Index to
Institutions by Category From Volume One

List of Categories

ART

Art Associations, Councils and Commissions, Foundations and
    Institutes 3
Art Museums and Galleries 3
Arts and Crafts Museums 17
China, Glass and Silver Museums 18
Civic Art and Cultural Centers 18
Decorative Arts Museums 19
Folk Art Museums 20
Textile Museums 21

CHILDREN'S MUSEUMS 22

COLLEGE AND UNIVERSITY MUSEUMS 26

COMPANY MUSEUMS 31

EXHIBIT AREAS 31

GENERAL MUSEUMS 33

HISTORY

Historic Agencies, Councils, Commissions, Foundations and
    Research Institutes 41
Historic Houses and Historic Buildings 43
Historic Sites 67
Historical and Preservation Societies 79
Historical Society Museums 82
History Museums 93
Maritime, Naval Museums and Historic Ships 122
Military Museums 123
Preservation Projects 126

LIBRARIES HAVING COLLECTIONS OF BOOKS 128

**LIBRARIES HAVING COLLECTIONS OTHER THAN
    BOOKS** 129

**NATIONAL AND STATE AGENCIES, COUNCILS AND
    COMMISSIONS** 131

NATURE CENTERS 132

PARK MUSEUMS AND VISITOR CENTERS 135

SCIENCE

Academies, Associations, Institutes and Foundations.............139
Aeronautics and Space Museums 139
Anthropology and Ethnology Museums 140
Aquariums, Marine Museums and Oceanariums 142
Arboretums 143
Archaeology Museums and Archaeological Sites....................145
Aviaries and Ornithology Museums 147
Botanical and Aquatic Gardens, Conservatories, and Horticulture

Societies 147
Entomology Museums 149
Geology, Mineralogy and Paleontology Museums 150
Herbariums 151
Herpetology Museums 151
Medical, Dental, Health, Pharmacology, Apothecary and
    Psychiatry Museums 151
Natural History and Natural Science Museums.......................152
Planetariums, Observatories and Astronomy Museums...........157
Science Museums and Centers 158
Wildlife Refuges and Bird Sanctuaries 161
Zoos 162

SPECIALIZED

Agriculture Museums 163
Antiques Museums 164
Architecture Museums 166
Audiovisual and Film Museums 167
Circus Museums 167
Comedy Museums 167
Communications Museums 167
Costume Museums 168
Crime Museums 168
Culturally Specific 168
Electricity Museums 173
Fire-Fighting Museums 173
Forestry Museums 174
Furniture Museums 174
Gun Museums 175
Hobby Museums 175
Horological Museums 175
Industrial Museums 175
Lapidary Arts Museums 176
Logging and Lumber Museums 176
Mappariums 176
Mining Museums 176
Money and Numismatics Museums 177
Musical Instruments Museums 177
Philatelic Museums 177
Photography Museums 177
Religious Museums 178
Scouting Museums 179
Sports Museums 179
Technology Museums 180
Theatre Museums 181
Toy and Doll Museums 181
Transportation Museums 182
Typography Museums 184
Village Museums 184
Wax Museums 185
Whaling Museums 185
Woodcarving Museums 185

List of Categories

ART

Art Associations, Councils and Commissions, Foundations and Institutes

Alexandria Museum of Art, Alexandria, LA 584

American Museum of Ceramic Art, Pomona, CA 143

Anderson Museum of Contemporary Art, Roswell, NM 945

Art Association of Henry County, Inc., New Castle, IN 494

Art Association of Randolph County, Inc., Union City, IN 501

Art Guild of Burlington, Inc., Burlington, IA 507

Barnes Foundation, Merion, PA 1271

Blue Star Contemporary Art Center, San Antonio, TX 1448

Chinati Foundation, Marfa, TX 1436

Gilmer Arts and Heritage Association, Ellijay, GA 371

Humboldt Arts Council/Morris Graves Museum of Art, Eureka, CA 94

Hus Var Fine Art, Buffalo, NY 973

Indianapolis Museum of Contemporary Art, Indianapolis, IN 485

Island Museum of Art, Westcott Bay Institute, Friday Harbor, WA 1554

Laurel Arts, Somerset, PA 1300

Madison Museum of Fine Art, Madison, GA 378

Maridon Museum, Butler, PA 1245

The Museum of Contemporary Art of Georgia (MOCA GA), Atlanta, GA 362

The Museum of Russian Art, Minneapolis, MN 783

New York State Council on the Arts/Museum Program, New York, NY 1036

O. Winston Link Museum, Roanoke, VA ...1535

Pasadena Museum of California Art, Pasadena, CA 140

Pence Gallery, Davis, CA 90

Provisions Library, Washington, DC 289

South Shore Arts, Munster, IN 493

Southern Arts Federation, Atlanta, GA 363

STAX Museum of American Soul Music, Memphis, TN 1376

Torrance Art Museum, Torrance, CA 192

Virginia Holocaust Museum, Richmond, VA 1533

The Walker African American Museum & Research Center, Las Vegas, NV 880

West Chicago City Museum, West Chicago, IL 464

Woodstock Artists Association, Woodstock, NY 1087

World Erotic Art Museum, Miami Beach, FL 327

Art Museums and Galleries

A.D. German Warehouse, Designed By Frank Lloyd Wright, Richland Center, WI 1620

A.K.C. Museum of The Dog, Saint Louis, MO 831

The APEX Museum, Atlanta, GA 357

A.R. Mitchell Museum, Trinidad, CO 233

Abby Aldrich Rockefeller Folk Art Museum, Williamsburg, VA 1544

Abington Art Center, Jenkintown, PA 1263

Academy Art Museum, Easton, MD 642

Ackland Art Museum, Chapel Hill, NC 1093

Adams County Historical Society Museum, Brighton, CO 204

Adams State College Luther Bean Museum, Alamosa, CO 201

Addison Gallery of American Art, Andover, MA 659

The Adirondack Museum, Blue Mountain Lake, NY 963

African American Museum, Dallas, TX 1403

African-American Museum and Library at Oakland, Oakland, CA 132

The African American Museum in Philadelphia, Philadelphia, PA 1275

African American Museum of the Arts, De Land, FL 303

African Art Museum of Maryland, Columbia, MD 641

African Art Museum of the S.M.A. Fathers, Tenafly, NJ 926

Aiken Center for the Arts, Aiken, SC 1320

Akron Art Museum, Akron, OH 1138

Akwesasne Museum, Hogansburg, NY 998

Alabama Artist's Gallery, Montgomery, AL 15

Alan Short Gallery, Stockton, CA 189

Alaska Heritage Museum at Wells Fargo, Anchorage, AK 21

Albany Institute of History & Art, Albany, NY 954

Albany Museum of Art, Albany, GA 355

Albin Polasek Museum and Sculpture Gardens, Winter Park, FL 354

Albion College Department of Art and Art History, Albion, MI 722

The Albrecht-Kemper Museum of Art, Saint Joseph, MO 830

Albright-Knox Art Gallery, Buffalo, NY 971

Albuquerque Museum, Albuquerque, NM 932

Alden B. Dow Museum of Science and Art of the Midland Center for the Arts, Midland, MI 755

The Aldrich Contemporary Art Museum, Ridgefield, CT 259

Alexander Brest Museum and Gallery, Jacksonville, FL 313

Alexander House, Port Edwards, WI 1618

Alexandria Museum of Art, Alexandria, LA 584

Alice C. Sabatini Gallery-Topeka and Shawnee County Public Library, Topeka, KS 558

Aljira, A Center for Contemporary Art, Newark, NJ 916

Allegheny College Art Galleries (Bowman, Penelec & Megahan Galleries), Meadville, PA 1270

Allegheny Highlands Arts & Crafts Center, Inc., Clifton Forge, VA 1501

Allen Memorial Art Museum, Oberlin, OH 1180

Allen R. Hite Art Institute, Louisville, KY 575

Allentown Art Museum, Allentown, PA 1239

Allied Arts Council of Yakima Valley Gallery, Yakima, WA 1578

Allison-Antrim Museum, Inc., Greencastle, PA 1257

Altama Museum of Art & History, Vidalia, GA 390

Alternative Museum, New York, NY 1018

Alton Museum of History and Art, Inc., Alton, IL 410

Alva deMars Megan Chapel Art Center, Manchester, NH 891

Amarillo Museum of Art, Amarillo, TX 1386

American Academy of Arts and Letters, New York, NY 1018

American Hungarian Foundation/Museum of the American Hungarian Foundation, New Brunswick, NJ 915

American Museum of Asmat Art, Saint Paul, MN 789

American Museum of Ceramic Art, Pomona, CA 143

American Red Cross Visitors Center and Gift Shop, Washington, DC 275

American Saddlebred Museum, Lexington, KY 572

American Sport Art Museum and Archives, Daphne, AL 7

American University Museum at The Katzen Arts Center, Washington, DC 275

American Visionary Art Museum, Baltimore, MD 629

Americas Society, New York, NY 1020

Amon Carter Museum, Fort Worth, TX 1416

Anacostia Museum and Center for African American History & Culture, Washington, DC 275

Anadarko Heritage Museum, Anadarko, OK 1195

Anaheim Museum, Anaheim, CA 71

Anchorage Museum at Rasmuson Center, Anchorage, AK 22

Ancient Spanish Monastery of St. Bernard de Clairvaux Cloisters, North Miami Beach, FL 329

Anderson/Abruzzo Albuquerque International Balloon Museum, Albuquerque, NM 933

Anderson County Arts Center, Anderson, SC 1320

Anderson Fine Arts Center, Anderson, IN ...467

Anderson Gallery - Drake University, Des Moines, IA 514

Anderson Gallery, School of the Arts, Virginia Commonwealth University, Richmond, VA 1528

Anderson Museum of Contemporary Art, Roswell, NM 945

Anderson Ranch Arts Center & Museum, Snowmass Village, CO 232

Andrew County Museum & Historical Society, Savannah, MO 838

The Andy Warhol Museum, Pittsburgh, PA 1290

Angels Gate Cultural Center, San Pedro, CA 176

Anita S. Wooten Gallery at Valencia Community College East Campus, Orlando, FL 331

Ann Arbor Art Center, Ann Arbor, MI 724

Anna Lamar Switzer Center for Visual Arts, Pensacola, FL 335

Annmary Brown Memorial, Providence, RI 1316

The Ansel Adams Gallery, Yosemite, CA 199

Antelope Valley Indian Museum, Lancaster, CA 108

Anthology Film Archives, New York, NY 1020

Appleton Art Center, Appleton, WI 1589

Appleton Museum of Art, Ocala, FL 330

ARC Gallery (Artists, Residents of Chicago), Chicago, IL 417

Arcadia University Art Gallery, Glenside, PA 1256

Archer County Museum, Archer City, TX 1387

The Archer Gallery, Vancouver, WA 1576

Archives of J.S.G. Boggs, Brandon, FL 298

Arizona Museum For Youth, Mesa, AZ 37

Arizona State University Art Museum, Tempe, AZ 45

The Arkansas Arts Center, Little Rock, AR 61

Arkansas River Valley Arts Center, Russellville, AR 67

Arkansas State University Art Gallery, Jonesboro, AR 60

Arlington Arts Center, Arlington, VA 1495

Arlington Museum of Art, Arlington, TX 1387

Art Museums and Galleries–Continued

Armenian Library and Museum of America, Watertown, MA 716

The Armory Art Center, West Palm Beach, FL 353

Arnot Art Museum, Elmira, NY 987

Arrowmont School of Arts & Crafts, Gatlinburg, TN 1365

Art and Culture Center of Hollywood, Hollywood, FL 312

Art Association of Harrisburg, Harrisburg, PA 1258

Art Association of Randolph County, Inc., Union City, IN 501

The Art Center at Fuller Lodge, Los Alamos, NM 942

Art Center In Hargate, St. Paul's School, Concord, NH 884

Art Center Manatee, Bradenton, FL 297

Art Center of Battle Creek, Battle Creek, MI 726

Art Center Sarasota, Inc, Sarasota, FL 343

Art Center Waco, Waco, TX 1458

Art Complex Museum, Duxbury, MA 680

The Art Galleries at UAH, Huntsville, AL 11

Art Galleries, California State University, Northridge, Northridge, CA 131

The Art Gallery at the University of Maryland, College Park, College Park, MD 640

Art Gallery at the University of New England, Portland, ME 618

The Art Gallery, John C. Calhoun State Community College, Decatur, AL 7

The Art Gallery, Lower Columbia College Fine Arts Gallery, Longview, WA 1558

Art Gallery Marist College, Poughkeepsie, NY 1054

The Art Gallery, University of New Hampshire, Durham, NH 886

Art Guild of Burlington, Inc., Burlington, IA 507

The Art Gym, Marylhurst, OR 1228

The Art Institute of Boston Main Gallery, Boston, MA 663

The Art Institute of Chicago, Chicago, IL ...418

Art League of Houston, Houston, TX 1425

Art Museum of Greater Lafayette, Lafayette, IN 487

Art Museum of South Texas, Corpus Christi, TX 1401

Art Museum of Southeast Texas, Beaumont, TX 1393

Art Museum of the Americas, Oas, Washington, DC 276

Art Museum of The University of Memphis, Memphis, TN 1372

Art Museum of Western Virginia, Roanoke, VA 1534

ART Station, Stone Mountain, GA 387

The Art Studio, Inc., Beaumont, TX 1393

ArtCenter/South Florida, Miami Beach, FL 326

Arte Americas, Fresno, CA 96

Artesia Historical Museum & Art Center, Artesia, NM 936

Arthouse, Austin, TX 1388

Arthur A. Houghton Jr. Gallery & The Great Hall Gallery, New York, NY 1020

Arthur M. Sackler Gallery, Washington, DC 276

Arthur Ross Gallery, University of Pennsylvania, Philadelphia, PA 1276

Artists Association of Nantucket, Nantucket, MA 695

Artlink, Fort Wayne, IN 477

Artmobile, Newtown, PA 1274

Artpace San Antonio, San Antonio, TX 1448

Artrain USA, Ann Arbor, MI 724

The Arts & Science Center for Southeast Arkansas, Pine Bluff, AR 65

The Arts Center, Jamestown, ND 1133

Arts Center at Okaloosa-Walton College, Niceville, FL 329

The Arts Center in Orange, Orange, VA ...1524

The Arts Centre, Inc., Martinsville, WV 1584

Arts Club of Washington, Washington, DC 276

Arts Consortium of Cincinnati's African American Museum, Cincinnati, OH 1148

Arts Council of Fayetteville/Cumberland County, Fayetteville, NC 1100

Arts Council of Moore County - Campbell House, Southern Pines, NC ...1120

Arts Council of Wayne County, Goldsboro, NC 1102

Artspace, Raleigh, NC 1114

ARTSplace, Grand Forks, ND 1131

Arvada Center for the Arts and Humanities, Arvada, CO 201

The Ashby-Hodge Gallery of American Art, Central Methodist University, Fayette, MO 815

Asheville Art Museum, Asheville, NC 1088

Ashtabula Arts Center, Ashtabula, OH 1140

Asia Society Museum, New York, NY 1020

Asian American Arts Centre, New York, NY 1021

Asian Art Museum of San Francisco, Chong-Moon Lee Center for Asian Art and Culture, San Francisco, CA 163

Asian Arts & Culture Center, Towson University, Towson, MD 655

Aspen Art Museum, Aspen, CO 201

Associated Artists of Pittsburgh, Pittsburgh, PA 1290

Ataloa Lodge Museum, Muskogee, OK 1205

Atlanta College of Art, Atlanta, GA 358

Atlanta Contemporary Art Center, Atlanta, GA 358

The Atlanta Cyclorama, Atlanta, GA 358

Atrium Gallery Ltd., Saint Louis, MO 832

Attleboro Arts Museum, Attleboro, MA 661

Atwater Kent Museum of Philadelphia, Philadelphia, PA 1276

Augustana College Art Museum, Rock Island, IL 453

Aurora Public Art Commission, Aurora, IL 411

Austin Museum of Art - Downtown, Austin, TX 1388

The AXA Gallery, New York, NY 1021

The Bade Institute of Biblical Archaeology and The Howell Bible Collection, Berkeley, CA 75

Bailey House Museum - Maui Historical Society, Wailuku, HI 402

Bakersfield Museum of Art, Bakersfield, CA 73

Baldwin Photo Gallery, Murfreesboro, TN 1376

Ball State University Museum of Art, Muncie, IN 492

The Baltimore Museum of Art, Baltimore, MD 630

Balzekas Museum of Lithuanian Culture, Chicago, IL 418

Barnard's Mill Art Museum, Glen Rose, TX 1422

The Barnsdall Junior Arts Center & Barnsdall Art Center, Los Angeles, CA 113

Barron Arts Center & Museum, Woodbridge, NJ 931

Barton Museum, Wilson, NC 1124

Bass Museum of Art, Miami Beach, FL 326

Bates College Museum of Art, Lewiston, ME 613

Baum Gallery of Fine Art, University of Central Arkansas, Conway, AR 56

Baycrafters, Inc., Bay Village, OH 1141

Bayou Bend Collection and Gardens, Houston, TX 1425

Beall Center for Art and Technology, Irvine, CA 104

Beard Gallery, Norton, MA 700

Beaumont Art League, Beaumont, TX 1394

Bedford Gallery at the Dean Lesher Regional Center for the Arts, Walnut Creek, CA 196

The Belknap Mill Society, Laconia, NH 890

Bellagio Gallery of Fine Arts, Las Vegas, NV 878

Bellevue Arts Museum, Bellevue, WA 1548

Belskie Museum of Art & Science, Closter, NJ 902

Belvedere-Tiburon Landmarks Society, Tiburon, CA 192

Ben Maltz Gallery at OTIS College of Art and Design, Los Angeles, CA 113

Ben Shahn Galleries at William Paterson University of New Jersey, Wayne, NJ 929

Benedicta Arts Center, Saint Joseph, MN 789

Bennington Center for the Natural & Cultural Arts, Bennington, VT 1476

The Bennington Museum, Bennington, VT 1476

Berea College, Doris Ulmann Galleries, Berea, KY 565

Bergen Museum of Art & Science, Paramus, NJ 919

Bergstrom-Mahler Museum, Neenah, WI 1614

Berkeley Art Center, Berkeley, CA 75

Berkshire Artisans/Lichtenstein Center for the Arts, Pittsfield, MA 702

Berkshire Museum, Pittsfield, MA 702

Besser Museum for Northeast Michigan, Alpena, MI 723

Biblical Arts Center, Dallas, TX 1404

Bicentennial Art Center & Museum, Paris, IL 449

Biggs Museum of American Art, Dover, DE 269

Birger Sandzen Memorial Gallery, Lindsborg, KS 549

Birmingham Bloomfield Art Center, Birmingham, MI 730

Birmingham Museum of Art, Birmingham, AL 5

Black Arts National Diaspora Museum, New Orleans, LA 594

Black Mountain College Museum & Arts Center, Asheville, NC 1089

Blaffer Gallery, The Art Museum of the University of Houston, Houston, TX 1425

Blair Museum of Lithophanes, Toledo, OH 1187

Blanden Memorial Art Museum, Fort Dodge, IA 518

Blanton Museum of Art, Austin, TX 1389

Bloomington Art Center, Bloomington, MN 769

Blount-Bridgers House/Hobson Pittman Memorial Gallery, Tarboro, NC 1121

Blue Star Contemporary Art Center, San Antonio, TX 1448

B'nai B'rith Klutznick National Jewish Museum, Washington, DC 277

Bob Jones University Museum & Gallery, Inc., Greenville, SC 1333

Bob Rauschenberg Gallery, Edison Community College, Fort Myers, FL 308

Boca Raton Museum of Art, Boca Raton, FL 296

Boehm Gallery, San Marcos, CA 174

Boise Art Museum, Boise, ID 403

Bolinas Museum, Bolinas, CA 79

Bonnet House Museum & Gardens, Fort Lauderdale, FL 306

Booth Western Art Museum, Cartersville, GA 367

Boothbay Region Art Foundation, Inc., Boothbay Harbor, ME 607

Boston Athenaeum Library, Boston, MA 663
Boston Public Library, Boston, MA 664
Boston University Art Gallery, Boston, MA 665
Boulder Museum of Contemporary Art, Boulder, CO 203
Bountiful/Davis Art Center, Bountiful, UT 1463
Bowdoin College Museum of Art, Brunswick, ME 607
Bowers Museum, Santa Ana, CA 177
Bowling Green State University Fine Arts Center Galleries, Bowling Green, OH ...1143
Bradford Brinton Memorial & Museum, Big Horn, WY 1628
Bradley Gallery of Art, Plymouth, WI 1617
Braithwaite Fine Arts Gallery, Cedar City, UT 1464
Brand Library & Art Center, Glendale, CA 100
Brandywine River Museum, Chadds Ford, PA 1246
Branigan Cultural Center, Las Cruces, NM 940
Brattleboro Museum & Art Center, Brattleboro, VT 1477
Brauer Museum of Art, Valparaiso, IN 501
Bread & Puppet Museum, Glover, VT 1479
Brenau University Galleries, Brenau University, Gainesville, GA 373
Brevard Museum of Art and Science, Inc., Melbourne, FL 323
Brigham City Museum-Gallery, Brigham City, UT 1463
Bromfield Art Gallery, Boston, MA 665
The Bronx Museum of the Arts, Bronx, NY 965
Brookfield Craft Center, Brookfield, CT 237
Brookgreen Gardens, Murrells Inlet, SC 1337
Brookings Arts Council, Brookings, SD 1344
Brooklyn Museum, Brooklyn, NY 968
Brown County Art Gallery and Museum, Nashville, IN 493
Brownsville Museum of Fine Art - Brownsville Art League, Brownsville, TX 1398
Bruce Museum, Greenwich, CT 243
Brueckner Museum of Starr Commonwealth, Albion, MI 723
Brunnier Art Museum, Ames, IA 504
Buchanan Center for the Arts, Monmouth, IL 445
Buckaroo Hall of Fame, Winnemucca, NV 882
Buffalo Bill Historical Center, Cody, WY ..1631
Burchfield-Penney Art Center, Buffalo, NY 973
The Butler Institute of American Art, Youngstown, OH 1193
The Butler Institute of American Art - Salem Branch, Salem, OH 1184
Butte-Silver Bow Arts Chateau, Butte, MT 843

CFCC Webber Center Gallery, Ocala, FL 330
C.M. Russell Museum, Great Falls, MT 848
CU Art Galleries, Boulder, CO 203
Cabrillo Gallery, Aptos, CA 71
Cahoon Museum of American Art, Cotuit, MA 677
Caldwell Arts Council, Lenoir, NC 1109
California African-American Museum, Los Angeles, CA 113
California Center for the Arts, Escondido, Escondido, CA 93
California Heritage Museum, Santa Monica, CA 183
California Historical Society, San Francisco, CA 163
California Museum of Ancient Art, Beverly Hills, CA 78

California Route 66 Museum, Victorville, CA 195
California State Indian Museum, Sacramento, CA 151
California State University, Long Beach, University Art Museum, Long Beach, CA 110
Call-Booth House Gallery, Paso Robles, CA 141
Callanwolde Fine Arts Center, Atlanta, GA 359
Calvin College Center Art Gallery, Grand Rapids, MI 743
Cambridge Museum, Cambridge, NE 858
The Camron-Stanford House Preservation Association, Oakland, CA 133
Canajoharie Library and Art Gallery, Canajoharie, NY 974
Cando Arts Center/Gallery, Minot, ND 1134
The Cannon Village Visitor Center, Kannapolis, NC 1107
The Canton Museum of Art, Canton, OH ..1145
Cape Ann Historical Museum, Gloucester, MA 684
Cape Cod Museum of Art, Dennis, MA 680
Caramoor Center for Music & the Arts, Inc., Katonah, NY 1006
Carleton College Art Gallery, Northfield, MN 785
Carlsbad Museum & Art Center, Carlsbad, NM 938
Carnegie Art Museum, Oxnard, CA 136
Carnegie Center for Art & History, New Albany, IN 493
Carnegie Museum of Art, Pittsburgh, PA ...1290
Carnegie Museums of Pittsburgh (Carnegie Institute), Pittsburgh, PA 1291
Carnegie Resource Center, Mitchell, SD....1351
Carriage and Western Art Museum, Santa Barbara, CA 178
Carroll Reece Museum, Johnson City, TN.1367
Carson County Square House Museum, Panhandle, TX 1442
Cartoon Art Museum, San Francisco, CA....164
CAS Gallery, Union, NJ 928
Cass County Museum & Pioneer School, Walker, MN 795
Castellani Art Museum of Niagara University, Niagara University, NY 1043
Cathedral Cultural Center, Omaha, NE 870
Cazenovia College - Art & Design Gallery, Cazenovia, NY 976
CCA Wattis Institute for Contemporary Arts, San Francisco, CA 164
The CCC Weeks Gallery, Jamestown, NY.1004
Cecelia Coker Bell Gallery, Hartsville, SC 1335
Cedar Rapids Museum of Art, Cedar Rapids, IA 509
Cedarhurst Center for the Arts, Mount Vernon, IL 446
Center for Book Arts, New York, NY 1022
Center for Contemporary Printmaking, Norwalk, CT 257
Center for Creative Photography, Tucson, AZ 48
Center for Curatorial Studies, Annandale-on-Hudson, NY 958
Center for Exploratory and Perceptual Art, Buffalo, NY 973
Center For Maine Contemporary Art, Rockport, ME 621
Center for the Arts - Dalton Gallery, Rock Hill, SC 1340
Center for the Study of Political Graphics (CSPG), Los Angeles, CA 113
Center Galleries, College for Creative Studies, Detroit, MI 735
Center for Southwest Studies/Fort Lewis College, Durango, CO 214
Center on Contemporary Art, Seattle, WA.1565

Central Iowa Art Association, Marshalltown, IA 523
Chaffee Center for the Visual Arts, Rutland, VT 1486
Chaffey Community Art Association Museum of Art, Rancho Cucamonga, CA 145
Chandler Gallery, Randolph, VT 1485
Charles Allis Art Museum, Milwaukee, WI 1610
Charles B. Goddard Center for Visual and Performing Arts, Ardmore, OK....1196
The Charles Edward Choate Exhibit, Sandersville, GA 384
Charles H. MacNider Museum, Mason City, IA 523
Charles H. Taylor Arts Center, Hampton, VA 1509
The Charles Hosmer Morse Museum of American Art, Winter Park, FL 354
Charles M. Schulz Museum and Research Center, Santa Rosa, CA 184
Charlotte and Philip Hanes Art Gallery, Wake Forest University, Winston-Salem, NC 1124
Chattahoochee Valley Art Museum, LaGrange, GA 375
The Chattanooga Nature Center, Chattanooga, TN 1361
Chazen Museum of Art, Madison, WI ...1604
Cheekwood-Tennessee Botanical Garden & Museum of Art, Nashville, TN 1378
Cherokee National Museum, Park Hill, OK 1211
Chester Art Guild, Chester, VT 1478
The Chester Gould-Dick Tracy Museum, Woodstock, IL 467
Chesterwood, Stockbridge, MA 711
Cheyenne Frontier Days Old West Museum, Cheyenne, WY 1630
Chicago Botanic Garden, Glencoe, IL 438
Chicago Cultural Center, Chicago, IL 419
Children's Museum/Museo de Los Ninos, San Diego, CA 156
The Children's Museum of Science and Technology, Troy, NY 1079
Children's Museum of the Arts, New York, NY 1022
China Institute Gallery, China Institute In America, New York, NY 1023
Chinati Foundation, Marfa, TX 1436
Chinese Culture Center of San Francisco, San Francisco, CA 164
Chrysler Museum of Art, Norfolk, VA.......1521
Cigna Museum and Art Collection, Philadelphia, PA 1277
Cincinnati Art Galleries, Cincinnati, OH....1148
Cincinnati Art Museum, Cincinnati, OH....1148
Circle Gallery/College of Environment & Design - University of Georgia, Athens, GA 356
City Arts Center, Oklahoma City, OK........1207
City Hall Council Chamber Gallery, Charleston, SC 1324
City Island Nautical Museum, Bronx, NY...965
City of Brea Gallery, Brea, CA 79
City of Las Cruces Museum System, Las Cruces, NM 940
Clark Atlanta University Art Galleries, Atlanta, GA 359
Clark Humanities Museum-Study, Claremont, CA 85
Clay Center for Arts & Sciences West Virginia, Charleston, WV 1580
The Clell and Ruth Gannon Gallery at Bismarck State College, Bismarck, ND 1128
Cleveland Artists Foundation at Beck Center for the Arts, Lakewood, OH 1170
The Cleveland Museum of Art, Cleveland, OH 1152
Cleveland State University Art Gallery, Cleveland, OH 1153

Art Museums and Galleries–Continued

The Cloisters, New York, NY 1023
Clough-Hanson Gallery, Rhodes College,
    Memphis, TN 1372
Clymer Museum of Art, Ellensburg, WA ...1553
Coachella Valley Museum and Cultural
    Center, Indio, CA 104
Colby College Museum of Art,
    Waterville, ME 624
Colfax County Society of Art, History
    and Archaeology, Raton, NM 945
The College Art Gallery, Ewing, NJ 903
College of Eastern Utah Art Gallery,
    Gallery East, Price, UT 1469
College of the Redwoods Art Gallery,
    Eureka, CA 94
The College of Wooster Art Museum,
    Wooster, OH 1192
Colorado Gallery of the Arts/Araphoe
    Community College, Littleton, CO 226
Colorado Springs Fine Arts Center
    (Taylor Museum), Colorado Springs,
    CO 206
Columbia College Chicago Center for the
    Book & Paper Arts, Chicago, IL 420
Columbia Museum of Art, Columbia, SC ..1329
The Columbian Theatre, Museum & Art
    Center, Wamego, KS 560
Columbus Chapel, Boal Mansion
    Museum, Boalsburg, PA 1244
Columbus Cultural Arts Center,
    Columbus, OH 1157
The Columbus Museum, Columbus, GA 368
Columbus Museum of Art, Columbus,
    OH 1157
Columbus Museum of Art and Design,
    Columbus, IN 473
Community Council for the Arts,
    Kinston, NC 1108
Community Fine Arts Center, Rock
    Springs, WY 1637
Compton Art Collection, Upland, IN 501
Concord Art Association, Concord, MA 676
Concordia University-Wisconsin, Art
    Gallery, Mequon, WI 1609
Conejo Valley Art Museum, Thousand
    Oaks, CA 191
Connecticut Historical Society, Hartford,
    CT 244
Contemporary Art Center of Virginia,
    Virginia Beach, VA 1542
Contemporary Art Museum, Raleigh, NC ..1114
Contemporary Art Museum St. Louis,
    Saint Louis, MO 832
Contemporary Arts Center, New Orleans,
    LA 594
The Contemporary Arts Center,
    Cincinnati, OH 1150
Contemporary Arts Museum Houston,
    Houston, TX 1426
Contemporary Crafts Museum & Gallery,
    Portland, OR 1230
The Contemporary Jewish Museum, San
    Francisco, CA 164
The Contemporary Museum, Honolulu,
    HI 394
Contemporary Museum, Baltimore, MD 631
The Contemporary Museum at First
    Hawaiian Center, Honolulu, HI 394
Cook County Historical Museum, Grand
    Marais, MN 776
Coos Art Museum, Coos Bay, OR 1222
Copia: The American Center for Wine,
    Food & the Arts, Napa, CA 129
Copper King Mansion, Butte, MT 843
Copper Village Museum & Arts Center of
    Deer Lodge County, Anaconda, MT 840
Coral Springs Museum of Art, Coral
    Springs, FL 301
Corbin Art Center, Spokane, WA 1571
The Corcoran Gallery of Art,
    Washington, DC 277

Corita Art Center, Los Angeles, CA 114
Cornell Museum of Art & History,
    Delray Beach, FL 304
The Corning Museum of Glass, Corning,
    NY 981
Cornish Colony Museum, Windsor, VT 1490
Cottonlandia Museum, Greenwood, MS 800
Coutts Memorial Museum of Art, Inc., El
    Dorado, KS 537
Craft Alliance, Saint Louis, MO 833
Craft and Folk Art Museum - CAFAM,
    Los Angeles, CA 114
Cranbrook Art Museum, Bloomfield
    Hills, MI 730
Cranbrook House and Gardens Auxiliary,
    Bloomfield Hills, MI 730
Creative Arts Center, Pontiac, MI 760
Creative Arts Guild, Dalton, GA 370
Creative Photographic Art Center of
    Maine, Lewiston, ME 614
Cress Gallery of Art, Chattanooga, TN 1361
Cripple Creek District Museum, Inc.,
    Cripple Creek, CO 209
Crocker Art Museum, Sacramento, CA 152
Crook County Museum & Art Gallery,
    Sundance, WY 1638
Crooked Tree Arts Center, Petoskey, MI 760
Crossman Gallery, UW-Whitewater,
    Whitewater, WI 1628
Crowder College-Longwell Museum &
    Camp Crowder Collection, Neosho,
    MO 828
Crowley Art Association & Gallery,
    Crowley, LA 588
Culbertson Mansion State Historic Site,
    New Albany, IN 493
Cummer Museum of Art and Gardens,
    Jacksonville, FL 314
Cuneo Museum & Gardens, Vernon Hills,
    IL 463
Cupola House, Egg Harbor, WI 1596
Curfman Gallery & Duhesa Lounge, Fort
    Collins, CO 216
The Currier Museum of Art, Manchester,
    NH 891
Custer County Art & Heritage Center,
    Miles City, MT 851
Cy Twombly Gallery, Houston, TX 1426
Cyrus E. Dallin Art Museum, Arlington,
    MA 660
Czech Center New York, New York, NY ...1024

DAAP Galleries, Cincinnati, OH 1150
D.R. Barker Historical Museum,
    Fredonia, NY 992
Dahesh Museum of Art, New York, NY 1024
Dahl Arts Center, Rapid City, SD 1354
Dakota Discovery Museum, Mitchell, SD...1352
Dallam-Hartley XIT Museum, Dalhart,
    TX 1403
The Dallas Center for Contemporary Art
    - The Dallas Contemporary, Dallas,
    TX 1404
Dallas Museum of Art, Dallas, TX 1405
The Dalles Art Association, The Dalles,
    OR 1237
Dalton Galleries, Decatur, GA 370
Dane G. Hansen Memorial Museum,
    Logan, KS 550
Danforth Museum of Art, Framingham,
    MA 683
Danville Museum of Fine Arts & History,
    Danville, VA 1502
Daum Museum of Contemporary Art,
    Sedalia, MO 838
Daura Gallery, Lynchburg, VA 1515
David Strawn Art Gallery, Jacksonville,
    IL 440
David Winton Bell Gallery, Providence,
    RI 1316
Davis Art Gallery, Columbia, MO 813
Davis Museum and Cultural Center,
    Wellesley, MA 716

Davison Art Center, Wesleyan University,
    Middletown, CT 249
The Davistown Museum, Liberty, ME 614
Dawson Springs Museum and Art Center,
    Inc., Dawson Springs, KY 568
Dayton Art Institute, Dayton, OH 1161
De Saisset Museum, Santa Clara, CA 180
Decorative Arts Collection, Inc. Museum
    of Decorative Painting, Wichita, KS 561
DeCordova Museum and Sculpture Park,
    Lincoln, MA 690
Degrazia Gallery In The Sun, Tucson, AZ 48
Deines Cultural Center, Russell, KS.............556
The DeLand Museum of Art, De Land,
    FL 303
Delaware Art Museum, Wilmington, DE 273
Delaware Center for the Contemporary
    Arts, Wilmington, DE 273
Deming Luna Mimbres Museum,
    Deming, NM 939
Denison Museum, Granville, OH 1167
Dennos Museum Center of Northwestern
    Michigan College, Traverse City, MI 765
Denver Art Museum, Denver, CO 210
DePaul University Art Museum, Chicago,
    IL 420
DePree Art Center & Gallery, Holland,
    MI 746
Des Moines Art Center, Des Moines, IA 514
Desert Caballeros Western Museum,
    Wickenburg, AZ..53
The Design Center at Philadelphia
    University, Philadelphia, PA 1278
Detroit Artists Market, Detroit, MI 735
The Detroit Institute of Arts, Detroit, MI....736
Detroit Zoo, Royal Oak, MI 762
DeWitt Wallace Decorative Arts Museum,
    Williamsburg, VA 1545
Dia:Beacon, Riggio Galleries, Beacon,
    NY 960
Dia Center for the Arts, Quemado, NM 945
Dia: Chelsea, New York, NY 1024
Diggs Gallery at Winston-Salem State
    University, Winston-Salem, NC 1125
Dinnerware Contemporary Arts, Tucson,
    AZ 49
Diplomatic Reception Rooms,
    Department of State, Washington, DC 278
Dishman Art Museum, Beaumont, TX 1394
The Dixon Gallery and Gardens,
    Memphis, TN 1372
Donna Beam Fine Art Gallery, UNLV,
    Las Vegas, NV 878
The Douglas F. Cooley Memorial Art
    Gallery, Reed College, Portland, OR.....1231
Dowd Fine Arts Gallery, State University
    of New York College at Cortland,
    Cortland, NY 983
Downey Museum of Art, Downey, CA 91
Dragon Dreams Museum & Gift Shop,
    Chattanooga, TN 1362
The Drawing Center, New York, NY 1024
Dublin-Laurens Museum, Dublin, GA 370
Dubuque Museum of Art, Dubuque, IA.......516
Duluth Art Institute, Duluth, MN 772
Dumbarton Oaks Research Library &
    Collections, Washington, DC 278
The Duncan Gallery of Art, De Land, FL....304
Dupont Gallery, Lexington, VA 1513
The Dwight Frederick Boyden Gallery,
    Saint Mary's City, MD 652

Eagle Rock Art Museum and Education
    Center, Idaho Falls, ID 406
East Hawaii Cultural Center, Hilo, HI 393
East Jordan Portside Art & Historical
    Museum, East Jordan, MI 739
East-West Center, Honolulu, HI 394
Eastern Shore Art Center, Fairhope, AL 9
Eccles Community Arts Center, Ogden,
    UT 1467

Edmonds Art Festival Museum,
    Edmonds, WA 1553
Edsel & Eleanor Ford House, Grosse
    Pointe Shores, MI 745
Edward-Dean Museum and Gardens,
    Cherry Valley, CA 82
Edward Hopper Landmark Preservation
    Foundation, Nyack, NY 1044
Egan Maritime Foundation, Nantucket,
    MA 695
Eiteljorg Museum of American Indians
    and Western Art, Indianapolis, IN 482
El Museo Del Barrio, New York, NY 1025
El Museo Latino, Omaha, NE 870
El Paso Museum of Art, El Paso, TX 1411
Elder Art Gallery, Nebraska Wesleyan
    University, Lincoln, NE 865
Elegba Folklore Society Cultural Center,
    Richmond, VA 1529
Elisabet Ney Museum, Austin, TX 1390
Elizabeth Myers Mitchell Art Gallery at
    St. John's College, Annapolis, MD 627
Ella Sharp Museum, Jackson, MI 748
The Ellen Noel Art Museum of the
    Permian Basin, Odessa, TX 1441
Elliott Museum, Stuart, FL 346
Elmhurst Art Museum, Elmhurst, IL 433
Eloise Pickard Smith Gallery at Cowell
    College, Santa Cruz, CA 181
Elverhoj Museum of History and Art,
    Solvang, CA 187
The Emerson Gallery, Clinton, NY 979
Epcot at Walt Disney World Resort, Lake
    Buena Vista, FL 319
The Eric Carle Museum of Picture Book
    Art, Amherst, MA 658
Erie Art Museum, Erie, PA 1252
The Esther and John Clay Fine Arts
    Gallery, Cheyenne, WY 1630
Esther M. Klein Art Gallery at University
    City Science Center, Philadelphia, PA ...1279
Eubie Blake National Jazz Institute and
    Cultural Center, Baltimore, MD 632
Euphrat Museum of Art, Cupertino, CA 89
Evanston Art Center, Evanston, IL 434
Evansville Museum of Arts History &
    Science, Evansville, IN 475
Evergreen Galleries, Olympia, WA 1560
Everhart Museum: Natural History,
    Science and Art, Scranton, PA 1298
Everson Museum of Art, Syracuse, NY 1076
The Exploratorium, San Francisco, CA 164
Ezra and Cecile Zilkha Gallery,
    Middletown, CT 249

The Fabric Workshop and Museum,
    Philadelphia, PA 1279
Fairfield Art Association, Fairfield, IA 518
Fairview Museum of History & Art,
    Fairview, UT 1465
Falkirk Cultural Center, San Rafael, CA 176
The Fashion Institute of Design &
    Merchandising/FIDM Museum &
    Galleries, Los Angeles, CA 114
Faulconer Gallery at Grinnell College,
    Grinnell, IA 519
Faust Park Foundation, Chesterfield, MO 812
Favell Museum Inc., Klamath Falls, OR 1227
Fayette Art Museum, Fayette, AL 9
Fayetteville Museum of Art, Fayetteville,
    NC 1100
Federal Reserve Board, Washington, DC 278
Fender Museum of Music and the Arts,
    Corona, CA 87
Festival-Institute, James Dick Foundation,
    Round Top, TX 1446
Fielding L. Wright Art Center, Cleveland,
    MS 799
Figge Art Museum, Davenport, IA 512
Finch Lane Gallery, Salt Lake City, UT 1471
Fine Arts Center at Miriam Hall, Anna
    Maria College, Paxton, MA 701

Fine Arts Center for New River Valley,
    Pulaski, VA 1526
Fine Arts Center of Kershaw County,
    Inc., Camden, SC 1322
Fine Arts Collection, Luther College,
    Decorah, IA 513
The Fine Arts Museums of San
    Francisco, de Young Museum, San
    Francisco, CA 165
The Fine Arts Museums of San
    Francisco, Legion of Honor, San
    Francisco, CA 165
Firehouse Art Center, Norman, OK 1206
Firehouse Art Gallery, Nassau
    Community College, Garden City, NY ...992
The Firehouse Gallery, Burlington, VT 1478
Fisher Gallery, University of Southern
    California, Los Angeles, CA 115
The Fisk University Galleries, Nashville,
    TN 1379
Fitchburg Art Museum, Fitchburg, MA 683
The Five Civilized Tribes Museum,
    Muskogee, OK 1205
Flaten Art Museum of St. Olaf College,
    Northfield, MN 785
Flathead Indian Museum, Saint Ignatius,
    MT 853
Fleischer Museum, Scottsdale, AZ 43
Flint Institute of Arts, Flint, MI 741
Florence Griswold Museum, Old Lyme,
    CT 258
Florence Museum of Art, Science &
    History and the Florence Railroad
    Museum, Florence, SC 1332
Florida Community College, Kent
    Campus Museum/Gallery,
    Jacksonville, FL 314
Florida Gulf Coast University Art
    Gallery, Fort Myers, FL 309
Florida Holocaust Museum, Saint
    Petersburg, FL 341
Florida State University Museum of Fine
    Arts, Tallahassee, FL 347
Fondo Del Sol Visual Arts & Media
    Center/El Museo de Culturas y
    Herencias Americanas/MOCHA,
    Washington, DC 279
Foothills Art Center, Golden, CO 220
Fort Collins Museum of Contemporary
    Art, Fort Collins, CO 217
Fort Sill National Historic Landmark,
    Fort Sill, OK 1201
Fort Smith Art Center, Fort Smith, AR 57
Fort Walton Beach Art Museum, Fort
    Walton Beach, FL 310
Fort Wayne Museum of Art, Fort Wayne,
    IN 477
Fort Worth Zoological Park, Fort Worth,
    TX 1417
Foster-Tanner Fine Arts Gallery,
    Tallahassee, FL 347
The Frances Lehman Loeb Art Center,
    Poughkeepsie, NY 1055
Frances Young Tang Teaching Museum
    and Art Gallery, Saratoga Springs, NY .1064
Francis Colburn Gallery, Burlington, VT ...1478
Francis McCray Gallery, Silver City, NM 951
Frank Chiarenza Museum of Glass,
    Meriden, CT 248
Franklin Furnace Archive, Inc., Brooklyn,
    NY 969
Franklin G. Burroughs-Simeon B. Chapin
    Art Museum, Myrtle Beach, SC 1338
Fred Dana Marsh Museum, Ormond
    Beach, FL 333
Fred Harman Art Museum, Pagosa
    Springs, CO 229
The Fred Jones Jr. Museum of Art,
    Norman, OK 1206
Fred Wolf, Jr. Gallery/Klein Branch
    Jewish Community Center,
    Philadelphia, PA 1280

Frederic Remington Art Museum,
    Ogdensburg, NY 1044
Frederick R. Weisman Art Museum,
    Minneapolis, MN 781
Frederick R. Weisman Museum of Art,
    Malibu, CA 123
Freedman Gallery-Albright College,
    Reading, PA 1296
Freeport Arts Center, Freeport, IL 435
Freer Gallery of Art, Washington, DC 279
French Art Colony, Gallipolis, OH 1165
Fresno Art Museum, Fresno, CA 97
Fresno Metropolitan Museum, Fresno,
    CA 97
The Frick Art & Historical Center,
    Pittsburgh, PA 1292
The Frick Collection, New York, NY 1025
Frist Center for the Visual Arts,
    Nashville, TN 1379
Fruitlands Museums, Harvard, MA 686
Frye Art Museum, Seattle, WA 1566
Fuller Craft Museum, Brockton, MA 671

Gadsden Arts Center, Quincy, FL 338
Gadsden Museum of Art, Gadsden, AL 10
Galeria, Orchard Lake, MI 759
Galesburg Civic Art Center, Galesburg,
    IL 437
The Gallery at UTA, Arlington, TX 1387
Gallery 510 Arts Guild, Decatur, IL 430
Gallery North, Setauket, NY 1069
Gallery of Contemporary Art, University
    of Colorado, Colorado Springs,
    Colorado Springs, CO 207
Gallery of Henry Street
    Settlement/Abrons Arts Center, New
    York, NY 1026
Gallery on the York - Yorktown Arts
    Foundation, Yorktown, VA 1547
Gallery 101, River Falls, WI 1620
Gallery '76, Wenatchee, WA 1577
Galveston Arts Center, Galveston, TX 1420
Gardiner Art Gallery, Stillwater, OK 1214
The Gardner Museum, Inc., Gardner, MA ...684
Gari Melchers Home and Studio,
    Fredericksburg, VA 1506
Garibaldi and Meucci Museum, Staten
    Island, NY 1072
Garrison Art Center, Garrison, NY 993
Gary's Gallery, Bismarck, ND 1128
Gaston County Museum of Art and
    History, Dallas, NC 1097
Gemological Institute of America
    Museum, Carlsbad, CA 81
Genesee Country Village & Museum,
    Mumford, NY 1016
George A. Spiva Center for the Arts,
    Joplin, MO 820
The George D. and Harriet W. Cornell
    Fine Arts Museum, Winter Park, FL 354
George Eastman House/International
    Museum of Photography and Film,
    Rochester, NY 1058
George J. Doizaki Gallery, Los Angeles,
    CA 115
George Washington Masonic National
    Memorial, Alexandria, VA 1493
Georgetown University Art Collection,
    Washington, DC 279
Georgia Museum of Art, University of
    Georgia, Athens, GA 356
Georgia O'Keeffe Museum, Santa Fe,
    NM 947
Georgia State University School of Art &
    Design Gallery, Atlanta, GA 360
Gertrude Herbert Institute of Art,
    Augusta, GA 365
Gibbes Museum of Art, Charleston, SC 1325
The Gilbert Stuart Birthplace and
    Museum, Saunderstown, RI 1319
Gilcrease Museum, Tulsa, OK 1215

Art Museums and Galleries–Continued

Glencairn Museum: Academy of the New Church, Bryn Athyn, PA 1244

The Glynn Art Association, Inc., Saint Simons Island, GA 383

The Godwin-Ternbach Museum, Flushing, NY 990

The Golden Age of Trucking Museum, Middlebury, CT 249

The Goldie Paley Gallery at Moore College of Art and Design, Philadelphia, PA 1281

The Governor's Gallery, Santa Fe, NM 947

The Grace Museum, Abilene, TX...............1385

The Gracie Mansion Conservancy, New York, NY...1026

Grand Rapids Art Museum, Grand Rapids, MI 743

Grand Teton National Park, Colter Bay Indian Arts Museum, Colter Bay Village, WY 1631

Grant Wood Gallery, Anamosa, IA...............505

Grants Pass Museum of Art, Grants Pass, OR 1225

Graycliff Conservancy, Derby, NY 984

Great Harbor Maritime Museum, Northeast Harbor, ME 616

Great Plains Art Museum, Lincoln, NE 865

The Greater Reston Arts Center (GRACE), Reston, VA 1527

Green Hill Art Gallery, Greensboro, NC...1103

Greensboro Artists' League, Greensboro, NC 1103

Greenville County Museum of Art, Greenville, SC 1334

Greenville Museum of Art, Inc., Greenville, NC 1105

Gregory Kondos Gallery, Sacramento, CA 152

Grey Art Gallery, New York University Art Collection, New York, NY 1026

Griffin Museum of Photography, Winchester, MA 720

Grossmont College Hyde Art Gallery, El Cajon, CA 92

Grounds For Sculpture, Hamilton, NJ 906

Grunwald Center for the Graphic Arts, Hammer Museum, Los Angeles, CA....115

Guggenheim Hermitage Museum, Las Vegas, NV 878

Guild Hall Museum, East Hampton, NY 986

Guilford College Art Gallery, Greensboro, NC 1103

Gulf Beach Art Center, Indian Rocks Beach, FL..313

Gulf Coast Museum of Art, Inc., Largo, FL 321

GumTree Museum of Art, Tupelo, MS 808

The Haggin Museum, Stockton, CA 189

Hagood-Mauldin House and Irma Morris Museum of Fine Arts, Pickens, SC 1340

The Hall of Fame for Great Americans, Bronx, NY 966

Hallie Ford Museum of Art, Salem, OR 1235

Halsey Institute of Contemporary Art at the College of Charleston, Charleston, SC..1325

Hamline University Galleries, Department of Studio Arts & Art History, Saint Paul, MN 790

Hammer Museum, Los Angeles, CA 115

Hammond-Harwood House Association, Annapolis, MD 628

Hammond Museum and Japanese Stroll Garden, North Salem, NY.....................1043

Hampden-Booth Theatre Library at the Players, New York, NY.........................1027

Hampton University Museum, Hampton, VA 1509

The Handweaving Museum & Arts Center, Clayton, NY................................978

Handwerker Gallery, Ithaca, NY 1003

Harlow Gallery, Kennebec Valley Art Association, Hallowell, ME 611

Harry Ransom Center at the University of Texas at Austin, Austin, TX 1390

Harvard University Art Museums, Cambridge, MA..672

The Harwood Museum of Art of the University of New Mexico, Taos, NM 952

Hatton Gallery, Colorado State University, Fort Collins, CO 217

Hawaii Pacific University Gallery, Honolulu, HI..395

Hawaii State Foundation on Culture & the Arts and Hawaii State Art Museum, Honolulu, HI.............................395

Hayden Museum of American Art, Paris, TX 1442

Heard Museum, Phoenix, AZ........................40

Hearst Art Gallery, St. Mary's College, Moraga, CA 128

Hearst Castle, San Simeon, CA...................177

Heckscher Museum of Art, Huntington, NY 1000

Helen Day Art Center, Stowe, VT 1488

Helen E. Copeland Gallery, Bozeman, MT..842

Helena Gallery, Helena, MT 849

Henry Art Gallery, Seattle, WA 1566

Henry County Museum and Cultural Arts Center, Clinton, MO..............................813

The Henry Sheldon Museum of Vermont History, Middlebury, VT 1481

Herbert F. Johnson Museum of Art, Ithaca, NY...1003

The Heritage Center, Pine Ridge, SD.........1354

Heritage Center of Lancaster County, Inc., Lancaster, PA..................................1265

Heritage Library Museum, Anchorage, AK..22

The Heritage Museum, Baltimore, MD........632

Heritage of the Americas Museum, El Cajon, CA..92

The Hermitage Foundation, Norfolk, VA...1521

Hibel Museum of Art, Jupiter, FL 316

The Hickory Museum of Art, Hickory, NC 1106

Hiddenite Center, Inc., Hiddenite, NC........1106

Higgins Armory Museum, Worcester, MA...721

Higgins Art Gallery - Cape Cod Community College, West Barnstable, MA..717

The High Museum of Art, Atlanta, GA........360

High Plains Western Heritage Center, Spearfish, SD 1357

Highlands Art League, Sebring, FL...............345

Hill Cumorah Visitors Center & Historic Sites, Palmyra, NY 1050

Hill-Stead Museum, Farmington, CT 241

Hillstrom Museum of Art, Saint Peter, MN..793

Hillwood Art Museum, Brookville, NY 971

Hiram Blauvelt Art Museum, Oradell, NJ....919

Hirshhorn Museum and Sculpture Garden, Smithsonian Institution, Washington, DC...280

The Hispanic Society of America, New York, NY...1027

Historic Arkansas Museum, Little Rock, AR..62

Historical Museum-Archival Center, Mission Hills, CA.....................................126

Historical Society of Garden County, Oshkosh, NE..871

Hockaday Museum of Art, Kalispell, MT....850

Hofstra Museum, Hempstead, NY................997

Holland Area Arts Council, Holland, MI 746

Hollins University Eleanor D. Wilson Museum, Roanoke, VA 1535

Holocaust Museum Houston, Houston, TX 1426

Holter Museum of Art, Helena, MT............849

Honeywell Center, Wabash, IN.....................503

Honolulu Academy of Arts, Honolulu, HI ...395

Hood Museum of Art, Hanover, NH............888

Hoosier Salon Gallery, Indianapolis, IN.......483

Hopewell Museum, Paris, KY 582

Housatonic Museum of Art, Bridgeport, CT 236

Howard University Gallery of Art, Washington, DC...281

The Hoyt Institute of Fine Arts, New Castle, PA 1273

Hoyt Sherman Place, Des Moines, IA...........514

The Hubbard Museum of the American West, Ruidoso Downs, NM....................946

The Hudson River Museum, Yonkers, NY.1087

Hui No'eau Visual Arts Center, Makawao, Maui, HI 401

Humboldt Arts Council/Morris Graves Museum of Art, Eureka, CA 94

Hunt Institute for Botanical Documentation, Pittsburgh, PA 1292

Hunter College Art Galleries, New York, NY 1027

Hunter Museum of American Art, Chattanooga, TN 1362

Hunterdon Museum of Art, Clinton, NJ.......901

Huntington Library, Art Collections, and Botanical Gardens, San Marino, CA 174

Huntington Museum of Art, Inc., Huntington, WV 1583

Huntsville Museum of Art, Huntsville, AL 12

Hus Var Fine Art, Buffalo, NY 973

Hutchinson Art Center, Hutchinson, KS.......545

Hutchinson County Museum, Borger, TX..1397

The Hyde Collection, Glens Falls, NY 994

Hyde Park Art Center, Chicago, IL 421

IUPUI Cultural Arts Gallery, Indianapolis, IN...483

Ida Goodstein Visual Arts Center, Casper, WY...1629

Illinois State Museum, Springfield, IL 458

Illinois State Museum, Chicago Gallery, Chicago, IL..422

Illinois State Museum/Lockport Gallery, Lockport, IL...443

IMA - Indianapolis Museum of Art, Indianapolis, IN...483

Imperial Calcasieu Museum, Inc., Lake Charles, LA..590

Independence Historical Museum, Independence, KS.....................................545

Indian City U.S.A., Anadarko, OK.............1195

Indiana State Museum, Indianapolis, IN 484

Indiana University Art Museum, Bloomington, IN.......................................469

Indiana University Kokomo Art Gallery, Kokomo, IN...486

Indianapolis Art Center, Indianapolis, IN.....484

The Institute For American Indian Studies (IAIS), Washington Green, CT ...263

Institute of American Indian Arts Museum, Santa Fe, NM 947

The Institute of Contemporary Art, Boston, MA..666

Institute of Contemporary Art at Maine College of Art (ICA at MECA), Portland, ME...619

Institute of Contemporary Art, University of Pennsylvania, Philadelphia, PA 1282

Institute of Visual Arts, University of Wisconsin-Milwaukee, Milwaukee, WI.1611

The Interchurch Center, New York, NY.....1027

International Center of Photography, New York, NY...1028

International Children's Art Museum, San Francisco, CA..166

The International Clown Hall of Fame & Research Center, Inc., Milwaukee, WI.1611

International Images, Ltd., Sewickley, PA .1299

International Institute of Metropolitan Detroit, Detroit, MI 737

International Museum of Art and Science, McAllen, TX............................1437
International Museum of the Horse, Lexington, KY............................573
International Print Center New York, New York, NY............................1028
International Sculpture Center, Hamilton, NJ............................906
Intuit: The Center for Intuitive and Outsider Art, Chicago, IL......................422
Iredell Museum of Arts & Heritage, Statesville, NC............................1120
Irene Cullis Gallery, Greensboro College, Greensboro, NC............................1104
Iris & B. Gerald Cantor Center for Visual Arts at Stanford University, Stanford, CA............................188
Iron County Museum, Caspian, MI............731
Irvine Fine Arts Center, Irvine, CA.............105
The Irvine Museum, Irvine, CA 105
Irving Arts Center, Irving, TX 1430
Isabel Anderson Comer Museum & Arts Center, Sylacauga, AL............................18
Isabella Stewart Gardner Museum, Boston, MA 666
Isamu Noguchi Garden Museum, Long Island City, NY............................1010
Isla Center For the Arts at the University of Guam, Mangilao, GU 1640
Island Museum of Art, Westcott Bay Institute, Friday Harbor, WA..................1554
Islip Art Museum, East Islip, NY 986

The J. Paul Getty Museum, Los Angeles, CA............................116
J. Wayne Stark University Center Galleries, College Station, TX..............1401
Jacksonville Museum of Modern Art, Jacksonville, FL............................314
Jacqueline Casey Hudgens Center for the Arts, Duluth, GA............................371
Jacques Marchais Museum of Tibetan Art, Staten Island, NY............................1072
Jaffrey Civic Center, Jaffrey, NH..................889
Jamaica Center for Arts & Learning (JCAL), Jamaica, NY............................1004
James A. Michener Art Museum, Doylestown, PA............................1249
James & Meryl Hearst Center for the Arts and Sculpture Garden, Cedar Falls, IA............................508
James E. Lewis Museum of Art, Morgan State University, Baltimore, MD............633
James J. Hill House, Saint Paul, MN............790
James Prendergast Library Association, Art Gallery, Jamestown, NY..................1005
Jane L. and Robert H. Weiner Judaic Museum, Rockville, MD............................651
Jane Voorhees Zimmerli Art Museum, New Brunswick, NJ............................915
Janet Turner Print Museum, Chico, CA..........83
Japan Society Gallery, New York, NY.......1028
Japanese American National Museum, Los Angeles, CA............................117
Jasper Rand Art Museum, at Westfield Athenaeum, Westfield, MA......................718
Jay I. Kislak Foundation, Miami Lakes, FL............................327
Jean P. Haydon Museum, Pago Pago, AS ..1640
Jefferson Historical Society and Museum, Jefferson, TX............................1431
Jersey City Museum, Jersey City, NJ..........908
The Jewish Museum, New York, NY............1029
Jim Powers Junk Art Museum, Gage, OK.1201
Jim Savage Western Art and Gift Gallery and Memorial Studio, Sioux Falls, SD..1356
John A. Logan College Museum, Carterville, IL............................416
John and Mable Ringling Museum of Art, Sarasota, FL............................344
John Furlong Gallery, Menomonie, WI.....1609
John James Audubon Center at Mill Grove, Audubon, PA............................1241

John James Audubon Museum, Henderson, KY............................571
John Marlor Arts Center, Milledgeville, GA............................380
John Michael Kohler Arts Center, Sheboygan, WI............................1621
John Slade Ely House, New Haven, CT 253
The Johns Hopkins University Archaeological Collection, Baltimore, MD............................633
Johnson County Community College, Gallery of Art, Overland Park, KS.........555
Jonson Gallery of the University of New Mexico Art Museum, Albuquerque, NM............................933
Jordan Schnitzer Museum of Art, Eugene, OR............................1223
Joseloff Gallery, Hartford Art School, University of Hartford, West Hartford, CT............................264
Joslyn Art Museum, Omaha, NE..................871
Judah L. Magnes Museum, Berkeley, CA......76
Judaica Museum of Central Synagogue, New York, NY............................1029
The Judaica Museum of the Hebrew Home at Riverdale, Riverdale, NY........1057
Jule Collins Smith Museum of Fine Art, Auburn, AL............................3
Jundt Art Museum, Spokane, WA..............1571
Juniata College Museum of Art, Huntingdon, PA............................1262

Kala Art Institute Gallery, Berkeley, CA........76
Kalamazoo Institute of Arts, Kalamazoo, MI............................748
The Kansas African American Museum, Wichita, KS............................561
Karl Drerup Fine Arts Gallery at Plymouth State University, Plymouth, NH............................893
Katherine Dunham Dynamic Museum, East Saint Louis, IL............................431
Katherine Nash Gallery, Minneapolis, MN............................782
Katonah Museum of Art, Katonah, NY......1006
Kauai Museum, Lihue, HI 401
Kemp Center for the Arts, Wichita Falls, TX............................1461
Kemper Museum of Contemporary Art, Kansas City, MO............................821
Kennedy Art Center Gallery at Holy Names University, Oakland, CA..............133
Kennedy-Douglass Center for the Arts, Florence, AL............................9
Kennedy Museum of Art, Athens, OH 1140
Kenosha Public Museum, Kenosha, WI.....1602
The Kent Art Association, Kent, CT............247
Kent State University Museum, Kent, OH.1169
Kent State University, School of Art Galleries, Kent, OH............................1169
The Kentuck Museum Association/Art Center/Festival of the Arts, Northport, AL............................17
The Kentucky Folk Art Center, Morehead, KY............................580
Kentucky Gateway Museum Center, Maysville, KY............................579
Key West Museum of Art and History, Key West, FL............................318
Kimbell Art Museum, Fort Worth, TX.......1417
Kipp Gallery at Indiana University of Pennsylvania, Indiana, PA......................1262
Kirkland Arts Center, Kirkland, WA 1557
Kirkland Fine Arts Center-Perkinson Gallery, Decatur, IL............................430
Kirkland Museum of Fine & Decorative Art, Denver, CO............................212
Kittredge Gallery, University of Puget Sound Art Dept., Tacoma, WA 1573
Klein Museum, Mobridge, SD....................1352
Klemm Gallery, Adrian, MI........................722

Kluge-Ruhe Aboriginal Art Collection at the University of Virginia, Charlottesville, VA............................1499
Knoxville Museum of Art, Knoxville, TN .1370
Kokomo Art Association Art Center, Kokomo, IN............................487
Koreshan State Historic Site, Estero, FL....306
Koshare Indian Museum, Inc., La Junta, CO............................224
Koucky Gallery, Bokeelia, FL 297
Krannert Art Museum and Kinkead Pavilion, Champaign, IL............................416
Krasl Art Center, Saint Joseph, MI..............763
The Kreeger Museum, Washington, DC.......281
Krempp Gallery, Jasper, IN........................486
Kresge Art Museum, East Lansing, MI........739

L.D. "Brink" Brinkman Foundation, Kerrville, TX............................1431
La Raza/Galeria Posada, Sacramento, CA ...153
La Salle University Art Museum, Philadelphia, PA............................1282
Laband Art Gallery, Loyola Marymount University, Los Angeles, CA....................117
LACE (Los Angeles Contemporary Exhibitions), Los Angeles, CA..............117
Ladew Topiary Gardens, Monkton, MD.......649
Lafayette College Art Gallery, Williams Center for the Arts, Easton, PA 1250
Laguna Art Museum, Laguna Beach, CA 107
Lakes Art Center, Okoboji, IA.....................525
Lakeview Museum of Arts and Sciences, Peoria, IL............................450
Lamar Dodd Art Center, LaGrange College, LaGrange, GA............................375
The Lamont Gallery, Exeter, NH..................888
Lancaster Museum/Art Gallery, Lancaster, CA............................108
Lancaster Museum of Art, Lancaster, PA...1266
Lane Community College Art Gallery, Eugene, OR............................1223
Lansing Art Gallery, Lansing, MI................750
Laredo Center for the Arts, Laredo, TX....1434
Larson Museum and Gallery, Yakima, WA............................1578
Las Vegas Art Museum, Las Vegas, NV 879
Las Vegas Natural History Museum, Las Vegas, NV............................879
Latitudes Gallery, Bismarck, ND................1128
Latvian Folk Art Museum, Chicago, IL 423
Laumeier Sculpture Park & Museum, Saint Louis, MO............................834
Laura A. Sprague Art Gallery, Joliet, IL 440
Laurel Arts, Somerset, PA............................1300
Lauren Rogers Museum of Art, Laurel, MS............................804
Leanin' Tree Museum of Western Art, Boulder, CO............................203
Leedel Moorehead-Graham Fine Arts Gallery, Pine Bluff, AR............................66
Lehigh University Art Galleries/Museum Operations, Bethlehem, PA......................1242
Lehman College Art Gallery, Bronx, NY.....966
Leigh Yawkey Woodson Art Museum, Wausau, WI............................1626
LeMoyne Art Foundation, Inc., Tallahassee, FL............................347
Lentz Center for Asian Culture, Lincoln, NE............................865
Leslie Powell Foundation and Gallery, Lawton, OK............................1204
Levere Memorial Temple, Evanston, IL.......434
Lewistown Art Center, Lewistown, MT.......850
Libby Museum, Wolfeboro, NH 897
Liberty Village Arts Center & Gallery, Chester, MT............................844
Licking County Arts, Newark, OH.............1178
Light Crust Doughboys Hall of Fame & Museum - Governor Jim Hogg City Park, Quitman, TX............................1444
The Light Factory - Museum of Photography & Film, Charlotte, NC......1095

Art Museums and Galleries–Continued

Lighthouse Center for the Arts, Tequesta, FL...351
Lilian Fendig Art Gallery, Rensselaer, IN....497
The Lion and Lamb Peace Arts Center, Bluffton, OH...1143
The Lithuanian Museum, Chicago, IL...423
Littleton Historical Museum, Littleton, CO...227
The Living Arts and Science Center, Inc., Lexington, KY..573
The Living Word National Bible Museum, Aledo, TX...........................1386
Lois E. Woods Museum, Norfolk, VA........1522
Long Beach Museum of Art, Long Beach, CA...111
Long Island Museum of American Art, History & Carriages, Stony Brook, NY...1075
Longboat Key Center for the Arts, Longboat Key, FL......................................322
LongHouse Reserve, East Hampton, NY.....986
Longview Museum of Fine Arts, Longview, TX..1434
Longwood Center for the Visual Arts, Farmville, VA.......................................1504
Lore Degenstein Gallery, Selinsgrove, PA.1299
The Los Angeles Art Association/Gallery 825, Los Angeles, CA..............................117
Los Angeles County Museum of Art, Los Angeles, CA...118
Los Angeles Municipal Art Gallery - Barnsdall Art Park, Los Angeles, CA......118
Los Angeles Museum of the Holocaust, Los Angeles, CA...118
Los Medanos College Art Gallery, Pittsburg, CA...142
Louie-Meager Art Gallery, Fremont, CA.......96
Louisburg College Art Gallery, Louisburg, NC...1109
Louise Wells Cameron Art Museum, Wilmington, NC..1123
Louisiana Art & Science Museum - Irene W. Pennington Planetarium, Baton Rouge, LA...586
Louisiana State University Museum of Art, Baton Rouge, LA..............................586
Louisville Visual Art Association, Louisville, KY...578
Loveland Museum Gallery, Loveland, CO...227
Lowe Art Museum, University of Miami, Coral Gables, FL.....................................301
Lowell Telecommunications Corp., Lowell, MA...691
Loyola University Museum of Art, Chicago, IL..423
Lubeznik Center for the Arts, Michigan City, IN...490
Lucy Craft Laney Museum of Black History and Conference Center, Augusta, GA...365
The Luther W. Brady Art Gallery, Washington, DC..282
Lyman Allyn Art Museum, New London, CT..255
Lyndon House Art, Athens, GA...................356

MAK Center for Art and Architecture at the Schindler House, West Hollywood, CA...197
MIT-List Visual Arts Center, Cambridge, MA...673
M. Louise Aughinbaugh Gallery at Messiah College, Grantham, PA...........1257
MSC Forsyth Center Galleries, Texas A&M University, College Station, TX..1401
Mabee-Gerrer Museum of Art, Shawnee, OK...1213
Macalester College Art Gallery, Janet Wallace Fine Arts Center, Saint Paul, MN...790
MacDonald Art Gallery, Dallas, PA...........1249

MADI Museum, Dallas, TX......................1407
Madison-Morgan Cultural Center, Madison, GA..378
Madison Museum of Contemporary Art, Madison, WI..1605
Madison Museum of Fine Art, Madison, GA..378
Magnolia Plantation and Gardens, Charleston, SC......................................1326
Maier Museum of Art, Randolph-Macon Woman's College, Lynchburg, VA........1515
Main Art Gallery, California State University, Fullerton, Fullerton, CA..........99
Maine Art Gallery, Wiscasset, ME............626
Maitland Art Center, Maitland, FL..............322
Malden Public Library, Malden, MA..........692
Mandeville Gallery, Union College, Schenectady, NY.......................................1067
Manhattan Arts Center, Manhattan, KS........551
The Mansfield Art Center, Mansfield, OH.1173
Marblehead Arts Association - King Hooper Mansion, Marblehead, MA.........693
Marblehead Museum & Historical Society, Marblehead, MA......................693
Marcella Sembrich Opera Museum, Bolton Landing, NY.......................................963
Margaret Fort Trahern Gallery, Clarksville, TN...1363
Margaret Harwell Art Museum, Poplar Bluff, MO...829
Mariani Gallery, University of Northern Colorado, Greeley, CO.............................221
Marianna Kistler Beach Museum of Art at Kansas State University, Manhattan, KS...551
Marietta/Cobb Museum of Art, Marietta, GA..379
Mariposa Museum & World Culture Center, Peterborough, NH.....................893
Maritime & Seafood Industry Museum, Biloxi, MS...798
Marshall County Historical Museum, Holly Springs, MS....................................801
Marshall M. Fredericks Sculpture Museum, University Center, MI..............766
Martin and Osa Johnson Safari Museum, Inc., Chanute, KS.................535
Martin Art Gallery, Allentown, PA............1239
The Martin D'Arcy Museum of Art: The Loyola University Museum of Medieval, Renaissance and Baroque Art, Chicago, IL...424
Marxhausen Art Gallery, Seward, NE.........873
Mary and Leigh Block Museum of Art, Northwestern University, Evanston, IL...434
Mary Baldwin College/Hunt Gallery, Staunton, VA...1537
The Mary Brogan Museum of Art and Science, Tallahassee, FL.........................347
Mary G. Hardin Center for Cultural Arts, Gadsden, AL...10
Mary Porter Sesnon Art Gallery, Santa Cruz, CA...181
Maryhill Museum of Art, Goldendale, WA...1556
Maryland Art Place, Baltimore, MD............634
The Maryland Institute, College of Art: Decker, Meyerhoff and Pinkard Galleries, Baltimore, MD.......................634
Maryville University - Morton J. May Foundation Gallery, Saint Louis, MO.....834
Marywood University Art Galleries (Suraci Gallery and Mahady Gallery), Scranton, PA...1298
MASS MoCA, North Adams, MA...............698
Massee Lane Gardens, Home of American Camellia Society, Fort Valley, GA...373
The Massillon Museum, Massillon, OH.....1175
Masur Museum of Art, Monroe, LA.............592
The Mather Homestead Museum, Library and Memorial Park, Wellsville, NY......1084

The Mattatuck Museum Arts and History Center, Waterbury, CT.............................264
Mattress Factory, Ltd., Pittsburgh, PA.....1293
Maturango Museum of the Indian Wells Valley, Ridgecrest, CA.............................148
Maude I. Kerns Art Center, Eugene, OR...1223
Maui Arts and Cultural Center, Kahului, Maui, HI...399
Maui Okinawa Cultural Center, Waiehu, HI..402
The May Gallery, Patron's Lounge, Beaver Creek, CO.....................................202
MCAD Gallery, Minneapolis, MN..............782
McCarthy Arts Center Gallery, Colchester, VT...1479
McCone County Museum, Circle, MT........844
McCormick Gallery, Midland, TX..............1438
McGuffey Art Center, Charlottesville, VA.1499
McLean County Arts Center, Bloomington, IL..414
McMullen Museum of Art, Boston College, Chestnut Hill, MA.......................675
McNay Art Museum, San Antonio, TX......1448
McWethy Hall, Luce Gallery, Cornell College, Mount Vernon, IA.........................524
Mead Art Museum, Amherst, MA...............658
Meadows Museum, Dallas, TX.................1407
Meadows Museum of Art of Centenary College, Shreveport, LA.............................601
Meeteetse Museum District, Meeteetse, WY...1636
Memorial Art Gallery of the University of Rochester, Rochester, NY.....................1059
Memorial Union Art Gallery, Davis, CA.......90
Memorial Union Gallery, Fargo, ND.........1130
Memphis Brooks Museum of Art, Memphis, TN...1374
Memphis College of Art, Memphis, TN....1374
The Menil Collection, Houston, TX..........1428
Mennello Museum of American Art, Orlando, FL...331
Meridian International Center, Washington, DC..283
Meridian Museum of Art, Meridian, MS.....805
The Merrick Art Gallery, New Brighton, PA...1273
Metamora Museum of Ethnographic Art, Metamora, IN..490
The Metropolitan Museum of Art, New York, NY..1030
Metropolitan State College of Denver/Center for Visual Art, Denver, CO..212
Mexic-Arte Museum, Austin, TX..............1391
Mexican Fine Arts Center Museum, Chicago, IL..424
The Mexican Museum, San Francisco, CA...166
Miami Art Museum, Miami, FL.................324
Miami-Dade College Kendall Campus Art Gallery, Miami, FL.............................324
Miami University Art Museum, Oxford, OH...1181
Michael C. Carlos Museum, Atlanta, GA....361
Michael C. Rockefeller Arts Center Gallery, Fredonia, NY.................................992
Michelson Museum of Art, Marshall, TX..1436
Mid-America All Indian Center, Wichita, KS...562
Middlebury College Museum of Art, Middlebury, VT...1482
Midwest Museum of American Art, Elkhart, IN..474
Mildred Lane Kemper Art Museum, Saint Louis, MO...834
Miles B. Carpenter Museum, Waverly, VA...1543
Military Museum of Southern New England, Danbury, CT..............................238
Miller Art Museum, Sturgeon Bay, WI......1623
Millicent Rogers Museum of Northern New Mexico, Taos, NM.........................952

Milliken Gallery, Converse College, Spartanburg, SC........................1341
The Millionaires' Cars & Disney Collection, Saint Ignace, MI................763
Mills College Art Museum, Oakland, CA....133
Milton Art Museum, Canton, MA................674
Milwaukee Art Museum, Milwaukee, WI..1611
Mingei International Museum, San Diego, CA................157
Minneapolis Institute of Arts, Minneapolis, MN........................782
Minnesota Museum of American Art, Saint Paul, MN........................791
Minnesota State Capitol Historic Site, Saint Paul, MN........................791
Mint Museum of Art, Charlotte, NC..........1095
Mint Museum of Craft + Design, Charlotte, NC........................1096
Miramont Castle Museum, Manitou Springs, CO........................228
Miriam & Ira D. Wallach Art Gallery, New York, NY........................1030
Mission Cultural Center for Latino Arts, San Francisco, CA........................166
Mission Inn Foundation/Museum, Riverside, CA........................149
Mission San Juan Capistrano Museum, San Juan Capistrano, CA........................173
Mississippi Museum of Art, Jackson, MS....802
Missoula Art Museum, Missoula, MT.........851
Mizel Museum, Denver, CO........................213
Mobile Museum of Art, Mobile, AL................14
Modern Art Museum of Fort Worth, Fort Worth, TX........................1418
Mohave Museum of History and Arts, Kingman, AZ........................36
Mondak Heritage Center, Sidney, MT.........853
The Money Museum-Federal Reserve Bank of Kansas City, Kansas City, MO........................821
The Monhegan Museum, Monhegan, ME....615
Monmouth Museum & Cultural Center, Lincroft, NJ........................909
Monongalia Arts Center, Morgantown, WV........................1585
Monroe Community College, Mercer Gallery, Rochester, NY........................1059
Montalvo Arts Center, Saratoga, CA............185
Montana Historical Society, Helena, MT.....849
Montana Museum of Art and Culture, Missoula, MT........................852
Montclair Art Museum, Montclair, NJ.........912
Montclair State University Art Galleries, Upper Montclair, NJ........................929
Monterey Museum of Art, Monterey, CA....128
Montgomery Museum & Lewis Miller Regional Art Center, Christiansburg, VA........................1501
Montgomery Museum of Fine Arts, Montgomery, AL........................16
Moore County Art Association, Dumas, TX........................1410
The Morris Museum, Morristown, NJ.........914
Morris Museum of Art, Augusta, GA............365
Moses Lake Museum & Art Center, Moses Lake, WA........................1559
Mount Holyoke College Art Museum, South Hadley, MA........................709
The Muchnic Gallery, Atchison, KS.............533
Muckenthaler Cultural Center and Mansion Museum, Fullerton, CA..............99
Mulvane Art Museum, Topeka, KS.............559
Munson-Williams-Proctor Arts Institute Museum of Art, Utica, NY........................1079
Muscarelle Museum of Art, Williamsburg, VA........................1545
Muscatine Art Center, Muscatine, IA.........524
Museo de Arte de Ponce (The Luis A. Ferre Foundation, Inc.), Ponce, PR.......1642
Museo de las Americas, Denver, CO..........213
Museo de Las Americas, San Juan, PR......1642
Museo Del Nino, San Juan, PR.................1643

Museo Fuerte Conde de Mirasol de Vieques, Vieques, PR........................1644
Museo ItaloAmericano, San Francisco, CA........................167
Museum and Arts Center in the Sequim Dungeness Valley, Sequim, WA............1570
The Museum for African Art, Long Island City, NY........................1011
Museum in the Community, Hurricane, WV........................1583
Museum NECCA at New England Center for Contemporary Art, Inc., Brooklyn, CT........................237
The Museum of African American Art, Los Angeles, CA........................119
The Museum of African Culture, Portland, ME........................619
Museum of American Glass at Wheaton Village, Millville, NJ........................911
The Museum of American Illustration at the Society of Illustrators, New York, NY........................1031
Museum of Ancient & Modern Art, Penn Valley, CA........................141
Museum of Art, Pullman, WA........................1563
Museum of Art and Archaeology, University of Missouri - Columbia, Columbia, MO........................813
Museum of Art and History at the McPherson Center, Santa Cruz, CA........182
Museum of Art & History at Weston, Weston, CT........................266
Museum of Art at Brigham Young University, Provo, UT........................1469
Museum of Art/Fort Lauderdale, Fort Lauderdale, FL........................307
Museum of Art of Puerto Rico, Santurce, PR........................1643
Museum of Art, Rhode Island School of Design, Providence, RI........................1317
Museum of Arts & Design, New York, NY........................1032
Museum of Arts and Sciences, Macon, GA........................378
The Museum of Arts and Sciences, Inc. and Center for Florida History, Daytona Beach, FL........................303
Museum of Bad Art, Dedham, MA........................679
Museum of Biblical Art, New York, NY...1032
Museum of Chinese in the Americas, New York, NY........................1032
Museum of Church History and Art, Salt Lake City, UT........................1471
Museum of Contemporary Art, Chicago, IL........................424
Museum of Contemporary Art, Denver, CO........................213
Museum of Contemporary Art Cleveland, Cleveland, OH........................1155
The Museum of Contemporary Art, Los Angeles, Los Angeles, CA........................119
Museum of Contemporary Art (MoCA), North Miami, FL........................329
Museum of Contemporary Art of Puerto Rico, Santurce, PR........................1644
Museum of Contemporary Art San Diego, La Jolla, CA........................106
Museum of Contemporary Art San Diego - Downtown, San Diego, CA........................157
Museum of Contemporary Photography, Columbia College Chicago, Chicago, IL........................424
Museum of Contemporary Religious Art (MOCRA)-St. Louis University, Saint Louis, MO........................835
Museum of Craft and Folk Art, San Francisco, CA........................167
Museum of Design Atlanta, Atlanta, GA.....362
Museum of Early Southern Decorative Arts (MESDA), Winston-Salem, NC.....1125
The Museum of East Texas, Lufkin, TX....1436
Museum of Fine Arts, Boston, MA..............667
Museum of Fine Arts, Santa Fe, NM..........948

The Museum of Fine Arts, Houston, Houston, TX........................1428
Museum of Fine Arts of St. Petersburg, Florida, Saint Petersburg, FL................341
Museum of Glass: International Center for Contemporary Art, Tacoma, WA......1573
Museum of Great Christian Preachers & Ministries, Orange Park, FL........................331
Museum of History & Art, Ontario, Ontario, CA........................136
Museum of History, Anthropology and Art, San Juan, PR........................1643
Museum of Indian Arts & Culture/Laboratory of Anthropology, Santa Fe, NM........................948
Museum of Jurassic Technology, Culver City, CA........................88
Museum of Latin American Art, Long Beach, CA........................111
The Museum of Modern Art, New York, NY........................1033
Museum of Nebraska Art, Kearney, NE......864
Museum of Neon Art, Los Angeles, CA......120
Museum of New Mexico, Santa Fe, NM.....949
Museum of Northern Arizona, Flagstaff, AZ........................33
Museum of Northwest Art, La Conner, WA........................1557
The Museum of Outdoor Arts, Englewood, CO........................214
Museum of Overbeck Art Pottery, Cambridge City, IN........................471
Museum of Photographic Arts, San Diego, CA........................158
The Museum of Printing History, Houston, TX........................1428
The Museum of Prints and Printmaking, Albany, NY........................955
The Museum of Russian Art, Minneapolis, MN........................783
Museum of Spanish Colonial Art - MoSCA, Santa Fe, NM........................949
Museum of the African Diaspora, San Francisco, CA........................167
The Museum of the Alphabet, Waxhaw, NC........................1121
Museum of the American Philosophical Society, Philadelphia, PA........................1283
Museum of the American Quilter's Society (MAQS), Paducah, KY.............581
Museum of the Hudson Highlands, Cornwall-on-Hudson, NY........................982
Museum of the National Center of Afro-American Artists, Roxbury, MA.....706
Museum of the Plains Indian, Browning, MT........................843
Museum of the Red River, Idabel, OK....1203
Museum of the Southwest, Midland, TX....1439
Museum of Utah Art & History, Salt Lake City, UT........................1471
The Museum of Western Art, Kerrville, TX........................1431
Museum of Woodcarving, Shell Lake, WI.1621
Museums of Los Gatos, Los Gatos, CA......123
Muskegon Museum of Art, Muskegon, MI........................758
Mystic Arts Center, Mystic, CT.................250

NAU Art Museum, Flagstaff, AZ.................33
NCCU Art Museum, Durham, NC.............1099
NIU Art Museum, DeKalb, IL........................429
Napa Valley Museum, Yountville, CA.........200
Naples Museum of Art and the Philharmonic Center for the Arts Galleries, Naples, FL........................328
Nasher Museum of Art at Duke University, Durham, NC........................1099
Nasher Sculpture Center, Dallas, TX.........1407
Nassau County Museum of Art, Roslyn Harbor, NY........................1062
National Academy Museum and School of Fine Arts, New York, NY.................1033

Art Museums and Galleries–Continued

National Academy of Sciences, Washington, DC..........283

National Afro-American Museum & Cultural Center, Wilberforce, OH..........1191

The National Agricultural Center & Hall of Fame, Bonner Springs, KS..........534

National Art Museum of Sport, Inc., Indianapolis, IN..........485

National Arts Club, New York, NY..........1034

National Center for Children's Illustrated Literature, Abilene, TX..........1385

National Cowboy & Western Heritage Museum, Oklahoma City, OK..........1208

National Gallery of Art, Washington, DC....285

National Hall of Fame for Famous American Indians, Anadarko, OK..........1196

National Hispanic Cultural Center, Art Museum, Albuquerque, NM..........935

National Infantry Museum, Fort Benning, GA..........372

National Liberty Museum, Philadelphia, PA..........1284

National Museum of African Art, Smithsonian Institution, Washington, DC..........285

National Museum of American Illustration, Newport, RI..........1314

The National Museum of Catholic Art & History, New York, NY..........1034

National Museum of Ceramic Art and Glass, Baltimore, MD..........635

National Museum of Racing and Hall of Fame, Saratoga Springs, NY..........1065

National Museum of the American Indian, Smithsonian Institution, New York, NY..........1034

National Museum of Wildlife Art, Jackson, WY..........1634

National Museum of Women in the Arts, Washington, DC..........287

National Museum of Woodcarving, Custer, SD..........1346

National Portrait Gallery, Washington, DC..........287

National Road/Zane Grey Museum, Norwich, OH..........1180

National Shaving And Barbershop Museum, Meriden, CT..........249

National Society of the Children of the American Revolution Museum, Washington, DC..........287

National Steinbeck Center, Salinas, CA..........154

National Vietnam Veterans Art Museum, Chicago, IL..........425

Navajo Nation Museum, Window Rock, AZ..........53

Nave Museum, Victoria, TX..........1457

Nebraska State Capitol, Lincoln, NE..........866

The Nelson-Atkins Museum of Art, Kansas City, MO..........822

Neuberger Museum of Art, Purchase College, State University of New York, Purchase, NY..........1056

The Neustadt Collection of Tiffany Glass, Long Island City, NY..........1011

Nevada Museum of Art, Reno, NV..........881

New Britain Museum of American Art, Inc., New Britain, CT..........251

The New England Carousel Museum, Bristol, CT..........236

New England College Gallery, Henniker, NH..........889

New Hampshire Institute of Art, Manchester, NH..........892

New Harmony Gallery of Contemporary Art, New Harmony, IN..........494

New Jersey State Museum, Trenton, NJ..........927

New London County Historical Society, New London, CT..........255

New Mexico State Fair Fine Arts Gallery, Albuquerque, NM..........935

The New Milford Historical Society, New Milford, CT..........256

The New Museum of Contemporary Art, New York, NY..........1035

New Orleans Museum of Art, New Orleans, LA..........597

New Visions Gallery, Inc., Marshfield, WI..........1608

New World Art Center/T.F. Chen Cultural Center, New York, NY..........1035

The New York Historical Society, New York, NY..........1035

New York State Historical Association/Fenimore Art Museum, Cooperstown, NY..........981

The New York Studio School of Drawing, Painting & Sculpture, New York, NY..........1036

The Newark Museum, Newark, NJ..........916

Newcomb Art Gallery, New Orleans, LA....598

Newport Art Museum, Newport, RI..........1314

The Newsome House Museum & Cultural Center, Newport News, VA..........1520

Nicholas Roerich Museum, New York, NY..........1037

Nicolaysen Art Museum and Discovery Center, Casper, WY..........1629

Nishna Heritage Museum, Oakland, IA..........525

Nita Stewart Haley Memorial Library & J. Evetts Haley History Center, Midland, TX..........1439

The Noble Maritime Collection, Staten Island, NY..........1073

Nora Eccles Harrison Museum of Art, Logan, UT..........1466

Nordic Heritage Museum, Seattle, WA..........1567

Norman R. Eppink Art Gallery, Emporia State University, Emporia, KS..........539

Norman Rockwell Museum, Stockbridge, MA..........712

Norman Rockwell Museum, Rutland, VT..1486

North Carolina Museum of Art, Raleigh, NC..........1115

North Carolina Pottery Center, Seagrove, NC..........1119

North Carolina State University Gallery of Art & Design, Raleigh, NC..........1116

North Country Museum of Arts, Park Rapids, MN..........786

North Dakota Museum of Art, Grand Forks, ND..........1132

North Florida Community College Art Gallery, Madison, FL..........322

North Michigan University DeVos Art Museum, Marquette, MI..........754

North Seattle Community College Art Gallery, Seattle, WA..........1567

The North Shore Arts Association, Gloucester, MA..........684

Northeast Louisiana Delta African American Heritage Museum, Monroe, LA..........592

Northeastern Nevada Museum, Elko, NV..........876

Northern Galleries, Aberdeen, SD..........1344

Northern Illinois University Art Gallery in Chicago, Chicago, IL..........425

Northern Kentucky University Art Galleries, Highland Heights, KY..........571

The Northern Virginia Fine Arts Association at the Athenaeum, Alexandria, VA..........1493

Northwest Art Center, Minot, ND..........1134

Northwest Museum of Arts & Culture (Eastern Washington State Historical Society), Spokane, WA..........1571

Norton Museum of Art, West Palm Beach, FL..........353

Norton Simon Museum, Pasadena, CA..........140

The Noyes Museum of Art, Oceanville, NJ..........918

Oak Hill and The Martha Berry Museum, Rome, GA..........382

Oak Ridge Art Center, Oak Ridge, TN..........1382

Oakdale Museum, Oakdale, CA..........132

Oakland Museum of California, Oakland, CA..........134

Oakland Museum of California-Sculpture Court at City Center, Oakland, CA..........134

Oakland University Art Gallery, Rochester, MI..........761

Oceanside Museum of Art, Oceanside, CA..........135

The Octagon Center for the Arts, Ames, IA..........505

Office of Cultural Affairs & Museum Programs at Salisbury University, Salisbury, MD..........652

The Ogden Museum of Southern Art, University of New Orleans, New Orleans, LA..........598

Ogden Union Station Museums, Ogden, UT..........1468

Oglethorpe University Museum of Art, Atlanta, GA..........362

Ogunquit Museum of American Art, Ogunquit, ME..........617

Ohio University Art Gallery, Athens, OH..1140

Ohr-O'Keefe Museum of Art, Biloxi, MS...799

Ohrmann Museum and Gallery, Drummond, MT..........846

Ojai Valley Historical Society and Museum, Ojai, CA..........135

Okefenokee Heritage Center, Waycross, GA..........391

Oklahoma City Museum of Art, Oklahoma City, OK..........1208

Oklahoma Visual Arts Coalition, Oklahoma City, OK..........1210

Olana State Historic Site, Hudson, NY..........1000

Old Church Cultural Center School of Art, Demarest, NJ..........902

Old Davie School Historical Museum, Davie, FL..........302

Old Dominion University - University Gallery, Norfolk, VA..........1523

The Old Jail Art Center, Albany, TX..........1385

Old State House, Hartford, CT..........245

Olympic Sculpture Park, Seattle, WA..........1568

The Opelousas Museum of Art, Inc., Opelousas, LA..........599

Orange County Historical Museum, Hillsborough, NC..........1107

Orange County Museum of Art, Newport Beach, CA..........130

Oregon State University Memorial Union Concourse Gallery, Corvallis, OR..........1222

Oriental Institute Museum, University of Chicago, Chicago, IL..........426

Orlando Museum of Art, Orlando, FL..........332

Ormond Memorial Art Museum & Garden, Ormond Beach, FL..........333

Osceola Center for the Arts, Kissimmee, FL..........319

Ossining Historical Society Museum, Ossining, NY..........1047

Owatonna Arts Center, Owatonna, MN..........786

Owens Community College/Walter E. Terhune Gallery, Perrysburg, OH..........1182

Owensboro Museum of Fine Art, Inc., Owensboro, KY..........581

The Ozark Folk Center, Mountain View, AR..........65

P. Buckley Moss Museum, Waynesboro, VA..........1544

P.S. 1 Contemporary Art Center, Long Island City, NY..........1011

Pacem in Terris, Warwick, NY..........1082

Pacific Asia Museum, Pasadena, CA..........140

Pacific Grove Art Center Associates, Inc., Pacific Grove, CA..........137

Pacific Lutheran University Art Galleries, Tacoma, WA..........1574

Packwood House Museum, Lewisburg, PA..........1268

Paine Art Center and Gardens, Oshkosh,
    WI 1617
Painted Bride Art Center, Philadelphia,
    PA 1284
The Palette & Chisel, Chicago, IL 426
Palm Beach Institute of Contemporary
    Art, Lake Worth, FL...........................320
Palm Springs Art Museum, Palm Springs,
    CA 139
Palmer Museum of Art, The Pennsylvania
    State University, University Park, PA....1304
Palo Alto Art Center, Palo Alto, CA 139
Palos Verdes Art Center, Rancho Palos
    Verdes, CA.......................................145
The Paperweight Museum, Santa Cruz,
    CA 182
Paris Gibson Square Museum of Art,
    Great Falls, MT 848
Parkersburg Art Center, Parkersburg, WV .1586
Parkland College Art Gallery,
    Champaign, IL 417
The Parrish Art Museum, Southampton,
    NY 1070
Parson Fisher House, Blue Hill, ME...........606
The Parthenon, Nashville, TN 1379
Pasadena Museum of California Art,
    Pasadena, CA....................................140
Passaic County Community College,
    Paterson, NJ.....................................920
The Patricia & Phillip Frost Art Museum,
    Miami, FL...325
The Patrick & Beatrice Haggerty
    Museum of Art, Milwaukee, WI...........1613
Paul and Lulu Hilliard University Art
    Museum, University of Louisiana at
    Lafayette, Lafayette, LA 590
Paul Robeson Art Gallery, Newark, NJ........917
Paul Robeson Cultural and Performing
    Arts Center, Wilberforce, OH 1191
The Peace Museum, Chicago, IL.................426
Pearce Collections Museum, Corsicana,
    TX 1402
Pelham Art Center, Pelham, NY 1052
Pen & Brush, New York, NY 1037
The Pena-Peck House, Saint Augustine,
    FL 339
Pence Gallery, Davis, CA 90
Peninsula Fine Arts Center, Newport
    News, VA...1520
Peninsula Museum of Art, Belmont, CA........74
Pennsylvania Academy of the Fine Arts,
    Philadelphia, PA................................1284
Pensacola Museum of Art, Pensacola, FL....336
The Peoria Art Guild, Peoria, IL 451
Perkins Center for the Arts, Moorestown,
    NJ 912
Perspective Gallery, Blacksburg, VA 1497
Petersburg Area Art League, Petersburg,
    VA 1525
Petersburg Regional Art Center,
    Petersburg, VA..................................1525
Pettigrew Home and Museum, Sioux
    Falls, SD 1356
The Philadelphia Art Alliance,
    Philadelphia, PA 1285
Philadelphia Museum of Art,
    Philadelphia, PA 1285
Philadelphia Museum of
    Judaica/Congregation Rodeph Shalom,
    Philadelphia, PA 1286
The Philbrook Museum of Art, Inc.,
    Tulsa, OK...1215
Philip and Muriel Berman Museum of
    Art at Ursinus College, Collegeville,
    PA 1247
The Phillips Collection, Washington, DC.....289
The Phillips Museum of Art, Franklin &
    Marshall College, Lancaster, PA...........1267
Philmont Museums, Cimarron, NM.............938
Phippen Museum, Prescott, AZ 42
Phoenix Art Museum, Phoenix, AZ..............41

Photographic Investments Gallery,
    Atlanta, GA.......................................363
Piccadilly Museum of Transportation
    Memorabilia and Advertising Art,
    Butte, MT...843
Pickens County Museum of Art &
    History, Pickens, SC...........................1340
The Picker Art Gallery, Hamilton, NY........997
Piedmont Arts Association, Martinsville,
    VA 1516
The Pierpont Morgan Library, New York,
    NY 1037
Pioneer Town, Wimberley, TX...................1462
Pittsburgh Center for the Arts, Pittsburgh,
    PA 1293
Plains Art Museum, Fargo, ND 1130
Plainsman Museum, Aurora, NE 856
Plattsburgh State Art Museum S.U.N.Y.,
    Plattsburgh, NY.................................1053
Plaza de La Raza, Inc. & Boathouse
    Gallery, Los Angeles, CA 121
Polish American Museum, Port
    Washington, NY.................................1054
Polish Museum of America, Chicago, IL.....426
Polk County Heritage Gallery, Des
    Moines, IA..515
Polk Museum of Art, Lakeland, FL.............321
Pomerene Center for the Arts, Coshocton,
    OH 1159
Pomona College Museum of Art,
    Claremont, CA....................................85
Ponca City Art Center, Ponca City, OK....1212
Pope John Paul II Cultural Center,
    Washington, DC.................................289
Popular Arts Museum, San Juan, PR..........1643
Port Angeles Fine Arts Center &
    Webster's Woods Art Park, Port
    Angeles, WA.....................................1561
Port Discovery, The Children's Museum
    in Baltimore, Baltimore, MD.................636
Port Huron Museum, Port Huron, MI 761
Porter Thermometer Museum, Onset, MA...700
Portholes Into the Past, Medina, OH..........1176
Portland Art Museum, Portland, OR 1232
Portland Museum of Art, Portland, ME.......619
Portland State University Galleries,
    Portland, OR.....................................1233
Portsmouth Museums, Portsmouth, VA......1526
Pratt Manhattan Gallery, New York, NY ...1037
Price Tower Arts Center, Bartlesville, OK .1197
Princeton University Art Museum,
    Princeton, NJ.....................................922
The Print Center, Philadelphia, PA 1287
Project Art-University of Iowa and
    Clinics, Iowa City, IA 520
Provincetown Art Association and
    Museum, Provincetown, MA 704
Provisions Library, Washington, DC 289
Public Library of Charlotte and
    Mecklenburg County, Charlotte, NC 1096
Pueblo Art Guild and Gallery, Pueblo,
    CO 230
Pueblo of Pojoaque, Poeh Museum, Santa
    Fe, NM...949
Pump House Regional Arts Center, La
    Crosse, WI.......................................1603
Purdue University Galleries, West
    Lafayette, IN.....................................503
Putnam County Museum, Greencastle, IN...479
Pyramid Hill Sculpture Park & Museum,
    Hamilton, OH 1168

Quartersaw Gallery, Portland, OR 1233
Queens Library Gallery, Jamaica, NY........1004
Queens Museum of Art, Queens, NY.........1056
Quietude Garden Gallery, East
    Brunswick, NJ...................................903
Quincy Art Center, Quincy, IL....................452
Quinlan Visual Arts Center, Gainesville,
    GA 374

R.S. Barnwell Memorial Garden and Art
    Center, Shreveport, LA 601

The R.W. Norton Art Gallery, Shreveport,
    LA 601
Racine Art Museum (RAM), Racine, WI...1619
Radford University Art Museum,
    Radford, VA......................................1527
Rahr West Art Museum, Manitowoc, WI...1607
Ransom Visual Arts Center, Saint
    Petersburg, FL...................................342
Rawls Museum Arts, Courtland, VA 1502
The Ray Drew Gallery-New Mexico
    Highlands University, Las Vegas, NM 941
The Reader's Digest Association, Inc.,
    Pleasantville, NY...............................1053
Reading Public Museum, Reading, PA.......1296
Red Earth Museum, Oklahoma City, OK...1210
Red River Valley Museum, Vernon, TX.....1457
Redwood Library and Athenaeum,
    Newport, RI......................................1315
Reese Bullen Gallery, Arcata, CA................72
The Reeves Center, Washington and Lee
    University, Lexington, VA....................1513
The Regina A. Quick Center for the Arts,
    Saint Bonaventure, NY 1063
Regina Gouger Miller Gallery, Pittsburgh,
    PA 1294
Rehoboth Art League, Inc., Rehoboth
    Beach, DE...272
Renaissance Gallery, Northport, AL 17
The Renaissance Society at The
    University of Chicago, Chicago, IL........427
Renee and Chaim Gross Foundation,
    New York, NY 1037
Renwick Gallery of the Smithsonian
    American Art Museum, Washington,
    DC 290
Reynolda House Museum of American
    Art, Winston-Salem, NC 1126
Reynolds Homestead, Critz, VA 1502
Rhode Island Black Heritage Society,
    Providence, RI...................................1318
The Rice Museum, Georgetown, SC..........1333
Rice University Art Gallery, Houston, TX.1429
Richard E. Peeler Art Center,
    Greencastle, IN..................................479
Richard L. Nelson Gallery & The Fine
    Arts Collection, UC Davis, Davis, CA......90
Richmond Art Center, Richmond, CA..........148
Richmond Art Museum, Richmond, IN........497
Ringling School of Art and Design, Selby
    Gallery, Sarasota, FL..........................345
Ritz Theatre & LaVilla Museum,
    Jacksonville, FL.................................315
Riverside Art Museum, Riverside, CA.........149
Riverside Community College Art
    Gallery, Riverside, CA 149
Roane County Museum of History & Art,
    Kingston, TN....................................1369
Roanoke Island Festival Park; Homeport
    of the "Elizabeth II", Manteo, NC.........1110
Roberson Museum and Science Center,
    Binghamton, NY................................962
Robert E. Wilson Gallery, Huntington, IN ...481
Robert Else Gallery, Sacramento, CA 153
Robert Hull Fleming Museum,
    Burlington, VT..................................1478
Robert T. Wright Community Gallery of
    Art, Grayslake, IL..............................439
Robert V. Fullerton Art Museum,
    California State University, San
    Bernardino, San Bernardino, CA.............155
Rochester Art Center, Rochester, MN 788
Rockford Art Museum, Rockford, IL...........455
Rockford College Art Gallery/Clark Arts
    Center, Rockford, IL...........................455
Rockport Art Association, Rockport, MA 705
Rockwell Museum of Western Art,
    Corning, NY 982
Rocky Mount Arts Center, Rocky Mount,
    NC 1117
Rocky Mountain College of Art + Design
    Galleries, Lakewood, CO.....................225
Rocky Reach Dam, Wenatchee, WA 1577

Art Museums and Galleries–Continued

Rodin Museum, Philadelphia, PA 1287

Rogers House Museum Gallery, Ellsworth, KS....................................538

Roland Gibson Gallery, Potsdam, NY 1054

Romanian Ethnic Art Museum, Cleveland, OH 1156

Rome Art and Community Center, Rome, NY...1061

Rosa Ponselle Museum, Meriden, CT 249

The Rose Art Museum, Waltham, MA.........715

Rose Center Museum, Morristown, TN 1376

Rosenbach Museum & Library, Philadelphia, PA 1287

Rosenberg Gallery, Goucher College, Baltimore, MD...................................636

Rosenbruch Wildlife Museum, St. George, UT 1474

Rosenthal Gallery of Art, Caldwell, ID.......405

Roswell Museum and Art Center, Roswell, NM......................................946

Roswell Visual Arts Center & Gallery, Roswell, GA.....................................382

Rothko Chapel, Houston, TX....................1429

The Rotunda Gallery, Brooklyn, NY...........970

The Rubelle & Norman Schafler Gallery, Brooklyn, NY 970

Rudolph E. Lee Gallery, Clemson, SC.......1328

The Ruth & Sherman Lee Institute for Japanese Art, Hanford, CA 101

Ruth Chandler Williamson Gallery, Scripps College, Claremont, CA................86

Ruth Eckerd Hall, Clearwater, FL 300

Rutland Historical Society, Rutland, VT 1486

S.C.R.A.P. Gallery, Indio, CA.....................104

SITE Santa Fe, Santa Fe, NM 950

Saco Museum, Saco, ME 621

Saginaw Art Museum, Saginaw, MI............763

Saint-Gaudens National Historic Site, Cornish, NH......................................885

St. George Art Museum, Saint George, UT..1470

St. Johnsbury Athenaeum, Saint Johnsbury, VT...................................1487

Saint Joseph College Art Gallery, West Hartford, CT 265

Saint Joseph's University - University Gallery - Boland Hall, Philadelphia, PA...1288

St. Lawrence University - Richard F. Brush Art Gallery and Permanent Collection, Canton, NY 976

The Saint Louis Art Museum, Saint Louis, MO...836

St. Louis Artists' Guild, Saint Louis, MO....836

Salem Art Association-Bush House Museum and Bush Barn Art Center, Salem, OR..1236

Salina Art Center, Salina, KS 557

Salmagundi Museum of American Art, New York, NY....................................1038

Salt Lake Art Center, Salt Lake City, UT ..1472

Salvador Dali Museum, Saint Petersburg, FL...342

Samek Art Gallery, Lewisburg, PA.............1268

Samuel Cupples House of Saint Louis University, Saint Louis, MO 837

Samuel Dorsky Museum of Art, State University of New York at New Paltz, New Paltz, NY..................................1018

Samuel P. Harn Museum of Art, Gainesville, FL...................................311

Samuel S. Fleisher Art Memorial, Philadelphia, PA 1288

San Angelo Museum of Fine Arts, San Angelo, TX.......................................1447

San Antonio Art League Museum, San Antonio, TX......................................1449

San Antonio Museum of Art, San Antonio, TX......................................1450

San Diego Museum of Art, San Diego, CA...160

San Fernando Mission, Mission Hills, CA...126

San Francisco Art Institute - Walter & McBean Galleries, San Francisco, CA....168

San Francisco Camerawork, San Francisco, CA.....................................169

San Francisco Museum of Modern Art, San Francisco, CA..............................169

San Jose Museum of Art, San Jose, CA 172

San Jose State University Art Galleries, San Jose, CA......................................173

Sand Springs Cultural & Historical Museum, Sand Springs, OK................1213

The Sandor Teszler Library, Spartanburg, SC...1341

Sangre de Cristo Arts Center & Buell Children's Museum, Pueblo, CO 231

Santa Ana College Art Gallery, Santa Ana, CA..178

Santa Barbara Museum of Art, Santa Barbara, CA.......................................179

Santa Barbara Trust for Historic Preservation, Santa Barbara, CA 180

Santa Cruz Art League, Inc., Santa Cruz, CA...182

Santa Fe Gallery, Gainesville, FL...............311

Santa Monica Museum of Art, Santa Monica, CA..183

Santa Rosa Jr. College Art Gallery, Santa Rosa, CA..184

Santuario de Nuestra Senora de Guadalupe, Santa Fe, NM.....................950

Sarah Campbell Blaffer Foundation, Houston, TX.....................................1429

Sarah Moody Gallery of Art, The University of Alabama, Tuscaloosa, AL..20

Sautee-Nacoochee Center, Sautee, GA.........384

Savannah College of Art and Design Galleries, Savannah, GA 386

Sawhill Gallery, James Madison University, Harrisonburg, VA 1511

SCAD Museum of Art, Savannah, GA 386

Scarfone/Hartley Gallery, Tampa, FL 349

The Schein-Joseph International Museum of Ceramic Art, Alfred, NY 956

The Schick Art Gallery, Skidmore College, Saratoga Springs, NY 1065

Schmucker Art Gallery, Gettysburg, PA.....1256

Schneider Museum of Art, Ashland, OR.....1217

School of American Research, Indian Arts Research Center, Santa Fe, NM 950

School of Fine Arts Gallery, Indiana University, Bloomington, IN 470

School of the Art Institute of Chicago, Gallery 2, Chicago, IL.......................427

Schoolhouse History & Art Center, Colstrip, MT......................................844

The Schumacher Gallery, Capital University, Columbus, OH 1159

Schweinfurth Memorial Art Center, Auburn, NY......................................959

Scottsdale Museum of Contemporary Art, Scottsdale, AZ......................................44

Scranton Museum of Art, Scranton, PA 1299

Seagraves-Loop Museum and Art Center Inc., Seagraves, TX..............................1452

Seattle Art Museum, Seattle, WA 1568

Seattle Asian Art Museum, Seattle, WA.....1569

Second Street Gallery, Charlottesville, VA.1500

Sedona Arts Center, Inc., Sedona, AZ............44

Seippel Homestead and Center for the Arts, Beaver Dam, WI 1592

Seminole Nation Museum, Wewoka, OK...1217

Senate House State Historic Site, Kingston, NY....................................1008

1768 Jeremiah Lee Mansion, Marblehead, MA...693

The Sharon Arts Center, Inc., Sharon, NH...896

Shasta State Historic Park, Shasta, CA 186

Sheehan Gallery at Whitman College, Walla Walla, WA 1577

Shelburne Museum, Inc., Shelburne, VT ...1487

Sheldon Memorial Art Gallery and Sculpture Garden/University of Nebraska-Lincoln, Lincoln, NE..............867

Sheldon Peck Homestead, Lombard, IL.......444

Shemer Art Center & Museum, Phoenix, AZ...42

Sheppard Fine Arts Gallery, Reno, NV........881

Sid Richardson Museum, Fort Worth, TX..1418

Sidney Historical Association, Sidney, NY...1069

Sidney Mishkin Gallery of Baruch College, New York, NY 1038

Silvermine Guild Arts Center, New Canaan, CT.......................................252

Simpson College/Farnham Galleries, Indianola, IA.....................................519

Sioux City Art Center, Sioux City, IA 527

Sioux Indian Museum, Rapid City, SD 1355

Skirball Cultural Center, Los Angeles, CA...121

Skirball Museum Cincinnati Hebrew Union College-Jewish Institute of Religion, Cincinnati, OH....................1151

The Slater Memorial Museum - Norwich Free Academy, Norwich, CT 258

Slater Mill Historic Site, Pawtucket, RI.....1315

Slidell Cultural Center, Slidell, LA 602

Slifer House, Lewisburg, PA......................1268

Slocumb Galleries, Johnson City, TN.........1368

The Smart Museum of Art, Chicago, IL 427

Smith College Museum of Art, Northampton, MA...............................700

Smithsonian American Art Museum, Washington, DC.................................290

Smithsonian Institution, Washington, DC.....290

The Snite Museum of Art, University of Notre Dame, Notre Dame, IN..............495

Snyder Museum & Creative Arts Center, Bastrop, LA 585

Society for Contemporary Craft, Pittsburgh, PA 1294

The Society of California Pioneers, San Francisco, CA...................................170

The Society of the Cincinnati at Anderson House, Washington, DC 291

The Society of the Four Arts, Palm Beach, FL...334

Solomon R. Guggenheim Museum, New York, NY..1038

Sondra & Marvin Smalley Sculpture Garden, Bel Air, CA.............................74

Sonoma County Museum, Santa Rosa, CA...185

Sonoma Valley Museum of Art, Sonoma, CA...188

Sordoni Art Gallery, Wilkes-Barre, PA.......1307

South Arkansas Arts Center, El Dorado, AR...56

South Bend Regional Museum of Art, South Bend, IN 500

South Boston-Halifax County Museum of Fine Arts & History, South Boston, VA..1536

South Dakota Art Museum, Brookings, SD...1344

South Florida Community College Museum of Florida Art and Culture, Avon Park, FL.....................................295

South Seattle Community College Art Gallery, West Seattle, WA 1578

South Shore Arts, Munster, IN 493

South Street Seaport Museum, New York, NY...1039

Southeast Missouri Regional Museum, Cape Girardeau, MO...........................812

Southeastern Center for Contemporary Art, Winston-Salem, NC 1126

Southern Alleghenies Museum of Art, Loretto, PA.......................................1269

Southern Alleghenies Museum of Art at
Johnstown, Johnstown, PA 1264
Southern Illinois Art & Artisans Center,
Whittington, IL 466
Southern Ohio Museum, Portsmouth, OH..1183
Southern Plains Indian Museum,
Anadarko, OK 1196
Southern Ute Cultural Center and
Museum, Ignacio, CO 223
Southern Vermont Art Center,
Manchester, VT 1481
Southern Vermont College Art Gallery,
Bennington, VT 1477
Southwest Museum, Los Angeles, CA 121
Southwest School of Art & Craft, San
Antonio, TX 1450
The Spanish Institute, New York, NY 1039
Spartanburg County Museum of Art,
Spartanburg, SC 1341
The Speed Art Museum, Louisville, KY 579
Spelman College Museum of Fine Art,
Atlanta, GA 363
Spencer Museum of Art, The University
of Kansas, Lawrence, KS 548
Spertus Museum, Chicago, IL 427
Spiers Gallery, Brevard, NC 1092
Spirit Square Center for Arts and
Education, Charlotte, NC 1096
Spokane Arts Commission-Chase Gallery,
Spokane, WA 1572
Spokane Falls Community College Fine
Art Gallery, Spokane, WA 1572
The Sports Museum, Boston, MA 669
Springfield Art & Historical Society -
Miller Art Center, Springfield, VT 1488
Springfield Art Association, Springfield,
IL 460
Springfield Art Museum, Springfield, MO ...839
Springfield Museum of Art, Springfield,
OH 1186
Springfield Museums - George Walter
Vincent Smith Art Museum,
Springfield, MA 710
Springfield Museums - Museum of Fine
Arts, Springfield, MA 711
Springville Museum of Art, Springville,
UT 1474
Spruill Gallery, Atlanta, GA 364
Stables Art Gallery of Taos Art
Association, Taos, NM 952
Stanlee & Gerald Rubin Center for the
Visual Arts, University of Texas, El
Paso, El Paso, TX 1413
Stark Museum of Art, Orange, TX 1441
State Historical Society of Missouri,
Columbia, MO 814
Staten Island Institute of Arts & Sciences
(SIIAS), Staten Island, NY 1074
Station 15, Norton, KS 554
Staunton Augusta Art Center, Staunton,
VA 1537
Stedman Gallery, Camden, NJ 900
Steffen Thomas Museum and Archives,
Buckhead, GA 367
Stephens African-American Museum,
Shreveport, LA 602
Sterling and Francine Clark Art Institute,
Williamstown, MA 719
Stillman Art Gallery, Tuscaloosa, AL 20
Stone House Gallery, Fredonia, KS 540
Stone Quarry Hill Art Park, Inc.,
Cazenovia, NY 977
Storm King Art Center, Mountainville,
NY 1016
The Stowitts Museum & Library, Pacific
Grove, CA 137
Stuart Collection, La Jolla, CA 107
The Studio Museum in Harlem, New
York, NY 1040
Studio San Giuseppe Art Gallery,
Cincinnati, OH 1151

SUArt Galleries - Syracuse University,
Syracuse, NY 1077
The Suffolk Museum, Suffolk, VA 1540
SullivanMunce Cultural Center,
Zionsville, IN 504
Sumter Gallery of Art, Sumter, SC 1342
Sun Gallery, Hayward, CA 102
Sushi Performance and Visual Art, San
Diego, CA 161
Suzanne H. Arnold Art Gallery, Lebanon
Valley College, Annville, PA 1241
Sweeney Art Gallery, University of
California, Riverside, CA 150
Sweet Briar College Art Gallery, Sweet
Briar, VA 1540
Swope Art Museum, Terre Haute, IN 501
Sylvia Plotkin Judaica Museum of
Congregation Beth Israel, Scottsdale,
AZ 44

T.C. Steele State Historic Site, Nashville,
IN 493
T.W. Wood Gallery & Arts Center,
Montpelier, VT 1482
Tacoma Art Museum, Tacoma, WA 1574
Tacoma Public Library/Thomas
Handforth Gallery, Tacoma, WA 1574
The Taft Museum of Art, Cincinnati, OH ..1151
Tall Grass Arts Association, Park Forest,
IL 449
Tampa Museum of Art, Tampa, FL 350
Tarble Arts Center, Eastern Illinois
University, Charleston, IL 417
Tarpon Springs Heritage Museum, Tarpon
Springs, FL 351
Taube Museum of Art, Minot, ND 1135
Telfair Museum of Art, Savannah, GA 386
Temple Gallery, Tyler School of Art of
Temple University, Philadelphia, PA 1288
Tennent Art Foundation Gallery,
Honolulu, HI 398
Tennessee Valley Art Center, Tuscumbia,
AL 20
Terrace Gallery-City of Orlando,
Orlando, FL 332
Texas Woman's University Art Galleries,
Denton, TX 1409
The Textile Museum, Washington, DC 291
This Century Art Gallery, Williamsburg,
VA 1545
Thomas Center Galleries, Gainesville, FL ...311
Thomas J. Walsh Art Gallery, Quick
Center for the Arts at Fairfield
University, Fairfield, CT 241
Thomas Kinkade Museum, Morgan Hill,
CA 129
Thomasville Cultural Center, Inc.,
Thomasville, GA 388
Thorne-Sagendorph Art Gallery, Keene,
NH 890
Thornhill Gallery at Avila University,
Kansas City, MO 823
Thunderbird Foundation for the Arts,
Mount Carmel, UT 1467
Timken Museum of Art, San Diego, CA 162
Tohono Chul Park Inc., Tucson, AZ 51
The Toledo Museum of Art, Toledo, OH ..1187
Torpedo Factory Art Center, Alexandria,
VA 1494
Torrance Art Museum, Torrance, CA 192
Tougaloo College, Tougaloo, MS 808
Tower Fine Arts Gallery (SUNY
Brockport), Brockport, NY 964
The Trammell & Margaret Crow
Collection of Asian Art, Dallas, TX 1408
Trenton City Museum, Trenton, NJ 928
Triangle Tattoo & Museum, Fort Bragg,
CA 95
Triton Museum of Art, Santa Clara, CA 181
The Trout Gallery, Carlisle, PA 1245
Troy-Hayner Cultural Center, Troy, OH 1188
Tubac Center of the Arts, Tubac, AZ 47

Tubman African-American Museum,
Macon, GA 378
Tucson Museum of Art & Historic Block,
Tucson, AZ 51
Tufts University Art Gallery, Medford,
MA 694
Turabo University, Gurabo, PR 1641
Turner House Museum, Hattiesburg, MS 801
The Turner Museum, Sarasota, FL 345
Turtle Bay Exploration Park, Redding,
CA 146
Turtle Mountain Chippewa Historical
Society, Belcourt, ND 1127
Tweed Museum of Art, Duluth, MN 774
Tyler Art Gallery, Oswego, NY 1048
Tyler Museum of Art, Tyler, TX 1456

UCLA Fowler Museum of Cultural
History, Los Angeles, CA 122
UCR/California Museum of Photography,
Riverside, CA 150
USM Art Gallery, Gorham, ME 611
UWM Union-Art Gallery, Milwaukee, WI.1613
Ukrainian Institute of Modern Art,
Chicago, IL 428
The Ukrainian Museum, New York, NY 1040
Ukrainian Museum-Archives, Inc.,
Cleveland, OH 1156
Ulrich Museum of Art, Wichita, KS 563
Umlauf Sculpture Garden & Museum,
Austin, TX 1392
UNI Gallery of Art, University of
Northern Iowa, Cedar Falls, IA 508
United States Capitol, Washington, DC 293
United States Naval Academy Museum,
Annapolis, MD 628
University Art Galleries, Vermillion, SD....1358
University Art Galleries, Murray State
University, Murray, KY 580
University Art Gallery, Indiana State
University, Terre Haute, IN 501
University Art Gallery, New Mexico
State University, Las Cruces, NM 941
University Art Gallery San Diego State
University, San Diego, CA 162
University Art Gallery, Sonoma State
University, Rohnert Park, CA 151
University Art Gallery, State University
of New York at Stony Brook, Stony
Brook, NY 1075
University Art Gallery, Texas Christian
University, Fort Worth, TX 1418
University Art Gallery, University of
California, San Diego, La Jolla, CA 107
University Art Gallery, University of
Massachusetts Dartmouth, New
Bedford, MA 697
University Art Gallery, University of
Pittsburgh, Pittsburgh, PA 1294
University Art Gallery, University of the
South, Sewanee, TN 1384
University Art Museum, Binghamton, NY ...963
University Art Museum, Santa Barbara,
CA 180
University Art Museum, The University
of New Mexico, Albuquerque, NM 936
University Art Museum, University at
Albany, Albany, NY 956
University at Buffalo Art Galleries,
Buffalo, NY 974
University Galleries, Clarion, PA 1247
University Galleries, Florida Atlantic
University, Boca Raton, FL 296
University Gallery, Gainesville, FL 312
University Gallery, University of
Massachusetts at Amherst, Amherst,
MA 659
The University Museum, Edwardsville,
IL 432
The University Museum, Indiana, PA 1263
University Museums, University of
Delaware, Newark, DE 272

Art Museums and Galleries–Continued

University of Alaska Museum of the
North, Fairbanks, AK 24

The University of Arizona Museum of
Art, Tucson, AZ...52

University of Arizona Student Union
Galleries, Tucson, AZ.................................52

University of Arkansas at Little Rock Art
Department Gallery I & II & III,
Little Rock, AR 63

University of California Berkeley Art
Museum and Pacific Film Archive,
Berkeley, CA 77

University of Central Florida Art Gallery,
Orlando, FL...332

University of Denver, School of Art &
Art History, Victoria H. Myhren
Gallery, Denver, CO 213

University of Hawaii Art Gallery,
Honolulu, HI 398

University of Iowa Museum of Art, Iowa
City, IA 520

University of Kentucky Art Museum,
Lexington, KY..574

University of Maine Museum of Art,
Bangor, ME..605

University of Mary Washington Galleries,
Fredericksburg, VA 1507

The University of Michigan Museum of
Art, Ann Arbor, MI 726

University of Missouri-Kansas City
Gallery of Art, Kansas City, MO.............823

The University of Montana-Western Art
Gallery & Museum, Dillon, MT..............846

University of North Texas Art Gallery,
Denton, TX..1409

University of Rhode Island Fine Arts
Center Galleries, Kingston, RI...............1312

University of Richmond Museums,
Richmond, VA..1532

The University of South Carolina
McKissick Museum, Columbia, SC.......1331

University of South Florida
Contemporary Art Museum, Tampa,
FL..350

The University of Texas at San Antonio,
Art Gallery, San Antonio, TX 1451

The University of the Arts -
Rosenwald-Wolf Gallery, Philadelphia,
PA...1289

University of Virginia Art Museum,
Charlottesville, VA 1500

University of Wyoming Art Museum,
Laramie, WY...1636

Upper Snake River Valley Historical
Society, Rexburg, ID................................409

Urban Institute for Contemporary Arts,
Grand Rapids, MI......................................744

U.S. Army Signal Corps Museum, Fort
Gordon, GA...372

Utah Museum of Fine Arts, Salt Lake
City, UT...1472

Valdosta State University Fine Arts
Gallery, Valdosta, GA...............................389

Valley Art Center, Inc., Clarkston, WA 1551

Van Every/Smith Galleries, Davidson,
NC..1098

Van Wyck Homestead Museum, Fishkill,
NY...989

Vanderbilt University Fine Arts Gallery,
Nashville, TN...1381

Varner-Hogg Plantation State Historic
Site, West Columbia, TX........................1461

Venango Museum of Art, Science &
Industry, Oil City, PA.............................1274

Ventura County Maritime Museum, Inc.,
Oxnard, CA...137

Ventura County Museum of History &
Art, Ventura, CA.......................................195

Vermont Marble Museum, Proctor, VT......1485

Vero Beach Museum of Art, Inc., Vero
Beach, FL..352

Victor Valley Museum & Art Gallery,
Apple Valley, CA..71

Viking Union Gallery, Bellingham, WA.....1549

Villa Terrace Decorative Arts Museum,
Milwaukee, WI..1613

Village Gallery, La Jolla, CA......................107

Virginia Museum of Fine Arts,
Richmond, VA 1533

Visual Arts Center at the Washington
Pavilion, Sioux Falls, SD........................1357

Visual Arts Center of New Jersey,
Summit, NJ..925

Visual Arts Center of Northwest Florida,
Panama City, FL..334

Visual Arts Museum, New York, NY 1040

Volcano Art Center, Volcano, HI.................402

The von Liebig Art Center, Naples, FL 328

VSA Arts of Georgia - Arts for All
Gallery, Atlanta, GA.................................364

WARM (Women's Art Registry of
Minnesota), Saint Paul, MN....................792

Wadsworth Atheneum Museum of Art,
Hartford, CT..246

Wailoa Center for Culture and Arts, Hilo,
HI 393

Walker Art Center, Minneapolis, MN.........783

The Walker Art Collection of the Garnett
Public Library, Garnett, KS 541

Walter Anderson Museum of Art, Ocean
Springs, MS...806

Walters Art Museum, Baltimore, MD...........636

The Ward Museum of Wildfowl Art,
Salisbury University, Salisbury, MD 653

Warwick Museum of Art, Warwick, RI.....1320

Washakie Museum, Worland, WY.............1639

Washington & Jefferson College - Olin
Fine Arts Center, Washington, PA 1305

Washington County Museum of Fine
Arts, Hagerstown, MD 647

Washington Pavilion of Arts and Science,
Sioux Falls, SD.......................................1357

Waterloo Center for the Arts, Waterloo,
IA...529

Waterworks Visual Arts Center, Salisbury,
NC..1118

Watkins Institute, Nashville, TN................1381

Watts Towers Arts Center, Los Angeles,
CA..122

Wave Hill, Bronx, NY.................................967

Wayne Center for the Arts, Wooster, OH...1192

Wayne State University Art Galleries,
Detroit, MI..738

Weatherspoon Art Museum, Greensboro,
NC..1104

Weber State University Art Gallery,
Ogden, UT...1468

Wellington B. Gray Gallery, Greenville,
NC..1105

Wells County Museum, Fessenden, ND 1131

Wendell Gilley Museum, Southwest
Harbor, ME...623

Wentworth-Coolidge Mansion,
Portsmouth, NH..895

West Bend Art Museum, West Bend, WI...1627

West Valley Art Museum, Surprise, AZ........45

West Virginia State Museum, Charleston,
WV..1581

Westerly Public Library, Westerly, RI 1320

Western Colorado Center for the Arts,
Grand Junction, CO..................................221

Western Illinois University Art Gallery,
Macomb, IL...444

Western Kentucky University Gallery,
Bowling Green, KY...................................566

Western Michigan University Richmond
Center for Visual Arts School of Art,
Kalamazoo, MI...749

Westmoreland Museum of American Art,
Greensburg, PA.......................................1257

Weston Woods Institute, Weston, CT...........266

Wexner Center for the Arts, Columbus,
OH...1159

The Wharton Esherick Museum,
Malvern, PA...1269

Whatcom Museum of History and Art,
Bellingham, WA......................................1549

The Wheelwright Museum of the
American Indian, Santa Fe, NM..............950

Whistler House Museum of Art, Lowell,
MA...692

Whitney Museum of American Art, New
York, NY..1041

Wichita Art Museum, Wichita, KS..............563

Wichita Center for the Arts, Wichita, KS.....563

Wichita Falls Museum and Art Center,
Wichita Falls, TX...................................1461

Widener Gallery, Austin Arts Center,
Trinity College, Hartford, CT 246

Widener University Art Collection and
Gallery, Chester, PA 1247

The Wiegand Gallery, Belmont, CA..............74

Wignall Museum/Gallery, Rancho
Cucamonga, CA.......................................145

Wildling Art Museum, Los Olivos, CA 123

Wilkes Art Gallery, North Wilkesboro,
NC..1113

Willa Cather Pioneer Memorial and
Educational Foundation, Red Cloud,
NE...872

William A. Farnsworth Library and Art
Museum, Inc. d/b/a Farnsworth Art
Museum, Rockland, ME...........................621

The William Benton Museum of Art,
Storrs, CT..262

William Bonifas Fine Arts Center,
Escanaba, MI..741

William King Regional Arts Center,
Abingdon, VA...1491

William S. Hart County Park & Museum,
Newhall, CA..130

William Weston Clarke Emison Museum
of Art, Greencastle, IN 479

Williams College Museum of Art,
Williamstown, MA...................................719

Wilson Galleries, Anderson, IN...................467

Wing Luke Asian Museum, Seattle, WA...1569

Winterset Art Center, Winterset, IA.............531

Wiregrass Museum of Art, Dothan, AL..........8

Wisconsin Fine Arts Association, Inc.,
Cedarburg, WI..1594

The Wisconsin Union Galleries,
University of Wisconsin-Madison,
Madison, WI...1606

Wiseman & FireHouse Galleries, Rogue
Community College, Grants Pass, OR ..1225

Witter Gallery, Storm Lake, IA...................528

Wolf Point Area Historical Society, Inc.,
Wolf Point, MT...855

The Wolfsonian - Florida International
University, Miami Beach, FL...................327

Wood Street Galleries, Pittsburgh, PA........1295

Woodmere Art Museum, Philadelphia, PA.1289

Woodstock Artists Association,
Woodstock, NY.......................................1087

Woodstock Historical Society, Bryant
Pond, ME...608

Woolaroc Museum, Bartlesville, OK..........1197

Worcester Art Museum, Worcester, MA.......721

Worcester Center for Crafts, Worcester,
MA...721

Working Men's Institute, New Harmony,
IN..495

The Works: Ohio Center for History, Art
& Technology, Newark, OH...................1179

World Erotic Art Museum, Miami Beach,
FL..327

World Figure Skating Museum & Hall of
Fame, Colorado Springs, CO..................208

World of Wings Pigeon Center,
Oklahoma City, OK................................1211

The World Organization of China
Painters, Oklahoma City, OK................1211

Wright Museum of Art, Beloit College, Beloit, WI 1592

Wright State University Art Galleries, Dayton, OH..............1162

Wriston Art Center Galleries, Appleton, WI 1590

Wyoming Arts Council Gallery, Cheyenne, WY..............1630

Xavier University Art Gallery, Cincinnati, OH..............1152

Xochipilli Art Gallery, Birmingham, MI 730

The Yager Museum of Art & Culture, Oneonta, NY..............1046

Yale Center for British Art, New Haven, CT..............254

Yale University Art Gallery, New Haven, CT..............254

Yeiser Art Center, Paducah, KY 582

Yellowstone Art Museum, Billings, MT.......842

Yerba Buena Center for the Arts, San Francisco, CA..............170

Yeshiva University Museum at the Center for Jewish History, New York, NY..............1041

Yuma Art Center Museum - Yuma Fine Arts, Yuma, AZ..............54

Zabriskie Gallery, New York, NY 1041

Zado Gallery, Portland, OR 1233

ZAM - Zigler Art Museum, Jennings, LA ...589

Zanesville Art Center, Zanesville, OH........1194

Zenith Gallery, Washington, DC..............294

Zeum, San Francisco, CA..............170

Ziibiwing Center of Anishinabe Culture & Lifeways, Mount Pleasant, MI 757

Zora Neale Hurston National Museum of Fine Arts, Eatonville, FL..............305

Arts and Crafts Museums

Alexandria Museum of Art, Alexandria, LA 584

Allegheny Highlands Arts & Crafts Center, Inc., Clifton Forge, VA..............1501

American Craft Museum, New York, NY ..1018

American Museum of Ceramic Art, Pomona, CA..............143

The American Museum of Fly Fishing, Manchester, VT 1481

Anna Lamar Switzer Center for Visual Arts, Pensacola, FL..............335

Appalachian Center For Craft, Smithville, TN 1384

Armenian Library and Museum of America, Watertown, MA 716

Art Association of Harrisburg, Harrisburg, PA..............1258

Artisans Center of Virginia, Waynesboro, VA 1543

Attleboro Arts Museum, Attleboro, MA.......661

The Belknap Mill Society, Laconia, NH 890

Bethlehem Historical Association, Selkirk, NY..............1068

Billy Sunday Home Museum and Visitors Center, Winona Lake, IN 504

Black Heritage Museum, Miami, FL..............323

Buechel Memorial Lakota Museum, Saint Francis, SD 1355

Bunker Hill Museum, Charlestown, MA.......675

Cazenovia College - Art & Design Gallery, Cazenovia, NY 976

Center for Book Arts, New York, NY 1022

Center on Contemporary Art, Seattle, WA.1565

Chattahoochee Valley Art Museum, LaGrange, GA..............375

Children's Museum of Oak Ridge, Inc., Oak Ridge, TN..............1382

City Museum, Saint Louis, MO..............832

Clifton Community Historical Society, Clifton, KS..............535

Contemporary Crafts Museum & Gallery, Portland, OR..............1230

Craft Alliance, Saint Louis, MO..............833

Craft and Folk Art Museum - CAFAM, Los Angeles, CA..............114

Crafts Museum, Mequon, WI..............1609

Craftsmen's Guild of Mississippi, Jackson, MS..............802

Crossroads Museum, Corinth, MS..............800

Crossroads of America, Bethlehem, NH 883

Crow Canyon Archaeological Center, Cortez, CO..............208

Cultural Museum, Nashville, TN..............1378

Dawson Springs Museum and Art Center, Inc., Dawson Springs, KY..............568

Decorative Arts Collection, Inc. Museum of Decorative Painting, Wichita, KS 561

Delaware Center for the Contemporary Arts, Wilmington, DE..............273

Denver Museum of Miniatures, Dolls and Toys, Denver, CO 211

El Museo Latino, Omaha, NE 870

The Ethel Wright Mohamed Stitchery Museum, Belzoni, MS..............798

Firehouse Art Gallery, Nassau Community College, Garden City, NY ...992

Fondo Del Sol Visual Arts & Media Center/El Museo de Culturas y Herencias Americanas/MOCHA, Washington, DC..............279

Fort Delaware Museum of Colonial History, Narrowsburg, NY 1017

Foster Gallery, University of Wisconsin-Eau Claire, Eau Claire, WI..1596

Fred Wolf, Jr. Gallery/Klein Branch Jewish Community Center, Philadelphia, PA 1280

Galerie Trinitas, Great Falls, MT..............848

Gallery North, Setauket, NY..............1069

Golden State Model Railroad Museum, Point Richmond, CA 143

Hammond Museum and Japanese Stroll Garden, North Salem, NY..............1043

The Heritage Museum of Fine Arts for Youth, Detroit, MI..............736

Hiddenite Center, Inc., Hiddenite, NC.......1106

Historic Sauder Village, Archbold, OH 1140

Houston Center for Contemporary Craft, Houston, TX..............1426

Hui No'eau Visual Arts Center, Makawao, Maui, HI..............401

Hungarian Folk-Art Museum, Port Orange, FL..............338

Hus Var Fine Art, Buffalo, NY..............973

Immigration Museum of New Americans Post WWII, San Diego, CA..............156

Indian Pueblo Cultural Center, Albuquerque, NM..............933

Iroquois Indian Museum, Howes Cave, NY..............999

Irvine Fine Arts Center, Irvine, CA..............105

Island Museum of Art, Westcott Bay Institute, Friday Harbor, WA..............1554

Jamaica Center for Arts & Learning (JCAL), Jamaica, NY..............1004

James A. Michener Art Museum, Doylestown, PA..............1249

John Michael Kohler Arts Center, Sheboygan, WI..............1621

Julia A. Purnell Museum, Snow Hill, MD...654

The Kentuck Museum Association/Art Center/Festival of the Arts, Northport, AL..............17

Kentucky Museum of Art and Craft, Louisville, KY..............577

Koshare Indian Museum, Inc., La Junta, CO..............224

Liberty Village Arts Center & Gallery, Chester, MT..............844

The Little Cowboy Bar & Museum, Fromberg, MT..............847

The London Brass Rubbing Centre in Washington D.C., Inc., Gaithersburg, MD..............645

Longboat Key Center for the Arts, Longboat Key, FL..............322

LongHouse Reserve, East Hampton, NY 986

Lux Center for the Arts, Lincoln, NE 866

Lyndon House Art, Athens, GA..............356

Macalester College Art Gallery, Janet Wallace Fine Arts Center, Saint Paul, MN..............790

Marblehead Arts Association - King Hooper Mansion, Marblehead, MA.........693

The Mather Homestead Museum, Library and Memorial Park, Wellsville, NY 1084

Mississippi Crafts Center, Ridgeland, MS ...807

Museum of American Glass at Wheaton Village, Millville, NJ..............911

Museum of Arts & Design, New York, NY..............1032

Museum of Automobile Art and Design, Syracuse, NY..............1076

Museum of Craft and Folk Art, San Francisco, CA..............167

The Museum of Miniature Houses and Other Collections, Inc., Carmel, IN.........471

Museum of Robotics, Orinda, CA..............136

Nantucket Lightship Basket Museum, Nantucket, MA..............696

National Association of Miniature Enthusiasts, Carmel, IN..............472

National Ceramic Museum and Heritage Center, Roseville, OH..............1184

National Museum of Ceramic Art and Glass, Baltimore, MD..............635

New Braunfels Museum of Art & Music, New Braunfels, TX..............1440

New England Quilt Museum, Lowell, MA..............692

North Carolina A&T State University Galleries, Greensboro, NC..............1104

North Carolina Pottery Center, Seagrove, NC..............1119

Northeast Georgia History Center at Brenau University, Gainesville, GA 373

The Ogden Museum of Southern Art, University of New Orleans, New Orleans, LA..............598

Palo Alto Art Center, Palo Alto, CA 139

Petterson Museum of Intercultural Art, Claremont, CA..............85

Pewabic Pottery, Detroit, MI..............737

Port Discovery, The Children's Museum in Baltimore, Baltimore, MD..............636

Red Barn Museum, Morristown, NY 1016

Red Rock Museum, Church Rock, NM 938

Renwick Gallery of the Smithsonian American Art Museum, Washington, DC..............290

Ripley's Believe It or Not!, Key West, FL..............319

Ripley's Believe It or Not! Museum, Orlando, FL..............332

Schingoethe Center for Native American Cultures, Aurora, IL..............412

School of Nations Museum, Elsah, IL 433

Schweinfurth Memorial Art Center, Auburn, NY..............959

Shemer Art Center & Museum, Phoenix, AZ..............42

Slidell Museum, Slidell, LA..............602

Snug Harbor Cultural Center - Visitors' Center and Newhouse Center for Contemporary Art, Staten Island, NY ...1073

Arts and Crafts Museums–Continued

Society for Contemporary Craft,
   Pittsburgh, PA 1294
South Carolina Artisans Center,
   Walterboro, SC 1343
Southern Highland Craft Guild at the
   Folk Art Center, Asheville, NC.............1090
Southern Illinois Art & Artisans Center,
   Whittington, IL 466
Steppingstone Museum, Havre de Grace,
   MD 647

Tama County Historical Museum, Toledo,
   IA 528
Tamastslikt Cultural Institute, Pendleton,
   OR 1230
Thomas Center Galleries, Gainesville, FL ...311
Thornhill Gallery at Avila University,
   Kansas City, MO 823

UCLA Fowler Museum of Cultural
   History, Los Angeles, CA 122
Warther Museum Inc., Dover, OH.............1163
Webb House Museum, Newark, OH 1179
Western Colorado Center for the Arts,
   Grand Junction, CO 221
William King Regional Arts Center,
   Abingdon, VA 1491
Wilson Czech Opera House Corporation,
   Foundation, Inc. & House of
   Memories Museum, Wilson, KS 564
Worcester Center for Crafts, Worcester,
   MA 721
World Kite Museum & Hall of Fame,
   Long Beach, WA 1558

China, Glass and Silver Museums

A.L. Fetterman Educational Museum,
   Fort Valley, GA..................................372
Adsmore Museum, Princeton, KY.............583
American Museum of Ceramic Art,
   Pomona, CA 143
Anna B. Smith House Museum,
   Moundsville, WV 1585

Beauchamp Newman Museum, Elizabeth,
   WV 1581
Bergen County Historical Society, River
   Edge, NJ 923
Birks Museum, Decatur, IL....................430
Boonsborough Museum of History,
   Boonsboro, MD 637
Brunnier Art Museum, Ames, IA............504
Butter Pat Museum, Bigfork, MT.............841

Carbon County Museum, Rawlins, WY 1637
Casteel-Linn House and Museum,
   Princeton, MO 829
Clifton Community Historical Society,
   Clifton, KS..535
The Corning Museum of Glass, Corning,
   NY 981
Crescent Bend/The Armstrong-Lockett
   House and The William P. Toms
   Memorial Gardens, Knoxville, TN 1369

DAR-Hervey Ely House, Rochester, NY ...1058
Dedham Historical Society Museum,
   Dedham, MA 679
Degenhart Paperweight & Glass Museum,
   Inc., Cambridge, OH 1144

Farm House Museum, Ames, IA 505
Fenton Glass Museum, Williamstown,
   WV 1589
Frank Chiarenza Museum of Glass,
   Meriden, CT......................................248

The Glass Museum, Dunkirk, IN.............474
Glassboro Heritage Glass Museum,
   Glassboro, NJ....................................905

Glenview Area Historical Society,
   Glenview, IL 438
Glove Museum, New York, NY 1026
Goodman Museum, Tyler, TX 1456
Grand Encampment Museum, Inc.,
   Encampment, WY 1632
Greentown Glass Museum, Inc.,
   Greentown, IN 480

Historic Cherry Hill, Albany, NY 954
Historical Society of Old Yarmouth,
   Yarmouth Port, MA 722
Home Sweet Home Museum, East
   Hampton, NY 986
Horatio Colony House Museum & Nature
   Preserve, Keene, NH 890
Houston Museum of Decorative Arts,
   Chattanooga, TN................................1362
The 100th Meridian Museum, Cozad, NE ...859

Kaminski House Museum, Georgetown,
   SC...1333
Kirkland Museum of Fine & Decorative
   Art, Denver, CO 212

Laramie Plains Museum, Laramie, WY 1635
Lincoln County Historical Society, North
   Platte, NE...869

MSC Forsyth Center Galleries, Texas
   A&M University, College Station, TX..1401
Manchester Historical Society,
   Manchester, MA 692
Maridon Museum, Butler, PA 1245
Marvin Newton House, Brookfield, VT 1477
Mary Todd Lincoln House, Lexington,
   KY..574
Massee Lane Gardens, Home of
   American Camellia Society, Fort
   Valley, GA 373
Museum of American Cut and Engraved
   Glass, Highlands, NC 1107
Museum of American Glass at Wheaton
   Village, Millville, NJ 911
Museum of Ceramics, East Liverpool,
   OH..1163
The Museum of Miniature Houses and
   Other Collections, Inc., Carmel, IN.........471
The Museums of Oglebay Institute -
   Mansion Museum & Glass Museum,
   Wheeling, WV 1588

National Heisey Glass Museum, Newark,
   OH..1178
National Shaving And Barbershop
   Museum, Meriden, CT.........................249
Northern Pacific Railway Museum,
   Toppenish, WA 1575

The Ogden Museum of Southern Art,
   University of New Orleans, New
   Orleans, LA 598

The Paperweight Museum, Santa Cruz,
   CA 182
Polish American Museum, Port
   Washington, NY 1054
Project Art-University of Iowa and
   Clinics, Iowa City, IA 520

The Reeves Center, Washington and Lee
   University, Lexington, VA....................1513
Reuel B. Pritchett Museum, Bridgewater,
   VA 1497
Rosa Ponselle Museum, Meriden, CT.........249
Ryerss Museum & Library, Philadelphia,
   PA...1287

Sanborn Area Historical Society,
   Sanborn, NY 1064
Sandwich Glass Museum, Sandwich, MA ...708
Silvercreek Museum, Freeport, IL 435
The Stephen Phillips House, Salem, MA.....707
Sturdivant Hall, Selma, AL.....................18

Ten Broeck Mansion - Albany County
   Historical Association, Albany, NY 956

Wallace House, Somerville, NJ....................924
Wayne County Historical Society,
   Honesdale, PA...................................1261
West Virginia Museum of American
   Glass, Weston, WV.............................1587
West Virginia Northern Community
   College Alumni Association Museum,
   Wheeling, WV 1588
Whitewater Historical Museum,
   Whitewater, WI..................................1628
Wilder Memorial Museum, Strawberry
   Point, IA...528
Wilson Czech Opera House Corporation,
   Foundation, Inc. & House of
   Memories Museum, Wilson, KS.............564
The World Organization of China
   Painters, Oklahoma City, OK................1211

Zalud House, Porterville, CA........................144

Civic Art and Cultural Centers

Academy Art Museum, Easton, MD 642
Aliceville Museum, Aliceville, AL 3
The Arkansas Arts Center, Little Rock,
   AR..61
The Armory Art Center, West Palm
   Beach, FL..353
Art Association of Randolph County,
   Inc., Union City, IN.............................501
Art Center of Battle Creek, Battle Creek,
   MI..726
Ashtabula Arts Center, Ashtabula, OH 1140
Asian Arts & Culture Center, Towson
   University, Towson, MD 655
Atlanta Contemporary Art Center,
   Atlanta, GA.......................................358
Attleboro Arts Museum, Attleboro, MA.......661

Beck Cultural Exchange Center,
   Knoxville, TN....................................1369
Bedford Gallery at the Dean Lesher
   Regional Center for the Arts, Walnut
   Creek, CA 196
Birmingham Bloomfield Art Center,
   Birmingham, MI.................................730
Boone County Historical Center, Boone,
   IA 506
Boston Center for Jewish Heritage,
   Boston, MA 663
Brand Library & Art Center, Glendale,
   CA 100
Brattleboro Museum & Art Center,
   Brattleboro, VT..................................1477
Brookings Arts Council, Brookings, SD 1344
Bulloch Hall, Roswell, GA 382

Callanwolde Fine Arts Center, Atlanta,
   GA...359
Charles B. Goddard Center for Visual
   and Performing Arts, Ardmore, OK.......1196
Charles H. Taylor Arts Center, Hampton,
   VA 1509
Charles H. Wright Museum of African
   American History, Detroit, MI...............735
Chattahoochee Valley Art Museum,
   LaGrange, GA 375
Chinese Culture Center of San Francisco,
   San Francisco, CA..............................164
City of Las Cruces Museum System, Las
   Cruces, NM.......................................940
Cleveland Artists Foundation at Beck
   Center for the Arts, Lakewood, OH 1170
College Park Aviation Museum, College
   Park, MD 641
The Columbian Theatre, Museum & Art
   Center, Wamego, KS 560
Columbus Cultural Arts Center,
   Columbus, OH...................................1157
Contemporary Art Museum St. Louis,
   Saint Louis, MO 832

Contemporary Arts Center, New Orleans,
    LA 594
Copia: The American Center for Wine,
    Food & the Arts, Napa, CA 129
Creative Arts Center, Pontiac, MI 760
Custer County Art & Heritage Center,
    Miles City, MT 851
Czech Center New York, New York, NY 1024

Davis Art Center, Davis, CA 89
Delta Cultural Center, Helena, AR 59

Edsel & Eleanor Ford House, Grosse
    Pointe Shores, MI 745
Eldridge Street Project, New York, NY 1025
Exploris, Raleigh, NC 1115

Falkirk Cultural Center, San Rafael, CA 176
Four Rivers Cultural Center & Museum,
    Ontario, OR 1229
Frank Chiarenza Museum of Glass,
    Meriden, CT 248
French Art Colony, Gallipolis, OH 1165

Galesburg Civic Art Center, Galesburg,
    IL 437
George A. Spiva Center for the Arts,
    Joplin, MO 820
Gertrude Smith House, Mount Airy, NC 1111
Grants Pass Museum of Art, Grants Pass,
    OR 1225
The Greater Reston Arts Center
    (GRACE), Reston, VA 1527
Greensboro Artists' League, Greensboro,
    NC 1103

Hana Cultural Center, Hana, Maui, HI 392
Henry County Museum and Cultural Arts
    Center, Clinton, MO 813
The Hispanic Society of America, New
    York, NY 1027
Hiwan Homestead Museum, Evergreen,
    CO 215
Hot Springs County Museum and
    Cultural Center, Thermopolis, WY 1639

Immigration Museum of New Americans
    Post WWII, San Diego, CA 156
Irving Arts Center, Irving, TX 1430

Jacqueline Casey Hudgens Center for the
    Arts, Duluth, GA 371
Jaffrey Civic Center, Jaffrey, NH 889
James A. Michener Art Museum,
    Doylestown, PA 1249
James & Meryl Hearst Center for the
    Arts and Sculpture Garden, Cedar
    Falls, IA 508

Kennedy-Douglass Center for the Arts,
    Florence, AL 9

Lesbian Herstory Educational Foundation,
    Inc. aka Lesbian Herstory Archives,
    Brooklyn, NY 969
Limon Heritage Museum, Limon, CO 226
The Log House Museum of the Historical
    Society of Columbiana-Fairfield
    Township, Columbiana, OH 1157
Los Angeles Municipal Art Gallery -
    Barnsdall Art Park, Los Angeles, CA 118
Lou Holtz/Upper Ohio Valley Hall of
    Fame, East Liverpool, OH 1163
Loveland Museum Gallery, Loveland, CO ...227
Lubeznik Center for the Arts, Michigan
    City, IN 490
Lyndon House Art, Athens, GA 356

Madison-Morgan Cultural Center,
    Madison, GA 378
Mary G. Hardin Center for Cultural Arts,
    Gadsden, AL 10
Memphis Botanic Garden, Goldsmith
    Civic Garden Center, Memphis, TN 1374

Mission Cultural Center for Latino Arts,
    San Francisco, CA 166
Mount Dora Center for the Arts, Mount
    Dora, FL 327
Museo ItaloAmericano, San Francisco,
    CA 167

Naples Museum of Art and the
    Philharmonic Center for the Arts
    Galleries, Naples, FL 328
National Shaving And Barbershop
    Museum, Meriden, CT 249
The North Shore Arts Association,
    Gloucester, MA 684

Oceanside Museum of Art, Oceanside,
    CA 135
The Octagon Center for the Arts, Ames,
    IA 505
Old Church Cultural Center School of
    Art, Demarest, NJ 902

Palm Springs Art Museum, Palm Springs,
    CA 139
Pelham Art Center, Pelham, NY 1052
Pittsburgh Center for the Arts, Pittsburgh,
    PA 1293
The Portal of the Folded Wings Shrine to
    Aviation and Museum, North
    Hollywood, CA 131

Ralph Milliken Museum, Los Banos, CA 122
Rialto Historical Society, Rialto, CA 148
Rocky Mount Arts Center, Rocky Mount,
    NC 1117
Romanian Ethnic Art Museum,
    Cleveland, OH 1156
Rosa Ponselle Museum, Meriden, CT 249
Rose Center Museum, Morristown, TN 1376

San Francisco African American
    Historical and Cultural Society, Inc.,
    San Francisco, CA 168
Schingoethe Center for Native American
    Cultures, Aurora, IL 412
Schweinfurth Memorial Art Center,
    Auburn, NY 959
Sedona Arts Center, Inc., Sedona, AZ 44
Shoshone Tribal Cultural Center, Fort
    Washakie, WY 1633
Snake River Heritage Center, Weiser, ID 410
Snug Harbor Cultural Center - Visitors'
    Center and Newhouse Center for
    Contemporary Art, Staten Island, NY ...1073
South Arkansas Arts Center, El Dorado,
    AR 56
Southdown Plantation House/The
    Terrebonne Museum, Houma, LA 589
Southern Ohio Museum, Portsmouth, OH..1183
Southern Vermont Art Center,
    Manchester, VT 1481
The Spanish Institute, New York, NY 1039
Stauth Memorial Museum, Montezuma,
    KS 553
Stephen Foster Folk Culture Center State
    Park, White Springs, FL 354
SullivanMunce Cultural Center,
    Zionsville, IN 504

Tarpon Springs Cultural Center, Tarpon
    Springs, FL 351
Tennessee Valley Art Center, Tuscumbia,
    AL 20
Thomasville Cultural Center, Inc.,
    Thomasville, GA 388
Thornhill Gallery at Avila University,
    Kansas City, MO 823
Torpedo Factory Art Center, Alexandria,
    VA 1494
Troy-Hayner Cultural Center, Troy, OH 1188

Ukrainian-American Museum &
    Archives, Warren, MI 766
Urban Institute for Contemporary Arts,
    Grand Rapids, MI 744

UTSA's Institute of Texan Cultures, San
    Antonio, TX 1451

Virginia Museum of Fine Arts,
    Richmond, VA 1533
Volcano Art Center, Volcano, HI 402

The Walker African American Museum &
    Research Center, Las Vegas, NV 880
Washington Pavilion of Arts and Science,
    Sioux Falls, SD 1357
Western Folklife Center, Elko, NV 876
William Bonifas Fine Arts Center,
    Escanaba, MI 741
William King Regional Arts Center,
    Abingdon, VA 1491
Worcester Center for Crafts, Worcester,
    MA 721

Decorative Arts Museums

Adam Thoroughgood House, Virginia
    Beach, VA 1541
Adsmore Museum, Princeton, KY 583
African Art Museum of the S.M.A.
    Fathers, Tenafly, NJ 926
Allegheny Highlands Arts & Crafts
    Center, Inc., Clifton Forge, VA 1501
American Folk Art Museum, New York,
    NY 1018
American Museum of Ceramic Art,
    Pomona, CA 143
American Museum of Straw Art, Long
    Beach, CA 110
American Sign Museum, Cincinnati, OH...1148
Andrew Low House, Savannah, GA 384
Appalachian Center For Craft, Smithville,
    TN 1384
Ash Lawn-Highland, Charlottesville, VA ...1498
Atlantic Wildfowl Heritage Museum,
    Virginia Beach, VA 1541

Banning Residence Museum,
    Wilmington, CA 198
The Bard Graduate Center for Studies in
    the Decorative Arts, Design, &
    Culture, New York, NY 1021
Batsto Village, Hammonton, NJ 907
Bayou Bend Collection and Gardens,
    Houston, TX 1425
Belcourt Castle, Newport, RI 1313
Bellamy Mansion Museum of History
    and Design Arts, Wilmington, NC 1122
Bellport-Brookhaven Historical Society
    and Museum, Bellport, NY 961
The Bennington Museum, Bennington,
    VT 1476
Bergstrom-Mahler Museum, Neenah, WI...1614
Bernard Judaica Museum, Congregation
    Emanu-El of the City of New York,
    New York, NY 1021
Birks Museum, Decatur, IL 430
Blair Museum of Lithophanes, Toledo,
    OH 1187
Boscobel, Garrison, NY 993
Brunnier Art Museum, Ames, IA 504
Burlington County Historical Society,
    Burlington, NJ 898

Campbell House Museum, Saint Louis,
    MO 832
Caramoor Center for Music & the Arts,
    Inc., Katonah, NY 1006
Casa Navarro State Historical Park, San
    Antonio, TX 1448
Chinqua-Penn Plantation, Reidsville, NC...1117
The Cloisters, New York, NY 1023
The Columbian Theatre, Museum & Art
    Center, Wamego, KS 560
Concord Museum, Concord, MA 676
Connecticut Historical Society, Hartford,
    CT 244

Decorative Arts Museums–Continued

Cooper-Hewitt National Design Museum, Smithsonian Institution, New York, NY 1023

Crescent Bend/The Armstrong-Lockett House and The William P. Toms Memorial Gardens, Knoxville, TN 1369

Crooked Tree Arts Center, Petoskey, MI......760

Daughters of the American Revolution Museum, Washington, DC 277

The Decorative Arts Center of Ohio, Lancaster, OH 1171

Decorative Arts Collection, Inc. Museum of Decorative Painting, Wichita, KS 561

Dedham Historical Society Museum, Dedham, MA...679

Department of the Treasury, Washington, DC...278

DeWitt Wallace Decorative Arts Museum, Williamsburg, VA 1545

Dinsmore Homestead Foundation, Burlington, KY 566

EarlyWorks Museums, Huntsville, AL 11

East Tennessee Historical Society, Knoxville, TN 1369

Edsel & Eleanor Ford House, Grosse Pointe Shores, MI 745

Edward-Dean Museum and Gardens, Cherry Valley, CA 82

The 1890 House-Museum & Center for Arts, Cortland, NY 983

Festival-Institute, James Dick Foundation, Round Top, TX 1446

The Fluvanna County Historical Society Old Stone Jail Museum, Palmyra, VA...1524

Fonthill Museum of the Bucks County Historical Society, Doylestown, PA.......1249

Fort Hunter Mansion & Park, Harrisburg, PA...1258

Frederic Remington Art Museum, Ogdensburg, NY 1044

Fulton Mansion State Historic Site, Rockport, TX 1446

Gallier House, New Orleans, LA...................595

Gemological Institute of America Museum, Carlsbad, CA 81

General Daniel Bissell House, Saint Louis, MO...833

Glove Museum, New York, NY 1026

The Goldstein Museum of Design, Saint Paul, MN..789

Gomez Foundation for Mill House, Marlboro, NY 1014

Graycliff Conservancy, Derby, NY 984

Gropius House, Lincoln, MA.......................690

Hampton History Museum, Hampton, VA .1509

Headley-Whitney Museum, Lexington, KY...573

Heritage Center of Lancaster County, Inc., Lancaster, PA....................................1265

Hermann-Grima/Gallier Historic Houses, New Orleans, LA..595

Hershey Museum, Hershey, PA 1261

Hill-Hold Museum, Montgomery, NY........1015

Hills and Dales Estate, LaGrange, GA.........375

Hillwood Museum & Gardens, Washington, DC..280

Historic Brattonsville, McConnells, SC......1336

Historic Cherry Hill, Albany, NY 954

Historic Deerfield, Inc., Deerfield, MA........679

Historic Hope Foundation, Inc., Windsor, NC 1124

Historic Indian Agency House, Portage, WI 1618

Historic New England, Boston, MA............665

Historic New England/Cogswells Grant, Essex, MA 682

Historical Society of Saratoga Springs, Saratoga Springs, NY............................1064

Hopewell Museum, Paris, KY 582

Horatio Colony House Museum & Nature Preserve, Keene, NH...................................890

Houston Museum of Decorative Arts, Chattanooga, TN.......................................1362

Hus Var Fine Art, Buffalo, NY 973

Jefferson County Museum, Charles Town, WV 1580

The John Nicholas Brown Center for the Study of American Civilization, Providence, RI 1317

Julian H. Sleeper House, Saint Paul, MN 790

Kensington Mansion, Eastover, SC 1332

Kent State University Museum, Kent, OH.1169

Kentucky Museum of Art and Craft, Louisville, KY 577

Kimberly Crest House & Gardens, Redlands, CA..147

Kirkland Museum of Fine & Decorative Art, Denver, CO 212

Liberty Hall Historic Site, Frankfort, KY 569

Lightner Museum, Saint Augustine, FL 339

Lock Museum of America, Inc., Terryville, CT...262

Lower Cape Fear Historical Society, Inc., Wilmington, NC......................................1123

Madison Museum of Fine Art, Madison, GA...378

Manchester Historical Society, Manchester, MA...692

Massee Lane Gardens, Home of American Camellia Society, Fort Valley, GA 373

The Mattatuck Museum Arts and History Center, Waterbury, CT...............................264

May Museum & Farmville Heritage Center, Farmville, NC 1100

Maymont, Richmond, VA 1530

McMinn County Living Heritage Museum, Athens, TN 1360

Mechanicsburg Museum Association, Mechanicsburg, PA.....................................1270

Memorial Art Gallery of the University of Rochester, Rochester, NY.................1059

Memorial Hall Museum, Pocumtuck Valley Memorial Assoc., Deerfield, MA...679

Merchant's House Museum, New York, NY...1029

Middleton Place Foundation, Charleston, SC...1326

Mississippi Crafts Center, Ridgeland, MS ...807

Monmouth County Historical Association, Freehold, NJ...905

Montpelier Mansion, Laurel, MD...............648

Morris-Butler House Museum, Indianapolis, IN..485

Morris-Jumel Mansion, New York, NY 1030

Moses Myers House, Norfolk, VA 1522

Museum of American Architecture and Decorative Arts, Houston, TX 1428

Museum of Arts & Design, New York, NY...1032

Museum of Central Connecticut State University, New Britain, CT 251

Museum of Craft and Folk Art, San Francisco, CA 167

Museum of Early Southern Decorative Arts (MESDA), Winston-Salem, NC.....1125

Museum of the American Quilter's Society (MAQS), Paducah, KY 581

Museum of Yarmouth History, Yarmouth, ME..626

The Museums of Oglebay Institute - Mansion Museum & Glass Museum, Wheeling, WV 1588

National Ornamental Metal Museum, Memphis, TN..1375

New England Quilt Museum, Lowell, MA..692

New Hampshire Historical Society, Concord, NH..885

New Haven Colony Historical Society, New Haven, CT...253

New Visions Gallery, Inc., Marshfield, WI 1608

New York State Historical Association/Fenimore Art Museum, Cooperstown, NY...981

Newport Restoration Foundation, Newport, RI...1315

Nichols House Museum, Boston, MA..........668

Norfolk History Museum, Norfolk, VA......1523

The Ogden Museum of Southern Art, University of New Orleans, New Orleans, LA 598

Osborn-Jackson House, East Hampton, NY 986

The Parry Mansion Museum, New Hope, PA...1273

Patterson Homestead, Dayton, OH 1161

Potsdam Public Museum, Potsdam, NY.....1054

Raynham Hall Museum, Oyster Bay, NY ..1049

Renfrew Museum & Park, Waynesboro, PA...1306

Richardson-Bates House Museum, Oswego, NY 1048

Riverview at Hobson Grove, Bowling Green, KY 566

Ryerss Museum & Library, Philadelphia, PA...1287

Sam Bell Maxey House State Historic Site, Paris, TX 1442

Samuel Cupples House of Saint Louis University, Saint Louis, MO 837

Sanford Museum, Sanford, FL......................343

Scalamandre, Long Island City, NY 1011

Shelburne Museum, Inc., Shelburne, VT ...1487

Springfield Museums - George Walter Vincent Smith Art Museum, Springfield, MA...710

Stauth Memorial Museum, Montezuma, KS...553

The Stephen Girard Collection, Philadelphia, PA...1288

Texas State Museum of Asian Cultures & Educational Center, Corpus Christi, TX 1402

Valentine Richmond History Center, Richmond, VA...1532

The Vermont State House, Montpelier, VT...1483

Villa Terrace Decorative Arts Museum, Milwaukee, WI..1613

Vizcaya Museum and Gardens, Miami, FL 326

Washington County Historical Society and Miller House Museum, Hagerstown, MD...646

Webster House Museum, Elkhorn, WI.......1596

Wilkinson County Museum, Woodville, MS...810

Winterthur Museum & Country Estate, Winterthur, DE..274

The Wolfsonian - Florida International University, Miami Beach, FL..................327

Worcester County Horticultural Society/Tower Hill Botanic Garden, Boylston, MA...670

Wyck, Philadelphia, PA.................................1289

Folk Art Museums

Abby Aldrich Rockefeller Folk Art
 Museum, Williamsburg, VA 1544
African American Museum, Dallas, TX 1403
Alexandria Museum of Art, Alexandria,
 LA 584
Alice Moseley Folk Art and Antique
 Museum, Bay Saint Louis, MS 798
American Folk Art Museum, New York,
 NY..1018
American Hungarian Foundation/Museum
 of the American Hungarian
 Foundation, New Brunswick, NJ 915
American Museum of Straw Art, Long
 Beach, CA...110
Atlantic Wildfowl Heritage Museum,
 Virginia Beach, VA................................1541

Black Arts National Diaspora Museum,
 New Orleans, LA......................................594
Blue Ridge Institute and Museum,
 Ferrum, VA...1504
B'nai B'rith Klutznick National Jewish
 Museum, Washington, DC 277
Burlington County Historical Society,
 Burlington, NJ..898

Cabin Nature Center, Wood Dale, IL 466
California Route 66 Museum, Victorville,
 CA...195
Center for Puppetry Arts, Atlanta, GA 359
Chase Home Museum of Utah Folk Arts,
 Salt Lake City, UT.................................1470
Chenango County Historical Society
 Museum, Norwich, NY 1044
Children's Museum of Oak Ridge, Inc.,
 Oak Ridge, TN..1382
Clark Hotel Museum, Van Horn, TX 1457
Clinton County Museum, Frankfort, IN 478
Craft and Folk Art Museum - CAFAM,
 Los Angeles, CA.......................................114
Croatian Heritage Museum & Library,
 Eastlake, OH...1163

Dancing Bear Folk Center, Thermopolis,
 WY..1639
Decorative Arts Collection, Inc. Museum
 of Decorative Painting, Wichita, KS 561
Delta Blues Museum, Clarksdale, MS...........799

El Museo Latino, Omaha, NE 870
Ethnic Heritage Museum, Rockford, IL 455

Farragut Folklife Museum, Farragut, TN 1364
Fayette Art Museum, Fayette, AL 9
Folk Art Society of America, Richmond,
 VA...1529
Fossil Museum, Fossil, OR.........................1224

Gadsden Museum, Mesilla, NM 943
Gibbs Museum of Pioneer and Dakotah
 Life, Falcon Heights, MN 775

Havre de Grace Decoy Museum, Havre
 de Grace, MD..647
Hellenic Museum & Cultural Center,
 Chicago, IL...421
Heritage Center of Lancaster County,
 Inc., Lancaster, PA.................................1265
Highland Maple Museum, Monterey, VA...1518
Hungarian Folk-Art Museum, Port
 Orange, FL..338

International Bluegrass Music Museum,
 Owensboro, KY...581
International Institute of Metropolitan
 Detroit, Detroit, MI..................................737

Jamaica Center for Arts & Learning
 (JCAL), Jamaica, NY.............................1004
Jewish Museum of Florida, Miami
 Beach, FL...326
Jimmie Rodgers Museum, Meridian, MS.....805

The Kentuck Museum Association/Art
 Center/Festival of the Arts, Northport,
 AL..17
The Kentucky Folk Art Center,
 Morehead, KY 580
Kentucky Museum of Art and Craft,
 Louisville, KY...577

Liberty Village Arts Center & Gallery,
 Chester, MT...844
Little Norway, Inc., Blue Mounds, WI.......1593

Marblehead Museum & Historical
 Society, Marblehead, MA..........................693
Mennello Museum of American Art,
 Orlando, FL...331
Mennonite Heritage Center, Harleysville,
 PA..1258
Mercer Museum of the Bucks County
 Historical Society, Doylestown, PA.......1250
Miles B. Carpenter Museum, Waverly,
 VA..1543
Mingei International Museum, San
 Diego, CA..157
Mississippi Crafts Center, Ridgeland, MS ...807
The Morikami Museum and Japanese
 Gardens, Delray Beach, FL........................305
Museo de Las Americas, San Juan, PR....1642
Museum of Appalachia, Clinton, TN..........1363
Museum of Craft and Folk Art, San
 Francisco, CA...167
Museum of International Folk Art, Santa
 Fe, NM..948
Museum of New Mexico, Santa Fe, NM.....949
Museum of the American Quilter's
 Society (MAQS), Paducah, KY 581

Nantucket Lightship Basket Museum,
 Nantucket, MA..696
New Braunfels Museum of Art & Music,
 New Braunfels, TX 1440
The New England Carousel Museum,
 Bristol, CT...236
New England Quilt Museum, Lowell,
 MA..692
New York State Historical
 Association/Fenimore Art Museum,
 Cooperstown, NY.......................................981
The Noyes Museum of Art, Oceanville,
 NJ..918

The Ozark Folk Center, Mountain View,
 AR...65

Parson Fisher House, Blue Hill, ME............606
Pennsylvania German Cultural Heritage
 Center at Kutztown University,
 Kutztown, PA..1265
Petterson Museum of Intercultural Art,
 Claremont, CA...85
Philadelphia Mummers Museum,
 Philadelphia, PA......................................1285
Pioneer Settlement for the Creative Arts,
 Barberville, FL...295
Plaza de La Raza, Inc. & Boathouse
 Gallery, Los Angeles, CA 121
Polish American Museum, Port
 Washington, NY.......................................1054
Polish Museum of America, Chicago, IL.....426
Popular Arts Museum, San Juan, PR..........1643

Rangeley Lakes Region Logging
 Museum, Rangeley, ME.............................620
Richland County Museum, Lexington,
 OH...1172
Rocky Mountain Quilt Museum, Golden,
 CO...220
Romanian Ethnic Art Museum,
 Cleveland, OH...1156

S.C.R.A.P. Gallery, Indio, CA......................104
Shaker Museum, New Gloucester, ME 615
The Shaker Museum and Library, Old
 Chatham, NY...1045

Sheldon Peck Homestead, Lombard, IL.......444
Shoshone Tribal Cultural Center, Fort
 Washakie, WY...1633
South Carolina Artisans Center,
 Walterboro, SC..1343
Southern Ute Cultural Center and
 Museum, Ignacio, CO 223
Southwest Museum, Los Angeles, CA 121
Statue of Liberty National Monument &
 Ellis Island Immigration Museum,
 New York, NY...1039
Stephen Foster Folk Culture Center State
 Park, White Springs, FL...........................354
Swedish American Museum Association
 of Chicago, Chicago, IL............................428

Tarpon Springs Cultural Center, Tarpon
 Springs, FL..351
Tinkertown Museum, Sandia Park, NM.......947
Tuckerton Seaport, Tuckerton, NJ 928
Tucumcari Historical Research Institute,
 Tucumcari, NM..953
Tuskegee Institute National Historic Site,
 Tuskegee Institute, AL................................21

UCLA Fowler Museum of Cultural
 History, Los Angeles, CA 122
The Ukrainian Museum, New York, NY....1040
Ukrainian Museum-Archives, Inc.,
 Cleveland, OH...1156
Ukrainian National Museum, Inc.,
 Chicago, IL...428
The University of South Carolina
 McKissick Museum, Columbia, SC.......1331

Vermont Folklife Center, Middlebury, VT.1482
Vesterheim Norwegian-American
 Museum, Decorah, IA 513

Wendell Gilley Museum, Southwest
 Harbor, ME...623
The White River Museum, Meeker, CO 228
William Hammond Mathers Museum,
 Bloomington, IN..470
Wooden Sculpture Garden of Romano
 Gabriel, Eureka, CA....................................94
Wren's Nest, Atlanta, GA 364

Zoar State Memorial, Zoar, OH.................1194

Textile Museums

African Art Museum of the S.M.A.
 Fathers, Tenafly, NJ 926
Alling Coverlet Museum, Palmyra, NY 1050
American Labor Museum, Botto House
 National Landmark, Haledon, NJ 906
American Textile History Museum,
 Lowell, MA...691
Armenian Library and Museum of
 America, Watertown, MA 716

The Belknap Mill Society, Laconia, NH......890
Biltmore Homespun Shops - Grovewood
 Gallery, Asheville, NC 1089
Bosque Memorial Museum, Clifton, TX....1400
Brooks Academy Museum, Harwich, MA ...686

Caramoor Center for Music & the Arts,
 Inc., Katonah, NY 1006
Charles River Museum of Industry,
 Waltham, MA..715
The Chicago Athenaeum: Museum of
 Architecture and Design, Galena, IL........436
Croatian Heritage Museum & Library,
 Eastlake, OH...1163

Dancing Bear Folk Center, Thermopolis,
 WY..1639
The Design Center at Philadelphia
 University, Philadelphia, PA 1278

Elizabeth Sage Historic Costume
 Collection, Bloomington, IN...................469

Textile Museums–Continued

The Fabric Workshop and Museum,
Philadelphia, PA 1279

Gay Nineties Button and Doll Museum,
Eureka Springs, AR................................57

Gibbs Museum of Pioneer and Dakotah
Life, Falcon Heights, MN 775

Gustafson Gallery/Design &
Merchandising, Fort Collins, CO.............217

The Handweaving Museum & Arts
Center, Clayton, NY 978

Helen Louise Allen Textile Collection,
Madison, WI.....................................1605

Heritage House Museum of Montgomery
County, Mount Ida, AR............................64

Historic Costume & Textiles Collection,
Columbus, OH...................................1158

Historic Palmyra's Print Shop, Palmyra,
NY..1050

International Linen Registry Museum,
Tulsa, OK...1215

The Lace Museum, Sunnyvale, CA..............190

Lentz Center for Asian Culture, Lincoln,
NE..865

Liberty Hall Historic Site, Frankfort, KY 569

Marquette County Historical Society,
Westfield, WI....................................1627

May Museum & Farmville Heritage
Center, Farmville, NC...........................1100

Merchant's House Museum, New York,
NY..1029

Mission Mill Museum Association,
Salem, OR.......................................1236

The Museum at the Fashion Institute of
Technology, New York, NY.......................1031

Museum of the American Quilter's
Society (MAQS), Paducah, KY.....................581

New England Quilt Museum, Lowell,
MA..692

Old Iron County Courthouse Museum,
Hurley, WI.......................................1601

Petterson Museum of Intercultural Art,
Claremont, CA......................................85

Reuel B. Pritchett Museum, Bridgewater,
VA..1497

Rifle Creek Museum, Rifle, CO..................231

Rocky Mountain Quilt Museum, Golden,
CO..220

San Jose Museum of Quilts & Textiles,
San Jose, CA.....................................172

Scalamandre, Long Island City, NY 1011

School of American Research, Indian
Arts Research Center, Santa Fe, NM 950

Slater Mill Historic Site, Pawtucket, RI.....1315

Swarthout Memorial Museum, La Crosse,
WI..1603

The Textile Museum, Washington, DC 291

The Ukrainian Museum, New York, NY....1040

Wilmette Historical Museum, Wilmette,
IL...466

Yeshiva University Museum at the Center
for Jewish History, New York, NY........1041

Zalud House, Porterville, CA.....................144

CHILDREN'S MUSEUMS

A.C. Gilbert's Discovery Village, Salem,
OR..1235

A:shiwi A:wan Museum and Heritage
Center, Zuni, NM.................................954

Abby Aldrich Rockefeller Folk Art
Museum, Williamsburg, VA 1544

Adventure Science Center, Nashville, TN..1377

Agrirama, Georgia's Living History
Museum & Village, Tifton, GA................388

Alamo Township Museum-John E. Gray
Memorial Museum, Kalamazoo, MI........748

Alaska Museum of Natural History,
Anchorage, AK.....................................21

Alden Historical Society, Inc., Alden, NY ...956

Almond Historical Society/Hagadorn
House Museum, Almond, NY..................957

Alton Museum of History and Art, Inc.,
Alton, IL..410

Amazement Square, The Rightmire
Children's Museum, Lynchburg, VA 1514

Amelia Park Children's Museum,
Westfield, MA.....................................718

American Heart Association - Halle Heart
Center, Tempe, AZ.................................45

American Helicopter Museum &
Education Center, West Chester, PA......1307

American Royal Museum & Visitors
Center, Kansas City, MO 820

Anaheim Museum, Anaheim, CA................71

Ann Arbor Art Center, Ann Arbor, MI........724

Archer County Museum, Archer City, TX .1387

Arizona Museum For Youth, Mesa, AZ 37

Art Center Sarasota, Inc, Sarasota, FL.......343

The Art Institute of Chicago, Chicago, IL ...418

Art League of Houston, Houston, TX 1425

Arthur D. Feiro Marine Life Center c/o
Peninsula College, Port Angeles, WA ...1561

Artmobile, Newtown, PA 1274

ArtWorks Children's Museum, Ingleside,
IL..440

Austin Children's Museum, Austin, TX 1388

Aviation Museum of Kentucky Inc.,
Lexington, KY.....................................572

The Bailey-Matthews Shell Museum,
Sanibel, FL.......................................343

The Bakken Library and Museum,
Minneapolis, MN..................................781

Baltimore Museum of Industry,
Baltimore, MD.....................................630

Balzekas Museum of Lithuanian Culture,
Chicago, IL.......................................418

The Barker Character, Comic and
Cartoon Museum, Cheshire, CT 237

The Barnsdall Junior Arts Center &
Barnsdall Art Center, Los Angeles,
CA..113

Bay Area Discovery Museum, Sausalito,
CA..186

Beck Cultural Exchange Center,
Knoxville, TN....................................1369

Belvedere Castle-Henry Luce Nature
Observatory, New York, NY 1021

Bergen Museum of Art & Science,
Paramus, NJ......................................919

Berkshire Scenic Railway Museum, Inc.,
Lenox, MA..689

Betty Brinn Children's Museum,
Milwaukee, WI...................................1610

Big Thicket National Preserve, Kountze,
TX..1432

Black Arts National Diaspora Museum,
New Orleans, LA..................................594

Blue Hills Trailside Museum, Milton,
MA..695

Boonshoft Museum of Discovery,
Dayton, OH......................................1160

Bootheel Youth Museum, Malden, MO.......826

Boston Childrens Museum, Boston, MA......664

Boulder City/Hoover Dam Museum,
Boulder City, NV..................................875

Bowie Heritage Children's Museum &
Welcome Center, Bowie, MD 638

Brattleboro Museum & Art Center,
Brattleboro, VT..................................1477

Brazos Valley Museum of Natural
History, Bryan, TX...............................1398

Brevard Museum of Art and Science,
Inc., Melbourne, FL..............................323

Brevard Museum of History & Science,
Cocoa, FL..300

Briar Bush Nature Center, Abington, PA ..1238

Bronzeville Children's Museum,
Evergreen Park, IL..............................435

Brookings Arts Council, Brookings, SD 1344

Brooklyn Children's Museum, Brooklyn,
NY..968

The Building for Kids - Fox Cities
Children's Museum, Appleton, WI........1589

Butler County Historical Society, Allison,
IA..504

C.M. Russell Museum, Great Falls, MT 848

COSI Columbus, Columbus, OH...............1157

Cabin Nature Center, Wood Dale, IL 466

Cape Cod Children's Museum, Mashpee,
MA..693

Carrie Weedon Natural Science Museum,
Galesville, MD....................................645

Center for History, Wheaton, IL................465

Center for Puppetry Arts, Atlanta, GA 359

Charlotte at Play, Charlotte, NC 1094

Charlotte Nature Museum, Charlotte, NC ..1094

The Chattanooga Nature Center,
Chattanooga, TN................................1361

The Chesapeake Children's Museum,
Annapolis, MD....................................627

Chesapeake Planetarium, Chesapeake, VA.1501

Chicago Children's Museum, Chicago, IL ...419

Chickasaw National Recreation Area,
Sulphur, OK......................................1214

Chico Creek Nature Center, Chico, CA 83

Children's Discovery Center, Clinton, IA 511

Children's Discovery Museum, Normal,
IL..447

Children's Discovery Museum of North
San Diego, Carlsbad, CA 81

Children's Discovery Museum of San
Jose, San Jose, CA...............................171

Children's Discovery Museum of the
Desert, Rancho Mirage, CA....................145

Children's Discovery Workshop,
Williamsport, PA.................................1308

Children's Hands-On Museum (CHOM),
Tuscaloosa, AL.....................................19

Children's Health Museum,
Charlottesville, VA..............................1499

The Children's Metamorphosis,
Children's Museum, Derry, NH...............886

Children's Museum, Jacksonville, OR........1226

The Children's Museum, Seattle, WA 1565

Children's Museum at Holyoke, Inc.,
Holyoke, MA......................................687

Children's Museum at La Habra, La
Habra, CA..106

The Children's Museum at Saratoga,
Saratoga Springs, NY...........................1064

The Children's Museum at Yunker Farm,
Fargo, ND..1130

Children's Museum/Detroit Public
Schools, Detroit, MI.............................735

The Children's Museum in Easton, North
Easton, MA.......................................699

Children's Museum in Oak Lawn, Oak
Lawn, IL...448

Children's Museum, Inc., Boca Raton, FL...296

The Children's Museum, Inc.,
Bloomsburg, PA..................................1243

Children's Museum/Museo de Los Ninos,
San Diego, CA....................................156

Children's Museum of Acadiana,
Lafayette, LA.....................................589

Children's Museum of Bozeman,
Bozeman, MT......................................842

Children's Museum of Central Nebraska,
Hastings, NE......................................863

The Children's Museum of Cleveland,
Cleveland, OH...................................1152

Children's Museum of Denver, Denver,
CO..209

Children's Museum of Durango, Durango, CO..............214
Children's Museum of Eastern Oregon, Pendleton, OR..............1229
The Children's Museum of Green Bay, Green Bay, WI..............1598
Children's Museum of History, Natural History and Science at Utica, New York, Utica, NY..............1079
The Children's Museum of Houston, Houston, TX..............1425
Children's Museum of Illinois, Decatur, IL..............430
The Children's Museum of Indianapolis, Indianapolis, IN..............481
The Children's Museum of Kansas City, Kansas City, KS..............546
Children's Museum of Lake Charles, Inc., Lake Charles, LA..............590
Children's Museum of Los Angeles, Van Nuys, CA..............194
Children's Museum of Maine, Portland, ME..............618
Children's Museum of Manhattan, New York, NY..............1022
The Children's Museum of Memphis, Memphis, TN..............1372
Children's Museum of Missoula, Missoula, MT..............851
Children's Museum of Montana, Great Falls, MT..............848
Children's Museum of Northern Nevada, Carson City, NV..............875
Children's Museum of Oak Ridge, Inc., Oak Ridge, TN..............1382
Children's Museum of Pittsburgh, Pittsburgh, PA..............1291
The Children's Museum of Portsmouth, Portsmouth, NH..............894
Children's Museum of Richmond, Richmond, VA..............1528
The Children's Museum of Rose Hill Manor Park, Frederick, MD..............644
The Children's Museum of Science and Technology, Troy, NY..............1079
The Children's Museum of South Carolina, Myrtle Beach, SC..............1338
Children's Museum of Southeastern Connecticut, Niantic, CT..............256
Children's Museum of Stockton, Stockton, CA..............189
Children's Museum of Tacoma, Tacoma, WA..............1573
Children's Museum of the Arts, New York, NY..............1022
The Children's Museum of the Brazos Valley, Bryan, TX..............1398
Children's Museum of the East End, Bridgehampton, NY..............964
Children's Museum of the Highlands, Sebring, FL..............345
Children's Museum of the Lowcountry, Charleston, SC..............1324
Children's Museum of the Native American, New York, NY..............1023
Children's Museum of the Shoals, Florence, AL..............9
Children's Museum of the Sierra, Oakhurst, CA..............132
Children's Museum of the Three Rivers, Pasco, WA..............1561
Children's Museum of the Valley, Youngstown, OH..............1194
Children's Museum of Winston-Salem, Winston-Salem, NC..............1125
Children's Peace Pavilion, Independence, MO..............817
The Children's Playhouse, Boone, NC..............1092
Children's Science Explorium at Sugar Sand Park, Boca Raton, FL..............296
The Children's Toy & Doll Museum, Marietta, OH..............1174

Christa McAuliffe Planetarium, Concord, NH..............884
Chula Vista Nature Center, Chula Vista, CA..............84
Cincinnati Fire Museum, Cincinnati, OH...1149
Cincinnati Museum Center at Union Terminal, Cincinnati, OH..............1149
Circus World Museum, Baraboo, WI..............1591
City Museum, Saint Louis, MO..............832
Coastal Discovery Museum, Hilton Head Island, SC..............1335
Cobb County Youth Museum, Marietta, GA..............379
Community Children's Museum, Dover, NJ..............902
Confusion Hill Gravity House, Piercy, CA..............142
Connecticut Audubon Society, Fairfield, CT..............240
Connecticut Children's Museum, New Haven, CT..............253
Connecticut Trolley Museum, East Windsor, CT..............239
Copia: The American Center for Wine, Food & the Arts, Napa, CA..............129
Cora Hartshorn Arboretum and Bird Sanctuary, Short Hills, NJ..............924
The Corcoran Gallery of Art, Washington, DC..............277
Coyote Point Museum for Environmental Education, San Mateo, CA..............175
Crane Point, Marathon, FL..............323
Creative Discovery Museum, Chattanooga, TN..............1361
Crossroads of America, Bethlehem, NH..............883
Culbertson Mansion State Historic Site, New Albany, IN..............493
The Curious Kids' Museum, Saint Joseph, MI..............763
Cylburn Arboretum, Baltimore, MD..............631

D.R. Barker Historical Museum, Fredonia, NY..............992
De Graaf Nature Center, Holland, MI..............746
Deer Park Escondido Winery & Auto Museum, Escondido, CA..............93
Deerfield Beach Historical Society, Deerfield Beach, FL..............304
Denison Pequotsepos Nature Center, Mystic, CT..............250
Denver Firefighters Museum, Denver, CO...211
Denver Museum of Miniatures, Dolls and Toys, Denver, CO..............211
The Depot Museum Complex, Henderson, TX..............1424
Des Moines Botanical Center, Des Moines, IA..............514
DeWitt County Historical Museum, Cuero, TX..............1403
Discover Westfield Children's Museum, Westfield, MA..............718
The Discovery Center, Fresno, CA..............96
Discovery Center at Murfree Spring, Murfreesboro, TN..............1376
Discovery Center (East Tennessee Discovery Center), Knoxville, TN..............1369
Discovery Center Museum, Rockford, IL....454
Discovery Center of Springfield, Springfield, MO..............839
The Discovery Center of the Southern Tier, Binghamton, NY..............962
Discovery Creek Children's Museum of Washington DC, Glen Echo, MD..............645
Discovery Depot Children's Museum, Galesburg, IL..............437
Discovery Gateway, Salt Lake City, UT....1471
The Discovery Museum, Eureka, CA..............94
The Discovery Museums, Acton, MA..............657
Discovery Science and Outdoor Center, Ocala, FL..............330
Discovery Science Place, Tyler, TX..............1456
Don Harrington Discovery Center, Amarillo, TX..............1387

Dubuque Arboretum & Botanical Gardens, Dubuque, IA..............516
Duluth Children's Museum, Duluth, MN.....772
DuPage Children's Museum, Naperville, IL..............447
Durham Center Museum/Research Library, East Durham, NY..............985

EarlyWorks Museums, Huntsville, AL..............11
East Hampton Town Marine Museum, Amagansett, NY..............957
Eastchester Historical Society - 1835 Marble Schoolhouse, Bronxville, NY......967
Eastern Shore Art Center, Fairhope, AL..............9
ECHO at the Leahy Center for Lake Champlain, Burlington, VT..............1478
EdVenture, Inc., Columbia, SC..............1329
Effie Yeaw Nature Center, Carmichael, CA..............82
Elachee Nature Science Center, Gainesville, GA..............373
Ephraim Historical Foundation, Ephraim, WI..............1597
The Eric Carle Museum of Picture Book Art, Amherst, MA..............658
Escondido Children's Museum, Escondido, CA..............93
Eugene Field House and St. Louis Toy Museum, Saint Louis, MO..............833
Experience Children's Museum, Erie, PA ..1253
Explora, Albuquerque, NM..............933
Exploration Place, Inc., Wichita, KS..............561
Exploration Station - A Children's Museum, Bourbonnais, IL..............414
Explorations V Children's Museum, Lakeland, FL..............320
The Exploratorium, San Francisco, CA..............164
Explore & More...A Children's Museum, East Aurora, NY..............985
Exploris, Raleigh, NC..............1115
Explorit Science Center, Davis, CA..............89
Explorium of Lexington, Lexington, KY.....572
EXPO, The Children's Museum of Gainesville, Inc., Gainesville, FL..............310

Family Museum, Bettendorf, IA..............505
Farmington Museum, Farmington, NM..............939
Fascinate-U Children's Museum, Fayetteville, NC..............1100
Finnup Park and Lee Richardson Zoo, Garden City, KS..............541
Fire Museum of Texas, Beaumont, TX..............1394
Flathead Indian Museum, Saint Ignatius, MT..............853
Flint River Quarium, Albany, GA..............355
The Fort at No. 4 Living History Museum, Charlestown, NH..............884
Fort Inglish, Bonham, TX..............1396
Fort Winnebago Surgeons Quarters, Portage, WI..............1618
Fort Worth Museum of Science and History, Fort Worth, TX..............1417
Fresno Metropolitan Museum, Fresno, CA..............97
Frist Center for the Visual Arts, Nashville, TN..............1379
Frontier Culture Museum, Staunton, VA....1537

Garden State Discovery Museum, Cherry Hill, NJ..............901
Geddes Historic District Village, Geddes, SD..............1347
The Golden Age of Trucking Museum, Middlebury, CT..............249
Golden State Model Railroad Museum, Point Richmond, CA..............143
The Grace Museum, Abilene, TX..............1385
Graham County Historical Society, Thatcher, AZ..............46
Grand Rapids Children's Museum, Grand Rapids, MI..............743
Great Explorations, The Childrens Museum, Saint Petersburg, FL..............341

CHILDREN'S MUSEUMS–Continued

Great Lakes Children's Museum, Greilickville, MI.............................744

The Great Overland Station, Topeka, KS.....559

Greater Hazleton Historical Society, Hazleton, PA.............................1260

Green Hill Art Gallery, Greensboro, NC....1103

Greensboro Children's Museum, Greensboro, NC.............................1103

Grout Museum District: Grout Museum of History and Science, Bluedorn Science Imaginarium, Rensselaer Russell House Museum, Snowden House, Waterloo, IA.....................529

Guinness World of Records Museum, Las Vegas, NV..................................879

Gulf Coast Exploreum Science Center, Mobile, AL...................................13

Gull Wings Children's Museum, Oxnard, CA..137

Habitot Children's Museum, Berkeley, CA..75

Hall of Health, Berkeley, CA......................75

Hamilton Van Wagoner Museum, Clifton, NJ...901

Hands On Children's Museum, Olympia, WA...1560

Hands-on House, Children's Museum of Lancaster, Lancaster, PA 1265

Hands On! Regional Museum, Johnson City, TN.......................................1367

Hannah Lindahl Children's Museum, Mishawaka, IN..............................491

Hawaii Children's Discovery Center, Honolulu, HI...................................395

The Health Adventure, Asheville, NC.......1090

Health World Children's Museum, Barrington, IL..................................412

Healthworks! Kids' Museum, South Bend, IN...499

The Heritage Museum of Fine Arts for Youth, Detroit, MI.............................736

Hershey Gardens, Hershey, PA...................1260

Highland Park Historical Society, Highland Park, IL...............................439

Highlands Museum & Discovery Center, Ashland, KY.....................................564

Hilltop Garden and Nature Center, Bloomington, IN..................................469

Historic Bowens Mills & Pioneer Park, Middleville, MI....................................754

Historic Hermann Museum, Hermann, MO..817

Historic House Trust of New York City, New York, NY...............................1027

Historic Pullman Foundation, Chicago, IL...421

Historic Southwest Ohio, Inc., Sharonville, OH...................................1185

Historical Society of Garden County, Oshkosh, NE.....................................871

Historical Society of Stanton County Museums at Stanton and Pilger, Pilger, NE...872

Holy Trinity (Old Swedes) Church & Hendrickson House Museum, Wilmington, DE....................................274

The Houdini Museum & Theater, Scranton, PA..................................1298

Houston Fire Museum, Houston, TX 1427

Imaginarium Hands-On Museum, Fort Myers, FL...309

The Imaginarium Science Discovery Center, Anchorage, AK 22

Imagination Station Science Museum, Wilson, NC......................................1124

Imagination Workshop - Temecula Children's Museum, Temecula, CA.........191

Imagine Children's Museum, Everett, WA.1554

Imagine It! The Children's Museum of Atlanta, Atlanta, GA............................361

Imagine Nation Museum, Bristol, CT..........236

Imagine That!, Florham Park, NJ.................904

ImagineU Children's Museum, Visalia, CA..195

Impression 5 Science Center, Lansing, MI...750

Indian Pueblo Cultural Center, Albuquerque, NM...............................933

Insights-El Paso Science Center, Inc., El Paso, TX.......................................1412

International Children's Art Museum, San Francisco, CA...................................166

The International Clown Hall of Fame & Research Center, Inc., Milwaukee, WI..1611

International Institute of Metropolitan Detroit, Detroit, MI...............................737

The Iowa Children's Museum, Coralville, IA..511

Iroquois Indian Museum, Howes Cave, NY..999

Jacqueline Casey Hudgens Center for the Arts, Duluth, GA...................................371

James A. McFaul Environmental Center of Bergen County, Wyckoff, NJ.............931

Jasmine Moran Children's Museum, Seminole, OK.....................................1213

The Jefferson County Historical Assoc., Steubenville, OH................................1186

Junior Center of Art and Science, Oakland, CA.......................................133

The Junior Museum of Bay County, Panama City, FL....................................334

Kaleidoscope, Kansas City, MO 821

Kansas Aviation Museum, Wichita, KS........562

Kansas Learning Center for Health, Halstead, KS.......................................542

Kauai Children's Discovery Museum, Kapaa, HI..400

Kearney Area Children's Museum, Kearney, NE.......................................864

Keeler Tavern Museum, Ridgefield, CT.......259

Kern County Museum, Bakersfield, CA.........73

Kid City - The Children's Museum of Tampa, Tampa, FL.................................349

Kidcity Children's Museum, Middletown, CT..249

Kids' Imagination Discovery Space, Medford, OR.......................................1228

Kids 'N' Stuff Children's Museum, Albion, MI...723

Kidspace Children's Museum, Pasadena, CA..140

KidsQuest Children's Museum, Bellevue, WA...1548

KidZone Museum, Truckee, CA..................192

The KidZone Riverside County Youth Museum, Hemet, CA...............................103

Koch Family Children's Museum of Evansville, Evansville, IN.......................476

Kohl Children's Museum of Greater Chicago, Glenview, IL............................438

Kruger Street Toy & Train Museum, Wheeling, WV...................................1588

Lake Wales Depot Museum & Cultural Center, Lake Wales, FL............................320

Laredo Children's Museum, Laredo, TX...1434

Las Vegas Natural History Museum, Las Vegas, NV.......................................879

Laura Ingalls Wilder Museum and Tourist Center, Walnut Grove, MN.....................795

Laura Ingalls Wilder Park & Museum, Inc., Burr Oak, IA...................................507

Laura Ingalls Wilder-Rose Wilder Lane Historic Home & Museum, Mansfield, MO..827

Lefferts Historic House, Brooklyn, NY........969

Legends of the Game Baseball Museum and Learning Center, Arlington, TX......1388

Lehman College Art Gallery, Bronx, NY....966

Lewis Ginter Botanical Garden, Richmond, VA.......................................1530

Libby Museum, Wolfeboro, NH 897

Licking County Historical Society, Newark, OH.......................................1178

Lied Discovery Children's Museum, Las Vegas, NV.......................................879

Lincoln Children's Museum, Lincoln, NE ...865

Lindsay Wildlife Museum, Walnut Creek, CA..196

The Living Arts and Science Center, Inc., Lexington, KY.....................................573

Loggerhead Marinelife Center, Juno Beach, FL...316

Long Island Children's Museum, Garden City, NY...992

Long Island Culture History Lab & Museum, Commack, NY............................980

Lori Brock Children's Discovery Center, Bakersfield, CA..73

Louisiana Art & Science Museum - Irene W. Pennington Planetarium, Baton Rouge, LA...586

Louisiana Children's Museum, New Orleans, LA.......................................596

Lower East Side Tenement Museum, New York, NY.....................................1029

Lutz Children's Museum, Manchester, CT...248

Lynn Meadows Discovery Center, Gulfport, MS.......................................801

MacKenzie Environmental Education Center, Poynette, WI............................1618

Madison Children's Museum, Madison, WI..1605

The Magic House, St. Louis Children's Museum, Saint Louis, MO........................834

Maine Discovery Museum, Bangor, ME....605

Marathon County Historical Society, Wausau, WI.......................................1626

Mariposa Museum & World Culture Center, Peterborough, NH.........................893

The Maritime Aquarium, Norwalk, CT........257

Marshall County Historical Society Museum, Warren, MN...............................795

Mary G. Hardin Center for Cultural Arts, Gadsden, AL...10

Maryland Science Center, Baltimore, MD...634

Matagorda County Museum, Bay City, TX..1393

The Mather Homestead Museum, Library and Memorial Park, Wellsville, NY 1084

Mayborn Museum Complex, Waco, TX.....1459

McKenna Children's Museum, New Braunfels, TX...................................1440

McPherson Museum & Arts Foundation, McPherson, KS.....................................552

McWane Science Center, Birmingham, AL..5

Meadowlands Museum, Rutherford, NJ.......923

The Metropolitan Museum of Art, New York, NY...1030

Miami Children's Museum, Miami, FL........324

Mid-America Air Museum, Liberal, KS......549

Mid-Hudson Children's Museum, Poughkeepsie, NY.................................1055

Minnesota Children's Museum, Saint Paul, MN...791

Minnesota Transportation Museum, Inc., Saint Paul, MN.....................................792

Mission Cultural Center for Latino Arts, San Francisco, CA..................................166

MOBIUS Kids, Spokane, WA....................1571

Monmouth Museum & Cultural Center, Lincroft, NJ...909

Monroe Historical Society, Monroe, CT 250

Morningside Nature Center, Gainesville, FL..311

Muncie Children's Museum, Muncie, IN....492

Museo Del Nino, San Juan, PR..................1643

Museum at Southwestern Michigan College, Dowagiac, MI............................738

Museum of American Presidents, Strasburg, VA..............1539
Museum of Ancient & Modern Art, Penn Valley, CA..............141
Museum of Discovery: Arkansas Museum of Science and History, Little Rock, AR..............62
The Museum of Early Trades and Crafts, Madison, NJ..............910
Museum of Life and Science, Durham, NC..............1098
Museum of the Southwest, Midland, TX ..1439
Muskegon County Museum, Muskegon, MI..............757
My Jewish Discovery Place Children's Museum, Fort Lauderdale, FL..............308
MY Museum, Monterey, CA..............128
Mystic Seaport - The Museum of America and the Sea, Mystic, CT..........251

National Center for Children's Illustrated Literature, Abilene, TX..............1385
National Children's Museum, Washington, DC..............284
National Farm Toy Museum, Dyersville, IA..............517
National Liberty Museum, Philadelphia, PA..............1284
National Museum of Natural History, Washington, DC..............286
National Postal Museum, Smithsonian Institution, Washington, DC..............287
National Scouting Museum, Irving, TX.....1430
National Steinbeck Center, Salinas, CA....154
Netherland Inn House Museum & Boatyard Complex, Kingsport, TN........1368
New Britain Youth Museum, New Britain, CT..............252
New Britain Youth Museum at Hungerford Park, Kensington, CT..........247
New Canaan Nature Center, New Canaan, CT..............252
New Hampshire Farm Museum, Inc., Milton, NH..............892
The New Jersey Children's Museum, Paramus, NJ..............919
New Jersey Meadowlands Environment Center, Lyndhurst, NJ..............910
New Jersey Naval Museum, Hackensack, NJ..............905
The New York Botanical Garden, Bronx, NY..............966
New York City Police Museum, New York, NY..............1035
The Newark Museum, Newark, NJ.............916
The North Museum of Natural History & Science, Lancaster, PA..............1266
Northampton County Historical and Genealogical Society, Easton, PA..........1250
Northeast Louisiana Children's Museum, Monroe, LA..............592
Northern Indiana Center for History, South Bend, IN..............499
Northwoods Children's Museum, Eagle River, WI..............1595

Oceanographic Teaching Station Inc. - Roundhouse Marine Studies Lab & Aquarium, Manhattan Beach, CA............124
Odyssey Maritime Discovery Center, Seattle, WA..............1567
Old Davie School Historical Museum, Davie, FL..............302
Old Firehouse Museum, Greenville, MS....800
Old Salem Inc., Winston-Salem, NC..........1126
Old State House, Hartford, CT..............245
Old Sturbridge Village, Sturbridge, MA.......713
Omaha Children's Museum, Omaha, NE.....871
Orpheum Children's Science Museum, Champaign, IL..............417

Pacific Coast Air Museum, Santa Rosa, CA..............184

Palo Alto Junior Museum and Zoo, Palo Alto, CA..............139
Paul H. Karshner Memorial Museum, Puyallup, WA..............1564
Peter J. McGovern Little League Museum, South Williamsport, PA..........1301
Phoenix Police Museum, Phoenix, AZ..........41
Pioneer Farm Museum and Ohop Indian Village, Eatonville, WA..............1552
Pioneer-Krier Museum, Ashland, KS..........532
Pioneer Museum and Vereins Kirche, Fredericksburg, TX..............1419
Playspace, Raleigh, NC..............1117
Please Touch Museum, Philadelphia, PA...1286
Plumb Farm Learning Center, Greeley, CO..............222
Port Discovery, The Children's Museum in Baltimore, Baltimore, MD..............636
Port Townsend Marine Science Center, Port Townsend, WA..............1562
Porter Thermometer Museum, Onset, MA...700
Portland Children's Museum, Portland, OR..............1233
Portsmouth Museums, Portsmouth, VA.......1526
Presidential Pet Museum, Lothian, MD........649
Providence Children's Museum, Providence, RI..............1317

Queens Library Gallery, Jamaica, NY........1004
Queens Museum of Art, Queens, NY.........1056
Quiet Valley Living Historical Farm, Stroudsburg, PA..............1302
QV Historical Society at Carriage House Museum, Camden, NY..............974

Railroad Museum of Long Island, Riverhead, NY..............1057
The Ralph Foster Museum, Point Lookout, MO..............828
Randall Museum, San Francisco, CA..........168
Rattlesnake Museum (American International), Albuquerque, NM..........935
Red Butte Garden & Arboretum, Salt Lake City, UT..............1472
Regional Science & Discovery Center, Horseheads, NY..............999
River Hills Visitor Center, Wildwood, MO..............840
River Legacy Living Science Center, Arlington, TX..............1388
Roanoke Island Festival Park; Homeport of the "Elizabeth II", Manteo, NC....1110
Rock Creek Nature Center, Washington, DC..............290
Rockingham, Kingston, NJ..............909
Rocky Mount Children's Museum and Science Center, Inc., Rocky Mount, NC..............1118
The Root House Museum, Marietta, GA.....379
Runestone Museum, Alexandria, MN..........767
Rutland Historical Society, Rutland, VT....1486

S.C.R.A.P. Gallery, Indio, CA..............104
Sag Harbor Whaling & Historical Museum, Sag Harbor, NY..............1063
St. Petersburg Museum of History, Saint Petersburg, FL..............342
San Antonio Children's Museum, San Antonio, TX..............1449
The Sandbox, An Interactive Children's Museum, Hilton Head Island, SC..........1335
Sangre de Cristo Arts Center & Buell Children's Museum, Pueblo, CO.............231
Santa Fe Children's Museum, Santa Fe, NM..............950
Schminck Memorial Museum, Lakeview, OR..............1227
Schoolhouse Children's Museum, Boynton Beach, FL..............297
The Schuette Biermann Farmhouse Museum, Elk Grove Village, IL.............432
Sci-Tech Center of Northern New York, Watertown, NY..............1084

The Science Center, Carbondale, IL............415
Science Center of Connecticut, West Hartford, CT..............265
Science Central, Fort Wayne, IN.................478
Science Factory Children's Museum & Planetarium, Eugene, OR..............1224
Science Museum of Western Virginia, Roanoke, VA..............1535
Science Station-IMAX Dome Theatre, Cedar Rapids, IA..............510
Sciencenter, Ithaca, NY..............1004
ScienceWorks Hands-On Museum, Ashland, OR..............1218
SciTech, Aurora, IL..............412
Scitrek, The Science and Technology Museum of Atlanta, Valdosta, GA..........389
Sciworks, Winston-Salem, NC..............1126
Scotia-Glenville Children's Museum, Scotia, NY..............1068
SEE Science Center, Manchester, NH..........892
Seminole Nation Museum, Wewoka, OK...1217
Senator John Heinz Pittsburgh Regional History Center, Pittsburgh, PA..............1294
Shalom Street, West Bloomfield, MI..........766
Sharon Historical Society, Sharon, CT.........260
Shenandoal Valley Discovery Museum, Winchester, VA..............1546
Sherwood Forest Plantation, Charles City, VA..............1498
Shoal Creek Living History Museum, Kansas City, MO..............822
Silver River Museum & Environmental Education Center, Ocala, FL..............330
Simsbury Historical Society, Phelps Tavern, Museum & Homestead, Simsbury, CT..............260
Smith-Zimmermann Heritage Museum, Madison, SD..............1351
Smokey Bear Museum, Capitan, NM..........937
The Somerville Museum, Somerville, MA..............709
Sony Wonder Technology Lab, New York, NY..............1039
South Florida Science Museum, West Palm Beach, FL..............353
Southern Museum of Flight, Birmingham, AL..............6
Southern Oregon Historical Society, Jacksonville, OR..............1226
Southwest Museum of Science and Technology, The Science Place & TI Founders IMAX Theater, Dallas, TX....1407
Space Farms Zoological Park and Museum, Sussex, NJ..............925
Spertus Museum, Chicago, IL..............427
The Sports Museum, Boston, MA..............669
Star Eco Station, Culver City, CA..............88
Staten Island Children's Museum, Staten Island, NY..............1073
Steele County Historical Society, Hope, ND..............1133
Stepping Stones Museum for Children, Norwalk, CT..............257
Stonewall Jackson Museum at Hupp's Hill, Strasburg, VA..............1539
The Stratford Historical Society & Catherine B. Mitchell Museum, Stratford, CT..............262
Strong - National Museum of Play, Rochester, NY..............1060
Sulphur Creek Nature Center, Hayward, CA..............102
Sun Inn Preservation Association Inc., Bethlehem, PA..............1243
Susquehanna Museum of Havre de Grace Inc. at the Lock House, Havre de Grace, MD..............647
Swedish American Museum Association of Chicago, Chicago, IL..............428

T.R.E.E. House - The Rapides Exploratory Education House, Alexandria, LA..............585

CHILDREN'S MUSEUMS–Continued

T Rex Museum, Tucson, AZ............50

Texarkana Museums System, Texarkana, TX............1455

Texas Air Museum, Slaton, TX....1453

Texas City Museum, Texas City, TX........1455

Tolland Historical Society - Tolland County Jail and Warden's Home Museum, Tolland, CT............262

Trailside Nature and Science Center, Mountainside, NJ............915

Treehouse Children's Museum, Ogden, UT............1468

T.T. Wentworth, Jr. Florida State Museum, Pensacola, FL............336

Tucson Children's Museum, Tucson, AZ......51

The Turner Museum, Sarasota, FL............345

Union Station Kansas City, Inc., Kansas City, MO............823

University of Washington Botanic Garden, Seattle, WA............1569

Upper Peninsula Children's Museum, Marquette, MI............754

Uppertown Firefighters Museum, Astoria, OR............1219

Valley County Pioneer Museum, Glasgow, MT............847

Venango Museum of Art, Science & Industry, Oil City, PA............1274

Victor Valley Museum & Art Gallery, Apple Valley, CA............71

Virginia Aquarium & Marine Science Center, Virginia Beach, VA............1542

The Virginia Discovery Museum, Charlottesville, VA............1500

Visual Arts Center at the Washington Pavilion, Sioux Falls, SD............1357

Visual Arts Center of Northwest Florida, Panama City, FL............334

W.H. Over Museum, Vermillion, SD............1358

Walter Reed Birthplace, Gloucester County, VA............1508

Ward W. O'Hara Agricultural Museum, Auburn, NY............959

Washburn County Historical Society Museum, Shell Lake, WI............1621

Washington County Historical Association, Fort Calhoun, NE............860

Waterloo Center for the Arts, Waterloo, IA............529

Watts Towers Arts Center, Los Angeles, CA............122

Wells County Historical Museum, Bluffton, IN............470

West Bay Common School Children's Museum, League City, TX............1434

Western Springs Historical Society, Western Springs, IL............464

Weston Woods Institute, Weston, CT............266

Whatcom Museum of History and Art, Bellingham, WA............1549

White River Valley Museum, Auburn, WA............1547

Wilbur D. May Museum, Reno, NV............882

Wildlife Museum at Petaluma High School, Petaluma, CA............142

Will Rogers Memorial Museum, Claremore, OK............1198

William McKinley Presidential Library & Museum, Canton, OH............1146

William S. Hart County Park & Museum, Newhall, CA............130

Wing Luke Asian Museum, Seattle, WA....1569

Wings Over Miami Museum, Inc., Miami, FL............326

Wisconsin Maritime Museum, Manitowoc, WI............1607

Witte Museum, San Antonio, TX............1451

Wonder Works, Oak Park, IL............449

Wonder Workshop Children's Museum, Manhattan, KS............552

Wonderscope Children's Museum, Shawnee, KS............558

Working Wonders Children's Museum, Bend, OR............1220

World Awareness Children's Museum, Glen Falls, NY............994

World Kite Museum & Hall of Fame, Long Beach, WA............1558

World of Wings Pigeon Center, Oklahoma City, OK............1211

Worldways Children's Museum, Ballwin, MO............811

WOW! Children's Museum (World of Wonder), Lafayette, CO............225

Wyandot County Historical Society, Upper Sandusky, OH............1188

Wyoming Children's Museum & Nature Center, Laramie, WY............1636

Yakima Valley Museum and Historical Association, Yakima, WA............1579

Young at Art Children's Museum, Davie, FL............302

Youth Museum of Southern West Virginia, Beckley, WV............1579

Youth Science Institute, San Jose, CA............173

Youth Science Institute at Vasona Park, Los Gatos, CA............123

Youth Science Institute, Sanborn Nature Center, Saratoga, CA............185

Zeum, San Francisco, CA............170

Zimmer Children's Museum, Los Angeles, CA............122

Zoo Montana, Billings, MT............842

COLLEGE AND UNIVERSITY MUSEUMS

The A.D. Buck Museum of Natural History & Science, Tonkawa, OK............1215

A. E. Seaman Mineral Museum, Houghton, MI............747

Adams State College Luther Bean Museum, Alamosa, CO............201

Adan E. Treganza Anthropology Museum, Dept. of Anthropology, San Francisco State University, San Francisco, CA............162

Alabama Museum of Natural History, Tuscaloosa, AL............19

Alabama Women's Hall of Fame, Marion, AL............13

The Albin O. Kuhn Library & Gallery, University of Maryland-Baltimore County, Baltimore, MD............628

Albion College Department of Art and Art History, Albion, MI............722

Alexander Brest Museum and Gallery, Jacksonville, FL............313

Allen R. Hite Art Institute, Louisville, KY............575

Alumni Center - Husky Heritage Sports Museum, Storrs, CT............261

Alva deMars Megan Chapel Art Center, Manchester, NH............891

American Sport Art Museum and Archives, Daphne, AL............7

American University Museum at The Katzen Arts Center, Washington, DC............275

American West Heritage Center, Wellsville, UT............1475

Anderson Gallery, School of the Arts, Virginia Commonwealth University, Richmond, VA............1528

Anna Lamar Switzer Center for Visual Arts, Pensacola, FL............335

Annmary Brown Memorial, Providence, RI............1316

The Anthropology Museum, DeKalb, IL............429

Arboretum at UC Santa Cruz, Santa Cruz, CA............181

Arizona State Museum, Tucson, AZ............48

Arkansas State University Art Gallery, Jonesboro, AR............60

Arkansas State University Museum, Jonesboro, AR............60

Armstrong Browning Library, Waco, TX...1458

Art Galleries, California State University, Northridge, Northridge, CA............131

The Art Gallery at the University of Maryland, College Park, College Park, MD............640

Art Gallery at the University of New England, Portland, ME............618

The Art Gallery, John C. Calhoun State Community College, Decatur, AL............7

The Art Gallery, Lower Columbia College Fine Arts Gallery, Longview, WA............1558

The Art Gallery, University of New Hampshire, Durham, NH............886

The Art Gym, Marylhurst, OR............1228

The Art Institute of Boston Main Gallery, Boston, MA............663

The Arthur & Kriebel Herbaria, Purdue University, West Lafayette, IN............503

Artmobile, Newtown, PA............1274

Baker University, William A. Quayle Bible Collection, Baldwin City, KS............533

Ball State University Museum of Art, Muncie, IN............492

The Ballard Institute & Museum of Puppetry, Storrs, CT............261

Barton Museum, Wilson, NC............1124

Bates College Museum of Art, Lewiston, ME............613

Beard Gallery, Norton, MA............700

Ben Shahn Galleries at William Paterson University of New Jersey, Wayne, NJ............929

Benedicta Arts Center, Saint Joseph, MN............789

Berea College Burroughs Geological Museum, Berea, KY............565

Berea College, Doris Ulmann Galleries, Berea, KY............565

Berea College Weatherford Planetarium, Berea, KY............565

Birch Aquarium at Scripps, Scripps Institution of Oceanography, University of California, San Diego, La Jolla, CA............106

Birks Museum, Decatur, IL............430

Blanton Museum of Art, Austin, TX............1389

Bob Campbell Geology Museum, Clemson, SC............1328

Bob Rauschenberg Gallery, Edison Community College, Fort Myers, FL............308

The Botanic Garden of Smith College, Northampton, MA............699

Botanical Museum of Harvard University, Cambridge, MA............672

Bowdoin College Museum of Art, Brunswick, ME............607

Bowers Science Museum, Cortland, NY............982

Bowling Green State University Fine Arts Center Galleries, Bowling Green, OH...1143

Braithwaite Fine Arts Gallery, Cedar City, UT............1464

Brauer Museum of Art, Valparaiso, IN............501

Brenau University Galleries, Brenau University, Gainesville, GA............373

Brigham Young University Earth Science Museum, Provo, UT............1469

Brunnier Art Museum, Ames, IA............504

CFCC Webber Center Gallery, Ocala, FL............330

C.H. Nash Museum-Chucalissa Archaeological Museum, Memphis, TN............1372

CU Heritage Center, Boulder, CO............203

CWU Anthropology Department, Ellensburg, WA............1553

California State University, Long Beach, University Art Museum, Long Beach, CA 110
Calkins Nature Area/Field Museum, Iowa Falls, IA 521
Calvin College Center Art Gallery, Grand Rapids, MI 743
The Campus Arboretum Association Haverford College, Haverford, PA 1260
Carleton College Art Gallery, Northfield, MN 785
Carroll Reece Museum, Johnson City, TN.1367
CAS Gallery, Union, NJ 928
Castellani Art Museum of Niagara University, Niagara University, NY.......1043
Cazenovia College - Art & Design Gallery, Cazenovia, NY 976
CCA Wattis Institute for Contemporary Arts, San Francisco, CA..............164
The Centennial Museum at the University of Texas at El Paso, El Paso, TX 1411
Center for Creative Photography, Tucson, AZ..............48
Center for Meteorite Studies, Tempe, AZ 46
Center Galleries, College for Creative Studies, Detroit, MI..............735
Central Missouri State University Archives and Museum, Warrensburg, MO..............839
Charlotte and Philip Hanes Art Gallery, Wake Forest University, Winston-Salem, NC..............1124
Chazen Museum of Art, Madison, WI 1604
The Citadel Archives & Museum, Charleston, SC..............1324
Clark Atlanta University Art Galleries, Atlanta, GA..............359
Clark Humanities Museum-Study, Claremont, CA..............85
Cleveland State University Art Gallery, Cleveland, OH..............1153
Clough-Hanson Gallery, Rhodes College, Memphis, TN..............1372
Colby College Museum of Art, Waterville, ME..............624
College of Eastern Utah Art Gallery, Gallery East, Price, UT..............1469
College of Eastern Utah Prehistoric Museum, Price, UT..............1469
The College of Wooster Art Museum, Wooster, OH..............1192
Colorado Plateau Biodiversity Center, Flagstaff, AZ..............32
Colorado School of Mines Geology Museum, Golden, CO..............220
Comer Museum, Morgantown, WV..........1585
Concordia University-Wisconsin, Art Gallery, Mequon, WI..............1609
Connecticut State Museum of Natural History and Connecticut Archaeology Center, Storrs, CT..............261
The Cornell Plantations, Ithaca, NY..........1003
Creative Photographic Art Center of Maine, Lewiston, ME..............614
Cress Gallery of Art, Chattanooga, TN......1361
Crowder College-Longwell Museum & Camp Crowder Collection, Neosho, MO..............828
Culinary Archives & Museum, Johnson & Wales University, Providence, RI......1316

D. Ralph Hostetter Museum of Natural History, Harrisonburg, VA..............1510
Dalton Galleries, Decatur, GA..............370
Davis Museum and Cultural Center, Wellesley, MA..............716
Davison Art Center, Wesleyan University, Middletown, CT..............249
De Saisset Museum, Santa Clara, CA..........180
Denison Museum, Granville, OH..............1167
Dennos Museum Center of Northwestern Michigan College, Traverse City, MI......765

DePaul University Art Museum, Chicago, IL..............420
Diggs Gallery at Winston-Salem State University, Winston-Salem, NC............1125
Doak House Museum, Greeneville, TN.....1366
Dowd Fine Arts Gallery, State University of New York College at Cortland, Cortland, NY..............983
The Duncan Gallery of Art, De Land, FL....304
Dunn-Seiler Museum, Mississippi State University, MS..............805
Dupont Gallery, Lexington, VA..............1513
The Dwight Frederick Boyden Gallery, Saint Mary's City, MD..............652

E.M. Violette Museum, Kirksville, MO.......824
Elder Art Gallery, Nebraska Wesleyan University, Lincoln, NE..............865
Eleanor Barbour Cook Museum of Geology, Chadron, NE..............859
Elizabeth Myers Mitchell Art Gallery at St. John's College, Annapolis, MD.........627
The Emerson Gallery, Clinton, NY.............979
Entomology Research Museum, Riverside, CA..............149
Essig Museum of Entomology, University of California, Berkeley, Berkeley, CA.......75
The Esther Thomas Atkinson Museum, Hampden-Sydney, VA..............1509
Evergreen Galleries, Olympia, WA.............1560
Ezra and Cecile Zilkha Gallery, Middletown, CT..............249

Farm House Museum, Ames, IA..............505
The Fashion Institute of Design & Merchandising/FIDM Museum & Galleries, Los Angeles, CA..............114
Faulconer Gallery at Grinnell College, Grinnell, IA..............519
The Fay Hyland Botanical Plantation, Orono, ME..............617
Fiedler Memorial Museum, Seguin, TX.....1452
Fielding L. Wright Art Center, Cleveland, MS..............799
Firehouse Art Gallery, Nassau Community College, Garden City, NY...992
Fisher Gallery, University of Southern California, Los Angeles, CA..............115
The Fisk University Galleries, Nashville, TN..............1379
Florida Museum of Natural History, Gainesville, FL..............310
Foster Gallery, University of Wisconsin-Eau Claire, Eau Claire, WI..1596
Francis Colburn Gallery, Burlington, VT...1478
Frank H. McClung Museum, Knoxville, TN..............1370
The Fred Jones Jr. Museum of Art, Norman, OK..............1206
Frederick R. Weisman Art Museum, Minneapolis, MN..............781
Freedman Gallery-Albright College, Reading, PA..............1296
The Frost Entomological Museum, Dept. of Entomology, The Pennsylvania State University, University Park, PA....1304

The Gallery at UTA, Arlington, TX...........1387
Gallery of Contemporary Art, University of Colorado, Colorado Springs, Colorado Springs, CO..............207
Gardiner Art Gallery, Stillwater, OK.........1214
The General Douglas L. McBride Museum, New Mexico Military Institute, Roswell, NM..............945
The Geological Museum, The University of Wyoming, Laramie, WY..............1635
Geology Museum, Huntington, WV.........1583
The George D. and Harriet W. Cornell Fine Arts Museum, Winter Park, FL.......354
George Washington Carver Museum, Tuskegee Institute, AL..............20

Georgetown University Art Collection, Washington, DC..............279
Georgia Museum of Art, University of Georgia, Athens, GA..............356
Georgia Museum of Natural History, Athens, GA..............356
Georgia Southern University Museum, Statesboro, GA..............387
Georgia State University School of Art & Design Gallery, Atlanta, GA..............360
Gheens Science Hall and Rauch Planetarium, Louisville, KY..............576
The Gillespie Museum - Stetson University, De Land, FL..............304
Glen Helen Ecology Institute Trailside Museum, Yellow Springs, OH..............1193
Glencairn Museum: Academy of the New Church, Bryn Athyn, PA..............1244
The Godwin-Ternbach Museum, Flushing, NY..............990
The Goldstein Museum of Design, Saint Paul, MN..............789
Grey Art Gallery, New York University Art Collection, New York, NY..............1026
Grossmont College Hyde Art Gallery, El Cajon, CA..............92
Guilford College Art Gallery, Greensboro, NC..............1103
Gustafson Gallery/Design & Merchandising, Fort Collins, CO.............217
Gustav Jeeninga Museum of Bible and Near Eastern Studies, Anderson, IN........467

Haffenreffer Museum of Anthropology, Brown University, Bristol, RI..............1310
Hallie Ford Museum of Art, Salem, OR....1235
Halsey Institute of Contemporary Art at the College of Charleston, Charleston, SC..............1325
Hamline University Galleries, Department of Studio Arts & Art History, Saint Paul, MN..............790
Hammer Museum, Los Angeles, CA............115
Hampton University Museum, Hampton, VA..............1509
Handwerker Gallery, Ithaca, NY..............1003
Harvard Museum of Natural History, Cambridge, MA..............672
Harvard University Art Museums, Cambridge, MA..............672
Harvard University Semitic Museum, Cambridge, MA..............673
Harvey Cushing/John Hay Whitney Medical Library, New Haven, CT..........253
The Harwood Museum of Art of the University of New Mexico, Taos, NM....952
Hatfield Marine Science Center, Oregon State University, Newport, OR..............1228
Hatton Gallery, Colorado State University, Fort Collins, CO..............217
Hearst Art Gallery, St. Mary's College, Moraga, CA..............128
Hefner Zoology Museum, Oxford, OH.......1181
Helen E. Copeland Gallery, Bozeman, MT..............842
Helen Louise Allen Textile Collection, Madison, WI..............1605
Henry Art Gallery, Seattle, WA..............1566
Herbarium of the University of Michigan, Ann Arbor, MI..............724
Herbert F. Johnson Museum of Art, Ithaca, NY..............1003
Herrett Center for Arts & Science, Faulkner Planetarium and Centennial Observatory, Twin Falls, ID..............410
Higgins Art Gallery - Cape Cod Community College, West Barnstable, MA..............717
Hillstrom Museum of Art, Saint Peter, MN..............793
Hillwood Art Museum, Brookville, NY.......971
Historic Bethany, Bethany, WV..............1580
Historic Pensacola Village, Pensacola, FL...335

COLLEGE AND UNIVERSITY MUSEUMS–Continued

History of Medicine Collections, Durham, NC...1098

History of Pharmacy Museum, Tucson, AZ...49

Hofstra Museum, Hempstead, NY..............997

Homewood House Museum, Baltimore, MD...633

Hood Museum of Art, Hanover, NH...........888

Housatonic Museum of Art, Bridgeport, CT..236

Howard University Museum, Moorland Spingarn Research Center, Washington, DC...................................281

Humboldt State University Natural History Museum, Arcata, CA.................72

Hunt Institute for Botanical Documentation, Pittsburgh, PA..............1292

I.P. Stanback Museum & Planetarium, Orangeburg, SC..............................1338

Idaho Museum of Natural History, Pocatello, ID....................................408

Indiana University Art Museum, Bloomington, IN.............................469

Institute of Contemporary Art, University of Pennsylvania, Philadelphia, PA.........1282

Institute of Meteoritics Meteorite Museum, Albuquerque, NM.....................933

Institute of Visual Arts, University of Wisconsin-Milwaukee, Milwaukee, WI.1611

Intermountain Herbarium, Utah State University, Logan, UT.....................1466

Irene Cullis Gallery, Greensboro College, Greensboro, NC................................1104

Iris & B. Gerald Cantor Art Gallery-College of the Holy Cross, Worcester, MA................................721

Iris & B. Gerald Cantor Center for Visual Arts at Stanford University, Stanford, CA..188

J.I. Holcomb Observatory and Planetarium, Indianapolis, IN...................485

J. Wayne Stark University Center Galleries, College Station, TX...............1401

James E. Lewis Museum of Art, Morgan State University, Baltimore, MD.............633

James Ford Bell Museum of Natural History, Minneapolis, MN....................782

James R. Slater Museum of Natural History, Tacoma, WA 1573

Jane Voorhees Zimmerli Art Museum, New Brunswick, NJ........................915

Jensen Arctic Museum, Monmouth, OR 1228

John A. Logan College Museum, Carterville, IL.................................416

John C. Wells Planetarium, Harrisonburg, VA...1511

John Deere Planetarium, Rock Island, IL 454

John E. Conner Museum, Kingsville, TX..1432

John Furlong Gallery, Menomonie, WI......1609

The Johns Hopkins University Archaeological Collection, Baltimore, MD...633

Johnson County Community College, Gallery of Art, Overland Park, KS.........555

Jonson Gallery of the University of New Mexico Art Museum, Albuquerque, NM...933

Jordan Schnitzer Museum of Art, Eugene, OR...1223

Joseloff Gallery, Hartford Art School, University of Hartford, West Hartford, CT 264

Joseph Moore Museum, Richmond, IN........497

Jule Collins Smith Museum of Fine Art, Auburn, AL...3

Juniata College Museum of Art, Huntingdon, PA.................................1262

Jurica Nature Museum, Lisle, IL.................442

Kansas State University Herbarium, Manhattan, KS.....................................551

Kauffman Museum, North Newton, KS.......553

Kelsey Museum of Archaeology, Ann Arbor, MI...724

Kennedy Museum of Art, Athens, OH 1140

Kent State University, School of Art Galleries, Kent, OH..............................1169

The Kentucky Library & Museum, Bowling Green, KY.............................565

Kipp Gallery at Indiana University of Pennsylvania, Indiana, PA.....................1262

Kirkland Fine Arts Center-Perkinson Gallery, Decatur, IL...........................430

Kresge Art Museum, East Lansing, MI.......739

L.H. Bailey Hortorium, Ithaca, NY............1003

La Salle University Art Museum, Philadelphia, PA................................1282

Laband Art Gallery, Loyola Marymount University, Los Angeles, CA....................117

Lafayette College Art Gallery, Williams Center for the Arts, Easton, PA.............1250

Lamar Dodd Art Center, LaGrange College, LaGrange, GA.........................375

The Lamont Gallery, Exeter, NH.................888

Leander J. McCormick Observatory, Charlottesville, VA...............................1499

Lehigh University Art Galleries/Museum Operations, Bethlehem, PA 1242

Lehman College Art Gallery, Bronx, NY....966

Lentz Center for Asian Culture, Lincoln, NE..865

Logan Museum of Anthropology, Beloit, WI 1592

Longwood Center for the Visual Arts, Farmville, VA.....................................1504

Lore Degenstein Gallery, Selinsgrove, PA .1299

Louden-Henritze Archaeology Museum, Trinidad, CO.......................................234

Louie-Meager Art Gallery, Fremont, CA 96

Louisburg College Art Gallery, Louisburg, NC....................................1109

Louisiana State University Herbarium, Baton Rouge, LA.................................586

Louisiana State University Museum of Art, Baton Rouge, LA.............................586

Louisiana Tech Museum, Ruston, LA 600

Lowe Art Museum, University of Miami, Coral Gables, FL................................301

Loyola University Museum of Art, Chicago, IL..423

The Luther W. Brady Art Gallery, Washington, DC.................................282

MIT-List Visual Arts Center, Cambridge, MA...673

MIT Museum, Cambridge, MA...................674

M. Louise Aughinbaugh Gallery at Messiah College, Grantham, PA.............1257

MSC Forsyth Center Galleries, Texas A&M University, College Station, TX..1401

M.T. Brackbill Planetarium, Harrisonburg, VA.................................1511

Mabee-Gerrer Museum of Art, Shawnee, OK...1213

Macalester College Art Gallery, Janet Wallace Fine Arts Center, Saint Paul, MN...790

Main Art Gallery, California State University, Fullerton, Fullerton, CA...........99

Mandeville Gallery, Union College, Schenectady, NY...............................1067

Margaret Fort Trahern Gallery, Clarksville, TN...................................1363

Mariani Gallery, University of Northern Colorado, Greeley, CO.........................221

Marianna Kistler Beach Museum of Art at Kansas State University, Manhattan, KS...551

Marshall M. Fredericks Sculpture Museum, University Center, MI.............766

Martin Art Gallery, Allentown, PA.............1239

The Martin D'Arcy Museum of Art: The Loyola University Museum of Medieval, Renaissance and Baroque Art, Chicago, IL................................424

Marvin Samson Center for History of Pharmacy/USP Museum, Philadelphia, PA...1283

Mary and Leigh Block Museum of Art, Northwestern University, Evanston, IL ...434

Mary Baldwin College/Hunt Gallery, Staunton, VA....................................1537

The Maryland Institute, College of Art: Decker, Meyerhoff and Pinkard Galleries, Baltimore, MD....................634

Maryville University - Morton J. May Foundation Gallery, Saint Louis, MO 834

Marywood University Art Galleries (Suraci Gallery and Mahady Gallery), Scranton, PA....................................1298

Matthaei Botanical Gardens and Nichols Arboretum, Ann Arbor, MI 725

Maxwell Museum of Anthropology, Albuquerque, NM..............................934

Mayborn Museum Complex, Waco, TX.....1459

MCAD Gallery, Minneapolis, MN..............782

McMullen Museum of Art, Boston College, Chestnut Hill, MA..................675

McWethy Hall, Luce Gallery, Cornell College, Mount Vernon, IA...................524

Mead Art Museum, Amherst, MA................658

Meadows Museum, Dallas, TX 1407

Meadows Museum of Art of Centenary College, Shreveport, LA.......................601

Memorial Art Gallery of the University of Rochester, Rochester, NY.................1059

Memorial Union Art Gallery, Davis, CA 90

Memphis College of Art, Memphis, TN 1374

Merritt Museum of Anthropology, Oakland, CA.......................................133

Miami-Dade College Kendall Campus Art Gallery, Miami, FL.......................324

Miami University Art Museum, Oxford, OH...1181

Michael C. Carlos Museum, Atlanta, GA 361

Michael C. Rockefeller Arts Center Gallery, Fredonia, NY...........................992

Michigan State University Herbarium, East Lansing, MI................................740

The Michigan State University Museum, East Lansing, MI................................740

Middlebury College Museum of Art, Middlebury, VT.................................1482

Mildred Lane Kemper Art Museum, Saint Louis, MO...834

Milliken Gallery, Converse College, Spartanburg, SC..............................1341

Mills College Art Museum, Oakland, CA....133

Mineral Museum, Butte, MT.......................843

Minnesota Landscape Arboretum, University of Minnesota, Chaska, MN....770

Mississippi Entomological Museum, Mississippi State University, MS............805

Mississippi University for Women, Archives and Museum, Columbus, MS...800

Montclair State University Art Galleries, Upper Montclair, NJ..........................929

Morris Arboretum of the University of Pennsylvania, Philadelphia, PA.............1283

Mount Holyoke College Art Museum, South Hadley, MA.............................709

Mountain Heritage Center, Cullowhee, NC...1097

Mulvane Art Museum, Topeka, KS 559

Museum & Archives of Georgia Education, Milledgeville, GA.................380

Museum at Southwestern Michigan College, Dowagiac, MI.........................738

Museum of Anthropology, Winston-Salem, NC.............................1125

Museum of Anthropology, Pullman, WA ...1563

Museum of Anthropology, Chico, CA............83

Museum of Anthropology, University of Denver, Denver, CO.............................213

Museum of Anthropology, University of Missouri, Columbia, MO 813
Museum of Art, Pullman, WA 1563
Museum of Art and Archaeology, University of Missouri - Columbia, Columbia, MO...813
Museum of Art at Brigham Young University, Provo, UT 1469
Museum of Art, Rhode Island School of Design, Providence, RI.............................1317
Museum of Comparative Zoology, Cambridge, MA..674
Museum of Contemporary Photography, Columbia College Chicago, Chicago, IL...424
Museum of Contemporary Religious Art (MOCRA)-St. Louis University, Saint Louis, MO...835
Museum of Cultural & Natural History, Mount Pleasant, MI................................757
Museum of Earth and Life History, Lynchburg, VA...1515
Museum of Geology and Paleontology, South Dakota School of Mines and Technology, Rapid City, SD..................1355
Museum of History, Anthropology and Art, San Juan, PR.....................................1643
Museum of Long Island Natural Sciences, Stony Brook, NY 1075
Museum of Natural History, Marshall, MN...780
Museum of Natural Science, Baton Rouge, LA..587
Museum of Peoples and Cultures, Provo, UT...1470
Museum of Southwestern Biology, Albuquerque, NM.....................................934
Museum of Texas Tech University, Lubbock, TX...1435
Museum of the Geosciences, Blacksburg, VA..1497
Museum of the Llano Estacado, Plainview, TX...1443
Museum of the Rockies, Bozeman, MT.......842
Museum of Vertebrate Zoology, Berkeley, CA...76
Museum of World Cultures/University of North Carolina at Wilmington, Wilmington, NC.....................................1123
Museum of Zoology, Amherst, MA.............659

NAU Art Museum, Flagstaff, AZ 33
NCCU Art Museum, Durham, NC 1099
NIU Art Museum, DeKalb, IL......................429
Nasher Museum of Art at Duke University, Durham, NC.....................1099
Native American Resource Center, Pembroke, NC...1114
Natural History Museum, Portales, NM.......944
Neuberger Museum of Art, Purchase College, State University of New York, Purchase, NY...............................1056
New England College Gallery, Henniker, NH...889
Newcomb Art Gallery, New Orleans, LA 598
No Man's Land Historical Society, Goodwell, OK...1201
Nora Eccles Harrison Museum of Art, Logan, UT...1466
Norman R. Eppink Art Gallery, Emporia State University, Emporia, KS.................539
North Carolina A&T State University Galleries, Greensboro, NC 1104
North Carolina Botanical Garden, Chapel Hill, NC...1093
North Florida Community College Art Gallery, Madison, FL..............................322
North Michigan University DeVos Art Museum, Marquette, MI..........................754
Northern Galleries, Aberdeen, SD 1344
Northern Illinois University Art Gallery in Chicago, Chicago, IL............................425

The Northern Maine Museum of Science, University of Maine, Presque Isle, ME...620
Northwestern Oklahoma State University Museum, Alva, OK.....................................1195
Norwegian-American Historical Association, Northfield, MN...................786

Oak Hill and The Martha Berry Museum, Rome, GA..382
Oakes Museum Messiah College, Grantham, PA 1257
Oakland University Art Gallery, Rochester, MI...761
The Ogden Museum of Southern Art, University of New Orleans, New Orleans, LA...598
Oglethorpe University Museum of Art, Atlanta, GA..362
Ohio University Art Gallery, Athens, OH ..1140
Old Dominion University - University Gallery, Norfolk, VA 1523
Oregon State University Memorial Union Concourse Gallery, Corvallis, OR.........1222
Oriental Institute Museum, University of Chicago, Chicago, IL 426
Orton Geological Museum, Ohio State University, Columbus, OH 1158
Owens Community College/Walter E. Terhune Gallery, Perrysburg, OH...........1182

Pacific Lutheran University Art Galleries, Tacoma, WA 1574
Pacific University Museum, Forest Grove, OR...1224
Palmer Foundation Chiropractic History, Davenport, IA...513
Palmer Museum of Art, The Pennsylvania State University, University Park, PA....1304
Passaic County Community College, Paterson, NJ..920
The Patricia & Phillip Frost Art Museum, Miami, FL..325
The Patrick & Beatrice Haggerty Museum of Art, Milwaukee, WI............1613
Peabody Museum of Archaeology & Ethnology, Cambridge, MA.....................674
Peabody Museum of Natural History, New Haven, CT...253
The Pearson Museum, Springfield, IL..........460
Philip and Muriel Berman Museum of Art at Ursinus College, Collegeville, PA...1247
Philip L. Wright Zoological Museum and University of Montana Herbarium, Missoula, MT...852
Phoebe Apperson Hearst Museum of Anthropology, Berkeley, CA 77
Photographic Archives, University of Louisville Libraries, Louisville, KY........578
Plattsburgh State Art Museum S.U.N.Y., Plattsburgh, NY...1053
Pomona College Museum of Art, Claremont, CA...85
Pratt Manhattan Gallery, New York, NY ...1037
The Pratt Museum of Natural History, Amherst, MA...659
President Andrew Johnson Museum and Library, Greeneville, TN 1366
Princeton University Museum of Natural History, Princeton, NJ 922
Purdue University Galleries, West Lafayette, IN..503

QCC Art Gallery, Bayside, NY 960

R.M. Bohart Museum of Entomology, Davis, CA..90
Radford University Art Museum, Radford, VA..1527
The Ralph Foster Museum, Point Lookout, MO...828
The Regina A. Quick Center for the Arts, Saint Bonaventure, NY 1063

Regina Gouger Miller Gallery, Pittsburgh, PA...1294
Reuel B. Pritchett Museum, Bridgewater, VA...1497
Rice University Art Gallery, Houston, TX.1429
Richard H. Schmidt Museum of Natural History, Emporia, KS 539
Richard L. Nelson Gallery & The Fine Arts Collection, UC Davis, Davis, CA......90
Robert Bebb Herbarium, Norman, OK.......1206
Robert E. Wilson Gallery, Huntington, IN ...481
Robert Hull Fleming Museum, Burlington, VT...1478
Rockford College Art Gallery/Clark Arts Center, Rockford, IL.................................455
Rocky Mountain College of Art + Design Galleries, Lakewood, CO.........................225
Roland Gibson Gallery, Potsdam, NY.........1054
The Rose Art Museum, Waltham, MA.........715
Rosenthal Gallery of Art, Caldwell, ID........405
The Rotunda, University of Virginia, Charlottesville, VA 1500
The Rubelle & Norman Schafler Gallery, Brooklyn, NY...970
Rudolph E. Lee Gallery, Clemson, SC.......1328
Rural Farming & Agriculture Museum, Warner, OK..1216
Ruth Chandler Williamson Gallery, Scripps College, Claremont, CA...............86

Saint Joseph College Art Gallery, West Hartford, CT...265
Saint Joseph's University - University Gallery - Boland Hall, Philadelphia, PA...1288
St. Lawrence University - Richard F. Brush Art Gallery and Permanent Collection, Canton, NY...............................976
Samek Art Gallery, Lewisburg, PA.............1268
Samuel Cupples House of Saint Louis University, Saint Louis, MO.....................837
Samuel Dorsky Museum of Art, State University of New York at New Paltz, New Paltz, NY...1018
Samuel P. Harn Museum of Art, Gainesville, FL...311
The Sandor Teszler Library, Spartanburg, SC...1341
Santa Ana College Art Gallery, Santa Ana, CA...178
Santa Fe Community College Teaching Zoo, Gainesville, FL.................................311
Santa Rosa Jr. College Art Gallery, Santa Rosa, CA...184
Sarah Moody Gallery of Art, The University of Alabama, Tuscaloosa, AL...20
Savannah College of Art and Design Galleries, Savannah, GA 386
Sawhill Gallery, James Madison University, Harrisonburg, VA.................1511
SCAD Museum of Art, Savannah, GA 386
Scarfone/Hartley Gallery, Tampa, FL...........349
The Schick Art Gallery, Skidmore College, Saratoga Springs, NY 1065
Schingoethe Center for Native American Cultures, Aurora, IL 412
Schmucker Art Gallery, Gettysburg, PA.....1256
School of Nations Museum, Elsah, IL 433
School of the Art Institute of Chicago, Gallery 2, Chicago, IL 427
The Schumacher Gallery, Capital University, Columbus, OH 1159
Shasta College Museum & Research Center, Redding, CA.................................146
Sheehan Gallery at Whitman College, Walla Walla, WA 1577
Sheldon Memorial Art Gallery and Sculpture Garden/University of Nebraska-Lincoln, Lincoln, NE 867
Sheppard Fine Arts Gallery, Reno, NV 881
Sidney Mishkin Gallery of Baruch College, New York, NY 1038

COLLEGE AND UNIVERSITY MUSEUMS–Continued

Simpson College/Farnham Galleries, Indianola, IA 519

Skirball Museum Cincinnati Hebrew Union College-Jewish Institute of Religion, Cincinnati, OH 1151

The Smart Museum of Art, Chicago, IL 427

Smith College Museum of Art, Northampton, MA 700

The Snite Museum of Art, University of Notre Dame, Notre Dame, IN 495

Southeast Missouri Regional Museum, Cape Girardeau, MO 812

Southern Oregon University Museum of Vertebrate Natural History, Ashland, OR 1218

Southern Vermont College Art Gallery, Bennington, VT 1477

Spencer Museum of Art, The University of Kansas, Lawrence, KS 548

Spiers Gallery, Brevard, NC 1092

Spindletop/Gladys City Boomtown Museum, Beaumont, TX 1395

Spokane Falls Community College Fine Art Gallery, Spokane, WA 1572

Spurlock Museum, University of Illinois at Urbana-Champaign, Urbana, IL 462

State Agricultural Heritage Museum, Brookings, SD 1344

The State Botanical Garden of Georgia, Athens, GA 357

The Stephens Museum, Fayette, MO 815

Sternberg Museum of Natural History, Hays, KS 543

Stuart Collection, La Jolla, CA 107

Studio San Giuseppe Art Gallery, Cincinnati, OH 1151

Sullivan Museum and History Center, Northfield, VT 1483

Suzanne H. Arnold Art Gallery, Lebanon Valley College, Annville, PA 1241

Sweet Briar Museum, Sweet Briar, VA 1540

Tarble Arts Center, Eastern Illinois University, Charleston, IL 417

Texas Woman's University Art Galleries, Denton, TX 1409

Thomas E. McMillan Museum, Brewton, AL 6

Thomas J. Walsh Art Gallery, Quick Center for the Arts at Fairfield University, Fairfield, CT 241

Thornhill Gallery at Avila University, Kansas City, MO 823

Tougaloo College, Tougaloo, MS 808

Tri-State University, General Lewis B. Hershey Museum, Angola, IN 468

T.T. Wentworth, Jr. Florida State Museum, Pensacola, FL 336

Tufts University Art Gallery, Medford, MA 694

Tweed Museum of Art, Duluth, MN 774

Tyler Art Gallery, Oswego, NY 1048

UCR/California Museum of Photography, Riverside, CA 150

UNLV Marjorie Barrick Museum, Las Vegas, NV 880

USM Art Gallery, Gorham, ME 611

UWM Union-Art Gallery, Milwaukee, WI.1613

Ulrich Museum of Art, Wichita, KS 563

UNI Gallery of Art, University of Northern Iowa, Cedar Falls, IA 508

University Art Galleries, Vermillion, SD....1358

University Art Galleries, Murray State University, Murray, KY 580

University Art Gallery, CSU Dominguez Hills, Carson, CA 82

University Art Gallery, Indiana State University, Terre Haute, IN 501

University Art Gallery, New Mexico State University, Las Cruces, NM 941

University Art Gallery, Sonoma State University, Rohnert Park, CA 151

University Art Gallery, State University of New York at Stony Brook, Stony Brook, NY 1075

University Art Gallery, University of California, San Diego, La Jolla, CA........107

University Art Gallery, University of the South, Sewanee, TN 1384

University Art Museum, Binghamton, NY...963

University Art Museum, Santa Barbara, Santa Barbara, CA 180

University Art Museum, The University of New Mexico, Albuquerque, NM 936

University Art Museum, University at Albany, Albany, NY 956

University at Buffalo Art Galleries, Buffalo, NY 974

University Galleries, Florida Atlantic University, Boca Raton, FL 296

University Gallery, Gainesville, FL 312

University Gallery, University of Massachusetts at Amherst, Amherst, MA 659

University Herbarium & Jepson Herbarium, Berkeley, CA 77

University Museum, Carbondale, IL 415

The University Museum, Edwardsville, IL 432

The University Museum, Indiana, PA 1263

University Museum, Martin, TN 1371

University Museum & Historic Houses, The University of Mississippi, Oxford, MS 806

The University Museum Collections, Fayetteville, AR 57

University Museum, New Mexico State University, Las Cruces, NM 941

University Museums, University of Delaware, Newark, DE 272

University of Alaska Museum of the North, Fairbanks, AK 24

University of Arizona Mineral Museum, Tucson, AZ 52

The University of Arizona Museum of Art, Tucson, AZ 52

University of Arkansas at Little Rock Art Department Gallery I & II & III, Little Rock, AR 63

University of California Berkeley Art Museum and Pacific Film Archive, Berkeley, CA 77

University of California Botanical Garden, Berkeley, CA 77

University of Central Florida Art Gallery, Orlando, FL 332

University of Hawaii Art Gallery, Honolulu, HI 398

University of Iowa Museum of Natural History, Iowa City, IA 520

University of Kansas Medical Center, Clendening History of Medicine Library and Museum, Kansas City, KS...546

University of Kentucky Art Museum, Lexington, KY 574

University of Kentucky Basketball Museum, Lexington, KY 574

University of Maine Museum of Art, Bangor, ME 605

University of Mary Washington Galleries, Fredericksburg, VA 1507

The University of Michigan Exhibit Museum of Natural History, Ann Arbor, MI 725

University of Michigan Museum of Anthropology, Ann Arbor, MI 725

The University of Michigan Museum of Art, Ann Arbor, MI 726

University of Michigan, Museum of Zoology, Ann Arbor, MI 726

University of Missouri-Kansas City Gallery of Art, Kansas City, MO 823

University of Missouri-Rolla Minerals Museum, Rolla, MO 829

The University of Montana-Western Art Gallery & Museum, Dillon, MT 846

University of Nebraska State Museum, Lincoln, NE 867

University of North Dakota Zoology Museum, Grand Forks, ND 1132

University of Northern Iowa Museums & Collections, Cedar Falls, IA 508

University of Pennsylvania Museum of Archaeology and Anthropology, Philadelphia, PA 1288

University of Puerto Rico Department of Marine Sciences Museum, Mayaguez, PR 1641

University of Richmond Museums, Richmond, VA 1532

The University of South Carolina McKissick Museum, Columbia, SC.......1331

University of South Florida Contemporary Art Museum, Tampa, FL 350

University of Tennessee Arboretum, Oak Ridge, TN 1382

The University of Texas at San Antonio, Art Gallery, San Antonio, TX 1451

The University of the Arts - Rosenwald-Wolf Gallery, Philadelphia, PA 1289

University of Wisconsin-Madison Arboretum, Madison, WI 1605

University of Wisconsin Zoological Museum, Madison, WI 1606

University of Wyoming Anthropology Museum, Laramie, WY 1636

University of Wyoming Art Museum, Laramie, WY 1636

U.S. Air Force Academy Visitor Center, USAF Academy, CO 234

Utah Museum of Fine Arts, Salt Lake City, UT 1472

UTSA's Institute of Texan Cultures, San Antonio, TX 1451

Valdosta State University Fine Arts Gallery, Valdosta, GA 389

Van Every/Smith Galleries, Davidson, NC 1098

Vanderbilt University Fine Arts Gallery, Nashville, TN 1381

Viking Union Gallery, Bellingham, WA......1549

Virginia Institute of Marine Science, Gloucester Point, VA 1508

Wake Forest College Birthplace Society, Inc., Wake Forest, NC 1121

Waring Historical Library, Charleston, SC.1327

Washington & Jefferson College - Olin Fine Arts Center, Washington, PA 1305

Wayne State University Art Galleries, Detroit, MI 738

Wayne State University Museum of Anthropology, Detroit, MI 738

The Wayne State University Museum of Natural History, Detroit, MI 738

Weatherspoon Art Museum, Greensboro, NC 1104

Weber State University Art Gallery, Ogden, UT 1468

Weitkamp Observatory and Planetarium, Westerville, OH 1191

Wellington B. Gray Gallery, Greenville, NC 1105

West Point Museum, West Point, NY 1085

West Virginia University-Mesaros Galleries, Morgantown, WV 1585

Western Gallery, Western Washington University, Bellingham, WA 1549

Western Illinois University Art Gallery, Macomb, IL 444

Western Kentucky University Gallery, Bowling Green, KY..........566

Western Michigan University Richmond Center for Visual Arts School of Art, Kalamazoo, MI..........749

Wexner Center for the Arts, Columbus, OH..........1159

Widener Gallery, Austin Arts Center, Trinity College, Hartford, CT..........246

The Wiegand Gallery, Belmont, CA..........74

The William Benton Museum of Art, Storrs, CT..........262

William Brewster Nickerson Memorial Room, Cape Cod Community College, West Barnstable, MA..........717

William Hammond Mathers Museum, Bloomington, IN..........470

William S. Webb Museum of Anthropology, Lexington, KY..........575

Williams College Museum of Art, Williamstown, MA..........719

Winedale, Center for American History, University of Texas at Austin, Round Top, TX..........1446

Winnie Davis Museum of History, Gaffney, SC..........1333

Winston Churchill Memorial and Library, Fulton, MO..........816

Wright Museum of Art, Beloit College, Beloit, WI..........1592

Wright State University Art Galleries, Dayton, OH..........1162

The Yager Museum of Art & Culture, Oneonta, NY..........1046

Yale Center for British Art, New Haven, CT..........254

Yale University Art Gallery, New Haven, CT..........254

COMPANY MUSEUMS

American Airlines C.R. Smith Museum, Fort Worth, TX..........1416

Baker-Cederberg Museum & Archives, Rochester, NY..........1058

Biltmore Homespun Shops - Grovewood Gallery, Asheville, NC..........1089

CTS Turner Museum, Elkhart, IN..........474

The Cannon Village Visitor Center, Kannapolis, NC..........1107

Cigna Museum and Art Collection, Philadelphia, PA..........1277

Dupont Historical Society, DuPont, WA..........1552

Emil A. Blackmore Museum of The American Legion, Indianapolis, IN..........482

FPL Energy Encounter, Jensen Beach, FL...316

Fenton Glass Museum, Williamstown, WV..........1589

Four Wheel Drive Foundation, Clintonville, WI..........1594

Frye's Measure Mill, Wilton, NH..........897

Goodyear World of Rubber Museum, Akron, OH..........1139

Heddon Museum, Dowagiac, MI..........738

Herschell Carrousel Factory Museum, North Tonawanda, NY..........1043

Hoover Historical Center, North Canton, OH..........1179

Johnson Victrola Museum, Dover, DE..........270

Knights of Columbus Museum, New Haven, CT..........253

Louisville Slugger Museum & Factory, Louisville, KY..........577

Port Gamble Historic Museum, Port Gamble, WA..........1562

Remington Firearms Museum and Country Store, Ilion, NY..........1002

Rogers Daisy Airgun Museum, Rogers, AR..........67

Schwartz Collection of Skiing Heritage, Tiburon, CA..........192

Sony Wonder Technology Lab, New York, NY..........1039

Union Pacific Railroad Museum, Council Bluffs, IA..........512

Wal-Mart Visitor's Center, Bentonville, AR..........55

Wells Fargo History Exhibit, Portland, OR..........1233

Wells Fargo History Museum, Minneapolis, MN..........783

Wells Fargo History Museum, Phoenix, AZ..........42

Wells Fargo History Museum, Los Angeles, CA..........122

Wells Fargo History Museum, Sacramento, CA..........154

Wells Fargo History Museum, Sacramento, CA..........154

Wells Fargo History Museum, San Diego, CA..........162

Wells Fargo History Museum, San Francisco, CA..........170

Weston Woods Institute, Weston, CT..........266

Wooden Nickel Historical Museum, San Antonio, TX..........1452

World's First Wendy's Restaurant, Columbus, OH..........1159

Zippo/Case Visitors Center, Bradford, PA..1244

EXHIBIT AREAS

Abraham Lincoln Presidential Library & Museum, Springfield, IL..........458

Adirondack Park Visitor Interpretive Center, Paul Smiths, NY..........1051

Alexander Brest Museum and Gallery, Jacksonville, FL..........313

Alton Museum of History and Art, Inc., Alton, IL..........410

American Airlines C.R. Smith Museum, Fort Worth, TX..........1416

Anasazi Heritage Center, Dolores, CO..........214

The Andy Warhol Museum, Pittsburgh, PA..........1290

ARC Gallery (Artists, Residents of Chicago), Chicago, IL..........417

Arizona Historical Society Museum - Downtown, Tucson, AZ..........47

Arlington Heights Historical Museum, Arlington Heights, IL..........411

The Armory Art Center, West Palm Beach, FL..........353

Art Association of Harrisburg, Harrisburg, PA..........1258

Art Guild of Burlington, Inc., Burlington, IA..........507

The Art Institute of Boston Main Gallery, Boston, MA..........663

Arts Consortium of Cincinnati's African American Museum, Cincinnati, OH..........1148

Atlanta Botanical Garden, Atlanta, GA..........357

Atlantic Center for the Arts, Inc., New Smyrna Beach, FL..........329

Audubon Society of New Hampshire, Concord, NH..........884

The AXA Gallery, New York, NY..........1021

The Bard Graduate Center for Studies in the Decorative Arts, Design, & Culture, New York, NY..........1021

Ben Shahn Galleries at William Paterson University of New Jersey, Wayne, NJ..........929

Berkshire Artisans/Lichtenstein Center for the Arts, Pittsfield, MA..........702

Bicentennial Art Center & Museum, Paris, IL..........449

Big Hole National Battlefield, Wisdom, MT..........855

Black American West Museum & Heritage Center, Denver, CO..........209

Bob Campbell Geology Museum, Clemson, SC..........1328

Boca Raton Museum of Art, Boca Raton, FL..........296

Branchville Railroad Shrine and Museum, Inc., Branchville, SC..........1322

Brevard Museum of Art and Science, Inc., Melbourne, FL..........323

CFCC Webber Center Gallery, Ocala, FL....330

California Route 66 Museum, Victorville, CA..........195

Carroll County Farm Museum, Westminster, MD..........656

Cecelia Coker Bell Gallery, Hartsville, SC..........1335

Center for American Archaeology, Kampsville, IL..........440

Center for Creative Photography, Tucson, AZ..........48

Center on Contemporary Art, Seattle, WA.1565

The Chicago Athenaeum: Museum of Architecture and Design, Galena, IL..........436

Chinese House/O.R. & N. Museum & St. Peter's Catholic Church, Echo, OR..........1222

Chisholm Trail Heritage Center, Duncan, OK..........1199

Christa McAuliffe Planetarium, Concord, NH..........884

City of Brea Gallery, Brea, CA..........79

Clearwater Marine Aquarium, Clearwater, FL..........299

Clinton County Historical Society Paine-Gillam-Scott Museum, Saint Johns, MI..........763

Clough-Hanson Gallery, Rhodes College, Memphis, TN..........1372

Collier County Museum, Naples, FL..........328

Columbia River Exhibition of History, Science and Technology, Richland, WA..........1564

Contemporary Art Museum St. Louis, Saint Louis, MO..........832

Contemporary Arts Center, New Orleans, LA..........594

Contemporary Crafts Museum & Gallery, Portland, OR..........1230

Courthouse Square Association, Charlotte, MI..........731

Crazy Mountain Museum, Big Timber, MT..........841

Creative Arts Center, Pontiac, MI..........760

Creative Photographic Art Center of Maine, Lewiston, ME..........614

Curfman Gallery & Duhesa Lounge, Fort Collins, CO..........216

Dakota Sunset Museum, Gettysburg, SD...1348

The Dallas Center for Contemporary Art - The Dallas Contemporary, Dallas, TX..........1404

The Dan Quayle Center & Museum, Huntington, IN..........481

The Design Center at Philadelphia University, Philadelphia, PA..........1278

Diggs Gallery at Winston-Salem State University, Winston-Salem, NC..........1125

Dinosaur Valley State Park, Glen Rose, TX..........1422

Dishman Art Museum, Beaumont, TX..........1394

Door County Maritime Museum (at Sturgeon Bay), Sturgeon Bay, WI..........1623

Dry Tortugas National Park, Key West, FL..........317

EXHIBIT AREAS–Continued

East Kentucky Center for Science, Mathematics, and Technology, Prestonsburg, KY...................583

East-West Center, Honolulu, HI..................394

Edward Hopper Landmark Preservation Foundation, Nyack, NY 1044

Esther M. Klein Art Gallery at University City Science Center, Philadelphia, PA...1279

Fayetteville Museum of Art, Fayetteville, NC..1100

Federal Bureau of Investigation, Washington, DC.....................................278

Fine Arts Center at Miriam Hall, Anna Maria College, Paxton, MA 701

Fine Arts Center for New River Valley, Pulaski, VA...1526

The Florida International Museum, Saint Petersburg, FL...341

Fort Jones Museum, Fort Jones, CA.............96

Fort MacArthur Museum, San Pedro, CA....176

Foster Gallery, University of Wisconsin-Eau Claire, Eau Claire, WI..1596

Gallery of Henry Street Settlement/Abrons Arts Center, New York, NY...1026

Gateway to Science, Bismarck, ND 1128

Gerald R. Ford Library, Ann Arbor, MI.......724

Gig Harbor Peninsula Historical Society, Gig Harbor, WA....................................1555

The Glynn Art Association, Inc., Saint Simons Island, GA.................................383

Grants Pass Museum of Art, Grants Pass, OR..1225

Greeley History Museum, Greeley, CO.......221

Grissom Air Museum, Peru, IN...................496

Guinness World of Records Museum, Las Vegas, NV...879

H.G. Albee Memorial Museum, Estherville, IA.......................................517

Hana Cultural Center, Hana, Maui, HI........392

Headwaters Heritage Museum, Three Forks, MT..854

Higgins Art Gallery - Cape Cod Community College, West Barnstable, MA..717

Historic Langhorne Association, Langhorne, PA.....................................1267

Historical Society of Oak Park & River Forest, Oak Park, IL.............................448

Holland Area Arts Council, Holland, MI 746

Holocaust Museum Houston, Houston, TX 1426

Hull Lifesaving Museum Inc., the Museum of Boston Harbor Heritage, Hull, MA...687

Huntington Beach International Surfing Museum, Huntington Beach, CA............104

Imaginarium Hands-On Museum, Fort Myers, FL..309

Intuit: The Center for Intuitive and Outsider Art, Chicago, IL........................422

Irish American Heritage Museum, Albany, NY...954

Irving Arts Center, Irving, TX 1430

Jamaica Center for Arts & Learning (JCAL), Jamaica, NY............................1004

James A. Michener Art Museum, Doylestown, PA....................................1249

Jean Lafitte National Historical Park & Preserve, New Orleans, LA....................596

Jeane Dixon Museum and Library, Strasburg, VA.....................................1538

Julia A. Purnell Museum, Snow Hill, MD...654

Kansas Department of Wildlife & Parks, Pratt, KS...556

Key West Museum of Art and History, Key West, FL.......................................318

Keyport Historical Society-Steamboat Dock Museum, Keyport, NJ 909

Keystone Area Historical Society, Keystone, SD.....................................1350

Kid City - The Children's Museum of Tampa, Tampa, FL................................349

KidsQuest Children's Museum, Bellevue, WA...1548

Lafayette College Art Gallery, Williams Center for the Arts, Easton, PA 1250

Laurence C. Jones Museum, Piney Woods, MS...807

Library of Congress, Washington, DC.........282

Lillian and Albert Small Jewish Museum, Washington, DC.....................................282

Lopez Island Historical Museum, Lopez Island, WA...1558

Lou Holtz/Upper Ohio Valley Hall of Fame, East Liverpool, OH 1163

Louisiana's Old State Capitol, Political History Museum, Baton Rouge, LA........587

Loveland Museum Gallery, Loveland, CO...227

M. Louise Aughinbaugh Gallery at Messiah College, Grantham, PA............1257

Madison Children's Museum, Madison, WI..1605

Mamie Doud Eisenhower Birthplace, Boone, IA...506

Mandeville Gallery, Union College, Schenectady, NY.................................1067

Manhattan Arts Center, Manhattan, KS........551

Mansfield Township Historical Society (1849 Georgetown School/Museum), Columbus, NJ.......................................902

Marblehead Arts Association - King Hooper Mansion, Marblehead, MA.........693

The Mary Baker Eddy Library for the Betterment of Humanity, Boston, MA.....666

Mattress Factory, Ltd., Pittsburgh, PA........1293

Maude I. Kerns Art Center, Eugene, OR ...1223

McMullen Museum of Art, Boston College, Chestnut Hill, MA....................675

Meux Home Museum, Fresno, CA................98

Miami Art Museum, Miami, FL...................324

Mid-America Science Museum, Hot Springs, AR..60

Miller Art Museum, Sturgeon Bay, WI 1623

The Money Museum-Federal Reserve Bank of Kansas City, Kansas City, MO..821

Montclair State University Art Galleries, Upper Montclair, NJ..............................929

The Muchnic Gallery, Atchison, KS.............533

Museum of Chinese in the Americas, New York, NY.....................................1032

Museum of Design Atlanta, Atlanta, GA 362

Museum of Idaho, Idaho Falls, ID 406

Museum of the Southern Jewish Experience, Jackson, MS 803

Museum of Utah Art & History, Salt Lake City, UT.......................................1471

Naismith Memorial Basketball Hall of Fame, Springfield, MA...........................710

Napa Valley Museum, Yountville, CA 200

National Academy of Sciences, Washington, DC.....................................283

National Cryptologic Museum, Fort Meade, MD...643

National First Ladies' Library, Canton, OH..1145

National Museum of Dance & Hall of Fame, Saratoga Springs, NY..................1065

National Road/Zane Grey Museum, Norwich, OH.......................................1180

National Wildlife Visitor Center, Patuxent Research Refuge, Laurel, MD.................648

Nevada Museum of Art, Reno, NV.............881

New Bedford Whaling Museum, New Bedford, MA...696

New England College Gallery, Henniker, NH..889

New England Maple Museum, Pittsford, VT..1484

New World Art Center/T.F. Chen Cultural Center, New York, NY............................1035

North Carolina Aquarium at Pine Knoll Shores, Pine Knoll Shores, NC.............1114

Oceanside Museum of Art, Oceanside, CA..135

Old Church Cultural Center School of Art, Demarest, NJ.................................902

Old Hidalgo Pumphouse, Hidalgo, TX 1424

Opelousas Museum and Interpretive Center, Opelousas, LA 599

Oregon Trail Regional Museum, Baker City, OR...1219

The Palette & Chisel, Chicago, IL 426

Passaic County Community College, Paterson, NJ..920

The Peace Museum, Chicago, IL.................426

Pence Gallery, Davis, CA 90

Pewabic Pottery, Detroit, MI 737

Photographic Resource Center, Boston, MA..669

Piper Aviation Museum Foundation, Lock Haven, PA..1269

Port Angeles Fine Arts Center & Webster's Woods Art Park, Port Angeles, WA.......................................1561

Port Discovery, The Children's Museum in Baltimore, Baltimore, MD..................636

Portholes Into the Past, Medina, OH.........1176

Pound Ridge Society/Museum, Pound Ridge, NY...1055

R.S. Barnwell Memorial Garden and Art Center, Shreveport, LA 601

Randolph County Museum (At Beverly), Beverly, WV.......................................1580

Renville County Historical Society, Inc., Mohall, ND...1135

Rice University Art Gallery, Houston, TX.1429

Richmond Museum of History, Richmond, CA......................................148

Rio Grande Nature Center State Park, Albuquerque, NM..................................935

Rip Van Winkle Gardens on Jefferson Island, New Iberia, LA...........................593

River Legacy Living Science Center, Arlington, TX.......................................1388

Roger Tory Peterson Institute of Natural History, Jamestown, NY.......................1005

Rosenbruch Wildlife Museum, St. George, UT...1474

SITE Santa Fe, Santa Fe, NM.....................950

Saint Joseph's University - University Gallery - Boland Hall, Philadelphia, PA..1288

St. Louis Science Center, Saint Louis, MO..836

Samuel Cupples House of Saint Louis University, Saint Louis, MO..................837

San Francisco Camerawork, San Francisco, CA.......................................169

San Francisco International Airport; San Francisco Airport Museums, San Francisco, CA.......................................169

Sanborn Area Historical Society, Sanborn, NY.......................................1064

Sanibel-Captiva Conservation Foundation, Inc., Sanibel, FL......................................343

Saratoga Automobile Museum, Saratoga Springs, NY..1065

Savannah College of Art and Design Galleries, Savannah, GA 386

School of Fine Arts Gallery, Indiana University, Bloomington, IN....................470

School of the Art Institute of Chicago, Gallery 2, Chicago, IL 427

Sci-Tech Center of Northern New York, Watertown, NY........................1084

Scottsdale Museum of Contemporary Art, Scottsdale, AZ 44

The Sharon Arts Center, Inc., Sharon, NH...896

Shenandoal Valley Discovery Museum, Winchester, VA 1546

Slidell Museum, Slidell, LA 602

Socrates Sculpture Park, Long Island City, NY 1012

The Somerville Museum, Somerville, MA 709

Southdown Plantation House/The Terrebonne Museum, Houma, LA 589

Southeastern Architectural Archive, New Orleans, LA 598

Springbrook Nature Center, Fridley, MN 776

Spruill Gallery, Atlanta, GA.......................364

Stauth Memorial Museum, Montezuma, KS..553

STAX Museum of American Soul Music, Memphis, TN..............................1376

Stephens African-American Museum, Shreveport, LA 602

Studio San Giuseppe Art Gallery, Cincinnati, OH............................1151

The Suffolk Museum, Suffolk, VA 1540

Sushi Performance and Visual Art, San Diego, CA....................................161

Sweet Briar College Art Gallery, Sweet Briar, VA 1540

T.W. Wood Gallery & Arts Center, Montpelier, VT 1482

Tacoma Public Library/Thomas Handforth Gallery, Tacoma, WA...........1574

Taos County Historical Society, Inc., Taos, NM 953

Tennessee Museum of Aviation, Sevierville, TN 1383

Thomas Kinkade Museum, Morgan Hill, CA..129

Thornhill Gallery at Avila University, Kansas City, MO 823

Torrance Art Museum, Torrance, CA 192

Umpqua Discovery Center, Reedsport, OR..1234

University Art Gallery San Diego State University, San Diego, CA....................162

University Art Gallery, Texas Christian University, Fort Worth, TX 1418

University of Arizona Student Union Galleries, Tucson, AZ......................52

University of West Florida Art Gallery, Pensacola, FL................................336

Upper Musselshell Historical Society, Harlowton, MT...............................849

U.S. Naval Museum of Armament & Technology, China Lake, CA...................84

Victor Heritage Museum, Victor, MT..........854

Visual Arts Center of Northwest Florida, Panama City, FL............................334

Waterworks Visual Arts Center, Salisbury, NC.......................................1118

The Wayne State University Museum of Natural History, Detroit, MI....................738

Wells Fargo History Museum, Minneapolis, MN.............................783

Wilkes Art Gallery, North Wilkesboro, NC..1113

William King Regional Arts Center, Abingdon, VA.................................1491

Windham Textile and History Museum (The Mill Museum), Willimantic, CT 267

Wonders: Memphis International Cultural Series, Memphis, TN....................1376

Woodstock Historical Society, Bryant Pond, ME....................................608

Worcester County Horticultural Society/Tower Hill Botanic Garden, Boylston, MA 670

WordSpring Discovery Center, Orlando, FL...333

Wrangell Museum, Wrangell, AK..............29

Wyatt Earp Birthplace Home, Monmouth, IL..445

GENERAL MUSEUMS

Abraham Lincoln Presidential Library & Museum, Springfield, IL 458

Action Wildlife Foundation, Goshen, CT.....242

Adams County Historical Society, Gettysburg, PA...............................1255

Adams County Historical Society Museum, Brighton, CO....................204

Adams Museum & House, Deadwood, SD.......................................1346

Adams Old Stone Grist Mill, Bellows Falls, VT 1476

Adan E. Treganza Anthropology Museum, Dept. of Anthropology, San Francisco State University, San Francisco, CA 162

Adventure Science Center, Nashville, TN..1377

Advertising Icon Museum, Kansas City, MO..820

The African American Museum in Philadelphia, Philadelphia, PA 1275

Alabama Center for Traditional Culture, Montgomery, AL 15

Alabama Jazz Hall of Fame, Birmingham, AL.................................4

Alamo Township Museum-John E. Gray Memorial Museum, Kalamazoo, MI.......748

Alaska State Museum, Juneau, AK 25

Albany Historical Society, Inc., Sabetha, KS...557

Alden Historical Society, Inc., Alden, NY ...956

Alexander Brest Museum and Gallery, Jacksonville, FL.............................313

Aliceville Museum, Aliceville, AL 3

Allaire Village Inc., Farmingdale, NJ...........903

Allegan County Historical Society and Old Jail Museum, Allegan, MI.............723

Allegany County Museum, Belmont, NY 961

Allen County Museum, Lima, OH 1172

Almond Historical Society/Hagadorn House Museum, Almond, NY.................957

Amador County Museum, Jackson, CA 105

Amelia Island Museum of History, Fernandina Beach, FL 306

American Swedish Historical Foundation & Museum, Philadelphia, PA................1276

American Work Horse Museum, Lexington, VA...............................1513

Americana Museum, Terra Alta, WV 1587

Amory Regional Museum, Amory, MS........797

Anadarko Heritage Museum, Anadarko, OK...1195

Andrew County Museum & Historical Society, Savannah, MO 838

Anna Bemis Palmer Museum, York, NE......875

Annie E. Woodman Institute Museum, Dover, NH 886

Antelope Valley California Poppy Reserve, Lancaster, CA 108

Anthropology Teaching Museum, California State University, Fullerton, Fullerton, CA 98

Appomattox Court House National Historical Park, Appomattox, VA 1495

Arcadia Township Historical Commission, Arcadia, MI 726

Archer County Museum, Archer City, TX .1387

Arizona Historical Society-Yuma: Sarguinetti House Museum and Garden, Yuma, AZ...........................54

Arkansas Post Museum, Gillett, AR.............58

Arkansas State University Museum, Jonesboro, AR................................60

Arlington Heights Historical Museum, Arlington Heights, IL 411

The Arms Family Museum of Local History, Youngstown, OH.....................1193

Art and Culture Center of Hollywood, Hollywood, FL...............................312

Art Center Sarasota, Inc, Sarasota, FL 343

Art League of Houston, Houston, TX 1425

Ashland Historical Society Museum, Ashland, WI...................................1590

Atchison County Historical Society, Atchison, KS..................................533

Audrain Historical Museum, Graceland, Mexico, MO...................................827

Audubon County Historical Society, Exira, IA...................................517

Aurora Historical Society, Aurora, OH.......1140

Austin Museum of Art - Downtown, Austin, TX 1388

Avery County Museum, Newland, NC 1113

Badger Mine and Museum, Shullsburg, WI...1622

Baldwin-Reynolds House Museum, Meadville, PA.................................1270

The Ballard Institute & Museum of Puppetry, Storrs, CT.........................261

Banner County Historical Society, Harrisburg, NE................................862

Baranov Museum, Kodiak, AK...................26

The Barbara Fritchie House, Frederick, MD..644

The Barker Character, Comic and Cartoon Museum, Cheshire, CT............237

Barron County Historical Society's Pioneer Village Museum, Cameron, WI...1593

The Bartlett Museum, Amesbury, MA 657

Bay Area Museum, Seabrook, TX...............1452

Bead Museum, Washington, DC.................276

The Beaufort Arsenal, Beaufort, SC...........1321

Beauvais Heritage Center, Clark, SD 1345

Becker County Historical Society, Detroit Lakes, MN...................................772

Bedford City/County Museum, Bedford, VA...1496

Bedford Historical Society Museum and Library, Bedford, OH 1142

Behringer-Crawford Museum, Covington, KY...567

Belding Museum, Belding, MI 728

Bellflower Historical and Genealogical Society, Bellflower, IL.......................413

Belmont County Victorian Mansion Museum, Barnesville, OH.................1141

Benton County Historical Museum, Philomath, OR...............................1230

Benton County Historical Museum, Prosser, WA...................................1563

Bergen Museum of Art & Science, Paramus, NJ.................................919

Berkshire Museum, Pittsfield, MA 702

Berlin Art and Historical Collections, Berlin, MA....................................662

Bessemer Hall of History, Bessemer, AL.........3

Bethlehem Historical Association, Selkirk, NY...................................1068

Betts House Research Center, Cincinnati, OH...1148

Beyer Home, Oconto County Historical Society Museum, Oconto, WI...............1616

Big Springs Museum, Caledonia, NY 974

Big Thunder Gold Mine, Keystone, SD.....1349

Big Timbers Museum, Lamar, CO 225

Big Well, Greensburg, KS 542

Billy the Kid Museum, Fort Sumner, NM ...939

Birthplace of John Wayne, Winterset, IA.....530

Bisbee Mining & Historical Museum, Bisbee, AZ.....................................30

Bishop Museum, Honolulu, HI.................394

The Black Fashion Museum, Washington, DC..277

GENERAL MUSEUMS–Continued

Black Hills Mining Museum, Lead, SD.....1350

Black River Historical Society of Lorain, Lorain, OH................1172

Blackhawk Museum (Behring-Hofmann Educational Institute, Inc.), Danville, CA................89

Blaine County Historical Museum, Hailey, ID................406

Blue Hills Trailside Museum, Milton, MA................695

Blue Licks Battlefield Museum, Mount Olivet, KY................580

Bob Burns Museum & River Valley Museum of Van Buren, Van Buren, AR................69

Boone County Historical Museum, Belvidere, IL................413

Boothe Memorial Park and Museum, Stratford, CT................262

Boswell Museum of Music, Springfield Center, NY................1071

Boundary County Historical Society, Bonners Ferry, ID................404

Bowers Museum, Santa Ana, CA................177

Bradford Historical Society Inc., Bradford, VT................1477

Branigan Cultural Center, Las Cruces, NM................940

Brattleboro Museum & Art Center, Brattleboro, VT................1477

Brazos Valley Museum of Natural History, Bryan, TX................1398

Brevard Museum of History & Science, Cocoa, FL................300

Bridge Hampton Historical Society, Bridgehampton, NY................964

Brookings County Historical Society Museum, Volga, SD................1358

Brooklyn Children's Museum, Brooklyn, NY................968

Brooklyn Historical Society, Brooklyn, OH................1144

Brown County Historical Society Pioneer Museum, Nashville, IN................493

Brownville Historical Society Museum, Brownville, NE................858

Bruce Museum, Greenwich, CT................243

Bucyrus Historical Society, Bucyrus, OH..1144

Buffalo and Erie County Historical Society, Buffalo, NY................972

Buffalo Bill Museum of Le Claire, Iowa, Inc., Le Claire, IA................522

Buffalo Trails Museum, Epping, ND................1130

Burke County Historical Powers Lake Complex, Powers Lake, ND................1136

Burlington Historical Museum, Burlington, MA................672

Burritt on the Mountain-A Living Museum, Huntsville, AL................11

Burt County Museum, Tekamah, NE................873

Butte-Silver Bow Arts Chateau, Butte, MT................843

Byron Historical Museum, Byron, NY................974

CFCC Webber Center Gallery, Ocala, FL....330

C.H. Moore Homestead, Clinton, IL................428

CHTJ Southard House Museum, Brunswick, ME................607

Calhoun County Museum, Rockwell City, IA................527

Calhoun County Museum, Port Lavaca, TX................1444

Calhoun County Museum & Cultural Center, Saint Matthews, SC................1341

California Heritage Museum, Santa Monica, CA................183

California Museum For History, Women and the Arts, Sacramento, CA................151

California Oil Museum, Santa Paula, CA....183

California Surf Museum, Oceanside, CA.....135

Calumet County Historical Society, Inc., New Holstein, WI................1615

Cambria County Historical Society, Ebensburg, PA................1251

Camden County Historical Society, Camden, NJ................899

Campbell County Rockpile Museum, Gillette, WY................1633

Canadian County Historical Museum, El Reno, OK................1200

Caney Valley Historical Society, Caney, KS................534

Cannon Falls Area Historical Museum, Cannon Falls, MN................770

Cape Cod National Seashore, Wellfleet, MA................717

Cape Vincent Historical Museum, Cape Vincent, NY................976

Capitol Reef National Park Visitor Center, Torrey, UT................1475

Capitola Historical Museum, Capitola, CA................81

Carlsbad Caverns National Park, Carlsbad, NM................937

Carnegie Historical Museum, Fairfield, IA................517

Carriage and Western Art Museum, Santa Barbara, CA................178

Carson County Square House Museum, Panhandle, TX................1442

Carter County Museum, Ekalaka, MT................846

Cass County Historical Society, Logansport, IN................489

Cass County Historical Society Museum, Plattsmouth, NE................872

Cassia County Museum, Burley, ID................404

Castle Museum of Saginaw County History, Saginaw, MI................762

Catskill Fly Fishing Center & Museum, Livingston Manor, NY................1010

Cattaraugus Area Historical Center, Cattaraugus, NY................976

Cedar Falls Historical Society, Cedar Falls, IA................507

Cedar Key Historical Society Museum, Cedar Key, FL................298

Central Missouri State University Archives and Museum, Warrensburg, MO................839

Central Texas Area Museum, Inc., Salado, TX................1447

Chandler Gallery, Randolph, VT................1485

Chappell Hill Historical Society Museum, Chappell Hill, TX................1399

Charles M. Schulz Museum and Research Center, Santa Rosa, CA................184

The Charleston Museum, Charleston, SC ..1324

Chase County Historical Society, Inc., Cottonwood Falls, KS................536

Chemung Valley History Museum, Elmira, NY................988

Chenango County Historical Society Museum, Norwich, NY................1044

Cherokee County Historical Museum, Inc., Murphy, NC................1112

Cherokee Strip Museum, Alva, OK................1195

Cherry County Historical Society, Valentine, NE................874

Cherry Valley Museum, Cherry Valley, NY................978

Chesterfield County Museum, Chesterfield, VA................1501

Cheyenne Botanic Gardens, Cheyenne, WY................1630

Chickasaw Council House Museum, Tishomingo, OK................1214

Chickasaw County Historical Society Bradford Pioneer Village Museum, Nashua, IA................525

The Children's Museum of Indianapolis, Indianapolis, IN................481

The Children's Museum of Science and Technology, Troy, NY................1079

Chinese Cultural Garden/Overfelt Gardens, San Jose, CA................171

Chisholm Trail Historical Museum, Waurika, OK................1216

Chisholm Trail Museum, Kingfisher, OK...1203

Choctaw County Historical Society, Hugo, OK................1203

Churchill County Museum and Archives, Fallon, NV................877

City County Pioneer Museum, Sweetwater, TX................1454

Clark County Historical Museum, Vancouver, WA................1576

Clark County Historical Society - Heritage Center of Clark County, Springfield, OH................1186

Clark Hotel Museum, Van Horn, TX................1457

Clarkson Historical Museum, Clarkson, NE................859

Clarksville-Montgomery County Museum dba Customs House Museum & Cultural Center, Clarksville, TN................1363

Clay County Historical Society Museum and Archives, Moorhead, MN................784

Clear Lake Area Historical Museum, Clear Lake, WI................1594

Clearwater County Historical Society, Shevlin, MN................793

Cleo Redd Fisher Museum, Loudonville, OH................1172

Clewiston Museum, Inc., Clewiston, FL................300

Clinton County Historical Society, Wilmington, OH................1191

Cloud County Historical Society Museum, Concordia, KS................536

Coeur d'Alenes Old Mission State Park, Cataldo, ID................405

The Coleman House Museum and Brown County Historical Society, Ainsworth, NE................855

Colleton Museum, Walterboro, SC................1343

Colorado Springs Museum, Colorado Springs, CO................206

Columbia River Exhibition of History, Science and Technology, Richland, WA................1564

Columbus-Belmont Civil War Museum, Columbus, KY................567

Comanche Crossing Historical Society & Museum, Strasburg, CO................233

The Commonwealth Museum, Boston, MA................665

Community Historical Museum, Maxwell, IA................523

Concord Historical Society, Warner Museum, Springville, NY................1071

Confederate Memorial Hall-Bleak House, Knoxville, TN................1369

Conklin Reed Organ & History Museum, Hanover, MI................745

Connecticut Trolley Museum, East Windsor, CT................239

Constitution Square State Historic Site, Danville, KY................567

Cook County Historical Museum, Grand Marais, MN................776

Cordova Historical Museum, Cordova, AK................23

Coronado-Quivira Museum, Lyons, KS................550

Corpus Christi Museum of Science and History, Corpus Christi, TX................1401

Cortland County Historical Society, Cortland, NY................982

Cottage Grove Museum & Annex, Cottage Grove, OR................1222

Cottonlandia Museum, Greenwood, MS................800

County Center Historical Society, Wabasso, MN................795

The Cowley County Historical Society, Winfield, KS................564

Cracker Trail Museum, Zolfo Springs, FL...355

Crawford County Historical Museum, Pittsburg, KS................556

Cripple Creek District Museum, Inc., Cripple Creek, CO......................209
Crossroads of America, Bethlehem, NH 883
Custer County Historical Society, Inc., Broken Bow, NE 858

Dakota Sunset Museum, Gettysburg, SD ...1348
Dakotaland Museum, Huron, SD................1348
Dal-Paso Museum, Lamesa, TX 1433
Dallam-Hartley XIT Museum, Dalhart, TX 1403
Dalton Defenders Museum, Coffeyville, KS 535
Dane G. Hansen Memorial Museum, Logan, KS 550
Davidson County Historical Museum, Lexington, NC 1109
Dawes County Historical Society Museum, Chadron, NE........................859
Dawson County Historical Museum, Lexington, NE 864
De Smet Depot Museum, De Smet, SD.....1346
Dedham Historical Society Museum, Dedham, MA 679
Del Norte County Historical Society, Crescent City, CA.................................87
Delano Heritage Park, Delano, CA 91
Delaware Visitor's Center, Dover, DE..........270
Delta County Historical Society Museum, Escanaba, MI 741
Delta Music Museum, Ferriday, LA 588
Denali National Park and Preserve, Denali Park, AK 23
Desert Caballeros Western Museum, Wickenburg, AZ.......................................53
Desha County Museum, Dumas, AR.............56
Dexter Historical Society Campus, Dexter, ME 609
Discovery Museum, Sacramento Museum of History, Science and Technology, Sacramento, CA..152
Discovery Seashell Museum, Ocean City, NJ 918
Dodge County Historical Society, Mantorville, MN.....................................780
Dodge County Historical Society Museum, Beaver Dam, WI 1591
Donald E. Stephens Museum of Hummels, Rosemont, IL 456
Douglas County Museum of History and Natural History, Roseburg, OR..............1234
Douglass Historical Museum, Douglass, KS 537
Downieville Museum, Downieville, CA 91
Drummond Island Historical Museum, Drummond Island, MI............................739
Dublin-Laurens Museum, Dublin, GA 370
Dundy County Historical Society, Benkelman, NE...857
Dunham Tavern Museum, Cleveland, OH..1154
Dunklin County Museum, Inc., Kennett, MO 824
Durham Center Museum/Research Library, East Durham, NY 985
Durham Historic Association Museum, Durham, NH 886

East Brunswick Museum Corporation, East Brunswick, NJ.................................902
East Jordan Portside Art & Historical Museum, East Jordan, MI 739
Eastchester Historical Society - 1835 Marble Schoolhouse, Bronxville, NY......967
Eastern California Museum, Independence, CA 104
Eastern Museum of Motor Racing, York Springs, PA 1309
Eastern Oregon Museum on the Old Oregon Trail, Haines, OR.....................1226
Edgar Allan Poe Museum, Richmond, VA.1529
Edwards County Historical Museum, Kinsley, KS...547

Edwin Wolters Memorial Museum, Shiner, TX...1453
1880 Town, Murdo, SD.............................1352
The 1811 Old Lincoln County Jail and Lincoln County Museum, Wiscasset, ME...625
1859 Jail, Marshal's Home & Museum, Independence, MO....................................817
El Monte Historical Society Museum, El Monte, CA 92
Elkhart County Historical Museum, Bristol, IN 471
Elkhorn Valley Museum & Research Center, Norfolk, NE 869
Ella Sharp Museum, Jackson, MI.................748
Elliott Museum, Stuart, FL 346
Elvis Presley Birthplace and Museum, Tupelo, MS 808
Emmett Kelly Historical Museum, Sedan, KS 558
Empire Area Heritage Group, Empire, MI...740
The Endowment Fund of the Phi Kappa Psi Fraternity-Heritage Hall, Indianapolis, IN 482
Ernest Hemingway House Museum, Key West, FL 317
Essley-Noble Museum: Mercer County Historical Society, Aledo, IL.................410
Esther M. Klein Art Gallery at University City Science Center, Philadelphia, PA...1279
Eureka Pioneer Museum of McPherson County, Inc., Eureka, SD 1346
Evansville Museum of Arts History & Science, Evansville, IN 475
The Exhibition Alliance, Hamilton, NY.......997

Fairbanks Museum and Planetarium, Saint Johnsbury, VT 1486
Fairport Historical Museum, Fairport, NY ...989
Falmouth Historical Society, Falmouth, MA...682
Faninadahen Kosas Guahan-Guam Museum, Hagatna, GU............................1640
Farmington Museum, Farmington, NM........939
Fayette County Museum, Washington Court House, OH 1190
Feet First: The Scholl Story, Rosalind Franklin University, North Chicago, IL...448
Fillmore County Historical Center, Fountain, MN...776
Fillmore Historical Museum, Inc., Fillmore, CA..95
Finney County Kansas Historical Society, Inc., Garden City, KS.............................541
Firelands Historical Society Museum, Norwalk, OH...1180
The First Division Museum at Cantigny, Wheaton, IL...465
Flint Ridge State Memorial Museum, Glenford, OH...1166
Florence Griswold Museum, Old Lyme, CT 258
Florence Museum of Art, Science & History and the Florence Railroad Museum, Florence, SC 1332
Florence Price Pioneer Museum, Florence, CO...216
Florida Community College, Kent Campus Museum/Gallery, Jacksonville, FL...314
Floyd County Historical Museum, Charles City, IA...510
Folsom Museum, Inc., Folsom, NM.............939
Ford County Historical Society, Paxton, IL 450
Forest Capital State Museum, Perry, FL 337
Forest Lawn Museum, Glendale, CA 100
Forestiere Underground Gardens, Fresno, CA 97
Fort Abercrombie State Historic Site, Abercrombie, ND 1127
Fort Abraham Lincoln State Park, Mandan, ND 1134

Fort Collins Museum, Fort Collins, CO.......217
Fort Crawford Museum, Prairie du Chien, WI 1618
Fort Crook Historical Museum, Fall River Mills, CA..94
Fort Jones Museum, Fort Jones, CA 96
Fort Kearney Museum, Kearney, NE 863
Fort Morgan Museum, Fort Morgan, CO.....218
Fort Sidney Museum & Post Commander's Home, Sidney, NE............873
Fort Sisseton State Historic Park, Lake • City, SD 1350
Fort Wilkins Historic Complex, Copper Harbor, MI 733
Frances Willard House Museum, Evanston, IL..434
Frank Chiarenza Museum of Glass, Meriden, CT..248
Frank H. McClung Museum, Knoxville, TN 1370
Frankfort Area Historical Museum, West Frankfort, IL 464
Franklin County Historical & Museum Society & House of History, Malone, NY 1012
Franklin County Old Jail Museum, Winchester, TN 1385
Franklin Historical Society, Franklin, ME....611
The Franklin Pierce Homestead, Hillsborough, NH 889
Fraternal Order of Alaska State Troopers Museum, Anchorage, AK 22
Freeborn County Museum and Historical Village, Albert Lea, MN............................767
Freeport Historical Society, Freeport, ME....611
Freestone County Historical Museum, Fairfield, TX 1413
Fremont County Pioneer Museum, Lander, WY 1635
Fresno Metropolitan Museum, Fresno, CA 97
The Friends of the Caleb Pusey House, Inc., Upland, PA.......................................1304
Frontier Gateway Museum, Glendive, MT 847
Frontier Historical Society and Museum, Glenwood Springs, CO.............................219
Frontier Museum, Williston, ND 1138
Frontier Times Museum, Bandera, TX 1393
Fruitlands Museums, Harvard, MA 686
Fryer Memorial Museum, Munnsville, NY 1017
Fullerton Museum Center, Fullerton, CA.......98
Fulton County Historical Museum, Wauseon, OH...1190
Fulton County Historical Society Museum, Rochester, IN 498
Furnas-Gosper Historical Society & Museum, Arapahoe, NE 856

Gage County Historical Society and Museum, Beatrice, NE 857
Galloway House and Village - Blakely Museum, Fond du Lac, WI...................1597
The Gardner Museum, Inc., Gardner, MA ...684
Garnavillo Historical Museum, Garnavillo, IA...518
Gaston County Museum of Art and History, Dallas, NC.................................1097
Gates Mills Historical Society, Gates Mills, OH...1166
Gateway to the Panhandle, Gate, OK.........1201
Gene Autry Oklahoma Museum, Gene Autry, OK...1201
General Sterling Price Museum, Keytesville, MO...824
George I. Ashby Memorial Museum, Copper Center, AK 23
George Washington Carver Museum, Tuskegee Institute, AL...........................20
Georgia Capitol Museum, Atlanta, GA 360
Georgia Salzburger Society Museum, Rincon, GA...381

GENERAL MUSEUMS–Continued

Georgia's Stone Mountain Park, Stone Mountain, GA 387
Gig Harbor Peninsula Historical Society, Gig Harbor, WA 1555
Gilcrease Museum, Tulsa, OK 1215
Gilman Museum, Hellertown, PA 1260
Gilpin History Museum, Central City, CO...205
Gloucester County Historical Society, Woodbury, NJ 931
Gone With The Wind Movie Museum, Marietta, GA 379
Goshen Historical Society, Goshen, CT 242
The Goudreau Museum of Mathematics in Art and Science, aka The Math Museum, New Hyde Park, NY 1017
Gouverneur Historical Association, Gouverneur, NY 995
Grace Hudson Museum & Sun House, Ukiah, CA 193
The Grace Museum, Abilene, TX 1385
The Gracie Mansion Conservancy, New York, NY 1026
Graham County Historical Society, Thatcher, AZ 46
Grand Lake Area Historical Society, Grand Lake, CO 221
The Grand River Historical Society & Museum, Chillicothe, MO 813
Grant County Museum, Medford, OK 1205
Grant County Museum & Historic Society, Hyannis, NE 863
Graue Mill and Museum, Oak Brook, IL 448
Gravette Historical Museum, Gravette, AR 59
Great Basin Historical Society & Museum, Delta, UT 1464
Greater Hazleton Historical Society, Hazleton, PA 1260
Greenwood County Historical Society, Eureka, KS 539
Gregg County Historical Museum, Longview, TX 1434
Greybull Museum, Greybull, WY 1634
Grout Museum District: Grout Museum of History and Science, Bluedorn Science Imaginarium, Rensselaer Russell House Museum, Snowden House, Waterloo, IA 529
Gunn Memorial Library and Museum, Washington, CT 263
Gunnison County Pioneer and Historical Society, Gunnison, CO 222

H. Earl Clack Museum, Havre, MT 849
H.G. Albee Memorial Museum, Estherville, IA 517
Hamilton Township Historical Society - John Abbott II House, Hamilton, NJ 906
Hancock Historical Society, Hancock, NH 888
Hans Christian Andersen Museum, Solvang, CA 187
Harbor Defense Museum, Brooklyn, NY 969
Hardin County Historical Museums, Inc., Kenton, OH 1170
Harney County Historical Museum, Burns, OR 1221
Harper City Historical Society, Harper, KS 543
Harpers Ferry Center, Harpers Ferry, WV .1582
Harrison County Historical Museum, Marshall, TX 1436
Hastings Museum, Hastings, NE 863
Hatton-Eielson Museum & Historical Association, Hatton, ND 1132
Haverhill Historical Society, Haverhill, MA 686
Hawks Inn Historical Society, Inc., Delafield, WI 1595
Headwaters Heritage Museum, Three Forks, MT 854

Heart of West Texas Museum, Colorado City, TX 1401
Henry County Museum and Cultural Arts Center, Clinton, MO 813
Heritage-Hjemkomst Interpretive Center, Moorhead, MN 784
The Heritage Museum at Falfurrias, Inc., Falfurrias, TX 1413
Heritage Museums & Gardens, Sandwich, MA 707
Hibbing Historical Society and Museum, Hibbing, MN 778
Hiddenite Center, Inc., Hiddenite, NC 1106
Hillsboro Area Historical Society, Hillsboro, WI 1600
Historic Auto Attractions, Roscoe, IL 456
Historic Bowens Mills & Pioneer Park, Middleville, MI 754
Historic Hermann Museum, Hermann, MO 817
Historic Occoquan, Inc., Occoquan, VA 1523
Historic Palmyra's Print Shop, Palmyra, NY 1050
Historic Pullman Foundation, Chicago, IL ...421
Historic Renville Preservation Commission, Renville, MN 787
Historic St. Mary's City, Saint Mary's City, MD 652
Historic Shepherdstown Museum, Shepherdstown, WV 1586
Historical and Genealogical Society of Indiana County, Indiana, PA 1262
The Historical Museum at St. Gertrude, Cottonwood, ID 405
Historical Natural History & Library Society of Natick dba Natick Historical Society, South Natick, MA 709
Historical Shrine Foundation of San Diego County, San Diego, CA 156
Historical Society of Bloomfield New Jersey, Bloomfield, NJ 898
Historical Society of Cecil County, Elkton, MD 643
Historical Society of Columbia County, Saint Helens, OR 1234
Historical Society of Greenfield, Greenfield, MA 685
Historical Society of Middletown and the Wallkill Precinct, Inc., Middletown, NY 1014
Historical Society of Ocean Grove, New Jersey, Ocean Grove, NJ 918
Historical Society of Palm Beach County, Palm Beach, FL 334
Historical Society of the Town of Greenwich Inc. aka Bush-Holley Historic Site, Cos Cob, CT 237
The Historical Society of the Town of Warwick, Warwick, NY 1082
The Historical Society, serving Sleepy Hollow and Tarrytown, Tarrytown, NY.1078
The History Center in Tompkins County, Ithaca, NY 1003
Hodgden House Museum Complex, Ellsworth, KS 538
Hollywood Bowl Museum, Los Angeles, CA 116
Hollywood Guinness World of Records Museum, Hollywood, CA 103
Hood River County Historical Museum, Hood River, OR 1226
Hope Historical Society, Hope, NJ 908
Hopewell Museum, Hopewell, NJ 908
Horizons Unlimited Supplementary Educational Center, Salisbury, NC 1118
Hornby Museum, Hornby, NY 999
Hot Spring County Museum - The Boyle House/1876 Log Cabin, Malvern, AR 63
Houghton County Historical Museum Society, Lake Linden, MI 749
The House on the Rock, Spring Green, WI 1622
The Hudson River Museum, Yonkers, NY.1087

The 100th Meridian Museum, Cozad, NE ...859
Huntington County Historical Society Museum, Huntington, IN 481
Huron City Museums, Port Austin, MI 761
Illinois State Museum, Springfield, IL 458
Imperial Calcasieu Museum, Inc., Lake Charles, LA 590
Independence Historical Museum, Independence, KS 545
Indiana State Museum, Indianapolis, IN 484
Interlaken Historical Society, Interlaken, NY 1002
International Institute of Metropolitan Detroit, Detroit, MI 737
International Museum of Carousel Art, Hood River, OR 1226
International Spy Museum, Washington, DC 281
International Swimming Hall of Fame, Inc., Fort Lauderdale, FL 307
International UFO Museum and Research Center, Roswell, NM 946
Iowa Masonic Library and Museum, Cedar Rapids, IA 509
Iredell Museum of Arts & Heritage, Statesville, NC 1120
Iroquois County Historical Society, Watseka, IL 463
Isabel Miller Museum/Sitka Historical Society, Sitka, AK 27
Ischua Valley Historical Society, Inc., Franklinville, NY 992
Issaquah History Museum, Issaquah, WA ...1557

J.E. Reeves Home & Museum, Dover, OH 1163
J.M. Davis Arms & Historical Museum, Claremore, OK 1198
J.W. Parmley Historical Home Society, Ipswich, SD 1349
Jackson Hole Historical Society and Museum, Jackson, WY 1634
Jail Museum, Neligh, NE 869
The James Madison Museum, Orange, VA 1524
Jean Lafitte National Historical Park & Preserve, New Orleans, LA 596
Jeff Matthews Memorial Museum, Galax, VA 1508
The Jefferson County Historical Assoc., Steubenville, OH 1186
Jefferson Historical Society and Museum, Jefferson, TX 1431
Jekyll Island Museum, Jekyll Island, GA ...374
Jerome County Historical Society, Inc. and Idaho Farm & Ranch Museum, Jerome, ID 406
Jesse Peter Museum, Santa Rosa, CA 184
Jewell County Historical Museum, Mankato, KS 552
Jewish Museum of Maryland, Baltimore, MD 633
John A. Logan College Museum, Carterville, IL 416
John E. Conner Museum, Kingsville, TX ..1432
John S. Barry Historical Society, Constantine, MI 732
Johnson-Humrickhouse Museum, Coshocton, OH 1159
Johnstown Historical Society, Johnstown, NY 1005
Joliet Area Historical Museum, Joliet, IL 440
Jordan Schnitzer Museum of Art, Eugene, OR 1223
Joseph Smith Historic Site, Nauvoo, IL 447
Judith Basin County Museum, Stanford, MT 853
Juneau-Douglas City Museum, Juneau, AK 26
Juniata County Historical Society, Mifflintown, PA 1271

The Junior Museum of Bay County, Panama City, FL 334

Kalamazoo Valley Museum, Kalamazoo, MI 749
Kankakee County Museum, Kankakee, IL...441
The Kansas Teachers' Hall of Fame, Dodge City, KS 537
Kaw Mission State Historic Site, Council Grove, KS 536
Kearney County Historical Museum, Minden, NE 868
Kearney Mansion Museum, Fresno, CA 97
Kellogg Historical Society, Kellogg, IA.......521
Kemerer Museum of Decorative Arts, Bethlehem, PA 1242
The Kemp-McCarthy Memorial Museum of the Rowe Historical Society, Inc., Rowe, MA 706
Kenosha County Historical Society and Museum, Inc., Kenosha, WI 1602
The Kentucky Library & Museum, Bowling Green, KY...............................565
Ker Place, Onancock, VA 1523
Kewaunee County Historical Museum, Kewaunee, WI 1602
Keweenaw County Historical Society, Eagle Harbor, MI 739
Keyport Historical Society-Steamboat Dock Museum, Keyport, NJ 909
Keystone Area Historical Society, Keystone, SD 1350
KidsQuest Children's Museum, Bellevue, WA 1548
Kingman County Historical Museum, Kingman, KS 547
Kit Carson Historical Society, Kit Carson, CO 223
Kit Carson Museum, Las Animas, CO.........225
Kiwanis Van Slyke Museum Foundation Inc., Caldwell, ID...................................404
Klein Museum, Mobridge, SD 1352
Knight Museum, Alliance, NE......................855
Knox County Museum, Benjamin, TX.......1395
Kuhlmann King Historical House and Museum, Boerne, TX 1396

LaBelle Heritage Museum, LaBelle, FL 319
Lac Qui Parle County Historical Society, Madison, MN...779
Lacey Historical Society, Forked River, NJ..904
Lafayette Miners Museum, Lafayette, CO ...224
Lahaina Restoration Foundation, Lahaina, HI 400
Lake County Discovery Museum, Wauconda, IL..463
Lake County Historical Society, Two Harbors, MN.......................................794
Lake Guernsey Museum-Guernsey State Park, Guernsey, WY 1634
Lake Tahoe Historical Society & Museum, South Lake Tahoe, CA.............188
Lakewood's Heritage Center, Lakewood, CO 225
Laramie Plains Museum, Laramie, WY 1635
Las Vegas Natural History Museum, Las Vegas, NV 879
Laumeier Sculpture Park & Museum, Saint Louis, MO 834
Laura Ingalls Wilder Memorial Society, Inc., De Smet, SD 1346
Laura Ingalls Wilder Museum and Tourist Center, Walnut Grove, MN 795
The Laurel Museum, Laurel, MD.................648
Lawrence County Gray House Museum, Ironton, OH 1169
Lawrence County Historical and Genealogical Society, Bedford, IN 469
Laws Railroad Museum and Historical Site, Bishop, CA..78
Layland Museum, Cleburne, TX 1400

Lemhi County Historical Museum, Salmon, ID...409
Lesueur County Historical Museum-Chapter 1, Elysian, MN 774
Lewis County Historical Society Museum, Lowville, NY........................1012
Liberty County Museum, Chester, MT........844
Life on the Ohio River History Museum, Vevay, IN 502
Lightner Museum, Saint Augustine, FL 339
Lincoln County Historical Museum, Davenport, WA....................................1552
Lincoln County Museum, Hugo, CO...........222
Lincoln County Pioneer Museum, Hendricks, MN 778
Linn County Museum/Genealogy Library, Pleasanton, KS.............................556
Little Falls Historical Society Museum, Little Falls, NY.......................................1009
Little White House Historic Site, Warm Springs, GA 390
Livingston County Historical Society Museum, Geneseo, NY........................993
Livingston Depot Center, Livingston, MT ...850
The Log House Museum of the Historical Society of Columbiana-Fairfield Township, Columbiana, OH....................1157
Logan County Historical Society Museum, Bellefontaine, OH...................1142
Logan County Museum, Paris, AR................65
Long Island Museum of American Art, History & Carriages, Stony Brook, NY..1075
Los Nogales Museum, Seguin, TX.............1452
Lou Holtz/Upper Ohio Valley Hall of Fame, East Liverpool, OH 1163
Louis E. May Museum, Fremont, NE 861
The Louisiana Cotton Museum, Lake Providence, LA....................................590
Louisiana Marine Fisheries Museum, Lafitte, LA 590
Louisiana State Exhibit Museum, Shreveport, LA 600
Louisiana State Oil & Gas Museum, Oil City, LA 599
Lower Hudson Conference of Historical Agencies and Museums, Elmsford, NY..988
Lowndes County Historical Society and Museum, Valdosta, GA 389
Lubeznik Center for the Arts, Michigan City, IN 490
Lyman Museum, Hilo, HI 393
Lynden Pioneer Museum, Lynden, WA.......1559
Lyon County Historical Society and Museum, Emporia, KS.............................538
Lyon County Historical Society Museum, Marshall, MN..........................780

Mabee-Gerrer Museum of Art, Shawnee, OK..1213
Madeline Island Historical Museum, La Pointe, WI..1603
Madera County Museum, Madera, CA 123
Madison County Historical Society, Winterset, IA..531
Madison Historical Society, Madison, CT....247
Maine Historical Society, Portland, ME.......619
Maine State Museum, Augusta, ME.............604
Mann Wildlife Learning Museum, Montgomery, AL.......................................16
Mansfield Historical Society Museum, Storrs, CT...261
Maple Valley Historical Museum, Maple Valley, WA...1559
Mardi Gras Museum, Kenner, LA................589
Marias Museum of History and Art, Shelby, MT 853
Marion Public Library Museum, Marion, IN...490
Maritime and Yachting Museum of the Treasure Coast, Stuart, FL 346

Marquette County Historical Society, Westfield, WI.......................................1627
Marshall County Historical Museum, Holly Springs, MS..................................801
Marshall County Historical Society Museum, Warren, MN............................795
Martin County Historical Museum, Stanton, TX..1453
Mason County Historical Society/Historic White Pine Village, Ludington, MI 751
Mason County Museum, Mason, TX 1437
MASS MoCA, North Adams, MA 698
Matchless Mine Museum (Leadville Assembly), Leadville, CO......................226
Mattapoisett Museum and Carriage House, Mattapoisett, MA 693
The Mattatuck Museum Arts and History Center, Waterbury, CT...............................264
Mattress Factory, Ltd., Pittsburgh, PA........1293
Matt's Museum, Lawtell, LA........................590
Maturango Museum of the Indian Wells Valley, Ridgecrest, CA..............................148
Mayville Area Museum of History and Genealogy, Mayville, MI 754
Mazomanie Historical Society, Mazomanie, WI.....................................1608
Mc Cook County Historical Society and Museum, Salem, SD 1355
McCallum Museum, Sibley, IA 527
McCone County Museum, Circle, MT.........844
McCook House, Civil War Museum, Carrollton, OH.....................................1146
McDonald's #1 Store Museum, Des Plaines, IL 431
McDowell House Museum, Danville, KY ...567
McIntosh County Historical Society, Ashley, ND..1127
McLean County Historical Society Museum, Washburn, ND 1137
McPherson Museum & Arts Foundation, McPherson, KS.......................................552
McWane Science Center, Birmingham, AL 5
Meade County Historical Society Museum, Meade, KS 552
Meadowlands Museum, Rutherford, NJ 923
Mecosta County Historical Museum, Big Rapids, MI 729
Medina County Historical Society, The John Smart House, Medina, OH............1175
Meeker County Historical Society Museum & G.A.R. Hall, Litchfield, MN..779
Meeteetse Museum District, Meeteetse, WY 1636
Memorial Hall Museum, Pocumtuck Valley Memorial Assoc., Deerfield, MA..679
Mendocino County Museum, Willits, CA 198
Menominee County Heritage Museum, Menominee, MI 754
The Metropolitan Museum of Art, New York, NY...1030
Miami County Museum, Peru, IN 496
The Michigan State University Museum, East Lansing, MI....................................740
Mid-America Science Museum, Hot Springs, AR..60
Middleborough Historical Association, Inc., Middleborough, MA 694
Middlebury Historical Society, Wyoming, NY..1087
Middletown Valley Historical Society, Middletown, MD 649
Midland County Historical Museum, Midland, TX...1438
Midland County Historical Society, Midland, MI...755
Midway Museum, Inc., Midway, GA...........379
Milan Historical Museum, Inc., Milan, OH..1176
Minneapolis Institute of Arts, Minneapolis, MN..................................782

GENERAL MUSEUMS–Continued

Minnetrista, Muncie, IN...............................492
Miramont Castle Museum, Manitou
    Springs, CO 228
Mission Bell Museum, Coweta, OK...........1199
Mission Cultural Center for Latino Arts,
    San Francisco, CA 166
Mission San Miguel, San Miguel, CA 175
Mississippi Agriculture &
    Forestry/National Agricultural Aviation
    Museum, Jackson, MS 802
Mississippi County Historical Society,
    Charleston, MO 812
Mississippi University for Women,
    Archives and Museum, Columbus, MS...800
Missouri State Museum, Jefferson City,
    MO 819
Mitchell County Historical Museum,
    Osage, IA 526
Modern Western Museum, Mount
    Pleasant, TX..1440
Mondak Heritage Center, Sidney, MT.........853
The Monhegan Museum, Monhegan, ME....615
Monroe County Historical
    Association/Stroud Mansion,
    Stroudsburg, PA 1302
Monroe County Historical Museum,
    Monroe, MI...756
Monroe Historical Society, Monroe, CT 250
Montague Museum & Historical
    Association, Montague, MI 756
Montana Historical Society, Helena, MT 849
Montclair State University Art Galleries,
    Upper Montclair, NJ..................................929
Montville Township Historical Museum,
    Montville, NJ...912
Moravian Historical Society, Nazareth,
    PA...1273
The Morris Museum, Morristown, NJ.........914
Morven Museum & Garden, Princeton,
    NJ 922
Moundbuilders State Memorial &
    Museum, Newark, OH.............................1178
Moundville Archaeological Park,
    Moundville, AL 17
Mount Holly Community Historical
    Museum, Belmont, VT............................1476
Mount Pleasant Historical Society, Mount
    Pleasant, OH...1177
Muckenthaler Cultural Center and
    Mansion Museum, Fullerton, CA 99
The Musee Mecanique, San Francisco,
    CA...167
The Museum, Greenwood, SC..................1334
Museum and Arts Center in the Sequim
    Dungeness Valley, Sequim, WA.............1570
Museum of Arts and Sciences, Macon,
    GA...378
Museum of Central Connecticut State
    University, New Britain, CT....................251
Museum of Chicot County Arkansas,
    Lake Village, AR 61
Museum of Cosmetology, Chicago, IL.......425
Museum of Discovery: Arkansas Museum
    of Science and History, Little Rock,
    AR...62
The Museum of East Alabama, Opelika,
    AL...17
Museum of History & Art, Ontario,
    Ontario, CA 136
Museum of History & Industry
    (MOHAI), Seattle, WA...........................1567
Museum of Holography/Chicago,
    Chicago, IL...425
Museum of Lifestyle & Fashion History,
    Delray Beach, FL 305
The Museum of Mobile, Mobile, AL.............14
Museum of Science & History of
    Jacksonville, Jacksonville, FL..................315
Museum of Seminole County History,
    Sanford, FL 343
Museum of Small Town Life, Dover, DE....270

Museum of Texas Tech University,
    Lubbock, TX..1435
Museum of the Aleutians, Unalaska, AK 28
Museum of the Berkeley Springs,
    Berkeley Springs, WV.............................1580
Museum of the Big Bend, Alpine, TX 1386
Museum of the Cherokee Strip, Enid, OK.1200
Museum of the City of Lake Worth, Lake
    Worth, FL..320
Museum of the City of New York, New
    York, NY..1033
Museum of the Great Plains, Lawton, OK.1204
Museum of the High Plains, McCook,
    NE...868
Museum of the Islands, Pine Island
    Center, FL...337
Museum of the Llano Estacado,
    Plainview, TX...1443
Museum of the Southwest, Midland, TX ...1439
Museum of the Western Prairie, Altus,
    OK...1195
Museum of World Treasures, Wichita, KS...562
Museum of York County, Rock Hill, SC ...1340
Museum on Main, Pleasanton, CA..............142
Museum Village, Monroe, NY...................1015
Muskogee War Memorial Park &
    Military Museum, Muskogee, OK 1205

Nashville Zoo at Grassmere, Nashville,
    TN...1379
National Automotive & Truck Museum
    of the United States, Inc. (NATMUS),
    Auburn, IN..468
National Bird Dog Museum, Grand
    Junction, TN..1366
National Buffalo Museum, Jamestown,
    ND...1133
National Farm Toy Museum, Dyersville,
    IA 517
National Museum of Dance & Hall of
    Fame, Saratoga Springs, NY..................1065
National Park Service-Great Falls Park,
    McLean, VA...1517
National Route 66 Museum and Old
    Town Complex, Elk City, OK 1200
National Shaving And Barbershop
    Museum, Meriden, CT..............................249
National Society of the Sons of the
    American Revolution, Louisville, KY 578
National Steinbeck Center, Salinas, CA.......154
The National Watch & Clock Museum,
    Columbia, PA..1247
The Nature Museum at Grafton, Grafton,
    VT..1479
Nebraska Prairie Museum of the Phelps
    County Historical Society, Holdrege,
    NE...863
Neenah Historical Society, Hiram Smith,
    Neenah's Heritage Park, Octagon
    House & Ward House, Neenah, WI.......1614
Neeses Farm Museum, Neeses, SC 1338
Neill Museum, Fort Davis, TX...................1414
Netherland Inn House Museum &
    Boatyard Complex, Kingsport, TN........1368
Nevada State Museum, Carson City, NV.....876
Nevada State Museum, Las Vegas, Las
    Vegas, NV...880
Nevada State Railroad Museum, Carson
    City, NV..876
Neversink Valley Area Museum,
    Cuddebackville, NY...................................984
Neville Public Museum of Brown
    County, Green Bay, WI...........................1599
The New Berlin Historical Society, New
    Berlin, WI..1614
New Britain Industrial Museum, New
    Britain, CT..251
New Britain Youth Museum, New
    Britain, CT..252
New Haven Colony Historical Society,
    New Haven, CT...253
New Jersey State Museum, Trenton, NJ 927

New London Historical Society, New
    London, NH...892
New London Public Museum, New
    London, WI..1615
The New Milford Historical Society, New
    Milford, CT...256
New Sweden Historical Society, New
    Sweden, ME..616
New York State Military Museum and
    Veterans Research Center, Saratoga
    Springs, NY...1065
Nez Perce County Museum, Lewiston, ID...407
The Niagara County Historical Center
    and Niagara County Genealogical
    Society, Lockport, NY.............................1010
Nishna Heritage Museum, Oakland, IA 525
Nita Stewart Haley Memorial Library &
    J. Evetts Haley History Center,
    Midland, TX...1439
No Man's Land Historical Society,
    Goodwell, OK..1201
Noank Historical Society, Inc., Noank,
    CT...256
Nobles County Historical Society,
    Worthington, MN......................................797
The Norman Cleveland County Historical
    Museum, Norman, OK.............................1206
North Carolina Museum of History,
    Raleigh, NC...1115
North Carolina Office of Archives and
    History, Raleigh, NC 1116
North Dakota Fishing Hall of Fame and
    Museum, Garrison, ND............................1131
North House Museum, Lewisburg, WV.....1584
North Lee County Historic Center and
    Santa Fe Depot Museum Complex,
    Fort Madison, IA......................................518
Northampton County Historical and
    Genealogical Society, Easton, PA 1250
Northborough Historical Society, Inc.,
    Northborough, MA 700
Northeast Georgia History Center at
    Brenau University, Gainesville, GA 373
Northeast Texas Rural Heritage Museum,
    Pittsburg, TX...1443
Northeastern Nevada Museum, Elko, NV ...876
Northwest Museum of Arts & Culture
    (Eastern Washington State Historical
    Society), Spokane, WA...........................1571
Norwood Historical Association and
    Museum, Norwood, NY 1044
Nowata County Historical Society
    Museum, Nowata, OK.............................1207

Oak Hill and The Martha Berry Museum,
    Rome, GA...382
Oakdale Museum, Oakdale, CA 132
Ocean City Historical Museum, Inc.,
    Ocean City, NJ..918
Ocracoke Island Visitor Center,
    Ocracoke, NC...1113
Ogden Union Station Museums, Ogden,
    UT..1468
Ojai Valley Historical Society and
    Museum, Ojai, CA....................................135
Oklahoma Route 66 Museum, Clinton,
    OK...1198
Oktibbeha County Heritage Museum,
    Starkville, MS...808
Old Brutus Historical Society, Inc.,
    Weedsport, NY..1084
Old Cathedral Museum, Saint Louis, MO....836
Old Coal Mine Museum, Madrid, NM........943
Old Conway Homestead Complex and
    Museum, Camden, ME.............................608
Old Court House Museum-Eva Whitaker
    Davis Memorial, Vicksburg, MS 809
Old Florida Museum, Saint Augustine,
    FL...339
Old Fort Harrod State Park Mansion
    Museum, Harrodsburg, KY 570
Old Fort Johnson, Fort Johnson, NY...........991

Old Iron County Courthouse Museum, Hurley, WI 1601

Old Lighthouse Museum, Michigan City, IN 491

Old Monterey Jail, Monterey, CA 128

Old State House Museum, Little Rock, AR 63

Old Stone Fort Museum Complex, Schoharie, NY 1067

Old Sturbridge Village, Sturbridge, MA......713

Old Trail Museum, Choteau, MT 844

Old West Movie Poster Museum, Tucson, AZ 50

Old West Museum, Wimberley, TX 1462

The Oliver Tucker Museum, Beverly, OH .1142

Onslow County Museum, Richlands, NC ...1117

Ontario County Historical Society, Canandaigua, NY 975

Opelousas Museum and Interpretive Center, Opelousas, LA 599

The Opelousas Museum of Art, Inc., Opelousas, LA 599

Orchard Park Historical Society, Orchard Park, NY 1047

Oregon Coast History Center, Newport, OR 1229

Oregon-Jerusalem Historical Museum, Oregon, OH 1181

Osage County Historical Society Museum, Pawhuska, OK 1211

Osage Nation Tribal Museum, Pawhuska, OK 1212

Oshkosh Public Museum, Oshkosh, WI.....1616

Oswego Historical Museum, Inc., Oswego, KS 555

Overland Trail Museum, Sterling, CO 232

Owensboro Area Museum of Science & History, Owensboro, KY 581

Painted Post - Erwin Museum at the Depot, Painted Post, NY 1050

Palmer House, Historical Society of Olde Northfield, Northfield, OH 1180

Palmer Museum, Jewell, KS 546

Panhandle-Plains Historical Museum, Canyon, TX 1399

Parishville Museum, Parishville, NY 1050

The Park-McCullough House, North Bennington, VT 1483

Pascack Historical Society, Park Ridge, NJ 920

The Patricia & Phillip Frost Art Museum, Miami, FL 325

The Patuxent Rural Life Museums, Upper Marlboro, MD 655

Pawnee City Historical Society & Museum, Pawnee City, NE 871

The Peekskill Museum, Peekskill, NY 1051

Peirce Mill and Peirce Barn, Washington, DC 289

Perkins County Historical Society, Grant, NE 862

Peshtigo Fire Museum, Peshtigo, WI 1617

Peter Rice Homestead, Home of Marlborough Historical Society, Inc., Marlboro, MA 693

Peterborough Historical Society, Peterborough, NH 893

Petrified Forest National Park, Petrified Forest National Park, AZ 38

Pettis County Historical Society, Sedalia, MO 838

Phillips County Museum, Holyoke, CO 222

Phillips Historical Society, Phillips, ME 618

Philmont Museums, Cimarron, NM 938

Phoenix Police Museum, Phoenix, AZ 41

Piatt County Museum, Monticello, IL 446

Pierrepont Museum, Canton, NY 975

Pilgrim Monument and Provincetown Museum, Provincetown, MA 704

Pinal County Historical Society and Museum, Florence, AZ 34

Pioneer Auto Museum, Murdo, SD 1352

The Pioneer Memorial Association of Fenton and Mundy Townships, Fenton, MI 741

Pioneer Museum - Martin County Historical Society, Fairmont, MN 775

Plains Indians and Pioneers Museum, Woodward, OK 1217

Plainsman Museum, Aurora, NE 856

Plumas County Museum, Quincy, CA 144

Plymouth Historical Museum, Plymouth, MI 760

Plymouth Historical Society, Inc., Plymouth, PA 1295

The Polk County Historical Society, Cedartown, GA 368

Polk County Memorial Museum, Livingston, TX 1434

Polk County Museum, Balsam Lake, WI...1590

Pope County Historical Society, Glenwood, MN 776

Port Huron Museum, Port Huron, MI 761

Portage County Historical Society, Ravenna, OH 1183

Portage County Historical Society, Stevens Point, WI 1623

Portland Museum, Louisville, KY 578

Post Rock Museum, La Crosse, KS 547

Powell County Museum, Deer Lodge, MT 845

Prairie Trails Museum of Wayne County, Corydon, IA 512

Prairie Village, Madison, SD 1351

Pratt Museum, Homer, AK 25

Presidio La Bahia, Goliad, TX 1423

Presque Isle County Historical Museum, Rogers City, MI 762

Providence Canyon State Park, Lumpkin, GA 377

Putnam County Historical Society Museum, Kalida, OH 1169

Putnam County Museum, Greencastle, IN ...479

Putnam Museum of History & Natural Science, Davenport, IA 513

The Quincy Museum, Quincy, IL 452

Railroad Museum of Long Island, Riverhead, NY 1057

Railways to Yesterday, Inc., Rockhill Furnace, PA 1297

Ralls Historical Museum, Ralls, TX 1445

The Ralph Foster Museum, Point Lookout, MO 828

Randolph County Historical Museum, Winchester, IN 503

Randsburg Desert Museum, Randsburg, CA 146

Ransom County Historical Society, Fort Ransom, ND 1131

Raton Museum, Raton, NM 945

Reading Historical Society, Reading, VT...1485

Red Barn Museum, Morristown, NY 1016

Red River Historical Society Museum, Clay City, KY 566

Red River Valley Museum, Vernon, TX.....1457

Redwood County Historical Society, Redwood Falls, MN 787

Refugio County Museum, Refugio, TX 1445

Renville County Historical Society, Inc., Mohall, ND 1135

Reuel B. Pritchett Museum, Bridgewater, VA 1497

Rex Allen Museum, Willcox, AZ 53

Rhode Island Historical Society, Providence, RI 1318

Rialto Historical Society, Rialto, CA 148

Rice County Museum of History, Faribault, MN 775

Richland County Historical Museum, Wahpeton, ND 1137

Richland County Museum, Lexington, OH 1172

Rifle Creek Museum, Rifle, CO 231

Rimrocker Historical Museum of West Montrose County, Naturita, CO 229

Ripley County, Indiana, Historical Society Museum, Versailles, IN 502

Ripley's Believe It or Not! Museum, Orlando, FL 332

Ripley's Believe It or Not! Museum, Atlantic City, NJ 898

Riverton Museum, Riverton, WY 1637

Robert Newell House, DAR Museum, Saint Paul, OR 1235

Robert S. Kerr Museum, Poteau, OK 1212

Roberts County Museum, Miami, TX 1438

Rockbridge Historical Society, Lexington, VA 1513

Rockwell Museum of Western Art, Corning, NY 982

Rocky Ford Historical Museum, Rocky Ford, CO 231

Rocky Reach Dam, Wenatchee, WA 1577

Rokeby (Ancestral Estate of Rowland Evans Robinson), Ferrisburgh, VT 1479

Rome Historical Society Museum, Rome, NY 1061

Roniger Memorial Museum, Cottonwood Falls, KS 536

Rosa Ponselle Museum, Meriden, CT 249

Rose Center Museum, Morristown, TN 1376

Rosebud County Pioneer Museum, Forsyth, MT 846

Rosemount Museum, Pueblo, CO 230

Rosenberg Library, Galveston, TX 1422

Ross County Historical Society, Inc., Chillicothe, OH 1147

Roswell Museum and Art Center, Roswell, NM 946

Rothschild Petersen Patent Model Museum, Cazenovia, NY 977

The Roy Rogers-Dale Evans Museum and Theater, Branson, MO 811

Runestone Museum, Alexandria, MN 767

Rural Farming & Agriculture Museum, Warner, OK 1216

Rusk County Historical Society, Ladysmith, WI 1604

St. Albans Historical Museum, Saint Albans, VT 1486

St. Charles County Historical Society, Inc., Saint Charles, MO 830

St. Joseph Museum Inc., Saint Joseph, MO 831

St. Lucie County Historical Museum, Fort Pierce, FL 309

St. Paul Museum, Randleman, NC 1117

St. Petersburg Museum of History, Saint Petersburg, FL 342

St. Simons Island Lighthouse Museum, Saint Simons Island, GA 383

Ste. Genevieve Museum, Sainte Genevieve, MO 838

Salem County Historical Society, Salem, NJ 924

Salem Historical Society and Museum, Salem, OH 1184

Salida Museum, Salida, CO 232

Sam Noble Oklahoma Museum of Natural History, Norman, OK 1206

Samek Art Gallery, Lewisburg, PA 1268

Samuel Ullman Museum, Birmingham, AL 5

San Bernardino County Museum, Redlands, CA 147

San Buenaventura Mission Museum, Ventura, CA 195

San Dieguito Heritage Museum, Encinitas, CA 92

San Francisco International Airport; San Francisco Airport Museums, San Francisco, CA 169

San Jacinto Museum, San Jacinto, CA 171

GENERAL MUSEUMS–Continued

San Joaquin County Historical Society & Museum, Lodi, CA 109

San Juan County Historical Society Museum, Silverton, CO.....................232

San Luis Obispo County Historical Museum, San Luis Obispo, CA 174

Sanborn Area Historical Society, Sanborn, NY 1064

Sandusky Library Follett House Museum, Sandusky, OH 1185

Sandwich Historical Society, Sandwich, IL 457

Sandy Bay Historical Society & Museums, Inc., Rockport, MA................705

Sanford Museum and Planetarium, Cherokee, IA.....................................510

Sanilac County Historical Museum and Village, Port Sanilac, MI.................761

Santa Fe Trail Center, Larned, KS 547

Santa Fe Trail Museum, Ingalls, KS 545

Santa Maria Valley Historical Museum, Santa Maria, CA.................................183

Saratoga Automobile Museum, Saratoga Springs, NY 1065

Saratoga County Historical Society, Brookside Museum, Ballston Spa, NY....960

Sauk County Historical Museum, Baraboo, WI.....................................1591

Saunders Memorial Museum, Berryville, AR..55

Sawin Memorial Building, Dover, MA 680

Sawyer's Sandhills Museum, Valentine, NE..874

Scantic Academy Museum, East Windsor Historical Society, Inc., East Windsor, CT..239

Scarborough Historical Museum, Scarborough, ME.....................................621

Schiele Museum of Natural History and Lynn Planetarium, Gastonia, NC.........1102

Schminck Memorial Museum, Lakeview, OR...1227

School of Nations Museum, Elsah, IL 433

Schoolcraft County Historical Society, Manistique, MI.......................................753

Schwenkfelder Library & Heritage Center, Pennsburg, PA...........................1275

The Science Fiction Museum and Hall of Fame, Seattle, WA..............................1568

The Science Museum of Minnesota, Saint Paul, MN...792

Scott & Zelda Fitzgerald Museum, Montgomery, AL 17

Seagraves-Loop Museum and Art Center Inc., Seagraves, TX...............................1452

Searchlight Historic Museum & Mining Park, Searchlight, NV..............................882

Senator George Baldwin Hotel, Klamath Falls, OR...1227

Seneca County Museum, Tiffin, OH...........1186

Seneca Falls Historical Society, Seneca Falls, NY...1069

Sharlot Hall Museum, Prescott, AZ..............43

Shawano County Historical Society, Inc., Shawano, WI.......................................1621

Shelburne Museum, Inc., Shelburne, VT ...1487

Shenandoal Valley Discovery Museum, Winchester, VA..1546

Sherwood-Davidson House, Newark, OH ..1178

Shippensburg Historical Society Museum, Shippensburg, PA..................................1300

Shirley Plantation, Charles City, VA 1498

Shorter Mansion Museum, Eufaula, AL.........8

Silver Cliff Museum, Silver Cliff, CO.........232

Sioux City Public Museum, Sioux City, IA..528

Siouxland Heritage Museums, Sioux Falls, SD...1357

Sisson Museum, Mount Shasta, CA.............129

Sloan Museum, Flint, MI..........................742

The Smart Museum of Art, Chicago, IL 427

Smithsonian Institution, Washington, DC......290

Smokey Bear Museum, Capitan, NM...........937

Smyth County Museum, Marion, VA 1516

Snake River Heritage Center, Weiser, ID.....410

The Snyder County Historical Society, Middleburg, PA..1271

Snyder Museum & Creative Arts Center, Bastrop, LA...585

Somervell County Historical Museum, Glen Rose, TX.......................................1423

The Somerville Museum, Somerville, MA..709

Sonoma County Museum, Santa Rosa, CA..185

South Bannock County Historical Center, Lava Hot Springs, ID.............................407

South Carolina State Museum, Columbia, SC..1331

South Dakota Tractor Museum, Kimball, SD..1350

South Florida Museum, Bishop Planetarium & Parker Manatee Aquarium, Bradenton, FL 297

Southern Museum of Flight, Birmingham, AL..6

Southern Oregon Historical Society, Jacksonville, OR.....................................1226

Southold Historical Society and Museum, Southold, NY...1071

Space Farms Zoological Park and Museum, Sussex, NJ...............................925

The SPAM Museum, Austin, MN...............768

Spirit of '76 Museum, Wellington, OH 1190

SPJST Library Archives & Museum, Temple, TX...1455

Split Rock Lighthouse Historic Site, Two Harbors, MN...795

Spotsylvania Historical Association and Museum, Spotsylvania, VA.....................1537

Springfield Museum, Springfield, OR 1236

Springs Museum, Springs, PA 1301

Stamford Historical Society, Inc., Stamford, CT...260

Stamford Museum & Nature Center, Stamford, CT...261

State Historical Society of Iowa, Des Moines, IA...515

State Historical Society of North Dakota, Bismarck, ND...1128

The State Museum of Pennsylvania, Harrisburg, PA..1259

Staten Island Institute of Arts & Sciences (SIIAS), Staten Island, NY 1074

The Steamboat Arabia Museum, Kansas City, MO..822

Stengel-True Museum, Marion, OH 1174

Stephens County Historical Society and Museum, Duncan, OK.............................1199

Stephenson County Historical Society, Freeport, IL...436

Stephenville Museum, Stephenville, TX 1454

Sterling Historical Society and Little Red Schoolhouse Museum, Sterling, NY......1074

Sternberg Museum of Natural History, Hays, KS..543

Stevens County Historical Society Museum, Morris, MN................................784

Stevens Museum, Salem, IN.......................498

Stewart M. Lord Memorial Historical Society, Inc., Burlington, ME 608

Stockholm Historical Society Museum, Stockholm, ME..623

Stoughton Historical Society, Stoughton, WI..1623

Stratford, Robert E. Lee Memorial Association, Inc., Stratford, VA...............1539

Strawbery Banke Museum, Portsmouth, NH..895

Strom Thurmond Institute, Clemson, SC ...1328

Stutsman County Memorial Museum, Jamestown, ND..1133

Suffolk County Historical Society, Riverhead, NY..1057

Suffolk County Vanderbilt Museum, Centerport, NY..977

Sullivan County Historical Society, Inc., Hurleyville, NY..1001

Susquehanna Museum of Havre de Grace Inc. at the Lock House, Havre de Grace, MD..647

Sussex County Historical Society, Newton, NJ...917

Swampscott Historical Society (John Humphrey House), Swampscott, MA......714

Swiss Historical Village, New Glarus, WI.1615

Switzerland County Historical Museum, Vevay, IN...502

Talkeetna Historical Society and Museum, Talkeetna, AK................................28

Tallahassee Museum, Tallahassee, FL 348

The Teddy Bear Museum of Naples, Naples, FL...328

Telluride Historical Museum, Telluride, CO..233

Tempe Historical Museum, Tempe, AZ.........46

Temperance Tavern, Newcomerstown, OH..1179

Tenino Depot Museum, Tenino, WA 1575

Terwilliger Museum, Waterloo, NY............1083

Teutopolis Monastery Museum, Teutopolis, IL..461

Texana Museum and Library Association, Edna, TX...1410

Texas Prison Museum, Huntsville, TX.......1430

Texas Ranger Hall of Fame and Museum, Waco, TX...1459

Theodore Roosevelt National Park-Visitor Center, Medora, ND 1134

Thomasville Cultural Center, Inc., Thomasville, GA..388

Thousand Islands Museum, Clayton, NY....979

Three Rivers Museum, Muskogee, OK 1205

Tioga Point Museum, Athens, PA..............1241

Tobias Community Historical Society, Tobias, NE...873

Tombstone Courthouse State Historic Park, Tombstone, AZ.............................46

Tongass Historical Museum, Ketchikan, AK..26

Top of Oklahoma Historical Museum, Blackwell, OK..1197

Town of Yorktown Museum, Yorktown Heights, NY...1087

Traill County Historical Society, Hillsboro, ND..1132

Travellers Rest Plantation & Museum, Nashville, TN..1381

Traverse County Historical Society, Wheaton, MN..796

Trenton City Museum, Trenton, NJ 928

Tri-County Historical Society & Museum, Inc., Herington, KS...............544

Tsa Mo Ga Memorial Museum, Plains, TX..1443

Tuck Museum, Hampton, NH.....................888

Tucker Wildlife Sanctuary, Silverado, CA ..186

Tuckerton Seaport, Tuckerton, NJ 928

Tucumcari Historical Research Institute, Tucumcari, NM..953

Tularosa Basin Historical Society Museum, Alamogordo, NM 932

Tuskegee Institute National Historic Site, Tuskegee Institute, AL 21

Twin Falls County Historical Museum, Filer, ID...405

Twinsburg Historical Society, Twinsburg, OH..1188

Twister the Movie Museum, Wakita, OK...1216

Tyler Rose Museum, Tyler, TX 1457

UNLV Marjorie Barrick Museum, Las Vegas, NV...880

Ukrainian-American Museum & Archives, Warren, MI................766

Ukrainian Museum-Archives, Inc., Cleveland, OH.................1156

Union County Historical Complex, Creston, IA...............512

The Union County Historical Society, Marysville, OH.................1175

Union County Museum, Union, OR...........1238

University Museum, Carbondale, IL 415

The University Museum, Edwardsville, IL....................432

University Museum, Martin, TN 1371

University Museum & Historic Houses, The University of Mississippi, Oxford, MS....................806

The University Museum Collections, Fayetteville, AR.............................57

University Museum, New Mexico State University, Las Cruces, NM....................941

University of Alaska Museum of the North, Fairbanks, AK 24

University of Colorado Museum, Boulder, CO....................203

University of Northern Iowa Museums & Collections, Cedar Falls, IA....................508

University of Richmond Museums, Richmond, VA...............1532

Utica Museum, Utica, MT................854

UTSA's Institute of Texan Cultures, San Antonio, TX....................1451

Valentine Richmond History Center, Richmond, VA....................1532

Valley County Pioneer Museum, Glasgow, MT....................847

Vann House, Chatsworth, GA................368

Vent Haven Museum, Fort Mitchell, KY 568

Verde Historical Society, Clemenceau Heritage Museum, Cottonwood, AZ..........32

Vermont Soapworks Discount Factory Outlet and Soap Museum, Middlebury, VT....................1482

Vernon County Historical Museum, Viroqua, WI................1625

Vernon Historians, Inc., Vernon, VT 1489

Vest-Lindsey House, Frankfort, KY 570

Vesterheim Norwegian-American Museum, Decorah, IA.................513

Victor Heritage Museum, Victor, MT...........854

Victorian Dress Museum, Rugby, ND 1136

Vigo County Historical Museum, Terre Haute, IN....................501

Virginia Aquarium & Marine Science Center, Virginia Beach, VA................1542

Virginia Military Institute Museum, Lexington, VA................1514

Visual Arts Museum, New York, NY.........1040

Wabasha County Museum, Wabasha County Historical Society at Reads Landing, Reads Landing, MN................787

Wabaunsee County Historical Museum, Alma, KS....................532

The Wagnalls Memorial, Lithopolis, OH ...1172

Wahkiakum County Historical Museum, Cathlamet, WA................1550

Wakefield Museum Association, Wakefield, KS....................560

Wal-Mart Visitor's Center, Bentonville, AR....................55

Walter Elwood Museum, Amsterdam, NY ...957

Walter Reed Birthplace, Gloucester County, VA................1508

The Waltham Museum, Waltham, MA.........716

Wanapum Dam Heritage Center, Beverly, WA....................1549

Wantagh Historical & Preservation Society, Wantagh, NY................1081

Ward County Historical Society, Minot, ND....................1135

Warren ICBM & Heritage Museum, Frances E. Warren Air Force Base, WY....................1633

Waseca County Historical Society, Waseca, MN................796

Washington County Historical Society, Washington, KS................560

Washington County Historical Society Warden's House Museum, Stillwater, MN....................794

Waterford Historical Museum and Cultural Center, Inc., Waterford, NY.....1083

Waterloo Area Historical Society, Grass Lake, MI....................744

Watermen's Museum, Yorktown, VA..........1547

Watertown Historical Society, Inc., Watertown, CT................264

Watkins Museum, Taylorsville, MS.............808

Waveland State Historic Site, Lexington, KY....................574

Wayland Historical Society, Wayland, MA....................716

Wayne County Historical Museum, Richmond, IN 497

Wayne County Historical Society, Wooster, OH................1192

Wayne County Historical Society, Honesdale, PA................1261

Webster County Historical Museum, Red Cloud, NE................872

Wellfleet Historical Society Museum, Wellfleet, MA................717

Wenatchee Valley Museum and Cultural Center, Wenatchee, WA................1577

Werner Wildlife Museum, Casper, WY......1630

Weslaco Museum, Weslaco, TX 1461

West Allis Historical Society Museum, West Allis, WI................1626

West Baton Rouge Museum, Port Allen, LA....................599

West of the Pecos Museum, Pecos, TX 1443

West River Museum Society, Philip, SD....1353

Western Hennepin County Pioneers Association, Long Lake, MN................779

Western Springs Historical Society, Western Springs, IL................464

Westminster Historical Society, Westminster, VT................1490

The Wethersfield Historical Society, Wethersfield, CT................266

Wexford County Historical Society & Museum, Cadillac, MI................731

Wharton County Historical Museum, Wharton, TX................1461

Wheels O' Time Museum, Peoria, IL..........451

White County Historical Society, Cleveland, GA................368

White Deer Land Museum, Pampa, TX.....1442

White Pillars Museum, De Pere Historical Society, De Pere, WI.............1594

White Pine Public Museum, Ely, NV..........877

The White River Museum, Meeker, CO 228

Whitehead Memorial Museum, Del Rio, TX....................1409

Whitewater Historical Museum, Whitewater, WI................1628

Whitley County Historical Museum, Columbia City, IN................472

Wichita Falls Museum and Art Center, Wichita Falls, TX 1461

Wilber Czech Museum, Wilber, NE 875

Wilder Memorial Museum, Strawberry Point, IA................528

Wilderness Road Regional Museum, Newbern, VA 1519

Wildwood Historical Society, Inc., Wildwood, NJ................930

Wilkin County Historical Society, Breckenridge, MN................770

Will Rogers Memorial Museum, Claremore, OK................1198

William Clark Market House Museum, Paducah, KY................582

William Weston Clarke Emison Museum of Art, Greencastle, IN................479

Williams County Historical Museum, Montpelier, OH................1177

Wilson County Historical Society Museum, Fredonia, KS................540

Wilson Historical Museum, Wilson, NY....1086

Wilton Historical Museums, Wilton, CT......267

Wing Luke Asian Museum, Seattle, WA....1569

Wisconsin Historical Museum, Madison, WI....................1606

Wise County Heritage Museum, Decatur, TX....................1408

Wistariahurst Museum, Holyoke, MA..........687

Wolcott House Museum Complex, Maumee, OH................1175

Wolf Point Area Historical Society, Inc., Wolf Point, MT................855

Wolfeboro Historical Society, Wolfeboro, NH....................897

Woods Hole Oceanographic Institution Exhibit Center, Woods Hole, MA............720

Woodson County Historical Society, Yates Center, KS................564

Woodstock Historical Society, Inc., Woodstock, VT................1491

Woodstock Museum of Shenandoah County, Inc., Woodstock, VA................1546

Woodville Museum, Inc., Rogue River, OR....................1234

Woolaroc Museum, Bartlesville, OK..........1197

World's First Wendy's Restaurant, Columbus, OH................1159

World's Smallest Museum, Superior, AZ.......45

Wrangell Museum, Wrangell, AK.................29

Wright County Historical Society, Buffalo, MN................770

Wyandot County Historical Society, Upper Sandusky, OH................1188

Wyoming Pioneer Home, Thermopolis, WY....................1639

Wyoming Pioneer Memorial Museum, Douglas, WY................1632

The Yager Museum of Art & Culture, Oneonta, NY................1046

Yakima Valley Museum and Historical Association, Yakima, WA................1579

Yellow Medicine County Historical Society and Museum, Granite Falls, MN....................777

Yellowstone Gateway Museum of Park County, Livingston, MT................850

Yorktown Historical Museum, Yorktown, TX....................1462

The Yosemite Museum, National Park Service, Yosemite National Park, CA......199

Ypsilanti Historical Museum, Ypsilanti, MI....................767

Yuma Crossing State Historic Park, Yuma, AZ................54

HISTORY

Historic Agencies, Councils, Commissions, Foundations and Research Institutes

Alexandria Black History Resource Center, Alexandria, VA................1491

The Alice T. Miner Colonial Collection, Chazy, NY................977

American Antiquarian Society, Worcester, MA....................720

American Association for State and Local History, Nashville, TN................1377

Amos Herr House Foundation and Historic Society, Landisville, PA...........1267

Ano Nuevo State Reserve, Pescadero, CA...141

Anoka County Historical Society, Anoka, MN....................767

Arcadia Township Historical Commission, Arcadia, MI................726

Historic Agencies, Councils, Commissions, Foundations and Research Institutes–Continued

Archives of American Art, Smithsonian Institution, Washington, DC 276

Arizona State Parks Board, Phoenix, AZ 39

Ashtabula Historic House, Pendleton, SC ..1339

Aurora History Museum, Aurora, CO 202

Baldwin Historical Society and Museum, Baldwin, NY 960

Berrien County Historical Association, Berrien Springs, MI 729

Birmingham Historical Museum & Park, Birmingham, MI 730

Blaine County Museum, Chinook, MT 844

Bloomfield Academy Museum, Bloomfield, NY 963

Broward County Historical Commission, Fort Lauderdale, FL..........................307

Brush Country Museum, Cotulla, TX 1403

Bureau County Historical Society Museum, Princeton, IL............................452

C.M. Russell Museum, Great Falls, MT 848

The Calvin Coolidge Memorial Foundation, Inc., Plymouth, VT 1484

Castillo de San Marcos National Monument, Saint Augustine, FL............338

The Center for Western Studies, Sioux Falls, SD 1356

Central Nevada Museum & Historical Society, Tonopah, NV 882

Charnley-Persky House Museum, Chicago, IL 418

Chinese House/O.R. & N. Museum & St. Peter's Catholic Church, Echo, OR 1222

Chippokes Farm & Forestry Museum, Surry, VA 1540

Chisholm Trail Heritage Center, Duncan, OK 1199

City of Wayne Historical Museum, Wayne, MI 766

Colonial Burlington Foundation, Inc., Burlington, NJ 899

Columbia Gorge Discovery Center and Wasco County Museum, The Dalles, OR 1237

Concordia Historical Institute, Saint Louis, MO..................................832

The Conference House, Staten Island, NY 1072

Cornelius Low House/Middlesex County Museum, Piscataway, NJ 921

Dakota Sunset Museum, Gettysburg, SD ...1348

Denton County Historical Museum, Inc. and Texas Heritage Center, Denton, TX 1409

DeWitt County Historical Museum, Cuero, TX 1403

Dubois Museum, Dubois, WY 1632

Edgar Allan Poe House and Museum, Baltimore, MD..............................631

Edward Hopper Landmark Preservation Foundation, Nyack, NY 1044

Elmhurst Historical Museum, Elmhurst, IL 433

Flowerdew Hundred Foundation, Hopewell, VA..............................1511

Fort Dodge & Frontier Village, Fort Dodge, IA 518

Fort Ligonier Association, Ligonier, PA 1269

Fort Morgan Museum, Gulf Shores, AL 10

Fort Zachary Taylor State Historical Site, Key West, FL................................317

Foundation For Historic Christ Church, Inc., Irvington, VA..........................1511

Galveston Historical Foundation, Inc., Galveston, TX.............................1421

Gateway to the Panhandle, Gate, OK.........1201

Georgia Historical Society, Savannah, GA...385

Gilcrease Museum, Tulsa, OK 1215

Great Basin Historical Society & Museum, Delta, UT...............................1464

Grumman Memorial Park, Calverton, NY ...974

Haas-Lilienthal House, San Francisco, CA 166

Hackettstown Historical Society Museum & Library, Hackettstown, NJ 905

Harrimans Falls Educational Centre and Museum, Bath, NH...........................883

Hawaii State Foundation on Culture & the Arts and Hawaii State Art Museum, Honolulu, HI........................395

Held-Poage Memorial Home and Research Library, Ukiah, CA...................193

Heritage Museum Foundation of Tate County, Inc., Senatobia, MS 808

The Hermitage: Home of President Andrew Jackson, Hermitage, TN...........1367

Historic Annapolis Foundation, Annapolis, MD 628

Historic Charleston Foundation, Charleston, SC 1325

Historic Columbia Foundation, Columbia, SC 1329

Historic Columbus Foundation, Inc., Columbus, GA 369

Historic Crab Orchard Museum & Pioneer Park, Inc., Tazewell, VA 1541

Historic Homes Foundation, Inc., Louisville, KY..............................576

Historic House Trust of New York City, New York, NY 1027

Historic Jefferson College, Washington, MS 810

Historic Landmarks Foundation of Indiana, Indianapolis, IN 482

Historic Nashville, Inc., Nashville, TN 1379

Historic Newton Home, Decatur, MI 734

Historic Pensacola Village, Pensacola, FL ...335

Historic Shepherdstown Museum, Shepherdstown, WV 1586

Historic Waco Foundation, Waco, TX 1459

Historical Museum of Southern Florida, Miami, FL 324

Historical Society of Cheshire County, Keene, NH 890

Historical Society of the Town of North Hempstead, Manhasset, NY 1013

Hollywood Heritage Museum, Hollywood, CA..............................103

Indiana War Memorials, Indianapolis, IN ...484

International Spy Museum, Washington, DC 281

Ironworld Discovery Center, Chisholm, MN 771

Jacinto Foundation, Inc., Corinth, MS.........800

The James Dunklin House, Laurens, SC....1336

James S. Copley Library, La Jolla, CA........106

Jeff Matthews Memorial Museum, Galax, VA 1508

John F. Kennedy Presidential Library & Museum, Boston, MA 666

John G. Neihardt State Historic Site, Bancroft, NE..................................856

The John Nicholas Brown Center for the Study of American Civilization, Providence, RI 1317

Kit Carson Home & Museum, Inc., Taos, NM 952

LaGuardia and Wagner Archives, Long Island City, NY..............................1010

Lake City Columbia County Historical Museum, Inc., Lake City, FL...............319

Law Enforcement Memorial Association, Inc., Roselle, IL 456

The Library of Virginia, Richmond, VA.....1530

Linden Railroad Museum, Linden, IN..........488

The Log House Museum of the Historical Society of Columbiana-Fairfield Township, Columbiana, OH..................1157

Lower Hudson Conference of Historical Agencies and Museums, Elmsford, NY...988

Mackinac State Historic Parks-Colonial Michilimackinac & Old Mackinac Point Lighthouse, Mackinaw City, MI 752

Mackinac State Historic Parks-Fort Mackinac & Mackinac Island State Park, Mackinac Island, MI.....................752

Mackinac State Historic Parks-Historic Mill Creek, Mackinaw City, MI 753

Manatee Village Historical Park, Bradenton, FL..............................297

Marietta House Museum, Glenn Dale, MD...645

Mary Todd Lincoln House, Lexington, KY...574

Matagorda County Museum, Bay City, TX 1393

Middleton Historical Society - Lura Woodside Watkins Museum, Middleton, MA 694

Midway Museum, Inc., Midway, GA...........379

Milam County Museum and Annex, Cameron, TX 1399

Mississippi Baptist Historical Commission, Clinton, MS......................799

Molly Brown House Museum, Denver, CO..213

Monroe County Historical Museum, Monroe, MI..................................756

Monroe County Local History Room & Library, Sparta, WI............................1622

Moody-Bradley House Restoration Foundation, Fairfield, TX..................1413

Mordecai Historic Park, Raleigh, NC........1115

Museum of Ancient Artifacts, Las Vegas, NV..879

Museum of Chinese in the Americas, New York, NY 1032

Museum of Southern History, Jacksonville, FL..............................315

Museum of Southwestern Biology, Albuquerque, NM 934

Museum of the Great Plains, Lawton, OK.1204

Museum on Main: A History Museum for West Georgia, LaGrange, GA 375

Nantucket Historical Association, Nantucket, MA 696

National Archives and Records Administration, Washington, DC 284

National Archives and Records Administration - Mid-Atlantic Region, Philadelphia, PA 1284

National Park Service Vicksburg National Military Park-Cairo Museum, Vicksburg, MS 809

National Society of the Sons of the American Revolution, Louisville, KY 578

New York State Bureau of Historic Sites, Waterford, NY 1082

New York State Historical Association/Fenimore Art Museum, Cooperstown, NY 981

New York State Museum, Albany, NY.........955

New York State Office of Parks, Recreation & Historic Preservation, Albany, NY 955

Nobleboro Historical Society, Nobleboro, ME..616

Nordic Heritage Museum, Seattle, WA 1567

North Carolina Office of Archives and History, Raleigh, NC.........................1116

Office of Historic Alexandria, Alexandria, VA..1494

Ohio Historical Society, Columbus, OH.....1158

Oklahoma City National Memorial,
    Oklahoma City, OK................................1209
Oklahoma Heritage Association,
    Oklahoma City, OK................................1209
Oklahoma Historical Society, Oklahoma
    City, OK..1209
Old Mill Museum, El Molino Viejo - Old
    Mill Foundation, San Marino, CA..........175
Old Prison Museums, Deer Lodge, MT.......845
Orange County Regional History Center,
    Orlando, FL...331

P.H. Sullivan Museum and Genealogy
    Library, Zionsville, IN.............................504
Pendleton Historic Foundation,
    Pendleton, SC.......................................1339
Pennsylvania Federation of Museums and
    Historical Organizations, Harrisburg,
    PA...1259
Photographic Archives, University of
    Louisville Libraries, Louisville, KY........578
Platt R. Spencer Memorial Archives and
    Special Collections Area, Geneva, OH..1166
Pope's Tavern Museum, Florence, AL 9
Presbyterian Historical Society
    (Montreat), Montreat, NC.....................1111

RV/MH Heritage Foundation, Inc.,
    Elkhart, IN..475
Red Hill-Patrick Henry National
    Memorial, Brookneal, VA......................1498
Reginald F. Lewis Museum of Maryland
    African American History and Culture,
    Baltimore, MD..636
Rhode Island State Archives, Providence,
    RI..1318
The Rice Museum, Georgetown, SC..........1333
Rosenberg Library, Galveston, TX.............1422
Royalton Historical Society, Royalton,
    VT...1486

Sacramento Archives and Museum
    Collection Center, Sacramento, CA.........153
Safe Haven Museum and Education
    Center, Oswego, NY.............................1048
St. Lucie County Historical Museum,
    Fort Pierce, FL.......................................309
Sam Houston Historical Schoolhouse,
    Maryville, TN...1371
Santa Barbara Trust for Historic
    Preservation, Santa Barbara, CA 180
Santa Maria Valley Historical Museum,
    Santa Maria, CA.....................................183
Santuario de Nuestra Senora de
    Guadalupe, Santa Fe, NM......................950
Schmidt House Museum & Research
    Library, Grants Pass, OR......................1225
School of American Research, Indian
    Arts Research Center, Santa Fe, NM 950
1761 Pownalborough Courthouse,
    Dresden, ME...610
Sherman Gardens, Corona del Mar, CA........87
Shoshone Tribal Cultural Center, Fort
    Washakie, WY.......................................1633
Sioux City Public Museum, Sioux City,
    IA...528
The Skinner Museum of Mount Holyoke
    College, South Hadley, MA....................709
South Carolina Department of Archives
    & History, Columbia, SC.......................1330
South Carolina Historical Society,
    Charleston, SC......................................1327
South Carolina Institute of Archaeology
    & Anthropology, Columbia, SC.............1330
South Dakota Hall of Fame,
    Chamberlain, SD....................................1345
South Dakota State Archives, Pierre, SD...1353
South Dakota State Historical Society,
    Pierre, SD...1353
Southwest Arkansas Regional Archives
    (SARA), Washington, AR..........................70
The Sports Museum, Boston, MA...............669

Stanly County Historic Preservation
    Commission and Museum, Albemarle,
    NC...1088
State Historical Society of North Dakota,
    Bismarck, ND..1128
Sunnyvale Historical Museum,
    Sunnyvale, CA..190

Tamastslikt Cultural Institute, Pendleton,
    OR...1230
Tennessee Historical Commission,
    Nashville, TN..1380
Tennessee Museum of Aviation,
    Sevierville, TN......................................1383
Tennessee State Museum, Nashville, TN ...1381
Texas Historical Commission, Austin, TX .1391
Thomas E. McMillan Museum, Brewton,
    AL...6
Thomas Warne Historical Museum &
    Library, Old Bridge, NJ...........................918
Thomas Whaley House Museum, San
    Diego, CA...161
Tile Heritage Foundation, Healdsburg,
    CA..102
Tippecanoe County Historical
    Association, Lafayette, IN........................487
Troutdale Historical Society, Troutdale,
    OR...1237
Troy Museum & Historic Village, Troy,
    MI...765

United States Holocaust Memorial
    Museum, Washington, DC.......................293
Upstate History Alliance, Oneonta, NY 1046

Van Riper-Hopper House Museum,
    Wayne, NJ..929
The Verdier House, Beaufort, SC..............1321
Vest-Lindsey House, Frankfort, KY.............570
The Victorian Society in America,
    Philadelphia, PA....................................1289
Virginia Association of Museums,
    Richmond, VA.......................................1532
Virginia Historical Society, Richmond,
    VA..1533
Virginia Holocaust Museum, Richmond,
    VA..1533

Warrick County Museum, Inc., Boonville,
    IN...470
Watkins Community Museum of History,
    Lawrence, KS..548
Wellfleet Historical Society Museum,
    Wellfleet, MA..717
Wildwood Historical Society, Inc.,
    Wildwood, NJ..930
Willa Cather Pioneer Memorial and
    Educational Foundation, Red Cloud,
    NE..872
Woodburn Historic House, Pendleton, SC .1339
Wyandotte Museum, Wyandotte, MI............766

Historic Houses and Historic Buildings

A.C. Gilbert's Discovery Village, Salem,
    OR...1235
A.L. Fetterman Educational Museum,
    Fort Valley, GA.......................................372
The APEX Museum, Atlanta, GA 357
A.R. Bowman Memorial Museum,
    Prineville, OR..1234
A.R. Mitchell Museum, Trinidad, CO..........233
AT & SF Depot, Alden, KS.........................532
Abbie Gardner Cabin, Arnolds Park, IA 505
Abraham Lincoln Birthplace National
    Historic Site, Hodgenville, KY................571
Academy Art Museum, Easton, MD.............642
Academy Hall Museum of the Rocky
    Hill Historical Society, Inc., Rocky
    Hill, CT..259
The Accokeek Foundation, Inc.,
    Accokeek, MD...627
Ace of Clubs House, Texarkana, TX..........1455

Adam Thoroughgood House, Virginia
    Beach, VA...1541
Adams County Historical Society,
    Gettysburg, PA.....................................1255
Adams County Historical Society
    Museum, Lind, WA................................1558
Adams Museum & House, Deadwood,
    SD..1346
Adams National Historical Park, Quincy,
    MA..704
Adams National Historical Park-John
    Adams and John Quincy Adams
    Birthplaces, Quincy, MA.........................704
Adams Old Stone Grist Mill, Bellows
    Falls, VT...1476
Adena Mansion and Gardens, Chillicothe,
    OH...1147
Admiral Nimitz National Museum of the
    Pacific War, Fredericksburg, TX............1419
Adobe De Palomares, Pomona, CA.............143
Adsmore Museum, Princeton, KY...............583
Afro-American Cultural Center,
    Charlotte, NC..1094
Agecroft Hall, Richmond, VA....................1527
Agrirama, Georgia's Living History
    Museum & Village, Tifton, GA................388
Aiken County Historical Museum, Aiken,
    SC..1320
Ak-Sar-Ben Aquarium Outdoor Education
    Center, Gretna, NE.................................862
Akron Art Museum, Akron, OH.................1138
Alabama Mining Museum, Dora, AL..............7
Alachua County Historic Trust: Matheson
    Museum, Inc., Gainesville, FL................310
Alamance Battleground State Historic
    Site, Burlington, NC.............................1092
Alamance County Historical Museum,
    Burlington, NC.....................................1092
The Alamo, San Antonio, TX....................1447
Alamo Township Museum-John E. Gray
    Memorial Museum, Kalamazoo, MI........748
Albany Civil Rights Movement Museum
    at Old Mt. Zion Church, Albany, GA......355
Albany Historical Society, Inc., Sabetha,
    KS..557
Albany Regional Museum, Albany, OR......1217
Albuquerque Museum, Albuquerque, NM....932
Alden Historical Society, Inc., Alden, NY ...956
Alden House Historic Site, Duxbury, MA ...680
Alex Haley Home and Museum,
    Henning, TN...1367
Alexander Ramsey House, Minnesota
    Historical Society, Saint Paul, MN..........789
Alexandre Mouton House/Lafayette
    Museum, Lafayette, LA...........................589
Alexandria Black History Resource
    Center, Alexandria, VA..........................1491
Alfred B. Maclay State Gardens,
    Tallahassee, FL......................................346
Alger County Heritage Center, Munising,
    MI..757
Alice Austen House Museum, Staten
    Island, NY..1072
The Alice T. Miner Colonial Collection,
    Chazy, NY..977
Allan Shivers Museum, Woodville, TX......1462
Allegan County Historical Society and
    Old Jail Museum, Allegan, MI................723
Allegany County Historical Society, Inc.,
    Cumberland, MD.....................................641
Allegheny Portage Railroad National
    Historic Site and Johnstown Flood
    National Memorial, Gallitzin, PA..........1255
Allen County Historical Society, Iola, KS ...545
Almond Historical Society/Hagadorn
    House Museum, Almond, NY....................957
Alpine County Museum, Markleeville,
    CA..124
Altama Museum of Art & History,
    Vidalia, GA...390
Alton Museum of History and Art, Inc.,
    Alton, IL...410

Historic Houses and Historic Buildings–Continued

Amador County Museum, Jackson, CA 105

Amelia Earhart Birthplace Museum, Atchison, KS...532

American Independence Museum, Exeter, NH..887

American Labor Museum, Botto House National Landmark, Haledon, NJ 906

American Museum of Magic & Lund Memorial Library, Inc., Marshall, MI 754

American Precision Museum Association, Inc., Windsor, VT...................................1490

American Swedish Institute, Minneapolis, MN...781

Americana Museum, Terra Alta, WV 1587

America's Ice Cream & Dairy Museum, Medina, OH...1175

Americas Society, New York, NY 1020

Amherst County Museum & Historical Society, Amherst, VA 1495

Amherst History Museum at the Strong House - Amherst Historical Society, Amherst, MA 658

Amherst Museum, Amherst, NY 957

Amity and Woodbridge Historical Society, Woodbridge, CT....................268

Amory Regional Museum, Amory, MS........797

Amos Herr House Foundation and Historic Society, Landisville, PA 1267

Anacortes Museum, Anacortes, WA 1547

Anadarko Heritage Museum, Anadarko, OK...1195

Anaheim Museum, Anaheim, CA................71

Anderson County Arts Center, Anderson, SC...1320

Anderson County Historical Museum, Garnett, KS...541

Anderson Fine Arts Center, Anderson, IN ...467

Andover Historical Society, Andover, MA...660

Andrew County Museum & Historical Society, Savannah, MO 838

Andrew J. Blackbird Museum, Harbor Springs, MI...745

Anna Miller Museum, Newcastle, WY 1637

The Anne Spencer Memorial Foundation, Inc., Lynchburg, VA 1515

Annie Riggs Memorial Museum, Fort Stockton, TX...1415

Ano Nuevo State Reserve, Pescadero, CA...141

Anoka County Historical Society, Anoka, MN...767

Anson County Historical Society, Inc., Wadesboro, NC...1121

Antelope Valley Indian Museum, Lancaster, CA 108

Anti-Saloon League Museum, Westerville, OH...1190

Antietam National Battlefield-Visitor Center, Sharpsburg, MD..........................653

The Antiquarian and Landmarks Society, Inc., Hartford, CT...................................244

The Apple Trees Museum, Burlington, IA...506

Appomattox Court House National Historical Park, Appomattox, VA 1495

Aptucxet Trading Post Museum, Bourne, MA...670

APVA's John Marshall House, Richmond, VA..1528

Arbor Lodge State Historical Park, Nebraska City, NE................................868

Arcade Historical Society, Arcade, NY........958

Arcadia Township Historical Commission, Arcadia, MI 726

Archer County Museum, Archer City, TX .1387

Archibald Graham McIlwaine House & Visitors' Center (The Petersburg Museums), Petersburg, VA....................1524

Archives Museum, Temple Mickve Israel, Savannah, GA...384

Arden - The Helena Modjeska Historic House & Gardens, Modjeska Canyon, CA..126

Arizona Historical Society-Fort Lowell Museum, Tucson, AZ..................................47

Arizona Historical Society Museum, Tucson, AZ...47

Arizona Historical Society Pioneer Museum, Flagstaff, AZ...............................32

Arizona Historical Society-Yuma: Sarguinetti House Museum and Garden, Yuma, AZ.................................54

Arizona Mining and Mineral Museum, Phoenix, AZ..39

Arizona State Capitol Museum, Phoenix, AZ...39

Ark-La-Tex Antique & Classic Vehicle Museum, Shreveport, LA..........................600

The Arkansas Arts Center, Little Rock, AR..61

Arkansas Post Museum, Gillett, AR..............58

Arlington Heights Historical Museum, Arlington Heights, IL 411

Arlington Historical Museum, Arlington, VA..1495

The Arlington Historical Society, Arlington, MA...660

Arlington House, The Robert E. Lee Memorial, Arlington, VA.......................1495

The Armory Art Center, West Palm Beach, FL...353

The Arms Family Museum of Local History, Youngstown, OH......................1193

Arrow Rock State Historic Site, Arrow Rock, MO...810

Art and Culture Center of Hollywood, Hollywood, FL...312

Art Guild of Burlington, Inc., Burlington, IA..507

Art League of Houston, Houston, TX 1425

Artesia Historical Museum & Art Center, Artesia, NM...936

Arthurdale Heritage, Inc., Arthurdale, WV...1579

Artillery Company of Newport Military Museum, Newport, RI..........................1313

Artists Association of Nantucket, Nantucket, MA...695

Arts Club of Washington, Washington, DC..276

Arts Council of Fayetteville/Cumberland County, Fayetteville, NC.......................1100

Asa Packer Mansion, Jim Thorpe, PA........1263

Ash Lawn-Highland, Charlottesville, VA ...1498

Ashland Railroad Station Museum, Ashland, NH...883

Ashland, The Henry Clay Estate, Lexington, KY......................................572

Ashtabula County Historical Society, Geneva-on-the-Lake, OH.......................1166

Ashtabula Historic House, Pendleton, SC..1339

Ashton Villa & The Heritage Visitor Center, Galveston, TX.............................1420

Asistencia: San Gabriel Mission Outpost, Redlands, CA...146

Aspen Historical Society, Aspen, CO...........202

Association for the Preservation of Tennessee Antiquities, Nashville, TN 1377

Astor House Museum, Golden, CO.............219

Astors' Beechwood Mansion - Living History Museum, Newport, RI.............1313

Ataloa Lodge Museum, Muskogee, OK.....1205

The Athenaeum of Philadelphia, Philadelphia, PA 1276

Atlanta Historical Society, Atlanta, GA.......358

Atlantic Heritage Center, Somers Point, NJ...924

Atlantic Wildfowl Heritage Museum, Virginia Beach, VA.................................1541

Attmore-Oliver House, New Bern, NC.......1112

Atwater Kent Museum of Philadelphia, Philadelphia, PA 1276

Atwood House Museum, Home of Chatham Historical Society, Chatham, MA..675

Audie Murphy/American Cotton Museum, Inc, Greenville, TX 1423

Audrain Historical Museum, Graceland, Mexico, MO...827

Audubon House & Tropical Gardens, Key West, FL...317

Audubon Naturalist Society, Chevy Chase, MD...640

Audubon State Historic Site, Saint Francisville, LA...600

Aurora Historical Society, Aurora, IL..........411

Aurora Historical Society, Inc., East Aurora, NY...984

Avery County Museum, Newland, NC.......1113

Avila Adobe, Los Angeles, CA.....................113

The Avon Historical Society, Inc., Avon, CT..235

Awbury Arboretum, Philadelphia, PA........1277

Aztalan Museum, Jefferson, WI..................1601

B&O Railroad Museum: Ellicott City Station, Ellicott City, MD 643

The Babe Ruth Museum and Sports Legends at Camden Yards, Baltimore, MD..629

Baca House, Trinidad History Museum, Trinidad, CO...233

Bacon's Castle, Surry County, VA..............1540

Bailey House Museum - Maui Historical Society, Wailuku, HI................................402

The Bakken Library and Museum, Minneapolis, MN.................................781

Baldwin-Reynolds House Museum, Meadville, PA...1270

Bale Grist Mill State Historic Park, Calistoga, CA...80

Baltimore County Historical Society, Cockeysville, MD.................................640

Baltimore Public Works Museum, Inc., Baltimore, MD...630

Bangor Museum & Center for History, Bangor, ME...604

Banning Residence Museum, Wilmington, CA...198

Baranov Museum, Kodiak, AK......................26

The Barbara Fritchie House, Frederick, MD..644

Barker Mansion, Michigan City, IN 490

The Barnacle Historic State Park, Coconut Grove, FL.................................300

Barnard's Mill Art Museum, Glen Rose, TX..1422

Barnes Foundation, Merion, PA..................1271

Barnet Historical Society, Barnet, VT 1476

The Barnum Museum, Bridgeport, CT........235

Barratt's Chapel and Museum, Frederica, DE..270

Barre Historical Society, Inc., Barre, MA 662

Barrett House, Forest Hall, New Ipswich, NH..892

The Barrington Area Historical Society, Barrington, IL...412

Barrington Living History Farm, Washington, TX...1460

Barton County Historical Museum & Village, Great Bend, KS.............................542

Bartow-Pell Mansion Museum, Carriage House & Gardens, Bronx, NY.............964

Bartram's Garden, Philadelphia, PA 1277

Bassett Hall, Williamsburg, VA 1544

Batavia Depot Museum, Batavia, IL............412

Bates-Scofield Homestead, The Darien Historical Society, Darien, CT................238

Battersea (The Petersburg Museums), Petersburg, VA...1524

Battle of Lexington State Historic Site, Lexington, MO 826

Battleground Historical Society, Englishtown, NJ...903

The Battles Museums of Rural Life,
    Girard, PA..................................1256
Baxter House Museum, Gorham, ME..........611
Bay Area Museum, Seabrook, TX.............1452
Bay View Historical Museum, Bay View,
    MI...728
Bayless-Selby House Museum, Denton,
    TX...1409
Bayou Bend Collection and Gardens,
    Houston, TX...............................1425
Bear Butte State Park Visitors Center,
    Sturgis, SD...............................1358
Beau Fort Plantation Home, Bermuda,
    LA..587
Beauchamp Newman Museum, Elizabeth,
    WV..1581
Beaufort Historic Site, Beaufort, NC.........1091
Beauport, Sleeper-McCann House,
    Gloucester, MA.............................684
Beauvais Heritage Center, Clark, SD.........1345
Beauvoir, The Jefferson Davis Home and
    Presidential Library, Biloxi, MS............798
Beaver Island Historical Society, Beaver
    Island, MI.................................728
Beaverhead County Museum, Dillon, MT...845
Beavertail Lighthouse Museum,
    Jamestown, RI.............................1311
Bedford City/County Museum, Bedford,
    VA..1496
Bedingfield Inn Museum, Lumpkin, GA......376
Beehive House, Salt Lake City, UT...........1470
Beith House Museum, Saint Charles, IL......456
Belair Mansion, Bowie, MD..................638
Belair Stable Museum, Bowie, MD...........638
Belcourt Castle, Newport, RI................1313
Belding Museum, Belding, MI................728
The Belknap Mill Society, Laconia, NH......890
Bell County Museum, Belton, TX.............1395
Bellamy Mansion Museum of History
    and Design Arts, Wilmington, NC.........1122
Belle Grove Plantation, Middletown, VA....1517
Belle Meade Plantation, Nashville, TN......1377
Bellflower Historical and Genealogical
    Society, Bellflower, IL....................413
Bellingrath Gardens & Home, Theodore,
    AL...18
Belmont County Victorian Mansion
    Museum, Barnesville, OH..................1141
Beloit Historical Society, Beloit, WI..........1592
Belvedere-Tiburon Landmarks Society,
    Tiburon, CA................................192
Bement-Billings Farmstead, Newark
    Valley, NY................................1041
Benicia Historical Museum, Benicia, CA......74
Benjamin Harrison Presidential Site,
    Indianapolis, IN............................481
Bennett Place State Historic Site,
    Durham, NC...............................1098
Benton County Historical Museum,
    Philomath, OR............................1230
Bentonville Battlefield State Historic Site,
    Four Oaks, NC............................1102
Benzie Area Historical Museum,
    Benzonia, MI..............................729
Bergen County Historical Society, River
    Edge, NJ..................................923
Bergen Museum of Local History,
    Bergen, NY................................962
Berkeley Plantation, Charles City, VA.......1498
Berkshire County Historical Society, Inc.
    - Arrowhead, Pittsfield, MA...............702
Berkshire Scenic Railway Museum, Inc.,
    Lenox, MA.................................689
Berlin Area Historical Society Museum
    of Local History, Berlin, WI..............1592
Berlin Art and Historical Collections,
    Berlin, MA.................................662
Bernard Historical Society and Museum,
    Delton, MI.................................734
Berrien County Historical Association,
    Berrien Springs, MI........................729
The Berry Botanic Garden, Portland, OR..1230

Bess Streeter Aldrich House & Museum,
    Elmwood, NE..............................860
Bessemer Hall of History, Bessemer, AL....3
Besser Museum for Northeast Michigan,
    Alpena, MI................................723
Best Friend of Charleston, Charleston,
    SC..1324
Bethel Historical Society Regional
    History Center, Bethel, ME................606
Bethlehem Historical Association,
    Selkirk, NY...............................1068
Betsey Williams Cottage, Providence, RI..1316
Betsy Ross House and Flag Museum,
    Philadelphia, PA..........................1277
Betts House Research Center, Cincinnati,
    OH.......................................1148
Beverly Historical Society and Museum,
    Beverly, MA...............................662
Beyer Home, Oconto County Historical
    Society Museum, Oconto, WI.............1616
BG John C.L. Scribner Texas Military
    Forces Museum, Austin, TX...............1389
The Bidwell House Museum, Monterey,
    MA.......................................695
Bidwell Mansion State Historic Park,
    Chico, CA..................................83
Biedenharn Museum & Gardens, Monroe,
    LA..592
Big Bend National Park, Big Bend, TX.....1396
Big Timbers Museum, Lamar, CO...........225
Bigelow House Museum, Olympia, WA....1560
Bill Baggs Cape Florida State Park, Key
    Biscayne, FL...............................316
Billie Creek Village, Rockville, IN..........498
Billy Sunday Home Museum and Visitors
    Center, Winona Lake, IN...................504
Biltmore Estate, Asheville, NC.............1089
Bily Clock Museum/Antonin Dvorak
    Exhibit, Spillville, IA......................528
Birdsong Nature Center, Thomasville,
    GA..387
Birmingham Historical Museum & Park,
    Birmingham, MI...........................730
Birthplace of John Wayne, Winterset, IA....530
Bishop Hill Heritage Museum, Bishop
    Hill, IL...................................413
Bishop Hill State Historic Site, Bishop
    Hill, IL...................................413
The Bishop's Palace, Galveston, TX........1420
Black American West Museum &
    Heritage Center, Denver, CO..............209
Black River Academy Museum, Ludlow,
    VT.......................................1480
Black River Historical Society of Lorain,
    Lorain, OH...............................1172
Blackberry Farm's Pioneer Village,
    Aurora, IL.................................411
Blackman House Museum, Snohomish,
    WA......................................1570
Blacksmith Shop Museum,
    Dover-Foxcroft, ME.......................610
Blaine County Historical Museum,
    Hailey, ID.................................406
Blaine County Museum, Chinook, MT......844
Blaine House, Augusta, ME.................604
Blandford Church & Reception Ctr. (The
    Petersburg Museums), Petersburg, VA..1524
Blithewold Mansion, Gardens &
    Arboretum, Bristol, RI.....................1310
Bloom Mansion, Trinidad History
    Museum, Trinidad, CO.....................233
Bloomfield Academy Museum,
    Bloomfield, NY............................963
Bloomington Historical Society,
    Minneapolis, MN...........................781
Blount-Bridgers House/Hobson Pittman
    Memorial Gallery, Tarboro, NC...........1121
Blount Mansion, Knoxville, TN............1369
Blue Earth County Historical Society,
    Mankato, MN..............................780

Bob Burns Museum & River Valley
    Museum of Van Buren, Van Buren,
    AR..69
Boca Raton Historical Society, Boca
    Raton, FL.................................296
Bodie Island Visitor Center, South Nags
    Head, NC................................1120
Bolduc House Museum, Sainte
    Genevieve, MO.............................837
Bolton Historical Society, Inc., Bolton,
    MA.......................................663
Bonnet House Museum & Gardens, Fort
    Lauderdale, FL.............................306
Boone's Lick State Historic Site,
    Boonesboro, MO...........................811
Boot Hill Museum, Inc., Dodge City, KS...536
Boothe Memorial Park and Museum,
    Stratford, CT..............................262
Boscobel, Garrison, NY.....................993
Boston Athenaeum Library, Boston, MA....663
Boston Fire Museum, Boston, MA..........664
Boulder History Museum, Boulder, CO....202
Bowdoin College Museum of Art,
    Brunswick, ME.............................607
Bowers Mansion, Washoe Valley, NV........882
Bowie Railroad Station and Huntington
    Museum, Bowie, MD.......................638
The Bowne House Historical Society,
    Flushing, NY..............................990
Boyce Thompson Arboretum, Superior,
    AZ..44
Boyhood Home of President Woodrow
    Wilson, Augusta, GA.......................365
Boys Town Hall of History & Father
    Flanagan House, Boys Town, NE...........858
Bradford Brinton Memorial & Museum,
    Big Horn, WY.............................1628
Bradley House Museum, Jasper, AR.........60
Braintree Historical Society, Inc.,
    Braintree, MA.............................670
Branchville Railroad Shrine and Museum,
    Inc., Branchville, SC.......................1322
Brand Library & Art Center, Glendale,
    CA..100
Brandywine Battlefield Park, Chadds
    Ford, PA..................................1246
Brandywine River Museum, Chadds
    Ford, PA..................................1246
Branigan Cultural Center, Las Cruces,
    NM.......................................940
Brattleboro Museum & Art Center,
    Brattleboro, VT...........................1477
Brec's Magnolia Mound Plantation,
    Baton Rouge, LA...........................585
Brick House, Montgomery, NY.............1015
Brick Store Museum, Kennebunk, ME......612
Bridge Hampton Historical Society,
    Bridgehampton, NY........................964
Bridgton Historical Society, Bridgton,
    ME.......................................607
Brigham Young's Winter Home, Saint
    George, UT...............................1470
Brimstone Museum, Sulphur, LA...........602
Bronck Museum, Coxsackie, NY...........983
The Bronx County Historical Society,
    Bronx, NY................................964
Brookfield Craft Center, Brookfield, CT......237
Brookings County Historical Society
    Museum, Volga, SD........................1358
Brookline Historical Society, Brookline,
    MA.......................................671
Brown County Historical Society, New
    Ulm, MN..................................785
Brown County Historical Society Pioneer
    Museum, Nashville, IN.....................493
The Brown House Museum, Sandersville,
    GA..384
Brown Mansion, Coffeyville, KS............535
Brownella Cottage, Galion, OH.............1165
Brownsville Museum of Fine Art -
    Brownsville Art League, Brownsville,
    TX.......................................1398

Historic Houses and Historic Buildings–Continued

Brownville Historical Society Museum, Brownville, NE 858
Brucemore, Cedar Rapids, IA 509
Brueckner Museum of Starr Commonwealth, Albion, MI..................723
Brunnier Art Museum, Ames, IA.................504
Brush Country Museum, Cotulla, TX 1403
Bryant Cottage, Bement, IL.......................413
Buccleuch Mansion, New Brunswick, NJ ...915
Buckeye Furnace State Memorial, Wellston, OH 1190
Bucks County Civil War Library & Museum, Doylestown, PA......................1249
Bucksport Historical Society, Inc., Bucksport, ME 608
Bucyrus Historical Society, Bucyrus, OH ..1144
Buena Park Historical Society, Buena Park, CA 80
Buffalo and Erie County Historical Society, Buffalo, NY 972
Buffalo Bill Cody Homestead, Princeton, IA 527
Buffalo Bill Historical Center, Cody, WY ..1631
Buffalo Bill Museum of Le Claire, Iowa, Inc., Le Claire, IA 522
Buffalo Bill Ranch State Historical Park, North Platte, NE 869
Buffalo Historical Museum and One-Room Schoolhouse, Buffalo, SD ...1345
Buffalo National River, Harrison, AR 59
Buffalo Trails Museum, Epping, ND.........1130
Bulloch Hall, Roswell, GA 382
The Burgwin-Wright Museum, Wilmington, NC 1123
Burlington County Historical Society, Burlington, NJ 898
Burlington Historical Museum, Burlington, MA 672
Burlington-Rock Island Railroad and Historical Museum, Teague, TX 1454
Burnham Tavern, Machias, ME 614
Burnside Plantation, Inc., Bethlehem, PA ..1242
Burritt on the Mountain-A Living Museum, Huntsville, AL 11
Burrowes Mansion Museum, Matawan, NJ 911
Burt County Museum, Tekamah, NE 873
Burwell-Morgan Mill, Millwood, VA.........1518
Bushwhacker Museum, Nevada, MO...........828
Butler County Historical Society, Allison, IA 504
Butler County Museum, Hamilton, OH......1168
Butte-Silver Bow Arts Chateau, Butte, MT 843
Butterfield Trail Historical Museum, Russell Springs, KS 557
Byers-Evans House Museum, Denver, CO 209

C.F. Lott Historic Home, Oroville, CA 136
C.H. Moore Homestead, Clinton, IL 428
CHTJ Southard House Museum, Brunswick, ME 607
C.M. Russell Museum, Great Falls, MT 848
CSS Neuse State Historic Site and Gov. Richard Caswell Memorial, Kinston, NC 1108
Cabot Historical Society, Cabot, VT 1478
Cabrillo National Monument, San Diego, CA 156
Cades Cove Visitor Center and Open-Air Museum, Townsend, TN 1384
Cahokia Courthouse State Historic Site, Cahokia, IL 415
Cahoon Museum of American Art, Cotuit, MA 677
Calaveras County Archives, San Andreas, CA 155

Calaveras County Museum, San Andreas, CA 155
California Heritage Museum, Santa Monica, CA 183
California State Capitol Museum, Sacramento, CA 151
Callanwolde Fine Arts Center, Atlanta, GA 359
Calvert Marine Museum, Solomons, MD 654
Calvin Coolidge Historic Site, Plymouth Notch, VT 1484
Cambria County Historical Society, Ebensburg, PA 1251
Cambridge Historical Society, Cambridge, MA 672
Camden County Historical Society, Camden, NJ 899
Campbell Historical Museum & Ainsley House, Campbell, CA 80
Campbell House, Grand Forks, ND...........1131
Campbell House Museum, Saint Louis, MO 832
Campus Martius Museum, Marietta, OH ...1173
The Camron-Stanford House Preservation Association, Oakland, CA 133
Canaan Historical Society, Inc., Canaan, NY 974
Canadian County Historical Museum, El Reno, OK 1200
Canal Fulton Heritage Society, Canal Fulton, OH 1145
Canby Historical Society, Canby, OR 1221
Caney Valley Historical Society, Caney, KS 534
Cannon Falls Area Historical Museum, Cannon Falls, MN 770
Canton Historical Society, Canton, MA 674
Cape Ann Historical Museum, Gloucester, MA 684
Cape Cod National Seashore, Wellfleet, MA 717
Cape Henry Lighthouse, Virginia Beach, VA 1541
Cape May County Historical Museum and Genealogical Society, Cape May Court House, NJ 900
Cape Vincent Historical Museum, Cape Vincent, NY 976
Caples House Museum, Columbia City, OR 1222
Cappon & Settlers House Museums, Holland, MI 746
Captain Forbes House Museum, Milton, MA 695
Captain George Flavel House Museum, Astoria, OR 1218
Captain John Wilson House, Cohasset, MA 676
Captain Nathaniel B. Palmer House - Home of the Discoverer of Antarctica, Stonington, CT 261
Captain Salem Avery House Museum, Shady Side Rural Heritage Society, Inc., Shady Side, MD 653
Caramoor Center for Music & the Arts, Inc., Katonah, NY 1006
Carl Sandburg Home National Historic Site, Flat Rock, NC 1101
Carl Sandburg State Historic Site, Galesburg, IL 437
Carlen House Museum, Mobile, AL.............13
Carlyle House Historic Park, Alexandria, VA 1492
Carmel Heritage Society's First Murphy House, Carmel-by-the-Sea, CA 81
Carnegie Art Museum, Oxnard, CA 136
Carnegie Historical Museum, Fairfield, IA 517
Carnton Plantation, Franklin, TN.............1365
Carroll County Farm Museum, Westminster, MD 656

Carroll Mansion Museum Home of Leavenworth County Historical Society, Leavenworth, KS 549
Carry A. Nation Home Memorial, Medicine Lodge, KS 553
Carson County Square House Museum, Panhandle, TX 1442
Carter-Coile Country Doctors Museum, Winterville, GA 392
The Carter House Association, Inc., Franklin, TN 1365
Cary Cottage, Cincinnati, OH 1148
Caryl House and Fisher Barn, Dover, MA...680
Casa Adobe de San Rafael, Glendale, CA ...100
Casa Amesti, Monterey, CA......................127
Casa Blanca Museum, San Juan, PR.........1642
Casa de Rancho Cucamonga, Rancho Cucamonga, CA 144
The Casa del Herrero Foundation, Santa Barbara, CA 178
Casa Navarro State Historical Park, San Antonio, TX 1448
Cascade County Historical Society Museum, Great Falls, MT 848
Casemate Museum, Fort Monroe, VA 1505
Casey Farm, Saunderstown, RI 1319
Casey Jones Home and Railroad Museum, Jackson, TN 1367
Cason Cottage House Museum, Delray Beach, FL 304
Cass County Historical Society, Logansport, IN 489
Casteel-Linn House and Museum, Princeton, MO 829
Castillo de San Marcos National Monument, Saint Augustine, FL.............338
Castine Scientific Society, Castine, ME 609
The Castle, Marietta, OH 1174
Castle Tucker, Wiscasset, ME....................625
Castleton Historical Society, Castleton, VT 1478
The Casto House and Northfield Museum, Northfield, NJ 917
Catawba County Museum of History, Newton, NC 1113
The Cathedral of St. John the Divine, New York, NY 1022
Catherine V. Yost Museum & Arts Center, Pontiac, IL 451
Cedar Falls Historical Society, Cedar Falls, IA 507
Cedar Grove Historical Society, Cedar Grove, NJ 901
Cedar Grove Mansion Inn, Vicksburg, MS 809
Cedar Key Museum State Park, Cedar Key, FL 299
Center for History, Wheaton, IL 465
Centerville Historical Museum, Centerville, MA 675
Centerville - Washington Township Historical Society & Asahel Wright Community Center, Centerville, OH 1146
Centerville - Washington Township Historical Society & Walton House Museum, Centerville, OH 1147
Central City Opera House Association, Central City, CO 205
Centre County Historical Society, State College, PA 1301
Centre County Library and Historical Museum, Bellefonte, PA 1241
Centre Hill Museum (The Petersburg Museums), Petersburg, VA 1524
Century House Historical Society, Rosendale, NY 1061
Century Village Museum, Burton, OH 1144
Chalet of the Golden Fleece, New Glarus, WI 1614
Champaign County Historical Museum, Champaign, IL 416
Champion Mill State Historical Park, Champion, NE 859

Chandler Gallery, Randolph, VT 1485

The Chapman Historical Museum, Glens Falls, NY...994

Charles A. Grignon Mansion, Kaukauna, WI 1601

Charles A. Lindbergh Historic Site, Little Falls, MN...779

Charles Allis Art Museum, Milwaukee, WI 1610

Charles B. Aycock Birthplace State Historic Site, Fremont, NC...............1102

Charles Carroll House, Annapolis, MD........627

Charles H. Taylor Arts Center, Hampton, VA...1509

Charles Pinckney National Historic Site, Mount Pleasant, SC...........................1337

Charlotte Museum of History and Hezekiah Alexander Homesite, Charlotte, NC.................................1094

Charnley-Persky House Museum, Chicago, IL.....................................418

Chase County Historical Society, Inc., Cottonwood Falls, KS 536

Chase Home Museum of Utah Folk Arts, Salt Lake City, UT 1470

Chateau De Mores State Historic Site, Medora, ND.....................................1134

Chatillon-DeMenil Mansion, Saint Louis, MO..832

Chattahoochee River National Recreation Area, Atlanta, GA.............................359

Chautauqua County Historical Society, McClurg Museum, Westfield, NY 1086

Cheboygan County Historical Museum Complex, Cheboygan, MI......................732

Cheekwood-Tennessee Botanical Garden & Museum of Art, Nashville, TN..........1378

The Chelmsford Historical Society, Inc., South Chelmsford, MA 709

Chemung Valley History Museum, Elmira, NY....................................988

Cheney Homestead, Manchester, CT............248

Cheraw Lyceum Museum, Cheraw, SC.......1327

Cherokee Courthouse Visitors Information Center & Museum, Gore, OK...1201

Cherry County Historical Society, Valentine, NE...................................874

Chesapeake and Ohio Canal National Historical Park, Hagerstown, MD......646

Chesapeake Bay Maritime Museum, Saint Michaels, MD.................................652

The Chesapeake Beach Railway Museum, Chesapeake Beach, MD 639

Chesterfield County Museum, Chesterfield, VA.................................1501

Chesterwood, Stockbridge, MA 711

Cheyenne Depot Museum, Cheyenne, WY 1630

Chico Museum, Chico, CA.........................83

The Chief John Ross House, Rossville, GA...382

Chieftains Museum, Rome, GA..................381

The Children's Museum in Easton, North Easton, MA..................................699

Children's Museum of Pittsburgh, Pittsburgh, PA.................................1291

The Children's Museum of Portsmouth, Portsmouth, NH................................894

The Children's Museum of Rose Hill Manor Park, Frederick, MD...............644

Chimney Point State Historic Site, Addison, VT...................................1475

Chinese House/O.R. & N. Museum & St. Peter's Catholic Church, Echo, OR.......1222

Chino's Old Schoolhouse Museum, Chino, CA...84

Chinqua-Penn Plantation, Reidsville, NC...1117

Chippewa Valley Museum, Inc., Eau Claire, WI.....................................1595

Choctaw County Historical Society, Hugo, OK.......................................1203

Christiansted National Historic Site, Saint Croix, VI....................................1644

Church-Waddel-Brumby House Museum & Athens Welcome Center, Athens, GA...356

Cimarron Valley Railroad Museum, Cushing, OK.....................................1199

Cincinnati Fire Museum, Cincinnati, OH...1149

Circus World Museum, Baraboo, WI 1591

City County Pioneer Museum, Sweetwater, TX.................................1454

City Hall Council Chamber Gallery, Charleston, SC.................................1324

City Island Nautical Museum, Bronx, NY...965

City of Bowie Museums, Bowie, MD..........638

City of Gilroy Museum, Gilroy, CA............99

Clara Barton Birthplace, North Oxford, MA...699

Clara Barton National Historic Site, Glen Echo, MD.....................................645

Clarion County Historical Society, Sutton-Ditz House Museum, Clarion, PA...1247

Clark County Museum, Marshall, IL............444

Clark County Museum, Henderson, NV 878

Clark Hotel Museum, Van Horn, TX 1457

Clarke County Historical Association, Inc., Berryville, VA.............................1496

Clarke House Museum, Chicago, IL 420

Clarkson Historical Museum, Clarkson, NE 859

Clarksville-Montgomery County Museum dba Customs House Museum & Cultural Center, Clarksville, TN 1363

Clearfield County Historical Society, Clearfield, PA...................................1247

Clearwater County Historical Society, Shevlin, MN......................................793

Clermont State Historic Site, Clermont, NY 979

Clinton Academy, East Hampton, NY.........985

Clinton County Historical Society, Wilmington, OH.................................1191

Clinton County Museum, Frankfort, IN.......478

Cliveden of the National Trust, Philadelphia, PA 1278

Coachella Valley Museum and Cultural Center, Indio, CA...............................104

Coarsegold Historic Museum, Coarsegold, CA 86

Codington County Heritage Museum, Watertown, SD.................................1359

Codman Estate, The Grange, Lincoln, MA...690

Coe Hall, Oyster Bay, NY 1049

Coeur d'Alenes Old Mission State Park, Cataldo, ID......................................405

Coffin House, Newbury, MA 697

Coggeshall Farm Museum, Bristol, RI.......1310

Cohen-Bray House, Oakland, CA................133

Cole County Historical Museum, Jefferson City, MO 819

The Coleman House Museum and Brown County Historical Society, Ainsworth, NE...855

Colesville & Windsor Museum at St. Luke's Church, Harpursville, NY 997

The Coley Homestead & Barn Museum, Weston, CT.....................................265

Colfax County Society of Art, History and Archaeology, Raton, NM..................945

The Collectors Club, Inc., New York, NY.1023

Collin County Historical Society, Inc. & History Museum, McKinney, TX 1437

Collingsworth County Museum, Wellington, TX 1460

Collingwood Library and Museum on Americanism, Alexandria, VA...............1492

Collinsville Depot Museum, Collinsville, OK...1198

Col. Ashley House, Ashley Falls, MA 661

Colonel Davenport Historical Foundation, Rock Island, IL...................................453

Colonel William Jones State Historic Site/Lincoln State Park & Colonel Jones Home, Lincoln City, IN 488

Colonial Burlington Foundation, Inc., Burlington, NJ...................................899

Colonial Industrial Quarter, Bethlehem, PA..1242

Colonial National Historical Park: Jamestown & Yorktown, Yorktown, VA..1546

Colonial Pemaquid, New Harbor, ME..........615

Colony House, Newport, RI.......................1313

Colorado Historical Society, Denver, CO.....210

Colorado Springs Museum, Colorado Springs, CO.....................................206

Colton Hall Museum, Monterey, CA............127

Columbia County Historical Society, Inc., Kinderhook, NY 1007

Columbia State Historic Park, Columbia, CA...87

The Columbian Theatre, Museum & Art Center, Wamego, KS 560

Columbus-Belmont Civil War Museum, Columbus, KY...................................567

Columbus Chapel, Boal Mansion Museum, Boalsburg, PA.........................1244

Columbus Cultural Arts Center, Columbus, OH.................................1157

Comanche Crossing Historical Society & Museum, Strasburg, CO..........................233

Comstock Historic House, Moorhead, MN...784

Concord Art Association, Concord, MA 676

Concord Historical Society, Warner Museum, Springville, NY 1071

Concordia Historical Institute, Saint Louis, MO......................................832

Confederate Memorial Hall-Bleak House, Knoxville, TN...................................1369

Confederate Memorial State Historic Site, Higginsville, MO................................817

Confederate Museum, Crawfordville, GA....369

The Conference House, Staten Island, NY..1072

Conklin Reed Organ & History Museum, Hanover, MI.....................................745

Conneaut Railroad Museum, Conneaut, OH..1159

Connecticut Audubon Society, Fairfield, CT 240

Connecticut River Museum, Essex, CT........239

Conner Prairie, Fishers, IN 476

Conrad-Caldwell House Museum, Louisville, KY...................................575

Conrad Mansion National Historic Site Museum, Kalispell, MT.........................850

Conrad Weiser Homestead and Memorial Park, Womelsdorf, PA 1308

Constitution Island Association, West Point, NY.....................................1085

Constitution Square State Historic Site, Danville, KY.....................................567

The Contemporary Museum, Honolulu, HI 394

Conway Scenic Railroad, Inc., North Conway, NH.....................................892

Cook County Historical Museum, Grand Marais, MN......................................776

Cooper Regional History Museum, Upland, CA.....................................193

Copper King Mansion, Butte, MT...............843

Copper Village Museum & Arts Center of Deer Lodge County, Anaconda, MT.......840

Copshaholm House Museum & Historic Oliver Gardens, South Bend, IN............499

Coquille River Lighthouse/Bullards Beach State Park, Bandon, OR.............1220

The Corcoran Gallery of Art, Washington, DC.................................277

Cordell Hull Birthplace & Museum State Historic Park, Byrdstown, TN 1360

Historic Houses and Historic Buildings—Continued

Cornelius Low House/Middlesex County Museum, Piscataway, NJ 921
Cornell Museum of Art & History, Delray Beach, FL 304
Cornwall Iron Furnace, Cornwall, PA 1248
Coronado-Quivira Museum, Lyons, KS 550
Corydon Capitol Historic Site, Corydon, IN 473
The Country Doctor Museum, Bailey, NC.1091
County of Westchester, Department of Parks, Recreation and Conservation, Mount Kisco, NY 1016
Courthouse Square Association, Charlotte, MI 731
Cow Neck Peninsula Historical Society Sands-Willets House, Port Washington, NY 1053
Cowpens National Battlefield, Chesnee, SC 1327
Cozens Ranch Museum, Fraser, CO.............218
Cracker Country, Tampa, FL 348
Cragfont-Historic Cragfont, Inc., Castalian Springs, TN 1360
Crailo State Historic Site, Rensselaer, NY.1056
Cramer-Kenyon Heritage Home, Yankton, SD 1359
Cranbrook Art Museum, Bloomfield Hills, MI..730
Cranbrook House and Gardens Auxiliary, Bloomfield Hills, MI 730
Cranbury Historical & Preservation Society, Cranbury, NJ 902
Crane Point, Marathon, FL 323
Cranford Historical Society, Cranford, NJ ...902
Cravens House, Lookout Mountain, TN 1371
Crawford W. Long Museum, Jefferson, GA 374
Creative Arts Center, Pontiac, MI................760
Creative Photographic Art Center of Maine, Lewiston, ME..........................614
Creek Council House Museum, Okmulgee, OK 1211
Crescent Bend/The Armstrong-Lockett House and The William P. Toms Memorial Gardens, Knoxville, TN 1369
The Crescent, Valdosta Garden Center, Inc., Valdosta, GA 389
Crestline Shunk Museum, Crestline, OH ...1160
Cripple Creek District Museum, Inc., Cripple Creek, CO.............................209
Crocker Art Museum, Sacramento, CA........152
Crocker House, Mount Clemens, MI.........756
Crockett Tavern Museum, Morristown, TN 1376
Crooked Tree Arts Center, Petoskey, MI......760
Crowley Museum & Nature Center, Sarasota, FL 344
Crown Gardens and Archives, Dalton, GA 370
Crystal Lake Falls Historical Association, Barton, VT 1476
Culbertson Mansion State Historic Site, New Albany, IN 493
Cumberland County Historical Society, Greenwich, NJ 905
Cumberland Island National Seashore, Saint Marys, GA 382
Cuneo Museum & Gardens, Vernon Hills, IL 463
Cupertino Historical Society & Museum, Cupertino, CA......................................88
Cupola House, Egg Harbor, WI..................1596
The Currier Museum of Art, Manchester, NH 891
Custer County Art & Heritage Center, Miles City, MT 851
Custer County 1881 Courthouse Museum, Custer, SD..1345
Custer State Park, Custer, SD 1346

The Custom House Maritime Museum, Newburyport, MA 697
Cuyahoga Valley National Park, Brecksville, OH 1144
Cuyuna Range Historical Society & Museum, Crosby, MN 772
Cylburn Arboretum, Baltimore, MD............631
Cyrus E. Dallin Art Museum, Arlington, MA 660

DAR-Hervey Ely House, Rochester, NY ...1058
DAR John Strong Mansion Museum, Addison, VT 1475
D.C. Booth Historic National Fish Hatchery, Spearfish, SD 1357
D.R. Barker Historical Museum, Fredonia, NY 992
Dacotah Prairie Museum, Aberdeen, SD....1344
Dahlonega Gold Museum State Historic Site, Dahlonega, GA...............................369
Dakota County Historical Society, South Saint Paul, MN 793
Dakota Discovery Museum, Mitchell, SD..1352
Dakota Sunset Museum, Gettysburg, SD ...1348
Dakota Territorial Museum, Yankton, SD ..1359
Dakotaland Museum, Huron, SD................1348
Dal-Paso Museum, Lamesa, TX 1433
Dallas Arboretum & Botanical Garden, Dallas, TX 1404
Dalton Gang Hideout, Meade, KS................552
Dan Nagle Walnut Grove Pioneer Village, Long Grove, IA 522
The Dana-Thomas House State Historic Site, Springfield, IL 458
The Danbury Museum & Historical Society, Danbury, CT 238
Daniel Benton Homestead, Tolland, CT.......262
Daniel Boone Home and Boonesfield Village, Lindenwood University, Defiance, MO.......................................814
Daniel Boone Homestead, Birdsboro, PA ..1243
Daniels County Museum and Pioneer Town, Scobey, MT 853
The Danish Immigrant Museum, Elk Horn, IA 517
Danvers Historical Society, Danvers, MA....678
Danville Museum of Fine Arts & History, Danville, VA 1502
DAR Van Bunschooten Museum, Sussex, NJ 925
Darnall's Chance House Museum, M-NCPPC, Upper Marlboro, MD 655
Daughters of Utah Pioneers Pioneer Memorial Museum & International Society Daughters of Utah Pioneers, Salt Lake City, UT 1471
Davenport House Museum, Savannah, GA 384
David Bradford House, Washington, PA 1305
David Conklin Farmhouse, Huntington, NY 1000
David Crockett Cabin, Rutherford, TN 1383
The David Davis Mansion, Bloomington, IL 413
David Strawn Art Gallery, Jacksonville, IL 440
Davidson County Historical Museum, Lexington, NC 1109
Davison Art Center, Wesleyan University, Middletown, CT....................................249
The Dawes Arboretum, Newark, OH 1177
Dawes County Historical Society Museum, Chadron, NE 859
Dawson County Historical Museum, Lexington, NE 864
Dawson Springs Museum and Art Center, Inc., Dawson Springs, KY 568
Dayton Historical Depot Society, Dayton, WA 1552
Dayton History at Carillon Park, Dayton, OH 1161
Deaf Smith County Museum, Hereford, TX 1424

Dearborn Historical Museum, Dearborn, MI 733
Death Valley National Park Visitor Center and Museums, Death Valley, CA..............91
Decatur House Museum, Washington, DC...277
The Decorative Arts Center of Ohio, Lancaster, OH 1171
Deer Isle-Stonington Historical Society, Deer Isle, ME 609
Deerfield Beach Historical Society, Deerfield Beach, FL 304
DeKalb History Center Museum, Decatur, GA 370
The Dekker Huis/Zeeland Historical Museum, Zeeland, MI 767
Delano Heritage Park, Delano, CA 91
Delaware Agricultural Museum and Village, Dover, DE 269
Delaware Division of Historical & Cultural Affairs, Dover, DE 269
Deming Luna Mimbres Museum, Deming, NM 939
Dennys River Historical Society, Dennysville, ME....................................609
Denver Firefighters Museum, Denver, CO...211
Denver Museum of Miniatures, Dolls and Toys, Denver, CO 211
Depot Museum & Fort Sedgwick Museum, Julesburg, CO 223
Depreciation Lands Museum, Allison Park, PA 1240
Des Plaines History Center, Des Plaines, IL 430
Descanso Gardens Guild, Inc., La Canada Flintridge, CA...105
Devils Tower Visitor Center, Devils Tower, WY 1631
Dewey Hotel Museum, Dewey, OK 1199
DeWitt County Historical Museum, Cuero, TX 1403
Dexter Area Historical Society & Museum, Dexter, MI 738
Dexter Historical Society Campus, Dexter, ME 609
Dey Mansion/Washington's Headquarters Museum, Wayne, NJ 929
Dinsmore Homestead Foundation, Burlington, KY 566
Discovery Gateway, Salt Lake City, UT 1471
Divide County Historical Society Museum, Crosby, ND 1129
Doak House Museum, Greeneville, TN 1366
Dr. Daniel W. Kissam House, Huntington, NY 1000
Dr. Howe-Waffle House and Medical Museum, Santa Ana, CA.......................177
Dr. Increase Mathews House, Zanesville, OH 1194
Dr. John Harris Dental Museum, Bainbridge, OH..................................1141
Dr. Jose Celso Barbosa Museum & Library, Bayamon, PR 1641
Dr Pepper Museum and Free Enterprise Institute, Waco, TX.............................1458
Dr. William Robinson Plantation, Clark, NJ 901
Dodge County Historical Society, Mantorville, MN....................................780
Donald G. Trayser Memorial Museum/Barnstable County Customs House, Barnstable, MA 661
Donkey Milk House, Historic Home, Key West, FL 317
Door County Maritime Museum (at Sturgeon Bay), Sturgeon Bay, WI 1623
Doric House, Flemington, NJ.......................903
Dorothy G. Page Museum, Wasilla, AK 29
Douglas County Museum Complex, Armour, SD...1344
Downieville Museum, Downieville, CA 91
The Drake House Museum, Plainfield, NJ.921
Drake Well Museum, Titusville, PA 1303

Drayton Hall, Charleston, SC 1325
Drew County Historical Museum,
    Monticello, AR 64
Drum Barracks Civil War Museum,
    Wilmington, CA 198
Drummond Home, Hominy, OK.................1203
Dry Tortugas National Park, Key West,
    FL 317
Duke Homestead State Historic Site,
    Durham, NC 1098
Dumbarton House, Washington, DC............278
Dunbar House State Memorial, Dayton,
    OH 1161
Duncan Cottage Museum, Metlakatla, AK.....27
Dunedin Historical Society & Museum,
    Dunedin, FL 305
Dunham Tavern Museum, Cleveland, OH..1154
Dunklin County Museum, Inc., Kennett,
    MO 824
Dunsmuir Historic Estate & Gardens,
    Oakland, CA 133
Durant House Museum, Saint Charles, IL ...457
Durham Center Museum/Research
    Library, East Durham, NY 985
Durham Historic Association Museum,
    Durham, NH 886
Durham Western Heritage Museum,
    Omaha, NE 870
Dutchess County Historical Society,
    Poughkeepsie, NY 1054
Duxbury Rural and Historical Society,
    Inc., Duxbury, MA 681
Dwight D. Eisenhower Library-Museum,
    Abilene, KS 531
Dyckman Farmhouse Museum and Park,
    New York, NY 1025

E. St. Julien Cox House, Saint Peter, MN ...792
Eagle Bluff Lighthouse, Fish Creek, WI ...1597
Eagle Historical Society & Museums,
    Eagle, AK..23
Eagle Tavern Museum, Watkinsville, GA 391
The Earle-Harrison House and Gardens
    on 5th Street, Waco, TX 1458
EarlyWorks Museums, Huntsville, AL 11
East Brunswick Museum Corporation,
    East Brunswick, NJ 902
East Ely Railroad Depot Museum, Ely,
    NV 876
East End Seaport Museum and Marine
    Foundation, Greenport, NY......................996
East Hillsborough Historical Society, Inc.,
    Plant City, FL 337
East Jersey Olde Towne, Piscataway, NJ 921
East Lyme Historical Society/Thomas
    Lee House, Niantic, CT 256
East Martello Museum, Key West, FL 317
East Poultney Museum, East Poultney,
    VT 1479
East Tennessee Historical Society,
    Knoxville, TN 1369
Eastchester Historical Society - 1835
    Marble Schoolhouse, Bronxville, NY......967
Eastern Arizona Museum and Historical
    Society of Graham County Inc., Pima,
    AZ 42
Eastern Oregon Museum on the Old
    Oregon Trail, Haines, OR 1226
The Ebenezer Maxwell Mansion, Inc.,
    Philadelphia, PA 1278
Eccles Community Arts Center, Ogden,
    UT 1467
The Eckhart House, Wheeling, WV 1587
Edgar Allan Poe Cottage, Bronx, NY 965
Edgar Allan Poe House and Museum,
    Baltimore, MD 631
Edgar Allan Poe Museum, Richmond, VA.1529
Edgar Allan Poe National Historic Site,
    Philadelphia, PA 1278
Edgar County Historical Museum, Paris,
    IL 449
Edison & Ford Winter Estates, Fort
    Myers, FL 308

Edison Museum, Beaumont, TX................1394
Edison National Historic Site, West
    Orange, NJ 930
Edna Historical Museum, Edna, KS............537
Edsel & Eleanor Ford House, Grosse
    Pointe Shores, MI......................................745
Edward H. White II Memorial Museum,
    Brooks Air Force Base, TX 1397
Edward Hopper Landmark Preservation
    Foundation, Nyack, NY 1044
Edwin Wolters Memorial Museum,
    Shiner, TX 1453
The 1811 Old Lincoln County Jail and
    Lincoln County Museum, Wiscasset,
    ME...625
1859 Jail, Marshal's Home & Museum,
    Independence, MO......................................817
The 1890 House-Museum & Center for
    Arts, Cortland, NY 983
Eisenhower Birthplace State Historical
    Site, Denison, TX 1409
Eisenhower National Historic Site,
    Gettysburg, PA 1255
El Pueblo Historical Monument, Los
    Angeles, CA 114
Eldridge Street Project, New York, NY 1025
Eleanor Roosevelt National Historic Site,
    Hyde Park, NY 1002
Elfreth's Alley Association, Philadelphia,
    PA 1279
Elisabet Ney Museum, Austin, TX.............1390
Elkhart County Historical Museum,
    Bristol, IN 471
Ella Sharp Museum, Jackson, MI................748
Elliott Museum, Stuart, FL 346
Ellis County Historical Society, Hays, KS...543
Ellis County Museum, Inc., Waxahachie,
    TX 1460
Ellwood House Museum, DeKalb, IL...........429
Elvis Presley Birthplace and Museum,
    Tupelo, MS 808
Elwood Haynes Museum, Kokomo, IN........486
Emily Dickinson Museum: The
    Homestead and The Evergreens,
    Amherst, MA 658
Emily Kimbrough House, Muncie, IN 492
End-O-Line Railroad Park & Museum,
    Currie, MN...772
Enfield Historical Society Museum,
    Enfield Center, NH 887
Enfield Shaker Museum, Enfield, NH 887
Enoch Kelsey House, Newington, CT..........256
Enos Mills Cabin Museum & Gallery,
    Estes Park, CO...215
Ephraim Historical Foundation, Ephraim,
    WI 1597
Ephrata Cloister, Ephrata, PA 1251
Erie Canal Village, Rome, NY 1061
Erie County History Center & Cashier's
    House, Erie, PA 1252
Ernest Hemingway House Museum, Key
    West, FL 317
Ernie Pyle State Historic Site, Dana, IN 473
Escondido History Center, Escondido,
    CA 93
Essex Historical Society, Inc., Essex, CT 240
Essex Shipbuilding Museum, Essex, MA 681
Eugene Field House and St. Louis Toy
    Museum, Saint Louis, MO.........................833
Eugene O'Neill National Historic Site,
    Danville, CA 89
Eugene V. Debs Home, Terre Haute, IN 500
Eureka Pioneer Museum of McPherson
    County, Inc., Eureka, SD 1346
Eureka School House, Springfield, VT 1487
Eustis Historical Museum & Preservation
    Society, Inc., Eustis, FL 306
Evanston Historical Society and Charles
    Gates Dawes House, Evanston, IL 434
Evergreen House, The Johns Hopkins
    University, Baltimore, MD.........................632
Excelsior House, Jefferson, TX..................1431

The Exchange Hotel Civil War Museum,
    Gordonsville, VA 1509
Ezra Meeker Mansion, Puyallup, WA 1564

Fabyan Villa Museum, Geneva, IL..............437
Fairbanks House, Dedham, MA...................679
Fairfax County Park Authority, Resource
    Management Division, Fairfax, VA 1503
Fairfield Art Association, Fairfield, IA 518
Fairfield County Museum, Winnsboro,
    SC...1343
Fairfield Historical Society, Fairfield, CT 241
Fairlawn Mansion & Museum, Superior,
    WI 1624
Fairport Marine Museum, Fairport
    Harbor, OH 1164
Falkirk Cultural Center, San Rafael, CA......176
Fall River County Historical Museum,
    Hot Springs, SD 1348
Fall River Historical Society Museum,
    Fall River, MA 682
Fallingwater, Mill Run, PA 1272
Falmouth Historical Society, Falmouth,
    MA...682
Farm House Museum, Ames, IA 505
Farmers Bank (The Petersburg
    Museums), Petersburg, VA.......................1525
Farmers Branch Historical Park, Farmers
    Branch, TX 1413
Farmington Historic Home, Louisville,
    KY...575
Farrar-Mansur House & Old Mill
    Museum, Weston, VT 1490
Faulkner County Museum, Conway, AR.......56
Faust Park-Thornhill Historic Site & 19th
    Century Village, Chesterfield, MO 812
Fayette County Museum, Washington
    Court House, OH 1190
Fayette Historic State Park, Garden, MI 742
Federal Hall National Memorial, New
    York, NY..1025
Felix Valle State Historic Site, Sainte
    Genevieve, MO..837
Fenton History Center-Museum &
    Library, Jamestown, NY..........................1005
Fern Cottage, Ferndale, CA 94
Festival-Institute, James Dick Foundation,
    Round Top, TX 1446
Fifth Maine Regiment Museum, Peaks
    Island, ME 618
Fillmore Historical Museum, Inc.,
    Fillmore, CA 95
Filoli Center, Woodside, CA 199
Fine Arts Center for New River Valley,
    Pulaski, VA 1526
Fine Arts Center of Kershaw County,
    Inc., Camden, SC.....................................1322
The Finley House, Wayne, PA 1306
Fire Island National Seashore, Patchogue,
    NY..1051
Fire Museum of Texas, Beaumont, TX.......1394
Firelands Historical Society Museum,
    Norwalk, OH..1180
First Church of Christ Unitarian,
    Lancaster, MA 688
First Missouri State Capitol-State Historic
    Site, Saint Charles, MO 830
First Territorial Capitol of Kansas, Fort
    Riley, KS...540
First White House of the Confederacy,
    Montgomery, AL 16
Fisher Grove Country School/Fisher
    Grove State Park, Frankfort, SD............1347
The Fisk University Galleries, Nashville,
    TN 1379
The Five Civilized Tribes Museum,
    Muskogee, OK..1205
The Flag House and Star-Spangled
    Banner Museum, Baltimore, MD.............632
Flagler Museum, Palm Beach, FL...............333
Fleischmann Planetarium, Reno, NV...........880
Fleming Historical Society, Fleming, CO 216
Flint House, Scotia, NY 1068

Historic Houses and Historic Buildings—Continued

The Florence McLeod Hazard Museum, Columbus, MS 800

Florence Price Pioneer Museum, Florence, CO 216

Florence Ranch Homestead, Mesquite, TX 1438

Florewood State Park, Greenwood, MS 801

Florissant Fossil Beds National Monument, Florissant, CO 216

Florissant Valley Historical Society, Florissant, MO 815

Folsom History Museum, Folsom, CA..........95

The Folsom House Museum, Taylors Falls, MN 794

Folsom Museum, Inc., Folsom, NM............939

Fonthill Museum of the Bucks County Historical Society, Doylestown, PA 1249

Ford's Theatre National Historic Site (Lincoln Museum), Washington, DC 279

Forest Capital State Museum, Perry, FL 337

The Forges and Manor of Ringwood, Ringwood, NJ 923

Former Governors' Mansion State Historic Site, Bismarck, ND 1128

Fort Abraham Lincoln State Park, Mandan, ND 1134

Fort Bend Museum Association, Richmond, TX 1445

Fort Bowie National Historic Site, Bowie, AZ...30

Fort Bridger State Museum, Fort Bridger, WY 1632

Fort Buenaventura, Ogden, UT............1468

Fort Buford State Historic Site, Williston, ND 1137

Fort Casey Interpretive Center, Coupeville, WA 1551

Fort Caspar Museum, Casper, WY 1629

Fort Christmas Historical Park, Christmas, FL 299

Fort Clinch State Park, Fernandina Beach, FL 306

Fort Columbia House Museum, Chinook, WA 1550

Fort Columbia Interpretive Center, Chinook, WA 1551

Fort Concho National Historic Landmark, San Angelo, TX 1447

Fort Crawford Museum, Prairie du Chien, WI 1618

Fort Dalles Museum/Anderson Homestead, The Dalles, OR....1237

Fort Davis National Historic Site, Fort Davis, TX.....................................1414

Fort Douglas Military Museum, Fort Douglas, UT..................................1465

Fort Fetterman State Historic Site, Douglas, WY..................................1631

Fort Gibson Historic Site, Fort Gibson, OK 1200

Fort Harker Museum Complex, Kanopolis, KS....................................546

Fort Hartsuff State Historical Park, Burwell, NE.....................................858

Fort Hays State Historic Site, Hays, KS 543

Fort Hill (The John C. Calhoun House), Clemson, SC..................................1328

Fort Huachuca Museum, Fort Huachuca, AZ..34

Fort Hunter Mansion & Park, Harrisburg, PA.......................................1258

Fort Klock Historic Restoration, Saint Johnsville, NY..................................1063

Fort Laramie National Historic Site, Fort Laramie, WY..................................1633

Fort Lauderdale Historical Society, Fort Lauderdale, FL...............................307

Fort Leaton State Historical Site, Presidio, TX..................................1444

Fort Lewis Military Museum, Fort Lewis, WA 1554

Fort Macon State Park, Atlantic Beach, NC....................................1091

Fort Matanzas National Monument, Saint Augustine, FL 339

Fort McAllister, Richmond Hill, GA............381

Fort McKavett State Historical Site, Fort McKavett, TX.....................................1415

Fort Meigs State Memorial, Perrysburg, OH 1182

Fort Mifflin, Philadelphia, PA...............1279

Fort Nashborough, Nashville, TN............1379

Fort Nisqually Living History Museum, Tacoma, WA 1573

Fort Ontario State Historic Site, Oswego, NY 1048

Fort Payne Depot Museum, Fort Payne, AL 10

The Fort Pitt Block House, Pittsburgh, PA 1292

Fort Plain Museum, Fort Plain, NY 991

Fort Raleigh National Historic Site, Manteo, NC...............................1110

Fort Recovery Museum, Fort Recovery, OH 1164

Fort Richardson State Historical Park, Jacksboro, TX................................1431

Fort Robinson Museum, Crawford, NE.......860

Fort St. Joseph Museum, Niles, MI............758

Fort Scott National Historic Site, Fort Scott, KS..................................540

Fort Sidney Museum & Post Commander's Home, Sidney, NE............873

Fort Sill National Historic Landmark, Fort Sill, OK...................................1201

Fort Simcoe State Park, White Swan, WA.1578

Fort Sisseton State Historic Park, Lake City, SD 1350

Fort Spokane Visitor Center and Museum, Davenport, WA...................1552

Fort Sumter National Monument, Sullivan's Island, SC 1342

Fort Tejon State Historic Park, Lebec, CA 108

Fort Vasquez Museum, Platteville, CO 230

Fort Verde State Historic Park, Camp Verde, AZ...30

Fort Washington Park, Fort Washington, MD 643

Fort Wilkins Historic Complex, Copper Harbor, MI 733

Fort Winnebago Surgeons Quarters, Portage, WI 1618

Fort Yargo State Park, Winder, GA............391

Fort Zachary Taylor State Historical Site, Key West, FL.......................................317

Forts Folle Avoine Historic Park, Danbury, WI 1594

Fosterfields Living Historical Farm, Morristown, NJ................................913

Foundation For Historic Christ Church, Inc., Irvington, VA..........................1511

4-H Schoolhouse Museum, Clarion, IA 510

Four Mile Historic Park, Denver, CO 212

Four Wheel Drive Foundation, Clintonville, WI 1594

Fox Island Historical Society, Fox Island, WA 1554

The Foxfire Museum & Heritage Center, Mountain City, GA............................380

Frances Willard House Museum, Evanston, IL...................................434

Francis Land House Historic Site, Virginia Beach, VA...........................1542

Franconia Heritage Museum, Franconia, NH 888

Frank G. Ray House, Vinton, IA 529

Frank Lloyd Wright Home and Studio, Oak Park, IL 448

Frank Lloyd Wright's Pope-Leighey House, Alexandria, VA......................1492

Frank Murphy Memorial Museum, Harbor Beach, MI...............................745

Frank Phillips Home, Bartlesville, OK.......1197

Frankenmuth Historical Museum, Frankenmuth, MI................................742

Franklin County Historical Museum, Pasco, WA..................................1561

Franklin County Old Jail Museum, Winchester, TN...............................1385

Franklin Historical Society, Franklin, ME....611

The Franklin Pierce Homestead, Hillsborough, NH................................889

Fraunces Tavern Museum, New York, NY 1025

Fred Harman Art Museum, Pagosa Springs, CO 229

Frederic Remington Art Museum, Ogdensburg, NY..............................1044

Frederick C. Robie House, Chicago, IL 420

Frederick Douglass National Historic Site, Washington, DC 279

Frederick Law Olmsted National Historic Site, Brookline, MA 671

Fredericksburg Area Museum & Cultural Center, Inc., Fredericksburg, VA...........1506

Freeport Historical Society, Freeport, ME....611

Freestone County Historical Museum, Fairfield, TX 1413

French Art Colony, Gallipolis, OH 1165

French Azilum, Inc., Towanda, PA...........1303

The French Legation Museum, Austin, TX 1390

Fresno Flats Historical Park, Oakhurst, CA 132

Fresno Metropolitan Museum, Fresno, CA 97

The Frick Art & Historical Center, Pittsburgh, PA..................................1292

Friends of Arrow Rock, Inc., Arrow Rock, MO 811

Friends of Historic Kingston, Fred J. Johnston House Museum, Kingston, NY 1007

The Friends of Lucy Hayes Heritage Center, Chillicothe, OH 1147

The Friends of Peace Church, Camp Hill, PA 1245

The Friends of the Caleb Pusey House, Inc., Upland, PA..............................1304

Friends (Quaker) Meeting House, Mount Pleasant, OH....................................1177

Friendship Firehouse, Alexandria, VA........1492

Frisco Historic Park & Museum, Frisco, CO 218

Frontera Audubon Society, Weslaco, TX....1460

Frontier Culture Museum, Staunton, VA....1537

Frontier Historical Society and Museum, Glenwood Springs, CO 219

Frontier Museum, Williston, ND 1138

Fruitlands Museums, Harvard, MA 686

Fryer Memorial Museum, Munnsville, NY 1017

Frye's Measure Mill, Wilton, NH...............897

The Fullerton Arboretum, Fullerton, CA.....98

Fulton County Historical Society Museum, Rochester, IN........................498

Fulton Mansion State Historic Site, Rockport, TX..................................1446

Gadsby's Tavern Museum, Alexandria, VA 1492

Gaineswood, Demopolis, AL 7

Galion Historical Museum, Galion, OH 1165

Gallier House, New Orleans, LA................595

Galloping Road Compound & Poker Alley, Harbor Ranch, Dripping Springs, TX..................................1410

Galloway House and Village - Blakely Museum, Fond du Lac, WI..................1597

Galveston County Historical Museum, Galveston, TX.....................................1420

Galveston Historical Foundation, Inc., Galveston, TX.....................................1421

Gamble House, Pasadena, CA 140
Garden Grove Historical Society, Garden
    Grove, CA..99
Gardner House Museum, Albion, MI 723
The Gardner Museum, Inc., Gardner, MA ..684
Garfield Farm Museum, LaFox, IL 441
Gari Melchers Home and Studio,
    Fredericksburg, VA..................................1506
Garibaldi and Meucci Museum, Staten
    Island, NY..1072
Garnavillo Historical Museum,
    Garnavillo, IA..518
Garrett Historical Museum, Garrett, IN........479
Garst Museum, Greenville, OH 1167
Gatekeeper's Museum & Marion
    Steinbach Indian Basket Museum,
    Tahoe City, CA..190
Gates House, Machiasport Historical
    Society, Machiasport, ME..........................614
Gates Mills Historical Society, Gates
    Mills, OH...1166
Gateway NRA, Sandy Hook Unit, Fort
    Hancock, NJ..904
Gateway to the Panhandle, Gate, OK.........1201
Gathland State Park, Boonsboro, MD..........637
Geddes Historic District Village, Geddes,
    SD..1347
Gene Stratton-Porter State Historic Site,
    Rome City, IN..498
Genealogy Research Center and Museum,
    Sandersville, GA..384
General Adam Stephen House,
    Martinsburg, WV......................................1584
General Crook House Museum and
    Library/Archives Center, Omaha, NE......870
General Daniel Bissell House, Saint
    Louis, MO..833
General Douglas MacArthur Memorial,
    Norfolk, VA..1521
General Grant National Memorial, New
    York, NY..1026
General Jacob Brown Historical Society,
    Brownville, NY..971
General John J. Pershing Boyhood Home
    State Historic Site, Laclede, MO.............824
General Lew Wallace Study & Museum,
    Crawfordsville, IN......................................473
General Wait House, Waitsfield, VT...........1489
Genesee Country Village & Museum,
    Mumford, NY...1016
Geneva Historical Society &
    Prouty-Chew House & Museum,
    Geneva, NY..994
Geneva Historical Society & Rose Hill
    Mansion, Geneva, NY................................994
George Ade Memorial Association Inc.,
    Brook, IN...471
George Eastman House/International
    Museum of Photography and Film,
    Rochester, NY..1058
The George G. Frelinghuysen Arboretum,
    Morris Township, NJ..................................913
George Key Ranch, Placentia, CA 142
George Peabody House Museum,
    Peabody, MA..701
George Rogers Clark National Historical
    Park, Vincennes, IN..................................502
George Washington Birthplace National
    Monument, Colonial Beach, VA.............1502
George Washington Carver National
    Monument, Diamond, MO.........................814
George Washington's Fredericksburg
    Foundation, Historic Kenmore &
    Washington's Ferry Farm,
    Fredericksburg, VA..................................1506
George Washington's Headquarters,
    Cumberland, MD..642
Georgia Capitol Museum, Atlanta, GA 360
Georgia Historical Society, Savannah, GA...385
Georgia Salzburger Society Museum,
    Rincon, GA..381
Georgia State Cotton Museum, Vienna,
    GA..390

The Georgian Museum, Lancaster, OH 1171
Georgia's Old Capital Museum,
    Milledgeville, GA.......................................380
Georgia's Stone Mountain Park, Stone
    Mountain, GA...387
Gertrude Smith House, Mount Airy, NC 1111
The Gibson Society, Inc. dba Gibson
    House Museum, Boston, MA.......................665
Gila County Historical Museum, Globe,
    AZ..35
The Gilbert Stuart Birthplace and
    Museum, Saunderstown, RI......................1319
Gillespie County Historical Society,
    Fredericksburg, TX...................................1419
Gillette Castle State Park, East Haddam,
    CT..239
Gilliam County Historical Society -
    Depot Museum Complex, Condon, OR.1222
Gilman Garrison House, Exeter, NH...........887
Gilpin History Museum, Central City, CO...205
The Glebe House Museum and Gertrude
    Jekyll Garden, Woodbury, CT...................268
Glencairn Museum: Academy of the New
    Church, Bryn Athyn, PA 1244
Glendower State Memorial, Lebanon, OH.1171
Glenn House/Historical Association of
    Greater Cape Girardeau, Cape
    Girardeau, MO...812
Glensheen Historic Estate, Duluth, MN 773
Glenview Area Historical Society,
    Glenview, IL...438
Glessner House Museum, Chicago, IL.........421
Gold Coast Railroad Museum, Inc.,
    Miami, FL...323
Golden Ball Tavern Museum, Weston,
    MA..718
Golden Gate National Recreation Area,
    San Francisco, CA......................................165
Gomez Foundation for Mill House,
    Marlboro, NY...1014
Goodman Museum, Tyler, TX 1456
Goodnow Museum State Historic Site,
    Manhattan, KS...550
Gorgas House, Tuscaloosa, AL......................19
Goschenhoppen Folklife Library and
    Museum, Green Lane, PA.........................1257
Governor Bent Museum, Taos, NM 952
Governor Henry Lippitt House Museum,
    Providence, RI...1316
Governor John Langdon House,
    Portsmouth, NH...894
Governor John Sevier Memorial
    Association, Knoxville, TN......................1370
Governor Ross Plantation, Seaford, DE 272
Governor Seay Mansion, Kingfisher, OK...1204
Governor Stephen Hopkins House
    Museum, Providence, RI...........................1317
The Governor's Mansion, Frankfort, KY 569
Governor's Mansion, Columbia, SC...........1329
Governor's Mansion State Historic Park,
    Sacramento, CA...152
Graber Olive House Museum, Ontario,
    CA..135
Grace Hudson Museum & Sun House,
    Ukiah, CA..193
Graceland, Memphis, TN...........................1373
The Gracie Mansion Conservancy, New
    York, NY..1026
Graeme Park, Horsham, PA 1261
Grafton Historical Society, Grafton, VT.....1479
Grand Army of the Republic Civil War
    Museum, Philadelphia, PA.......................1281
Grand County Museum, Hot Sulphur
    Springs, CO...222
Grand Encampment Museum, Inc.,
    Encampment, WY....................................1632
Grand Gulf Military Park, Port Gibson,
    MS..807
Grand Lake Area Historical Society,
    Grand Lake, CO...221
The Granger Homestead Society, Inc.,
    Canandaigua, NY.......................................975

Grant County Museum aka Historic
    Adobe Museum, Ulysses, KS 560
Grant County Museum & Historic
    Society, Hyannis, NE................................863
Grant-Humphreys Mansion, Denver, CO 212
Grant's Birthplace State Memorial, Point
    Pleasant, OH..1182
Granville Historical Society Museum,
    Granville, OH...1167
Graue Mill and Museum, Oak Brook, IL.....448
Graycliff Conservancy, Derby, NY 984
Greater Loveland Historical Society
    Museum, Loveland, OH............................1173
Greenbelt Museum, Greenbelt, MD.............646
Greene County Historical Museum,
    Waynesburg, PA.......................................1306
Greene County Historical Society, Xenia,
    OH..1193
Greenfield Historical Society, Greenfield,
    WI...1599
Greensboro Historical Museum, Inc.,
    Greensboro, NC..1103
Gresham History Museum, Gresham, OR..1226
Grevemberg House Museum, Franklin,
    LA..588
Grier Musser Museum, Los Angeles, CA 115
Grinter Place State Historic Site, Kansas
    City, KS...546
Gropius House, Lincoln, MA.......................690
Grosse Ile Historical Society, Grosse Ile,
    MI..745
Groton Historical Society, Groton, MA........685
Grout Museum District: Grout Museum
    of History and Science, Bluedorn
    Science Imaginarium, Rensselaer
    Russell House Museum, Snowden
    House, Waterloo, IA..................................529
The Grove, Glenview, IL.............................438
Grover Cleveland Birthplace, Caldwell,
    NJ..899
Gruenewald Historic House, Anderson,
    IN...467
Guadalupe Mountains National Park, Salt
    Flat, TX...1447
Guernsey County Museum, Cambridge,
    OH..1144
The Guest House Museum, Fort Bragg,
    CA..95
Gulf Coast Exploreum Science Center,
    Mobile, AL...13
Gulf Islands National Seashore, Gulf
    Breeze, FL...312
GumTree Museum of Art, Tupelo, MS 808
Gunderson House, Kenyon, MN..................778
Gunn Memorial Library and Museum,
    Washington, CT...263
Gunnison County Pioneer and Historical
    Society, Gunnison, CO..............................222
Gunnison Museum of Natural History,
    Pawling, NY...1051
Gunston Hall Plantation, Mason Neck,
    VA..1517
Guy B. Woodward Museum, Ramona,
    CA..144
Gwinnett History Museum,
    Lawrenceville, GA.....................................376

H.G. Albee Memorial Museum,
    Estherville, IA..517
Haas-Lilienthal House, San Francisco,
    CA..166
Hackettstown Historical Society Museum
    & Library, Hackettstown, NJ.....................905
Hackley & Hume Historic Site,
    Muskegon, MI..757
Hadley Farm Museum, Hadley, MA 685
The Hagley Museum and Library,
    Wilmington, DE...273
Hahns Peak Area Historical Society and
    School House, Clark, CO...........................205
Haines Museum, Waukegan Historical
    Society, Waukegan, IL...............................463
Hale Farm and Village, Bath, OH 1141

Historic Houses and Historic Buildings—Continued

Hale Pa'ahao Prison, Lahaina, HI 400
The Hall of Fame for Great Americans, Bronx, NY 966
Hallockville Museum Farm, Riverhead, NY 1057
Hamburg State Park Museum, Mitchell, GA 380
Hamden Historical Society, Inc., Hamden, CT 244
Hamilton Grange National Memorial, New York, NY 1026
Hamilton House, South Berwick, ME 622
Hamilton Township Historical Society - John Abbott II House, Hamilton, NJ 906
Hamilton Van Wagoner Museum, Clifton, NJ 901
Hamlin Garland Homestead, West Salem, WI 1627
Hammond Castle Museum, Gloucester, MA 684
Hammond-Harwood House Association, Annapolis, MD 628
Hampden-Booth Theatre Library at the Players, New York, NY 1027
Hampton County Historical Museum, Hampton, SC 1334
Hampton National Historic Site, Towson, MD 655
Hampton Plantation State Historic Site, McClellanville, SC 1336
Hampton University Museum, Hampton, VA 1509
Hana Cultural Center, Hana, Maui, HI 392
Hanby House, Westerville, OH 1191
Hancock Historical Society, Hancock, NH 888
Hancock House, Hancock's Bridge, NJ 907
Hancock Shaker Village, Inc., Pittsfield, MA 703
Hanley House, Clayton, MO 813
Hanover Historical Society Museum, Hanover, VA 1510
Hanover House, Clemson, SC 1328
Harbour House Museum, Crystal Falls, MI 733
Harding Home and Museum, Marion, OH.1174
Harding Museum, Franklin, OH 1164
Hardwick Historical Society, Hardwick, MA 686
Hargitt House, Norwalk, CA 131
Harlan-Lincoln House, Mount Pleasant, IA 524
Harmonie Associates, Inc., Ambridge, PA .1240
Harn Homestead and 1889er Museum, Oklahoma City, OK 1207
The Harness Racing Museum and Hall of Fame, Goshen, NY 995
Harper City Historical Society, Harper, KS 543
Harriet Beecher Stowe Center, Hartford, CT 245
The Harriet Tubman Home, Auburn, NY 959
Harrimans Falls Educational Centre and Museum, Bath, NH 883
Harrison County Historical Museum, Marshall, TX 1436
Harrison House, Branford, CT......................235
Harrisonburg-Rockingham Historical Society, Dayton, VA 1503
Harry P. Leu Gardens, Orlando, FL 331
Harry S Truman Birthplace State Historic Site, Lamar, MO 825
Harry S. Truman Little White House Museum, Key West, FL 317
Harry S Truman National Historic Site - Truman Farm Home, Grandview, MO 816
Harry S Truman National Historic Site - Truman Home, Independence, MO........818
Hartford House Museum, Manhattan, KS 551

Hartsville Museum, Hartsville, SC 1335
Harvard Historical Society, Still River, MA 711
Harvey-Baker House, Salinas, CA...............154
Harvey County Historical Society, Newton, KS 553
Harvey House Museum, Florence, KS 539
Hathaway Ranch Museum, Santa Fe Springs, CA 182
Hatteras Island Visitor Center, Buxton, NC 1093
Hatton-Eielson Museum & Historical Association, Hatton, ND 1132
Haverford Township Historical Society, Havertown, PA 1260
Hawaii's Plantation Village, Waipahu, HI 402
Hawkeye Log Cabin, Burlington, IA...........507
Hawks Inn Historical Society, Inc., Delafield, WI 1595
Hay House Museum, Macon, GA 377
Headquarters House Museum, Fayetteville, AR 57
Headwaters Heritage Museum, Three Forks, MT 854
Healy House-Dexter Cabin, Leadville, CO 225
Hearst Castle, San Simeon, CA...................177
Hearthstone Historic House Museum, Appleton, WI 1589
Heisey Museum, Clinton County Historical Society, Lock Haven, PA 1269
Held-Poage Memorial Home and Research Library, Ukiah, CA 193
Helen Day Art Center, Stowe, VT 1488
Helvetia Museum, Helvetia, WV 1582
The Hemingway Museum and The Ernest Hemingway Birthplace, Oak Park, IL 448
Henrico County Historic Preservation & Museum Services, Richmond, VA 1529
Henry B. Plant Museum, Tampa, FL............349
Henry County Historical Society, New Castle, IN 494
Henry County Museum and Cultural Arts Center, Clinton, MO................................813
The Henry Ford, Dearborn, MI 733
Henry Ford Estate-Fair Lane, Dearborn, MI 734
Henry Guest House, New Brunswick, NJ....915
Henry Whitfield State Historical Museum, Guilford, CT 243
Heritage Center Museum, Berryville, AR 55
Heritage Conservancy, Doylestown, PA 1249
Heritage Farmstead Museum, Plano, TX ...1444
Heritage Hall Museum & Archives, Freeman, SD 1347
Heritage Hill State Historical Park, Green Bay, WI 1599
Heritage House, West Covina, CA 197
Heritage House of Orange County Association Inc., Orange, TX 1441
The Heritage Museum, Baltimore, MD........632
The Heritage Museum, Astoria, OR............1218
Heritage Museum & Gallery, Leadville, CO 226
Heritage Museum & Potton House, Big Spring, TX 1396
The Heritage Society, Houston, TX............1426
Heritage Square Museum, Ontario, NY 1047
Heritage Square Museum, Los Angeles, CA 116
Heritage Village, Largo, FL 321
Heritage Village, Mountain Lake, MN 785
Herkimer Home State Historic Site, Little Falls, NY 1009
Hermann-Grima/Gallier Historic Houses, New Orleans, LA 595
The Hermitage, Ho-Ho-Kus, NJ 907
The Hermitage Foundation, Norfolk, VA...1521
The Hermitage: Home of President Andrew Jackson, Hermitage, TN..........1367
Hernando Heritage Museum, Brooksville, FL 298

Herreshoff Marine Museum/America's Cup Hall of Fame, Bristol, RI 1311
Hettinger County Historical Society, Regent, ND 1136
Hibbing Historical Society and Museum, Hibbing, MN 778
The Hickories Museum of the Lorain County Historical Society, Elyria, OH ..1163
Hickory Grove Rural School Museum, Ogden, IA 525
Hickory Hill, Thomson, GA 388
Hickory Landmarks Society-Propst House & Maple Grove, Hickory, NC...............1106
The Hicksville Gregory Museum, Hicksville, NY 998
Hiddenite Center, Inc., Hiddenite, NC........1106
Higgins Armory Museum, Worcester, MA...721
High Cliff Historical Society & General Store Museum, Sherwood, WI 1622
High Point Museum & Historical Park, High Point, NC 1106
Highland House Museum, Hillsboro, OH ..1168
Highland Park Historical Society, Highland Park, IL 439
The Highlands, Fort Washington, PA 1254
Highlands Hammock State Park/Civilian Conservation Corps Museum, Sebring, FL 346
Hildene, The Lincoln Family Home, Manchester, VT 1481
Hill Cumorah Visitors Center & Historic Sites, Palmyra, NY 1050
Hill-Hold Museum, Montgomery, NY........1015
Hill-Stead Museum, Farmington, CT 241
Hillforest House Museum, Aurora, IN 468
Hills and Dales Estate, LaGrange, GA.........375
Hillsboro Area Historical Society, Hillsboro, WI 1600
Hillsboro Museums, Hillsboro, KS...............544
Hillwood Museum & Gardens, Washington, DC 280
Hinckley Fire Museum, Hinckley, MN 778
Historic Annapolis Foundation, Annapolis, MD 628
Historic Arkansas Museum, Little Rock, AR 62
Historic Bath State Historic Site, Bath, NC 1091
Historic Bethabara Park, Winston-Salem, NC 1125
Historic Bethany, Bethany, WV 1580
Historic Bowens Mills & Pioneer Park, Middleville, MI 754
Historic Brattonsville, McConnells, SC......1336
Historic Burlington County Prison Museum, Mount Holly, NJ 914
Historic Camden Revolutionary War Site, Camden, SC 1323
Historic Carson House, Marion, NC...........1110
Historic Charleston Foundation, Charleston, SC 1325
Historic Cherry Hill, Albany, NY 954
Historic Columbia Foundation, Columbia, SC 1329
Historic Columbus Foundation, Inc., Columbus, GA 369
Historic Crab Orchard Museum & Pioneer Park, Inc., Tazewell, VA 1541
Historic Deepwood Estate, Salem, OR.......1235
Historic Deerfield, Inc., Deerfield, MA........679
Historic Edenton State Historic Site, Edenton, NC 1099
Historic Fort Steilacoom, Lakewood, WA..1558
Historic General Dodge House, Council Bluffs, IA 512
Historic Georgetown Inc., Georgetown, CO 218
Historic Governors' Mansion, Cheyenne, WY 1630
Historic Halifax State Historic Site, Halifax, NC 1105

Historic Hartwood Mansion, Pittsburgh, PA 1292

Historic Hermann Museum, Hermann, MO 817

Historic Homes Foundation, Inc., Louisville, KY 576

Historic Hope Foundation, Inc., Windsor, NC 1124

Historic House Trust of New York City, New York, NY 1027

Historic Hudson Valley, Tarrytown, NY 1077

Historic Indian Agency House, Portage, WI 1618

Historic Jefferson College, Washington, MS 810

Historic Landmarks Foundation of Indiana, Indianapolis, IN 482

Historic Langhorne Association, Langhorne, PA 1267

Historic Latta Plantation, Huntersville, NC 1107

Historic London Town and Gardens, Edgewater, MD 642

Historic Lyme Village Association, Bellevue, OH 1142

Historic Macon Foundation, Inc. - Sidney Lanier Cottage House Museum, Macon, GA 377

Historic Madison, Inc., Madison, IN 489

Historic Mann House, Concord, MI 732

Historic Mobile Preservation Society, Mobile, AL 14

Historic New England, Boston, MA 665

Historic New England/Cogswells Grant, Essex, MA 682

Historic New Harmony, New Harmony, IN 494

The Historic New Orleans Collection, New Orleans, LA 595

Historic Newton Home, Decatur, MI 734

Historic Northampton, Northampton, MA ...699

Historic Oakland Cemetery, Atlanta, GA ...360

Historic Occoquan, Inc., Occoquan, VA ...1523

Historic Palmyra's Print Shop, Palmyra, NY 1050

Historic Palmyra's - Wm. Phelps General Store, Palmyra, NY 1050

Historic Pensacola Village, Pensacola, FL ...335

Historic Pittsford, Pittsford, NY 1052

Historic Price House, Woodruff, SC 1343

Historic Renville Preservation Commission, Renville, MN 787

Historic Richmond Town, Staten Island, NY 1072

Historic Rosedale, Charlotte, NC 1095

Historic Rugby, Rugby, TN 1383

Historic St. Mary's City, Saint Mary's City, MD 652

Historic Shepherdstown Museum, Shepherdstown, WV 1586

Historic Smithfield, Blacksburg, VA 1497

Historic Southwest Ohio, Inc., Sharonville, OH 1185

Historic Stagville, Durham, NC 1098

Historic Waco Foundation, Waco, TX 1459

Historic Walnford, Upper Freehold Twp., NJ 929

Historic Warrior Run Church, Watsontown, PA 1306

Historic Wolcott House, Wolcott, IN 504

Historical Center for Southeast New Mexico, Roswell, NM 946

The Historical Museum at St. Gertrude, Cottonwood, ID 405

Historical Museum of Bay County, Bay City, MI 727

Historical Shrine Foundation of San Diego County, San Diego, CA 156

Historical Society of Brookfield, Brookfield Center, VT 1477

Historical Society of Carroll County, Westminster, MD 656

Historical Society of Cheshire County, Keene, NH 890

Historical Society of Columbia County, Saint Helens, OR 1234

The Historical Society of Dauphin County, Harrisburg, PA 1258

Historical Society of Delaware, Wilmington, DE 274

Historical Society of Fort Washington, Fort Washington, PA 1254

Historical Society of Garden County, Oshkosh, NE 871

Historical Society of Glastonbury, Glastonbury, CT 242

Historical Society of Greater Port Jefferson, Port Jefferson, NY 1053

Historical Society of Haddonfield, Haddonfield, NJ 905

Historical Society of Kent County, Inc., Chestertown, MD 640

Historical Society of Middletown and the Wallkill Precinct, Inc., Middletown, NY 1014

Historical Society of Millersburg & Upper Paxton Township Museum, Millersburg, PA 1272

Historical Society of Newburgh Bay & the Highlands - David Crawford House, Newburgh, NY 1042

Historical Society of Old Newbury, Cushing House Museum, Newburyport, MA 698

Historical Society of Old Yarmouth, Yarmouth Port, MA 722

Historical Society of Princeton, Princeton, NJ 921

Historical Society of Quaker Hill & Pawling, Pawling, NY 1051

Historical Society of Quincy and Adams County, Quincy, IL 452

Historical Society of Santuit and Cotuit, Cotuit, MA 677

Historical Society of Saratoga Springs, Saratoga Springs, NY 1064

Historical Society of Stanton County Museums at Stanton and Pilger, Pilger, NE 872

Historical Society of Talbot County, Easton, MD 642

Historical Society of the Cocalico Valley, Ephrata, PA 1252

Historical Society of the Tonawandas, Inc., Tonawanda, NY 1078

Historical Society of the Town of Clarence, Clarence, NY 978

Historical Society of the Town of Greenwich Inc. aka Bush-Holley Historic Site, Cos Cob, CT 237

The Historical Society of the Town of Warwick, Warwick, NY 1082

The Historical Society of Trappe, Collegeville, Perkiomen Valley, Inc., Trappe, PA 1303

Historical Society of Walden & Wallkill Valley, Walden, NY 1081

Historical Society of Wells and Ogunquit, Wells, ME 625

The History Center, Fort Wayne, IN 477

The History Museum, Lake Placid-North Elba Historical Society, Lake Placid, NY 1009

Hiwan Homestead Museum, Evergreen, CO 215

Hixon House, La Crosse, WI 1603

Hoard Historical Museum and National Dairy Shrine's Visitors Center, Fort Atkinson, WI 1598

Hobart Historical Society Museum, Hobart, IN 480

Hodgden House Museum Complex, Ellsworth, KS 538

Hofwyl-Broadfield Plantation State Historic Site, Brunswick, GA 366

Hoiles-Davis Museum, Greenville, IL 439

Holland Historical Society Museum, Inc., Holland, VT 1480

The Holland Land Office Museum, Batavia, NY 960

The Holland Museum, Holland, MI 746

Hollenberg Station State Historic Site, Hanover, KS 543

Holly History Center & Hutchinson House Museum, Waupaca, WI 1626

Hollywood Heritage Museum, Hollywood, CA 103

Holmes County Historical Society, Millersburg, OH 1176

Holy Trinity (Old Swedes) Church & Hendrickson House Museum, Wilmington, DE 274

Home of Franklin D. Roosevelt National Historic Site, Hyde Park, NY 1002

Home of Stone (The Mueller-Schmidt House 1881), a Ford County Museum, curated by Ford County Historic Society, Dodge City, KS 537

Home Sweet Home Museum, East Hampton, NY 986

Homestead Acre and the Hill-Palmer House, Chatsworth, CA 82

Homestead National Monument of America, Beatrice, NE 857

Homewood House Museum, Baltimore, MD 633

Honolulu House Museum, Marshall, MI 754

Hoover Historical Center, North Canton, OH 1179

Hope Historical Society, Hope, NJ 908

Hope Lodge and Mather Mill, Fort Washington, PA 1254

Hopsewee Plantation, Georgetown, SC 1333

Horatio Colony House Museum & Nature Preserve, Keene, NH 890

Horridge House, Vinton, IA 529

Hose 5 Fire Museum, Bangor, ME 604

Hot Spring County Museum - The Boyle House/1876 Log Cabin, Malvern, AR 63

Hot Springs National Park Visitor Center, Hot Springs, AR 60

Hotel de Paris Museum, Georgetown, CO ...219

House in the Horseshoe State Historic Site, Sanford, NC 1119

House of Refuge Museum, Stuart, FL 346

The House of the Seven Gables, Salem, MA 706

House of Wickersham State Historical Site, Juneau, AK 25

House with the Eye Museum, Leadville, CO 226

Houston Fire Museum, Houston, TX 1427

Houston Museum of Decorative Arts, Chattanooga, TN 1362

Howard County Historical Society, Ellicott City, MD 643

Howard-Dickinson House Museum, Henderson, TX 1424

Howard Steamboat Museum and Mansion, Jeffersonville, IN 486

Howell Historical Society & Committee Museum, Howell, NJ 908

Howland House, Plymouth, MA 703

The Hoyt Institute of Fine Arts, New Castle, PA 1273

Hoyt Sherman Place, Des Moines, IA 514

The Hubbard Museum of the American West, Ruidoso Downs, NM 946

Hubbell Trading Post National Historic Site, Ganado, AZ 34

Huddleston Farmhouse Inn Museum, Cambridge City, IN 471

Hudson Library and Historical Society, Hudson, OH 1168

The Hudson River Museum, Yonkers, NY.1087

*Historic Houses and Historic
Buildings–Continued*

Huerfano County Historical Society,
    including The Walsenburg Mining
    Museum & Ft. Francisco Museum of
    La Veta, Walsenburg, CO 234
Hugh Mercer Apothecary Shop,
    Fredericksburg, VA 1506
The Huguenot Historical Society, New
    Paltz, NY 1017
Hui No'eau Visual Arts Center,
    Makawao, Maui, HI 401
Hulihee Palace, Kailua-Kona, HI.................399
Hull Lifesaving Museum Inc., the
    Museum of Boston Harbor Heritage,
    Hull, MA 687
Humboldt Historical Museum, Humboldt,
    KS 544
Humpback Rocks Mountain Farm &
    Visitor Center, Waynesboro, VA 1544
Hunt-Morgan House, Lexington, KY 573
Hunter-Dawson State Historic Site, New
    Madrid, MO 828
Hunter House Victorian Museum,
    Norfolk, VA 1522
Hunter Museum of American Art,
    Chattanooga, TN 1362
Hunterdon Museum of Art, Clinton, NJ 901
Huntington Sewing & Trade School,
    Huntington, NY 1001
Huron City Museums, Port Austin, MI 761
Hurricane Valley Heritage Park Museum,
    Hurricane, UT 1466
Hutchinson County Museum, Borger, TX ..1397
The Hyde Collection, Glens Falls, NY 994
Hyde Hall, Inc., Cooperstown, NY 980
The Hyland House, Guilford, CT 243
Hyser Rivers Museum, Belmont, MI 728

Illinois Railway Museum, Union, IL 461
Immaculate Conception Catholic Church,
    Natchitoches, LA 593
Imperial Calcasieu Museum, Inc., Lake
    Charles, LA 590
Independence National Historical Park,
    Philadelphia, PA 1281
Indian King Tavern Museum,
    Haddonfield, NJ 906
Indian Pay Station Museum, Saint Marys,
    KS 557
Indiana Medical History Museum,
    Indianapolis, IN 484
Indiana State Museum, Indianapolis, IN 484
International Museum of Surgical
    Science, Chicago, IL 422
International Tennis Hall of Fame &
    Museum, Newport, RI 1313
Iolani Palace, Honolulu, HI 396
Iosco County Historical Museum, East
    Tawas, MI 740
Iowa Department of Natural Resources,
    Des Moines, IA 515
Ipswich Historical Society and Museum,
    Ipswich, MA 688
Iredell Museum of Arts & Heritage,
    Statesville, NC 1120
Iron & Steel Museum of Alabama,
    Tannehill Ironworks Historical State
    Park, McCalla, AL 13
Ironwood Area Historical Museum,
    Ironwood, MI 747
Iroquois County Historical Society,
    Watseka, IL 463
Isaac Farrar Mansion, Bangor, ME.............604
Isaac Winslow House, Marshfield, MA 693
Isabella Stewart Gardner Museum,
    Boston, MA 666
Isanti County Historical Society,
    Cambridge, MN 770
Ischua Valley Historical Society, Inc.,
    Franklinville, NY 992
Isle of Wight Courthouse, Smithfield, VA ..1536

Isle Royale National Park, Houghton, MI....747
Islesboro Historical Society, Islesboro,
    ME 612
Issaquah History Museum, Issaquah, WA ..1557
Itasca County Historical Society, Grand
    Rapids, MN 777
Ivy Green, Birthplace of Helen Keller,
    Tuscumbia, AL 20

J.E. Reeves Home & Museum, Dover,
    OH 1163
J.W. Parmley Historical Home Society,
    Ipswich, SD 1349
Jacinto Foundation, Inc., Corinth, MS.........800
Jackson County Historical Museum,
    Lakefield, MN 778
Jackson County Historical Society, Black
    River Falls, WI 1592
Jackson-Washabaugh Historical Museum,
    Kadoka, SD 1349
Jacksonport State Park, Jacksonport, AR 60
Jackson's Mill Historic Area, Weston,
    WV 1587
Jacksonville Fire Museum, Jacksonville,
    FL 314
Jacob Hamblin Home, Santa Clara, UT 1474
Jacob Kelley House Museum, Hartsville,
    SC 1335
Jail Museum, Neligh, NE 869
James A. Garfield National Historic Site,
    Mentor, OH 1176
James Buchanan Foundation for the
    Preservation of Wheatland, Lancaster,
    PA 1266
The James Dunklin House, Laurens, SC....1336
James J. Hill House, Saint Paul, MN...........790
James K. Polk Ancestral Home,
    Columbia, TN 1364
James Madison's Montpelier, Montpelier
    Station, VA 1518
James Mitchell Varnum House and
    Museum, East Greenwich, RI 1311
James W. Dillon House Museum, Dillon,
    SC 1331
James Whitcomb Riley Birthplace &
    Museum, Greenfield, IN 480
James Whitcomb Riley Museum Home,
    Indianapolis, IN 485
Jamestown Museum, Jamestown, RI 1312
Jane Addams Hull-House Museum,
    University of Illinois Chicago,
    Chicago, IL 422
Jarrell Plantation Georgia State Historic
    Site, Juliette, GA 374
Jean P. Haydon Museum, Pago Pago, AS ..1640
Jefferson Barracks Historic Site, Saint
    Louis, MO 833
The Jefferson County Historical Assoc.,
    Steubenville, OH 1186
Jefferson County Historical Society,
    Watertown, NY 1083
Jefferson County Historical Society, Inc.,
    Madison, IN 489
Jefferson Historical Society and Museum,
    Jefferson, TX 1431
Jefferson Landing State Historic Site,
    Jefferson City, MO 819
Jefferson National Expansion Memorial,
    Saint Louis, MO 833
Jefferson Patterson Park & Museum,
    Saint Leonard, MD 651
Jekyll Island Museum, Jekyll Island, GA 374
Jemez State Monument, Jemez Springs,
    NM 940
Jenkins Plantation Museum, Lesage, WV ..1584
Jennings-Brown House Female Academy,
    Bennettsville, SC 1322
Jericho Historical Society, Jericho
    Corners, VT 1480
Jesse James Bank Museum, Liberty, MO 826
Jesse James Farm & Museum, Kearney,
    MO 823

Jesse James Home Museum, Saint
    Joseph, MO 830
The Jewish Museum, New York, NY.........1029
Jewish Museum of Florida, Miami
    Beach, FL 326
Jewish Museum of Maryland, Baltimore,
    MD 633
Jim Thorpe Home, Yale, OK 1217
John A. Logan College Museum,
    Carterville, IL 416
John and Mable Ringling Museum of Art,
    Sarasota, FL 344
John Brown Farm State Historic Site,
    Lake Placid, NY 1009
John Brown Museum State Historic Site,
    Osawatomie, KS 554
John Burroughs Association, Inc., West
    Park, NY 1085
John Deere Historic Site, Dixon, IL 431
John Fitzgerald Kennedy National
    Historic Site, Brookline, MA 671
John G. Neihardt State Historic Site,
    Bancroft, NE 856
John G. Voigt House, Plymouth, WI 1618
John James Audubon Center at Mill
    Grove, Audubon, PA 1241
John James Audubon Museum,
    Henderson, KY 571
John Jay French House, Beaumont
    Heritage Society, Beaumont, TX 1395
John Jay Homestead State Historic Site,
    Katonah, NY 1006
John Michael Kohler Arts Center,
    Sheboygan, WI 1621
John Nance Garner Museum, Uvalde, TX .1457
The John Nicholas Brown Center for the
    Study of American Civilization,
    Providence, RI 1317
John Paul Jones House Museum,
    Portsmouth, NH 894
John R. Jackson House, Winlock, WA 1578
John Rains House, Rancho Cucamonga,
    CA 145
John Rivers Communications Museum,
    Charleston, SC 1325
John S. Barry Historical Society,
    Constantine, MI 732
John Slade Ely House, New Haven, CT 253
John Stark Edwards House, Warren, OH ...1189
John Sydnor's 1847 Powhatan House,
    Galveston, TX 1421
John Waddey Carter House, Martinsville,
    VA 1516
John Woolman Memorial, Mount Holly,
    NJ 915
John Wornall House Museum, Kansas
    City, MO 821
Johnson County Historical Society,
    Coralville, IA 511
Johnson County Historical Society, Inc.,
    Tecumseh, NE 873
Johnson County Historical Society
    Museum, Warrensburg, MO 840
Johnson Ferry House Museum, Titusville,
    NJ 926
Johnson Hall State Historic Site,
    Johnstown, NY 1005
Johnstown Area Heritage Association,
    Johnstown, PA 1263
Johnstown Flood National Memorial,
    South Fork, PA 1300
Johnstown Historical Society, Johnstown,
    NY 1005
Jonathan Bailey Home, Whittier, CA 198
Jonathan Hager House & Museum,
    Hagerstown, MD 646
Joseph A. Tallman Museum, Cherokee,
    IA 510
Joseph Priestley House, Northumberland,
    PA 1274
Joseph Smith Historic Site, Nauvoo, IL......447
Josiah Quincy House, Quincy, MA 705

Juan Matias Sanchez Adobe, Montebello, CA..............127
The Judah P. Benjamin Confederate Memorial at Gamble Plantation Historic State Park, Ellenton, FL..............306
Judaica Museum of Central Synagogue, New York, NY..............1029
Judy Garland Museum, Grand Rapids, MN..............777
Julian H. Sleeper House, Saint Paul, MN...790
Juliette Gordon Low Birthplace, Savannah, GA..............385
Junction City Historical Society, Junction City, OR..............1226
Juniata County Historical Society, Mifflintown, PA..............1271
Justin Smith Morrill Homestead, Strafford, VT..............1488

Kalamazoo Nature Center, Inc., Kalamazoo, MI..............748
Kalkaska County Historical Museum, Kalkaska, MI..............749
Kaminski House Museum, Georgetown, SC..............1333
Kankakee County Museum, Kankakee, IL...441
Kansas Aviation Museum, Wichita, KS..............562
The Kate Chopin House & Bayou Folk Museum, Cloutierville, LA..............588
Kauai Museum, Lihue, HI..............401
Kaw Mission State Historic Site, Council Grove, KS..............536
Kearney County Historical Museum, Minden, NE..............868
Kearney Mansion Museum, Fresno, CA..............97
The Kearny Cottage, Perth Amboy, NJ..............921
Keeler Tavern Museum, Ridgefield, CT..............259
Kell House Museum, Wichita Falls, TX....1461
Kellogg-Eddy House and Museum, Newington, CT..............256
Kelly-Griggs House Museum, Red Bluff, CA..............146
The Kelso House Museum, Kent, OH..............1169
Kelton House Museum & Garden, Columbus, OH..............1158
The Kemp-McCarthy Memorial Museum of the Rowe Historical Society, Inc., Rowe, MA..............706
Kennebunkport Historical Society, Kennebunkport, ME..............612
Kennedy Museum of Art, Athens, OH..............1140
Kensington Mansion, Eastover, SC..............1332
Kent-Delord House Museum, Plattsburgh, NY..............1052
Kent Plantation House, Alexandria, LA..............585
Kentucky Historical Society, Frankfort, KY..............569
The Kentucky Library & Museum, Bowling Green, KY..............565
Kentucky Military History Museum, Frankfort, KY..............569
Kentucky State Capitol, Frankfort, KY..............569
Ker Place, Onancock, VA..............1523
Kerbyville Museum, Kerby, OR..............1227
Kern County Museum, Bakersfield, CA..............73
Kershaw County Historical Society, Camden, SC..............1323
Kewaunee County Historical Museum, Kewaunee, WI..............1602
Keweenaw County Historical Society, Eagle Harbor, MI..............739
Key West Lighthouse Museum, Key West, FL..............318
Key West Museum of Art and History, Key West, FL..............318
Keystone Area Historical Society, Keystone, SD..............1350
Kimball House Museum, Battle Creek, MI..............727
Kimberly Crest House & Gardens, Redlands, CA..............147
Kimble County Historical Museum, Junction, TX..............1431

King Kamehameha V-Judiciary History Center, Honolulu, HI..............397
Kingman County Historical Museum, Kingman, KS..............547
Kingman Tavern Historical Museum, Cummington, MA..............678
Kings Mountain National Military Park, Blacksburg, SC..............1322
Kingsburg Historical Park, Kingsburg, CA..............105
Kingsley Plantation, Jacksonville, FL..............315
Kirkland Arts Center, Kirkland, WA..............1557
Kit Carson Home & Museum, Inc., Taos, NM..............952
Kitsap County Historical Society Museum, Bremerton, WA..............1549
Klickitat County Historical Society, Goldendale, WA..............1555
Klondike Gold Rush National Historical Park, Seattle, WA..............1566
Knott House Museum, Tallahassee, FL..............347
Knox Headquarters State Historic Site, Vails Gate, NY..............1080
Knox House Museum, El Cajon, CA..............92
Knudt Salle Log Cabin, Adams, ND..............1127
Koester House Museum, Marysville, KS..............552
Koreshan State Historic Site, Estero, FL..............306
Korner's Folly, Kernersville, NC..............1108
Kruse House Museum, West Chicago, IL....464
Kuhlmann King Historical House and Museum, Boerne, TX..............1396
Kuser Farm Mansion, Hamilton, NJ..............907

L.C. Bates Museum, Hinckley, ME..............612
La Miranda, Monterey, CA..............127
La Puente Valley Historical Society City Hall, LaPuente, CA..............107
La Purisima Mission State Historic Park, Lompoc, CA..............109
Lacey Historical Society, Forked River, NJ..............904
Ladew Topiary Gardens, Monkton, MD..............649
Lafayette Miners Museum, Lafayette, CO...224
Lagrange County Historical Society, Inc., Lagrange, IN..............488
LaGrange Plantation, Cambridge, MD..............639
Lahaina Restoration Foundation, Lahaina, HI..............400
Lake City Columbia County Historical Museum, Inc., Lake City, FL..............319
Lake County Historic Courthouse Museum, Lakeport, CA..............108
Lake County Historical Society, Kirtland Hills, OH..............1170
Lake Guernsey Museum-Guernsey State Park, Guernsey, WY..............1634
Lake Hopatcong Historical Museum, Landing, NJ..............909
Lake of the Red Cedars Museum, Cedar Lake, IN..............472
Lake Shore Railway Museum, North East, PA..............1274
Lake Waccamaw Depot Museum, Lake Waccamaw, NC..............1109
Lake Wales Depot Museum & Cultural Center, Lake Wales, FL..............320
Lakewood's Heritage Center, Lakewood, CO..............225
LaMoure County Museum, Grand Rapids, ND..............1132
Lancaster Historical Society, Lancaster, NH..............890
Land of the Yankee Fork Historic Association Museum, Stanley, ID..............410
The Landmark Society of Western New York, Rochester, NY..............1058
Landmarks Foundation/Old Alabama Town, Montgomery, AL..............16
Lane House, Roseburg, OR..............1234
Lane Place, Crawfordsville, IN..............473
Langlade County Historical Society Museum, Antigo, WI..............1589

Lanier Mansion State Historic Site, Madison, IN..............489
Lansing Manor House Museum, North Blenheim, NY..............1043
Lanterman House, La Canada Flintridge, CA..............105
Lapham-Patterson House, Thomasville, GA..............388
The LaPointe-Krebs House & Old Spanish Fort Museum, Pascagoula, MS..............807
Laramie Plains Museum, Laramie, WY..............1635
Laredo Children's Museum, Laredo, TX..............1434
Lars Noak Blacksmith Shop, Larsson/Ostlund Log Home & One-Room Capitol School, New Sweden, ME..............616
Las Cabezas de San Juan Nature Reserve (El Faro), Fajardo, PR..............1641
Lathrop House, Redwood City, CA..............147
Laura Ingalls Wilder Park & Museum, Inc., Burr Oak, IA..............507
The Laurel Museum, Laurel, MD..............648
Laurence C. Jones Museum, Piney Woods, MS..............807
Lawrence Heritage State Park, Lawrence, MA..............689
Lawrence History Center: Immigrant City Archives & Museum, Lawrence, MA..............689
Le Sault de Sainte Marie Historical Sites, Inc., Sault Ste. Marie, MI..............764
Leaming's Run Garden & Colonial Farm, Swainton, NJ..............926
Leander J. McCormick Observatory, Charlottesville, VA..............1499
Lee Chapel and Museum, Lexington, VA..1513
Lee-Fendall House Museum and Garden, Alexandria, VA..............1493
Lee Hall Mansion, Newport News, VA..............1519
Lefferts Historic House, Brooklyn, NY..............969
The Leffingwell House Museum, Norwich, CT..............258
Lehigh County Historical Society, Allentown, PA..............1239
The Lemee House, Natchitoches, LA..............593
Lemon Hill Mansion, Philadelphia, PA..............1282
LeMoyne Art Foundation, Inc., Tallahassee, FL..............347
Lesueur County Historical Museum-Chapter 1, Elysian, MN..............774
Leverett Historical Society, Leverett, MA..............689
Levi Coffin House, Fountain City, IN..............478
Lewes Historical Society, Lewes, DE..............271
Lewis County Historical Museum, Chehalis, WA..............1550
Lewis County Historical Society Museum, Lowville, NY..............1012
Lewis Ginter Botanical Garden, Richmond, VA..............1530
Lexington County Museum, Lexington, SC..............1336
Lexington Historical Society, Lexington, MA..............689
Liberty County Museum, Chester, MT..............844
Liberty Hall Historic Center, Lamoni, IA...522
Liberty Hall Historic Site, Frankfort, KY....569
Liberty Hall Museum, Union, NJ..............928
Liberty Jail Historic Site, Liberty, MO..............826
Libertyville-Mundelein Historical Society, Inc., Libertyville, IL..............442
Library of Congress, Washington, DC..............282
Licking County Historical Society, Newark, OH..............1178
Light Crust Doughboys Hall of Fame & Museum - Governor Jim Hogg City Park, Quitman, TX..............1444
Lightner Museum, Saint Augustine, FL..............339
Lilacia Park-Lombard Park District, Lombard, IL..............443
Lillian and Albert Small Jewish Museum, Washington, DC..............282

Historic Houses and Historic Buildings—Continued

Limberlost State Historic Site, Geneva, IN 479

Lincoln Boyhood National Memorial, Lincoln City, IN.................................488

Lincoln County Historical Society, Lincoln, KS.................................549

Lincoln County Historical Society, North Platte, NE.................................869

Lincoln County Historical Society Museum of Pioneer History, Chandler, OK.................................1197

Lincoln County Museum, Hugo, CO...........222

Lincoln Herdon Law Offices State Historic Site, Springfield, IL.................................458

Lincoln Home National Historic Site, Springfield, IL.................................459

Lincoln Log Cabin State Historic Site, Lerna, IL.................................442

Lincoln Parish Museum & Historical Society, Ruston, LA 600

Lincoln Park Historical Museum, Lincoln Park, MI.................................751

The Lincoln-Tallman Restorations, Janesville, WI.................................1601

Lincoln Tomb State Historic Site, Springfield, IL.................................459

Linn County Historical Museum and Moyer House, Brownsville, OR...........1220

Lisbon Historical Society, Lisbon, OH.......1172

Lisle Station Museum, Lisle, IL 443

The Little Brick House, Vandalia, IL 462

Little Compton Historical Society, Little Compton, RI 1312

Little Falls Historical Society Museum, Little Falls, NY.................................1009

Little Log Church & Museum, Yachats, OR.................................1238

Little Red School House Museum, Weyauwega, WI.................................1628

Little Red Schoolhouse-Living Library, Beloit, KS 534

Little Traverse Historical Society, Petoskey, MI.................................760

Little White House Historic Site, Warm Springs, GA.................................390

Little White Schoolhouse, Ripon, WI.........1620

Littleton Historical Museum, Littleton, CO.................................227

Livingston Depot Center, Livingston, MT ...850

Lock Museum of America, Inc., Terryville, CT 262

Lockehaven Schoolhouse Museum, Enfield, NH.................................887

Lockwood-Mathews Mansion Museum, Norwalk, CT 257

Locust Creek Covered Bridge State Historic Site, Laclede, MO.................825

Locust Grove, Louisville, KY.................577

Locust Grove, The Samuel Morse Historic Site, Poughkeepsie, NY 1055

Locust Lawn and Terwilliger House, Gardiner, NY 993

Log Cabin Village, Fort Worth, TX...........1417

The Log House Museum of the Historical Society of Columbiana-Fairfield Township, Columbiana, OH.................1157

Logan County Historical Society Museum, Bellefontaine, OH.................1142

Logan County Museum, Paris, AR.................65

Loghurst Farm Museum, Canfield, OH......1145

Lombard Historical Museum, Lombard, IL.................................443

Lompoc Museum, Lompoc, CA 109

Lompoc Valley Historical Society, Inc., Lompoc, CA.................................110

Long Branch Historical Museum, Long Branch, NJ.................................910

Long Island Culture History Lab & Museum, Commack, NY.................980

Long Island Museum of American Art, History & Carriages, Stony Brook, NY.................................1075

Longfellow Evangeline State Historic Site, Saint Martinville, LA.................600

Longfellow National Historic Site, Cambridge, MA.................................673

Longfellow's Wayside Inn, Sudbury, MA 714

Longstreet Farm, Holmdel, NJ.................908

Longue Vue House & Gardens, New Orleans, LA.................................596

Longyear Museum, Chestnut Hill, MA 675

Lorenzo State Historic Site, Cazenovia, NY.................................976

Loriks Peterson Heritage House, Oldham, SD.................................1352

Los Altos History Museum aka Association of the Los Altos Historical Museum, Los Altos, CA.................112

The Los Angeles County Arboretum & Botanic Garden, Arcadia, CA.................71

Los Angeles Maritime Museum, San Pedro, CA 176

Los Angeles Municipal Art Gallery - Barnsdall Art Park, Los Angeles, CA......118

Los Nogales Museum, Seguin, TX.................1452

Lost River State Park, Mathias, WV 1584

Louise Wells Cameron Art Museum, Wilmington, NC.................................1123

Louisiana State Exhibit Museum, Shreveport, LA.................................600

Louisiana State Museum, New Orleans, LA.................................596

Louisiana State Oil & Gas Museum, Oil City, LA.................................599

Louisiana's Old State Capitol, Political History Museum, Baton Rouge, LA.........587

Louisville Science Center, Louisville, KY ...577

Louisville Visual Art Association, Louisville, KY.................................578

Lowell Area Historical Museum, Lowell, MI.................................751

Lowell Damon House, Wauwatosa, WI......1626

Lowell's Boat Shop, Amesbury, MA...........658

Lower Cape Fear Historical Society, Inc., Wilmington, NC.................................1123

Lower East Side Tenement Museum, New York, NY.................................1029

Lower Hudson Conference of Historical Agencies and Museums, Elmsford, NY.................................988

Loxahatchee River Historical Society, Jupiter, FL.................................316

Luckhard Museum - The Indian Mission, Sebewaing, MI.................................764

Lucy Craft Laney Museum of Black History and Conference Center, Augusta, GA.................................365

Ludwig Welk Farmstead, Strasburg, ND....1136

Luis Munoz Rivera Library & Museum, Barranquitas, PR.................................1641

Lum & Abner Museum & Jot 'Em Down Store, Pine Ridge, AR.................................66

Lummis Home: El Alisal, Los Angeles, CA.................................119

Luther Burbank Home & Gardens, Santa Rosa, CA.................................184

The Lyceum, Alexandria's History Museum, Alexandria, VA.................1493

Lyman Allyn Art Museum, New London, CT.................................255

Lyman Estate, The Vale, Waltham, MA.......715

Lyman Museum, Hilo, HI.................................393

Lyndhurst, Tarrytown, NY.................................1078

Lyndon B. Johnson National Historical Park, Johnson City, TX.................1431

Lyndon House Art, Athens, GA.................356

Lynnhaven House, Virginia Beach, VA 1542

The Lyons Redstone Museum, Lyons, CO...227

Mabee Farm Historic Site, Rotterdam Junction, NY.................................1062

Mabel Hartzell Historical Home, Alliance, OH.................................1139

Mabry-Hazen House, Knoxville, TN..........1371

Macartney House Museum, Oakland, ME ...616

Macculloch Hall Historical Museum & Gardens, Morristown, NJ.................913

Macedon Historical Society, Inc., Macedon, NY.................................1012

MacGregor Ranch, Estes Park, CO 215

Mackinac Island State Park Commission-Mackinac State Historic Parks, Mackinaw City, MI.................752

Mackinac State Historic Parks-Fort Mackinac & Mackinac Island State Park, Mackinac Island, MI.................752

Macktown Living History Education Center, Inc., Rockton, IL.................456

The Madam Brett Homestead, Beacon, NY.................................961

Madison County Historical Museum & Archival Library, Edwardsville, IL.........432

Madison County Historical Society, Winterset, IA.................................531

Madison County Historical Society-Cottage Lawn, Oneida, NY...1045

Madison Historical Society, Madison, CT....247

Madison-Morgan Cultural Center, Madison, GA.................................378

Magevney House, Memphis, TN.................1373

Maggie L. Walker National Historic Site, Richmond, VA.................................1530

Magnolia Grove-Historic House Museum, Greensboro, AL.................................10

Magnolia Manor, Cairo, IL.................................415

Magoffin Home State Historic Site, El Paso, TX.................................1412

Mahaffie Stagecoach Stop and Farm, Olathe, KS.................................554

Maine Historical Society, Portland, ME.......619

Maitland Historical Museums, Maitland, FL.................................322

The Major General Frederick Funston Boyhood Home and Museum, Iola, KS.................................546

Major John Bradford House, Kingston, MA.................................688

Makoti Threshers' Museum, Makoti, ND...1133

Malabar Farm State Park, Lucas, OH.........1173

Malheur Historical Project, Stonehouse Museum, Vale, OR 1238

Malibu Lagoon Museum, Malibu, CA 123

Mallory-Neely House, Memphis, TN.........1373

Mamie Doud Eisenhower Birthplace, Boone, IA.................................506

Mandeville Gallery, Union College, Schenectady, NY 1067

Manistee County Historical Museum, Manistee, MI.................................753

Mansfield Historical Society Museum, Storrs, CT.................................261

Mansfield State Historic Site - Civil War Battlefield, Mansfield, LA.................591

Mansfield Township Historical Society (1849 Georgetown School/Museum), Columbus, NJ.................................902

Manship House Museum, Jackson, MS.......802

Maple Valley Historical Museum, Maple Valley, WA.................................1559

Marathon County Historical Society, Wausau, WI.................................1626

Marblehead Arts Association - King Hooper Mansion, Marblehead, MA.........693

Marcella Sembrich Opera Museum, Bolton Landing, NY.................................963

Mardi Gras Museum, Biloxi, MS.................798

The Margaret Mitchell House & Museum, Atlanta, GA.................................361

Marianna-Lee County Museum Assoc. Inc., Marianna, AR.................................64

Marietta House Museum, Glenn Dale, MD.................................645

Marietta Museum of History, Marietta, GA.................................379

Marin History Museum, San Rafael, CA 177

Marinette County Historical Museum,
Marinette, WI................1607

Marion Historical Museums, Inc. -
Granger House, Marion, IA 523

Marion Public Library Museum, Marion,
IN................490

Marjorie Kinnan Rawlings Historic State
Park, Cross Creek, FL..................301

Mark Twain Birthplace State Historic
Site, Florida, MO................815

Mark Twain Home and Museum,
Hannibal, MO................816

The Mark Twain House & Museum,
Hartford, CT..................245

Marlboro County Historical Museum,
Bennettsville, SC..................1322

Marlboro Historical Society, Marlboro,
VT................1481

Marquette County Historical Society,
Westfield, WI..................1627

Marrett House, Standish, ME................623

Marshall Center School, Cedar Falls, IA 508

Marshall County Historical Museum,
Holly Springs, MS..................801

Marshall County Historical Society
Museum, Warren, MN................795

Marshall Gold Discovery State Historic
Park, Coloma, CA................86

The Marston House/San Diego Historical
Society, San Diego, CA 157

Martha A. Parsons House Museum,
Enfield, CT..................239

Martha's Vineyard Museum, Edgartown,
MA................681

Martin County Historical Museum,
Stanton, TX..................1453

Martin Luther King, Jr. Center for
Nonviolent Social Change, Inc.,
Atlanta, GA..................361

Martin Luther King, Jr. National Historic
Site and Preservation District, Atlanta,
GA..................361

Martin Van Buren National Historic Site,
Kinderhook, NY..................1007

Marvin Newton House, Brookfield, VT 1477

Mary Aaron Memorial Museum,
Marysville, CA..................125

The Mary Baker Eddy Library for the
Betterment of Humanity, Boston, MA.....666

Mary Ball Washington Museum &
Library, Inc., Lancaster, VA..................1512

Mary McLeod Bethune Council House
National Historic Site, Washington,
DC..................283

Mary Todd Lincoln House, Lexington,
KY..................574

Mary Washington House, Fredericksburg,
VA..................1507

Maryhill Museum of Art, Goldendale,
WA..................1556

Maryland Historical Society, Baltimore,
MD..................634

The Maryland Institute, College of Art:
Decker, Meyerhoff and Pinkard
Galleries, Baltimore, MD..................634

The Maryland Zoo in Baltimore,
Baltimore, MD..................635

Mason County Historical Society/Historic
White Pine Village, Ludington, MI 751

Mason County Museum, Mason, TX 1437

The Masonic Library and Museum of
Pennsylvania, Philadelphia, PA..................1283

Massee Lane Gardens, Home of
American Camellia Society, Fort
Valley, GA..................373

Matagorda County Museum, Bay City,
TX..................1393

Matchless Mine Museum (Leadville
Assembly), Leadville, CO..................226

The Mather Homestead Museum, Library
and Memorial Park, Wellsville, NY 1084

Mathias Ham House Historic Site,
Dubuque, IA..................516

Mattapoisett Museum and Carriage
House, Mattapoisett, MA..................693

Matthews Museum of Maine Heritage,
Union, ME..................624

Matt's Museum, Lawtell, LA..................590

Maude I. Kerns Art Center, Eugene, OR ...1223

May Museum & Farmville Heritage
Center, Farmville, NC..................1100

Mayflower Society Museum, Plymouth,
MA..................703

Maymont, Richmond, VA..................1530

Mayville Historical Society, Inc.,
Mayville, WI..................1608

Mazomanie Historical Society,
Mazomanie, WI..................1608

Mc Cook County Historical Society and
Museum, Salem, SD..................1355

McAllister House Museum, Colorado
Springs, CO..................207

McCallum Museum, Sibley, IA..................527

McConaghy House, Hayward, CA..................102

McCone County Museum, Circle, MT........844

McConnell Mansion, Moscow, ID..................407

McCook House, Civil War Museum,
Carrollton, OH..................1146

McCoy House, Lewistown, PA..................1269

McCutchen Overland Inn,
McCutchenville, OH..................1175

McDowell House Museum, Danville, KY...567

McFaddin-Ward House, Beaumont, TX 1395

McFarland State Historic Park, Florence,
AZ..................34

McKee Botanical Garden, Vero Beach,
FL..................352

McKinley Birthplace Home, Niles, OH 1179

McLarty Treasure Museum, Vero Beach,
FL..................352

McLean County Historical Society
Museum, Washburn, ND..................1137

McNamara House Museum, Victoria, TX..1457

McPherson Museum & Arts Foundation,
McPherson, KS..................552

Meadow Brook Hall, Rochester, MI............761

Meadow Garden Museum, Augusta, GA......365

Meadowlands Museum, Rutherford, NJ......923

Meagher County Historical Association
Castle Museum, White Sulphur
Springs, MT..................855

Mechanicsburg Museum Association,
Mechanicsburg, PA..................1270

Medina Railroad Museum, Medina, NY 1014

Medora Doll House, Medora, ND..................1134

Meeker County Historical Society
Museum & G.A.R. Hall, Litchfield,
MN..................779

Meeker Home Museum, Greeley, CO..........222

Mellette House, Watertown, SD..................1359

Melrose Plantation Home Complex,
Melrose, LA..................592

The Memorial Day Museum, Waterloo,
NY..................1083

Mendocino Historical Research,
Inc./Kelley House Museum,
Mendocino, CA..................125

Merced County Courthouse Museum,
Merced, CA..................125

Mercer County Historical Museum, The
Riley Home, Celina, OH..................1146

Mercer County Historical Society,
Mercer, PA..................1271

Merchant's House Museum, New York,
NY..................1029

Meriden Historical Society, Inc.,
Meriden, CT..................249

Meridian International Center,
Washington, DC..................283

Meriwether Lewis Dredge Museum,
Brownville, NE..................858

The Merrick Art Gallery, New Brighton,
PA..................1273

Merwin House, Tranquility, Stockbridge,
MA..................712

Metamora Courthouse Historic Site,
Metamora, IL..................444

Meux Home Museum, Fresno, CA..................98

Michel Brouillet House & Museum,
Vincennes, IN..................502

Michie Tavern ca. 1784, Charlottesville,
VA..................1499

Michigan Historical Museum, Michigan
Historical Center, Lansing, MI..................750

Mid-Atlantic Center for the Arts/Emlen
Physick Estate/Cape May Lighthouse,
Cape May, NJ..................900

Middlebury Historical Society, Wyoming,
NY..................1087

Middleton Place Foundation, Charleston,
SC..................1326

Middletown Valley Historical Society,
Middletown, MD..................649

Midland County Historical Society,
Midland, MI..................755

Mifflinburg Buggy Museum Association,
Inc., Mifflinburg, PA..................1271

Milam County Museum and Annex,
Cameron, TX..................1399

Milan Historical Museum, Inc., Milan,
OH..................1176

Milford Historical Museum, Milford, MI.....756

Milford Historical Society, Milford, CT.....250

Milford Museum, Milford, DE..................271

Mill Race Historical Village, Northville,
MI..................758

Millard Fillmore House, East Aurora, NY ...985

Miller-Cory House Museum, Westfield,
NJ..................930

Millerton Courthouse, Friant, CA..................98

Milton House Museum Historic Site,
Milton, WI..................1610

Milwaukee County Historical Society,
Milwaukee, WI..................1611

Minisink Valley Historical Society, Port
Jervis, NY..................1053

Minnesota Historical Society, Saint Paul,
MN..................791

Minnesota Pioneer Park Museum,
Annandale, MN..................767

Minnesota Transportation Museum, Inc.,
Saint Paul, MN..................792

Minute Man National Historical Park,
Concord, MA..................676

Miramont Castle Museum, Manitou
Springs, CO..................228

Mission Bell Museum, Coweta, OK..........1199

The Mission House, Stockbridge, MA..........712

Mission Houses Museum, Honolulu, HI......397

Mission Inn Foundation/Museum,
Riverside, CA..................149

Mission Mill Museum Association,
Salem, OR..................1236

Mission San Antonio de Padua, Jolon,
CA..................105

Mission San Francisco de Asis (Mission
Dolores), San Francisco, CA 167

Mission San Juan Capistrano Museum,
San Juan Capistrano, CA..................173

Mission San Luis Obispo de Tolosa, San
Luis Obispo, CA..................174

Mission San Luis Rey Museum,
Oceanside, CA..................135

Mission San Miguel, San Miguel, CA 175

Missisquoi Valley Historical Society,
North Troy, VT..................1483

Mississippi County Historical Society,
Charleston, MO..................812

Mississippi Governor's Mansion,
Jackson, MS..................802

Mississippi Society Daughters of the
American Revolution Rosalie House
Museum, Natchez, MS..................805

Mississippi University for Women,
Archives and Museum, Columbus, MS...800

Historic Houses and Historic Buildings—Continued

Missouri Botanical Garden, Saint Louis, MO.................834

Missouri State Museum, Jefferson City, MO.................819

Mitchell County Historical Museum, Osage, IA.................526

Moffatt-Ladd House and Garden, Portsmouth, NH.................894

Moland House, Warrington, PA.................1305

Molly Brown House Museum, Denver, CO.................213

The Money Museum-Federal Reserve Bank of Kansas City, Kansas City, MO.................821

The Monhegan Museum, Monhegan, ME....615

Monmouth County Historical Association, Freehold, NJ.................905

Monroe County Heritage Museum, Monroeville, AL.................15

Monroe County Historical Association/Stroud Mansion, Stroudsburg, PA.................1302

Monroe County Historical Museum, Monroe, MI.................756

Monroe Historical Society, Monroe, CT......250

Montalvo Arts Center, Saratoga, CA.................185

Montauk, Clermont, IA.................511

Montauk Point Lighthouse Museum, Montauk, NY.................1015

Montclair Historical Society, Montclair, NJ.................912

Monterey History and Art Association, Monterey, CA.................127

Monterey Museum of Art, Monterey, CA....128

Monterey State Historic Park, Monterey, CA.................128

The Montgomery County Historical Society, Dayton, OH.................1161

The Montgomery County Historical Society, Inc., Rockville, MD.................651

Montgomery Museum & Lewis Miller Regional Art Center, Christiansburg, VA.................1501

Monticello, Home of Thomas Jefferson, Thomas Jefferson Foundation, Inc., Charlottesville, VA.................1499

Montpelier Mansion, Laurel, MD.................648

Montpelier-The General Henry Knox Museum, Thomaston, ME.................624

Montrose County Historical Museum, Montrose, CO.................228

Moody-Bradley House Restoration Foundation, Fairfield, TX.................1413

The Moody Mansion Museum, Galveston, TX.................1421

Moore Home, Lerna, IL.................442

The Moore-Youse Home Museum, Muncie, IN.................492

Moravian Museum of Bethlehem, Inc., Bethlehem, PA.................1242

Mordecai Historic Park, Raleigh, NC.................1115

Morgan Row Museum and Harrodsburg-Mercer County Research Library, Harrodsburg, KY.................570

Mormon Station State Historic Park, Genoa, NV.................877

Morris-Butler House Museum, Indianapolis, IN.................485

Morris County Historical Society (Acorn Hall House Museum), Morristown, NJ ...914

Morris-Jumel Mansion, New York, NY 1030

Morristown National Historical Park, Morristown, NJ.................914

Morton Grove Historical Museum/Haupt-Yehl House, Morton Grove, IL.................446

Morton Homestead, Prospect Park, PA 1295

Morton House Museum, Benton Harbor, MI.................728

Morton Museum of Cooke County, Gainesville, TX.................1420

Morven Museum & Garden, Princeton, NJ.................922

Morven Park, Leesburg, VA.................1512

Moses Myers House, Norfolk, VA.................1522

Moss Mansion Historic House Museum, Billings, MT.................841

Mother Colony House Museum, Anaheim, CA.................71

Motown Historical Museum, Detroit, MI.....737

Mount Clare Museum House, Baltimore, MD.................635

Mount Desert Island Historical Society, Mount Desert, ME.................615

Mount Holly Community Historical Museum, Belmont, VT.................1476

Mount Pleasant Historical Society, Mount Pleasant, OH.................1177

Mount Prospect Historical Society Museums, Mount Prospect, IL.................446

Mt. Pulaski Courthouse State Historic Site, Mount Pulaski, IL.................446

Mount Vernon Hotel Museum & Garden, New York, NY.................1031

Mount Vernon Ladies' Association, Mount Vernon, VA.................1518

Mountain Farm Museum-Great Smoky Mountains National Park, Cherokee, NC.................1096

Mountain Gateway Museum, Old Fort, NC.................1113

The Muchnic Gallery, Atchison, KS.................533

Muckenthaler Cultural Center and Mansion Museum, Fullerton, CA.................99

Mulford Farm, East Hampton, NY.................986

Muller House Museum, San Pedro, CA.................176

The Municipal Art Society of New York, New York, NY.................1031

Munson-Williams-Proctor Arts Institute Museum of Art, Utica, NY.................1079

Murfreesboro Historical Association, Murfreesboro, NC.................1112

Murray-Lindsay Mansion, Lindsay, OK.....1204

Murrell Home, Park Hill, OK.................1211

Muscatine Art Center, Muscatine, IA.................524

Museo Fuerte Conde de Mirasol de Vieques, Vieques, PR.................1644

Museum, Mission San Juan Bautista, San Juan Bautista, CA.................173

Museum of Afro-American History, Boston, MA.................667

The Museum of Early Trades and Crafts, Madison, NJ.................910

The Museum of East Texas, Lufkin, TX....1436

Museum of Florida History, Tallahassee, FL.................348

Museum of History & Art, Ontario, Ontario, CA.................136

Museum of Indian Culture, Allentown, PA.................1239

The Museum of Mobile, Mobile, AL.................14

Museum of Nebraska Art, Kearney, NE.......864

Museum of Northern Arizona, Flagstaff, AZ.................33

Museum of Northwest Colorado, Craig, CO.................208

Museum of Rural Life, Denton, MD.................642

Museum of Small Town Life, Dover, DE....270

Museum of South Texas History, Edinburg, TX.................1410

Museum of the Arkansas Grand Prairie, Stuttgart, AR.................69

Museum of the Bedford Historical Society, Bedford, NY.................961

Museum of the Berkeley Springs, Berkeley Springs, WV.................1580

Museum of the Cape Fear Historical Complex, Fayetteville, NC.................1101

Museum of the Cherokee Strip, Enid, OK.1200

Museum of the City of Lake Worth, Lake Worth, FL.................320

Museum of the Fur Trade, Chadron, NE......859

Museum of the Great Plains, Lawton, OK.1204

Museum of the Puerto Rican Family of the 19th Century, San Juan, PR.................1643

Museum of the Rockies, Bozeman, MT.......842

Museum of the Weston Historical Society, Inc., Weston, MA.................718

Museum of Wildlife, Science & Industry, Webster, SD.................1359

Museum on Main: A History Museum for West Georgia, LaGrange, GA.................375

The Museums of Oglebay Institute - Mansion Museum & Glass Museum, Wheeling, WV.................1588

Muskegon County Museum, Muskegon, MI.................757

My Old Kentucky Home State Park, Bardstown, KY.................564

Mystic Arts Center, Mystic, CT.................250

NAU Art Museum, Flagstaff, AZ.................33

Nantucket Historical Association, Nantucket, MA.................696

Nantucket Maria Mitchell Association, Nantucket, MA.................696

Naomi Wood Collection at Woodford Mansion, Philadelphia, PA.................1284

Naper Settlement, Naperville, IL.................447

Narcissa Prentiss House, Prattsburgh, NY .1055

Narragansett Historical Society, Templeton, MA.................714

Nashville Zoo at Grassmere, Nashville, TN.................1379

Nassau County, Division of Museum Services, Department of Recreation, Parks & Museums, East Meadow, NY....987

Nassau County Museum of Art, Roslyn Harbor, NY.................1062

Nathan Denison Advocates, Forty Fort, PA.................1254

Nathaniel W. Faison Home and Museum, La Grange, TX.................1432

National Academy Museum and School of Fine Arts, New York, NY.................1033

National Apple Museum, Biglerville, PA ...1243

National Arts Club, New York, NY.................1034

National Building Museum, Washington, DC.................284

National Canal Museum, Hugh Moore Historical Park and Museums, Easton, PA.................1250

National Czech & Slovak Museum & Library, Cedar Rapids, IA.................509

National Heisey Glass Museum, Newark, OH.................1178

National Hispanic Cultural Center, Art Museum, Albuquerque, NM.................935

National Museum of American Illustration, Newport, RI.................1314

National Museum of Natural History, Washington, DC.................286

National New York Central Railroad Museum, Elkhart, IN.................475

National Postal Museum, Smithsonian Institution, Washington, DC.................287

National Railroad Museum and Hall of Fame, Inc., Hamlet, NC.................1105

National Temple Hill Association, Inc., New Windsor, NY.................1018

National Women's Hall of Fame, Seneca Falls, NY.................1068

National World War I Museum at Liberty Memorial, Kansas City, MO.................822

Native American Resource Center, Pembroke, NC.................1114

Natural History Museum, Portales, NM......944

Natural History Museum of Los Angeles County, Los Angeles, CA.................120

Naugatuck Historical Society, Naugatuck, CT.................251

Naumkeag, Stockbridge, MA.................712

Nauvoo Historical Society Museum, Nauvoo, IL.................447

Naval War College Museum, Newport, RI 1314
Navarro County Historical Society, Pioneer Village, Corsicana, TX 1402
Nebraska State Historical Society's Thomas P. Kennard House, Lincoln, NE 867
Neenah Historical Society, Hiram Smith, Neenah's Heritage Park, Octagon House & Ward House, Neenah, WI 1614
Neill-Cochran Museum House, Austin, TX 1391
Neill Museum, Fort Davis, TX 1414
Neligh Mills, Neligh, NE 869
Nelson Pioneer Farm and Museum, Oskaloosa, IA 526
Nemours Mansion and Gardens, Wilmington, DE.....................274
Netherland Inn House Museum & Boatyard Complex, Kingsport, TN 1368
Nevada County Historical Society, Inc., Nevada City, CA 130
Nevada State Museum, Carson City, NV 876
Neversink Valley Area Museum, Cuddebackville, NY 984
New Almaden Quicksilver Mining Museum, San Jose, CA 172
The New Berlin Historical Society, New Berlin, WI.........................1614
New Braunfels Conservation Society, New Braunfels, TX 1440
New Castle Historical Society, New Castle, DE.......................272
New Castle Historical Society - Horace Greeley House, Chappaqua, NY 977
New England Quilt Museum, Lowell, MA 692
New England Wireless & Steam Museum Inc., East Greenwich, RI 1311
New Hampshire Farm Museum, Inc., Milton, NH 892
New Harmony State Historic Site/Historic New Harmony, New Harmony, IN 494
New Haven Colony Historical Society, New Haven, CT.......................253
New Jersey Botanical Garden at Skylands (NJBG), Ringwood, NJ 923
New Jersey Office of Historic Sites, Trenton, NJ 927
New Jersey State House, Trenton, NJ 927
New London County Historical Society, New London, CT.........................255
The New Milford Historical Society, New Milford, CT.......................256
New Orleans Pharmacy Museum, New Orleans, LA 597
New Richmond Preservation Society, New Richmond, WI.......................1615
New Sweden Historical Society, New Sweden, ME.......................616
New Windsor Cantonment State Historic Site and National Purple Heart Hall of Honor, Vails Gate, NY 1080
The New York Public Library, Astor, Lenox and Tilden Foundations, New York, NY.......................1036
The New York Studio School of Drawing, Painting & Sculpture, New York, NY.......................1036
Newaygo County Museum, Newaygo, MI...758
Newell Museum, Newell, SD 1352
Newport Art Museum, Newport, RI 1314
Newport Historical Society & The Museum of Newport History, Newport, RI 1315
Newport Restoration Foundation, Newport, RI 1315
The Newsome House Museum & Cultural Center, Newport News, VA 1520
Newton Fire Department, Newton, NJ 917
The Newton History Museum at The Jackson Homestead, Newton, MA 698

Newtown Historic Association, Newtown, PA 1274
Newtown History Center, Stephens City, VA 1538
The Niagara County Historical Center and Niagara County Genealogical Society, Lockport, NY.......................1010
Nichols House Museum, Boston, MA..........668
Nici Self Museum, Centennial, WY 1630
Nickels-Sortwell House, Wiscasset, ME 626
Niles Hotel and Saloon, Alturas, CA.............70
Ninety Six National Historic Site, Ninety Six, SC.......................1338
Nishna Heritage Museum, Oakland, IA 525
Noah Webster House/West Hartford Historical Society, West Hartford, CT.....265
Nobleboro Historical Society, Nobleboro, ME.......................616
Nordica Homestead, Farmington, ME..........610
Norfolk History Museum, Norfolk, VA........1523
The Norman Cleveland County Historical Museum, Norman, OK.......................1206
Norman Rockwell Museum, Stockbridge, MA.......................712
North Andover Historical Society, North Andover, MA.......................698
North Carolina Transportation Museum, Spencer, NC.......................1120
North Castle Historical Society, Armonk, NY.......................958
North Country Museum of Arts, Park Rapids, MN.......................786
North Haven Historical Society, North Haven, CT.......................257
North House Museum, Lewisburg, WV 1584
North Lee County Historic Center and Santa Fe Depot Museum Complex, Fort Madison, IA.......................518
North Platte Valley Museum, Gering, NE....861
The North Shore Arts Association, Gloucester, MA.......................684
Northampton County Historical and Genealogical Society, Easton, PA 1250
Northborough Historical Society, Inc., Northborough, MA.......................700
Northeast Georgia History Center at Brenau University, Gainesville, GA 373
The Northern Virginia Fine Arts Association at the Athenaeum, Alexandria, VA.......................1493
Northfield Historical Society Museum, Northfield, MN.......................785
Northwest Museum of Arts & Culture (Eastern Washington State Historical Society), Spokane, WA.......................1571
Northwest Railway Museum, Snoqualmie, WA.......................1570
Norwalk Museum, South Norwalk, CT........260
Nottawa Stone School, Centreville, MI........731
Novato History Museum, Novato, CA 132
Noyes House Museum, Morrisville, VT 1483
Nutter D. Marvel Museum, Georgetown, DE.......................271

O. Henry Museum, Austin, TX.....................1391
Oak Creek Historical Society-Pioneer Village, Oak Creek, WI.......................1615
Oak Hill and The Martha Berry Museum, Rome, GA.......................382
Oakdale Museum, Oakdale, CA 132
Oakland County Pioneer and Historical Society, Pontiac, MI.......................760
Oaklands Historic House Museum, Murfreesboro, TN.......................1376
Oakleigh Period House Museum, Mobile, AL.......................15
Oakley Park, UDC Shrine, Edgefield, SC..1332
The Oaks House Museum, Jackson, MS......804
Oatlands, Leesburg, VA.......................1512
Oberlin Heritage Center, Oberlin, OH.......1180
Ocean County Historical Museum, Toms River, NJ.......................926

Oceanside Museum of Art, Oceanside, CA.......................135
The Octagon, Washington, DC....................288
Octagon House, San Francisco, CA 168
The Octagon House, Hudson, WI.............1600
Octagon House-First Kindergarten in America, Watertown, WI.......................1625
O'Fallon Historical Museum, Baker, MT.....840
Office of Historic Alexandria, Alexandria, VA.......................1494
Ogden Historical Society, Spencerport, NY.......................1071
Ogden Union Station Museums, Ogden, UT.......................1468
Ohio Historical Society, Columbus, OH.....1158
Ohr-O'Keefe Museum of Art, Biloxi, MS ...799
Okefenokee Heritage Center, Waycross, GA.......................391
Oklahoma Heritage Association, Oklahoma City, OK.......................1209
Oklahoma Historical Society, Oklahoma City, OK.......................1209
Oklahoma Territorial Museum, Guthrie, OK.......................1202
Oktibbeha County Heritage Museum, Starkville, MS.......................808
Olana State Historic Site, Hudson, NY.......1000
Old Barracks Museum, Trenton, NJ............927
Old Bethpage Village Restoration, Old Bethpage, NY.......................1045
Old Bohemia Historical Society, Warwick, MD.......................656
Old Capitol Museum, Iowa City, IA 520
Old Castle Museum, Baldwin City, KS........533
Old Cathedral Museum, Saint Louis, MO....836
The Old Church Society, Inc., Portland, OR.......................1231
Old Colony Historical Society, Taunton, MA.......................714
Old Conway Homestead Complex and Museum, Camden, ME.......................608
Old Court House Museum-Eva Whitaker Davis Memorial, Vicksburg, MS.........809
Old Courthouse Museum, Santa Ana, CA....178
Old Cowtown Museum, Wichita, KS 562
Old Davie School Historical Museum, Davie, FL.......................302
Old Dutch Parsonage, Somerville, NJ.........924
Old Economy Village, Ambridge, PA.........1240
Old Exchange & Provost Dungeon, Charleston, SC.......................1326
Old Falls Village, Menomonee Falls, WI...1609
Old Firehouse Museum, Greenville, MS......800
Old Fort Bissell, Phillipsburg, KS 555
Old Fort Harrod State Park Mansion Museum, Harrodsburg, KY.......................570
Old Fort House Museum, Fort Edward, NY.......................991
Old Fort Jackson, Savannah, GA.................385
Old Fort Johnson, Fort Johnson, NY...........991
Old Fort Niagara, Youngstown, NY 1088
Old Fort Western, Augusta, ME 604
The Old Governor's Mansion, Frankfort, KY.......................570
Old Greer County Museum & Hall of Fame, Mangum, OK.......................1204
Old Hidalgo Pumphouse, Hidalgo, TX 1424
The Old Hoxie House, Sandwich, MA 708
Old Idaho Penitentiary, Boise, ID..............404
Old Iron County Courthouse Museum, Hurley, WI.......................1601
The Old Jail Art Center, Albany, TX..........1385
Old Jail Museum, Albion, IN.......................467
The Old Jail Museum, Crawfordsville, IN....473
The Old Jail Museum, Warrenton, VA 1543
Old Jefferson Town, Oskaloosa, KS............555
Old Lighthouse Museum, Michigan City, IN.......................491
Old Lighthouse Museum, Stonington, CT....261
Old Lincoln County Courthouse Museum, Lincoln, NM.......................942

Historic Houses and Historic Buildings—Continued

Old Log Jail and Chapel Museums, Greenfield, IN 480
The Old Manse, Concord, MA 677
Old Market House State Historic Site, Galena, IL 436
Old Mill Museum, Cimarron, NM 938
Old Monterey Jail, Monterey, CA 128
Old Ordinary House Museum, Hingham, MA 687
Old Prairie Town at Ward-Meade Historic Site, Topeka, KS 560
Old Prison Museums, Deer Lodge, MT 845
Old St. Ferdinand's Shrine, Florissant, MO 815
Old Salem Inc., Winston-Salem, NC 1126
Old Santee Canal Park, Moncks Corner, SC 1337
The Old Schwamb Mill, Arlington, MA 660
Old South Meeting House, Boston, MA 668
Old State Capitol, Springfield, IL 459
Old State House, Hartford, CT 245
Old State House Museum, Little Rock, AR 63
Old State House-The Bostonian Society, Boston, MA 668
Old Stone Fort Museum Complex, Schoharie, NY 1067
The Old Stone House, Washington, DC 289
Old Stone House Museum, Windsor, NY ..1086
Old Sussex County Courthouse, Georgetown, DE 271
The Old Tavern Museum, Tuscaloosa, AL 19
Old Town Museum, Old Town, ME 617
Old Town Museum, Burlington, CO 204
Old Town San Diego State Historic Park, San Diego, CA 158
Old Trail Museum, Choteau, MT 844
Old Village Hall Museum, Lindenhurst, NY 1009
Old Westbury Gardens, Old Westbury, NY 1045
Old World Wisconsin, Eagle, WI 1595
Old York Historical Society, York, ME 626
Olde Colonial Courthouse, Tales of Cape Cod, Inc., Barnstable, MA 661
Oldest House Museum Complex, Saint Augustine, FL 339
The Oldest House Museum/Wrecker's Museum, Key West, FL 318
Oldest Stone House Museum, Lakewood, OH 1170
Oldest Store Museum, Saint Augustine, FL 339
Oliver Kelley Farm, Elk River, MN 774
The Oliver Tucker Museum, Beverly, OH .1142
Olmstead Place State Park, Ellensburg, WA 1553
Olmsted County Historical Society, Rochester, MN 788
103rd Ohio Volunteer Infantry Civil War Museum, Sheffield Lake, OH 1185
Oneida Community Mansion House, Oneida, NY 1046
The Opelousas Museum of Art, Inc., Opelousas, LA 599
Orange Beach Indian and Sea Museum, Orange Beach, AL 18
Orange County Historical Museum, Hillsborough, NC 1107
Orangetown Historical Museum and Archives, Pearl River, NY 1051
Orcas Island Historical Museum, Orcas Island, WA 1560
Orchard House, Concord, MA 677
Orchard Park Historical Society, Orchard Park, NY 1047
Orcutt Ranch, Canoga Park, CA 81
Oregon-Jerusalem Historical Museum, Oregon, OH 1181

Oregon Trail Regional Museum, Baker City, OR 1219
Orland E. White Arboretum, Boyce, VA 1497
Orland Historical Society, Orland, ME 617
Orleans County Historical Society & The Old Stone House Museum, Brownington, VT 1477
Oroville Chinese Temple, Oroville, CA 136
Ortega Adobe, Ventura, CA 195
Osage County Historical Society Museum, Pawhuska, OK 1211
Osborn-Jackson House, East Hampton, NY 986
The Oscar Anderson House Museum, Anchorage, AK 22
Ossining Historical Society Museum, Ossining, NY 1047
Osterville Historical Society, Inc., Osterville, MA 701
Otero Museum Association, La Junta, CO ...224
Ouachita County Historical Society, Camden, AR 55
Our House State Memorial, Gallipolis, OH 1165
Outagamie Museum, Appleton, WI 1589
Overfield Tavern Museum, Troy, OH 1188
Overholser Mansion, Oklahoma City, OK .1210
Overstreet-Kerr Historical Farm, Keota, OK 1203
Oyster Bay Historical Society, Oyster Bay, NY 1049
Oysterponds Historical Society: The Museum of Orient and East Marion History, Orient, NY 1047
Ozark National Scenic Riverways, Van Buren, MO 839

Pacem in Terris, Warwick, NY 1082
Pacific Asia Museum, Pasadena, CA 140
Pacific Grove Museum of Natural History, Pacific Grove, CA 137
Pacific University Museum, Forest Grove, OR 1224
Packwood House Museum, Lewisburg, PA 1268
Paine Art Center and Gardens, Oshkosh, WI 1617
Painted Post - Erwin Museum at the Depot, Painted Post, NY 1050
Pajaro Valley Historical Association, Watsonville, CA 196
Palace of the Governors/New Mexico History Museum, Santa Fe, NM 949
PALCO, Scotia, CA 186
The Palette & Chisel, Chicago, IL 426
Palmer/Gullickson Octagon Home, West Salem, WI 1627
Palmer House, Historical Society of Olde Northfield, Northfield, OH 1180
Pamplin Historical Park and The National Museum of the Civil War Soldier, Petersburg, VA 1525
The Pardee Home Museum, Oakland, CA ...134
Paris Gibson Square Museum of Art, Great Falls, MT 848
Paris-Henry County Heritage Center, Paris, TN 1382
Parishville Museum, Parishville, NY 1050
The Park-McCullough House, North Bennington, VT 1483
Parker Tavern, Reading, MA 705
Parks, Recreation & Historic Sites Division, Georgia Dept. of Natural Resources, Atlanta, GA 362
The Parrish Art Museum, Southampton, NY 1070
The Parry Mansion Museum, New Hope, PA 1273
Parson Fisher House, Blue Hill, ME 606
Parsonsfield-Porter Historical Society, Porter, ME 618
The Parthenon, Nashville, TN 1379

Pasadena Museum of History, Pasadena, CA 140
Pascack Historical Society, Park Ridge, NJ 920
Passaic County Historical Society & Lambert Castle Museum, Paterson, NJ ...920
Patee House Museum, Saint Joseph, MO 831
The Paterson Museum, Paterson, NJ 920
Patterson Homestead, Dayton, OH 1161
Patterson Inn Museum/Corning - Painted Post Historical Society, Corning, NY 982
Paul Dresser Memorial Birthplace, Terre Haute, IN 500
Paul Revere House/Paul Revere Memorial Association, Boston, MA 668
Paulson House, Au Train, MI 726
Pawnee Bill Ranch and Museum, Pawnee, OK 1212
Pawnee City Historical Society & Museum, Pawnee City, NE 871
Paynes Creek Historic State Park, Bowling Green, FL 297
Pea Ridge National Military Park, Garfield, AR 58
Peabody Essex Museum, Salem, MA 706
Pearl S. Buck Birthplace Foundation, Hillsboro, WV 1582
The Pearl S. Buck House, Perkasie, PA 1275
Pebble Hill Plantation, Thomasville, GA 388
The Peekskill Museum, Peekskill, NY 1051
Peel Mansion Museum & Historic Gardens, Bentonville, AR 55
Peirce Mill and Peirce Barn, Washington, DC 289
Pejepscot Historical Society, Brunswick, ME 608
Pembroke Historical Society, Inc., Pembroke, MA 701
Pendarvis State Historic Site, Mineral Point, WI 1614
Pendleton Historic Foundation, Pendleton, SC 1339
Pennsbury Manor, Morrisville, PA 1272
Pennsylvania Academy of the Fine Arts, Philadelphia, PA 1284
Pennsylvania German Cultural Heritage Center at Kutztown University, Kutztown, PA 1265
Pennsylvania Historical & Museum Commission, Harrisburg, PA 1259
Pennypacker Mills, Schwenksville, PA 1297
Pensacola Historical Society Museum, Pensacola, FL 336
Pensacola Museum of Art, Pensacola, FL 336
Peoria Historical Society, Peoria, IL 451
Peralta Adobe, San Jose, CA 172
Perkins Center for the Arts, Moorestown, NJ 912
Perkins County Historical Society, Grant, NE 862
Peshtigo Fire Museum, Peshtigo, WI 1617
Petaluma Adobe State Historic Park, Petaluma, CA 142
Peter Conser House, Heavener, OK 1202
Peter Rice Homestead, Home of Marlborough Historical Society, Inc., Marlboro, MA 693
Peter Wentz Farmstead, Worcester, PA 1308
Peter Whitmer Sr. Home and Visitors Center, Waterloo, NY 1083
Peter Yegen Jr. Yellowstone County Museum, Billings, MT 841
Pettaquamscutt Historical Society, Kingston, RI 1312
Pettigrew Home and Museum, Sioux Falls, SD 1356
Pettis County Historical Society, Sedalia, MO 838
Pewabic Pottery, Detroit, MI 737
Phelps House, Burlington, IA 507
The Philadelphia Art Alliance, Philadelphia, PA 1285

Philadelphia Museum of Art, Philadelphia, PA 1285

Philadelphia Museum of Judaica/Congregation Rodeph Shalom, Philadelphia, PA 1286

Philadelphia Society for the Preservation of Landmarks, Philadelphia, PA 1286

The Philbrook Museum of Art, Inc., Tulsa, OK.....................1215

Philipse Manor Hall State Historic Site, Yonkers, NY.....................1087

Phillips County Museum, Helena, AR............59

Phillips Historical Society, Phillips, ME 618

Philmont Museums, Cimarron, NM.............938

Piatt Castles, West Liberty, OH 1190

Pickler Mansion, Faulkton, SD...................1347

The Pierce Manse/New Hampshire Political Library, Concord, NH................885

The Pierpont Morgan Library, New York, NY.....................1037

Pierre Menard Home State Historic Site, Ellis Grove, IL.....................433

Pima Air & Space Museum, Tucson, AZ.......50

Pimeria Alta Historical Society, Nogales, AZ.....................37

Pine Creek Grist Mill, Muscatine, IA 525

Pine Lodge (Ehrman Mansion), Tahoma, CA.....................190

Pioneer Arizona Living History Village & Museum, Phoenix, AZ.....................41

Pioneer Corner Museum, New Holstein, WI 1615

Pioneer Farm Museum and Ohop Indian Village, Eatonville, WA.....................1552

Pioneer Historical Museum of South Dakota, Hot Springs, SD.................1348

Pioneer Log Cabin, Manhattan, KS.............551

The Pioneer Memorial Association of Fenton and Mundy Townships, Fenton, MI 741

Pioneer Museum and Vereins Kirche, Fredericksburg, TX.....................1419

Pioneer Settlement for the Creative Arts, Barberville, FL.....................295

Pioneer Village & Virgil Grissom Memorial at Spring Mill State Park, Mitchell, IN 491

Pioneers, Trail Drivers and Texas Rangers Memorial Museum, San Antonio, TX.....................1449

Pipestone County Historical Museum, Pipestone, MN.....................786

Piqua Historical Area State Memorial, Piqua, OH 1182

Pitot House Museum, New Orleans, LA.......598

Pittock Mansion, Portland, OR 1232

Plains Indians and Pioneers Museum, Woodward, OK.....................1217

Plainsman Museum, Aurora, NE 856

Planting Fields Arboretum State Historic Park, Oyster Bay, NY.....................1049

Plum Grove Historic Home, Iowa City, IA.....................520

Plumb Farm Learning Center, Greeley, CO.....................222

Plymouth Antiquarian Society, Plymouth, MA.....................704

Pocahontas County Museum, Marlinton, WV.....................1584

Pohick Episcopal Church, Lorton, VA 1514

Point Arena Lighthouse and Museum, Point Arena, CA.....................142

Point Fermin Lighthouse, San Pedro, CA....176

Point of Honor, Lynchburg, VA.................1515

Point Reyes National Seashore, Point Reyes, CA.....................143

Pointe Coupee Museum, New Roads, LA....599

Polk County Historical Museum, Bartow, FL.....................295

The Polk County Historical Society, Cedartown, GA.....................368

Polk County Historical Society, Des Moines, IA.....................515

Polson Museum, Hoquiam, WA.................1556

Pomeroy Living History Farm, Yacolt, WA.....................1578

Ponca City Art Center, Ponca City, OK 1212

Ponce DeLeon Inlet Lighthouse Preservation Association, Inc., Ponce Inlet, FL.....................337

Pony Express Museum, Saint Joseph, MO.....................831

Pope's Tavern Museum, Florence, AL 9

Poplar Grove Historic Plantation, Wilmington, NC.....................1123

Poricy Park Nature Center, Middletown, NJ.....................911

Portage County Historical Society, Stevens Point, WI.....................1623

The Portal of the Folded Wings Shrine to Aviation and Museum, North Hollywood, CA.....................131

Porter-Phelps-Huntington Foundation, Inc., Hadley, MA.....................685

Porterville Historical Museum, Porterville, CA.....................144

Portland Museum, Louisville, KY.............578

Portland Museum of Art, Portland, ME.......619

Portsmouth Athenaeum, Portsmouth, NH.....894

Portsmouth Historical Association, Portsmouth, VA.....................1526

Portsmouth Historical Society, Portsmouth, RI.....................1316

Portsmouth Museums, Portsmouth, VA......1526

Potts Inn Museum, Pottsville, AR 66

Pottsgrove Manor, Pottstown, PA 1295

Prairie Homestead, Philip, SD 1353

The Prairie Museum of Art & History, Colby, KS.....................535

Praters Mill Foundation, Varnell, GA...........390

Preservation Resource Center, New Orleans, LA.....................598

The Preservation Society of Newport County/The Newport Mansions, Newport, RI.....................1315

President Andrew Johnson Museum and Library, Greeneville, TN.....................1366

President Chester A. Arthur Historic Site, Fairfield, VT.....................1479

President James K. Polk State Historic Site, Pineville, NC.....................1114

President's Cottage Museum-The Greenbrier, White Sulphur Springs, WV.....................1588

Presidio La Bahia, Goliad, TX 1423

Presque Isle County Historical Museum, Rogers City, MI.....................762

Prestwould Foundation, Clarksville, VA.....1501

Price Tower Arts Center, Bartlesville, OK .1197

Pricketts Fort, Fairmont, WV.....................1581

Promont House Museum, Milford, OH 1176

Proprietary House, The Royal Governor's Mansion, Perth Amboy, NJ.....................921

Providence Preservation Society, Providence, RI.....................1318

Prudence Crandall Museum, Canterbury, CT.....................237

Public Museum of West Michigan, Grand Rapids, MI.....................744

Pueblo Zoo, Pueblo, CO.....................230

Putnam Cottage, Greenwich, CT 243

Putnam County Historical Society & Foundry School Museum, Cold Spring, NY.....................979

Putney Historical Society, Putney, VT 1485

Pyle House Museum, Huron, SD................1349

Quasdorf Blacksmith and Wagon Museum, Dows, IA 516

Queen Emma Summer Palace, Honolulu, HI.....................398

Queens County Farm Museum, Floral Park, NY.....................989

Queens Historical Society, Flushing, NY.....990

The Quilters Hall of Fame, Inc., Marion, IN.....................490

Quincy Art Center, Quincy, IL.....................452

Quincy Historical Society, Quincy, MA 705

The Quincy Museum, Quincy, IL.................452

R.P. Strathearn Historical Park and Museum, Simi Valley, CA.....................187

Rachel Carson Homestead, Springdale, PA.....................1301

Racine Heritage Museum, Racine, WI 1619

Railroad House Historical Association Museum, Sanford, NC.....................1119

Ralls Historical Museum, Ralls, TX...........1445

Ralph Waldo Emerson House, Concord, MA.....................677

Ralston Historical Association, John Ralston Museum, Mendham, NJ.....................911

Ramapogue Historical Society, West Springfield, MA.....................718

Ramsay House Visitors Center, Alexandria, VA.....................1494

Ramsey House Museum Plantation, Knoxville, TN.....................1371

Rancho La Patera - The Stow House G.V.H.S., Goleta, CA 100

Rancho Los Alamitos, Long Beach, CA 111

Randolph County Historical Museum, Winchester, IN.....................503

Randolph County Museum (At Beverly), Beverly, WV.....................1580

Rangely Outdoor Museum, Rangely, CO.....231

Rankin Museum, Rankin, TX 1445

Raton Museum, Raton, NM 945

Ravalli County Museum/Bitter Root Valley Historical Society, Hamilton, MT.....................848

Raynham Hall Museum, Oyster Bay, NY ..1049

Reading Historical Society Museum, Reading, OH.....................1184

Readsboro Historical Society, Readsboro, VT.....................1486

Rebecca Nurse Homestead, Danvers, MA ...678

Red Hill-Patrick Henry National Memorial, Brookneal, VA.....................1498

Red River Historical Society Museum, Clay City, KY.....................566

Redington Museum, Waterville, ME............625

Reedville Fishermen's Museum, Reedville, VA.....................1527

Reeves-Reed Arboretum, Summit, NJ..........925

Rehoboth Art League, Inc., Rehoboth Beach, DE.....................272

Reitz Home Museum, Evansville, IN...........476

Remick Country Doctor Museum and Farm, Tamworth, NH.....................896

Renfrew Museum & Park, Waynesboro, PA.....................1306

Rensselaer County Historical Society, Troy, NY.....................1079

Rensselaer Russell House Museum, Waterloo, IA.....................529

Renton Historical Society and Museum, Renton, WA.....................1564

Reverend Dan Foster House, Museum of the Weathersfield Historical Society, Weathersfield, VT.....................1489

Reynolda House Museum of American Art, Winston-Salem, NC 1126

Reynolds Homestead, Critz, VA.................1502

Rhode Island Historical Preservation and Heritage, Providence, RI.....................1318

Rhode Island Historical Society, Providence, RI.....................1318

Rialto Historical Society, Rialto, CA............148

Rice County Museum of History, Faribault, MN.....................775

The Rice Museum, Georgetown, SC..........1333

Richard Salter Storrs House, Longmeadow, MA.....................691

Richard Sparrow House Inc., Plymouth, MA.....................704

Historic Houses and Historic Buildings–Continued

Richards DAR House Museum, Mobile, AL 15

Richardson-Bates House Museum, Oswego, NY 1048

Richey Historical Society, Richey, MT 852

Richland County Museum, Lexington, OH 1172

Richmond National Battlefield Park, Richmond, VA 1531

Riddick's Folly, Suffolk, VA 1539

Riley House Museum of African American History & Culture, Tallahassee, FL 348

Rim Country Museum, Payson, AZ............38

Rio Grande Valley Museum, Harlingen, TX 1423

Riordan Mansion State Historic Park, Flagstaff, AZ 33

Rios-Caledonia Adobe, San Miguel, CA......175

Rip Van Winkle Gardens on Jefferson Island, New Iberia, LA............593

Rising Sun Tavern, Fredericksburg, VA 1507

Rittman Historical Society, Rittman, OH ...1184

River Museum, Wellsville, OH 1190

Riversdale House Mansion, Riverdale Park, MD 651

Riverside Heritage House, Riverside, CA ...150

Riverside Metropolitan Museum, Riverside, CA 150

Riverside, The Farnsley-Moremen Landing, Louisville, KY............579

Riverview at Hobson Grove, Bowling Green, KY............566

Robbins Hunter Museum, Avery-Downer House, Granville, OH 1167

Robert Frost Stone House Museum, Shaftsbury, VT 1487

Robert Fulton Birthplace, Quarryville, PA .1295

Robert Louis Stevenson House, Monterey, CA 128

Robert Louis Stevenson Memorial Cottage, Saranac Lake, NY............1064

Robert Newell House, DAR Museum, Saint Paul, OR 1235

Robert R. McCormick Museum at Cantigny, Wheaton, IL 465

Robert S. Kerr Museum, Poteau, OK 1212

Robert Toombs House, Washington, GA......391

Roberts County Museum, Miami, TX 1438

Robinson-Rose House, San Diego, CA 159

Rochester Hills Museum at Van Hoosen Farm, Rochester Hills, MI 762

Rochester Historical Society, Rochester, NY............1059

Rock County Historical Society, Janesville, WI 1601

Rock Ford Plantation, Lancaster, PA............1267

Rock House Museum, Wytheville, VA 1546

Rock Island County Historical Society, Moline, IL 445

Rock Island State Park, Washington Island, WI 1625

Rock Ledge Ranch Historic Site, Colorado Springs, CO 208

Rockbridge Historical Society, Lexington, VA 1513

Rockingham, Kingston, NJ 909

Rockwood Park, Wilmington, DE 274

Rodgers Tavern, Perryville, MD 650

Rogers Historical Museum, Rogers, AR 67

Rokeby (Ancestral Estate of Rowland Evans Robinson), Ferrisburgh, VT 1479

Ronald Reagan Boyhood Home, Dixon, IL 431

Roosevelt Campobello International Park Commission, Lubec, ME............614

The Root House Museum, Marietta, GA 379

Rosalie House, Eureka Springs, AR 57

Roscoe Village Foundation, Coshocton, OH............1159

Rose Center Museum, Morristown, TN 1376

Rose Hill Museum, Bay Village, OH 1141

Rose Hill Plantation State Historic Site, Union, SC 1343

Rose Lawn Museum, Cartersville, GA.........368

Roseland Cottage, Woodstock, CT 268

Rosemont Plantation, Woodville, MS.........810

Rosemount Museum, Pueblo, CO............230

Rosenbach Museum & Library, Philadelphia, PA 1287

Roslyn Landmark Society, Roslyn, NY......1061

The Rotch-Jones-Duff House & Garden Museum, Inc., New Bedford, MA 697

Rothschild House State Park, Port Townsend, WA 1562

The Rotunda, University of Virginia, Charlottesville, VA 1500

Rowan Museum, Inc., Salisbury, NC.........1118

Rowan Oak, William Faulkner's Home, Oxford, MS............806

Rowley Historical Society, Rowley, MA......706

Roxbury Heritage State Park, Roxbury, MA............706

Royal Gorge Regional Museum & History Center, Canon City, CO............205

Royall House Association, Medford, MA 694

Royalton Historical Society, Royalton, VT............1486

Ruggles House Society, Columbia Falls, ME............609

Rumford Historical Association, North Woburn, MA 699

Rundlet-May House, Portsmouth, NH.........895

Rural Life Museum & Windrush Gardens, Baton Rouge, LA............587

Rusk County Historical Society, Ladysmith, WI 1604

Russell County Historical Society/Fossil Station Museum, Russell, KS............556

Rutherford B. Hayes Presidential Center, Fremont, OH 1165

Ruthmere Museum, Elkhart, IN............475

Rutland Historical Society, Rutland, VT 1486

The Rye Historical Society and Square House Museum, Rye, NY 1062

Sackets Harbor Battlefield State Historic Site, Sackets Harbor, NY 1062

Sacramento Mountains Historical Museum, Cloudcroft, NM 938

Safe Haven Museum and Education Center, Oswego, NY 1048

Safford House Historic House Museum, Tarpon Springs, FL............351

Sag Harbor Whaling & Historical Museum, Sag Harbor, NY............1063

Sagamore Hill National Historic Site, Oyster Bay, NY 1049

Saginaw Art Museum, Saginaw, MI............763

Saguache County Museum, Saguache, CO............231

Sahuaro Ranch Historical Area, Glendale, AZ............35

Sailor's Memorial Museum, Islesboro, ME............612

St. Augustine Lighthouse & Museum, Inc., Saint Augustine, FL............340

St. Charles County Historical Society, Inc., Saint Charles, MO............830

St. Clair County Historical Society, Belleville, IL............412

Saint-Gaudens National Historic Site, Cornish, NH............885

St. James' House, Fredericksburg, VA 1507

St. John's Episcopal Church, Richmond, VA............1531

St. Johnsbury Athenaeum, Saint Johnsbury, VT............1487

St. Joseph Museum Inc., Saint Joseph, MO............831

St. Lawrence County Historical Association - Silas Wright House, Canton, NY............975

The Saint Louis Art Museum, Saint Louis, MO............836

The St. Louis County Historical Society, Duluth, MN............773

St. Paul Museum, Randleman, NC 1117

St. Simons Island Lighthouse Museum, Saint Simons Island, GA............383

Salem Art Association-Bush House Museum and Bush Barn Art Center, Salem, OR............1236

Salem Historical Society and Museum, Salem, OH............1184

The Salem Museum, Salem, VA............1536

Saline County Historical Society, Inc., Dorchester, NE............860

Salisbury House Foundation, Des Moines, IA............515

Salmagundi Museum of American Art, New York, NY............1038

Salmon Brook Historical Society, Inc., Granby, CT............242

Saltbox Museum, New Providence, NJ.........916

Salter Museum, Argonia, KS 532

Sam Bell Maxey House State Historic Site, Paris, TX 1442

Sam Brown Log House, Browns Valley, MN............770

Sam Houston Historical Schoolhouse, Maryville, TN 1371

Sam Houston Memorial Museum, Huntsville, TX............1430

Sam Houston Regional Library & Research Center, Liberty, TX............1434

Sam Rayburn House Museum, Bonham, TX............1397

Samuel Cupples House of Saint Louis University, Saint Louis, MO............837

San Antonio Botanical Garden, San Antonio, TX............1449

San Antonio Conservation Society, San Antonio, TX............1449

San Antonio de Pala Asistencia, Pala, CA ...138

San Antonio Missions National Historical Park, San Antonio, TX............1449

San Antonio Museum of Art, San Antonio, TX............1450

San Fernando Mission, Mission Hills, CA...126

San Fernando Valley Historical Society, Inc., Mission Hills, CA............126

San Gabriel Mission Museum, San Gabriel, CA............171

San Jacinto Museum of History Association, La Porte, TX............1433

San Joaquin County Historical Society & Museum, Lodi, CA............109

San Jose Museum of Art, San Jose, CA 172

San Juan Bautista State Historic Park, San Juan Bautista, CA............173

San Juan Historical Society, Friday Harbor, WA............1555

San Luis Obispo County Historical Museum, San Luis Obispo, CA............174

San Mateo Arboretum Society, Inc., San Mateo, CA............175

San Miguel Mission Church, Santa Fe, NM............950

Sanchez Adobe Historic Site, Pacifica, CA............138

Sandown Historical Society and Museum, Sandown, NH............896

Sandusky Library Follett House Museum, Sandusky, OH............1185

Sandwich Historical Society, Center Sandwich, NH............884

Sandy Bay Historical Society & Museums, Inc., Rockport, MA............705

Sanilac County Historical Museum and Village, Port Sanilac, MI............761

The Santa Barbara Historical Museum, Santa Barbara, CA............179

Santa Barbara Mission Museum, Santa Barbara, CA.................................179

Santa Barbara Trust for Historic Preservation, Santa Barbara, CA.............180

Santa Fe Trail Museum/Trinidad History Museum, Trinidad, CO..............234

Santa Ynez Valley Historical Society, Santa Ynez, CA............................185

Santa Ysabel Asistencia, Santa Ysabel, CA...185

Sappington House Museum, Crestwood, MO..814

Sarah A. Mooney Memorial Museum, Lemoore, CA....................................109

Sarah Orne Jewett House, South Berwick, ME..622

Saratoga County Historical Society, Brookside Museum, Ballston Spa, NY....960

The Sargent House Museum, Gloucester, MA..684

Sarpy County Historical Museum, Bellevue, NE...857

Satterlee Clark House, Horicon, WI...........1600

Saugus Iron Works National Historic Site, Saugus, MA.............................708

Sauk County Historical Museum, Baraboo, WI...1591

Sauk Prairie Area Historical Society, Inc., Prairie du Sac, WI..................1619

Saunders County Historical Complex, Wahoo, NE......................................874

Sawin Memorial Building, Dover, MA........680

Sayward-Wheeler House, York Harbor, ME...627

Scantic Academy Museum, East Windsor Historical Society, Inc., East Windsor, CT..239

The Scarsdale Historical Society, Scarsdale, NY.......................................1066

Schenectady County Historical Society, Schenectady, NY..........................1067

Schifferstadt Architectural Museum, Frederick, MD...................................644

Schmidt House Museum & Research Library, Grants Pass, OR.....................1225

Schoenbrunn Village State Memorial, New Philadelphia, OH.....................1177

Schofield House, Madison, IN.....................489

Schoharie Colonial Heritage Association, Schoharie, NY.............................1067

Scholte House Museum, Pella, IA..............527

Schoolcraft County Historical Society, Manistique, MI................................753

Schoolhouse Museum of the Ridgewood Historical Society, Inc., Ridgewood, NJ...923

The Schuette Biermann Farmhouse Museum, Elk Grove Village, IL.............432

Schuyler County Historical Society, Inc., Montour Falls, NY........................1015

Schuyler-Hamilton House, Morristown, NJ..914

Schuyler Jail Museum, Rushville, IL...........456

Schuyler Mansion State Historic Site, Albany, NY...955

Science Museum of Virginia, Richmond, VA...1531

SciTech, Aurora, IL...................................412

Scotchtown, Beaverdam, VA.....................1496

Scotland Heritage Chapel & Museum, Scotland, SD..1355

Seaford Historical Museum, Seaford, NY..1068

Seagraves-Loop Museum and Art Center Inc., Seagraves, TX.............................1452

The Seay House, Spartanburg, SC.............1341

Sedgwick-Brooklin Historical Society, Sedgwick, ME..622

Seguine-Burke Plantation, Staten Island, NY...1073

Senator George Baldwin Hotel, Klamath Falls, OR.....................................1227

Senator George Norris State Historic Site, McCook, NE..............................868

Seneca County Museum, Tiffin, OH...........1186

Seneca Falls Historical Society, Seneca Falls, NY......................................1069

Seneca Schoolhouse Museum, Poolesville, MD......................................650

Sepulveda House, Los Angeles, CA............121

Sequoyah Cabin, Sallisaw, OK..................1213

Serra Museum/San Diego Historical Society, San Diego, CA.....................161

1719 Hans Herr House & Museum, Willow Street, PA...............................1308

The 1719 William Trent House Museum, Trenton, NJ.......................................928

1797 Ezekiel Harris House, Augusta, GA....366

1768 Jeremiah Lee Mansion, Marblehead, MA...693

1761 Pownalborough Courthouse, Dresden, ME..610

Sewall-Belmont House and Museum, Washington, DC....................................290

Seward County Historical Society Museum, Goehner, NE............................861

Seward House, Auburn, NY.........................959

Seymour Community Museum, Seymour, WI...1621

The Shadows-on-the-Teche, New Iberia, LA..593

Shafer Historical Museum, Winthrop, WA.1578

Shaker Heritage Society, Albany, NY..........956

Shaker Historical Society, Shaker Heights, OH..1185

Shandy Hall, Geneva, OH...........................1166

Sharlot Hall Museum, Prescott, AZ.............43

Sharon Historical Society, Sharon, CT........260

Sharpsteen Museum, Calistoga, CA............80

Shasta State Historic Park, Shasta, CA........186

Shawano County Historical Society, Inc., Shawano, WI.....................................1621

Shawnee Town, Shawnee, KS....................558

Sheboygan County Historical Museum, Sheboygan, WI.....................................1621

Shelburne Museum, Inc., Shelburne, VT...1487

Sheldon Jackson Museum, Sitka, AK..........27

Sheldon Peck Homestead, Lombard, IL......444

Shelter House Society, Emmaus, PA..........1251

Shelter Island Historical Society, Shelter Island, NY......................................1069

Shemer Art Center & Museum, Phoenix, AZ...42

The Sherman House, Lancaster, OH..........1171

Sherwood-Davidson House, Newark, OH..1178

Sherwood Forest Plantation, Charles City, VA..1498

Shiloh Museum of Ozark History, Springdale, AR..68

Shippensburg Historical Society Museum, Shippensburg, PA...............1300

Ships of the Sea Maritime Museum/William Scarbrough House, Savannah, GA..386

Shirley-Eustis House, Boston, MA..............669

Shirley Plantation, Charles City, VA...........1498

Shoreline Historical Museum, Seattle, WA..1569

Shorter Mansion Museum, Eufaula, AL........8

Shortgrass Country Museum Society, Sayre, OK...1213

Shoshone County Mining and Smelting Museum d/b/a The Staff House Museum, Kellogg, ID.............................406

Shoshone Tribal Cultural Center, Fort Washakie, WY...................................1633

Shrewsbury Windle House, Madison, IN.....489

Sibley County Historical Museum, Henderson, MN...................................777

Sibley House Historic Site, Mendota, MN...780

Siege Museum (The Petersburg Museums), Petersburg, VA.....................1525

Silver City Museum, Silver City, NM..........951

Simonian Farms, Fresno, CA.......................98

Sinclair Lewis House Museum & Interpretive Center/Museum, Sauk Centre, MN......................................793

Sioux City Public Museum, Sioux City, IA...528

Siouxland Heritage Museums, Sioux Falls, SD...1357

The Sixth Floor Museum at Dealey Plaza, Dallas, TX.................................1407

Skagway Museum & Archives, Skagway, AK...28

Skirball Museum Cincinnati Hebrew Union College-Jewish Institute of Religion, Cincinnati, OH.....................1151

Skowhegan History House Inc., Skowhegan, ME......................................622

Sky City Cultural Center, Pueblo of Acoma, NM..944

Slate Run Living Historical Farm, Metro Parks, Ashville, OH...........................1140

Slater Mill Historic Site, Pawtucket, RI.....1315

Slaughter Ranch Museum, Douglas, AZ........32

Slidell Museum, Slidell, LA.........................602

Slifer House, Lewisburg, PA.......................1268

Smallwood State Park, Marbury, MD..........649

Smith-McDowell House Museum, Asheville, NC..1090

Smith Robertson Museum & Cultural Center, Jackson, MS.............................804

Smith's Fort Plantation, Surry, VA.............1540

Smithsonian American Art Museum, Washington, DC......................................290

Smithtown Historical Society, Smithtown, NY..1070

Smoki Museum - American Indian Art & Culture, Prescott, AZ..............................43

Smyth County Museum, Marion, VA..........1516

Society for the Preservation of Long Island Antiquities, Cold Spring Harbor, NY..980

The Society of the Cincinnati at Anderson House, Washington, DC.....291

Sod House Museum, Gothenburg, NE.........862

Sod House Museum, Aline, OK..................1195

SoDus Bay Historical Society, Sodus Point, NY...1070

Soldiers & Sailors Memorial Building, Huntington, NY....................................1001

Soldiers National Museum, Gettysburg, PA...1256

Somers Historical Society, Somers, NY.....1070

Somers Mansion, Somers Point, NJ............924

The Somerset County Historical Society, Inc., Princess Anne, MD...................650

Somerset Place State Historic Site, Creswell, NC...1097

Somervell County Historical Museum, Glen Rose, TX.....................................1423

Sonnenberg Gardens & Mansion State Historic Park, Canandaigua, NY............975

Sonoma State Historic Park, Sonoma, CA...188

Sosa-Carrillo-Fremont House Museum, Tucson, AZ...50

Sotterley Plantation, Hollywood, MD.........647

South Carolina Department of Parks, Recreation and Tourism, Columbia, SC...1330

South Coast Railroad Museum at Goleta Depot, Goleta, CA.................................100

South County Historical Society, Arroyo Grande, CA...72

South Hero Bicentennial Museum, South Hero, VT...1487

South Holland Historical Society, South Holland, IL..457

South Park City Museum, Fairplay, CO......215

South River Meeting House, Lynchburg, VA...1516

South Sutton Old Store Museum, South Sutton, NH..896

South Texas Museum, Alice, TX.................1386

Historic Houses and Historic Buildings–Continued

South Wood County Historical Corp.,
Wisconsin Rapids, WI 1628
Southampton Historical Museum,
Southampton, NY 1070
Southern Oregon Historical Society,
Jacksonville, OR....................................1226
Southern Vermont College Art Gallery,
Bennington, VT......................................1477
Southwest Arkansas Regional Archives
(SARA), Washington, AR 70
Southwest Florida Museum of History,
Fort Myers, FL..309
Southwest School of Art & Craft, San
Antonio, TX..1450
Southwest Virginia Museum Historical
State Park, Big Stone Gap, VA..............1497
Spanish Governor's Palace, San Antonio,
TX 1450
Spencer-Peirce-Little Farm, Newbury,
MA 697
Spirit of '76 Museum, Wellington, OH 1190
Spring Street Historical Museum,
Shreveport, LA 602
Spring Valley Community Historical
Society, Inc., Spring Valley, MN 794
Springfield Armory National Historic
Site, Springfield, MA................................710
Springfield Art & Historical Society -
Miller Art Center, Springfield, VT........1488
Springfield Art Association, Springfield,
IL..460
Springfield Historical Society,
Springfield, NJ..925
Springfield Museum of Old Domestic
Life, High Point, NC................................1107
Springfield Museums - George Walter
Vincent Smith Art Museum,
Springfield, MA..710
Spruill Gallery, Atlanta, GA..........................364
Staatsburgh State Historic Site,
Staatsburg, NY..1071
Stables Art Gallery of Taos Art
Association, Taos, NM 952
Stacy's Tavern Museum and Glen Ellyn
Historical Society, Glen Ellyn, IL 437
Stagecoach Inn Museum Complex,
Newbury Park, CA....................................130
Stamford Historical Society, Inc.,
Stamford, CT..260
Stan Hywet Hall and Gardens, Inc.,
Akron, OH..1139
Stanley Museum, Inc., Kingfield, ME..........613
Stanley-Whitman House, Farmington,
Farmington, CT 241
Stanly County Historic Preservation
Commission and Museum, Albemarle,
NC..1088
Stanton House, Clinton, CT..........................237
Stanzel Model Aircraft Museum,
Schulenburg, TX......................................1452
State Capital Publishing Museum,
Guthrie, OK..1202
State Capitol, Hartford, Conn., Hartford,
CT 246
State Historic Site of Fort Loudoun,
Chambersburg, PA..................................1246
State Historical Society of Iowa, Des
Moines, IA..515
The State House Museum, Dover, DE 270
Staten Island Historical Society, Staten
Island, NY..1074
Statue of Liberty National Monument &
Ellis Island Immigration Museum,
New York, NY..1039
Steele County Historical Society, Hope,
ND..1133
Steilacoom Historical Museum
Association, Steilacoom, WA................1572
Stengel-True Museum, Marion, OH 1174

The Stephen Girard Collection,
Philadelphia, PA 1288
The Stephen Phillips House, Salem, MA.....707
Stephens County Historical Society and
Museum, Duncan, OK............................1199
Stephenson County Historical Society,
Freeport, IL..436
Stephenville Museum, Stephenville, TX 1454
Stepping Stones, Katonah, NY 1006
Steppingstone Museum, Havre de Grace,
MD..647
Sterling Historical Society and Little Red
Schoolhouse Museum, Sterling, NY......1074
Steuben House, River Edge, NJ....................923
The Stevens-Coolidge Place, a property
of The Trustees of Reservations, North
Andover, MA..698
Stevens County Gas and Historical
Museum, Hugoton, KS..............................544
Steves Homestead, San Antonio, TX..........1450
Stewart M. Lord Memorial Historical
Society, Inc., Burlington, ME..................608
The Stickley Museum at Craftsman
Farms, Parsippany, NJ 920
Still National Osteopathic Museum,
Kirksville, MO..824
Stockholm Historical Society Museum,
Stockholm, ME..623
Stone House Gallery, Fredonia, KS..............540
The Stone House Museum, Belchertown,
MA..662
Stone Lagoon Red Schoolhouse Museum
at Redwood Trails, Trinidad, CA..............192
Stonefield Historic Site, Cassville, WI.......1593
Stone's Tavern, Ligonier, IN..........................488
Stonewall House, Rocky Mount, NC..........1118
Stonewall Jackson House, Lexington, VA..1514
Stoughton Historical Society, Stoughton,
WI..1623
Stow West School Museum, Stow, MA 713
Stranahan House, Inc., Fort Lauderdale,
FL..308
Strater Hotel, Durango, CO 214
The Stratford Historical Society &
Catherine B. Mitchell Museum,
Stratford, CT..262
Stratford, Robert E. Lee Memorial
Association, Inc., Stratford, VA 1539
Stuart House City Museum, Mackinac
Island, MI..752
Stuhr Museum of the Prairie Pioneer,
Grand Island, NE....................................862
Sturdivant Hall, Selma, AL............................18
Sturgis Library, Barnstable, MA..................662
Stutsman County Memorial Museum,
Jamestown, ND......................................1133
Suffolk County Vanderbilt Museum,
Centerport, NY..977
Suffolk Resolves House, Milton, MA 695
Summit County Historical Society,
Akron, OH..1139
Summit Historical Society, Breckenridge,
CO..204
The Sumter County Museum, Sumter, SC.1342
Sun Inn Preservation Association Inc.,
Bethlehem, PA..1243
The Supreme Court of the United States,
Washington, DC......................................291
Surratt House Museum, Clinton, MD..........640
Susan B. Anthony House, Rochester, NY..1060
Susquehanna Museum of Havre de Grace
Inc. at the Lock House, Havre de
Grace, MD..647
Sutton County Historical Society - Miers
Home Museum, Sonora, TX 1453
Swampscott Historical Society (John
Humphrey House), Swampscott, MA......714
Swarthout Memorial Museum, La Crosse,
WI..1603
Sweetwater Creek State Park, Lithia
Springs, GA..376

Swenson Memorial Museum of Stephens
County, Breckenridge, TX....................1397
Swinney Homestead, Fort Wayne, IN 478
Swisher County Archives and Museum
Association, Tulia, TX 1456
Swope Art Museum, Terre Haute, IN...........501

T.B. Ferguson Home, Watonga, OK...........1216
T.C. Steele State Historic Site, Nashville,
IN..493
T.J. Elder Community Center,
Sandersville, GA......................................384
Tabor Opera House Museum, Leadville,
CO..226
Tacoma Public Library/Thomas
Handforth Gallery, Tacoma, WA............1574
The Taft Museum of Art, Cincinnati, OH ..1151
Talkeetna Historical Society and
Museum, Talkeetna, AK..............................28
Tallahassee Museum, Tallahassee, FL 348
Tante Blanche Museum, Madawaska, ME ...614
Tate House Museum, Portland, ME..............620
Taube Museum of Art, Minot, ND 1135
Taylor-Grady House, Athens, GA..................357
Taylor House Museum, Berlin, MD..............637
Telfair Museum of Art, Savannah, GA 386
Telluride Historical Museum, Telluride,
CO..233
Tempe Historical Museum, Tempe, AZ.........46
Temperance Tavern, Newcomerstown,
OH..1179
The Temple Museum of Religious Art,
Cleveland, OH 1156
Ten Broeck Mansion - Albany County
Historical Association, Albany, NY.........956
Terrace Hill Historic Site and Governor's
Mansion, Des Moines, IA 516
Territorial Capital-Lane Museum,
Lecompton, KS..549
Territorial Statehouse State Park &
Museum, Fillmore, UT............................1465
Terwilliger Museum, Waterloo, NY...........1083
Texarkana Museums System, Texarkana,
TX..1455
Texas Baptist Historical Center Museum,
Brenham, TX 1397
Texas Discovery Gardens, Dallas, TX........1408
Texas Governor's Mansion, Austin, TX.....1391
Texas Historical Commission, Austin, TX.1391
Theodore Roosevelt Inaugural National
Historic Site, Buffalo, NY......................973
Theodore Roosevelt National Park-Visitor
Center, Medora, ND 1134
This Is The Place Heritage Park, Salt
Lake City, UT..1472
Thomas Clarke House/Princeton
Battlefield State Park, Princeton, NJ 922
Thomas Edison Birthplace Museum,
Milan, OH..1176
Thomas Edison House, Louisville, KY.......579
Thomas-Foreman Home, Muskogee, OK...1205
The Thomas Griswold House and
Museum, Guilford, CT............................243
Thomas Hart Benton Home and Studio
State Historic Site, Kansas City, MO......823
Thomas Jefferson's Poplar Forest, Forest,
VA..1504
Thomas Kinkade Museum, Morgan Hill,
CA..129
Thomas L. Kane Memorial Chapel, Kane,
PA..1264
Thomas Warne Historical Museum &
Library, Old Bridge, NJ 918
Thomas Whaley House Museum, San
Diego, CA..161
Thomas Wolfe Memorial, Asheville, NC ...1090
Thomaston Historical Society,
Thomaston, ME..624
Thomasville Cultural Center, Inc.,
Thomasville, GA......................................388
Thornton W. Burgess Museum,
Sandwich, MA..708

Thousand Islands Museum, Clayton, NY.....979
Thunderbird Foundation for the Arts, Mount Carmel, UT 1467
Tillamook County Pioneer Museum, Tillamook, OR 1237
Timucuan Ecological and Historic Preserve and Fort Caroline National Memorial, Jacksonville, FL.....................315
Tinker Swiss Cottage Museum, Rockford, IL...456
Tinley Park Historical Society, Tinley Park, IL..461
Tintic Mining Museum, Eureka, UT 1464
Tippecanoe County Historical Association, Lafayette, IN......................487
Tipton-Haynes Historic Site, Johnson City, TN...1368
Tobias Community Historical Society, Tobias, NE..873
Tolland Historical Society - Tolland County Jail and Warden's Home Museum, Tolland, CT.........................262
Tomball Community Museum Center, Tomball, TX.....................................1455
Tombstone Courthouse State Historic Park, Tombstone, AZ..............................46
Top of Oklahoma Historical Museum, Blackwell, OK 1197
Toppenish Museum, Toppenish, WA 1575
Topsfield Historical Society, Topsfield, MA..714
Torreya State Park, Bristol, FL...................298
Torrington Historical Society, Inc., Torrington, CT.....................................263
Tournament House and Wrigley Gardens, Pasadena, CA..141
Trail End State Historic Site, Sheridan, WY..1638
Traill County Historical Society, Hillsboro, ND 1132
Transylvania Museum, Lexington, KY.........574
Traveler's Rest State Historic Site, Toccoa, GA..389
Travellers Rest Plantation & Museum, Nashville, TN....................................1381
Trenton City Museum, Trenton, NJ.............928
Trenton Historical Museum, Trenton, MI.....765
Tri-Cities Museum, Grand Haven, MI 743
Trinity Museum of the Parish of Trinity Church, New York, NY.........................1040
Troutdale Historical Society, Troutdale, OR...1237
Troy-Hayner Cultural Center, Troy, OH.....1188
Truckee-Donner Historical Society Jail Museum, Truckee, CA 193
The Trustees of Reservations, Beverly, MA..662
Tryon Palace Historic Sites and Gardens, New Bern, NC 1112
Tsa Mo Ga Memorial Museum, Plains, TX..1443
T.T. Wentworth, Jr. Florida State Museum, Pensacola, FL 336
Tu-Endie-Wei State Park, Point Pleasant, WV..1586
Tucson Museum of Art & Historic Block, Tucson, AZ 51
Tucumcari Historical Research Institute, Tucumcari, NM..................................953
Tudor Place Foundation, Inc., Washington, DC.....................................292
Tumacacori National Historical Park, Tumacacori, AZ.......................................52
Turner House Museum, Hattiesburg, MS.....801
Twin Falls County Historical Museum, Filer, ID...405
Twin Falls State Park & Museum, Mullens, WV......................................1585
Twinsburg Historical Society, Twinsburg, OH..1188
Tybee Island Light Station and Tybee Museum, Tybee Island, GA 389

U.S. Navy Museum, Washington, DC..........292
Ulysses S. Grant Cottage State Historic Site, Wilton, NY.....................................1086
Uncle Remus Museum, Eatonton, GA 371
The Union County Historical Society, Marysville, OH 1175
Union County Historical Society, Lewisburg, PA 1268
Union County Museum, Union, OR...........1238
Union Covered Bridge State Historic Site, Paris, MO...828
Union Mills Homestead & Grist Mill, Westminster, MD......................................656
Union Station Kansas City, Inc., Kansas City, MO...823
United States Army Heritage and Education Center - Army Heritage Museum, Carlisle, PA...........................1246
United States Golf Association Museum & Archives, Far Hills, NJ 903
United States Senate Commission on Art, Washington, DC....................................293
University Museum & Historic Houses, The University of Mississippi, Oxford, MS..806
University Museums, University of Delaware, Newark, DE..........................272
University of Washington Botanic Garden, Seattle, WA 1569
Upham Mansion, Marshfield, WI.............1608
Uppertown Firefighters Museum, Astoria, OR...1219
U.S. Army Engineer Museum, Fort Leonard Wood, MO...........................815
U.S. Capitol Historical Society, Washington, DC....................................293
U.S. Grant's Home State Historic Site, Galena, IL..436
USS Alabama Battleship Memorial Park, Mobile, AL...15
USS Constellation Museum, Baltimore, MD..636
Utah State Historical Society, Salt Lake City, UT...1473

Vachel Lindsay Home State Historic Site, Springfield, IL...460
Vaile Mansion-Dewitt Museum, Independence, MO...............................819
Valentine Richmond History Center, Richmond, VA 1532
Valentine-Varian House/Museum of Bronx History, Bronx, NY.....................967
Valley Community Historical Society, Inc., Valley, NE...874
Valley Forge National Historical Park, King of Prussia, PA...............................1264
Van Buren County Historical Society, Keosauqua, IA.....................................521
Van Cortlandt House Museum, Bronx, NY...967
Van Riper-Hopper House Museum, Wayne, NJ...929
Van Wyck Homestead Museum, Fishkill, NY...989
Vandalia Statehouse State Historic Site, Vandalia, IL...462
Vanderbilt Mansion National Historic Site, Hyde Park, NY.................................1002
Vann House, Chatsworth, GA.....................368
Varner-Hogg Plantation State Historic Site, West Columbia, TX 1461
Venango Museum of Art, Science & Industry, Oil City, PA............................1274
The Verdier House, Beaufort, SC...............1321
Vermilion County Museum Society, Danville, IL..429
The Vermont State House, Montpelier, VT..1483
Vernon Historians, Inc., Vernon, VT.........1489
Vernonia Pioneer Museum, Vernonia, OR..1238
Vest-Lindsey House, Frankfort, KY............570

Vesterheim Norwegian-American Museum, Decorah, IA 513
Victor Heritage Museum, Victor, MT..........854
Victoria Mansion, Portland, ME.................620
Victorian Dress Museum, Rugby, ND 1136
Vigo County Historical Museum, Terre Haute, IN...501
Vikingsholm, Tahoma, CA..........................191
Villa Louis Historic Site, Prairie du Chien, WI..1619
Villa Montezuma Museum/San Diego Historical Society, San Diego, CA 162
Villa Terrace Decorative Arts Museum, Milwaukee, WI.....................................1613
Village Historical Society, Inc., Harrison, OH...1168
Village of Elsah Museum, Elsah, IL 433
Vincennes State Historic Site, Indiana Territory, Vincennes, IN 503
Vincennes State Historic Site, Old State Bank, Vincennes, IN.............................503
Virgin Islands National Park, St. John, VI.1644
Virginia Beach Maritime Museum, Inc./The Old Coast Guard Station, Virginia Beach, VA.............................1543
Virginia Department of Conservation and Recreation, Richmond, VA.......................1533
Virginia Historical Society, Richmond, VA...1533
Vista House, Corbett, OR..........................1222
Vizcaya Museum and Gardens, Miami, FL...326
Volcano Art Center, Volcano, HI 402

W.C. Handy Home Museum and Library, Florence, AL...9
The W.H. Stark House, Orange, TX..........1442
W.W. Seymour Botanical Conservatory, Tacoma, WA......................................1574
Wabasha County Museum, Wabasha County Historical Society at Reads Landing, Reads Landing, MN................787
Wade House Stagecoach Inn & Wesley Jung Carriage Museum State Historic Site, Greenbush, WI..............................1599
The Wagnalls Memorial, Lithopolis, OH ...1172
Wagner Free Institute of Science, Philadelphia, PA..................................1289
Wake Forest College Birthplace Society, Inc., Wake Forest, NC...........................1121
Wakefield House Museum, Blue Earth, MN..769
Walkersville, Southern Railroad Museum, Walkersville, MD......................................656
Wallace House, Somerville, NJ...................924
Wallingford Historical Society, Inc., Wallingford, CT.....................................263
Walnut Grove Plantation, Roebuck, SC 1340
Walt Whitman Birthplace State Historic Site and Interpretive Center, Huntington Station, NY.........................1001
Walt Whitman House Museum and Library, Camden, NJ..............................900
Walter F. George Law Office Museum, Vienna, GA..390
Walter P. Chrysler Boyhood Home and Museum, Ellis, KS.................................538
Walter Reed Birthplace, Gloucester County, VA...1508
Ward County Historical Society, Minot, ND...1135
Ward Hall, Georgetown, KY.......................570
Warner House, Portsmouth, NH..................895
Warren County Historical Society, Warren, PA...1304
Warren ICBM & Heritage Museum, Frances E. Warren Air Force Base, WY..1633
Warwick Museum of Art, Warwick, RI......1320
Washburn County Historical Society Museum, Shell Lake, WI 1621

Historic Houses and Historic Buildings—Continued

Washburn Historical Museum & Cultural Center, Inc. aka Washburn Cultural Center, Washburn, WI 1625

Washington County Historical Association, Fort Calhoun, NE................860

Washington County Historical Society, Washington, PA 1305

Washington County Historical Society and Miller House Museum, Hagerstown, MD 646

Washington County Historical Society Inc., West Bend, WI 1627

Washington County Historical Society Warden's House Museum, Stillwater, MN..794

Washington Historical Museum, Washington, GA 391

Washington National Cathedral, Washington, DC 294

Washington Pavilion of Arts and Science, Sioux Falls, SD..............................1357

Washington State Capital Museum and Outreach Center, Olympia, WA 1560

Washington's Headquarters State Historic Site, Newburgh, NY 1042

Water Mill Museum, Water Mill, NY 1082

Waterfront Museum, Brooklyn, NY 970

Waterloo Area Historical Society, Grass Lake, MI 744

Watertown Historical Society, Inc., Watertown, CT.................................264

Watervliet Arsenal's Museum of the Big Guns, Watervliet, NY 1084

Watkins Woolen Mill State Historic Site & Park, Lawson, MO 825

Watson-Curtze Mansion, Erie, PA 1253

Watters Smith Memorial State Park, Lost Creek, WV 1584

Watts Towers Arts Center, Los Angeles, CA 122

Wauconda Township Historical Society, Wauconda, IL.................................463

Wave Hill, Bronx, NY............................967

Waveland State Historic Site, Lexington, KY 574

Wayland Historical Society, Wayland, MA 716

Wayne County Historical Museum, Richmond, IN 497

Wayne County Historical Society, Wooster, OH 1192

Wayne County Historical Society, Honesdale, PA 1261

Weaverville Joss House, Weaverville, CA ...197

The Webb-Deane-Stevens Museum, Wethersfield, CT.............................266

Webb House Museum, Newark, OH 1179

Webster House Museum, Elkhorn, WI 1596

Weems-Botts Museum, Dumfries, VA......1503

Weir Farm National Historic Site, Wilton, CT 267

Wells County Historical Museum, Bluffton, IN.....................................470

Wells County Museum, Fessenden, ND 1131

Wenham Museum, Wenham, MA 717

Wentworth-Coolidge Mansion, Portsmouth, NH 895

Wentworth Gardner & Tobias Lear Houses Association, Portsmouth, NH 895

West Allis Historical Society Museum, West Allis, WI 1626

West Chicago City Museum, West Chicago, IL 464

West Milford Museum, West Milford, NJ....930

West of the Pecos Museum, Pecos, TX 1443

West Pasco Historical Society Museum and Library, New Port Richey, FL 329

West River Museum Society, Philip, SD....1353

West Virginia Independence Hall, Wheeling, WV 1588

West Virginia State Farm Museum, Point Pleasant, WV 1586

Westerly Public Library, Westerly, RI 1320

Western Heritage Center, Billings, MT 841

Western Reserve Historical Society, Cleveland, OH 1156

Western Springs Historical Society, Western Springs, IL............................464

Westminster Historical Society, Westminster, VT 1490

Westport Historical Society, Westport, CT...266

Westport Maritime Museum, Westport, WA 1578

The Wethersfield Historical Society, Wethersfield, CT...............................266

Wexford County Historical Society & Museum, Cadillac, MI.......................731

The Whalehead Club, Corolla, NC............1097

Wharton County Historical Museum, Wharton, TX 1461

Whatcom Museum of History and Art, Bellingham, WA 1549

Wheat Ridge Historic Park, Wheat Ridge, CO 235

Wheeler Historic Farm, Salt Lake City, UT 1474

Whipple House Museum, Ashland Historical Society, Ashland, NH 883

Whiskeytown Unit, Whiskeytown-Shasta-Trinity National Recreation Area, Whiskeytown, CA........198

Whistler House Museum of Art, Lowell, MA 692

White County Historical Society, Carmi, IL 415

White Deer Land Museum, Pampa, TX 1442

White Hall State Historic Site, Richmond, KY 583

The White House, Washington, DC............294

The White River Museum, Meeker, CO 228

Whitehall Museum House, Middletown, RI 1312

Whitehaven Tourist Welcome Center, Paducah, KY 582

Whitehead Memorial Museum, Del Rio, TX 1409

Whitewater Canal State Historic Site, Metamora, IN 490

Whitewater Historical Museum, Whitewater, WI 1628

Whitley County Historical Museum, Columbia City, IN 472

Whittier Home Association, Amesbury, MA 658

Wichita-Sedgwick County Historical Museum Association, Wichita, KS 563

Wickersham House Museum (Tanana-Yukon Historical Society), Fairbanks, AK..................................24

Wilbur Wright Birthplace & Interpretive Center, Hagerstown, IN....................480

Wilderness Road Regional Museum, Newbern, VA 1519

Wildling Art Museum, Los Olivos, CA 123

Wildwood Center, Nebraska City, NE 869

Wilhelm Reich Museum - Orgonon, Rangeley, ME 621

Wilkinson County Museum, Woodville, MS 810

Will Rogers State Historic Park, Pacific Palisades, CA 137

Willa Cather Pioneer Memorial and Educational Foundation, Red Cloud, NE 872

Willard House and Clock Museum, Inc., Grafton, MA 685

William A. Farnsworth Library and Art Museum, Inc. d/b/a Farnsworth Art Museum, Rockland, ME....................621

William B. Ide Adobe State Historic Park, Red Bluff, CA 146

William Clark Market House Museum, Paducah, KY 582

William Cullen Bryant Homestead, Cummington, MA 678

William Heath Davis House Museum administered by Gaslamp Quarter Historical Foundation, San Diego, CA....162

William Henry Harrison Mansion, Grouseland, Vincennes, IN...................503

William Holmes McGuffey Museum, Oxford, OH 1181

William Howard Taft National Historic Site, Cincinnati, OH 1151

William S. Hart County Park & Museum, Newhall, CA 130

William Whitley House State Historic Site, Stanford, KY 584

Williamson County Historical Society, Marion, IL 444

Wilmington Railroad Museum, Wilmington, NC 1124

Wilson Castle, Proctor, VT 1485

Wilson County Historical Society Museum, Fredonia, KS........................540

Wilton Historical Museums, Wilton, CT......267

Wilton House Museum, Richmond, VA 1534

Winchendon Historical Society, Inc., Winchendon, MA 720

Winchester-Frederick County Historical Society, Inc., Winchester, VA 1546

Windham Textile and History Museum (The Mill Museum), Willimantic, CT 267

Windmill Island Municipal Park, Holland, MI 747

The Wine Museum of Greyton H. Taylor, Hammondsport, NY..........................997

Winedale, Center for American History, University of Texas at Austin, Round Top, TX 1446

Winnie Davis Museum of History, Gaffney, SC 1333

Winslow Crocker House, Yarmouth Port, MA 722

Winston Churchill Memorial and Library, Fulton, MO 816

Winterset Art Center, Winterset, IA............531

Winterthur Museum & Country Estate, Winterthur, DE 274

Wise County Heritage Museum, Decatur, TX 1408

Wistariahurst Museum, Holyoke, MA.........687

Witte Museum, San Antonio, TX 1451

Wolcott House Museum Complex, Maumee, OH 1175

Woldumar Nature Center, Lansing, MI 751

Wolf House Museum, Manhattan, KS.........552

Wolfeboro Historical Society, Wolfeboro, NH 897

Wood County Historical Center and Museum, Bowling Green, OH 1143

Woodburn Historic House, Pendleton, SC .1339

Woodlawn Museum/The Black House, Ellsworth, ME 610

Woodlawn Plantation Museum, Alexandria, VA 1494

Woodmere Art Museum, Philadelphia, PA.1289

Woodrow Wilson House, Washington, DC 294

Woodrow Wilson Presidential Library at His Birthplace, Staunton, VA................1537

Woodside Store Historic Site, Woodside, CA 199

Woodson County Historical Society, Yates Center, KS..............................564

Woodstock Historical Society, Inc., Woodstock, VT 1491

Woodstock Museum of Shenandoah County, Inc., Woodstock, VA................1546

Workman & Temple Family Homestead Museum, City of Industry, CA 85

Worthington Historical Society, Worthington, OH 1192

Wren's Nest, Atlanta, GA 364

Wright's Ferry Mansion, Columbia, PA 1248
Wyandot County Historical Society,
    Upper Sandusky, OH 1188
Wyandotte Museum, Wyandotte, MI 766
Wyatt Earp Birthplace Home, Monmouth,
    IL 445
Wyck, Philadelphia, PA 1289
The Wyckoff Farmhouse Museum,
    Brooklyn, NY 970
Wylie House Museum, Bloomington, IN 470
The Wyman Tavern, Keene, NH.................890

Yankee Air Force, Inc. (Yankee Air
    Museum), Ypsilanti, MI 766
Yates County Genealogical and Historical
    Society and Oliver House Museum
    and L. Caroline Underwood Museum,
    Penn Yan, NY 1052
Ybor City Museum State Park, Tampa,
    FL 351
Yellowstone Gateway Museum of Park
    County, Livingston, MT 850
Yesteryear House-Central Mine,
    Clarkston, MI 732
Yolo County Historical Museum,
    Woodland, CA 199
Yorba and Slaughter Families Adobe,
    Chino, CA 84
York County Heritage Trust, Fire
    Museum, York, PA 1309
Yorktown Historical Museum, Yorktown,
    TX 1462
The Yosemite Museum, National Park
    Service, Yosemite National Park, CA......199
Ypsilanti Historical Museum, Ypsilanti,
    MI 767
Yucaipa Adobe, Yucaipa, CA 200
Yuma Crossing State Historic Park,
    Yuma, AZ 54
Yuma Territorial Prison State Historic
    Park, Yuma, AZ 54

Z. Taylor Brown-Sarah Dorsey House,
    Midland, TX 1439
Zalud House, Porterville, CA......................144
Zane Grey Museum, Lackawaxen, PA 1265
Zebulon B. Vance Birthplace State
    Historic Site, Weaverville, NC..............1122
Zelienople Historical Society, Zelienople,
    PA 1309
Zion Historical Society, Zion, IL.................467

Historic Sites

Abbie Gardner Cabin, Arnolds Park, IA 505
Abington Art Center, Jenkintown, PA 1263
Abraham Lincoln Birthplace National
    Historic Site, Hodgenville, KY...............571
Adams County Historical Museum,
    Decatur, IN 474
Adams County Historical Society,
    Gettysburg, PA..1255
Adams National Historical Park, Quincy,
    MA 704
Adams National Historical Park-John
    Adams and John Quincy Adams
    Birthplaces, Quincy, MA..........................704
Adena Mansion and Gardens, Chillicothe,
    OH 1147
Adobe De Palomares, Pomona, CA.............143
Agate Fossil Beds National Monument,
    Harrison, NE...862
Agua Mansa Pioneer Memorial Cemetery,
    Colton, CA..87
Aiken County Historical Museum, Aiken,
    SC 1320
Air Mobility Command Museum, Dover
    AFB, DE..270
Alamance Battleground State Historic
    Site, Burlington, NC...............................1092
The Alamo, San Antonio, TX 1447
Alaska Indian Arts, Inc., Haines, AK............24
Alcatraz Island, San Francisco, CA.............163

Alden Historical Society, Inc., Alden, NY ...956
Alden House Historic Site, Duxbury, MA ...680
Alexander Ramsey House, Minnesota
    Historical Society, Saint Paul, MN..........789
Alfred B. Maclay State Gardens,
    Tallahassee, FL...346
Allaire Village Inc., Farmingdale, NJ...........903
Allegan County Historical Society and
    Old Jail Museum, Allegan, MI 723
Allegany County Historical Society, Inc.,
    Cumberland, MD 641
Allegheny Portage Railroad National
    Historic Site and Johnstown Flood
    National Memorial, Gallitzin, PA 1255
Amador County Museum, Jackson, CA 105
Amelia Earhart Birthplace Museum,
    Atchison, KS...532
Amelia Island Museum of History,
    Fernandina Beach, FL 306
American Independence Museum, Exeter,
    NH 887
American Labor Museum, Botto House
    National Landmark, Haledon, NJ 906
American Precision Museum Association,
    Inc., Windsor, VT 1490
American West Heritage Center,
    Wellsville, UT 1475
Americas Society, New York, NY 1020
America's Stonehenge, North Salem, NH....893
Amherst History Museum at the Strong
    House - Amherst Historical Society,
    Amherst, MA..658
Anasazi State Park Museum, Boulder, UT.1463
Ancient Spanish Monastery of St.
    Bernard de Clairvaux Cloisters, North
    Miami Beach, FL 329
Andersonville National Historic Site,
    Andersonville, GA....................................355
Andover Historical Society, Andover, MA...660
Andrew Johnson National Historic Site,
    Greeneville, TN 1366
Andrew Low House, Savannah, GA 384
Angel Mounds State Historic Site,
    Evansville, IN 475
Anson County Historical Society, Inc.,
    Wadesboro, NC 1121
Antelope Valley Indian Museum,
    Lancaster, CA 108
Antietam National Battlefield-Visitor
    Center, Sharpsburg, MD...........................653
Apostles Islands National Lakeshore,
    Bayfield, WI 1591
Appomattox Court House National
    Historical Park, Appomattox, VA 1495
APVA Preservation Virginia, Richmond,
    VA 1528
APVA's John Marshall House, Richmond,
    VA 1528
Argo Gold Mine & Mill Museum, Idaho
    Springs, CO 223
Arizona Historical Society-Fort Lowell
    Museum, Tucson, AZ 47
Arizona Jewish Historical Society,
    Phoenix, AZ 39
Armand Bayou Nature Center, Houston,
    TX 1424
The Arms Family Museum of Local
    History, Youngstown, OH.......................1193
Arrow Rock State Historic Site, Arrow
    Rock, MO 810
Art and Culture Center of Hollywood,
    Hollywood, FL..312
Art Association of Randolph County,
    Inc., Union City, IN 501
Arthurdale Heritage, Inc., Arthurdale,
    WV 1579
Ash Hollow State Historical Park,
    Lewellen, NE..864
Ashland, The Henry Clay Estate,
    Lexington, KY...572
Ashtabula County Historical Society,
    Geneva-on-the-Lake, OH 1166

Asistencia: San Gabriel Mission Outpost,
    Redlands, CA..146
Astor House Museum, Golden, CO.............219
Astors' Beechwood Mansion - Living
    History Museum, Newport, RI...............1313
The Athenaeum of Philadelphia,
    Philadelphia, PA 1276
Atlantic Heritage Center, Somers Point,
    NJ 924
Atwater Kent Museum of Philadelphia,
    Philadelphia, PA 1276
Atwood House Museum, Home of
    Chatham Historical Society, Chatham,
    MA 675
Audubon County Historical Society,
    Exira, IA 517
Audubon House & Tropical Gardens,
    Key West, FL..317
Avery Research Center for African
    American History & Culture,
    Charleston, SC 1323
Awbury Arboretum, Philadelphia, PA.........1277
Aztalan Museum, Jefferson, WI................1601

The Babe Ruth Museum and Sports
    Legends at Camden Yards, Baltimore,
    MD 629
Bacon's Castle, Surry County, VA.............1540
The Bade Institute of Biblical
    Archaeology and The Howell Bible
    Collection, Berkeley, CA 75
Badger Mine and Museum, Shullsburg,
    WI 1622
Baltimore & Ohio Railroad Museum,
    Baltimore, MD..629
Baltimore Civil War Museum, Baltimore,
    MD 629
Baltimore Maritime Museum, Baltimore,
    MD 630
Bandelier National Monument, Los
    Alamos, NM 942
Baranov Museum, Kodiak, AK......................26
The Barbara Fritchie House, Frederick,
    MD 644
The Barnacle Historic State Park,
    Coconut Grove, FL...................................300
Barnard's Mill Art Museum, Glen Rose,
    TX 1422
Barre Historical Society, Inc., Barre, MA....662
Barrington Living History Farm,
    Washington, TX 1460
Bartow History Center, Cartersville, GA 367
Batsto Village, Hammonton, NJ.................907
Battle of Lexington State Historic Site,
    Lexington, MO 826
Battleground Historical Society,
    Englishtown, NJ 903
Battles for Chattanooga Museum,
    Lookout Mountain, TN 1371
Battleship Texas State Historic Site, La
    Porte, TX 1433
Baxter Springs Heritage Center and
    Museum, Baxter Springs, KS....................533
Bay Area Museum, Seabrook, TX.............1452
Bayard Cutting Arboretum, Great River,
    NY 996
Bayou Bend Collection and Gardens,
    Houston, TX 1425
Bear Mountain Trailside Museums and
    Zoo, Bear Mountain, NY 961
Beauvais Heritage Center, Clark, SD 1345
Beauvoir, The Jefferson Davis Home and
    Presidential Library, Biloxi, MS..............798
Beck Cultural Exchange Center,
    Knoxville, TN 1369
Bedford Historical Society Museum and
    Library, Bedford, OH 1142
Belcourt Castle, Newport, RI....................1313
Bellamy Mansion Museum of History
    and Design Arts, Wilmington, NC.........1122
Belle Grove Plantation, Middletown, VA..1517
Belle Meade Plantation, Nashville, TN 1377

Historic Sites–Continued

Bellingrath Gardens & Home, Theodore, AL 18

Beloit Historical Society, Beloit, WI 1592

Belvedere Castle-Henry Luce Nature Observatory, New York, NY 1021

Bement-Billings Farmstead, Newark Valley, NY 1041

The Benjamin Banneker Park & Museum, Baltimore, MD 631

Bennett Place State Historic Site, Durham, NC 1098

Bennington Battle Monument, Old Bennington, VT 1484

Bennington Battlefield State Historic Site, Walloomsac, NY 1081

Benson Grist Mill, Stansbury Park, UT 1475

Bentonville Battlefield State Historic Site, Four Oaks, NC 1102

Bent's Old Fort National Historic Site, La Junta, CO 224

Berkeley Plantation, Charles City, VA 1498

Berkshire County Historical Society, Inc. - Arrowhead, Pittsfield, MA 702

Berkshire Scenic Railway Museum, Inc., Lenox, MA 689

Bernard Judaica Museum, Congregation Emanu-El of the City of New York, New York, NY 1021

Berrien County Historical Association, Berrien Springs, MI...........................729

The Berry Botanic Garden, Portland, OR ..1230

Bethel Historical Society Regional History Center, Bethel, ME.....................606

Betsy Ross House and Flag Museum, Philadelphia, PA 1277

Betts House Research Center, Cincinnati, OH 1148

The Bidwell House Museum, Monterey, MA 695

Biedenharn Coca-Cola Museum, Vicksburg, MS 809

Big Bone Lick State Park Museum, Union, KY 584

The Big Duck, Hampton Bays, NY.............997

Big Hole National Battlefield, Wisdom, MT 855

Big Thunder Gold Mine, Keystone, SD 1349

Big Well, Greensburg, KS......................542

Bill Baggs Cape Florida State Park, Key Biscayne, FL 316

Biltmore Estate, Asheville, NC.................1089

Birmingham Historical Museum & Park, Birmingham, MI 730

Birthplace of John Wayne, Winterset, IA.....530

Bishop Hill Heritage Museum, Bishop Hill, IL 413

Bishop Hill State Historic Site, Bishop Hill, IL 413

Black Hawk State Historic Site: Hauberg Indian Museum, Rock Island, IL.............453

Blackman House Museum, Snohomish, WA 1570

Blandford Church & Reception Ctr. (The Petersburg Museums), Petersburg, VA ..1524

Blount Mansion, Knoxville, TN 1369

Bluff Hall Antebellum Home and Museum, Demopolis, AL.....................7

Boca Raton Historical Society, Boca Raton, FL 296

Bodie State Historic Park, Bridgeport, CA 79

Bollinger Mill State Historic Site, Burfordville, MO 811

Bonnet House Museum & Gardens, Fort Lauderdale, FL 306

Bonneyville Mill, Bristol, IN.......................471

Booker T. Washington National Monument, Hardy, VA 1510

Boone's Lick State Historic Site, Boonesboro, MO...............................811

The Boorman House - The Juneau County Historical Society, Mauston, WI 1608

Boot Hill Museum, Inc., Dodge City, KS 536

Boston Center for Jewish Heritage, Boston, MA 663

Boston Fire Museum, Boston, MA.............664

Boston National Historical Park, Boston, MA 664

Botanical Gardens at Asheville, Asheville, NC 1089

Boulder City/Hoover Dam Museum, Boulder City, NV 875

Bowdoin College Museum of Art, Brunswick, ME 607

Bowers Mansion, Washoe Valley, NV 882

The Bowne House Historical Society, Flushing, NY 990

Boys Town Hall of History & Father Flanagan House, Boys Town, NE...........858

Bradford Brinton Memorial & Museum, Big Horn, WY 1628

Bradford Ohio Railroad Museum, Bradford, OH 1143

Brandywine Battlefield Park, Chadds Ford, PA 1246

Brandywine River Museum, Chadds Ford, PA 1246

Brimstone Museum, Sulphur, LA 602

Bronck Museum, Coxsackie, NY 983

Brown Mansion, Coffeyville, KS.................535

Brownsville Museum of Fine Art - Brownsville Art League, Brownsville, TX 1398

Browntown Museum, Lake City, SC...........1336

Brucemore, Cedar Rapids, IA......................509

Brunswick Town/Fort Anderson State Historic Site, Winnabow, NC 1124

Buccleuch Mansion, New Brunswick, NJ....915

Bucyrus Historical Society, Bucyrus, OH ..1144

Buena Park Historical Society, Buena Park, CA 80

Buffalo and Erie County Historical Society, Buffalo, NY 972

Buffalo Bill Cody Homestead, Princeton, IA 527

Buffalo National River, Harrison, AR 59

Burlington Historical Museum, Burlington, MA 672

Burnham Tavern, Machias, ME...................614

Burnside Plantation, Inc., Bethlehem, PA ..1242

Burrowes Mansion Museum, Matawan, NJ 911

Bushy Run Battlefield, Jeannette, PA.........1263

Butterfield Trail Historical Museum, Russell Springs, KS...........................557

C.H. Nash Museum-Chucalissa Archaeological Museum, Memphis, TN 1372

CSS Neuse State Historic Site and Gov. Richard Caswell Memorial, Kinston, NC 1108

Cabrillo National Monument, San Diego, CA 156

Cahokia Courthouse State Historic Site, Cahokia, IL 415

California Oil Museum, Santa Paula, CA 183

Calvin Coolidge Historic Site, Plymouth Notch, VT 1484

The Calvin Coolidge Memorial Foundation, Inc., Plymouth, VT 1484

Cambridge Historical Society, Cambridge, MA 672

Camp Atterbury Museum, Edinburgh, IN 474

Camp Five Museum Foundation, Inc., Laona, WI 1604

Camp Floyd/Stagecoach Inn State Park, Fairfield, UT 1465

Camp Hancock State Historic Site, Bismarck, ND 1127

Campbell Historical Museum & Ainsley House, Campbell, CA.........................80

Campo de Cahuenga, North Hollywood, CA 131

Canterbury Shaker Village, Inc., Canterbury, NH...............................883

Caparra Museum and Historic Park, Guaynabo, PR 1641

Capitol Visitors Center, a Division of the State Preservation Board, Austin, TX....1389

Captain George Flavel House Museum, Astoria, OR 1218

Carl Sandburg Home National Historic Site, Flat Rock, NC 1101

Carlyle House Historic Park, Alexandria, VA 1492

Carroll County Farm Museum, Westminster, MD 656

Carroll Mansion Museum Home of Leavenworth County Historical Society, Leavenworth, KS.....................549

Carry A. Nation Home Memorial, Medicine Lodge, KS 553

The Carter House Association, Inc., Franklin, TN 1365

Carter's Grove, Williamsburg, VA.............1544

Cary Cottage, Cincinnati, OH 1148

Casa Adobe de San Rafael, Glendale, CA ...100

Casa Grande Ruins National Monument, Coolidge, AZ 31

Casa Grande Valley Historical Society & Museum, Casa Grande, AZ.................30

Casa Navarro State Historical Park, San Antonio, TX 1448

Casemate Museum, Fort Monroe, VA 1505

Castillo de San Marcos National Monument, Saint Augustine, FL.............338

Castle Clinton National Monument, New York, NY 1021

Catawba County Museum of History, Newton, NC 1113

Cattaraugus Area Historical Center, Cattaraugus, NY 976

Cayuga Museum & Case Research Lab Museum, Auburn, NY 959

Cayuga-Owasco Lakes Historical Society, Moravia, NY 1015

Centennial Village Museum, Greeley, CO ...221

Center for American History, Austin, TX....1390

Center for Wooden Boats, Seattle, WA 1565

Centerville - Washington Township Historical Society & Asahel Wright Community Center, Centerville, OH 1146

Centerville - Washington Township Historical Society & Walton House Museum, Centerville, OH 1147

Central High School National Historic Site, Little Rock, AR...............................61

Central Park Conservancy, New York, NY 1022

Centre County Historical Society, State College, PA 1301

Century House Historical Society, Rosendale, NY 1061

Charles A. Lindbergh Historic Site, Little Falls, MN 779

Charles B. Aycock Birthplace State Historic Site, Fremont, NC 1102

Charles Pinckney National Historic Site, Mount Pleasant, SC 1337

Charles River Museum of Industry, Waltham, MA 715

Charles Towne Landing State Historic Site, Charleston, SC 1324

Charlotte Museum of History and Hezekiah Alexander Homesite, Charlotte, NC 1094

Chateau De Mores State Historic Site, Medora, ND 1134

Chattahoochee River National Recreation Area, Atlanta, GA 359

Cherokee National Museum, Park Hill, OK 1211

Cherokee Strip Museum, Alva, OK...........1195

Cherry Valley Museum, Cherry Valley, NY 978

Chesapeake and Ohio Canal National Historical Park, Hagerstown, MD 646

The Chesapeake Beach Railway Museum, Chesapeake Beach, MD 639

Chickasaw Council House Museum, Tishomingo, OK 1214

Chickasaw County Historical Society Bradford Pioneer Village Museum, Nashua, IA 525

Chief Plenty Coups Museum, Pryor, MT 852

The Children's Museum of Rose Hill Manor Park, Frederick, MD 644

Chimney Point State Historic Site, Addison, VT 1475

Chippewa Valley Museum, Inc., Eau Claire, WI 1595

Chittenango Landing Canal Boat Museum, Chittenango, NY 978

Christiansted National Historic Site, Saint Croix, VI 1644

City of Burlington Historical Society, Burlington, NJ 899

City of Las Cruces Museum System, Las Cruces, NM 940

Civil War Museum of Lonejack, Jackson County, Lone Jack, MO 826

Clara Barton Birthplace, North Oxford, MA 699

Clara Barton National Historic Site, Glen Echo, MD 645

Clarke House Museum, Chicago, IL 420

Clearfield County Historical Society, Clearfield, PA 1247

Clermont State Historic Site, Clermont, NY 979

Clinton Academy, East Hampton, NY 985

Cliveden of the National Trust, Philadelphia, PA 1278

Clovis Big Dry Creek Historical Museum, Clovis, CA 86

Coarsegold Historic Museum, Coarsegold, CA 86

Coe Hall, Oyster Bay, NY 1049

Coggeshall Farm Museum, Bristol, RI 1310

Cokato Museum & Akerlund Photography Studio, Cokato, MN...........771

Colfax County Society of Art, History and Archaeology, Raton, NM...................945

College Park Aviation Museum, College Park, MD 641

Collis P. Huntington Railroad Historical Society, Inc., Huntington, WV 1583

Colonel Allensworth State Historic Park, Allensworth, CA 70

Colonel Davenport Historical Foundation, Rock Island, IL 453

Colonel William Jones State Historic Site/Lincoln State Park & Colonel Jones Home, Lincoln City, IN 488

Colonial National Historical Park: Jamestown & Yorktown, Yorktown, VA 1546

The Colonial Spanish Quarter Museum, Saint Augustine, FL 338

Colony House, Newport, RI......................1313

Colton Area Museum, Colton, CA 87

Columbia State Historic Park, Columbia, CA 87

Comanche Crossing Historical Society & Museum, Strasburg, CO 233

Compass Inn Museum, Laughlintown, PA .1267

Comstock Historic House, Moorhead, MN 784

Confederate Memorial State Historic Site, Higginsville, MO 817

Connecticut Audubon Birdcraft Museum, Fairfield, CT 240

Conrad Mansion National Historic Site Museum, Kalispell, MT 850

Constitution Island Association, West Point, NY 1085

Constitution Square State Historic Site, Danville, KY 567

The Contemporary Museum, Honolulu, HI 394

Cookeville Depot Museum, Cookeville, TN 1364

Coos Art Museum, Coos Bay, OR.............1222

The Corcoran Gallery of Art, Washington, DC......................................277

Cornell Museum of Art & History, Delray Beach, FL 304

Coronado State Monument, Bernalillo, NM 937

Corydon Capitol Historic Site, Corydon, IN 473

Courthouse Square Association, Charlotte, MI 731

The Cowley County Historical Society, Winfield, KS 564

Cowpens National Battlefield, Chesnee, SC 1327

Cragfont-Historic Cragfont, Inc., Castalian Springs, TN 1360

Crailo State Historic Site, Rensselaer, NY.1056

Cranbrook Art Museum, Bloomfield Hills, MI 730

Cranbury Historical & Preservation Society, Cranbury, NJ 902

Crater of Diamonds State Park Museum, Murfreesboro, AR 65

Cravens House, Lookout Mountain, TN 1371

Crawford W. Long Museum, Jefferson, GA 374

Crow Wing County Historical Society, Brainerd, MN 769

Crown Point State Historic Site, Crown Point, NY 984

Crystal Caverns at Hupp's Hill, Strasburg, VA 1538

Crystal Lake Falls Historical Association, Barton, VT 1476

Culbertson Mansion State Historic Site, New Albany, IN 493

Cultural Rights and Protection Department/Ute Indian Tribe, Fort Duchesne, UT 1465

Cumberland Island National Seashore, Saint Marys, GA 382

The Currier Museum of Art, Manchester, NH 891

Curwood Castle, Owosso, MI...................759

Custer Battlefield Museum, Garryowen, MT 847

Custer State Park, Custer, SD 1346

Dade Battlefield Historic State Park, Bushnell, FL 298

Dakota County Historical Society, South Saint Paul, MN 793

Dakota Discovery Museum, Mitchell, SD..1352

Dakotaland Museum, Huron, SD...............1348

Dallas Arboretum & Botanical Garden, Dallas, TX 1404

Dallas Heritage Village at Old City Park, Dallas, TX 1405

Daniel Boone Home and Boonesfield Village, Lindenwood University, Defiance, MO 814

Daniel Boone Homestead, Birdsboro, PA ..1243

Darnall's Chance House Museum, M-NCPPC, Upper Marlboro, MD 655

Davenport House Museum, Savannah, GA 384

David Bradford House, Washington, PA ...1305

David Conklin Farmhouse, Huntington, NY 1000

Dayton Historical Depot Society, Dayton, WA 1552

Dayton History at Carillon Park, Dayton, OH 1161

Dearborn Historical Museum, Dearborn, MI 733

Decatur County Last Indian Raid Museum, Oberlin, KS...........................554

Decatur House Museum, Washington, DC...277

Deer Isle-Stonington Historical Society, Deer Isle, ME 609

Delaware Division of Historical & Cultural Affairs, Dover, DE 269

The Dennison Railroad Depot Museum, Dennison, OH 1162

Denver Botanic Gardens, Inc., Denver, CO 210

Department of the Treasury, Washington, DC 278

The Depot Museum Complex, Henderson, TX 1424

Depot Park Museum, Sonoma, CA 187

Descanso Gardens Guild, Inc., La Canada Flintridge, CA 105

Deutschheim State Historic Site, Hermann, MO 817

Dewey Hotel Museum, Dewey, OK 1199

Dickson Mounds Museum, Lewistown, IL 442

Dr Pepper Museum and Free Enterprise Institute, Waco, TX......................................1458

Dodge County Historical Society, Mantorville, MN 780

Dodge County Historical Society Museum, Beaver Dam, WI 1591

Donald G. Trayser Memorial Museum/Barnstable County Customs House, Barnstable, MA 661

Donkey Milk House, Historic Home, Key West, FL 317

Donner Memorial State Park and Emigrant Trail Museum, Truckee, CA 192

Door County Maritime Museum (at Gills Rock), Gills Rock, WI 1598

Dorothy G. Page Museum, Wasilla, AK 29

Douglas County Historical Society - Carson Valley Museum & Cultural Center, Gardnerville, NV 877

Douglas County Historical Society - Genoa Courthouse Museum, Genoa, NV 877

Downieville Museum, Downieville, CA 91

Dows Depot Welcome Center, Dows, IA.....516

Drake Well Museum, Titusville, PA 1303

Drayton Hall, Charleston, SC 1325

Drum Barracks Civil War Museum, Wilmington, CA 198

Duke Homestead State Historic Site, Durham, NC 1098

Dumbarton Oaks Research Library & Collections, Washington, DC 278

Duncan Cottage Museum, Metlakatla, AK.....27

Durham Center Museum/Research Library, East Durham, NY 985

Durham Western Heritage Museum, Omaha, NE 870

Dutchess County Historical Society, Poughkeepsie, NY 1054

The Dwight Frederick Boyden Gallery, Saint Mary's City, MD 652

Dyckman Farmhouse Museum and Park, New York, NY 1025

E. St. Julien Cox House, Saint Peter, MN ...792

Eagle Bluff Lighthouse, Fish Creek, WI 1597

East Hampton Historical Society, Inc., East Hampton, NY 985

East Hillsborough Historical Society, Inc., Plant City, FL 337

Eastern State Penitentiary Historic Site, Philadelphia, PA 1278

Eastside Heritage Center, Bellevue, WA 1548

The Eckhart House, Wheeling, WV 1587

Edgar Allan Poe Museum, Richmond, VA.1529

Edgar Allan Poe National Historic Site, Philadelphia, PA 1278

Edge of the Cedars State Park Museum, Blanding, UT 1463

Historic Sites–Continued

Edmonds South Snohomish County Historical Society, Inc., Edmonds, WA .1553

Edna Historical Museum, Edna, KS.............537

Edsel & Eleanor Ford House, Grosse Pointe Shores, MI....................................745

Edward Hopper Landmark Preservation Foundation, Nyack, NY 1044

Egan Maritime Foundation, Nantucket, MA 695

1859 Jail, Marshal's Home & Museum, Independence, MO.................................817

Eisenhower Birthplace State Historical Site, Denison, TX.................................1409

Eisenhower National Historic Site, Gettysburg, PA..................................1255

El Morro National Monument, Ramah, NM 945

El Pueblo Historical Monument, Los Angeles, CA......................................114

El Rancho de Las Golondrinas Museum, Santa Fe, NM......................................947

Elbert Hubbard-Roycroft Museum, East Aurora, NY...985

Elfreth's Alley Association, Philadelphia, PA 1279

Eli Whitney Museum, Inc., Hamden, CT.....244

Elisabet Ney Museum, Austin, TX.............1390

Ella Sharp Museum, Jackson, MI.............748

Ellis County Museum, Inc., Waxahachie, TX..1460

Elverhoj Museum of History and Art, Solvang, CA..187

Emil A. Blackmore Museum of The American Legion, Indianapolis, IN 482

Emmett Kelly Historical Museum, Sedan, KS 558

End-O-Line Railroad Park & Museum, Currie, MN...772

Enfield Shaker Museum, Enfield, NH.........887

Enos Mills Cabin Museum & Gallery, Estes Park, CO......................................215

Environmental Education Center, Somerset County Park Commission, Basking Ridge, NJ....................................898

Ephrata Cloister, Ephrata, PA 1251

Erie Canal Village, Rome, NY 1061

Ernest Hemingway House Museum, Key West, FL..317

Ethan Allen Homestead Museum & Historic Site, Burlington, VT.................1478

Eugene O'Neill National Historic Site, Danville, CA..89

Ezra Meeker Mansion, Puyallup, WA 1564

Fairbanks House, Dedham, MA.....................679

Fairfax County Park Authority, Resource Management Division, Fairfax, VA........1503

Fairfax Museum & Visitor Center, Fairfax, VA..1503

Fairfield County Museum, Winnsboro, SC 1343

Fairlawn Mansion & Museum, Superior, WI 1624

Fairmount Historical Museum & Gift Shop, Fairmount, IN...............................476

Faith Trumbull Chapter, Daughters of the American Revolution, Inc., Museum and Chapter House, Norwich, CT 258

Fall River County Historical Museum, Hot Springs, SD...................................1348

Fall River Historical Society Museum, Fall River, MA......................................682

Falls of the Ohio State Park, Clarksville, IN 472

Farm House Museum, Ames, IA 505

Faust Park Foundation, Chesterfield, MO 812

Faust Park-Thornhill Historic Site & 19th Century Village, Chesterfield, MO.........812

Fayette Historic State Park, Garden, MI 742

Filoli Center, Woodside, CA.......................199

First Consolidated School in Minnesota, Saum, MN...793

Fisher Grove Country School/Fisher Grove State Park, Frankfort, SD............1347

Flagler Museum, Palm Beach, FL.................333

Flint Ridge State Memorial Museum, Glenford, OH......................................1166

Florence Griswold Museum, Old Lyme, CT 258

Florence Ranch Homestead, Mesquite, TX..1438

Florida Gulf Coast Railroad Museum, Parrish, FL...335

Flowerdew Hundred Foundation, Hopewell, VA......................................1511

Folsom History Museum, Folsom, CA...........95

The Folsom House Museum, Taylors Falls, MN...794

Ford's Theatre National Historic Site (Lincoln Museum), Washington, DC.......279

Forest Capital State Museum, Perry, FL 337

Forest History Center, Grand Rapids, MN...777

Forestiere Underground Gardens, Fresno, CA 97

Former Governors' Mansion State Historic Site, Bismarck, ND.................1128

Fort Abercrombie State Historic Site, Abercrombie, ND 1127

Fort Ancient Museum, Oregonia, OH.........1181

The Fort at No. 4 Living History Museum, Charlestown, NH.................884

Fort Atkinson State Historical Park, Fort Calhoun, NE..860

Fort Bedford Museum, Bedford, PA...........1241

Fort Benton Museum of the Upper Missouri, Fort Benton, MT.................846

Fort Bowie National Historic Site, Bowie, AZ...30

Fort Bridger State Museum, Fort Bridger, WY..1632

Fort Buenaventura, Ogden, UT..................1468

Fort Buford State Historic Site, Williston, ND..1137

Fort Casey Interpretive Center, Coupeville, WA......................................1551

Fort Caspar Museum, Casper, WY 1629

Fort Clark Trading Post State Historic Site, Center, ND 1129

Fort Clatsop National Memorial, Astoria, OR..1218

Fort Columbia Interpretive Center, Chinook, WA......................................1551

Fort Concho National Historic Landmark, San Angelo, TX...................................1447

Fort Croghan Museum, Burnet, TX.............1398

Fort Davidson State Historic Site, Pilot Knob, MO...828

Fort Davis National Historic Site, Fort Davis, TX...1414

Fort de Chartres State Historic Site & Museum, Prairie du Rocher, IL 451

Fort Delaware Society, Delaware City, DE..268

Fort Dobbs State Historic Site, Statesville, NC......................................1120

Fort Douglas Military Museum, Fort Douglas, UT......................................1465

Fort Fetterman State Historic Site, Douglas, WY......................................1631

Fort Fisher State Historic Site, Kure Beach, NC...1108

Fort Frederick State Park, Big Pool, MD.....637

Fort Garland Museum, Fort Garland, CO 217

Fort Harker Museum Complex, Kanopolis, KS......................................546

Fort Henrietta Interpretive Park, Echo, OR..1223

Fort Hill (The John C. Calhoun House), Clemson, SC......................................1328

Fort Hunter Mansion & Park, Harrisburg, PA..1258

Fort Inglish, Bonham, TX.............................1396

Fort Jones Museum, Fort Jones, CA 96

Fort Kearny State Historical Park, Kearney, NE......................................864

Fort King George Historic Site, Darien, GA..370

Fort Knox State Historic Site, Prospect, ME..620

Fort Laramie National Historic Site, Fort Laramie, WY......................................1633

Fort Larned National Historic Site, Larned, KS...547

Fort Laurens State Memorial, Bolivar, OH..1143

Fort Leaton State Historical Site, Presidio, TX......................................1444

Fort Lee Historic Park & Museum, Fort Lee, NJ...904

Fort Ligonier Association, Ligonier, PA....1269

Fort MacArthur Museum, San Pedro, CA....176

Fort Massac State Park and Historic Site, Metropolis, IL......................................445

Fort McAllister, Richmond Hill, GA...........381

Fort McHenry National Monument and Historic Shrine, Baltimore, MD.......632

Fort McKavett State Historical Site, Fort McKavett, TX...................................1415

Fort Mifflin, Philadelphia, PA 1279

Fort Mountain State Park, Chatsworth, GA..368

Fort Nashborough, Nashville, TN.............1379

Fort Necessity National Battlefield, Farmington, PA...................................1253

Fort Nisqually Living History Museum, Tacoma, WA......................................1573

Fort Okanogan Interpretive Center, Brewster, WA......................................1550

Fort Ontario State Historic Site, Oswego, NY..1048

Fort Osage National Historic Landmark, Sibley, MO...838

Fort Phil Kearny, Banner, WY..................1628

Fort Pike State Historic Site, New Orleans, LA......................................595

Fort Plain Museum, Fort Plain, NY 991

Fort Point National Historic Site, San Francisco, CA......................................165

Fort Pulaski National Monument, Savannah, GA......................................385

Fort Raleigh National Historic Site, Manteo, NC......................................1110

Fort Richardson State Historical Park, Jacksboro, TX...................................1431

Fort St. Jean Baptiste State Historic Site, Natchitoches, LA.................................593

Fort Sam Houston Museum, Fort Sam Houston, TX...................................1415

Fort Scott National Historic Site, Fort Scott, KS...540

Fort Sidney Museum & Post Commander's Home, Sidney, NE...........873

Fort Sill National Historic Landmark, Fort Sill, OK......................................1201

Fort Sisseton State Historic Park, Lake City, SD...1350

Fort Smith National Historic Site, Fort Smith, AR...58

Fort Spokane Visitor Center and Museum, Davenport, WA.....................1552

Fort Stanwix National Monument, Rome, NY..1061

Fort Sumner State Monument, Fort Sumner, NM......................................939

Fort Sumter National Monument, Sullivan's Island, SC.................................1342

Fort Tejon State Historic Park, Lebec, CA..108

Fort Ticonderoga, Ticonderoga, NY...........1078

Fort Totten State Historic Site, Fort Totten, ND......................................1131

Fort Towson Historic Site, Fort Towson, OK..1201

Fort Uncompahgre Living History Museum, Delta, CO.................................209

Fort Union National Monument, Watrous, NM 954
Fort Union Trading Post National Historic Site, Williston, ND 1138
Fort Vancouver National Historic Site, Vancouver, WA 1576
Fort Verde State Historic Park, Camp Verde, AZ....................................30
Fort Walla Walla Museum, Walla Walla, WA 1576
Fort Ward Museum and Historic Site, Alexandria, VA 1492
Fort Washita, Durant, OK 1199
Fort Wayne Firefighters Museum, Fort Wayne, IN..477
Fort William Henry Museum, Lake George, NY 1008
Fort Winnebago Surgeons Quarters, Portage, WI 1618
Fort Worth Zoological Park, Fort Worth, TX 1417
Fort Yargo State Park, Winder, GA 391
Fort Zachary Taylor State Historical Site, Key West, FL 317
Forts Folle Avoine Historic Park, Danbury, WI 1594
Fosterfields Living Historical Farm, Morristown, NJ...................................913
Foundation For Historic Christ Church, Inc., Irvington, VA.............................1511
Fountain Rock Nature Center, Walkersville, MD...................................656
4-H Schoolhouse Museum, Clarion, IA 510
Four Mile Historic Park, Denver, CO 212
Francisco Fort Museum, La Veta, CO..........224
Frank Lloyd Wright's Pope-Leighey House, Alexandria, VA...........................1492
Franklin D. Roosevelt Presidential Library-Museum, Hyde Park, NY 1002
The Franklin Pierce Homestead, Hillsborough, NH...................................889
Frederick Douglass National Historic Site, Washington, DC 279
Frederick Law Olmsted National Historic Site, Brookline, MA 671
Fredericksburg & Spotsylvania National Military Park, Fredericksburg, VA.........1506
French Azilum, Inc., Towanda, PA 1303
French Cable Station Museum in Orleans, Orleans, MA 701
The French Legation Museum, Austin, TX 1390
The Friends of Peace Church, Camp Hill, PA 1245
The Friends of the Caleb Pusey House, Inc., Upland, PA..................................1304
Friendship Hill National Historic Site, Point Marion, PA..................................1295
Front Street, Ogallala, NE...........................869
Frontera Audubon Society, Weslaco, TX.....1460
The Fullerton Arboretum, Fullerton, CA........98
Fulton County Historical Society Museum, Rochester, IN............................498
Fulton County Museum, Groversville, NY 996
Furnace Town Living Heritage Museum, Snow Hill, MD 654

Gadsby's Tavern Museum, Alexandria, VA 1492
Gage County Historical Society and Museum, Beatrice, NE 857
Gaineswood, Demopolis, AL 7
Gallier House, New Orleans, LA..................595
Galloway House and Village - Blakely Museum, Fond du Lac, WI 1597
Ganondagan State Historic Site, Victor, NY 1081
Gardner House Museum, Albion, MI 723
The Gardner Museum of Architecture & Design, Quincy, IL 452
Garfield Farm Museum, LaFox, IL 441

Garibaldi and Meucci Museum, Staten Island, NY 1072
Gathland State Park, Boonsboro, MD 637
Gene Stratton-Porter State Historic Site, Rome City, IN......................................498
General Daniel Bissell House, Saint Louis, MO 833
General Grant National Memorial, New York, NY 1026
General Patton Memorial Museum, Chiriaco Summit, CA............................84
General Wait House, Waitsfield, VT..........1489
Geneva Historical Society & Rose Hill Mansion, Geneva, NY 994
Geographical Center Historical Museum, Rugby, ND 1136
George Ade Memorial Association Inc., Brook, IN 471
George Washington Birthplace National Monument, Colonial Beach, VA 1502
George Washington Carver National Monument, Diamond, MO 814
George Washington's Ferry Farm, Stafford County, VA 1537
George Washington's Fredericksburg Foundation, Historic Kenmore & Washington's Ferry Farm, Fredericksburg, VA 1506
Georgia Capitol Museum, Atlanta, GA 360
Georgia's Old Capital Museum, Milledgeville, GA 380
Gettysburg National Military Park, Gettysburg, PA 1255
Gibbs Museum of Pioneer and Dakotah Life, Falcon Heights, MN 775
The Gilbert Stuart Birthplace and Museum, Saunderstown, RI 1319
Gilman Museum, Hellertown, PA 1260
Gingras Trading Post State Historic Site, Walhalla, ND 1137
The Glebe House Museum and Gertrude Jekyll Garden, Woodbury, CT................268
Glendower State Memorial, Lebanon, OH.1171
Glensheen Historic Estate, Duluth, MN 773
Gnadenhutten Historical Park & Museum, Gnadenhutten, OH 1167
Golden Ball Tavern Museum, Weston, MA 718
Golden Spike National Historic Site, Brigham City, UT..................................1463
Goliad State Park, Goliad, TX....................1423
Gomez Foundation for Mill House, Marlboro, NY 1014
Goodman Museum, Tyler, TX 1456
Goodnow Museum State Historic Site, Manhattan, KS......................................550
Gore Place, Waltham, MA 715
Governor Bent Museum, Taos, NM 952
Governor Henry Lippitt House Museum, Providence, RI......................................1316
Governor John Sevier Memorial Association, Knoxville, TN....................1370
Governor Printz Park, Essington, PA 1253
Governor Ross Plantation, Seaford, DE 272
Governor's Mansion, Columbia, SC...........1329
Governor's Mansion State Historic Park, Sacramento, CA......................................152
The Gracie Mansion Conservancy, New York, NY 1026
Graeme Park, Horsham, PA 1261
Graham County Historical Society, Thatcher, AZ..46
Grand Forks County Historical Society, Grand Forks, ND..................................1132
Grand Lake Area Historical Society, Grand Lake, CO......................................221
Grand Portage National Monument, Grand Marais, MN 776
Grand Traverse Heritage Center, Traverse City, MI 765
Grand Village of the Natchez Indians, Natchez, MS......................................805

Grant County Historical Museum, Canyon City, OR..................................1221
Grant County Museum, Medford, OK........1205
Grant-Kohrs Ranch National Historic Site, Deer Lodge, MT.............................845
Grants Pass Museum of Art, Grants Pass, OR 1225
Granville Museum, Inc., Granville, TN....1366
Grave Creek Mound Archaeology Complex, Moundsville, WV 1585
Gravette Historical Museum, Gravette, AR 59
Great Explorations, The Childrens Museum, Saint Petersburg, FL............341
Great Lakes Shipwreck Museum, Paradise, MI 760
The Great Overland Station, Topeka, KS.....559
Greater Loveland Historical Society Museum, Loveland, OH 1173
Greenbelt Museum, Greenbelt, MD............646
Greene County Historical Museum, Waynesburg, PA 1306
Grinter Place State Historic Site, Kansas City, KS 546
Grissom Air Museum, Peru, IN 496
Grosse Ile Historical Society, Grosse Ile, MI 745
Guernsey County Museum, Cambridge, OH 1144
Gulf Islands National Seashore, Gulf Breeze, FL 312
Gunston Hall Plantation, Mason Neck, VA 1517
Gwinnett Historical Society, Lawrenceville, GA.............................376

Hacienda Buena Vista, Ponce, PR 1642
The Hagley Museum and Library, Wilmington, DE......................................273
Hahns Peak Area Historical Society and School House, Clark, CO......................205
Hallockville Museum Farm, Riverhead, NY 1057
Hamden Historical Society, Inc., Hamden, CT......................................244
Hamilton Van Wagoner Museum, Clifton, NJ 901
Hampton County Historical Museum, Hampton, SC......................................1334
Hampton National Historic Site, Towson, MD 655
Hana Cultural Center, Hana, Maui, HI.........392
Hancock Shaker Village, Inc., Pittsfield, MA 703
Hanford Mills Museum, East Meredith, NY 987
Hanley House, Clayton, MO........................813
Hanover House, Clemson, SC 1328
Harbor Defense Museum, Brooklyn, NY.....969
Harn Homestead and 1889er Museum, Oklahoma City, OK...............................1207
The Harness Racing Museum and Hall of Fame, Goshen, NY..................................995
Harpers Ferry Center, Harpers Ferry, WV .1582
Harpers Ferry National Historical Park, Harpers Ferry, WV..................................1582
Harriet Beecher Stowe Center, Hartford, CT 245
Harrison House, Branford, CT....................235
Harry P. Leu Gardens, Orlando, FL 331
Harry S. Truman Little White House Museum, Key West, FL.........................317
Harry S Truman National Historic Site - Truman Farm Home, Grandview, MO 816
Harry S Truman National Historic Site - Truman Home, Independence, MO.........818
Harry S. Truman Office & Courtroom, Independence, MO..................................818
Harvard Historical Society, Still River, MA 711
Hatton-Eielson Museum & Historical Association, Hatton, ND 1132
Hawkeye Log Cabin, Burlington, IA............507

Historic Sites–Continued

Hawks Nest State Park, Ansted, WV 1579

Hay House Museum, Macon, GA 377

Hearthstone Historic House Museum, Appleton, WI 1589

Heavener Runestone State Park, Heavener, OK 1202

Hemet Museum, Hemet, CA........................103

Henrico County Historic Preservation & Museum Services, Richmond, VA 1529

Henry B. Plant Museum, Tampa, FL............349

The Henry Ford, Dearborn, MI 733

Henry Ford Estate-Fair Lane, Dearborn, MI..734

Herbert Hoover National Historic Site, West Branch, IA 530

Hereford Inlet Lighthouse, North Wildwood, NJ...917

Heritage Farmstead Museum, Plano, TX ..1444

Heritage Hill State Historical Park, Green Bay, WI 1599

The Heritage Society, Houston, TX............1426

Heritage Village, Largo, FL 321

Herkimer Home State Historic Site, Little Falls, NY 1009

Hermann-Grima/Gallier Historic Houses, New Orleans, LA.....................................595

The Hermitage, Ho-Ho-Kus, NJ 907

Hernando Heritage Museum, Brooksville, FL..298

Herschell Carrousel Factory Museum, North Tonawanda, NY 1043

Hershey Gardens, Hershey, PA 1260

The Hickories Museum of the Lorain County Historical Society, Elyria, OH ..1163

Hickory Hill, Thomson, GA 388

Hiddenite Center, Inc., Hiddenite, NC........1106

Higgins Armory Museum, Worcester, MA...721

High Cliff Historical Society & General Store Museum, Sherwood, WI...............1622

Hillforest House Museum, Aurora, IN 468

Hillsboro Museums, Hillsboro, KS................544

Hillwood Museum & Gardens, Washington, DC......................................280

Hinckley Fire Museum, Hinckley, MN 778

Historic Annapolis Foundation, Annapolis, MD 628

Historic Arkansas Museum, Little Rock, AR..62

Historic Bath State Historic Site, Bath, NC..1091

Historic Bethabara Park, Winston-Salem, NC..1125

Historic Bethany, Bethany, WV 1580

Historic Bok Sanctuary, Lake Wales, FL ...320

Historic Brattonsville, McConnells, SC......1336

Historic Charlton Park Village and Museum, Hastings, MI............................745

Historic Cherry Hill, Albany, NY 954

Historic Columbia Foundation, Columbia, SC..1329

Historic Crab Orchard Museum & Pioneer Park, Inc., Tazewell, VA 1541

Historic Deerfield, Inc., Deerfield, MA 679

Historic Edenton State Historic Site, Edenton, NC...1099

Historic Fort Snelling, Saint Paul, MN 790

Historic Fort Steilacoom, Lakewood, WA...1558

Historic Fort Stockton, Fort Stockton, TX.1416

Historic General Dodge House, Council Bluffs, IA 512

Historic Governors' Mansion, Cheyenne, WY..1630

Historic Halifax State Historic Site, Halifax, NC...1105

Historic Homes Foundation, Inc., Louisville, KY...576

Historic Hope Foundation, Inc., Windsor, NC..1124

Historic House Trust of New York City, New York, NY...1027

Historic Hudson Valley, Tarrytown, NY.....1077

Historic Indian Agency House, Portage, WI...1618

Historic Jamestowne, Jamestown, VA 1512

Historic Jefferson College, Washington, MS..810

Historic Latta Plantation, Huntersville, NC..1107

Historic Lincoln, Lincoln, NM 941

Historic London Town and Gardens, Edgewater, MD 642

Historic Lyme Village Association, Bellevue, OH 1142

Historic Macon Foundation, Inc. - Sidney Lanier Cottage House Museum, Macon, GA 377

Historic Mobile Preservation Society, Mobile, AL..14

Historic New Harmony, New Harmony, IN 494

Historic Oakland Cemetery, Atlanta, GA ...360

Historic Occoquan, Inc., Occoquan, VA.....1523

Historic Preservation Association of Bourbon County, Inc., Fort Scott, KS 540

Historic Pullman Foundation, Chicago, IL...421

Historic Richmond Town, Staten Island, NY..1072

Historic St. Mary's City, Saint Mary's City, MD 652

Historic Spanish Point, Osprey, FL 333

Historic Speedwell, Morristown, NJ............913

Historic Waco Foundation, Waco, TX 1459

Historic Walnford, Upper Freehold Twp., NJ...929

Historic Warrior Run Church, Watsontown, PA......................................1306

Historical and Genealogical Society of Indiana County, Indiana, PA 1262

Historical Museum-Archival Center, Mission Hills, CA.....................................126

Historical Museum at Fort Missoula, Missoula, MT...851

The Historical Museum at St. Gertrude, Cottonwood, ID 405

Historical Shrine Foundation of San Diego County, San Diego, CA.................156

Historical Society of Brookfield, Brookfield Center, VT 1477

The Historical Society of Dauphin County, Harrisburg, PA 1258

Historical Society of Fort Washington, Fort Washington, PA 1254

The Historical Society of Frederick County, Inc., Frederick, MD 644

Historical Society of Glastonbury, Glastonbury, CT.......................................242

Historical Society of Old Newbury, Cushing House Museum, Newburyport, MA..................................698

Historical Society of Old Yarmouth, Yarmouth Port, MA.................................722

Historical Society of Quaker Hill & Pawling, Pawling, NY...........................1051

Historical Society of Quincy and Adams County, Quincy, IL....................................452

Historical Society of Rockland County, New City, NY..1017

Historical Society of Stanton County Museums at Stanton and Pilger, Pilger, NE..872

Historical Society of the Tonawandas, Inc., Tonawanda, NY..............................1078

Historical Society of the Town of Clarence, Clarence, NY...........................978

The Historical Society of Trappe, Collegeville, Perkiomen Valley, Inc., Trappe, PA 1303

History San Jose, San Jose, CA...................171

Hiwan Homestead Museum, Evergreen, CO..215

Hixon House, La Crosse, WI...................1603

Hockaday Museum of Art, Kalispell, MT....850

Hodgden House Museum Complex, Ellsworth, KS..538

Holy Trinity (Old Swedes) Church & Hendrickson House Museum, Wilmington, DE......................................274

Home of Stone (The Mueller-Schmidt House 1881), a Ford County Museum, curated by Ford County Historic Society, Dodge City, KS 537

Home Sweet Home Museum, East Hampton, NY..986

Homolovi Ruins State Park, Winslow, AZ.....53

Hoover Historical Center, North Canton, OH..1179

Hope Lodge and Mather Mill, Fort Washington, PA 1254

Hopewell Furnace National Historic Site, Elverson, PA 1251

Hopewell Museum, Paris, KY 582

Horseshoe Bend National Military Park, Daviston, AL..7

Hot Spring County Museum - The Boyle House/1876 Log Cabin, Malvern, AR 63

Houghton County Historical Museum Society, Lake Linden, MI.......................749

House in the Horseshoe State Historic Site, Sanford, NC....................................1119

The House of the Seven Gables, Salem, MA...706

House of the Temple, Washington, DC 280

House of Wickersham State Historical Site, Juneau, AK..25

Howard County Historical Museum, Kokomo, IN 486

Howell Historical Society & Committee Museum, Howell, NJ.................................908

Hubbardton Battlefield Museum, Hubbardton, VT....................................1480

Hubbell Trading Post National Historic Site, Ganado, AZ.......................................34

Huddleston Farmhouse Inn Museum, Cambridge City, IN.................................471

Hugh Mercer Apothecary Shop, Fredericksburg, VA.................................1506

The Huguenot Historical Society, New Paltz, NY 1017

Hunter Museum of American Art, Chattanooga, TN...................................1362

Hurst Ranch Historical Foundation, West Covina, CA...197

Hutchinson County Museum, Borger, TX..1397

Hyde Hall, Inc., Cooperstown, NY 980

The Hyland House, Guilford, CT 243

Ice House Museum, Cedar Falls, IA 508

Illinois and Michigan Canal Commissioners Office Museum, Lockport, IL..443

IMA - Indianapolis Museum of Art, Indianapolis, IN......................................483

Imaginarium Hands-On Museum, Fort Myers, FL..309

Immaculate Conception Catholic Church, Natchitoches, LA.....................................593

Independence Historical Museum, Independence, KS...................................545

Independence National Historical Park, Philadelphia, PA......................................1281

Indian City U.S.A., Anadarko, OK............1195

Indian Hill Historical Society, Cincinnati, OH..1150

Indian Mill Museum State Memorial, Upper Sandusky, OH..............................1188

Indian Springs State Park Museum, Flovilla, GA..372

Indiana State Museum, Indianapolis, IN 484

Indiana War Memorials, Indianapolis, IN 484

Indianapolis Motor Speedway Hall of Fame Museum, Indianapolis, IN..............484

Institute of American Indian Arts Museum, Santa Fe, NM 947

International Images, Ltd., Sewickley, PA .1299

Iolani Palace, Honolulu, HI 396

Iowa Department of Natural Resources, Des Moines, IA 515

Iraan Museum, Iraan, TX 1430

Iron & Steel Museum of Alabama, Tannehill Ironworks Historical State Park, McCalla, AL 13

Ironwood Area Historical Museum, Ironwood, MI...747

Ironworld Discovery Center, Chisholm, MN 771

Island County Historical Society Museum, Coupeville, WA 1551

Isle Royale National Park, Houghton, MI....747

Islesford Historical Museum, Islesford, ME 612

Itasca County Historical Society, Grand Rapids, MN.....................................777

J.W. Parmley Historical Home Society, Ipswich, SD 1349

Jackson County Historical Museum, Lakefield, MN...778

Jacob Hamblin Home, Santa Clara, UT 1474

Jacob Kelley House Museum, Hartsville, SC..1335

James A. Garfield National Historic Site, Mentor, OH......................................1176

James Buchanan Foundation for the Preservation of Wheatland, Lancaster, PA 1266

James K. Polk Ancestral Home, Columbia, TN 1364

Jane Addams Hull-House Museum, University of Illinois Chicago, Chicago, IL..422

Japanese American National Museum, Los Angeles, CA..............................117

Jarrell Plantation Georgia State Historic Site, Juliette, GA...................................374

J.C. Penney Homestead & Historical Foundation, Kemmerer, WY 1635

Jean Lafitte National Historical Park & Preserve, New Orleans, LA 596

Jeffers Petroglyphs Historic Site, Comfrey, MN..771

Jefferson Barracks Historic Site, Saint Louis, MO...833

Jefferson Landing State Historic Site, Jefferson City, MO.....................................819

Jekyll Island Museum, Jekyll Island, GA 374

Jemez State Monument, Jemez Springs, NM 940

Jesse James Farm & Museum, Kearney, MO 823

John Brown Farm State Historic Site, Lake Placid, NY 1009

John Brown Museum State Historic Site, Osawatomie, KS.................................554

John Burroughs Memorial State Historic Site, Roxbury, NY...............................1062

John Deere Historic Site, Dixon, IL.............431

John James Audubon Center at Mill Grove, Audubon, PA 1241

John Jay Homestead State Historic Site, Katonah, NY.......................................1006

John Muir National Historic Site, Martinez, CA 124

John Rains House, Rancho Cucamonga, CA...145

John S. Barry Historical Society, Constantine, MI...732

John Wornall House Museum, Kansas City, MO...821

Johnson County Museums, Shawnee, KS 558

Johnstown Area Heritage Association, Johnstown, PA 1263

Johnstown Flood National Memorial, South Fork, PA 1300

The Jordan House, West Des Moines, IA 530

Jordan Schnitzer Museum of Art, Eugene, OR..1223

Joseph Smith Historic Site, Nauvoo, IL.......447

Joshua Tree National Park, Oasis Visitor Center, Twentynine Palms, CA................193

The Judah P. Benjamin Confederate Memorial at Gamble Plantation Historic State Park, Ellenton, FL.............306

Julia A. Purnell Museum, Snow Hill, MD...654

Kalaupapa National Historical Park, Kalaupapa, HI..400

Kankakee County Museum, Kankakee, IL...441

The Kate Chopin House & Bayou Folk Museum, Cloutierville, LA 588

Kate Shelley Railroad Museum, Boone, IA 506

Kateri Galleries, The National Shrine of the North American Martyrs, Auriesville, NY...959

Kaw Mission State Historic Site, Council Grove, KS..536

Kearney Mansion Museum, Fresno, CA 97

Keeler Tavern Museum, Ridgefield, CT.......259

Kell House Museum, Wichita Falls, TX 1461

Kent Plantation House, Alexandria, LA 585

Ker Place, Onancock, VA 1523

Kerbyville Museum, Kerby, OR 1227

Keweenaw County Historical Society, Eagle Harbor, MI.......................................739

Key West Lighthouse Museum, Key West, FL..318

Key West Tropical Forest & Botanical Garden, Key West, FL...............................318

Kimberly Crest House & Gardens, Redlands, CA..147

King Manor, Jamaica, NY 1004

Kingsley Plantation, Jacksonville, FL 315

Kirkland Museum of Fine & Decorative Art, Denver, CO..212

Kirtland Temple Historic Center, Kirtland, OH...1170

Kit Carson Home & Museum, Inc., Taos, NM 952

Kiwanis Van Slyke Museum Foundation Inc., Caldwell, ID.......................................404

Kline Creek Farm, Winfield, IL....................466

Klondike Gold Rush National Historical Park, Seattle, WA.......................................1566

Klyne Esopus Museum, Ulster Park, NY...1079

Knife River Indian Villages National Historic Site, Stanton, ND.....................1136

Knott House Museum, Tallahassee, FL........347

Knox County Museum, Knoxville, IL...........441

Knox Headquarters State Historic Site, Vails Gate, NY..1080

Kolomoki Mounds State Park Museum, Blakely, GA..366

Kuhlmann King Historical House and Museum, Boerne, TX.................................1396

Kuser Farm Mansion, Hamilton, NJ.............907

Lahaina Restoration Foundation, Lahaina, HI..400

Lake County Historical Society, Two Harbors, MN.....................................794

Lake George Historical Association Museum, Lake George, NY 1008

Lake Jackson Mounds Archaeological State Park, Tallahassee, FL 347

Lake of the Red Cedars Museum, Cedar Lake, IN...472

Lake Wales Depot Museum & Cultural Center, Lake Wales, FL............................320

Lakewood's Heritage Center, Lakewood, CO..225

Land of the Yankee Fork Historic Association Museum, Stanley, ID............410

Landmarks Foundation/Old Alabama Town, Montgomery, AL................................16

Langlade County Historical Society Museum, Antigo, WI..............................1589

Lanier Mansion State Historic Site, Madison, IN...489

The LaPointe-Krebs House & Old Spanish Fort Museum, Pascagoula, MS...807

Laramie Plains Museum, Laramie, WY 1635

Laredo Children's Museum, Laredo, TX....1434

Lars Noak Blacksmith Shop, Larsson/Ostlund Log Home & One-Room Capitol School, New Sweden, ME...616

Laura Ingalls Wilder Museum and Tourist Center, Walnut Grove, MN 795

Laura Ingalls Wilder Park & Museum, Inc., Burr Oak, IA......................................507

Laura Ingalls Wilder-Rose Wilder Lane Historic Home & Museum, Mansfield, MO...827

Laurence C. Jones Museum, Piney Woods, MS..807

Lawrence County Gray House Museum, Ironton, OH...1169

Layland Museum, Cleburne, TX 1400

Le Sault de Sainte Marie Historical Sites, Inc., Sault Ste. Marie, MI.......................764

Leander J. McCormick Observatory, Charlottesville, VA.....................................1499

Lee Chapel and Museum, Lexington, VA ..1513

The Leffingwell House Museum, Norwich, CT..258

The Lemee House, Natchitoches, LA...........593

Lemon Hill Mansion, Philadelphia, PA......1282

Lewis & Clark Boat House and Nature Center, Saint Charles, MO 830

The Lexington Cemetery, Lexington, KY....573

Lexington Historical Society, Lexington, MA...689

Liberty Hall Historic Site, Frankfort, KY 569

Licking County Historical Society, Newark, OH...1178

Light Crust Doughboys Hall of Fame & Museum - Governor Jim Hogg City Park, Quitman, TX 1444

Limberlost State Historic Site, Geneva, IN..479

Lincoln County Historical Museum, Davenport, WA..1552

Lincoln County Historical Society Museum of Pioneer History, Chandler, OK..1197

Lincoln County Museum, Hugo, CO............222

Lincoln Herdon Law Offices State Historic Site, Springfield, IL.....................458

Lincoln Home National Historic Site, Springfield, IL...459

Lincoln Homestead State Park, Springfield, KY..583

Lincoln Log Cabin State Historic Site, Lerna, IL...442

Lincoln Memorial Garden and Nature Center, Springfield, IL................................459

Lincoln State Monument, Lincoln, NM 941

Lincoln Tomb State Historic Site, Springfield, IL...459

Lincoln's New Salem State Historic Site, Petersburg, IL...451

Lisle Station Museum, Lisle, IL...................443

Litchfield Historical Society and Museum, Litchfield, CT...........................247

The Little Brick House, Vandalia, IL...........462

Little Norway, Inc., Blue Mounds, WI.......1593

Little White House Historic Site, Warm Springs, GA..390

The Living Arts and Science Center, Inc., Lexington, KY...573

Living History Farms, Urbandale, IA...........529

Locust Creek Covered Bridge State Historic Site, Laclede, MO 825

Locust Grove, Louisville, KY......................577

Locust Grove, The Samuel Morse Historic Site, Poughkeepsie, NY 1055

Locust Lawn and Terwilliger House, Gardiner, NY...993

Longfellow National Historic Site, Cambridge, MA..673

Historic Sites—Continued

Longstreet Farm, Holmdel, NJ......................908
Lopez Adobe, San Fernando, CA..............162
Loriks Peterson Heritage House, Oldham,
　SD...1352
Los Alamos Historical Museum, Los
　Alamos, NM...942
The Los Angeles County Arboretum &
　Botanic Garden, Arcadia, CA.....................71
Louisiana State Museum, New Orleans,
　LA...596
Louisiana's Old State Capitol, Political
　History Museum, Baton Rouge, LA......587
Lowell National Historical Park, Lowell,
　MA...691
Lowell's Boat Shop, Amesbury, MA...........658
Lower Hudson Conference of Historical
　Agencies and Museums, Elmsford,
　NY..988
Luckhard Museum - The Indian Mission,
　Sebewaing, MI..764
Luther Burbank Home & Gardens, Santa
　Rosa, CA..184
Lutheran Heritage Center & Museum of
　the Perry County Lutheran Historical
　Society, Altenburg, MO...........................810
Lyndhurst, Tarrytown, NY 1078
Lyndon B. Johnson National Historical
　Park, Johnson City, TX..........................1431
Lyndon House Art, Athens, GA...................356
Lynnhaven House, Virginia Beach, VA......1542

Mabee Farm Historic Site, Rotterdam
　Junction, NY..1062
Mabel Hartzell Historical Home,
　Alliance, OH...1139
Mabry-Hazen House, Knoxville, TN.........1371
Mackinac Island State Park
　Commission-Mackinac State Historic
　Parks, Mackinaw City, MI.......................752
Mackinac State Historic Parks-Colonial
　Michilimackinac & Old Mackinac
　Point Lighthouse, Mackinaw City, MI 752
Mackinac State Historic Parks-Fort
　Mackinac & Mackinac Island State
　Park, Mackinac Island, MI......................752
Mackinac State Historic Parks-Historic
　Mill Creek, Mackinaw City, MI 753
Macon County Historical Society
　Museum Complex, Decatur, IL...............430
The Madam Brett Homestead, Beacon,
　NY..961
Madeline Island Historical Museum, La
　Pointe, WI..1603
Madison County Historical Society,
　Winterset, IA..531
Madison Historical Society, Madison, CT....247
Madison Museum of Fine Art, Madison,
　GA..378
Magevney House, Memphis, TN................1373
Maggie L. Walker National Historic Site,
　Richmond, VA 1530
Magnolia Plantation and Gardens,
　Charleston, SC.......................................1326
Mahaffie Stagecoach Stop and Farm,
　Olathe, KS..554
Maidu Interpretive Center, Roseville, CA....151
Maine Historical Society, Portland, ME....619
Maine Maritime Museum, Bath, ME...........606
The Major General Frederick Funston
　Boyhood Home and Museum, Iola,
　KS..546
Malibu Lagoon Museum, Malibu, CA 123
Mallory-Neely House, Memphis, TN.........1373
Mamie Doud Eisenhower Birthplace,
　Boone, IA..506
Mammoth Site of Hot Springs, Inc., Hot
　Springs, SD..1348
Manassas Museum System, Manassas,
　VA..1516
Manassas National Battlefield Park,
　Manassas, VA 1516

Manatee Village Historical Park,
　Bradenton, FL...297
Manchester Historical Society,
　Manchester, MA.......................................692
Mandeville Gallery, Union College,
　Schenectady, NY....................................1067
Mansfield State Historic Site - Civil War
　Battlefield, Mansfield, LA.......................591
Marble Historical Society, Marble, CO........228
Marblehead Arts Association - King
　Hooper Mansion, Marblehead, MA........693
Marietta House Museum, Glenn Dale,
　MD...645
Marietta Museum of History, Marietta,
　GA..379
Marin Museum of the American Indian,
　Novato, CA...131
Marion Historical Museums, Inc. -
　Granger House, Marion, IA.....................523
Maritime Industry Museum at Fort
　Schuyler, Bronx, NY..............................966
Maritime Museum at Historic Coast
　Guard Station, Saint Simons Island,
　GA..383
Marjorie Kinnan Rawlings Historic State
　Park, Cross Creek, FL.............................301
Mark Twain Birthplace State Historic
　Site, Florida, MO....................................815
The Mark Twain House & Museum,
　Hartford, CT...245
Marland's Grand Home, Ponca City, OK...1212
Marshall Gold Discovery State Historic
　Park, Coloma, CA.....................................86
The Marston House/San Diego Historical
　Society, San Diego, CA 157
Martin Luther King, Jr. Center for
　Nonviolent Social Change, Inc.,
　Atlanta, GA...361
Martin Luther King, Jr. National Historic
　Site and Preservation District, Atlanta,
　GA..361
Mary McLeod Bethune Council House
　National Historic Site, Washington,
　DC..283
Mary Todd Lincoln House, Lexington,
　KY..574
MASS MoCA, North Adams, MA 698
Mathias Ham House Historic Site,
　Dubuque, IA..516
Matthew Edel Blacksmith Shop,
　Haverhill, IA...519
Maude I. Kerns Art Center, Eugene, OR ...1223
Mc Cook County Historical Society and
　Museum, Salem, SD...............................1355
McAllister House Museum, Colorado
　Springs, CO..207
McConaghy House, Hayward, CA 102
McCone County Museum, Circle, MT........844
McKee Botanical Garden, Vero Beach,
　FL..352
McLarty Treasure Museum, Vero Beach,
　FL..352
McLean County Museum of History,
　Bloomington, IL.....................................414
McPherson County Old Mill Museum
　and Park, Lindsborg, KS.........................550
Meadow Garden Museum, Augusta, GA.....365
Medina County Historical Society, The
　John Smart House, Medina, OH............1175
Melrose Plantation Home Complex,
　Melrose, LA..592
Memorial Art Gallery of the University
　of Rochester, Rochester, NY.................1059
Merced County Courthouse Museum,
　Merced, CA...125
Meriwether Lewis National Monument,
　Hohenwald, TN.....................................1367
Merrill Historical Museum, Merrill, WI...1609
Mesa Historical Museum, Mesa, AZ.............37
Mesa Verde National Park Museum,
　Mesa Verde National Park, CO...............228
Metamora Courthouse Historic Site,
　Metamora, IL..444

Michie Tavern ca. 1784, Charlottesville,
　VA..1499
Michigan Historical Museum, Michigan
　Historical Center, Lansing, MI 750
Michigan Transit Museum, Inc., Mount
　Clemens, MI..756
Middleborough Historical Association,
　Inc., Middleborough, MA.......................694
Middleton Place Foundation, Charleston,
　SC..1326
Miles B. Carpenter Museum, Waverly,
　VA..1543
Mill Race Historical Village, Northville,
　MI..758
Milton Historical Museum, Milton, VT 1482
Milton House Museum Historic Site,
　Milton, WI...1610
Milwaukee County Historical Society,
　Milwaukee, WI......................................1611
Miners Foundry Cultural Center, Nevada
　City, CA...129
Minnesota Historical Society, Saint Paul,
　MN...791
Minnesota Historical Society's North
　West Company Fur Post, Pine City,
　MN...786
Minnesota State Capitol Historic Site,
　Saint Paul, MN..791
Minter Field Air Museum, Shafter, CA........186
The Mission House, Stockbridge, MA 712
Mission Inn Foundation/Museum,
　Riverside, CA..149
Mission San Antonio de Padua, Jolon,
　CA..105
Mission San Diego de Alcala, San Diego,
　CA..157
Mission San Juan Capistrano Museum,
　San Juan Capistrano, CA 173
Mission San Luis Rey Museum,
　Oceanside, CA...135
Mississippi Governor's Mansion,
　Jackson, MS..802
Mississippi Society Daughters of the
　American Revolution Rosalie House
　Museum, Natchez, MS............................805
Missouri State Museum, Jefferson City,
　MO...819
Missouri Town 1855, Lee's Summit, MO....825
Moanalua Gardens Foundation, Honolulu,
　HI..397
Moffatt-Ladd House and Garden,
　Portsmouth, NH......................................894
Mohave Museum of History and Arts,
　Kingman, AZ...36
Mohonk Preserve, Inc., Gardiner, NY........993
Moland House, Warrington, PA.................1305
Molly Brown House Museum, Denver,
　CO..213
Molokai Museum and Cultural Center,
　Kualapua, HI...400
Monocacy National Battlefield, Frederick,
　MD...644
Monroe County Historical
　Association/Stroud Mansion,
　Stroudsburg, PA.....................................1302
Montauk Point Lighthouse Museum,
　Montauk, NY...1015
Monterey History and Art Association,
　Monterey, CA..127
Monterey State Historic Park, Monterey,
　CA..128
Montgomery Museum & Lewis Miller
　Regional Art Center, Christiansburg,
　VA..1501
Montpelier Mansion, Laurel, MD...............648
Montpelier-The General Henry Knox
　Museum, Thomaston, ME.......................624
Montrose County Historical Museum,
　Montrose, CO..228
Moody-Bradley House Restoration
　Foundation, Fairfield, TX.....................1413
Moore Home, Lerna, IL..............................442

Moores Creek National Battlefield, Currie, NC 1097

Moorten Botanic Garden and Cactarium, Palm Springs, CA..............138

Mordecai Historic Park, Raleigh, NC.........1115

Morris Arboretum of the University of Pennsylvania, Philadelphia, PA..............1283

Morris-Butler House Museum, Indianapolis, IN 485

Morris-Jumel Mansion, New York, NY 1030

Morristown National Historical Park, Morristown, NJ..............914

Morven Museum & Garden, Princeton, NJ..............922

Morven Park, Leesburg, VA..............1512

Mount Airy Arboretum, Cincinnati, OH.....1150

Mount Clare Museum House, Baltimore, MD..............635

Mount Independence Historic Site, Orwell, VT..............1484

Mt. Pulaski Courthouse State Historic Site, Mount Pulaski, IL 446

Mount Vernon Hotel Museum & Garden, New York, NY..............1031

Mount Vernon Ladies' Association, Mount Vernon, VA..............1518

Mount Washington Museum and The Weather Discovery Center, North Conway, NH..............893

Mountain Farm Museum-Great Smoky Mountains National Park, Cherokee, NC..............1096

Mulford Farm, East Hampton, NY..............986

Museum and Arts Center in the Sequim Dungeness Valley, Sequim, WA..............1570

Museum, Mission San Juan Bautista, San Juan Bautista, CA..............173

Museum of Appalachia, Clinton, TN..........1363

Museum of Chicot County Arkansas, Lake Village, AR..............61

Museum of Florida History, Tallahassee, FL..............348

Museum of Seminole County History, Sanford, FL..............343

Museum of the Cape Fear Historical Complex, Fayetteville, NC..............1101

The Museum of the Confederacy, Richmond, VA..............1531

Museum of the Fur Trade, Chadron, NE......859

Museum of the Great Plains, Lawton, OK.1204

Museum of the Moving Image, Astoria, NY..............958

Museum of the Northern Great Plains, Fort Benton, MT..............846

Museum of the Weston Historical Society, Inc., Weston, MA 718

Museum of Transportation, Saint Louis, MO..............835

Museum of Western Colorado, Grand Junction, CO..............220

Museum of Yachting, Newport, RI............1314

My Old Kentucky Home State Park, Bardstown, KY..............564

Mystic Arts Center, Mystic, CT..............250

Mystic Seaport - The Museum of America and the Sea, Mystic, CT 251

Nantucket Lightship Basket Museum, Nantucket, MA 696

Naper Settlement, Naperville, IL..............447

Nassau County Museum of Art, Roslyn Harbor, NY..............1062

Natchez Trace Parkway, Tupelo, MS............808

Nathaniel W. Faison Home and Museum, La Grange, TX..............1432

The National Aquarium, Washington, DC....284

National Automotive & Truck Museum of the United States, Inc. (NATMUS), Auburn, IN..............468

National Baseball Hall of Fame and Museum, Inc., Cooperstown, NY 981

National Capital Parks-East, Washington, DC..............284

National Civil Rights Museum, Memphis, TN..............1375

National First Ladies' Library, Canton, OH..............1145

National Historic Oregon Trail Interpretive Center, Baker City, OR 1219

National Mississippi River Museum & Aquarium, Dubuque, IA..............516

National Museum of Industrial History, Bethlehem, PA..............1243

National Museum of the American Indian, Smithsonian Institution, New York, NY..............1034

National Park Service-Great Falls Park, McLean, VA..............1517

National Park Service Museum Resource Center, Landover, MD..............648

National Park Service Vicksburg National Military Park-Cairo Museum, Vicksburg, MS..............809

National Railroad Museum and Hall of Fame, Inc., Hamlet, NC 1105

National Route 66 Museum and Old Town Complex, Elk City, OK 1200

National Temple Hill Association, Inc., New Windsor, NY..............1018

Native American Exhibit, National Kateri Shrine, Fonda, NY..............991

Natural Center for the American Revolution, Wayne, PA..............1306

The Nature Center at Shaker Lakes, Cleveland, OH..............1155

Naumkeag, Stockbridge, MA..............712

Nauvoo Historical Society Museum, Nauvoo, IL..............447

Navarro County Historical Society, Pioneer Village, Corsicana, TX..............1402

Navy UDT-SEAL Museum, Fort Pierce, FL..............309

Neill Museum, Fort Davis, TX..............1414

Netherland Inn House Museum & Boatyard Complex, Kingsport, TN........1368

Nevada Northern Railway Museum, Ely, NV..............876

Neversink Valley Area Museum, Cuddebackville, NY 984

The New Berlin Historical Society, New Berlin, WI..............1614

New Castle Historical Society - Horace Greeley House, Chappaqua, NY..........977

New Echota State Historic Site, Calhoun, GA..............367

New England Wireless & Steam Museum Inc., East Greenwich, RI..............1311

New Harmony State Historic Site/Historic New Harmony, New Harmony, IN..............494

New Jersey Botanical Garden at Skylands (NJBG), Ringwood, NJ..............923

New Jersey Naval Museum, Hackensack, NJ..............905

New Jersey Office of Historic Sites, Trenton, NJ..............927

New Jersey State House, Trenton, NJ..........927

New London County Historical Society, New London, CT..............255

New Market Battlefield State Historical Park, New Market, VA..............1519

New Windsor Cantonment State Historic Site and National Purple Heart Hall of Honor, Vails Gate, NY..............1080

The New York Public Library, Astor, Lenox and Tilden Foundations, New York, NY..............1036

New York State Office of Parks, Recreation & Historic Preservation, Albany, NY..............955

New York Transit Museum, Brooklyn Heights, NY..............970

Newark Valley Depot Museum, Newark Valley, NY..............1042

Newaygo County Museum, Newaygo, MI...758

Newport Restoration Foundation, Newport, RI..............1315

The Niagara County Historical Center and Niagara County Genealogical Society, Lockport, NY..............1010

Ninety Six National Historic Site, Ninety Six, SC..............1338

Noden-Reed Farm Museum, Windsor Locks, CT..............268

Nohwike Bagowa, The White Mountain Apache Cultural Center and Museum, Fort Apache, AZ..............34

Nordica Homestead, Farmington, ME.........610

Norfolk Historical Society, Norfolk, VA 1522

Norman #1 Oil Well Museum, Neodesha, KS..............553

Norman Rockwell Museum, Stockbridge, MA..............712

North Carolina Transportation Museum, Spencer, NC..............1120

Northfield Historical Society Museum, Northfield, MN..............785

The Northumberland County Historical Society, Sunbury, PA..............1302

Oak Glen School House Museum, Yucaipa, CA..............200

Oak Hill and The Martha Berry Museum, Rome, GA..............382

Oaklands Historic House Museum, Murfreesboro, TN..............1376

Oatlands, Leesburg, VA..............1512

Oceanographic Teaching Station Inc. - Roundhouse Marine Studies Lab & Aquarium, Manhattan Beach, CA............124

Octagon House, San Francisco, CA 168

The Octagon House, Hudson, WI..............1600

Oklahoma Historical Society, Oklahoma City, OK..............1209

Olana State Historic Site, Hudson, NY 1000

Old Arsenal Powder Magazine Museum, Baton Rouge, LA..............587

Old Barracks Museum, Trenton, NJ 927

Old Bethpage Village Restoration, Old Bethpage, NY..............1045

Old Bohemia Historical Society, Warwick, MD..............656

The Old Church Society, Inc., Portland, OR..............1231

Old Constitution House, Windsor, VT........1490

Old Courthouse Museum, Santa Ana, CA....178

Old Davie School Historical Museum, Davie, FL..............302

Old Dorchester State Historic Site, Summerville, SC..............1342

Old Economy Village, Ambridge, PA.........1240

Old Exchange & Provost Dungeon, Charleston, SC..............1326

Old Fort Jackson, Savannah, GA..............385

Old Fort Johnson, Fort Johnson, NY...........991

Old Fort Meade Museum and Historic Research Association, Fort Meade, SD .1347

Old Fort Niagara, Youngstown, NY 1088

Old Fort Western, Augusta, ME 604

The Old Governor's Mansion, Frankfort, KY..............570

Old Lighthouse Museum, Michigan City, IN..............491

The Old Manse, Concord, MA 677

Old Market House State Historic Site, Galena, IL..............436

Old Mill Museum, El Molino Viejo - Old Mill Foundation, San Marino, CA...........175

Old Mission Santa Ines, Solvang, CA.........187

Old New-Gate Prison and Copper Mine, East Granby, CT..............238

Old Ordinary House Museum, Hingham, MA..............687

Old Prairie Town at Ward-Meade Historic Site, Topeka, KS..............560

Old Prison Museums, Deer Lodge, MT 845

Old Sacramento State Historic Park, Old Sacramento, CA..............135

Historic Sites—Continued

Old St. Paul's Cemetery, Baltimore, MD 636
Old Salem Inc., Winston-Salem, NC 1126
Old Santee Canal Park, Moncks Corner,
  SC...1337
Old Sod Post Office, Grassy Butte, ND 1132
Old South Meeting House, Boston, MA 668
Old State Capitol, Springfield, IL.................459
Old State House Museum, Little Rock,
  AR..63
The Old Tavern Museum, Tuscaloosa, AL.....19
Old Washington Historic State Park,
  Washington, AR..69
Olde Colonial Courthouse, Tales of Cape
  Cod, Inc., Barnstable, MA 661
The Oldest House Museum/Wrecker's
  Museum, Key West, FL................................318
Oliver Kelley Farm, Elk River, MN............774
Olmstead Place State Park, Ellensburg,
  WA...1553
Olmsted County Historical Society,
  Rochester, MN...788
Olustee Battlefield Historic State Park,
  Olustee, FL..331
103rd Ohio Volunteer Infantry Civil War
  Museum, Sheffield Lake, OH.....................1185
Oneida Community Mansion House,
  Oneida, NY 1046
Orange County Historical Museum,
  Hillsborough, NC 1107
Oriskany Battlefield State Historic Site,
  Oriskany, NY 1047
Osage County Historical Society
  Museum, Pawhuska, OK 1211
Osage Nation Tribal Museum, Pawhuska,
  OK...1212
Oswego Historical Museum, Inc.,
  Oswego, KS 555
Ouachita County Historical Society,
  Camden, AR...55
Overfield Tavern Museum, Troy, OH 1188
Overland Trail Museum, Sterling, CO..........232
Overstreet-Kerr Historical Farm, Keota,
  OK...1203
Owensboro Museum of Fine Art, Inc.,
  Owensboro, KY 581
Ozaukee County Pioneer Village,
  Saukville, WI 1620

Pacific Aviation Museum - Pearl Harbor,
  Honolulu, HI..397
Padre Island National Seashore, Corpus
  Christi, TX..1402
Pajaro Valley Historical Association,
  Watsonville, CA...196
PALCO, Scotia, CA.......................................186
Pamplin Historical Park and The National
  Museum of the Civil War Soldier,
  Petersburg, VA...1525
The Pardee Home Museum, Oakland, CA...134
The Park-McCullough House, North
  Bennington, VT..1483
Parks, Recreation & Historic Sites
  Division, Georgia Dept. of Natural
  Resources, Atlanta, GA 362
Parris Island Museum, Parris Island, SC....1338
Parson Fisher House, Blue Hill, ME............606
Patterson Inn Museum/Corning - Painted
  Post Historical Society, Corning, NY 982
Paynes Creek Historic State Park,
  Bowling Green, FL...297
Pea Ridge National Military Park,
  Garfield, AR..58
The Pearl S. Buck House, Perkasie, PA 1275
Pebble Hill Plantation, Thomasville, GA 388
Pecos National Historical Park, Pecos,
  NM...944
Peirce Mill and Peirce Barn, Washington,
  DC...289
Pella Historical Village, Pella, IA.................526

Pendleton District Historical, Recreational
  and Tourism Commission, Pendleton,
  SC...1339
Pendleton Historic Foundation,
  Pendleton, SC...1339
Pennsylvania German Cultural Heritage
  Center at Kutztown University,
  Kutztown, PA...1265
Pennypacker Mills, Schwenksville, PA 1297
Peoria Historical Society, Peoria, IL 451
Perry's Victory & International Peace
  Memorial, Put-in-Bay, OH 1183
Peshtigo Fire Museum, Peshtigo, WI.........1617
Petaluma Adobe State Historic Park,
  Petaluma, CA...142
Peter Conser House, Heavener, OK............1202
Peter Wentz Farmstead, Worcester, PA.......1308
Peter Whitmer Sr. Home and Visitors
  Center, Waterloo, NY 1083
Petersburg National Battlefield,
  Petersburg, VA...1525
Petrified Sea Gardens, Saratoga Springs,
  NY...1065
Pettis County Historical Society, Sedalia,
  MO...838
Philipse Manor Hall State Historic Site,
  Yonkers, NY 1087
Philmont Museums, Cimarron, NM..............938
Piatt Castles, West Liberty, OH 1190
Piatt County Museum, Monticello, IL..........446
The Pierce Manse/New Hampshire
  Political Library, Concord, NH................885
Pierre Menard Home State Historic Site,
  Ellis Grove, IL..433
Pierrepont Museum, Canton, NY 975
Pine Creek Grist Mill, Muscatine, IA 525
Pioneer Arizona Living History Village &
  Museum, Phoenix, AZ.....................................41
Pioneer Heritage Center, Cavalier, ND.......1129
Pioneer Museum and Vereins Kirche,
  Fredericksburg, TX......................................1419
Pioneer Village & Virgil Grissom
  Memorial at Spring Mill State Park,
  Mitchell, IN...491
Pioneer Woman Statue & Museum,
  Ponca City, OK...1212
Pioneers, Trail Drivers and Texas
  Rangers Memorial Museum, San
  Antonio, TX..1449
Pipestone National Monument, Pipestone,
  MN...787
Piqua Historical Area State Memorial,
  Piqua, OH...1182
Pithole Visitor Center, Pleasantville, PA ...1295
Planting Fields Arboretum State Historic
  Park, Oyster Bay, NY..................................1049
Plum Grove Historic Home, Iowa City,
  IA...520
Plumas-Eureka State Park, Blairsden, CA......78
Plumb Farm Learning Center, Greeley,
  CO...222
Pohick Episcopal Church, Lorton, VA 1514
Point Arena Lighthouse and Museum,
  Point Arena, CA...142
Point Fermin Lighthouse, San Pedro, CA....176
Pointe Coupee Museum, New Roads, LA....599
Polk County Historical Society, Des
  Moines, IA...515
Polson Museum, Hoquiam, WA 1556
Pomeroy Living History Farm, Yacolt,
  WA...1578
Ponce DeLeon Inlet Lighthouse
  Preservation Association, Inc., Ponce
  Inlet, FL..337
Pony Express Museum, Saint Joseph,
  MO...831
Poplar Grove Historic Plantation,
  Wilmington, NC..1123
Poricy Park Nature Center, Middletown,
  NJ...911
Port Orford Lifeboat Station, Port Orford,
  OR...1230

The Portal of the Folded Wings Shrine to
  Aviation and Museum, North
  Hollywood, CA...131
Porterville Historical Museum,
  Porterville, CA...144
Portsmouth Historical Association,
  Portsmouth, VA..1526
Postville Courthouse State Historic Site,
  Lincoln, IL...442
Pottsgrove Manor, Pottstown, PA 1295
Pound Ridge Society/Museum, Pound
  Ridge, NY...1055
Prairie Grove Battlefield State Park,
  Prairie Grove, AR..66
Prairie Homestead, Philip, SD....................1353
Prairie Village, Madison, SD.......................1351
Praters Mill Foundation, Varnell, GA..........390
The Preservation Society of Newport
  County/The Newport Mansions,
  Newport, RI..1315
President Chester A. Arthur Historic Site,
  Fairfield, VT...1479
President James K. Polk State Historic
  Site, Pineville, NC.......................................1114
Presidio La Bahia, Goliad, TX....................1423
Prestwould Foundation, Clarksville, VA.....1501
Pricketts Fort, Fairmont, WV.....................1581
Prince William Forest Park Visitor
  Center, Triangle, VA....................................1541
Proprietary House, The Royal Governor's
  Mansion, Perth Amboy, NJ............................921
Puget Sound Coast Artillery Museum at
  Fort Worden, Port Townsend, WA.........1562
Putney Historical Society, Putney, VT.......1485
Puukohola Heiau National Historic Site,
  Kamuela, HI..400

Queen Mary Museum, Long Beach, CA......111
Queens Historical Society, Flushing, NY.....990
Quiet Valley Living Historical Farm,
  Stroudsburg, PA..1302

R.P. Strathearn Historical Park and
  Museum, Simi Valley, CA.............................187
Rachel Carson Homestead, Springdale,
  PA...1301
Railroad Museum of Long Island,
  Riverhead, NY..1057
Ramsey House Museum Plantation,
  Knoxville, TN...1371
Rancho Los Alamitos, Long Beach, CA 111
Rancho Los Cerritos Historic Site, Long
  Beach, CA..111
Randolph Historical Society, Inc.,
  Randolph, VT...1485
Rankin House State Memorial, Ripley,
  OH...1184
Ransom County Historical Society, Fort
  Ransom, ND 1131
Ravine Gardens State Park, Palatka, FL 333
Rebel State Historic Site & Louisiana
  Country Music Museum, Marthaville,
  LA...592
Red Clay State Historic Park, Cleveland,
  TN...1363
Red Hill-Patrick Henry National
  Memorial, Brookneal, VA 1498
Red Mill Museum Village, Clinton, NJ........901
Redington Museum, Waterville, ME............625
Reed Gold Mine State Historic Site,
  Midland, NC...1111
Reynolds Homestead, Critz, VA.................1502
The Ridges Sanctuary, Inc., Baileys
  Harbor, WI...1590
Rikard's Mill Historical Park, Beatrice,
  AL..3
Riordan Mansion State Historic Park,
  Flagstaff, AZ...33
Rip Van Winkle Gardens on Jefferson
  Island, New Iberia, LA..................................593
Rising Sun Tavern, Fredericksburg, VA 1507
Roanoke Island Festival Park; Homeport
  of the "Elizabeth II", Manteo, NC.........1110

Robbins Hunter Museum, Avery-Downer
  House, Granville, OH.............................1167
Robert Frost Farm, Derry, NH.....................886
Robert Louis Stevenson House,
  Monterey, CA......................................128
Robert Toombs House, Washington, GA......391
Robidoux Row Museum, Saint Joseph,
  MO...831
Rock County Historical Society,
  Janesville, WI....................................1601
Rock Creek Station State Historic Park,
  Fairbury, NE..860
Rock Island State Park, Washington
  Island, WI..1625
Rock Ledge Ranch Historic Site,
  Colorado Springs, CO...........................208
Rock Springs Historical Museum, Rock
  Springs, WY.......................................1638
Rockwood Park, Wilmington, DE.............274
Rocky Mount Children's Museum and
  Science Center, Inc., Rocky Mount,
  NC...1118
Rocky Mount Museum, Piney Flats, TN....1383
Rodgers Tavern, Perryville, MD.................650
Roger Williams National Memorial,
  Providence, RI....................................1318
Ronald Reagan Boyhood Home, Dixon,
  IL...431
Roosevelt Campobello International Park
  Commission, Lubec, ME........................614
The Root House Museum, Marietta, GA.....379
Rosalie House, Eureka Springs, AR...........57
Roscoe Village Foundation, Coshocton,
  OH...1159
Rose Hill Museum, Bay Village, OH.........1141
Rose Hill Plantation State Historic Site,
  Union, SC...1343
Rose Lawn Museum, Cartersville, GA.........368
Rosemount Museum, Pueblo, CO...............230
Rosenbach Museum & Library,
  Philadelphia, PA..................................1287
Roslyn Landmark Society, Roslyn, NY......1061
Royalton Historical Society, Royalton,
  VT..1486
Ruggles House Society, Columbia Falls,
  ME...609
Rural Life Museum & Windrush
  Gardens, Baton Rouge, LA.....................587
Rutherford B. Hayes Presidential Center,
  Fremont, OH.......................................1165

S.S. Meteor Maritime Museum, Superior,
  WI..1624
Sacajawea Interpretive Center, Pasco, WA.1561
Sackets Harbor Battlefield State Historic
  Site, Sackets Harbor, NY.......................1062
Sacramento Mountains Historical
  Museum, Cloudcroft, NM.......................938
Sagamore Hill National Historic Site,
  Oyster Bay, NY....................................1049
Sahuaro Ranch Historical Area, Glendale,
  AZ..35
St. Clements Island and Piney Point
  Museums, Colton's Point, MD................641
St. Francis County Museum, Forrest City,
  AR..57
St. James' House, Fredericksburg, VA.......1507
St. John's Church and Parish Museum,
  Hampton, VA.......................................1510
St. John's Episcopal Church, Richmond,
  VA..1531
St. John's Northwestern Military
  Academy Archives & Museum,
  Delafield, WI......................................1595
Salem Maritime National Historic Site,
  Salem, MA...707
Saline County Historical Society, Inc.,
  Dorchester, NE....................................860
Salt Museum, Liverpool, NY....................1010
Sam Bell Maxey House State Historic
  Site, Paris, TX....................................1442
Sam Houston Historical Schoolhouse,
  Maryville, TN......................................1371

Sam Houston Memorial Museum,
  Huntsville, TX.....................................1430
San Antonio Conservation Society, San
  Antonio, TX..1449
San Antonio Missions National Historical
  Park, San Antonio, TX..........................1449
San Buenaventura Mission Museum,
  Ventura, CA..195
San Fernando Mission, Mission Hills, CA...126
San Gabriel Mission Museum, San
  Gabriel, CA...171
San Juan Bautista State Historic Park,
  San Juan Bautista, CA..........................173
San Juan County Historical Society
  Museum, Silverton, CO.........................232
San Juan Island National Historical Park,
  Friday Harbor, WA...............................1555
San Juan National Historic Site, San
  Juan, PR...1643
San Mateo Arboretum Society, Inc., San
  Mateo, CA..175
San Miguel Mission Church, Santa Fe,
  NM...950
Sanchez Adobe Historic Site, Pacifica,
  CA..138
Sandwich Historical Society, Center
  Sandwich, NH......................................884
Sandy Creek Covered Bridge State
  Historic Site, Goldman, MO...................816
Santa Barbara Botanic Garden, Santa
  Barbara, CA..178
Santa Fe Trail Museum/Trinidad History
  Museum, Trinidad, CO..........................234
Santa Monica Mountains National
  Recreation Area, Thousand Oaks, CA.....191
Santuario de Nuestra Senora de
  Guadalupe, Santa Fe, NM......................950
Sappington Cemetery State Historic Site,
  Nelson, MO...827
Sappington House Museum, Crestwood,
  MO...814
Sarasota Classic Car Museum, Sarasota,
  FL..345
Saratoga National Historical Park,
  Stillwater, NY......................................1075
Sarpy County Historical Museum,
  Bellevue, NE.......................................857
Satterlee Clark House, Horicon, WI...........1600
Saugus Iron Works National Historic
  Site, Saugus, MA..................................708
Sauk Prairie Area Historical Society, Inc.,
  Prairie du Sac, WI................................1619
Scantic Academy Museum, East Windsor
  Historical Society, Inc., East Windsor,
  CT..239
Schenectady County Historical Society,
  Schenectady, NY..................................1067
Schifferstadt Architectural Museum,
  Frederick, MD.....................................644
Schminck Memorial Museum, Lakeview,
  OR...1227
Schoenbrunn Village State Memorial,
  New Philadelphia, OH..........................1177
Schoharie Crossing State Historic Site,
  Fort Hunter, NY...................................991
Schuyler Jail Museum, Rushville, IL..........456
Scotland Heritage Chapel & Museum,
  Scotland, SD.......................................1355
Sedgwick-Brooklin Historical Society,
  Sedgwick, ME......................................622
Senate House State Historic Site,
  Kingston, NY.......................................1008
Seneca Falls Historical Society, Seneca
  Falls, NY..1069
Sequoyah Cabin, Sallisaw, OK.................1213
Serra Museum/San Diego Historical
  Society, San Diego, CA.........................161
1719 Hans Herr House & Museum,
  Willow Street, PA................................1308
The 1719 William Trent House Museum,
  Trenton, NJ...928
1797 Ezekiel Harris House, Augusta, GA....366

1768 Jeremiah Lee Mansion, Marblehead,
  MA...693
1761 Pownalborough Courthouse,
  Dresden, ME..610
Seward House, Auburn, NY......................959
Shafer Historical Museum, Winthrop, WA.1578
Shaker Heritage Society, Albany, NY..........956
Shaker Historical Society, Shaker
  Heights, OH...1185
Shaker Museum, New Gloucester, ME........615
Shaker Museum at South Union, South
  Union, KY...583
Shakespeare Ghost Town, Lordsburg, NM...942
Shako:wi Cultural Center, Oneida, NY......1046
Sheldon Peck Homestead, Lombard, IL......444
Shelter House Society, Emmaus, PA..........1251
Sherwood Forest Plantation, Charles City,
  VA..1498
Shippensburg Historical Society Museum,
  Shippensburg, PA.................................1300
Shirley-Eustis House, Boston, MA.............669
Shirley Plantation, Charles City, VA..........1498
Shore Line Trolley Museum, East Haven,
  CT..239
Sibley House Historic Site, Mendota, MN...780
Silent Wings Museum, Lubbock, TX..........1435
Silver Cliff Museum, Silver Cliff, CO.........232
Silver River Museum & Environmental
  Education Center, Ocala, FL....................330
Silvercreek Museum, Freeport, IL.............435
Simonian Farms, Fresno, CA....................98
Sitka National Historical Park, Sitka, AK......28
The Sixth Floor Museum at Dealey
  Plaza, Dallas, TX.................................1407
Skagway Museum & Archives, Skagway,
  AK..28
Slate Run Living Historical Farm, Metro
  Parks, Ashville, OH.............................1140
Sleeping Bear Dunes National Lakeshore,
  Empire, MI..741
Sleepy Eye Depot Museum, Sleepy Eye,
  MN...793
Slifer House, Lewisburg, PA.....................1268
Sloss Furnaces National Historic
  Landmark, Birmingham, AL.....................5
Smyth County Museum, Marion, VA..........1516
Snug Harbor Cultural Center - Visitors'
  Center and Newhouse Center for
  Contemporary Art, Staten Island, NY ...1073
Sod House Museum, Gothenburg, NE.........862
Soldiers National Museum, Gettysburg,
  PA..1256
Somerset Place State Historic Site,
  Creswell, NC.......................................1097
Somervell County Historical Museum,
  Glen Rose, TX.....................................1423
Sonnenberg Gardens & Mansion State
  Historic Park, Canandaigua, NY.............975
Sophienburg Museum & Archives Inc.,
  New Braunfels, TX...............................1440
Sotterley Plantation, Hollywood, MD........647
The South Carolina Botanical Garden,
  Clemson, SC..1328
South Carolina Department of Parks,
  Recreation and Tourism, Columbia,
  SC..1330
South Charleston Museum, South
  Charleston, WV...................................1586
South Holland Historical Society, South
  Holland, IL...457
South Park City Museum, Fairplay, CO.......215
South Pass City State Historic Site, South
  Pass City, WY......................................1638
South River Meeting House, Lynchburg,
  VA..1516
South Sutton Old Store Museum, South
  Sutton, NH..896
Southampton Historical Museum,
  Southampton, NY..................................1070
Southern Alleghenies Museum of Art,
  Loretto, PA..1269

Historic Sites—Continued

Southern Forest Heritage Museum, Long
  Leaf, LA..591

The Southern Museum of Civil War and
  Locomotive History, Kennesaw, GA.......375

Southwest Florida Museum of History,
  Fort Myers, FL....................................309

Spanish Governor's Palace, San Antonio,
  TX...1450

Spindletop/Gladys City Boomtown
  Museum, Beaumont, TX 1395

Split Rock Lighthouse Historic Site, Two
  Harbors, MN......................................795

Spokane House Interpretive Center, Nine
  Mile Falls, WA..................................1559

Spring Grove Hospital Center, Alumni
  Museum, Catonsville, MD 639

Spring Street Historical Museum,
  Shreveport, LA...................................602

Spring Valley Community Historical
  Society, Inc., Spring Valley, MN 794

Springfield Museum of Old Domestic
  Life, High Point, NC...........................1107

Staatsburgh State Historic Site,
  Staatsburg, NY..................................1071

Stan Hywet Hall and Gardens, Inc.,
  Akron, OH..1139

Stanton House, Clinton, CT.....................237

Star of the Republic Museum,
  Washington, TX.................................1460

State Historic Site of Fort Loudoun,
  Chambersburg, PA..............................1246

The State House Museum, Dover, DE........270

Staten Island Historical Society, Staten
  Island, NY..1074

Station 15, Norton, KS...........................554

STAX Museum of American Soul Music,
  Memphis, TN.....................................1376

Steamboat Bertrand Collection, Missouri
  Valley, IA...524

Steamship William G. Mather Museum,
  Cleveland, OH...................................1156

Stephen A. Douglas Tomb, Chicago, IL.......427

The Stephen Girard Collection,
  Philadelphia, PA................................1288

The Stephen Phillips House, Salem, MA.....707

Stephens County Historical Society and
  Museum, Duncan, OK..........................1199

Sterling Hill Mining Museum, Inc.,
  Ogdensburg, NJ.................................918

Sterne-Hoya House Museum and Library,
  Nacogdoches, TX...............................1440

Steuben Memorial State Historic Site,
  Remsen, NY......................................1056

The Stevens-Coolidge Place, a property
  of The Trustees of Reservations, North
  Andover, MA.....................................698

Stevens County Gas and Historical
  Museum, Hugoton, KS.........................544

The Stickley Museum at Craftsman
  Farms, Parsippany, NJ.........................920

Stonefield Historic Site, Cassville, WI.......1593

Stony Point Battlefield State Historic
  Site, Stony Point, NY..........................1075

Storrowton Village Museum, West
  Springfield, MA.................................718

Stranahan House, Inc., Fort Lauderdale,
  FL...308

Strater Hotel, Durango, CO.....................214

The Stratford Historical Society &
  Catherine B. Mitchell Museum,
  Stratford, CT.....................................262

Stratford, Robert E. Lee Memorial
  Association, Inc., Stratford, VA.............1539

Strawbery Banke Museum, Portsmouth,
  NH...895

Stuart House City Museum, Mackinac
  Island, MI...752

Stuhr Museum of the Prairie Pioneer,
  Grand Island, NE................................862

Suffolk County Vanderbilt Museum,
  Centerport, NY...................................977

Sun Inn Preservation Association Inc.,
  Bethlehem, PA...................................1243

Sun Prairie Historical Library &
  Museum, Sun Prairie, WI.....................1624

SunWatch Indian Village/Archaeological
  Park, Dayton, OH...............................1162

The Supreme Court of the United States,
  Washington, DC..................................291

Susan B. Anthony House, Rochester, NY..1060

Susquehanna Museum of Havre de Grace
  Inc. at the Lock House, Havre de
  Grace, MD..647

Sutter's Fort State Historic Park,
  Sacramento, CA.................................153

Swarthout Memorial Museum, La Crosse,
  WI...1603

Sweet Briar Museum, Sweet Briar, VA......1540

Sweetwater Creek State Park, Lithia
  Springs, GA......................................376

T.B. Ferguson Home, Watonga, OK..........1216

Tannenbaum Historic Park, Greensboro,
  NC...1104

Tante Blanche Museum, Madawaska, ME..614

Taos Historic Museums, Taos, NM 953

Tappantown Historical Society, Tappan,
  NY...1077

Tarpon Springs Cultural Center, Tarpon
  Springs, FL.......................................351

Ted Smallwood's Store, Inc.,
  Chokoloskee, FL................................299

Tempe Historical Museum, Tempe, AZ.........46

Tennessee Valley Railroad Museum Inc.,
  Chattanooga, TN................................1363

Terrace Hill Historic Site and Governor's
  Mansion, Des Moines, IA.....................516

Territorial Capital-Lane Museum,
  Lecompton, KS..................................549

Texas Baptist Historical Center Museum,
  Brenham, TX.....................................1397

Texas Governor's Mansion, Austin, TX.....1391

Theodore Roosevelt Birthplace National
  Historic Site, New York, NY................1040

Theodore Roosevelt Inaugural National
  Historic Site, Buffalo, NY....................973

This Is The Place Heritage Park, Salt
  Lake City, UT....................................1472

Thomas Center Galleries, Gainesville, FL ...311

Thomas Clarke House/Princeton
  Battlefield State Park, Princeton, NJ 922

The Thomas Griswold House and
  Museum, Guilford, CT.........................243

Thomas Hart Benton Home and Studio
  State Historic Site, Kansas City, MO......823

Thomas L. Kane Memorial Chapel, Kane,
  PA...1264

Thomas Warne Historical Museum &
  Library, Old Bridge, NJ.......................918

Thomas Whaley House Museum, San
  Diego, CA..161

Thomaston Historical Society,
  Thomaston, ME..................................624

Three Rivers Museum, Muskogee, OK......1205

Thunderbird Foundation for the Arts,
  Mount Carmel, UT.............................1467

Timucuan Ecological and Historic
  Preserve and Fort Caroline National
  Memorial, Jacksonville, FL...................315

Tippecanoe Battlefield, Battle Ground, IN..468

Tippecanoe County Historical
  Association, Lafayette, IN.....................487

Town Creek Indian Mound State Historic
  Site, Mount Gilead, NC.......................1111

Traill County Historical Society,
  Hillsboro, ND....................................1132

Trailside Nature and Science Center,
  Mountainside, NJ...............................915

Traveler's Rest State Historic Site,
  Toccoa, GA.......................................389

Travellers Rest Plantation & Museum,
  Nashville, TN....................................1381

Trenton City Museum, Trenton, NJ............928

Troutdale Historical Society, Troutdale,
  OR..1237

The Trustees of Reservations, Beverly,
  MA..662

Tsa Mo Ga Memorial Museum, Plains,
  TX...1443

Tu-Endie-Wei State Park, Point Pleasant,
  WV..1586

Tubac Presidio State Historic Park,
  Tubac, AZ...47

Tulare County Museum at Mooney Grove
  Park, Visalia, CA...............................195

Tumacacori National Historical Park,
  Tumacacori, AZ...................................52

Turabo University, Gurabo, PR................1641

Tybee Island Light Station and Tybee
  Museum, Tybee Island, GA 389

USDA Forest Service - Land Between
  the Lakes, Golden Pond, KY.................570

Ulster County Historical Society,
  Marbletown, NY................................1013

Ulysses S. Grant Cottage State Historic
  Site, Wilton, NY................................1086

Union County Historical Complex,
  Creston, IA..512

Union Covered Bridge State Historic
  Site, Paris, MO..................................828

United States Department of the Interior
  Museum, Washington, DC.....................293

United States Senate Commission on Art,
  Washington, DC..................................293

University Museum & Historic Houses,
  The University of Mississippi, Oxford,
  MS...806

University of Northern Iowa Museums &
  Collections, Cedar Falls, IA..................508

U.S. Army Communications-Electronics
  Museum, Fort Monmouth, NJ................904

U.S. Army Museum of Hawaii, Fort
  DeRussy, HI......................................392

U.S. Grant's Home State Historic Site,
  Galena, IL...436

U.S. Navy Supply Corps Museum,
  Athens, GA.......................................357

USS Arizona Memorial, Honolulu, HI........398

USS Constellation Museum, Baltimore,
  MD..636

USS Lexington Museum on the Bay,
  Corpus Christi, TX............................1402

Ute Indian Museum/Montrose Visitor
  Center, Montrose, CO 228

Valley Community Historical Society,
  Inc., Valley, NE.................................874

Valley Forge National Historical Park,
  King of Prussia, PA............................1264

Van Buren County Historical Society,
  Keosauqua, IA...................................521

Van Meter State Park, Miami, MO............827

Van Wyck Homestead Museum, Fishkill,
  NY...989

Vandalia Statehouse State Historic Site,
  Vandalia, IL......................................462

Vann House, Chatsworth, GA...................368

Varner-Hogg Plantation State Historic
  Site, West Columbia, TX.....................1461

Verde Historical Society, Clemenceau
  Heritage Museum, Cottonwood, AZ.........32

Vermilion County Museum Society,
  Danville, IL.......................................429

Vernon County Historical Museum,
  Viroqua, WI......................................1625

Vesterheim Norwegian-American
  Museum, Decorah, IA..........................513

Victoria Mansion, Portland, ME................620

Vikingsholm, Tahoma, CA.......................191

Villa Louis Historic Site, Prairie du
  Chien, WI...1619

Vincennes State Historic Site, Indiana
  Territory, Vincennes, IN......................503

Virginia Department of Conservation and
  Recreation, Richmond, VA...................1533

Virginia Military Institute Museum, Lexington, VA............1514
Virginia Robinson Gardens, Beverly Hills, CA.............78
Vista House, Corbett, OR............1222
Volunteer Firemen's Mall and Museum of Kingston, Kingston, NY............1008

The W.H. Stark House, Orange, TX............1442
Wabasha County Museum, Wabasha County Historical Society at Reads Landing, Reads Landing, MN............787
Wade House Stagecoach Inn & Wesley Jung Carriage Museum State Historic Site, Greenbush, WI............1599
Wahkiakum County Historical Museum, Cathlamet, WA............1550
Waimea Arboretum and Botanical Garden in Waimea Valley Audubon Center, Haleiwa, HI............392
Walney Visitor Center-At Ellanor C. Lawrence Park, Chantilly, VA............1498
Walnut Canyon National Monument, Flagstaff, AZ............34
Walt Whitman Birthplace State Historic Site and Interpretive Center, Huntington Station, NY............1001
Walter Reed Birthplace, Gloucester County, VA............1508
Wantagh Historical & Preservation Society, Wantagh, NY............1081
War in the Pacific National Historical Park, Piti, GU............1640
Ward County Historical Society, Minot, ND............1135
Warner Hall Graveyard, Gloucester County, VA............1508
Warner House, Portsmouth, NH............895
Warwick Museum of Art, Warwick, RI............1320
Washburn County Historical Society Museum, Shell Lake, WI............1621
Washington County Historical Association, Fort Calhoun, NE............860
Washington County Historical Society Inc., West Bend, WI............1627
Washington Crossing Historic Park, Washington Crossing, PA............1305
Washington Museum & Tourist Center, Washington, LA............603
Washington National Cathedral, Washington, DC............294
Washington State Capital Museum and Outreach Center, Olympia, WA............1560
Watkins Woolen Mill State Historic Site & Park, Lawson, MO............825
Watson Farm, Jamestown, RI............1312
Wauconda Township Historical Society, Wauconda, IL............463
Waveland State Historic Site, Lexington, KY............574
Wayland Historical Society, Wayland, MA............716
Wayne County Historical Society, Wooster, OH............1192
Weir Farm National Historic Site, Wilton, CT............267
West Overton Museums, Scottdale, PA............1298
West Virginia Camp Washington-Carver, Clifftop, WV............1581
West Virginia State Farm Museum, Point Pleasant, WV............1586
Western Reserve Historical Society, Cleveland, OH............1156
Westport Historical Society, Westport, CT...266
Westport Maritime Museum, Westport, WA............1578
The Wethersfield Historical Society, Wethersfield, CT............266
The Whalehead Club, Corolla, NC............1097
Whiskeytown Unit, Whiskeytown-Shasta-Trinity National Recreation Area, Whiskeytown, CA............198

White County Historical Society, Carmi, IL............415
White Hall State Historic Site, Richmond, KY............583
White River Valley Museum, Auburn, WA............1547
Whitehead Memorial Museum, Del Rio, TX............1409
Whitestone Hill Battlefield State Historic Site, Kulm, ND............1133
Whitewater Canal State Historic Site, Metamora, IN............490
Whitman Mission National Historic Site, Walla Walla, WA............1577
Wilbur Wright Birthplace & Interpretive Center, Hagerstown, IN............480
Wilderness Road Regional Museum, Newbern, VA............1519
Wilkinson County Museum, Woodville, MS............810
Will Rogers Memorial Museum, Claremore, OK............1198
William Clark Market House Museum, Paducah, KY............582
William Cullen Bryant Homestead, Cummington, MA............678
William Henry Harrison Mansion, Grouseland, Vincennes, IN............503
William Howard Taft National Historic Site, Cincinnati, OH............1151
William McKinley Presidential Library & Museum, Canton, OH............1146
William S. Hart County Park & Museum, Newhall, CA............130
Williamson County Historical Society, Marion, IL............444
Willowbrook Museum Village, Newfield, ME............616
Wilson County Historical Society Museum, Fredonia, KS............540
Wilton House Museum, Richmond, VA............1534
Windham Textile and History Museum (The Mill Museum), Willimantic, CT............267
The Wine Museum of Greyton H. Taylor, Hammondsport, NY............997
Winnie Davis Museum of History, Gaffney, SC............1333
Wisconsin National Guard Museum, Camp Douglas, WI............1593
Woodlawn Plantation Museum, Alexandria, VA............1494
Woodstock Museum of Shenandoah County, Inc., Woodstock, VA............1546
Working Men's Institute, New Harmony, IN............495
Workman & Temple Family Homestead Museum, City of Industry, CA............85
World Museum of Mining, Butte, MT............843
Wormsloe State Historic Site, Savannah, GA............387
Wright County Historical Society, Buffalo, MN............770
Wupatki National Monument, Flagstaff, AZ............34
Wyandot County Historical Society, Upper Sandusky, OH............1188
Wyck, Philadelphia, PA............1289
Wyoming Territorial Prison State Historic Site, Laramie, WY............1636

Yankee Air Force, Inc. (Yankee Air Museum), Ypsilanti, MI............766
Yates County Genealogical and Historical Society and Oliver House Museum and L. Caroline Underwood Museum, Penn Yan, NY............1052
Yolo County Historical Museum, Woodland, CA............199
Yorba and Slaughter Families Adobe, Chino, CA............84
York County Heritage Trust, Fire Museum, York, PA............1309

Ypsilanti Historical Museum, Ypsilanti, MI............767
Yucaipa Adobe, Yucaipa, CA............200
Yuma Territorial Prison State Historic Park, Yuma, AZ............54

Zalud House, Porterville, CA............144
Zebulon B. Vance Birthplace State Historic Site, Weaverville, NC............1122
Zelienople Historical Society, Zelienople, PA............1309
Zoar State Memorial, Zoar, OH............1194

Historical and Preservation Societies

Aiken County Historical Museum, Aiken, SC............1320
Alutiiq Museum and Archaeological Repository, Kodiak, AK............26
American Antiquarian Society, Worcester, MA............720
American Association for State and Local History, Nashville, TN............1377
American Truck Historical Society, Kansas City, MO............820
Amos Herr House Foundation and Historic Society, Landisville, PA............1267
APVA Preservation Virginia, Richmond, VA............1528
Arizona Jewish Historical Society, Phoenix, AZ............39
The Arms Family Museum of Local History, Youngstown, OH............1193
Ashtabula Historic House, Pendleton, SC...1339
Associated American Jewish Museums, Pittsburgh, PA............1290
The Association for Gravestone Studies, Greenfield, MA............685
Association for the Preservation of Tennessee Antiquities, Nashville, TN...1377
Astor House Museum, Golden, CO............219
Atlantic City Historical Museum, Atlantic City, NJ............897
Atlantic Heritage Center, Somers Point, NJ............924

Barnes County Historical Museum, Valley City, ND............1136
Barnet Historical Society, Barnet, VT............1476
Beacon Historical Society, Beacon, NY............960
Beauchamp Newman Museum, Elizabeth, WV............1581
Beaufort Historic Site, Beaufort, NC............1091
Bement-Billings Farmstead, Newark Valley, NY............1041
Bethel Historical Society Regional History Center, Bethel, ME............606
Biedenharn Coca-Cola Museum, Vicksburg, MS............809
Boca Raton Historical Society, Boca Raton, FL............296
Boulder City/Hoover Dam Museum, Boulder City, NV............875
Braintree Historical Society, Inc., Braintree, MA............670
The Bronx County Historical Society, Bronx, NY............964
Buffalo Bill Museum of Le Claire, Iowa, Inc., Le Claire, IA............522
Buffalo County Historical Society, Kearney, NE............863
Burke County Historical Powers Lake Complex, Powers Lake, ND............1136
Burleson County Historical Museum, Caldwell, TX............1399
Burlington-Rock Island Railroad and Historical Museum, Teague, TX............1454
Burrowes Mansion Museum, Matawan, NJ............911

Cabot Historical Society, Cabot, VT............1478
The Camron-Stanford House Preservation Association, Oakland, CA............133

Historical and Preservation Societies–Continued

Canal Fulton Heritage Society, Canal Fulton, OH 1145

Caney Valley Historical Society, Caney, KS 534

Captain Salem Avery House Museum, Shady Side Rural Heritage Society, Inc., Shady Side, MD 653

Carpenter Home Museum and Gallery, Cle Elum, WA 1551

Castine Scientific Society, Castine, ME 609

Center for Agricultural Science and Heritage, Indianapolis, IN 481

The Center for Civil War Photography, Gettysburg, PA 1255

Centerville - Washington Township Historical Society & Asahel Wright Community Center, Centerville, OH 1146

Central Nevada Museum & Historical Society, Tonopah, NV 882

Centre County Historical Society, State College, PA 1301

Cheboygan County Historical Museum Complex, Cheboygan, MI 732

Cherry County Historical Society, Valentine, NE 874

Chippewa County Historical Society, Montevideo, MN 783

Circle Gallery/College of Environment & Design - University of Georgia, Athens, GA 356

Clay County Historical Society Museum and Archives, Moorhead, MN 784

Columbia County Historical and Genealogical Society, Bloomsburg, PA .1243

Cragfont-Historic Cragfont, Inc., Castalian Springs, TN 1360

Cranbury Historical & Preservation Society, Cranbury, NJ 902

Crazy Mountain Museum, Big Timber, MT 841

The Crescent, Valdosta Garden Center, Inc., Valdosta, GA 389

Croatian Heritage Museum & Library, Eastlake, OH 1163

Crockett Tavern Museum, Morristown, TN 1376

Crown Gardens and Archives, Dalton, GA 370

Cupertino Historical Society & Museum, Cupertino, CA 88

Dallas Heritage Village at Old City Park, Dallas, TX 1405

Dennys River Historical Society, Dennysville, ME 609

Department of Historic Resources, Richmond, VA 1529

Deschutes County Historical Society, Bend, OR 1220

Desha County Museum, Dumas, AR 56

DeSoto County Museum, Hernando, MS 801

Dutchess County Historical Society, Poughkeepsie, NY 1054

East Hillsborough Historical Society, Inc., Plant City, FL 337

East Lyme Historical Society/Thomas Lee House, Niantic, CT 256

Eastern Arizona Museum and Historical Society of Graham County Inc., Pima, AZ 42

Edisto Island Historic Preservation Society Museum, Edisto Island, SC 1332

Edmond Historical Society Museum, Edmond, OK 1200

Ellis County Historical Society, Hays, KS ...543

Empire Area Heritage Group, Empire, MI...740

Essley-Noble Museum: Mercer County Historical Society, Aledo, IL 410

Eugene Historical Society, Eugene, OR 1223

Eustis Historical Museum & Preservation Society, Inc., Eustis, FL 306

Excelsior House, Jefferson, TX 1431

Excelsior-Lake Minnetonka Historical Society, Excelsior, MN 775

The Exchange Hotel Civil War Museum, Gordonsville, VA 1509

Fairbanks House, Dedham, MA 679

The Fishermen's Museum, New Harbor, ME 615

Florida Gulf Coast Railroad Museum, Parrish, FL 335

The Fluvanna County Historical Society Old Stone Jail Museum, Palmyra, VA .1524

Fort Jones Museum, Fort Jones, CA 96

Fort Leavenworth Historical Society, Fort Leavenworth, KS 539

The Fort Pitt Block House, Pittsburgh, PA 1292

Fort Point and Presidio Historical Association, Presidio of San Francisco, CA 144

Fossil Museum, Fossil, OR 1224

Franklin County Historical Museum, Pasco, WA 1561

Friends of Historic Kingston, Fred J. Johnston House Museum, Kingston, NY 1007

Frisco Historic Park & Museum, Frisco, CO 218

Fulton County Museum, Groversville, NY 996

Gage County Historical Society and Museum, Beatrice, NE 857

Geddes Historic District Village, Geddes, SD 1347

George Ade Memorial Association Inc., Brook, IN 471

Gillespie County Historical Society, Fredericksburg, TX 1419

Gilliam County Historical Society - Depot Museum Complex, Condon, OR.1222

Glenview Area Historical Society, Glenview, IL 438

Golden Gate Railroad Museum, San Francisco, CA 166

Grand County Museum, Hot Sulphur Springs, CO 222

Gravette Historical Museum, Gravette, AR 59

Grevemberg House Museum, Franklin, LA 588

Grinnell Historical Museum, Grinnell, IA...519

Hancock County Historical Society, Carthage, IL 416

Hancock Historical Museum, Findlay, OH 1164

Har-Ber Village, Grove, OK 1202

Harding Museum, Franklin, OH 1164

Harmonie Associates, Inc., Ambridge, PA .1240

Harn Homestead and 1889er Museum, Oklahoma City, OK 1207

Harpers Ferry National Historical Park, Harpers Ferry, WV 1582

Hayward Area Historical Society, Hayward, CA 102

Held-Poage Memorial Home and Research Library, Ukiah, CA 193

Helvetia Museum, Helvetia, WV 1582

Heritage Conservancy, Doylestown, PA 1249

Heritage Preservation, Washington, DC 280

Heritage Village Museum, Woodville, TX .1462

Hernando Heritage Museum, Brooksville, FL 298

Hettinger County Historical Society, Regent, ND 1136

Highland Park Historical Society, Highland Park, IL 439

The Hill Country Museum, Kerrville, TX .1431

Hillforest House Museum, Aurora, IN 468

Historic Annapolis Foundation, Annapolis, MD 628

Historic Charleston Foundation, Charleston, SC 1325

Historic Columbus Foundation, Inc., Columbus, GA 369

Historic Fallsington, Inc., Fallsington, PA .1253

Historic Gardner's Basin, Atlantic City, NJ 898

Historic Landmarks Foundation of Indiana, Indianapolis, IN 482

Historic Langhorne Association, Langhorne, PA 1267

Historic Madison, Inc., Madison, IN 489

Historic Mobile Preservation Society, Mobile, AL 14

Historic Nashville, Inc., Nashville, TN 1379

Historic Oakland Cemetery, Atlanta, GA 360

Historic Preservation Association of Bourbon County, Inc., Fort Scott, KS 540

Historic Preservation League of Oregon, Portland, OR 1231

Historic Renville Preservation Commission, Renville, MN 787

Historic Richmond Town, Staten Island, NY 1072

Historical Museum at Fort Missoula, Missoula, MT 851

Historical Society of Carroll County, Westminster, MD 656

The Historical Society of Dauphin County, Harrisburg, PA 1258

Historical Society of Old Newbury, Cushing House Museum, Newburyport, MA 698

Historical Society of Quaker Hill & Pawling, Pawling, NY 1051

Historical Society of the Town of Clarence, Clarence, NY 978

Historical Society of the Town of North Hempstead, Manhasset, NY 1013

Holocaust Documentation & Education Center, Inc., Hollywood, FL 313

The 100th Meridian Museum, Cozad, NE ...859

Indian Hill Historical Society, Cincinnati, OH 1150

Indiana Historical Society, Indianapolis, IN 483

Islesboro Historical Society, Islesboro, ME 612

Jackson County Historical Society, Black River Falls, WI 1592

James Mitchell Varnum House and Museum, East Greenwich, RI 1311

Jennings-Brown House Female Academy, Bennettsville, SC 1322

Jewish Museum of Florida, Miami Beach, FL 326

John Jay French House, Beaumont Heritage Society, Beaumont, TX 1395

Kaminski House Museum, Georgetown, SC 1333

Kelly-Griggs House Museum, Red Bluff, CA 146

Kershaw County Historical Society, Camden, SC 1323

King Manor, Jamaica, NY 1004

Klyne Esopus Museum, Ulster Park, NY...1079

Koochiching County Historical Museum, International Falls, MN 778

Kuhlmann King Historical House and Museum, Boerne, TX 1396

The Landmark Society of Western New York, Rochester, NY 1058

Landmarks Foundation/Old Alabama Town, Montgomery, AL 16

Lars Noak Blacksmith Shop, Larsson/Ostlund Log Home & One-Room Capitol School, New Sweden, ME 616

Lee County Historical Society,
Loachapoka, AL..............13
Lesbian Herstory Educational Foundation,
Inc. aka Lesbian Herstory Archives,
Brooklyn, NY..............969
Levere Memorial Temple, Evanston, IL......434
Lewes Historical Society, Lewes, DE..........271
Lexington History Museum, Lexington,
KY..............573
Licking County Historical Society,
Newark, OH..............1178
Light Crust Doughboys Hall of Fame &
Museum - Governor Jim Hogg City
Park, Quitman, TX..............1444
Limon Heritage Museum, Limon, CO..........226
Lincoln Parish Museum & Historical
Society, Ruston, LA..............600
Litchfield Historical Society and
Museum, Litchfield, CT..............247
The Living Word National Bible
Museum, Aledo, TX..............1386
Los Alamos Historical Museum, Los
Alamos, NM..............942
Louisiana State Museum, New Orleans,
LA..............596

Madison County Historical Society,
Winterset, IA..............531
Magnolia Manor, Cairo, IL..............415
Maitland Historical Museums, Maitland,
FL..............322
Malibu Lagoon Museum, Malibu, CA..........123
Marblehead Museum & Historical
Society, Marblehead, MA..............693
Mariposa Museum and History Center
Inc., Mariposa, CA..............124
Marlboro County Historical Museum,
Bennettsville, SC..............1322
Marlboro Historical Society, Marlboro,
VT..............1481
The Marston House/San Diego Historical
Society, San Diego, CA..............157
Masonic Grand Lodge Library and
Museum of Texas, Waco, TX..............1459
Massachusetts Historical Society, Boston,
MA..............667
McHenry County Historical Society and
Museum, Union, IL..............461
McLean-Alanreed Area Museum,
McLean, TX..............1438
Mendocino Historical Research,
Inc./Kelley House Museum,
Mendocino, CA..............125
Merced County Courthouse Museum,
Merced, CA..............125
Merrill Historical Museum, Merrill, WI.....1609
Metropolitan Historic Structures
Association, New York, NY..............1030
Middlebury Historical Society, Wyoming,
NY..............1087
Middleton Historical Society - Lura
Woodside Watkins Museum,
Middleton, MA..............694
Mill Race Historical Village, Northville,
MI..............758
Minnesota Pioneer Park Museum,
Annandale, MN..............767
Mississippi Society Daughters of the
American Revolution Rosalie House
Museum, Natchez, MS..............805
Molly Brown House Museum, Denver,
CO..............213
Montague Museum & Historical
Association, Montague, MI..............756
Montana Historical Society, Helena, MT.....849
Morris-Jumel Mansion, New York, NY.....1030
The Municipal Art Society of New York,
New York, NY..............1031
Murfreesboro Historical Association,
Murfreesboro, NC..............1112
Museum of History & Industry
(MOHAI), Seattle, WA..............1567

The Museum of Nursing History, Inc.,
Philadelphia, PA..............1283
Museum of Rural Life, Denton, MD..........642
Museum of the High Plains, McCook,
NE..............868
Museum on Main: A History Museum for
West Georgia, LaGrange, GA..............375

Naper Settlement, Naperville, IL..............447
National Apple Museum, Biglerville, PA...1243
National Temple Hill Association, Inc.,
New Windsor, NY..............1018
National Trust for Historic Preservation,
Washington, DC..............288
Neenah Historical Society, Hiram Smith,
Neenah's Heritage Park, Octagon
House & Ward House, Neenah, WI.......1614
Nevada Northern Railway Museum, Ely,
NV..............876
New Braunfels Conservation Society,
New Braunfels, TX..............1440
New Richmond Preservation Society,
New Richmond, WI..............1615
New York State Bureau of Historic Sites,
Waterford, NY..............1082
New York State Office of Parks,
Recreation & Historic Preservation,
Albany, NY..............955
Newark Valley Depot Museum, Newark
Valley, NY..............1042
Newport Historical Society & The
Museum of Newport History,
Newport, RI..............1315
Newport Restoration Foundation,
Newport, RI..............1315
Newtown Historic Association, Newtown,
PA..............1274
Newtown History Center, Stephens City,
VA..............1538
Noah Webster House/West Hartford
Historical Society, West Hartford, CT.....265
Nobleboro Historical Society, Nobleboro,
ME..............616
Norwood Historical Association and
Museum, Norwood, NY..............1044

Oakleigh Period House Museum, Mobile,
AL..............15
The Octagon House, Hudson, WI..............1600
Ojai Valley Historical Society and
Museum, Ojai, CA..............135
Oklahoma Heritage Association,
Oklahoma City, OK..............1209
Old Brutus Historical Society, Inc.,
Weedsport, NY..............1084
The Old Jail Museum, Warrenton, VA......1543
Old York Historical Society, York, ME........626
Old York Road Historical Society,
Jenkintown, PA..............1263
The Oldest House Museum/Wrecker's
Museum, Key West, FL..............318
Oneida County Historical Society, Utica,
NY..............1080
Oregon-Jerusalem Historical Museum,
Oregon, OH..............1181
Orland Historical Society, Orland, ME........617
Osterville Historical Society, Inc.,
Osterville, MA..............701
Overstreet-Kerr Historical Farm, Keota,
OK..............1203

Palmer Museum, Jewell, KS..............546
Park City Historical Society & Museum,
Park City, UT..............1468
Parson Fisher House, Blue Hill, ME..........606
Phelps House, Burlington, IA..............507
Philadelphia Society for the Preservation
of Landmarks, Philadelphia, PA..............1286
Pilgrim Hall Museum, Plymouth, MA.........703
Pinal County Historical Society and
Museum, Florence, AZ..............34

The Pioneer Memorial Association of
Fenton and Mundy Townships,
Fenton, MI..............741
Pitot House Museum, New Orleans, LA......598
Pocahontas County Iowa Historical
Society Museum, Laurens, IA..............522
Pope County Historical Society,
Glenwood, MN..............776
Portage County Historical Society,
Stevens Point, WI..............1623
Pratt Building - Cohasset Historical
Society, Cohasset, MA..............676
Preservation Resource Center, New
Orleans, LA..............598
The Preservation Society of Newport
County/The Newport Mansions,
Newport, RI..............1315
Providence Preservation Society,
Providence, RI..............1318

Queens Historical Society, Flushing, NY.....990

Ramsey House Museum Plantation,
Knoxville, TN..............1371
Rancho La Patera - The Stow House
G.V.H.S., Goleta, CA..............100
Randolph County Historical Museum,
Winchester, IN..............503
Reginald F. Lewis Museum of Maryland
African American History and Culture,
Baltimore, MD..............636
Reitz Home Museum, Evansville, IN...........476
Reverend Dan Foster House, Museum of
the Weathersfield Historical Society,
Weathersfield, VT..............1489
Rhode Island Historical Preservation and
Heritage, Providence, RI..............1318
Rock County Historical Society,
Janesville, WI..............1601
Ronald Reagan Boyhood Home, Dixon,
IL..............431
Rosalie House, Eureka Springs, AR..............57
Ruggles House Society, Columbia Falls,
ME..............609

Safe Haven Museum and Education
Center, Oswego, NY..............1048
The Salgo Trust for Education, Port
Washington, NY..............1054
San Dieguito Heritage Museum,
Encinitas, CA..............92
Santuario de Nuestra Senora de
Guadalupe, Santa Fe, NM..............950
Schmidt House Museum & Research
Library, Grants Pass, OR..............1225
Scholte House Museum, Pella, IA..............527
Schoolhouse Museum of the Ridgewood
Historical Society, Inc., Ridgewood,
NJ..............923
Shaker Village of Pleasant Hill,
Harrodsburg, KY..............571
Sharlot Hall Museum, Prescott, AZ..............43
Sidney Historical Association, Sidney,
NY..............1069
Slaughter Ranch Museum, Douglas, AZ........32
Society for the Preservation of Long
Island Antiquities, Cold Spring
Harbor, NY..............980
South Bannock County Historical Center,
Lava Hot Springs, ID..............407
Southern California Chapter Railway &
Locomotive Historical Society,
Pomona, CA..............143
Spring Street Historical Museum,
Shreveport, LA..............602
Strawbery Banke Museum, Portsmouth,
NH..............895
Sun Inn Preservation Association Inc.,
Bethlehem, PA..............1243
Swedish American Museum Association
of Chicago, Chicago, IL..............428

Taos County Historical Society, Inc.,
Taos, NM..............953

Historical and Preservation Societies–Continued

Tennessee Historical Commission, Nashville, TN............................1380

The Thomas Griswold House and Museum, Guilford, CT.....................243

Three Village Historical Society, Setauket, NY....................................1069

Triangle Tattoo & Museum, Fort Bragg, CA...95

Troutdale Historical Society, Troutdale, OR..1237

Tybee Island Light Station and Tybee Museum, Tybee Island, GA 389

Union County Museum, Union, OR..........1238

Union Pacific Historical Society (UPHS), Laramie, WY 1635

Upper Musselshell Historical Society, Harlowton, MT...............................849

Upstate History Alliance, Oneonta, NY 1046

Utah State Historical Society, Salt Lake City, UT..1473

Vaile Mansion-Dewitt Museum, Independence, MO...........................819

Van Riper-Hopper House Museum, Wayne, NJ..929

Vashon Maury Island Heritage Association, Vashon, WA.....................1576

The Walker African American Museum & Research Center, Las Vegas, NV 880

Walt Whitman Birthplace State Historic Site and Interpretive Center, Huntington Station, NY....................1001

Watermen's Museum, Yorktown, VA......1547

Weems-Botts Museum, Dumfries, VA.......1503

West Chicago City Museum, West Chicago, IL..464

West Virginia State Farm Museum, Point Pleasant, WV.....................................1586

Westport Historical Society, Westport, CT...266

Winnebago Area Museum, Winnebago, MN...797

Woodbine International Fire Museum, Woodbine, GA.....................................392

Woodburn Historic House, Pendleton, SC .1339

Wren's Nest, Atlanta, GA 364

Yorktown Historical Museum, Yorktown, TX...1462

Historical Society Museums

A.R. Bowman Memorial Museum, Prineville, OR..1234

Adair County Historical Society, Inc., Kirksville, MO..................................824

Adams County Historical Museum, Decatur, IN..474

Adams County Historical Society, Gettysburg, PA.....................................1255

Adams County Historical Society Museum, Lind, WA.........................1558

Adams County Historical Society Museum, Brighton, CO 204

Adams Old Stone Grist Mill, Bellows Falls, VT...1476

African-American Museum and Library at Oakland, Oakland, CA......................132

Albany Historical Society, Inc., Sabetha, KS...557

Albion Academy Historical Museum, Edgerton, WI.....................................1596

Alden B. Dow Museum of Science and Art of the Midland Center for the Arts, Midland, MI..............................755

Alger County Heritage Center, Munising, MI..757

Allegan County Historical Society and Old Jail Museum, Allegan, MI................723

Allegany County Historical Society, Inc., Cumberland, MD............................641

Allen County Historical Society, Iola, KS ...545

Allen County Museum, Lima, OH 1172

Almond Historical Society/Hagadorn House Museum, Almond, NY..................957

Alpine County Museum, Markleeville, CA...124

Amana Heritage Museum, Amana, IA 504

American Historical Society of Germans from Russia, Lincoln, NE.....................865

American Jewish Historical Society, New York, NY...1019

Amity and Woodbridge Historical Society, Woodbridge, CT 268

Amory Regional Museum, Amory, MS........797

Anderson County Historical Museum, Garnett, KS...541

Andover Historical Society, Andover, MA...660

Androscoggin Historical Society, Auburn, ME...603

Animas Museum, Durango, CO...................214

Anna Miller Museum, Newcastle, WY 1637

Anoka County Historical Society, Anoka, MN...767

Anson County Historical Society, Inc., Wadesboro, NC......................................1121

The Antiquarian and Landmarks Society, Inc., Hartford, CT..................................244

The Apple Trees Museum, Burlington, IA...506

APVA Preservation Virginia, Richmond, VA...1528

Arcade Historical Society, Arcade, NY 958

Archer County Museum, Archer City, TX.1387

Arches Museum of Pioneer Life, Winona, MN...797

Arizona Historical Society Pioneer Museum, Flagstaff, AZ.........................32

Arizona Historical Society-Yuma: Sarguinetti House Museum and Garden, Yuma, AZ..............................54

Arlington Heights Historical Museum, Arlington Heights, IL............................411

The Arlington Historical Society, Arlington, MA.......................................660

Aspen Historical Society, Aspen, CO...........202

Atchison County Historical Society, Atchison, KS...533

Atlanta Historical Society, Atlanta, GA........358

Atlantic City Historical Museum, Atlantic City, NJ...897

Atwood House Museum, Home of Chatham Historical Society, Chatham, MA...675

Au Glaize Village, Defiance, OH................1162

Audrain Historical Museum, Graceland, Mexico, MO...827

Auglaize County Historical Society, Saint Marys, OH...1184

Aurora Historical Society, Aurora, IL...........411

Aurora Historical Society, Aurora, OH.......1140

Aurora Historical Society, Inc., East Aurora, NY...984

The Avon Historical Society, Inc., Avon, CT 235

Badger Mine and Museum, Shullsburg, WI...1622

Bailey House Museum - Maui Historical Society, Wailuku, HI............................402

Baker-Cederberg Museum & Archives, Rochester, NY.....................................1058

Baldwin Historical Society and Museum, Baldwin, NY..960

Bale Grist Mill State Historic Park, Calistoga, CA..80

Baltimore County Historical Society, Cockeysville, MD..................................640

Bandon Historical Society Museum, Bandon, OR...1219

Bangor Museum & Center for History, Bangor, ME...604

Bar Harbor Historical Society, Bar Harbor, ME...605

Baranov Museum, Kodiak, AK.....................26

Barnes County Historical Museum, Valley City, ND 1136

Barnet Historical Society, Barnet, VT.....1476

Barre Historical Society, Inc., Barre, MA 662

The Barrington Area Historical Society, Barrington, IL..412

Barron County Historical Society's Pioneer Village Museum, Cameron, WI...1593

Bartholomew County Historical Society, Columbus, IN..472

Barton County Historical Museum & Village, Great Bend, KS.........................542

Batavia Depot Museum, Batavia, IL 412

Bath County Historical Society, Warm Springs, VA..1543

Battleground Historical Society, Englishtown, NJ...................................903

Baxter Springs Heritage Center and Museum, Baxter Springs, KS.................533

Beatty Museum and Historical Society, Beatty, NV...875

Beaver Island Historical Society, Beaver Island, MI...728

Becker County Historical Society, Detroit Lakes, MN..772

Bedford Historical Society Museum and Library, Bedford, OH 1142

Bellport-Brookhaven Historical Society and Museum, Bellport, NY.....................961

Belmont County Victorian Mansion Museum, Barnesville, OH....................1141

Beloit Historical Society, Beloit, WI..........1592

Beltrami County History Center, Bemidji, MN...768

Belvedere-Tiburon Landmarks Society, Tiburon, CA..192

The Bennett School, West Des Moines, IA...530

Benton County Historical Museum, Philomath, OR......................................1230

Benton County Historical Museum, Prosser, WA..1563

Benzie Area Historical Museum, Benzonia, MI...729

Bergen County Historical Society, River Edge, NJ...923

Bergen Museum of Local History, Bergen, NY..962

Berkshire County Historical Society, Inc. - Arrowhead, Pittsfield, MA...................702

Berlin Area Historical Society Museum of Local History, Berlin, WI..................1592

Bernard Historical Society and Museum, Delton, MI..734

Bethlehem Historical Association, Selkirk, NY...1068

Beverly Historical Society and Museum, Beverly, MA..662

Bexley Historical Society, Bexley, OH.......1143

Beyer Home, Oconto County Historical Society Museum, Oconto, WI...............1616

Big Horn County Historical Museum, Hardin, MT...849

Big Springs Museum, Caledonia, NY 974

Birmingham Historical Museum & Park, Birmingham, MI...................................730

Black River Academy Museum, Ludlow, VT...1480

Black River Historical Society of Lorain, Lorain, OH..1172

Blackman House Museum, Snohomish, WA...1570

Blacksmith Shop Museum, Dover-Foxcroft, ME...............................610

Blaine County Historical Museum, Hailey, ID..406

Block Island Historical Society, Block Island, RI..1310

Bloomington Historical Society, Minneapolis, MN............781

Blue Earth County Historical Society, Mankato, MN............780

Bluff Hall Antebellum Home and Museum, Demopolis, AL............7

Boca Raton Historical Society, Boca Raton, FL............296

Bolton Historical Society, Inc., Bolton, MA............663

Bonner County Historical Museum, Sandpoint, ID............409

Boone County Historical Museum, Belvidere, IL............413

The Boorman House - The Juneau County Historical Society, Mauston, WI............1608

Botetourt County Historical Society, Fincastle, VA............1504

Boulder History Museum, Boulder, CO............202

Boundary County Historical Society, Bonners Ferry, ID............404

Bowie Heritage Children's Museum & Welcome Center, Bowie, MD............638

Bowie Railroad Station and Huntington Museum, Bowie, MD............638

The Bowne House Historical Society, Flushing, NY............990

Bradford County Historical Society, Towanda, PA............1303

Bradford Historical Society Inc., Bradford, VT............1477

Braintree Historical Society, Inc., Braintree, MA............670

Bridge Hampton Historical Society, Bridgehampton, NY............964

Bridgton Historical Society, Bridgton, ME............607

Brimstone Museum, Sulphur, LA............602

Bronck Museum, Coxsackie, NY............983

Brookings County Historical Society Museum, Volga, SD............1358

Brookline Historical Society, Brookline, MA............671

Brooks Academy Museum, Harwich, MA............686

The Broome County Historical Society, Binghamton, NY............962

Brown County Historical Society, New Ulm, MN............785

Brown County Historical Society Pioneer Museum, Nashville, IN............493

The Brown House Museum, Sandersville, GA............384

Bucksport Historical Society, Inc., Bucksport, ME............608

Bucyrus Historical Society, Bucyrus, OH............1144

Buena Park Historical Society, Buena Park, CA............80

Buffalo and Erie County Historical Society, Buffalo, NY............972

Buffalo County Historical Society, Kearney, NE............863

Bunker Hill Museum, Charlestown, MA............675

Bureau County Historical Society Museum, Princeton, IL............452

Burlington County Historical Society, Burlington, NJ............898

Burrowes Mansion Museum, Matawan, NJ............911

Burwell-Morgan Mill, Millwood, VA............1518

Bushwhacker Museum, Nevada, MO............828

Butler County Historical Society, Allison, IA............504

Butler County History Center & Kansas Oil Museum, El Dorado, KS............537

Butler County Museum, Hamilton, OH............1168

Byron Historical Museum, Byron, NY............974

Calhoun County Museum, Rockwell City, IA............527

California Historical Society, San Francisco, CA............163

California Route 66 Museum, Victorville, CA............195

Cambria County Historical Society, Ebensburg, PA............1251

Cambridge Historical Society, Cambridge, MA............672

Camden County Historical Society, Camden, NJ............899

Campus Martius Museum, Marietta, OH............1173

Canaan Historical Society, Inc., Canaan, NY............974

Canadian County Historical Museum, El Reno, OK............1200

Canal Society of New York State, Inc., Syracuse, NY............1076

Canby Historical Society, Canby, OR............1221

Caney Valley Historical Society, Caney, KS............534

Cannon Falls Area Historical Museum, Cannon Falls, MN............770

Canton Historical Society, Canton, MA............674

Canyon County Historical Society & Museum, Nampa, ID............408

Cape May County Historical Museum and Genealogical Society, Cape May Court House, NJ............900

Captain George Flavel House Museum, Astoria, OR............1218

Captain John Wilson House, Cohasset, MA............676

Carlton County Historical Society, Cloquet, MN............771

Carpenter Home Museum and Gallery, Cle Elum, WA............1551

Carroll Mansion Museum Home of Leavenworth County Historical Society, Leavenworth, KS............549

Carver County Historical Society, Waconia, MN............795

Casa Grande Valley Historical Society & Museum, Casa Grande, AZ............30

Cascade County Historical Society Museum, Great Falls, MT............848

Cashmere Museum & Pioneer Village, Cashmere, WA............1550

Cason Cottage House Museum, Delray Beach, FL............304

Cass County Historical Society, Logansport, IN............489

Cass County Historical Society at Bonanzaville, West Fargo, ND............1137

Cass County Historical Society Museum, Plattsmouth, NE............872

Catalina Island Museum Society, Inc., Avalon, CA............73

Catholic Historical Society of the Roanoke Valley, Roanoke, VA............1535

Cattaraugus Area Historical Center, Cattaraugus, NY............976

Cayuga-Owasco Lakes Historical Society, Moravia, NY............1015

Cedar Falls Historical Society, Cedar Falls, IA............507

Cedar Grove Historical Society, Cedar Grove, NJ............901

Cedar Key Historical Society Museum, Cedar Key, FL............298

The Center for Western Studies, Sioux Falls, SD............1356

Centerville - Washington Township Historical Society & Asahel Wright Community Center, Centerville, OH............1146

Central Montana Historical Association, Inc. Museum, Lewistown, MT............850

The Central Museum, Central, AK............23

Central Nevada Museum & Historical Society, Tonopah, NV............882

Centre County Historical Society, State College, PA............1301

Century Village Museum, Burton, OH............1144

Chagrin Falls Historical Society, Chagrin Falls, OH............1147

Champaign County Historical Museum, Urbana, OH............1188

Chandler Museum, Chandler, AZ............31

The Chapman Historical Museum, Glens Falls, NY............994

Chappell Hill Historical Society Museum, Chappell Hill, TX............1399

Charles A. Lindbergh Historic Site, Little Falls, MN............779

Charles A. Weyerhaeuser Memorial Museum, Little Falls, MN............779

Chase County Historical Society, Inc., Cottonwood Falls, KS............536

Chautauqua County Historical Society, McClurg Museum, Westfield, NY............1086

Cheboygan County Historical Museum Complex, Cheboygan, MI............732

The Chelmsford Historical Society, Inc., South Chelmsford, MA............709

Chemung Valley History Museum, Elmira, NY............988

Chenango County Historical Society Museum, Norwich, NY............1044

Cherokee County Historical Museum, Inc., Murphy, NC............1112

Cherokee Strip Museum and Henry S. Johnston Library, Perry, OK............1212

Cherry County Historical Society, Valentine, NE............874

Chester County Historical Society Museum, Chester, SC............1327

Chetopa Historical Museum, Chetopa, KS............535

Chicago History Museum, Chicago, IL............419

Chickasaw Council House Museum, Tishomingo, OK............1214

Chickasaw County Historical Society Bradford Pioneer Village Museum, Nashua, IA............525

Chippewa County Historical Society, Montevideo, MN............783

Chippewa Valley Museum, Inc., Eau Claire, WI............1595

Choctaw County Historical Society, Hugo, OK............1203

Clallam County Historical Society, Port Angeles, WA............1561

The Claremont, New Hampshire Historical Society, Inc., Claremont, NH............884

Clarion County Historical Society, Sutton-Ditz House Museum, Clarion, PA............1247

Clark County Historical Museum, Vancouver, WA............1576

Clark County Historical Society - Heritage Center of Clark County, Springfield, OH............1186

Clark County Museum, Marshall, IL............444

Clarke County Historical Association, Inc., Berryville, VA............1496

Clay County Historical Museum, Liberty, MO............826

Clay County Historical Society Museum and Archives, Moorhead, MN............784

Cle Elum Telephone Museum, Cle Elum, WA............1551

Clear Lake Area Historical Museum, Clear Lake, WI............1594

Clearfield County Historical Society, Clearfield, PA............1247

Clearwater County Historical Society, Shevlin, MN............793

Clearwater Historical Museum, Orofino, ID............408

Cleo Redd Fisher Museum, Loudonville, OH............1172

Cleveland County Historical Museum, Shelby, NC............1119

Cleveland Police Historical Society & Museum, Cleveland, OH............1153

Clinton County Historical Association & Museum, Plattsburgh, NY............1052

Historical Society Museums–Continued

Clinton County Historical Society, Clinton, IA 511

Clinton County Historical Society, Wilmington, OH 1191

Clinton County Historical Society Paine-Gillam-Scott Museum, Saint Johns, MI 763

Clinton County Museum, Frankfort, IN 478

Cloud County Historical Society Museum, Concordia, KS 536

Coachella Valley Museum and Cultural Center, Indio, CA 104

Coal Miners' Museum/Van Lear Historical Society, Inc., Van Lear, KY 584

The Coffey County Historical Museum, Burlington, KS 534

Cole County Historical Museum, Jefferson City, MO 819

The Coley Homestead & Barn Museum, Weston, CT 265

Colfax County Society of Art, History and Archaeology, Raton, NM 945

Collin County Historical Society, Inc. & History Museum, McKinney, TX 1437

Collinsville Depot Museum, Collinsville, OK 1198

Colorado Historical Society, Denver, CO.....210

Columbia County Historical and Genealogical Society, Bloomsburg, PA .1243

Columbia County Historical Society, Inc., Kinderhook, NY 1007

Columbia Gorge Interpretive Center Museum, Stevenson, WA 1572

Comanche Crossing Historical Society & Museum, Strasburg, CO 233

Community Historical Museum, Maxwell, IA 523

Comstock Historic House, Moorhead, MN 784

Concord Historical Society, Warner Museum, Springville, NY 1071

Conklin Reed Organ & History Museum, Hanover, MI 745

Connecticut Historical Society, Hartford, CT 244

Constitution Island Association, West Point, NY 1085

Cook County Historical Museum, Grand Marais, MN 776

The Coopersville Area Historical Society Museum, Coopersville, MI.....................733

Coos Historical & Maritime Museum, North Bend, OR....................................1229

Cordova Historical Museum, Cordova, AK 23

Coronado-Quivira Museum, Lyons, KS.....550

Corry Area Historical Society, Corry, PA...1248

Cortland County Historical Society, Cortland, NY 982

Cottonwood County Historical Society, Windom, MN 796

County Center Historical Society, Wabasso, MN 795

Cow Neck Peninsula Historical Society Sands-Willets House, Port Washington, NY 1053

The Cowley County Historical Society, Winfield, KS 564

Cranbury Historical & Preservation Society, Cranbury, NJ 902

Cranford Historical Society, Cranford, NJ ...902

Crawford County Historical Museum, Pittsburg, KS 556

Crazy Mountain Museum, Big Timber, MT 841

Crocker House, Mount Clemens, MI.......756

Crockett County Museum, Ozona, TX 1442

Crow Wing County Historical Society, Brainerd, MN 769

Crystal Rice Plantation, Crowley, LA 588

Cumberland County Historical Society, Greenwich, NJ 905

Cumberland County Historical Society, The Hamilton Library and The Two Mile House, Carlisle, PA.....................1245

Cupertino Historical Society & Museum, Cupertino, CA......................................88

Curry Historical Society Museum, Gold Beach, OR...1225

Custer County 1881 Courthouse Museum, Custer, SD..1345

Cuyuna Range Historical Society & Museum, Crosby, MN 772

DAR John Strong Mansion Museum, Addison, VT 1475

Dakota County Historical Society, South Saint Paul, MN 793

Dallam-Hartley XIT Museum, Dalhart, TX 1403

Dallas Historical Society, Dallas, TX 1405

Danvers Historical Society, Danvers, MA....678

Dawes County Historical Society Museum, Chadron, NE............................859

Dawson County Historical Museum, Lexington, NE 864

Dayton Historical Depot Society, Dayton, WA 1552

Decatur County Last Indian Raid Museum, Oberlin, KS 554

Deer Isle-Stonington Historical Society, Deer Isle, ME 609

Deerfield Beach Historical Society, Deerfield Beach, FL 304

DeKalb History Center Museum, Decatur, GA 370

Del Norte County Historical Society, Crescent City, CA................................87

Delta County Historical Society Museum, Escanaba, MI 741

Delta County Museum, Delta, CO................209

Deming Luna Mimbres Museum, Deming, NM 939

Dennys River Historical Society, Dennysville, ME 609

Depot Museum & Fort Sedgwick Museum, Julesburg, CO 223

Depot Park Museum, Sonoma, CA 187

Des Plaines History Center, Des Plaines, IL 430

DeSoto County Museum, Hernando, MS.....801

DeWitt County Historical Museum, Cuero, TX 1403

Dexter Area Historical Society & Museum, Dexter, MI 738

Dexter Historical Society Campus, Dexter, ME 609

Dickinson County Heritage Center, Abilene, KS 531

Diego Sepulveda Adobe Estancia, Costa Mesa, CA 87

Disciples of Christ Historical Society, Nashville, TN.......................................1378

Divide County Historical Society Museum, Crosby, ND 1129

Dr. Increase Mathews House, Zanesville, OH 1194

Dodge County Historical Society Museum, Beaver Dam, WI 1591

Door County Historical Museum, Sturgeon Bay, WI 1623

Doric House, Flemington, NJ 903

Dorothea B. Hoover Historical Museum, Joplin, MO 819

Douglas County Historical Society, Superior, WI 1624

Douglas County Historical Society - Carson Valley Museum & Cultural Center, Gardnerville, NV 877

Douglas County Historical Society - Genoa Courthouse Museum, Genoa, NV 877

Douglas County Museum Complex, Armour, SD...1344

Douglass Historical Museum, Douglass, KS 537

The Drake House Museum, Plainfield, NJ...921

Drew County Historical Museum, Monticello, AR 64

Drummond Home, Hominy, OK................1203

Drummond Island Historical Museum, Drummond Island, MI.........................739

Dublin-Laurens Museum, Dublin, GA 370

Dumbarton House, Washington, DC.............278

Dunbar House State Memorial, Dayton, OH 1161

Dundee Township Historical Society, Inc., Dundee, IL 431

Dundy County Historical Society, Benkelman, NE 857

Dunedin Historical Society & Museum, Dunedin, FL 305

Dunn County Historical Society, Menomonie, WI 1609

Dupont Historical Society, DuPont, WA 1552

Durham Historic Association Museum, Durham, NH 886

Dutchess County Historical Society, Poughkeepsie, NY 1054

Duxbury Rural and Historical Society, Inc., Duxbury, MA 681

Eagle Historical Society & Museums, Eagle, AK...23

East Hampton Historical Society, Inc., East Hampton, NY 985

East Hampton Town Marine Museum, Amagansett, NY 957

East Hillsborough Historical Society, Inc., Plant City, FL 337

East Jordan Portside Art & Historical Museum, East Jordan, MI.....................739

East Poultney Museum, East Poultney, VT 1479

East Tennessee Historical Society, Knoxville, TN.......................................1369

Eastchester Historical Society - 1835 Marble Schoolhouse, Bronxville, NY......967

Eastern Arizona Museum and Historical Society of Graham County Inc., Pima, AZ 42

Eastman Lord House, Conway, NH.............885

Eastside Heritage Center, Bellevue, WA ...1548

Edgar County Historical Museum, Paris, IL 449

Edisto Island Historic Preservation Society Museum, Edisto Island, SC 1332

Edmond Historical Society Museum, Edmond, OK 1200

Edmonds South Snohomish County Historical Society, Inc., Edmonds, WA .1553

Edna Historical Museum, Edna, KS 537

Edwards County Historical Museum, Kinsley, KS 547

1859 Jail, Marshal's Home & Museum, Independence, MO................................817

82nd Airborne Division War Memorial Museum, Fort Bragg, NC......................1101

El Dorado County Historical Museum, Placerville, CA..142

El Monte Historical Society Museum, El Monte, CA 92

El Pueblo History Museum, Pueblo, CO......230

Elbert Hubbard-Roycroft Museum, East Aurora, NY 985

Elgin Area Historical Society, Elgin, IL.......432

Ellis County Historical Society, Hays, KS...543

Enfield Historical Society Museum, Enfield Center, NH 887

Erie County History Center & Cashier's House, Erie, PA 1252

Escondido History Center, Escondido, CA 93

Essex Historical Society, Inc., Essex, CT 240

Evanston Historical Society and Charles
 Gates Dawes House, Evanston, IL 434

Fairfield Historical Society, Fairfield, CT 241
Fairmount Historical Museum & Gift
 Shop, Fairmount, IN...............................476
Fairport Historical Museum, Fairport, NY ...989
Faith Trumbull Chapter, Daughters of the
 American Revolution, Inc., Museum
 and Chapter House, Norwich, CT 258
Fall River County Historical Museum,
 Hot Springs, SD.....................................1348
Fall River Historical Society Museum,
 Fall River, MA 682
Falls Village-Canaan Historical Society,
 Falls Village, CT....................................241
Falmouth Historical Society, Falmouth,
 MA 682
Farrar-Mansur House & Old Mill
 Museum, Weston, VT.............................1490
Faulkner County Museum, Conway, AR........56
Fayette County Helpers Club &
 Historical Society, West Union, IA..........530
Fayette County Museum, Washington
 Court House, OH 1190
Fenton History Center-Museum &
 Library, Jamestown, NY.........................1005
Fifth Maine Regiment Museum, Peaks
 Island, ME 618
Fillmore Historical Museum, Inc.,
 Fillmore, CA..95
The Filson Historical Society, Inc.,
 Louisville, KY 576
The Finley House, Wayne, PA 1306
Finney County Kansas Historical Society,
 Inc., Garden City, KS.............................541
Fitchburg Historical Society, Fitchburg,
 MA 683
Fleming Historical Society, Fleming, CO 216
Florence Griswold Museum, Old Lyme,
 CT 258
The Florence McLeod Hazard Museum,
 Columbus, MS..800
Florence Price Pioneer Museum,
 Florence, CO..216
Florissant Valley Historical Society,
 Florissant, MO.......................................815
Floyd County Historical Museum,
 Charles City, IA.....................................510
Folsom History Museum, Folsom, CA...........95
Fort Abercrombie State Historic Site,
 Abercrombie, ND 1127
Fort Bend Museum Association,
 Richmond, TX 1445
Fort Buford State Historic Site, Williston,
 ND..1137
Fort Croghan Museum, Burnet, TX............1398
Fort Inglish, Bonham, TX...........................1396
Fort Lauderdale Historical Society, Fort
 Lauderdale, FL.......................................307
Fort Robinson Museum, Crawford, NE........860
Fort Totten State Historic Site, Fort
 Totten, ND 1131
Fort Towson Historic Site, Fort Towson,
 OK...1201
Fort Vasquez Museum, Platteville, CO 230
Fort Washita, Durant, OK 1199
Fostoria Area Historical Museum,
 Fostoria, OH 1164
Fox Island Historical Society, Fox Island,
 WA 1554
Fox Lake Historical Museum, Inc., Fox
 Lake, WI..1598
Framingham Historical Society &
 Museum, Framingham, MA 683
Francisco Fort Museum, La Veta, CO..........224
Frank Phillips Home, Bartlesville, OK.......1197
Frankfort Area Historical Museum, West
 Frankfort, IL..464
Franklin County Historical & Museum
 Society & House of History, Malone,
 NY..1012

Franklin County Historical Museum,
 Pasco, WA..1561
Franklin County Old Jail Museum,
 Winchester, TN.......................................1385
Franklin County Seminary and Museum,
 Brookville, IN...471
Franklin Historical Society, Franklin, ME....611
Freeborn County Museum and Historical
 Village, Albert Lea, MN.........................767
Freeport Historical Society, Freeport, ME....611
Fresno Flats Historical Park, Oakhurst,
 CA...132
Friends of Historic Kingston, Fred J.
 Johnston House Museum, Kingston,
 NY..1007
Frisco Historic Park & Museum, Frisco,
 CO...218
Front Street, Ogallala, NE...........................869
Frontier Historical Society and Museum,
 Glenwood Springs, CO 219
Fulton County Historical Society
 Museum, Rochester, IN...........................498

Gage County Historical Society and
 Museum, Beatrice, NE.............................857
Gaineswood, Demopolis, AL 7
Galena-Jo Daviess County Historical
 Society & Museum, Galena, IL................436
Galion Historical Museum, Galion, OH 1165
Galveston County Historical Museum,
 Galveston, TX..1420
Garden Grove Historical Society, Garden
 Grove, CA..99
Garnavillo Historical Museum,
 Garnavillo, IA..518
Garrett County Historical Museum,
 Oakland, MD..649
Garrett Historical Museum, Garrett, IN........479
Garst Museum, Greenville, OH...................1167
Gatekeeper's Museum & Marion
 Steinbach Indian Basket Museum,
 Tahoe City, CA.......................................190
Gates House, Machiasport Historical
 Society, Machiasport, ME........................614
Gates Mills Historical Society, Gates
 Mills, OH 1166
Gateway to the Panhandle, Gate, OK.........1201
Gem County Historical Society and
 Museum, Emmett, ID..............................405
Genealogy Research Center and Museum,
 Sandersville, GA....................................384
General Crook House Museum and
 Library/Archives Center, Omaha, NE......870
General Jacob Brown Historical Society,
 Brownville, NY 971
Geneva Historical Society &
 Prouty-Chew House & Museum,
 Geneva, NY 994
Geographical Center Historical Museum,
 Rugby, ND 1136
Georgia Historical Society, Savannah, GA...385
Georgia Salzburger Society Museum,
 Rincon, GA..381
The Georgian Museum, Lancaster, OH 1171
Gerald R. Ford Conservation Center,
 Omaha, NE 871
Germantown Historical Society,
 Philadelphia, PA 1280
The Gibson Society, Inc. dba Gibson
 House Museum, Boston, MA...................665
Gig Harbor Peninsula Historical Society,
 Gig Harbor, WA.....................................1555
Gila County Historical Museum, Globe,
 AZ...35
Gillespie County Historical Society,
 Fredericksburg, TX.................................1419
Gilliam County Historical Society -
 Depot Museum Complex, Condon, OR.1222
Gilpin History Museum, Central City, CO...205
Gloucester County Historical Society,
 Woodbury, NJ..931
Gnadenhutten Historical Park & Museum,
 Gnadenhutten, OH 1167

Goochland County Museum & Historical
 Center, Goochland, VA...........................1508
Goodhue County Historical Society, Red
 Wing, MN..787
Gore Place, Waltham, MA............................715
Goschenhoppen Folklife Library and
 Museum, Green Lane, PA 1257
Gouverneur Historical Association,
 Gouverneur, NY 995
Governor Ross Plantation, Seaford, DE.......272
Grafton Historical Society, Grafton, VT.....1479
Graham County Historical Society,
 Thatcher, AZ...46
Grand County Museum, Hot Sulphur
 Springs, CO 222
Grand Forks County Historical Society,
 Grand Forks, ND....................................1132
Grant County Historical Museum,
 Ephrata, WA...1553
Grant County Historical Society, Elbow
 Lake, MN...774
Grant County Museum, Carson, ND 1129
Grant County Museum aka Historic
 Adobe Museum, Ulysses, KS 560
Grant County Museum & Historic
 Society, Hyannis, NE..............................863
Grant's Birthplace State Memorial, Point
 Pleasant, OH 1182
Granville County Historical Society
 Museum, Oxford, NC..............................1114
Granville Historical Society Museum,
 Granville, OH...1167
Great Basin Historical Society &
 Museum, Delta, UT................................1464
Greater Harvard Area Historical Society,
 Harvard, IL...439
Greater Hazleton Historical Society,
 Hazleton, PA..1260
Greene County Historical Museum,
 Waynesburg, PA.....................................1306
Greene County Historical Society, Xenia,
 OH..1193
Greenfield Historical Society, Greenfield,
 WI 1599
Greensboro Historical Museum, Inc.,
 Greensboro, NC......................................1103
Greenwood County Historical Society,
 Eureka, KS...539
Gresham History Museum, Gresham, OR..1226
Grevemberg House Museum, Franklin,
 LA...588
Grinnell Historical Museum, Grinnell, IA....519
Grinter Place State Historic Site, Kansas
 City, KS...546
Grosse Ile Historical Society, Grosse Ile,
 MI...745
Groton Historical Society, Groton, MA........685
Groveland Yosemite Gateway Museum,
 Groveland, CA..101
Gunnison County Pioneer and Historical
 Society, Gunnison, CO 222
Gwinnett Historical Society,
 Lawrenceville, GA..................................376

H.G. Albee Memorial Museum,
 Estherville, IA..517
Hackettstown Historical Society Museum
 & Library, Hackettstown, NJ 905
Hahns Peak Area Historical Society and
 School House, Clark, CO 205
Haines Museum, Waukegan Historical
 Society, Waukegan, IL............................463
Halifax Historical Museum, Daytona
 Beach, FL...303
Hamden Historical Society, Inc.,
 Hamden, CT..244
Hamilton Township Historical Society -
 John Abbott II House, Hamilton, NJ.......906
Hamlin Garland Homestead, West Salem,
 WI 1627
Hampton County Historical Museum,
 Hampton, SC..1334

Historical Society Museums–Continued

Hancock County Historical Society, Carthage, IL.................................416

Hanover Historical Society Museum, Hanover, VA 1510

Hardwick Historical Society, Hardwick, MA 686

Harper City Historical Society, Harper, KS 543

Harrison County Historical Museum, Marshall, TX.............................1436

Harrisonburg-Rockingham Historical Society, Dayton, VA....................1503

Harvard Historical Society, Still River, MA 711

Harvey County Historical Society, Newton, KS 553

Harvey House Museum, Florence, KS........539

Hattiesburg Area Historical Society and HAHS Museum, Hattiesburg, MS 801

Hatton-Eielson Museum & Historical Association, Hatton, ND 1132

Haverford Township Historical Society, Havertown, PA............................1260

Haverhill Historical Society, Haverhill, MA 686

Hawkeye Log Cabin, Burlington, IA............507

Hawks Inn Historical Society, Inc., Delafield, WI...............................1595

Hayward Area Historical Society, Hayward, CA....................................102

Headwaters Heritage Museum, Three Forks, MT..854

Healdton Oil Museum, Healdton, OK.........1202

Healy House-Dexter Cabin, Leadville, CO 225

Heisey Museum, Clinton County Historical Society, Lock Haven, PA ...1269

Hennepin History Museum, Minneapolis, MN 782

Henry County Historical Society, New Castle, IN.....................................494

The Henry Sheldon Museum of Vermont History, Middlebury, VT 1481

Heritage Center Museum, Berryville, AR 55

The Heritage Museum, Astoria, OR 1218

The Heritage Museum & Underhill Museum, Idaho Springs, CO.............223

The Heritage Society, Houston, TX............1426

Heritage Square Museum, Ontario, NY 1047

Heritage Station, Umatilla County Historical Society Museum, Pendleton, OR......................................1230

Heritage Village Museum, Woodville, TX.1462

Herkimer County Historical Society, Herkimer, NY..................................998

Hernando Heritage Museum, Brooksville, FL..298

Hettinger County Historical Society, Regent, ND...................................1136

Hibbing Historical Society and Museum, Hibbing, MN...................................778

The Hickories Museum of the Lorain County Historical Society, Elyria, OH ..1163

Hickory Landmarks Society-Propst House & Maple Grove, Hickory, NC............1106

High Cliff Historical Society & General Store Museum, Sherwood, WI..............1622

High Point Museum & Historical Park, High Point, NC.................................1106

Highland County Museum and Heritage Center, McDowell, VA......................1517

Highland House Museum, Hillsboro, OH ..1168

Hillsboro Area Historical Society, Hillsboro, WI.................................1600

Hinsdale Historical Society, Hinsdale, IL 440

Historic Columbia Foundation, Columbia, SC...1329

Historic Georgetown Inc., Georgetown, CO...218

Historic Hermann Museum, Hermann, MO...817

Historic Lyme Village Association, Bellevue, OH.................................1142

Historic Macon Foundation, Inc. - Sidney Lanier Cottage House Museum, Macon, GA 377

Historic Preservation Association of Bourbon County, Inc., Fort Scott, KS 540

Historic Richmond Town, Staten Island, NY..1072

Historic Shepherdstown Museum, Shepherdstown, WV.........................1586

Historical and Genealogical Society of Indiana County, Indiana, PA............1262

Historical and Genealogical Society of Somerset County, Somerset, PA 1300

Historical Museum of Bay County, Bay City, MI.......................................727

Historical Natural History & Library Society of Natick dba Natick Historical Society, South Natick, MA 709

Historical Society of Berks County, Reading, PA...................................1296

Historical Society of Bloomfield New Jersey, Bloomfield, NJ...................898

Historical Society of Brookfield, Brookfield Center, VT.......................1477

Historical Society of Cecil County, Elkton, MD....................................643

Historical Society of Columbia County, Saint Helens, OR...............................1234

The Historical Society of Dauphin County, Harrisburg, PA......................1258

Historical Society of Delaware, Wilmington, DE.................................274

Historical Society of Fort Washington, Fort Washington, PA.......................1254

The Historical Society of Frederick County, Inc., Frederick, MD..................644

Historical Society of Garden County, Oshkosh, NE....................................871

Historical Society of Glastonbury, Glastonbury, CT................................242

Historical Society of Greater Port Jefferson, Port Jefferson, NY 1053

Historical Society of Haddonfield, Haddonfield, NJ...............................905

Historical Society of Kent County, Inc., Chestertown, MD.................................640

Historical Society of Middletown and the Wallkill Precinct, Inc., Middletown, NY......................................1014

Historical Society of Millersburg & Upper Paxton Township Museum, Millersburg, PA.................................1272

Historical Society of Newburgh Bay & the Highlands - David Crawford House, Newburgh, NY.........................1042

Historical Society of Oak Park & River Forest, Oak Park, IL.....................448

Historical Society of Ocean Grove, New Jersey, Ocean Grove, NJ...................918

Historical Society of Old Randolph, Randolph, NJ..................................922

Historical Society of Palm Beach County, Palm Beach, FL..............................334

Historical Society of Princeton, Princeton, NJ...................................921

Historical Society of Quaker Hill & Pawling, Pawling, NY.........................1051

Historical Society of Quincy and Adams County, Quincy, IL.............................452

Historical Society of Rockland County, New City, NY...................................1017

Historical Society of St. Marys and Benzinger Township, Saint Marys, PA ..1297

Historical Society of Santuit and Cotuit, Cotuit, MA......................................677

Historical Society of Saratoga Springs, Saratoga Springs, NY.........................1064

Historical Society of Stanton County Museums at Stanton and Pilger, Pilger, NE..872

Historical Society of Talbot County, Easton, MD.....................................642

Historical Society of the Cocalico Valley, Ephrata, PA......................................1252

Historical Society of the Phoenixville Area, Phoenixville, PA......................1290

Historical Society of the Tonawandas, Inc., Tonawanda, NY.........................1078

Historical Society of the Town of Clarence, Clarence, NY............................978

Historical Society of the Town of Greenwich Inc. aka Bush-Holley Historic Site, Cos Cob, CT................237

Historical Society of the Town of North Hempstead, Manhasset, NY.................1013

The Historical Society of the Town of Warwick, Warwick, NY........................1082

The Historical Society of Trappe, Collegeville, Perkiomen Valley, Inc., Trappe, PA.....................................1303

Historical Society of Wells and Ogunquit, Wells, ME.......................................625

Historical Society Porter County Old Jail Museum, Valparaiso, IN.......................502

The Historical Society, serving Sleepy Hollow and Tarrytown, Tarrytown, NY.1078

The History Center, Fort Wayne, IN 477

The History Center in Tompkins County, Ithaca, NY.....................................1003

The History Museum, Lake Placid-North Elba Historical Society, Lake Placid, NY..1009

History Museum of Western Virginia, Roanoke, VA....................................1535

The History Place, Morehead City, NC 1111

The History Place, Morehead City, NC 1111

Hixon House, La Crosse, WI.......................1603

Hoard Historical Museum and National Dairy Shrine's Visitors Center, Fort Atkinson, WI...................................1598

Hobart Historical Society Museum, Hobart, IN.....................................480

Hocking Valley Museum of Theatrical History, Inc., Nelsonville, OH.............1177

Hodgden House Museum Complex, Ellsworth, KS...................................538

Hoiles-Davis Museum, Greenville, IL.........439

Holland Historical Society Museum, Inc., Holland, VT.....................................1480

The Holland Land Office Museum, Batavia, NY....................................960

Hollywood Heritage Museum, Hollywood, CA.................................103

Holmes County Historical Society, Millersburg, OH...............................1176

Home of Stone (The Mueller-Schmidt House 1881), a Ford County Museum, curated by Ford County Historic Society, Dodge City, KS 537

Honolulu House Museum, Marshall, MI......754

Hood River County Historical Museum, Hood River, OR.................................1226

Hope Historical Society, Hope, NJ.............908

Hornby Museum, Hornby, NY....................999

Hose 5 Fire Museum, Bangor, ME.............604

Howard County Historical Museum, Kokomo, IN...................................486

Howard County Historical Society, Ellicott City, MD...............................643

Howell Historical Society & Committee Museum, Howell, NJ.........................908

Howland House, Plymouth, MA.................703

Hudson Library and Historical Society, Hudson, OH...................................1168

Huerfano County Historical Society, including The Walsenburg Mining Museum & Ft. Francisco Museum of La Veta, Walsenburg, CO....................234

The Huguenot Historical Society, New Paltz, NY......................................1017

Humboldt County Historical Association Museum, Dakota City, IA.................512

The 100th Meridian Museum, Cozad, NE ...859

Huntingdon County Historical Society, Huntingdon, PA 1262
Huntington County Historical Society Museum, Huntington, IN 481
The Hyland House, Guilford, CT 243

Idaho State Historical Museum, Boise, ID...404
Illinois and Michigan Canal Commissioners Office Museum, Lockport, IL..........443
Indian Pay Station Museum, Saint Marys, KS..........557
Indiana Historical Society, Indianapolis, IN..........483
Inland Seas Maritime Museum, Vermilion, OH..........1189
Interlaken Historical Society, Interlaken, NY..........1002
Iosco County Historical Museum, East Tawas, MI..........740
Iowa Railroad Historical Society, Boone, IA..........506
Iron County Museum, Caspian, MI..........731
Iroquois County Historical Society, Watseka, IL..........463
Isanti County Historical Society, Cambridge, MN..........770
Ischua Valley Historical Society, Inc., Franklinville, NY..........992
Island County Historical Society Museum, Coupeville, WA..........1551
Isle La Motte Historical Society, Isle La Motte, VT..........1480
Issaquah History Museum, Issaquah, WA..1557
Itasca County Historical Society, Grand Rapids, MN..........777

J.E. Reeves Home & Museum, Dover, OH..........1163
JFK Special Warfare Museum, Fort Bragg, NC..........1101
J.J. Jackson Memorial Museum, Weaverville, CA..........197
Jackson County Historical Museum & Research Library, Maquoketa, IA..........522
Jackson County Historical Society, Black River Falls, WI..........1592
Jackson-Washabaugh Historical Museum, Kadoka, SD..........1349
Jaffrey Civic Center, Jaffrey, NH..........889
Jail Museum, Neligh, NE..........869
James W. Dillon House Museum, Dillon, SC..........1331
Jamestown Museum, Jamestown, RI..........1312
Jeffers Petroglyphs Historic Site, Comfrey, MN..........771
The Jefferson County Historical Assoc., Steubenville, OH..........1186
Jefferson County Historical Society, Watertown, NY..........1083
Jefferson County Historical Society Museum, Port Townsend, WA..........1562
Jefferson Historical Society and Museum, Jefferson, TX..........1431
Jericho Historical Society, Jericho Corners, VT..........1480
Jerome County Historical Society, Inc. and Idaho Farm & Ranch Museum, Jerome, ID..........406
Jewish Museum of Maryland, Baltimore, MD..........633
Jim Thorpe Home, Yale, OK..........1217
John Brown Museum State Historic Site, Osawatomie, KS..........554
John G. Neihardt State Historic Site, Bancroft, NE..........856
John Jay French House, Beaumont Heritage Society, Beaumont, TX..........1395
John S. Barry Historical Society, Constantine, MI..........732
John Stark Edwards House, Warren, OH...1189
Johnson County Historical Society, Coralville, IA..........511

Johnson County Historical Society, Inc., Tecumseh, NE..........873
Johnson County Historical Society Museum, Warrensburg, MO..........840
Johnstown Historical Society, Johnstown, NY..........1005
Junction City Historical Society, Junction City, OR..........1226

Kalkaska County Historical Museum, Kalkaska, MI..........749
Kanabec History Center, Mora, MN..........784
Kandiyohi County Historical Society, Willmar, MN..........796
Kankakee County Museum, Kankakee, IL..441
Kansas Museum of History, Topeka, KS....559
Kaw Mission State Historic Site, Council Grove, KS..........536
Kearney County Historical Museum, Minden, NE..........868
Kearney Mansion Museum, Fresno, CA........97
Kell House Museum, Wichita Falls, TX....1461
Kellogg Historical Society, Kellogg, IA......521
The Kemp-McCarthy Memorial Museum of the Rowe Historical Society, Inc., Rowe, MA..........706
The Kenilworth Historical Society, Kenilworth, IL..........441
Kenosha County Historical Society and Museum, Inc., Kenosha, WI..........1602
Kentucky Gateway Museum Center, Maysville, KY..........579
Kentucky Historical Society, Frankfort, KY..........569
Kentucky Military History Museum, Frankfort, KY..........569
Ker Place, Onancock, VA..........1523
Keweenaw County Historical Society, Eagle Harbor, MI..........739
Keyport Historical Society-Steamboat Dock Museum, Keyport, NJ..........909
Keystone Area Historical Society, Keystone, SD..........1350
Kimball House Museum, Battle Creek, MI..........727
Kingman County Historical Museum, Kingman, KS..........547
Kinney Pioneer Museum and Historical Society of North Iowa, Clear Lake, IA..510
Kit Carson Museum, Las Animas, CO........225
Kitsap County Historical Society Museum, Bremerton, WA..........1549
Kittson County History Center Museum, Lake Bronson, MN..........778
Klickitat County Historical Society, Goldendale, WA..........1555
Klyne Esopus Museum, Ulster Park, NY...1079
Knox County Historical Society Museum, Edina, MO..........814
Knox County Museum, Knoxville, IL..........441
Knudt Salle Log Cabin, Adams, ND..........1127
Koochiching County Historical Museum, International Falls, MN..........778

La Casa Primera de Rancho San Jose, Pomona, CA..........143
La Porte County Historical Society Museum, La Porte, IN..........487
La Puente Valley Historical Society City Hall, LaPuente, CA..........107
Lac Qui Parle County Historical Society, Madison, MN..........779
Lacey Historical Society, Forked River, NJ..........904
The Lackawanna Historical Society at the Catlin House, Scranton, PA..........1298
Lagrange County Historical Society, Inc., Lagrange, IN..........488
LaGrange Plantation, Cambridge, MD........639
Lahaina Restoration Foundation, Lahaina, HI..........400
Lake County Historical Society, Kirtland Hills, OH..........1170

Lake Forest-Lake Bluff Historical Society, Lake Forest, IL..........441
Lake George Historical Association Museum, Lake George, NY..........1008
Lake Hopatcong Historical Museum, Landing, NJ..........909
Lake of the Red Cedars Museum, Cedar Lake, IN..........472
Lake Tahoe Historical Society & Museum, South Lake Tahoe, CA..........188
Lake Tomahawk Historical Society, Lake Tomahawk, WI..........1604
Lancaster County Historical Society, Lancaster, PA..........1266
Lancaster Historical Society, Lancaster, NH..........890
Lane County Historical Museum, Dighton, KS..........536
Lane House, Roseburg, OR..........1234
Lane Place, Crawfordsville, IN..........473
Langlade County Historical Society Museum, Antigo, WI..........1589
Larchmont Historical Society, Mamaroneck, NY..........1013
Lars Noak Blacksmith Shop, Larsson/Ostlund Log Home & One-Room Capitol School, New Sweden, ME..........616
LaSalle County Historical Society Museum, Utica, IL..........462
Lassen Historical Museum, Susanville, CA..........190
Lauder Museum - Amityville Historical Society, Amityville, NY..........957
Laura Ingalls Wilder Museum and Tourist Center, Walnut Grove, MN..........795
Lawrence History Center: Immigrant City Archives & Museum, Lawrence, MA......689
Laws Railroad Museum and Historical Site, Bishop, CA..........78
The Lebanon County Historical Society, Lebanon, PA..........1268
Lee County Historical Society, Loachapoka, AL..........13
Leelanau Historical Museum, Leland, MI....751
Lehigh County Historical Society, Allentown, PA..........1239
Lemhi County Historical Museum, Salmon, ID..........409
LeRoy House & JELL-O Gallery, LeRoy, NY..........1009
Lesbian Herstory Educational Foundation, Inc. aka Lesbian Herstory Archives, Brooklyn, NY..........969
Lesueur County Historical Museum-Chapter 1, Elysian, MN..........774
Leverett Historical Society, Leverett, MA....689
Lewis County Historical Museum, Chehalis, WA..........1550
Lewis County Historical Society Museum, Lowville, NY..........1012
Lexington Historical Society, Lexington, MA..........689
Libertyville-Mundelein Historical Society, Inc., Libertyville, IL..........442
Lillian and Albert Small Jewish Museum, Washington, DC..........282
Lincoln County Historical Museum, Davenport, WA..........1552
Lincoln County Historical Society Museum of Pioneer History, Chandler, OK..........1197
Lincoln County Pioneer Museum, Hendricks, MN..........778
Lincoln Parish Museum & Historical Society, Ruston, LA..........600
The Lincoln-Tallman Restorations, Janesville, WI..........1601
Lisbon Historical Society, Lisbon, OH......1172
Litchfield Historical Society and Museum, Litchfield, CT..........247
Little Compton Historical Society, Little Compton, RI..........1312

Historical Society Museums—Continued

Little Falls Historical Society Museum, Little Falls, NY 1009

Little Log Church & Museum, Yachats, OR 1238

Little Traverse Historical Society, Petoskey, MI 760

Livingston County Historical Society Museum, Geneseo, NY 993

Lockehaven Schoolhouse Museum, Enfield, NH 887

The Log House Museum of the Historical Society of Columbiana-Fairfield Township, Columbiana, OH 1157

Logan County Historical Society Museum, Bellefontaine, OH 1142

Lombard Historical Museum, Lombard, IL 443

Lompoc Valley Historical Society, Inc., Lompoc, CA 110

Long Branch Historical Museum, Long Branch, NJ 910

Lopez Island Historical Museum, Lopez Island, WA 1558

Los Angeles Police Historical Society & Museum, Los Angeles, CA 119

Los Nogales Museum, Seguin, TX 1452

Lou Holtz/Upper Ohio Valley Hall of Fame, East Liverpool, OH 1163

Louis E. May Museum, Fremont, NE 861

Louis H. & Lena Firn Grover Museum, Shelbyville, IN 498

Louisa County Historical Society, Louisa, VA 1514

Louisiana State Oil & Gas Museum, Oil City, LA 599

Lovettsville Historical Society Museum, Lovettsville, VA 1514

Lowell Area Historical Museum, Lowell, MI 751

Lower Cape Fear Historical Society, Inc., Wilmington, NC 1123

Lowndes County Historical Society and Museum, Valdosta, GA 389

Lucretia Vaile Museum, Palmer Lake, CO 229

Lummis Home: El Alisal, Los Angeles, CA 119

Lutheran Heritage Center & Museum of the Perry County Lutheran Historical Society, Altenburg, MO 810

Luzerne County Historical Society, Wilkes-Barre, PA 1307

Lynn Museum & Historical Society, Lynn, MA 692

Lyon County Historical Society and Museum, Emporia, KS 538

Lyon County Historical Society Museum, Marshall, MN 780

The Lyons Redstone Museum, Lyons, CO ...227

Macartney House Museum, Oakland, ME ...616

Macedon Historical Society, Inc., Macedon, NY 1012

Macktown Living History Education Center, Inc., Rockton, IL 456

Macon County Historical Society Museum Complex, Decatur, IL 430

Madison County Historical Museum & Archival Library, Edwardsville, IL 432

Madison County Historical Society, Winterset, IA 531

Madison County Historical Society-Cottage Lawn, Oneida, NY 1045

Madison Historical Society, Madison, CT 247

Maine Historical Society, Portland, ME 619

Maitland Historical Museums, Maitland, FL 322

The Major General Frederick Funston Boyhood Home and Museum, Iola, KS 546

Manchester Historic Association Millyard Museum, Manchester, NH 891

Manchester Historical Society, Manchester, MA 692

Mansfield Historical Society Museum, Storrs, CT 261

Maple Valley Historical Museum, Maple Valley, WA 1559

Marathon County Historical Society, Wausau, WI 1626

Marblehead Museum & Historical Society, Marblehead, MA 693

Marietta House Museum, Glenn Dale, MD 645

Marilla Historical Society Museum, Marilla, NY 1014

Marion County Historical Society, Salem, OR 1236

The Marion County Historical Society Museum, Marion, OH 1174

Mariposa Museum and History Center Inc., Mariposa, CA 124

Maritime Museum at Historic Coast Guard Station, Saint Simons Island, GA 383

Maritime Museum - Cohasset Historical Society, Cohasset, MA 676

Marlboro County Historical Museum, Bennettsville, SC 1322

Marquette County Historical Society, Westfield, WI 1627

Marquette County History Museum, Marquette, MI 753

Marshall County Historical Museum, Plymouth, IN 496

Marshall County Historical Museum, Holly Springs, MS 801

Marshall County Historical Society Museum, Warren, MN 795

Martha A. Parsons House Museum, Enfield, CT 239

Martha's Vineyard Museum, Edgartown, MA 681

Martin County Historical Museum, Stanton, TX 1453

Marvin Newton House, Brookfield, VT 1477

Maryland Historical Society, Baltimore, MD 634

Mason County Historical Society/Historic White Pine Village, Ludington, MI 751

Masonic Grand Lodge Library and Museum of Texas, Waco, TX 1459

Massachusetts Historical Society, Boston, MA 667

Matagorda County Museum, Bay City, TX 1393

Mathias Ham House Historic Site, Dubuque, IA 516

The Mattatuck Museum Arts and History Center, Waterbury, CT 264

Mayflower Society Museum, Plymouth, MA 703

Mayville Area Museum of History and Genealogy, Mayville, MI 754

Mayville Historical Society, Inc., Mayville, WI 1608

Mazomanie Historical Society, Mazomanie, WI 1608

McAllister House Museum, Colorado Springs, CO 207

McConnell Mansion, Moscow, ID 407

McCook House, Civil War Museum, Carrollton, OH 1146

McCutchen Overland Inn, McCutchenville, OH 1175

McFarland Historical Society, McFarland, WI 1609

McHenry County Historical Society and Museum, Union, IL 461

McIntosh County Historical Society, Ashley, ND 1127

McLean-Alanreed Area Museum, McLean, TX 1438

McLean County Historical Society Museum, Washburn, ND 1137

McLean County Museum of History, Bloomington, IL 414

McMinn County Living Heritage Museum, Athens, TN 1360

Meagher County Historical Association Castle Museum, White Sulphur Springs, MT 855

Medina County Historical Society, The John Smart House, Medina, OH 1175

Meigs County Museum, Pomeroy, OH 1183

Mem-Erie Historical Museum, Erie, KS 539

Memorial Hall Museum, Pocumtuck Valley Memorial Assoc., Deerfield, MA 679

Mendocino Historical Research, Inc./Kelley House Museum, Mendocino, CA 125

Menominee County Heritage Museum, Menominee, MI 754

Merced County Courthouse Museum, Merced, CA 125

Mercer County Genealogical and Historical Society, Princeton, MO 829

Mercer County Historical Museum, The Riley Home, Celina, OH 1146

Mercer County Historical Society, Mercer, PA 1271

Meriden Historical Society, Inc., Meriden, CT 249

Merrill Historical Museum, Merrill, WI 1609

Mesa Historical Museum, Mesa, AZ 37

Mid-Continent Railway Museum, North Freedom, WI 1615

Middleborough Historical Association, Inc., Middleborough, MA 694

Middlebury Historical Society, Wyoming, NY 1087

Middlesex County Historical Society, Middletown, CT 249

Middleton Historical Society - Lura Woodside Watkins Museum, Middleton, MA 694

Middletown Valley Historical Society, Middletown, MD 649

Midland County Historical Museum, Midland, TX 1438

Midland County Historical Society, Midland, MI 755

Milford Historical Museum, Milford, MI 756

Milford Historical Society, Milford, CT 250

Mill Race Historical Village, Northville, MI 758

Millard Fillmore House, East Aurora, NY ...985

Mills County Historical Society and Museum, Glenwood, IA 519

Milton House Museum Historic Site, Milton, WI 1610

Milwaukee County Historical Society, Milwaukee, WI 1611

Mineral County Museum & Historical Society, Superior, MT 854

Minisink Valley Historical Society, Port Jervis, NY 1053

Minnesota Historical Society, Saint Paul, MN 791

Minnilusa Pioneer Museum, Rapid City, SD 1354

Miramont Castle Museum, Manitou Springs, CO 228

Mission Bell Museum, Coweta, OK 1199

Missisquoi Valley Historical Society, North Troy, VT 1483

Missouri Historical Society, Saint Louis, MO 835

Monmouth County Historical Association, Freehold, NJ 905

Monroe County Historical Association/Stroud Mansion, Stroudsburg, PA 1302

Monroe County Historical Society, Bloomington, IN 469

Monroe County Local History Room & Library, Sparta, WI 1622
Monroe Historical Society, Monroe, CT 250
Montague Museum & Historical Association, Montague, MI.......................756
Montclair Historical Society, Montclair, NJ 912
Monterey History and Art Association, Monterey, CA 127
The Montgomery County Historical Society, Dayton, OH...................1161
The Montgomery County Historical Society, Inc., Rockville, MD...................651
Montrose County Historical Museum, Montrose, CO 228
Montville Township Historical Museum, Montville, NJ 912
Moravian Historical Society, Nazareth, PA 1273
Morgan Row Museum and Harrodsburg-Mercer County Research Library, Harrodsburg, KY 570
Moriarty Historical Museum, Moriarty, NM..943
Morris County Historical Society (Acorn Hall House Museum), Morristown, NJ ...914
Morton Grove Historical Museum/Haupt-Yehl House, Morton Grove, IL 446
Mount Desert Island Historical Society, Mount Desert, ME..........................615
Mount Holly Community Historical Museum, Belmont, VT...........................1476
Mount Pleasant Historical Society, Mount Pleasant, OH 1177
Mount Prospect Historical Society Museums, Mount Prospect, IL.................446
Murray-Lindsay Mansion, Lindsay, OK.....1204
Museum of Ceramics, East Liverpool, OH..1163
Museum of History & Industry (MOHAI), Seattle, WA...........................1567
Museum of Idaho, Idaho Falls, ID 406
Museum of Indian Culture, Allentown, PA 1239
The Museum of Mobile, Mobile, AL 14
Museum of San Diego History and Research Library, San Diego, CA 158
Museum of Seminole County History, Sanford, FL 343
Museum of the Bedford Historical Society, Bedford, NY 961
Museum of the Cherokee Strip, Enid, OK.1200
Museum of the High Plains, McCook, NE 868
Museum of the Western Prairie, Altus, OK 1195
Museum of the Weston Historical Society, Inc., Weston, MA 718
Museum of Yarmouth History, Yarmouth, ME 626
Museum on Main, Pleasanton, CA..............142
Museum on Main: A History Museum for West Georgia, LaGrange, GA 375

Napoleonic Society of America, Inc., Clearwater, FL 300
Narragansett Historical Society, Templeton, MA......................................714
National Apple Museum, Biglerville, PA ...1243
National Archives and Records Administration - Mid-Atlantic Region, Philadelphia, PA 1284
National Railroad Museum, Green Bay, WI 1599
National Road/Zane Grey Museum, Norwich, OH...1180
National Society of the Children of the American Revolution Museum, Washington, DC.......................................287
National Society of the Sons of the American Revolution, Louisville, KY 578

Naugatuck Historical Society, Naugatuck, CT 251
Nauvoo Historical Society Museum, Nauvoo, IL...447
Navarro County Historical Society, Pioneer Village, Corsicana, TX.............1402
Nebraska Prairie Museum of the Phelps County Historical Society, Holdrege, NE 863
Nebraska State Historical Society's Museum of Nebraska History, Lincoln, NE 866
Neenah Historical Society, Hiram Smith, Neenah's Heritage Park, Octagon House & Ward House, Neenah, WI.......1614
Neill-Cochran Museum House, Austin, TX 1391
Nevada County Historical Society, Inc., Nevada City, CA 130
Nevada Historical Society, Reno, NV 881
The New Berlin Historical Society, New Berlin, WI...1614
New Canaan Historical Society, New Canaan, CT 252
New Castle Historical Society, New Castle, DE 272
New Hampshire Antiquarian Society, Hopkinton, NH..889
New Hampshire Historical Society, Concord, NH..885
New Hartford Historical Society, New Hartford, NY..1017
New Hartford Historical Society, Pine Meadow, CT 258
New Haven Colony Historical Society, New Haven, CT......................................253
New London County Historical Society, New London, CT.....................................255
New London Historical Society, New London, NH..892
The New Milford Historical Society, New Milford, CT..256
New Richmond Preservation Society, New Richmond, WI...............................1615
New Sweden Historical Society, New Sweden, ME..616
The New York Historical Society, New York, NY...1035
Newaygo County Museum, Newaygo, MI...758
Newton Public Library and Museum, Newton, IL...447
Newtown History Center, Stephens City, VA 1538
The Niagara County Historical Center and Niagara County Genealogical Society, Lockport, NY 1010
Nicollet County Historical Society, Saint Peter, MN..793
No Man's Land Historical Society, Goodwell, OK..1201
Noank Historical Society, Inc., Noank, CT 256
Nobleboro Historical Society, Nobleboro, ME 616
Nobles County Historical Society, Worthington, MN....................................797
Nordica Homestead, Farmington, ME.........610
Norfolk Historical Museum, Norfolk, CT 257
The Norman Cleveland County Historical Museum, Norman, OK 1206
North Andover Historical Society, North Andover, MA..698
North Brevard Historical Museum, Titusville, FL 352
North Castle Historical Society, Armonk, NY 958
North Haven Historical Society, North Haven, CT 257
North House Museum, Lewisburg, WV 1584
North Lee County Historic Center and Santa Fe Depot Museum Complex, Fort Madison, IA......................................518
North Platte Valley Museum, Gering, NE....861

Northampton County Historical and Genealogical Society, Easton, PA 1250
Northborough Historical Society, Inc., Northborough, MA 700
Northeast Oakland Historical Museum, Oxford, MI..759
Northeastern Nevada Museum, Elko, NV 876
Northfield Historical Society Museum, Northfield, MN..785
Northport Historical Society Museum, Northport, NY..1044
Northwest Museum of Arts & Culture (Eastern Washington State Historical Society), Spokane, WA..........................1571
Norwich Historical Society, Norwich, VT .1484
Nowata County Historical Society Museum, Nowata, OK...........................1207
Noyes House Museum, Morrisville, VT 1483

Oak Creek Historical Society-Pioneer Village, Oak Creek, WI.........................1615
Oakdale Museum, Oakdale, CA 132
Oakland County Pioneer and Historical Society, Pontiac, MI.................................760
The Oaks House Museum, Jackson, MS......804
Ocean County Historical Museum, Toms River, NJ 926
Octagon House-First Kindergarten in America, Watertown, WI..........................1625
Octave Chanute Aerospace Museum, Rantoul, IL...453
O'Fallon Historical Museum, Baker, MT.....840
Ogden Historical Society, Spencerport, NY 1071
Ohio River Museum, Marietta, OH 1174
Ojai Valley Historical Society and Museum, Ojai, CA 135
Oklahoma Historical Society, Oklahoma City, OK...1209
Oklahoma Museum of History, Oklahoma City, OK...1210
Oklahoma Territorial Museum, Guthrie, OK 1202
Old Bohemia Historical Society, Warwick, MD..656
Old Brutus Historical Society, Inc., Weedsport, NY..1084
Old Colony Historical Society, Taunton, MA 714
Old Conway Homestead Complex and Museum, Camden, ME...........................608
Old Court House Museum-Eva Whitaker Davis Memorial, Vicksburg, MS 809
Old Depot Museum, Ottawa, KS.................555
Old Dominion Railway Museum, Richmond, VA..1531
Old Falls Village, Menomonee Falls, WI...1609
Old Fort Bissell, Phillipsburg, KS 555
Old Fort House Museum, Fort Edward, NY 991
Old Fort Johnson, Fort Johnson, NY...........991
The Old Jail Museum, Warrenton, VA 1543
Old Jefferson Town, Oskaloosa, KS.............555
Old Lighthouse Museum, Stonington, CT....261
Old Log Jail and Chapel Museums, Greenfield, IN..480
Old Ordinary House Museum, Hingham, MA 687
Old State House-The Bostonian Society, Boston, MA..668
Old Stone Fort Museum Complex, Schoharie, NY..1067
Old Sussex County Courthouse, Georgetown, DE..271
Old Village Hall Museum, Lindenhurst, NY 1009
Old York Road Historical Society, Jenkintown, PA..1263
Oldest House Museum Complex, Saint Augustine, FL..339
Oldest Stone House Museum, Lakewood, OH 1170
Oliver Kelley Farm, Elk River, MN............774

Historical Society Museums–Continued

Olmsted County Historical Society,
  Rochester, MN 788
103rd Ohio Volunteer Infantry Civil War
  Museum, Sheffield Lake, OH 1185
Oneida County Historical Society, Utica,
  NY 1080
Onondaga Historical Association Museum
  & Research Center, Syracuse, NY 1077
Ontario County Historical Society,
  Canandaigua, NY 975
Orcas Island Historical Museum, Orcas
  Island, WA 1560
Orchard Park Historical Society, Orchard
  Park, NY 1047
Oregon Coast History Center, Newport,
  OR 1229
Oregon Historical Society, Portland, OR....1231
Oregon-Jerusalem Historical Museum,
  Oregon, OH 1181
Orleans County Historical Society & The
  Old Stone House Museum,
  Brownington, VT 1477
Osage County Historical Society
  Museum, Pawhuska, OK 1211
Osage County Historical Society
  Research Center, Lyndon, KS 550
Osborn-Jackson House, East Hampton,
  NY 986
Ossining Historical Society Museum,
  Ossining, NY 1047
Osterville Historical Society, Inc.,
  Osterville, MA 701
Oswego Historical Museum, Inc.,
  Oswego, KS 555
Otter Tail County Historical Society,
  Fergus Falls, MN 775
Ouachita County Historical Society,
  Camden, AR 55
Outagamie Museum, Appleton, WI 1589
Overholser Mansion, Oklahoma City, OK .1210
Overland Trail Museum, Sterling, CO..........232
Oyster Bay Historical Society, Oyster
  Bay, NY 1049
Oysterponds Historical Society: The
  Museum of Orient and East Marion
  History, Orient, NY 1047
Ozaukee County Pioneer Village,
  Saukville, WI 1620

Pacific County Historical Museum, South
  Bend, WA 1571
Pajaro Valley Historical Association,
  Watsonville, CA 196
Palmer/Gullickson Octagon Home, West
  Salem, WI 1627
Parker Tavern, Reading, MA 705
Parsons Historical Commission Museum,
  Parsons, KS 555
Parsonsfield-Porter Historical Society,
  Porter, ME 618
Pasadena Museum of History, Pasadena,
  CA 140
Pascack Historical Society, Park Ridge,
  NJ 920
Passaic County Historical Society &
  Lambert Castle Museum, Paterson, NJ ...920
Patterson Inn Museum/Corning - Painted
  Post Historical Society, Corning, NY......982
Pauline E. Glidden Toy Museum,
  Ashland, NH 883
Pawnee City Historical Society &
  Museum, Pawnee City, NE 871
Pejepscot Historical Society, Brunswick,
  ME 608
Pembroke Historical Society, Inc.,
  Pembroke, MA..701
Pensacola Historical Society Museum,
  Pensacola, FL..336
Perkins County Historical Society, Grant,
  NE 862
Peshtigo Fire Museum, Peshtigo, WI 1617

Peter Conser House, Heavener, OK 1202
Peter Rice Homestead, Home of
  Marlborough Historical Society, Inc.,
  Marlboro, MA..693
Peterborough Historical Society,
  Peterborough, NH 893
Petersham Historical Society, Inc.,
  Petersham, MA...702
Pettaquamscutt Historical Society,
  Kingston, RI..1312
Pettis County Historical Society, Sedalia,
  MO 838
Phelps House, Burlington, IA 507
Phillips County Museum, Holyoke, CO.......222
Phillips Historical Society, Phillips, ME 618
Pike County Historical Society, Milford,
  PA 1272
Pimeria Alta Historical Society, Nogales,
  AZ 37
Pinal County Historical Society and
  Museum, Florence, AZ...............................34
Pine County Historical Society, Askov,
  MN 768
Pioneer Corner Museum, New Holstein,
  WI 1615
Pioneer-Krier Museum, Ashland, KS 532
Pioneer Log Cabin, Manhattan, KS 551
The Pioneer Memorial Association of
  Fenton and Mundy Townships,
  Fenton, MI 741
Pioneer Museum, Watford City, ND..........1137
Pioneer Museum, Wild Rose, WI 1628
Pioneer Museum and Vereins Kirche,
  Fredericksburg, TX 1419
Pioneer Museum - Martin County
  Historical Society, Fairmont, MN 775
Pioneer Village, Rison, AR 67
Piqua Historical Area State Memorial,
  Piqua, OH 1182
Pittsford Historical Society Museum,
  Pittsford, VT 1484
Plainsman Museum, Aurora, NE 856
Plantation Historical Museum, Plantation,
  FL 337
Plymouth Historical Museum, Plymouth,
  MI 760
Plymouth Historical Society, Inc.,
  Plymouth, PA..1295
Pocahontas County Iowa Historical
  Society Museum, Laurens, IA 522
Pocahontas County Museum, Marlinton,
  WV 1584
The Polk County Historical Society,
  Cedartown, GA 368
Polk County Historical Society, Des
  Moines, IA 515
Polk County Museum, Balsam Lake, WI....1590
Pope County Historical Society,
  Glenwood, MN 776
Portage County Historical Society,
  Ravenna, OH 1183
Portage County Historical Society,
  Stevens Point, WI 1623
Portsmouth Historical Society,
  Portsmouth, RI 1316
Post Rock Museum, La Crosse, KS 547
Potter County Historical Society,
  Coudersport, PA 1248
Pound Ridge Society/Museum, Pound
  Ridge, NY 1055
The Prairie Museum of Art & History,
  Colby, KS 535
Prairie Trails Museum of Wayne County,
  Corydon, IA 512
Prairie Village, Madison, SD 1351
Pratt County Historical Society Museum,
  Pratt, KS 556
Presbyterian Historical Society,
  Philadelphia, PA 1286
Prestwould Foundation, Clarksville, VA.....1501
Promont House Museum, Milford, OH 1176

Pueblo County Historical Society
  Museum and Edward H. Broadhead
  Library, Pueblo, CO 230
Putnam County Historical Society &
  Foundry School Museum, Cold
  Spring, NY 979
Queens Historical Society, Flushing, NY 990
Quincy Historical Society, Quincy, MA.......705
QV Historical Society at Carriage House
  Museum, Camden, NY 974

R.P. Strathearn Historical Park and
  Museum, Simi Valley, CA 187
Ralston Historical Association, John
  Ralston Museum, Mendham, NJ..............911
Ramapogue Historical Society, West
  Springfield, MA 718
Rancho La Patera - The Stow House
  G.V.H.S., Goleta, CA 100
Randall Library, Stow, MA 713
Randolph County Museum (At Beverly),
  Beverly, WV 1580
Randolph Historical Society, Inc.,
  Randolph, VT 1485
Ransom County Historical Society, Fort
  Ransom, ND 1131
Raton Museum, Raton, NM 945
Ravalli County Museum/Bitter Root
  Valley Historical Society, Hamilton,
  MT..848
Reading Historical Society, Reading, VT...1485
Reading Railroad Heritage Museum,
  Reading, PA 1296
Readsboro Historical Society, Readsboro,
  VT 1486
Rebecca Nurse Homestead, Danvers, MA ...678
Red River Historical Society Museum,
  Clay City, KY 566
Redington Museum, Waterville, ME 625
Redwood County Historical Society,
  Redwood Falls, MN 787
Refugio County Museum, Refugio, TX 1445
Reno County Museum, Hutchinson, KS 545
Rensselaer County Historical Society,
  Troy, NY 1079
Renton Historical Society and Museum,
  Renton, WA 1564
Renville County Historical Society, Inc.,
  Mohall, ND 1135
Republic County Historical Society
  Museum, Belleville, KS 534
Reverend Dan Foster House, Museum of
  the Weathersfield Historical Society,
  Weathersfield, VT 1489
Rhode Island Black Heritage Society,
  Providence, RI 1318
Rhode Island Historical Preservation and
  Heritage, Providence, RI 1318
Rhode Island Historical Society,
  Providence, RI 1318
Rialto Historical Society, Rialto, CA............148
Rice County Museum of History,
  Faribault, MN 775
Richard Salter Storrs House,
  Longmeadow, MA 691
Richardson-Bates House Museum,
  Oswego, NY 1048
Richey Historical Society, Richey, MT 852
Richland County Historical Museum,
  Wahpeton, ND 1137
Riley County Historical Museum,
  Manhattan, KS 551
Rim Country Museum, Payson, AZ..............38
Rimrocker Historical Museum of West
  Montrose County, Naturita, CO 229
Ripley County, Indiana, Historical
  Society Museum, Versailles, IN..............502
Rittman Historical Society, Rittman, OH ...1184
River Museum, Wellsville, OH 1190
Riverside Metropolitan Museum,
  Riverside, CA 150

Robert Louis Stevenson Memorial Cottage, Saranac Lake, NY...................1064
Rochester Historical Society, Rochester, NY..1059
Rock County Historical Society, Janesville, WI..1601
Rock House Museum, Wytheville, VA...1546
Rockbridge Historical Society, Lexington, VA..1513
Rodgers Tavern, Perryville, MD.................650
Rome Historical Society Museum, Rome, NY...1061
Ronald Reagan Boyhood Home, Dixon, IL..431
The Root House Museum, Marietta, GA.....379
Rose Center Museum, Morristown, TN.....1376
Roseau County Historical Museum and Interpretive Center, Roseau, MN.............788
Ross County Historical Society, Inc., Chillicothe, OH..1147
Rowley Historical Society, Rowley, MA......706
Royall House Association, Medford, MA....694
Royalton Historical Society, Royalton, VT..1486
Ruggles House Society, Columbia Falls, ME...609
Rusk County Historical Society, Ladysmith, WI..1604
Russell County Historical Society/Fossil Station Museum, Russell, KS..................556
Rutland Historical Society, Rutland, VT....1486

Sacramento Mountains Historical Museum, Cloudcroft, NM........................938
St. Albans Historical Museum, Saint Albans, VT..1486
St. Charles County Historical Society, Inc., Saint Charles, MO........................830
St. Charles Heritage Center, Saint Charles, IL..457
St. Clair County Historical Society, Belleville, IL...412
St. Francis County Museum, Forrest City, AR..57
St. Lawrence County Historical Association - Silas Wright House, Canton, NY...975
The St. Louis County Historical Society, Duluth, MN......................................773
St. Petersburg Museum of History, Saint Petersburg, FL.......................................342
St. Simons Island Lighthouse Museum, Saint Simons Island, GA.......................383
Salem County Historical Society, Salem, NJ..924
Salem Historical Society and Museum, Salem, OH..1184
The Salem Museum, Salem, VA.................1536
Saline County Historical Society, Inc., Dorchester, NE.......................................860
Salisbury Historical Society, Salisbury, NH...896
Salmon Brook Historical Society, Inc., Granby, CT..242
Sam Brown Log House, Browns Valley, MN...770
Sam Houston Historical Schoolhouse, Maryville, TN.......................................1371
San Antonio Conservation Society, San Antonio, TX...1449
San Fernando Valley Historical Society, Inc., Mission Hills, CA.............................126
San Joaquin County Historical Society & Museum, Lodi, CA..................................109
San Juan County Historical Society Museum, Silverton, CO........................232
San Juan Historical Society, Friday Harbor, WA..1555
San Luis Obispo County Historical Museum, San Luis Obispo, CA..............174
San Mateo County Historical Association and Museum, Redwood City, CA............147

Sandown Historical Society and Museum, Sandown, NH...............................896
Sandpoint Lighthouse, Escanaba, MI...........741
Sandwich Historical Society, Sandwich, IL...457
Sandwich Historical Society, Center Sandwich, NH...884
Sandy Bay Historical Society & Museums, Inc., Rockport, MA.............705
The Santa Barbara Historical Museum, Santa Barbara, CA.....................................179
Santa Ynez Valley Historical Society, Santa Ynez, CA..185
Saratoga County Historical Society, Brookside Museum, Ballston Spa, NY....960
Saratoga Museum, Saratoga, WY..............1638
Sarpy County Historical Museum, Bellevue, NE..857
Satterlee Clark House, Horicon, WI...........1600
Sauk County Historical Museum, Baraboo, WI...1591
Sauk Prairie Area Historical Society, Inc., Prairie du Sac, WI...............................1619
Saunders County Historical Complex, Wahoo, NE..874
Sawin Memorial Building, Dover, MA........680
Sayville Historical Society, Sayville, NY...1066
Scantic Academy Museum, East Windsor Historical Society, Inc., East Windsor, CT...239
The Scarsdale Historical Society, Scarsdale, NY..1066
Schenectady County Historical Society, Schenectady, NY......................................1067
Schmidt House Museum & Research Library, Grants Pass, OR....................1225
Schoenbrunn Village State Memorial, New Philadelphia, OH..........................1177
Scholte House Museum, Pella, IA...............527
Schuyler County Historical Society, Inc., Montour Falls, NY.................................1015
Schuyler Jail Museum, Rushville, IL...........456
Scituate Historical Society, Scituate, MA....708
Scituate Maritime and Irish Mossing Museum, Scituate, MA..........................709
Scotland Heritage Chapel & Museum, Scotland, SD.......................................1355
Seaside Museum & Historical Society, Seaside, OR.......................................1236
Sedgwick-Brooklin Historical Society, Sedgwick, ME...622
Senator John Heinz Pittsburgh Regional History Center, Pittsburgh, PA...............1294
Seneca Falls Historical Society, Seneca Falls, NY...1069
Serpent Mound Museum, Peebles, OH.......1182
Serra Museum/San Diego Historical Society, San Diego, CA 161
Seward County Historical Society Museum, Goehner, NE............................861
Seward Museum, Seward, AK......................27
Seymour Community Museum, Seymour, WI...1621
Shaftsbury Historical Society, Shaftsbury, VT...1487
Shaker Heritage Society, Albany, NY..........956
Shaker Historical Society, Shaker Heights, OH..1185
Sharlot Hall Museum, Prescott, AZ...............43
Sharon Historical Society, Sharon, CT.........260
Sharpsteen Museum, Calistoga, CA...............80
Shaw Island Library & Historical Society, Shaw Island, WA.......................1570
Shawano County Historical Society, Inc., Shawano, WI....................................1621
Sheboygan County Historical Museum, Sheboygan, WI...................................1621
Shelter House Society, Emmaus, PA...........1251
Shelter Island Historical Society, Shelter Island, NY..1069
Sherburne History Center, Becker, MN........768
The Sherman House, Lancaster, OH...........1171

Sherwood-Davidson House, Newark, OH..1178
Shippensburg Historical Society Museum, Shippensburg, PA.............................1300
Shortgrass Country Museum Society, Sayre, OK...1213
Sibley County Historical Museum, Henderson, MN......................................777
Sidney Historical Association, Sidney, NY...1069
Silt Historical Society, Silt, CO.................232
Simsbury Historical Society, Phelps Tavern, Museum & Homestead, Simsbury, CT..260
Sioux City Public Museum, Sioux City, IA..528
Skagit County Historical Museum, La Conner, WA.......................................1557
Smith-McDowell House Museum, Asheville, NC...1090
Smithtown Historical Society, Smithtown, NY...1070
Smyth County Museum, Marion, VA...........1516
Snake River Heritage Center, Weiser, ID.....410
Snoqualmie Valley Historical Museum, North Bend, WA...1559
The Snyder County Historical Society, Middleburg, PA..1271
The Society of California Pioneers, San Francisco, CA.......................................170
Sod House Museum, Aline, OK..................1195
Soldiers & Sailors Memorial Building, Huntington, NY......................................1001
Somers Historical Society, Somers, NY.....1070
Sophienburg Museum & Archives Inc., New Braunfels, TX................................1440
South County Historical Society, Arroyo Grande, CA..72
South Holland Historical Society, South Holland, IL..457
South Milwaukee Historical Society Museum, South Milwaukee, WI...........1622
South Wood County Historical Corp., Wisconsin Rapids, WI..........................1628
Southeastern Railway Museum, Duluth, GA..371
Southold Historical Society and Museum, Southold, NY..1071
Spotsylvania Historical Association and Museum, Spotsylvania, VA.................1537
Spring Street Historical Museum, Shreveport, LA.......................................602
Spring Valley Community Historical Society, Inc., Spring Valley, MN.............794
Springfield Historical Society, Springfield, NJ..925
Springs Museum, Springs, PA.................1301
Stafford County Historical Society Museum, Stafford, KS...........................558
Stamford Historical Society, Inc., Stamford, CT..260
State Capital Publishing Museum, Guthrie, OK...1202
Staten Island Historical Society, Staten Island, NY...1074
Stearns History Museum, Saint Cloud, MN...788
Steele County Historical Society, Hope, ND..1133
Steilacoom Historical Museum Association, Steilacoom, WA...............1572
Stengel-True Museum, Marion, OH...........1174
Sterling Historical Society and Little Red Schoolhouse Museum, Sterling, NY......1074
Sterling-Rock Falls Historical Society Museum, Sterling, IL..............................461
Steuben House, River Edge, NJ.................923
Stevens County Historical Society Museum, Morris, MN............................784
Stevens Museum, Salem, IN.......................498
Steves Homestead, San Antonio, TX.........1450
Stewart M. Lord Memorial Historical Society, Inc., Burlington, ME.................608

Historical Society Museums—Continued

Stockholm Historical Society Museum, Stockholm, ME 623

The Stone House Museum, Belchertown, MA 662

Stone's Tavern, Ligonier, IN 488

Stoughton Historical Society, Stoughton, MA 713

Stoughton Historical Society, Stoughton, WI 1623

The Stratford Historical Society & Catherine B. Mitchell Museum, Stratford, CT 262

Stutsman County Memorial Museum, Jamestown, ND 1133

Suffolk County Historical Society, Riverhead, NY 1057

Sullivan County Historical Society, Inc., Hurleyville, NY 1001

Summit County Historical Society, Akron, OH 1139

Summit Historical Society, Breckenridge, CO 204

Sunnyvale Historical Museum, Sunnyvale, CA 190

Sussex County Historical Society, Newton, NJ 917

Suzanne G. Long Local History Room, Hammond, IN 480

Swampscott Historical Society (John Humphrey House), Swampscott, MA 714

Swarthout Memorial Museum, La Crosse, WI 1603

Swedish American Historical Society, Inc., Chicago, IL 428

Swift County Historical Society, Benson, MN 769

Switzerland County Historical Museum, Vevay, IN 502

T.J. Elder Community Center, Sandersville, GA 384

Table Rock Historical Society and Museums, Table Rock, NE 873

Tama County Historical Museum, Toledo, IA 528

Tante Blanche Museum, Madawaska, ME ... 614

Tappantown Historical Society, Tappan, NY 1077

Tarpon Springs Area Historical Society - Depot Museum, Tarpon Springs, FL 351

Telluride Historical Museum, Telluride, CO 233

Temperance Tavern, Newcomerstown, OH 1179

Tennessee Historical Commission, Nashville, TN 1380

Tennessee Historical Society, Nashville, TN 1380

Tennessee Valley Railroad Museum Inc., Chattanooga, TN 1363

Territorial Capital-Lane Museum, Lecompton, KS 549

Terwilliger Museum, Waterloo, NY 1083

Thetford Historical Society Library and Museum, Thetford, VT 1488

Thomas-Foreman Home, Muskogee, OK .. 1205

The Thomas Griswold House and Museum, Guilford, CT 243

The Thomas T. Taber Museum of the Lycoming County Historial Society, Williamsport, PA 1308

Thomas Warne Historical Museum & Library, Old Bridge, NJ 918

The Thoreau Institute at Walden Woods, Lincoln, MA 691

Tinley Park Historical Society, Tinley Park, IL 461

Tioga County Historical Society Museum, Owego, NY 1048

Tobias Community Institutions, Tobias, NE 873

Tolland Historical Society - Tolland County Jail and Warden's Home Museum, Tolland, CT 262

Tom Mix Museum, Dewey, OK 1199

Tomball Community Museum Center, Tomball, TX 1455

Top of Oklahoma Historical Museum, Blackwell, OK 1197

Topsfield Historical Society, Topsfield, MA 714

Torrington Historical Society, Inc., Torrington, CT 263

Towe Auto Museum, Sacramento, CA 154

Town of Manlius Historical Society with Museum, Manlius, NY 1013

Traill County Historical Society, Hillsboro, ND 1132

Trails & Rails Museum, Kearney, NE 864

Traverse County Historical Society, Wheaton, MN 796

Tri-Cities Museum, Grand Haven, MI 743

Tri-County Historical Society & Museum, Inc., Herington, KS 544

Troutdale Historical Society, Troutdale, OR 1237

Tuck Museum, Hampton, NH 888

Tularosa Basin Historical Society Museum, Alamogordo, NM 932

Twinsburg Historical Society, Twinsburg, OH 1188

Tybee Island Light Station and Tybee Museum, Tybee Island, GA 389

Ulster County Historical Society, Marbletown, NY 1013

The Union County Historical Society, Marysville, OH 1175

Union County Historical Society, Lewisburg, PA 1268

Union County Historical Society Museum, Blairsville, GA 366

Upper Musselshell Historical Society, Harlowton, MT 849

Upper Snake River Valley Historical Society, Rexburg, ID 409

Uppertown Firefighters Museum, Astoria, OR 1219

U.S. Capitol Historical Society, Washington, DC 293

Utah State Historical Society, Salt Lake City, UT 1473

Utica Museum, Utica, MT 854

Valley Community Historical Society, Inc., Valley, NE 874

Van Buren County Historical Museum, Clinton, AR 55

Van Buren County Historical Society, Keosauqua, IA 521

Van Wyck Homestead Museum, Fishkill, NY 989

Verde Historical Society, Clemenceau Heritage Museum, Cottonwood, AZ 32

Verendrye Museum, Fort Pierre, SD 1347

Vermilion County Museum Society, Danville, IL 429

Vermont Historical Society Museum, Montpelier, VT 1482

Vernon County Historical Museum, Viroqua, WI 1625

Vernonia Pioneer Museum, Vernonia, OR .. 1238

The Vestal Museum, Vestal, NY 1081

Vigo County Historical Museum, Terre Haute, IN 501

Villa Montezuma Museum/San Diego Historical Society, San Diego, CA 162

The Vinalhaven Historical Society Museum, Vinalhaven, ME 624

Virginia Baptist Historical Society, Richmond, VA 1532

Virginia City J. Spencer Watkins Memorial Museum, Virginia City, MT 854

Virginia Historical Society, Richmond, VA 1533

Vista Historical Museum, Vista, CA 196

Wahkiakum County Historical Museum, Cathlamet, WA 1550

Wakefield Historical Society, Wakefield, MA 715

Wakefield House Museum, Blue Earth, MN 769

Wakefield Museum Association, Wakefield, KS 560

Wallingford Historical Society, Inc., Wallingford, CT 263

Walt Whitman Birthplace State Historic Site and Interpretive Center, Huntington Station, NY 1001

Waltham Historical Society, Waltham, MA 716

Wapello County Historical Museum, Ottumwa, IA 526

Ward County Historical Society, Minot, ND 1135

Ward W. O'Hara Agricultural Museum, Auburn, NY 959

Warren County Historical Society, Warren, PA 1304

Warren County Historical Society Museum, Lebanon, OH 1171

Warren Historical Society, Warren, ME 624

Warren Rifles Confederate Museum, Front Royal, VA 1508

Warsaw Historical Museum, Warsaw, NY . 1082

Waseca County Historical Society, Waseca, MN 796

Washburn County Historical Society Museum, Shell Lake, WI 1621

Washington County Historical Association, Fort Calhoun, NE 860

Washington County Historical Society, Washington, KS 560

Washington County Historical Society, Portland, OR 1233

Washington County Historical Society, Washington, PA 1305

Washington County Historical Society and Miller House Museum, Hagerstown, MD 646

Washington County Historical Society Inc., West Bend, WI 1627

Washington County Historical Society Warden's House Museum, Stillwater, MN 794

Washington Historical Museum, Washington, GA 391

Washington State Capital Museum and Outreach Center, Olympia, WA 1560

Washington State Historical Society, Tacoma, WA 1574

Washington's Lands Museum & Sayre Log House, Ravenswood, WV 1586

Waterloo Area Historical Society, Grass Lake, MI 744

Watertown Historical Society, Inc., Watertown, CT 264

Watkins Community Museum of History, Lawrence, KS 548

Wauconda Township Historical Society, Wauconda, IL 463

Wayland Historical Society, Wayland, MA 716

Wayne County Historical Museum, Richmond, IN 497

Wayne County Historical Society, Lyons, NY 1012

Wayne County Historical Society, Wooster, OH 1192

Wayne County Historical Society, Honesdale, PA 1261

Webb House Museum, Newark, OH 1179

Webster County Historical Museum, Red Cloud, NE 872

Webster House Museum, Elkhorn, WI 1596

Wellesley Historical Society, Inc.,
    Wellesley Hills, MA 717
Wellfleet Historical Society Museum,
    Wellfleet, MA 717
Wells County Historical Museum,
    Bluffton, IN..470
Wells County Museum, Fessenden, ND 1131
Wenham Museum, Wenham, MA................717
Wentworth Gardner & Tobias Lear
    Houses Association, Portsmouth, NH......895
West Overton Museums, Scottdale, PA 1298
West River Museum Society, Philip, SD....1353
Western Reserve Historical Society,
    Cleveland, OH 1156
Western Rhode Island Civic Historical
    Society, Coventry, RI............................1311
Westminster Historical Society,
    Westminster, VT 1490
The Wethersfield Historical Society,
    Wethersfield, CT 266
Wexford County Historical Society &
    Museum, Cadillac, MI............................731
Wheat Ridge Historic Park, Wheat Ridge,
    CO...235
Whipple House Museum, Ashland
    Historical Society, Ashland, NH 883
White County Historical Society,
    Cleveland, GA 368
White County Historical Society, Carmi,
    IL...415
White County Historical Society
    Museum, Monticello, IN 491
White Pillars Museum, De Pere
    Historical Society, De Pere, WI.............1594
Wickersham House Museum
    (Tanana-Yukon Historical Society),
    Fairbanks, AK...24
Wilderness Road Regional Museum,
    Newbern, VA 1519
Wilkin County Historical Society,
    Breckenridge, MN 770
Williamson County Historical Society,
    Marion, IL...444
Wilson County Historical Society
    Museum, Fredonia, KS............................540
Wilson Historical Museum, Wilson, NY....1086
Wilton Historical Museums, Wilton, CT......267
Winchester-Frederick County Historical
    Society, Inc., Winchester, VA.................1546
Winona County Historical Museum,
    Winona, MN 797
Wolcott House Museum Complex,
    Maumee, OH.......................................1175
Wolf Point Area Historical Society, Inc.,
    Wolf Point, MT 855
Wolfeboro Historical Society, Wolfeboro,
    NH...897
Wood County Historical\Center and
    Museum, Bowling Green, OH 1143
Woodford County Historical Society
    Museum, Versailles, KY..........................584
Woodson County Historical Society,
    Yates Center, KS....................................564
Woodstock Historical Society, Bryant
    Pond, ME..608
Woodstock Historical Society, Inc.,
    Woodstock, CT 268
Woodstock Historical Society, Inc.,
    Woodstock, VT 1491
Woodville Museum, Inc., Rogue River,
    OR...1234
Worcester Historical Museum, Worcester,
    MA...721
Worthington Historical Society,
    Worthington, OH 1192
Wyandotte County Museum, Bonner
    Springs, KS..534
Wyandotte Museum, Wyandotte, MI..........766
The Wyman Tavern, Keene, NH.................890

Yakima Valley Museum and Historical
    Association, Yakima, WA......................1579

Yellowstone Gateway Museum of Park
    County, Livingston, MT 850
York County Heritage Trust, Museum &
    Library, York, PA.................................1309
Ypsilanti Historical Museum, Ypsilanti,
    MI...767

Z. Taylor Brown-Sarah Dorsey House,
    Midland, TX 1439
Zion Historical Society, Zion, IL.................467

History Museums

The A.D. Buck Museum of Natural
    History & Science, Tonkana, OK 1215
The APEX Museum, Atlanta, GA 357
A.R. Bowman Memorial Museum,
    Prineville, OR......................................1234
A:shiwi A:wan Museum and Heritage
    Center, Zuni, NM 954
Abby Aldrich Rockefeller Folk Art
    Museum, Williamsburg, VA 1544
Aberdeen Museum of History, Aberdeen,
    WA 1547
Abraham Lincoln Library & Museum,
    Lincoln Memorial University,
    Harrogate, TN 1366
Abraham Lincoln Presidential Library &
    Museum, Springfield, IL 458
Academy Hall Museum of the Rocky
    Hill Historical Society, Inc., Rocky
    Hill, CT...259
The Accokeek Foundation, Inc.,
    Accokeek, MD.......................................627
Ace of Clubs House, Texarkana, TX..........1455
Adam Thoroughgood House, Virginia
    Beach, VA 1541
Adams County Historical Museum,
    Decatur, IN 474
Adams County Historical Society
    Museum, Lind, WA 1558
Adams County Historical Society
    Museum, Brighton, CO 204
Adams National Historical Park, Quincy,
    MA 704
Adams National Historical Park-John
    Adams and John Quincy Adams
    Birthplaces, Quincy, MA.........................704
Adams Old Stone Grist Mill, Bellows
    Falls, VT 1476
Adams State College Luther Bean
    Museum, Alamosa, CO 201
Adena Mansion and Gardens, Chillicothe,
    OH...1147
Adirondack History Center,
    Elizabethtown, NY 987
The Adirondack Museum, Blue Mountain
    Lake, NY 963
Adler Planetarium & Astronomy
    Museum, Chicago, IL 417
Admiral Nimitz National Museum of the
    Pacific War, Fredericksburg, TX...........1419
Admiral Peary Monument, Cresson, PA....1248
Adobe De Palomares, Pomona, CA..............143
African American Historical Museum &
    Cultural Center of Iowa, Cedar
    Rapids, IA..508
African American Museum, Cleveland,
    OH...1152
African American Museum, Dallas, TX 1403
African-American Museum and Library
    at Oakland, Oakland, CA 132
The African American Museum in
    Philadelphia, Philadelphia, PA 1275
Afro American Historical Association of
    Fauquier County, The Plains, VA 1541
Afro-American Historical Society
    Museum, Jersey City, NJ 908
Age of Steam Railroad Museum, Dallas,
    TX 1404
Agricultural and Industrial Museum, York
    County Heritage Trust, York, PA 1309

Agricultural Heritage Museum, Boerne,
    TX 1396
Agriculture Museum, Merced, CA 125
Agrirama, Georgia's Living History
    Museum & Village, Tifton, GA 388
Agua Caliente Cultural Museum, Palm
    Springs, CA 138
Agua Mansa Pioneer Memorial Cemetery,
    Colton, CA...87
Ah-Tah-Thi-Ki Museum, Big Cypress
    Seminole Indian Reservation, FL 295
Ah-Tah-Thi-Ki Museum at Okalee,
    Hollywood, FL......................................312
Aiken County Historical Museum, Aiken,
    SC..1320
Aiken Thoroughbred Racing Hall of
    Fame and Museum, Aiken, SC 1320
Air Acres Museum, Cartersville, GA 367
Air Force Flight Test Center Museum,
    Edwards AFB, CA...................................92
Air Mobility Command Museum, Dover
    AFB, DE...270
The Air Museum - Planes of Fame,
    Chino, CA..84
Air Power Park & Museum, Hampton,
    VA 1509
The Airborne & Special Operations
    Museum, Fayetteville, NC.....................1100
Airline History Museum, Kansas City,
    MO..820
Airmen Memorial Museum, Suitland,
    MD..655
Ak-Sar-Ben Aquarium Outdoor Education
    Center, Gretna, NE................................862
Akta Lakota Museum and Cultural
    Center, Chamberlain, SD......................1345
Akwesasne Museum, Hogansburg, NY 998
Al Goin Historical Museum, Portage, IN....496
Alabama Department of Archives &
    History, Montgomery, AL 15
Alabama River Museum, Finchburg, AL 9
Alabama Women's Hall of Fame, Marion,
    AL 13
Alachua County Historic Trust: Matheson
    Museum, Inc., Gainesville, FL.................310
Alamance Battleground State Historic
    Site, Burlington, NC.............................1092
The Alamo, San Antonio, TX 1447
Alaska Heritage Museum at Wells Fargo,
    Anchorage, AK..21
Alaska Native Heritage Center,
    Anchorage, AK..22
Albany Civil Rights Movement Museum
    at Old Mt. Zion Church, Albany, GA......355
Albany Institute of History & Art,
    Albany, NY 954
Albany Regional Museum, Albany, OR 1217
Albuquerque Museum, Albuquerque, NM....932
Alcatraz Island, San Francisco, CA..............163
Alden Historical Society, Inc., Alden, NY ...956
Alden House Historic Site, Duxbury, MA ...680
Alexander & Baldwin Sugar Museum,
    Puunene, HI 401
Alexander House, Port Edwards, WI..........1618
Alexandria Black History Resource
    Center, Alexandria, VA..........................1491
Alger County Heritage Center, Munising,
    MI...757
Aliceville Museum, Aliceville, AL 3
Allaire Village Inc., Farmingdale, NJ..........903
Allan Shivers Museum, Woodville, TX......1462
Allegan County Historical Society and
    Old Jail Museum, Allegan, MI 723
Allegany County Historical Society, Inc.,
    Cumberland, MD..................................641
Allegany County Museum, Belmont, NY 961
Allegheny Portage Railroad National
    Historic Site and Johnstown Flood
    National Memorial, Gallitzin, PA 1255
Allen County Historical Society, Iola, KS ...545
Allen County Museum, Lima, OH 1172
Alling Coverlet Museum, Palmyra, NY 1050

History Museums–Continued

Allison-Antrim Museum, Inc.,
Greencastle, PA..............................1257

Almond Historical Society/Hagadorn
House Museum, Almond, NY.................957

Alpine County Museum, Markleeville,
CA..124

Altama Museum of Art & History,
Vidalia, GA.....................................390

Alton Museum of History and Art, Inc.,
Alton, IL..410

Alumni Center - Husky Heritage Sports
Museum, Storrs, CT...........................261

Alvarado Adobe & The Blume House,
San Pablo, CA..................................175

Amador County Museum, Jackson, CA........105

Amana Heritage Museum, Amana, IA.........504

Amelia Earhart Birthplace Museum,
Atchison, KS....................................532

Amelia Island Museum of History,
Fernandina Beach, FL..........................306

American Airlines C.R. Smith Museum,
Fort Worth, TX................................1416

American Airpower Heritage Museum,
Inc. & Commemorative Air Force
Headquarters, Midland, TX..................1438

American Catholic Historical Society,
Philadelphia, PA...............................1276

American Clock and Watch Museum,
Inc., Bristol, CT................................236

American Hungarian Foundation/Museum
of the American Hungarian
Foundation, New Brunswick, NJ.............915

American Independence Museum, Exeter,
NH...887

American Irish Historical Society, New
York, NY......................................1019

American Jewish Historical Society, New
York, NY......................................1019

American Labor Museum, Botto House
National Landmark, Haledon, NJ............906

American Maple Museum, Croghan, NY.....983

The American Museum of Fly Fishing,
Manchester, VT...............................1481

American Museum of Nursing, Tempe,
AZ...45

American Museum of Radio and
Electricity, Bellingham, WA.................1548

American Museum of Science & Energy,
Oak Ridge, TN................................1382

The American Numismatic Society, New
York, NY......................................1020

American Printing House for the Blind,
Callahan Museum, Louisville, KY...........575

American Quarter Horse Hall of Fame &
Museum, Amarillo, TX.......................1386

American Red Cross Visitors Center and
Gift Shop, Washington, DC..................275

American Royal Museum & Visitors
Center, Kansas City, MO.....................820

American Saddlebred Horse Museum,
Mexico, MO....................................827

American Saddlebred Museum,
Lexington, KY..................................572

American Sign Museum, Cincinnati, OH...1148

American Swedish Historical Foundation
& Museum, Philadelphia, PA................1276

American Swedish Institute, Minneapolis,
MN..781

American Textile History Museum,
Lowell, MA.....................................691

American Watchmakers-Clockmakers
Institute, Harrison, OH......................1168

American Water Ski Educational
Foundation, Polk City, FL....................337

American Wings Air Museum, Blaine,
MN..769

American Work Horse Museum,
Lexington, VA.................................1513

America's Black Holocaust Museum,
Milwaukee, WI...............................1610

America's Ice Cream & Dairy Museum,
Medina, OH...................................1175

Amherst County Museum & Historical
Society, Amherst, VA........................1495

Amherst History Museum at the Strong
House - Amherst Historical Society,
Amherst, MA..................................658

Amherst Museum, Amherst, NY.............957

Amity and Woodbridge Historical
Society, Woodbridge, CT....................268

Amory Regional Museum, Amory, MS.......797

Amos Herr House Foundation and
Historic Society, Landisville, PA...........1267

Anacortes Museum, Anacortes, WA........1547

Anacostia Museum and Center for
African American History & Culture,
Washington, DC...............................275

Anadarko Heritage Museum, Anadarko,
OK...1195

Anaheim Museum, Anaheim, CA..............71

Anchorage Museum at Rasmuson Center,
Anchorage, AK.................................22

Ancient and Honorable Artillery
Company, Boston, MA........................663

Anderson/Abruzzo Albuquerque
International Balloon Museum,
Albuquerque, NM.............................933

Anderson County Historical Museum,
Garnett, KS.....................................541

Anderson County Museum, Anderson, SC.1321

Anderson Museum of Contemporary Art,
Roswell, NM...................................945

Andersonville National Historic Site,
Andersonville, GA.............................355

Andover Historical Society, Andover, MA...660

Andrew County Museum & Historical
Society, Savannah, MO.......................838

Andrew Johnson National Historic Site,
Greeneville, TN...............................1366

Androscoggin Historical Society, Auburn,
ME...603

Angels Camp Museum & Carriage
House, Angels Camp, CA......................71

Animas Museum, Durango, CO................214

Anna B. Smith House Museum,
Moundsville, WV.............................1585

Anna Bemis Palmer Museum, York, NE....875

Anna Miller Museum, Newcastle, WY......1637

Annie E. Woodman Institute Museum,
Dover, NH.....................................886

Annie Riggs Memorial Museum, Fort
Stockton, TX..................................1415

Anoka County Historical Society, Anoka,
MN...767

Anti-Saloon League Museum,
Westerville, OH...............................1190

The Antique Boat Museum, Clayton, NY...978

Antique Gas & Steam Engine Museum,
Inc., Vista, CA.................................196

The Appaloosa Museum and Heritage
Center, Moscow, ID..........................407

The Apple Trees Museum, Burlington, IA...506

Appomattox Court House National
Historical Park, Appomattox, VA..........1495

Aptucxet Trading Post Museum, Bourne,
MA...670

Arab American National Museum,
Dearborn, MI.................................733

Arbor Lodge State Historical Park,
Nebraska City, NE.............................868

Arcadia Township Historical
Commission, Arcadia, MI....................726

Arches Museum of Pioneer Life, Winona,
MN...797

Archives Museum, Temple Mickve Israel,
Savannah, GA..................................384

Ardenwood Historic Farm, Fremont, CA....96

Argo Gold Mine & Mill Museum, Idaho
Springs, CO....................................223

Arizona Historical Society-Fort Lowell
Museum, Tucson, AZ...........................47

Arizona Historical Society Museum,
Tucson, AZ.....................................47

Arizona Historical Society Museum at
Papago Park, Tempe, AZ.......................45

Arizona Historical Society Museum -
Downtown, Tucson, AZ.........................47

Arizona Historical Society Pioneer
Museum, Flagstaff, AZ.........................32

Arizona State Capitol Museum, Phoenix,
AZ...39

Arkansas Historic Wine Museum, Paris,
AR...65

Arkansas Museum of Natural Resources,
Smackover, AR.................................68

Arkansas Post Museum, Gillett, AR...........58

Arkansas Post National Memorial, Gillett,
AR...58

Arkansas State University Museum,
Jonesboro, AR..................................60

Arkansas Tech University Museum of
Prehistory and History, Russellville,
AR...67

Arlington Heights Historical Museum,
Arlington Heights, IL..........................411

Arlington Historical Museum, Arlington,
VA...1495

The Arlington Historical Society,
Arlington, MA..................................660

Arlington House, The Robert E. Lee
Memorial, Arlington, VA.....................1495

Armand Bayou Nature Center, Houston,
TX...1424

The Arms Family Museum of Local
History, Youngstown, OH....................1193

Art League of Houston, Houston, TX.......1425

Artesia Historical Museum & Art Center,
Artesia, NM....................................936

Arts Consortium of Cincinnati's African
American Museum, Cincinnati, OH......1148

Arvada Center for the Arts and
Humanities, Arvada, CO......................201

Ash Hollow State Historical Park,
Lewellen, NE...................................864

Ashland Historical Society, Ashland, MA....661

Ashland Historical Society Museum,
Ashland, WI...................................1590

Ashtabula County Historical Society,
Geneva-on-the-Lake, OH.....................1166

Ashtabula Historic House, Pendleton, SC..1339

Asistencia: San Gabriel Mission Outpost,
Redlands, CA...................................146

Aspen Historical Society, Aspen, CO........202

Atchison County Historical Society,
Atchison, KS....................................533

The Atlanta Cyclorama, Atlanta, GA........358

Atlanta Historical Society, Atlanta, GA......358

Atlantic City Historical Museum, Atlantic
City, NJ..897

Atlantic Heritage Center, Somers Point,
NJ...924

Attmore-Oliver House, New Bern, NC......1112

Atwater Kent Museum of Philadelphia,
Philadelphia, PA...............................1276

Atwood House Museum, Home of
Chatham Historical Society, Chatham,
MA...675

Audie Murphy/American Cotton
Museum, Inc, Greenville, TX...............1423

Audrain Historical Museum, Graceland,
Mexico, MO....................................827

Audubon County Historical Society,
Exira, IA.......................................517

Augusta Historical Museum &
Genealogy, Augusta, KS.......................533

Augusta Museum of History, Augusta,
GA...364

Aurora Historical Society, Inc., East
Aurora, NY.....................................984

Aurora History Museum, Aurora, CO........202

Automobile Driving Museum, Los
Angeles, CA....................................112

Autry National Center of the American
West, Los Angeles, CA........................112

Avery Research Center for African American History & Culture, Charleston, SC 1323

Aviation Hall of Fame and Museum of New Jersey, Teterboro, NJ 926

Aztalan Museum, Jefferson, WI.................1601

Aztec Museum and Pioneer Village, Aztec, NM 936

B&O Railroad Museum: Ellicott City Station, Ellicott City, MD 643

Babe Didrikson Zaharias Museum, Beaumont, TX 1394

Baca House, Trinidad History Museum, Trinidad, CO 233

Bagg Bonanza Historical Farm, Mooreton, ND...1135

Bailey House Museum - Maui Historical Society, Wailuku, HI 402

The Bakken Library and Museum, Minneapolis, MN 781

Baldwin County Heritage Museum, Elberta, AL...8

Baldwin Historical Society and Museum, Baldwin, NY 960

Bale Grist Mill State Historic Park, Calistoga, CA...80

Baltimore & Ohio Railroad Museum, Baltimore, MD...629

Baltimore Civil War Museum, Baltimore, MD 629

Baltimore County Historical Society, Cockeysville, MD...................................640

Baltimore Maritime Museum, Baltimore, MD 630

Baltimore Museum of Industry, Baltimore, MD...630

Baltimore Public Works Museum, Inc., Baltimore, MD...630

Balzekas Museum of Lithuanian Culture, Chicago, IL...418

The Band Museum, Pine Bluff, AR.............66

Bandon Historical Society Museum, Bandon, OR..1219

Bangor Museum & Center for History, Bangor, ME..604

Banner County Historical Society, Harrisburg, NE.......................................862

Bannock County Historical Museum, Pocatello, ID...408

Bar Harbor Historical Society, Bar Harbor, ME...605

The Barbara Fritchie House, Frederick, MD 644

Barbed Wire Museum, La Crosse, KS 547

The Bare Cove Fire Museum, Hingham, MA 687

Barker Mansion, Michigan City, IN 490

Barnes County Historical Museum, Valley City, ND 1136

Barnes Museum, Southington, CT.............260

The Barnum Museum, Bridgeport, CT.........235

Barnwell County Museum, Barnwell, SC ..1321

Barre Historical Society, Inc., Barre, MA 662

Barrett House, Forest Hall, New Ipswich, NH...892

The Barrington Area Historical Society, Barrington, IL..412

Barrington Living History Farm, Washington, TX...1460

Barron County Historical Society's Pioneer Village Museum, Cameron, WI 1593

Barstow Route 66 Mother Road Museum, Barstow, CA...74

Bartholomew County Historical Society, Columbus, IN...472

Bartlesville Area History Museum, Bartlesville, OK....................................1196

The Bartlett Museum, Amesbury, MA 657

Bartow History Center, Cartersville, GA 367

Bartram's Garden, Philadelphia, PA 1277

Batavia Depot Museum, Batavia, IL 412

Bates-Scofield Homestead, The Darien Historical Society, Darien, CT.................238

Batsto Village, Hammonton, NJ 907

Battle of Lexington State Historic Site, Lexington, MO 826

Battles for Chattanooga Museum, Lookout Mountain, TN.............................1371

Bay of Pigs Museum & Library, Miami, FL...323

Bear Mountain Trailside Museums and Zoo, Bear Mountain, NY 961

The Beaufort Arsenal, Beaufort, SC............1321

Beauvais Heritage Center, Clark, SD 1345

Beaver Island Historical Society, Beaver Island, MI..728

Beaverhead County Museum, Dillon, MT ...845

Beck Cultural Exchange Center, Knoxville, TN...1369

Becker County Historical Society, Detroit Lakes, MN...772

Beckman Coulter Heritage Exhibit, Fullerton, CA..98

Bedford City/County Museum, Bedford, VA..1496

Bedford Historical Society Museum and Library, Bedford, OH.............................1142

Beith House Museum, Saint Charles, IL......456

Belair Stable Museum, Bowie, MD.............638

Belding Museum, Belding, MI 728

Belhaven Memorial Museum, Inc., Belhaven, NC...1092

Bell County Museum, Belton, TX...............1395

Bella Vista Historical Museum, Bella Vista, AR...55

Bellamy Mansion Museum of History and Design Arts, Wilmington, NC....1122

Belleville Area Museum, Belleville, MI......728

Bellflower Historical and Genealogical Society, Bellflower, IL.............................413

Bellport-Brookhaven Historical Society and Museum, Bellport, NY.....................961

Beloit Historical Society, Beloit, WI 1592

Beltrami County History Center, Bemidji, MN..768

Belvedere-Tiburon Landmarks Society, Tiburon, CA..192

Benicia Historical Museum, Benicia, CA 74

The Benjamin Banneker Park & Museum, Baltimore, MD 631

Bennington Covered Bridge Museum, Bennington, VT 1476

The Bennington Museum, Bennington, VT...1476

Benson Grist Mill, Stansbury Park, UT 1475

Benton County Historical Museum, Philomath, OR..1230

Bentonville Battlefield State Historic Site, Four Oaks, NC..1102

Bent's Old Fort National Historic Site, La Junta, CO..224

Bergen County Historical Society, River Edge, NJ..923

Bergen Museum of Local History, Bergen, NY...962

Berkeley County Museum & Heritage Center, Moncks Corner, SC.................1336

Berkeley Plantation, Charles City, VA 1498

Berkshire County Historical Society, Inc. - Arrowhead, Pittsfield, MA................702

Berkshire Museum, Pittsfield, MA 702

Berman Museum of World History, Anniston, AL 3

Bernard Historical Society and Museum, Delton, MI...734

Bernhard Museum Complex, Auburn, CA 72

Berrien County Historical Association, Berrien Springs, MI.................................729

Bess Streeter Aldrich House & Museum, Elmwood, NE...860

Bessemer Hall of History, Bessemer, AL.........3

Besser Museum for Northeast Michigan, Alpena, MI...723

Beth Ahabah Museum & Archives, Richmond, VA..1528

Bethel Historical Society Regional History Center, Bethel, ME....................606

Betsy Ross House and Flag Museum, Philadelphia, PA 1277

Betts House Research Center, Cincinnati, OH...1148

Beverly Historical Society and Museum, Beverly, MA...662

Bexley Historical Society, Bexley, OH.......1143

Beyer Home, Oconto County Historical Society Museum, Oconto, WI................1616

BG John C.L. Scribner Texas Military Forces Museum, Austin, TX 1389

Biblical Resource Center & Museum, Collierville, TN.......................................1364

Big Horn County Historical Museum, Hardin, MT...849

Big Thunder Gold Mine, Keystone, SD......1349

Big Timbers Museum, Lamar, CO 225

Bigelow House Museum, Olympia, WA 1560

Billie Creek Village, Rockville, IN 498

Billings Farm & Museum, Woodstock, VT...1490

Billy the Kid Museum, Fort Sumner, NM ...939

Birmingham Civil Rights Institute, Birmingham, AL..4

Bisbee Mining & Historical Museum, Bisbee, AZ...30

Biscayne National Park, Homestead, FL......313

Bishop Hill Heritage Museum, Bishop Hill, IL...413

Bishop Hill State Historic Site, Bishop Hill, IL...413

Black American West Museum & Heritage Center, Denver, CO.................209

Black Arts National Diaspora Museum, New Orleans, LA.......................................594

The Black Fashion Museum, Washington, DC..277

Black Hawk State Historic Site: Hauberg Indian Museum, Rock Island, IL............453

Black Heritage Museum, Miami, FL............323

Black Hills Mining Museum, Lead, SD.....1350

Black History Museum and Cultural Center, Richmond, VA 1528

Black Kettle Museum, Cheyenne, OK 1198

Black River Academy Museum, Ludlow, VT...1480

Black River Historical Society of Lorain, Lorain, OH..1172

Blackberry Farm's Pioneer Village, Aurora, IL..411

Blackhawk Museum (Behring-Hofmann Educational Institute, Inc.), Danville, CA...89

Blaine County Historical Museum, Hailey, ID...406

Blaine County Museum, Chinook, MT 844

Block Island Historical Society, Block Island, RI...1310

Bloom Mansion, Trinidad History Museum, Trinidad, CO..........................233

Bloomfield Academy Museum, Bloomfield, NY 963

Bloomington Historical Society, Minneapolis, MN....................................781

Blount-Bridgers House/Hobson Pittman Memorial Gallery, Tarboro, NC............1121

Blount County Memorial Museum, Oneonta, AL...17

Blue and Gray Museum, Fitzgerald, GA......371

Blue Earth County Historical Society, Mankato, MN...780

Blue Hills Trailside Museum, Milton, MA...695

Blue Ridge Institute and Museum, Ferrum, VA...1504

Bluff Hall Antebellum Home and Museum, Demopolis, AL...........................7

History Museums–Continued

B'nai B'rith Klutznick National Jewish
 Museum, Washington, DC 277

Bob Burns Museum & River Valley
 Museum of Van Buren, Van Buren,
 AR 69

Boca Raton Historical Society, Boca
 Raton, FL 296

Bodley-Bullock House, Lexington, KY 572

Bolinas Museum, Bolinas, CA 79

Bolton Hall Historical Museum, Tujunga,
 CA 193

Bonnet House Museum & Gardens, Fort
 Lauderdale, FL 306

Bonneyville Mill, Bristol, IN 471

Booker T. Washington National
 Monument, Hardy, VA 1510

Boone County Heritage Museum,
 Harrison, AR 59

Boone County Historical Center, Boone,
 IA 506

Boone County Historical Museum,
 Belvidere, IL 413

Boonsborough Museum of History,
 Boonsboro, MD 637

The Boorman House - The Juneau
 County Historical Society, Mauston,
 WI 1608

Boot Hill Museum, Inc., Dodge City, KS 536

Boscobel, Garrison, NY 993

Bosque Memorial Museum, Clifton, TX 1400

Boston Fire Museum, Boston, MA 664

Bottineau County Historical Museum,
 Bottineau, ND 1129

Boulder City/Hoover Dam Museum,
 Boulder City, NV 875

Boulder History Museum, Boulder, CO 202

Bowers Museum, Santa Ana, CA 177

Boys Town Hall of History & Father
 Flanagan House, Boys Town, NE 858

Bradford County Historical Society,
 Towanda, PA 1303

Bradford Historical Society Inc.,
 Bradford, VT 1477

Bradford Ohio Railroad Museum,
 Bradford, OH 1143

Bradley County Historical Museum,
 Warren, AR 69

Branigan Cultural Center, Las Cruces,
 NM 940

Brazoria County Historical Museum,
 Angleton, TX 1387

Brazos Valley Museum of Natural
 History, Bryan, TX 1398

Bremerton Naval Museum, Bremerton,
 WA 1549

Brick Store Museum, Kennebunk, ME 612

Bridger Valley Heritage Museum, Lyman,
 WY 1636

Brigham City Museum-Gallery, Brigham
 City, UT 1463

Brimstone Museum, Sulphur, LA 602

Bronck Museum, Coxsackie, NY 983

The Bronx County Historical Society,
 Bronx, NY 964

Brookings County Historical Society
 Museum, Volga, SD 1358

The Brooklyn Historical Society,
 Brooklyn, NY 968

Brooklyn Historical Society, Brooklyn,
 OH 1144

Broward County Historical Commission,
 Fort Lauderdale, FL 307

Brown County Historical Society, New
 Ulm, MN 785

Brown County Historical Society Pioneer
 Museum, Nashville, IN 493

The Brown House Museum, Sandersville,
 GA 384

Brownville Historical Society Museum,
 Brownville, NE 858

Brunswick Railroad Museum and C&O
 Canal Visitors Center, Brunswick, MD ...639

Brunswick Town/Fort Anderson State
 Historic Site, Winnabow, NC 1124

Brush Country Museum, Cotulla, TX 1403

Bucks County Civil War Library &
 Museum, Doylestown, PA 1249

Bucksport Historical Society, Inc.,
 Bucksport, ME 608

Bucyrus Historical Society, Bucyrus, OH ..1144

Buddy Holly Center, Lubbock, TX 1435

Buechel Memorial Lakota Museum, Saint
 Francis, SD 1355

Buena Vista Heritage Museum, Buena
 Vista, CO 204

Buffalo and Erie County Historical
 Society, Buffalo, NY 972

Buffalo Bill Cody Homestead, Princeton,
 IA 527

Buffalo Bill Historical Center, Cody, WY ..1631

Buffalo Bill Museum & Grave, Golden,
 CO 219

Buffalo Bill Museum of Le Claire, Iowa,
 Inc., Le Claire, IA 522

Buffalo Bill Ranch State Historical Park,
 North Platte, NE 869

Buffalo Gap Historic Village, Buffalo
 Gap, TX 1398

Buffalo Historical Museum and
 One-Room Schoolhouse, Buffalo, SD ..1345

Buffalo Trails Museum, Epping, ND 1130

Bulow Plantation Ruins Historic State
 Park, Bunnell, FL 298

Bunker Hill Museum, Charlestown, MA 675

Bureau County Historical Society
 Museum, Princeton, IL 452

The Burgwin-Wright Museum,
 Wilmington, NC 1123

Burleson County Historical Museum,
 Caldwell, TX 1399

Burlington Historical Museum,
 Burlington, MA 672

Burlington-Rock Island Railroad and
 Historical Museum, Teague, TX 1454

Burnham Tavern, Machias, ME 614

Burritt on the Mountain-A Living
 Museum, Huntsville, AL 11

Burrowes Mansion Museum, Matawan,
 NJ 911

Burt County Museum, Tekamah, NE 873

Burwell-Morgan Mill, Millwood, VA 1518

Bushwhacker Museum, Nevada, MO 828

Butler County Historical Society, Allison,
 IA 504

Butler County History Center & Kansas
 Oil Museum, El Dorado, KS 537

Butler County Museum, Hamilton, OH 1168

Butte County Pioneer Memorial Museum,
 Oroville, CA 136

Butte-Silver Bow Arts Chateau, Butte,
 MT 843

Butterfield Trail Historical Museum,
 Russell Springs, KS 557

Butterfly Lodge Museum, Greer, AZ 36

CHTJ Southard House Museum,
 Brunswick, ME 607

COSI Columbus, Columbus, OH 1157

CSS Neuse State Historic Site and Gov.
 Richard Caswell Memorial, Kinston,
 NC 1108

CU Heritage Center, Boulder, CO 203

Cabin Nature Center, Wood Dale, IL 466

Cabot Historical Society, Cabot, VT 1478

Calaboose African American History
 Museum, San Marcos, TX 1452

Calaveras County Archives, San Andreas,
 CA 155

Calaveras County Museum, San Andreas,
 CA 155

Calhoun County Museum, Port Lavaca,
 TX 1444

Calico Ghost Town and the Lane House
 & Museum, Yermo, CA 199

California African-American Museum,
 Los Angeles, CA 113

California Historical Society, San
 Francisco, CA 163

California History Center & Foundation,
 Cupertino, CA 88

The California Memorial and Museum,
 Clovis, CA 86

California Museum For History, Women
 and the Arts, Sacramento, CA 151

California Museum of Ancient Art,
 Beverly Hills, CA 78

California State Capitol Museum,
 Sacramento, CA 151

California State Railroad Museum,
 Sacramento, CA 152

Call-Booth House Gallery, Paso Robles,
 CA 141

Callahan County Pioneer Museum, Baird,
 TX 1393

Calvin Coolidge Presidential Library &
 Museum, Northampton, MA 699

Cambridge Museum, Cambridge, NE 858

Camden Archives & Museum, Camden,
 SC 1322

Camden County Historical Society,
 Camden, NJ 899

Camp Atterbury Museum, Edinburgh, IN 474

Camp Five Museum Foundation, Inc.,
 Laona, WI 1604

Camp Floyd/Stagecoach Inn State Park,
 Fairfield, UT 1465

Camp Moore Cemetery and Museum,
 Tangipahoa, LA 603

Campbell County Rockpile Museum,
 Gillette, WY 1633

Campbell Historical Museum & Ainsley
 House, Campbell, CA 80

Campbell House, Grand Forks, ND 1131

Campo de Cahuenga, North Hollywood,
 CA 131

Canadian County Historical Museum, El
 Reno, OK 1200

Cannon Falls Area Historical Museum,
 Cannon Falls, MN 770

The Cannon Village Visitor Center,
 Kannapolis, NC 1107

Canoga-Owensmouth Historical Museum,
 Canoga Park, CA 81

Canton Historical Museum, Collinsville,
 CT 237

Canton Historical Society, Canton, MA 674

Cape Ann Historical Museum,
 Gloucester, MA 684

Cape Cod National Seashore, Wellfleet,
 MA 717

Cape Fear Museum of History and
 Science, Wilmington, NC 1123

Cape May County Historical Museum
 and Genealogical Society, Cape May
 Court House, NJ 900

Cape Vincent Historical Museum, Cape
 Vincent, NY 976

Capitol Reef National Park Visitor
 Center, Torrey, UT 1475

Capitol Visitors Center, a Division of the
 State Preservation Board, Austin, TX 1389

Capitola Historical Museum, Capitola,
 CA 81

Captain John Mullan Museum, Mullan,
 ID 407

Captain John Wilson House, Cohasset,
 MA 676

Captain Salem Avery House Museum,
 Shady Side Rural Heritage Society,
 Inc., Shady Side, MD 653

Carbon County Museum, Rawlins, WY 1637

Carlsbad Caverns National Park,
 Carlsbad, NM 937

Carlsbad Museum & Art Center,
 Carlsbad, NM 938

Carlton County Historical Society, Cloquet, MN 771

Carmel Heritage Society's First Murphy House, Carmel-by-the-Sea, CA 81

Carnegie Center for Art & History, New Albany, IN 493

Carnifex Ferry Battlefield State Park & Museum, Summersville, WV 1587

Carolinas Aviation Museum, Charlotte, NC 1094

Carpenter Home Museum and Gallery, Cle Elum, WA 1551

Carpenter Museum, Rehoboth, MA 705

Carpinteria Valley Historical Society & Museum of History, Carpinteria, CA 82

Carriage and Western Art Museum, Santa Barbara, CA 178

Carroll County Farm Museum, Westminster, MD 656

Carroll County Historical Museum, Delphi, IN 474

Carroll Mansion Museum Home of Leavenworth County Historical Society, Leavenworth, KS 549

Carroll Reece Museum, Johnson City, TN.1367

Carson County Square House Museum, Panhandle, TX 1442

Carter-Coile Country Doctors Museum, Winterville, GA 392

Carter County Museum, Ekalaka, MT 846

The Carter House Association, Inc., Franklin, TN 1365

Carver County Historical Society, Waconia, MN 795

Casa Blanca Museum, San Juan, PR 1642

Casa de Rancho Cucamonga, Rancho Cucamonga, CA 144

The Casa del Herrero Foundation, Santa Barbara, CA 178

Casa Grande Valley Historical Society & Museum, Casa Grande, AZ 30

Cascade County Historical Society Museum, Great Falls, MT 848

Casemate Museum, Fort Monroe, VA 1505

Cashmere Museum & Pioneer Village, Cashmere, WA 1550

Cass County Historical Society, Logansport, IN 489

Cass County Historical Society at Bonanzaville, West Fargo, ND 1137

Cass County Historical Society Museum, Plattsmouth, NE 872

Cass County Museum & Pioneer School, Walker, MN 795

Cassia County Museum, Burley, ID 404

Casteel-Linn House and Museum, Princeton, MO 829

Castle Clinton National Monument, New York, NY 1021

Castle Museum of Saginaw County History, Saginaw, MI 762

The Casto House and Northfield Museum, Northfield, NJ 917

Catalina Island Museum Society, Inc., Avalon, CA 73

Catawba County Museum of History, Newton, NC 1113

Catholic Historical Society of the Roanoke Valley, Roanoke, VA 1535

Cattle Raisers Museum, Fort Worth, TX 1416

Cave Creek Museum, Cave Creek, AZ 31

Cayuga Museum & Case Research Lab Museum, Auburn, NY 959

Cayuga-Owasco Lakes Historical Society, Moravia, NY 1015

Cedar Falls Historical Society, Cedar Falls, IA 507

Cedar Grove Historical Society, Cedar Grove, NJ 901

Cedar Key Museum State Park, Cedar Key, FL 299

Cedar Valley Memories, Osage, IA 526

Centennial Village Museum, Greeley, CO ...221

Center for American History, Austin, TX...1390

Center for American Music, Pittsburgh, PA 1291

The Center for Civil War Photography, Gettysburg, PA 1255

Center for History, Wheaton, IL 465

Center for the Study of Political Graphics (CSPG), Los Angeles, CA 113

The Center for Western Studies, Sioux Falls, SD 1356

Center for Wooden Boats, Seattle, WA 1565

Center of Southwest Studies/Fort Lewis College, Durango, CO 214

Centerville - Washington Township Historical Society & Walton House Museum, Centerville, OH 1147

Central Delta Depot Museum, Brinkley, AR 55

Central High School National Historic Site, Little Rock, AR 61

Central Montana Historical Association, Inc. Museum, Lewistown, MT 850

Central Nevada Museum & Historical Society, Tonopah, NV 882

Central Rappahannock Heritage Center, Fredericksburg, VA 1505

Centre County Library and Historical Museum, Bellefonte, PA 1241

Century House Historical Society, Rosendale, NY 1061

Century Village Museum, Burton, OH 1144

Chagrin Falls Historical Society, Chagrin Falls, OH 1147

Champaign County Historical Museum, Champaign, IL 416

Champaign County Historical Museum, Urbana, OH 1188

Champoeg State Heritage Area Visitor Center, Saint Paul, OR 1235

Chancellor Robert R. Livingston Masonic Library & Museum, New York, NY 1022

Chandler Museum, Chandler, AZ 31

The Chapman Historical Museum, Glens Falls, NY 994

Chappell Hill Historical Society Museum, Chappell Hill, TX 1399

Charles A. Grignon Mansion, Kaukauna, WI 1601

Charles H. Wright Museum of African American History, Detroit, MI 735

Charles Pinckney National Historic Site, Mount Pleasant, SC 1337

Charles River Museum of Industry, Waltham, MA 715

Charles Towne Landing State Historic Site, Charleston, SC 1324

Charlotte County Historical Center, Charlotte Harbor, FL 299

Charlotte Museum of History and Hezekiah Alexander Homesite, Charlotte, NC 1094

Chase County Historical Society, Inc., Cottonwood Falls, KS 536

Chatillon-DeMenil Mansion, Saint Louis, MO 832

Chattanooga African Museum/Bessie Smith Hall, Chattanooga, TN 1360

Chattanooga Regional History Museum, Chattanooga, TN 1361

Chautauqua County Historical Society, McClurg Museum, Westfield, NY 1086

Cheboygan County Historical Museum Complex, Cheboygan, MI 732

The Chelmsford Historical Society, Inc., South Chelmsford, MA 709

Chemung Valley History Museum, Elmira, NY 988

Chenango County Historical Society Museum, Norwich, NY 1044

Cheraw Lyceum Museum, Cheraw, SC 1327

Cherokee County Historical Museum, Inc., Murphy, NC 1112

Cherokee Courthouse Visitors Information Center & Museum, Gore, OK 1201

Cherokee National Museum, Park Hill, OK 1211

Cherokee Strip Land Rush Museum, Arkansas City, KS 532

Cherokee Strip Museum, Alva, OK 1195

Cherokee Strip Museum and Henry S. Johnston Library, Perry, OK 1212

Cherry County Historical Society, Valentine, NE 874

Cherry Valley Museum, Cherry Valley, NY 978

Chesapeake and Ohio Canal National Historical Park, Hagerstown, MD 646

Chesapeake Bay Maritime Museum, Saint Michaels, MD 652

The Chesapeake Beach Railway Museum, Chesapeake Beach, MD 639

Chester County Historical Society, West Chester, PA 1307

Chester County Historical Society Museum, Chester, SC 1327

The Chester Gould-Dick Tracy Museum, Woodstock, IL 467

Chesterfield County Museum, Chesterfield, VA 1501

Chetopa Historical Museum, Chetopa, KS...535

Cheyenne County Museum, Saint Francis, KS 557

Cheyenne Depot Museum, Cheyenne, WY 1630

Cheyenne Frontier Days Old West Museum, Cheyenne, WY 1630

Chicago History Museum, Chicago, IL........419

Chicago Public Library, Chicago, IL............419

Chickamauga-Chattanooga National Military Park, Fort Oglethorpe, GA 372

Chickasaw County Historical Society Bradford Pioneer Village Museum, Nashua, IA 525

Chico Museum, Chico, CA 83

Chief Plenty Coups Museum, Pryor, MT 852

Chieftains Museum, Rome, GA 381

Children's Museum of History, Natural History and Science at Utica, New York, Utica, NY 1079

The Children's Museum of Rose Hill Manor Park, Frederick, MD 644

Childress County Heritage Museum, Childress, TX 1400

Chimney Point State Historic Site, Addison, VT 1475

Chinese House/O.R. & N. Museum & St. Peter's Catholic Church, Echo, OR 1222

Chinese Joss House Museum, Evanston, WY 1632

Chino's Old Schoolhouse Museum, Chino, CA 84

Chippewa County Historical Society, Montevideo, MN 783

Chippewa Valley Museum, Inc., Eau Claire, WI 1595

Chisholm Trail Heritage Center, Duncan, OK 1199

Chisholm Trail Historical Museum, Waurika, OK 1216

Chisholm Trail Museum, Wellington, KS 561

Chisholm Trail Museum, Kingfisher, OK...1203

Chittenango Landing Canal Boat Museum, Chittenango, NY 978

The Christian C. Sanderson Museum, Chadds Ford, PA 1246

Church Landing Farmhouse, Pennsville, NJ 920

Churchill County Museum and Archives, Fallon, NV 877

Cimarron Valley Railroad Museum, Cushing, OK 1199

Cincinnati Fire Museum, Cincinnati, OH...1149

Cincinnati Museum Center at Union Terminal, Cincinnati, OH 1149

History Museums–Continued

Circus World Museum, Baraboo, WI 1591
The Citadel Archives & Museum,
   Charleston, SC...1324
City Island Nautical Museum, Bronx, NY...965
City Museum, Saint Louis, MO.....................832
City of Fort Walton Beach Heritage Park
   & Cultural Center, Fort Walton Beach,
   FL..310
City of Gilroy Museum, Gilroy, CA 99
City of Las Cruces Museum System, Las
   Cruces, NM...940
City of Las Vegas Museum and Rough
   Rider Memorial Collection, Las Vegas,
   NM 941
City of Wayne Historical Museum,
   Wayne, MI...766
Civil War and Underground Railroad
   Museum of Philadelphia, Philadelphia,
   PA..1278
Civil War Museum of Lonejack, Jackson
   County, Lone Jack, MO 826
Civil War Soldiers Museum, Pensacola,
   FL..335
Clallam County Historical Society, Port
   Angeles, WA...1561
The Claremont, New Hampshire
   Historical Society, Inc., Claremont,
   NH...884
Clarion County Historical Society,
   Sutton-Ditz House Museum, Clarion,
   PA..1247
Clark County Historical Museum,
   Vancouver, WA.......................................1576
Clark County Historical Society -
   Heritage Center of Clark County,
   Springfield, OH......................................1186
Clark County Museum, Marshall, IL...........444
Clark County Museum, Henderson, NV 878
Clarke County Historical Association,
   Inc., Berryville, VA................................1496
Clarke Historical Museum, Eureka, CA.........94
Clarke House Museum, Chicago, IL............420
Clark's Fork Valley Museum, Fromberg,
   MT...846
Clarkson Historical Museum, Clarkson,
   NE...859
Clarksville-Montgomery County Museum
   dba Customs House Museum &
   Cultural Center, Clarksville, TN............1363
Clausen Memorial Museum, Petersburg,
   AK...27
Clawson Historical Museum, Clawson,
   MI...732
Clay County Historical Museum, Liberty,
   MO..826
Clay County Historical Society Museum
   and Archives, Moorhead, MN.................784
Clear Creek History Park, Golden, CO........219
Clearfield County Historical Society,
   Clearfield, PA...1247
Clearwater Historical Museum, Orofino,
   ID...408
Clermont State Historic Site, Clermont,
   NY...979
Cleveland County Historical Museum,
   Shelby, NC..1119
Cleveland Police Historical Society &
   Museum, Cleveland, OH........................1153
Clewiston Museum, Inc., Clewiston, FL......300
Clinton Academy, East Hampton, NY.........985
Clinton County Historical Association &
   Museum, Plattsburgh, NY......................1052
Clinton County Historical Society,
   Wilmington, OH.....................................1191
Clinton County Museum, Frankfort, IN.......478
Clovis Big Dry Creek Historical
   Museum, Clovis, CA..................................86
Clovis Depot Model Train Museum,
   Clovis, NM...939
Coachella Valley Museum and Cultural
   Center, Indio, CA.....................................104

Coarsegold Historic Museum,
   Coarsegold, CA 86
Coastal Discovery Museum, Hilton Head
   Island, SC..1335
Coastal Heritage Museum, Crystal River,
   FL..301
Codington County Heritage Museum,
   Watertown, SD.......................................1359
Coggeshall Farm Museum, Bristol, RI.......1310
Cokato Museum & Akerlund
   Photography Studio, Cokato, MN...........771
Cold Spring Harbor Whaling Museum,
   Cold Spring Harbor, NY 979
Cole County Historical Museum,
   Jefferson City, MO 819
The Coleman House Museum and Brown
   County Historical Society, Ainsworth,
   NE...855
Colesville & Windsor Museum at St.
   Luke's Church, Harpursville, NY............997
College Park Aviation Museum, College
   Park, MD...641
Colleton Museum, Walterboro, SC.............1343
Collier County Museum, Naples, FL............328
Collier Memorial State Park & Logging
   Museum, Chiloquin, OR........................1221
Collin County Historical Society, Inc. &
   History Museum, McKinney, TX 1437
Collingwood Library and Museum on
   Americanism, Alexandria, VA................1492
Collinsville Depot Museum, Collinsville,
   OK...1198
Colonial National Historical Park:
   Jamestown & Yorktown, Yorktown,
   VA 1546
Colonial Pennsylvania Plantation, Media,
   PA..1270
Colonial Williamsburg, Williamsburg, VA .1544
Colorado Historical Society, Denver, CO....210
Colorado National Monument, Fruita, CO...218
Colorado Railroad Museum, Golden, CO 220
Colorado Ski Museum-Ski & Snowboard
   Hall of Fame, Vail, CO............................234
Colorado Springs Museum, Colorado
   Springs, CO..206
Colton Area Museum, Colton, CA 87
Colton Hall Museum, Monterey, CA............127
Columbia County Historical and
   Genealogical Society, Bloomsburg, PA .1243
Columbia Gorge Discovery Center and
   Wasco County Museum, The Dalles,
   OR...1237
Columbia Gorge Interpretive Center
   Museum, Stevenson, WA.......................1572
Columbia River Exhibition of History,
   Science and Technology, Richland,
   WA 1564
Columbia River Maritime Museum,
   Astoria, OR...1218
Columbia State Historic Park, Columbia,
   CA...87
The Columbian Theatre, Museum & Art
   Center, Wamego, KS................................560
Columbus-Belmont Civil War Museum,
   Columbus, KY..567
The Columbus Museum, Columbus, GA 368
Combat Air Museum, Inc., Topeka, KS 559
Command Museum, Marine Corps
   Recruit Depot, San Diego, San Diego,
   CA...156
The Commonwealth Museum, Boston,
   MA..665
Commonwealth of the Northern Mariana
   Islands Museum of History and
   Culture, Saipan, MP 1640
Communal Kitchen and Coopershop
   Museum, Middle Amana, IA 523
Community Historical Museum,
   Maxwell, IA..523
Community Memorial Museum of Sutter
   County, Yuba City, CA.............................200
Community of Christ, Independence, MO ...817
Compass Inn Museum, Laughlintown, PA.1267

Computer History Museum, Mountain
   View, CA 129
Concord Historical Society, Warner
   Museum, Springville, NY 1071
Concord Museum, Concord, MA.................676
Concordia Historical Institute, Saint
   Louis, MO..832
Coney Island Museum, Brooklyn, NY 969
Confederate Memorial Hall-Bleak House,
   Knoxville, TN...1369
Confederate Museum, Crawfordville, GA....369
Confederate Museum, New Orleans, LA 594
Confederate Tribes and Bands of the
   Yakama Indian Nation - Cultural
   Heritage Center Museum, Toppenish,
   WA..1575
Confederated Tribes of Grand Ronde
   Cultural Resources Department, Grand
   Ronde, OR..1225
The Conference House, Staten Island,
   NY...1072
Conneaut Railroad Museum, Conneaut,
   OH..1159
Connecticut Audubon Birdcraft Museum,
   Fairfield, CT...240
Connecticut Historical Society, Hartford,
   CT...244
Connecticut River Museum, Essex, CT........239
Conner Prairie, Fishers, IN 476
Conrad-Caldwell House Museum,
   Louisville, KY..575
Conrad Mansion National Historic Site
   Museum, Kalispell, MT 850
Constitution Convention Museum State
   Park, Port St. Joe, FL...............................338
Cooper Regional History Museum,
   Upland, CA..193
Coos Historical & Maritime Museum,
   North Bend, OR......................................1229
Copper Range Historical Museum, South
   Range, MI...764
Copper Village Museum & Arts Center of
   Deer Lodge County, Anaconda, MT........840
The Corcoran Gallery of Art,
   Washington, DC.......................................277
Cordell Hull Birthplace & Museum State
   Historic Park, Byrdstown, TN 1360
Cordova Historical Museum, Cordova,
   AK...23
Cornelius Low House/Middlesex County
   Museum, Piscataway, NJ.........................921
Cornell Museum of Art & History,
   Delray Beach, FL 304
The Corning Museum of Glass, Corning,
   NY...981
Coronado National Memorial, Hereford,
   AZ...36
Coronado State Monument, Bernalillo,
   NM..937
Corry Area Historical Society, Corry, PA...1248
Cortland County Historical Society,
   Cortland, NY..982
Cottage Grove Museum & Annex,
   Cottage Grove, OR 1222
Cottonlandia Museum, Greenwood, MS 800
Cottonwood County Historical Society,
   Windom, MN...796
The Country Doctor Museum, Bailey, NC.1091
Country Music Hall of Fame and
   Museum, Country Music Foundation,
   Nashville, TN...1378
Country Relics Little Village, Stanhope,
   IA..528
Courthouse Square Association,
   Charlotte, MI..731
The Cowley County Historical Society,
   Winfield, KS...564
Cowlitz County Historical Museum,
   Kelso, WA...1557
Cozens Ranch Museum, Fraser, CO.............218
Cracker Country, Tampa, FL........................348
Crailo State Historic Site, Rensselaer, NY.1056

Cranbury Historical & Preservation Society, Cranbury, NJ..................902
Crandall Historical Printing Museum, Provo, UT........................1469
Crane Point, Marathon, FL.............323
Cranford Historical Society, Cranford, NJ...902
Crawford County Historical Museum, Pittsburg, KS..........................556
Crawford W. Long Museum, Jefferson, GA........................374
Crazy Mountain Museum, Big Timber, MT........................841
Creek Council House Museum, Okmulgee, OK......................1211
Crested Butte Mountain Heritage Museum, Crested Butte, CO..............208
Crestline Shunk Museum, Crestline, OH...1160
Cripple Creek District Museum, Inc., Cripple Creek, CO....................209
Crispus Attucks Center Museum, Indianapolis, IN....................482
Crocker House, Mount Clemens, MI...........756
Crockett County Museum, Ozona, TX.......1442
Crockett Tavern Museum, Morristown, TN........................1376
Crook County Museum & Art Gallery, Sundance, WY......................1638
Crosby County Pioneer Memorial Museum, Crosbyton, TX................1403
Crossroads Museum, Corinth, MS.............800
Crow Wing County Historical Society, Brainerd, MN......................769
Crowley Museum & Nature Center, Sarasota, FL........................344
Crown Gardens and Archives, Dalton, GA........................370
Crystal Caverns at Hupp's Hill, Strasburg, VA......................1538
Culbertson Museum, Culbertson, MT.........845
Culinary Archives & Museum, Johnson & Wales University, Providence, RI...1316
Cullman County Museum, Cullman, AL.........6
Cumberland Gap National Historical Park, Middlesboro, KY..............580
Cupertino Historical Society & Museum, Cupertino, CA......................88
Custer Battlefield Museum, Garryowen, MT........................847
Custer County Historical Society, Inc., Broken Bow, NE....................858
The Custom House Maritime Museum, Newburyport, MA......................697
Cuyahoga Valley National Park, Brecksville, OH....................1144
Cuyuna Range Historical Society & Museum, Crosby, MN....................772
Cyrus H. McCormick Memorial Museum, Steeles Tavern, VA................1538

D.C. Booth Historic National Fish Hatchery, Spearfish, SD..............1357
D.R. Barker Historical Museum, Fredonia, NY......................992
Dacotah Prairie Museum, Aberdeen, SD....1344
Dade Battlefield Historic State Park, Bushnell, FL......................298
Dahlonega Gold Museum State Historic Site, Dahlonega, GA..............369
Dakota County Historical Society, South Saint Paul, MN....................793
Dakota Discovery Museum, Mitchell, SD..1352
Dakota Sunset Museum, Gettysburg, SD....1348
Dakota Territorial Museum, Yankton, SD...1359
Dakota Territory Air Museum, Minot, ND.1134
Dakotaland Museum, Huron, SD.............1348
Dale & Martha Hawk Museum, Wolford, ND........................1138
Dallam-Hartley XIT Museum, Dalhart, TX........................1403
Dallas Heritage Village at Old City Park, Dallas, TX........................1405
Dallas Historical Society, Dallas, TX.........1405
Dallas Holocaust Museum, Dallas, TX......1405

Dallidet Adobe and Gardens, San Luis Obispo, CA......................174
Dalton Defenders Museum, Coffeyville, KS........................535
Dan O'Laurie Museum of Moab, Moab, UT........................1467
The Dan Quayle Center & Museum, Huntington, IN....................481
Dana Adobe, Nipomo, CA.............130
The Danbury Museum & Historical Society, Danbury, CT................238
Dancing Bear Folk Center, Thermopolis, WY........................1639
Daniel Boone Home and Boonesfield Village, Lindenwood University, Defiance, MO......................814
Daniels County Museum and Pioneer Town, Scobey, MT....................853
The Danish Immigrant Museum, Elk Horn, IA........................517
Danvers Historical Society, Danvers, MA....678
Darnall's Chance House Museum, M-NCPPC, Upper Marlboro, MD...........655
Daughters of the American Revolution Museum, Washington, DC..............277
Daughters of Utah Pioneers Pioneer Memorial Museum & International Society Daughters of Utah Pioneers, Salt Lake City, UT................1471
David Bradford House, Washington, PA...1305
David Conklin Farmhouse, Huntington, NY........................1000
David Crockett Cabin, Rutherford, TN......1383
Davidson County Historical Museum, Lexington, NC....................1109
The Davistown Museum, Liberty, ME.........614
The Dawes Arboretum, Newark, OH.........1177
Dawes County Historical Society Museum, Chadron, NE....................859
Dawson County Historical Museum, Lexington, NE....................864
Dawson Springs Museum and Art Center, Inc., Dawson Springs, KY..............568
Dayton Historical Depot Society, Dayton, WA........................1552
Dayton History at Carillon Park, Dayton, OH........................1161
De Saisset Museum, Santa Clara, CA.........180
De Smet Depot Museum, De Smet, SD....1346
Deaf Smith County Museum, Hereford, TX........................1424
Dearborn Historical Museum, Dearborn, MI........................733
Decatur County Last Indian Raid Museum, Oberlin, KS....................554
Decatur House Museum, Washington, DC...277
Dedham Historical Society Museum, Dedham, MA......................679
Deer Isle-Stonington Historical Society, Deer Isle, ME......................609
Deere & Company, Administrative Center, Moline, IL....................445
Deerfield Beach Historical Society, Deerfield Beach, FL................304
Degenhart Paperweight & Glass Museum, Inc., Cambridge, OH................1144
DeKalb History Center Museum, Decatur, GA........................370
The Dekker Huis/Zeeland Historical Museum, Zeeland, MI................767
Del Norte County Historical Society, Crescent City, CA................87
Delano Heritage Park, Delano, CA.............91
Delaware Agricultural Museum and Village, Dover, DE....................269
Delaware and Hudson Canal Historical Society and Museum, High Falls, NY.....998
Delaware Division of Historical & Cultural Affairs, Dover, DE..............269
Delaware Visitor's Center, Dover, DE.........270
Delta Blues Museum, Clarksdale, MS...........799
Delta County Museum, Delta, CO.............209

Delta Cultural Center, Helena, AR................59
Deming Luna Mimbres Museum, Deming, NM......................939
The Dennison Railroad Depot Museum, Dennison, OH....................1162
Dennys River Historical Society, Dennysville, ME....................609
Denton County Historical Museum, Inc. and Texas Heritage Center, Denton, TX........................1409
Denver Museum of Miniatures, Dolls and Toys, Denver, CO....................211
Depot Museum & Fort Sedgwick Museum, Julesburg, CO................223
The Depot Museum Complex, Henderson, TX....................1424
Depot Park Museum, Sonoma, CA.............187
Depreciation Lands Museum, Allison Park, PA......................1240
Des Plaines History Center, Des Plaines, IL........................430
Deschutes County Historical Society, Bend, OR......................1220
Desert Caballeros Western Museum, Wickenburg, AZ....................53
Desha County Museum, Dumas, AR.............56
DeSoto County Museum, Hernando, MS.......801
Detroit Historical Society, Detroit, MI.........735
Deutschheim State Historic Site, Hermann, MO....................817
Dewey Hotel Museum, Dewey, OK...........1199
DeWitt Wallace Decorative Arts Museum, Williamsburg, VA................1545
Dexter Area Historical Society & Museum, Dexter, MI....................738
Dickinson County Heritage Center, Abilene, KS......................531
Diego Sepulveda Adobe Estancia, Costa Mesa, CA........................87
The Dinosaur Museum, Blanding, UT.......1463
Dinsmore Homestead Foundation, Burlington, KY....................566
DiscoverSea Shipwreck Museum, Fenwick Island, DE................270
The Discovery Center, Fresno, CA.............96
Discovery Museum, Sacramento Museum of History, Science and Technology, Sacramento, CA....................152
Doak House Museum, Greeneville, TN......1366
Dr. Daniel W. Kissam House, Huntington, NY....................1000
Dr Pepper Museum and Free Enterprise Institute, Waco, TX................1458
Dr. Samuel D. Harris National Museum of Dentistry, Baltimore, MD...........631
Dr. William Robinson Plantation, Clark, NJ........................901
Doctors' House Museum, Glendale, CA......100
Dodge County Historical Society, Mantorville, MN....................780
Dog Mushing Museum, Fairbanks, AK.........24
Don F. Pratt Memorial Museum, Fort Campbell, KY....................568
Don Garlits Museum of Drag Racing Inc., Ocala, FL....................330
Donald G. Trayser Memorial Museum/Barnstable County Customs House, Barnstable, MA................661
Donner Memorial State Park and Emigrant Trail Museum, Truckee, CA....192
Door County Historical Museum, Sturgeon Bay, WI................1623
Door County Maritime Museum (at Sturgeon Bay), Sturgeon Bay, WI.........1623
Doric House, Flemington, NJ................903
Dorothy G. Page Museum, Wasilla, AK........29
Douglas County Historical Society - Carson Valley Museum & Cultural Center, Gardnerville, NV................877
Douglas County Historical Society - Genoa Courthouse Museum, Genoa, NV........................877

History Museums–Continued

Douglas County Museum Complex, Armour, SD............1344

Douglass Historical Museum, Douglass, KS............537

The Downers Grove Park District Museum, Downers Grove, IL 431

Downieville Museum, Downieville, CA 91

Downing House Museum, Memphis, MO....827

Drew County Historical Museum, Monticello, AR............64

Drum Barracks Civil War Museum, Wilmington, CA 198

Drummond Island Historical Museum, Drummond Island, MI............739

Dublin-Laurens Museum, Dublin, GA 370

Dubois Museum, Dubois, WY............1632

Dugger Coal Museum, Dugger, IN............474

Duke Homestead State Historic Site, Durham, NC............1098

Dundee Township Historical Society, Inc., Dundee, IL............431

Dunedin Historical Society & Museum, Dunedin, FL............305

Dunham Tavern Museum, Cleveland, OH..1154

Dunklin County Museum, Inc., Kennett, MO............824

DuPage County Historical Museum, Wheaton, IL............465

Dupont Historical Society, DuPont, WA 1552

Durant House Museum, Saint Charles, IL ...457

Durham Western Heritage Museum, Omaha, NE............870

Dusable Museum of African-American History, Inc., Chicago, IL............420

Dwight D. Eisenhower Library-Museum, Abilene, KS............531

Dyckman Farmhouse Museum and Park, New York, NY............1025

E.M. Violette Museum, Kirksville, MO 824

E. St. Julien Cox House, Saint Peter, MN...792

EAA AirVenture Museum, Oshkosh, WI...1616

Eagle Tavern Museum, Watkinsville, GA ...391

Early American Museum, Mahomet, IL......444

EarlyWorks Museums, Huntsville, AL 11

East Brunswick Museum Corporation, East Brunswick, NJ............902

East Contra Costa Museum, Brentwood, CA............79

East End Seaport Museum and Marine Foundation, Greenport, NY............996

East Hampton Historical Society, Inc., East Hampton, NY............985

East Jersey Olde Towne, Piscataway, NJ ...921

East Martello Museum, Key West, FL........317

East Tennessee Historical Society, Knoxville, TN............1369

East Texas Oil Museum at Kilgore College, Kilgore, TX............1432

East-West Center, Honolulu, HI............394

Eastern Arizona Museum and Historical Society of Graham County Inc., Pima, AZ............42

Eastern California Museum, Independence, CA............104

Eastside Heritage Center, Bellevue, WA 1548

Edgar Allan Poe Cottage, Bronx, NY 965

Edgar Allan Poe Museum, Richmond, VA.1529

Edison & Ford Winter Estates, Fort Myers, FL............308

Edison Museum, Beaumont, TX............1394

Edison National Historic Site, West Orange, NJ............930

Edisto Island Historic Preservation Society Museum, Edisto Island, SC 1332

Edmond Historical Society Museum, Edmond, OK............1200

Edmonds South Snohomish County Historical Society, Inc., Edmonds, WA .1553

Edwards County Historical Museum, Kinsley, KS............547

The 1811 Old Lincoln County Jail and Lincoln County Museum, Wiscasset, ME............625

1859 Jail, Marshal's Home & Museum, Independence, MO............817

82nd Airborne Division War Memorial Museum, Fort Bragg, NC............1101

Eisenhower Birthplace State Historical Site, Denison, TX............1409

El Camino Real International Heritage Center, San Antonio, NM............947

El Cazador Museum, Grand Bay, AL............10

El Dorado County Historical Museum, Placerville, CA............142

El Monte Historical Society Museum, El Monte, CA............92

El Museo Latino, Omaha, NE............870

El Paso Holocaust Museum & Study Center, El Paso, TX............1411

El Paso Museum of History, El Paso, TX..1412

El Pueblo Historical Monument, Los Angeles, CA............114

El Pueblo History Museum, Pueblo, CO......230

El Rancho de Las Golondrinas Museum, Santa Fe, NM............947

Elbert Hubbard-Roycroft Museum, East Aurora, NY............985

Eldridge Street Project, New York, NY 1025

Elgin Area Historical Society, Elgin, IL......432

Eli Whitney Museum, Inc., Hamden, CT.....244

Elijah Clark Memorial Museum, Lincolnton, GA............376

Elisabet Ney Museum, Austin, TX............1390

Elkhart County Historical Museum, Bristol, IN............471

Ellingson Car Museum, Rogers, MN............788

Elliott Museum, Stuart, FL............346

Ellis County Historical Society, Hays, KS...543

Ellis County Museum, Inc., Waxahachie, TX............1460

Ellwood House Museum, DeKalb, IL............429

Elmhurst Historical Museum, Elmhurst, IL............433

Elverhoj Museum of History and Art, Solvang, CA............187

Elwood Haynes Museum, Kokomo, IN........486

Emil A. Blackmore Museum of The American Legion, Indianapolis, IN 482

Emily Kimbrough House, Muncie, IN............492

Emmett Kelly Historical Museum, Sedan, KS............558

Empire Area Heritage Group, Empire, MI...740

End-O-Line Railroad Park & Museum, Currie, MN............772

Enfield Historical Society Museum, Enfield Center, NH............887

Enfield Shaker Museum, Enfield, NH............887

Englewood Textile Museum, Englewood, TN............1364

Epcot at Walt Disney World Resort, Lake Buena Vista, FL............319

Ephraim Historical Foundation, Ephraim, WI............1597

Erie Canal Museum, Syracuse, NY............1076

Erie Canal Village, Rome, NY............1061

Erie County History Center & Cashier's House, Erie, PA............1252

Erie Maritime Museum, Homeport U.S. Brig Niagara, Erie, PA............1252

The Erlander Home Museum, Rockford, IL............454

Ernie Pyle State Historic Site, Dana, IN......473

Erskine Caldwell Birthplace Museum, Moreland, GA............380

Escondido History Center, Escondido, CA............93

Essex Historical Society, Inc., Essex, CT ...240

Essex Shipbuilding Museum, Essex, MA 681

Essley-Noble Museum: Mercer County Historical Society, Aledo, IL............410

Estes Park Museum, Estes Park, CO............215

The Esther Thomas Atkinson Museum, Hampden-Sydney, VA............1509

Ethan Allen Homestead Museum & Historic Site, Burlington, VT............1478

Ethnic Heritage Museum, Rockford, IL.......455

Eubie Blake National Jazz Institute and Cultural Center, Baltimore, MD............632

Eugene Field House and St. Louis Toy Museum, Saint Louis, MO............833

Eureka Pioneer Museum of McPherson County, Inc., Eureka, SD............1346

Eustis Historical Museum & Preservation Society, Inc., Eustis, FL............306

Evanston Historical Society and Charles Gates Dawes House, Evanston, IL..........434

Evansville Museum of Arts History & Science, Evansville, IN............475

Excelsior-Lake Minnetonka Historical Society, Excelsior, MN............775

The Exchange Hotel Civil War Museum, Gordonsville, VA............1509

Fabyan Villa Museum, Geneva, IL............437

Fairfax Museum & Visitor Center, Fairfax, VA............1503

Fairfield Historical Society, Fairfield, CT 241

Fairmount Historical Museum & Gift Shop, Fairmount, IN............476

Fairport Historical Museum, Fairport, NY...989

Fairport Marine Museum, Fairport Harbor, OH............1164

Fairview Museum of History & Art, Fairview, UT............1465

Fall River Historical Society Museum, Fall River, MA............682

Falls Village-Canaan Historical Society, Falls Village, CT............241

Farmers Branch Historical Park, Farmers Branch, TX............1413

The Farmers' Museum, Inc., Cooperstown, NY............980

Farmington Historic Home, Louisville, KY............575

Farragut Folklife Museum, Farragut, TN ...1364

Farrar-Mansur House & Old Mill Museum, Weston, VT............1490

Faulkner County Museum, Conway, AR........56

Faust Park-Thornhill Historic Site & 19th Century Village, Chesterfield, MO 812

Favell Museum Inc., Klamath Falls, OR....1227

Fayette County Museum, Washington Court House, OH............1190

Fayette Heritage Museum & Archives, La Grange, TX............1432

Federal Hall National Memorial, New York, NY............1025

Feet First: The Scholl Story, Rosalind Franklin University, North Chicago, IL...448

Fenton History Center-Museum & Library, Jamestown, NY............1005

Ferndale Museum, Ferndale, CA............95

Fick Fossil & History Museum, Oakley, KS............554

Fillmore County Historical Center, Fountain, MN............776

Fillmore Historical Museum, Inc., Fillmore, CA............95

The Filson Historical Society, Inc., Louisville, KY............576

The Finley House, Wayne, PA............1306

Finney County Kansas Historical Society, Inc., Garden City, KS............541

1st Cavalry Division Museum, Fort Hood, TX............1414

First Consolidated School in Minnesota, Saum, MN............793

The First Division Museum at Cantigny, Wheaton, IL............465

First Landing State Park, Virginia Beach, VA............1542

First Territorial Capitol of Kansas, Fort Riley, KS............540

First White House of the Confederacy, Montgomery, AL 16
Fischer-Hanlon House, Benicia, CA 75
Fitchburg Historical Society, Fitchburg, MA 683
The Five Civilized Tribes Museum, Muskogee, OK 1205
The Flag House and Star-Spangled Banner Museum, Baltimore, MD 632
Flagler Museum, Palm Beach, FL 333
Flathead Indian Museum, Saint Ignatius, MT 853
Fleming Historical Society, Fleming, CO 216
Flickertail Village and Museum, Stanley, ND 1136
Flint House, Scotia, NY 1068
The Florence McLeod Hazard Museum, Columbus, MS 800
Florence Museum of Art, Science & History and the Florence Railroad Museum, Florence, SC 1332
Florence Price Pioneer Museum, Florence, CO 216
Florewood State Park, Greenwood, MS 801
Florida Agricultural Museum, Palm Coast, FL 334
Florida Gulf Coast Railroad Museum, Parrish, FL 335
Florida Holocaust Museum, Saint Petersburg, FL 341
The Fluvanna County Historical Society Old Stone Jail Museum, Palmyra, VA 1524
Folsom History Museum, Folsom, CA 95
Folsom Museum, Inc., Folsom, NM 939
Ford County Historical Society, Paxton, IL 450
Ford House Visitor Center and Museum, Mendocino, CA 125
Ford's Theatre National Historic Site (Lincoln Museum), Washington, DC 279
Forest Capital State Museum, Perry, FL 337
Forest History Center, Grand Rapids, MN 777
Forest Lawn Museum, Glendale, CA 100
Forest Park Museum and Arboretum, Perry, IA 527
Foresthill Divide Museum, Foresthill, CA 95
Forney Museum of Transportation, Denver, CO 212
Fort Abraham Lincoln State Park, Mandan, ND 1134
Fort Ancient Museum, Oregonia, OH 1181
The Fort at No. 4 Living History Museum, Charlestown, NH 884
Fort Atkinson State Historical Park, Fort Calhoun, NE 860
Fort Bedford Museum, Bedford, PA 1241
Fort Belknap Museum and Archives, Inc., Newcastle, TX 1441
Fort Benton Museum of the Upper Missouri, Fort Benton, MT 846
Fort Bliss Museum, Fort Bliss, TX 1413
Fort Boonesborough Museum, Richmond, KY 583
Fort Bridger State Museum, Fort Bridger, WY 1632
Fort Caspar Museum, Casper, WY 1629
Fort Christmas Historical Park, Christmas, FL 299
Fort Clatsop National Memorial, Astoria, OR 1218
Fort Clinch State Park, Fernandina Beach, FL 306
Fort Collins Museum, Fort Collins, CO 217
Fort Columbia Interpretive Center, Chinook, WA 1551
Fort Concho National Historic Landmark, San Angelo, TX 1447
Fort Crawford Museum, Prairie du Chien, WI 1618
Fort Croghan Museum, Burnet, TX 1398
Fort Crook Historical Museum, Fall River Mills, CA 94

Fort Dalles Museum/Anderson Homestead, The Dalles, OR 1237
Fort Davis National Historic Site, Fort Davis, TX 1414
Fort de Chartres State Historic Site & Museum, Prairie du Rocher, IL 451
Fort Delaware Museum of Colonial History, Narrowsburg, NY 1017
Fort Dix Museum, Fort Dix, NJ 904
Fort Dodge & Frontier Village, Fort Dodge, IA 518
Fort Douglas Military Museum, Fort Douglas, UT 1465
Fort Fetterman State Historic Site, Douglas, WY 1631
Fort Fisher State Historic Site, Kure Beach, NC 1108
Fort Frederica National Monument, Saint Simons Island, GA 383
Fort Frederick State Park, Big Pool, MD 637
Fort Garland Museum, Fort Garland, CO 217
Fort Gibson Historic Site, Fort Gibson, OK 1200
Fort Harker Museum Complex, Kanopolis, KS 546
Fort Hartsuff State Historical Park, Burwell, NE 858
Fort Henrietta Interpretive Park, Echo, OR 1223
Fort Hill (The John C. Calhoun House), Clemson, SC 1328
Fort Huachuca Museum, Fort Huachuca, AZ 34
Fort Inglish, Bonham, TX 1396
Fort Jackson Museum, Fort Jackson, SC 1332
Fort Jones Museum, Fort Jones, CA 96
Fort Kearny State Historical Park, Kearney, NE 864
Fort King George Historic Site, Darien, GA 370
Fort Larned National Historic Site, Larned, KS 547
Fort Lauderdale Historical Society, Fort Lauderdale, FL 307
Fort Leaton State Historical Site, Presidio, TX 1444
Fort Leboeuf, Waterford, PA 1306
Fort Lee Historic Park & Museum, Fort Lee, NJ 904
Fort Ligonier Association, Ligonier, PA 1269
Fort MacArthur Museum, San Pedro, CA 176
Fort Macon State Park, Atlantic Beach, NC 1091
Fort Massac State Park and Historic Site, Metropolis, IL 445
Fort McAllister, Richmond Hill, GA 381
Fort McHenry National Monument and Historic Shrine, Baltimore, MD 632
Fort Meigs State Memorial, Perrysburg, OH 1182
Fort Morgan Museum, Gulf Shores, AL 10
Fort Morgan Museum, Fort Morgan, CO 218
Fort Morris State Historic Site, Midway, GA 379
Fort Necessity National Battlefield, Farmington, PA 1253
Fort Okanogan Interpretive Center, Brewster, WA 1550
Fort Osage National Historic Landmark, Sibley, MO 838
Fort Payne Depot Museum, Fort Payne, AL 10
Fort Peck Interpretive Center, Fort Peck, MT 846
Fort Pike State Historic Site, New Orleans, LA 595
The Fort Pitt Block House, Pittsburgh, PA 1292
Fort Pitt Museum, Pittsburgh, PA 1292
Fort Plain Museum, Fort Plain, NY 991
Fort Polk Museum Activity, Fort Polk, LA 588

Fort Pulaski National Monument, Savannah, GA 385
Fort Recovery Museum, Fort Recovery, OH 1164
Fort St. Joseph Museum, Niles, MI 758
Fort Sam Houston Museum, Fort Sam Houston, TX 1415
Fort Selden State Monument, Radium Springs, NM 945
Fort Sidney Museum & Post Commander's Home, Sidney, NE 873
Fort Sill National Historic Landmark, Fort Sill, OK 1201
Fort Smith Museum of History, Fort Smith, AR 58
Fort Smith National Historic Site, Fort Smith, AR 58
Fort Smith Trolley Museum, Fort Smith, AR 58
Fort Stanwix National Monument, Rome, NY 1061
Fort Stewart Museum, Fort Stewart, GA 372
Fort Sumter National Monument, Sullivan's Island, SC 1342
Fort Tejon State Historic Park, Lebec, CA 108
Fort Ticonderoga, Ticonderoga, NY 1078
Fort Totten State Historic Site, Fort Totten, ND 1131
Fort Uncompahgre Living History Museum, Delta, CO 209
Fort Vasquez Museum, Platteville, CO 230
Fort Walla Walla Museum, Walla Walla, WA 1576
Fort Ward Museum and Historic Site, Alexandria, VA 1492
Fort Washington Park, Fort Washington, MD 643
Fort Washita, Durant, OK 1199
Fort William Henry Museum, Lake George, NY 1008
Fort Winnebago Surgeons Quarters, Portage, WI 1618
Fort Worth Museum of Science and History, Fort Worth, TX 1417
Forts Folle Avoine Historic Park, Danbury, WI 1594
Fortuna Depot Museum, Fortuna, CA 96
Fossil Country Museum, Kemmerer, WY 1635
Fosterfields Living Historical Farm, Morristown, NJ 913
Foundation For Historic Christ Church, Inc., Irvington, VA 1511
4-H Schoolhouse Museum, Clarion, IA 510
Four Rivers Cultural Center & Museum, Ontario, OR 1229
Four Wheel Drive Foundation, Clintonville, WI 1594
4th Infantry Division Museum, Fort Hood, TX 1415
Fox Island Historical Society, Fox Island, WA 1554
Fox Lake Historical Museum, Inc., Fox Lake, WI 1598
The Foxfire Museum & Heritage Center, Mountain City, GA 380
Framingham Historical Society & Museum, Framingham, MA 683
Francisco Fort Museum, La Veta, CO 224
Frank G. Ray House, Vinton, IA 529
Frank H. Woods Telephone Museum, Lincoln, NE 865
Frank Murphy Memorial Museum, Harbor Beach, MI 745
Frankenmuth Historical Museum, Frankenmuth, MI 742
Franklin County Historical & Museum Society & House of History, Malone, NY 1012
Franklin County Historical Museum, Mount Vernon, TX 1440
Franklin County Old Jail Museum, Winchester, TN 1385

History Museums–Continued

Franklin County Seminary and Museum, Brookville, IN............471

Franklin D. Roosevelt Presidential Library-Museum, Hyde Park, NY 1002

The Franklin Pierce Homestead, Hillsborough, NH 889

Fraternal Order of Alaska State Troopers Museum, Anchorage, AK 22

Fraunces Tavern Museum, New York, NY............1025

The Frazier International History Museum, Louisville, KY 576

Fred Dana Marsh Museum, Ormond Beach, FL............333

Fred Harman Art Museum, Pagosa Springs, CO............229

Fredericksburg Area Museum & Cultural Center, Inc., Fredericksburg, VA...1506

Freeborn County Museum and Historical Village, Albert Lea, MN............767

Freestone County Historical Museum, Fairfield, TX............1413

Fremont County Pioneer Museum, Lander, WY............1635

Fresno Flats Historical Park, Oakhurst, CA............132

Friends of Arrow Rock, Inc., Arrow Rock, MO............811

The Friends of Peace Church, Camp Hill, PA............1245

Friendship Hill National Historic Site, Point Marion, PA............1295

Frisco Historic Park & Museum, Frisco, CO............218

Frisco Native American Museum and Natural History Center, Frisco, NC 1102

Front Street, Ogallala, NE............869

Frontier Army Museum, Fort Leavenworth, KS............539

Frontier Culture Museum, Staunton, VA 1537

Frontier Gateway Museum, Glendive, MT............847

Frontier Historical Society and Museum, Glenwood Springs, CO 219

Frontier Times Museum, Bandera, TX............1393

Frontier Village Association, Inc., Jamestown, ND............1133

Frontiers of Flight Museum, Dallas, TX 1406

Fruitlands Museums, Harvard, MA 686

The Fryeburg Fair Farm Museum, Fryeburg, ME............611

Fryer Memorial Museum, Munnsville, NY............1017

Frye's Measure Mill, Wilton, NH............897

Fullerton Museum Center, Fullerton, CA.......98

Fulton County Historical Museum, Wauseon, OH............1190

Fulton County Museum, Groversville, NY............996

Furnas-Gosper Historical Society & Museum, Arapahoe, NE 856

Gadsden Museum, Mesilla, NM 943

Gadsden Museum of Art, Gadsden, AL 10

Gage County Historical Society and Museum, Beatrice, NE............857

Galena-Jo Daviess County Historical Society & Museum, Galena, IL............436

Galion Historical Museum, Galion, OH 1165

Galloway House and Village - Blakely Museum, Fond du Lac, WI............1597

Galveston County Historical Museum, Galveston, TX............1420

Garden Grove Historical Society, Garden Grove, CA............99

Gardner House Museum, Albion, MI 723

The Gardner Museum, Inc., Gardner, MA ...684

The Gardner Museum of Architecture & Design, Quincy, IL............452

Garibaldi and Meucci Museum, Staten Island, NY............1072

Garrett County Historical Museum, Oakland, MD............649

Garrett Historical Museum, Garrett, IN........479

Gaston County Museum of Art and History, Dallas, NC 1097

Gatekeeper's Museum & Marion Steinbach Indian Basket Museum, Tahoe City, CA............190

Gates Mills Historical Society, Gates Mills, OH............1166

Gateway NRA, Sandy Hook Unit, Fort Hancock, NJ............904

Gateway to the Panhandle, Gate, OK.........1201

Gathland State Park, Boonsboro, MD 637

Genealogy Research Center and Museum, Sandersville, GA............384

General Adam Stephen House, Martinsburg, WV............1584

General Daniel Bissell House, Saint Louis, MO............833

General Douglas MacArthur Memorial, Norfolk, VA............1521

General John J. Pershing Boyhood Home State Historic Site, Laclede, MO............824

General Lew Wallace Study & Museum, Crawfordsville, IN............473

General Patton Memorial Museum, Chiriaco Summit, CA............84

Genesee Country Village & Museum, Mumford, NY............1016

Geneva Historical Society & Prouty-Chew House & Museum, Geneva, NY............994

Geneva Historical Society & Rose Hill Mansion, Geneva, NY............994

Geographical Center Historical Museum, Rugby, ND............1136

The George Bush Presidential Library and Museum, College Station, TX 1400

George C. Marshall Museum, Lexington, VA............1513

George I. Ashby Memorial Museum, Copper Center, AK............23

George Meany Memorial Archives, Silver Spring, MD............654

George Peabody House Museum, Peabody, MA............701

George Washington Carver Museum and Cultural Center, Phoenix, AZ............40

George Washington Carver National Monument, Diamond, MO............814

George Washington Masonic National Memorial, Alexandria, VA............1493

George Washington's Ferry Farm, Stafford County, VA............1537

George Washington's Fredericksburg Foundation, Historic Kenmore & Washington's Ferry Farm, Fredericksburg, VA............1506

Georgetown Energy Museum, Georgetown, CO............218

Georgetown University Art Collection, Washington, DC............279

Georgia Music Hall of Fame and Museum, Macon, GA............377

Georgia Rural Telephone Museum, Leslie, GA............376

Georgia Salzburger Society Museum, Rincon, GA............381

Georgia's Old Capital Museum, Milledgeville, GA............380

Georgia's Stone Mountain Park, Stone Mountain, GA............387

Gerald R. Ford Conservation Center, Omaha, NE............871

Gerald R. Ford Library, Ann Arbor, MI.......724

Gerald R. Ford Presidential Museum, Grand Rapids, MI............743

German American Heritage Center, Davenport, IA............513

Germantown Historical Society, Philadelphia, PA............1280

Geronimo Springs Museum, Truth or Consequences, NM............953

Gettysburg National Military Park, Gettysburg, PA............1255

Ghost Town Museum, Colorado Springs, CO............207

Gibbs Museum of Pioneer and Dakotah Life, Falcon Heights, MN............775

Gig Harbor Peninsula Historical Society, Gig Harbor, WA............1555

Gila County Historical Museum, Globe, AZ............35

Gilcrease Museum, Tulsa, OK............1215

Gillespie County Historical Society, Fredericksburg, TX............1419

Gilliam County Historical Society - Depot Museum Complex, Condon, OR.1222

Gilman Historic Ranch and Wagon Museum, Banning, CA............74

Gilmore Car Museum, Hickory Corners, MI............746

Gilpin History Museum, Central City, CO...205

Glenn H. Curtiss Museum, Hammondsport, NY............997

Glenview Area Historical Society, Glenview, IL............438

Glove Museum, New York, NY 1026

Gnadenhutten Historical Park & Museum, Gnadenhutten, OH............1167

Gold Coast Railroad Museum, Inc., Miami, FL............323

Gold Nugget Museum, Paradise, CA 139

The Golden Age of Trucking Museum, Middlebury, CT............249

Golden Ball Tavern Museum, Weston, MA............718

Golden Gate National Recreation Area, San Francisco, CA............165

Golden Gate Railroad Museum, San Francisco, CA............166

Golden Pioneer Museum, Golden, CO.........220

Golden State Model Railroad Museum, Point Richmond, CA............143

Golden Valley County Museum, Beach, ND............1127

Goliad State Park, Goliad, TX............1423

Gonzales Memorial Museum, Gonzales, TX............1423

Goochland County Museum & Historical Center, Goochland, VA............1508

Goodhue County Historical Society, Red Wing, MN............787

Goodman Museum, Tyler, TX 1456

Goodyear World of Rubber Museum, Akron, OH............1139

Gore Place, Waltham, MA............715

Gorgas House, Tuscaloosa, AL............19

Goschenhoppen Folklife Library and Museum, Green Lane, PA............1257

Goshen Historical Society, Goshen, CT 242

Gouverneur Historical Association, Gouverneur, NY............995

Governor Bent Museum, Taos, NM 952

Grace Armantrout Museum, George West, TX............1422

The Grace Museum, Abilene, TX............1385

The Gracie Mansion Conservancy, New York, NY............1026

Grafton Historical Society, Grafton, VT.....1479

Graham County Historical Society, Thatcher, AZ............46

Grand Army of the Republic Civil War Museum, Philadelphia, PA............1281

Grand County Museum, Hot Sulphur Springs, CO............222

Grand Encampment Museum, Inc., Encampment, WY............1632

Grand Gulf Military Park, Port Gibson, MS............807

Grand Lodge AF&AM of Virginia - Allen E. Roberts Masonic Library and Museum, Richmond, VA............1529

Grand Portage National Monument, Grand Marais, MN 776
The Grand River Historical Society & Museum, Chillicothe, MO......813
Grand River Museum, Lemmon, SD 1351
Grand Traverse Heritage Center, Traverse City, MI......765
Grant County Historical Museum, Canyon City, OR 1221
Grant County Historical Museum, Ephrata, WA......1553
Grant County Museum, Medford, OK......1205
Grant County Museum, Sheridan, AR......68
Grant County Museum aka Historic Adobe Museum, Ulysses, KS 560
Grant County Museum & Historic Society, Hyannis, NE 863
Granville County Historical Society Museum, Oxford, NC......1114
Granville Historical Society Museum, Granville, OH 1167
Granville Museum, Inc., Granville, TN......1366
Grass Valley Museum, Grass Valley, CA 100
Graue Mill and Museum, Oak Brook, IL......448
Graycliff Conservancy, Derby, NY 984
Great Basin Historical Society & Museum, Delta, UT......1464
Great Harbor Maritime Museum, Northeast Harbor, ME 616
Great Lakes Naval Memorial and Museum, Muskegon, MI 757
The Great Overland Station, Topeka, KS......559
Great Smoky Mountains Heritage Center, Townsend, TN......1384
Greater Hazleton Historical Society, Hazleton, PA 1260
Greater Loveland Historical Society Museum, Loveland, OH 1173
Greeley History Museum, Greeley, CO......221
Green Mountain Club, Inc., Waterbury Center, VT 1489
Green River Valley Museum, Big Piney, WY 1629
Greenbelt Museum, Greenbelt, MD......646
Greene County Historical Society, Xenia, OH......1193
Greenfield Historical Society, Greenfield, WI 1599
Greensboro Historical Museum, Inc., Greensboro, NC 1103
Greentown Glass Museum, Inc., Greentown, IN 480
Greenwood County Historical Society, Eureka, KS......539
Gregg County Historical Museum, Longview, TX......1434
Grier Musser Museum, Los Angeles, CA 115
Griggs County Historical Museum, Prairies, ND 1136
Grinnell Historical Museum, Grinnell, IA......519
Groton Historical Society, Groton, MA......685
Grover Cleveland Birthplace, Caldwell, NJ......899
Gruenewald Historic House, Anderson, IN......467
Guadalupe Mountains National Park, Salt Flat, TX......1447
Guernsey County Museum, Cambridge, OH......1144
The Guest House Museum, Fort Bragg, CA......95
Guilford Courthouse National Military Park, Greensboro, NC 1104
Gulf Shores Museum, Gulf Shores, AL 11
Gunn Memorial Library and Museum, Washington, CT 263
Gunnison Museum of Natural History, Pawling, NY 1051
Gustafson Gallery/Design & Merchandising, Fort Collins, CO......217
Guy B. Woodward Museum, Ramona, CA 144

Gwinnett Historical Society, Lawrenceville, GA......376
Gwinnett History Museum, Lawrenceville, GA......376
H.E.A.R.T.S. Veterans Museum of Texas, Huntsville, TX 1430
H. Earl Clack Museum, Havre, MT 849
H.G. Albee Memorial Museum, Estherville, IA......517
Haas-Lilienthal House, San Francisco, CA 166
Hackettstown Historical Society Museum & Library, Hackettstown, NJ 905
The Haggin Museum, Stockton, CA 189
The Hagley Museum and Library, Wilmington, DE......273
Hahns Peak Area Historical Society and School House, Clark, CO 205
Haines Museum, Waukegan Historical Society, Waukegan, IL......463
Hale Farm and Village, Bath, OH 1141
Halifax Historical Museum, Daytona Beach, FL......303
The Hall of Fame for Great Americans, Bronx, NY......966
Hall of Flame Museum of Firefighting, Phoenix, AZ......40
Hallockville Museum Farm, Riverhead, NY......1057
Hamden Historical Society, Inc., Hamden, CT......244
Hamilton Grange National Memorial, New York, NY......1026
Hamilton Township Historical Society - John Abbott II House, Hamilton, NJ......906
Hamilton Van Wagoner Museum, Clifton, NJ......901
Hamilton Wood Type Printing Museum, Two Rivers, WI......1625
Hamlin Garland Homestead, West Salem, WI......1627
Hammel Museum, Socorro, NM......951
Hammond Castle Museum, Gloucester, MA......684
Hammond-Harwood House Association, Annapolis, MD......628
Hammond Museum of Bells, Eureka Springs, AR......57
Hampton County Historical Museum, Hampton, SC......1334
Hampton History Museum, Hampton, VA......1509
Hampton Plantation State Historic Site, McClellanville, SC......1336
Hampton Roads Naval Museum, Norfolk, VA......1521
Hampton University Museum, Hampton, VA......1509
Hancock County Historical Society, Carthage, IL......416
Hancock Historical Museum, Findlay, OH......1164
Hancock House, Hancock's Bridge, NJ......907
Hancock Memorial Museum, Los Angeles, CA......116
Hanford Carnegie Museum, Hanford, CA....101
Hanford Mills Museum, East Meredith, NY......987
Hank Williams Museum, Montgomery, AL......16
Hanna Basin Museum, Hanna, WY......1634
Hannah Lindahl Children's Museum, Mishawaka, IN......491
Hanover Historical Society Museum, Hanover, VA......1510
Hanover House, Clemson, SC......1328
Har-Ber Village, Grove, OK......1202
Harbor Defense Museum, Brooklyn, NY......969
Harbour House Museum, Crystal Falls, MI......733
Hardin County Historical Museums, Inc., Kenton, OH......1170
Harding Home and Museum, Marion, OH.1174

Hardwick Historical Society, Hardwick, MA......686
Harlan-Lincoln House, Mount Pleasant, IA......524
Harney County Historical Museum, Burns, OR......1221
Harold M. Freund American Museum of Baking, Manhattan, KS......550
Harold Warp Pioneer Village Foundation, Minden, NE......868
Harper City Historical Society, Harper, KS......543
Harpers Ferry Center, Harpers Ferry, WV .1582
Harpers Ferry National Historical Park, Harpers Ferry, WV......1582
Harriet Beecher Stowe Center, Hartford, CT......245
The Harriet Tubman Home, Auburn, NY.....959
Harrison County Historical Museum, Marshall, TX......1436
Harrison House, Branford, CT......235
Harrison Museum of African-American Culture, Roanoke, VA......1535
Harrisonburg-Rockingham Historical Society, Dayton, VA......1503
Harry S. Truman Library-Museum, Independence, MO......818
Harry S Truman National Historic Site - Truman Farm Home, Grandview, MO 816
Harry S. Truman Office & Courtroom, Independence, MO......818
Hartslog Heritage Museum, Alexandria, PA......1239
Hartsville Museum, Hartsville, SC......1335
Harvard Historical Society, Still River, MA......711
Harvey-Baker House, Salinas, CA......154
Harvey County Historical Society, Newton, KS......553
Haskell County Historical Society, Sublette, KS......558
Hathaway Ranch Museum, Santa Fe Springs, CA......182
Hattie Weber Museum of Davis, Davis, CA......89
Haverford Township Historical Society, Havertown, PA......1260
Haverhill Historical Society, Haverhill, MA......686
Hawaii Maritime Center, Honolulu, HI......395
Hawaii's Plantation Village, Waipahu, HI....402
Hawkeye Log Cabin, Burlington, IA......507
Hawks Inn Historical Society, Inc., Delafield, WI......1595
Hawks Nest State Park, Ansted, WV 1579
Hayward Area Historical Society, Hayward, CA......102
Hazel Kibler Museum, Girard, PA 1256
Headquarters House Museum, Fayetteville, AR......57
Headwaters Heritage Museum, Three Forks, MT......854
Healdton Oil Museum, Healdton, OK 1202
Heart of West Texas Museum, Colorado City, TX......1401
Heddon Museum, Dowagiac, MI......738
Hellenic Museum & Cultural Center, Chicago, IL......421
Hemet Museum, Hemet, CA......103
Henager "Memories and Nostalgia" Museum, Buckskin, IN......471
Hendricks Hill Museum, Southport, ME......623
Hennepin History Museum, Minneapolis, MN......782
Henrico County Historic Preservation & Museum Services, Richmond, VA 1529
The Henry Ford, Dearborn, MI 733
Henry S. Reuss Ice Age Visitor Center, Campbellsport, WI......1593
The Henry Sheldon Museum of Vermont History, Middlebury, VT 1481

History Museums–Continued

Henry Whitfield State Historical Museum, Guilford, CT...............243

Henryetta Territorial Museum, Henryetta, OK....................1203

Herbert Hoover Presidential Library-Museum, West Branch, IA.........530

Hereford Inlet Lighthouse, North Wildwood, NJ....................917

The Heritage Center and Citrus Museum, Vero Beach, FL....................352

Heritage Center Museum, Berryville, AR......55

Heritage Center of Lancaster County, Inc., Lancaster, PA....................1265

Heritage Farm Museum & Village, Huntington, WV....................1583

Heritage Hall Museum & Archives, Freeman, SD....................1347

Heritage-Hjemkomst Interpretive Center, Moorhead, MN....................784

Heritage House, West Covina, CA...............197

Heritage House Museum and Robert Frost Cottage, Key West, FL...................318

Heritage House Museum of Montgomery County, Mount Ida, AR....................64

Heritage House of Orange County Association Inc., Orange, TX...............1441

The Heritage Museum, Baltimore, MD........632

The Heritage Museum, Astoria, OR...........1218

Heritage Museum & Cultural Center, Baker, LA....................585

Heritage Museum & Gallery, Leadville, CO....................226

Heritage Museum & Potton House, Big Spring, TX....................1396

The Heritage Museum at Falfurrias, Inc., Falfurrias, TX....................1413

Heritage Museum Foundation of Tate County, Inc., Senatobia, MS....................808

Heritage Museum of Northwest Florida, Valparaiso, FL....................352

Heritage Museums & Gardens, Sandwich, MA....................707

The Heritage Society, Houston, TX............1426

Heritage Square Museum, Los Angeles, CA....................116

Heritage Station, Umatilla County Historical Society Museum, Pendleton, OR....................1230

Heritage Village, Largo, FL.........321

Heritage Village, Mountain Lake, MN........785

Heritage Village Museum, Woodville, TX.1462

Herkimer County Historical Society, Herkimer, NY....................998

The Hermitage: Home of President Andrew Jackson, Hermitage, TN...........1367

Herschell Carrousel Factory Museum, North Tonawanda, NY....................1043

Hershey Museum, Hershey, PA.................1261

Hesston Steam Museum, LaPorte, IN..........487

Hettinger County Historical Society, Regent, ND....................1136

Hi-Desert Nature Museum, Yucca Valley, CA....................201

Hibbing Historical Society and Museum, Hibbing, MN....................778

The Hickories Museum of the Lorain County Historical Society, Elyria, OH..1163

Hickory Grove Rural School Museum, Ogden, IA....................525

Higgins Armory Museum, Worcester, MA...721

High Cliff Historical Society & General Store Museum, Sherwood, WI....................1622

High Plains Museum, Goodland, KS...........542

High Plains Western Heritage Center, Spearfish, SD....................1357

High Point Museum & Historical Park, High Point, NC....................1106

Highland House Museum, Hillsboro, OH..1168

Highland Maple Museum, Monterey, VA...1518

Highland Park Historical Society, Highland Park, IL....................439

Highlands Hammock State Park/Civilian Conservation Corps Museum, Sebring, FL....................346

Highlands Museum & Discovery Center, Ashland, KY....................564

Hildene, The Lincoln Family Home, Manchester, VT....................1481

Hill Cumorah Visitors Center & Historic Sites, Palmyra, NY....................1050

Hill-Hold Museum, Montgomery, NY........1015

Hill-Stead Museum, Farmington, CT.........241

Hillsboro Area Historical Society, Hillsboro, WI....................1600

Hillsboro Museums, Hillsboro, KS.........544

Hinckley Fire Museum, Hinckley, MN........778

Hinsdale Historical Society, Hinsdale, IL....440

Historic Arkansas Museum, Little Rock, AR....................62

Historic Auto Attractions, Roscoe, IL.........456

Historic Bowens Mills & Pioneer Park, Middleville, MI....................754

Historic Burlington County Prison Museum, Mount Holly, NJ....................914

Historic Camden Revolutionary War Site, Camden, SC....................1323

Historic Carson House, Marion, NC.........1110

Historic Charlton Park Village and Museum, Hastings, MI....................745

Historic Columbus Foundation, Inc., Columbus, GA....................369

Historic Crab Orchard Museum & Pioneer Park, Inc., Tazewell, VA...........1541

Historic Fort Steilacoom, Lakewood, WA..1558

Historic Fort Stockton, Fort Stockton, TX.1416

Historic General Dodge House, Council Bluffs, IA....................512

Historic Halifax State Historic Site, Halifax, NC....................1105

Historic Hartwood Mansion, Pittsburgh, PA....................1292

Historic Hope Foundation, Inc., Windsor, NC....................1124

Historic Hudson Valley, Tarrytown, NY.....1077

Historic Jefferson College, Washington, MS....................810

Historic Landmarks Foundation of Indiana, Indianapolis, IN....................482

Historic Langhorne Association, Langhorne, PA....................1267

Historic Latta Plantation, Huntersville, NC....................1107

Historic Lincoln, Lincoln, NM....................941

Historic Lyme Village Association, Bellevue, OH....................1142

Historic New Harmony, New Harmony, IN....................494

The Historic New Orleans Collection, New Orleans, LA....................595

Historic Northampton, Northampton, MA....699

Historic Palmyra's Print Shop, Palmyra, NY....................1050

Historic Pensacola Village, Pensacola, FL...335

Historic Preservation Association of Bourbon County, Inc., Fort Scott, KS.....540

Historic Pullman Foundation, Chicago, IL...421

Historic Renville Preservation Commission, Renville, MN....................787

Historic Richmond Town, Staten Island, NY....................1072

Historic St. Mary's City, Saint Mary's City, MD....................652

Historic Sauder Village, Archbold, OH......1140

Historic Schaefferstown, Inc., Schaefferstown, PA....................1297

Historic Smithfield, Blacksburg, VA...........1497

Historic Southwest Ohio, Inc., Sharonville, OH....................1185

Historic Spanish Point, Osprey, FL.............333

Historic Westville, Inc., Lumpkin, GA.........376

Historical and Genealogical Society of Indiana County, Indiana, PA.................1262

Historical and Genealogical Society of Somerset County, Somerset, PA............1300

Historical and Wildlife Museum, Gridley, CA....................101

Historical Center for Southeast New Mexico, Roswell, NM....................946

Historical Electronics Museum, Linthicum, MD....................648

Historical Museum-Archival Center, Mission Hills, CA....................126

Historical Museum at Fort Missoula, Missoula, MT....................851

The Historical Museum at St. Gertrude, Cottonwood, ID....................405

Historical Museum of Bay County, Bay City, MI....................727

Historical Museum of Southern Florida, Miami, FL....................324

Historical Natural History & Library Society of Natick dba Natick Historical Society, South Natick, MA.....709

Historical Shrine Foundation of San Diego County, San Diego, CA................156

Historical Society of Berks County, Reading, PA....................1296

Historical Society of Bloomfield New Jersey, Bloomfield, NJ....................898

Historical Society of Cecil County, Elkton, MD....................643

Historical Society of Cheshire County, Keene, NH....................890

Historical Society of Delaware, Wilmington, DE....................274

Historical Society of Fort Washington, Fort Washington, PA....................1254

The Historical Society of Frederick County, Inc., Frederick, MD.................644

Historical Society of Garden County, Oshkosh, NE....................871

Historical Society of Glastonbury, Glastonbury, CT....................242

Historical Society of Greater Port Jefferson, Port Jefferson, NY.................1053

Historical Society of Greenfield, Greenfield, MA....................685

Historical Society of Haddonfield, Haddonfield, NJ....................905

Historical Society of Kent County, Inc., Chestertown, MD....................640

Historical Society of Middletown and the Wallkill Precinct, Inc., Middletown, NY....................1014

Historical Society of Millersburg & Upper Paxton Township Museum, Millersburg, PA....................1272

Historical Society of Oak Park & River Forest, Oak Park, IL....................448

Historical Society of Ocean Grove, New Jersey, Ocean Grove, NJ....................918

Historical Society of Old Newbury, Cushing House Museum, Newburyport, MA....................698

Historical Society of Palm Beach County, Palm Beach, FL....................334

Historical Society of Princeton, Princeton, NJ....................921

Historical Society of Quaker Hill & Pawling, Pawling, NY....................1051

Historical Society of Quincy and Adams County, Quincy, IL....................452

Historical Society of Rockland County, New City, NY....................1017

Historical Society of St. Marys and Benzinger Township, Saint Marys, PA..1297

Historical Society of Saratoga Springs, Saratoga Springs, NY....................1064

Historical Society of Stanton County Museums at Stanton and Pilger, Pilger, NE....................872

Historical Society of the Cocalico Valley, Ephrata, PA....................1252

Historical Society of the Tonawandas, Inc., Tonawanda, NY 1078
Historical Society of the Town of Clarence, Clarence, NY 978
Historical Society of the Town of Greenwich Inc. aka Bush-Holley Historic Site, Cos Cob, CT 237
The Historical Society of Trappe, Collegeville, Perkiomen Valley, Inc., Trappe, PA 1303
Historical Society of Walden & Wallkill Valley, Walden, NY 1081
Historical Society of Wells and Ogunquit, Wells, ME 625
Historical Society Porter County Old Jail Museum, Valparaiso, IN 502
History and Traditions Museum, Lackland Air Force Base, TX 1433
The History Center, Fort Wayne, IN 477
The History Center, Cedar Rapids, IA 509
The History Center in Tompkins County, Ithaca, NY 1003
History Museum for Springfield-Greene County, Springfield, MO 839
The History Museum, Lake Placid-North Elba Historical Society, Lake Placid, NY 1009
History Museum of Western Virginia, Roanoke, VA 1535
The History Place, Morehead City, NC 1111
History San Jose, San Jose, CA 171
Hiwan Homestead Museum, Evergreen, CO 215
Hoard Historical Museum and National Dairy Shrine's Visitors Center, Fort Atkinson, WI 1598
Hoboken Historical Museum, Hoboken, NJ 907
Hofwyl-Broadfield Plantation State Historic Site, Brunswick, GA 366
Holland Historical Society Museum, Inc., Holland, VT 1480
The Holland Museum, Holland, MI 746
Holly History Center & Hutchinson House Museum, Waupaca, WI..............1626
Hollyhock House, Los Angeles, CA.............116
Hollywood Heritage Museum, Hollywood, CA 103
Hollywood History Museum, Hollywood, CA 103
Holocaust Memorial Center, Farmington Hills, MI 741
Holocaust Memorial Resource and Education Center of Florida, Inc., Maitland, FL 322
Holocaust Museum Houston, Houston, TX 1426
Holocaust Museum of Southwest Florida, Naples, FL 328
Holt-Atherton Special Collections, Stockton, CA 189
Holy Trinity (Old Swedes) Church & Hendrickson House Museum, Wilmington, DE 274
Home of Franklin D. Roosevelt National Historic Site, Hyde Park, NY 1002
Home of Stone (The Mueller-Schmidt House 1881), a Ford County Museum, curated by Ford County Historic Society, Dodge City, KS 537
Homeopathy Works, Berkeley Springs, WV 1580
Homestake Gold Mine Visitor Center, Lead, SD 1351
Homestead Acre and the Hill-Palmer House, Chatsworth, CA..............82
Homestead National Monument of America, Beatrice, NE 857
Homesteader Museum, Powell, WY 1637
Homeville Antique Fire Department, Homer, NY 999
Homeville Museum, Homer, NY 999

Honolulu Police Department Law Enforcement Museum, Honolulu, HI.......396
Hood River County Historical Museum, Hood River, OR..............1226
Hoofprints of the Past Museum, Kaycee, WY 1634
Hoover Historical Center, North Canton, OH..............1179
Hopewell Museum, Paris, KY 582
Hopewell Museum, Hopewell, NJ 908
Horatio Colony House Museum & Nature Preserve, Keene, NH 890
Hornby Museum, Hornby, NY 999
Horry County Museum, Conway, SC 1331
Horseshoe Bend National Military Park, Daviston, AL..............7
Hot Springs County Museum and Cultural Center, Thermopolis, WY 1639
Hot Springs National Park Visitor Center, Hot Springs, AR 60
Hotel de Paris Museum, Georgetown, CO ...219
The Houdini Museum & Theater, Scranton, PA 1298
Houghton County Historical Museum Society, Lake Linden, MI..............749
House of Broadcasting Radio & Television Museum, Scottsdale, AZ 44
The House on the Rock, Spring Green, WI 1622
Houston Police Museum, Houston, TX 1427
Howard County Center of African American Culture, Columbia, MD..........641
Howard County Historical Museum, Kokomo, IN 486
Howard County Historical Society, Ellicott City, MD..............643
Howard Steamboat Museum and Mansion, Jeffersonville, IN 486
Howard University Museum, Moorland Spingarn Research Center, Washington, DC 281
Howard Weeden House Museum, Huntsville, AL 11
Howell Living History Farm, Titusville, NJ 926
Howland House, Plymouth, MA..............703
The Hubbard Museum of the American West, Ruidoso Downs, NM..............946
Hubbell Trading Post National Historic Site, Ganado, AZ 34
Hudson Library and Historical Society, Hudson, OH 1168
Hudson River Maritime Museum, Kingston, NY 1007
Huerfano County Historical Society, including The Walsenburg Mining Museum & Ft. Francisco Museum of La Veta, Walsenburg, CO..............234
Hugh Mercer Apothecary Shop, Fredericksburg, VA..............1506
Hui No'eau Visual Arts Center, Makawao, Maui, HI 401
Hull Lifesaving Museum Inc., the Museum of Boston Harbor Heritage, Hull, MA..............687
Humboldt Historical Museum, Humboldt, KS 544
Humboldt Redwoods State Park Visitor Center, Weott, CA 197
The Humphrey Forum, Minneapolis, MN....782
Hungarian Folk-Art Museum, Port Orange, FL..............338
Hunter House Victorian Museum, Norfolk, VA 1522
Huntingdon County Historical Society, Huntingdon, PA 1262
Huntington County Historical Society Museum, Huntington, IN 481
Huntington Library, Art Collections, and Botanical Gardens, San Marino, CA 174
Huntington Sewing & Trade School, Huntington, NY 1001
Huron City Museums, Port Austin, MI 761

Hurricane Valley Heritage Park Museum, Hurricane, UT 1466
Hurst Ranch Historical Foundation, West Covina, CA 197
Hutchinson County Museum, Borger, TX..1397
Hyrum City Museum, Hyrum, UT 1466
Ice House Museum, Cedar Falls, IA 508
Idaho Black History Museum, Boise, ID 403
Idaho Military History Museum, Boise, ID 404
Idaho Museum of Mining and Geology, Boise, ID..............404
Idaho State Historical Museum, Boise, ID...404
Ilwaco Heritage Museum, Ilwaco, WA.......1556
Immigration Station Barracks Museum, Tiburon, CA 192
Imperial Calcasieu Museum, Inc., Lake Charles, LA..............590
Independence Historical Museum, Independence, KS..............545
Independence National Historical Park, Philadelphia, PA 1281
Indian City U.S.A., Anadarko, OK............1195
Indian Heritage Museum, Rancocas, NJ 922
Indian Hill Historical Society, Cincinnati, OH..............1150
Indian Museum of Lake County, Ohio, Willoughby, OH..............1191
Indian Pueblo Cultural Center, Albuquerque, NM..............933
Indian Springs State Park Museum, Flovilla, GA..............372
Indiana Historical Society, Indianapolis, IN..............483
Indianapolis Motor Speedway Hall of Fame Museum, Indianapolis, IN.............484
The Institute For American Indian Studies (IAIS), Washington Green, CT...263
Intel Museum, Santa Clara, CA..............181
Interlaken Historical Society, Interlaken, NY..............1002
International Bluegrass Music Museum, Owensboro, KY..............581
International Bowling Museum and Hall of Fame, Saint Louis, MO 833
The International Clown Hall of Fame & Research Center, Inc., Milwaukee, WI..1611
International Institute of Metropolitan Detroit, Detroit, MI..............737
International Museum of Surgical Science, Chicago, IL 422
International Museum of the Horse, Lexington, KY..............573
International Museum of Women, San Francisco, CA 166
The International Printing Museum, Carson, CA 82
International Spy Museum, Washington, DC..............281
International Swimming Hall of Fame, Inc., Fort Lauderdale, FL..............307
International Women's Air and Space Museum, Inc., Cleveland, OH..............1155
Intrepid Sea-Air-Space Museum, New York, NY..............1028
Iolani Palace, Honolulu, HI..............396
Iosco County Historical Museum, East Tawas, MI..............740
Iowa Aviation Museum, Greenfield, IA........519
Iowa Great Lakes Maritime Museum, Arnolds Park, IA 505
Iowa Masonic Library and Museum, Cedar Rapids, IA 509
Ipswich Historical Society and Museum, Ipswich, MA..............688
Iraan Museum, Iraan, TX..............1430
Iredell Museum of Arts & Heritage, Statesville, NC..............1120
Iron & Steel Museum of Alabama, Tannehill Ironworks Historical State Park, McCalla, AL..............13
Iron County Museum, Caspian, MI............731

History Museums–Continued

Iron Hill Museum, Newark, DE 272
Iron Mission State Park & Museum, Cedar City, UT 1464
Ironworld Discovery Center, Chisholm, MN 771
Isabel Anderson Comer Museum & Arts Center, Sylacauga, AL 18
Isabel Miller Museum/Sitka Historical Society, Sitka, AK 27
Isanti County Historical Society, Cambridge, MN 770
Ischua Valley Historical Society, Inc., Franklinville, NY 992
Island County Historical Society Museum, Coupeville, WA 1551
Isle La Motte Historical Society, Isle La Motte, VT 1480
Islesford Historical Museum, Islesford, ME 612
Issaquah History Museum, Issaquah, WA ..1557
Itasca County Historical Society, Grand Rapids, MN 777

J.E. Reeves Home & Museum, Dover, OH 1163
J.J. Jackson Memorial Museum, Weaverville, CA 197
J.M. Davis Arms & Historical Museum, Claremore, OK 1198
J.W. Parmley Historical Home Society, Ipswich, SD 1349
Jack London State Historic Park, Glen Ellen, CA 99
Jackson County Historical Museum, Lakefield, MN 778
Jackson County Historical Museum & Research Library, Maquoketa, IA 522
Jackson County Historical Society, Black River Falls, WI 1592
Jackson Hole Historical Society and Museum, Jackson, WY 1634
Jacksonport State Park, Jacksonport, AR 60
Jacksonville Fire Museum, Jacksonville, FL 314
Jacob Kelley House Museum, Hartsville, SC 1335
The Jacqueline House African American Museum, Vicksburg, MS 809
Jail Museum, Neligh, NE 869
The James Madison Museum, Orange, VA 1524
James Madison's Montpelier, Montpelier Station, VA 1518
James Monroe Museum and Memorial Library, Fredericksburg, VA 1507
James S. Copley Library, La Jolla, CA 106
James Whitcomb Riley Birthplace & Museum, Greenfield, IN 480
Jamestown Museum, Jamestown, RI 1312
Jamestown Settlement, Yorktown Victory Center, The Jamestown-Yorktown Foundation, Williamsburg, VA 1545
Jane L. and Robert H. Weiner Judaic Museum, Rockville, MD 651
Japanese American National Museum, Los Angeles, CA 117
Japanese Cultural Center of Hawaii, Honolulu, HI 397
J.C. Penney Homestead & Historical Foundation, Kemmerer, WY 1635
Jean P. Haydon Museum, Pago Pago, AS ..1640
Jeanerette Bicentennial Park and Museum, Jeanerette, LA 589
Jefferson Barracks Historic Site, Saint Louis, MO 833
The Jefferson County Historical Assoc., Steubenville, OH 1186
Jefferson County Historical Society, Watertown, NY 1083

Jefferson County Historical Society and Farnsworth TV Pioneer Museum, Rigby, ID 409
Jefferson County Historical Society, Inc., Madison, IN 489
Jefferson County Historical Society Museum, Port Townsend, WA 1562
Jefferson County Museum, Charles Town, WV 1580
Jefferson Historical Society and Museum, Jefferson, TX 1431
Jefferson National Expansion Memorial, Saint Louis, MO 833
Jefferson Patterson Park & Museum, Saint Leonard, MD 651
Jefferson Valley Museum, Whitehall, MT 855
Jemez State Monument, Jemez Springs, NM 940
Jerome State Historic Park, Jerome, AZ 36
Jesse James Bank Museum, Liberty, MO 826
Jesse James Farm & Museum, Kearney, MO 823
Jewell County Historical Museum, Mankato, KS 552
The Jewish Museum, New York, NY 1029
Jewish Museum of Florida, Miami Beach, FL 326
Jim Crow Museum - Ferris State University, Big Rapids, MI 729
Jim Gatchell Memorial Museum, Buffalo, WY 1629
Jimmie Rodgers Museum, Meridian, MS.....805
Jimmy Carter National Historic Site, Plains, GA 381
The Jimmy Stewart Museum, Indiana, PA.1262
Joachim Regional Museum, Dickinson, ND 1130
John Brown Museum State Historic Site, Osawatomie, KS 554
John Burroughs Association, Inc., West Park, NY 1085
John E. Conner Museum, Kingsville, TX ..1432
John F. Kennedy Presidential Library & Museum, Boston, MA 666
John G. Neihardt State Historic Site, Bancroft, NE 856
John Gorrie Museum State Park, Apalachicola, FL 295
John Hutchings Museum of Natural History, Lehi, UT 1466
John Jay French House, Beaumont Heritage Society, Beaumont, TX 1395
John Jay Homestead State Historic Site, Katonah, NY 1006
John Nance Garner Museum, Uvalde, TX .1457
John Paul Jones House Museum, Portsmouth, NH 894
The John Q. Adams Center for the History of Otolaryngology - Head and Neck Surgery, Alexandria, VA 1493
John Rains House, Rancho Cucamonga, CA 145
John Rivers Communications Museum, Charleston, SC 1325
John Sydnor's 1847 Powhatan House, Galveston, TX 1421
John Waddey Carter House, Martinsville, VA 1516
John Wesley Powell Memorial Museum, Page, AZ 37
John Wesley Powell Museum, Green River, UT 1466
Johnny Appleseed Society Museum, Urbana, OH 1189
Johnson County Historical Society Museum, Warrensburg, MO 840
Johnson County Museum of History, Franklin, IN 478
Johnson County Museums, Shawnee, KS 558
Johnson Ferry House Museum, Titusville, NJ 926
Johnstown Area Heritage Association, Johnstown, PA 1263

Joliet Area Historical Museum, Joliet, IL 440
Jonathan Bailey Home, Whittier, CA 198
Jonesborough-Washington County History Museum, Jonesborough, TN 1368
Joshua Tree National Park, Oasis Visitor Center, Twentynine Palms, CA 193
The Journey Museum, Rapid City, SD 1354
Juan Matias Sanchez Adobe, Montebello, CA 127
Judge Roy Bean Visitor Center, Langtry, TX 1433
Judith Basin County Museum, Stanford, MT 853
Jugville Museum, Grafton, ND 1131
Julia A. Purnell Museum, Snow Hill, MD ...654
Julian H. Sleeper House, Saint Paul, MN 790
Junction City Historical Society, Junction City, OR 1226
Juneau-Douglas City Museum, Juneau, AK 26
Juneteenth Creative Cultural Center & Museum, Saginaw, MI 762
Juniata County Historical Society, Mifflintown, PA 1271

Kalamazoo Valley Museum, Kalamazoo, MI 749
Kalkaska County Historical Museum, Kalkaska, MI 749
Kanabec History Center, Mora, MN............784
Kandiyohi County Historical Society, Willmar, MN 796
Kankakee County Museum, Kankakee, IL...441
Kansas Museum of History, Topeka, KS 559
Karl C. Harrison Museum of George Washington, Columbiana, AL 6
Karl E. Mundt Historical & Educational Foundation, Madison, SD 1351
Karpeles Manuscript Library Museum, Duluth, MN 773
The Kate Chopin House & Bayou Folk Museum, Cloutierville, LA 588
Kate Shelley Railroad Museum, Boone, IA 506
Kauai Museum, Lihue, HI 401
Kauffman Museum, North Newton, KS 553
Kearney County Historical Museum, Minden, NE 868
Kearney Mansion Museum, Fresno, CA 97
Keeler Tavern Museum, Ridgefield, CT 259
Kell House Museum, Wichita Falls, TX 1461
Kelly-Griggs House Museum, Red Bluff, CA 146
The Kelso House Museum, Kent, OH........1169
Kelton House Museum & Garden, Columbus, OH 1158
The Kemp-McCarthy Memorial Museum of the Rowe Historical Society, Inc., Rowe, MA 706
The Kenilworth Historical Society, Kenilworth, IL 441
Kennebunkport Historical Society, Kennebunkport, ME 612
Kennesaw Mountain National Battlefield Park, Kennesaw, GA 374
Kenosha County Historical Society and Museum, Inc., Kenosha, WI 1602
Kentucky Gateway Museum Center, Maysville, KY 579
Kentucky Historical Society, Frankfort, KY 569
The Kentucky Library & Museum, Bowling Green, KY 565
Kentucky Military History Museum, Frankfort, KY 569
Kerbyville Museum, Kerby, OR 1227
Kern County Museum, Bakersfield, CA.........73
Kewaunee County Historical Museum, Kewaunee, WI 1602
Key West Lighthouse Museum, Key West, FL 318
Key West Museum of Art and History, Key West, FL 318

Keyport Historical Society-Steamboat Dock Museum, Keyport, NJ 909

Keystone Area Historical Society, Keystone, SD..................1350

Kidwell Farm at Frying Pan Park, Herndon, VA..................1511

Kimball House Museum, Battle Creek, MI..................727

Kimble County Historical Museum, Junction, TX..................1431

King Kamehameha V-Judiciary History Center, Honolulu, HI..................397

King Manor, Jamaica, NY..................1004

King Saddlery Museum, Sheridan, WY 1638

Kingman County Historical Museum, Kingman, KS..................547

Kingman Tavern Historical Museum, Cummington, MA..................678

Kinney Pioneer Museum and Historical Society of North Iowa, Clear Lake, IA ...510

Kit Carson Historical Society, Kit Carson, CO..................223

Kit Carson Home & Museum, Inc., Taos, NM..................952

Kitsap County Historical Society Museum, Bremerton, WA..................1549

Kittery Historical & Naval Museum, Kittery, ME..................613

Klamath County Museum, Klamath Falls, OR..................1227

Klickitat County Historical Society, Goldendale, WA..................1555

Knife River Indian Villages National Historic Site, Stanton, ND..................1136

Knight Museum, Alliance, NE..................855

Knights of Columbus Museum, New Haven, CT..................253

Knott House Museum, Tallahassee, FL.....347

Knox County Historical Society Museum, Edina, MO..................814

Knox County Museum, Knoxville, IL..........441

Knox County Museum, Benjamin, TX.......1395

Knox House Museum, El Cajon, CA...........92

Knoxville Public Library, Knoxville, PA ...1265

Knudt Salle Log Cabin, Adams, ND..........1127

Koester House Museum, Marysville, KS.....552

Kolomoki Mounds State Park Museum, Blakely, GA..................366

Koochiching County Historical Museum, International Falls, MN..................778

Korean War Veterans National Museum & Library, Rantoul, IL..................453

Kuhlmann King Historical House and Museum, Boerne, TX..................1396

Kuser Farm Mansion, Hamilton, NJ............907

La Casa Primera de Rancho San Jose, Pomona, CA..................143

La Miranda, Monterey, CA..................127

La Porte County Historical Society Museum, La Porte, IN..................487

La Puente Valley Historical Society City Hall, LaPuente, CA..................107

La Purisima Mission State Historic Park, Lompoc, CA..................109

Lac Qui Parle County Historical Society, Madison, MN..................779

The Lace Museum, Sunnyvale, CA............190

Lacey Historical Society, Forked River, NJ..................904

The Lackawanna Historical Society at the Catlin House, Scranton, PA..................1298

Lafayette Miners Museum, Lafayette, CO ...224

Lagrange County Historical Society, Inc., Lagrange, IN..................488

LaGrange Plantation, Cambridge, MD........639

LaGuardia and Wagner Archives, Long Island City, NY..................1010

Lahaina Restoration Foundation, Lahaina, HI..................400

The Lake Champlain Maritime Museum, Vergennes, VT..................1488

Lake City Columbia County Historical Museum, Inc., Lake City, FL..................319

Lake County Historic Courthouse Museum, Lakeport, CA..................108

Lake County Historical Museum, Tavares, FL..................351

Lake County Historical Society, Kirtland Hills, OH..................1170

Lake George Historical Association Museum, Lake George, NY..................1008

Lake Hopatcong Historical Museum, Landing, NJ..................909

Lake Jackson Historical Museum, Lake Jackson, TX..................1433

Lake Mead National Recreation Area, Boulder City, NV..................875

Lake of the Red Cedars Museum, Cedar Lake, IN..................472

Lake of the Woods County Museum, Baudette, MN..................768

Lake Superior Maritime Visitors Center, Duluth, MN..................773

Lake Superior Railroad Museum, Duluth, MN..................773

Lake Waccamaw Depot Museum, Lake Waccamaw, NC..................1109

Lake Wales Depot Museum & Cultural Center, Lake Wales, FL..................320

Lakewood's Heritage Center, Lakewood, CO..................225

LaMoure County Museum, Grand Rapids, ND..................1132

Lancaster County Historical Society, Lancaster, PA..................1266

Lancaster Museum/Art Gallery, Lancaster, CA..................108

Land of the Yankee Fork Historic Association Museum, Stanley, ID............410

Landis Valley Museum, Lancaster, PA 1266

Lane County Historical Museum, Dighton, KS..................536

Lane County Historical Society & Museum, Eugene, OR..................1223

Lane House, Roseburg, OR..................1234

Lane Place, Crawfordsville, IN..................473

Langlade County Historical Society Museum, Antigo, WI..................1589

Lanterman House, La Canada Flintridge, CA..................105

The LaPointe-Krebs House & Old Spanish Fort Museum, Pascagoula, MS..................807

Laramie Plains Museum, Laramie, WY 1635

Larchmont Historical Society, Mamaroneck, NY..................1013

Larz Anderson Auto Museum, Brookline, MA..................671

Lassen Historical Museum, Susanville, CA..................190

Lathrop House, Redwood City, CA..................147

Latvian Museum, Rockville, MD..................651

Lauder Museum - Amityville Historical Society, Amityville, NY..................957

Laura Ingalls Wilder Park & Museum, Inc., Burr Oak, IA..................507

Laura Ingalls Wilder-Rose Wilder Lane Historic Home & Museum, Mansfield, MO..................827

The Laurel Museum, Laurel, MD..................648

Laurence C. Jones Museum, Piney Woods, MS..................807

Lawrence County Gray House Museum, Ironton, OH..................1169

Lawrence County Historical and Genealogical Society, Bedford, IN..........469

Lawrence Heritage State Park, Lawrence, MA..................689

Lawrence History Center: Immigrant City Archives & Museum, Lawrence, MA 689

Lawrence L. Lee Scouting Museum, Manchester, NH..................891

Layland Museum, Cleburne, TX 1400

Le Sueur Museum, Le Sueur, MN 779

Lea County Cowboy Hall of Fame and Western Heritage Center, Hobbs, NM.....940

Lea County Museum, Lovington, NM 943

Leaming's Run Garden & Colonial Farm, Swainton, NJ..................926

The Lebanon County Historical Society, Lebanon, PA..................1268

Lee Chapel and Museum, Lexington, VA ..1513

Lee County Historical Society, Loachapoka, AL..................13

Leelanau Historical Museum, Leland, MI....751

Lefferts Historic House, Brooklyn, NY........969

The Leffingwell House Museum, Norwich, CT..................258

Legacy Museum of African-American History, Lynchburg, VA..................1515

Legends of New Mexico Museum, Algodones, NM..................936

Legends of the Game Baseball Museum and Learning Center, Arlington, TX......1388

Lehigh County Historical Society, Allentown, PA..................1239

Lemhi County Historical Museum, Salmon, ID..................409

Levere Memorial Temple, Evanston, IL......434

Levine Museum of the New South, Charlotte, NC..................1095

Lewes Historical Society, Lewes, DE 271

Lewis & Clark Boat House and Nature Center, Saint Charles, MO..................830

Lewis & Clark Interpretive Center, Ilwaco, WA..................1556

Lewis County Historical Museum, Chehalis, WA..................1550

Lewis County Historical Society Museum, Lowville, NY..................1012

Lexington Historical Society, Lexington, MA..................689

Lexington History Museum, Lexington, KY..................573

Liberace Museum & Foundation, Las Vegas, NV..................879

Liberty Bell Memorial Museum, Melbourne, FL..................323

Liberty County Museum, Chester, MT........844

Liberty Jail Historic Site, Liberty, MO 826

Libertyville-Mundelein Historical Society, Inc., Libertyville, IL..................442

Library of the Supreme Council, 33 Degrees, Washington, DC..................282

Licking County Historical Society, Newark, OH..................1178

Life on the Ohio River History Museum, Vevay, IN..................502

Ligonier Historical Museum, Ligonier, IN....488

Lillian and Albert Small Jewish Museum, Washington, DC..................282

Lillian Jones Museum, Jackson, OH..........1169

Limon Heritage Museum, Limon, CO..........226

Lincoln Boyhood National Memorial, Lincoln City, IN..................488

Lincoln County Historical Society, North Platte, NE..................869

Lincoln County Historical Society Museum of Pioneer History, Chandler, OK..................1197

Lincoln County Pioneer Museum, Hendricks, MN..................778

Lincoln Log Cabin State Historic Site, Lerna, IL..................442

Lincoln Memorial Shrine, Redlands, CA 147

The Lincoln Museum, Fort Wayne, IN 478

Lincoln Parish Museum & Historical Society, Ruston, LA..................600

Lincoln Park Historical Museum, Lincoln Park, MI..................751

Lincoln State Monument, Lincoln, NM 941

Lincoln Train Museum, Gettysburg, PA......1255

Linn County Historical Museum and Moyer House, Brownsville, OR............1220

History Museums–Continued

Linn County Museum/Geneaology Library, Pleasanton, KS.....556
Lisle Station Museum, Lisle, IL.....443
Litchfield Historical Society and Museum, Litchfield, CT.....247
The Lithuanian Museum, Chicago, IL.....423
Little Bighorn Battlefield National Monument, Crow Agency, MT.....844
The Little Brick House, Vandalia, IL.....462
Little Compton Historical Society, Little Compton, RI.....1312
Little Falls Historical Society Museum, Little Falls, NY.....1009
Little Norway, Inc., Blue Mounds, WI.....1593
Little Red Schoolhouse-Living Library, Beloit, KS.....534
Little Snake River Museum, Savery, WY..1638
Little White House Historic Site, Warm Springs, GA.....390
Little White Schoolhouse, Ripon, WI.....1620
Littleton Historical Museum, Littleton, CO.....227
Living Bible Museum, Mansfield, OH.....1173
Living History Farms, Urbandale, IA.....529
Living Memorial Sculpture Garden, Weed, CA.....197
The Living Word National Bible Museum, Aledo, TX.....1386
Locust Grove, The Samuel Morse Historic Site, Poughkeepsie, NY.....1055
Log House Museum, Seattle, WA.....1566
Logan County Historical Society Museum, Bellefontaine, OH.....1142
Logan County Museum, Paris, AR.....65
Loghurst Farm Museum, Canfield, OH.....1145
Logoly State Park, McNeil, AR.....64
Lola Montez Home, Grass Valley, CA.....101
Lombard Historical Museum, Lombard, IL.....443
Lompoc Museum, Lompoc, CA.....109
Lompoc Valley Historical Society, Inc., Lompoc, CA.....110
Lone Star Flight Museum/Texas Aviation Hall of Fame, Galveston, TX.....1421
Long Branch Historical Museum, Long Branch, NJ.....910
Long Island Museum of American Art, History & Carriages, Stony Brook, NY.....1075
Longfellow Evangeline State Historic Site, Saint Martinville, LA.....600
Longhorn Museum, Pleasanton, TX.....1444
Longmont Museum, Longmont, CO.....227
Longyear Museum, Chestnut Hill; MA.....675
Lopez Adobe, San Fernando, CA.....162
Lopez Island Historical Museum, Lopez Island, WA.....1558
Loriks Peterson Heritage House, Oldham, SD.....1352
Los Altos History Museum aka Association of the Los Altos Historical Museum, Los Altos, CA.....112
Los Angeles Museum of the Holocaust, Los Angeles, CA.....118
Los Angeles Police Historical Society & Museum, Los Angeles, CA.....119
Los Nogales Museum, Seguin, TX.....1452
Lost City Museum, Overton, NV.....880
Loudoun Museum, Inc., Leesburg, VA.....1512
Louis E. May Museum, Fremont, NE.....861
Louis H. & Lena Firn Grover Museum, Shelbyville, IN.....498
Louisa County Historical Society, Louisa, VA.....1514
Louisiana Political Museum and Hall of Fame, Winnfield, LA.....603
Louisiana State Museum, New Orleans, LA.....596
Louisiana State Oil & Gas Museum, Oil City, LA.....599

Louisiana's Old State Capitol, Political History Museum, Baton Rouge, LA.....587
Louisville Slugger Museum & Factory, Louisville, KY.....577
Loveland Museum Gallery, Loveland, CO.....227
Lowell Area Historical Museum, Lowell, MI.....751
Lowell National Historical Park, Lowell, MA.....691
Lower East Side Tenement Museum, New York, NY.....1029
Lower Hudson Conference of Historical Agencies and Museums, Elmsford, NY.....988
Lower White River Museum, Des Arc, AR.....56
Lowndes County Historical Society and Museum, Valdosta, GA.....389
Loxahatchee River Historical Society, Jupiter, FL.....316
Lucretia Vaile Museum, Palmer Lake, CO.....229
Lucy Craft Laney Museum of Black History and Conference Center, Augusta, GA.....365
Lucy-Desi Museum, Jamestown, NY.....1005
Ludwig Welk Farmstead, Strasburg, ND....1136
Luis Munoz Rivera Library & Museum, Barranquitas, PR.....1641
Lum & Abner Museum & Jot 'Em Down Store, Pine Ridge, AR.....66
Luther Burbank Home & Gardens, Santa Rosa, CA.....184
Lutheran Heritage Center & Museum of the Perry County Lutheran Historical Society, Altenburg, MO.....810
Lux Center for the Arts, Lincoln, NE.....866
Luzerne County Historical Society, Wilkes-Barre, PA.....1307
The Lyceum, Alexandria's History Museum, Alexandria, VA.....1493
Lyman Museum, Hilo, HI.....393
Lynchburg Museum System, Lynchburg, VA.....1515
Lyndon Baines Johnson Library and Museum, Austin, TX.....1391
Lynn Museum & Historical Society, Lynn, MA.....692
Lyon County Historical Society and Museum, Emporia, KS.....538
The Lyons Redstone Museum, Lyons, CO...227

MIT Museum, Cambridge, MA.....674
Mabee Farm Historic Site, Rotterdam Junction, NY.....1062
MacArthur Museum of Arkansas Military History, Little Rock, AR.....62
Macartney House Museum, Oakland, ME...616
Macaulay Museum of Dental History, Charleston, SC.....1326
MacCallum More Museum and Gardens, Chase City, VA.....1500
Macculloch Hall Historical Museum & Gardens, Morristown, NJ.....913
Macedon Historical Society, Inc., Macedon, NY.....1012
MacGregor Ranch, Estes Park, CO.....215
Mackinac Island State Park Commission-Mackinac State Historic Parks, Mackinaw City, MI.....752
Mackinac State Historic Parks-Colonial Michilimackinac & Old Mackinac Point Lighthouse, Mackinaw City, MI....752
Mackinac State Historic Parks-Fort Mackinac & Mackinac Island State Park, Mackinac Island, MI.....752
Mackinac State Historic Parks-Historic Mill Creek, Mackinaw City, MI.....753
Macon County Historical Society Museum Complex, Decatur, IL.....430
Mac's Antique Car Museum, Tulsa, OK....1215
The Madam Brett Homestead, Beacon, NY.....961

Madeline Island Historical Museum, La Pointe, WI.....1603
Madera County Museum, Madera, CA.....123
Madison County Historical Museum & Archival Library, Edwardsville, IL.....432
Madison County Historical Society-Cottage Lawn, Oneida, NY.....1045
Madison Historical Society, Madison, CT....247
Madison-Morgan Cultural Center, Madison, GA.....378
Magevney House, Memphis, TN.....1373
Maggie L. Walker National Historic Site, Richmond, VA.....1530
Mai Wah Society, Butte, MT.....843
Maine Historical Society, Portland, ME.....619
Maine Lighthouse Museum, Rockland, ME.....621
Maine Maritime Museum, Bath, ME.....606
Maine State Museum, Augusta, ME.....604
The Major General Frederick Funston Boyhood Home and Museum, Iola, KS.....546
Makoti Threshers' Museum, Makoti, ND...1133
Malheur Historical Project, Stonehouse Museum, Vale, OR.....1238
Malibu Lagoon Museum, Malibu, CA.....123
Malki Museum, Banning, CA.....74
Mammoth Spring State Park, Depot Museum, Mammoth Spring, AR.....64
Manassas Museum System, Manassas, VA.....1516
Manatee Village Historical Park, Bradenton, FL.....297
Manchester Historic Association Millyard Museum, Manchester, NH.....891
Manchester Historical Society, Manchester, MA.....692
Manistee County Historical Museum, Manistee, MI.....753
Manitowoc County Historical Society, Manitowoc, WI.....1607
Mann Wildlife Learning Museum, Montgomery, AL.....16
Mansfield Historical Society Museum, Storrs, CT.....261
Mansfield State Historic Site - Civil War Battlefield, Mansfield, LA.....591
Maramec Museum, The James Foundation, Saint James, MO.....830
Marathon County Historical Society, Wausau, WI.....1626
Marble Historical Society, Marble, CO.....228
Marblehead Museum & Historical Society, Marblehead, MA.....693
Marcellus Historical Society, Marcellus, NY.....1013
March Field Air Museum, Riverside, CA...149
Mardi Gras Museum, Kenner, LA.....589
Mardi Gras Museum, Biloxi, MS.....798
Marfa and Presidio County Museum, Marfa, TX.....1436
The Margaret Mitchell House & Museum, Atlanta, GA.....361
Marianna-Lee County Museum Assoc. Inc., Marianna, AR.....64
Marias Museum of History and Art, Shelby, MT.....853
Maridon Museum, Butler, PA.....1245
Marietta Museum of History, Marietta, GA.....379
Marilla Historical Society Museum, Marilla, NY.....1014
Marin History Museum, San Rafael, CA.....177
The Mariners' Museum, Newport News, VA.....1519
Marinette County Historical Museum, Marinette, WI.....1607
Marion County Historical Society, Salem, OR.....1236
The Marion County Historical Society Museum, Marion, OH.....1174
Marion Heritage Center, Marion, IA.....522

Marion Public Library Museum, Marion, IN 490

Mariposa Museum & World Culture Center, Peterborough, NH 893

Maritime & Seafood Industry Museum, Biloxi, MS 798

Maritime and Yachting Museum of the Treasure Coast, Stuart, FL 346

Maritime Museum - Cohasset Historical Society, Cohasset, MA 676

Maritime Museum of Monterey, Monterey, CA 127

Mark Twain Home and Museum, Hannibal, MO 816

The Mark Twain House & Museum, Hartford, CT 245

Marland's Grand Home, Ponca City, OK ...1212

Marlboro Historical Society, Marlboro, VT 1481

Marquette County History Museum, Marquette, MI 753

Marshall Center School, Cedar Falls, IA 508

Marshall County Historical Museum, Plymouth, IN 496

Marshall County Historical Museum, Holly Springs, MS 801

Marshall County Historical Society Museum, Warren, MN 795

Marshall Gold Discovery State Historic Park, Coloma, CA 86

Marshall Point Lighthouse Museum, Saint George, ME 621

Martha's Vineyard Museum, Edgartown, MA 681

Martin and Osa Johnson Safari Museum, Inc., Chanute, KS 535

Martin County Historical Museum, Stanton, TX 1453

Martin County Museum, Shoals, IN 499

Martin Luther King, Jr. Center for Nonviolent Social Change, Inc., Atlanta, GA 361

Martinez Museum, Martinez, CA 124

Marvin Samson Center for History of Pharmacy/USP Museum, Philadelphia, PA 1283

Mary Aaron Memorial Museum, Marysville, CA 125

The Mary Baker Eddy Library for the Betterment of Humanity, Boston, MA 666

Mary Ball Washington Museum & Library, Inc., Lancaster, VA 1512

Mary McLeod Bethune Council House National Historic Site, Washington, DC 283

Mary Washington House, Fredericksburg, VA 1507

Maryland Historical Society, Baltimore, MD 634

Mashantucket Pequot Museum and Research Center, Mashantucket, CT 248

Mason County Historical Society/Historic White Pine Village, Ludington, MI 751

Mason County Museum, Mason, TX 1437

The Masonic Library and Museum of Pennsylvania, Philadelphia, PA 1283

Massachusetts Historical Society, Boston, MA 667

The Massillon Museum, Massillon, OH 1175

Matagorda County Museum, Bay City, TX 1393

Mathias Ham House Historic Site, Dubuque, IA 516

Mattapoisett Museum and Carriage House, Mattapoisett, MA 693

The Mattatuck Museum Arts and History Center, Waterbury, CT 264

Matthew Edel Blacksmith Shop, Haverhill, IA 519

Maturango Museum of the Indian Wells Valley, Ridgecrest, CA 148

May Museum & Farmville Heritage Center, Farmville, NC 1100

Mayborn Museum Complex, Waco, TX 1459

Maynard Pioneer Museum & Park, Maynard, AR 64

Mayville Area Museum of History and Genealogy, Mayville, MI 754

Mc Cook County Historical Society and Museum, Salem, SD 1355

McCallum Museum, Sibley, IA 527

McCone County Museum, Circle, MT 844

McConnell Mansion, Moscow, ID 407

McCook House, Civil War Museum, Carrollton, OH 1146

McDowell House Museum, Danville, KY ...567

McFarland Historical Society, McFarland, WI 1609

McFarland State Historic Park, Florence, AZ 34

McHenry Museum, Modesto, CA 126

McIntosh County Historical Society, Ashley, ND 1127

McKinley Birthplace Home, Niles, OH 1179

McLarty Treasure Museum, Vero Beach, FL 352

McLean-Alanreed Area Museum, McLean, TX 1438

McLean County Historical Society Museum, Washburn, ND 1137

McLean County Museum of History, Bloomington, IL 414

McNamara House Museum, Victoria, TX ..1457

McPherson County Old Mill Museum and Park, Lindsborg, KS 550

McPherson Museum & Arts Foundation, McPherson, KS 552

Meade County Historical Society Museum, Meade, KS 552

Meadowlands Museum, Rutherford, NJ 923

Meagher County Historical Association Castle Museum, White Sulphur Springs, MT 855

Mechanicsburg Museum Association, Mechanicsburg, PA 1270

Mecosta County Historical Museum, Big Rapids, MI 729

Medicine Bow Museum, Medicine Bow, WY 1636

Medina County Historical Society, The John Smart House, Medina, OH 1175

Medina Railroad Museum, Medina, NY 1014

Meeker County Historical Society Museum & G.A.R. Hall, Litchfield, MN 779

Meeteetse Museum District, Meeteetse, WY 1636

Meigs County Museum, Pomeroy, OH 1183

Memorial Hall Museum, Pocumtuck Valley Memorial Assoc., Deerfield, MA 679

The Menczer Museum of Medicine & Dentistry, Hartford, CT 245

Mendocino County Museum, Willits, CA 198

Mendocino Historical Research, Inc./Kelley House Museum, Mendocino, CA 125

Mennonite Heritage Center, Harleysville, PA 1258

Mennonite Heritage Museum, Goessel, KS 542

Menominee County Heritage Museum, Menominee, MI 754

Merced County Courthouse Museum, Merced, CA 125

Mercer County Historical Museum, The Riley Home, Celina, OH 1146

Mercer County Historical Society, Mercer, PA 1271

Mercer Museum of the Bucks County Historical Society, Doylestown, PA 1250

Meriwether Lewis Dredge Museum, Brownville, NE 858

Mesa Historical Museum, Mesa, AZ 37

Metamora Courthouse Historic Site, Metamora, IL 444

The Metropolitan Museum of Art, New York, NY 1030

Meux Home Museum, Fresno, CA 98

Miami County Museum, Peru, IN 496

Michel Brouillet House & Museum, Vincennes, IN 502

Michigan Historical Museum, Michigan Historical Center, Lansing, MI 750

Michigan Maritime Museum, South Haven, MI 764

The Michigan State University Museum, East Lansing, MI 740

Michigan Transit Museum, Inc., Mount Clemens, MI 756

Mid-America Air Museum, Liberal, KS 549

Mid-America Windmill Museum, Kendallville, IN 486

Mid-Continent Railway Museum, North Freedom, WI 1615

Middleborough Historical Association, Inc., Middleborough, MA 694

Middlebury Historical Society, Wyoming, NY 1087

Middlesex Canal Collection, Lowell, MA ...691

Middleton Place Foundation, Charleston, SC 1326

Midland County Historical Society, Midland, MI 755

Midland Pioneer Museum, Midland, SD ...1351

Midway Museum, Inc., Midway, GA 379

Midway Village & Museum Center, Rockford, IL 455

Mighty Eighth Air Force Museum, Pooler, GA 381

Milam County Museum and Annex, Cameron, TX 1399

Milan Historical Museum, Inc., Milan, OH 1176

Milford Museum, Milford, DE 271

Military Museum of Southern New England, Danbury, CT 238

Millard Fillmore House, East Aurora, NY ...985

Mille Lacs Indian Museum, Onamia, MN ...786

Miller-Cory House Museum, Westfield, NJ 930

Millerton Courthouse, Friant, CA 98

Mills County Historical Society and Museum, Glenwood, IA 519

Milton Historical Museum, Milton, VT 1482

Milton House Museum Historic Site, Milton, WI 1610

Milwaukee County Historical Society, Milwaukee, WI 1611

Mineral County Museum, Hawthorne, NV 878

Mineral County Museum & Historical Society, Superior, MT 854

Minisink Valley Historical Society, Port Jervis, NY 1053

Minnesota Air National Guard Historical Foundation, Inc., Saint Paul, MN 790

Minnesota Historical Society, Saint Paul, MN 791

Minnesota Pioneer Park Museum, Annandale, MN 767

Minnesota Transportation Museum, Inc., Saint Paul, MN 792

Minnetrista, Muncie, IN 492

Minnilusa Pioneer Museum, Rapid City, SD 1354

Minter Field Air Museum, Shafter, CA 186

Minute Man National Historical Park, Concord, MA 676

Miracle of America Museum Inc., Polson, MT 852

Mission Bell Museum, Coweta, OK 1199

The Mission House, Stockbridge, MA 712

Mission Houses Museum, Honolulu, HI 397

Mission Inn Foundation/Museum, Riverside, CA 149

Mission Mill Museum Association, Salem, OR 1236

History Museums–Continued

Mission San Carlos Borromeo Del Rio Carmelo, Carmel, CA 81
Mission San Diego de Alcala, San Diego, CA 157
Mission San Francisco de Asis (Mission Dolores), San Francisco, CA 167
Mission San Jose Chapel and Museum, Fremont, CA 96
Mission San Juan Capistrano Museum, San Juan Capistrano, CA 173
Mission San Luis Obispo de Tolosa, San Luis Obispo, CA 174
Mission San Luis Rey Museum, Oceanside, CA 135
Mission San Rafael Arcangel, San Rafael, CA 177
Mission Santa Cruz, Santa Cruz, CA 182
Mississippi Armed Forces Museum, Camp Shelby, MS 799
Mississippi River Museum at Mud Island River Park, Memphis, TN 1375
Mississippi University for Women, Archives and Museum, Columbus, MS 800
Missouri Historical Society, Saint Louis, MO 835
Missouri State Museum, Jefferson City, MO 819
Missouri Town 1855, Lee's Summit, MO 825
Mitchell County Historical Museum, Osage, IA 526
The Mitchell Museum of the American Indian, Evanston, IL 435
Moanalua Gardens Foundation, Honolulu, HI 397
Mobile Medical Museum, Mobile, AL 14
Modoc County Historical Museum, Alturas, CA 70
Moffatt-Ladd House and Garden, Portsmouth, NH 894
Mohave Museum of History and Arts, Kingman, AZ 36
Mojave River Valley Museum, Barstow, CA 74
Moland House, Warrington, PA 1305
Molly Brown House Museum, Denver, CO 213
Molokai Museum and Cultural Center, Kualapua, HI 400
Mondak Heritage Center, Sidney, MT 853
The Money Museum-Federal Reserve Bank of Kansas City, Kansas City, MO 821
Monmouth County Historical Association, Freehold, NJ 905
Monroe County Heritage Museum, Monroeville, AL 15
Monroe County Historical Association/Stroud Mansion, Stroudsburg, PA 1302
Monroe County Historical Museum, Monroe, MI 756
Monroe County Historical Society, Bloomington, IN 469
Monroe County Local History Room & Library, Sparta, WI 1622
Monroe Historical Society, Monroe, CT 250
Montana Masonic Museum, Helena, MT 850
Monterey State Historic Park, Monterey, CA 128
The Montgomery County Historical Society, Dayton, OH 1161
The Montgomery County Historical Society, Inc., Rockville, MD 651
Montgomery Museum & Lewis Miller Regional Art Center, Christiansburg, VA 1501
Montpelier-The General Henry Knox Museum, Thomaston, ME 624
Montrose County Historical Museum, Montrose, CO 228
Montrose Historical & Telephone Pioneer Museum, Montrose, MI 756
Montville Township Historical Museum, Montville, NJ 912
Moody County Museum, Flandreau, SD 1347
The Moody Mansion Museum, Galveston, TX 1421
Moore County Historical Museum, Dumas, TX 1410
The Moore-Youse Home Museum, Muncie, IN 492
Moravian Historical Society, Nazareth, PA 1273
Moravian Museum of Bethlehem, Inc., Bethlehem, PA 1242
Mordecai Historic Park, Raleigh, NC 1115
Moriarty Historical Museum, Moriarty, NM 943
The Morikami Museum and Japanese Gardens, Delray Beach, FL 305
Mormon Station State Historic Park, Genoa, NV 877
Mormon Visitors Center, Independence, MO 818
Morningside Nature Center, Gainesville, FL 311
Morris-Butler House Museum, Indianapolis, IN 485
Morris-Jumel Mansion, New York, NY 1030
The Morris Museum, Morristown, NJ 914
Morrison's Heritage Museum, Morrison, IL 446
Morristown National Historical Park, Morristown, NJ 914
Morton Grove Historical Museum/Haupt-Yehl House, Morton Grove, IL 446
Morton Museum of Cooke County, Gainesville, TX 1420
Moses Lake Museum & Art Center, Moses Lake, WA 1559
Moses Myers House, Norfolk, VA 1522
Motown Historical Museum, Detroit, MI 737
Moundbuilders State Memorial & Museum, Newark, OH 1178
Mount Clare Museum House, Baltimore, MD 635
Mount Desert Island Historical Society, Mount Desert, ME 615
Mount Holly Community Historical Museum, Belmont, VT 1476
Mt. Horeb Area Museum, Mount Horeb, WI 1614
Mt. Kearsarge Indian Museum, Warner, NH 897
Mount Pleasant Historical Society, Mount Pleasant, OH 1177
Mount Rushmore National Memorial, Keystone, SD 1350
Mount Vernon Hotel Museum & Garden, New York, NY 1031
Mount Vernon Ladies' Association, Mount Vernon, VA 1518
Mount Washington Museum and The Weather Discovery Center, North Conway, NH 893
Mountain Heritage Center, Cullowhee, NC 1097
Mountain Life Museum, London, KY 575
Muir Woods National Monument, Mill Valley, CA 125
Mulford Farm, East Hampton, NY 986
Murfreesboro Historical Association, Murfreesboro, NC 1112
Murphy African American Museum, Tuscaloosa, AL 19
Muscatine History & Industry Center/Pearl Button Museum, Muscatine, IA 524
Museo de las Americas, Denver, CO 213
Museo de Las Americas, San Juan, PR 1642
Museo Fuerte Conde de Mirasol de Vieques, Vieques, PR 1644
The Museum, Greenwood, SC 1334
Museum & Archives of Georgia Education, Milledgeville, GA 380
Museum and Arts Center in the Sequim Dungeness Valley, Sequim, WA 1570
Museum at Southwestern Michigan College, Dowagiac, MI 738
Museum, Mission San Juan Bautista, San Juan Bautista, CA 173
Museum of Afro-American History, Boston, MA 667
Museum of Alaska Transportation & Industry, Inc., Wasilla, AK 29
Museum of American Architecture and Decorative Arts, Houston, TX 1428
Museum of American Finance, New York, NY 1031
Museum of American Political Life, West Hartford, CT 265
Museum of American Presidents, Strasburg, VA 1539
Museum of Appalachia, Clinton, TN 1363
Museum of Art and History at the McPherson Center, Santa Cruz, CA 182
Museum of Art & History at Weston, Weston, CT 266
The Museum of Arts and Sciences, Inc. and Center for Florida History, Daytona Beach, FL 303
Museum of Automobile Art and Design, Syracuse, NY 1076
Museum of Carousel Art & History, Sandusky, OH 1185
Museum of Ceramics, East Liverpool, OH 1163
Museum of Chicot County Arkansas, Lake Village, AR 61
Museum of Chinese in the Americas, New York, NY 1032
Museum of Church History and Art, Salt Lake City, UT 1471
Museum of Colorado Prisons, Canon City, CO 205
The Museum of Communications, Seattle, WA 1566
Museum of Connecticut History, Hartford, CT 245
Museum of Cultural & Natural History, Mount Pleasant, MI 757
Museum of disAbility History, Williamsville, NY 1086
Museum of Discovery: Arkansas Museum of Science and History, Little Rock, AR 62
The Museum of Early Trades and Crafts, Madison, NJ 910
The Museum of East Alabama, Opelika, AL 17
The Museum of East Texas, Lufkin, TX 1436
Museum of Family Camping, Allenstown, NH 883
Museum of Fife and Drum, Ivoryton, CT 246
Museum of Florida History, Tallahassee, FL 348
Museum of Funeral Customs, Springfield, IL 459
Museum of History & Art, Ontario, Ontario, CA 136
Museum of History & Industry (MOHAI), Seattle, WA 1567
Museum of History, Anthropology and Art, San Juan, PR 1643
Museum of Indian Arts & Culture/Laboratory of Anthropology, Santa Fe, NM 948
Museum of Indian Culture, Allentown, PA 1239
Museum of Jewish Heritage-A Living Memorial to the Holocaust, New York, NY 1032
Museum of Jurassic Technology, Culver City, CA 88

Museum of Lifestyle & Fashion History, Delray Beach, FL 305

Museum of Lighthouse History, Wells, ME 625

The Museum of Man in the Sea, Inc., Panama City Beach, FL 335

Museum of Migrating People, Bronx, NY ...966

Museum of Mississippi History, Jackson, MS 803

The Museum of Mobile, Mobile, AL 14

Museum of New Mexico, Santa Fe, NM 949

Museum of North Idaho, Coeur d'Alene, ID 405

Museum of Northwest Colorado, Craig, CO 208

The Museum of Printing History, Houston, TX 1428

Museum of Radio & Technology, Inc., Huntington, WV 1583

Museum of San Diego History and Research Library, San Diego, CA 158

Museum of San Rafael, Castle Dale, UT ...1464

Museum of Science & History of Jacksonville, Jacksonville, FL.................315

Museum of Seminole County History, Sanford, FL 343

Museum of South Texas History, Edinburg, TX 1410

Museum of Southern History, Jacksonville, FL 315

The Museum of Southern History, Sugarland, TX 1454

Museum of Surveying, Lansing, MI............750

Museum of the Albemarle, Elizabeth City, NC 1099

Museum of the Aleutians, Unalaska, AK 28

The Museum of the Alphabet, Waxhaw, NC 1121

Museum of the American Philosophical Society, Philadelphia, PA 1283

Museum of the Bedford Historical Society, Bedford, NY 961

Museum of the Berkeley Springs, Berkeley Springs, WV.......................1580

Museum of the Big Bend, Alpine, TX 1386

Museum of the Cape Fear Historical Complex, Fayetteville, NC 1101

Museum of the Cherokee Indian, Cherokee, NC 1096

Museum of the Cherokee Strip, Enid, OK.1200

Museum of the City of Lake Worth, Lake Worth, FL..................................320

Museum of the City of New York, New York, NY..................................1033

The Museum of the Confederacy, Richmond, VA 1531

Museum of the Fur Trade, Chadron, NE......859

Museum of the Great Plains, Lawton, OK.1204

Museum of the Gulf Coast, Port Arthur, TX 1444

Museum of the High Plains, McCook, NE......................................868

Museum of the Jimmy Carter Library, Atlanta, GA...............................362

Museum of the Llano Estacado, Plainview, TX 1443

Museum of the Middle Appalachians, Saltville, VA..............................1536

Museum of the Mountain Man, Pinedale, WY......................................1637

Museum of the Moving Image, Astoria, NY......................................958

Museum of the Northern Great Plains, Fort Benton, MT.............................846

Museum of the Occidental, Buffalo, WY ...1629

Museum of the Plains, Perryton, TX..........1443

Museum of the Rockies, Bozeman, MT.......842

Museum of the Southern Jewish Experience, Jackson, MS 803

Museum of the Waxhaws & Andrew Jackson Memorial, Waxhaw, NC 1122

Museum of the Western Prairie, Altus, OK 1195

Museum of the Weston Historical Society, Inc., Weston, MA 718

Museum of Tolerance, Los Angeles, CA 120

Museum of Transportation, Saint Louis, MO 835

Museum of Utah Art & History, Salt Lake City, UT 1471

Museum of Vision, San Francisco, CA 167

Museum of Weapons and Early American History, Saint Augustine, FL.....................339

Museum of West Louisiana, Leesville, LA 591

The Museum of Western Art, Kerrville, TX 1431

Museum of Western Colorado, Grand Junction, CO 220

Museum of Women's History, Billings, MT......................................841

Museum of Woodcarving, Shell Lake, WI.1621

Museum of Work & Culture, Woonsocket, RI 1320

Museum of Yarmouth History, Yarmouth, ME......................................626

Museum on York County, Rock Hill, SC ...1340

Museum on Main: A History Museum for West Georgia, LaGrange, GA 375

Museum Village, Monroe, NY..................1015

Museums of Los Gatos, Los Gatos, CA 123

The Museums of Oglebay Institute - Mansion Museum & Glass Museum, Wheeling, WV 1588

Muskegon County Museum, Muskegon, MI......................................757

Musselshell Valley Historical Museum, Roundup, MT 853

My Jewish Discovery Place Children's Museum, Fort Lauderdale, FL 308

Mystic Seaport - The Museum of America and the Sea, Mystic, CT 251

Naismith Memorial Basketball Hall of Fame, Springfield, MA.......................710

Nanticoke Indian Museum, Millsboro, DE 271

Nantucket Historical Association, Nantucket, MA 696

Nantucket Life-Saving Museum, Nantucket, MA 696

Napa Valley Museum, Yountville, CA 200

Naper Settlement, Naperville, IL................447

Napoleonic Society of America, Inc., Clearwater, FL 300

Nathan Denison Advocates, Forty Fort, PA 1254

Nathan Hale Homestead Museum, Coventry, CT 238

The National African-American Archives and Museum, Mobile, AL 15

National Afro-American Museum & Cultural Center, Wilberforce, OH 1191

The National Agricultural Center & Hall of Fame, Bonner Springs, KS..................534

National Air and Space Museum, Washington, DC...........................283

National Apple Museum, Biglerville, PA ...1243

National Archives and Records Administration, Washington, DC 284

National Baseball Hall of Fame and Museum, Inc., Cooperstown, NY 981

The National Border Patrol Museum and Memorial Library, El Paso, TX 1412

National Building Museum, Washington, DC 284

National Ceramic Museum and Heritage Center, Roseville, OH...........................1184

National Christmas Center, Paradise, PA ...1275

National Civil Rights Museum, Memphis, TN......................................1375

The National Civil War Museum, Harrisburg, PA 1258

National Cowboy & Western Heritage Museum, Oklahoma City, OK 1208

National Cowgirl Museum and Hall of Fame, Fort Worth, TX...........................1418

National Cryptologic Museum, Fort Meade, MD..................................643

National Czech & Slovak Museum & Library, Cedar Rapids, IA.....................509

National Farm Toy Museum, Dyersville, IA......................................517

National Firearms Museum, Fairfax, VA ...1504

National First Ladies' Library, Canton, OH......................................1145

National Football Museum, Inc., Canton, OH......................................1145

National Frontier Trails Museum, Independence, MO.............................818

The National Great Blacks in Wax Museum, Inc., Baltimore, MD.................635

National Hall of Fame for Famous American Indians, Anadarko, OK..........1196

National Heritage Museum, Lexington, MA......................................690

National Historic Oregon Trail Interpretive Center, Baker City, OR 1219

National Infantry Museum, Fort Benning, GA......................................372

National Knife Museum, Inc., Chattanooga, TN.............................1362

National Liberty Museum, Philadelphia, PA......................................1284

National Medal of Honor Museum of Military History, Chattanooga, TN 1362

National Mississippi River Museum & Aquarium, Dubuque, IA.....................516

National Museum of American History, Washington, DC...........................285

National Museum of American Jewish History, Philadelphia, PA 1284

National Museum of American Jewish Military History, Washington, DC 286

The National Museum of Catholic Art & History, New York, NY.....................1034

National Museum of Civil War Medicine, Frederick, MD..............................644

National Museum of Dance & Hall of Fame, Saratoga Springs, NY.................1065

National Museum of Funeral History, Houston, TX 1429

National Museum of Health and Medicine, Washington, DC 286

National Museum of Industrial History, Bethlehem, PA 1243

National Museum of Patriotism, Atlanta, GA......................................362

National Museum of Roller Skating, Lincoln, NE 866

National Museum of the American Indian, Washington, DC 286

National Museum of the American Indian, Smithsonian Institution, New York, NY..................................1034

National Museum of the Morgan Horse, Shelburne, VT..............................1487

National Museum of the United States Air Force, Wright-Patterson Air Force Base, OH..................................1193

National New York Central Railroad Museum, Elkhart, IN...........................475

National Packard Museum, Warren, OH ...1189

National Portrait Gallery, Washington, DC 287

National Postal Museum, Smithsonian Institution, Washington, DC 287

National Railroad Museum, Green Bay, WI......................................1599

National Railroad Museum and Hall of Fame, Inc., Hamlet, NC 1105

National Road/Zane Grey Museum, Norwich, OH..............................1180

National Route 66 Museum and Old Town Complex, Elk City, OK 1200

National Scouting Museum, Irving, TX 1430

History Museums–Continued

The National Soccer Hall of Fame, Oneonta, NY..1046

National Society of the Sons of the American Revolution, Louisville, KY.....578

National Steeplechase Museum, Camden, SC..1323

National Steinbeck Center, Salinas, CA.......154

National Temple Hill Association, Inc., New Windsor, NY..................................1018

National Tropical Botanical Garden, Kalaheo, HI.......................................399

National Underground Railroad Freedom Center, Cincinnati, OH..........................1150

National Vietnam Veterans Art Museum, Chicago, IL...425

National Voting Rights Museum and Institute, Selma, AL......................................18

The National Watch & Clock Museum, Columbia, PA.................................1247

National Women's Hall of Fame, Seneca Falls, NY..1068

National World War I Museum at Liberty Memorial, Kansas City, MO..................822

The National World War II Museum, New Orleans, LA.................................597

National Yiddish Book Center, Amherst, MA..659

Native American Exhibit, National Kateri Shrine, Fonda, NY..............................991

Native American Heritage Museum at Highland Mission State Historic Site, Highland, KS..544

Native American Museum, Terre Haute, IN..500

Natural Center for the American Revolution, Wayne, PA..........................1306

Natural History Museum of Los Angeles County, Los Angeles, CA......................120

Natural History Museum of Western Wyoming College, Rock Springs, WY..1638

Naugatuck Historical Society, Naugatuck, CT..251

Navajo Nation Museum, Window Rock, AZ..53

Naval War College Museum, Newport, RI..1314

Navarro County Historical Society, Pioneer Village, Corsicana, TX..............1402

Navy UDT-SEAL Museum, Fort Pierce, FL...309

Nebraska Conference United Methodist Historical Center, Lincoln, NE................866

Nebraska Prairie Museum of the Phelps County Historical Society, Holdrege, NE...863

Nebraska State Historical Society's Museum of Nebraska History, Lincoln, NE...866

Nebraska State Historical Society's Thomas P. Kennard House, Lincoln, NE...867

Negro Leagues Baseball Museum, Kansas City, MO...822

Neill Museum, Fort Davis, TX................1414

Netherland Inn House Museum & Boatyard Complex, Kingsport, TN........1368

Nevada County Depot Museum, Prescott, AR..67

Nevada County Historical Society, Inc., Nevada City, CA.......................................130

Nevada Historical Society, Reno, NV..........881

Nevada Northern Railway Museum, Ely, NV...876

Nevada State Fire Museum & Comstock Firemen's Museum, Virginia City, NV....882

Nevada State Museum, Carson City, NV.....876

Nevada State Museum, Las Vegas, Las Vegas, NV..880

Nevada State Railroad Museum, Carson City, NV...876

New Almaden Quicksilver Mining Museum, San Jose, CA............................172

New Bedford Whaling Museum, New Bedford, MA...696

New Canaan Historical Society, New Canaan, CT...252

New Castle Historical Society, New Castle, DE...272

New Castle Historical Society - Horace Greeley House, Chappaqua, NY..............977

The New England Carousel Museum, Bristol, CT...236

New England Civil War Museum, Vernon, CT..263

New England Fire and History Museum, Brewster, MA...670

New England Maple Museum, Pittsford, VT...1484

New England Pirate Museum, Salem, MA..706

New England Wireless & Steam Museum Inc., East Greenwich, RI......................1311

New Hampshire Antiquarian Society, Hopkinton, NH...889

New Hampshire Farm Museum, Inc., Milton, NH...892

New Hampshire Historical Society, Concord, NH...885

New Harmony State Historic Site/Historic New Harmony, New Harmony, IN...494

New Hartford Historical Society, New Hartford, NY...1017

New Haven Colony Historical Society, New Haven, CT...253

The New Jersey Historical Society, Newark, NJ...916

The New Jersey Museum of Agriculture, North Brunswick, NJ.............................917

New Jersey Naval Museum, Hackensack, NJ..905

New Jersey Office of Historic Sites, Trenton, NJ...927

New Jersey State Museum, Trenton, NJ......927

New Jersey State Police Museum, West Trenton, NJ...930

New Market Battlefield State Historical Park, New Market, VA.........................1519

New Mexico Farm & Ranch Heritage Museum, Las Cruces, NM......................940

New Mexico Museum of Natural History & Science, Albuquerque, NM...............935

New Mexico Museum of Space History, Alamogordo, NM...932

The New Milford Historical Society, New Milford, CT...256

New Orleans Fire Dept. Museum & Educational Center, New Orleans, LA....597

New Orleans Pharmacy Museum, New Orleans, LA...597

New Richmond Preservation Society, New Richmond, WI...1615

New Sweden Farmstead Museum, Inc., Bridgeton, NJ...898

New Sweden Historical Society, New Sweden, ME...616

New Windsor Cantonment State Historic Site and National Purple Heart Hall of Honor, Vails Gate, NY.........................1080

New York City Fire Museum, New York, NY..1035

New York City Police Museum, New York, NY..1035

The New York Historical Society, New York, NY..1035

New York Museum of Transportation, West Henrietta, NY...1084

The New York Public Library for the Performing Arts, New York, NY...........1036

New York State Historical Association/Fenimore Art Museum, Cooperstown, NY...981

New York State Military Museum and Veterans Research Center, Saratoga Springs, NY..1065

New York State Museum, Albany, NY.........955

Newaygo County Museum, Newaygo, MI...758

Newell Museum, Newell, SD....................1352

Newport Historical Society & The Museum of Newport History, Newport, RI...1315

Newseum, Washington, DC.........................288

Newton Fire Department, Newton, NJ.........917

The Newton History Museum at The Jackson Homestead, Newton, MA...........698

Newton Public Library and Museum, Newton, IL...447

Newtown History Center, Stephens City, VA...1538

Nez Perce County Museum, Lewiston, ID...407

The Niagara County Historical Center and Niagara County Genealogical Society, Lockport, NY.............................1010

Nici Self Museum, Centennial, WY...........1630

Nicollet County Historical Society, Saint Peter, MN...793

Niles Hotel and Saloon, Alturas, CA.............70

Ninety Six National Historic Site, Ninety Six, SC...1338

Nishna Heritage Museum, Oakland, IA.......525

Nita Stewart Haley Memorial Library & J. Evetts Haley History Center, Midland, TX...1439

Nixon Presidential Materials Staff, College Park, MD...641

No Man's Land Historical Society, Goodwell, OK...1201

Noah Webster House/West Hartford Historical Society, West Hartford, CT.....265

Noank Historical Society, Inc., Noank, CT..256

Noden-Reed Farm Museum, Windsor Locks, CT...268

Nordic Heritage Museum, Seattle, WA......1567

Nordica Homestead, Farmington, ME........610

Norfolk History Museum, Norfolk, VA......1523

The Norman Cleveland County Historical Museum, Norman, OK.........................1206

Norman #1 Oil Well Museum, Neodesha, KS..553

North Andover Historical Society, North Andover, MA...698

North Brevard Historical Museum, Titusville, FL...352

North Carolina A&T State University Galleries, Greensboro, NC....................1104

North Carolina Maritime Museum, Beaufort, NC...1091

North Carolina Museum of History, Raleigh, NC...1115

North Carolina Pottery Center, Seagrove, NC..1119

North Carolina Transportation Museum, Spencer, NC...1120

The North Dakota Lewis & Clark Interpretive Center, Washburn, ND........1137

North Dakota State Railroad Museum, Mandan, ND...1134

North Haven Historical Society, North Haven, CT...257

North House Museum, Lewisburg, WV.....1584

North Lee County Historic Center and Santa Fe Depot Museum Complex, Fort Madison, IA...518

North Plainfield Exempt Firemen's Association, North Plainfield, NJ.............917

North Platte Valley Museum, Gering, NE....861

North Star Museum of Boy Scouting and Girl Scouting, North Saint Paul, MN......785

North Tonawanda History Museum, North Tonawanda, NY.........................1043

Northeast Georgia History Center at Brenau University, Gainesville, GA........373

Northeast Louisiana Delta African
  American Heritage Museum, Monroe,
  LA 592
Northeast Oakland Historical Museum,
  Oxford, MI 759
Northeast Texas Rural Heritage Museum,
  Pittsburg, TX 1443
Northeastern Montana Threshers and
  Antique Association, Culbertson, MT 845
Northeastern Nevada Museum, Elko, NV 876
Northern Indiana Center for History,
  South Bend, IN 499
Northern New York Agricultural
  Historical Society, Agricultural
  Museum at Stone Mills, LaFargeville,
  NY 1008
Northfield Historical Society Museum,
  Northfield, MN 785
Northport Historical Society Museum,
  Northport, NY 1044
The Northumberland County Historical
  Society, Sunbury, PA 1302
The Northwest Carriage Museum,
  Raymond, WA 1564
Northwest Railway Museum,
  Snoqualmie, WA 1570
Northwestern Oklahoma State University
  Museum, Alva, OK 1195
Norwalk Museum, South Norwalk, CT 260
Norwegian-American Historical
  Association, Northfield, MN 786
Novato History Museum, Novato, CA 132
Nowata County Historical Society
  Museum, Nowata, OK 1207

O. Winston Link Museum, Roanoke, VA ...1535
Oak Glen School House Museum,
  Yucaipa, CA 200
Oakdale Cowboy Museum, Oakdale, CA 132
Oakdale Museum, Oakdale, CA 132
Oakland Museum of California, Oakland,
  CA 134
Oaklands Historic House Museum,
  Murfreesboro, TN 1376
The Oaks House Museum, Jackson, MS 804
Oberlin Heritage Center, Oberlin, OH 1180
Occoneechee State Park, Clarksville, VA ...1501
Ocean City Historical Museum, Inc.,
  Ocean City, NJ 918
Ocean City Life-Saving Station Museum,
  Ocean City, MD 650
Ocean County Historical Museum, Toms
  River, NJ 926
The Octagon House, Hudson, WI 1600
Octagon House-First Kindergarten in
  America, Watertown, WI 1625
Octave Chanute Aerospace Museum,
  Rantoul, IL 453
O'Fallon Historical Museum, Baker, MT 840
Office of Historic Alexandria, Alexandria,
  VA 1494
Ogden Union Station Museums, Ogden,
  UT 1468
Ohef Sholom Temple Archives, Norfolk,
  VA 1523
Ohio Historical Society, Columbus, OH ...1158
Okefenokee Heritage Center, Waycross,
  GA 391
Oklahoma City National Memorial,
  Oklahoma City, OK 1209
Oklahoma Museum of History, Oklahoma
  City, OK 1210
Oklahoma Route 66 Museum, Clinton,
  OK 1198
Oklahoma Territorial Museum, Guthrie,
  OK 1202
Oktibbeha County Heritage Museum,
  Starkville, MS 808
Old Arsenal Powder Magazine Museum,
  Baton Rouge, LA 587
Old Barracks Museum, Trenton, NJ 927
Old Brutus Historical Society, Inc.,
  Weedsport, NY 1084

Old Capitol Museum, Iowa City, IA 520
Old Cathedral Museum, Saint Louis, MO....836
Old Coal Mine Museum, Madrid, NM.........943
Old Colony Historical Society, Taunton,
  MA 714
Old Court House Museum-Eva Whitaker
  Davis Memorial, Vicksburg, MS 809
The Old Courthouse Heritage Museum,
  Inverness, FL 313
Old Courthouse Museum, Santa Ana, CA....178
Old Cowtown Museum, Wichita, KS 562
Old Davie School Historical Museum,
  Davie, FL 302
Old Depot Museum, Selma, AL 18
Old Dominion Railway Museum,
  Richmond, VA 1531
Old Exchange & Provost Dungeon,
  Charleston, SC 1326
Old Firehouse Museum, Greenville, MS......800
Old Florida Museum, Saint Augustine,
  FL 339
Old Fort Harrod State Park Mansion
  Museum, Harrodsburg, KY 570
Old Fort House Museum, Fort Edward,
  NY 991
Old Fort Meade Museum and Historic
  Research Association, Fort Meade, SD .1347
Old Greer County Museum & Hall of
  Fame, Mangum, OK 1204
Old Independence Regional Museum,
  Batesville, AR 54
Old Iron County Courthouse Museum,
  Hurley, WI 1601
Old Jail Museum, Albion, IN.......................467
The Old Jail Museum, Crawfordsville, IN...473
The Old Jail Museum, Warrenton, VA 1543
Old Lighthouse Museum, Michigan City,
  IN 491
Old Lighthouse Museum, Stonington, CT....261
Old Lincoln County Courthouse Museum,
  Lincoln, NM 942
Old Manchester Museum, Manchester,
  CT 248
Old Market House State Historic Site,
  Galena, IL 436
Old Mill Museum, Cimarron, NM................938
Old Mill Museum, El Molino Viejo - Old
  Mill Foundation, San Marino, CA............175
Old Ordinary House Museum, Hingham,
  MA 687
Old Prairie Town at Ward-Meade Historic
  Site, Topeka, KS 560
Old Sacramento Schoolhouse Museum,
  Sacramento, CA 153
Old St. Ferdinand's Shrine, Florissant,
  MO 815
Old Salem Inc., Winston-Salem, NC 1126
Old Sod Post Office, Grassy Butte, ND 1132
Old South Meeting House, Boston, MA......668
Old State House, Hartford, CT 245
Old State House Museum, Little Rock,
  AR 63
Old State House-The Bostonian Society,
  Boston, MA 668
Old Stone Fort Museum Complex,
  Schoharie, NY 1067
Old Stone House Museum, Windsor, NY ..1086
Old Sturbridge Village, Sturbridge, MA.....713
The Old Tavern Museum, Tuscaloosa, AL.....19
Old Town Hall Museum, Fifield, WI..........1597
Old Town Museum, Old Town, ME.............617
Old Town San Diego State Historic Park,
  San Diego, CA 158
Old Trail Museum, Choteau, MT 844
Old Village Hall Museum, Lindenhurst,
  NY 1009
Old Washington Historic State Park,
  Washington, AR 69
Old World Wisconsin, Eagle, WI................1595
Oldest House Museum Complex, Saint
  Augustine, FL 339

Oldest Store Museum, Saint Augustine,
  FL 339
Oldham County History Center, La
  Grange, KY 572
The Oliver Tucker Museum, Beverly, OH .1142
Olmstead Funeral & Historical Museum,
  Heber Springs, AR 59
Olympic Flight Museum, Olympia, WA 1560
103rd Ohio Volunteer Infantry Civil War
  Museum, Sheffield Lake, OH.................1185
Oneida County Historical Society, Utica,
  NY 1080
Oneida County Pioneer Museum, Malad,
  ID 407
Oneida Nation Museum, De Pere, WI........1594
Onondaga Historical Association Museum
  & Research Center, Syracuse, NY.........1077
Onslow County Museum, Richlands, NC...1117
Ontario County Historical Society,
  Canandaigua, NY 975
Ontonagon County Historical Society
  Museum, Ontonagon, MI 758
Opelousas Museum and Interpretive
  Center, Opelousas, LA 599
Opus 40 and the Quarryman's Museum,
  Saugerties, NY 1066
Orange Beach Indian and Sea Museum,
  Orange Beach, AL 18
Orange County Historical Museum,
  Hillsborough, NC 1107
Orange County Natural History Museum,
  Laguna Niguel, CA 107
Orange County Regional History Center,
  Orlando, FL 331
Orangetown Historical Museum and
  Archives, Pearl River, NY 1051
Orcas Island Historical Museum, Orcas
  Island, WA 1560
Orchard House, Concord, MA 677
Oregon Coast History Center, Newport,
  OR 1229
Oregon Historical Society, Portland, OR....1231
Oregon-Jerusalem Historical Museum,
  Oregon, OH 1181
Oregon Military Museum, Clackamas,
  OR 1221
Oregon Trail Regional Museum, Baker
  City, OR 1219
Orleans County Historical Society & The
  Old Stone House Museum,
  Brownington, VT 1477
Ortega Adobe, Ventura, CA 195
Osage County Historical Society
  Museum, Pawhuska, OK 1211
Osage County Historical Society
  Research Center, Lyndon, KS 550
Osborne Homestead Museum, Derby, CT....238
Oscar Getz Museum of Whiskey History
  And The Bardstown Historical
  Museum, Bardstown, KY 565
Ossining Historical Society Museum,
  Ossining, NY 1047
Oswego Historical Museum, Inc.,
  Oswego, KS 555
Otero Museum Association, La Junta, CO...224
Otoe County Museum of Memories,
  Syracuse, NE 873
Ottawa County Historical Museum, Port
  Clinton, OH 1183
Otter Tail County Historical Society,
  Fergus Falls, MN 775
Our House State Memorial, Gallipolis,
  OH 1165
Outagamie Museum, Appleton, WI 1589
Overfield Tavern Museum, Troy, OH 1188
Owyhee County Historical Museum,
  Murphy, ID 407
Oxford Library Museum, Oxford, MA.........701
Oxford Museum, Inc., Oxford, MD.............650
The Oyster and Maritime Museum of
  Chincoteague, Chincoteague, VA...........1501

History Museums–Continued

Oyster Bay Historical Society, Oyster Bay, NY 1049

Oysterponds Historical Society: The Museum of Orient and East Marion History, Orient, NY 1047

Ozark Heritage Arts Center & Museum, Leslie, AR...61

Ozark National Scenic Riverways, Van Buren, MO...................................839

Ozaukee County Pioneer Village, Saukville, WI................................1620

P.H. Sullivan Museum and Genealogy Library, Zionsville, IN.....................504

Pacific Aviation Museum - Pearl Harbor, Honolulu, HI....................................397

Pacific Coast Air Museum, Santa Rosa, CA...184

Pacific County Historical Museum, South Bend, WA..................................1571

Pacific University Museum, Forest Grove, OR......................................1224

Packwood House Museum, Lewisburg, PA...1268

Padre Island National Seashore, Corpus Christi, TX....................................1402

Painted Post - Erwin Museum at the Depot, Painted Post, NY........................1050

Pajaro Valley Historical Association, Watsonville, CA..........................196

Palace of the Governors/New Mexico History Museum, Santa Fe, NM..............949

Palmer Foundation Chiropractic History, Davenport, IA................................513

Palmer/Gullickson Octagon Home, West Salem, WI................................1627

Panhandle-Plains Historical Museum, Canyon, TX...................................1399

Paris-Henry County Heritage Center, Paris, TN......................................1382

Parishville Museum, Parishville, NY.........1050

Park City Historical Society & Museum, Park City, UT................................1468

The Park-McCullough House, North Bennington, VT..............................1483

Parker Tavern, Reading, MA 705

Parks, Recreation & Historic Sites Division, Georgia Dept. of Natural Resources, Atlanta, GA.....................362

Parsonsfield-Porter Historical Society, Porter, ME...618

Pasadena Museum of History, Pasadena, CA...140

Pascack Historical Society, Park Ridge, NJ...920

Passaic County Historical Society & Lambert Castle Museum, Paterson, NJ ...920

Patten Lumbermen's Museum, Inc., Patten, ME...618

Patterson Inn Museum/Corning - Painted Post Historical Society, Corning, NY 982

Paul Bunyan Logging Camp Museum, Eau Claire, WI................................1596

Paul Dresser Memorial Birthplace, Terre Haute, IN...500

Paul H. Karshner Memorial Museum, Puyallup, WA................................1564

Paul Revere House/Paul Revere Memorial Association, Boston, MA 668

Pauline E. Glidden Toy Museum, Ashland, NH...883

Paunsaugunt Wildlife Museum, Bryce, UT...1464

Pawnee Bill Ranch and Museum, Pawnee, OK...1212

Pawnee City Historical Society & Museum, Pawnee City, NE.....................871

Paynes Creek Historic State Park, Bowling Green, FL..............................297

The Peace Museum, Chicago, IL.................426

Peaks of Otter Visitor Center, Bedford, VA...1496

Pearce Collections Museum, Corsicana, TX...1402

Pearl S. Buck Birthplace Foundation, Hillsboro, WV................................1582

Pearson Air Museum, Vancouver, WA 1576

The Peary-MacMillan Arctic Museum, Brunswick, ME.......................................608

Pedaling History Bicycle Museum, Orchard Park, NY................................1047

The Peekskill Museum, Peekskill, NY.......1051

Peirce Mill and Peirce Barn, Washington, DC...289

Pejepscot Historical Society, Brunswick, ME...608

Pembina State Museum, Pembina, ND.......1135

The Pena-Peck House, Saint Augustine, FL...339

Pendarvis State Historic Site, Mineral Point, WI..1614

Pendleton District Historical, Recreational and Tourism Commission, Pendleton, SC...1339

Pendleton Historic Foundation, Pendleton, SC......................................1339

Pennsylvania Anthracite Heritage Museum, Scranton, PA.........................1299

Pennsylvania Historical & Museum Commission, Harrisburg, PA..................1259

Pennsylvania Longrifle Museum, Nazareth, PA......................................1273

Pennsylvania Lumber Museum, Galeton, PA...1254

Pennsylvania Trolley Museum, Washington, PA......................................1305

Pennyroyal Area Museum, Hopkinsville, KY...572

Penobscot Marine Museum, Searsport, ME...622

Pensacola Historical Society Museum, Pensacola, FL......................................336

Perkins History Museum, Perkins School for the Blind, Watertown, MA.................716

Perry's Victory & International Peace Memorial, Put-in-Bay, OH.................1183

Peshtigo Fire Museum, Peshtigo, WI 1617

Peter Rice Homestead, Home of Marlborough Historical Society, Inc., Marlboro, MA.......................................693

Peter Whitmer Sr. Home and Visitors Center, Waterloo, NY...........................1083

Peter Yegen Jr. Yellowstone County Museum, Billings, MT.........................841

Petersburg National Battlefield, Petersburg, VA......................................1525

Petersen Automotive Museum, Los Angeles, CA...121

Petersham Historical Society, Inc., Petersham, MA.......................................702

Petrified Forest of the Black Hills, Piedmont, SD......................................1353

The Petroleum Museum, Midland, TX.......1439

Pettaquamscutt Historical Society, Kingston, RI......................................1312

Pettis County Historical Society, Sedalia, MO...838

Phillips County Museum, Helena, AR...........59

Phillips County Museum, Holyoke, CO.......222

Phillips Historical Society, Phillips, ME 618

Philmont Museums, Cimarron, NM.............938

Phoenix Fire Museum, Mobile, AL................15

Phoenix Museum of History, Phoenix, AZ...41

Piatt Castles, West Liberty, OH 1190

Piatt County Museum, Monticello, IL.........446

Pickens County Museum of Art & History, Pickens, SC.................................1340

The Pierce Manse/New Hampshire Political Library, Concord, NH...............885

Pike County Historical Society, Milford, PA...1272

Pilgrim Hall Museum, Plymouth, MA 703

Pilgrim Monument and Provincetown Museum, Provincetown, MA.................704

Pima Air & Space Museum, Tucson, AZ.......50

Pimeria Alta Historical Society, Nogales, AZ...37

Pinal County Historical Society and Museum, Florence, AZ.........................34

Pine Bluff/Jefferson County Historical Museum, Pine Bluff, AR.........................66

Pine County Historical Society, Askov, MN...768

Pink Palace Family of Museums, Memphis, TN......................................1375

Pioneer Arizona Living History Village & Museum, Phoenix, AZ..........................41

Pioneer Auto Museum, Murdo, SD 1352

Pioneer Corner Museum, New Holstein, WI...1615

Pioneer Farm Museum and Ohop Indian Village, Eatonville, WA........................1552

Pioneer Florida Museum Association, Inc., Dade City, FL...............................302

Pioneer Heritage Center, Cavalier, ND.......1129

Pioneer Heritage Center, LSU-Shreveport, Shreveport, LA......................................601

Pioneer Historical Museum of South Dakota, Hot Springs, SD.....................1348

Pioneer-Krier Museum, Ashland, KS 532

Pioneer Mothers Memorial Cabin, Saint Paul, OR...1235

Pioneer Museum, Watford City, ND.........1137

Pioneer Museum, Wild Rose, WI 1628

Pioneer Museum & The Big Stampede, Fairbanks, AK..24

Pioneer Museum and Vereins Kirche, Fredericksburg, TX................................1419

Pioneer Museum - Martin County Historical Society, Fairmont, MN............775

Pioneer Museum of Alabama, Troy, AL.........18

Pioneer Settlement for the Creative Arts, Barberville, FL......................................295

Pioneer Trails Regional Museum, Bowman, ND......................................1129

Pioneer Village, Farmington, UT...............1465

Pioneer Woman Statue & Museum, Ponca City, OK......................................1212

Pioneers, Trail Drivers and Texas Rangers Memorial Museum, San Antonio, TX......................................1449

Piper Aviation Museum Foundation, Lock Haven, PA......................................1269

Pipestone County Historical Museum, Pipestone, MN......................................786

Pipestone National Monument, Pipestone, MN...787

Pirate Soul Museum, Key West, FL 319

Pittsford Historical Society Museum, Pittsford, VT......................................1484

Placer County Museums, Auburn, CA...........72

Plains Conservation Center, Aurora, CO......202

Plains Indians and Pioneers Museum, Woodward, OK......................................1217

Plainsman Museum, Aurora, NE 856

Plantation Agriculture Museum, Scott, AR...67

Plantation Historical Museum, Plantation, FL...337

Plimoth Plantation Inc., Plymouth, MA 703

Plumas County Museum, Quincy, CA..........144

Plymouth Historical Museum, Plymouth, MI...760

Plymouth Historical Society, Inc., Plymouth, PA......................................1295

Pocahontas County Iowa Historical Society Museum, Laurens, IA 522

Pocahontas County Museum, Marlinton, WV...1584

Point Fermin Lighthouse, San Pedro, CA....176

Pointe Coupee Museum, New Roads, LA.....599

Polish American Museum, Port Washington, NY.....................................1054

Polish Museum of America, Chicago, IL.....426
Polk County Historical Museum, Bartow, FL................295
The Polk County Historical Society, Cedartown, GA................368
Polk County Historical Society, Crookston, MN................771
Polk County Memorial Museum, Livingston, TX................1434
Polk County Museum, Balsam Lake, WI...1590
Polson Museum, Hoquiam, WA................1556
Ponce DeLeon Inlet Lighthouse Preservation Association, Inc., Ponce Inlet, FL................337
Pony Express Museum, Saint Joseph, MO................831
Pope County Historical Society, Glenwood, MN................776
Pope's Tavern Museum, Florence, AL............9
Poplar Grove Historic Plantation, Wilmington, NC................1123
Port Gamble Historic Museum, Port Gamble, WA................1562
Port Huron Museum, Port Huron, MI.........761
Portage County Historical Society, Ravenna, OH................1183
Portage County Historical Society, Stevens Point, WI................1623
Porter-Phelps-Huntington Foundation, Inc., Hadley, MA................685
Porterville Historical Museum, Porterville, CA................144
Portholes Into the Past, Medina, OH.........1176
Portland Harbor Museum, South Portland, ME................623
Portsmouth Athenaeum, Portsmouth, NH.....894
Portsmouth Historical Society, Portsmouth, RI................1316
Portsmouth Museums, Portsmouth, VA......1526
Post Rock Museum, La Crosse, KS.............547
Postville Courthouse State Historic Site, Lincoln, IL................442
Potsdam Public Museum, Potsdam, NY.....1054
Potter County Historical Society, Coudersport, PA................1248
Pound Ridge Society/Museum, Pound Ridge, NY................1055
Powder Magazine, Charleston, SC.............1326
Powell County Museum, Deer Lodge, MT................845
Powers Museum, Carthage, MO................812
Prairie Homestead, Philip, SD................1353
Prairie Trails Museum of Wayne County, Corydon, IA................512
Prairie Village, Madison, SD................1351
Pratt Building - Cohasset Historical Society, Cohasset, MA................676
Pratt County Historical Society Museum, Pratt, KS................556
Pratt Museum, Homer, AK................25
President Andrew Johnson Museum and Library, Greeneville, TN................1366
The Presidential Museum and Leadership Library, Odessa, TX................1441
Presidential Pet Museum, Lothian, MD.......649
Presidents Park Sculpture Garden, Lead, SD................1351
Presidio La Bahia, Goliad, TX................1423
Prestwould Foundation, Clarksville, VA.....1501
Pricketts Fort, Fairmont, WV................1581
Prince William Forest Park Visitor Center, Triangle, VA................1541
Pro Rodeo Hall of Fame & Museum of the American Cowboy, Colorado Springs, CO................207
Proprietary House, The Royal Governor's Mansion, Perth Amboy, NJ................921
Providence Canyon State Park, Lumpkin, GA................377
Prudence Crandall Museum, Canterbury, CT................237

The Public Library of Nashville and Davidson County, Nashville, TN...........1380
Public Museum of West Michigan, Grand Rapids, MI................744
Pueblo County Historical Society Museum and Edward H. Broadhead Library, Pueblo, CO................230
Pueblo Weisbrod Aircraft Museum, Pueblo, CO................230
Puget Sound Coast Artillery Museum at Fort Worden, Port Townsend, WA.........1562
Putnam Cottage, Greenwich, CT................243
Putnam County Historical Society & Foundry School Museum, Cold Spring, NY................979
Putnam County Historical Society Museum, Kalida, OH................1169
Putnam County Museum, Greencastle, IN...479
Putnam Museum of History & Natural Science, Davenport, IA................513
Putney Historical Society, Putney, VT.......1485

Quasdorf Blacksmith and Wagon Museum, Dows, IA................516
Queen Emma Summer Palace, Honolulu, HI................398
Queen Mary Museum, Long Beach, CA......111
Quiet Valley Living Historical Farm, Stroudsburg, PA................1302
The Quilters Hall of Fame, Inc., Marion, IN................490

R.E. Olds Transportation Museum, Lansing, MI................751
R.P. Strathearn Historical Park and Museum, Simi Valley, CA................187
Rachel Carson Homestead, Springdale, PA................1301
Racine Heritage Museum, Racine, WI.......1619
Radio & Television Museum, Bowie, MD...638
Railroad and Heritage Museum Inc., Temple, TX................1454
Railroad Museum of Long Island, Riverhead, NY................1057
Railroad Museum of Pennsylvania, Strasburg, PA................1302
Railroaders Memorial Museum, Altoona, PA................1240
Railways to Yesterday, Inc., Rockhill Furnace, PA................1297
Raleigh City Museum, Raleigh, NC...........1117
Ralls Historical Museum, Ralls, TX...........1445
Ralph Mark Gilbert Civil Rights Museum, Savannah, GA................386
Ralph Milliken Museum, Los Banos, CA....122
Ralston Historical Association, John Ralston Museum, Mendham, NJ................911
Rancho La Patera - The Stow House G.V.H.S., Goleta, CA................100
Rancho Los Cerritos Historic Site, Long Beach, CA................111
Randall Library, Stow, MA................713
Randolph County Historical Museum, Winchester, IN................503
Randolph County Museum (At Beverly), Beverly, WV................1580
Randolph Historical Society, Inc., Randolph, VT................1485
Rangeley Lakes Region Logging Museum, Rangeley, ME................620
Rangely Outdoor Museum, Rangely, CO.....231
Rankin Museum, Rankin, TX................1445
Rankin Museum, Inc., Ellerbe, NC................1100
Ransom County Historical Society, Fort Ransom, ND................1131
Raton Museum, Raton, NM................945
Reading Historical Society Museum, Reading, OH................1184
Red Clay State Historic Park, Cleveland, TN................1363
Red Hill-Patrick Henry National Memorial, Brookneal, VA................1498

Red River Historical Museum, Sherman, TX................1452
Red River Valley Museum, Vernon, TX.....1457
Redington Museum, Waterville, ME............625
Reedville Fishermen's Museum, Reedville, VA................1527
Refugio County Museum, Refugio, TX.....1445
Reginald F. Lewis Museum of Maryland African American History and Culture, Baltimore, MD................636
Rehoboth Art League, Inc., Rehoboth Beach, DE................272
Remick Country Doctor Museum and Farm, Tamworth, NH................896
Reno County Museum, Hutchinson, KS......545
Rensselaer County Historical Society, Troy, NY................1079
Renton Historical Society and Museum, Renton, WA................1564
Reshaw Exhibit, Evansville, WY................1632
Reston Museum, Reston, VA................1527
Retired Correctional Peace Officers Museum at Folsom Prison, Represa, CA................148
Reverend Dan Foster House, Museum of the Weathersfield Historical Society, Weathersfield, VT................1489
Rhode Island Black Heritage Society, Providence, RI................1318
Rhode Island Historical Society, Providence, RI................1318
Rice County Museum of History, Faribault, MN................775
The Rice Museum, Georgetown, SC...........1333
Richard I. Bong WWII Heritage Center, Superior, WI................1624
Richard Salter Storrs House, Longmeadow, MA................691
Richardson-Bates House Museum, Oswego, NY................1048
Richey Historical Society, Richey, MT.........852
Richland County Historical Museum, Wahpeton, ND................1137
Richland County Museum, Lexington, OH................1172
Richmond Museum of History, Richmond, CA................148
Riddick's Folly, Suffolk, VA................1539
Rifle Creek Museum, Rifle, CO................231
Rikard's Mill Historical Park, Beatrice, AL................3
Riley County Historical Museum, Manhattan, KS................551
Riley House Museum of African American History & Culture, Tallahassee, FL................348
Rim Country Museum, Payson, AZ................38
Rimrocker Historical Museum of West Montrose County, Naturita, CO................229
Rio Grande Valley Museum, Harlingen, TX................1423
Rio Vista Museum, Rio Vista, CA................148
Riordan Mansion State Historic Park, Flagstaff, AZ................33
Rios-Caledonia Adobe, San Miguel, CA......175
Ritz Theatre & LaVilla Museum, Jacksonville, FL................315
River Museum, Wellsville, OH................1190
Riversdale House Mansion, Riverdale Park, MD................651
Riverside Museum, La Crosse, WI............1603
Riverton Museum, Riverton, WY................1637
Roane County Museum of History & Art, Kingston, TN................1369
Roanoke Island Festival Park; Homeport of the "Elizabeth II", Manteo, NC.........1110
Roaring Twenties Antique Car Museum, Hood, VA................1511
Roberson Museum and Science Center, Binghamton, NY................962

History Museums–Continued

Robert C. Williams American Museum of Papermaking at Georgia Tech, Atlanta, GA.................363

Robert Frost Stone House Museum, Shaftsbury, VT.................1487

Robert Louis Stevenson House, Monterey, CA.................128

Robert Louis Stevenson Silverado Museum, Saint Helena, CA.................154

Robert S. Kerr Museum, Poteau, OK.................1212

Robert Toombs House, Washington, GA.................391

Roberts County Museum, Miami, TX.................1438

Robidoux Row Museum, Saint Joseph, MO.................831

Rochester Hills Museum at Van Hoosen Farm, Rochester Hills, MI.................762

Rochester Museum & Science Center, Rochester, NY.................1059

The Rock and Roll Hall of Fame and Museum, Cleveland, OH.................1155

Rock County Historical Society, Janesville, WI.................1601

Rock Creek Station State Historic Park, Fairbury, NE.................860

Rock Island Arsenal Museum, Rock Island, IL.................454

Rock Island County Historical Society, Moline, IL.................445

Rock Springs Historical Museum, Rock Springs, WY.................1638

Rockbridge Historical Society, Lexington, VA.................1513

Rockingham Free Public Library and Museum, Bellows Falls, VT.................1476

Rocky Ford Historical Museum, Rocky Ford, CO.................231

Rocky Mount Museum, Piney Flats, TN.....1383

Rocky Reach Dam, Wenatchee, WA.................1577

Rogers Historical Museum, Rogers, AR.................67

Rollo Jamison Museum, Platteville, WI.....1617

Rome Area History Museum, Rome, GA.....382

Rome Historical Society Museum, Rome, NY.................1061

Ronald Reagan Presidential Library and Museum, Simi Valley, CA.................187

Roniger Memorial Museum, Cottonwood Falls, KS.................536

Roosevelt Campobello International Park Commission, Lubec, ME.................614

Roosevelt County Museum, Portales, NM.....944

Roscoe Village Foundation, Coshocton, OH.................1159

Rose Hill Museum, Bay Village, OH.................1141

Rose Hill Plantation State Historic Site, Union, SC.................1343

Rose Island Lighthouse, Rose Island, RI.....1319

Rose Lawn Museum, Cartersville, GA.................368

Roseau County Historical Museum and Interpretive Center, Roseau, MN.................788

Rosebud County Pioneer Museum, Forsyth, MT.................846

Rosenbach Museum & Library, Philadelphia, PA.................1287

Rosicrucian Egyptian Museum, San Jose, CA.................172

The Rotch-Jones-Duff House & Garden Museum, Inc., New Bedford, MA.................697

Roth Living Farm Museum of Delaware Valley College, North Wales, PA.................1274

Rothschild Petersen Patent Model Museum, Cazenovia, NY.................977

Rowan Museum, Inc., Salisbury, NC.................1118

Rowley Historical Society, Rowley, MA.....706

Roxbury Heritage State Park, Roxbury, MA.................706

Royal Gorge Regional Museum & History Center, Canon City, CO.................205

Royall House Association, Medford, MA.....694

Royellou Museum, Mount Dora, FL.................327

Ruggles House Society, Columbia Falls, ME.................609

Rumford Historical Association, North Woburn, MA.................699

Runestone Museum, Alexandria, MN.................767

Rural Farming & Agriculture Museum, Warner, OK.................1216

Rural Life Museum & Windrush Gardens, Baton Rouge, LA.................587

Rushmore Borglum Story, Keystone, SD.....1350

Rusk County Historical Society, Ladysmith, WI.................1604

Ruth and Charles Gilb Arcadia Historical Museum, Arcadia, CA.................71

Rutherford B. Hayes Presidential Center, Fremont, OH.................1165

Rutland Historical Society, Rutland, VT.....1486

The Rye Historical Society and Square House Museum, Rye, NY.................1062

S.C. Tobacco Museum, Mullins, SC.................1337

S.S. Meteor Maritime Museum, Superior, WI.................1624

Sacajawea Interpretive Center, Pasco, WA.1561

Saco Museum, Saco, ME.................621

Sacramento Archives and Museum Collection Center, Sacramento, CA.................153

Sacramento Mountains Historical Museum, Cloudcroft, NM.................938

Safe Haven Museum and Education Center, Oswego, NY.................1048

Safety Harbor Museum of Regional History, Safety Harbor, FL.................338

Sag Harbor Whaling & Historical Museum, Sag Harbor, NY.................1063

Saguache County Museum, Saguache, CO.................231

St. Albans Historical Museum, Saint Albans, VT.................1486

St. Augustine Lighthouse & Museum, Inc., Saint Augustine, FL.................340

St. Charles County Historical Society, Inc., Saint Charles, MO.................830

St. Charles Heritage Center, Saint Charles, IL.................457

St. Clair County Historical Society, Belleville, IL.................412

St. Clements Island and Piney Point Museums, Colton's Point, MD.................641

St. Francis County Museum, Forrest City, AR.................57

Saint-Gaudens National Historic Site, Cornish, NH.................885

St. John's Northwestern Military Academy Archives & Museum, Delafield, WI.................1595

St. Joseph Museum Inc., Saint Joseph, MO.................831

St. Lawrence County Historical Association - Silas Wright House, Canton, NY.................975

The St. Louis County Historical Society, Duluth, MN.................773

St. Petersburg Museum of History, Saint Petersburg, FL.................342

St. Photios Greek Orthodox National Shrine, Saint Augustine, FL.................340

Ste. Genevieve Museum, Sainte Genevieve, MO.................838

Sainte Marie among the Iroquois, Liverpool, NY.................1010

The Salem Museum, Salem, VA.................1536

Salem Witch Museum, Salem, MA.................707

Salisbury Historical Society, Salisbury, NH.................896

Salmon Brook Historical Society, Inc., Granby, CT.................242

Salt Museum, Liverpool, NY.................1010

Salter Museum, Argonia, KS.................532

The Salvation Army Southern Historical Center & Museum, Atlanta, GA.................363

Sam Brown Log House, Browns Valley, MN.................770

Sam Houston Memorial Museum, Huntsville, TX.................1430

Sam Houston Regional Library & Research Center, Liberty, TX.................1434

Samoa Cookhouse & Logging Museum, Samoa, CA.................155

San Antonio Conservation Society, San Antonio, TX.................1449

San Antonio de Pala Asistencia, Pala, CA.....138

San Antonio Missions National Historical Park, San Antonio, TX.................1449

San Benito County Historical Society Museum, Hollister, CA.................103

San Bernardino County Museum, Redlands, CA.................147

San Buenaventura Mission Museum, Ventura, CA.................195

San Diego Air & Space Museum, San Diego, CA.................159

San Diego Model Railroad Museum, Inc., San Diego, CA.................159

San Dieguito Heritage Museum, Encinitas, CA.................92

San Fernando Mission, Mission Hills, CA.....126

San Fernando Valley Historical Society, Inc., Mission Hills, CA.................126

San Francisco African American Historical and Cultural Society, Inc., San Francisco, CA.................168

San Francisco Maritime National Historical Park, San Francisco, CA.................169

San Gabriel Mission Museum, San Gabriel, CA.................171

San Jacinto Museum, San Jacinto, CA.................171

San Jacinto Museum of History Association, La Porte, TX.................1433

San Joaquin County Historical Society & Museum, Lodi, CA.................109

San Juan Bautista State Historic Park, San Juan Bautista, CA.................173

San Juan County Historical Society Museum, Silverton, CO.................232

San Juan Historical Society, Friday Harbor, WA.................1555

San Juan Island National Historical Park, Friday Harbor, WA.................1555

San Juan National Historic Site, San Juan, PR.................1643

San Lorenzo Valley Museum, Boulder Creek, CA.................79

San Luis Obispo County Historical Museum, San Luis Obispo, CA.................174

San Marcos de Apalache Historic State Park, Saint Marks, FL.................340

San Mateo County Historical Association and Museum, Redwood City, CA.................147

San Quentin Prison Museum, San Quentin, CA.................176

Sanchez Adobe Historic Site, Pacifica, CA.................138

Sand Springs Cultural & Historical Museum, Sand Springs, OK.................1213

Sandusky Library Follett House Museum, Sandusky, OH.................1185

Sandwich Glass Museum, Sandwich, MA.....708

Sandwich Historical Society, Center Sandwich, NH.................884

Sandy Bay Historical Society & Museums, Inc., Rockport, MA.................705

Sandy Spring Museum, Sandy Spring, MD.................653

Sanford Museum, Sanford, FL.................343

Sanilac County Historical Museum and Village, Port Sanilac, MI.................761

Santa Barbara Courthouse, Santa Barbara, CA.................179

The Santa Barbara Historical Museum, Santa Barbara, CA.................179

Santa Barbara Trust for Historic Preservation, Santa Barbara, CA.................180

Santa Fe Trail Center, Larned, KS.................547

Santa Fe Trail Museum, Ingalls, KS.................545

Santa Fe Trail Museum/Trinidad History Museum, Trinidad, CO......234
Santa Maria Museum of Flight, Inc., Santa Maria, CA......183
Santa Maria Valley Historical Museum, Santa Maria, CA......183
Santa Monica Mountains National Recreation Area, Thousand Oaks, CA.....191
Sappington House Museum, Crestwood, MO......814
Sapulpa Historical Museum, Sapulpa, OK.1213
Saratoga County Historical Society, Brookside Museum, Ballston Spa, NY....960
Saratoga Museum, Saratoga, WY......1638
The Sargent House Museum, Gloucester, MA......684
Satterlee Clark House, Horicon, WI......1600
Saugus Iron Works National Historic Site, Saugus, MA......708
Sauk Prairie Area Historical Society, Inc., Prairie du Sac, WI......1619
Saunders County Historical Complex, Wahoo, NE......874
Sautee-Nacoochee Center, Sautee, GA......384
Savannah History Museum, Savannah, GA......386
Sawin Memorial Building, Dover, MA......680
Scantic Academy Museum, East Windsor Historical Society, Inc., East Windsor, CT......239
Scarborough Historical Museum, Scarborough, ME......621
Schenectady County Historical Society, Schenectady, NY......1067
Schenectady Museum and Suits-Bueche Planetarium, Schenectady, NY......1067
Schiele Museum of Natural History and Lynn Planetarium, Gastonia, NC......1102
Schmidt House Museum & Research Library, Grants Pass, OR......1225
Schminck Memorial Museum, Lakeview, OR......1227
Scholte House Museum, Pella, IA......527
The Schomburg Center for Research in Black Culture, New York, NY......1038
School of Nations Museum, Elsah, IL......433
Schoolcraft County Historical Society, Manistique, MI......753
Schoolhouse History & Art Center, Colstrip, MT......844
Schoolhouse Museum of the Ridgewood Historical Society, Inc., Ridgewood, NJ......923
The Schuette Biermann Farmhouse Museum, Elk Grove Village, IL......432
Schuyler County Historical Society, Inc., Montour Falls, NY......1015
Schuyler-Hamilton House, Morristown, NJ......914
Schuyler Jail Museum, Rushville, IL......456
Schwenkfelder Library & Heritage Center, Pennsburg, PA......1275
Scotts Bluff National Monument, Gering, NE......861
Scottsville Museum, Scottsville, VA......1536
Scurry County Museum, Snyder, TX......1453
Sea Cliff Village Museum, Sea Cliff, NY..1068
Seabrook Village, Midway, GA......380
Seaford Historical Museum, Seaford, NY..1068
Seagraves-Loop Museum and Art Center Inc., Seagraves, TX......1452
Searchlight Historic Museum & Mining Park, Searchlight, NV......882
Seashore Trolley Museum, Kennebunkport, ME......613
Seaside Museum & Historical Society, Seaside, OR......1236
Sedgwick-Brooklin Historical Society, Sedgwick, ME......622
Seminole Canyon State Park and Historic Site, Comstock, TX......1401
Seminole Nation Museum, Wewoka, OK...1217

Senate House State Historic Site, Kingston, NY......1008
Senator John Heinz Pittsburgh Regional History Center, Pittsburgh, PA......1294
Seneca County Museum, Tiffin, OH......1186
The Sequoyah Birthplace Museum, Vonore, TN......1385
Serra Museum/San Diego Historical Society, San Diego, CA......161
1768 Jeremiah Lee Mansion, Marblehead, MA......693
1761 Pownalborough Courthouse, Dresden, ME......610
The Sevier County Historical Museum, De Queen, AR......56
Sewall-Belmont House and Museum, Washington, DC......290
Seward Museum, Seward, AK......27
Seymour Community Museum, Seymour, WI......1621
Shaftsbury Historical Society, Shaftsbury, VT......1487
Shaker Historical Society, Shaker Heights, OH......1185
The Shaker Museum and Library, Old Chatham, NY......1045
Shaker Museum at South Union, South Union, KY......583
Shaker Village of Pleasant Hill, Harrodsburg, KY......571
Sharon Historical Society, Sharon, CT......260
Sharpsteen Museum, Calistoga, CA......80
Shasta College Museum & Research Center, Redding, CA......146
Shaw Island Library & Historical Society, Shaw Island, WA......1570
Shawano County Historical Society, Inc., Shawano, WI......1621
Shawnee Town, Shawnee, KS......558
Shelburne Museum, Inc., Shelburne, VT...1487
Shelby County Museum, Center, TX......1399
Sheldon Museum and Cultural Center, Inc., Haines, AK......25
Shelter House Society, Emmaus, PA......1251
Sherman Gardens, Corona del Mar, CA......87
Sherwin Miller Museum of Jewish Art, Tulsa, OK......1216
Sherwood-Davidson House, Newark, OH..1178
Shiloh Museum of Ozark History, Springdale, AR......68
Shimmin Tveit Museum, Forbes, ND......1131
Shippensburg Historical Society Museum, Shippensburg, PA......1300
Shirley Plantation, Charles City, VA......1498
Shoal Creek Living History Museum, Kansas City, MO......822
Shore Line Trolley Museum, East Haven, CT......239
Shoreline Historical Museum, Seattle, WA......1569
Shores Memorial Museum, Lyndon Center, VT......1481
Shorter Mansion Museum, Eufaula, AL......8
Shortgrass Country Museum Society, Sayre, OK......1213
Shoshone Bannock Tribal Museum, Fort Hall, ID......406
Sidney Historical Association, Sidney, NY......1069
Siege Museum (The Petersburg Museums), Petersburg, VA......1525
Silent Wings Museum, Lubbock, TX......1435
Siloam Springs Museum, Siloam Springs, AR......68
Silt Historical Society, Silt, CO......232
Silver City Museum, Silver City, NM......951
Silver Cliff Museum, Silver Cliff, CO......232
Silver River Museum & Environmental Education Center, Ocala, FL......330
Silvercreek Museum, Freeport, IL......435
The Simon Paneak Memorial Museum, Anaktuvuk Pass, AK......21

Simsbury Historical Society, Phelps Tavern, Museum & Homestead, Simsbury, CT......260
Sinclair Lewis House Museum & Interpretive Center/Museum, Sauk Centre, MN......793
Sioux City Public Museum, Sioux City, IA......528
Sioux Empire Medical Museum, Sioux Falls, SD......1356
Siouxland Heritage Museums, Sioux Falls, SD......1357
Siskiyou County Museum, Yreka, CA......200
Sisson Museum, Mount Shasta, CA......129
Sitka National Historical Park, Sitka, AK......28
The Sixth Floor Museum at Dealey Plaza, Dallas, TX......1407
Skagit County Historical Museum, La Conner, WA......1557
Skagway Museum & Archives, Skagway, AK......28
Skiatook Museum, Skiatook, OK......1214
The Skinner Museum of Mount Holyoke College, South Hadley, MA......709
Skirball Cultural Center, Los Angeles, CA......121
Skirball Museum Cincinnati Hebrew Union College-Jewish Institute of Religion, Cincinnati, OH......1151
Skowhegan History House Inc., Skowhegan, ME......622
Sky City Cultural Center, Pueblo of Acoma, NM......944
The Skyscraper Museum, New York, NY..1038
Slate Valley Museum, Granville, NY......996
Slater Mill Historic Site, Pawtucket, RI.....1315
Slidell Museum, Slidell, LA......602
Sloan Museum, Flint, MI......742
Sloane-Stanley Museum and Kent Furnace, Kent, CT......247
Smith County Historical Society, Tyler, TX......1456
Smith-McDowell House Museum, Asheville, NC......1090
Smith Robertson Museum & Cultural Center, Jackson, MS......804
Smith-Zimmermann Heritage Museum, Madison, SD......1351
Smithsonian Institution, Washington, DC.....290
Smokey Bear Museum, Capitan, NM......937
Smoky Hill Museum, Salina, KS......557
Smyrna Museum, Smyrna, DE......272
Snake River Heritage Center, Weiser, ID.....410
Snoqualmie Valley Historical Museum, North Bend, WA......1559
Snowmobile Hall of Fame and Museum, Saint Germain, WI......1620
Snyder Museum & Creative Arts Center, Bastrop, LA......585
The Society of the Cincinnati at Anderson House, Washington, DC......291
Sod House Museum, Gothenburg, NE......862
Sod House Museum, Aline, OK......1195
Soldiers & Sailors Memorial Building, Huntington, NY......1001
The Somerset County Historical Society, Inc., Princess Anne, MD......650
Somerset Historical Center, Somerset, PA.1300
Sonoma County Museum, Santa Rosa, CA......185
Sonoma State Historic Park, Sonoma, CA...188
Sophienburg Museum & Archives Inc., New Braunfels, TX......1440
South Bannock County Historical Center, Lava Hot Springs, ID......407
South Boston-Halifax County Museum of Fine Arts & History, South Boston, VA......1536
South Carolina Confederate Relic Room and Museum, Columbia, SC......1330
South Carolina Cotton Museum, Bishopville, SC......1322

History Museums–Continued

South Carolina Department of Parks, Recreation and Tourism, Columbia, SC..........1330

South Carolina Law Enforcement Officers Hall of Fame, Columbia, SC.................1330

South Carolina Tennis Hall of Fame, Belton, SC..........1321

South Charleston Museum, South Charleston, WV..........1586

South Coast Railroad Museum at Goleta Depot, Goleta, CA..........100

South County Museum Inc., Narragansett, RI..........1313

South Dakota Hall of Fame, Chamberlain, SD..........1345

South Dakota National Guard Museum, Pierre, SD..........1353

South Dakota Tractor Museum, Kimball, SD..........1350

South Florida Museum, Bishop Planetarium & Parker Manatee Aquarium, Bradenton, FL..........297

South Hero Bicentennial Museum, South Hero, VT..........1487

South Holland Historical Society, South Holland, IL..........457

South Park City Museum, Fairplay, CO.......215

South Pass City State Historic Site, South Pass City, WY..........1638

South Street Seaport Museum, New York, NY..........1039

South Sutton Old Store Museum, South Sutton, NH..........896

South Texas Museum, Alice, TX..........1386

Southampton Historical Museum, Southampton, NY..........1070

Southdown Plantation House/The Terrebonne Museum, Houma, LA..........589

Southeast Florida Regional Preservation Office, Florida Division of Historical Resources, Fort Lauderdale, FL..........308

Southeast Missouri Regional Museum, Cape Girardeau, MO..........812

Southeast Museum Association, Inc., Brewster, NY..........964

Southeastern Architectural Archive, New Orleans, LA..........598

Southern Forest Heritage Museum, Long Leaf, LA..........591

The Southern Museum of Civil War and Locomotive History, Kennesaw, GA.......375

Southern Museum of Flight, Birmingham, AL..........6

Southern Oregon Historical Society, Jacksonville, OR..........1226

Southern Ute Cultural Center and Museum, Ignacio, CO..........223

Southwest Dairy Museum, Sulphur Springs, TX..........1454

Southwest Florida Museum of History, Fort Myers, FL..........309

Southwest School of Art & Craft, San Antonio, TX..........1450

Southwest Virginia Museum Historical State Park, Big Stone Gap, VA..........1497

Space Farms Zoological Park and Museum, Sussex, NJ..........925

The Spanish Institute, New York, NY........1039

Spartanburg County Regional Museum of History, Spartanburg, SC..........1341

Spellman Museum of Stamps and Postal History, Weston, MA..........719

Spirit of '76 Museum, Wellington, OH......1190

SPJST Library Archives & Museum, Temple, TX..........1455

Spokane House Interpretive Center, Nine Mile Falls, WA..........1559

The Sports Museum, Boston, MA..........669

Spring Grove Hospital Center, Alumni Museum, Catonsville, MD..........639

Spring Street Historical Museum, Shreveport, LA..........602

Spring Valley Community Historical Society, Inc., Spring Valley, MN..........794

Springfield Armory National Historic Site, Springfield, MA..........710

Springfield Art & Historical Society - Miller Art Center, Springfield, VT.........1488

Springfield Historical Society, Springfield, NJ..........925

Springfield Museums - Connecticut Valley Historical Museum, Springfield, MA..........710

Springs Museum, Springs, PA..........1301

Spurlock Museum, University of Illinois at Urbana-Champaign, Urbana, IL..........462

Stagecoach Inn Museum Complex, Newbury Park, CA..........130

Stamford Historical Society, Inc., Stamford, CT..........260

Stanley Museum, Inc., Kingfield, ME..........613

Stanley-Whitman House, Farmington, Farmington, CT..........241

Stanly County Historic Preservation Commission and Museum, Albemarle, NC..........1088

Stanzel Model Aircraft Museum, Schulenburg, TX..........1452

Star of the Republic Museum, Washington, TX..........1460

Stars and Stripes Museum/Library, Bloomfield, MO..........811

State Agricultural Heritage Museum, Brookings, SD..........1344

State Historic Site of Fort Loudoun, Chambersburg, PA..........1246

State Historical Society of Iowa, Des Moines, IA..........515

State Historical Society of North Dakota, Bismarck, ND..........1128

The State House Museum, Dover, DE.........270

The State Museum of Pennsylvania, Harrisburg, PA..........1259

Staten Island Historical Society, Staten Island, NY..........1074

Staten Island Institute of Arts & Sciences (SIIAS), Staten Island, NY..........1074

Station 15, Norton, KS..........554

Statue of Liberty National Monument & Ellis Island Immigration Museum, New York, NY..........1039

STAX Museum of American Soul Music, Memphis, TN..........1376

Steam Railroading Institute, Owosso, MI....759

The Steamboat Arabia Museum, Kansas City, MO..........822

Steamboat Bertrand Collection, Missouri Valley, IA..........524

Steamtown National Historic Site, Scranton, PA..........1299

Stearns History Museum, Saint Cloud, MN..........788

Steele County Historical Society, Hope, ND..........1133

Steilacoom Historical Museum Association, Steilacoom, WA..........1572

Stephen Foster Folk Culture Center State Park, White Springs, FL..........354

Stephens County Historical Society and Museum, Duncan, OK..........1199

The Stephens Museum, Fayette, MO..........815

Stephenson County Historical Society, Freeport, IL..........436

Stephenville Museum, Stephenville, TX....1454

Steppingstone Museum, Havre de Grace, MD..........647

Sterling-Rock Falls Historical Society Museum, Sterling, IL..........461

Sterne-Hoya House Museum and Library, Nacogdoches, TX..........1440

Stevens County Gas and Historical Museum, Hugoton, KS..........544

Stevens Museum, Salem, IN..........498

Steves Homestead, San Antonio, TX..........1450

Stewart M. Lord Memorial Historical Society, Inc., Burlington, ME..........608

Stockbridge Library Historical Collection, Stockbridge, MA..........713

Stockholm Historical Society Museum, Stockholm, ME..........623

Stone Fort Museum, Nacogdoches, TX......1440

Stonewall House, Rocky Mount, NC..........1118

Stonewall Jackson Museum at Hupp's Hill, Strasburg, VA..........1539

Stony Point Battlefield State Historic Site, Stony Point, NY..........1075

Storrowton Village Museum, West Springfield, MA..........718

Stoughton Historical Society, Stoughton, MA..........713

Stow West School Museum, Stow, MA.......713

Stranahan House, Inc., Fort Lauderdale, FL..........308

Strasburg Museum, Strasburg, VA..........1539

Strategic Air & Space Museum, Ashland, NE..........856

Strater Hotel, Durango, CO..........214

The Stratford Historical Society & Catherine B. Mitchell Museum, Stratford, CT..........262

Strawbery Banke Museum, Portsmouth, NH..........895

Strong - National Museum of Play, Rochester, NY..........1060

Stuart Heritage Museum, Stuart, FL..........346

Studebaker National Museum, Inc., South Bend, IN..........500

Stuhr Museum of the Prairie Pioneer, Grand Island, NE..........862

Sturgis Library, Barnstable, MA..........662

Submarine Force Museum and Historic Ship Nautilus, Groton, CT..........243

Suffolk County Historical Society, Riverhead, NY..........1057

Sullivan County Historical Society, Inc., Hurleyville, NY..........1001

Sullivan Museum and History Center, Northfield, VT..........1483

SullivanMunce Cultural Center, Zionsville, IN..........504

Summit County Historical Society, Akron, OH..........1139

Summit Historical Society, Breckenridge, CO..........204

The Sumter County Museum, Sumter, SC.1342

Sun Prairie Historical Library & Museum, Sun Prairie, WI..........1624

Sunnyside Historical Museum, Sunnyside, WA..........1572

Sunnyvale Historical Museum, Sunnyvale, CA..........190

Superstition Mountain Lost Dutchman Museum, Apache Junction, AZ..........30

Susan B. Anthony House, Rochester, NY..1060

Susquehanna County Historical Society & Free Library Association, Montrose, PA..........1272

Susquehanna Museum of Havre de Grace Inc. at the Lock House, Havre de Grace, MD..........647

Sussex County Historical Society, Newton, NJ..........917

Sutton County Historical Society - Miers Home Museum, Sonora, TX..........1453

Suzanne G. Long Local History Room, Hammond, IN..........480

Swarthout Memorial Museum, La Crosse, WI..........1603

Sweet Briar Museum, Sweet Briar, VA......1540

Sweetwater County Historical Museum, Green River, WY..........1633

Swenson Memorial Museum of Stephens County, Breckenridge, TX..........1397

Swift County Historical Society, Benson, MN..........769

Swisher County Archives and Museum
Association, Tulia, TX 1456
Swiss Historical Village, New Glarus, WI.1615
Sylvia Plotkin Judaica Museum of
Congregation Beth Israel, Scottsdale,
AZ 44

Talkeetna Historical Society and
Museum, Talkeetna, AK.............................28
Tallahassee Museum, Tallahassee, FL 348
Tama County Historical Museum, Toledo,
IA 528
Tamastslikt Cultural Institute, Pendleton,
OR...1230
Tampa Bay History Center, Inc., Tampa,
FL...350
Tantaquidgeon Indian Museum,
Uncasville, CT...263
Taoist Temple and Museum, Hanford, CA...101
Taos Historic Museums, Taos, NM 953
Tarpon Springs Cultural Center, Tarpon
Springs, FL...351
Tarpon Springs Heritage Museum, Tarpon
Springs, FL...351
Tate House Museum, Portland, ME..............620
Taylor House Museum, Berlin, MD 637
Ted Smallwood's Store, Inc.,
Chokoloskee, FL..299
Telephone Museum of New Mexico,
Albuquerque, NM.....................................935
Telluride Historical Museum, Telluride,
CO..233
Temecula Valley Museum, Temecula, CA.....191
Tempe Historical Museum, Tempe, AZ..........46
Temperance Tavern, Newcomerstown,
OH...1179
Ten Sleep Pioneer Museum, Ten Sleep,
WY..1639
Tenino Depot Museum, Tenino, WA 1575
Tennessee Museum of Aviation,
Sevierville, TN...1383
Tennessee State Museum, Nashville, TN ...1381
Territorial Capital-Lane Museum,
Lecompton, KS...549
Territorial Statehouse State Park &
Museum, Fillmore, UT............................1465
Territory Town, Okemah, OK.....................1207
Teutopolis Monastery Museum,
Teutopolis, IL...461
Texana Museum and Library Association,
Edna, TX...1410
Texarkana Museums System, Texarkana,
TX 1455
Texas Baptist Historical Center Museum,
Brenham, TX 1397
Texas City Museum, Texas City, TX..........1455
Texas Civil War Museum, Fort Worth,
TX 1418
Texas Cowboy Hall of Fame, Fort Worth,
TX 1418
Texas Energy Museum, Beaumont, TX........1395
Texas Forestry Museum, Lufkin, TX..........1436
Texas Heritage Museum, Hillsboro, TX......1424
Texas Maritime Museum, Rockport, TX......1446
Texas Music Museum, Austin, TX 1392
Texas Ranger Hall of Fame and Museum,
Waco, TX...1459
Texas Seaport Museum, Galveston, TX 1422
Texas State Library, Austin, TX 1392
Theodore Roosevelt Birthplace National
Historic Site, New York, NY 1040
Thomas Downs House, Charlestown, IN 472
Thomas Edison House, Louisville, KY.........579
The Thomas J. Boyd, Wytheville, VA.........1546
Thomas L. Kane Memorial Chapel, Kane,
PA..1264
The Thomas T. Taber Museum of the
Lycoming County Historial Society,
Williamsport, PA 1308
Thomas Warne Historical Museum &
Library, Old Bridge, NJ 918

Thomaston Historical Society,
Thomaston, ME..624
Thousand Islands Museum, Clayton, NY.....979
Thrasher Carriage Museum, Frostburg,
MD...645
Three Rivers Museum, Muskogee, OK 1205
Three Valley Museum, Durant, OK............1200
Thronateeska Heritage Foundation, Inc.,
Albany, GA...355
Tillamook County Pioneer Museum,
Tillamook, OR 1237
Tillamook Naval Air Station Museum,
Tillamook, OR 1237
Timexpo Museum, Waterbury, CT...............264
Timucuan Ecological and Historic
Preserve and Fort Caroline National
Memorial, Jacksonville, FL......................315
Tintic Mining Museum, Eureka, UT 1464
Tioga County Historical Society
Museum, Owego, NY...............................1048
Tippecanoe County Historical
Association, Lafayette, IN........................487
Tipton County Museum, Veteran's
Memorial & Nature Center,
Covington, TN...1364
Titan Missile Museum, Green Valley, AZ......36
Tobacco Farm Life Museum, Inc., Kenly,
NC...1107
Tobias Community Historical Society,
Tobias, NE...873
Tolland Historical Society - Tolland
County Jail and Warden's Home
Museum, Tolland, CT...............................262
Tom Mix Museum, Dewey, OK..................1199
Tomaquag Indian Memorial Museum,
Exeter, RI..1311
Tongass Historical Museum, Ketchikan,
AK...26
Tooele County Railroad Museum, Tooele,
UT...1475
Toppenish Museum, Toppenish, WA 1575
Topsfield Historical Society, Topsfield,
MA...714
Towe Auto Museum, Sacramento, CA 154
Town of Yorktown Museum, Yorktown
Heights, NY...1087
Toy Train Depot Museum and Train
Ride, Alamogordo, NM.............................932
Trails & Rails Museum, Kearney, NE..........864
Trapper Creek Museum, Trapper Creek,
AK...28
Travel Town Museum, Los Angeles, CA 121
Tread of Pioneers Museum, Steamboat
Springs, CO..232
Trenton City Museum, Trenton, NJ.............928
Trenton Historical Museum, Trenton, MI.....765
Tri-Cities Museum, Grand Haven, MI 743
Triangle Tattoo & Museum, Fort Bragg,
CA...95
Trinity Museum of the Parish of Trinity
Church, New York, NY...........................1040
Troy Museum & Historic Village, Troy,
MI...765
Truckee-Donner Historical Society Jail
Museum, Truckee, CA 193
Trust for the Preservation of Maine
Industrial History and Technology
d/b/a Maine Narrow Gauge Railroad
Co. & Museum, Portland, ME..................620
Tryon Palace Historic Sites and Gardens,
New Bern, NC 1112
Tsa Mo Ga Memorial Museum, Plains,
TX 1443
T.T. Wentworth, Jr. Florida State
Museum, Pensacola, FL 336
Tu-Endie-Wei State Park, Point Pleasant,
WV..1586
Tubac Presidio State Historic Park,
Tubac, AZ..47
Tubman African-American Museum,
Macon, GA...378
Tuck Museum, Hampton, NH.....................888

Tucker Wildlife Sanctuary, Silverado, CA ...186
Tuckerton Seaport, Tuckerton, NJ 928
Tucson Rodeo Parade Museum, Tucson,
AZ...52
Tucumcari Historical Research Institute,
Tucumcari, NM...953
Tulare County Museum at Mooney Grove
Park, Visalia, CA......................................195
Tularosa Basin Historical Society
Museum, Alamogordo, NM 932
Tumacacori National Historical Park,
Tumacacori, AZ..52
Tunica-Biloxi Native American Museum,
Marksville, LA..591
Turabo University, Gurabo, PR..................1641
Turtle Bay Exploration Park, Redding,
CA...146
Turtle Mountain Chippewa Historical
Society, Belcourt, ND.............................1127
Twin Falls County Historical Museum,
Filer, ID...405
Tybee Island Light Station and Tybee
Museum, Tybee Island, GA 389

USDA Forest Service - Land Between
the Lakes, Golden Pond, KY 570
U.S. Navy Museum, Washington, DC..........292
Ukrainian-American Museum &
Archives, Warren, MI...............................766
Ukrainian Museum-Archives, Inc.,
Cleveland, OH 1156
Ukrainian National Museum, Inc.,
Chicago, IL...428
Ulysses S. Grant Cottage State Historic
Site, Wilton, NY.....................................1086
Umpqua Discovery Center, Reedsport,
OR...1234
Uncle Remus Museum, Eatonton, GA 371
Union County Heritage Museum, New
Albany, MS..806
Union County Historical Complex,
Creston, IA...512
The Union County Historical Society,
Marysville, OH 1175
Union County Historical Society
Museum, Blairsville, GA 366
Union County Museum, Union, OR...........1238
Union Mills Homestead & Grist Mill,
Westminster, MD......................................656
Union Pacific Railroad Museum, Council
Bluffs, IA...512
Union Station Kansas City, Inc., Kansas
City, MO...823
Unionville Museum, Farmington, CT..........242
United States Army Heritage and
Education Center - Army Heritage
Museum, Carlisle, PA.............................1246
The United States Army Quartermaster
Museum, Fort Lee, VA............................1505
United States Department of the Interior
Museum, Washington, DC 293
United States Hockey Hall of Fame,
Eveleth, MN...774
United States Holocaust Memorial
Museum, Washington, DC 293
United States Marine Corps Air-Ground
Museum, Quantico, VA 1526
United States Naval Academy Museum,
Annapolis, MD...628
United States Senate Commission on Art,
Washington, DC..293
University Art Museum, Binghamton, NY...963
The University Museum, Indiana, PA 1263
The University of South Carolina
McKissick Museum, Columbia, SC.......1331
University Saint Thomas Art History,
Saint Paul, MN..792
Upham Mansion, Marshfield, WI 1608
Upper Musselshell Historical Society,
Harlowton, MT...849
Upper Snake River Valley Historical
Society, Rexburg, ID 409

History Museums–Continued

Uppertown Firefighters Museum, Astoria, OR 1219

Upton Red Onion Museum, Upton, WY 1639

U.S. Army Center of Military History, Museum Division, Fort McNair, DC 275

U.S. Army Chaplain Museum, Fort Jackson, SC 1332

U.S. Army Communications-Electronics Museum, Fort Monmouth, NJ.................904

U.S. Army Engineer Museum, Fort Leonard Wood, MO......................815

U.S. Army Museum of Hawaii, Fort DeRussy, HI 392

U.S. Army Ordnance Museum, Aberdeen Proving Ground, MD......................627

U.S. Army Signal Corps Museum, Fort Gordon, GA 372

U.S. Army Women's Museum, Fort Lee, VA 1505

U.S. Cavalry Museum, Fort Riley, KS 540

U.S. Coast Guard Museum, New London, CT 255

U.S. Grant's Home State Historic Site, Galena, IL 436

U.S. Navy Seabee Museum, Port Hueneme, CA 143

U.S. Navy Supply Corps Museum, Athens, GA 357

The U.S. Space & Rocket Center, Huntsville, AL 12

USS Alabama Battleship Memorial Park, Mobile, AL 15

USS Bowfin Submarine Museum & Park, Honolulu, HI 398

USS Constellation Museum, Baltimore, MD 636

USS Constitution Museum, Boston, MA 669

Utah State Historical Society, Salt Lake City, UT 1473

Utica Museum, Utica, MT 854

UTSA's Institute of Texan Cultures, San Antonio, TX 1451

Vacaville Museum, Vacaville, CA 194

The Valdez Museum & Historical Archive Association, Inc., Valdez, AK 29

Valentine Richmond History Center, Richmond, VA 1532

Valentown Museum, Victor, NY 1081

Valiant Air Command Warbird Air Museum, Titusville, FL 352

Vallejo Naval & Historical Museum, Vallejo, CA 194

Valley Community Historical Society, Inc., Valley, NE 874

Valley County Pioneer Museum, Glasgow, MT 847

Van Meter State Park, Miami, MO..............827

Vann House, Chatsworth, GA 368

Varner-Hogg Plantation State Historic Site, West Columbia, TX 1461

Vashon Maury Island Heritage Association, Vashon, WA 1576

Ventura County Museum of History & Art, Ventura, CA 195

Verde Historical Society, Clemenceau Heritage Museum, Cottonwood, AZ..........32

The Verdier House, Beaufort, SC 1321

Verendrye Museum, Fort Pierre, SD 1347

Vermilion County Museum Society, Danville, IL 429

Vermont Historical Society Museum, Montpelier, VT 1482

Vermont Marble Museum, Proctor, VT 1485

The Vermont State House, Montpelier, VT 1483

Vernonia Pioneer Museum, Vernonia, OR..1238

Vesterheim Norwegian-American Museum, Decorah, IA 513

Veterans Memorial Museum, Laurel, MS 804

Vicksburg Battlefield Museum, Vicksburg, MS 809

Victor Heritage Museum, Victor, MT..........854

Victor Valley Museum & Art Gallery, Apple Valley, CA 71

Vietnam Era Educational Center, Holmdel, NJ 908

Vietnam War National Museum, Nelson, NE 869

Village of Elsah Museum, Elsah, IL 433

The Vinalhaven Historical Society Museum, Vinalhaven, ME 624

Virginia Aviation Museum, Richmond International Airport, VA 1534

Virginia Beach Maritime Museum, Inc./The Old Coast Guard Station, Virginia Beach, VA 1543

Virginia City J. Spencer Watkins Memorial Museum, Virginia City, MT 854

Virginia Historical Society, Richmond, VA 1533

Virginia Holocaust Museum, Richmond, VA 1533

Virginia War Memorial, Richmond, VA 1534

The Virginia War Museum, Newport News, VA 1520

Vista Historical Museum, Vista, CA 196

Vista House, Corbett, OR 1222

Volendam Windmill Museum Inc., Milford, NJ 911

W.H. Over Museum, Vermillion, SD..........1358

Wabasha County Museum, Wabasha County Historical Society at Reads Landing, Reads Landing, MN.................787

Wabaunsee County Historical Museum, Alma, KS 532

Wade House Stagecoach Inn & Wesley Jung Carriage Museum State Historic Site, Greenbush, WI 1599

Wake Forest College Birthplace Society, Inc., Wake Forest, NC 1121

Wakefield Historical Society, Wakefield, MA 715

Wal-Mart Visitor's Center, Bentonville, AR 55

Waldensian Heritage Museum, Valdese, NC 1121

The Walker African American Museum & Research Center, Las Vegas, NV 880

Walkersville, Southern Railroad Museum, Walkersville, MD..............................656

Wallace District Mining Museum, Wallace, ID 410

Walter Elwood Museum, Amsterdam, NY ...957

Walter P. Chrysler Boyhood Home and Museum, Ellis, KS 538

Walter Reed Birthplace, Gloucester County, VA 1508

Waltham Historical Society, Waltham, MA 716

The Waltham Museum, Waltham, MA 716

Wanapum Dam Heritage Center, Beverly, WA 1549

Wantagh Historical & Preservation Society, Wantagh, NY 1081

Wapello County Historical Museum, Ottumwa, IA 526

War Between the States Museum, Florence, SC 1332

War Eagle Air Museum, Santa Teresa, NM 951

Ward County Historical Society, Minot, ND 1135

Ward W. O'Hara Agricultural Museum, Auburn, NY 959

Warhawk Air Museum, Nampa, ID 408

Waring Historical Library, Charleston, SC.1327

Warner House, Portsmouth, NH 895

Warren County Historical Society, Warren, PA 1304

Warren County Historical Society Museum, Lebanon, OH 1171

Warren Historical Society, Warren, ME 624

Warren ICBM & Heritage Museum, Frances E. Warren Air Force Base, WY 1633

Warrick County Museum, Inc., Boonville, IN 470

Waseca County Historical Society, Waseca, MN 796

Washakie Museum, Worland, WY..............1639

Washington County Fair Farm Museum, Greenwich, NY 996

Washington County Historical Association, Fort Calhoun, NE 860

Washington County Historical Society, Portland, OR 1233

Washington County Historical Society, Washington, PA 1305

Washington County Historical Society and Miller House Museum, Hagerstown, MD 646

Washington County Historical Society Inc., West Bend, WI 1627

Washington County Historical Society Warden's House Museum, Stillwater, MN 794

Washington County Rural Heritage Museum, Boonsboro, MD 637

Washington Historical Museum, Washington, GA 391

Washington Irving Trail Museum, Ripley, OK 1213

Washington Museum & Tourist Center, Washington, LA 603

Washington State Capital Museum and Outreach Center, Olympia, WA 1560

Washington State Historical Society, Tacoma, WA 1574

Waterford Historical Museum and Cultural Center, Inc., Waterford, NY ...1083

Waterloo Area Historical Society, Grass Lake, MI 744

Watermen's Museum, Yorktown, VA..........1547

Watkins Community Museum of History, Lawrence, KS 548

Watson-Curtze Mansion, Erie, PA 1253

Watts Towers Arts Center, Los Angeles, CA 122

Waukesha County Museum, Waukesha, WI 1625

Wayland Historical Society, Wayland, MA 716

Wayne County Historical Museum, Richmond, IN 497

Wayne County Historical Society, Lyons, NY 1012

Wayne County Historical Society, Wooster, OH 1192

Wayne County Historical Society, Honesdale, PA 1261

The Webb-Deane-Stevens Museum, Wethersfield, CT 266

Webster House Museum, Elkhorn, WI 1596

Weems-Botts Museum, Dumfries, VA.........1503

Weeping Water Valley Historical Society, Weeping Water, NE 874

Wellesley Historical Society, Inc., Wellesley Hills, MA 717

Wellfleet Historical Society Museum, Wellfleet, MA 717

Wells County Historical Museum, Bluffton, IN 470

Wells County Museum, Fessenden, ND 1131

Wells Fargo History Exhibit, Portland, OR 1233

Wells Fargo History Museum, Minneapolis, MN..............................783

Wells Fargo History Museum, Phoenix, AZ 42

Wells Fargo History Museum, Los Angeles, CA 122

Wells Fargo History Museum, Sacramento, CA 154

Wells Fargo History Museum, Sacramento, CA 154

Wells Fargo History Museum, San Diego, CA 162

Wells Fargo History Museum, San Francisco, CA 170

Welsh-American Heritage Museum, Oak Hill, OH 1180

Wenham Museum, Wenham, MA 717

Weslaco Museum, Weslaco, TX 1461

West Allis Historical Society Museum, West Allis, WI 1626

West Baton Rouge Museum, Port Allen, LA 599

West Chicago City Museum, West Chicago, IL 464

West Florida Railroad Museum, Milton, FL 327

West Milford Museum, West Milford, NJ ...930

West of the Pecos Museum, Pecos, TX 1443

West Overton Museums, Scottdale, PA 1298

West Pasco Historical Society Museum and Library, New Port Richey, FL 329

West Point Museum, West Point, NY 1085

West River Museum Society, Philip, SD....1353

West Virginia Independence Hall, Wheeling, WV 1588

West Virginia Northern Community College Alumni Association Museum, Wheeling, WV 1588

West Virginia Penitentiary, Moundsville, WV 1585

West Virginia State Museum, Charleston, WV 1581

Westerly Public Library, Westerly, RI 1320

Western Archeological & Conservation Center, Tucson, AZ 52

Western Hennepin County Pioneers Association, Long Lake, MN 779

Western Heritage Center, Billings, MT 841

Western Historic Radio Museum, Virginia City, NV 882

Western Hotel/Museum, Lancaster, CA........108

Western Museum of Mining & Industry, Colorado Springs, CO 208

Western Rhode Island Civic Historical Society, Coventry, RI............................1311

Westminster Historical Society, Westminster, VT 1490

Westport Historical Society, Westport, CT ...266

The Wethersfield Historical Society, Wethersfield, CT 266

Wexford County Historical Society & Museum, Cadillac, MI............................731

Weymouth Woods-Sandhills Nature Preserve Museum, Southern Pines, NC.1120

The Whalehead Club, Corolla, NC.............1097

Wharton County Historical Museum, Wharton, TX............................1461

Whatcom Museum of History and Art, Bellingham, WA 1549

Wheat Ridge Historic Park, Wheat Ridge, CO............................235

Wheeler Historic Farm, Salt Lake City, UT 1474

Wheels O' Time Museum, Peoria, IL...........451

Whipple House Museum, Ashland Historical Society, Ashland, NH 883

Whiskeytown Unit, Whiskeytown-Shasta-Trinity National Recreation Area, Whiskeytown, CA 198

White County Historical Society, Cleveland, GA 368

White County Historical Society, Carmi, IL............................415

White County Historical Society Museum, Monticello, IN 491

White 1 Foundation, Kissimmee, FL...........319

The White River Museum, Meeker, CO 228

White River Valley Museum, Auburn, WA 1547

Whitehall Museum House, Middletown, RI............................1312

Whitehead Memorial Museum, Del Rio, TX............................1409

Whitingham Historical Museum, Whitingham, VT............................1490

Whitley County Historical Museum, Columbia City, IN............................472

Whitman Mission National Historic Site, Walla Walla, WA 1577

Whittier Home Association, Amesbury, MA 658

Wibaux Museum, Wibaux, MT............855

Wichita-Sedgwick County Historical Museum Association, Wichita, KS 563

Wilber Czech Museum, Wilber, NE.............875

Wilbur Wright Birthplace & Interpretive Center, Hagerstown, IN............................480

Wild Turkey Center and Winchester Museum, Edgefield, SC............................1332

Wilder Memorial Museum, Strawberry Point, IA............................528

Wilderness Road Regional Museum, Newbern, VA............................1519

Wilkin County Historical Society, Breckenridge, MN 770

Wilkinson County Museum, Woodville, MS............................810

Will Rogers Memorial Museum, Claremore, OK............................1198

Will Rogers State Historic Park, Pacific Palisades, CA............................137

Willa Cather Pioneer Memorial and Educational Foundation, Red Cloud, NE............................872

Willard House and Clock Museum, Inc., Grafton, MA............................685

William Brewster Nickerson Memorial Room, Cape Cod Community College, West Barnstable, MA 717

William Clark Market House Museum, Paducah, KY............................582

William Hammond Mathers Museum, Bloomington, IN............................470

William Heath Davis House Museum administered by Gaslamp Quarter Historical Foundation, San Diego, CA....162

William Henry Harrison Mansion, Grouseland, Vincennes, IN............................503

William Holmes McGuffey Museum, Oxford, OH............................1181

William J. Clinton Presidential Library & Museum, Little Rock, AR............................63

William M. Colmer Visitor Center, Ocean Springs, MS............................806

William McKinley Presidential Library & Museum, Canton, OH............................1146

William Pryor Letchworth Museum, Castile, NY 976

Williamson County Historical Society, Marion, IL............................444

Willow Creek - China Flat Museum, Willow Creek, CA............................198

Willowbrook Museum Village, Newfield, ME............................616

Willows Museum, Willows, CA 198

Wilmette Historical Museum, Wilmette, IL............................466

Wilmington Railroad Museum, Wilmington, NC............................1124

Wilson County Historical Society Museum, Fredonia, KS............................540

Wilson's Creek National Battlefield, Republic, MO............................829

Winchendon Historical Society, Inc., Winchendon, MA 720

Winchester-Frederick County Historical Society, Inc., Winchester, VA.................1546

Windham Textile and History Museum (The Mill Museum), Willimantic, CT 267

Wing Luke Asian Museum, Seattle, WA....1569

Wings of History Air Museum, San Martin, CA............................175

Wings Over Miami Museum, Inc., Miami, FL............................326

Winnebago Area Museum, Winnebago, MN............................797

Winnetka Historical Society, Winnetka, IL............................466

Winnie Davis Museum of History, Gaffney, SC............................1333

Winona County Historical Museum, Winona, MN............................797

Winston Churchill Memorial and Library, Fulton, MO............................816

Winterthur Museum & Country Estate, Winterthur, DE............................274

Wisconsin Historical Museum, Madison, WI............................1606

Wisconsin Maritime Museum, Manitowoc, WI............................1607

Wisconsin National Guard Museum, Camp Douglas, WI............................1593

Wisconsin Veterans Museum-Madison, Madison, WI............................1606

Wise County Heritage Museum, Decatur, TX............................1408

Wistariahurst Museum, Holyoke, MA.........687

Witte Museum, San Antonio, TX 1451

Wolcott House Museum Complex, Maumee, OH............................1175

Wolf Creek Indian Village and Museum, Bastian, VA............................1496

Wolf Point Area Historical Society, Inc., Wolf Point, MT............................855

Wolfeboro Historical Society, Wolfeboro, NH............................897

Women's History Museum, West Liberty, WV............................1587

The Women's Museum: An Institute for the Future, Dallas, TX............................1408

Wood County Historical Center and Museum, Bowling Green, OH 1143

Woodbine International Fire Museum, Woodbine, GA............................392

Woodlawn Museum/The Black House, Ellsworth, ME............................610

Woodson County Historical Society, Yates Center, KS............................564

Woodstock Historical Society, Bryant Pond, ME............................608

Woodstock Historical Society, Inc., Woodstock, VT............................1491

Woodstock Museum of Shenandoah County, Inc., Woodstock, VA.................1546

Woolaroc Museum, Bartlesville, OK.........1197

Worcester Historical Museum, Worcester, MA............................721

Workman & Temple Family Homestead Museum, City of Industry, CA 85

The Works: Ohio Center for History, Art & Technology, Newark, OH............................1179

World Figure Skating Museum & Hall of Fame, Colorado Springs, CO..................208

World Kite Museum & Hall of Fame, Long Beach, WA 1558

World Methodist Museum, Lake Junaluska, NC............................1109

World Museum of Mining, Butte, MT.........843

World's First Wendy's Restaurant, Columbus, OH............................1159

World's Largest Toy Museum and Harold Bell Wright, Branson, MO............................811

Wormsloe State Historic Site, Savannah, GA............................387

Worthington Historical Society, Worthington, OH............................1192

Wounded Knee Museum, Wall, SD...........1358

Wrangell Museum, Wrangell, AK...................29

Wrather West Kentucky Museum, Murray, KY............................580

Wray Museum, Wray, CO............................235

Wren's Nest, Atlanta, GA 364

Wright Brothers National Memorial, Kill Devil Hills, NC............................1108

Wright Centennial Museum, Wright, WY ..1639

History Museums–Continued

Wright County Historical Society, Buffalo, MN..................770

Wright Museum, Wolfeboro, NH.................897

Wyalusing Valley Museum, Wyalusing, PA......................1309

Wyandot County Historical Society, Upper Sandusky, OH..................1188

Wyandotte County Museum, Bonner Springs, KS..................534

Wyandotte Museum, Wyandotte, MI............766

Wyatt Earp Birthplace Home, Monmouth, IL.......................445

Wyoming Frontier Prison Museum, Rawlings, WY......................1637

Wyoming State Museum, Cheyenne, WY..1631

Wyoming Territorial Prison State Historic Site, Laramie, WY......................1636

Yates County Genealogical and Historical Society and Oliver House Museum and L. Caroline Underwood Museum, Penn Yan, NY.....................1052

Ybor City Museum State Park, Tampa, FL....................351

Yellow Medicine County Historical Society and Museum, Granite Falls, MN.......................777

Yellowstone Gateway Museum of Park County, Livingston, MT..................850

Yellowstone National Park, Gardiner, MT...847

Yeshiva University Museum at the Center for Jewish History, New York, NY.......1041

Yesteryear House-Central Mine, Clarkston, MI........................732

Yesteryear Village, West Palm Beach, FL....354

Yolo County Historical Museum, Woodland, CA....................199

Yorba and Slaughter Families Adobe, Chino, CA........................84

York County Heritage Trust, Fire Museum, York, PA......................1309

York County Heritage Trust, Museum & Library, York, PA....................1309

York W. Bailey Museum at Penn Center, Saint Helena Island, SC 1340

Youth Museum of Southern West Virginia, Beckley, WV..................1579

Ypsilanti Historical Museum, Ypsilanti, MI.......................767

Yucaipa Adobe, Yucaipa, CA......................200

Yucaipa Valley Historical Society Museum, Yucaipa, CA......................201

Yuma Crossing State Historic Park, Yuma, AZ.......................54

Yuma Territorial Prison State Historic Park, Yuma, AZ......................54

Zane Grey Museum, Lackawaxen, PA.......1265

Ziibiwing Center of Anishinabe Culture & Lifeways, Mount Pleasant, MI......757

Zippo/Case Visitors Center, Bradford, PA..1244

Maritime, Naval Museums and Historic Ships

Admiral Nimitz National Museum of the Pacific War, Fredericksburg, TX............1419

American Merchant Marine Museum, Kings Point, NY......................1007

The Antique Boat Museum, Clayton, NY....978

Atlantic Heritage Center, Somers Point, NJ.......................924

Baltimore Maritime Museum, Baltimore, MD......................630

Bandon Historical Society Museum, Bandon, OR......................1219

Battleship New Jersey Museum & Memorial, Camden, NJ......................899

Battleship North Carolina, Wilmington, NC......................1122

Battleship Texas State Historic Site, La Porte, TX......................1433

Beavertail Lighthouse Museum, Jamestown, RI......................1311

Beverly Historical Society and Museum, Beverly, MA......................662

Bremerton Naval Museum, Bremerton, WA......................1549

Brooks Academy Museum, Harwich, MA...686

Bucksport Historical Society, Inc., Bucksport, ME......................608

Buffalo and Erie County Naval & Military Park, Buffalo, NY......................972

Calvert Marine Museum, Solomons, MD....654

Canal Fulton Heritage Society, Canal Fulton, OH......................1145

Cape Ann Historical Museum, Gloucester, MA......................684

The Cape Cod Maritime Museum, Hyannis, MA......................688

Captain Charles H. Hurley Library, Buzzards Bay, MA......................672

Captain Salem Avery House Museum, Shady Side Rural Heritage Society, Inc., Shady Side, MD......................653

Center for Wooden Boats, Seattle, WA......1565

Centerville Historical Museum, Centerville, MA......................675

Chesapeake Bay Maritime Museum, Saint Michaels, MD......................652

City Island Nautical Museum, Bronx, NY...965

Coastal Science Center at Hutchinson Island, Stuart, FL......................346

Cold Spring Harbor Whaling Museum, Cold Spring Harbor, NY......................979

Columbia River Maritime Museum, Astoria, OR......................1218

Confederate Memorial Museum, Atoka, OK......................1196

Connecticut River Museum, Essex, CT........239

Cumberland County Historical Society, Greenwich, NJ......................905

The Custom House Maritime Museum, Newburyport, MA......................697

Detroit Historical Society, Detroit, MI.........735

DiscoverSea Shipwreck Museum, Fenwick Island, DE......................270

Door County Maritime Museum (at Gills Rock), Gills Rock, WI......................1598

Door County Maritime Museum (at Sturgeon Bay), Sturgeon Bay, WI.........1623

Dossin Great Lakes Museum, Detroit, MI...736

East End Seaport Museum and Marine Foundation, Greenport, NY......................996

East Hampton Town Marine Museum, Amagansett, NY......................957

Egan Maritime Foundation, Nantucket, MA......................695

El Cazador Museum, Grand Bay, AL............10

Erie Maritime Museum, Homeport U.S. Brig Niagara, Erie, PA......................1252

Essex Shipbuilding Museum, Essex, MA 681

Fairport Marine Museum, Fairport Harbor, OH......................1164

Fort Morgan Museum, Gulf Shores, AL 10

Galveston Historical Foundation, Inc., Galveston, TX......................1421

Great Harbor Maritime Museum, Northeast Harbor, ME......................616

Great Lakes Naval Memorial and Museum, Muskegon, MI......................757

Great Lakes Shipwreck Museum, Paradise, MI......................760

Grumman Memorial Park, Calverton, NY ...974

Gulf Shores Museum, Gulf Shores, AL 11

Hampton Roads Naval Museum, Norfolk, VA......................1521

Hawaii Maritime Center, Honolulu, HI........395

Hereford Inlet Lighthouse, North Wildwood, NJ......................917

Herreshoff Marine Museum/America's Cup Hall of Fame, Bristol, RI 1311

Historic Gardner's Basin, Atlantic City, NJ......................898

Historical Society of Greater Port Jefferson, Port Jefferson, NY 1053

Howard Steamboat Museum and Mansion, Jeffersonville, IN.................486

Hudson River Maritime Museum, Kingston, NY......................1007

Hull Lifesaving Museum Inc., the Museum of Boston Harbor Heritage, Hull, MA......................687

Independence Seaport Museum, Philadelphia, PA 1281

Inland Seas Maritime Museum, Vermilion, OH......................1189

Intrepid Sea-Air-Space Museum, New York, NY......................1028

Iowa Great Lakes Maritime Museum, Arnolds Park, IA......................505

Ipswich Historical Society and Museum, Ipswich, MA......................688

Jacksonville Maritime Museum Society, Jacksonville, FL......................314

Keokuk River Museum, Keokuk, IA............521

Keweenaw County Historical Society, Eagle Harbor, MI......................739

Kittery Historical & Naval Museum, Kittery, ME......................613

The Lake Champlain Maritime Museum, Vergennes, VT......................1488

Lake Pontchartrain Basin Maritime Museum, Madisonville, LA 591

Lake Superior Maritime Visitors Center, Duluth, MN......................773

Le Sault de Sainte Marie Historical Sites, Inc., Sault Ste. Marie, MI......................764

Lewes Historical Society, Lewes, DE 271

Long Island Maritime Museum, West Sayville, NY......................1085

Los Angeles Maritime Museum, San Pedro, CA......................176

Louisiana Naval War Memorial/U.S.S. Kidd, Baton Rouge, LA......................586

MIT Museum, Cambridge, MA 674

Maine Lighthouse Museum, Rockland, ME......................621

Maine Maritime Museum, Bath, ME............606

The Marine Museum at Fall River, Inc., Fall River, MA......................682

Marine Science Institute, Redwood City, CA......................147

The Mariners' Museum, Newport News, VA......................1519

Maritime and Yachting Museum of the Treasure Coast, Stuart, FL......................346

Maritime Industry Museum at Fort Schuyler, Bronx, NY......................966

Maritime Museum at Historic Coast Guard Station, Saint Simons Island, GA......................383

Maritime Museum - Cohasset Historical Society, Cohasset, MA......................676

Maritime Museum of Monterey, Monterey, CA......................127

Maritime Museum of San Diego, San Diego, CA......................157

Mel Fisher Maritime Heritage Society, Key West, FL......................318

Meriwether Lewis Dredge Museum, Brownville, NE......................858

Michigan Maritime Museum, South Haven, MI......................764

Montauk Point Lighthouse Museum, Montauk, NY......................1015

Monterey History and Art Association, Monterey, CA 127

Moosehead Marine Museum, Greenville, ME...611

Museum of Yachting, Newport, RI............1314

Museum of Yarmouth History, Yarmouth, ME...626

Muskogee War Memorial Park & Military Museum, Muskogee, OK 1205

Mystic Seaport - The Museum of America and the Sea, Mystic, CT 251

National Atomic Museum, Albuquerque, NM...934

National Civil War Naval Museum at Port Columbus, Columbus, GA 369

National Liberty Ship Memorial/S.S. Jeremiah O'Brien, San Francisco, CA.....168

National Mississippi River Museum & Aquarium, Dubuque, IA............................516

National Park Service Vicksburg National Military Park-Cairo Museum, Vicksburg, MS 809

Nauticus, The National Maritime Center, Norfolk, VA...1522

Naval Undersea Museum, Keyport, WA ...1557

Naval War College Museum, Newport, RI...1314

Navy UDT-SEAL Museum, Fort Pierce, FL...309

The Noble Maritime Collection, Staten Island, NY...1073

North Carolina Maritime Museum, Beaufort, NC...1091

Ocean Institute, Dana Point, CA 89

Odyssey Maritime Discovery Center, Seattle, WA...1567

Ohio River Museum, Marietta, OH 1174

Old Fort Jackson, Savannah, GA...................385

Old State House-The Bostonian Society, Boston, MA...668

The Oldest House Museum/Wrecker's Museum, Key West, FL 318

The P.T. Boat Museum & Library, Germantown, TN..................................1365

Patriots Point Naval and Maritime Museum, Mount Pleasant, SC...............1337

Peabody Essex Museum, Salem, MA...........706

Penobscot Marine Museum, Searsport, ME...622

Point Fermin Lighthouse, San Pedro, CA 176

Ponce DeLeon Inlet Lighthouse Preservation Association, Inc., Ponce Inlet, FL...337

Port Orford Lifeboat Station, Port Orford, OR...1230

Porter Thermometer Museum, Onset, MA ...700

Portland Harbor Museum, South Portland, ME...623

Presque Isle County Historical Museum, Rogers City, MI.......................................762

Queen Mary Museum, Long Beach, CA 111

Quoddy Maritime Museum, Eastport, ME ...610

Reedville Fishermen's Museum, Reedville, VA...1527

Richardson Maritime Museum, Cambridge, MD...................................639

Ripley's Believe It or Not!, Key West, FL...319

River Heritage Museum, Paducah, KY 582

S.S. Meteor Maritime Museum, Superior, WI...1624

Sackets Harbor Battlefield State Historic Site, Sackets Harbor, NY.....................1062

Sailor's Memorial Museum, Islesboro, ME...612

St. Augustine Lighthouse & Museum, Inc., Saint Augustine, FL 340

St. Clements Island and Piney Point Museums, Colton's Point, MD.................641

San Francisco Maritime National Historical Park, San Francisco, CA.........169

Santa Barbara Maritime Museum, Santa Barbara, CA...179

The Sargent House Museum, Gloucester, MA...684

Scituate Maritime and Irish Mossing Museum, Scituate, MA...........................709

Ship Ashore Resort Museum, Smith River, CA...187

Ships of the Sea Maritime Museum/William Scarbrough House, Savannah, GA...386

SoDus Bay Historical Society, Sodus Point, NY...1070

South Street Seaport Museum, New York, NY...1039

Split Rock Lighthouse Historic Site, Two Harbors, MN.......................................795

Steamship Historical Society of America, Providence, RI.......................................1319

Steamship Keewatin, Douglas, MI 738

Steamship William G. Mather Museum, Cleveland, OH.......................................1156

Submarine Force Museum and Historic Ship Nautilus, Groton, CT 243

Texas Maritime Museum, Rockport, TX....1446

Texas Seaport Museum, Galveston, TX 1422

Tillamook Naval Air Station Museum, Tillamook, OR.......................................1237

Treasures of the Sea Exhibit, Georgetown, DE.......................................271

Tuckerton Seaport, Tuckerton, NJ...............928

U.S. Navy Museum, Washington, DC..........292

USS Massachusetts Memorial Committee, Inc., Fall River, MA...........................682

United States Naval Academy Museum, Annapolis, MD...................................628

United States Naval Shipbuilding Museum, Quincy, MA...........................705

U.S. Coast Guard Museum, New London, CT...255

U.S. Merchant Marine Museum, Anderson, IN.......................................467

U.S. Naval Museum of Armament & Technology, China Lake, CA.....................84

U.S. Navy Memorial Foundation and Naval Heritage Center, Washington, DC...294

U.S. Navy Supply Corps Museum, Athens, GA...357

USS Alabama Battleship Memorial Park, Mobile, AL...15

USS Constellation Museum, Baltimore, MD...636

USS Constitution Museum, Boston, MA 669

USS Lexington Museum on the Bay, Corpus Christi, TX...............................1402

Vallejo Naval & Historical Museum, Vallejo, CA...194

Varnum Memorial Armory & Military Museum, East Greenwich, RI...............1311

Ventura County Maritime Museum, Inc., Oxnard, CA...137

Virginia Beach Maritime Museum, Inc./The Old Coast Guard Station, Virginia Beach, VA...............................1543

Waterfront Museum, Brooklyn, NY 970

Watermen's Museum, Yorktown, VA...........1547

Westport Maritime Museum, Westport, WA...1578

Willapa Seaport Museum, Raymond, WA..1564

Wisconsin Maritime Museum, Manitowoc, WI.......................................1607

Military Museums

Admiral Nimitz National Museum of the Pacific War, Fredericksburg, TX............1419

Air Acres Museum, Cartersville, GA 367

Air Classic Inc. Museum of Aviation, Sugar Grove, IL.......................................461

Air Force Armament Museum, Eglin Air Force Base, FL...305

Air Force Flight Test Center Museum, Edwards AFB, CA...................................92

Air Mobility Command Museum, Dover AFB, DE...270

The Airborne & Special Operations Museum, Fayetteville, NC.....................1100

Airmen Memorial Museum, Suitland, MD...655

The Alamo, San Antonio, TX 1447

Albany Regional Museum, Albany, OR 1217

Aliceville Museum, Aliceville, AL 3

American Airpower Heritage Museum, Inc. & Commemorative Air Force Headquarters, Midland, TX...................1438

American Independence Museum, Exeter, NH...887

American Military Museum, Charleston, SC...1323

American Wings Air Museum, Blaine, MN...769

Ancient and Honorable Artillery Company, Boston, MA.............................663

Antietam National Battlefield-Visitor Center, Sharpsburg, MD.........................653

Arizona Historical Society-Fort Lowell Museum, Tucson, AZ...............................47

Arizona Military Museum, Phoenix, AZ........39

Arkansas National Guard Museum, North Little Rock, AR.......................................65

Artillery Company of Newport Military Museum, Newport, RI...........................1313

Audie Murphy/American Cotton Museum, Inc, Greenville, TX...............1423

Aviation Cadet Museum, Eureka Springs, AR...57

Aviation Hall of Fame and Museum of New Jersey, Teterboro, NJ 926

Aviation Museum of Kentucky Inc., Lexington, KY.......................................572

Baltimore Civil War Museum, Baltimore, MD...629

Bandon Historical Society Museum, Bandon, OR...1219

Battles for Chattanooga Museum, Lookout Mountain, TN 1371

Battleship New Jersey Museum & Memorial, Camden, NJ...........................899

Battleship North Carolina, Wilmington, NC...1122

Battleship South Dakota Memorial, Sioux Falls, SD...1356

Baxter Springs Heritage Center and Museum, Baxter Springs, KS.................533

Benicia Historical Museum, Benicia, CA 74

Bentonville Battlefield State Historic Site, Four Oaks, NC...1102

BG John C.L. Scribner Texas Military Forces Museum, Austin, TX...................1389

Boone County Historical Center, Boone, IA...506

Boonsborough Museum of History, Boonsboro, MD...................................637

Buffalo Soldiers National Museum, Houston, TX...1425

Bushy Run Battlefield, Jeannette, PA.........1263

The California State Military Museum, Sacramento, CA...................................151

Camp Atterbury Museum, Edinburgh, IN 474

Camp Moore Cemetery and Museum, Tangipahoa, LA...................................603

Canaan Historical Society, Inc., Canaan, NY...974

Carolinas Aviation Museum, Charlotte, NC...1094

Military Museums–Continued

Casemate Museum, Fort Monroe, VA 1505
Castle Air Museum, Atwater, CA 72
The Center for Civil War Photography,
  Gettysburg, PA.................................1255
Centerville Historical Museum,
  Centerville, MA 675
Chicago Public Library, Chicago, IL...........419
Chickamauga-Chattanooga National
  Military Park, Fort Oglethorpe, GA 372
The Citadel Archives & Museum,
  Charleston, SC 1324
Civil War Life - The Soldier's Museum,
  Fredericksburg, VA...........................1505
Civil War Museum of Lonejack, Jackson
  County, Lone Jack, MO 826
Civil War Soldiers Museum, Pensacola,
  FL...335
Cole Land Transportation Museum,
  Bangor, ME 604
Collingwood Library and Museum on
  Americanism, Alexandria, VA...............1492
Columbus-Belmont Civil War Museum,
  Columbus, KY 567
Columbus Chapel, Boal Mansion
  Museum, Boalsburg, PA......................1244
Combat Air Museum, Inc., Topeka, KS 559
Command Museum, Marine Corps
  Recruit Depot, San Diego, San Diego,
  CA...156
Confederate Memorial Museum, Atoka,
  OK...1196
Confederate Museum, New Orleans, LA 594
Cowpens National Battlefield, Chesnee,
  SC...1327
Crossroads Museum, Corinth, MS...............800
Crown Point State Historic Site, Crown
  Point, NY 984
Custer Battlefield Museum, Garryowen,
  MT...847

The Dennison Railroad Depot Museum,
  Dennison, OH 1162
Don F. Pratt Memorial Museum, Fort
  Campbell, KY 568
Drum Barracks Civil War Museum,
  Wilmington, CA 198

Eagle Historical Society & Museums,
  Eagle, AK...23
East Tennessee Historical Society,
  Knoxville, TN..................................1369
82nd Airborne Division War Memorial
  Museum, Fort Bragg, NC....................1101
Emil A. Blackmore Museum of The
  American Legion, Indianapolis, IN 482
Enlisted Heritage Hall, Maxwell AFB -
  Gunter Annex, AL 13
The Exchange Hotel Civil War Museum,
  Gordonsville, VA 1509

Fifth Maine Regiment Museum, Peaks
  Island, ME 618
1st Cavalry Division Museum, Fort
  Hood, TX 1414
The First Division Museum at Cantigny,
  Wheaton, IL.....................................465
Flying Heritage Collection, Arlington,
  WA...1547
Fort Belknap Museum and Archives, Inc.,
  Newcastle, TX.................................1441
Fort Bliss Museum, Fort Bliss, TX 1413
Fort Bowie National Historic Site,
  Bowie, AZ...30
Fort Bridger State Museum, Fort Bridger,
  WY...1632
Fort Building, Fort Bragg, CA....................95
Fort Casey Interpretive Center,
  Coupeville, WA 1551
Fort Caspar Museum, Casper, WY............1629
Fort Christmas Historical Park,
  Christmas, FL....................................299

Fort Columbia Interpretive Center,
  Chinook, WA 1551
Fort Crawford Museum, Prairie du Chien,
  WI..1618
Fort Dalles Museum/Anderson
  Homestead, The Dalles, OR.................1237
Fort Davis National Historic Site, Fort
  Davis, TX.......................................1414
Fort de Chartres State Historic Site &
  Museum, Prairie du Rocher, IL 451
Fort Delaware Society, Delaware City,
  DE...268
Fort Dodge & Frontier Village, Fort
  Dodge, IA 518
Fort Donelson National Battlefield,
  Dover, TN 1364
Fort Douglas Military Museum, Fort
  Douglas, UT....................................1465
Fort Fetterman State Historic Site,
  Douglas, WY 1631
Fort Frederick State Park, Big Pool, MD.....637
Fort Garland Museum, Fort Garland, CO 217
Fort George G. Meade Museum, Fort
  Meade, MD.......................................643
Fort Gibson Historic Site, Fort Gibson,
  OK...1200
Fort Harker Museum Complex,
  Kanopolis, KS 546
Fort Hartsuff State Historical Park,
  Burwell, NE......................................858
Fort Hays State Historic Site, Hays, KS 543
Fort Huachuca Museum, Fort Huachuca,
  AZ...34
Fort Jackson Museum, Fort Jackson, SC ...1332
Fort Kearny State Historical Park,
  Kearney, NE......................................864
Fort King George Historic Site, Darien,
  GA...370
Fort Knox State Historic Site, Prospect,
  ME...620
Fort Laramie National Historic Site, Fort
  Laramie, WY 1633
Fort Larned National Historic Site,
  Larned, KS.......................................547
Fort Laurens State Memorial, Bolivar,
  OH...1143
Fort Lee Historic Park & Museum, Fort
  Lee, NJ...904
Fort Lewis Military Museum, Fort Lewis,
  WA...1554
Fort MacArthur Museum, San Pedro, CA....176
Fort McAllister, Richmond Hill, GA...........381
Fort McKavett State Historical Site, Fort
  McKavett, TX..................................1415
Fort Meigs State Memorial, Perrysburg,
  OH...1182
Fort Morgan Museum, Gulf Shores, AL 10
Fort Morris State Historic Site, Midway,
  GA...379
Fort Ontario State Historic Site, Oswego,
  NY...1048
Fort Pike State Historic Site, New
  Orleans, LA......................................595
Fort Pitt Museum, Pittsburgh, PA.............1292
Fort Polk Museum Activity, Fort Polk,
  LA...588
Fort Pulaski National Monument,
  Savannah, GA....................................385
Fort Robinson Museum, Crawford, NE........860
Fort Sam Houston Museum, Fort Sam
  Houston, TX....................................1415
Fort Selden State Monument, Radium
  Springs, NM.....................................945
Fort Sill National Historic Landmark,
  Fort Sill, OK...................................1201
Fort Simcoe State Park, White Swan, WA.1578
Fort Spokane Visitor Center and
  Museum, Davenport, WA.....................1552
Fort Stanwix National Monument, Rome,
  NY...1061
Fort Stewart Museum, Fort Stewart, GA 372

Fort Sumter National Monument,
  Sullivan's Island, SC 1342
Fort Ticonderoga, Ticonderoga, NY 1078
Fort Totten State Historic Site, Fort
  Totten, ND 1131
Fort Towson Historic Site, Fort Towson,
  OK...1201
Fort Union National Monument, Watrous,
  NM...954
Fort Verde State Historic Park, Camp
  Verde, AZ...30
Fort Washington Park, Fort Washington,
  MD...643
Fort Washita, Durant, OK 1199
Fort Wilkins Historic Complex, Copper
  Harbor, MI.......................................733
45th Infantry Division Museum,
  Oklahoma City, OK............................1207
Fountain County War Museum, Inc.,
  Veedersburg, IN 502
442nd Veterans Club Archives, Honolulu,
  HI...395
4th Infantry Division Museum, Fort
  Hood, TX...1415
Frankfort Area Historical Museum, West
  Frankfort, IL....................................464
Fredericksburg & Spotsylvania National
  Military Park, Fredericksburg, VA.........1506
Frontier Army Museum, Fort
  Leavenworth, KS 539

Gateway NRA, Sandy Hook Unit, Fort
  Hancock, NJ.....................................904
Gathland State Park, Boonsboro, MD.........637
General Crook House Museum and
  Library/Archives Center, Omaha, NE......870
General Daniel Bissell House, Saint
  Louis, MO.......................................833
The General Douglas L. McBride
  Museum, New Mexico Military
  Institute, Roswell, NM 945
General Douglas MacArthur Memorial,
  Norfolk, VA....................................1521
General John J. Pershing Boyhood Home
  State Historic Site, Laclede, MO............824
General Patton Memorial Museum,
  Chiriaco Summit, CA 84
Georgia Veterans Memorial Museum,
  Cordele, GA......................................369
Golden Gate National Recreation Area,
  San Francisco, CA...............................165
Granville Museum, Inc., Granville, TN......1366
Great Lakes Museum of Military History,
  Michigan City, IN 490
Great Lakes Naval Museum, Great
  Lakes, IL...439
Grissom Air Museum, Peru, IN 496
Guilford Courthouse National Military
  Park, Greensboro, NC 1104

H.E.A.R.T.S. Veterans Museum of Texas,
  Huntsville, TX..................................1430
Hampton History Museum, Hampton, VA .1509
Harbor Defense Museum, Brooklyn, NY 969
Harrisonburg-Rockingham Historical
  Society, Dayton, VA...........................1503
Heartland Museum of Military Vehicles,
  Lexington, NE...................................865
Higgins Armory Museum, Worcester, MA...721
Highland County Museum and Heritage
  Center, McDowell, VA.........................1517
Hill Aerospace Museum, Hill Air Force
  Base, UT..1466
Historic Auto Attractions, Roscoe, IL........456
Historic Fort Snelling, Saint Paul, MN 790
Historic Fort Steilacoom, Lakewood, WA..1558
Historic Fort Stockton, Fort Stockton, TX.1416
History and Traditions Museum,
  Lackland Air Force Base, TX................1433
Homeville Museum, Homer, NY................999
Horseshoe Bend National Military Park,
  Daviston, AL......................................7

Idaho Military History Museum, Boise, ID 404

Illinois Citizen Soldier Museum, Galesburg, IL 437

Independence National Historical Park, Philadelphia, PA 1281

Indiana War Memorials, Indianapolis, IN 484

Intrepid Sea-Air-Space Museum, New York, NY 1028

JFK Special Warfare Museum, Fort Bragg, NC 1101

The Jackson Barracks Military Museum, New Orleans, LA 596

Jefferson Barracks Historic Site, Saint Louis, MO 833

Kalamazoo Aviation History Museum, Kalamazoo, MI 748

Kennesaw Mountain National Battlefield Park, Kennesaw, GA 374

Kenosha Military Museum, Pleasant Prairie, WI 1617

Kentucky Military History Museum, Frankfort, KY 569

Kings Mountain National Military Park, Blacksburg, SC 1322

Kodiak Military History Museum, Kodiak, AK 27

Korean War Veterans National Museum & Library, Rantoul, IL 453

Legion of Valor Veterans Museum, Fresno, CA 98

Lesueur County Historical Museum-Chapter 1, Elysian, MN 774

The Lithuanian Museum, Chicago, IL 423

Lone Star Flight Museum/Texas Aviation Hall of Fame, Galveston, TX 1421

Louisiana Naval War Memorial/U.S.S. Kidd, Baton Rouge, LA 586

MacArthur Museum of Arkansas Military History, Little Rock, AR 62

Mackinac Island State Park Commission-Mackinac State Historic Parks, Mackinaw City, MI 752

The Major General Frederick Funston Boyhood Home and Museum, Iola, KS 546

Manassas National Battlefield Park, Manassas, VA 1516

March Field Air Museum, Riverside, CA 149

Maritime Museum at Historic Coast Guard Station, Saint Simons Island, GA 383

McChord Air Museum, Tacoma, WA 1573

McCoy House, Lewistown, PA 1269

The Memorial Day Museum, Waterloo, NY 1083

Memphis Belle B17 Flying Fortress, Memphis, TN 1374

Mighty Eighth Air Force Museum, Pooler, GA 381

Military Aviation Museum, Virginia Beach, VA 1542

Military Historians, Headquarters & Museum, Westbrook, CT 265

Military Museum of Southern New England, Danbury, CT 238

Military Veterans Museum, Inc., Oshkosh, WI 1616

Millville Army Air Field Museum, Millville, NJ 911

Minter Field Air Museum, Shafter, CA 186

Miracle of America Museum Inc., Polson, MT 852

Mississippi Armed Forces Museum, Camp Shelby, MS 799

Mississippi County Historical Society, Charleston, MO 812

Moores Creek National Battlefield, Currie, NC 1097

Morristown National Historical Park, Morristown, NJ 914

Motts Military Museum, Groveport, OH 1167

Museum at Mountain Home - East Tennessee State University, Johnson City, TN 1368

Museum of Southern History, Jacksonville, FL 315

The Museum of Southern History, Sugarland, TX 1454

The Museum of the Confederacy, Richmond, VA 1531

Museum of the Soldier, Portland, IN 496

National Atomic Museum, Albuquerque, NM 934

The National Civil War Museum, Harrisburg, PA 1258

National Civil War Naval Museum at Port Columbus, Columbus, GA 369

National Infantry Museum, Fort Benning, GA 372

National Liberty Ship Memorial/S.S. Jeremiah O'Brien, San Francisco, CA 168

National Medal of Honor Museum of Military History, Chattanooga, TN 1362

National Museum of American Jewish Military History, Washington, DC 286

National Museum of Health and Medicine, Washington, DC 286

National Museum of Naval Aviation, Pensacola, FL 336

National Museum of the United States Air Force, Wright-Patterson Air Force Base, OH 1193

National Park Service Vicksburg National Military Park-Cairo Museum, Vicksburg, MS 809

National Vietnam Veterans Art Museum, Chicago, IL 425

National World War I Museum at Liberty Memorial, Kansas City, MO 822

Naval War College Museum, Newport, RI 1314

Navy UDT-SEAL Museum, Fort Pierce, FL 309

New England Civil War Museum, Vernon, CT 263

New Jersey Naval Museum, Hackensack, NJ 905

New Windsor Cantonment State Historic Site and National Purple Heart Hall of Honor, Vails Gate, NY 1080

New York State Military Museum and Veterans Research Center, Saratoga Springs, NY 1065

Newell Museum, Newell, SD 1352

The Northumberland County Historical Society, Sunbury, PA 1302

Novato History Museum, Novato, CA 132

Noyes House Museum, Morrisville, VT 1483

Octave Chanute Aerospace Museum, Rantoul, IL 453

Old Fort Jackson, Savannah, GA 385

Old Fort Meade Museum and Historic Research Association, Fort Meade, SD .1347

Old Fort Niagara, Youngstown, NY 1088

The Old Guard Museum, Fort Myer, VA ...1505

The Old Jail Museum, Warrenton, VA 1543

Old Stone House Museum, Windsor, NY ..1086

Oldest House Museum Complex, Saint Augustine, FL 339

Olustee Battlefield Historic State Park, Olustee, FL 331

103rd Ohio Volunteer Infantry Civil War Museum, Sheffield Lake, OH 1185

Oregon Military Museum, Clackamas, OR 1221

Pacific Aviation Museum - Pearl Harbor, Honolulu, HI 397

Pamplin Historical Park and The National Museum of the Civil War Soldier, Petersburg, VA 1525

Paper Airplane Museum and the Tin Can Man of Maui, Kahului Central Maui, HI 399

Parris Island Museum, Parris Island, SC 1338

Patrol Squadron Colorado, Aurora, CO 202

Patton Museum of Cavalry and Armor, Fort Knox, KY 568

Pea Ridge National Military Park, Garfield, AR 58

Pennsylvania Military Museum and 28th Division Shrine, Boalsburg, PA 1244

Perryville Battlefield Museum, Perryville, KY 582

Petersburg National Battlefield, Petersburg, VA 1525

Peterson Air & Space Museum, Peterson Air Force Base, CO 229

Phillips County Museum, Helena, AR 59

Polish Museum of America, Chicago, IL 426

Portsmouth Museum of Military History Inc., Portsmouth, VA 1526

Pratt County Historical Society Museum, Pratt, KS 556

Pueblo Weisbrod Aircraft Museum, Pueblo, CO 230

Puget Sound Coast Artillery Museum at Fort Worden, Port Townsend, WA 1562

Ravalli County Museum/Bitter Root Valley Historical Society, Hamilton, MT 848

Richard I. Bong WWII Heritage Center, Superior, WI 1624

Richmond National Battlefield Park, Richmond, VA 1531

Rock Island Arsenal Museum, Rock Island, IL 454

Sackets Harbor Battlefield State Historic Site, Sackets Harbor, NY 1062

St. Marys Submarine Museum, Saint Marys, GA 382

Sandown Historical Society and Museum, Sandown, NH 896

Santa Fe Trail Museum, Ingalls, KS 545

Saratoga National Historical Park, Stillwater, NY 1075

Shiloh National Military Park & Cemetery, Shiloh, TN 1384

Siege Museum (The Petersburg Museums), Petersburg, VA 1525

Silent Wings Museum, Lubbock, TX 1435

Soldiers' Memorial Military Museum, Saint Louis, MO 837

Soldiers National Museum, Gettysburg, PA 1256

South Carolina Military Museum, Columbia, SC 1330

South Dakota National Guard Museum, Pierre, SD 1353

Stars and Stripes Museum/Library, Bloomfield, MO 811

Stones River National Battlefield, Murfreesboro, TN 1377

Stonewall Jackson Museum at Hupp's Hill, Strasburg, VA 1539

Stony Point Battlefield State Historic Site, Stony Point, NY 1075

Strategic Air & Space Museum, Ashland, NE 856

Tennessee Museum of Aviation, Sevierville, TN 1383

Texas Air Museum, Slaton, TX 1453

Texas Heritage Museum, Hillsboro, TX 1424

Texas Ranger Hall of Fame and Museum, Waco, TX 1459

Third Cavalry Museum, Fort Carson, CO 216

Tillamook Naval Air Station Museum, Tillamook, OR 1237

Military Museums–Continued

Tipton County Museum, Veteran's Memorial & Nature Center, Covington, TN 1364

Titan Missile Museum, Green Valley, AZ 36

Tri-State University, General Lewis B. Hershey Museum, Angola, IN 468

Triangle Tattoo & Museum, Fort Bragg, CA 95

Tropic Lightning Museum, Schofield Barracks, HI 402

U.S. Navy Museum, Washington, DC 292

United States Army Heritage and Education Center - Army Heritage Museum, Carlisle, PA 1246

The United States Army Quartermaster Museum, Fort Lee, VA 1505

United States Marine Corps Air-Ground Museum, Quantico, VA 1526

U.S. Air Force Academy Visitor Center, USAF Academy, CO 234

U.S. Army Air Defense Artillery Museum, Fort Bliss, TX 1414

U.S. Army Aviation Museum, Fort Rucker, AL 10

U.S. Army Center of Military History, Museum Division, Fort McNair, DC 275

U.S. Army Chaplain Museum, Fort Jackson, SC 1332

U.S. Army Communications-Electronics Museum, Fort Monmouth, NJ 904

U.S. Army Engineer Museum, Fort Leonard Wood, MO 815

U.S. Army Finance Corps Museum, Fort Jackson, SC 1333

U.S. Army Medical Department Museum, Fort Sam Houston, TX 1415

U.S. Army Military Police Corps Museum, Fort Leonard Wood, MO 816

U.S. Army Museum of Hawaii, Fort DeRussy, HI 392

U.S. Army Ordnance Museum, Aberdeen Proving Ground, MD 627

U.S. Army Signal Corps Museum, Fort Gordon, GA 372

U.S. Army Transportation Museum, Fort Eustis, VA 1504

U.S. Army Women's Museum, Fort Lee, VA 1505

U.S. Cavalry Museum, Fort Riley, KS 540

U.S. Naval Museum of Armament & Technology, China Lake, CA 84

U.S. Navy Seabee Museum, Port Hueneme, CA 143

U.S. Navy Supply Corps Museum, Athens, GA 357

USS Alabama Battleship Memorial Park, Mobile, AL 15

USS Arizona Memorial, Honolulu, HI 398

USS Bowfin Submarine Museum & Park, Honolulu, HI 398

USS Constellation Museum, Baltimore, MD 636

USS Constitution Museum, Boston, MA 669

USS Lexington Museum on the Bay, Corpus Christi, TX 1402

USS Radford National Naval Museum, Newcomerstown, OH 1179

Valiant Air Command Warbird Air Museum, Titusville, FL 352

Varnum Memorial Armory & Military Museum, East Greenwich, RI 1311

Veterans Depot Museum, West Frankfort, IL 464

Veterans Memorial Museum, Laurel, MS 804

Vietnam Era Educational Center, Holmdel, NJ 908

Vietnam War National Museum, Nelson, NE 869

Vintage Flying Museum, Fort Worth, TX .. 1419

Virginia Military Institute Museum, Lexington, VA 1514

Virginia War Memorial, Richmond, VA 1534

The Virginia War Museum, Newport News, VA 1520

Volo Antique Auto Museum and Village, Volo, IL 463

War Between the States Museum, Florence, SC 1332

War Eagle Air Museum, Santa Teresa, NM 951

War in the Pacific National Historical Park, Piti, GU 1640

Warhawk Air Museum, Nampa, ID 408

Warren ICBM & Heritage Museum, Frances E. Warren Air Force Base, WY 1633

Warren Rifles Confederate Museum, Front Royal, VA 1508

Washington's Headquarters State Historic Site, Newburgh, NY 1042

Watervliet Arsenal's Museum of the Big Guns, Watervliet, NY 1084

West Point Museum, West Point, NY 1085

White 1 Foundation, Kissimmee, FL 319

Wilson's Creek National Battlefield, Republic, MO 829

Wings Over Miami Museum, Inc., Miami, FL 326

Wings Over The Rockies Air & Space Museum, Denver, CO 213

Wisconsin National Guard Museum, Camp Douglas, WI 1593

Wisconsin Veterans Museum-King, King, WI 1602

Wisconsin Veterans Museum-Madison, Madison, WI 1606

Wright Museum, Wolfeboro, NH 897

Yankee Air Force, Inc. (Yankee Air Museum), Ypsilanti, MI 766

Yanks Air Museum, Chino, CA 84

Preservation Projects

Albany Civil Rights Movement Museum at Old Mt. Zion Church, Albany, GA 355

Allaire Village Inc., Farmingdale, NJ 903

Amelia Earhart Birthplace Museum, Atchison, KS 532

The American Film Institute, Los Angeles, CA 112

The American Film Institute, Washington, DC 275

America's Stonehenge, North Salem, NH 893

Anthology Film Archives, New York, NY. 1020

The Antiquarian and Landmarks Society, Inc., Hartford, CT 244

The Appalachian Trail Conservancy, Harpers Ferry, WV 1581

APVA Preservation Virginia, Richmond, VA 1528

Ark-La-Tex Antique & Classic Vehicle Museum, Shreveport, LA 600

Arthurdale Heritage, Inc., Arthurdale, WV 1579

The Association for Gravestone Studies, Greenfield, MA 685

Atlanta Historical Society, Atlanta, GA 358

Au Glaize Village, Defiance, OH 1162

Audubon House & Tropical Gardens, Key West, FL 317

Aurora History Museum, Aurora, CO 202

Battleground Historical Society, Englishtown, NJ 903

Baxter Springs Heritage Center and Museum, Baxter Springs, KS 533

Beaufort Historic Site, Beaufort, NC 1091

Bennington Battle Monument, Old Bennington, VT 1484

Berkshire Scenic Railway Museum, Inc., Lenox, MA 689

Big Bone Lick State Park Museum, Union, KY 584

Big Cypress National Preserve, Ochopee, FL 330

Biltmore Estate, Asheville, NC 1089

Birthplace of John Wayne, Winterset, IA 530

Blue Ridge Institute and Museum, Ferrum, VA 1504

Bolduc House Museum, Sainte Genevieve, MO 837

Browntown Museum, Lake City, SC 1336

Buckeye Furnace State Memorial, Wellston, OH 1190

Buffalo Bill Museum of Le Claire, Iowa, Inc., Le Claire, IA 522

Burke County Historical Powers Lake Complex, Powers Lake, ND 1136

Cades Cove Visitor Center and Open-Air Museum, Townsend, TN 1384

Cahokia Courthouse State Historic Site, Cahokia, IL 415

The Camron-Stanford House Preservation Association, Oakland, CA 133

Canal Fulton Heritage Society, Canal Fulton, OH 1145

Cedar Bog Nature Preserve, Urbana, OH ... 1188

The Center for Civil War Photography, Gettysburg, PA 1255

The Central Museum, Central, AK 23

Charles Pinckney National Historic Site, Mount Pleasant, SC 1337

Chesapeake Bay Maritime Museum, Saint Michaels, MD 652

The Chesapeake Beach Railway Museum, Chesapeake Beach, MD 639

Chittenango Landing Canal Boat Museum, Chittenango, NY 978

Coggeshall Farm Museum, Bristol, RI 1310

Colonel Allensworth State Historic Park, Allensworth, CA 70

Colonel Davenport Historical Foundation, Rock Island, IL 453

The Colonial Spanish Quarter Museum, Saint Augustine, FL 338

Colonial Williamsburg, Williamsburg, VA . 1544

Columbia County Historical Society, Inc., Kinderhook, NY 1007

Columbia State Historic Park, Columbia, CA 87

Congaree National Park, Hopkins, SC 1336

Connecticut River Museum, Essex, CT 239

Cookeville Depot Museum, Cookeville, TN 1364

Coppertown U.S.A., Calumet, MI 731

Courthouse Square Association, Charlotte, MI 731

Crafts Museum, Mequon, WI 1609

Cragfont-Historic Cragfont, Inc., Castalian Springs, TN 1360

Crocker House, Mount Clemens, MI 756

Crockett Tavern Museum, Morristown, TN 1376

Crow Canyon Archaeological Center, Cortez, CO 208

Crystal Caverns at Hupp's Hill, Strasburg, VA 1538

Culbertson Museum, Culbertson, MT 845

Davenport House Museum, Savannah, GA 384

Deerfield Beach Historical Society, Deerfield Beach, FL 304

The Dennison Railroad Depot Museum, Dennison, OH 1162

Department of the Treasury, Washington, DC 278

Detroit Historical Society, Detroit, MI 735

Dinsmore Homestead Foundation, Burlington, KY 566

Drayton Hall, Charleston, SC 1325

Drummond Home, Hominy, OK 1203

Dry Tortugas National Park, Key West, FL 317
Durham Western Heritage Museum, Omaha, NE 870

E. St. Julien Cox House, Saint Peter, MN ...792
East End Seaport Museum and Marine Foundation, Greenport, NY.....................996
Edison National Historic Site, West Orange, NJ......................................930
The 1890 House-Museum & Center for Arts, Cortland, NY 983
Eldridge Street Project, New York, NY 1025
Ellis County Museum, Inc., Waxahachie, TX 1460
End-O-Line Railroad Park & Museum, Currie, MN 772

Faust Park Foundation, Chesterfield, MO 812
Faust Park-Thornhill Historic Site & 19th Century Village, Chesterfield, MO 812
Fayette Historic State Park, Garden, MI 742
Florence Ranch Homestead, Mesquite, TX 1438
Fort Abercrombie State Historic Site, Abercrombie, ND 1127
Fort Bend Museum Association, Richmond, TX 1445
Fort Concho National Historic Landmark, San Angelo, TX...............................1447
Fort Garland Museum, Fort Garland, CO 217
Fort Hartsuff State Historical Park, Burwell, NE 858
Fort Larned National Historic Site, Larned, KS.......................................547
Fort Lauderdale Historical Society, Fort Lauderdale, FL..................................307
Fort St. Jean Baptiste State Historic Site, Natchitoches, LA...............................593
Fort Scott National Historic Site, Fort Scott, KS.......................................540
Fort Sumter National Monument, Sullivan's Island, SC 1342

Garfield Farm Museum, LaFox, IL 441
Gaston County Museum of Art and History, Dallas, NC 1097
Geddes Historic District Village, Geddes, SD 1347
General Crook House Museum and Library/Archives Center, Omaha, NE......870
Geneva Historical Society & Prouty-Chew House & Museum, Geneva, NY 994
The Great Overland Station, Topeka, KS.....559
Grissom Air Museum, Peru, IN 496

Haas-Lilienthal House, San Francisco, CA 166
Hacienda Buena Vista, Ponce, PR 1642
Hamilton Van Wagoner Museum, Clifton, NJ 901
Hanford Mills Museum, East Meredith, NY 987
The Heritage Society, Houston, TX............1426
Heritage Village, Mountain Lake, MN 785
The Hermitage, Ho-Ho-Kus, NJ 907
Hernando Heritage Museum, Brooksville, FL 298
Hickory Landmarks Society-Propst House & Maple Grove, Hickory, NC...............1106
Hillforest House Museum, Aurora, IN 468
Historic Arkansas Museum, Little Rock, AR 62
Historic Bethany, Bethany, WV 1580
Historic Brattonsville, McConnells, SC......1336
Historic Charleston Foundation, Charleston, SC 1325
Historic Columbia Foundation, Columbia, SC 1329
Historic Hudson Valley, Tarrytown, NY.....1077
Historic Jamestowne, Jamestown, VA 1512

Historic Jefferson College, Washington, MS..810
Historic London Town and Gardens, Edgewater, MD 642
Historic New England, Boston, MA.............665
Historic New Harmony, New Harmony, IN 494
Historic Pensacola Village, Pensacola, FL ...335
Historic Pullman Foundation, Chicago, IL...421
Historic Rugby, Rugby, TN 1383
Historic Schaefferstown, Inc., Schaefferstown, PA 1297
Historic Stagville, Durham, NC 1098
Holly History Center & Hutchinson House Museum, Waupaca, WI..............1626
Holocaust Documentation & Education Center, Inc., Hollywood, FL 313

Ironwood Area Historical Museum, Ironwood, MI.....................................747

Jacinto Foundation, Inc., Corinth, MS..........800
Jack London State Historic Park, Glen Ellen, CA 99
James Buchanan Foundation for the Preservation of Wheatland, Lancaster, PA 1266
Japanese American National Museum, Los Angeles, CA.................................117
Jarrell Plantation Georgia State Historic Site, Juliette, GA 374
Jefferson Barracks Historic Site, Saint Louis, MO.......................................833
Jekyll Island Museum, Jekyll Island, GA 374
Jensen Arctic Museum, Monmouth, OR 1228
Jim Thorpe Home, Yale, OK 1217
Johnson County Museum of History, Franklin, IN 478
Jonathan Hager House & Museum, Hagerstown, MD 646

The Kelso House Museum, Kent, OH 1169
Kentucky Gateway Museum Center, Maysville, KY 579
Kimberly Crest House & Gardens, Redlands, CA 147
Knudt Salle Log Cabin, Adams, ND 1127
Korner's Folly, Kernersville, NC 1108

La Purisima Mission State Historic Park, Lompoc, CA 109
The Landmark Society of Western New York, Rochester, NY 1058
Las Cabezas de San Juan Nature Reserve (El Faro), Fajardo, PR 1641
Leaming's Run Garden & Colonial Farm, Swainton, NJ 926
Lewes Historical Society, Lewes, DE 271
Lincoln's New Salem State Historic Site, Petersburg, IL 451
Lockwood-Mathews Mansion Museum, Norwalk, CT 257
Locust Lawn and Terwilliger House, Gardiner, NY 993
Louisiana Naval War Memorial/U.S.S. Kidd, Baton Rouge, LA 586
Lum & Abner Museum & Jot 'Em Down Store, Pine Ridge, AR 66
The Lyons Redstone Museum, Lyons, CO...227

Madison-Morgan Cultural Center, Madison, GA 378
Magnolia Plantation and Gardens, Charleston, SC 1326
Manatee Village Historical Park, Bradenton, FL 297
Martin Luther King, Jr. National Historic Site and Preservation District, Atlanta, GA 361
Mary Todd Lincoln House, Lexington, KY 574
Mary Washington House, Fredericksburg, VA 1507

Mississippi University for Women, Archives and Museum, Columbus, MS...800
Monroe County Heritage Museum, Monroeville, AL 15
Morton Museum of Cooke County, Gainesville, TX 1420
Morven Museum & Garden, Princeton, NJ 922
Morven Park, Leesburg, VA.....................1512
Moundbuilders State Memorial & Museum, Newark, OH 1178
Mt. Pulaski Courthouse State Historic Site, Mount Pulaski, IL 446
Mount Vernon Ladies' Association, Mount Vernon, VA................................1518
Murfreesboro Historical Association, Murfreesboro, NC 1112
Museum of Florida History, Tallahassee, FL 348
Museum of the City of Lake Worth, Lake Worth, FL 320

Naper Settlement, Naperville, IL 447
National Audubon Society, New York, NY 1034
National Building Museum, Washington, DC 284
National Historic Oregon Trail Interpretive Center, Baker City, OR 1219
National Museum of Industrial History, Bethlehem, PA 1243
New Harmony State Historic Site/Historic New Harmony, New Harmony, IN 494
Newport Restoration Foundation, Newport, RI 1315
Ninety Six National Historic Site, Ninety Six, SC 1338
Northeast Document Conservation Center, Andover, MA 660

Old Courthouse Museum, Santa Ana, CA....178
Old Dorchester State Historic Site, Summerville, SC 1342
Old Economy Village, Ambridge, PA.........1240
Old Fort Johnson, Fort Johnson, NY...........991
Old Prison Museums, Deer Lodge, MT.......845
The Old Schwamb Mill, Arlington, MA 660
Old Town San Diego State Historic Park, San Diego, CA 158
Overholser Mansion, Oklahoma City, OK .1210
Overstreet-Kerr Historical Farm, Keota, OK 1203

Patterson Inn Museum/Corning - Painted Post Historical Society, Corning, NY 982
Pearson Air Museum, Vancouver, WA 1576
Pendleton Historic Foundation, Pendleton, SC 1339
The Pierce Manse/New Hampshire Political Library, Concord, NH 885
Pioneer Settlement for the Creative Arts, Barberville, FL 295
Pittock Mansion, Portland, OR 1232
Plains Conservation Center, Aurora, CO......202
Port Gamble Historic Museum, Port Gamble, WA 1562
The Portal of the Folded Wings Shrine to Aviation and Museum, North Hollywood, CA 131
Potts Inn Museum, Pottsville, AR 66
The Preservation Society of Newport County/The Newport Mansions, Newport, RI 1315

Queens County Farm Museum, Floral Park, NY 989

Reitz Home Museum, Evansville, IN...........476
Restoration House, Mantorville, MN...........780
Riverview at Hobson Grove, Bowling Green, KY 566
Rose Hill Museum, Bay Village, OH 1141
Rosemount Museum, Pueblo, CO................230

Preservation Projects–Continued

The Rotch-Jones-Duff House & Garden
  Museum, Inc., New Bedford, MA 697

St. Lawrence County Historical
  Association - Silas Wright House,
  Canton, NY 975
The Scarsdale Historical Society,
  Scarsdale, NY 1066
Schoenbrunn Village State Memorial,
  New Philadelphia, OH..............................1177
Schoharie Colonial Heritage Association,
  Schoharie, NY 1067
The Schuette Biermann Farmhouse
  Museum, Elk Grove Village, IL 432
Shaker Heritage Society, Albany, NY 956
Shaker Museum at South Union, South
  Union, KY 583
Slaughter Ranch Museum, Douglas, AZ 32
Sloss Furnaces National Historic
  Landmark, Birmingham, AL 5
Snyder Museum & Creative Arts Center,
  Bastrop, LA 585
South River Meeting House, Lynchburg,
  VA 1516
South Sutton Old Store Museum, South
  Sutton, NH 896
Spiro Mounds Archaeological Center,
  Spiro, OK..1214
Split Rock Lighthouse Historic Site, Two
  Harbors, MN..795
The Steamboat Arabia Museum, Kansas
  City, MO..822
The Stickley Museum at Craftsman
  Farms, Parsippany, NJ..............................920
Susan B. Anthony House, Rochester, NY ..1060

Tarpon Springs Cultural Center, Tarpon
  Springs, FL 351
Ted Smallwood's Store, Inc.,
  Chokoloskee, FL..299
Tennessee Central Railway Museum,
  Nashville, TN..1380
Thomas Jefferson's Poplar Forest, Forest,
  VA 1504
Totem Heritage Center, Ketchikan, AK 26
Travellers Rest Plantation & Museum,
  Nashville, TN..1381
The Trustees of Reservations, Beverly,
  MA 662
Tunica-Biloxi Native American Museum,
  Marksville, LA 591

United States Capitol, Washington, DC 293

Vaile Mansion-Dewitt Museum,
  Independence, MO.....................................819
Valley Forge National Historical Park,
  King of Prussia, PA..................................1264
The Vermont State House, Montpelier,
  VT 1483
Vernon Historians, Inc., Vernon, VT 1489

Washington County Fair Farm Museum,
  Greenwich, NY 996
West Virginia Independence Hall,
  Wheeling, WV...1588
West Virginia State Museum, Charleston,
  WV 1581
The Wetlands Institute, Stone Harbor, NJ 925
Wheat Ridge Historic Park, Wheat Ridge,
  CO 235
Wheeler Historic Farm, Salt Lake City,
  UT 1474
The White House, Washington, DC..............294
White 1 Foundation, Kissimmee, FL............319
Whitehaven Tourist Welcome Center,
  Paducah, KY..582
Wickersham House Museum
  (Tanana-Yukon Historical Society),
  Fairbanks, AK..24
William King Regional Arts Center,
  Abingdon, VA...1491

Woodstock Historical Society, Inc.,
  Woodstock, CT...268
Workman & Temple Family Homestead
  Museum, City of Industry, CA 85
World Figure Skating Museum & Hall of
  Fame, Colorado Springs, CO....................208
Wyandotte Museum, Wyandotte, MI 766
Wyoming Territorial Prison State Historic
  Site, Laramie, WY...................................1636

LIBRARIES HAVING
COLLECTIONS OF BOOKS

A.L. Fetterman Educational Museum,
  Fort Valley, GA..372
Abraham Lincoln Presidential Library &
  Museum, Springfield, IL 458
Academy of Model Aeronautics/National
  Model Aviation Museum, Muncie, IN.....492
Adirondack Park Visitor Interpretive
  Center, Paul Smiths, NY..........................1051
The African American Museum in
  Philadelphia, Philadelphia, PA 1275
Alachua County Historic Trust: Matheson
  Museum, Inc., Gainesville, FL.................310
Alaska Heritage Museum at Wells Fargo,
  Anchorage, AK..21
Amelia Island Museum of History,
  Fernandina Beach, FL 306
American Baptist Historical Society,
  Rochester, NY...1058
The American Film Institute, Los
  Angeles, CA..112
The American Film Institute, Washington,
  DC 275
American Independence Museum, Exeter,
  NH 887
American Irish Historical Society, New
  York, NY..1019
American Quarter Horse Hall of Fame &
  Museum, Amarillo, TX 1386
American Truck Historical Society,
  Kansas City, MO.......................................820
Anasazi Heritage Center, Dolores, CO.........214
Androscoggin Historical Society, Auburn,
  ME 603
The Andy Warhol Museum, Pittsburgh,
  PA 1290
Anthology Film Archives, New York, NY .1020
The Appalachian Trail Conservancy,
  Harpers Ferry, WV...................................1581
Arizona Jewish Historical Society,
  Phoenix, AZ..39
Armenian Library and Museum of
  America, Watertown, MA 716
The Armory Art Center, West Palm
  Beach, FL 353
Atlanta College of Art, Atlanta, GA............358
Audubon Society of New Hampshire,
  Concord, NH..884
Audubon Society of Rhode Island,
  Smithfield, RI...1319
Austin History Center, Austin, TX 1388

Bay of Pigs Museum & Library, Miami,
  FL 323
Bob Campbell Geology Museum,
  Clemson, SC...1328
Brand Library & Art Center, Glendale,
  CA 100
Browntown Museum, Lake City, SC.........1336
Bucks County Civil War Library &
  Museum, Doylestown, PA........................1249

California African-American Museum,
  Los Angeles, CA.......................................113
California Historical Society, San
  Francisco, CA..163
Casteel-Linn House and Museum,
  Princeton, MO...829
Center for American History, Austin, TX ..1390
Center for Curatorial Studies,
  Annandale-on-Hudson, NY 958

Centerville Historical Museum,
  Centerville, MA...675
Central Nevada Museum & Historical
  Society, Tonopah, NV 882
Chancellor Robert R. Livingston Masonic
  Library & Museum, New York, NY......1022
Chattanooga African Museum/Bessie
  Smith Hall, Chattanooga, TN.................1360
Cleo Redd Fisher Museum, Loudonville,
  OH 1172
Clinton County Historical Society,
  Wilmington, OH.......................................1191
Colorado Springs Fine Arts Center
  (Taylor Museum), Colorado Springs,
  CO 206
Connecticut Historical Society, Hartford,
  CT 244
Croatian Heritage Museum & Library,
  Eastlake, OH..1163
Crossroads Museum, Corinth, MS..............800
Culinary Archives & Museum, Johnson
  & Wales University, Providence, RI......1316
Czech Center New York, New York, NY ..1024

D.R. Barker Historical Museum,
  Fredonia, NY..992
Dallas Holocaust Museum, Dallas, TX 1405
The Danish Immigrant Museum, Elk
  Horn, IA...517
Danvers Archival Center, Danvers, MA......678
Dawes County Historical Society
  Museum, Chadron, NE.............................859
Dedham Historical Society Museum,
  Dedham, MA...679
Drum Barracks Civil War Museum,
  Wilmington, CA..198
Dubuque Arboretum & Botanical
  Gardens, Dubuque, IA..............................516

Eastchester Historical Society - 1835
  Marble Schoolhouse, Bronxville, NY......967
Egan Maritime Foundation, Nantucket,
  MA 695
Emil A. Blackmore Museum of The
  American Legion, Indianapolis, IN 482

Feet First: The Scholl Story, Rosalind
  Franklin University, North Chicago, IL...448
The First Division Museum at Cantigny,
  Wheaton, IL..465
Forest Park Museum and Arboretum,
  Perry, IA...527
Fossil Museum, Fossil, OR......................1224
Fresno Flats Historical Park, Oakhurst,
  CA 132

Gatekeeper's Museum & Marion
  Steinbach Indian Basket Museum,
  Tahoe City, CA...190
Gemological Institute of America
  Museum, Carlsbad, CA 81
General Douglas MacArthur Memorial,
  Norfolk, VA...1521
Grand Lodge AF&AM of Virginia - Allen
  E. Roberts Masonic Library and
  Museum, Richmond, VA 1529
Grand Traverse Heritage Center, Traverse
  City, MI..765

Haines Museum, Waukegan Historical
  Society, Waukegan, IL.............................463
Harold M. Freund American Museum of
  Baking, Manhattan, KS.............................550
Harry Ransom Center at the University
  of Texas at Austin, Austin, TX 1390
Held-Poage Memorial Home and
  Research Library, Ukiah, CA...................193
Heritage Library Museum, Anchorage,
  AK 22
Hiller Aviation Institute, San Carlos, CA 155
Historic Langhorne Association,
  Langhorne, PA...1267
Historical Society of Haddonfield,
  Haddonfield, NJ..905

Historical Society of Pennsylvania, Philadelphia, PA 1281
Historical Society of Quincy and Adams County, Quincy, IL 452
Holocaust Museum Houston, Houston, TX 1426
Homeopathy Works, Berkeley Springs, WV 1580
Horseless Carriage Foundation & Automotive Research Library, La Mesa, CA 107
House of the Temple, Washington, DC 280
The Humphrey Forum, Minneapolis, MN....782
Huntington Library, Art Collections, and Botanical Gardens, San Marino, CA 174

Indiana Historical Society, Indianapolis, IN 483
The International Clown Hall of Fame & Research Center, Inc., Milwaukee, WI..1611
International Motor Racing Research Center at Watkins Glen, Watkins Glen, NY 1084
The International Printing Museum, Carson, CA 82
International Women's Air and Space Museum, Inc., Cleveland, OH................1155
Intuit: The Center for Intuitive and Outsider Art, Chicago, IL.........................422
Irish American Heritage Museum, Albany, NY 954

Jaffrey Civic Center, Jaffrey, NH.................889
James S. Copley Library, La Jolla, CA 106
Jay I. Kislak Foundation, Miami Lakes, FL 327
Jeane Dixon Museum and Library, Strasburg, VA..1538
John F. Kennedy Presidential Library & Museum, Boston, MA..............................666
John Sydnor's 1847 Powhatan House, Galveston, TX 1421

Klyne Esopus Museum, Ulster Park, NY...1079

Lady Bird Johnson Wildflower Center, Austin, TX 1390
Lauder Museum - Amityville Historical Society, Amityville, NY 957
Law Enforcement Memorial Association, Inc., Roselle, IL......................................456
Lawrence L. Lee Scouting Museum, Manchester, NH 891
Lesbian Herstory Educational Foundation, Inc. aka Lesbian Herstory Archives, Brooklyn, NY 969
The Lithuanian Museum, Chicago, IL..........423
The Living Word National Bible Museum, Aledo, TX 1386
Lone Star Flight Museum/Texas Aviation Hall of Fame, Galveston, TX.................1421
Los Angeles (Central) Public Library, Los Angeles, CA 117

Malden Public Library, Malden, MA 692
Maridon Museum, Butler, PA 1245
Marion Public Library Museum, Marion, IN 490
The Mary Baker Eddy Library for the Betterment of Humanity, Boston, MA.....666
Melton Art Reference Library, Oklahoma City, OK..1208
Mendocino Historical Research, Inc./Kelley House Museum, Mendocino, CA 125
Mighty Eighth Air Force Museum, Pooler, GA 381
Mississippi Baptist Historical Commission, Clinton, MS.....................799
Missouri Botanical Garden, Saint Louis, MO 834
Monroe County Local History Room & Library, Sparta, WI...............................1622

Museum of Ancient Artifacts, Las Vegas, NV 879
Museum of Art and History at the McPherson Center, Santa Cruz, CA 182
Museum of Chinese in the Americas, New York, NY 1032
Museum of Comparative Zoology, Cambridge, MA 674
Museum of Funeral Customs, Springfield, IL 459
Museum of Indian Culture, Allentown, PA 1239
Museum of San Diego History and Research Library, San Diego, CA 158
Museum of Southern History, Jacksonville, FL..315
Museum of the Mountain Man, Pinedale, WY 1637
Museum of Women's History, Billings, MT 841

Napoleonic Society of America, Inc., Clearwater, FL 300
National Czech & Slovak Museum & Library, Cedar Rapids, IA...........................509
National First Ladies' Library, Canton, OH 1145
National Frontier Trails Museum, Independence, MO....................................818
National Hispanic Cultural Center, Art Museum, Albuquerque, NM...................935
National Yiddish Book Center, Amherst, MA 659
Native American Museum, Terre Haute, IN 500
The New York Historical Society, New York, NY 1035
Newport Historical Society & The Museum of Newport History, Newport, RI 1315
The Newsome House Museum & Cultural Center, Newport News, VA 1520
Northampton County Historical and Genealogical Society, Easton, PA 1250

Old Jefferson Town, Oskaloosa, KS 555

Photographic Resource Center, Boston, MA 669
Platt R. Spencer Memorial Archives and Special Collections Area, Geneva, OH..1166
Provisions Library, Washington, DC 289
Pueblo County Historical Society Museum and Edward H. Broadhead Library, Pueblo, CO 230

Queens Historical Society, Flushing, NY.....990

Roger Tory Peterson Institute of Natural History, Jamestown, NY........................1005
Ronald Reagan Presidential Library and Museum, Simi Valley, CA.......................187

San Francisco International Airport; San Francisco Airport Museums, San Francisco, CA 169
Sanford Museum, Sanford, FL.....................343
Sanibel-Captiva Conservation Foundation, Inc., Sanibel, FL..343
Sappington House Museum, Crestwood, MO 814
Senator John Heinz Pittsburgh Regional History Center, Pittsburgh, PA..............1294
Slidell Museum, Slidell, LA 602
Snyder Museum & Creative Arts Center, Bastrop, LA 585
The Society of California Pioneers, San Francisco, CA 170
SoDus Bay Historical Society, Sodus Point, NY 1070
South Carolina Historical Society, Charleston, SC..1327
South Carolina Institute of Archaeology & Anthropology, Columbia, SC.............1330

Stephens African-American Museum, Shreveport, LA...602
The Stowitts Museum & Library, Pacific Grove, CA 137

Texas Air Museum, Slaton, TX 1453
Tile Heritage Foundation, Healdsburg, CA 102
Tunica-Biloxi Native American Museum, Marksville, LA 591

United States Golf Association Museum & Archives, Far Hills, NJ 903
United States Holocaust Memorial Museum, Washington, DC 293
UTSA's Institute of Texan Cultures, San Antonio, TX....................................1451

Virginia Historical Society, Richmond, VA 1533
Virginia Holocaust Museum, Richmond, VA 1533
The Virginia War Museum, Newport News, VA 1520

Washington County Historical Society, Portland, OR...1233
Weems-Botts Museum, Dumfries, VA........1503
Weinman Mineral Museum, White, GA.......391
West Pasco Historical Society Museum and Library, New Port Richey, FL 329
Westchester County Historical Society, Elmsford, NY..988
The Wolfsonian - Florida International University, Miami Beach, FL.................327
World of Wings Pigeon Center, Oklahoma City, OK 1211
The World Organization of China Painters, Oklahoma City, OK.................1211

LIBRARIES HAVING COLLECTIONS OTHER THAN BOOKS

Abraham Lincoln Presidential Library & Museum, Springfield, IL 458
Academy of Model Aeronautics/National Model Aviation Museum, Muncie, IN.....492
The African American Museum in Philadelphia, Philadelphia, PA 1275
Alice C. Sabatini Gallery-Topeka and Shawnee County Public Library, Topeka, KS 558
Amelia Island Museum of History, Fernandina Beach, FL.............................306
American Antiquarian Society, Worcester, MA 720
The American Film Institute, Los Angeles, CA 112
The American Film Institute, Washington, DC 275
American Hungarian Foundation/Museum of the American Hungarian Foundation, New Brunswick, NJ.............915
American Labor Museum, Botto House National Landmark, Haledon, NJ 906
The American Museum of Fly Fishing, Manchester, VT...1481
American Quarter Horse Hall of Fame & Museum, Amarillo, TX 1386
American Truck Historical Society, Kansas City, MO......................................820
Amos Herr House Foundation and Historic Society, Landisville, PA 1267
Androscoggin Historical Society, Auburn, ME 603
The Andy Warhol Museum, Pittsburgh, PA 1290
Anti-Saloon League Museum, Westerville, OH 1190
Archives of American Art, Smithsonian Institution, Washington, DC....................276
Arizona Jewish Historical Society, Phoenix, AZ 39

LIBRARIES HAVING COLLECTIONS OTHER THAN BOOKS–Continued

Armstrong Browning Library, Waco, TX ...1458

The Association for Gravestone Studies, Greenfield, MA 685

The Athenaeum of Philadelphia, Philadelphia, PA 1276

Audubon Society of Rhode Island, Smithfield, RI.................1319

Austin History Center, Austin, TX 1388

Avery Research Center for African American History & Culture, Charleston, SC 1323

Bagpipe Music Museum, Manchester, NH...891

Balzekas Museum of Lithuanian Culture, Chicago, IL.................418

Boston Athenaeum Library, Boston, MA 663

Boston Public Library, Boston, MA 664

Brand Library & Art Center, Glendale, CA.................100

Brooks Free Library, Harwich, MA.............686

California African-American Museum, Los Angeles, CA.................113

California Historical Society, San Francisco, CA.................163

California State Railroad Museum, Sacramento, CA.................152

The Calvin Coolidge Memorial Foundation, Inc., Plymouth, VT 1484

Calvin Coolidge Presidential Library & Museum, Northampton, MA 699

Camden Archives & Museum, Camden, SC.................1322

Canajoharie Library and Art Gallery, Canajoharie, NY.................974

Captain Charles H. Hurley Library, Buzzards Bay, MA 672

Casa Grande Valley Historical Society & Museum, Casa Grande, AZ.................30

Casemate Museum, Fort Monroe, VA 1505

Center for American History, Austin, TX...1390

Center for Curatorial Studies, Annandale-on-Hudson, NY.................958

Chancellor Robert R. Livingston Masonic Library & Museum, New York, NY......1022

Chapin Library of Rare Books, Williamstown, MA 719

Charles A. Weyerhaeuser Memorial Museum, Little Falls, MN.................779

Charleston Library Society, Charleston, SC.................1324

Chemung Valley History Museum, Elmira, NY.................988

Chicago Public Library, Chicago, IL...........419

The Collectors Club, Inc., New York, NY.1023

Collin County Historical Society, Inc. & History Museum, McKinney, TX 1437

Concordia Historical Institute, Saint Louis, MO.................832

Creative Photographic Art Center of Maine, Lewiston, ME.................614

Cumberland County Historical Society, The Hamilton Library and The Two Mile House, Carlisle, PA.................1245

Dallas Holocaust Museum, Dallas, TX 1405

The Danish Immigrant Museum, Elk Horn, IA.................517

Danvers Archival Center, Danvers, MA.......678

Dearborn Historical Museum, Dearborn, MI.................733

The Design Center at Philadelphia University, Philadelphia, PA 1278

Dutchess County Historical Society, Poughkeepsie, NY.................1054

Dyer Memorial Library, Abington, MA 657

Evanston Environmental Association/Evanston Ecology Center, Evanston, IL.................434

Feet First: The Scholl Story, Rosalind Franklin University, North Chicago, IL...448

Folger Shakespeare Library, Washington, DC.................278

Forest Park Museum and Arboretum, Perry, IA.................527

Free Library of Philadelphia Rare Book Department, Philadelphia, PA 1280

Freeborn County Museum and Historical Village, Albert Lea, MN.................767

Gemological Institute of America Museum, Carlsbad, CA 81

The Genealogical Society of Pennsylvania, Philadelphia, PA.................1280

The George Bush Presidential Library and Museum, College Station, TX 1400

George C. Marshall Museum, Lexington, VA.................1513

Gerald R. Ford Library, Ann Arbor, MI.......724

Glenview Area Historical Society, Glenview, IL.................438

Greeley History Museum, Greeley, CO.......221

Harold M. Freund American Museum of Baking, Manhattan, KS 550

Harry Ransom Center at the University of Texas at Austin, Austin, TX 1390

Harvey Cushing/John Hay Whitney Medical Library, New Haven, CT 253

The Heritage Museum, Baltimore, MD.......632

Historic Bethany, Bethany, WV.................1580

Historic Macon Foundation, Inc. - Sidney Lanier Cottage House Museum, Macon, GA.................377

Historical and Genealogical Society of Indiana County, Indiana, PA 1262

The Historical Society of Dauphin County, Harrisburg, PA 1258

Historical Society of Haddonfield, Haddonfield, NJ.................905

Holocaust Documentation & Education Center, Inc., Hollywood, FL 313

Horseless Carriage Foundation & Automotive Research Library, La Mesa, CA.................107

The Humphrey Forum, Minneapolis, MN....782

Indiana Historical Society, Indianapolis, IN.................483

The Interchurch Center, New York, NY.....1027

International Motor Racing Research Center at Watkins Glen, Watkins Glen, NY.................1084

International Women's Air and Space Museum, Inc., Cleveland, OH.................1155

Iowa Masonic Library and Museum, Cedar Rapids, IA.................509

Jackson County Historical Museum & Research Library, Maquoketa, IA.............522

James Monroe Museum and Memorial Library, Fredericksburg, VA.................1507

James Prendergast Library Association, Art Gallery, Jamestown, NY 1005

James S. Copley Library, La Jolla, CA........106

John F. Kennedy Presidential Library & Museum, Boston, MA.................666

John Sydnor's 1847 Powhatan House, Galveston, TX.................1421

Johnstown Historical Society, Johnstown, NY.................1005

Karpeles Manuscript Library Museum, Duluth, MN.................773

Klyne Esopus Museum, Ulster Park, NY...1079

Knoxville Public Library, Knoxville, PA...1265

Koreshan State Historic Site, Estero, FL......306

Lancaster County Historical Society, Lancaster, PA.................1266

Law Enforcement Memorial Association, Inc., Roselle, IL.................456

Lesbian Herstory Educational Foundation, Inc. aka Lesbian Herstory Archives, Brooklyn, NY.................969

Library Company of Philadelphia, Philadelphia, PA.................1282

Library of Congress, Washington, DC.........282

The Library of Virginia, Richmond, VA.....1530

Lincoln Memorial Shrine, Redlands, CA 147

Lone Star Flight Museum/Texas Aviation Hall of Fame, Galveston, TX.................1421

Longfellow National Historic Site, Cambridge, MA.................673

Los Angeles (Central) Public Library, Los Angeles, CA.................117

Luis Munoz Rivera Library & Museum, Barranquitas, PR.................1641

Lyndon Baines Johnson Library and Museum, Austin, TX.................1391

Madison County Historical Museum & Archival Library, Edwardsville, IL.........432

Malden Public Library, Malden, MA 692

Marion Public Library Museum, Marion, IN.................490

Martin Luther King, Jr. Center for Nonviolent Social Change, Inc., Atlanta, GA.................361

Martinez Museum, Martinez, CA 124

Maryland Historical Society, Baltimore, MD.................634

Masonic Grand Lodge Library and Museum of Texas, Waco, TX 1459

The Masonic Library and Museum of Pennsylvania, Philadelphia, PA.................1283

Melton Art Reference Library, Oklahoma City, OK.................1208

Mercer County Historical Society, Mercer, PA.................1271

Merrill Historical Museum, Merrill, WI.....1609

Mighty Eighth Air Force Museum, Pooler, GA.................381

Minnetrista, Muncie, IN.................492

Mondak Heritage Center, Sidney, MT.........853

Monroe County Local History Room & Library, Sparta, WI.................1622

Monterey History and Art Association, Monterey, CA.................127

Museum of American Finance, New York, NY.................1031

Museum of Ancient Artifacts, Las Vegas, NV.................879

Museum of Early Southern Decorative Arts (MESDA), Winston-Salem, NC.....1125

Museum of San Diego History and Research Library, San Diego, CA 158

Museum of the Jimmy Carter Library, Atlanta, GA.................362

Napoleonic Society of America, Inc., Clearwater, FL.................300

National Afro-American Museum & Cultural Center, Wilberforce, OH.........1191

National Archives and Records Administration - Mid-Atlantic Region, Philadelphia, PA.................1284

National Hispanic Cultural Center, Art Museum, Albuquerque, NM.................935

National Voting Rights Museum and Institute, Selma, AL.................18

Naval War College Museum, Newport, RI.................1314

Nebraska Conference United Methodist Historical Center, Lincoln, NE 866

The New Jersey Historical Society, Newark, NJ.................916

New London County Historical Society, New London, CT.................255

The New York Public Library, Astor, Lenox and Tilden Foundations, New York, NY.................1036

The New York Public Library for the
   Performing Arts, New York, NY 1036
New York State Military Museum and
   Veterans Research Center, Saratoga
   Springs, NY 1065
Newport Historical Society & The
   Museum of Newport History,
   Newport, RI 1315
The Newsome House Museum &
   Cultural Center, Newport News, VA 1520
Novato History Museum, Novato, CA 132

Oakland Museum of California, Oakland,
   CA 134
Old State House-The Bostonian Society,
   Boston, MA 668
The Ozark Folk Center, Mountain View,
   AR 65

Peabody Essex Museum, Salem, MA...........706
Photographic Archives, Lexington, KY........574
The Pierpont Morgan Library, New York,
   NY 1037
Platt R. Spencer Memorial Archives and
   Special Collections Area, Geneva, OH..1166
Polish American Museum, Port
   Washington, NY 1054
Portsmouth Athenaeum, Portsmouth, NH....894
President Andrew Johnson Museum and
   Library, Greeneville, TN 1366
Pro Rodeo Hall of Fame & Museum of
   the American Cowboy, Colorado
   Springs, CO 207
Provisions Library, Washington, DC 289
Public Library of Charlotte and
   Mecklenburg County, Charlotte, NC 1096
The Public Library of Nashville and
   Davidson County, Nashville, TN 1380
Pueblo County Historical Society
   Museum and Edward H. Broadhead
   Library, Pueblo, CO 230

Quincy Historical Society, Quincy, MA.......705

RV/MH Heritage Foundation, Inc.,
   Elkhart, IN 475
Randall Library, Stow, MA.........................713
Ravalli County Museum/Bitter Root
   Valley Historical Society, Hamilton,
   MT 848
Reading Railroad Heritage Museum,
   Reading, PA 1296
Redwood Library and Athenaeum,
   Newport, RI 1315
The Regina A. Quick Center for the Arts,
   Saint Bonaventure, NY 1063
Rhode Island State Archives, Providence,
   RI 1318
Rhododendron Species Botanical Garden,
   Federal Way, WA 1554
The Rock and Roll Hall of Fame and
   Museum, Cleveland, OH 1155
Rockingham Free Public Library and
   Museum, Bellows Falls, VT 1476
Rosenbach Museum & Library,
   Philadelphia, PA 1287
Rosenberg Library, Galveston, TX 1422
Rutherford B. Hayes Presidential Center,
   Fremont, OH 1165

Sam Houston Regional Library &
   Research Center, Liberty, TX................1434
The Sam Rayburn Library and Museum,
   a Division of the Center for American
   History of the University of Texas at
   Austin, Bonham, TX 1397
San Fernando Mission, Mission Hills, CA...126
The Sandor Teszler Library, Spartanburg,
   SC 1341
Santa Fe Trail Center, Larned, KS 547
The Schomburg Center for Research in
   Black Culture, New York, NY 1038
Shaker Museum, New Gloucester, ME 615

The Society of California Pioneers, San
   Francisco, CA 170
The Society of the Four Arts, Palm
   Beach, FL..334
South Carolina Department of Archives
   & History, Columbia, SC 1330
South Carolina Historical Society,
   Charleston, SC 1327
South Dakota Hall of Fame,
   Chamberlain, SD 1345
Statue of Liberty National Monument &
   Ellis Island Immigration Museum,
   New York, NY 1039
Steamship Historical Society of America,
   Providence, RI 1319
Stearns History Museum, Saint Cloud,
   MN 788
Sterne-Hoya House Museum and Library,
   Nacogdoches, TX 1440
Stevens Museum, Salem, IN 498
Stockbridge Library Historical Collection,
   Stockbridge, MA 713
The Stowitts Museum & Library, Pacific
   Grove, CA...137
Sturgis Library, Barnstable, MA.................662
Sun Prairie Historical Library &
   Museum, Sun Prairie, WI....................1624
Swedish American Historical Society,
   Inc., Chicago, IL 428

Territorial Capital-Lane Museum,
   Lecompton, KS 549
Texas State Library, Austin, TX 1392
The Thoreau Institute at Walden Woods,
   Lincoln, MA 691
Tile Heritage Foundation, Healdsburg,
   CA 102

Ukrainian National Museum, Inc.,
   Chicago, IL 428
Union for Reform Judaism, New York,
   NY 1040
Upper Snake River Valley Historical
   Society, Rexburg, ID 409

The Wagnalls Memorial, Lithopolis, OH ...1172
Walt Whitman House Museum and
   Library, Camden, NJ 900
Waring Historical Library, Charleston, SC.1327
Weems-Botts Museum, Dumfries, VA........1503
Westchester County Historical Society,
   Elmsford, NY.....................................988
Winchendon Historical Society, Inc.,
   Winchendon, MA 720
Wood Library-Museum of
   Anesthesiology, Park Ridge, IL 450
Woodruff Museum of Indian Artifacts,
   Bridgeton, NJ 898
Working Men's Institute, New Harmony,
   IN 495
Wyck, Philadelphia, PA 1289

Yolo County Historical Museum,
   Woodland, CA 199

NATIONAL AND STATE AGENCIES, COUNCILS AND COMMISSIONS

Alabama Music Hall of Fame,
   Tuscumbia, AL 20
Archives of American Art, Smithsonian
   Institution, Washington, DC................276
Arizona State Parks Board, Phoenix, AZ.......39
Art In Embassies Program, U.S.
   Department of State, Washington, DC 276
Arts Council of Fayetteville/Cumberland
   County, Fayetteville, NC.....................1100
Audubon State Historic Site, Saint
   Francisville, LA 600

CDC/Global Health Odyssey, Atlanta,
   GA 358
California State Capitol Museum,
   Sacramento, CA.................................151

Carnifex Ferry Battlefield State Park &
   Museum, Summersville, WV 1587
Cedar Key Museum State Park, Cedar
   Key, FL 299
Chase Home Museum of Utah Folk Arts,
   Salt Lake City, UT 1470
Colonial Pemaquid, New Harbor, ME..........615
Creative Arts Guild, Dalton, GA 370
Czech Center New York, New York, NY....1024

Dead Horse Point State Park, Moab, UT ...1467
Delaware Division of Historical &
   Cultural Affairs, Dover, DE 269
Devils Tower Visitor Center, Devils
   Tower, WY 1631
Dinosaur Valley State Park, Glen Rose,
   TX 1422
Diplomatic Reception Rooms,
   Department of State, Washington, DC 278

Elijah Clark Memorial Museum,
   Lincolnton, GA 376

Father Marquette National Memorial,
   Saint Ignace, MI 763
Fayette Historic State Park, Garden, MI 742
Florida Association of Museums,
   Tallahassee, FL..................................347
Fort Abraham Lincoln State Park,
   Mandan, ND 1134
Fort Frederick State Park, Big Pool, MD.....637
Fort Kearny State Historical Park,
   Kearney, NE......................................864
Fort Knox State Historic Site, Prospect,
   ME 620
Fort Lee Historic Park & Museum, Fort
   Lee, NJ...904
Fort Pulaski National Monument,
   Savannah, GA 385
Fort Washington Park, Fort Washington,
   MD 643
Frontier Culture Museum, Staunton, VA....1537

General John J. Pershing Boyhood Home
   State Historic Site, Laclede, MO............824
George Washington Carver National
   Monument, Diamond, MO....................814
Ginkgo Petrified Forest State Park,
   Vantage, WA 1576
Governor John Sevier Memorial
   Association, Knoxville, TN...................1370
Grand Gulf Military Park, Port Gibson,
   MS 807
Grand Teton National Park, Colter Bay
   Indian Arts Museum, Colter Bay
   Village, WY 1631
Grant's Birthplace State Memorial, Point
   Pleasant, OH 1182
Grinter Place State Historic Site, Kansas
   City, KS 546

Harpers Ferry National Historical Park,
   Harpers Ferry, WV 1582
Hawaii State Foundation on Culture &
   the Arts and Hawaii State Art
   Museum, Honolulu, HI........................395
Historical Resources and Museum
   Services, Little Rock, AR.....................62
Homolovi Ruins State Park, Winslow, AZ.....53
Horseshoe Bend National Military Park,
   Daviston, AL......................................7

Illinois State Museum, Springfield, IL 458
Indian Arts and Crafts Board,
   Washington, DC.................................281
Iowa Department of Natural Resources,
   Des Moines, IA 515
Iron & Steel Museum of Alabama,
   Tannehill Ironworks Historical State
   Park, McCalla, AL 13

J.M. Davis Arms & Historical Museum,
   Claremore, OK 1198
Jefferson Davis Monument State Park,
   Fairview, KY 568

NATIONAL AND STATE AGENCIES, COUNCILS AND COMMISSIONS–Continued

John F. Kennedy Presidential Library & Museum, Boston, MA 666
Joseph A. Tallman Museum, Cherokee, IA 510
Judge Roy Bean Visitor Center, Langtry, TX 1433

Kentucky Department of Fish & Wildlife Resources-Salato Wildlife Education Center, Frankfort, KY 569
Knights of Columbus Museum, New Haven, CT...253

Lawrence Heritage State Park, Lawrence, MA 689
Library of Congress, Washington, DC 282
The Library of Virginia, Richmond, VA.....1530
Lost River State Park, Mathias, WV 1584
Louisiana State Museum, New Orleans, LA 596

Mammoth Cave National Park, Mammoth Cave, KY 579
Manassas National Battlefield Park, Manassas, VA 1516
Maryland State Archives, Annapolis, MD....628
Mid-Atlantic Association of Museums, Washington, DC...283
Minute Man National Historical Park, Concord, MA 676
Missouri State Museum, Jefferson City, MO 819
Mormon Station State Historic Park, Genoa, NV 877

National Archives and Records Administration, Washington, DC 284
National Park Service, Washington, DC......287
National Park Service Museum Resource Center, Landover, MD...............................648
National Trust for Historic Preservation, Washington, DC...288
Nebraska State Capitol, Lincoln, NE............866
New Jersey Association of Museums, Newark, NJ 916
New Jersey State House, Trenton, NJ 927
New York State Bureau of Historic Sites, Waterford, NY 1082
New York State Office of Parks, Recreation & Historic Preservation, Albany, NY 955
Northwest Museum of Arts & Culture (Eastern Washington State Historical Society), Spokane, WA...............................1571

Oklahoma Historical Society, Oklahoma City, OK 1209
Oklahoma Museums Association, Oklahoma City, OK 1210
Organ Pipe Cactus National Monument Museum, Ajo, AZ 29

Pendleton District Historical, Recreational and Tourism Commission, Pendleton, SC 1339
Pennsylvania Federation of Museums and Historical Organizations, Harrisburg, PA 1259
Pennsylvania Historical & Museum Commission, Harrisburg, PA...............1259
Pioneer Heritage Center, Cavalier, ND.......1129
Pioneer Woman Statue & Museum, Ponca City, OK..1212
Plantation Agriculture Museum, Scott, AR 67

Rails-to-Trails Conservancy, Washington, DC 289
Rhode Island State Archives, Providence, RI 1318

Roosevelt Campobello International Park Commission, Lubec, ME.........................614
Rose Hill Plantation State Historic Site, Union, SC 1343
Russell Cave National Monument, Bridgeport, AL 6

Sharlot Hall Museum, Prescott, AZ...............43
Sheldon Jackson Museum, Sitka, AK............27
Shenandoah National Park, Luray, VA 1514
South Carolina Department of Archives & History, Columbia, SC......................1330
South Carolina Institute of Archaeology & Anthropology, Columbia, SC............1330
South Dakota State Archives, Pierre, SD...1353
The State House Museum, Dover, DE 270
State of Illinois-Historic Preservation Agency, Historic Sites Division, Springfield, IL...460
Steamboat Bertrand Collection, Missouri Valley, IA 524

Texas Association of Museums, Austin, TX 1391
Texas Historical Commission, Austin, TX .1391
Texas Parks and Wildlife Department, Austin, TX 1392

United States Capitol, Washington, DC 293
United States Senate Commission on Art, Washington, DC...293
The University of Arizona Museum of Art, Tucson, AZ 52

Washington Oaks Gardens State Park, Palm Coast, FL...334
Washington State Capital Museum and Outreach Center, Olympia, WA 1560
Watters Smith Memorial State Park, Lost Creek, WV 1584
Weir Farm National Historic Site, Wilton, CT 267
West Virginia Independence Hall, Wheeling, WV 1588
West Virginia State Museum, Charleston, WV 1581
William J. Clinton Presidential Library & Museum, Little Rock, AR 63
William Pryor Letchworth Museum, Castile, NY 976
Wyoming State Museum, Cheyenne, WY ..1631

Zane Grey Museum, Lackawaxen, PA 1265

NATURE CENTERS

ASRI Environmental Education Center, Bristol, RI 1310
Abilene Zoological Gardens, Abilene, TX .1385
The Accokeek Foundation, Inc., Accokeek, MD...627
Action Wildlife Foundation, Goshen, CT.....242
Adirondack Park Visitor Interpretive Center, Paul Smiths, NY 1051
Ak-Sar-Ben Aquarium Outdoor Education Center, Gretna, NE 862
Alley Pond Environmental Center, Inc., Douglaston, NY 984
Ano Nuevo State Reserve, Pescadero, CA...141
Antelope Valley California Poppy Reserve, Lancaster, CA 108
Applegate Park Zoo, Merced, CA 125
The Arboretum at Flagstaff, Flagstaff, AZ 32
Arboretum at UC Santa Cruz, Santa Cruz, CA 181
Arizona-Sonora Desert Museum, Tucson, AZ 48
Armand Bayou Nature Center, Houston, TX 1424
Audubon Canyon Ranch, Stinson Beach, CA 188
Audubon Greenwich, Greenwich, CT 242
Audubon Louisiana Nature Center, New Orleans, LA 594

Audubon Naturalist Society, Chevy Chase, MD...640
Audubon Society of New Hampshire, Concord, NH...884
Audubon Society of Rhode Island, Smithfield, RI...1319
Aullwood Audubon Center and Farm, Dayton, OH...1160
Austin Nature & Science Center, Austin, TX 1389
Awbury Arboretum, Philadelphia, PA.........1277

Batsto Village, Hammonton, NJ 907
Bayard Cutting Arboretum, Great River, NY 996
Bear Brook Nature Center, Suncook, NH 896
Belle Isle Nature Zoo, Detroit, MI 735
Belvedere Castle-Henry Luce Nature Observatory, New York, NY 1021
The Benjamin Banneker Park & Museum, Baltimore, MD 631
Bernheim Arboretum and Research Forest, Clermont, KY 567
Big Thicket National Preserve, Kountze, TX 1432
Birdsong Nature Center, Thomasville, GA 387
Biscayne National Park, Homestead, FL......313
Blue Hills Trailside Museum, Milton, MA 695
Botanica, The Wichita Gardens, Wichita, KS 561
Bowman's Hill Wildflower Preserve, New Hope, PA...1273
Bradford Brinton Memorial & Museum, Big Horn, WY 1628
Brazos Valley Museum of Natural History, Bryan, TX 1398
Brevard Museum of History & Science, Cocoa, FL...300
Briar Bush Nature Center, Abington, PA ...1238
Brookgreen Gardens, Murrells Inlet, SC ...1337
Buffalo Museum of Science, Buffalo, NY ...972
Buffalo National River, Harrison, AR 59

Cabin Nature Center, Wood Dale, IL 466
Calusa Nature Center and Planetarium, Fort Myers, FL...308
Camp Five Museum Foundation, Inc., Laona, WI 1604
Cape Cod Museum of Natural History, Inc., Brewster, MA 670
Carl G. Fenner Nature Center, Lansing, MI 749
Catherine Montgomery Interpretive Center, Greenwater, WA 1556
Cedar Bog Nature Preserve, Urbana, OH...1188
Charlotte Nature Museum, Charlotte, NC..1094
The Chattanooga Nature Center, Chattanooga, TN...1361
Cheekwood-Tennessee Botanical Garden & Museum of Art, Nashville, TN.......1378
Chicago Botanic Garden, Glencoe, IL.........438
Chickasaw Council House Museum, Tishomingo, OK 1214
Chickasaw National Recreation Area, Sulphur, OK 1214
Chico Creek Nature Center, Chico, CA 83
Chihuahuan Desert Research Institute, Fort Davis, TX...1414
The Children's Metamorphosis, Children's Museum, Derry, NH 886
Chippewa Nature Center, Midland, MI 755
Chula Vista Nature Center, Chula Vista, CA 84
Cincinnati Museum Center at Union Terminal, Cincinnati, OH 1149
Cleveland Metroparks Outdoor Education Division, Garfield Heights, OH.............1165
Cliffs of the Neuse State Park, Seven Springs, NC...1119
Clyde E. Buckley Wildlife Sanctuary, Frankfort, KY...568

Coastal Discovery Museum, Hilton Head Island, SC..................................1335
Congaree National Park, Hopkins, SC.......1336
Connecticut Audubon Birdcraft Museum, Fairfield, CT.................................240
Connecticut Audubon Center at Fairfield, Fairfield, CT.................................240
Connecticut Audubon Society, Fairfield, CT.................................240
Conservancy Nature Center, Naples, FL......328
Cora Hartshorn Arboretum and Bird Sanctuary, Short Hills, NJ......................924
County of Westchester, Department of Parks, Recreation and Conservation, Mount Kisco, NY....................................1016
Coyote Point Museum for Environmental Education, San Mateo, CA.....................175
Cranbrook House and Gardens Auxiliary, Bloomfield Hills, MI...............................730
Cranbrook Institute of Science, Bloomfield Hills, MI...............................730
Crane Point, Marathon, FL.............................323
The Crescent, Valdosta Garden Center, Inc., Valdosta, GA................................389
The Crosby Arboretum, Mississippi State University, Picayune, MS......................807
Crowley Museum & Nature Center, Sarasota, FL...344
Cuneo Museum & Gardens, Vernon Hills, IL..463
Cylburn Arboretum, Baltimore, MD............631

The Dawes Arboretum, Newark, OH.........1177
De Graaf Nature Center, Holland, MI..........746
Deer Valley Rock Art Center, Glendale, AZ...35
Delaware Nature Society, Hockessin, DE....271
Denison Pequotsepos Nature Center, Mystic, CT...250
Denver Botanic Gardens, Inc., Denver, CO...210
Des Moines Botanical Center, Des Moines, IA...514
The Discovery Center, Fresno, CA.................96
Discovery Museum, Sacramento Museum of History, Science and Technology, Sacramento, CA.....................................152
Discovery Park, Safford, AZ.............................43
Discovery Place, Inc., Charlotte, NC..........1094
Discovery Science and Outdoor Center, Ocala, FL...330
Dodge Nature Center, West Saint Paul, MN...796
Drumlin Farm Education Center, Lincoln, MA...690
Dubuque Arboretum & Botanical Gardens, Dubuque, IA............................516
Dungeness River Audubon Center, Sequim, WA..1570

Earthplace - The Nature Discovery Center, Westport, CT.............................266
Edison & Ford Winter Estates, Fort Myers, FL...308
Effie Yeaw Nature Center, Carmichael, CA...82
El Dorado Nature Center, Long Beach, CA...110
El Paso Museum of Archaeology, El Paso, TX..1411
Elachee Nature Science Center, Gainesville, GA.....................................373
Eloise Butler Wildflower Garden and Bird Sanctuary, Minneapolis, MN...........781
Environmental Education Center, Somerset County Park Commission, Basking Ridge, NJ..............................898
Evanston Environmental Association/Evanston Ecology Center, Evanston, IL...434

Fairfax County Park Authority, Resource Management Division, Fairfax, VA.......1503

Farmington Museum, Farmington, NM........939
Ferndell Nature Museum, Los Angeles, CA...115
Fernwood Botanical Garden & Nature Preserve, Niles, MI...............................758
Filoli Center, Woodside, CA.........................199
Finnup Park and Lee Richardson Zoo, Garden City, KS.....................................541
First Landing State Park, Virginia Beach, VA...1542
Flowerdew Hundred Foundation, Hopewell, VA.......................................1511
Fontenelle Nature Association, Bellevue, NE...857
Ford Nature Education Center, Youngstown, OH.....................................1194
Fort Leaton State Historical Site, Presidio, TX...1444
Fort Roosevelt Natural Science and History Museum, Hanford, CA..............101
Fountain Rock Nature Center, Walkersville, MD...................................656
Fox Lake Historical Museum, Inc., Fox Lake, WI...1598
Frisco Native American Museum and Natural History Center, Frisco, NC.......1102

Gardenview Horticultural Park, Strongsville, OH.....................................1186
Genesee Country Village & Museum, Mumford, NY.....................................1016
Glen Helen Ecology Institute Trailside Museum, Yellow Springs, OH..............1193
The Greenburgh Nature Center, Scarsdale, NY.....................................1066
The Grove, Glenview, IL................................438
Gulf Branch Nature Center, Arlington, VA...1496
Gwinnett County Parks & Recreation Outdoor Interpretive Section, Lawrenceville, GA....................................375

Harriet Alexander Nature Center, Roseville, MN...788
Hartman Reserve Nature Center, Cedar Falls, IA...507
Hawaii Volcanoes National Park, Kilauea Visitor Center, Hawaii Volcanoes National Park, HI.....................................393
Hawk Mountain Sanctuary, Kempton, PA..1264
Hayes Regional Arboretum, Richmond, IN...497
Heard Natural Science Museum and Wildlife Sanctuary, Inc., McKinney, TX...1437
Henry Ford Estate-Fair Lane, Dearborn, MI...734
High Cliff Historical Society & General Store Museum, Sherwood, WI..............1622
High Desert Museum, Bend, OR.................1220
Highlands Center for Natural History, Prescott, AZ...42
Highlands Hammock State Park/Civilian Conservation Corps Museum, Sebring, FL...346
Hilltop Garden and Nature Center, Bloomington, IN.....................................469
Historic Bok Sanctuary, Lake Wales, FL.....320
Historic Spanish Point, Osprey, FL..............333
Historical Society of Old Yarmouth, Yarmouth Port, MA...............................722
Humboldt Redwoods State Park Visitor Center, Weott, CA.....................................197

The Institute For American Indian Studies (IAIS), Washington Green, CT....263
Iowa Department of Natural Resources, Des Moines, IA...515
Ipswich River Wildlife Sanctuary (Massachusetts Audubon Society), Topsfield, MA...714

James A. McFaul Environmental Center of Bergen County, Wyckoff, NJ...............931

Jekyll Island Museum, Jekyll Island, GA 374
Jerome Ford Nature Center, Alexandria, VA...1493
John D. MacArthur Beach State Park & Nature Center, North Palm Beach, FL 329
John Hutchings Museum of Natural History, Lehi, UT.....................................1466
John James Audubon Center at Mill Grove, Audubon, PA.............................1241
John James Audubon Museum, Henderson, KY...571
Joshua Tree National Park, Oasis Visitor Center, Twentynine Palms, CA.............193
The Junior Museum of Bay County, Panama City, FL.....................................334
Jurupa Mountains Cultural Center, Riverside, CA...149

Kalamazoo Nature Center, Inc., Kalamazoo, MI.....................................748
Kansas Department of Wildlife & Parks, Pratt, KS.................................556
Kauai Children's Discovery Museum, Kapaa, HI.................................400
Kensington Metropark Nature Center, Milford, MI.................................755
Kentucky Department of Fish & Wildlife Resources-Salato Wildlife Education Center, Frankfort, KY.............................569
Kerbyville Museum, Kerby, OR.................1227
Key West Tropical Forest & Botanical Garden, Key West, FL.............................318

L.C. Bates Museum, Hinckley, ME.............612
Lady Bird Johnson Wildflower Center, Austin, TX...1390
Lake Erie Nature & Science Center, Bay Village, OH...1141
Lake View Nature Center, Oakbrook Terrace, IL...449
Lake Waccamaw Depot Museum, Lake Waccamaw, NC.....................................1109
Landmark Park, Dothan, AL.............................8
Las Cabezas de San Juan Nature Reserve (El Faro), Fajardo, PR...........................1641
Laughing Brook Education Center & Wildlife Sanctuary, Hampden, MA..........686
Leaming's Run Garden & Colonial Farm, Swainton, NJ...926
Lewis & Clark Boat House and Nature Center, Saint Charles, MO.....................830
Lewis Ginter Botanical Garden, Richmond, VA...1530
Libby Museum, Wolfeboro, NH.................897
Lichterman Nature Center, Memphis, TN..1373
Lincoln Memorial Garden and Nature Center, Springfield, IL.............................459
Lindsay Wildlife Museum, Walnut Creek, CA...196
Living Desert Zoo and Gardens State Park, Carlsbad, NM.....................................938
Locust Grove, The Samuel Morse Historic Site, Poughkeepsie, NY...........1055
Logoly State Park, McNeil, AR.........................64
Long Branch Nature Center, Arlington, VA...1496
Long Island Culture History Lab & Museum, Commack, NY.............................980
Lower Rio Grande Valley Nature Center, Weslaco, TX...1460
Luther Burbank Home & Gardens, Santa Rosa, CA...184
Lutz Children's Museum, Manchester, CT..248

MacCallum More Museum and Gardens, Chase City, VA.....................................1500
MacKenzie Environmental Education Center, Poynette, WI.............................1618
Mackinac Island State Park Commission-Mackinac State Historic Parks, Mackinaw City, MI...................752
Mackinac State Historic Parks-Historic Mill Creek, Mackinaw City, MI.............753

NATURE CENTERS—Continued

Magnolia Plantation and Gardens, Charleston, SC................1326

Mammoth Cave Wildlife Museum, Cave City, KY................566

Mary Vagle Museum & Nature Center, Fontana, CA................95

Massachusetts Audubon at Connecticut River Valley Sanctuaries, Easthampton, MA................681

Matthaei Botanical Gardens and Nichols Arboretum, Ann Arbor, MI................725

Maymont, Richmond, VA................1530

Miami Museum of Science & Planetarium, Miami, FL................325

The Minna Anthony Common Nature Center at Wellesley State Park, Fineview, NY................989

Minnesota Zoo, Apple Valley, MN................768

Missouri Botanical Garden, Saint Louis, MO................834

Moccasin Lake Nature Park, An Environmental & Energy Education Center, Clearwater, FL................299

Mohonk Preserve, Inc., Gardiner, NY................993

Moore County Historical Museum, Dumas, TX................1410

Morningside Nature Center, Gainesville, FL................311

Moundville Archaeological Park, Moundville, AL................17

Mount Pisgah Arboretum, Eugene, OR................1224

Muir Woods National Monument, Mill Valley, CA................125

The Murie Museum, Kelly, WY................1634

Museum of Idaho, Idaho Falls, ID................406

Museum of Life and Science, Durham, NC................1098

Myriad Botanical Gardens, Oklahoma City, OK................1208

Myrtle Beach State Park Nature Center, Myrtle Beach, SC................1338

Nantucket Maria Mitchell Association, Nantucket, MA................696

Nassau County, Division of Museum Services, Department of Recreation, Parks & Museums, East Meadow, NY................987

National Audubon Society, New York, NY................1034

National Aviary in Pittsburgh, Inc., Pittsburgh, PA................1293

National Bighorn Sheep Interpretive Center, Dubois, WY................1632

National Capital Parks-East, Washington, DC................284

The Natural Science Center of Greensboro, Inc., Greensboro, NC................1104

The Nature Center at Shaker Lakes, Cleveland, OH................1155

The Nature Conservancy, Arlington, VA................1496

Nature Interpretive Center, Lebanon, MO................825

New Britain Youth Museum at Hungerford Park, Kensington, CT................247

New Canaan Nature Center, New Canaan, CT................252

New Jersey Meadowlands Environment Center, Lyndhurst, NJ................910

The New York Botanical Garden, Bronx, NY................966

North Carolina Aquarium at Pine Knoll Shores, Pine Knoll Shores, NC................1114

North Carolina Botanical Garden, Chapel Hill, NC................1093

Northwest Trek Wildlife Park, Eatonville, WA................1552

Oakwoods Metropark Nature Center, Belleville, MI................728

Oatland Island Education Center, Savannah, GA................385

Old Santee Canal Park, Moncks Corner, SC................1337

Oneida Nation Museum, De Pere, WI................1594

Organ Pipe Cactus National Monument Museum, Ajo, AZ................29

Orland E. White Arboretum, Boyce, VA................1497

Ormond Memorial Art Museum & Garden, Ormond Beach, FL................333

Padre Island National Seashore, Corpus Christi, TX................1402

Panola Mountain State Conservation Park, Stockbridge, GA................387

Paradise Point Nature Center, East Hebron, NH................887

Parks, Recreation & Historic Sites Division, Georgia Dept. of Natural Resources, Atlanta, GA................362

Pember Museum of Natural History, Granville, NY................995

Petrified Forest of the Black Hills, Piedmont, SD................1353

Piedmont Environmental Center, High Point, NC................1107

Pine Lodge (Ehrman Mansion), Tahoma, CA................190

Pink Palace Family of Museums, Memphis, TN................1375

Pioneer Village & Virgil Grissom Memorial at Spring Mill State Park, Mitchell, IN................491

Pioneers Park Nature Center, Lincoln, NE................867

Plains Conservation Center, Aurora, CO................202

Poricy Park Nature Center, Middletown, NJ................911

Prince William Forest Park Visitor Center, Triangle, VA................1541

Providence Canyon State Park, Lumpkin, GA................377

Rachel Carson Homestead, Springdale, PA................1301

Randall Museum, San Francisco, CA................168

Rattlesnake Museum (American International), Albuquerque, NM................935

Red Butte Garden & Arboretum, Salt Lake City, UT................1472

Renfrew Museum & Park, Waynesboro, PA................1306

Rhododendron Species Botanical Garden, Federal Way, WA................1554

The Ridges Sanctuary, Inc., Baileys Harbor, WI................1590

Rikard's Mill Historical Park, Beatrice, AL................3

Rio Grande Nature Center State Park, Albuquerque, NM................935

River Hills Visitor Center, Wildwood, MO................840

River Legacy Living Science Center, Arlington, TX................1388

Riverbend Environmental Education Center, Gladwyne, PA................1256

Riverside Metropolitan Museum, Riverside, CA................150

Riverside Nature Center, Kerrville, TX................1432

Rochester Museum & Science Center, Rochester, NY................1059

Rock Creek Nature Center, Washington, DC................290

Rock Island State Park, Washington Island, WI................1625

Rockwoods Reservation, Wildwood, MO................840

Roger Tory Peterson Institute of Natural History, Jamestown, NY................1005

Roper Mountain Science Center, Greenville, SC................1334

Rotary Nature Center, Oakland, CA................134

San Antonio Botanical Garden, San Antonio, TX................1449

San Francisco Zoological Gardens, San Francisco, CA................170

Sanibel-Captiva Conservation Foundation, Inc., Sanibel, FL................343

Sanilac County Historical Museum and Village, Port Sanilac, MI................761

Santa Monica Mountains National Recreation Area, Thousand Oaks, CA................191

Sarett Nature Center, Benton Harbor, MI................729

Schiele Museum of Natural History and Lynn Planetarium, Gastonia, NC................1102

The Schuylkill Center for Environmental Education, Philadelphia, PA................1288

Science Center of Connecticut, West Hartford, CT................265

Sciworks, Winston-Salem, NC................1126

Seacoast Science Center, Rye, NH................896

Seney National Wildlife Refuge Visitor Center, Seney, MI................764

Sharon Audubon Center, Sharon, CT................259

Sieur de Monts Springs Nature Center, Bar Harbor, ME................605

Silver River Museum & Environmental Education Center, Ocala, FL................330

Six Flags Marine World, Vallejo, CA................194

Slaughter Ranch Museum, Douglas, AZ................32

Sleeping Bear Dunes National Lakeshore, Empire, MI................741

The South Carolina Botanical Garden, Clemson, SC................1328

South Carolina Department of Parks, Recreation and Tourism, Columbia, SC................1330

South Shore Natural Science Center, Inc., Norwell, MA................700

Southern Vermont Natural History Museum, West Marlboro, VT................1489

Spartanburg Science Center, Spartanburg, SC................1342

Spring Valley Nature Center & Heritage Farm, Schaumburg, IL................457

Springbrook Nature Center, Fridley, MN................776

Squam Lakes Natural Science Center, Holderness, NH................889

Stanwood Wildlife Sanctuary, Ellsworth, ME................610

Star Eco Station, Culver City, CA................88

Starhill Forest Arboretum, Petersburg, IL................451

Starved Rock State Park, Utica, IL................462

Steamboat Bertrand Collection, Missouri Valley, IA................524

Stone Quarry Hill Art Park, Inc., Cazenovia, NY................977

Stonewall Jackson Museum at Hupp's Hill, Strasburg, VA................1539

Sulphur Creek Nature Center, Hayward, CA................102

T.C. Steele State Historic Site, Nashville, IN................493

Tanglewood Nature Center and Museum, Elmira, NY................988

Texas Discovery Gardens, Dallas, TX................1408

Thornton W. Burgess Museum, Sandwich, MA................708

Tilden Nature Area Environmental Education Center, Berkeley, CA................77

Tohono Chul Park Inc., Tucson, AZ................51

Trailside Nature and Science Center, Mountainside, NJ................915

Trailside Nature Center, Cincinnati, OH................1151

Trailside Nature Museum, Cross River, NY................983

The Trustees of Reservations, Beverly, MA................662

Tucker Tower Nature Center, Ardmore, OK................1196

Tulsa Zoo & Living Museum, Tulsa, OK................1216

Turtle Bay Exploration Park, Redding, CA................146

USDA Forest Service - Land Between the Lakes, Golden Pond, KY................570

University of Washington Botanic Garden, Seattle, WA................1569

University of Wisconsin-Madison
Arboretum, Madison, WI 1605

Virginia Living Museum, Newport News,
VA..1520

W.K. Kellogg Bird Sanctuary of
Michigan State University, Augusta,
MI..726

Wahkeena Nature Preserve, Sugar Grove,
OH..1186

Waimea Arboretum and Botanical Garden
in Waimea Valley Audubon Center,
Haleiwa, HI...392

Walney Visitor Center-At Ellanor C.
Lawrence Park, Chantilly, VA..............1498

Walter B. Jacobs Memorial Nature Park,
Shreveport, LA 602

Walter E. Heller Nature Center, Highland
Park, IL 439

Washington Park Zoological Gardens,
Michigan City, IN....................................491

Wave Hill, Bronx, NY...................................967

Weinberg Nature Center, Scarsdale, NY 1066

West Rock Nature Center, New Haven,
CT..254

Western North Carolina Nature Center,
Asheville, NC 1090

Westmoreland Sanctuary, Inc., Bedford
Corners, NY...961

The Wetlands Institute, Stone Harbor, NJ 925

Weymouth Woods-Sandhills Nature
Preserve Museum, Southern Pines, NC.1120

White Memorial Conservation Center,
Inc., Litchfield, CT..................................247

Whitefish Dunes State Park, Sturgeon
Bay, WI..1624

Whitehouse Nature Center, Albion, MI........723

The Wilderness Center Inc., Wilmot, OH ..1192

Wildlife Museum at Petaluma High
School, Petaluma, CA..............................142

Wildlife Prairie State Park, Hanna City,
IL...439

William S. Hart County Park & Museum,
Newhall, CA..130

Wing Haven Garden and Bird Sanctuary,
Charlotte, NC...1096

Woldumar Nature Center, Lansing, MI 751

Wood County Historical Center and
Museum, Bowling Green, OH 1143

Youth Science Institute, San Jose, CA 173

Youth Science Institute, Sanborn Nature
Center, Saratoga, CA...............................185

Zion Human History Museum,
Springdale, UT......................................1474

Zoo Montana, Billings, MT 842

PARK MUSEUMS AND VISITOR CENTERS

Agate Fossil Beds National Monument,
Harrison, NE...862

Alamance Battleground State Historic
Site, Burlington, NC..............................1092

Aliceville Museum, Aliceville, AL...................3

Allegheny Portage Railroad National
Historic Site and Johnstown Flood
National Memorial, Gallitzin, PA 1255

American Royal Museum & Visitors
Center, Kansas City, MO 820

Ano Nuevo State Reserve, Pescadero, CA...141

Antelope Valley California Poppy
Reserve, Lancaster, CA 108

Apostles Islands National Lakeshore,
Bayfield, WI...1591

The Appalachian Trail Conservancy,
Harpers Ferry, WV 1581

Arizona Historical Society-Fort Lowell
Museum, Tucson, AZ................................47

Arkansas Post National Memorial, Gillett,
AR...58

Armand Bayou Nature Center, Houston,
TX..1424

Arts Council of Fayetteville/Cumberland
County, Fayetteville, NC........................1100

Ash Hollow State Historical Park,
Lewellen, NE...864

Audubon State Historic Site, Saint
Francisville, LA..600

Aztec Ruins National Monument, Aztec,
NM...937

Badlands National Park, Interior, SD 1349

Bale Grist Mill State Historic Park,
Calistoga, CA..80

Bandelier National Monument, Los
Alamos, NM...942

Barataria Preserve, Jean Lafitte National
Historical Park and Preserve, Marrero,
LA...591

The Barnacle Historic State Park,
Coconut Grove, FL...................................300

Baton Rouge Zoo, Baton Rouge, LA............585

Battle of Lexington State Historic Site,
Lexington, MO...826

Bay Area Museum, Seabrook, TX...............1452

Bayard Cutting Arboretum, Great River,
NY..996

Bear Brook Nature Center, Suncook, NH 896

Bennett Place State Historic Site,
Durham, NC...1098

Bentonville Battlefield State Historic Site,
Four Oaks, NC.......................................1102

Bernheim Arboretum and Research
Forest, Clermont, KY 567

Bidwell Mansion State Historic Park,
Chico, CA...83

Big Basin Redwoods State Park, Boulder
Creek, CA...79

Big Bend National Park, Big Bend, TX.....1396

Big Cypress National Preserve, Ochopee,
FL...330

Big Hole National Battlefield, Wisdom,
MT...855

Big Thicket National Preserve, Kountze,
TX..1432

Bill Baggs Cape Florida State Park, Key
Biscayne, FL..316

Biscayne National Park, Homestead, FL......313

Black Hawk State Historic Site: Hauberg
Indian Museum, Rock Island, IL..............453

Bodie Island Visitor Center, South Nags
Head, NC..1120

Brasstown Bald Visitor Center,
Hiawassee, GA...374

Brigham Young University Earth Science
Museum, Provo, UT...............................1469

Brunswick Town/Fort Anderson State
Historic Site, Winnabow, NC................1124

Bryce Canyon National Park Visitor
Center, Bryce, UT..................................1464

Buffalo National River, Harrison, AR 59

Bulow Plantation Ruins Historic State
Park, Bunnell, FL.....................................298

CSS Neuse State Historic Site and Gov.
Richard Caswell Memorial, Kinston,
NC..1108

Cabrillo National Monument, San Diego,
CA..156

Caddoan Mounds State Historic Site,
Cherokee County, TX.............................1399

California State Indian Museum,
Sacramento, CA..151

Canyon de Chelly National Monument,
Chinle, AZ...31

Caparra Museum and Historic Park,
Guaynabo, PR..1641

Capitol Reef National Park Visitor
Center, Torrey, UT.................................1475

Capitol Visitors Center, a Division of the
State Preservation Board, Austin, TX....1389

Capulin Volcano National Monument,
Capulin, NM...937

Carlsbad Caverns National Park,
Carlsbad, NM...937

Carnifex Ferry Battlefield State Park &
Museum, Summersville, WV.................1587

Casa Grande Ruins National Monument,
Coolidge, AZ..31

Castillo de San Marcos National
Monument, Saint Augustine, FL.............338

Cedar Breaks National Monument, Cedar
City, UT...1464

Cedar Key Museum State Park, Cedar
Key, FL..299

Centerville - Washington Township
Historical Society & Walton House
Museum, Centerville, OH 1147

Central Park Conservancy, New York,
NY..1022

Chaco Culture National Historical Park,
Nageezi, NM..943

Chamizal National Memorial, El Paso,
TX..1411

Champion Mill State Historical Park,
Champion, NE..859

Champoeg State Heritage Area Visitor
Center, Saint Paul, OR..........................1235

Channel Islands National Park, Robert J.
Lagomarsino Visitor Center, Ventura,
CA..194

Charles A. Lindbergh Historic Site, Little
Falls, MN...779

Charles B. Aycock Birthplace State
Historic Site, Fremont, NC 1102

Chicago Botanic Garden, Glencoe, IL..........438

Chickamauga-Chattanooga National
Military Park, Fort Oglethorpe, GA 372

Chickasaw National Recreation Area,
Sulphur, OK...1214

Chico Creek Nature Center, Chico, CA 83

Chihuahuan Desert Research Institute,
Fort Davis, TX.......................................1414

Chiricahua National Monument, Willcox,
AZ..53

Christa McAuliffe Planetarium, Concord,
NH...884

Cleveland Metroparks Outdoor Education
Division, Garfield Heights, OH..............1165

Cliffs of the Neuse State Park, Seven
Springs, NC..1119

Coeur d'Alenes Old Mission State Park,
Cataldo, ID..405

Colonel Allensworth State Historic Park,
Allensworth, CA...70

Colonial National Historical Park:
Jamestown & Yorktown, Yorktown,
VA..1546

Colonial Pemaquid, New Harbor, ME..........615

Colorado National Monument, Fruita, CO...218

Columbia State Historic Park, Columbia,
CA..87

Confederate Museum, Crawfordville, GA....369

Congaree National Park, Hopkins, SC 1336

Connecticut Audubon Society, Fairfield,
CT..240

Cora Hartshorn Arboretum and Bird
Sanctuary, Short Hills, NJ......................924

Coronado National Memorial, Hereford,
AZ..36

County of Westchester, Department of
Parks, Recreation and Conservation,
Mount Kisco, NY...................................1016

Cracker Trail Museum, Zolfo Springs, FL...355

Crater Lake National Park, Crater Lake,
OR..1222

Crater of Diamonds State Park Museum,
Murfreesboro, AR......................................65

Craters of the Moon National Monument,
Arco, ID...403

Crystal River State Archaeological Site,
Crystal River, FL.....................................302

Cumberland Gap National Historical
Park, Middlesboro, KY 580

Cumberland Island National Seashore,
Saint Marys, GA......................................382

PARK MUSEUMS AND VISITOR CENTERS–Continued

Custer State Park, Custer, SD 1346

Cuyahoga Valley National Park, Brecksville, OH 1144

D.C. Booth Historic National Fish Hatchery, Spearfish, SD 1357

Dade Battlefield Historic State Park, Bushnell, FL 298

Dead Horse Point State Park, Moab, UT ...1467

Death Valley National Park Visitor Center and Museums, Death Valley, CA............91

Delano Heritage Park, Delano, CA 91

Denali National Park and Preserve, Denali Park, AK 23

DeSoto National Memorial, Bradenton, FL...297

Devils Postpile National Monument, Mammoth Lakes, CA 124

Devils Tower Visitor Center, Devils Tower, WY 1631

Dinosaur State Park, Rocky Hill, CT 259

Dinosaur Valley State Park, Glen Rose, TX 1422

Discovery Park, Safford, AZ 43

Dorothy G. Page Museum, Wasilla, AK 29

Dry Tortugas National Park, Key West, FL...317

Duke Homestead State Historic Site, Durham, NC 1098

East Kentucky Center for Science, Mathematics, and Technology, Prestonsburg, KY 583

Edge of the Cedars State Park Museum, Blanding, UT 1463

El Morro National Monument, Ramah, NM 945

El Pueblo Historical Monument, Los Angeles, CA 114

Elachee Nature Science Center, Gainesville, GA 373

Elijah Clark Memorial Museum, Lincolnton, GA 376

Environmental Education Center, Somerset County Park Commission, Basking Ridge, NJ 898

Everglades National Park, Homestead, FL ...313

Explorit Science Center, Davis, CA 89

FPL Energy Encounter, Jensen Beach, FL ...316

Fairfax Museum & Visitor Center, Fairfax, VA 1503

Fairmont Park Horticulture Center, Philadelphia, PA 1279

Falls of the Ohio State Park, Clarksville, IN 472

Faust Park Foundation, Chesterfield, MO ...812

Fayette Historic State Park, Garden, MI 742

Fire Island National Seashore, Patchogue, NY 1051

First Landing State Park, Virginia Beach, VA 1542

Fisher Grove Country School/Fisher Grove State Park, Frankfort, SD............1347

Florewood State Park, Greenwood, MS 801

Florissant Fossil Beds National Monument, Florissant, CO 216

Ford Nature Education Center, Youngstown, OH..................................1194

Fort Abraham Lincoln State Park, Mandan, ND 1134

Fort Atkinson State Historical Park, Fort Calhoun, NE 860

Fort Bedford Museum, Bedford, PA...........1241

Fort Boonesborough Museum, Richmond, KY 583

Fort Bowie National Historic Site, Bowie, AZ 30

Fort de Chartres State Historic Site & Museum, Prairie du Rocher, IL 451

Fort Donelson National Battlefield, Dover, TN 1364

Fort Fisher State Historic Site, Kure Beach, NC 1108

Fort Frederica National Monument, Saint Simons Island, GA..................................383

Fort Frederick State Park, Big Pool, MD.....637

Fort Hartsuff State Historical Park, Burwell, NE 858

Fort King George Historic Site, Darien, GA..370

Fort Knox State Historic Site, Prospect, ME..620

Fort Lee Historic Park & Museum, Fort Lee, NJ..904

Fort Macon State Park, Atlantic Beach, NC..1091

Fort Massac State Park and Historic Site, Metropolis, IL..445

Fort Matanzas National Monument, Saint Augustine, FL.......................................339

Fort McHenry National Monument and Historic Shrine, Baltimore, MD..............632

Fort Mountain State Park, Chatsworth, GA..368

Fort Necessity National Battlefield, Farmington, PA....................................1253

Fort Okanogan Interpretive Center, Brewster, WA..1550

Fort Peck Interpretive Center, Fort Peck, MT..846

Fort Pulaski National Monument, Savannah, GA..385

Fort Raleigh National Historic Site, Manteo, NC..1110

Fort Richardson State Historical Park, Jacksboro, TX.......................................1431

Fort Scott National Historic Site, Fort Scott, KS..540

Fort Selden State Monument, Radium Springs, NM..945

Fort Sisseton State Historic Park, Lake City, SD..1350

Fort Stanwix National Monument, Rome, NY..1061

Fort Totten State Historic Site, Fort Totten, ND..1131

Fort Uncompahgre Living History Museum, Delta, CO................................209

Fort Union National Monument, Watrous, NM..954

Fort Vancouver National Historic Site, Vancouver, WA..1576

Fort Verde State Historic Park, Camp Verde, AZ..30

Fort Wilkins Historic Complex, Copper Harbor, MI..733

Fred Dana Marsh Museum, Ormond Beach, FL..333

Fredericksburg & Spotsylvania National Military Park, Fredericksburg, VA.........1506

Friendship Hill National Historic Site, Point Marion, PA....................................1295

Gateway NRA, Sandy Hook Unit, Fort Hancock, NJ..904

Gathland State Park, Boonsboro, MD 637

General Grant National Memorial, New York, NY..1026

George Rogers Clark National Historical Park, Vincennes, IN................................502

George Washington Birthplace National Monument, Colonial Beach, VA 1502

George Washington Carver National Monument, Diamond, MO......................814

Georgia Veterans Memorial Museum, Cordele, GA..369

Georgia's Stone Mountain Park, Stone Mountain, GA..387

Gettysburg National Military Park, Gettysburg, PA..1255

Ginkgo Petrified Forest State Park, Vantage, WA..1576

Glacier National Park Museum, West Glacier, MT..854

Glen Helen Ecology Institute Trailside Museum, Yellow Springs, OH 1193

Gnadenhutten Historical Park & Museum, Gnadenhutten, OH....................1167

Golden Gate National Recreation Area, San Francisco, CA.....................................165

Golden Spike National Historic Site, Brigham City, UT.......................................1463

Goliad State Park, Goliad, TX 1423

Governor's Mansion State Historic Park, Sacramento, CA...152

Graham Cave State Park, Montgomery City, MO..827

Grand Canyon National Park Museum Collection, Grand Canyon National Park, AZ..36

Grand Gulf Military Park, Port Gibson, MS..807

Grand Portage National Monument, Grand Marais, MN.......................................776

Grand Teton National Park, Colter Bay Indian Arts Museum, Colter Bay Village, WY..1631

Grant-Kohrs Ranch National Historic Site, Deer Lodge, MT.................................845

Great Basin National Park, Baker, NV........875

Great Sand Dunes National Monument and Preserve, Mosca, CO.........................229

Grizzly & Wolf Discovery Center, West Yellowstone, MT.......................................854

Guadalupe Mountains National Park, Salt Flat, TX..1447

Guilford Courthouse National Military Park, Greensboro, NC................................1104

Gulf Islands National Seashore, Gulf Breeze, FL..312

Harkness Memorial State Park, Waterford, CT...264

Harpers Ferry National Historical Park, Harpers Ferry, WV......................................1582

Harry S Truman National Historic Site - Truman Home, Independence, MO.........818

Hatteras Island Visitor Center, Buxton, NC..1093

Hawaii Volcanoes National Park, Kilauea Visitor Center, Hawaii Volcanoes National Park, HI..393

Hawk Mountain Sanctuary, Kempton, PA...1264

Hawks Nest State Park, Ansted, WV 1579

Heavener Runestone State Park, Heavener, OK..1202

Henry S. Reuss Ice Age Visitor Center, Campbellsport, WI.....................................1593

Heritage Hill State Historical Park, Green Bay, WI..1599

Highlands Hammock State Park/Civilian Conservation Corps Museum, Sebring, FL..346

Historic Bath State Historic Site, Bath, NC..1091

Historic Charlton Park Village and Museum, Hastings, MI..............................745

Historic Edenton State Historic Site, Edenton, NC..1099

Historical Museum-Archival Center, Mission Hills, CA.......................................126

The Holden Arboretum, Kirtland, OH........1170

Homestead National Monument of America, Beatrice, NE.................................857

Homolovi Ruins State Park, Winslow, AZ.....53

Hopewell Culture National Historical Park, Chillicothe, OH.................................1147

Hopewell Furnace National Historic Site, Elverson, PA..1251

Horseshoe Bend National Military Park, Daviston, AL..7

Hot Springs National Park Visitor Center, Hot Springs, AR...60

Howard B. Owens Science Center and
  Challenger Learning Center,
  Lanham-Seabrook, MD 648
Hubbardton Battlefield Museum,
  Hubbardton, VT..1480
Hubbell Trading Post National Historic
  Site, Ganado, AZ...34
Humboldt Redwoods State Park Visitor
  Center, Weott, CA 197
Humpback Rocks Mountain Farm &
  Visitor Center, Waynesboro, VA 1544

Imagination Station Science Museum,
  Wilson, NC 1124
Impression 5 Science Center, Lansing,
  MI...750
Independence National Historical Park,
  Philadelphia, PA 1281
Indian City U.S.A., Anadarko, OK 1195
Indian Springs State Park Museum,
  Flovilla, GA 372
Indiana Dunes National Lakeshore,
  Porter, IN 496
Iron & Steel Museum of Alabama,
  Tannehill Ironworks Historical State
  Park, McCalla, AL 13
Iron Mission State Park & Museum,
  Cedar City, UT 1464
Island Museum of Art, Westcott Bay
  Institute, Friday Harbor, WA...................1554
Isle Royale National Park, Houghton, MI....747

Jack London State Historic Park, Glen
  Ellen, CA 99
Jacksonport State Park, Jacksonport, AR 60
Jacques Marchais Museum of Tibetan
  Art, Staten Island, NY..............................1072
James A. McFaul Environmental Center
  of Bergen County, Wyckoff, NJ................931
Jean Lafitte National Historical Park &
  Preserve, New Orleans, LA 596
Jefferson Barracks Historic Site, Saint
  Louis, MO...833
Jefferson Davis Monument State Park,
  Fairview, KY 568
Jefferson Landing State Historic Site,
  Jefferson City, MO......................................819
Jefferson National Expansion Memorial,
  Saint Louis, MO..833
Jerome State Historic Park, Jerome, AZ 36
John D. MacArthur Beach State Park &
  Nature Center, North Palm Beach, FL 329
John Day Fossil Beds National
  Monument, Kimberly, OR.......................1227
John Fitzgerald Kennedy National
  Historic Site, Brookline, MA 671
John James Audubon Museum,
  Henderson, KY 571
John R. Jackson House, Winlock, WA 1578
Johnstown Flood National Memorial,
  South Fork, PA 1300
Joshua Tree National Park, Oasis Visitor
  Center, Twentynine Palms, CA................193
The Judah P. Benjamin Confederate
  Memorial at Gamble Plantation
  Historic State Park, Ellenton, FL 306
Judge Roy Bean Visitor Center, Langtry,
  TX...1433

Ka-Do-Ha Indian Village Museum,
  Murfreesboro, AR 65
Kenilworth Aquatic Gardens, Washington,
  DC...281
Kennesaw Mountain National Battlefield
  Park, Kennesaw, GA 374
Kings Mountain National Military Park,
  Blacksburg, SC 1322
Kingsley Plantation, Jacksonville, FL 315
Klondike Gold Rush National Historical
  Park, Skagway, AK 28
Klondike Gold Rush National Historical
  Park, Seattle, WA 1566

Knife River Indian Villages National
  Historic Site, Stanton, ND......................1136
Kolomoki Mounds State Park Museum,
  Blakely, GA 366

Lake Mead National Recreation Area,
  Boulder City, NV 875
Lake Perris Regional Indian Museum
  (Home of the Wind), Perris, CA..............141
Las Cabezas de San Juan Nature Reserve
  (El Faro), Fajardo, PR 1641
Laughing Brook Education Center &
  Wildlife Sanctuary, Hampden, MA..........686
Laumeier Sculpture Park & Museum,
  Saint Louis, MO..834
Laura Ingalls Wilder Park & Museum,
  Inc., Burr Oak, IA 507
Lawrence Hall of Science, Berkeley, CA.......76
Lawrence Heritage State Park, Lawrence,
  MA..689
Lewis & Clark Interpretive Center,
  Ilwaco, WA 1556
Lewis and Clark Visitor Center, Yankton,
  SD 1360
Lincoln Boyhood National Memorial,
  Lincoln City, IN 488
Lincoln Homestead State Park,
  Springfield, KY...583
Lincoln Log Cabin State Historic Site,
  Lerna, IL...442
Little Bighorn Battlefield National
  Monument, Crow Agency, MT 844
Logoly State Park, McNeil, AR......................64
Lost River State Park, Mathias, WV 1584
Lowell National Historical Park, Lowell,
  MA..691

MacKenzie Environmental Education
  Center, Poynette, WI 1618
Mackinac State Historic Parks-Colonial
  Michilimackinac & Old Mackinac
  Point Lighthouse, Mackinaw City, MI 752
Mackinac State Historic Parks-Fort
  Mackinac & Mackinac Island State
  Park, Mackinac Island, MI 752
Mackinac State Historic Parks-Historic
  Mill Creek, Mackinaw City, MI 753
Malabar Farm State Park, Lucas, OH........1173
Mammoth Cave National Park, Mammoth
  Cave, KY 579
Manassas National Battlefield Park,
  Manassas, VA 1516
Manatee Village Historical Park,
  Bradenton, FL...297
Mansfield State Historic Site - Civil War
  Battlefield, Mansfield, LA 591
Marjorie McNeely Conservatory at Como
  Park, Saint Paul, MN 790
Martin Luther King, Jr. Center for
  Nonviolent Social Change, Inc.,
  Atlanta, GA...361
Massacre Rocks State Park, American
  Falls, ID..402
McArthur-Burney Falls Memorial State
  Park, Burney, CA 80
McFarland State Historic Park, Florence,
  AZ 34
Memphis Botanic Garden, Goldsmith
  Civic Garden Center, Memphis, TN 1374
Miami Seaquarium, Miami, FL 325
Mineral County Museum & Historical
  Society, Superior, MT 854
Minute Man National Historical Park,
  Concord, MA 676
Mississippi Crafts Center, Ridgeland, MS ...807
Mississippi Petrified Forest, Flora, MS 800
Monterey State Historic Park, Monterey,
  CA..128
Montezuma Castle National Monument,
  Camp Verde, AZ 30
Montshire Museum of Science, Inc.,
  Norwich, VT...1483

Moores Creek National Battlefield,
  Currie, NC 1097
Mormon Station State Historic Park,
  Genoa, NV..877
Morningside Nature Center, Gainesville,
  FL...311
Morrow Mountain State Park, Albemarle,
  NC...1088
Mt. Rainier National Park, Ashford, WA ...1547
Mount Rushmore National Memorial,
  Keystone, SD..1350
Mount Washington Museum and The
  Weather Discovery Center, North
  Conway, NH 893
Mountain Farm Museum-Great Smoky
  Mountains National Park, Cherokee,
  NC...1096
Mountain Life Museum, London, KY..........575
Museum of New Mexico, Santa Fe, NM 949
Museum of North Carolina Minerals,
  Spruce Pine, NC.......................................1120
Museum of Rural Life, Denton, MD...........642
Museum of San Diego History and
  Research Library, San Diego, CA 158
Museum of Yachting, Newport, RI.............1314
Myriad Botanical Gardens, Oklahoma
  City, OK 1208
Myrtle Beach State Park Nature Center,
  Myrtle Beach, SC 1338

Nashville Zoo at Grassmere, Nashville,
  TN...1379
Natchez Trace Parkway, Tupelo, MS............808
Nathan Manilow Sculpture Park,
  Governors State University, University
  Park, IL 461
National Audubon Society, New York,
  NY..1034
National Capital Parks-East, Washington,
  DC..284
National Great Rivers Museum, East
  Alton, IL..431
National Hall of Fame for Famous
  American Indians, Anadarko, OK...........1196
National Park Service, Washington, DC.......287
National Park Service-Great Falls Park,
  McLean, VA..1517
National Park Service Vicksburg National
  Military Park-Cairo Museum,
  Vicksburg, MS 809
National Wildlife Visitor Center, Patuxent
  Research Refuge, Laurel, MD 648
Nauvoo Historical Society Museum,
  Nauvoo, IL...447
Navajo Nation Museum, Window Rock,
  AZ 53
Neversink Valley Area Museum,
  Cuddebackville, NY 984
New Echota State Historic Site, Calhoun,
  GA..367
New Jersey Office of Historic Sites,
  Trenton, NJ 927
New Market Battlefield State Historical
  Park, New Market, VA.............................1519
Newport State Park, Ellison Bay, WI.........1597
Nez Perce National Historical Park,
  Spalding, ID...409
Niagara Gorge Discovery Center, Niagara
  Falls, NY...1042
North Cascades National Park Service
  Complex, Marblemount, WA 1559

Ocmulgee National Monument, Macon,
  GA..378
Ocracoke Island Visitor Center,
  Ocracoke, NC...1113
Old Sacramento State Historic Park, Old
  Sacramento, CA 135
Old Santee Canal Park, Moncks Corner,
  SC...1337
Old Town San Diego State Historic Park,
  San Diego, CA 158

PARK MUSEUMS AND VISITOR CENTERS–Continued

Olmstead Place State Park, Ellensburg, WA 1553

Olympic National Park Visitor Center, Port Angeles, WA 1561

Olympic Sculpture Park, Seattle, WA 1568

Oregon Trail Museum, Gering, NE 861

Organ Pipe Cactus National Monument Museum, Ajo, AZ 29

Ozark National Scenic Riverways, Van Buren, MO 839

Padre Island National Seashore, Corpus Christi, TX 1402

Panola Mountain State Conservation Park, Stockbridge, GA 387

Pea Ridge National Military Park, Garfield, AR 58

Peaks of Otter Visitor Center, Bedford, VA 1496

Pearson Air Museum, Vancouver, WA 1576

Pecos National Historical Park, Pecos, NM 944

Peirce Mill and Peirce Barn, Washington, DC 289

Peninsula State Park, Fish Creek, WI 1597

Perry's Victory & International Peace Memorial, Put-in-Bay, OH 1183

Petaluma Adobe State Historic Park, Petaluma, CA 142

Petrified Forest National Park, Petrified Forest National Park, AZ 38

Pine Lodge (Ehrman Mansion), Tahoma, CA 190

Pinnacle Mountain State Park, Little Rock, AR 63

Pinson Mounds State Archaeological Area, Pinson, TN 1383

Pioneer Heritage Center, Cavalier, ND 1129

Pioneer Village & Virgil Grissom Memorial at Spring Mill State Park, Mitchell, IN 491

Pioneer Woman Statue & Museum, Ponca City, OK 1212

Point Reyes National Seashore, Point Reyes, CA 143

Polson Museum, Hoquiam, WA 1556

Potawatomi State Park, Sturgeon Bay, WI.1624

Prairie Grove Battlefield State Park, Prairie Grove, AR 66

President James K. Polk State Historic Site, Pineville, NC 1114

Pricketts Fort, Fairmont, WV 1581

Prince William Forest Park Visitor Center, Triangle, VA 1541

Providence Canyon State Park, Lumpkin, GA 377

Puukohola Heiau National Historic Site, Kamuela, HI 400

Pyramid Hill Sculpture Park & Museum, Hamilton, OH 1168

Quoddy Head State Park, Lubec, ME 614

Red Clay State Historic Park, Cleveland, TN 1363

Redwood National and State Parks, Crescent City, CA 88

Renfrew Museum & Park, Waynesboro, PA 1306

Richmond National Battlefield Park, Richmond, VA 1531

The Ridges Sanctuary, Inc., Baileys Harbor, WI 1590

Rio Grande Nature Center State Park, Albuquerque, NM 935

Riordan Mansion State Historic Park, Flagstaff, AZ 33

River Hills Visitor Center, Wildwood, MO 840

Robert Louis Stevenson House, Monterey, CA 128

Rock Creek Station State Historic Park, Fairbury, NE 860

Rock Island State Park, Washington Island, WI 1625

Rocky Reach Dam, Wenatchee, WA 1577

Roger Williams National Memorial, Providence, RI 1318

Roosevelt Campobello International Park Commission, Lubec, ME 614

Rose Hill Plantation State Historic Site, Union, SC 1343

Russell Cave National Monument, Bridgeport, AL 6

Sacajawea Interpretive Center, Pasco, WA.1561

Sagamore Hill National Historic Site, Oyster Bay, NY 1049

St. Croix National Scenic Riverway, Saint Croix Falls, WI 1620

Saint-Gaudens National Historic Site, Cornish, NH 885

Salinas Pueblo Missions National Monument, Mountainair, NM 943

San Diego Zoo, San Diego, CA 161

San Francisco Bay Model Visitor Center, Sausalito, CA 186

San Juan Bautista State Historic Park, San Juan Bautista, CA 173

San Juan Island National Historical Park, Friday Harbor, WA 1555

San Marcos de Apalache Historic State Park, Saint Marks, FL 340

Santa Barbara Zoological Gardens, Santa Barbara, CA 180

Santa Monica Mountains National Recreation Area, Thousand Oaks, CA 191

Saratoga National Historical Park, Stillwater, NY 1075

Saugus Iron Works National Historic Site, Saugus, MA 708

The Science Center of West Virginia, Bluefield, WV 1580

Sciencenter, Ithaca, NY 1004

Scotts Bluff National Monument, Gering, NE 861

Seacoast Science Center, Rye, NH 896

SEE Science Center, Manchester, NH 892

Seminole Canyon State Park and Historic Site, Comstock, TX 1401

Sequoia and Kings Canyon National Parks, Three Rivers, CA 191

Serra Museum/San Diego Historical Society, San Diego, CA 161

Shasta State Historic Park, Shasta, CA 186

Sheboygan County Historical Museum, Sheboygan, WI 1621

Shenandoah National Park, Luray, VA 1514

Sitka National Historical Park, Sitka, AK 28

Sleeping Bear Dunes National Lakeshore, Empire, MI 741

Smallwood State Park, Marbury, MD 649

Socrates Sculpture Park, Long Island City, NY 1012

Southern Illinois Art & Artisans Center, Whittington, IL 466

Space Center Houston, Houston, TX 1429

Spiro Mounds Archaeological Center, Spiro, OK 1214

Split Rock Lighthouse Historic Site, Two Harbors, MN 795

Starved Rock State Park, Utica, IL 462

Statue of Liberty National Monument & Ellis Island Immigration Museum, New York, NY 1039

Steamboat Bertrand Collection, Missouri Valley, IA 524

Stephen C. Foster State Park, Fargo, GA 371

Stephen Foster Folk Culture Center State Park, White Springs, FL 354

Stones River National Battlefield, Murfreesboro, TN 1377

Stonewall Jackson Museum at Hupp's Hill, Strasburg, VA 1539

Stow West School Museum, Stow, MA 713

Sugarlands Visitor Center, Gatlinburg, TN.1365

Sunset Crater Volcano National Monument, Flagstaff, AZ 33

Sutter's Fort State Historic Park, Sacramento, CA 153

Sweetwater Creek State Park, Lithia Springs, GA 376

Tannenbaum Historic Park, Greensboro, NC 1104

Theodore Roosevelt Birthplace National Historic Site, New York, NY 1040

Theodore Roosevelt National Park-Visitor Center, Medora, ND 1134

This Is The Place Heritage Park, Salt Lake City, UT 1472

Thomas Clarke House/Princeton Battlefield State Park, Princeton, NJ 922

Timpanogos Cave National Monument, American Fork, UT 1462

Tippecanoe Battlefield, Battle Ground, IN..468

Tohono Chul Park Inc., Tucson, AZ 51

Toltec Mounds Archeological State Park, Scott, AR 68

Tombstone Courthouse State Historic Park, Tombstone, AZ 46

Tonto National Monument, Roosevelt, AZ 43

Topeka Zoological Park, Topeka, KS 560

Town Creek Indian Mound State Historic Site, Mount Gilead, NC 1111

Trailside Nature and Science Center, Mountainside, NJ 915

Tu-Endie-Wei State Park, Point Pleasant, WV 1586

Tubac Presidio State Historic Park, Tubac, AZ 47

Tucker Tower Nature Center, Ardmore, OK 1196

Tucker Wildlife Sanctuary, Silverado, CA ...186

Tumacacori National Historical Park, Tumacacori, AZ 52

Tuskegee Institute National Historic Site, Tuskegee Institute, AL 21

Tuzigoot National Monument, Clarkdale, AZ 31

Twin Falls State Park & Museum, Mullens, WV 1585

USDA Forest Service - Land Between the Lakes, Golden Pond, KY 570

United States Capitol, Washington, DC 293

University of California Irvine Arboretum, Irvine, CA 105

U.S. Air Force Academy Visitor Center, USAF Academy, CO 234

U.S. Army Engineer Museum, Fort Leonard Wood, MO 815

USS Arizona Memorial, Honolulu, HI 398

Valley Forge National Historical Park, King of Prussia, PA 1264

Van Meter State Park, Miami, MO 827

Varner-Hogg Plantation State Historic Site, West Columbia, TX 1461

Vikingsholm, Tahoma, CA 191

Virgin Islands National Park, St. John, VI.1644

Virginia Department of Conservation and Recreation, Richmond, VA 1533

The Voas Nature Area/Voas Museum, Minburn, IA 523

Volcano Art Center, Volcano, HI 402

Walney Visitor Center-At Ellanor C. Lawrence Park, Chantilly, VA 1498

Walnut Canyon National Monument, Flagstaff, AZ 34

War in the Pacific National Historical Park, Piti, GU 1640

Washington Oaks Gardens State Park, Palm Coast, FL 334

Watkins Woolen Mill State Historic Site & Park, Lawson, MO...................825
Watters Smith Memorial State Park, Lost Creek, WV.................................1584
West Virginia Camp Washington-Carver, Clifftop, WV.................................1581
Western Skisport Museum, Donner Pass, CA...91
Westmoreland Sanctuary, Inc., Bedford Corners, NY....................................961
Weymouth Woods-Sandhills Nature Preserve Museum, Southern Pines, NC.1120
White Sands National Monument, Alamogordo, NM.....................................932
Whitefish Dunes State Park, Sturgeon Bay, WI...1624
Whitehaven Tourist Welcome Center, Paducah, KY.......................................582
Whitman Mission National Historic Site, Walla Walla, WA..........................1577
Wildlife Prairie State Park, Hanna City, IL...439
Will Rogers State Historic Park, Pacific Palisades, CA.................................137
William B. Ide Adobe State Historic Park, Red Bluff, CA.............................146
William M. Colmer Visitor Center, Ocean Springs, MS.................................806
William Pryor Letchworth Museum, Castile, NY..976
Wilson's Creek National Battlefield, Republic, MO....................................829
Wind Cave National Park, Hot Springs, SD...1348
Windham Textile and History Museum (The Mill Museum), Willimantic, CT.....267
Windmill Island Municipal Park, Holland, MI..747
Worcester County Horticultural Society/Tower Hill Botanic Garden, Boylston, MA..................................670
Wormsloe State Historic Site, Savannah, GA...387
Wright Brothers National Memorial, Kill Devil Hills, NC.............................1108
Wupatki National Monument, Flagstaff, AZ...34

Yellowstone National Park, Gardiner, MT...847
The Yosemite Museum, National Park Service, Yosemite National Park, CA......199
Youth Science Institute, San Jose, CA.........173
Youth Science Institute, Sanborn Nature Center, Saratoga, CA..........................185
Yuma Territorial Prison State Historic Park, Yuma, AZ.....................................54

Zebulon B. Vance Birthplace State Historic Site, Weaverville, NC...........1122
Zion Human History Museum, Springdale, UT...1474

SCIENCE

Academies, Associations, Institutes and Foundations

The Academy of Natural Sciences of Philadelphia, Philadelphia, PA..............1275
American Heart Association - Halle Heart Center, Tempe, AZ...........................45

Brigham Young University Earth Science Museum, Provo, UT..........................1469

The Children's Museum of Indianapolis, Indianapolis, IN.............................481
Crow Canyon Archaeological Center, Cortez, CO..208

Discovery World - The James Lovell Museum of Science, Economics and Technology, Milwaukee, WI.................1610

Explora, Albuquerque, NM...........................933

Flandrau Science Center and Planetarium, Tucson, AZ.......................................49
Fullerton Museum Center, Fullerton, CA.......98

Heartland, The California Museum of the Heart, Rancho Mirage, CA.....................145
Hunt Institute for Botanical Documentation, Pittsburgh, PA..............1292

The John Q. Adams Center for the History of Otolaryngology - Head and Neck Surgery, Alexandria, VA...............1493

Lakeview Museum of Arts and Sciences, Peoria, IL.......................................450
Louisville Science Center, Louisville, KY...577

Mammoth Site of Hot Springs, Inc., Hot Springs, SD......................................1348
Marian Koshland Science Museum, Washington, DC.......................................283
Maryland Science Center, Baltimore, MD...634
Mayborn Museum Complex, Waco, TX.....1459
Mote Marine Laboratory/Aquarium, Sarasota, FL..345
The Murie Museum, Kelly, WY..................1634
Museum of Science and Industry, Tampa, FL...349

The Nature Conservancy, Arlington, VA....1496

Robert S. Peabody Museum of Archaeology, Andover, MA....................660

The Science Center of Pinellas County, Saint Petersburg, FL................................342
Spartanburg Science Center, Spartanburg, SC...1342

University of Washington Botanic Garden, Seattle, WA................................1569

Virginia Institute of Marine Science, Gloucester Point, VA.............................1508

Western North Carolina Nature Center, Asheville, NC......................................1090
The Wetlands Institute, Stone Harbor, NJ....925
Wilbur D. May Museum, Reno, NV............882
The World of Energy, Seneca, SC..............1341

Aeronautics and Space Museums

Academy of Model Aeronautics/National Model Aviation Museum, Muncie, IN.....492
Adler Planetarium & Astronomy Museum, Chicago, IL................................417
Air Classic Inc. Museum of Aviation, Sugar Grove, IL.......................................461
Air Force Flight Test Center Museum, Edwards AFB, CA..................................92
Air Mobility Command Museum, Dover AFB, DE...270
Air Power Park & Museum, Hampton, VA...1509
Air Victory Museum, Inc., Lumberton, NJ...910
Airline History Museum, Kansas City, MO...820
Airpower Museum Inc., Ottumwa, IA..........526
Alaska Aviation Heritage Museum, Anchorage, AK...21
Amelia Earhart Birthplace Museum, Atchison, KS..532
American Airlines C.R. Smith Museum, Fort Worth, TX..1416
American Airpower Heritage Museum, Inc. & Commemorative Air Force Headquarters, Midland, TX....................1438
American Helicopter Museum & Education Center, West Chester, PA....1307
American Wings Air Museum, Blaine, MN...769
Anderson/Abruzzo Albuquerque International Balloon Museum, Albuquerque, NM.................................933

Arkansas Air Museum, Fayetteville, AR........57
Astronaut Ellison S. Onizuka Space Center, Kailua-Kona, HI.........................399
Aviation Museum of Kentucky Inc., Lexington, KY..572

BG John C.L. Scribner Texas Military Forces Museum, Austin, TX.................1389
Buehler Challenger & Science Center, Paramus, NJ..919

Challenger Learning Center of Arizona, Peoria, AZ..38
Charles A. Lindbergh Historic Site, Little Falls, MN..779
Chesapeake Planetarium, Chesapeake, VA.1501
Children's Science Explorium at Sugar Sand Park, Boca Raton, FL.....................296
Christa McAuliffe Planetarium, Concord, NH..884
Clark County Museum, Henderson, NV......878
Clark Planetarium, Salt Lake City, UT......1470
College Park Aviation Museum, College Park, MD..641
Cradle of Aviation Museum, Garden City, NY...992

EAA AirVenture Museum, Oshkosh, WI....1616
Edward H. White II Memorial Museum, Brooks Air Force Base, TX.................1397
Empire State Aerosciences Museum, Glenville, NY..995
Evergreen Aviation Museum, McMinnville, OR.......................................1228

Fargo Air Museum, Fargo, ND.................1130
Fleischmann Planetarium, Reno, NV...........880
Florida Air Museum At Sun'n Fun, Lakeland, FL..321
Frontiers of Flight Museum, Dallas, TX....1406

Glenn H. Curtiss Museum, Hammondsport, NY.................................997
Grissom Air Museum, Peru, IN....................496

Harold Warp Pioneer Village Foundation, Minden, NE...868
Hill Aerospace Museum, Hill Air Force Base, UT..1466
Hiller Aviation Institute, San Carlos, CA.....155
History and Traditions Museum, Lackland Air Force Base, TX...............1433
Howard W. Cannon Aviation Museum, Henderson, NV..878

Institute of Meteoritics Meteorite Museum, Albuquerque, NM................933
International Women's Air and Space Museum, Inc., Cleveland, OH...............1155
Iowa Aviation Museum, Greenfield, IA......519

Kalamazoo Aviation History Museum, Kalamazoo, MI..748
Kansas Aviation Museum, Wichita, KS.......562
Kansas Cosmosphere and Space Center, Hutchinson, KS..545

Lone Star Flight Museum/Texas Aviation Hall of Fame, Galveston, TX..............1421
Long Island Museum of Science and Technology, Garden City, NY...............993
Louisiana State Museum-Patterson, Patterson, LA...599
Louisville Science Center, Louisville, KY...577

March Field Air Museum, Riverside, CA....149
May Natural History Museum and Museum of Space Exploration, Colorado Springs, CO...............................207
Mid-America Air Museum, Liberal, KS.......549
Mid Atlantic Air Museum, Reading, PA....1296
Mighty Eighth Air Force Museum, Pooler, GA...381
Military Aviation Museum, Virginia Beach, VA..1542

Aeronautics and Space Museums–Continued

Minnesota Air National Guard Historical Foundation, Inc., Saint Paul, MN............790

Minter Field Air Museum, Shafter, CA........186

Mitchell Gallery of Flight, Milwaukee, WI...1612

Museum of Astrogeology, Meteor Crater, Winslow, AZ...53

Museum of Aviation at Robins Air Force Base, GA, Warner Robins, GA................390

The Museum of Flight, Seattle, WA........1567

Museum of Flying, Santa Monica, CA........183

NASA Glenn Research Center's Visitor Center, Cleveland, OH 1155

NASA Kennedy Space Center, Merritt Island, FL...323

National Air and Space Museum, Washington, DC...............................283

National Museum of Naval Aviation, Pensacola, FL....................................336

National Museum of the United States Air Force, Wright-Patterson Air Force Base, OH...1193

National Soaring Museum, Elmira, NY.......988

National Warplane Museum, Horseheads, NY..999

Neil Armstrong Air & Space Museum, Wapakoneta, OH................................1189

New England Air Museum of the Connecticut Aeronautical Historical Association, Inc., Windsor Locks, CT.....267

New Mexico Museum of Space History, Alamogordo, NM................................932

Octave Chanute Aerospace Museum, Rantoul, IL..453

Oregon Air & Space Museum, Eugene, OR...1224

Pacific Aviation Museum - Pearl Harbor, Honolulu, HI......................................397

Parker-O'Malley Air Museum, Ghent, NY..994

Pearson Air Museum, Vancouver, WA 1576

Pima Air & Space Museum, Tucson, AZ.......50

Pioneer Air Museum, Fairbanks, AK..............24

Piper Aviation Museum Foundation, Lock Haven, PA.......................................1269

The Portal of the Folded Wings Shrine to Aviation and Museum, North Hollywood, CA................................131

Rhinebeck Aerodrome Museum, Rhinebeck, NY 1056

San Diego Air & Space Museum, San Diego, CA...159

San Francisco International Airport; San Francisco Airport Museums, San Francisco, CA.....................................169

Santa Maria Museum of Flight, Inc., Santa Maria, CA....................................183

Space Center Houston, Houston, TX..........1429

Stafford Air and Space Museum, Weatherford, OK................................1217

Stanzel Model Aircraft Museum, Schulenburg, TX................................1452

Tennessee Museum of Aviation, Sevierville, TN....................................1383

Texas Air Museum, Slaton, TX 1453

Tillamook Naval Air Station Museum, Tillamook, OR....................................1237

United States Marine Corps Air-Ground Museum, Quantico, VA.....................1526

U.S. Naval Museum of Armament & Technology, China Lake, CA..............84

The U.S. Space & Rocket Center, Huntsville, AL......................................12

Vintage Flying Museum, Fort Worth, TX ..1419

Virginia Air & Space Center, Hampton, VA...1510

Virginia Aviation Museum, Richmond International Airport, VA.......................1534

Western Aerospace Museum, Oakland, CA...134

White 1 Foundation, Kissimmee, FL...........319

Wings of History Air Museum, San Martin, CA...175

Wings Over Miami Museum, Inc., Miami, FL...326

Wright Brothers National Memorial, Kill Devil Hills, NC...................................1108

Yankee Air Force, Inc. (Yankee Air Museum), Ypsilanti, MI 766

Anthropology and Ethnology Museums

A:shiwi A:wan Museum and Heritage Center, Zuni, NM 954

Abbe Museum, Bar Harbor, ME.................605

Adams State College Luther Bean Museum, Alamosa, CO 201

Adan E. Treganza Anthropology Museum, Dept. of Anthropology, San Francisco State University, San Francisco, CA.......................................162

Afro-American Cultural Center, Charlotte, NC....................................1094

Agate Fossil Beds National Monument, Harrison, NE.......................................862

Agua Caliente Cultural Museum, Palm Springs, CA...138

Ah-Tah-Thi-Ki Museum, Big Cypress Seminole Indian Reservation, FL...........295

Ah-Tah-Thi-Ki Museum at Okalee, Hollywood, FL....................................312

Akwesasne Museum, Hogansburg, NY 998

Alabama Museum of Natural History, Tuscaloosa, AL......................................19

Alaska Heritage Museum at Wells Fargo, Anchorage, AK......................................21

Alaska Indian Arts, Inc., Haines, AK............24

Alutiiq Museum and Archaeological Repository, Kodiak, AK.......................26

American Museum of Asmat Art, Saint Paul, MN..789

American Museum of Natural History, New York, NY....................................1019

American Museum of Straw Art, Long Beach, CA..110

America's Stonehenge, North Salem, NH....893

The Amerind Foundation, Inc., Dragoon, AZ...32

Anasazi Heritage Center, Dolores, CO.........214

Anchorage Museum at Rasmuson Center, Anchorage, AK.......................................22

Andrew J. Blackbird Museum, Harbor Springs, MI...745

Antelope Valley Indian Museum, Lancaster, CA.......................................108

The Anthropology Museum, DeKalb, IL......429

Anthropology Museum, University of San Diego, San Diego, CA 155

Anthropology Teaching Museum, California State University, Fullerton, Fullerton, CA...98

Anza-Borrego Desert State Park, Borrego Springs, CA...79

The Appaloosa Museum and Heritage Center, Moscow, ID...............................407

Arches National Park Visitor Center, Moab, UT...1467

Arizona State Museum, Tucson, AZ..............48

Arizona State University Museum of Anthropology, Tempe, AZ.......................46

Armenian Library and Museum of America, Watertown, MA 716

Ataloa Lodge Museum, Muskogee, OK.....1205

Audubon County Historical Society, Exira, IA...517

Avery Research Center for African American History & Culture, Charleston, SC...................................1323

Aztalan Museum, Jefferson, WI.................1601

The Bade Institute of Biblical Archaeology and The Howell Bible Collection, Berkeley, CA 75

Bandelier National Monument, Los Alamos, NM...942

Bay Area Museum, Seabrook, TX..............1452

The Bead Museum, Glendale, AZ.................35

Bear Butte State Park Visitors Center, Sturgis, SD...1358

Besser Museum for Northeast Michigan, Alpena, MI...723

Bishop Museum, Honolulu, HI...................394

Black Arts National Diaspora Museum, New Orleans, LA...................................594

Blackwater Draw Museum, Portales, NM....944

Boone County Historical Center, Boone, IA...506

Boot Hill Museum, Inc., Dodge City, KS....536

Buechel Memorial Lakota Museum, Saint Francis, SD...1355

Buffalo Bill Historical Center, Cody, WY..1631

Buffalo Museum of Science, Buffalo, NY ...972

Burke Museum of Natural History and Culture, Seattle, WA...........................1565

C.E. Smith Museum of Anthropology, Hayward, CA..101

C.H. Nash Museum-Chucalissa Archaeological Museum, Memphis, TN...1372

CWU Anthropology Department, Ellensburg, WA...............................1553

Cable Natural History Museum, Cable, WI...1593

Caddoan Mounds State Historic Site, Cherokee County, TX...........................1399

Caguana Indian Ceremonial Park & Museum, Utuado, PR 1644

Cahokia Mounds State Historic Site, Collinsville, IL....................................428

California State Indian Museum, Sacramento, CA.....................................151

Cambridge Museum, Cambridge, NE..........858

Canyon de Chelly National Monument, Chinle, AZ...31

Carnegie Museum of Natural History, Pittsburgh, PA...................................1291

Carter County Museum, Ekalaka, MT.........846

Casa Grande Ruins National Monument, Coolidge, AZ...31

Cass County Museum & Pioneer School, Walker, MN...795

Castine Scientific Society, Castine, ME 609

Catalina Island Museum Society, Inc., Avalon, CA...73

Center of Southwest Studies/Fort Lewis College, Durango, CO.........................214

The Central Museum, Central, AK.................23

Chaco Culture National Historical Park, Nageezi, NM.......................................943

Cheraw Lyceum Museum, Cheraw, SC......1327

Cherokee National Museum, Park Hill, OK...1211

Chester County Historical Society Museum, Chester, SC...........................1327

Chickasaw Council House Museum, Tishomingo, OK...............................1214

Chief Oshkosh Native American Arts, Egg Harbor, WI................................1596

Chief Plenty Coups Museum, Pryor, MT....852

Churchill County Museum and Archives, Fallon, NV..877

City of Fort Walton Beach Heritage Park & Cultural Center, Fort Walton Beach, FL...310

Clearwater Historical Museum, Orofino, ID...408

Cliffs of the Neuse State Park, Seven Springs, NC......1119
College of Eastern Utah Prehistoric Museum, Price, UT......1469
Colorado River Indian Tribes Museum, Parker, AZ......38
Colorado Springs Fine Arts Center (Taylor Museum), Colorado Springs, CO......206
Commonwealth of the Northern Mariana Islands Museum of History and Culture, Saipan, MP......1640
Confederated Tribes and Bands of the Yakama Indian Nation - Cultural Heritage Center Museum, Toppenish, WA......1575
Cottonlandia Museum, Greenwood, MS......800
Creek Council House Museum, Okmulgee, OK......1211
Crockett County Museum, Ozona, TX......1442
Crow Canyon Archaeological Center, Cortez, CO......208
Cultural Museum, Nashville, TN......1378
Cultural Rights and Protection Department/Ute Indian Tribe, Fort Duchesne, UT......1465
Curry Historical Society Museum, Gold Beach, OR......1225

Deer Valley Rock Art Center, Glendale, AZ......35
Deming Luna Mimbres Museum, Deming, NM......939
Denison Museum, Granville, OH......1167
Dickson Mounds Museum, Lewistown, IL......442
Douglas County Museum of History and Natural History, Roseburg, OR......1234
Durham Center Museum/Research Library, East Durham, NY......985

Eastern California Museum, Independence, CA......104
Edge of the Cedars State Park Museum, Blanding, UT......1463
Effigy Mounds National Monument, Harpers Ferry, IA......519
Eiteljorg Museum of American Indians and Western Art, Indianapolis, IN......482
El Paso Museum of Archaeology, El Paso, TX......1411
Elgin Public Museum, Elgin, IL......432
Etowah Indian Mounds Historical Site, Cartersville, GA......367
Everhart Museum: Natural History, Science and Art, Scranton, PA......1298

Favell Museum Inc., Klamath Falls, OR....1227
The Five Civilized Tribes Museum, Muskogee, OK......1205
Flathead Indian Museum, Saint Ignatius, MT......853
Flint Ridge State Memorial Museum, Glenford, OH......1166
Florence Hawley Ellis Museum of Anthropology and Ruth Hall Museum of Paleontology, Abiquiu, NM......931
Fort Ancient Museum, Oregonia, OH......1181
Fort Belknap Museum and Archives, Inc., Newcastle, TX......1441
Fort Bridger State Museum, Fort Bridger, WY......1632
Fort Buford State Historic Site, Williston, ND......1137
Fort Caspar Museum, Casper, WY......1629
Fort Henrietta Interpretive Park, Echo, OR......1223
Fort Okanogan Interpretive Center, Brewster, WA......1550
Fort Recovery Museum, Fort Recovery, OH......1164

Gadsden Museum, Mesilla, NM......943

Galveston County Historical Museum, Galveston, TX......1420
Georgia Museum of Natural History, Athens, GA......356
Georgia Southern University Museum, Statesboro, GA......387
Grand Teton National Park, Colter Bay Indian Arts Museum, Colter Bay Village, WY......1631
Grand Village of the Natchez Indians, Natchez, MS......805
Graves Museum of Archaeology and Natural History, Dania Beach, FL......302
Greybull Museum, Greybull, WY......1634

Haffenreffer Museum of Anthropology, Brown University, Bristol, RI......1310
Hampson Archeological Museum State Park, Wilson, AR......70
Heard Museum, Phoenix, AZ......40
Helen Louise Allen Textile Collection, Madison, WI......1605
Helvetia Museum, Helvetia, WV......1582
The Heritage Center, Pine Ridge, SD......1354
Heritage Library Museum, Anchorage, AK......22
Heritage of the Americas Museum, El Cajon, CA......92
Herrett Center for Arts & Science, Faulkner Planetarium and Centennial Observatory, Twin Falls, ID......410
Hi-Desert Nature Museum, Yucca Valley, CA......201
High Desert Museum, Bend, OR......1220
Historic Bowens Mills & Pioneer Park, Middleville, MI......754
Historic Halifax State Historic Site, Halifax, NC......1105
Homolovi Ruins State Park, Winslow, AZ......53
Horry County Museum, Conway, SC......1331
Housatonic Museum of Art, Bridgeport, CT......236
Hudson Museum, The University of Maine, Orono, ME......617

Idaho Museum of Natural History, Pocatello, ID......408
Illinois State Museum, Springfield, IL......458
Immigration Museum of New Americans Post WWII, San Diego, CA......156
Indian City U.S.A., Anadarko, OK......1195
Indian Museum of Lake County, Ohio, Willoughby, OH......1191
Indian Museum of North America at Crazy Horse Memorial, Crazy Horse, SD......1345
Indian Pueblo Cultural Center, Albuquerque, NM......933
International Bluegrass Music Museum, Owensboro, KY......581
International Museum of Cultures, Dallas, TX......1406
Iraan Museum, Iraan, TX......1430
Iroquois Indian Museum, Howes Cave, NY......999
Italian American Museum, New York, NY......1028

Jane L. and Robert H. Weiner Judaic Museum, Rockville, MD......651
Jensen Arctic Museum, Monmouth, OR....1228
Jesse Peter Museum, Santa Rosa, CA......184

Ka-Do-Ha Indian Village Museum, Murfreesboro, AR......65
Kateri Galleries, The National Shrine of the North American Martyrs, Auriesville, NY......959
Kaw Mission State Historic Site, Council Grove, KS......536
Klein Museum, Mobridge, SD......1352

L.C. Bates Museum, Hinckley, ME......612
Latvian Museum, Rockville, MD......651

Libby Museum, Wolfeboro, NH......897
Logan Museum of Anthropology, Beloit, WI......1592
Lompoc Museum, Lompoc, CA......109
Los Alamos Historical Museum, Los Alamos, NM......942
Lost City Museum, Overton, NV......880
Louden-Henritze Archaeology Museum, Trinidad, CO......234
Louisiana State Exhibit Museum, Shreveport, LA......600
Lower East Side Tenement Museum, New York, NY......1029
Lynden Pioneer Museum, Lynden, WA......1559

MacCallum More Museum and Gardens, Chase City, VA......1500
Maidu Interpretive Center, Roseville, CA....151
Malki Museum, Banning, CA......74
Maltz Museum of Jewish Heritage, Beachwood, OH......1142
Marianna-Lee County Museum Assoc. Inc., Marianna, AR......64
Marin Museum of the American Indian, Novato, CA......131
Martin and Osa Johnson Safari Museum, Inc., Chanute, KS......535
Maryhill Museum of Art, Goldendale, WA......1556
Maxwell Museum of Anthropology, Albuquerque, NM......934
Mercer County Historical Museum, The Riley Home, Celina, OH......1146
Merritt Museum of Anthropology, Oakland, CA......133
Mesa Southwest Museum, Mesa, AZ......37
Miami County Museum, Peru, IN......496
Michel Brouillet House & Museum, Vincennes, IN......502
Mid-America All Indian Center, Wichita, KS......562
Millicent Rogers Museum of Northern New Mexico, Taos, NM......952
The Mitchell Museum of the American Indian, Evanston, IL......435
The Morikami Museum and Japanese Gardens, Delray Beach, FL......305
Moundville Archaeological Park, Moundville, AL......17
Mountain Heritage Center, Cullowhee, NC......1097
Museo de Las Americas, San Juan, PR......1642
Museum of Anthropology, Highland Heights, KY......571
Museum of Anthropology, Winston-Salem, NC......1125
Museum of Anthropology, Pullman, WA...1563
Museum of Anthropology, Chico, CA......83
Museum of Anthropology, University of Denver, Denver, CO......213
Museum of Anthropology, University of Missouri, Columbia, MO......813
Museum of Cultural & Natural History, Mount Pleasant, MI......757
Museum of History, Anthropology and Art, San Juan, PR......1643
Museum of Indian Arts & Culture/Laboratory of Anthropology, Santa Fe, NM......948
Museum of Natural History and Planetarium, Providence, RI......1317
Museum of Northern Arizona, Flagstaff, AZ......33
Museum of Northwest Colorado, Craig, CO......208
Museum of Peoples and Cultures, Provo, UT......1470
Museum of Primitive Art and Culture, Peace Dale, RI......1316
Museum of the African Diaspora, San Francisco, CA......167
Museum of the Aleutians, Unalaska, AK......28

Anthropology and Ethnology Museums–Continued

The Museum of the Alphabet, Waxhaw, NC.........1121

Museum of the Cherokee Indian, Cherokee, NC.........1096

Museum of the Red River, Idabel, OK......1203

Museum of Vertebrate Zoology, Berkeley, CA.........76

Napa Valley Museum, Yountville, CA.........200

National Hall of Fame for Famous American Indians, Anadarko, OK.........1196

National Museum of the American Indian, Smithsonian Institution, New York, NY.........1034

Native American Museum, Terre Haute, IN.........500

Native American Resource Center, Pembroke, NC.........1114

The Nature Museum at Grafton, Grafton, VT.........1479

Navajo Nation Museum, Window Rock, AZ.........53

Nevada State Museum, Las Vegas, Las Vegas, NV.........880

Nez Perce National Historical Park, Spalding, ID.........409

No Man's Land Historical Society, Goodwell, OK.........1201

Norwegian-American Historical Association, Northfield, MN.........786

Oakwoods Metropark Nature Center, Belleville, MI.........728

Oklahoma Museum of History, Oklahoma City, OK.........1210

Old Fort Meade Museum and Historic Research Association, Fort Meade, SD.1347

Oneida Nation Museum, De Pere, WI.........1594

Oregon Coast History Center, Newport, OR.........1229

The Ozark Folk Center, Mountain View, AR.........65

Parks, Recreation & Historic Sites Division, Georgia Dept. of Natural Resources, Atlanta, GA.........362

Pawnee Indian Village State Historic Site, Republic, KS.........556

Peabody Museum of Archaeology & Ethnology, Cambridge, MA.........674

The Peary-MacMillan Arctic Museum, Brunswick, ME.........608

Petrified Forest of the Black Hills, Piedmont, SD.........1353

Petterson Museum of Intercultural Art, Claremont, CA.........85

Phoebe Apperson Hearst Museum of Anthropology, Berkeley, CA.........77

Pipestone County Historical Museum, Pipestone, MN.........786

Pipestone National Monument, Pipestone, MN.........787

Piqua Historical Area State Memorial, Piqua, OH.........1182

Plains Indians and Pioneers Museum, Woodward, OK.........1217

Plaza de La Raza, Inc. & Boathouse Gallery, Los Angeles, CA.........121

Porterville Historical Museum, Porterville, CA.........144

Pueblo Grande Museum and Archaeological Park, Phoenix, AZ.........42

Putnam County Historical Society Museum, Kalida, OH.........1169

Putnam Museum of History & Natural Science, Davenport, IA.........513

Rancho Los Alamitos, Long Beach, CA.........111

Rankin Museum, Inc., Ellerbe, NC.........1100

Red Earth Museum, Oklahoma City, OK.........1210

Red Rock Museum, Church Rock, NM.........938

Reuel B. Pritchett Museum, Bridgewater, VA.........1497

Riverside Metropolitan Museum, Riverside, CA.........150

Robert Hull Fleming Museum, Burlington, VT.........1478

Robert S. Kerr Museum, Poteau, OK.........1212

Robert S. Peabody Museum of Archaeology, Andover, MA.........660

Royal Gorge Regional Museum & History Center, Canon City, CO.........205

Sacajawea Interpretive Center, Pasco, WA.1561

St. Clements Island and Piney Point Museums, Colton's Point, MD.........641

St. Joseph Museum Inc., Saint Joseph, MO.........831

Samuel K. Fox Museum, Dillingham, AK.....23

San Diego Archaeological Center, Escondido, CA.........93

San Diego Museum of Man, San Diego, CA.........160

San Juan County Archaeological Research Center and Library at the Salmon Ruin/San Juan County Museum Association, Bloomfield, NM...937

Santa Ynez Valley Historical Society, Santa Ynez, CA.........185

Schingoethe Center for Native American Cultures, Aurora, IL.........412

The Schomburg Center for Research in Black Culture, New York, NY.........1038

School of American Research, Indian Arts Research Center, Santa Fe, NM.........950

Seminole Canyon State Park and Historic Site, Comstock, TX.........1401

Seminole Nation Museum, Wewoka, OK...1217

Seneca-Iroquois National Museum, Salamanca, NY.........1063

Serpent Mound Museum, Peebles, OH.........1182

Sheldon Jackson Museum, Sitka, AK.........27

The Simon Paneak Memorial Museum, Anaktuvuk Pass, AK.........21

Siouxland Heritage Museums, Sioux Falls, SD.........1357

Sitka National Historical Park, Sitka, AK.........28

Six Nations Indian Museum, Onchiota, NY.........1045

Sky City Cultural Center, Pueblo of Acoma, NM.........944

Smoki Museum - American Indian Art & Culture, Prescott, AZ.........43

Southeast Missouri Regional Museum, Cape Girardeau, MO.........812

Southern Plains Indian Museum, Anadarko, OK.........1196

Southern Ute Cultural Center and Museum, Ignacio, CO.........223

Southold Indian Museum, Southold, NY...1071

Southwest Museum, Los Angeles, CA.........121

Spiro Mounds Archaeological Center, Spiro, OK.........1214

Stagecoach Inn Museum Complex, Newbury Park, CA.........130

Stone Fort Museum, Nacogdoches, TX.........1440

Sunnyside Historical Museum, Sunnyside, WA.........1572

SunWatch Indian Village/Archaeological Park, Dayton, OH.........1162

Suquamish Museum, Poulsbo, WA.........1563

Tamastslikt Cultural Institute, Pendleton, OR.........1230

Tantaquidgeon Indian Museum, Uncasville, CT.........263

Tonto National Monument, Roosevelt, AZ.........43

Totem Heritage Center, Ketchikan, AK.........26

Trailside Nature Museum, Cross River, NY.........983

Turabo University, Gurabo, PR.........1641

UCLA Fowler Museum of Cultural History, Los Angeles, CA.........122

United States Department of the Interior Museum, Washington, DC.........293

The University Museum, Edwardsville, IL.........432

University Museum, New Mexico State University, Las Cruces, NM.........941

The University of Michigan Exhibit Museum of Natural History, Ann Arbor, MI.........725

University of Michigan Museum of Anthropology, Ann Arbor, MI.........725

University of Northern Iowa Museums & Collections, Cedar Falls, IA.........508

University of Oregon Museum of Natural and Cultural History, Eugene, OR.........1224

University of Pennsylvania Museum of Archaeology and Anthropology, Philadelphia, PA.........1288

University of Wyoming Anthropology Museum, Laramie, WY.........1636

Utah State University's Museum of Anthropology, Logan, UT.........1467

Ute Indian Museum/Montrose Visitor Center, Montrose, CO.........228

Van Meter State Park, Miami, MO.........827

Wayne State University Museum of Anthropology, Detroit, MI.........738

West Pasco Historical Society Museum and Library, New Port Richey, FL.........329

Western Archeological & Conservation Center, Tucson, AZ.........52

Western New Mexico University Museum, Silver City, NM.........951

Weymouth Woods-Sandhills Nature Preserve Museum, Southern Pines, NC.1120

The Wheelwright Museum of the American Indian, Santa Fe, NM.........950

Whiskeytown Unit, Whiskeytown-Shasta-Trinity National Recreation Area, Whiskeytown, CA.........198

William Hammond Mathers Museum, Bloomington, IN.........470

William S. Webb Museum of Anthropology, Lexington, KY.........575

Winnebago Area Museum, Winnebago, MN.........797

Woodruff Museum of Indian Artifacts, Bridgeton, NJ.........898

Woolaroc Museum, Bartlesville, OK.........1197

WordSpring Discovery Center, Orlando, FL.........333

Wrangell Museum, Wrangell, AK.........29

Wriston Art Center Galleries, Appleton, WI.........1590

Wyoming Pioneer Home, Thermopolis, WY.........1639

The Yager Museum of Art & Culture, Oneonta, NY.........1046

Yellowstone National Park, Gardiner, MT...847

Aquariums, Marine Museums and Oceanariums

ASRI Environmental Education Center, Bristol, RI.........1310

Abilene Zoological Gardens, Abilene, TX.1385

Adventure Aquarium, Camden, NJ.........899

Ak-Sar-Ben Aquarium Outdoor Education Center, Gretna, NE.........862

Alaska SeaLife Center, Seward, AK.........27

Albuquerque Biological Park, Albuquerque, NM.........932

Aquarium of Niagara, Niagara Falls, NY..1042

Aquarium of the Pacific, Long Beach, CA.........110

Arthur D. Feiro Marine Life Center c/o Peninsula College, Port Angeles, WA...1561

Audubon Aquarium of the Americas, New Orleans, LA.........593

The Bailey-Matthews Shell Museum, Sanibel, FL...............................343
Belle Isle Aquarium, Detroit, MI.................734
Berkshire Museum, Pittsfield, MA 702
Birch Aquarium at Scripps, Scripps Institution of Oceanography, University of California, San Diego, La Jolla, CA...106
Bramble Park Zoo, Watertown, SD 1359

Cabrillo Marine Aquarium, San Pedro, CA...176
California Academy of Sciences, San Francisco, CA...163
Calvert Marine Museum, Solomons, MD 654
Cameron Park Zoo, Waco, TX.................1458
Carrie Weedon Natural Science Museum, Galesville, MD...645
Chicago Zoological Park (Brookfield Zoo), Brookfield, IL 414
Chula Vista Nature Center, Chula Vista, CA...84
City Museum, Saint Louis, MO...................832
Clearwater Marine Aquarium, Clearwater, FL...299
Columbus Zoo and Aquarium, Powell, OH..1183

D.C. Booth Historic National Fish Hatchery, Spearfish, SD 1357
The Dallas Aquarium at Fair Park, Dallas, TX..1404
The Dallas World Aquarium, Dallas, TX ..1406
Detroit Zoo, Royal Oak, MI 762

East End Seaport Museum and Marine Foundation, Greenport, NY.....................996
ECHO at the Leahy Center for Lake Champlain, Burlington, VT...................1478
Epcot at Walt Disney World Resort, Lake Buena Vista, FL.......................................319

Falls of the Ohio State Park, Clarksville, IN..472
Flint River Quarium, Albany, GA 355
Florida Aquarium, Tampa, FL.....................349
Fort Peck Interpretive Center, Fort Peck, MT...846
Fort Worth Zoological Park, Fort Worth, TX...1417

Gavins Point National Fish Hatchery and Aquarium, Yankton, SD 1359
Georgia Aquarium, Atlanta, GA 360
Gladys Porter Zoo, Brownsville, TX...........1398
Great Harbor Maritime Museum, Northeast Harbor, ME 616

Hatfield Marine Science Center, Oregon State University, Newport, OR 1228
Hereford Inlet Lighthouse, North Wildwood, NJ...917
Houston Zoo, Inc., Houston, TX 1427

Imaginarium Hands-On Museum, Fort Myers, FL...309
Indianapolis Zoo, Indianapolis, IN 485

J.L. Scott Marine Education Center and Aquarium, Gulf Coast Research Laboratory College of Marine Sciences, The U. of Southern Mississippi, Biloxi, MS...........................798
James A. McFaul Environmental Center of Bergen County, Wyckoff, NJ............931
John D. MacArthur Beach State Park & Nature Center, North Palm Beach, FL 329
John G. Shedd Aquarium, Chicago, IL 422

Kansas Department of Wildlife & Parks, Pratt, KS...556

Lake Meredith Aquatic and Wildlife Museum, Fritch, TX 1420

Las Vegas Natural History Museum, Las Vegas, NV..879
Loggerhead Marinelife Center, Juno Beach, FL..316
Logoly State Park, McNeil, AR.....................64

Maramec Museum, The James Foundation, Saint James, MO.................830
The Maritime Aquarium, Norwalk, CT........257
Maui Ocean Center, Maalaea, HI 401
McWane Science Center, Birmingham, AL..5
Miami Seaquarium, Miami, FL 325
Minnesota Zoo, Apple Valley, MN 768
Mississippi Museum of Natural Science, Jackson, MS...803
Mississippi River Museum at Mud Island River Park, Memphis, TN.....................1375
Montauk Point Lighthouse Museum, Montauk, NY...1015
Monterey Bay Aquarium, Monterey, CA 127
Morro Bay Aquarium, Morro Bay, CA 129
Mote Marine Laboratory/Aquarium, Sarasota, FL...345
Mount Desert Oceanarium, Southwest Harbor, ME...623
Mystic Aquarium & Institute for Exploration, Mystic, CT.........................250

Nantucket Maria Mitchell Association, Nantucket, MA 696
Natchitoches National Fish Hatchery, Natchitoches, LA 593
The National Aquarium, Washington, DC....284
National Aquarium in Baltimore, Baltimore, MD...635
National Mississippi River Museum & Aquarium, Dubuque, IA.........................516
Natural History Museum, Portales, NM.......944
Nauticus, The National Maritime Center, Norfolk, VA..1522
New England Aquarium Corporation, Boston, MA...668
New York Aquarium, Brooklyn, NY 969
North Carolina Aquarium at Fort Fisher, Kure Beach, NC 1109
North Carolina Aquarium at Pine Knoll Shores, Pine Knoll Shores, NC..............1114
North Carolina Aquarium on Roanoke Island, Manteo, NC...................................1110

Oceanographic Teaching Station Inc. - Roundhouse Marine Studies Lab & Aquarium, Manhattan Beach, CA.............124
Odyssey Maritime Discovery Center, Seattle, WA..1567
Oregon Coast Aquarium, Newport, OR.......1229
The Oyster and Maritime Museum of Chincoteague, Chincoteague, VA...........1501

Paducah Aquarium, Paducah, KY................582
The Pier Aquarium, Saint Petersburg, FL 341
Pittsburgh Zoo and Aquarium, Pittsburgh, PA..1293
Point Defiance Zoo & Aquarium, Tacoma, WA 1574
Port Townsend Marine Science Center, Port Townsend, WA.................................1562
Pratt Museum, Homer, AK 25

Ripley's Believe It or Not!, Key West, FL...319
River Heritage Museum, Paducah, KY 582
Roper Mountain Science Center, Greenville, SC...1334

Santa Barbara Museum of Natural History, Santa Barbara, CA.......................179
Science Museum of Virginia, Richmond, VA...1531
Seacoast Science Center, Rye, NH 896
Seattle Aquarium, Seattle, WA....................1568
SeaWorld San Diego, San Diego, CA...........161
Six Flags Marine World, Vallejo, CA...........194

South Carolina Aquarium, Charleston, SC.1326
South Dakota Discovery Center and Aquarium, Pierre, SD 1353
South Florida Museum, Bishop Planetarium & Parker Manatee Aquarium, Bradenton, FL........................297
South Florida Science Museum, West Palm Beach, FL...353
Star Eco Station, Culver City, CA.................88

Tennessee Aquarium, Chattanooga, TN......1362
The Toledo Zoo, Toledo, OH.....................1187
Tulsa Zoo & Living Museum, Tulsa, OK ..1216

University of Puerto Rico Department of Marine Sciences Museum, Mayaguez, PR..1641

Virginia Aquarium & Marine Science Center, Virginia Beach, VA....................1542
Virginia Living Museum, Newport News, VA...1520

Waikiki Aquarium, Honolulu, HI..................399
The Wetlands Institute, Stone Harbor, NJ 925
Whalers Village Museum, Lahaina, HI 401
Wildlife Museum at Petaluma High School, Petaluma, CA.................................142
Woods Hole Science Aquarium, Woods Hole, MA...720
The World of Energy, Seneca, SC 1341

Arboretums

A.L. Fetterman Educational Museum, Fort Valley, GA...372
Abington Art Center, Jenkintown, PA 1263
The Accokeek Foundation, Inc., Accokeek, MD...627
Ak-Sar-Ben Aquarium Outdoor Education Center, Gretna, NE....................862
Albuquerque Biological Park, Albuquerque, NM.....................................932
American Museum of Science & Energy, Oak Ridge, TN...1382
Arbor Lodge State Historical Park, Nebraska City, NE.......................................868
The Arboretum at Flagstaff, Flagstaff, AZ 32
Arboretum at UC Santa Cruz, Santa Cruz, CA..181
Arizona State Parks Board, Phoenix, AZ 39
Arkansas Museum of Natural Resources, Smackover, AR...68
Arnold Arboretum of Harvard University, Jamaica Plain, MA.....................................688
Atlanta Botanical Garden, Atlanta, GA.........357
Atlanta Historical Society, Atlanta, GA.........358
Audubon House & Tropical Gardens, Key West, FL...317
Awbury Arboretum, Philadelphia, PA.........1277

Bailey House Museum - Maui Historical Society, Wailuku, HI 402
Barnes Foundation, Merion, PA.................1271
Bartlett Arboretum & Gardens, Stamford, CT...260
Bartram's Garden, Philadelphia, PA 1277
Bayard Cutting Arboretum, Great River, NY...996
Berkshire Botanical Garden, Stockbridge, MA...711
Bernheim Arboretum and Research Forest, Clermont, KY 567
The Berry Botanic Garden, Portland, OR ..1230
Bickelhaupt Arboretum, Clinton, IA............511
Black Hills Reptile Gardens, Inc., Rapid City, SD...1354
Blackberry Farm's Pioneer Village, Aurora, IL..411
Blithewold Mansion, Gardens & Arboretum, Bristol, RI.............................1310
Bonner County Historical Museum, Sandpoint, ID...409

Arboretums–Continued

The Botanic Garden of Smith College, Northampton, MA 699

Botanica, The Wichita Gardens, Wichita, KS 561

Botanical Gardens at Asheville, Asheville, NC 1089

Bowman's Hill Wildflower Preserve, New Hope, PA 1273

Boyce Thompson Arboretum, Superior, AZ 44

Brooklyn Botanic Garden, Brooklyn, NY 967

Brownville Historical Society Museum, Brownville, NE 858

Buffalo and Erie County Botanical Gardens, Buffalo, NY 972

Cabin Nature Center, Wood Dale, IL 466

The Campus Arboretum Association Haverford College, Haverford, PA 1260

Carleen Bright Arboretum, Woodway, TX .1462

The Cathedral of St. John the Divine, New York, NY 1022

The Centennial Museum at the University of Texas at El Paso, El Paso, TX 1411

The Chattanooga Nature Center, Chattanooga, TN 1361

Cheekwood-Tennessee Botanical Garden & Museum of Art, Nashville, TN 1378

Cherokee National Museum, Park Hill, OK 1211

Chicago Botanic Garden, Glencoe, IL 438

Chihuahuan Desert Research Institute, Fort Davis, TX 1414

Cincinnati Zoo & Botanical Garden, Cincinnati, OH 1149

Civic Garden Center of Greater Cincinnati, Cincinnati, OH 1149

Cleveland Botanical Garden, Cleveland, OH 1152

Coe Hall, Oyster Bay, NY 1049

Coker Arboretum of the North Carolina Botanical Garden, Chapel Hill, NC 1093

Confederate Memorial Hall-Bleak House, Knoxville, TN 1369

Connecticut College Arboretum, New London, CT 255

The Conservatory Garden, New York, NY 1023

The Contemporary Museum, Honolulu, HI 394

Cora Hartshorn Arboretum and Bird Sanctuary, Short Hills, NJ 924

Core Arboretum, Morgantown, WV 1585

The Cornell Plantations, Ithaca, NY 1003

Cox Arboretum & Gardens MetroPark, Dayton, OH 1160

Cranbrook House and Gardens Auxiliary, Bloomfield Hills, MI 730

Crane Point, Marathon, FL 323

Crawford W. Long Museum, Jefferson, GA 374

The Crescent, Valdosta Garden Center, Inc., Valdosta, GA 389

The Crosby Arboretum, Mississippi State University, Picayune, MS 807

Cuneo Museum & Gardens, Vernon Hills, IL 463

Cylburn Arboretum, Baltimore, MD 631

Dallas Arboretum & Botanical Garden, Dallas, TX 1404

The Dawes Arboretum, Newark, OH 1177

Denver Botanic Gardens, Inc., Denver, CO 210

Des Moines Botanical Center, Des Moines, IA 514

Descanso Gardens Guild, Inc., La Canada Flintridge, CA 105

Dinosaur State Park, Rocky Hill, CT 259

Dodge Nature Center, West Saint Paul, MN 796

Dow Gardens, Midland, MI 755

Dubuque Arboretum & Botanical Gardens, Dubuque, IA 516

The Earle-Harrison House and Gardens on 5th Street, Waco, TX 1458

Edison & Ford Winter Estates, Fort Myers, FL 308

Effie Yeaw Nature Center, Carmichael, CA 82

Eloise Butler Wildflower Garden and Bird Sanctuary, Minneapolis, MN 781

Ernest Hemingway House Museum, Key West, FL 317

Evanston Environmental Association/Evanston Ecology Center, Evanston, IL 434

Fairfax County Park Authority, Resource Management Division, Fairfax, VA 1503

Fairmont Park Horticulture Center, Philadelphia, PA 1279

The Fay Hyland Botanical Plantation, Orono, ME 617

Fernwood Botanical Garden & Nature Preserve, Niles, MI 758

Filoli Center, Woodside, CA 199

Finnup Park and Lee Richardson Zoo, Garden City, KS 541

Forest Park Museum and Arboretum, Perry, IA 527

Fort Raleigh National Historic Site, Manteo, NC 1110

Fort Ticonderoga, Ticonderoga, NY 1078

Fort Worth Botanic Garden, Fort Worth, TX 1416

Fort Worth Zoological Park, Fort Worth, TX 1417

Frontera Audubon Society, Weslaco, TX 1460

Fuller Gardens, North Hampton, NH 893

The Fullerton Arboretum, Fullerton, CA 98

Garden in the Woods of the New England Wild Flower Society, Framingham, MA 683

Gardens at Callaway, Pine Mountain, GA 380

Gardenview Horticultural Park, Strongsville, OH 1186

Garfield Park Conservatory, Chicago, IL 421

Gene Stratton-Porter State Historic Site, Rome City, IN 498

General Crook House Museum and Library/Archives Center, Omaha, NE 870

Genesee Country Village & Museum, Mumford, NY 1016

The George G. Frelinghuysen Arboretum, Morris Township, NJ 913

George L. Luthy Memorial Botanical Garden, Peoria, IL 450

George Landis Arboretum, Esperance, NY 989

The Gilbert Stuart Birthplace and Museum, Saunderstown, RI 1319

The Glebe House Museum and Gertrude Jekyll Garden, Woodbury, CT 268

Goodman Museum, Tyler, TX 1456

The Greenburgh Nature Center, Scarsdale, NY 1066

Hammond Museum and Japanese Stroll Garden, North Salem, NY 1043

Hanover House, Clemson, SC 1328

Harold L. Lyon Arboretum, Honolulu, HI ...395

Hathaway Ranch Museum, Santa Fe Springs, CA 182

Hayes Regional Arboretum, Richmond, IN 497

Heritage Hall Museum & Archives, Freeman, SD 1347

The Heritage Museum, Baltimore, MD 632

Heritage Museums & Gardens, Sandwich, MA 707

Hershey Gardens, Hershey, PA 1260

Hidden Lake Gardens, Tipton, MI 765

Highland Botanical Park, Rochester, NY ...1058

Highland Community College Arboretum, Freeport, IL 435

Hildene, The Lincoln Family Home, Manchester, VT 1481

Hilltop Garden and Nature Center, Bloomington, IN 469

Historic London Town and Gardens, Edgewater, MD 642

Hofstra Museum, Hempstead, NY 997

The Holden Arboretum, Kirtland, OH 1170

Hoyt Arboretum, Portland, OR 1231

Humboldt Redwoods State Park Visitor Center, Weott, CA 197

Huntington Library, Art Collections, and Botanical Gardens, San Marino, CA 174

Hurricane Valley Heritage Park Museum, Hurricane, UT 1466

Idaho Museum of Natural History, Pocatello, ID 408

Indianapolis Zoo, Indianapolis, IN 485

The Institute For American Indian Studies (IAIS), Washington Green, CT ...263

Institute of Ecosystem Studies, Millbrook, NY 1014

International Peace Garden, Dunseith, ND 1130

Isabella Stewart Gardner Museum, Boston, MA 666

Jacksonville Zoo and Gardens, Jacksonville, FL 315

James A. McFaul Environmental Center of Bergen County, Wyckoff, NJ 931

JC Raulston Arboretum at NC State University, Raleigh, NC 1115

Jenkins Arboretum, Devon, PA 1249

Jesse Hepler Lilac Arboretum, University of New Hampshire, Durham, NH 886

John A. Finch Arboretum, Spokane, WA ...1571

The Journey Museum, Rapid City, SD 1354

Judge Roy Bean Visitor Center, Langtry, TX 1433

Kalamazoo Nature Center, Inc., Kalamazoo, MI 748

Key West Tropical Forest & Botanical Garden, Key West, FL 318

Kingwood Center, Mansfield, OH 1173

Klehm Arboretum & Botanical Garden, Rockford, IL 455

L.C. Bates Museum, Hinckley, ME 612

L.H. Bailey Hortorium, Ithaca, NY 1003

Ladew Topiary Gardens, Monkton, MD 649

Lady Bird Johnson Wildflower Center, Austin, TX 1390

Lancaster County Historical Society, Lancaster, PA 1266

Laurens Henry Cohn, Sr. Memorial Plant Arboretum, Baton Rouge, LA 586

Lewis Ginter Botanical Garden, Richmond, VA 1530

The Lexington Cemetery, Lexington, KY 573

Lichterman Nature Center, Memphis, TN ..1373

Lilacia Park-Lombard Park District, Lombard, IL 443

Lincoln Children's Zoo, Lincoln, NE 866

Lincoln Memorial Garden and Nature Center, Springfield, IL 459

Lincoln Park Conservatory, Chicago, IL 423

Living Desert Zoo and Gardens State Park, Carlsbad, NM 938

LongHouse Reserve, East Hampton, NY 986

Longwood Gardens, Kennett Square, PA 1264

The Los Angeles County Arboretum & Botanic Garden, Arcadia, CA 71

Louis E. May Museum, Fremont, NE 861

Louisiana Arboretum, State Preservation Area, Ville Platte, LA 603

Luther Burbank Home & Gardens, Santa Rosa, CA 184

MacKenzie Environmental Education Center, Poynette, WI 1618

The Marie Selby Botanical Gardens, Inc., Sarasota, FL 344

Marjorie McNeely Conservatory at Como Park, Saint Paul, MN 790

Massee Lane Gardens, Home of American Camellia Society, Fort Valley, GA 373

Matthaei Botanical Gardens and Nichols Arboretum, Ann Arbor, MI 725

Maymont, Richmond, VA 1530

McCrory Gardens at South Dakota State University, Brookings, SD 1344

Memphis Botanic Garden, Goldsmith Civic Garden Center, Memphis, TN 1374

Mildred E. Mathias Botanical Garden, Los Angeles, CA 119

Minnesota Landscape Arboretum, University of Minnesota, Chaska, MN 770

Miramont Castle Museum, Manitou Springs, CO 228

Mitchell Park Horticultural Conservatory, Milwaukee, WI 1612

Moanalua Gardens Foundation, Honolulu, HI 397

Montalvo Arts Center, Saratoga, CA 185

Moorten Botanic Garden and Cactarium, Palm Springs, CA 138

Morehead Planetarium and Science Center, Chapel Hill, NC 1093

Morris Arboretum of the University of Pennsylvania, Philadelphia, PA 1283

Morris County Historical Society (Acorn Hall House Museum), Morristown, NJ ...914

The Morton Arboretum, Lisle, IL 443

Mount Pisgah Arboretum, Eugene, OR 1224

Museum of Life and Science, Durham, NC 1098

Myriad Botanical Gardens, Oklahoma City, OK 1208

Nassau County Museum of Art, Roslyn Harbor, NY 1062

National Capital Parks-East, Washington, DC 284

National Tropical Botanical Garden, Kalaheo, HI 399

Nebraska State Capitol, Lincoln, NE 866

New Jersey Botanical Garden at Skylands (NJBG), Ringwood, NJ 923

New Richmond Preservation Society, New Richmond, WI 1615

The New York Botanical Garden, Bronx, NY 966

New York State Office of Parks, Recreation & Historic Preservation, Albany, NY 955

Norfolk Botanical Garden, Norfolk, VA.....1522

North Carolina Botanical Garden, Chapel Hill, NC 1093

Northland Arboretum, Brainerd, MN 769

Oatlands, Leesburg, VA 1512

Oklahoma City Zoo, Oklahoma City, OK..1209

Oklahoma State University Botanical Garden, Stillwater, OK 1214

Old Westbury Gardens, Old Westbury, NY 1045

Oldest House Museum Complex, Saint Augustine, FL 339

Omniplex Science Museum, Oklahoma City, OK 1210

Oregon Trail Arboretum, Echo, OR 1223

Orland E. White Arboretum, Boyce, VA 1497

Ormond Memorial Art Museum & Garden, Ormond Beach, FL 333

Paine Art Center and Gardens, Oshkosh, WI 1617

Parrot Jungle Island, Miami, FL 325

Phipps Conservatory and Botanical Gardens, Pittsburgh, PA 1293

Pink Palace Family of Museums, Memphis, TN 1375

Planting Fields Arboretum State Historic Park, Oyster Bay, NY 1049

Potawatomi Zoo, South Bend, IN 499

Pyramid Hill Sculpture Park & Museum, Hamilton, OH 1168

Queens Botanical Garden, Flushing, NY 990

R.S. Barnwell Memorial Garden and Art Center, Shreveport, LA 601

Rancho Santa Ana Botanic Garden at Claremont, Claremont, CA 85

Red Butte Garden & Arboretum, Salt Lake City, UT 1472

Reeves-Reed Arboretum, Summit, NJ 925

Rehoboth Art League, Inc., Rehoboth Beach, DE 272

Rhododendron Species Botanical Garden, Federal Way, WA 1554

Riverbanks Zoological Park & Botanical Garden, Columbia, SC 1329

Riverside Nature Center, Kerrville, TX 1432

Robert A. Vines Environmental Science Center, Houston, TX 1429

Rockwood Park, Wilmington, DE 274

Rose Hill Museum, Bay Village, OH 1141

Rosicrucian Egyptian Museum, San Jose, CA 172

The Rutgers Gardens, New Brunswick, NJ 916

Saint-Gaudens National Historic Site, Cornish, NH 885

San Antonio Botanical Garden, San Antonio, TX 1449

San Diego Wild Animal Park, Escondido, CA 93

San Diego Zoo, San Diego, CA 161

San Francisco Botanical Garden at Strybing Arboretum, San Francisco, CA 168

San Mateo Arboretum Society, Inc., San Mateo, CA 175

Santarella, Tyringham, MA 715

Schedel Arboretum & Gardens, Elmore, OH 1163

Sciworks, Winston-Salem, NC 1126

Scott Arboretum of Swarthmore College, Swarthmore, PA 1302

Sherman Gardens, Corona del Mar, CA 87

Ships of the Sea Maritime Museum/William Scarbrough House, Savannah, GA 386

Slifer House, Lewisburg, PA 1268

The South Carolina Botanical Garden, Clemson, SC 1328

Stagecoach Inn Museum Complex, Newbury Park, CA 130

Stan Hywet Hall and Gardens, Inc., Akron, OH 1139

Starhill Forest Arboretum, Petersburg, IL 451

The State Botanical Garden of Georgia, Athens, GA 357

Stephenson County Historical Society, Freeport, IL 436

Still National Osteopathic Museum, Kirksville, MO 824

Texas Discovery Gardens, Dallas, TX 1408

Tohono Chul Park Inc., Tucson, AZ..............51

The Toledo Zoo, Toledo, OH 1187

Tucker Wildlife Sanctuary, Silverado, CA ...186

Tucson Botanical Gardens, Tucson, AZ 51

Tulsa Zoo & Living Museum, Tulsa, OK..1216

Turtle Bay Exploration Park, Redding, CA 146

Tyler Arboretum, Media, PA 1271

UNLV Marjorie Barrick Museum, Las Vegas, NV 880

U.S National Arboretum, Washington, DC 292

UC Davis Arboretum, Davis, CA 90

University of Alabama Arboretum, Tuscaloosa, AL 20

University of California Botanical Garden, Berkeley, CA 77

University of California Irvine Arboretum, Irvine, CA 105

University of Tennessee Arboretum, Oak Ridge, TN 1382

University of Washington Botanic Garden, Seattle, WA 1569

University of Wisconsin-Madison Arboretum, Madison, WI 1605

Virginia Zoological Park, Norfolk, VA.......1523

W.H. Over Museum, Vermillion, SD 1358

W.J. Beal Botanical Garden, East Lansing, MI 740

W.W. Seymour Botanical Conservatory, Tacoma, WA 1574

Waimea Arboretum and Botanical Garden in Waimea Valley Audubon Center, Haleiwa, HI 392

Washington National Cathedral, Washington, DC 294

Wave Hill, Bronx, NY 967

Whitehouse Nature Center, Albion, MI 723

Wilbur D. May Museum, Reno, NV 882

Winterthur Museum & Country Estate, Winterthur, DE 274

Woodland Park Zoo, Seattle, WA 1570

Worcester County Horticultural Society/Tower Hill Botanic Garden, Boylston, MA 670

World Museum of Natural History, Riverside, CA 150

Yakima Area Arboretum & Botanical Garden, Yakima, WA 1579

The Zoo, Gulf Breeze, FL 312

Archaeology Museums and Archaeological Sites

A:shiwi A:wan Museum and Heritage Center, Zuni, NM 954

Abbe Museum, Bar Harbor, ME 605

Adams State College Luther Bean Museum, Alamosa, CO 201

Adan E. Treganza Anthropology Museum, Dept. of Anthropology, San Francisco State University, San Francisco, CA 162

Agua Caliente Cultural Museum, Palm Springs, CA 138

Albinger Archeological Museum, Ventura, CA 194

Alexandria Archaeology Museum, Alexandria, VA 1491

Alutiiq Museum and Archaeological Repository, Kodiak, AK 26

America's Stonehenge, North Salem, NH 893

The Amerind Foundation, Inc., Dragoon, AZ 32

Anasazi Heritage Center, Dolores, CO 214

Anasazi State Park Museum, Boulder, UT.1463

Angel Mounds State Historic Site, Evansville, IN 475

Animas Museum, Durango, CO 214

The Anthropology Museum, DeKalb, IL....429

Anthropology Museum, University of San Diego, San Diego, CA 155

Anthropology Teaching Museum, California State University, Fullerton, Fullerton, CA 98

Anza-Borrego Desert State Park, Borrego Springs, CA 79

Apostles Islands National Lakeshore, Bayfield, WI 1591

Arkansas Tech University Museum of Prehistory and History, Russellville, AR 67

Archaeology Museums and
Archaeological Sites–Continued

Associated American Jewish Museums,
   Pittsburgh, PA.....................................1290
Aztec Ruins National Monument, Aztec,
   NM..937

The Bade Institute of Biblical
   Archaeology and The Howell Bible
   Collection, Berkeley, CA 75
Bandelier National Monument, Los
   Alamos, NM..942
Bear Butte State Park Visitors Center,
   Sturgis, SD..1358
Besh-Ba-Gowah Archaeological Park,
   Globe, AZ..35
Biblical Resource Center & Museum,
   Collierville, TN.....................................1364
Billings Curation Center, Billings, MT.......841
Black Kettle Museum, Cheyenne, OK.......1198
Blackwater Draw Museum, Portales, NM....944
Boonsborough Museum of History,
   Boonsboro, MD.....................................637
Boonshoft Museum of Discovery,
   Dayton, OH...1160
Bosque Memorial Museum, Clifton, TX....1400
Brunswick Town/Fort Anderson State
   Historic Site, Winnabow, NC.................1124

C.H. Nash Museum-Chucalissa
   Archaeological Museum, Memphis,
   TN..1372
Cahokia Mounds State Historic Site,
   Collinsville, IL.......................................428
California Museum of Ancient Art,
   Beverly Hills, CA......................................78
Canyon de Chelly National Monument,
   Chinle, AZ...31
Carlsbad Museum & Art Center,
   Carlsbad, NM...938
Carter's Grove, Williamsburg, VA.............1544
Casa Grande Ruins National Monument,
   Coolidge, AZ..31
Cashmere Museum & Pioneer Village,
   Cashmere, WA.......................................1550
Center for American Archaeology,
   Kampsville, IL..440
Center of Southwest Studies/Fort Lewis
   College, Durango, CO............................214
Chaco Culture National Historical Park,
   Nageezi, NM..943
Chenango County Historical Society
   Museum, Norwich, NY.........................1044
Chittenango Landing Canal Boat
   Museum, Chittenango, NY.......................978
Churchill County Museum and Archives,
   Fallon, NV...877
Cobb Institute of Archaeology,
   Mississippi State University, MS.............805
College of Eastern Utah Prehistoric
   Museum, Price, UT...............................1469
Collier County Museum, Naples, FL..........328
Colonial National Historical Park:
   Jamestown & Yorktown, Yorktown,
   VA..1546
Colonial Pemaquid, New Harbor, ME.........615
Commonwealth of the Northern Mariana
   Islands Museum of History and
   Culture, Saipan, MP..............................1640
Crow Canyon Archaeological Center,
   Cortez, CO..208
Crystal River State Archaeological Site,
   Crystal River, FL....................................302
Curry Historical Society Museum, Gold
   Beach, OR..1225
Custer Battlefield Museum, Garryowen,
   MT..847

Dan O'Laurie Museum of Moab, Moab,
   UT..1467
Deer Valley Rock Art Center, Glendale,
   AZ...35

Delaware Archaeology Museum, Dover,
   DE..269
Delaware Division of Historical &
   Cultural Affairs, Dover, DE....................269
Dickson Mounds Museum, Lewistown,
   IL..442
The Dinosaur Museum, Blanding, UT...1463
Dinosaur Walk Museum, Pigeon Forge,
   TN..1383

Effigy Mounds National Monument,
   Harpers Ferry, IA..................................519
El Morro National Monument, Ramah,
   NM..945
El Paso Museum of Archaeology, El
   Paso, TX...1411
El Paso Museum of Art, El Paso, TX.......1411
Erie Canal Village, Rome, NY.................1061
Etowah Indian Mounds Historical Site,
   Cartersville, GA....................................367

Fairfax County Park Authority, Resource
   Management Division, Fairfax, VA.......1503
Favell Museum Inc., Klamath Falls, OR....1227
Flowerdew Hundred Foundation,
   Hopewell, VA.......................................1511
Folsom Museum, Inc., Folsom, NM...........939
Ford County Historical Society, Paxton,
   IL..450
Fort Fetterman State Historic Site,
   Douglas, WY..1631
Fort Henrietta Interpretive Park, Echo,
   OR...1223
Fort Zachary Taylor State Historical Site,
   Key West, FL..317
Furnace Town Living Heritage Museum,
   Snow Hill, MD......................................654

Gila County Historical Museum, Globe,
   AZ...35
Grand Village of the Natchez Indians,
   Natchez, MS...805
Grave Creek Mound Archaeology
   Complex, Moundsville, WV..................1585
Graves Museum of Archaeology and
   Natural History, Dania Beach, FL..........302
Gulf Islands National Seashore, Gulf
   Breeze, FL..312
Gustav Jeeninga Museum of Bible and
   Near Eastern Studies, Anderson, IN.......467

H. Earl Clack Museum, Havre, MT...........849
Hampson Archeological Museum State
   Park, Wilson, AR....................................70
Hampton History Museum, Hampton, VA.1509
Hanley House, Clayton, MO....................813
Harvard University Semitic Museum,
   Cambridge, MA....................................673
Heritage of the Americas Museum, El
   Cajon, CA...92
Highland County Museum and Heritage
   Center, McDowell, VA..........................1517
Historic Bethabara Park, Winston-Salem,
   NC..1125
Historic Camden Revolutionary War Site,
   Camden, SC..1323
Historic Spanish Point, Osprey, FL...........333
Historic Walnford, Upper Freehold Twp.,
   NJ...929
History Museum of Western Virginia,
   Roanoke, VA..1535
Homolovi Ruins State Park, Winslow, AZ....53
Hopewell Culture National Historical
   Park, Chillicothe, OH..........................1147
Hot Springs County Museum and
   Cultural Center, Thermopolis, WY.......1639
Howland House, Plymouth, MA................703
Hudson Museum, The University of
   Maine, Orono, ME.................................617

Iraan Museum, Iraan, TX.......................1430
Iroquois Indian Museum, Howes Cave,
   NY..999

Isabel Anderson Comer Museum & Arts
   Center, Sylacauga, AL.............................18
Jay I. Kislak Foundation, Miami Lakes,
   FL...327
Jefferson Patterson Park & Museum,
   Saint Leonard, MD................................651
The Johns Hopkins University
   Archaeological Collection, Baltimore,
   MD..633
The Joseph A. Callaway Archaeological
   Museum, Louisville, KY........................576
Jurupa Mountains Cultural Center,
   Riverside, CA.......................................149

Ka-Do-Ha Indian Village Museum,
   Murfreesboro, AR...................................65
Kelsey Museum of Archaeology, Ann
   Arbor, MI...724
Kolomoki Mounds State Park Museum,
   Blakely, GA..366

Lake Guernsey Museum-Guernsey State
   Park, Guernsey, WY.............................1634
Long Island Culture History Lab &
   Museum, Commack, NY........................980
Los Alamos Historical Museum, Los
   Alamos, NM...942
Lost City Museum, Overton, NV..............880
Louisiana Tech Museum, Ruston, LA.........600
Lynden Pioneer Museum, Lynden, WA....1559

Maidu Interpretive Center, Roseville, CA....151
Malheur Historical Project, Stonehouse
   Museum, Vale, OR...............................1238
Manassas Museum System, Manassas,
   VA..1516
Marianna-Lee County Museum Assoc.
   Inc., Marianna, AR.................................64
Marin Museum of the American Indian,
   Novato, CA...131
Maturango Museum of the Indian Wells
   Valley, Ridgecrest, CA..........................148
Maxwell Museum of Anthropology,
   Albuquerque, NM.................................934
Merritt Museum of Anthropology,
   Oakland, CA...133
Mesa Verde National Park Museum,
   Mesa Verde National Park, CO...............228
Michael C. Carlos Museum, Atlanta, GA....361
Minute Man National Historical Park,
   Concord, MA..676
Mission San Juan Capistrano Museum,
   San Juan Capistrano, CA.......................173
Mississippi County Historical Society,
   Charleston, MO.....................................812
Moanalua Gardens Foundation, Honolulu,
   HI...397
Montezuma Castle National Monument,
   Camp Verde, AZ.....................................30
Moundville Archaeological Park,
   Moundville, AL.......................................17
Museo Fuerte Conde de Mirasol de
   Vieques, Vieques, PR............................1644
Museum of Ancient & Modern Art, Penn
   Valley, CA..141
Museum of Anthropology, Highland
   Heights, KY..571
Museum of Anthropology,
   Winston-Salem, NC..............................1125
Museum of Anthropology, University of
   Denver, Denver, CO..............................213
Museum of Anthropology, University of
   Missouri, Columbia, MO........................813
Museum of Archaeology & Material
   Culture, Cedar Crest, NM......................938
Museum of Art and Archaeology,
   University of Missouri - Columbia,
   Columbia, MO......................................813
Museum of Florida History, Tallahassee,
   FL...348
Museum of History, Anthropology and
   Art, San Juan, PR.................................1643

Museum of Primitive Art and Culture,
    Peace Dale, RI 1316
Museum of the Aleutians, Unalaska, AK 28
Museum of the Middle Appalachians,
    Saltville, VA 1536
Museum of the Red River, Idabel, OK 1203

National Museum of the American
    Indian, Washington, DC 286
Native American Exhibit, National Kateri
    Shrine, Fonda, NY 991
Native American Museum, Terre Haute,
    IN 500
Navajo National Monument, Tonalea, AZ......47
Newell Museum, Newell, SD 1352

Ocmulgee National Monument, Macon,
    GA 378
Ogden's George S. Eccles Dinosaur Park,
    Ogden, UT 1468
Old Fort House Museum, Fort Edward,
    NY 991
Old Santee Canal Park, Moncks Corner,
    SC 1337
Oriental Institute Museum, University of
    Chicago, Chicago, IL 426
Osage Village State Historic Site, Lamar,
    MO 825

Page Museum at the La Brea Tar Pits,
    Los Angeles, CA 121
Peabody Museum of Archaeology &
    Ethnology, Cambridge, MA 674
The Peary-MacMillan Arctic Museum,
    Brunswick, ME 608
Pecos National Historical Park, Pecos,
    NM 944
Phoebe Apperson Hearst Museum of
    Anthropology, Berkeley, CA 77
Pinson Mounds State Archaeological
    Area, Pinson, TN 1383
The Prehistoric Life Museum, Evanston,
    IL 435
Pueblo Grande Museum and
    Archaeological Park, Phoenix, AZ............42

Rankin Museum, Inc., Ellerbe, NC............1100
Riverside Museum, La Crosse, WI............1603
Robbins Museum of Archaeology,
    Middleborough, MA 694
Robert S. Peabody Museum of
    Archaeology, Andover, MA 660
Russell Cave National Monument,
    Bridgeport, AL 6

Safety Harbor Museum of Regional
    History, Safety Harbor, FL.....................338
St. Clements Island and Piney Point
    Museums, Colton's Point, MD...............641
Salinas Pueblo Missions National
    Monument, Mountainair, NM 943
San Diego Archaeological Center,
    Escondido, CA 93
San Diego Museum of Man, San Diego,
    CA 160
San Juan County Archaeological
    Research Center and Library at the
    Salmon Ruin/San Juan County
    Museum Association, Bloomfield, NM ...937
Santa Barbara Trust for Historic
    Preservation, Santa Barbara, CA 180
Saratoga Museum, Saratoga, WY.............1638
Scotts Bluff National Monument, Gering,
    NE 861
Seminole Canyon State Park and Historic
    Site, Comstock, TX 1401
Sidney Historical Association, Sidney,
    NY 1069
Siegfried H. Horn Archaeological
    Museum, Berrien Springs, MI 729
The Simon Paneak Memorial Museum,
    Anaktuvuk Pass, AK 21
Skirball Cultural Center, Los Angeles,
    CA 121

Smoki Museum - American Indian Art &
    Culture, Prescott, AZ 43
Southold Indian Museum, Southold, NY ...1071
Southwest Museum, Los Angeles, CA 121
Spertus Museum, Chicago, IL 427
Spiro Mounds Archaeological Center,
    Spiro, OK 1214
Stone Fort Museum, Nacogdoches, TX......1440
SunWatch Indian Village/Archaeological
    Park, Dayton, OH 1162

Tampa Bay History Center, Inc., Tampa,
    FL 350
Tarpon Springs Heritage Museum, Tarpon
    Springs, FL 351
Thomas E. McMillan Museum, Brewton,
    AL 6
Toltec Mounds Archeological State Park,
    Scott, AR 68
Tonto National Monument, Roosevelt,
    AZ 43
T.T. Wentworth, Jr. Florida State
    Museum, Pensacola, FL 336
Tubac Presidio State Historic Park,
    Tubac, AZ 47
Turabo University, Gurabo, PR................1641
Tuzigoot National Monument, Clarkdale,
    AZ 31

UCLA Fowler Museum of Cultural
    History, Los Angeles, CA 122
University of Michigan Museum of
    Anthropology, Ann Arbor, MI.................725
University of Oregon Museum of Natural
    and Cultural History, Eugene, OR 1224
University of Pennsylvania Museum of
    Archaeology and Anthropology,
    Philadelphia, PA 1288
Utah State Historical Society, Salt Lake
    City, UT 1473
Utah State University's Museum of
    Anthropology, Logan, UT....................1467

Van Riper-Hopper House Museum,
    Wayne, NJ 929

Walnut Canyon National Monument,
    Flagstaff, AZ 34
Washakie Museum, Worland, WY.............1639
West Virginia State Museum, Charleston,
    WV 1581
Western Archeological & Conservation
    Center, Tucson, AZ 52
Wickliffe Mounds State Historic Site,
    Wickliffe, KY 584
William S. Webb Museum of
    Anthropology, Lexington, KY 575
Winnebago Area Museum, Winnebago,
    MN 797
Woodruff Museum of Indian Artifacts,
    Bridgeton, NJ.....................................898
Wormsloe State Historic Site, Savannah,
    GA 387
Wray Museum, Wray, CO 235

The Yager Museum of Art & Culture,
    Oneonta, NY 1046

Aviaries and Ornithology Museums

Bronx Zoo, Bronx, NY 965

Carrie Weedon Natural Science Museum,
    Galesville, MD....................................645
Connecticut Audubon Birdcraft Museum,
    Fairfield, CT 240

Denison Pequotsepos Nature Center,
    Mystic, CT 250
Detroit Zoo, Royal Oak, MI 762
Disney's Animal Kingdom Theme Park,
    Bay Lake, FL 295

Epcot at Walt Disney World Resort, Lake
    Buena Vista, FL 319

Finnup Park and Lee Richardson Zoo,
    Garden City, KS 541
Frontera Audubon Society, Weslaco, TX....1460

International Crane Foundation, Baraboo,
    WI 1591

Kansas Department of Wildlife & Parks,
    Pratt, KS 556

Minnesota Zoo, Apple Valley, MN.............768
Museum of Comparative Zoology,
    Cambridge, MA 674

National Aviary in Pittsburgh, Inc.,
    Pittsburgh, PA 1293
The Natural History Museum, Santa
    Maria, CA 182
The Nature Museum at Grafton, Grafton,
    VT 1479

Oakes Museum Messiah College,
    Grantham, PA 1257

Parrot Jungle Island, Miami, FL..............325

Rotary Nature Center, Oakland, CA............134

Sauk Prairie Area Historical Society, Inc.,
    Prairie du Sac, WI 1619
Seneca Park Zoo, Rochester, NY 1060
Six Flags Marine World, Vallejo, CA...........194
South Carolina Aquarium, Charleston, SC.1326
Southern Vermont Natural History
    Museum, West Marlboro, VT 1489
Stanwood Wildlife Sanctuary, Ellsworth,
    ME 610

Tracy Aviary, Salt Lake City, UT 1472

Westmoreland Sanctuary, Inc., Bedford
    Corners, NY 961
Weymouth Woods-Sandhills Nature
    Preserve Museum, Southern Pines, NC.1120

Zoo New England, Boston, MA 669

Botanical and Aquatic Gardens, Conservatories, and Horticulture Societies

A.L. Fetterman Educational Museum,
    Fort Valley, GA...................................372
Abilene Zoological Gardens, Abilene, TX.1385
Ah-Tah-Thi-Ki Museum, Big Cypress
    Seminole Indian Reservation, FL 295
Alfred B. Maclay State Gardens,
    Tallahassee, FL 346
Amy B.H. Greenwell Ethnobotanical
    Garden, Captain Cook, HI 392
Anna Scripps Whitcomb Conservatory,
    Detroit, MI 734
The Arboretum at Flagstaff, Flagstaff, AZ 32
Arboretum at UC Santa Cruz, Santa
    Cruz, CA 181
Arnold Arboretum of Harvard University,
    Jamaica Plain, MA 688
Atlanta Botanical Garden, Atlanta, GA........357
Audubon Zoo, New Orleans, LA.................594

Bartlett Arboretum & Gardens, Stamford,
    CT 260
Bartram's Garden, Philadelphia, PA 1277
Beaumont Botanical Gardens, Beaumont,
    TX 1394
Bellingrath Gardens & Home, Theodore,
    AL 18
Belvedere-Tiburon Landmarks Society,
    Tiburon, CA 192
Berkeley Rose Garden, Berkeley, CA 75
Berkshire Botanical Garden, Stockbridge,
    MA 711
Bernheim Arboretum and Research
    Forest, Clermont, KY 567
The Berry Botanic Garden, Portland, OR ..1230
Bickelhaupt Arboretum, Clinton, IA............511

Botanical and Aquatic Gardens,
Conservatories, and Horticulture
Societies–Continued

Biedenharn Museum & Gardens, Monroe, LA...592

Big Thicket National Preserve, Kountze, TX..1432

Biltmore Estate, Asheville, NC..................1089

Birmingham Botanical Gardens, Birmingham, AL.....................................4

Boerner Botanical Gardens, Hales Corners, WI...1600

Bolsa Chica Conservancy, Huntington Beach, CA...104

The Botanic Garden of Smith College, Northampton, MA.................................699

Botanica, The Wichita Gardens, Wichita, KS...561

Botanical Gardens at Asheville, Asheville, NC...1089

Bowman's Hill Wildflower Preserve, New Hope, PA...1273

Boyce Thompson Arboretum, Superior, AZ..44

Brookgreen Gardens, Murrells Inlet, SC....1337

Brooklyn Botanic Garden, Brooklyn, NY....967

Brookside Gardens, Wheaton, MD.............657

Buffalo and Erie County Botanical Gardens, Buffalo, NY.............................972

Cal State Northridge Botanic Garden, Northridge, CA..131

Cameron Park Zoo, Waco, TX...............1458

Cape May County Park and Zoo, Cape May Court House, NJ...............................901

Carl S. English Botanical Gardens, Seattle, WA..1565

The Casa del Herrero Foundation, Santa Barbara, CA...178

The Cathedral of St. John the Divine, New York, NY..1022

Charles Towne Landing State Historic Site, Charleston, SC.................................1324

Cheekwood-Tennessee Botanical Garden & Museum of Art, Nashville, TN.........1378

Cheyenne Botanic Gardens, Cheyenne, WY..1630

Chicago Botanic Garden, Glencoe, IL......438

Chicago Zoological Park (Brookfield Zoo), Brookfield, IL................................414

Chihuahuan Desert Research Institute, Fort Davis, TX...1414

Chinqua-Penn Plantation, Reidsville, NC...1117

Civic Garden Center of Greater Cincinnati, Cincinnati, OH.....................1149

Clark Botanic Garden, Albertson, NY.........956

Cleveland Botanical Garden, Cleveland, OH..1152

Collier County Museum, Naples, FL...........328

The Conservatory Garden, New York, NY..1023

Copia: The American Center for Wine, Food & the Arts, Napa, CA.....................129

County of Westchester, Department of Parks, Recreation and Conservation, Mount Kisco, NY...1016

Cuneo Museum & Gardens, Vernon Hills, IL...463

Cutler Botanic Garden, Binghamton, NY....962

Dallas Arboretum & Botanical Garden, Dallas, TX..1404

Daniel Stowe Botanical Garden, Belmont, NC..1092

The Dawes Arboretum, Newark, OH.........1177

Denver Botanic Gardens, Inc., Denver, CO..210

Des Moines Botanical Center, Des Moines, IA...514

Descanso Gardens Guild, Inc., La Canada Flintridge, CA...105

Desert Botanical Garden, Phoenix, AZ..........40

Discovery Park, Safford, AZ.......................43

Disney's Animal Kingdom Theme Park, Bay Lake, FL...295

The Dixon Gallery and Gardens, Memphis, TN...1372

Dothan Area Botanical Gardens, Dothan, AL..8

Dow Gardens, Midland, MI.......................755

Dubuque Arboretum & Botanical Gardens, Dubuque, IA.........................516

Earl Burns Miller Japanese Garden, Long Beach, CA...110

The Ebenezer Maxwell Mansion, Inc., Philadelphia, PA...1278

EcoTarium, Worcester, MA.......................720

Edison & Ford Winter Estates, Fort Myers, FL...308

Eloise Butler Wildflower Garden and Bird Sanctuary, Minneapolis, MN.........781

Epcot at Walt Disney World Resort, Lake Buena Vista, FL...319

Erie Zoological Park & Botanical Gardens of Northwestern Pennsylvania, Erie, PA.........................1253

Fairchild Tropical Botanic Garden, Coral Gables, FL...301

The Fay Hyland Botanical Plantation, Orono, ME...617

Fernbank Science Center, Atlanta, GA.........360

Fernwood Botanical Garden & Nature Preserve, Niles, MI...758

Florida Institute of Technology Botanical Gardens, Melbourne, FL.........................323

Foellinger-Freimann Botanical Conservatory, Fort Wayne, IN.................477

Fort Worth Botanic Garden, Fort Worth, TX..1416

Foster Botanical Garden, Honolulu, HI.......395

Four Rivers Cultural Center & Museum, Ontario, OR...1229

Franklin Park Conservatory, Columbus, OH..1158

Fuller Gardens, North Hampton, NH.........893

Garden in the Woods of the New England Wild Flower Society, Framingham, MA...683

Gardens at Callaway, Pine Mountain, GA...380

Garfield Park Conservatory, Chicago, IL.....421

George Eastman House/International Museum of Photography and Film, Rochester, NY...1058

The George G. Frelinghuysen Arboretum, Morris Township, NJ.........................913

George L. Luthy Memorial Botanical Garden, Peoria, IL...450

George Landis Arboretum, Esperance, NY..989

Gillespie County Historical Society, Fredericksburg, TX...1419

Gladys Porter Zoo, Brownsville, TX.........1398

Graycliff Conservancy, Derby, NY.............984

Green Bay Botanical Garden, Green Bay, WI...1598

The Grove, Glenview, IL.........................438

Hakone Gardens, Saratoga, CA.................185

Hampton Plantation State Historic Site, McClellanville, SC...1336

Harold L. Lyon Arboretum, Honolulu, HI...395

Harry P. Leu Gardens, Orlando, FL.........331

Harvard Museum of Natural History, Cambridge, MA...672

Hawaii Tropical Botanical Garden, Papaikou, HI...401

Heathcote Botanical Gardens, Inc., Fort Pierce, FL...309

Henry Foundation for Botanical Research, Gladwyne, PA.........................1256

Hereford Inlet Lighthouse, North Wildwood, NJ...917

Hershey Gardens, Hershey, PA.................1260

High Desert Museum, Bend, OR...............1220

Highland Botanical Park, Rochester, NY...1058

Hills and Dales Estate, LaGrange, GA.........375

Hillwood Museum & Gardens, Washington, DC...280

Historic Bok Sanctuary, Lake Wales, FL.....320

Historic London Town and Gardens, Edgewater, MD...642

Historic Oakland Cemetery, Atlanta, GA.....360

Historic Rosedale, Charlotte, NC...............1095

The Holden Arboretum, Kirtland, OH.......1170

Honolulu Botanical Gardens, Honolulu, HI..396

Huntington Library, Art Collections, and Botanical Gardens, San Marino, CA.......174

Huntington Museum of Art, Inc., Huntington, WV...1583

Huntsville/Madison County Botanical Garden, Huntsville, AL.........................11

Idaho Botanical Garden, Boise, ID.............403

International Peace Garden, Dunseith, ND..1130

Japanese Friendship Garden, San Diego, CA..156

The Japanese Garden, Van Nuys, CA.........194

Jenkins Arboretum, Devon, PA.................1249

Jurupa Mountains Cultural Center, Riverside, CA...149

Kalamazoo Nature Center, Inc., Kalamazoo, MI...748

Kanapaha Botanical Gardens, Gainesville, FL..311

Kenilworth Aquatic Gardens, Washington, DC..281

Key West Tropical Forest & Botanical Garden, Key West, FL.........................318

Kimberly Crest House & Gardens, Redlands, CA...147

Kingwood Center, Mansfield, OH.............1173

Klehm Arboretum & Botanical Garden, Rockford, IL...455

Koreshan State Historic Site, Estero, FL.......306

Krohn Conservatory, Cincinnati, OH.........1150

L.H. Bailey Hortorium, Ithaca, NY...........1003

Ladew Topiary Gardens, Monkton, MD.......649

Lady Bird Johnson Wildflower Center, Austin, TX...1390

Laurens Henry Cohn, Sr. Memorial Plant Arboretum, Baton Rouge, LA.................586

Lewis Ginter Botanical Garden, Richmond, VA...1530

The Lexington Cemetery, Lexington, KY....573

Lilacia Park-Lombard Park District, Lombard, IL...443

Lincoln Children's Zoo, Lincoln, NE.........866

Lincoln Park Conservatory, Chicago, IL......423

The Living Desert, Palm Desert, CA.........138

Longwood Gardens, Kennett Square, PA...1264

The Los Angeles County Arboretum & Botanic Garden, Arcadia, CA.................71

Louisville Zoological Garden, Louisville, KY..578

Lower Rio Grande Valley Nature Center, Weslaco, TX...1460

MacCallum More Museum and Gardens, Chase City, VA...1500

Madison Museum of Fine Art, Madison, GA..378

Magnolia Plantation and Gardens, Charleston, SC...1326

Malheur Historical Project, Stonehouse Museum, Vale, OR...1238

The Marie Selby Botanical Gardens, Inc., Sarasota, FL...344

Marjorie McNeely Conservatory at Como Park, Saint Paul, MN.........................790

Matthaei Botanical Gardens and Nichols Arboretum, Ann Arbor, MI.................725

Maymont, Richmond, VA.........................1530

McKee Botanical Garden, Vero Beach, FL 352
Memphis Botanic Garden, Goldsmith Civic Garden Center, Memphis, TN 1374
Mendocino Coast Botanic Garden, Fort Bragg, CA 95
Miami Seaquarium, Miami, FL 325
Mildred E. Mathias Botanical Garden, Los Angeles, CA 119
Minnesota Landscape Arboretum, University of Minnesota, Chaska, MN 770
Minnetrista, Muncie, IN 492
Mississippi Society Daughters of the American Revolution Rosalie House Museum, Natchez, MS 805
Missouri Botanical Garden, Saint Louis, MO 834
Mitchell Park Horticultural Conservatory, Milwaukee, WI 1612
Mobile Botanic Gardens, Mobile, AL 14
Moorten Botanic Garden and Cactarium, Palm Springs, CA 138
The Morikami Museum and Japanese Gardens, Delray Beach, FL 305
Morris Arboretum of the University of Pennsylvania, Philadelphia, PA 1283
Morven Museum & Garden, Princeton, NJ 922
Mount Airy Arboretum, Cincinnati, OH 1150
Mounts Botanical Garden, West Palm Beach, FL 353
Muckenthaler Cultural Center and Mansion Museum, Fullerton, CA 99
Myriad Botanical Gardens, Oklahoma City, OK 1208
Nani Mau Gardens, Hilo, HI 393
Nassau County Museum of Art, Roslyn Harbor, NY 1062
National Aviary in Pittsburgh, Inc., Pittsburgh, PA 1293
National Tropical Botanical Garden, Kalaheo, HI 399
Nemours Mansion and Gardens, Wilmington, DE 274
New Canaan Nature Center, New Canaan, CT 252
New Jersey Botanical Garden at Skylands (NJBG), Ringwood, NJ 923
The New York Botanical Garden, Bronx, NY 966
Norfolk Botanical Garden, Norfolk, VA 1522
North Carolina Botanical Garden, Chapel Hill, NC 1093
North Central Oklahoma Cactus Botanical Garden, Covington, OK 1198
The Oak Park Conservatory, Oak Park, IL 449
Oklahoma State University Botanical Garden, Stillwater, OK 1214
Olbrich Botanical Gardens, Madison, WI ..1605
Old Prairie Town at Ward-Meade Historic Site, Topeka, KS 560
Old Westbury Gardens, Old Westbury, NY 1045
Ormond Memorial Art Museum & Garden, Ormond Beach, FL 333
Pacific Grove Museum of Natural History, Pacific Grove, CA 137
Pacific Rim Bonsai Collection, Federal Way, WA 1554
Parrot Jungle Island, Miami, FL 325
Peel Mansion Museum & Historic Gardens, Bentonville, AR 55
Pennsylvania Historical & Museum Commission, Harrisburg, PA 1259
The Philadelphia Zoo, Philadelphia, PA 1286
Phipps Conservatory and Botanical Gardens, Pittsburgh, PA 1293
Pickens County Museum of Art & History, Pickens, SC 1340

The Presby Memorial Iris Gardens, Upper Montclair, NJ 929
Quail Botanical Gardens, Encinitas, CA 92
Quail Ridge Wilderness Conservancy, Davis, CA 90
Queens Botanical Garden, Flushing, NY 990
R.S. Barnwell Memorial Garden and Art Center, Shreveport, LA 601
Rancho Los Alamitos, Long Beach, CA 111
Rancho Santa Ana Botanic Garden at Claremont, Claremont, CA 85
Ravine Gardens State Park, Palatka, FL 333
Red Butte Garden & Arboretum, Salt Lake City, UT 1472
Reeves-Reed Arboretum, Summit, NJ 925
Reynolda Gardens of Wake Forest University, Winston-Salem, NC 1126
Rhododendron Species Botanical Garden, Federal Way, WA 1554
Rip Van Winkle Gardens on Jefferson Island, New Iberia, LA 593
Rodef Shalom Biblical Botanical Garden, Pittsburgh, PA 1294
Roper Mountain Science Center, Greenville, SC 1334
The Rotch-Jones-Duff House & Garden Museum, Inc., New Bedford, MA 697
Rural Life Museum & Windrush Gardens, Baton Rouge, LA 587
Rusch Botanical Garden, Citrus Heights, CA 84
The Rutgers Gardens, New Brunswick, NJ 916
San Antonio Botanical Garden, San Antonio, TX 1449
San Diego Zoo, San Diego, CA 161
San Francisco Bay Bird Observatory, Alviso, CA 70
San Francisco Botanical Garden at Strybing Arboretum, San Francisco, CA 168
San Mateo Arboretum Society, Inc., San Mateo, CA 175
Sanibel-Captiva Conservation Foundation, Inc., Sanibel, FL 343
Santa Barbara Botanic Garden, Santa Barbara, CA 178
Santa Barbara Orchid Estate, Santa Barbara, CA 180
Scott Arboretum of Swarthmore College, Swarthmore, PA 1302
Senator Fong's Plantation & Gardens, Kaneohe, HI 400
Sherman Gardens, Corona del Mar, CA 87
Sieur de Monts Springs Nature Center, Bar Harbor, ME 605
Snug Harbor Cultural Center - Visitors' Center and Newhouse Center for Contemporary Art, Staten Island, NY ...1073
The Society of the Four Arts, Palm Beach, FL 334
Sonnenberg Gardens & Mansion State Historic Park, Canandaigua, NY 975
South Carolina Aquarium, Charleston, SC .1326
The South Carolina Botanical Garden, Clemson, SC 1328
Southwest Museum, Los Angeles, CA 121
Stan Hywet Hall and Gardens, Inc., Akron, OH 1139
Starhill Forest Arboretum, Petersburg, IL 451
The State Botanical Garden of Georgia, Athens, GA 357
Staten Island Botanical Garden, Staten Island, NY 1073
The Stevens-Coolidge Place, a property of The Trustees of Reservations, North Andover, MA 698
Terrace Hill Historic Site and Governor's Mansion, Des Moines, IA 516
Texas Discovery Gardens, Dallas, TX 1408

Texas Forestry Museum, Lufkin, TX 1436
Tohono Chul Park Inc., Tucson, AZ 51
Toledo Botanical Garden, Toledo, OH 1187
Tryon Palace Historic Sites and Gardens, New Bern, NC 1112
Tucson Botanical Gardens, Tucson, AZ 51
U.S National Arboretum, Washington, DC 292
Umlauf Sculpture Garden & Museum, Austin, TX 1392
United States Botanic Garden, Washington, DC 292
University of California Botanical Garden, Berkeley, CA 77
University of California Irvine Arboretum, Irvine, CA 105
University of South Florida Botanical Garden, Tampa, FL 350
Virginia Robinson Gardens, Beverly Hills, CA 78
The Voas Nature Area/Voas Museum, Minburn, IA 523
W.J. Beal Botanical Garden, East Lansing, MI 740
W.W. Seymour Botanical Conservatory, Tacoma, WA 1574
Washington National Cathedral, Washington, DC 294
Washington Park Botanical Garden, Springfield, IL 460
Wave Hill, Bronx, NY 967
Western North Carolina Nature Center, Asheville, NC 1090
Wildlife Prairie State Park, Hanna City, IL 439
Wing Haven Garden and Bird Sanctuary, Charlotte, NC 1096
Worcester County Horticultural Society/Tower Hill Botanic Garden, Boylston, MA 670
Yakima Area Arboretum & Botanical Garden, Yakima, WA 1579
Zoo Montana, Billings, MT 842

Entomology Museums

Colorado Plateau Biodiversity Center, Flagstaff, AZ 32
Cook's Natural Science Museum, Decatur, AL 7
Disney's Animal Kingdom Theme Park, Bay Lake, FL 295
Ehrhart Museum, Antwerp, OH 1139
Entomology Research Museum, Riverside, CA 149
Essig Museum of Entomology, University of California, Berkeley, Berkeley, CA 75
The Frost Entomological Museum, Dept. of Entomology, The Pennsylvania State University, University Park, PA ...1304
Hershey Gardens, Hershey, PA 1260
The Little Cowboy Bar & Museum, Fromberg, MT 847
May Natural History Museum and Museum of Space Exploration, Colorado Springs, CO 207
The Merrick Art Gallery, New Brighton, PA 1273
Mississippi Entomological Museum, Mississippi State University, MS 805
Moorten Botanic Garden and Cactarium, Palm Springs, CA 138
Museum of Long Island Natural Sciences, Stony Brook, NY 1075

Entomology Museums–Continued

Oakes Museum Messiah College, Grantham, PA 1257

Pacific Grove Museum of Natural History, Pacific Grove, CA 137

R.M. Bohart Museum of Entomology, Davis, CA 90

Rattlesnake Museum (American International), Albuquerque, NM 935

Rosenbruch Wildlife Museum, St. George, UT 1474

Geology, Mineralogy and Paleontology Museums

A. E. Seaman Mineral Museum, Houghton, MI 747

Agate Fossil Beds National Monument, Harrison, NE...862

Anza-Borrego Desert State Park, Borrego Springs, CA 79

Arizona Mining and Mineral Museum, Phoenix, AZ 39

Aurora Fossil Museum, Aurora, NC 1091

Aztec Museum and Pioneer Village, Aztec, NM 936

Badlands Petrified Gardens, Kadoka, SD...1349

The Bailey-Matthews Shell Museum, Sanibel, FL 343

Bear Butte State Park Visitors Center, Sturgis, SD..1358

Bear Mountain Trailside Museums and Zoo, Bear Mountain, NY 961

Big Well, Greensburg, KS...........................542

Bisbee Mining & Historical Museum, Bisbee, AZ 30

Black Hills Museum of Natural History, Hill City, SD.....................................1348

Bob Campbell Geology Museum, Clemson, SC...1328

Bosque Memorial Museum, Clifton, TX...1400

Brigham Young University Earth Science Museum, Provo, UT...............................1469

Bruce Museum, Greenwich, CT 243

California State Mining & Mineral Museum, Mariposa, CA 124

Capulin Volcano National Monument, Capulin, NM 937

Carlsbad Museum & Art Center, Carlsbad, NM...938

Carter County Museum, Ekalaka, MT.........846

Castine Scientific Society, Castine, ME.......609

Chapman's Gem and Mineral Museum, Fortuna, CA 96

Children's Science Explorium at Sugar Sand Park, Boca Raton, FL 296

Colburn Earth Science Museum, Asheville, NC 1089

College of Eastern Utah Prehistoric Museum, Price, UT...............................1469

Colorado Plateau Biodiversity Center, Flagstaff, AZ...32

Colorado School of Mines Geology Museum, Golden, CO...........................220

Crater of Diamonds State Park Museum, Murfreesboro, AR......................................65

Craters of the Moon National Monument, Arco, ID...403

Crossroads Museum, Corinth, MS...............800

Crystal Caverns at Hupp's Hill, Strasburg, VA...1538

Curry Historical Society Museum, Gold Beach, OR..1225

Dakota Dinosaur Museum, Dickinson, ND...1129

Dan O'Laurie Museum of Moab, Moab, UT...1467

Devils Tower Visitor Center, Devils Tower, WY..1631

Dinosaur Depot Museum, Canon City, CO..204

Dinosaur Discovery Museum, Kenosha, WI...1602

Dinosaur Gardens, LLC, Ossineke, MI.......759

Dinosaur Journey, Fruita, CO 218

The Dinosaur Museum, Blanding, UT 1463

Dinosaur State Park, Rocky Hill, CT..........259

Dinosaur Walk Museum, Pigeon Forge, TN...1383

Drake Well Museum, Titusville, PA 1303

Dunn-Seiler Museum, Mississippi State University, MS.......................................805

Earth & Mineral Sciences Museum and Art Gallery, University Park, PA 1303

East Texas Oil Museum at Kilgore College, Kilgore, TX...........................1432

ECHO at the Leahy Center for Lake Champlain, Burlington, VT................1478

EcoTarium, Worcester, MA.........................720

Ed Clark Museum of Missouri Geology, Rolla, MO...829

Elberton Granite Museum & Exhibit, Elberton, GA..371

Eleanor Barbour Cook Museum of Geology, Chadron, NE 859

Elsing Museum, Tulsa, OK......................1215

Emporia State University Johnston Geology Museum, Emporia, KS.............538

Falls of the Ohio State Park, Clarksville, IN...472

Fick Fossil & History Museum, Oakley, KS...554

Fiedler Memorial Museum, Seguin, TX.....1452

Florence Hawley Ellis Museum of Anthropology and Ruth Hall Museum of Paleontology, Abiquiu, NM 931

Florissant Fossil Beds National Monument, Florissant, CO....................216

Fort Peck Interpretive Center, Fort Peck, MT..846

Franklin Mineral Museum, Franklin, NJ....904

Fryxell Geology Museum, Rock Island, IL..454

Galena Mining & Historical Museum, Galena, KS...541

Gemological Institute of America Museum, Carlsbad, CA...........................81

The Geological Museum, The University of Wyoming, Laramie, WY................1635

Geology Museum, Huntington, WV...........1583

Georgia Southern University Museum, Statesboro, GA.......................................387

Gerald E. Eddy Discovery Center, Chelsea, MI..732

The Gillespie Museum - Stetson University, De Land, FL 304

Glenrock Paleontological Museum, Glenrock, WY.......................................1633

Grand River Museum, Lemmon, SD..........1351

Great Basin Historical Society & Museum, Delta, UT...............................1464

Greene Memorial Museum, University of Wisconsin-Milwaukee, Milwaukee, WI.1611

Groveland Yosemite Gateway Museum, Groveland, CA.......................................101

Harvard Museum of Natural History, Cambridge, MA....................................672

Held-Poage Memorial Home and Research Library, Ukiah, CA..................193

Henry S. Reuss Ice Age Visitor Center, Campbellsport, WI...............................1593

Heritage House Museum of Montgomery County, Mount Ida, AR...........................64

Hot Springs County Museum and Cultural Center, Thermopolis, WY........1639

Idaho Museum of Mining and Geology, Boise, ID...404

Institute of Meteoritics Meteorite Museum, Albuquerque, NM...................933

Iraan Museum, Iraan, TX.........................1430

Isabel Anderson Comer Museum & Arts Center, Sylacauga, AL.............................18

Jerome State Historic Park, Jerome, AZ 36

John Day Fossil Beds National Monument, Kimberly, OR....................1227

Jurupa Mountains Cultural Center, Riverside, CA...149

Kentucky Coal Mining Museum, Benham, KY...565

The Little Cowboy Bar & Museum, Fromberg, MT......................................847

Los Alamos Historical Museum, Los Alamos, NM..942

Lost City Museum, Overton, NV 880

Louisiana Tech Museum, Ruston, LA..........600

Luzerne County Historical Society, Wilkes-Barre, PA...............................1307

Makoshika Dinosaur Museum, Glendive, MT..848

Mammoth Site of Hot Springs, Inc., Hot Springs, SD..1348

The Merrick Art Gallery, New Brighton, PA..1273

Mesa Southwest Museum, Mesa, AZ.............37

Mesalands Community College's Dinosaur Museum, Tucumcari, NM 953

Miles Mineral Museum, Portales, NM.........944

Mineral and Lapidary Museum of Henderson County Inc., Hendersonville, NC 1105

Mineral County Museum & Historical Society, Superior, MT............................854

Mineral Museum, Butte, MT.......................843

Mississippi Petrified Forest, Flora, MS 800

Museum of Astrogeology, Meteor Crater, Winslow, AZ...53

Museum of Earth and Life History, Lynchburg, VA....................................1515

Museum of Geology and Paleontology, South Dakota School of Mines and Technology, Rapid City, SD.................1355

Museum of Long Island Natural Sciences, Stony Brook, NY...................1075

Museum of North Carolina Minerals, Spruce Pine, NC...................................1120

Museum of Paleontology, Berkeley, CA 76

Museum of the Geosciences, Blacksburg, VA...1497

Museum of the Middle Appalachians, Saltville, VA...1536

Nassau County, Division of Museum Services, Department of Recreation, Parks & Museums, East Meadow, NY....987

The Natural Science Center of Greensboro, Inc., Greensboro, NC....1104

The Nature Museum at Grafton, Grafton, VT..1479

New Almaden Quicksilver Mining Museum, San Jose, CA............................172

New Mexico Bureau of Geology Mineral Museum, Socorro, NM.........................951

Niagara Gorge Discovery Center, Niagara Falls, NY...1042

Norman #1 Oil Well Museum, Neodesha, KS...553

Oakes Museum Messiah College, Grantham, PA.....................................1257

Ogden's George S. Eccles Dinosaur Park, Ogden, UT...1468

Old Coal Mine Museum, Madrid, NM.........943

Oregon Trail Regional Museum, Baker City, OR...1219

Orton Geological Museum, Ohio State University, Columbus, OH 1158
Overland Trail Museum, Sterling, CO..........232

Paleontological Research Institution, Ithaca, NY..1004
Petrified Creatures Museum of Natural History, Richfield Springs, NY 1057
Petrified Forest Museum, Calistoga, CA 80
Petrified Forest of the Black Hills, Piedmont, SD....................................1353
Petrified Sea Gardens, Saratoga Springs, NY..1065
Post Rock Museum, La Crosse, KS 547
The Prehistoric Life Museum, Evanston, IL..435

Rankin Museum, Inc., Ellerbe, NC.............1100
Rifle Creek Museum, Rifle, CO....................231
Rocky Mountain Dinosaur Resource Center, Woodland Park, CO....................235

Scotts Bluff National Monument, Gering, NE..861
Ship Ashore Resort Museum, Smith River, CA....................................187
Slate Valley Museum, Granville, NY 996
Sterling Hill Mining Museum, Inc., Ogdensburg, NJ..........................918
The Stone Museum, Monroe Township, NJ..912

Tate Geological Museum, Casper, WY 1629
Texas Energy Museum, Beaumont, TX......1395
Tri-State Mineral Museum, Joplin, MO 820
Turquoise Museum, Albuquerque, NM 936
Two Medicine Dinosaur Center, Bynum, MO..812

University of Arizona Mineral Museum, Tucson, AZ....................................52
University of Missouri-Rolla Minerals Museum, Rolla, MO..........................829
University of Nebraska State Museum, Lincoln, NE..................................867
University of Oregon Museum of Natural and Cultural History, Eugene, OR 1224
University of Richmond Museums, Richmond, VA....................................1532
The University of South Carolina McKissick Museum, Columbia, SC.......1331

Vermont Marble Museum, Proctor, VT 1485
The Voas Nature Area/Voas Museum, Minburn, IA..................................523

W.M. Keck Museum, Reno, NV................881
Washakie Museum, Worland, WY 1639
Weinman Mineral Museum, White, GA.......391
Working Men's Institute, New Harmony, IN..495
World Museum of Natural History, Riverside, CA..................................150
The Wyoming Dinosaur Center, Thermopolis, WY............................1639

Yellow Medicine County Historical Society and Museum, Granite Falls, MN..777
Yellowstone National Park, Gardiner, MT ...847

Herbariums

The Arthur & Kriebel Herbaria, Purdue University, West Lafayette, IN.................503

Bartlett Arboretum & Gardens, Stamford, CT..260
Birmingham Botanical Gardens, Birmingham, AL....................................4
Brooklyn Botanic Garden, Brooklyn, NY 967

The Cloisters, New York, NY...................1023
Crater Lake National Park, Crater Lake, OR..1222

Craters of the Moon National Monument, Arco, ID..403

Denver Botanic Gardens, Inc., Denver, CO..210

Garden in the Woods of the New England Wild Flower Society, Framingham, MA 683
Greene-Nieuwland Herbarium, Notre Dame, IN 495

The Harvard University Herbaria, Cambridge, MA....................................673
Herbarium of the University of Michigan, Ann Arbor, MI....................................724
The Herbarium of the University of the Pacific, Stockton, CA 189
Hi-Desert Nature Museum, Yucca Valley, CA..201
Highland Botanical Park, Rochester, NY ...1058

Intermountain Herbarium, Utah State University, Logan, UT............................1466
International Crane Foundation, Baraboo, WI..1591

Kansas State University Herbarium, Manhattan, KS....................................551

L.H. Bailey Hortorium, Ithaca, NY 1003
Laurens Henry Cohn, Sr. Memorial Plant Arboretum, Baton Rouge, LA......586
The Los Angeles County Arboretum & Botanic Garden, Arcadia, CA 71
Louisiana Arboretum, State Preservation Area, Ville Platte, LA........................603
Louisiana State University Herbarium, Baton Rouge, LA..............................586

The Marie Selby Botanical Gardens, Inc., Sarasota, FL....................................344
Michigan State University Herbarium, East Lansing, MI....................................740
Mildred E. Mathias Botanical Garden, Los Angeles, CA..............................119
Missouri Botanical Garden, Saint Louis, MO..834
Muir Woods National Monument, Mill Valley, CA....................................125
Museum of Long Island Natural Sciences, Stony Brook, NY 1075

The New York Botanical Garden, Bronx, NY..966

Pacific Grove Museum of Natural History, Pacific Grove, CA 137
Philip L. Wright Zoological Museum and University of Montana Herbarium, Missoula, MT....................................852
Planting Fields Arboretum State Historic Park, Oyster Bay, NY............................1049

Rancho Santa Ana Botanic Garden at Claremont, Claremont, CA..........85
Riverside Nature Center, Kerrville, TX......1432
Robert Bebb Herbarium, Norman, OK.......1206
Rocky Mountain Herbarium, Laramie, WY..1635

University Herbarium & Jepson Herbarium, Berkeley, CA.....................77

Whitehouse Nature Center, Albion, MI........723

Herpetology Museums

Colorado Plateau Biodiversity Center, Flagstaff, AZ....................................32
Creepy Hollow Living Museum, Oklahoma City, OK............................1207

Detroit Zoo, Royal Oak, MI 762

Museum of Comparative Zoology, Cambridge, MA....................................674

Rattlesnake Museum (American International), Albuquerque, NM 935
Seneca Park Zoo, Rochester, NY 1060
South Carolina Aquarium, Charleston, SC.1326
Southern Oregon University Museum of Vertebrate Natural History, Ashland, OR..1218

World Museum of Natural History, Riverside, CA..................................150

Zoo Montana, Billings, MT 842

Medical, Dental, Health, Pharmacology, Apothecary and Psychiatry Museums

Alabama Museum of the Health Sciences, Birmingham, AL....................................4
Allison-Antrim Museum, Inc., Greencastle, PA....................................1257
American Heart Association - Halle Heart Center, Tempe, AZ 45
American Red Cross Visitors Center and Gift Shop, Washington, DC 275
Arkansas Country Doctor Museum, Lincoln, AR....................................61

Baker-Cederberg Museum & Archives, Rochester, NY..........................1058

CDC/Global Health Odyssey, Atlanta, GA..358
Carter-Coile Country Doctors Museum, Winterville, GA....................................392
Children's Health Museum, Charlottesville, VA..............................1499
The Country Doctor Museum, Bailey, NC.1091
Crawford W. Long Museum, Jefferson, GA..374

DeWitt Stetten, Jr., Museum of Medical Research, Bethesda, MD 637
Discovery Center (East Tennessee Discovery Center), Knoxville, TN.........1369
Dittrick Museum of Medical History, Cleveland, OH....................................1154
Dr. Francis Medical and Apothecary Museum, Jacksonville, AL..................12
Dr. Howe-Waffle House and Medical Museum, Santa Ana, CA........................177
Dr. John Harris Dental Museum, Bainbridge, OH....................................1141
Dr. Samuel D. Harris National Museum of Dentistry, Baltimore, MD 631

Edward H. White II Memorial Museum, Brooks Air Force Base, TX 1397

Feet First: The Scholl Story, Rosalind Franklin University, North Chicago, IL...448
Fort Winnebago Surgeons Quarters, Portage, WI....................................1618

Hall of Health, Berkeley, CA........................75
Harvey Cushing/John Hay Whitney Medical Library, New Haven, CT 253
The Health Adventure, Asheville, NC........1090
HealthSpace Cleveland, Cleveland, OH 1154
Heartland, The California Museum of the Heart, Rancho Mirage, CA 145
History of Medicine Collections, Durham, NC....................................1098
History of Pharmacy Museum, Tucson, AZ..49
Homeopathy Works, Berkeley Springs, WV..1580
Hugh Mercer Apothecary Shop, Fredericksburg, VA..............................1506

Indiana Medical History Museum, Indianapolis, IN..................................484
International Museum of Surgical Science, Chicago, IL 422

Medical, Dental, Health, Pharmacology, Apothecary and Psychiatry Museums—Continued

John P. McGovern Museum of Health & Medical Science, Houston, TX 1427
The John Q. Adams Center for the History of Otolaryngology - Head and Neck Surgery, Alexandria, VA 1493

Kansas Learning Center for Health, Halstead, KS 542

The Lithuanian Museum, Chicago, IL..........423

Macaulay Museum of Dental History, Charleston, SC 1326
Marvin Samson Center for History of Pharmacy/USP Museum, Philadelphia, PA.................................1283
The Menczer Museum of Medicine & Dentistry, Hartford, CT 245
Mobile Medical Museum, Mobile, AL...........14
Museum at Mountain Home - East Tennessee State University, Johnson City, TN 1368
Museum of Chicot County Arkansas, Lake Village, AR 61
Museum of disAbility History, Williamsville, NY 1086
Museum of Funeral Customs, Springfield, IL 459
The Museum of Nursing History, Inc., Philadelphia, PA 1283
Museum of Science, Boston, MA..........667
Museum of Small Town Life, Dover, DE 270
The Museum of Southern History, Sugarland, TX 1454
Museum of Vision, San Francisco, CA 167
Mutter Museum, College of Physicians of Philadelphia, Philadelphia, PA 1283

National Museum of Health and Medicine, Washington, DC 286
New Orleans Pharmacy Museum, New Orleans, LA 597

The Pearson Museum, Springfield, IL..........460
Pocahontas County Iowa Historical Society Museum, Laurens, IA 522

Remick Country Doctor Museum and Farm, Tamworth, NH 896
Robert Crown Center for Health Education, Hinsdale, IL.........................440

Sheboygan County Historical Museum, Sheboygan, WI 1621
Sierra Sacramento Valley Medical Society Museum of Medical History, Sacramento, CA 153
Sindecuse Museum of Dentistry, Ann Arbor, MI.................................725
Sioux Empire Medical Museum, Sioux Falls, SD 1356
Southwest Museum of Science and Technology, The Science Place & TI Founders IMAX Theater, Dallas, TX 1407
Stabler-Leadbeater Apothecary Museum and Museum Shop, Alexandria, VA 1494
Still National Osteopathic Museum, Kirksville, MO.................................824

Texas Pharmacy Museum, Amarillo, TX ...1387
Transylvania Museum, Lexington, KY.........574

University of Iowa Hospitals & Clinics Medical Museum, Iowa City, IA 520
University of Kansas Medical Center, Clendening History of Medicine Library and Museum, Kansas City, KS...546
U.S. Army Medical Department Museum, Fort Sam Houston, TX.........................1415

Waring Historical Library, Charleston, SC.1327

Weeping Water Valley Historical Society, Weeping Water, NE 874
Wood Library-Museum of Anesthesiology, Park Ridge, IL 450

Natural History and Natural Science Museums

The A.D. Buck Museum of Natural History & Science, Tonkawa, OK 1215
ASRI Environmental Education Center, Bristol, RI 1310
The Academy of Natural Sciences of Philadelphia, Philadelphia, PA 1275
Adan E. Treganza Anthropology Museum, Dept. of Anthropology, San Francisco State University, San Francisco, CA 162
Adventure Science Center, Nashville, TN..1377
Agate Fossil Beds National Monument, Harrison, NE.................................862
Aiken County Historical Museum, Aiken, SC.................................1320
Alabama Museum of Natural History, Tuscaloosa, AL.................................19
Alaska Museum of Natural History, Anchorage, AK.................................21
Alley Pond Environmental Center, Inc., Douglaston, NY.................................984
American Bald Eagle Foundation, Haines, AK.................................25
American Museum of Asmat Art, Saint Paul, MN.................................789
American Museum of Natural History, New York, NY.................................1019
American Saddlebred Museum, Lexington, KY.................................572
Anaheim Museum, Anaheim, CA.................71
Angel Mounds State Historic Site, Evansville, IN.................................475
Annie E. Woodman Institute Museum, Dover, NH.................................886
Anniston Museum of Natural History, Anniston, AL.................................3
Anza-Borrego Desert State Park, Borrego Springs, CA.................................79
Arches National Park Visitor Center, Moab, UT.................................1467
Arizona-Sonora Desert Museum, Tucson, AZ.................................48
Arizona State Parks Board, Phoenix, AZ.......39
Arkansas State University Museum, Jonesboro, AR.................................60
Ash Hollow State Historical Park, Lewellen, NE.................................864
Ataloa Lodge Museum, Muskogee, OK.....1205
Audubon County Historical Society, Exira, IA.................................517
Audubon Louisiana Nature Center, New Orleans, LA.................................594
Audubon Society of New Hampshire, Concord, NH.................................884
Austin Nature & Science Center, Austin, TX.................................1389

Badlands National Park, Interior, SD 1349
Badlands Petrified Gardens, Kadoka, SD...1349
The Bailey-Matthews Shell Museum, Sanibel, FL.................................343
Bandon Historical Society Museum, Bandon, OR.................................1219
The Bartlett Museum, Amesbury, MA 657
Battle Hill Museum of Natural History, Battle Creek, IA.................................505
Bear Brook Nature Center, Suncook, NH 896
Bear Mountain Trailside Museums and Zoo, Bear Mountain, NY 961
Becker County Historical Society, Detroit Lakes, MN.................................772
Bergen Museum of Art & Science, Paramus, NJ.................................919
Berkshire Museum, Pittsfield, MA 702

Big Basin Redwoods State Park, Boulder Creek, CA.................................79
Big Bend National Park, Big Bend, TX.....1396
Big Bone Lick State Park Museum, Union, KY.................................584
Big Cypress National Preserve, Ochopee, FL.................................330
Big Thicket National Preserve, Kountze, TX.................................1432
Big Thunder Gold Mine, Keystone, SD.....1349
Billings Curation Center, Billings, MT 841
Biscayne National Park, Homestead, FL......313
Bishop Museum, Honolulu, HI...................394
Black Hills Museum of Natural History, Hill City, SD.................................1348
Blackwater Draw Museum, Portales, NM....944
Blue Hills Trailside Museum, Milton, MA.................................695
Bolin Wildlife Exhibit & Antique Collection, McKinney, TX....................1437
Boone County Historical Center, Boone, IA.................................506
Boone County Historical Museum, Belvidere, IL.................................413
Boone's Lick State Historic Site, Boonesboro, MO.................................811
Boonshoft Museum of Discovery, Dayton, OH.................................1160
Boyce Thompson Arboretum, Superior, AZ.................................44
Bramble Park Zoo, Watertown, SD 1359
Brazos Valley Museum of Natural History, Bryan, TX.................................1398
Brazosport Museum of Natural Science, Clute, TX.................................1400
Brevard Museum of History & Science, Cocoa, FL.................................300
Briar Bush Nature Center, Abington, PA ...1238
Brown County Historical Society Pioneer Museum, Nashville, IN.................................493
Bruce Museum, Greenwich, CT 243
Bryce Canyon National Park Visitor Center, Bryce, UT.................................1464
Buckhorn Saloon & Museum, San Antonio, TX.................................1448
Buena Vista Museum of Natural History, Bakersfield, CA.................................73
Buffalo Bill Historical Center, Cody, WY..1631
Buffalo Museum of Science, Buffalo, NY ...972
Buffalo National River, Harrison, AR 59
Buffalo Trails Museum, Epping, ND..........1130
Burke Museum of Natural History and Culture, Seattle, WA.................................1565
Burlington Historical Museum, Burlington, MA.................................672
Burpee Museum of Natural History, Rockford, IL.................................454
Burritt on the Mountain-A Living Museum, Huntsville, AL.................................11

C.E. Smith Museum of Anthropology, Hayward, CA.................................101
C.H. Nash Museum-Chucalissa Archaeological Museum, Memphis, TN.................................1372
Cable Natural History Museum, Cable, WI.................................1593
Cabrillo National Monument, San Diego, CA.................................156
Caguana Indian Ceremonial Park & Museum, Utuado, PR.................................1644
California Academy of Sciences, San Francisco, CA.................................163
California State Indian Museum, Sacramento, CA.................................151
Calkins Nature Area/Field Museum, Iowa Falls, IA.................................521
Call of the Wild Museum, Gaylord, MI.......742
Calvert Marine Museum, Solomons, MD 654
Cape Cod Museum of Natural History, Inc., Brewster, MA.................................670
Cape Cod National Seashore, Wellfleet, MA.................................717

Cape Fear Museum of History and Science, Wilmington, NC 1123

Capitol Reef National Park Visitor Center, Torrey, UT 1475

Capulin Volcano National Monument, Capulin, NM 937

Carl G. Fenner Nature Center, Lansing, MI 749

Carlsbad Caverns National Park, Carlsbad, NM 937

Carlsbad Museum & Art Center, Carlsbad, NM 938

Carnegie Museum of Natural History, Pittsburgh, PA 1291

Carnegie Museums of Pittsburgh (Carnegie Institute), Pittsburgh, PA 1291

Carrie Weedon Natural Science Museum, Galesville, MD 645

Cashmere Museum & Pioneer Village, Cashmere, WA 1550

Catherine Montgomery Interpretive Center, Greenwater, WA 1556

Cedar Bog Nature Preserve, Urbana, OH ..1188

Cedar Breaks National Monument, Cedar City, UT 1464

Cedar Key Museum State Park, Cedar Key, FL 299

The Centennial Museum at the University of Texas at El Paso, El Paso, TX 1411

Center for American Archaeology, Kampsville, IL 440

Center for Meteorite Studies, Tempe, AZ 46

Central Missouri State University Archives and Museum, Warrensburg, MO 839

Channel Islands National Park, Robert J. Lagomarsino Visitor Center, Ventura, CA 194

Charles R. Conner Museum, Pullman, WA 1563

Charlotte County Historical Center, Charlotte Harbor, FL 299

Cheraw Lyceum Museum, Cheraw, SC 1327

Chickasaw National Recreation Area, Sulphur, OK 1214

Chief Plenty Coups Museum, Pryor, MT 852

Children's Museum of History, Natural History and Science at Utica, New York, Utica, NY 1079

The Children's Museum of Indianapolis, Indianapolis, IN 481

Chippewa Nature Center, Midland, MI 755

Chiricahua National Monument, Willcox, AZ 53

Cincinnati Museum Center at Union Terminal, Cincinnati, OH 1149

City of Las Cruces Museum System, Las Cruces, NM 940

Cleveland County Historical Museum, Shelby, NC 1119

Cleveland Metroparks Outdoor Education Division, Garfield Heights, OH 1165

The Cleveland Museum of Natural History, Cleveland, OH 1153

Cliff Dwellings Museum, Manitou Springs, CO 227

Cliffs of the Neuse State Park, Seven Springs, NC 1119

Coastal Discovery Museum, Hilton Head Island, SC 1335

Coke Hallowell Center for River Studies, Fresno, CA 96

Colburn Earth Science Museum, Asheville, NC 1089

College of Eastern Utah Prehistoric Museum, Price, UT 1469

Colleton Museum, Walterboro, SC 1343

Collier County Museum, Naples, FL............328

Colorado National Monument, Fruita, CO...218

Colorado Plateau Biodiversity Center, Flagstaff, AZ 32

Columbia Gorge Discovery Center and Wasco County Museum, The Dalles, OR 1237

Columbus-Belmont Civil War Museum, Columbus, KY 567

Community Historical Museum, Maxwell, IA 523

Congaree National Park, Hopkins, SC 1336

Connecticut Audubon Birdcraft Museum, Fairfield, CT 240

Connecticut Audubon Society, Fairfield, CT 240

Connecticut State Museum of Natural History and Connecticut Archaeology Center, Storrs, CT 261

Cook's Natural Science Museum, Decatur, AL 7

The Cornell Plantations, Ithaca, NY...........1003

Coronado State Monument, Bernalillo, NM 937

Coyote Point Museum for Environmental Education, San Mateo, CA......................175

Cranbrook Institute of Science, Bloomfield Hills, MI 730

Craters of the Moon National Monument, Arco, ID 403

Creation Museum, Petersburg, KY 583

Crystal River State Archaeological Site, Crystal River, FL 302

Cylburn Arboretum, Baltimore, MD............631

D. Ralph Hostetter Museum of Natural History, Harrisonburg, VA......................1510

Dallas Museum of Natural History, Dallas, TX 1406

Dan Nicholas Park Nature Center, Salisbury, NC 1118

Dawson County Historical Museum, Lexington, NE 864

De Graaf Nature Center, Holland, MI..........746

Death Valley National Park Visitor Center and Museums, Death Valley, CA...............91

Delaware Museum of Natural History, Wilmington, DE 273

Denison Pequotsepos Nature Center, Mystic, CT 250

Denver Museum of Nature & Science, Denver, CO 211

Dickson Mounds Museum, Lewistown, IL 442

Dinosaur State Park, Rocky Hill, CT 259

The Discovery Center, Fresno, CA...............96

Drumlin Farm Education Center, Lincoln, MA 690

Dry Falls Interpretive Center, Coulee City, WA 1551

Dubois Museum, Dubois, WY.....................1632

Dunn-Seiler Museum, Mississippi State University, MS 805

Earthplace - The Nature Discovery Center, Westport, CT 266

East-West Center, Honolulu, HI...................394

Eastern California Museum, Independence, CA 104

ECHO at the Leahy Center for Lake Champlain, Burlington, VT 1478

EcoTarium, Worcester, MA..........................720

Edgar County Historical Museum, Paris, IL 449

Edge of the Cedars State Park Museum, Blanding, UT 1463

Edisto Island Historic Preservation Society Museum, Edisto Island, SC 1332

Effie Yeaw Nature Center, Carmichael, CA 82

Ehrhart Museum, Antwerp, OH 1139

El Campo Museum of Natural History, El Campo, TX 1411

El Dorado Nature Center, Long Beach, CA 110

El Morro National Monument, Ramah, NM 945

Elachee Nature Science Center, Gainesville, GA 373

Elgin Public Museum, Elgin, IL..................432

Elkhorn Slough National Estuarine Research, Wastonville, CA..................196

Environmental Education Center, Somerset County Park Commission, Basking Ridge, NJ 898

Essex Shipbuilding Museum, Essex, MA 681

Essig Museum of Entomology, University of California, Berkeley, Berkeley, CA........75

Estelle H. Womack Museum of Natural History, Danville, VA 1503

Everglades National Park, Homestead, FL...313

Everhart Museum: Natural History, Science and Art, Scranton, PA...............1298

Explorium of Lexington, Lexington, KY 572

Fairbanks Museum and Planetarium, Saint Johnsbury, VT 1486

Fairview Museum of History & Art, Fairview, UT 1465

Faulkner County Museum, Conway, AR........56

Fernbank Museum of Natural History, Atlanta, GA 359

Fernbank Science Center, Atlanta, GA.........360

Field Museum of Natural History, Chicago, IL 420

Fisher Museum of Forestry, Petersham, MA 702

Flint Ridge State Memorial Museum, Glenford, OH 1166

Flint River Quarium, Albany, GA 355

Florence Hawley Ellis Museum of Anthropology and Ruth Hall Museum of Paleontology, Abiquiu, NM 931

Florence Museum of Art, Science & History and the Florence Railroad Museum, Florence, SC 1332

Florence Price Pioneer Museum, Florence, CO 216

Florida Agricultural Museum, Palm Coast, FL 334

Florida Museum of Natural History, Gainesville, FL 310

Florissant Fossil Beds National Monument, Florissant, CO 216

Fontenelle Nature Association, Bellevue, NE 857

Forest History Center, Grand Rapids, MN...777

Forest Park Museum and Arboretum, Perry, IA 527

Fort Atkinson State Historical Park, Fort Calhoun, NE 860

Fort Harker Museum Complex, Kanopolis, KS 546

Fort McKavett State Historical Site, Fort McKavett, TX 1415

Fort Peck Interpretive Center, Fort Peck, MT 846

Fort Roosevelt Natural Science and History Museum, Hanford, CA 101

Fort Vasquez Museum, Platteville, CO 230

Fort Worth Museum of Science and History, Fort Worth, TX 1417

Forts Folle Avoine Historic Park, Danbury, WI 1594

Fred Dana Marsh Museum, Ormond Beach, FL 333

Fresno Flats Historical Park, Oakhurst, CA 132

The Frost Entomological Museum, Dept. of Entomology, The Pennsylvania State University, University Park, PA....1304

Fruitlands Museums, Harvard, MA 686

Galloway House and Village - Blakely Museum, Fond du Lac, WI 1597

Garden in the Woods of the New England Wild Flower Society, Framingham, MA 683

Natural History and Natural Science Museums—Continued

Gatekeeper's Museum & Marion Steinbach Indian Basket Museum, Tahoe City, CA.................190

Geddes Historic District Village, Geddes, SD...............1347

George Washington Carver Museum, Tuskegee Institute, AL...............20

Georgia Museum of Natural History, Athens, GA.................356

Georgia Southern University Museum, Statesboro, GA...............387

Gerald E. Eddy Discovery Center, Chelsea, MI.................732

George B. Dorr Museum of Natural History, Bar Harbor, ME...............605

Gilman Museum, Hellertown, PA.............1260

Ginkgo Petrified Forest State Park, Vantage, WA.................1576

Golden Gate National Recreation Area, San Francisco, CA...............165

Graves Museum of Archaeology and Natural History, Dania Beach, FL...........302

Great Basin National Park, Baker, NV.........875

Great Harbor Maritime Museum, Northeast Harbor, ME.................616

Great Plains Zoo & Delbridge Museum, Sioux Falls, SD...............1356

Great Sand Dunes National Monument and Preserve, Mosca, CO.................229

Great Valley Museum of Natural History, Modesto, CA.................126

Greater Hazleton Historical Society, Hazleton, PA.................1260

Greene-Nieuwland Herbarium, Notre Dame, IN.................495

Greybull Museum, Greybull, WY.............1634

The Grove, Glenview, IL.................438

Gunnison Museum of Natural History, Pawling, NY.................1051

Gwinnett County Parks & Recreation Outdoor Interpretive Section, Lawrenceville, GA.................375

Hampton County Historical Museum, Hampton, SC.................1334

Harmonie Associates, Inc., Ambridge, PA.1240

Harpers Ferry Center, Harpers Ferry, WV.1582

Harvard Museum of Natural History, Cambridge, MA.................672

Hastings Museum, Hastings, NE.................863

Heard Natural Science Museum and Wildlife Sanctuary, Inc., McKinney, TX.................1437

Hefner Zoology Museum, Oxford, OH.........1181

Henry S. Reuss Ice Age Visitor Center, Campbellsport, WI.................1593

Heritage of the Americas Museum, El Cajon, CA.................92

Herrett Center for Arts & Science, Faulkner Planetarium and Centennial Observatory, Twin Falls, ID.................410

Hi-Desert Nature Museum, Yucca Valley, CA.................201

High Desert Museum, Bend, OR.............1220

Highlands Center for Natural History, Prescott, AZ.................42

Hilltop Garden and Nature Center, Bloomington, IN.................469

Hiram Blauvelt Art Museum, Oradell, NJ....919

Historic Bethabara Park, Winston-Salem, NC.................1125

Historic Charlton Park Village and Museum, Hastings, MI.................745

Historic Crab Orchard Museum & Pioneer Park, Inc., Tazewell, VA...........1541

Historic New Harmony, New Harmony, IN.................494

Historical Natural History & Library Society of Natick dba Natick Historical Society, South Natick, MA.....709

Horizons Unlimited Supplementary Educational Center, Salisbury, NC.........1118

Horry County Museum, Conway, SC.........1331

Hot Springs National Park Visitor Center, Hot Springs, AR.................60

Houston Museum of Natural Science, Houston, TX.................1427

Humboldt Redwoods State Park Visitor Center, Weott, CA.................197

Humboldt State University Natural History Museum, Arcata, CA.................72

Humpback Rocks Mountain Farm & Visitor Center, Waynesboro, VA...........1544

Hutchinson County Museum, Borger, TX..1397

Idaho Museum of Natural History, Pocatello, ID.................408

Illinois State Museum, Springfield, IL.........458

Indiana State Museum, Indianapolis, IN.....484

The Institute For American Indian Studies (IAIS), Washington Green, CT...263

International Museum of Art and Science, McAllen, TX.................1437

International Museum of Cultures, Dallas, TX.................1406

International Wildlife Museum, Tucson, AZ.................49

Iosco County Historical Museum, East Tawas, MI.................740

Iron Hill Museum, Newark, DE.................272

Isle Royale National Park, Houghton, MI....747

James Ford Bell Museum of Natural History, Minneapolis, MN.................782

James R. Slater Museum of Natural History, Tacoma, WA.................1573

Jean Lafitte National Historical Park & Preserve, New Orleans, LA.................596

Jean P. Haydon Museum, Pago Pago, AS..1640

Jefferson Patterson Park & Museum, Saint Leonard, MD.................651

Jensen Arctic Museum, Monmouth, OR....1228

John Day Fossil Beds National Monument, Kimberly, OR.................1227

John E. Conner Museum, Kingsville, TX..1432

John Hutchings Museum of Natural History, Lehi, UT.................1466

Joseph A. Tallman Museum, Cherokee, IA.................510

Joseph Moore Museum, Richmond, IN.........497

Joshua Tree National Park, Oasis Visitor Center, Twentynine Palms, CA.................193

The Journey Museum, Rapid City, SD.......1354

Jurupa Mountains Cultural Center, Riverside, CA.................149

KU Natural History Museum and Biodiversity Research Center, Lawrence, KS.................548

Kalamazoo Nature Center, Inc., Kalamazoo, MI.................748

Kansas Department of Wildlife & Parks, Pratt, KS.................556

Kauffman Museum, North Newton, KS.......553

Kenosha Public Museum, Kenosha, WI.....1602

Kentucky Coal Mining Museum, Benham, KY.................565

Kingman Museum, Battle Creek, MI..........727

Klamath County Museum, Klamath Falls, OR.................1227

Koke'e Natural History Museum, Kauai, HI.................400

L.C. Bates Museum, Hinckley, ME.............612

L.H. Bailey Hortorium, Ithaca, NY...........1003

Lady Bird Johnson Wildflower Center, Austin, TX.................1390

Lafayette Natural History Museum and Planetarium, Lafayette, LA.................589

Lake Erie Nature & Science Center, Bay Village, OH.................1141

Lake Mead National Recreation Area, Boulder City, NV.................875

Lake Meredith Aquatic and Wildlife Museum, Fritch, TX.................1420

Lake Perris Regional Indian Museum (Home of the Wind), Perris, CA.............141

Lake Waccamaw Depot Museum, Lake Waccamaw, NC.................1109

Las Vegas Natural History Museum, Las Vegas, NV.................879

Laughing Brook Education Center & Wildlife Sanctuary, Hampden, MA.........686

Lava Beds National Monument, Tulelake, CA.................193

Libby Museum, Wolfeboro, NH.................897

Lincoln Memorial Garden and Nature Center, Springfield, IL.................459

Lindsay Wildlife Museum, Walnut Creek, CA.................196

Living Desert Zoo and Gardens State Park, Carlsbad, NM.................938

Lompoc Museum, Lompoc, CA.................109

Long Island Culture History Lab & Museum, Commack, NY.................980

Louden-Henritze Archaeology Museum, Trinidad, CO.................234

Louisiana State Exhibit Museum, Shreveport, LA.................600

Louisiana State University Herbarium, Baton Rouge, LA.................586

Louisiana Tech Museum, Ruston, LA.........600

Lower Rio Grande Valley Nature Center, Weslaco, TX.................1460

M.T. Brackbill Planetarium, Harrisonburg, VA.................1511

MacCallum More Museum and Gardens, Chase City, VA.................1500

Maidu Interpretive Center, Roseville, CA....151

Maine State Museum, Augusta, ME.................604

Mammoth Site of Hot Springs, Inc., Hot Springs, SD.................1348

Mann Wildlife Learning Museum, Montgomery, AL.................16

Maramec Museum, The James Foundation, Saint James, MO.................830

Marengo Cave, Marengo, IN.................489

Marianna-Lee County Museum Assoc. Inc., Marianna, AR.................64

Marin Museum of the American Indian, Novato, CA.................131

Maritime Museum at Historic Coast Guard Station, Saint Simons Island, GA.................383

Martin and Osa Johnson Safari Museum, Inc., Chanute, KS.................535

Maryhill Museum of Art, Goldendale, WA.................1556

Mashantucket Pequot Museum and Research Center, Mashantucket, CT........248

Maturango Museum of the Indian Wells Valley, Ridgecrest, CA.................148

May Natural History Museum and Museum of Space Exploration, Colorado Springs, CO.................207

Mayborn Museum Complex, Waco, TX....1459

McCone County Museum, Circle, MT........844

McLean County Historical Society Museum, Washburn, ND.................1137

McPherson Museum & Arts Foundation, McPherson, KS.................552

Menominee County Heritage Museum, Menominee, MI.................754

Merritt Museum of Anthropology, Oakland, CA.................133

Mesa Southwest Museum, Mesa, AZ.............37

The Michigan State University Museum, East Lansing, MI.................740

Midland County Historical Museum, Midland, TX.................1438

Milwaukee Public Museum, Milwaukee, WI.................1612

Mission Houses Museum, Honolulu, HI.....397

Mississippi Museum of Natural Science, Jackson, MS.................803

Mississippi River Museum at Mud Island River Park, Memphis, TN 1375
Mohave Museum of History and Arts, Kingman, AZ 36
Mohonk Preserve, Inc., Gardiner, NY 993
The Monhegan Museum, Monhegan, ME....615
Monroe County Historical Society, Bloomington, IN...469
Montauk Point Lighthouse Museum, Montauk, NY 1015
Monte L. Bean Life Science Museum, Provo, UT 1469
Montezuma Castle National Monument, Camp Verde, AZ.....................................30
The Morris Museum, Morristown, NJ..........914
Morro Bay State Park Museum of Natural History, Morro Bay, CA 129
Morrow Mountain State Park, Albemarle, NC 1088
Moses Lake Museum & Art Center, Moses Lake, WA 1559
Mote Marine Laboratory/Aquarium, Sarasota, FL..345
Moundbuilders State Memorial & Museum, Newark, OH.........................1178
Moundville Archaeological Park, Moundville, AL 17
Mt. Rainier National Park, Ashford, WA ...1547
Mount Washington Museum and The Weather Discovery Center, North Conway, NH 893
Mountain Heritage Center, Cullowhee, NC 1097
Mulberry Phospate Museum, Mulberry, FL 327
The Murie Museum, Kelly, WY 1634
The Museum, Greenwood, SC....................1334
Museum and Arts Center in the Sequim Dungeness Valley, Sequim, WA.............1570
Museum of Ancient & Modern Art, Penn Valley, CA..141
Museum of Anthropology, Chico, CA...........83
The Museum of Arts and Sciences, Inc. and Center for Florida History, Daytona Beach, FL....................................303
Museum of Chicot County Arkansas, Lake Village, AR...................................61
Museum of Comparative Zoology, Cambridge, MA...................................674
Museum of Cultural & Natural History, Mount Pleasant, MI..............................757
Museum of Discovery: Arkansas Museum of Science and History, Little Rock, AR 62
Museum of Earth and Life History, Lynchburg, VA...................................1515
Museum of Idaho, Idaho Falls, ID 406
Museum of Indian Arts & Culture/Laboratory of Anthropology, Santa Fe, NM...948
Museum of Jurassic Technology, Culver City, CA 88
Museum of Long Island Natural Sciences, Stony Brook, NY 1075
Museum of Natural History, Marshall, MN...780
The Museum of Natural History, Stevens Point, WI...1622
Museum of Natural History and Planetarium, Providence, RI....................1317
Museum of Natural Science, Baton Rouge, LA...587
Museum of North Carolina Minerals, Spruce Pine, NC...................................1120
Museum of Northern Arizona, Flagstaff, AZ 33
Museum of Paleontology, Berkeley, CA 76
Museum of Rim Country Archaeology, Payson, AZ...38
Museum of Science, Boston, MA................667
Museum of Science and Industry, Chicago, IL...425

Museum of Southwestern Biology, Albuquerque, NM.................................934
Museum of the Gulf Coast, Port Arthur, TX 1444
Museum of the Hudson Highlands, Cornwall-on-Hudson, NY 982
Museum of the Llano Estacado, Plainview, TX 1443
Museum of the Middle Appalachians, Saltville, VA...1536
Museum of the Red River, Idabel, OK 1203
Museum of the Rockies, Bozeman, MT......842
Museum of Vertebrate Zoology, Berkeley, CA 76
Museum of Western Colorado, Grand Junction, CO...220
Museum of York County, Rock Hill, SC ...1340
Museums of Los Gatos, Los Gatos, CA 123
Muskegon County Museum, Muskegon, MI..757
Myriad Botanical Gardens, Oklahoma City, OK...1208
Mystic Aquarium & Institute for Exploration, Mystic, CT.........................250

Nantucket Maria Mitchell Association, Nantucket, MA 696
Napa Valley Museum, Yountville, CA 200
Nassau County, Division of Museum Services, Department of Recreation, Parks & Museums, East Meadow, NY 987
National Geographic Museum at Explorers Hall, Washington, DC..............285
National Museum of Natural History, Washington, DC.....................................286
National Park Service Museum Resource Center, Landover, MD........................648
National Tropical Botanical Garden, Kalaheo, HI...399
Natural History Museum, Portales, NM......944
The Natural History Museum, Santa Maria, CA..182
Natural History Museum of Los Angeles County, Los Angeles, CA.........................120
The Natural Science Center of Greensboro, Inc., Greensboro, NC....1104
Nature Interpretive Center, Lebanon, MO....825
The Nature Museum at Grafton, Grafton, VT 1479
Nevada State Museum, Carson City, NV 876
Nevada State Museum, Las Vegas, Las Vegas, NV..880
Nevada State Railroad Museum, Carson City, NV..876
New Canaan Nature Center, New Canaan, CT...252
New Jersey Meadowlands Environment Center, Lyndhurst, NJ.............................910
New Jersey State Museum, Trenton, NJ 927
New Mexico Museum of Natural History & Science, Albuquerque, NM.................935
New York State Museum, Albany, NY........955
The Newark Museum, Newark, NJ.............916
Nohwike Bagowa, The White Mountain Apache Cultural Center and Museum, Fort Apache, AZ.......................................34
North Carolina Aquarium at Fort Fisher, Kure Beach, NC 1109
North Carolina Maritime Museum, Beaufort, NC...1091
North Carolina Museum of Forestry, Whiteville, NC.......................................1122
North Carolina Museum of Natural Sciences, Raleigh, NC 1116
North Cascades National Park Service Complex, Marblemount, WA.................1559
The North Museum of Natural History & Science, Lancaster, PA...........................1266
Northeastern Nevada Museum, Elko, NV....876
Northwestern Oklahoma State University Museum, Alva, OK....................................1195
The Nylander Museum of Natural History, Caribou, ME 609

Oakes Museum Messiah College, Grantham, PA 1257
Oakland Museum of California, Oakland, CA..134
Oatland Island Education Center, Savannah, GA..385
Oceanographic Teaching Station Inc. - Roundhouse Marine Studies Lab & Aquarium, Manhattan Beach, CA..........124
Ogden Union Station Museums, Ogden, UT 1468
Ohio Historical Society, Columbus, OH.....1158
Ojai Valley Historical Society and Museum, Ojai, CA 135
Old Economy Village, Ambridge, PA.........1240
Old Trail Museum, Choteau, MT 844
Olympic National Park Visitor Center, Port Angeles, WA 1561
Oneida County Historical Society, Utica, NY 1080
Oregon Trail Arboretum, Echo, OR............1223
Orma J. Smith Museum of Natural History, Caldwell, ID 405
Orpheum Children's Science Museum, Champaign, IL.......................................417
Orton Geological Museum, Ohio State University, Columbus, OH 1158
Osage Village State Historic Site, Lamar, MO..825
Overland Trail Museum, Sterling, CO..........232
The Oyster and Maritime Museum of Chincoteague, Chincoteague, VA...........1501
Ozark National Scenic Riverways, Van Buren, MO...839

Pacific Grove Museum of Natural History, Pacific Grove, CA 137
Pacific Tsunami Museum, Hilo, HI 393
Padre Island National Seashore, Corpus Christi, TX..1402
Paleontological Research Institution, Ithaca, NY...1004
The Paterson Museum, Paterson, NJ 920
Peabody Museum of Natural History, New Haven, CT..253
Peaks of Otter Visitor Center, Bedford, VA 1496
The Peary-MacMillan Arctic Museum, Brunswick, ME..608
The Peggy Notebaert Nature Museum, Chicago, IL..426
Pember Museum of Natural History, Granville, NY..995
Petrified Creatures Museum of Natural History, Richfield Springs, NY 1057
Petrified Forest National Park, Petrified Forest National Park, AZ 38
Petrified Forest of the Black Hills, Piedmont, SD...1353
Philip L. Wright Zoological Museum and University of Montana Herbarium, Missoula, MT..852
Pink Palace Family of Museums, Memphis, TN..1375
Pinnacle Mountain State Park, Little Rock, AR..63
Pinnacles National Monument, Paicines, CA..138
Pioneer Farm Museum and Ohop Indian Village, Eatonville, WA.........................1552
Pioneer-Krier Museum, Ashland, KS 532
Pioneers, Trail Drivers and Texas Rangers Memorial Museum, San Antonio, TX..1449
Pipestone National Monument, Pipestone, MN..787
Plains Conservation Center, Aurora, CO......202
Plumas County Museum, Quincy, CA..........144
Port Townsend Marine Science Center, Port Townsend, WA................................1562
Prairie Grove Battlefield State Park, Prairie Grove, AR.....................................66
Pratt Museum, Homer, AK 25

Natural History and Natural Science Museums—Continued

The Pratt Museum of Natural History, Amherst, MA..............659

Prince William Forest Park Visitor Center, Triangle, VA..............1541

Princeton University Museum of Natural History, Princeton, NJ..............922

Providence Canyon State Park, Lumpkin, GA..............377

Public Museum of West Michigan, Grand Rapids, MI..............744

Putnam County Historical Society Museum, Kalida, OH..............1169

Putnam Museum of History & Natural Science, Davenport, IA..............513

The Quincy Museum, Quincy, IL..............452

R.M. Bohart Museum of Entomology, Davis, CA..............90

The Raymond M. Alf Museum of Paleontology, Claremont, CA..............86

Reading Public Museum, Reading, PA..............1296

Red River Valley Museum, Vernon, TX..............1457

Red Rock Museum, Church Rock, NM..............938

Richard H. Schmidt Museum of Natural History, Emporia, KS..............539

Rio Grande Valley Museum, Harlingen, TX..............1423

River Heritage Museum, Paducah, KY..............582

River Hills Visitor Center, Wildwood, MO..............840

River Legacy Living Science Center, Arlington, TX..............1388

Riverside Metropolitan Museum, Riverside, CA..............150

Riverside Museum, La Crosse, WI..............1603

Robert A. Vines Environmental Science Center, Houston, TX..............1429

Rochester Museum & Science Center, Rochester, NY..............1059

Rock Creek Nature Center, Washington, DC..............290

Rock Island State Park, Washington Island, WI..............1625

Rocky Mountain National Park, Estes Park, CO..............215

Roger Tory Peterson Institute of Natural History, Jamestown, NY..............1005

Rosenbruch Wildlife Museum, St. George, UT..............1474

Rotary Nature Center, Oakland, CA..............134

Royal Gorge Regional Museum & History Center, Canon City, CO..............205

Runestone Museum, Alexandria, MN..............767

Sag Harbor Whaling & Historical Museum, Sag Harbor, NY..............1063

St. Croix National Scenic Riverway, Saint Croix Falls, WI..............1620

St. Joseph Museum Inc., Saint Joseph, MO..............831

St. Petersburg Museum of History, Saint Petersburg, FL..............342

Sam Noble Oklahoma Museum of Natural History, Norman, OK..............1206

San Bernardino County Museum, Redlands, CA..............147

San Diego Museum of Man, San Diego, CA..............160

San Diego Natural History Museum, San Diego, CA..............160

Sanford Museum and Planetarium, Cherokee, IA..............510

Santa Barbara Museum of Natural History, Santa Barbara, CA..............179

Santa Cruz Museum of Natural History, Santa Cruz, CA..............182

Santa Monica Mountains National Recreation Area, Thousand Oaks, CA..............191

Schiele Museum of Natural History and Lynn Planetarium, Gastonia, NC..............1102

School of American Research, Indian Arts Research Center, Santa Fe, NM..............950

The Science Museum of Minnesota, Saint Paul, MN..............792

Sheldon Jackson Museum, Sitka, AK..............27

Shelter House Society, Emmaus, PA..............1251

Sieur de Monts Springs Nature Center, Bar Harbor, ME..............605

Silver River Museum & Environmental Education Center, Ocala, FL..............330

The Simon Paneak Memorial Museum, Anaktuvuk Pass, AK..............21

Sky City Cultural Center, Pueblo of Acoma, NM..............944

Sleeping Bear Dunes National Lakeshore, Empire, MI..............741

Smithsonian Institution, Washington, DC..............290

Snoqualmie Valley Historical Museum, North Bend, WA..............1559

South Carolina Department of Parks, Recreation and Tourism, Columbia, SC..............1330

South Florida Museum, Bishop Planetarium & Parker Manatee Aquarium, Bradenton, FL..............297

South Shore Natural Science Center, Inc., Norwell, MA..............700

Southern Oregon University Museum of Vertebrate Natural History, Ashland, OR..............1218

Southern Vermont Natural History Museum, West Marlboro, VT..............1489

Space Farms Zoological Park and Museum, Sussex, NJ..............925

Spartanburg Science Center, Spartanburg, SC..............1342

Spring Valley Nature Center & Heritage Farm, Schaumburg, IL..............457

Springbrook Nature Center, Fridley, MN..............776

Springfield Museums - Springfield Science Museum, Springfield, MA..............711

Squam Lakes Natural Science Center, Holderness, NH..............889

Staten Island Institute of Arts & Sciences (SIIAS), Staten Island, NY..............1074

Stephen C. Foster State Park, Fargo, GA..............371

The Stephens Museum, Fayette, MO..............815

Sternberg Museum of Natural History, Hays, KS..............543

Strasenburgh Planetarium/Rochester Museum & Science Center, Rochester, NY..............1060

Suffolk County Vanderbilt Museum, Centerport, NY..............977

Sugarlands Visitor Center, Gatlinburg, TN..............1365

SunWatch Indian Village/Archaeological Park, Dayton, OH..............1162

Sweet Briar Museum, Sweet Briar, VA..............1540

T Rex Museum, Tucson, AZ..............50

Tallahassee Museum, Tallahassee, FL..............348

Texas Natural Science Center, Austin, TX..............1392

Theodore Roosevelt National Park-Visitor Center, Medora, ND..............1134

Thornton W. Burgess Museum, Sandwich, MA..............708

Tillamook County Pioneer Museum, Tillamook, OR..............1237

Timberlake Rose Rock Museum, Noble, OK..............1206

Timucuan Ecological and Historic Preserve and Fort Caroline National Memorial, Jacksonville, FL..............315

Toltec Mounds Archeological State Park, Scott, AR..............68

Trailside Nature and Science Center, Mountainside, NJ..............915

Trailside Nature Museum, Cross River, NY..............983

The Trustees of Reservations, Beverly, MA..............662

Tucumcari Historical Research Institute, Tucumcari, NM..............953

Tularosa Basin Historical Society Museum, Alamogordo, NM..............932

Tulsa Zoo & Living Museum, Tulsa, OK..............1216

Turtle Bay Exploration Park, Redding, CA..............146

Umpqua Discovery Center, Reedsport, OR..............1234

Union Station Kansas City, Inc., Kansas City, MO..............823

United States Hockey Hall of Fame, Eveleth, MN..............774

University Herbarium & Jepson Herbarium, Berkeley, CA..............77

University of Alaska Museum of the North, Fairbanks, AK..............24

University of Colorado Museum, Boulder, CO..............203

University of Iowa Museum of Natural History, Iowa City, IA..............520

The University of Michigan Exhibit Museum of Natural History, Ann Arbor, MI..............725

University of Michigan, Museum of Zoology, Ann Arbor, MI..............726

University of Nebraska State Museum, Lincoln, NE..............867

University of North Dakota Zoology Museum, Grand Forks, ND..............1132

University of Northern Iowa Museums & Collections, Cedar Falls, IA..............508

University of Oregon Museum of Natural and Cultural History, Eugene, OR..............1224

University of Pennsylvania Museum of Archaeology and Anthropology, Philadelphia, PA..............1288

University of Richmond Museums, Richmond, VA..............1532

University of Wisconsin Zoological Museum, Madison, WI..............1606

Utah Field House of Natural History State Park, Vernal, UT..............1475

Utah Museum of Natural History, Salt Lake City, UT..............1473

Vashon Maury Island Heritage Association, Vashon, WA..............1576

Verde Historical Society, Clemenceau Heritage Museum, Cottonwood, AZ..............32

Vermont Institute of Natural Science, Quechee, VT..............1485

Victor Valley Museum & Art Gallery, Apple Valley, CA..............71

Virgin Islands National Park, St. John, VI..............1644

Virginia Department of Conservation and Recreation, Richmond, VA..............1533

Virginia Living Museum, Newport News, VA..............1520

Virginia Museum of Natural History, Martinsville, VA..............1516

The Voas Nature Area/Voas Museum, Minburn, IA..............523

W.H. Over Museum, Vermillion, SD..............1358

Wagner Free Institute of Science, Philadelphia, PA..............1289

Wahkiakum County Historical Museum, Cathlamet, WA..............1550

Waikiki Aquarium, Honolulu, HI..............399

Waimea Arboretum and Botanical Garden in Waimea Valley Audubon Center, Haleiwa, HI..............392

Wanapum Dam Heritage Center, Beverly, WA..............1549

The Wayne State University Museum of Natural History, Detroit, MI..............738

Weinberg Nature Center, Scarsdale, NY..............1066

Weinman Mineral Museum, White, GA..............391

Wells County Museum, Fessenden, ND..............1131

Westmoreland Sanctuary, Inc., Bedford Corners, NY..............961

Westport Maritime Museum, Westport, WA 1578

The Whale Museum, Friday Harbor, WA...1555

White County Historical Society, Carmi, IL 415

White Memorial Conservation Center, Inc., Litchfield, CT 247

White Pine Public Museum, Ely, NV..........877

White Sands National Monument, Alamogordo, NM..................................932

Wilbur D. May Museum, Reno, NV 882

Wildcare: Terwilliger Nature Education & Wildlife, San Rafael, CA 177

Wildlife Experience Museum, Parker, CO ...229

Wildlife Prairie State Park, Hanna City, IL 439

William Pryor Letchworth Museum, Castile, NY 976

Wind Cave National Park, Hot Springs, SD 1348

Witte Museum, San Antonio, TX 1451

Working Men's Institute, New Harmony, IN 495

World Museum of Natural History, Riverside, CA 150

Wupatki National Monument, Flagstaff, AZ 34

The Wyoming Dinosaur Center, Thermopolis, WY 1639

Yellowstone National Park, Gardiner, MT ...847

Yorktown Historical Museum, Yorktown, TX 1462

Yucaipa Valley Historical Society Museum, Yucaipa, CA..............................201

Planetariums, Observatories and Astronomy Museums

Abrams Planetarium, Michigan State University, East Lansing, MI 739

Adler Planetarium & Astronomy Museum, Chicago, IL 417

Adventure Science Center, Nashville, TN..1377

Alexander F. Morrison Planetarium, San Francisco, CA 163

American Museum of Natural History, New York, NY 1019

Argus Planetarium, Ann Arbor, MI 724

Arizona Science Center, Phoenix, AZ 39

Astronaut Memorial Planetarium and Observatory, Cocoa, FL 300

Audubon Louisiana Nature Center, New Orleans, LA 594

Berea College Weatherford Planetarium, Berea, KY 565

Besser Museum for Northeast Michigan, Alpena, MI..723

Big Bear Solar Observatory, Big Bear City, CA 78

Bishop Museum, Honolulu, HI.....................394

Boonshoft Museum of Discovery, Dayton, OH 1160

Buffalo Museum of Science, Buffalo, NY ...972

California Academy of Sciences, San Francisco, CA 163

Calusa Nature Center and Planetarium, Fort Myers, FL 308

Carnegie Museums of Pittsburgh (Carnegie Institute), Pittsburgh, PA 1291

Carnegie Science Center, Pittsburgh, PA....1291

Cernan Earth & Space Center, River Grove, IL 453

Chesapeake Planetarium, Chesapeake, VA.1501

Children's Museum/Detroit Public Schools, Detroit, MI 735

The Children's Museum of Indianapolis, Indianapolis, IN 481

The Children's Museum of Science and Technology, Troy, NY 1079

Children's Science Explorium at Sugar Sand Park, Boca Raton, FL 296

Christa McAuliffe Planetarium, Concord, NH 884

Clark Planetarium, Salt Lake City, UT 1470

Clay Center for Arts & Sciences West Virginia, Charleston, WV 1580

The Cleveland Museum of Natural History, Cleveland, OH 1153

Cranbrook House and Gardens Auxiliary, Bloomfield Hills, MI 730

Cranbrook Institute of Science, Bloomfield Hills, MI 730

D. Ralph Hostetter Museum of Natural History, Harrisonburg, VA....................1510

De Anza Planetarium, Cupertino, CA 88

Denver Museum of Nature & Science, Denver, CO 211

Detroit Science Center, Detroit, MI..............736

Discovery Center (East Tennessee Discovery Center), Knoxville, TN.........1369

Discovery Center Museum, Rockford, IL 454

The Discovery Museum, Inc., Bridgeport, CT 236

Discovery Museum, Sacramento Museum of History, Science and Technology, Sacramento, CA 152

Discovery Park, Safford, AZ 43

Don Harrington Discovery Center, Amarillo, TX 1387

Downing Planetarium, Fresno, CA 96

East Kentucky Center for Science, Mathematics, and Technology, Prestonsburg, KY 583

EcoTarium, Worcester, MA 720

Erie Planetarium, Erie, PA 1253

Evansville Museum of Arts History & Science, Evansville, IN 475

Fairbanks Museum and Planetarium, Saint Johnsbury, VT 1486

Fernbank Science Center, Atlanta, GA.........360

Flandrau Science Center and Planetarium, Tucson, AZ 49

Fleischmann Planetarium, Reno, NV............880

Fort Worth Museum of Science and History, Fort Worth, TX 1417

The Franklin Institute, Philadelphia, PA.....1280

Gheens Science Hall and Rauch Planetarium, Louisville, KY....................576

Goldendale Observatory, Goldendale, WA .1555

Good Zoo, Wheeling, WV 1587

Griffith Observatory, Los Angeles, CA.........115

Grout Museum District: Grout Museum of History and Science, Bluedorn Science Imaginarium, Rensselaer Russell House Museum, Snowden House, Waterloo, IA 529

Hardin Planetarium, Bowling Green, KY 565

Hastings Museum, Hastings, NE 863

Herrett Center for Arts & Science, Faulkner Planetarium and Centennial Observatory, Twin Falls, ID 410

Houston Museum of Natural Science, Houston, TX 1427

Howard B. Owens Science Center and Challenger Learning Center, Lanham-Seabrook, MD 648

The Hudson River Museum, Yonkers, NY.1087

I.P. Stanback Museum & Planetarium, Orangeburg, SC 1338

J.I. Holcomb Observatory and Planetarium, Indianapolis, IN..................485

Robert H. Johnson Planetarium, Lakewood, CO 225

Jefferson Planetarium, Richmond, VA........1530

John C. Wells Planetarium, Harrisonburg, VA 1511

John Deere Planetarium, Rock Island, IL 454

Joseph Moore Museum, Richmond, IN........497

Kalamazoo Valley Museum, Kalamazoo, MI...749

Kansas Cosmosphere and Space Center, Hutchinson, KS.......................................545

Kauai Children's Discovery Museum, Kapaa, HI...400

Kingman Museum, Battle Creek, MI 727

Kitt Peak National Observatory, Tucson, AZ...49

Lafayette Natural History Museum and Planetarium, Lafayette, LA 589

Lake Afton Public Observatory, Goddard, KS 541

Lake Erie Nature & Science Center, Bay Village, OH 1141

Lakeview Museum of Arts and Sciences, Peoria, IL 450

Landmark Park, Dothan, AL 8

Lawrence Hall of Science, Berkeley, CA.......76

Layton P. Ott Planetarium, Ogden, UT 1468

Leander J. McCormick Observatory, Charlottesville, VA 1499

The Living Arts and Science Center, Inc., Lexington, KY 573

Louisiana Art & Science Museum - Irene W. Pennington Planetarium, Baton Rouge, LA 586

Lowell Observatory, Flagstaff, AZ.................33

M.T. Brackbill Planetarium, Harrisonburg, VA 1511

Maryland Science Center, Baltimore, MD ...634

Merrillville Community Planetarium, Merrillville, IN 490

Miami Museum of Science & Planetarium, Miami, FL 325

Mid-Hudson Children's Museum, Poughkeepsie, NY 1055

Milton J. Rubenstein Museum of Science & Technology, Syracuse, NY 1076

Minnesota Planetarium & Space Discovery Center, Minneapolis, MN 783

Morehead Planetarium and Science Center, Chapel Hill, NC.........................1093

Mount Wilson Observatory & Museum, Atlanta, GA...362

Museum of Arts and Sciences, Macon, GA...378

The Museum of Arts and Sciences, Inc. and Center for Florida History, Daytona Beach, FL 303

Museum of Natural History and Planetarium, Providence, RI..................1317

Museum of Science, Boston, MA..................667

Museum of Science & History of Jacksonville, Jacksonville, FL.................315

Museum of the Rockies, Bozeman, MT.......842

Museum of the Southwest, Midland, TX 1439

Museum of York County, Rock Hill, SC 1340

Mystic Seaport - The Museum of America and the Sea, Mystic, CT 251

Nantucket Maria Mitchell Association, Nantucket, MA 696

National Air and Space Museum, Washington, DC.....................................283

The Natural Science Center of Greensboro, Inc., Greensboro, NC..........1104

New Jersey State Museum, Trenton, NJ 927

New Mexico Museum of Natural History & Science, Albuquerque, NM.................935

New Mexico Museum of Space History, Alamogordo, NM....................................932

The Newark Museum, Newark, NJ 916

The North Museum of Natural History & Science, Lancaster, PA 1266

Oatland Island Education Center, Savannah, GA...385

Planetariums, Observatories and Astronomy Museums–Continued

Omniplex Science Museum, Oklahoma City, OK.................1210

Oregon Museum of Science and Industry, Portland, OR.................1231

Orlando Science Center, Inc., Orlando, FL.................332

Pacific Science Center, Seattle, WA.........1568

Palomar Observatory, Palomar Mountain, CA.................139

Pink Palace Family of Museums, Memphis, TN.................1375

Planetarium at the Reading Public Museum, Reading, PA.................1296

Portland Planetarium, Portland, ME.........620

Portsmouth Museums, Portsmouth, VA......1526

Pretlow Planetarium, Norfolk, VA.............1523

Public Museum of West Michigan, Grand Rapids, MI.................744

Reading Public Museum, Reading, PA.......1296

Reuben H. Fleet Science Center, San Diego, CA.................158

Robert R. Meyer Planetarium, Birmingham, AL.................5

Robert T. Longway Planetarium, Flint, MI.................742

Robeson Planetarium and Science Center, Lumberton, NC.................1110

Rochester Museum & Science Center, Rochester, NY.................1059

Rock Creek Nature Center, Washington, DC.................290

Rocky Mount Children's Museum and Science Center, Inc., Rocky Mount, NC.................1118

Roper Mountain Science Center, Greenville, SC.................1334

Rosicrucian Egyptian Museum, San Jose, CA.................172

Roswell Museum and Art Center, Roswell, NM.................946

Russell C. Davis Planetarium, Jackson, MS.................804

St. Louis Science Center, Saint Louis, MO.................836

Sanford Museum and Planetarium, Cherokee, IA.................510

Santa Barbara Museum of Natural History, Santa Barbara, CA.................179

Schenectady Museum and Suits-Bueche Planetarium, Schenectady, NY.........1067

Schiele Museum of Natural History and Lynn Planetarium, Gastonia, NC.........1102

Science Center of Connecticut, West Hartford, CT.................265

Science Center of Iowa, Des Moines, IA.....515

Science Factory Children's Museum & Planetarium, Eugene, OR.................1224

Science Museum of Virginia, Richmond, VA.................1531

Science Museum of Western Virginia, Roanoke, VA.................1535

Sciworks, Winston-Salem, NC.................1126

South Dakota Discovery Center and Aquarium, Pierre, SD.................1353

South Florida Museum, Bishop Planetarium & Parker Manatee Aquarium, Bradenton, FL.................297

South Florida Science Museum, West Palm Beach, FL.................353

Southern Vermont Natural History Museum, West Marlboro, VT.................1489

Southwest Museum of Science and Technology, The Science Place & TI Founders IMAX Theater, Dallas, TX....1407

Springfield Museums - Springfield Science Museum, Springfield, MA.........711

The State Museum of Pennsylvania, Harrisburg, PA.................1259

Strasenburgh Planetarium/Rochester Museum & Science Center, Rochester, NY.................1060

Suffolk County Vanderbilt Museum, Centerport, NY.................977

SunWatch Indian Village/Archaeological Park, Dayton, OH.................1162

Thronateeska Heritage Foundation, Inc., Albany, GA.................355

The University of Michigan Exhibit Museum of Natural History, Ann Arbor, MI.................725

University of Nebraska State Museum, Lincoln, NE.................867

Virginia Living Museum, Newport News, VA.................1520

W.A. Gayle Planetarium, Montgomery, AL.................17

Weitkamp Observatory and Planetarium, Westerville, OH.................1191

Wichita Falls Museum and Art Center, Wichita Falls, TX.................1461

The Wilderness Center Inc., Wilmot, OH..1192

William McKinley Presidential Library & Museum, Canton, OH.................1146

Science Museums and Centers

A.C. Gilbert's Discovery Village, Salem, OR.................1235

A.W.A. Electronic-Communication Museum, Bloomfield, NY.................963

Adler Planetarium & Astronomy Museum, Chicago, IL.................417

American Heart Association - Halle Heart Center, Tempe, AZ.................45

American Museum of Nursing, Tempe, AZ.................45

American Museum of Radio and Electricity, Bellingham, WA.................1548

American Museum of Science & Energy, Oak Ridge, TN.................1382

Anderson/Abruzzo Albuquerque International Balloon Museum, Albuquerque, NM.................933

Aquarium of the Pacific, Long Beach, CA.................110

Arizona Science Center, Phoenix, AZ.........39

The Arts & Science Center for Southeast Arkansas, Pine Bluff, AR.................65

The Atomic Testing Museum, Las Vegas, NV.................878

Audubon Society of Rhode Island, Smithfield, RI.................1319

BRIMS - Barren River Imaginative Museum of Science, Bowling Green, KY.................565

The Bakken Library and Museum, Minneapolis, MN.................781

Baldwin-Reynolds House Museum, Meadville, PA.................1270

Baltimore Public Works Museum, Inc., Baltimore, MD.................630

Beall Center for Art and Technology, Irvine, CA.................104

Berea College Burroughs Geological Museum, Berea, KY.................565

Bergen Museum of Art & Science, Paramus, NJ.................919

Birch Aquarium at Scripps, Scripps Institution of Oceanography, University of California, San Diego, La Jolla, CA.................106

Black Hills Museum of Natural History, Hill City, SD.................1348

Bowers Science Museum, Cortland, NY.....982

Bradbury Science Museum, Los Alamos, NM.................942

Brazosport Museum of Natural Science, Clute, TX.................1400

Brevard Museum of Art and Science, Inc., Melbourne, FL.................323

Brookhaven National Laboratory-Science Museum, Upton, NY.................1079

Bruce Museum, Greenwich, CT.................243

Buehler Challenger & Science Center, Paramus, NJ.................919

COSI Columbus, Columbus, OH.................1157

COSI Toledo, Toledo, OH.................1187

California Oil Museum, Santa Paula, CA....183

California Science Center, Los Angeles, CA.................113

The Cannon Village Visitor Center, Kannapolis, NC.................1107

Carnegie Museums of Pittsburgh (Carnegie Institute), Pittsburgh, PA.......1291

Carnegie Science Center, Pittsburgh, PA....1291

Carrie Weedon Natural Science Museum, Galesville, MD.................645

Catawba Science Center, Hickory, NC.......1106

Center for Agricultural Science and Heritage, Indianapolis, IN.................481

Center for Meteorite Studies, Tempe, AZ......46

Chabot Space & Science Center, Oakland, CA.................133

Charles River Museum of Industry, Waltham, MA.................715

Children's Health Museum, Charlottesville, VA.................1499

The Children's Metamorphosis, Children's Museum, Derry, NH.................886

Children's Museum of History, Natural History and Science at Utica, New York, Utica, NY.................1079

The Children's Museum of Science and Technology, Troy, NY.................1079

Children's Science Explorium at Sugar Sand Park, Boca Raton, FL.................296

Cincinnati Museum Center at Union Terminal, Cincinnati, OH.................1149

Clark Planetarium, Salt Lake City, UT......1470

Clarke County Historical Association, Inc., Berryville, VA.................1496

Clay Center for Arts & Sciences West Virginia, Charleston, WV.................1580

Coastal Discovery Museum, Hilton Head Island, SC.................1335

Coca-Cola Space Science Center, Columbus, GA.................368

Columbia River Exhibition of History, Science and Technology, Richland, WA.................1564

Congaree National Park, Hopkins, SC.......1336

Cook's Natural Science Museum, Decatur, AL.................7

The Corning Museum of Glass, Corning, NY.................981

Cranbrook Institute of Science, Bloomfield Hills, MI.................730

Creation Evidence Museum, Glen Rose, TX.................1422

D.C. Booth Historic National Fish Hatchery, Spearfish, SD.................1357

Danville Science Center, Danville, VA.......1502

Delaware County Institute of Science, Media, PA.................1270

Detroit Science Center, Detroit, MI.............736

The Discovery Center, Fresno, CA.................96

Discovery Center (East Tennessee Discovery Center), Knoxville, TN.........1369

Discovery Center Museum, Rockford, IL....454

The Discovery Center of Idaho, Boise, ID.................403

Discovery Center of Springfield, Springfield, MO.................839

Discovery Creek Children's Museum of Washington DC, Glen Echo, MD.................645

The Discovery Museum, Inc., Bridgeport, CT.................236

Discovery Museum, Sacramento Museum of History, Science and Technology, Sacramento, CA..152
The Discovery Museums, Acton, MA...........657
Discovery Park, Safford, AZ.............................43
Discovery Place, Inc., Charlotte, NC..........1094
Discovery Science and Outdoor Center, Ocala, FL...330
Discovery Science Center, Fort Collins, CO..216
Discovery World - The James Lovell Museum of Science, Economics and Technology, Milwaukee, WI...................1610
Don Harrington Discovery Center, Amarillo, TX..1387

East Kentucky Center for Science, Mathematics, and Technology, Prestonsburg, KY.....................................583
East Texas Oil Museum at Kilgore College, Kilgore, TX.............................1432
ECHO at the Leahy Center for Lake Champlain, Burlington, VT....................1478
Edgerton Explorit Center, Aurora, NE..........856
Evansville Museum of Arts History & Science, Evansville, IN.............................475
Everhart Museum: Natural History, Science and Art, Scranton, PA...............1298
Explora, Albuquerque, NM..............................933
Exploration Place, Inc., Wichita, KS..............561
The Exploratorium, San Francisco, CA..........164
Explorit Science Center, Davis, CA................89
Explorium of Lexington, Lexington, KY.....572

FPL Energy Encounter, Jensen Beach, FL...316
Farmington Museum, Farmington, NM..........939
Fernbank Science Center, Atlanta, GA..........360
Fiedler Memorial Museum, Seguin, TX.....1452
Flandrau Science Center and Planetarium, Tucson, AZ...49
Fleischmann Planetarium, Reno, NV...........880
Fontenelle Nature Association, Bellevue, NE...857
Fort Roosevelt Natural Science and History Museum, Hanford, CA...............101
Fort Worth Museum of Science and History, Fort Worth, TX.......................1417
The Franklin Institute, Philadelphia, PA.....1280
Fresno Metropolitan Museum, Fresno, CA..97
The Frost Entomological Museum, Dept. of Entomology, The Pennsylvania State University, University Park, PA....1304

Gateway to Science, Bismarck, ND 1128
Geology Museum, Huntington, WV 1583
George Westinghouse Museum, Wilmerding, PA.....................................1308
The Gillespie Museum - Stetson University, De Land, FL 304
Grand Gulf Military Park, Port Gibson, MS...807
Granville County Historical Society Museum, Oxford, NC..........................1114
Great Lakes Science Center, Cleveland, OH...1154
Greybull Museum, Greybull, WY 1634
Griffith Observatory, Los Angeles, CA.........115
Grout Museum District: Grout Museum of History and Science, Bluedorn Science Imaginarium, Rensselaer Russell House Museum, Snowden House, Waterloo, IA.............................529
Gulf Coast Exploreum Science Center, Mobile, AL..13
Gulfcoast Wonder and Imagination Zone, dba G.WIZ, Sarasota, FL.......................344

Hall of Health, Berkeley, CA..........................75
Hands On! Regional Museum, Johnson City, TN...1367
Hatfield Marine Science Center, Oregon State University, Newport, OR 1228

The Health Adventure, Asheville, NC........1090
HealthSpace Cleveland, Cleveland, OH 1154
Hefner Zoology Museum, Oxford, OH 1181
The Henry Ford, Dearborn, MI 733
The Hicksville Gregory Museum, Hicksville, NY.....................................998
Highlands Center for Natural History, Prescott, AZ..42
Hilltop Garden and Nature Center, Bloomington, IN....................................469
Houston Museum of Natural Science, Houston, TX...1427
Howard B. Owens Science Center and Challenger Learning Center, Lanham-Seabrook, MD...........................648

ICR Museum of Creation & Earth History, Santee, CA................................185
Imaginarium Hands-On Museum, Fort Myers, FL...309
The Imaginarium Science Discovery Center, Anchorage, AK 22
Imagination Station Science Museum, Wilson, NC...1124
Impression 5 Science Center, Lansing, MI..750
Indiana Transportation Museum, Noblesville, IN......................................495
Insights-El Paso Science Center, Inc., El Paso, TX...1412
Institute of Meteoritics Meteorite Museum, Albuquerque, NM...................933
Intel Museum, Santa Clara, CA.....................181
International Museum of Art and Science, McAllen, TX..1437
The International Printing Museum, Carson, CA...82
Intrepid Sea-Air-Space Museum, New York, NY...1028

John P. McGovern Museum of Health & Medical Science, Houston, TX 1427

Kansas Aviation Museum, Wichita, KS........562
Kansas Learning Center for Health, Halstead, KS..542
Kauai Children's Discovery Museum, Kapaa, HI..400
Kern County Museum, Bakersfield, CA.........73
Kirby Science Discovery Center at the Washington Pavilion, Sioux Falls, SD...1356

Lake Shore Railway Museum, North East, PA..1274
Lakeview Museum of Arts and Sciences, Peoria, IL...450
Lars Noak Blacksmith Shop, Larsson/Ostlund Log Home & One-Room Capitol School, New Sweden, ME...616
Lawrence Hall of Science, Berkeley, CA.......76
Leander J. McCormick Observatory, Charlottesville, VA.................................1499
Liberty Science Center, Jersey City, NJ.......909
Lichterman Nature Center, Memphis, TN...1373
The Living Arts and Science Center, Inc., Lexington, KY...573
Loggerhead Marinelife Center, Juno Beach, FL...316
Long Island Museum of Science and Technology, Garden City, NY.................993
Louisiana Art & Science Museum - Irene W. Pennington Planetarium, Baton Rouge, LA...586
Louisville Science Center, Louisville, KY...577

MIT Museum, Cambridge, MA...................674
The Magic Lantern Castle Museum, San Antonio, TX..1448
Marian Koshland Science Museum, Washington, DC......................................283
Marine Science Institute, Redwood City, CA..147
The Maritime Aquarium, Norwalk, CT........257

The Mary Brogan Museum of Art and Science, Tallahassee, FL 347
Mary G. Hardin Center for Cultural Arts, Gadsden, AL...10
Maryland Science Center, Baltimore, MD ...634
Maxwell Museum of Anthropology, Albuquerque, NM....................................934
McWane Science Center, Birmingham, AL...5
Mesa Southwest Museum, Mesa, AZ............37
Miami Museum of Science & Planetarium, Miami, FL.........................325
The Michigan State University Museum, East Lansing, MI.....................................740
Mid-America Air Museum, Liberal, KS.......549
Mid-America Science Museum, Hot Springs, AR...60
Mid Atlantic Air Museum, Reading, PA 1296
Military Museum of Southern New England, Danbury, CT..............................238
Milton J. Rubenstein Museum of Science & Technology, Syracuse, NY...............1076
Mineral Museum, Butte, MT 843
Minnesota Transportation Museum, Inc., Saint Paul, MN..792
Minnesota Veterinary Historical Museum, Saint Paul, MN..792
Minnetrista, Muncie, IN.................................492
Monmouth Museum & Cultural Center, Lincroft, NJ...909
Monte L. Bean Life Science Museum, Provo, UT...1469
Montshire Museum of Science, Inc., Norwich, VT...1483
Morehead Planetarium and Science Center, Chapel Hill, NC..........................1093
Mote Marine Laboratory/Aquarium, Sarasota, FL...345
Mount Washington Museum and The Weather Discovery Center, North Conway, NH..893
Mount Wilson Observatory & Museum, Atlanta, GA...362
Mountain Skies Astronomical Society & Science Center, Lake Arrowhead, CA.....107
Museum at Southwestern Michigan College, Dowagiac, MI.............................738
Museum of Ancient & Modern Art, Penn Valley, CA..141
Museum of Arts and Sciences, Macon, GA..378
The Museum of Arts and Sciences, Inc. and Center for Florida History, Daytona Beach, FL...................................303
Museum of Aviation at Robins Air Force Base, GA, Warner Robins, GA...............390
Museum of Discovery and Science, Fort Lauderdale, FL..307
Museum of Discovery: Arkansas Museum of Science and History, Little Rock, AR...62
Museum of Earth and Life History, Lynchburg, VA..1515
Museum of Flying, Santa Monica, CA 183
Museum of Geology and Paleontology, South Dakota School of Mines and Technology, Rapid City, SD...................1355
Museum of Independent Telephony, Abilene, KS...531
Museum of Jurassic Technology, Culver City, CA..88
Museum of Life and Science, Durham, NC...1098
The Museum of Man in the Sea, Inc., Panama City Beach, FL 335
Museum of Natural Science, Ogden, UT...1468
Museum of Radio & Technology, Inc., Huntington, WV....................................1583
Museum of Robotics, Orinda, CA.................136
Museum of Science, Boston, MA................667
Museum of Science & History of Jacksonville, Jacksonville, FL.................315

Science Museums and Centers–Continued

Museum of Science and Industry, Tampa, FL 349

Museum of Science and Industry, Chicago, IL 425

The Museum of the Alphabet, Waxhaw, NC 1121

Museum of the American Philosophical Society, Philadelphia, PA 1283

Museum of Vertebrate Zoology, Berkeley, CA 76

Museum of Wildlife, Science & Industry, Webster, SD 1359

Muskegon County Museum, Muskegon, MI 757

Mystic Aquarium & Institute for Exploration, Mystic, CT 250

NASA Glenn Research Center's Visitor Center, Cleveland, OH 1155

National Air and Space Museum, Washington, DC.......................................283

National Atomic Museum, Albuquerque, NM 934

National Cryptologic Museum, Fort Meade, MD 643

National Geographic Museum at Explorers Hall, Washington, DC.............285

National Inventors Hall of Fame, Akron, OH 1139

National Museum of Civil War Medicine, Frederick, MD 644

National Museum of Health and Medicine, Washington, DC 286

National Museum of Natural History, Washington, DC 286

National Park Service Museum Resource Center, Landover, MD 648

The National Science Center's Fort Discovery, Augusta, GA 366

National Steinbeck Center, Salinas, CA 154

National Warplane Museum, Horseheads, NY 999

National Wildlife Visitor Center, Patuxent Research Refuge, Laurel, MD 648

Nauticus, The National Maritime Center, Norfolk, VA 1522

Neil Armstrong Air & Space Museum, Wapakoneta, OH 1189

New Britain Youth Museum at Hungerford Park, Kensington, CT 247

New Canaan Nature Center, New Canaan, CT 252

New England Aquarium Corporation, Boston, MA 668

New England Wireless & Steam Museum Inc., East Greenwich, RI 1311

The New Jersey Center for Life Science, Trenton, NJ 927

New Jersey Meadowlands Environment Center, Lyndhurst, NJ 910

New Mexico Farm & Ranch Heritage Museum, Las Cruces, NM 940

New Mexico Museum of Natural History & Science, Albuquerque, NM 935

New York Hall of Science, Flushing Meadows, NY 990

North Anna Nuclear Information Center, Mineral, VA 1518

North Carolina Transportation Museum, Spencer, NC 1120

The North Museum of Natural History & Science, Lancaster, PA 1266

The Northern Maine Museum of Science, University of Maine, Presque Isle, ME ...620

Northwest Railway Museum, Snoqualmie, WA..1570

Oatland Island Education Center, Savannah, GA 385

Ocean Institute, Dana Point, CA 89

Ocean Star Offshore Drilling Rig & Museum, Galveston, TX 1421

Omaha Children's Museum, Omaha, NE 871

Omniplex Science Museum, Oklahoma City, OK 1210

Optical Science Center & Museum, Hannibal, MO 817

Oregon Museum of Science and Industry, Portland, OR 1231

Orlando Science Center, Inc., Orlando, FL 332

Orpheum Children's Science Museum, Champaign, IL 417

Orton Geological Museum, Ohio State University, Columbus, OH 1158

The Oyster and Maritime Museum of Chincoteague, Chincoteague, VA..........1501

Pacific Coast Air Museum, Santa Rosa, CA 184

Pacific Science Center, Seattle, WA 1568

Paper Discovery Center, Appleton, WI 1590

The Paterson Museum, Paterson, NJ 920

Pearson Air Museum, Vancouver, WA 1576

The Peggy Notebaert Nature Museum, Chicago, IL 426

Pennsylvania Historical & Museum Commission, Harrisburg, PA 1259

Petersen Automotive Museum, Los Angeles, CA 121

Piedmont Environmental Center, High Point, NC 1107

Pima Air & Space Museum, Tucson, AZ 50

Pioneer-Krier Museum, Ashland, KS 532

Port Discovery, The Children's Museum in Baltimore, Baltimore, MD 636

Porter Thermometer Museum, Onset, MA ...700

Poulsbo Marine Science Center, Poulsbo, WA 1563

Racine Heritage Museum, Racine, WI 1619

Radio & Television Museum, Bowie, MD ...638

Railroad Museum of Long Island, Riverhead, NY 1057

Rattlesnake Museum (American International), Albuquerque, NM 935

Ravalli County Museum/Bitter Root Valley Historical Society, Hamilton, MT 848

Reading Public Museum, Reading, PA 1296

Regional Science & Discovery Center, Horseheads, NY 999

Reuben H. Fleet Science Center, San Diego, CA 158

Rhinebeck Aerodrome Museum, Rhinebeck, NY 1056

River Heritage Museum, Paducah, KY 582

River Legacy Living Science Center, Arlington, TX 1388

Roberson Museum and Science Center, Binghamton, NY 962

Robeson Planetarium and Science Center, Lumberton, NC 1110

Rochester Museum & Science Center, Rochester, NY 1059

Rocky Mount Children's Museum and Science Center, Inc., Rocky Mount, NC 1118

Roper Mountain Science Center, Greenville, SC 1334

St. John Science Museum, Saint John, KS 557

St. Louis Science Center, Saint Louis, MO 836

San Francisco Bay Model Visitor Center, Sausalito, CA 186

Sanilac County Historical Museum and Village, Port Sanilac, MI 761

Schenectady Museum and Suits-Bueche Planetarium, Schenectady, NY..............1067

Sci-Port Discovery Center, Shreveport, LA 601

Sci-Quest, the North Alabama Science Center, Huntsville, AL....................12

Sci-Tech Center of Northern New York, Watertown, NY 1084

The Science Center, Carbondale, IL...........415

Science Center of Connecticut, West Hartford, CT 265

Science Center of Iowa, Des Moines, IA.....515

The Science Center of West Virginia, Bluefield, WV 1580

Science Central, Fort Wayne, IN 478

Science Discovery Center of Oneonta, Oneonta, NY 1046

Science Factory Children's Museum & Planetarium, Eugene, OR 1224

The Science Fiction Museum and Hall of Fame, Seattle, WA 1568

Science Museum of Long Island, Manhasset, NY 1013

The Science Museum of Minnesota, Saint Paul, MN..................................792

Science Museum of Virginia, Richmond, VA 1531

Science Museum of Western Virginia, Roanoke, VA 1535

Science Spectrum, Lubbock, TX 1435

Science Station-IMAX Dome Theatre, Cedar Rapids, IA 510

Sciencenter, Ithaca, NY 1004

ScienceWorks Hands-On Museum, Ashland, OR 1218

SciTech, Aurora, IL 412

Scitrek, The Science and Technology Museum of Atlanta, Valdosta, GA..........389

Sciworks, Winston-Salem, NC 1126

Seashore Trolley Museum, Kennebunkport, ME 613

SEE Science Center, Manchester, NH..........892

Shenandoal Valley Discovery Museum, Winchester, VA 1546

Sloan Museum, Flint, MI 742

Sony Wonder Technology Lab, New York, NY 1039

South Dakota Discovery Center and Aquarium, Pierre, SD 1353

South Florida Science Museum, West Palm Beach, FL 353

Southern Forest World, Waycross, GA.........391

Southern Museum of Flight, Birmingham, AL 6

Southwest Museum of Science and Technology, The Science Place & TI Founders IMAX Theater, Dallas, TX 1407

Springfield Museums - Springfield Science Museum, Springfield, MA..........711

Stanley Museum, Inc., Kingfield, ME..........613

Star Eco Station, Culver City, CA 88

Sterling Hill Mining Museum, Inc., Ogdensburg, NJ 918

Sternberg Museum of Natural History, Hays, KS 543

The Tech Museum of Innovation, San Jose, CA 173

Texas Energy Museum, Beaumont, TX......1395

Texas Natural Science Center, Austin, TX .1392

Thomas Edison House, Louisville, KY 579

Thronateeska Heritage Foundation, Inc., Albany, GA 355

Titan Missile Museum, Green Valley, AZ......36

Union Station Kansas City, Inc., Kansas City, MO 823

University of Puerto Rico Department of Marine Sciences Museum, Mayaguez, PR 1641

U.S. Army Aviation Museum, Fort Rucker, AL...10

U.S. Army Communications-Electronics Museum, Fort Monmouth, NJ................904

U.S. Army Signal Corps Museum, Fort Gordon, GA 372

U.S. Naval Museum of Armament & Technology, China Lake, CA 84
U.S. Patent and Trademark Office - Museum, Alexandria, VA 1494
The U.S. Space & Rocket Center, Huntsville, AL 12

Venango Museum of Art, Science & Industry, Oil City, PA 1274
Virginia Air & Space Center, Hampton, VA 1510
Virginia Aquarium & Marine Science Center, Virginia Beach, VA 1542
Virginia Institute of Marine Science, Gloucester Point, VA 1508
Virginia Living Museum, Newport News, VA 1520

Warhawk Air Museum, Nampa, ID 408
Washington Pavilion of Arts and Science, Sioux Falls, SD 1357
Weinman Mineral Museum, White, GA 391
Whitaker Center for Science and the Arts, Harrisburg, PA 1259
Wilbur D. May Museum, Reno, NV 882
Wildlife Museum at Petaluma High School, Petaluma, CA 142
William McKinley Presidential Library & Museum, Canton, OH 1146
Wisconsin Maritime Museum, Manitowoc, WI 1607
Witte Museum, San Antonio, TX 1451
The Women's Museum: An Institute for the Future, Dallas, TX 1408
WonderLab Museum of Science, Health and Technology, Bloomington, IN 470
Woods Hole Oceanographic Institution Exhibit Center, Woods Hole, MA 720
The Works: Ohio Center for History, Art & Technology, Newark, OH 1179
The Wyoming Dinosaur Center, Thermopolis, WY 1639

Youth Science Center, Hacienda Heights, CA 101
Youth Science Institute, San Jose, CA 173
Youth Science Institute at Vasona Park, Los Gatos, CA 123
Youth Science Institute, Sanborn Nature Center, Saratoga, CA 185

Zeum, San Francisco, CA 170

Wildlife Refuges and Bird Sanctuaries

ASRI Environmental Education Center, Bristol, RI 1310
Armand Bayou Nature Center, Houston, TX 1424
Audubon Louisiana Nature Center, New Orleans, LA 594
Audubon Naturalist Society, Chevy Chase, MD 640
Audubon Society of New Hampshire, Concord, NH 884
Audubon Society of Rhode Island, Smithfield, RI 1319

Benson Memorial Museum, Malheur National Wildlife Refuge, Princeton, OR 1233
Bernheim Arboretum and Research Forest, Clermont, KY 567
Birdsong Nature Center, Thomasville, GA 387
Biscayne National Park, Homestead, FL 313
Black Hills Reptile Gardens, Inc., Rapid City, SD 1354
Briar Bush Nature Center, Abington, PA ...1238
Burritt on the Mountain-A Living Museum, Huntsville, AL 11

Catoctin Wildlife Preserve & Zoo, Thurmont, MD 655
Cedar Bog Nature Preserve, Urbana, OH...1188

Charles Towne Landing State Historic Site, Charleston, SC 1324
The Chattanooga Nature Center, Chattanooga, TN 1361
Clyde E. Buckley Wildlife Sanctuary, Frankfort, KY 568
Cora Hartshorn Arboretum and Bird Sanctuary, Short Hills, NJ 924

Dan Nicholas Park Nature Center, Salisbury, NC 1118
De Graaf Nature Center, Holland, MI..........746
Denison Pequotsepos Nature Center, Mystic, CT 250
Descanso Gardens Guild, Inc., La Canada Flintridge, CA 105
Dodge Nature Center, West Saint Paul, MN 796
Dry Tortugas National Park, Key West, FL 317

Eloise Butler Wildflower Garden and Bird Sanctuary, Minneapolis, MN 781
Environmental Education Center, Somerset County Park Commission, Basking Ridge, NJ 898
Evanston Environmental Association/Evanston Ecology Center, Evanston, IL 434

Falls of the Ohio State Park, Clarksville, IN 472
Fire Island National Seashore, Patchogue, NY 1051
Fontenelle Nature Association, Bellevue, NE 857
Fort Niobrara National Wildlife Refuge, Valentine, NE 874
Fossil Rim Wildlife Center, Glen Rose, TX 1422
Frontera Audubon Society, Weslaco, TX....1460

Garden in the Woods of the New England Wild Flower Society, Framingham, MA 683
The George G. Frelinghuysen Arboretum, Morris Township, NJ 913
Grizzly & Wolf Discovery Center, West Yellowstone, MT 854
The Grove, Glenview, IL 438

Heard Natural Science Museum and Wildlife Sanctuary, Inc., McKinney, TX 1437
The Holden Arboretum, Kirtland, OH........1170

International Crane Foundation, Baraboo, WI 1591
Ipswich River Wildlife Sanctuary (Massachusetts Audubon Society), Topsfield, MA 714

James A. McFaul Environmental Center of Bergen County, Wyckoff, NJ...............931
John James Audubon Center at Mill Grove, Audubon, PA 1241
John James Audubon Museum, Henderson, KY 571

Kentucky Department of Fish & Wildlife Resources-Salato Wildlife Education Center, Frankfort, KY 569

Las Cabezas de San Juan Nature Reserve (El Faro), Fajardo, PR 1641
Laughing Brook Education Center & Wildlife Sanctuary, Hampden, MA..........686
Lichterman Nature Center, Memphis, TN..1373
Lincoln Memorial Garden and Nature Center, Springfield, IL 459
Lincoln Park Zoological Gardens, Chicago, IL 423

Massachusetts Audubon at Connecticut River Valley Sanctuaries, Easthampton, MA 681

Miami Seaquarium, Miami, FL 325
Minnesota Zoo, Apple Valley, MN 768
Morningside Nature Center, Gainesville, FL 311

National Audubon Society, New York, NY 1034
National Wildlife Visitor Center, Patuxent Research Refuge, Laurel, MD 648
The Nature Conservancy, Arlington, VA 1496
New Jersey Meadowlands Environment Center, Lyndhurst, NJ 910
North Carolina Aquarium at Pine Knoll Shores, Pine Knoll Shores, NC 1114

Paradise Point Nature Center, East Hebron, NH 887
Pember Museum of Natural History, Granville, NY 995
Pinnacle Mountain State Park, Little Rock, AR 63

Quail Botanical Gardens, Encinitas, CA 92

Reynolda Gardens of Wake Forest University, Winston-Salem, NC 1126
The Ridges Sanctuary, Inc., Baileys Harbor, WI 1590
Rio Grande Nature Center State Park, Albuquerque, NM 935
Rip Van Winkle Gardens on Jefferson Island, New Iberia, LA 593
Rockwoods Reservation, Wildwood, MO 840
Rotary Nature Center, Oakland, CA............134

St. Catherine's Wildlife Survival Center, Midway, GA 380
San Diego Wild Animal Park, Escondido, CA 93
Sanibel-Captiva Conservation Foundation, Inc., Sanibel, FL 343
Sarett Nature Center, Benton Harbor, MI.....729
Seney National Wildlife Refuge Visitor Center, Seney, MI 764
Sharon Audubon Center, Sharon, CT 259
Slaughter Ranch Museum, Douglas, AZ 32
The South Carolina Botanical Garden, Clemson, SC 1328
Spiro Mounds Archaeological Center, Spiro, OK 1214
Spring Valley Nature Center & Heritage Farm, Schaumburg, IL 457
Stanwood Wildlife Sanctuary, Ellsworth, ME 610
Star Eco Station, Culver City, CA 88

Tewaukon National Wildlife Refuge, Cayuga, ND 1129
Tucker Wildlife Sanctuary, Silverado, CA ...186

University of Wisconsin-Madison Arboretum, Madison, WI 1605
Upper Souris National Wildlife Refuge, Berthhold, ND 1127

The Voas Nature Area/Voas Museum, Minburn, IA 523

W.K. Kellogg Bird Sanctuary of Michigan State University, Augusta, MI 726
Wahkeena Nature Preserve, Sugar Grove, OH 1186
Walter E. Heller Nature Center, Highland Park, IL 439
Welder Wildlife Foundation & Refuge, Sinton, TX 1453
Westmoreland Sanctuary, Inc., Bedford Corners, NY 961
The Wetlands Institute, Stone Harbor, NJ 925
Whitehouse Nature Center, Albion, MI........723
The Wilderness Center Inc., Wilmot, OH ..1192
Wing Haven Garden and Bird Sanctuary, Charlotte, NC 1096

Zoos

Abilene Zoological Gardens, Abilene, TX .1385
Action Wildlife Foundation, Goshen, CT.....242
Agrirama, Georgia's Living History
    Museum & Village, Tifton, GA 388
Akron Zoological Park, Akron, OH...........1138
Alameda Park Zoo, Alamogordo, NM.........931
Alaska Zoo, Anchorage, AK......................22
Albuquerque Biological Park,
    Albuquerque, NM.............................932
Applegate Park Zoo, Merced, CA 125
Arizona Zoological Society, dba the
    Phoenix Zoo, Phoenix, AZ.....................40
Arkansas Game and Fish Commission,
    Little Rock, AR 61
Audubon Zoo, New Orleans, LA.................594

Baton Rouge Zoo, Baton Rouge, LA 585
Bear Country U.S.A., Rapid City, SD........1354
Bear Mountain Trailside Museums and
    Zoo, Bear Mountain, NY 961
Belle Isle Nature Zoo, Detroit, MI 735
Bergen County Zoological Park,
    Paramus, NJ...................................919
Binder Park Zoo, Battle Creek, MI 727
Binghamton Zoo at Ross Park,
    Binghamton, NY...............................962
Birmingham Zoo, Birmingham, AL.................5
Black Hills Reptile Gardens, Inc., Rapid
    City, SD......................................1354
Blackberry Farm's Pioneer Village,
    Aurora, IL.....................................411
Blank Park Zoo, Des Moines, IA 514
Boonshoft Museum of Discovery,
    Dayton, OH...................................1160
Bramble Park Zoo, Watertown, SD 1359
Brandywine Zoo, Wilmington, DE 272
Bronx Zoo, Bronx, NY...........................965
Brookgreen Gardens, Murrells Inlet, SC ...1337
Buffalo Zoological Gardens, Buffalo, NY 972

Caldwell Zoo, Tyler, TX 1456
Cameron Park Zoo, Waco, TX 1458
Cape May County Park and Zoo, Cape
    May Court House, NJ 901
Capron Park Zoo, Attleboro, MA 661
Catoctin Wildlife Preserve & Zoo,
    Thurmont, MD.................................655
Central Florida Zoo, Sanford, FL 342
Charles Paddock Zoo, Atascadero, CA 72
Charles Towne Landing State Historic
    Site, Charleston, SC 1324
Chattanooga Zoo at Warner Park,
    Chattanooga, TN..............................1361
Cheyenne Mountain Zoological Park,
    Colorado Springs, CO 206
Chicago Zoological Park (Brookfield
    Zoo), Brookfield, IL 414
Cincinnati Zoo & Botanical Garden,
    Cincinnati, OH.................................1149
Cleveland Metroparks Zoo, Cleveland,
    OH...1152
Clyde Peeling's Reptiland, Allenwood,
    PA...1240
Columbian Park Zoo, Lafayette, IN 487
Columbus Zoo and Aquarium, Powell,
    OH...1183
Como Park Zoo and Conservatory, Saint
    Paul, MN......................................789
Connecticut's Beardsley Zoo, Bridgeport,
    CT 236

Dakota Zoo, Bismarck, ND.....................1128
Dallas Zoo, Dallas, TX 1406
Dan Nicholas Park Nature Center,
    Salisbury, NC.................................1118
David Trayol Zoo of Emporia, Emporia,
    KS 538
Denver Zoological Gardens, Denver, CO.....211
Detroit Zoo, Royal Oak, MI 762
Dickerson Park Zoo, Springfield, MO........838

Disney's Animal Kingdom Theme Park,
    Bay Lake, FL:.................................295

EcoTarium, Worcester, MA 720
El Paso Zoo, El Paso, TX 1412
Ellen Trout Zoo, Lufkin, TX 1435
Erie Zoological Park & Botanical
    Gardens of Northwestern
    Pennsylvania, Erie, PA 1253
Essex County's Turtle Back Zoo, West
    Orange, NJ....................................930

Fejervary Zoo, Davenport, IA...................512
Finnup Park and Lee Richardson Zoo,
    Garden City, KS 541
Fort Roosevelt Natural Science and
    History Museum, Hanford, CA................101
Fort Wayne Children's Zoo, Fort Wayne,
    IN 477
Fort Worth Zoological Park, Fort Worth,
    TX 1417
Fresno Chaffee Zoo, Fresno, CA 97

Georgia's Stone Mountain Park, Stone
    Mountain, GA..................................387
Gladys Porter Zoo, Brownsville, TX 1398
Glen Oak Zoo, Peoria, IL 450
Good Zoo, Wheeling, WV 1587
Great Plains Zoo & Delbridge Museum,
    Sioux Falls, SD................................1356
The Greenburgh Nature Center,
    Scarsdale, NY.................................1066
Greenville Zoo, Greenville, SC 1334

Happy Hollow Park & Zoo, San Jose,
    CA 171
Henry Doorly Zoo, Omaha, NE.................871
Henry Vilas Park Zoo, Madison, WI.........1605
Henson Robinson Zoo, Springfield, IL........458
Hi-Desert Nature Museum, Yucca Valley,
    CA 201
High Desert Museum, Bend, OR..............1220
Honolulu Zoo, Honolulu, HI......................396
Houston Zoo, Inc., Houston, TX 1427

Indianapolis Zoo, Indianapolis, IN 485

Jackson Zoological Park, Inc., Jackson,
    MS..802
Jacksonville Zoo and Gardens,
    Jacksonville, FL...............................315
John Ball Zoological Garden, Grand
    Rapids, MI....................................744
Jurica Nature Museum, Lisle, IL...............442

Kansas City Zoo, Kansas City, MO 821
Kentucky Department of Fish & Wildlife
    Resources-Salato Wildlife Education
    Center, Frankfort, KY 569
Knoxville Zoological Gardens, Knoxville,
    TN..1370

Lake Erie Nature & Science Center, Bay
    Village, OH....................................1141
Lake Superior Zoological Gardens,
    Duluth, MN....................................773
Lincoln Children's Zoo, Lincoln, NE..........866
Lincoln Park Zoo, Manitowoc, WI............1607
Lincoln Park Zoological Gardens,
    Chicago, IL....................................423
Little River Zoo, Norman, OK 1206
Little Rock Zoological Gardens, Little
    Rock, AR 62
The Living Desert, Palm Desert, CA 138
Living Desert Zoo and Gardens State
    Park, Carlsbad, NM 938
The Los Angeles Zoo and Botanical
    Gardens, Los Angeles, CA 119
Louisville Zoological Garden, Louisville,
    KY 578

MacKenzie Environmental Education
    Center, Poynette, WI 1618
Manchester Zoo, Manchester, CT...............248

The Maryland Zoo in Baltimore,
    Baltimore, MD..................................635
Memphis Zoo, Memphis, TN....................1374
The Merrick Art Gallery, New Brighton,
    PA...1273
ME's Zoo, Parker City, IN 495
Mesker Park Zoo & Botanic Garden,
    Evansville, IN..................................476
Miami Metrozoo, Miami, FL.....................324
Micke Grove Zoo, Lodi, CA 109
Mill Mountain Zoo, Roanoke, VA.............1535
Millbrook School, Trevor Zoo, Millbrook,
    NY..1014
Miller Park Zoo, Bloomington, IL...............414
Milwaukee County Zoological Gardens,
    Milwaukee, WI................................1612
Minnesota Zoo, Apple Valley, MN.............768
Montgomery Zoo, Montgomery, AL 17
Museum of Life and Science, Durham,
    NC..1098
Museum of Zoology, Amherst, MA............659

Nashville Zoo at Grassmere, Nashville,
    TN..1379
National Aviary in Pittsburgh, Inc.,
    Pittsburgh, PA.................................1293
National Zoological Park, Smithsonian
    Institution, Washington, DC...................288
Natural Bridge Zoological Park, Natural
    Bridge, VA....................................1519
Natural History Museum, Portales, NM.......944
The Natural Science Center of
    Greensboro, Inc., Greensboro, NC.........1104
New Britain Youth Museum at
    Hungerford Park, Kensington, CT...........247
The Newark Museum, Newark, NJ 916
Niabi Zoo, Coal Valley, IL.......................428
North Carolina Zoological Park,
    Asheboro, NC.................................1088
Northwest Trek Wildlife Park, Eatonville,
    WA 1552

Oakland Zoo, Oakland, CA 134
Oatland Island Education Center,
    Savannah, GA.................................385
Oklahoma City Zoo, Oklahoma City, OK..1209
Oregon Zoo, Portland, OR 1232

Palm Beach Zoo at Dreher Park, West
    Palm Beach, FL................................353
Palo Alto Junior Museum and Zoo, Palo
    Alto, CA.......................................139
Panaewa Rainforest Zoo, Hilo, HI.............393
Parrot Jungle Island, Miami, FL.................325
The Philadelphia Zoo, Philadelphia, PA....1286
Pittsburgh Zoo and Aquarium, Pittsburgh,
    PA...1293
Pocatello Zoo, Pocatello, ID....................409
Point Defiance Zoo & Aquarium,
    Tacoma, WA 1574
Potawatomi Zoo, South Bend, IN..............499
Potter Park Zoo, Lansing, MI...................750
Prospect Park Zoo, Brooklyn, NY..............970
Pueblo Zoo, Pueblo, CO 230

Racine Zoological Gardens, Racine, WI 1619
Rattlesnake Museum (American
    International), Albuquerque, NM.............935
Reid Park Zoo, Tucson, AZ 50
Riverbanks Zoological Park & Botanical
    Garden, Columbia, SC........................1329
Riverside Zoo, Scottsbluff, NE.................872
Roger Williams Park Zoo, Providence, RI.1318
Roosevelt Park Zoo, Minot, ND................1135
Rosamond Gifford Zoo at Burnet Park,
    Syracuse, NY..................................1077

Sacramento Zoo, Sacramento, CA.............153
Saginaw Valley Zoological Society,
    Saginaw, MI...................................763
St. Augustine Alligator Farm, Saint
    Augustine, FL..................................340
Saint Louis Zoo, Saint Louis, MO 837

The Salisbury Zoological Park, Salisbury, MD 652
San Antonio Zoological Society, San Antonio, TX 1450
San Diego Wild Animal Park, Escondido, CA 93
San Diego Zoo, San Diego, CA 161
San Francisco Zoological Gardens, San Francisco, CA 170
Santa Ana Zoo, Santa Ana, CA 178
Santa Barbara Zoological Gardens, Santa Barbara, CA 180
Santa Fe Community College Teaching Zoo, Gainesville, FL 311
Scovill Children's Zoo, Decatur, IL 430
Sedgwick County Zoo, Wichita, KS 562
Seneca Park Zoo, Rochester, NY 1060
Sierra Safari Zoo, Reno, NV 881
Six Flags Marine World, Vallejo, CA 194
Smithsonian Institution, Washington, DC...290
South Carolina Aquarium, Charleston, SC.1326
Space Farms Zoological Park and Museum, Sussex, NJ 925
Spring River Park & Zoo, Roswell, NM.....946
Staten Island Zoo, Staten Island, NY 1074
Sunset Zoological Park, Manhattan, KS......552

Tallahassee Museum, Tallahassee, FL 348
Tampa's Lowry Park Zoo, Tampa, FL 350
Tautphaus Park Zoo, Idaho Falls, ID............406
The Texas Zoo, Victoria, TX 1457
The Toledo Zoo, Toledo, OH 1187
Topeka Zoological Park, Topeka, KS 560
Tulsa Zoo & Living Museum, Tulsa, OK ..1216

Utah's Hogle Zoo, Salt Lake City, UT.......1473
Utica Zoo, Utica, NY 1080

Virginia Zoological Park, Norfolk, VA.......1523

Washington Park Zoological Gardens, Michigan City, IN............491
West Virginia State Wildlife Center, French Creek, WV 1581
Western North Carolina Nature Center, Asheville, NC 1090
Wildlife Conservation Society, Queens Zoo, Flushing, NY 990
Wildlife Museum at Petaluma High School, Petaluma, CA 142
Wildlife Prairie State Park, Hanna City, IL............439
Wildlife World Zoo, Litchfield Park, AZ 37
Willow Park Zoo, Logan, UT 1467
Woodland Park Zoo, Seattle, WA 1570

The Zoo, Gulf Breeze, FL 312
Zoo Atlanta, Atlanta, GA 364
Zoo Boise, Boise, ID............404
Zoo Montana, Billings, MT 842
Zoo New England, Boston, MA 669
Zooamerica North America Wildlife Park, Hershey, PA 1261

SPECIALIZED

Agriculture Museums

The Accokeek Foundation, Inc., Accokeek, MD............627
Adams County Historical Society Museum, Brighton, CO 204
Agricultural and Industrial Museum, York County Heritage Trust, York, PA 1309
Agricultural Heritage Museum, Boerne, TX............1396
The Agricultural Memories Museum, Penn Yan, NY 1052
Agriculture Museum, Merced, CA 125
Agrirama, Georgia's Living History Museum & Village, Tifton, GA 388
Alabama Agricultural Museum, Dothan, AL 8

Alexander & Baldwin Sugar Museum, Puunene, HI 401
Allison-Antrim Museum, Inc., Greencastle, PA............1257
American Maple Museum, Croghan, NY.....983
American Royal Museum & Visitors Center, Kansas City, MO 820
American West Heritage Center, Wellsville, UT............1475
Anson County Historical Society, Inc., Wadesboro, NC............1121
Antique Gas & Steam Engine Museum, Inc., Vista, CA............196
Arkansas Historic Wine Museum, Paris, AR............65
Audie Murphy/American Cotton Museum, Inc, Greenville, TX 1423
Aullwood Audubon Center and Farm, Dayton, OH............1160

Baldwin County Heritage Museum, Elberta, AL............8
Banner County Historical Society, Harrisburg, NE............862
The Battles Museums of Rural Life, Girard, PA 1256
Bergen County Zoological Park, Paramus, NJ............919
Big Horn County Historical Museum, Hardin, MT............849
Billings Farm & Museum, Woodstock, VT............1490
Brooks Academy Museum, Harwich, MA ...686
Burnside Plantation, Inc., Bethlehem, PA ..1242
Burwell-Morgan Mill, Millwood, VA.........1518

Calumet County Historical Society, Inc., New Holstein, WI............1615
Canby Historical Society, Canby, OR 1221
Carroll County Farm Museum, Westminster, MD............656
Cassia County Museum, Burley, ID............404
Cedar Grove Historical Society, Cedar Grove, NJ............901
Center for Agricultural Science and Heritage, Indianapolis, IN............481
Central Washington Agricultural Museum, Union Gap, WA............1575
The Children's Museum of Rose Hill Manor Park, Frederick, MD............644
Chippokes Farm & Forestry Museum, Surry, VA 1540
Clearwater County Historical Society, Shevlin, MN............793
Clinton County Historical Society Paine-Gillam-Scott Museum, Saint Johns, MI............763
Coachella Valley Museum and Cultural Center, Indio, CA............104
Coggeshall Farm Museum, Bristol, RI.......1310
The Coley Homestead & Barn Museum, Weston, CT............265
Collin County Farm Museum, McKinney, TX............1437
Colonial Pennsylvania Plantation, Media, PA............1270
Communal Agriculture Museum, South Amana, IA............528
Copia: The American Center for Wine, Food & the Arts, Napa, CA............129
Culbertson Museum, Culbertson, MT 845
Cumberland County Historical Society, Greenwich, NJ............905

De Smet Depot Museum, De Smet, SD.....1346
Deer Park Escondido Winery & Auto Museum, Escondido, CA............93
Deere & Company, Administrative Center, Moline, IL............445
Delaware Agricultural Museum and Village, Dover, DE............269
Divide County Historical Society Museum, Crosby, ND............1129

Drumlin Farm Education Center, Lincoln, MA............690
East Jordan Portside Art & Historical Museum, East Jordan, MI 739
East Texas Oil Museum at Kilgore College, Kilgore, TX............1432
The Farm, Sturgeon Bay, WI............1623
Farm and Ranch Museum, Gering, NE........861
Farmamerica, The Minnesota Agricultural Interpretive Center, Waseca, MN............796
The Farmers' Museum, Inc., Cooperstown, NY 980
Florewood State Park, Greenwood, MS 801
Florida Agricultural Museum, Palm Coast, FL............334
Flowerdew Hundred Foundation, Hopewell, VA............1511
Fort Abercrombie State Historic Site, Abercrombie, ND............1127
Fort Walla Walla Museum, Walla Walla, WA 1576
Fosterfields Living Historical Farm, Morristown, NJ............913
Fostoria Area Historical Museum, Fostoria, OH 1164
Four Mile Historic Park, Denver, CO 212
The Fryeburg Fair Farm Museum, Fryeburg, ME............611

Garfield Farm Museum, LaFox, IL 441
Georgia State Cotton Museum, Vienna, GA............390
Graber Olive House Museum, Ontario, CA............135
Granville Museum, Inc., Granville, TN......1366

Hacienda Buena Vista, Ponce, PR............1642
Hadley Farm Museum, Hadley, MA 685
Hallockville Museum Farm, Riverhead, NY............1057
Harold M. Freund American Museum of Baking, Manhattan, KS............550
Harold Warp Pioneer Village Foundation, Minden, NE............868
Haskell County Historical Society, Sublette, KS............558
Hathaway Ranch Museum, Santa Fe Springs, CA............182
Helvetia Museum, Helvetia, WV............1582
The Heritage Center and Citrus Museum, Vero Beach, FL............352
Heritage Complex Farm Equipment Museum and Learning Center, Tulare, CA............193
Heritage Farm Museum & Village, Huntington, WV 1583
Heritage Hall Museum & Archives, Freeman, SD............1347
Heritage Museum Foundation of Tate County, Inc., Senatobia, MS............808
Highland County Museum and Heritage Center, McDowell, VA............1517
Highland Maple Museum, Monterey, VA...1518
Hillsboro Museums, Hillsboro, KS............544
Historic Prophetstown, Battle Ground, IN ...468
Historic Schaefferstown, Inc., Schaefferstown, PA............1297
Hofwyl-Broadfield Plantation State Historic Site, Brunswick, GA 366
Hot Springs County Museum and Cultural Center, Thermopolis, WY........1639
Howell Living History Farm, Titusville, NJ............926
Hurst Ranch Historical Foundation, West Covina, CA............197

Jackson County Historical Museum & Research Library, Maquoketa, IA............522
Jackson's Mill Historic Area, Weston, WV............1587
Jarrell Plantation Georgia State Historic Site, Juliette, GA 374

Agriculture Museums–Continued

Jefferson Patterson Park & Museum,
Saint Leonard, MD..................................651
Jerome County Historical Society, Inc.
and Idaho Farm & Ranch Museum,
Jerome, ID...406
Jewell County Historical Museum,
Mankato, KS..552
John Muir National Historic Site,
Martinez, CA..124
Johnson County Historical Society
Museum, Warrensburg, MO....................840

Kittson County History Center Museum,
Lake Bronson, MN..................................778
Kiwanis Van Slyke Museum Foundation
Inc., Caldwell, ID....................................404
Kline Creek Farm, Winfield, IL.................466

LaGrange Plantation, Cambridge, MD........639
Landis Valley Museum, Lancaster, PA.......1266
Landmark Park, Dothan, AL...........................8
Lexington County Museum, Lexington,
SC..1336
Lincoln County Historical Society,
Lincoln, KS...549
Living History Farms, Urbandale, IA..........529
Longstreet Farm, Holmdel, NJ....................908
Loudoun Heritage Farm Museum,
Sterling, VA..1538

Madison County Historical
Society-Cottage Lawn, Oneida, NY......1045
Malabar Farm State Park, Lucas, OH.........1173
Malheur Historical Project, Stonehouse
Museum, Vale, OR..................................1238
Matthews Museum of Maine Heritage,
Union, ME..624
Menominee County Heritage Museum,
Menominee, MI.......................................754
Mercer County Historical Museum, The
Riley Home, Celina, OH........................1146
Midwest Old Settlers & Threshers
Association, Inc., Mount Pleasant, IA.....524
Miles B. Carpenter Museum, Waverly,
VA..1543
Minnesota's Machinery Museum, Hanley
Falls, MN..777
Miracle of America Museum Inc., Polson,
MT..852
Mississippi Agriculture &
Forestry/National Agricultural Aviation
Museum, Jackson, MS............................802
Mitchell County Historical Museum,
Osage, IA..526
Moriarty Historical Museum, Moriarty,
NM..943
Mountain Farm Museum-Great Smoky
Mountains National Park, Cherokee,
NC...1096
Museum of Rural Life, Denton, MD...........642
Museum of Seminole County History,
Sanford, FL...343
Museum of the Arkansas Grand Prairie,
Stuttgart, AR..69

The National Agricultural Center & Hall
of Fame, Bonner Springs, KS.................534
National Apple Museum, Biglerville, PA...1243
Neeses Farm Museum, Neeses, SC............1338
Neligh Mills, Neligh, NE............................869
Nelson Pioneer Farm and Museum,
Oskaloosa, IA...526
New Hampshire Farm Museum, Inc.,
Milton, NH...892
The New Jersey Museum of Agriculture,
North Brunswick, NJ..............................917
New Mexico Farm & Ranch Heritage
Museum, Las Cruces, NM......................940
Norman #1 Oil Well Museum, Neodesha,
KS..553
Northeastern Montana Threshers and
Antique Association, Culbertson, MT.....845

Northern New York Agricultural
Historical Society, Agricultural
Museum at Stone Mills, LaFargeville,
NY...1008
Old Hidalgo Pumphouse, Hidalgo, TX......1424
Old Stone Fort Museum Complex,
Schoharie, NY.......................................1067
Old World Wisconsin, Eagle, WI...............1595
Oliver Kelley Farm, Elk River, MN............774
Olmstead Place State Park, Ellensburg,
WA..1553
Oxon Cove Park, Oxon Hill, MD................650

The Patuxent Rural Life Museums, Upper
Marlboro, MD...655
Pendleton District Agricultural Museum,
Pendleton, SC..1339
Pendleton District Historical, Recreational
and Tourism Commission, Pendleton,
SC..1339
Pioneer Florida Museum Association,
Inc., Dade City, FL.................................302
Pioneer Museum of Alabama, Troy, AL.........18
Plantation Agriculture Museum, Scott,
AR..67
Pomeroy Living History Farm, Yacolt,
WA..1578
Prairie Homestead, Philip, SD..................1353
The Prairie Museum of Art & History,
Colby, KS...535
Pratt County Historical Society Museum,
Pratt, KS...556

Queens County Farm Museum, Floral
Park, NY...989
Quiet Valley Living Historical Farm,
Stroudsburg, PA.....................................1302

Redwood County Historical Society,
Redwood Falls, MN................................787
Remick Country Doctor Museum and
Farm, Tamworth, NH..............................896
Renville County Historical Society, Inc.,
Mohall, ND..1135
Rice County Museum of History,
Faribault, MN...775
The Rice Museum, Georgetown, SC..........1333
Rochester Hills Museum at Van Hoosen
Farm, Rochester Hills, MI......................762
Roth Living Farm Museum of Delaware
Valley College, North Wales, PA...........1274
Rough & Tumble Engineers Historical
Association, Kinzers, PA.......................1265
Rutherford County Farm Museum, Forest
City, NC...1101

Sahuaro Ranch Historical Area, Glendale,
AZ...35
Saline County Historical Society, Inc.,
Dorchester, NE.......................................860
San Joaquin County Historical Society &
Museum, Lodi, CA..................................109
Sanborn Area Historical Society,
Sanborn, NY..1064
1719 Hans Herr House & Museum,
Willow Street, PA..................................1308
Seward County Historical Society
Museum, Goehner, NE............................861
Silt Historical Society, Silt, CO..................232
Silvercreek Museum, Freeport, IL..............435
Simonian Farms, Fresno, CA.......................98
Slate Run Living Historical Farm, Metro
Parks, Ashville, OH..............................1140
South Carolina Cotton Museum,
Bishopville, SC......................................1322
South Dakota Tractor Museum, Kimball,
SD..1350
Southdown Plantation House/The
Terrebonne Museum, Houma, LA...........589
State Agricultural Heritage Museum,
Brookings, SD.......................................1344
Steppingstone Museum, Havre de Grace,
MD..647

Sterling Historical Society and Little Red
Schoolhouse Museum, Sterling, NY......1074
Stonefield Historic Site, Cassville, WI.......1593
Stutsman County Memorial Museum,
Jamestown, ND.......................................1133

Ted Smallwood's Store, Inc.,
Chokoloskee, FL....................................299
Tennessee Agricultural Museum,
Nashville, TN...1380
Thetford Historical Society Library and
Museum, Thetford, VT...........................1488
Tipton-Haynes Historic Site, Johnson
City, TN...1368
Tobacco Farm Life Museum, Inc., Kenly,
NC...1107
Troy Museum & Historic Village, Troy,
MI..765

Ward W. O'Hara Agricultural Museum,
Auburn, NY..959
Washington County Fair Farm Museum,
Greenwich, NY.......................................996
Waterloo Area Historical Society, Grass
Lake, MI..744
Watters Smith Memorial State Park, Lost
Creek, WV..1584
Weslaco Museum, Weslaco, TX.................1461
West Virginia State Farm Museum, Point
Pleasant, WV...1586
Wheeler Historic Farm, Salt Lake City,
UT..1474
Winedale, Center for American History,
University of Texas at Austin, Round
Top, TX...1446

Antiques Museums

Adsmore Museum, Princeton, KY...............583
The Agricultural Memories Museum,
Penn Yan, NY..1052
Albany Regional Museum, Albany, OR.....1217
The Alice T. Miner Colonial Collection,
Chazy, NY..977
American Radio Relay League-Museum
of Amateur Radio, Newington, CT.........256
American Sign Museum, Cincinnati, OH...1148
America's Ice Cream & Dairy Museum,
Medina, OH...1175
Amherst History Museum at the Strong
House - Amherst Historical Society,
Amherst, MA..658
Antique Gas & Steam Engine Museum,
Inc., Vista, CA.......................................196
Arches Museum of Pioneer Life, Winona,
MN..797
Ark-La-Tex Antique & Classic Vehicle
Museum, Shreveport, LA.......................600
Arlington, Birmingham, AL............................4
Artesia Historical Museum & Art Center,
Artesia, NM..936
Ash Lawn-Highland, Charlottesville, VA...1498
Astor House Museum, Golden, CO..............219
Atlantic 1, Swampscott, MA.......................714
Aviation Museum of Kentucky Inc.,
Lexington, KY..572

Baldwin County Heritage Museum,
Elberta, AL...8
The Barbara Fritchie House, Frederick,
MD..644
The Barnacle Historic State Park,
Coconut Grove, FL.................................300
Beauchamp Newman Museum, Elizabeth,
WV..1581
Belcourt Castle, Newport, RI....................1313
Big Horn County Historical Museum,
Hardin, MT...849
Bishop Hill Heritage Museum, Bishop
Hill, IL...413
Black Heritage Museum, Miami, FL............323
Blair Museum of Lithophanes, Toledo,
OH..1187

Bob Jones University Museum & Gallery, Inc., Greenville, SC 1333
Bolin Wildlife Exhibit & Antique Collection, McKinney, TX 1437
Boonsborough Museum of History, Boonsboro, MD 637
Boot Hill Museum, Inc., Dodge City, KS 536
Boundary County Historical Society, Bonners Ferry, ID 404
Bragg-Mitchell Mansion, Mobile, AL 13
Braintree Historical Society, Inc., Braintree, MA 670
Brookings County Historical Society Museum, Volga, SD 1358
Brooklyn Historical Society, Brooklyn, OH 1144
Brunswick Railroad Museum and C&O Canal Visitors Center, Brunswick, MD ...639
Burke County Historical Powers Lake Complex, Powers Lake, ND 1136
Burlington County Historical Society, Burlington, NJ 898

Canadian County Historical Museum, El Reno, OK...1200
Canby Historical Society, Canby, OR 1221
Caney Valley Historical Society, Caney, KS 534
Carbon County Museum, Rawlins, WY 1637
The Casa del Herrero Foundation, Santa Barbara, CA 178
Cassia County Museum, Burley, ID 404
Casteel-Linn House and Museum, Princeton, MO 829
Center of Southwest Studies/Fort Lewis College, Durango, CO.........................214
Chancellor Robert R. Livingston Masonic Library & Museum, New York, NY 1022
Chinese House/O.R. & N. Museum & St. Peter's Catholic Church, Echo, OR......1222
Chinqua-Penn Plantation, Reidsville, NC ...1117
Chippokes Farm & Forestry Museum, Surry, VA 1540
Cimarron Valley Railroad Museum, Cushing, OK 1199
Clifton Community Historical Society, Clifton, KS...535
Clinton County Historical Society Paine-Gillam-Scott Museum, Saint Johns, MI 763
Clinton County Museum, Frankfort, IN 478
Collinsville Depot Museum, Collinsville, OK..1198
Conklin Reed Organ & History Museum, Hanover, MI 745
The Crescent, Valdosta Garden Center, Inc., Valdosta, GA 389
Culinary Archives & Museum, Johnson & Wales University, Providence, RI 1316

DAR-Hervey Ely House, Rochester, NY ...1058
Daniels County Museum and Pioneer Town, Scobey, MT 853
De Smet Depot Museum, De Smet, SD.....1346
Denver Firefighters Museum, Denver, CO...211
DeWitt Wallace Decorative Arts Museum, Williamsburg, VA 1545
Divide County Historical Society Museum, Crosby, ND............................1129
Dubois Museum, Dubois, WY....................1632

Early American Museum, Mahomet, IL.......444
East Brunswick Museum Corporation, East Brunswick, NJ 902
East Poultney Museum, East Poultney, VT 1479
Eastern Arizona Museum and Historical Society of Graham County Inc., Pima, AZ 42
Ellingson Car Museum, Rogers, MN 788
Escondido History Center, Escondido, CA 93

Fairbanks House, Dedham, MA....................679
Fall River County Historical Museum, Hot Springs, SD.....................................1348
Fayette County Museum, Washington Court House, OH..................................1190
Fenton Glass Museum, Williamstown, WV...1589
Florewood State Park, Greenwood, MS 801
Ford County Historical Society, Paxton, IL...450
Fort Christmas Historical Park, Christmas, FL 299
Fort Inglish, Bonham, TX 1396
Fostoria Area Historical Museum, Fostoria, OH...1164
Frank Chiarenza Museum of Glass, Meriden, CT...248
Frankfort Area Historical Museum, West Frankfort, IL..464
The French Legation Museum, Austin, TX 1390
Friends of Historic Kingston, Fred J. Johnston House Museum, Kingston, NY 1007
Frontier Times Museum, Bandera, TX.......1393
Frontier Village Association, Inc., Jamestown, ND 1133

Gay Nineties Button and Doll Museum, Eureka Springs, AR..................................57
Georgia State Cotton Museum, Vienna, GA 390
The Gilbert Stuart Birthplace and Museum, Saunderstown, RI...................1319
Gilliam County Historical Society - Depot Museum Complex, Condon, OR.1222
The Golden Age of Trucking Museum, Middlebury, CT...249
Gomez Foundation for Mill House, Marlboro, NY 1014
Governor Henry Lippitt House Museum, Providence, RI..1316
Granville Museum, Inc., Granville, TN......1366
Green Mountain Club, Inc., Waterbury Center, VT..1489
Grevemberg House Museum, Franklin, LA 588
Grier Musser Museum, Los Angeles, CA 115
Groveland Yosemite Gateway Museum, Groveland, CA..101

Hammond Museum of Bells, Eureka Springs, AR 57
Hanley House, Clayton, MO........................813
Har-Ber Village, Grove, OK 1202
Hartung's Auto and License Plate Museum, Glenview, IL............................438
Harvey House Museum, Florence, KS 539
Haskell County Historical Society, Sublette, KS 558
Hawks Inn Historical Society, Inc., Delafield, WI 1595
Heisey Museum, Clinton County Historical Society, Lock Haven, PA 1269
Henry B. Plant Museum, Tampa, FL...........349
Henry County Museum and Cultural Arts Center, Clinton, MO................................813
Heritage Museum Foundation of Tate County, Inc., Senatobia, MS 808
Highland County Museum and Heritage Center, McDowell, VA 1517
Hills and Dales Estate, LaGrange, GA.........375
Historic Columbus Foundation, Inc., Columbus, GA 369
Historic New England, Boston, MA............665
Historic New England/Cogswells Grant, Essex, MA 682
Historic Shepherdstown Museum, Shepherdstown, WV.............................1586
Historical Society of Saratoga Springs, Saratoga Springs, NY...........................1064
Holmes County Historical Society, Millersburg, OH................................1176

Home of Stone (The Mueller-Schmidt House 1881), a Ford County Museum, curated by Ford County Historic Society, Dodge City, KS 537
Homeopathy Works, Berkeley Springs, WV...1580
Homeville Antique Fire Department, Homer, NY 999
Homewood House Museum, Baltimore, MD...633
Hood River County Historical Museum, Hood River, OR.....................................1226
Horatio Colony House Museum & Nature Preserve, Keene, NH.............................890
The House on the Rock, Spring Green, WI...1622
House with the Eye Museum, Leadville, CO...226
Houston Museum of Decorative Arts, Chattanooga, TN......................................1362
Howard Steamboat Museum and Mansion, Jeffersonville, IN 486
The Huguenot Historical Society, New Paltz, NY 1017
The 100th Meridian Museum, Cozad, NE ...859
Hurricane Valley Heritage Park Museum, Hurricane, UT..1466
The Hyland House, Guilford, CT.................243

Iowa Great Lakes Maritime Museum, Arnolds Park, IA...505
Ipswich Historical Society and Museum, Ipswich, MA...688
Isabel Anderson Comer Museum & Arts Center, Sylacauga, AL...............................18

Jackson County Historical Museum & Research Library, Maquoketa, IA...........522
Jackson-Washabaugh Historical Museum, Kadoka, SD...1349
John Rivers Communications Museum, Charleston, SC 1325
Johnson County Museum of History, Franklin, IN 478
Johnson Victrola Museum, Dover, DE.........270

Kaminski House Museum, Georgetown, SC...1333
Kelton House Museum & Garden, Columbus, OH...1158
Kensington Mansion, Eastover, SC 1332
Kewaunee County Historical Museum, Kewaunee, WI...1602

The Lace Museum, Sunnyvale, CA..............190
LaGrange Plantation, Cambridge, MD.........639
Lane Place, Crawfordsville, IN....................473
The Leffingwell House Museum, Norwich, CT..258
Liberty Hall Historic Site, Frankfort, KY 569
Lincoln County Historical Society, Lincoln, KS..549
The Little Cowboy Bar & Museum, Fromberg, MT...847
The Living Word National Bible Museum, Aledo, TX..................................1386
Long Branch Historical Museum, Long Branch, NJ...910
Lux Center for the Arts, Lincoln, NE 866
Lynden Pioneer Museum, Lynden, WA......1559

Mac's Antique Car Museum, Tulsa, OK ...1215
Marietta House Museum, Glenn Dale, MD...645
Marilla Historical Society Museum, Marilla, NY...1014
Marvin Newton House, Brookfield, VT 1477
The Mather Homestead Museum, Library and Memorial Park, Wellsville, NY 1084
Mc Cook County Historical Society and Museum, Salem, SD................................1355
McAllister House Museum, Colorado Springs, CO 207

Antiques Museums–Continued

McMinn County Living Heritage Museum, Athens, TN 1360
Mem-Erie Historical Museum, Erie, KS 539
Memoryville USA, Inc., Rolla, MO 829
Meux Home Museum, Fresno, CA................98
Middleton Historical Society - Lura Woodside Watkins Museum, Middleton, MA 694
Middletown Valley Historical Society, Middletown, MD 649
Midway Museum, Inc., Midway, GA 379
Monroe County Heritage Museum, Monroeville, AL 15
Montpelier Mansion, Laurel, MD 648
Morton House Museum, Benton Harbor, MI 728
Museum of Art & History at Weston, Weston, CT 266
Museum of Automobile Art and Design, Syracuse, NY..........................1076
Museum of Ceramics, East Liverpool, OH 1163
Museum of Idaho, Idaho Falls, ID 406
The Museum of Miniature Houses and Other Collections, Inc., Carmel, IN.........471
Museum of Radio & Technology, Inc., Huntington, WV 1583
Museum of Small Town Life, Dover, DE....270
Museum of Southern History, Jacksonville, FL 315
The Museum of Southern History, Sugarland, TX 1454
Museum of the American Quilter's Society (MAQS), Paducah, KY 581
Museum of the City of Lake Worth, Lake Worth, FL 320
Museum of Women's History, Billings, MT..841
The Music House Museum, Acme, MI 722

Nantucket Lightship Basket Museum, Nantucket, MA 696
National Cryptologic Museum, Fort Meade, MD 643
National Fresh Water Fishing Hall of Fame, Hayward, WI 1600
National Knife Museum, Inc., Chattanooga, TN 1362
National Shaving And Barbershop Museum, Meriden, CT 249
The National Toy Train Museum, Strasburg, PA 1301
Nevada County Historical Society, Inc., Nevada City, CA 130
New England Maple Museum, Pittsford, VT..1484
Newell Museum, Newell, SD 1352
Newtown Historic Association, Newtown, PA..1274
Newtown History Center, Stephens City, VA..1538
Nichols House Museum, Boston, MA.........668
Nobleboro Historical Society, Nobleboro, ME.......................................616
North House Museum, Lewisburg, WV 1584
North Plainfield Exempt Firemen's Association, North Plainfield, NJ...........917
Northeast Classic Car Museum, Norwich, NY..1044
Northeast Louisiana Delta African American Heritage Museum, Monroe, LA...592
Northeastern Montana Threshers and Antique Association, Culbertson, MT 845

Old Firehouse Museum, Greenville, MS......800
Old Prairie Town at Ward-Meade Historic Site, Topeka, KS...........................560
The Old Stone House, Washington, DC.......289
Oldest Stone House Museum, Lakewood, OH..1170

Otero Museum Association, La Junta, CO...224
Ouachita County Historical Society, Camden, AR................................55
Overfield Tavern Museum, Troy, OH 1188
Overstreet-Kerr Historical Farm, Keota, OK..1203

The Parry Mansion Museum, New Hope, PA..1273
Patee House Museum, Saint Joseph, MO 831
Peel Mansion Museum & Historic Gardens, Bentonville, AR.....................55
The Pena-Peck House, Saint Augustine, FL..339
Pierrepont Museum, Canton, NY................975
Pocahontas County Iowa Historical Society Museum, Laurens, IA 522
Pointe Coupee Museum, New Roads, LA....599
Porter Thermometer Museum, Onset, MA...700
The Prairie Museum of Art & History, Colby, KS.................................535
Pratt County Historical Society Museum, Pratt, KS.................................556
Presque Isle County Historical Museum, Rogers City, MI 762
Prestwould Foundation, Clarksville, VA.....1501

The Ralph Foster Museum, Point Lookout, MO 828
Randolph County Historical Museum, Winchester, IN 503
Randolph County Museum (At Beverly), Beverly, WV 1580
Rankin Museum, Inc., Ellerbe, NC............1100
The Reeves Center, Washington and Lee University, Lexington, VA....................1513
Reitz Home Museum, Evansville, IN..........476
Renville County Historical Society, Inc., Mohall, ND................................1135
Rhinebeck Aerodrome Museum, Rhinebeck, NY 1056
Rising Sun Tavern, Fredericksburg, VA 1507
Roaring Twenties Antique Car Museum, Hood, VA..................................1511
Rosa Ponselle Museum, Meriden, CT.........249
Rose Lawn Museum, Cartersville, GA........368
Ruthmere Museum, Elkhart, IN..................475

Salem Historical Society and Museum, Salem, OH...............................1184
Sandown Historical Society and Museum, Sandown, NH 896
Sandusky Library Follett House Museum, Sandusky, OH 1185
Santa Ynez Valley Historical Society, Santa Ynez, CA 185
Sappington House Museum, Crestwood, MO..814
The Sargent House Museum, Gloucester, MA..684
Saunders Memorial Museum, Berryville, AR..55
The Scarsdale Historical Society, Scarsdale, NY 1066
Shakespeare Ghost Town, Lordsburg, NM...942
Siloam Springs Museum, Siloam Springs, AR..68
Silvercreek Museum, Freeport, IL...............435
Sisson Museum, Mount Shasta, CA 129
Society for the Preservation of Long Island Antiquities, Cold Spring Harbor, NY 980
South Dakota Tractor Museum, Kimball, SD..1350
Southdown Plantation House/The Terrebonne Museum, Houma, LA 589
Springfield Museum of Old Domestic Life, High Point, NC........................1107
Stan Hywet Hall and Gardens, Inc., Akron, OH................................1139
Stanzel Model Aircraft Museum, Schulenburg, TX 1452
Stengel-True Museum, Marion, OH 1174

The Stephen Girard Collection, Philadelphia, PA 1288
Strater Hotel, Durango, CO 214
Sun Inn Preservation Association Inc., Bethlehem, PA 1243

Ten Broeck Mansion - Albany County Historical Association, Albany, NY 956
Terrace Hill Historic Site and Governor's Mansion, Des Moines, IA..................516
Teutopolis Monastery Museum, Teutopolis, IL............................461
The Thomas Griswold House and Museum, Guilford, CT 243
Thousand Islands Museum, Clayton, NY.....979
Tinkertown Museum, Sandia Park, NM 947
Troy Museum & Historic Village, Troy, MI..765

Upham Mansion, Marshfield, WI 1608
Upper Musselshell Historical Society, Harlowton, MT 849

Volo Antique Auto Museum and Village, Volo, IL..................................463

Wakefield Museum Association, Wakefield, KS............................560
Washburn Historical Museum & Cultural Center, Inc. aka Washburn Cultural Center, Washburn, WI 1625
Washington County Fair Farm Museum, Greenwich, NY 996
Washington County Historical Society and Miller House Museum, Hagerstown, MD 646
Wilder Memorial Museum, Strawberry Point, IA.................................528
Wilkinson County Museum, Woodville, MS..810
William Henry Harrison Mansion, Grouseland, Vincennes, IN...................503
Wilson Castle, Proctor, VT 1485
Wilson Czech Opera House Corporation, Foundation, Inc. & House of Memories Museum, Wilson, KS.............564
World O' Tools Museum, Waverly, TN......1385
World of Wings Pigeon Center, Oklahoma City, OK 1211
Wright Museum, Wolfeboro, NH................897
Wright's Ferry Mansion, Columbia, PA 1248
Wyoming Pioneer Home, Thermopolis, WY..1639

Yellow Medicine County Historical Society and Museum, Granite Falls, MN..777
Yesterday's Children Antique Doll & Toy Museum, Vicksburg, MS.....................809

Zalud House, Porterville, CA......................144

Architecture Museums

A.D. German Warehouse, Designed By Frank Lloyd Wright, Richland Center, WI..1620

Battleground Historical Society, Englishtown, NJ............................903
Belcourt Castle, Newport, RI....................1313
Bellamy Mansion Museum of History and Design Arts, Wilmington, NC.........1122
Betts House Research Center, Cincinnati, OH..1148
Boston Center for Jewish Heritage, Boston, MA...............................663
Bragg-Mitchell Mansion, Mobile, AL 13

The Casa del Herrero Foundation, Santa Barbara, CA..............................178
Cathedral Cultural Center, Omaha, NE 870
The Cathedral of St. John the Divine, New York, NY 1022

Charnley-Persky House Museum, Chicago, IL 418
Chicago Architecture Foundation, Chicago, IL 418
The Chicago Athenaeum: Museum of Architecture and Design, Galena, IL 436
Circle Gallery/College of Environment & Design - University of Georgia, Athens, GA 356
The Dana-Thomas House State Historic Site, Springfield, IL 458
Department of the Treasury, Washington, DC 278
Escondido History Center, Escondido, CA 93
Fallingwater, Mill Run, PA 1272
Festival-Institute, James Dick Foundation, Round Top, TX 1446
Frederick Law Olmsted National Historic Site, Brookline, MA 671
The Gardner Museum of Architecture & Design, Quincy, IL 452
Hacienda Buena Vista, Ponce, PR 1642
Hawaii's Plantation Village, Waipahu, HI 402
Heritage Square Museum, Los Angeles, CA 116
Historic Oakland Cemetery, Atlanta, GA 360
The Hyland House, Guilford, CT 243
Kensington Mansion, Eastover, SC 1332
Korner's Folly, Kernersville, NC 1108
Lower East Side Tenement Museum, New York, NY 1029
MAK Center for Art and Architecture at the Schindler House, West Hollywood, CA 197
Merchant's House Museum, New York, NY 1029
Minnesota State Capitol Historic Site, Saint Paul, MN 791
Museo Fuerte Conde de Mirasol de Vieques, Vieques, PR 1644
Museum of Rural Life, Denton, MD 642
National Building Museum, Washington, DC 284
Nichols House Museum, Boston, MA 668
The Octagon, Washington, DC 288
Old World Wisconsin, Eagle, WI 1595
Peel Mansion Museum & Historic Gardens, Bentonville, AR 55
The Pena-Peck House, Saint Augustine, FL 339
Point Fermin Lighthouse, San Pedro, CA 176
Price Tower Arts Center, Bartlesville, OK .1197
Rothko Chapel, Houston, TX 1429
The Sargent House Museum, Gloucester, MA 684
Schifferstadt Architectural Museum, Frederick, MD 644
Shoal Creek Living History Museum, Kansas City, MO 822
The Skyscraper Museum, New York, NY ..1038
Southeastern Architectural Archive, New Orleans, LA 598
The State House Museum, Dover, DE 270
Stow West School Museum, Stow, MA 713
Strater Hotel, Durango, CO 214
Terrace Hill Historic Site and Governor's Mansion, Des Moines, IA 516
The Vermont State House, Montpelier, VT 1483

West Virginia Independence Hall, Wheeling, WV 1588
William Henry Harrison Mansion, Grouseland, Vincennes, IN 503
The Wolfsonian - Florida International University, Miami Beach, FL 327

Audiovisual and Film Museums

Alabama Music Hall of Fame, Tuscumbia, AL 20
American Royal Museum & Visitors Center, Kansas City, MO 820
The Andy Warhol Museum, Pittsburgh, PA 1290
Anthology Film Archives, New York, NY .1020
Ava Gardner Museum, Smithfield, NC 1119
California Route 66 Museum, Victorville, CA 195
Captain Salem Avery House Museum, Shady Side Rural Heritage Society, Inc., Shady Side, MD 653
Country Music Hall of Fame and Museum, Country Music Foundation, Nashville, TN 1378
Crafts Museum, Mequon, WI 1609
Field of Dreams Movie Site, Dyersville, IA 517
George Eastman House/International Museum of Photography and Film, Rochester, NY 1058
Gerald R. Ford Library, Ann Arbor, MI 724
Groveland Yosemite Gateway Museum, Groveland, CA 101
Harry Ransom Center at the University of Texas at Austin, Austin, TX 1390
Hollywood Heritage Museum, Hollywood, CA 103
Holocaust Documentation & Education Center, Inc., Hollywood, FL 313
International Center of Photography, New York, NY 1028
The Jimmy Stewart Museum, Indiana, PA .1262
The Light Factory - Museum of Photography & Film, Charlotte, NC 1095
Lowell Telecommunications Corp., Lowell, MA 691
Lucy-Desi Museum, Jamestown, NY 1005
The Magic Lantern Castle Museum, San Antonio, TX 1448
Mario Lanza Institute/Museum, Philadelphia, PA 1282
Martin and Osa Johnson Safari Museum, Inc., Chanute, KS 535
McLarty Treasure Museum, Vero Beach, FL 352
The Movie Museum, Owosso, MI 759
The Museum of Television & Radio, New York, NY 1033
Museum of the Moving Image, Astoria, NY 958
The National Museum of Communications, Richardson, TX 1445
National Postal Museum, Smithsonian Institution, Washington, DC 287
The New York Public Library for the Performing Arts, New York, NY 1036
Olde Colonial Courthouse, Tales of Cape Cod, Inc., Barnstable, MA 661
Philadelphia Mummers Museum, Philadelphia, PA 1285
Photographic Archives, Lexington, KY 574
The Rock and Roll Hall of Fame and Museum, Cleveland, OH 1155

Russell C. Davis Planetarium, Jackson, MS 804
Salem Witch Museum, Salem, MA 707
Tillamook Naval Air Station Museum, Tillamook, OR 1237
Virginia Holocaust Museum, Richmond, VA 1533
Weston Woods Institute, Weston, CT 266
Wilson Czech Opera House Corporation, Foundation, Inc. & House of Memories Museum, Wilson, KS 564
Yerba Buena Center for the Arts, San Francisco, CA 170

Circus Museums

Circus City Festival Museum, Peru, IN 495
Circus World Museum, Baraboo, WI 1591
City Museum, Saint Louis, MO 832
Emmett Kelly Historical Museum, Sedan, KS 558
John and Mable Ringling Museum of Art, Sarasota, FL 344
Norman #1 Oil Well Museum, Neodesha, KS 553
Somers Historical Society, Somers, NY 1070

Comedy Museums

Cartoon Art Museum, San Francisco, CA 164
The International Clown Hall of Fame & Research Center, Inc., Milwaukee, WI ..1611
Lucy-Desi Museum, Jamestown, NY 1005
Lum & Abner Museum & Jot 'Em Down Store, Pine Ridge, AR 66
Philadelphia Mummers Museum, Philadelphia, PA 1285

Communications Museums

The American Film Institute, Washington, DC 275
American Museum of Radio and Electricity, Bellingham, WA 1548
American Sign Museum, Cincinnati, OH ..1148
Carroll Reece Museum, Johnson City, TN .1367
Cartoon Art Museum, San Francisco, CA 164
Cle Elum Telephone Museum, Cle Elum, WA 1551
Conway Scenic Railroad, Inc., North Conway, NH 892
Deer Park Escondido Winery & Auto Museum, Escondido, CA 93
French Cable Station Museum in Orleans, Orleans, MA 701
Hamilton Wood Type Printing Museum, Two Rivers, WI 1625
Historic Speedwell, Morristown, NJ 913
The International Printing Museum, Carson, CA 82
John Rivers Communications Museum, Charleston, SC 1325
The Mary Baker Eddy Library for the Betterment of Humanity, Boston, MA 666
The Movie Museum, Owosso, MI 759
Mulvane Art Museum, Topeka, KS 559
Museum of Independent Telephony, Abilene, KS 531
The Museum of Television & Radio, New York, NY 1033

Communications Museums–Continued

The Museum of Television & Radio, Beverly Hills, CA 78

Museum of Transportation, Saint Louis, MO 835

National Cryptologic Museum, Fort Meade, MD 643

National Italian American Sports Hall of Fame, Chicago, IL 425

The National Museum of Communications, Richardson, TX 1445

The National Science Center's Fort Discovery, Augusta, GA 366

The New York Public Library, Astor, Lenox and Tilden Foundations, New York, NY 1036

Patee House Museum, Saint Joseph, MO 831

Pavek Museum of Broadcasting, St. Louis Park, MN 794

Platen Press Printing Museum, Zion, IL 467

The Telephone Museum, Ellsworth, ME......610

Telephone Museum of New Mexico, Albuquerque, NM 935

Telephone Pioneer Museum, Phoenix, AZ 42

U.S. Army Communications-Electronics Museum, Fort Monmouth, NJ..................904

U.S. Marconi Museum, Bedford, NH..........883

Weston Woods Institute, Weston, CT 266

Costume Museums

Adsmore Museum, Princeton, KY 583

Allison-Antrim Museum, Inc., Greencastle, PA 1257

American Museum of Straw Art, Long Beach, CA 110

Amherst History Museum at the Strong House - Amherst Historical Society, Amherst, MA 658

Ark-La-Tex Antique & Classic Vehicle Museum, Shreveport, LA 600

Brooks Academy Museum, Harwich, MA ...686

Brunswick Railroad Museum and C&O Canal Visitors Center, Brunswick, MD ...639

Carpenter Home Museum and Gallery, Cle Elum, WA 1551

Centerville Historical Museum, Centerville, MA 675

Country Music Hall of Fame and Museum, Country Music Foundation, Nashville, TN..1378

Cumberland County Historical Society, Greenwich, NJ 905

DAR Museum First Ladies of Texas Historic Costumes Collection, Denton, TX 1409

Elizabeth Sage Historic Costume Collection, Bloomington, IN 469

Enfield Historical Society Museum, Enfield Center, NH 887

The Fashion Institute of Design & Merchandising/FIDM Museum & Galleries, Los Angeles, CA......................114

Glove Museum, New York, NY 1026

The Goldstein Museum of Design, Saint Paul, MN 789

Graceland, Memphis, TN 1373

Gustafson Gallery/Design & Merchandising, Fort Collins, CO............217

Historic Costume & Textiles Collection, Columbus, OH 1158

Historical Society of Oak Park & River Forest, Oak Park, IL................................448

The International Clown Hall of Fame & Research Center, Inc., Milwaukee, WI..1611

Kelton House Museum & Garden, Columbus, OH 1158

Kent State University Museum, Kent, OH.1169

The Lace Museum, Sunnyvale, CA.............190

Liberace Museum & Foundation, Las Vegas, NV 879

Lincoln County Historical Society, Lincoln, KS..549

Mardi Gras Museum, Kenner, LA 589

Milan Historical Museum, Inc., Milan, OH 1176

Mississippi County Historical Society, Charleston, MO 812

Monroe County Heritage Museum, Monroeville, AL 15

Mount Mary College Historic Costume Collection, Milwaukee, WI 1613

The Museum at the Fashion Institute of Technology, New York, NY 1031

Museum of the Bedford Historical Society, Bedford, NY 961

North Carolina A&T State University Galleries, Greensboro, NC 1104

Old Fort Meade Museum and Historic Research Association, Fort Meade, SD .1347

Owatonna Arts Center, Owatonna, MN........786

Pascack Historical Society, Park Ridge, NJ 920

Philadelphia Mummers Museum, Philadelphia, PA 1285

The Rock and Roll Hall of Fame and Museum, Cleveland, OH........................1155

Santa Ynez Valley Historical Society, Santa Ynez, CA 185

Shippensburg University Fashion Archives and Museum, Shippensburg, PA 1300

Siloam Springs Museum, Siloam Springs, AR 68

Ukrainian National Museum, Inc., Chicago, IL 428

Valentine Richmond History Center, Richmond, VA 1532

World Figure Skating Museum & Hall of Fame, Colorado Springs, CO 208

Crime Museums

Cleveland Police Historical Society & Museum, Cleveland, OH 1153

Federal Bureau of Investigation, Washington, DC..278

Historic Burlington County Prison Museum, Mount Holly, NJ......................914

Honolulu Police Department Law Enforcement Museum, Honolulu, HI......396

House of the Temple, Washington, DC 280

Houston Police Museum, Houston, TX......1427

Law Enforcement Memorial Association, Inc., Roselle, IL......................................456

Museum of Colorado Prisons, Canon City, CO 205

The National Border Patrol Museum and Memorial Library, El Paso, TX 1412

New York City Police Museum, New York, NY..1035

Old New-Gate Prison and Copper Mine, East Granby, CT 238

Old Prison Museums, Deer Lodge, MT 845

Rock Springs Historical Museum, Rock Springs, WY 1638

San Quentin Prison Museum, San Quentin, CA..176

Wayne County Historical Society, Lyons, NY 1012

Culturally Specific

A.C. Gilbert's Discovery Village, Salem, OR 1235

A.D. German Warehouse, Designed By Frank Lloyd Wright, Richland Center, WI 1620

A.R. Mitchell Museum, Trinidad, CO..........233

A:shiwi A:wan Museum and Heritage Center, Zuni, NM 954

Abbe Museum, Bar Harbor, ME..................605

Abby Aldrich Rockefeller Folk Art Museum, Williamsburg, VA 1544

Abraham Lincoln Birthplace National Historic Site, Hodgenville, KY............571

African American Historical Museum & Cultural Center of Iowa, Cedar Rapids, IA..508

African American Museum, Cleveland, OH 1152

African-American Museum and Library at Oakland, Oakland, CA 132

African American Museum of the Arts, De Land, FL 303

African Art Museum of the S.M.A. Fathers, Tenafly, NJ 926

Afro-American Cultural Center, Charlotte, NC..1094

Ah-Tah-Thi-Ki Museum, Big Cypress Seminole Indian Reservation, FL 295

Ah-Tah-Thi-Ki Museum at Okalee, Hollywood, FL..312

Airmen Memorial Museum, Suitland, MD 655

Akta Lakota Museum and Cultural Center, Chamberlain, SD......................1345

Alamance Battleground State Historic Site, Burlington, NC..............................1092

Alaska Heritage Museum at Wells Fargo, Anchorage, AK..21

Alaska Native Heritage Center, Anchorage, AK..22

Alaska State Museum, Juneau, AK...............25

Albion Academy Historical Museum, Edgerton, WI..1596

Alexandria Black History Resource Center, Alexandria, VA..............................1491

Alutiiq Museum and Archaeological Repository, Kodiak, AK 26

Amana Heritage Museum, Amana, IA 504

American Hungarian Foundation/Museum of the American Hungarian Foundation, New Brunswick, NJ.............915

American Irish Historical Society, New York, NY..1019

American Jewish Historical Society, New York, NY..1019

American Museum of Asmat Art, Saint Paul, MN..789

American Museum of Magic & Lund Memorial Library, Inc., Marshall, MI 754

American Red Cross Visitors Center and Gift Shop, Washington, DC 275

American Swedish Historical Foundation & Museum, Philadelphia, PA..................1276

American Swedish Institute, Minneapolis, MN 781

American Watchmakers-Clockmakers Institute, Harrison, OH 1168

American West Heritage Center, Wellsville, UT..1475

America's Black Holocaust Museum, Milwaukee, WI..1610

Amherst County Museum & Historical Society, Amherst, VA 1495

Amon Carter Museum, Fort Worth, TX 1416
Anasazi Heritage Center, Dolores, CO.........214
Anderson County Historical Museum, Garnett, KS 541
Angel Mounds State Historic Site, Evansville, IN 475
Antelope Valley African American Museum, Lancaster, CA...........................108
Antelope Valley Indian Museum, Lancaster, CA 108
Archives Museum, Temple Mickve Israel, Savannah, GA 384
Arizona Jewish Historical Society, Phoenix, AZ 39
Armenian Library and Museum of America, Watertown, MA 716
Armstrong Browning Library, Waco, TX ...1458
Art Association of Harrisburg, Harrisburg, PA 1258
Art Association of Randolph County, Inc., Union City, IN.............................501
Art In Embassies Program, U.S. Department of State, Washington, DC 276
Art Museum of the Americas, Oas, Washington, DC...................................276
Art Museum of Western Virginia, Roanoke, VA...1534
Arthur M. Sackler Gallery, Washington, DC..276
Arts Consortium of Cincinnati's African American Museum, Cincinnati, OH 1148
Arts Council of Wayne County, Goldsboro, NC 1102
Asia Society Museum, New York, NY.......1020
Asian Art Museum of San Francisco, Chong-Moon Lee Center for Asian Art and Culture, San Francisco, CA 163
Asian Arts & Culture Center, Towson University, Towson, MD 655
Astor House Museum, Golden, CO.............219
Ataloa Lodge Museum, Muskogee, OK....1205
Atrium Gallery Ltd., Saint Louis, MO.........832
Audie Murphy/American Cotton Museum, Inc, Greenville, TX 1423
Avery County Museum, Newland, NC 1113
Avery Research Center for African American History & Culture, Charleston, SC 1323

Baca House, Trinidad History Museum, Trinidad, CO 233
Balzekas Museum of Lithuanian Culture, Chicago, IL..418
Barbed Wire Museum, La Crosse, KS 547
Bartram's Garden, Philadelphia, PA 1277
Bay of Pigs Museum & Library, Miami, FL...323
Beacon Historical Society, Beacon, NY.......960
Bear Butte State Park Visitors Center, Sturgis, SD 1358
Beau Fort Plantation Home, Bermuda, LA..587
Beaufort Historic Site, Beaufort, NC.........1091
Beck Cultural Exchange Center, Knoxville, TN 1369
Bement-Billings Farmstead, Newark Valley, NY 1041
The Benjamin & Dr. Edgar R. Cofeld Judaic Museum of Temple Beth Zion, Buffalo, NY 971
Bernard Judaica Museum, Congregation Emanu-El of the City of New York, New York, NY 1021
Beth Ahabah Museum & Archives, Richmond, VA 1528
Big Cypress National Preserve, Ochopee, FL...330
Big Timbers Museum, Lamar, CO 225
Birmingham Civil Rights Institute, Birmingham, AL..4
Bishop Hill Heritage Museum, Bishop Hill, IL...413

Black American West Museum & Heritage Center, Denver, CO 209
The Black Fashion Museum, Washington, DC...277
Black Hawk State Historic Site: Hauberg Indian Museum, Rock Island, IL.............453
Black Heritage Museum, Miami, FL............323
Black Kettle Museum, Cheyenne, OK 1198
Bloom Mansion, Trinidad History Museum, Trinidad, CO......................................233
B'nai B'rith Klutznick National Jewish Museum, Washington, DC 277
Boerner Botanical Gardens, Hales Corners, WI 1600
Boone's Lick State Historic Site, Boonesboro, MO....................................811
Boothbay Region Art Foundation, Inc., Boothbay Harbor, ME............................607
Boston Center for Jewish Heritage, Boston, MA 663
Brevard Museum of History & Science, Cocoa, FL 300
Brick Store Museum, Kennebunk, ME 612
Bridgton Historical Society, Bridgton, ME..607
Brookfield Craft Center, Brookfield, CT 237
Brush Country Museum, Cotulla, TX 1403
Bucksport Historical Society, Inc., Bucksport, ME...608
Buechel Memorial Lakota Museum, Saint Francis, SD 1355
Buffalo Trails Museum, Epping, ND 1130
Burke Museum of Natural History and Culture, Seattle, WA 1565
Burlington-Rock Island Railroad and Historical Museum, Teague, TX 1454
Bushwhacker Museum, Nevada, MO..........828
Butler County Museum, Hamilton, OH......1168

Calaveras County Museum, San Andreas, CA 155
California Heritage Museum, Santa Monica, CA 183
California Indian Museum & Cultural Center, Santa Rosa, CA.........................184
California State Indian Museum, Sacramento, CA..151
California State Railroad Museum, Sacramento, CA..152
Calvin Coolidge Historic Site, Plymouth Notch, VT 1484
The Calvin Coolidge Memorial Foundation, Inc., Plymouth, VT 1484
Caramoor Center for Music & the Arts, Inc., Katonah, NY 1006
Carl Sandburg State Historic Site, Galesburg, IL 437
Carlsbad Caverns National Park, Carlsbad, NM..937
Carroll Mansion Museum Home of Leavenworth County Historical Society, Leavenworth, KS 549
Carter County Museum, Ekalaka, MT.........846
Cary Cottage, Cincinnati, OH 1148
Casa Grande Ruins National Monument, Coolidge, AZ 31
Casa Navarro State Historical Park, San Antonio, TX..1448
Cass County Museum & Pioneer School, Walker, MN 795
Center for Latino Arts & Culture, New Brunswick, NJ 915
Chaco Culture National Historical Park, Nageezi, NM...943
Charles A. Grignon Mansion, Kaukauna, WI...1601
Charles H. Wright Museum of African American History, Detroit, MI.................735
Charlotte Museum of History and Hezekiah Alexander Homesite, Charlotte, NC......................................1094
Chattanooga African Museum/Bessie Smith Hall, Chattanooga, TN.................1360

Cheboygan County Historical Museum Complex, Cheboygan, MI 732
Cherry Valley Museum, Cherry Valley, NY...978
Chesapeake and Ohio Canal National Historical Park, Hagerstown, MD...........646
Chester Art Guild, Chester, VT 1478
Chetopa Historical Museum, Chetopa, KS...535
The Chicago Athenaeum: Museum of Architecture and Design, Galena, IL.......436
Chicago Cultural Center, Chicago, IL..........419
Chickasaw National Recreation Area, Sulphur, OK...1214
Chief Plenty Coups Museum, Pryor, MT.....852
The Children's Museum, Seattle, WA 1565
China Institute Gallery, China Institute In America, New York, NY 1023
Chinese American Museum, Los Angeles, CA...114
Chinese Culture Center of San Francisco, San Francisco, CA....................................164
Chinese Joss House Museum, Evanston, WY...1632
Chisholm Trail Museum, Kingfisher, OK...1203
Christiansted National Historic Site, Saint Croix, VI...1644
City Island Nautical Museum, Bronx, NY ...965
Clarke County Historical Association, Inc., Berryville, VA 1496
Coarsegold Historic Museum, Coarsegold, CA 86
Coastal Heritage Museum, Crystal River, FL...301
Coeur d'Alenes Old Mission State Park, Cataldo, ID...405
College Park Aviation Museum, College Park, MD 641
The Colonial Spanish Quarter Museum, Saint Augustine, FL....................................338
Colorado Ski Museum-Ski & Snowboard Hall of Fame, Vail, CO............................234
Confederate Memorial State Historic Site, Higginsville, MO...817
Confederate Tribes of Grand Ronde Cultural Resources Department, Grand Ronde, OR 1225
The Conference House, Staten Island, NY...1072
Connecticut River Museum, Essex, CT........239
Conrad Mansion National Historic Site Museum, Kalispell, MT...............................850
Cottonlandia Museum, Greenwood, MS 800
Country Music Hall of Fame and Museum, Country Music Foundation, Nashville, TN...1378
The Cowley County Historical Society, Winfield, KS 564
Creek Council House Museum, Okmulgee, OK...1211
Croatian Heritage Museum & Library, Eastlake, OH 1163
Crook County Museum & Art Gallery, Sundance, WY 1638
Crowley Art Association & Gallery, Crowley, LA 588
Crystal Rice Plantation, Crowley, LA 588
Crystal River State Archaeological Site, Crystal River, FL..302
Custer County 1881 Courthouse Museum, Custer, SD..1345

Daniel Boone Homestead, Birdsboro, PA ..1243
The Danish Immigrant Museum, Elk Horn, IA..517
David Crockett Cabin, Rutherford, TN 1383
Death Valley National Park Visitor Center and Museums, Death Valley, CA...............91
DeCordova Museum and Sculpture Park, Lincoln, MA...690
The DeLand Museum of Art, De Land, FL...303
Delta Blues Museum, Clarksdale, MS.........799
Delta Cultural Center, Helena, AR 59

Culturally Specific–Continued

The Depot Museum Complex, Henderson, TX...............................1424

Deutschheim State Historic Site, Hermann, MO...............................817

DeWitt Stetten, Jr., Museum of Medical Research, Bethesda, MD..........................637

DeWitt Wallace Decorative Arts Museum, Williamsburg, VA.............................1545

Dickson Mounds Museum, Lewistown, IL...442

Diggs Gallery at Winston-Salem State University, Winston-Salem, NC............1125

Disney's Animal Kingdom Theme Park, Bay Lake, FL.....................................295

Dr. John Harris Dental Museum, Bainbridge, OH......................................1141

Donald G. Trayser Memorial Museum/Barnstable County Customs House, Barnstable, MA..........................661

Drew County Historical Museum, Monticello, AR...64

Dubuque Museum of Art, Dubuque, IA....516

Dunbar House State Memorial, Dayton, OH..1161

Duncan Cottage Museum, Metlakatla, AK.....27

Dunedin Historical Society & Museum, Dunedin, FL...305

EarlyWorks Museums, Huntsville, AL............11

East-West Center, Honolulu, HI..................394

Eastern Oregon Museum on the Old Oregon Trail, Haines, OR.......................1226

Effie Yeaw Nature Center, Carmichael, CA..82

The 1811 Old Lincoln County Jail and Lincoln County Museum, Wiscasset, ME..625

Eiteljorg Museum of American Indians and Western Art, Indianapolis, IN..........482

El Museo Latino, Omaha, NE....................870

El Paso Museum of Archaeology, El Paso, TX..1411

El Rancho de Las Golondrinas Museum, Santa Fe, NM...947

Elbert Hubbard-Roycroft Museum, East Aurora, NY..985

Elfreth's Alley Association, Philadelphia, PA..1279

Elkhart County Historical Museum, Bristol, IN..471

Elliott Museum, Stuart, FL..........................346

Ephraim Historical Foundation, Ephraim, WI..1597

Ephrata Cloister, Ephrata, PA....................1251

The Erlander Home Museum, Rockford, IL..454

Ethnic Heritage Museum, Rockford, IL.......455

Eubie Blake National Jazz Institute and Cultural Center, Baltimore, MD..............632

Eureka Pioneer Museum of McPherson County, Inc., Eureka, SD.......................1346

Fairfield County Museum, Winnsboro, SC..1343

Faninadahen Kosas Guahan-Guam Museum, Hagatna, GU........................1640

The Farm, Sturgeon Bay, WI....................1623

Farrar-Mansur House & Old Mill Museum, Weston, VT.............................1490

Federal Hall National Memorial, New York, NY...1025

Felix Valle State Historic Site, Sainte Genevieve, MO.......................................837

First White House of the Confederacy, Montgomery, AL...16

The Five Civilized Tribes Museum, Muskogee, OK..1205

The Florida International Museum, Saint Petersburg, FL..341

The Folsom House Museum, Taylors Falls, MN..794

Fort Clatsop National Memorial, Astoria, OR..1218

Fort Davidson State Historic Site, Pilot Knob, MO...828

Fort Davis National Historic Site, Fort Davis, TX...1414

Fort Delaware Museum of Colonial History, Narrowsburg, NY.....................1017

Fort Leaton State Historical Site, Presidio, TX..1444

Fort Recovery Museum, Fort Recovery, OH..1164

Fort St. Jean Baptiste State Historic Site, Natchitoches, LA.......................................593

Fort Verde State Historic Park, Camp Verde, AZ...30

Fort Worth Botanic Garden, Fort Worth, TX..1416

Four Rivers Cultural Center & Museum, Ontario, OR..1229

Fox Lake Historical Museum, Inc., Fox Lake, WI...1598

Framingham Historical Society & Museum, Framingham, MA.....................683

Francisco Fort Museum, La Veta, CO.........224

Frankenmuth Historical Museum, Frankenmuth, MI......................................742

The Franklin Pierce Homestead, Hillsborough, NH.....................................889

Frederick Douglass National Historic Site, Washington, DC.................................279

Freestone County Historical Museum, Fairfield, TX..1413

The Frick Collection, New York, NY.........1025

Frontier Culture Museum, Staunton, VA...1537

Fryer Memorial Museum, Munnsville, NY..1017

General Adam Stephen House, Martinsburg, WV......................................1584

General Sterling Price Museum, Keytesville, MO...824

George Washington Birthplace National Monument, Colonial Beach, VA.............1502

Georgia Capitol Museum, Atlanta, GA........360

Georgia Music Hall of Fame and Museum, Macon, GA...................................377

German American Heritage Center, Davenport, IA..513

Gig Harbor Peninsula Historical Society, Gig Harbor, WA.......................................1555

The Glebe House Museum and Gertrude Jekyll Garden, Woodbury, CT.................268

Golden Gate Railroad Museum, San Francisco, CA..166

Golden Spike National Historic Site, Brigham City, UT....................................1463

Goliad State Park, Goliad, TX....................1423

Gomez Foundation for Mill House, Marlboro, NY...1014

Goschenhoppen Folklife Library and Museum, Green Lane, PA.....................1257

Grand Canyon National Park Museum Collection, Grand Canyon National Park, AZ..36

Great Smoky Mountains Heritage Center, Townsend, TN..1384

Greensboro Artists' League, Greensboro, NC..1103

Gunston Hall Plantation, Mason Neck, VA..1517

Hammond Castle Museum, Gloucester, MA..684

Hammond-Harwood House Association, Annapolis, MD...628

Hampton County Historical Museum, Hampton, SC..1334

Hampton University Museum, Hampton, VA..1509

Hana Cultural Center, Hana, Maui, HI.........392

Harbour House Museum, Crystal Falls, MI..733

Harding Home and Museum, Marion, OH.1174

Harrison House, Branford, CT....................235

Harvard University Semitic Museum, Cambridge, MA.......................................673

Heard Museum, Phoenix, AZ........................40

Heathcote Botanical Gardens, Inc., Fort Pierce, FL...309

Heddon Museum, Dowagiac, MI.................738

Hellenic Museum & Cultural Center, Chicago, IL..421

The Heritage Center, Pine Ridge, SD........1354

Heritage Center of Lancaster County, Inc., Lancaster, PA....................................1265

Heritage Hall Museum & Archives, Freeman, SD...1347

Heritage Village, Largo, FL..........................321

Heritage Village, Mountain Lake, MN.........785

The Hermitage, Ho-Ho-Kus, NJ...................907

Highland Maple Museum, Monterey, VA...1518

Highland Park Historical Society, Highland Park, IL.......................................439

Hill Cumorah Visitors Center & Historic Sites, Palmyra, NY.................................1050

Historic Deerfield, Inc., Deerfield, MA........679

Historic Schaefferstown, Inc., Schaefferstown, PA..................................1297

Historic Southwest Ohio, Inc., Sharonville, OH.......................................1185

Historic Westville, Inc., Lumpkin, GA.........376

Historical and Genealogical Society of Somerset County, Somerset, PA............1300

Historical Society of Old Newbury, Cushing House Museum, Newburyport, MA....................................698

Hiwan Homestead Museum, Evergreen, CO..215

Holly History Center & Hutchinson House Museum, Waupaca, WI..............1626

Holocaust Museum Houston, Houston, TX..1426

Hoopa Valley Tribal Museum, Hoopa, CA..103

Hoover Historical Center, North Canton, OH..1179

Hopewell Culture National Historical Park, Chillicothe, OH................................1147

Horry County Museum, Conway, SC.........1331

The Houdini Museum & Theater, Scranton, PA...1298

Howard County Center of African American Culture, Columbia, MD...........641

Hubbell Trading Post National Historic Site, Ganado, AZ...34

The Hudson River Museum, Yonkers, NY.1087

Hui No'eau Visual Arts Center, Makawao, Maui, HI....................................401

Hulihee Palace, Kailua-Kona, HI.................399

Hungarian Folk-Art Museum, Port Orange, FL...338

Hyde Hall, Inc., Cooperstown, NY..............980

Illinois and Michigan Canal Commissioners Office Museum, Lockport, IL...443

Immaculate Conception Catholic Church, Natchitoches, LA......................................593

Indian Arts and Crafts Board, Washington, DC.......................................281

Indian Heritage Museum, Rancocas, NJ......922

Indian Museum of Lake County, Ohio, Willoughby, OH......................................1191

Indian Museum of North America at Crazy Horse Memorial, Crazy Horse, SD..1345

Indian Pueblo Cultural Center, Albuquerque, NM.....................................933

Institute of American Indian Arts Museum, Santa Fe, NM...............................947

The Interchurch Center, New York, NY.....1027

International Motor Racing Research Center at Watkins Glen, Watkins Glen, NY..1084

International Museum of Women, San Francisco, CA 166
Iolani Palace, Honolulu, HI 396
Iowa Railroad Historical Society, Boone, IA 506
Irish American Heritage Museum, Albany, NY 954
Iroquois Indian Museum, Howes Cave, NY......................999

James Madison's Montpelier, Montpelier Station, VA......................1518
James Monroe Museum and Memorial Library, Fredericksburg, VA......................1507
Jane L. and Robert H. Weiner Judaic Museum, Rockville, MD......................651
Japan Society Gallery, New York, NY 1028
Jean P. Haydon Museum, Pago Pago, AS ..1640
Jensen Arctic Museum, Monmouth, OR 1228
The Jewish Museum, New York, NY 1029
Jewish Museum of Florida, Miami Beach, FL......................326
Jewish Museum of Maryland, Baltimore, MD......................633
Jim Crow Museum - Ferris State University, Big Rapids, MI 729
John Nance Garner Museum, Uvalde, TX .1457
Jonathan Hager House & Museum, Hagerstown, MD......................646
The Journey Museum, Rapid City, SD.......1354
Judaica Museum of Central Synagogue, New York, NY 1029
The Judaica Museum of the Hebrew Home at Riverdale, Riverdale, NY........1057
Julia A. Purnell Museum, Snow Hill, MD...654
Juneteenth Creative Cultural Center & Museum, Saginaw, MI 762

Kalamazoo Institute of Arts, Kalamazoo, MI......................748
Kanabec History Center, Mora, MN,............784
Kateri Galleries, The National Shrine of the North American Martyrs, Auriesville, NY......................959
The Kelso House Museum, Kent, OH........1169
Kelton House Museum & Garden, Columbus, OH......................1158
Ker Place, Onancock, VA 1523
Kerbyville Museum, Kerby, OR 1227
Kershaw County Historical Society, Camden, SC......................1323
Knife River Indian Villages National Historic Site, Stanton, ND......................1136
Knoxville Zoological Gardens, Knoxville, TN 1370
Koshare Indian Museum, Inc., La Junta, CO 224
The Kurdish Museum, Brooklyn, NY 969

La Purisima Mission State Historic Park, Lompoc, CA......................109
La Raza/Galeria Posada, Sacramento, CA ...153
The Lacrosse Museum & National Hall of Fame/US Lacrosse, Baltimore, MD 633
Lake City Columbia County Historical Museum, Inc., Lake City, FL......................319
Lake County Historical Society, Kirtland Hills, OH......................1170
Lake Perris Regional Indian Museum (Home of the Wind), Perris, CA..............141
Lake Wales Depot Museum & Cultural Center, Lake Wales, FL......................320
Land of the Yankee Fork Historic Association Museum, Stanley, ID......................410
Landis Valley Museum, Lancaster, PA 1266
Lars Noak Blacksmith Shop, Larsson/Ostlund Log Home & One-Room Capitol School, New Sweden, ME......................616
Latvian Museum, Rockville, MD 651
Layland Museum, Cleburne, TX 1400
The Leffingwell House Museum, Norwich, CT......................258

Lillian and Albert Small Jewish Museum, Washington, DC......................282
Lincoln County Historical Society, North Platte, NE......................869
Lincoln Herdon Law Offices State Historic Site, Springfield, IL......................458
Linn County Historical Museum and Moyer House, Brownsville, OR............1220
Little White Schoolhouse, Ripon, WI.........1620
Locust Creek Covered Bridge State Historic Site, Laclede, MO 825
Lompoc Museum, Lompoc, CA 109
Luis Munoz Rivera Library & Museum, Barranquitas, PR......................1641
Lutheran Heritage Center & Museum of the Perry County Lutheran Historical Society, Altenburg, MO......................810
Lyman Museum, Hilo, HI......................393
Lyon County Historical Society and Museum, Emporia, KS......................538

Macon County Historical Society Museum Complex, Decatur, IL................430
Madison Museum of Contemporary Art, Madison, WI......................1605
Mai Wah Society, Butte, MT 843
Maier Museum of Art, Randolph-Macon Woman's College, Lynchburg, VA.........1515
Malki Museum, Banning, CA 74
Maltz Museum of Jewish Heritage, Beachwood, OH......................1142
Manassas Museum System, Manassas, VA......................1516
Maramec Museum, The James Foundation, Saint James, MO.................830
Maridon Museum, Butler, PA 1245
Marin Museum of the American Indian, Novato, CA......................131
Maritime Museum - Cohasset Historical Society, Cohasset, MA 676
Mark Twain Birthplace State Historic Site, Florida, MO......................815
Marland's Grand Home, Ponca City, OK...1212
Marquette County Historical Society, Westfield, WI......................1627
Martin County Historical Museum, Stanton, TX......................1453
The Martin D'Arcy Museum of Art: The Loyola University Museum of Medieval, Renaissance and Baroque Art, Chicago, IL......................424
The Mary Brogan Museum of Art and Science, Tallahassee, FL 347
Mary G. Hardin Center for Cultural Arts, Gadsden, AL......................10
Mary McLeod Bethune Council House National Historic Site, Washington, DC......................283
Mashantucket Pequot Museum and Research Center, Mashantucket, CT........248
Maui Ocean Center, Maalaea, HI 401
Maxwell Museum of Anthropology, Albuquerque, NM......................934
Mazomanie Historical Society, Mazomanie, WI......................1608
McNamara House Museum, Victoria, TX ..1457
McPherson County Old Mill Museum and Park, Lindsborg, KS......................550
Meadows Museum of Art of Centenary College, Shreveport, LA......................601
Melrose Plantation Home Complex, Melrose, LA......................592
Mennonite Heritage Center, Harleysville, PA......................1258
Meriden Historical Society, Inc., Meriden, CT......................249
Meriwether Lewis Dredge Museum, Brownville, NE......................858
Mesa Verde National Park Museum, Mesa Verde National Park, CO..............228
Mexic-Arte Museum, Austin, TX 1391
Mexican Fine Arts Center Museum, Chicago, IL......................424

The Mexican Museum, San Francisco, CA......................166
Mid-America All Indian Center, Wichita, KS......................562
Midland County Historical Museum, Midland, TX......................1438
Military Veterans Museum, Inc., Oshkosh, WI......................1616
Millicent Rogers Museum of Northern New Mexico, Taos, NM......................952
Milton House Museum Historic Site, Milton, WI......................1610
Mineral Museum, Butte, MT......................843
Minnesota Museum of American Art, Saint Paul, MN......................791
Mission Houses Museum, Honolulu, HI 397
Mission San Antonio de Padua, Jolon, CA......................105
Mississippi Armed Forces Museum, Camp Shelby, MS......................799
Mississippi Crafts Center, Ridgeland, MS ...807
Mississippi Society Daughters of the American Revolution Rosalie House Museum, Natchez, MS......................805
Missoula Art Museum, Missoula, MT.........851
The Mitchell Museum of the American Indian, Evanston, IL......................435
Mizel Museum, Denver, CO......................213
Montclair Historical Society, Montclair, NJ......................912
Montgomery Museum of Fine Arts, Montgomery, AL 16
Moores Creek National Battlefield, Currie, NC......................1097
The Morikami Museum and Japanese Gardens, Delray Beach, FL......................305
Mormon Visitors Center, Independence, MO......................818
Morristown National Historical Park, Morristown, NJ......................914
Moses Myers House, Norfolk, VA 1522
Mote Marine Laboratory/Aquarium, Sarasota, FL......................345
Mount Clare Museum House, Baltimore, MD......................635
Mount Dora Center for the Arts, Mount Dora, FL......................327
Mount Independence Historic Site, Orwell, VT......................1484
Mt. Kearsarge Indian Museum, Warner, NH......................897
Mountain Heritage Center, Cullowhee, NC......................1097
Museo de las Americas, Denver, CO 213
Museo de Las Americas, San Juan, PR.......1642
Museo ItaloAmericano, San Francisco, CA......................167
The Museum at Warm Springs, Warm Springs, OR......................1238
The Museum for African Art, Long Island City, NY......................1011
Museum of Ancient Artifacts, Las Vegas, NV......................879
Museum of Appalachia, Clinton, TN.........1363
Museum of Craft and Folk Art, San Francisco, CA......................167
Museum of Indian Arts & Culture/Laboratory of Anthropology, Santa Fe, NM......................948
Museum of Indian Culture, Allentown, PA......................1239
Museum of Jewish Heritage-A Living Memorial to the Holocaust, New York, NY......................1032
Museum of New Mexico, Santa Fe, NM.....949
Museum of Northern Arizona, Flagstaff, AZ......................33
Museum of Small Town Life, Dover, DE 270
Museum of Spanish Colonial Art - MoSCA, Santa Fe, NM......................949
Museum of the African Diaspora, San Francisco, CA......................167

Culturally Specific—Continued

The Museum of the Confederacy, Richmond, VA..........1531

Museum of the Gulf Coast, Port Arthur, TX..........1444

Museum of the Mountain Man, Pinedale, WY..........1637

Museum of the Plains Indian, Browning, MT..........843

Museum of the Southern Jewish Experience, Jackson, MS..........803

Museum of Women's History, Billings, MT..........841

My Jewish Discovery Place Children's Museum, Fort Lauderdale, FL..........308

Mystic Arts Center, Mystic, CT..........250

Nantucket Historical Association, Nantucket, MA..........696

The National African-American Archives and Museum, Mobile, AL..........15

National Afro-American Museum & Cultural Center, Wilberforce, OH..........1191

National Czech & Slovak Museum & Library, Cedar Rapids, IA..........509

National Firearms Museum, Fairfax, VA..1504

National Football Museum, Inc., Canton, OH..........1145

The National Great Blacks in Wax Museum, Inc., Baltimore, MD..........635

National Hall of Fame for Famous American Indians, Anadarko, OK..........1196

National Hispanic Cultural Center, Art Museum, Albuquerque, NM..........935

National Museum of African Art, Smithsonian Institution, Washington, DC..........285

National Museum of American Jewish History, Philadelphia, PA..........1284

National Museum of the American Indian, Smithsonian Institution, New York, NY..........1034

National Museum of Women in the Arts, Washington, DC..........287

National Society of the Sons of the American Revolution, Louisville, KY.....578

National Yiddish Book Center, Amherst, MA..........659

Native American Exhibit, National Kateri Shrine, Fonda, NY..........991

Native American Heritage Museum at Highland Mission State Historic Site, Highland, KS..........544

Native American Museum, Terre Haute, IN..........500

Navajo Nation Museum, Window Rock, AZ..........53

Neill-Cochran Museum House, Austin, TX..........1391

Nevada State Fire Museum & Comstock Firemen's Museum, Virginia City, NV....882

New Braunfels Conservation Society, New Braunfels, TX..........1440

The New England Carousel Museum, Bristol, CT..........236

New England Fire and History Museum, Brewster, MA..........670

New Hampshire Historical Society, Concord, NH..........885

The New Museum of Contemporary Art, New York, NY..........1035

Newark Valley Depot Museum, Newark Valley, NY..........1042

Newaygo County Museum, Newaygo, MI...758

Nez Perce National Historical Park, Spalding, ID..........409

Niagara Gorge Discovery Center, Niagara Falls, NY..........1042

Nichols House Museum, Boston, MA..........668

Noah Webster House/West Hartford Historical Society, West Hartford, CT.....265

Nordic Heritage Museum, Seattle, WA......1567

North Carolina A&T State University Galleries, Greensboro, NC..........1104

North Carolina Pottery Center, Seagrove, NC..........1119

North Platte Valley Museum, Gering, NE....861

Northeast Louisiana Delta African American Heritage Museum, Monroe, LA..........592

Notah Dineh Museum, Cortez, CO..........208

Nowetah's American Indian Museum & Store, New Portland, ME..........615

Occoneechee State Park, Clarksville, VA...1501

The Octagon House, Hudson, WI..........1600

Odyssey Maritime Discovery Center, Seattle, WA..........1567

Old Exchange & Provost Dungeon, Charleston, SC..........1326

Old Lighthouse Museum, Michigan City, IN..........491

Old Ordinary House Museum, Hingham, MA..........687

The Old Schwamb Mill, Arlington, MA......660

The Oldest House Museum/Wrecker's Museum, Key West, FL..........318

Oneida Nation Museum, De Pere, WI........1594

Orange County Historical Museum, Hillsborough, NC..........1107

Orcas Island Historical Museum, Orcas Island, WA..........1560

Oregon Air & Space Museum, Eugene, OR..........1224

Orland Historical Society, Orland, ME........617

Oroville Chinese Temple, Oroville, CA.......136

Otis Chidester Scout Museum of Southern Arizona, Tucson, AZ..........50

Ottawa County Historical Museum, Port Clinton, OH..........1183

Outagamie Museum, Appleton, WI...........1589

The Oyster and Maritime Museum of Chincoteague, Chincoteague, VA...........1501

Ozark National Scenic Riverways, Van Buren, MO..........839

P.H. Sullivan Museum and Genealogy Library, Zionsville, IN..........504

Pacific Asia Museum, Pasadena, CA...........140

Pacific Coast Air Museum, Santa Rosa, CA..........184

Pacific Grove Art Center Associates, Inc., Pacific Grove, CA..........137

Pacific University Museum, Forest Grove, OR..........1224

Palace of the Governors/New Mexico History Museum, Santa Fe, NM..........949

Pamunkey Indian Museum, King William, VA..........1512

The Park-McCullough House, North Bennington, VT..........1483

Paul Bunyan Logging Camp Museum, Eau Claire, WI..........1596

Paul W. Bryant Museum, Tuscaloosa, AL......19

Paynes Creek Historic State Park, Bowling Green, FL..........297

Pendarvis State Historic Site, Mineral Point, WI..........1614

Pennsbury Manor, Morrisville, PA............1272

Pennsylvania German Cultural Heritage Center at Kutztown University, Kutztown, PA..........1265

Petaluma Adobe State Historic Park, Petaluma, CA..........142

Pewabic Pottery, Detroit, MI..........737

Piatt Castles, West Liberty, OH..........1190

Pimeria Alta Historical Society, Nogales, AZ..........37

Pinson Mounds State Archaeological Area, Pinson, TN..........1383

Pioneer Air Museum, Fairbanks, AK..........24

Pitot House Museum, New Orleans, LA......598

Placer County Museums, Auburn, CA..........72

Point of Honor, Lynchburg, VA..........1515

Polish Heritage Center, Ashton, NE..........856

Polynesian Cultural Center, Laie, HI..........401

Pony Express Museum, Saint Joseph, MO..........831

Pope County Historical Society, Glenwood, MN..........776

Pope John Paul II Cultural Center, Washington, DC..........289

Portuguese Historical Museum, San Jose, CA..........172

Post Rock Museum, La Crosse, KS..........547

Powers Museum, Carthage, MO..........812

Pratt Museum, Homer, AK..........25

Provincetown Art Association and Museum, Provincetown, MA..........704

Prudence Crandall Museum, Canterbury, CT..........237

Pueblo Grande Museum and Archaeological Park, Phoenix, AZ..........42

Putney Historical Society, Putney, VT.......1485

R.S. Barnwell Memorial Garden and Art Center, Shreveport, LA..........601

Red Clay State Historic Park, Cleveland, TN..........1363

Red Earth Museum, Oklahoma City, OK...1210

Redington Museum, Waterville, ME..........625

Redwood County Historical Society, Redwood Falls, MN..........787

Reitz Home Museum, Evansville, IN...........476

Renfrew Museum & Park, Waynesboro, PA..........1306

Reverend Dan Foster House, Museum of the Weathersfield Historical Society, Weathersfield, VT..........1489

Rhinelander Logging Museum, Rhinelander, WI..........1620

Richland County Museum, Lexington, OH..........1172

Ritz Theatre & LaVilla Museum, Jacksonville, FL..........315

Riverside Nature Center, Kerrville, TX......1432

Robert S. Peabody Museum of Archaeology, Andover, MA..........660

Rock House Museum, Wytheville, VA......1546

Rockport Art Association, Rockport, MA...705

Roger Williams National Memorial, Providence, RI..........1318

Rogue Gallery & Art Center, Medford, OR..........1228

Romanian Ethnic Art Museum, Cleveland, OH..........1156

The Root House Museum, Marietta, GA......379

Ross County Historical Society, Inc., Chillicothe, OH..........1147

Roswell Museum and Art Center, Roswell, NM..........946

Rowley Historical Society, Rowley, MA......706

Royalton Historical Society, Royalton, VT..........1486

Sacramento Mountains Historical Museum, Cloudcroft, NM..........938

St. Photios Greek Orthodox National Shrine, Saint Augustine, FL..........340

San Antonio Missions National Historical Park, San Antonio, TX..........1449

San Diego Air & Space Museum, San Diego, CA..........159

San Diego Museum of Man, San Diego, CA..........160

Sanchez Adobe Historic Site, Pacifica, CA..........138

Santa Fe Trail Center, Larned, KS..........547

Satterlee Clark House, Horicon, WI..........1600

Satwiwa Native American Indian Culture Center, Thousand Oaks, CA..........191

Schingoethe Center for Native American Cultures, Aurora, IL..........412

Schwenkfelder Library & Heritage Center, Pennsburg, PA..........1275

Scituate Maritime and Irish Mossing Museum, Scituate, MA..........709

The Scottish Tartans Museum, Franklin,
    NC...1102
Seabrook Village, Midway, GA 380
Seattle Asian Art Museum, Seattle, WA..1569
Second Street Gallery, Charlottesville, VA.1500
The Sequoyah Birthplace Museum,
    Vonore, TN...1385
1719 Hans Herr House & Museum,
    Willow Street, PA.......................................1308
1797 Ezekiel Harris House, Augusta, GA....366
1761 Pownalborough Courthouse,
    Dresden, ME..610
Sewall-Belmont House and Museum,
    Washington, DC...290
Seward House, Auburn, NY.........................959
Shaker Historical Society, Shaker
    Heights, OH..1185
The Shaker Museum and Library, Old
    Chatham, NY..1045
Sheldon Jackson Museum, Sitka, AK.............27
Sheldon Memorial Art Gallery and
    Sculpture Garden/University of
    Nebraska-Lincoln, Lincoln, NE 867
Sherman Indian Museum, Riverside, CA.....150
Shiloh Museum of Ozark History,
    Springdale, AR..68
Shimmin Tveit Museum, Forbes, ND.........1131
Shoshone Tribal Cultural Center, Fort
    Washakie, WY 1633
Sibley House Historic Site, Mendota, MN...780
Sierra Mono Indian Museum, North Fork,
    CA..131
Sioux Indian Museum, Rapid City, SD......1355
Skagit County Historical Museum, La
    Conner, WA...1557
Skirball Cultural Center, Los Angeles,
    CA..121
Skirball Museum Cincinnati Hebrew
    Union College-Jewish Institute of
    Religion, Cincinnati, OH.........................1151
Skowhegan History House Inc.,
    Skowhegan, ME..622
Sky City Cultural Center, Pueblo of
    Acoma, NM...944
Smoki Museum - American Indian Art &
    Culture, Prescott, AZ...................................43
Sod House Museum, Gothenburg, NE 862
The Somerset County Historical Society,
    Inc., Princess Anne, MD 650
Sophienburg Museum & Archives Inc.,
    New Braunfels, TX 1440
Sosa-Carrillo-Fremont House Museum,
    Tucson, AZ..50
South Bannock County Historical Center,
    Lava Hot Springs, ID 407
South Charleston Museum, South
    Charleston, WV...1586
South Dakota State Historical Society,
    Pierre, SD..1353
Southern Plains Indian Museum,
    Anadarko, OK..1196
Southern Ute Cultural Center and
    Museum, Ignacio, CO 223
Spertus Museum, Chicago, IL 427
Spokane House Interpretive Center, Nine
    Mile Falls, WA..1559
Spring Valley Nature Center & Heritage
    Farm, Schaumburg, IL 457
Stagecoach Inn Museum Complex,
    Newbury Park, CA 130
Stanley Museum, Inc., Kingfield, ME.........613
Stanly County Historic Preservation
    Commission and Museum, Albemarle,
    NC..1088
Stewart M. Lord Memorial Historical
    Society, Inc., Burlington, ME 608
Still National Osteopathic Museum,
    Kirksville, MO..824
Strasburg Museum, Strasburg, VA..............1539
Sunset Crater Volcano National
    Monument, Flagstaff, AZ 33

Swedish American Museum Association
    of Chicago, Chicago, IL..............................428
Sweet Briar Museum, Sweet Briar, VA..1540
Swiss Historical Village, New Glarus, WI.1615

Tamastslikt Cultural Institute, Pendleton,
    OR..1230
Tannenbaum Historic Park, Greensboro,
    NC..1104
Tarpon Springs Heritage Museum, Tarpon
    Springs, FL..351
The Temple Judea Museum of Reform
    Congregation Keneseth Israel, Elkins
    Park, PA...1251
Tennent Art Foundation Gallery,
    Honolulu, HI...398
Tennessee Historical Commission,
    Nashville, TN...1380
Texas Maritime Museum, Rockport, TX....1446
Texas Music Museum, Austin, TX 1392
This Is The Place Heritage Park, Salt
    Lake City, UT...1472
Thomas Hart Benton Home and Studio
    State Historic Site, Kansas City, MO 823
Thomaston Historical Society,
    Thomaston, ME...624
Thousand Islands Museum, Clayton, NY.....979
The Toledo Museum of Art, Toledo, OH....1187
The Toledo Zoo, Toledo, OH......................1187
Toltec Mounds Archeological State Park,
    Scott, AR...68
Tomaquag Indian Memorial Museum,
    Exeter, RI..1311
Tonto National Monument, Roosevelt,
    AZ..43
Town Creek Indian Mound State Historic
    Site, Mount Gilead, NC.............................1111
Trailside Nature Museum, Cross River,
    NY..983
Treasures of the Sea Exhibit,
    Georgetown, DE..271
Tri-County Historical Society &
    Museum, Inc., Herington, KS 544
Triangle Tattoo & Museum, Fort Bragg,
    CA..95
Tsa Mo Ga Memorial Museum, Plains,
    TX..1443
Tubman African-American Museum,
    Macon, GA 378
Tunica-Biloxi Native American Museum,
    Marksville, LA...591

The Ukrainian Museum, New York, NY....1040
Ukrainian Museum-Archives, Inc.,
    Cleveland, OH 1156
Umpqua Discovery Center, Reedsport,
    OR..1234
United States Capitol, Washington, DC 293
The University of Michigan Exhibit
    Museum of Natural History, Ann
    Arbor, MI..725
U.S. Army Signal Corps Museum, Fort
    Gordon, GA 372
U.S. Cavalry Museum, Fort Riley, KS.........540

Valley Community Historical Society,
    Inc., Valley, NE...874
Vann House, Chatsworth, GA 368
Ventura County Maritime Museum, Inc.,
    Oxnard, CA..137
Vernon County Historical Museum,
    Viroqua, WI...1625
The Virginia War Museum, Newport
    News, VA...1520

Waimea Arboretum and Botanical Garden
    in Waimea Valley Audubon Center,
    Haleiwa, HI...392
The Walker African American Museum &
    Research Center, Las Vegas, NV 880
Walt Whitman Birthplace State Historic
    Site and Interpretive Center,
    Huntington Station, NY..............................1001

Wanapum Dam Heritage Center, Beverly,
    WA 1549
Wapello County Historical Museum,
    Ottumwa, IA..526
Warner House, Portsmouth, NH 895
Washington Museum & Tourist Center,
    Washington, LA...603
Watermen's Museum, Yorktown, VA...........1547
Weir Farm National Historic Site, Wilton,
    CT..267
West of the Pecos Museum, Pecos, TX 1443
West Pasco Historical Society Museum
    and Library, New Port Richey, FL 329
Western Aerospace Museum, Oakland,
    CA..134
Western New Mexico University
    Museum, Silver City, NM 951
Whitingham Historical Museum,
    Whitingham, VT...1490
Wichita Center for the Arts, Wichita, KS.....563
Wickliffe Mounds State Historic Site,
    Wickliffe, KY..584
Willa Cather Pioneer Memorial and
    Educational Foundation, Red Cloud,
    NE..872
The William Breman Jewish Heritage
    Museum, Atlanta, GA..................................364
William Heath Davis House Museum
    administered by Gaslamp Quarter
    Historical Foundation, San Diego, CA....162
William Otis Sawtelle Collections and
    Research Center, Bar Harbor, ME............606
Wilson Czech Opera House Corporation,
    Foundation, Inc. & House of
    Memories Museum, Wilson, KS 564
Wing Luke Asian Museum, Seattle, WA....1569
Wisconsin Veterans Museum-King, King,
    WI..1602
Wisconsin Veterans Museum-Madison,
    Madison, WI..1606
Wolf Creek Indian Village and Museum,
    Bastian, VA..1496
Woodmere Art Museum, Philadelphia, PA.1289
Woodruff Museum of Indian Artifacts,
    Bridgeton, NJ..898
World O' Tools Museum, Waverly, TN......1385
Yale Center for British Art, New Haven,
    CT..254
Ybor City Museum State Park, Tampa,
    FL..351
Yeshiva University Museum at the Center
    for Jewish History, New York, NY........1041

Zimmer Children's Museum, Los
    Angeles, CA..122
Zoar State Memorial, Zoar, OH..................1194

Electricity Museums

A.W.A. Electronic-Communication
    Museum, Bloomfield, NY 963

FPL Energy Encounter, Jensen Beach, FL...316

Museum of Neon Art, Los Angeles, CA......120
Museum of Radio & Technology, Inc.,
    Huntington, WV 1583

New York Power Authority-Niagara
    Power Project Visitors' Center,
    Lewiston, NY...1009
North Anna Nuclear Information Center,
    Mineral, VA...1518

SEE Science Center, Manchester, NH..........892

The World of Energy, Seneca, SC 1341

Fire-Fighting Museums

The American Heritage "Big Red" Fire
    Museum, Louisville, MS.............................804
Ark-La-Tex Antique & Classic Vehicle
    Museum, Shreveport, LA 600

Fire-Fighting Museums—Continued

Atlantic 1, Swampscott, MA.........................714

Aurora Regional Fire Museum, Aurora,
   IL..411

The Bare Cove Fire Museum, Hingham,
   MA...687
Benicia Fire Museum, Benicia, CA...............74
Boston Fire Museum, Boston, MA..............664
Brockton Fire Museum, Brockton, MA.......671

Central Ohio Fire Museum, Columbus,
   OH...1157
Cincinnati Fire Museum, Cincinnati, OH...1149
Cole Land Transportation Museum,
   Bangor, ME...604
Columbia Fire Department Museum,
   Columbia, SC......................................1328
Connecticut Fire Museum, East Windsor,
   CT...239
County of Los Angeles Fire Museum,
   Los Angeles, CA....................................114
Crystal Lake Falls Historical Association,
   Barton, VT..1476

Dallas Firefighter's Museum, Inc., Dallas,
   TX..1404
Denver Firefighters Museum, Denver, CO...211

Eureka Fire Museum, Milltown, NJ............911

FASNY Museum of Fire Fighting,
   Hudson, NY..1000
Fire Museum of Maryland, Inc.,
   Lutherville, MD....................................649
Fire Museum of Memphis, Memphis, TN..1373
Fire Museum of Missouri, Willow
   Springs, MO...840
Fire Museum of Texas, Beaumont, TX......1394
The Firehouse Museum, Ellicott City,
   MD..643
Firehouse Museum, San Diego, CA............156
Fireman's Hall Museum, Philadelphia, PA.1279
Fort Wayne Firefighters Museum, Fort
   Wayne, IN..477
Fostoria Area Historical Museum,
   Fostoria, OH.......................................1164
Friends of Firemen's Museum, New
   Bern, NC...1112
Friendship Fire Company Museum,
   Woodbury, NJ.......................................931
Friendship Firehouse, Alexandria, VA........1492

Hall of Flame Museum of Firefighting,
   Phoenix, AZ...40
Homeville Antique Fire Department,
   Homer, NY..999
Hose 5 Fire Museum, Bangor, ME..............604
Houston Fire Museum, Houston, TX.........1427

Jacksonville Fire Museum, Jacksonville,
   FL..314
Jamestown Fire Department Memorial
   Museum, Jamestown, RI........................1312

Lincoln Fire & Rescue Department
   Museum, Lincoln, NE............................866

Long Beach Fire Museum, Long Beach,
   CA...111

Maple Valley Historical Museum, Maple
   Valley, WA..1559
The Museum of Mobile, Mobile, AL............14

Nevada State Fire Museum & Comstock
   Firemen's Museum, Virginia City, NV....882
New Bedford Fire Museum, New
   Bedford, MA...696
New England Fire and History Museum,
   Brewster, MA..670
New Orleans Fire Dept. Museum &
   Educational Center, New Orleans, LA....597
New York City Fire Museum, New York,
   NY..1035

Newton Fire Department, Newton, NJ.........917
North Plainfield Exempt Firemen's
   Association, North Plainfield, NJ............917
Northeast Georgia History Center at
   Brenau University, Gainesville, GA........373

Oklahoma Firefighters Museum,
   Oklahoma City, OK.............................1209
Old Firehouse Museum, Greenville, MS......800
Otero Museum Association, La Junta, CO...224

Plantation Historical Museum, Plantation,
   FL..337
Robert A. Bogan Fire Museum, Baton
   Rouge, LA..587
Rock Springs Historical Museum, Rock
   Springs, WY.......................................1638

San Francisco Fire Department Museum,
   San Francisco, CA.................................169
Smokey Bear Museum, Capitan, NM..........937

Toledo Firefighters Museum, Toledo, OH..1187

Uppertown Firefighters Museum, Astoria,
   OR...1219

Volunteer Firemen's Mall and Museum of
   Kingston, Kingston, NY.......................1008

Wildland Firefighters Museum, Capitan,
   NM...937
Woodbine International Fire Museum,
   Woodbine, GA......................................392

York County Heritage Trust, Fire
   Museum, York, PA..............................1309

Forestry Museums

Baldwin County Heritage Museum,
   Elberta, AL..8

Chippokes Farm & Forestry Museum,
   Surry, VA...1540

Dubois Museum, Dubois, WY.................1632

Fisher Museum of Forestry, Petersham,
   MA...702
Forest History Center, Grand Rapids, MN...777

Hoo-Hoo International Forestry Museum,
   Gurdon, AR..59

Mississippi Agriculture &
   Forestry/National Agricultural Aviation
   Museum, Jackson, MS...........................802

New England Maple Museum, Pittsford,
   VT...1484
North Carolina Museum of Forestry,
   Whiteville, NC.....................................1122

Oklahoma Forest Heritage Center,
   Broken Bow, OK..................................1197

Pennsylvania Lumber Museum, Galeton,
   PA..1254
Petrified Forest Museum, Calistoga, CA......80
Port Gamble Historic Museum, Port
   Gamble, WA..1562

Rangeley Lakes Region Logging
   Museum, Rangeley, ME..........................620

Southern Forest Heritage Museum, Long
   Leaf, LA..591
Southern Forest World, Waycross, GA........391

Texas Forestry Museum, Lufkin, TX.........1436

World Forestry Center, Portland, OR.........1233

Furniture Museums

Beauchamp Newman Museum, Elizabeth,
   WV..1581

Bergen County Historical Society, River
   Edge, NJ...923
Bob Jones University Museum & Gallery,
   Inc., Greenville, SC.............................1333
Boscobel, Garrison, NY...........................993
Buccleuch Mansion, New Brunswick, NJ....915

Carbon County Museum, Rawlins, WY.....1637
Casa Blanca Museum, San Juan, PR.........1642
Cassia County Museum, Burley, ID............404
The Chicago Athenaeum: Museum of
   Architecture and Design, Galena, IL........436
Chinqua-Penn Plantation, Reidsville, NC...1117
Clifton Community Historical Society,
   Clifton, KS...535
Clinton County Historical Society
   Paine-Gillam-Scott Museum, Saint
   Johns, MI...763
Crook County Museum & Art Gallery,
   Sundance, WY.....................................1638
Crystal Lake Falls Historical Association,
   Barton, VT..1476

The Dana-Thomas House State Historic
   Site, Springfield, IL..............................458
Dinsmore Homestead Foundation,
   Burlington, KY......................................566
Dr. Jose Celso Barbosa Museum &
   Library, Bayamon, PR..........................1641

Fall River County Historical Museum,
   Hot Springs, SD..................................1348
Fort Delaware Museum of Colonial
   History, Narrowsburg, NY....................1017
Fort Smith Museum of History, Fort
   Smith, AR..58
The French Legation Museum, Austin,
   TX...1390

General Adam Stephen House,
   Martinsburg, WV.................................1584

Hancock Historical Society, Hancock,
   NH..888
Hills and Dales Estate, LaGrange, GA.........375
Historic Auto Attractions, Roscoe, IL.........456
Historic General Dodge House, Council
   Bluffs, IA...512
The Historical Society of the Town of
   Warwick, Warwick, NY........................1082

Jeane Dixon Museum and Library,
   Strasburg, VA......................................1538
Johnson County Museum of History,
   Franklin, IN..478

Kensington Mansion, Eastover, SC...........1332
Kirkland Museum of Fine & Decorative
   Art, Denver, CO....................................212

Lexington County Museum, Lexington,
   SC..1336

Marvin Newton House, Brookfield, VT.....1477
McMinn County Living Heritage
   Museum, Athens, TN...........................1360
Merchant's House Museum, New York,
   NY...1029
Midway Museum, Inc., Midway, GA..........379
Montpelier Mansion, Laurel, MD..............648
The Museum of Miniature Houses and
   Other Collections, Inc., Carmel, IN.........471
The Museum of Southern History,
   Sugarland, TX.....................................1454
Museum of the Puerto Rican Family of
   the 19th Century, San Juan, PR.............1643

The Parry Mansion Museum, New Hope,
   PA...1273
Pioneer Florida Museum Association,
   Inc., Dade City, FL...............................302
Pointe Coupee Museum, New Roads, LA....599

Rensselaer County Historical Society,
   Troy, NY..1079

The Scarsdale Historical Society, Scarsdale, NY 1066
Silt Historical Society, Silt, CO 232
Society for the Preservation of Long Island Antiquities, Cold Spring Harbor, NY 980
The Stephen Phillips House, Salem, MA 707
The Stickley Museum at Craftsman Farms, Parsippany, NJ 920

Turner House Museum, Hattiesburg, MS 801

Wickersham House Museum (Tanana-Yukon Historical Society), Fairbanks, AK 24
Wilder Memorial Museum, Strawberry Point, IA 528
Wright's Ferry Mansion, Columbia, PA 1248

Gun Museums

Archives of J.S.G. Boggs, Brandon, FL 298

Bosque Memorial Museum, Clifton, TX 1400

Carbon County Museum, Rawlins, WY 1637
Civil War Life - The Soldier's Museum, Fredericksburg, VA 1505

Dane G. Hansen Memorial Museum, Logan, KS 550
Dixie Gun Works' Old Car Museum, Union City, TN 1384
Don F. Pratt Memorial Museum, Fort Campbell, KY 568

Favell Museum Inc., Klamath Falls, OR 1227
Ford County Historical Society, Paxton, IL 450
Fort Lewis Military Museum, Fort Lewis, WA 1554
Fort MacArthur Museum, San Pedro, CA 176
The Frazier International History Museum, Louisville, KY 576

The General Douglas L. McBride Museum, New Mexico Military Institute, Roswell, NM 945

Honolulu Police Department Law Enforcement Museum, Honolulu, HI 396
Hurst Ranch Historical Foundation, West Covina, CA 197

J.M. Davis Arms & Historical Museum, Claremore, OK 1198
Jefferson County Museum, Charles Town, WV 1580

Kentucky Military History Museum, Frankfort, KY 569

La Porte County Historical Society Museum, La Porte, IN 487
Law Enforcement Memorial Association, Inc., Roselle, IL 456
Lynden Pioneer Museum, Lynden, WA 1559

Museum of Southern History, Jacksonville, FL 315

National Firearms Museum, Fairfax, VA 1504
National Infantry Museum, Fort Benning, GA 372
Navy UDT-SEAL Museum, Fort Pierce, FL 309
New York State Military Museum and Veterans Research Center, Saratoga Springs, NY 1065

Oregon Military Museum, Clackamas, OR 1221

Pennsylvania Longrifle Museum, Nazareth, PA 1273

Remington Firearms Museum and Country Store, Ilion, NY 1002

Saunders Memorial Museum, Berryville, AR 55
Shakespeare Ghost Town, Lordsburg, NM 942
Springfield Armory National Historic Site, Springfield, MA 710

The Virginia War Museum, Newport News, VA 1520

Warren Rifles Confederate Museum, Front Royal, VA 1508
Watervliet Arsenal's Museum of the Big Guns, Watervliet, NY 1084
Woolaroc Museum, Bartlesville, OK 1197

Hobby Museums

American Radio Relay League-Museum of Amateur Radio, Newington, CT 256
Automobile Driving Museum, Los Angeles, CA 112

Carroll Reece Museum, Johnson City, TN 1367
Clovis Depot Model Train Museum, Clovis, NM 939
Crossroads of America, Bethlehem, NH 883

Decorative Arts Collection, Inc. Museum of Decorative Painting, Wichita, KS 561

Gay Nineties Button and Doll Museum, Eureka Springs, AR 57
Golden State Model Railroad Museum, Point Richmond, CA 143

Matchbox Road Museum, Newfield, NJ 917
Medina Railroad Museum, Medina, NY 1014
Mennonite Quilting Center, Reedley, CA 147
Museum of Automobile Art and Design, Syracuse, NY 1076

National Association of Miniature Enthusiasts, Carmel, IN 472
The National Toy Train Museum, Strasburg, PA 1301
North Dakota Fishing Hall of Fame and Museum, Garrison, ND 1131

O. Winston Link Museum, Roanoke, VA 1535

Paper Airplane Museum and the Tin Can Man of Maui, Kahului Central Maui, HI 399

San Diego Model Railroad Museum, Inc., San Diego, CA 159

Trainland U.S.A., Colfax, IA 511

Wooden Nickel Historical Museum, San Antonio, TX 1452
World Kite Museum & Hall of Fame, Long Beach, WA 1558
World O' Tools Museum, Waverly, TN 1385
World of Wings Pigeon Center, Oklahoma City, OK 1211

Yesterday's Children Antique Doll & Toy Museum, Vicksburg, MS 809

Horological Museums

American Clock and Watch Museum, Inc., Bristol, CT 236
American Watchmakers-Clockmakers Institute, Harrison, OH 1168

Bily Clock Museum/Antonin Dvorak Exhibit, Spillville, IA 528

The National Agricultural Center & Hall of Fame, Bonner Springs, KS 534
The National Watch & Clock Museum, Columbia, PA 1247

Old Clock Museum, Pharr, TX 1443

Willard House and Clock Museum, Inc., Grafton, MA 685

Industrial Museums

Agricultural and Industrial Museum, York County Heritage Trust, York, PA 1309
Alexander & Baldwin Sugar Museum, Puunene, HI 401
American Precision Museum Association, Inc., Windsor, VT 1490
American Textile History Museum, Lowell, MA 691
Antique Gas & Steam Engine Museum, Inc., Vista, CA 196
Arkansas Museum of Natural Resources, Smackover, AR 68
Attleboro Area Industrial Museum, Inc., Attleboro, MA 661

Baltimore & Ohio Railroad Museum, Baltimore, MD 629
Baltimore Museum of Industry, Baltimore, MD 630
Butler County History Center & Kansas Oil Museum, El Dorado, KS 537

C. Grier Beam Truck Museum, Cherryville, NC 1096
Champion Mill State Historical Park, Champion, NE 859
Charles River Museum of Industry, Waltham, MA 715
Comer Museum, Morgantown, WV 1585
Coolspring Power Museum, Coolspring, PA 1248
Cornwall Iron Furnace, Cornwall, PA 1248
Crawford Auto-Aviation Museum, Cleveland, OH 1154
Crown Gardens and Archives, Dalton, GA 370
Crystal Lake Falls Historical Association, Barton, VT 1476

Dr Pepper Museum and Free Enterprise Institute, Waco, TX 1458
Door County Maritime Museum (at Sturgeon Bay), Sturgeon Bay, WI 1623
Drake Well Museum, Titusville, PA 1303

East Ely Railroad Depot Museum, Ely, NV 876
Elberton Granite Museum & Exhibit, Elberton, GA 371
Eli Whitney Museum, Inc., Hamden, CT 244
Elwood Haynes Museum, Kokomo, IN 486

Fenton Glass Museum, Williamstown, WV 1589
Frye's Measure Mill, Wilton, NH 897
Furnace Town Living Heritage Museum, Snow Hill, MD 654

George Peabody House Museum, Peabody, MA 701

Hacienda Buena Vista, Ponce, PR 1642
Hamburg State Park Museum, Mitchell, GA 380
Hanford Mills Museum, East Meredith, NY 987
Historic Madison, Inc., Madison, IN 489
Historic Speedwell, Morristown, NJ 913
Historic Walnford, Upper Freehold Twp., NJ 929
Hopewell Furnace National Historic Site, Elverson, PA 1251

International Bluegrass Music Museum, Owensboro, KY 581

Johnson Victrola Museum, Dover, DE 270

Industrial Museums–Continued

Kellogg's Cereal City USA, Battle Creek, MI.................................727

Lightner Museum, Saint Augustine, FL.......339

Lock Museum of America, Inc., Terryville, CT.................................262

Louisville Slugger Museum & Factory, Louisville, KY.................................577

Lowell National Historical Park, Lowell, MA.................................691

Maramec Museum, The James Foundation, Saint James, MO.................830

Matchless Mine Museum (Leadville Assembly), Leadville, CO......................226

Mifflinburg Buggy Museum Association, Inc., Mifflinburg, PA.................1271

Mission Mill Museum Association, Salem, OR.................................1236

Muscatine History & Industry Center/Pearl Button Museum, Muscatine, IA.................................524

Museum of Alaska Transportation & Industry, Inc., Wasilla, AK.................29

Museum of Ceramics, East Liverpool, OH.................................1163

National Museum of Industrial History, Bethlehem, PA.................................1243

National Plastics Center and Museum, Leominster, MA.................................689

New Britain Industrial Museum, New Britain, CT.................................251

Old Dominion Railway Museum, Richmond, VA.................................1531

Old Hidalgo Pumphouse, Hidalgo, TX......1424

Old Iron County Courthouse Museum, Hurley, WI.................................1601

The Old Schwamb Mill, Arlington, MA......660

Petersen Automotive Museum, Los Angeles, CA.................................121

RV/MH Heritage Foundation, Inc., Elkhart, IN.................................475

Railroad Museum of Pennsylvania, Strasburg, PA.................................1302

Reed Gold Mine State Historic Site, Midland, NC.................................1111

Rough & Tumble Engineers Historical Association, Kinzers, PA.................1265

Russell County Historical Society/Fossil Station Museum, Russell, KS.................556

Salt Museum, Liverpool, NY.................................1010

Saugus Iron Works National Historic Site, Saugus, MA.................................708

Slate Valley Museum, Granville, NY.........996

Slater Mill Historic Site, Pawtucket, RI.....1315

Sloane-Stanley Museum and Kent Furnace, Kent, CT.................................247

Sloss Furnaces National Historic Landmark, Birmingham, AL......................5

Southern Forest Heritage Museum, Long Leaf, LA.................................591

The Southern Museum of Civil War and Locomotive History, Kennesaw, GA.......375

Southwest Dairy Museum, Sulphur Springs, TX.................................1454

The Telephone Museum, Ellsworth, ME......610

Texas City Museum, Texas City, TX.........1455

Texas Energy Museum, Beaumont, TX......1395

Venango Museum of Art, Science & Industry, Oil City, PA.................................1274

Vermont Marble Museum, Proctor, VT......1485

W.K. Gordon Center for Industrial History of Texas, Mingus, TX..............1439

The Waltham Museum, Waltham, MA.........716

Watkins Woolen Mill State Historic Site & Park, Lawson, MO.................................825

West Virginia Northern Community College Alumni Association Museum, Wheeling, WV.................................1588

Western Museum of Mining & Industry, Colorado Springs, CO.................................208

The Wolfsonian - Florida International University, Miami Beach, FL.................327

Ybor City Museum State Park, Tampa, FL.................................351

Lapidary Arts Museums

Arizona Mining and Mineral Museum, Phoenix, AZ.................................39

Badlands Petrified Gardens, Kadoka, SD...1349

Comer Museum, Morgantown, WV...........1585

Ginkgo Petrified Forest State Park, Vantage, WA.................................1576

Lizzadro Museum of Lapidary Art, Elmhurst, IL.................................433

Mineral and Lapidary Museum of Henderson County Inc., Hendersonville, NC.................................1105

Mississippi Petrified Forest, Flora, MS.......800

Oregon Trail Regional Museum, Baker City, OR.................................1219

Turquoise Museum, Albuquerque, NM.......936

World Museum of Natural History, Riverside, CA.................................150

Logging and Lumber Museums

Ashland Logging Museum, Inc., Ashland, ME.................................603

Camp Five Museum Foundation, Inc., Laona, WI.................................1604

Camp 6 Logging Museum, Tacoma, WA...1572

Clearwater County Historical Society, Shevlin, MN.................................793

Collier Memorial State Park & Logging Museum, Chiloquin, OR........................1221

Dunn County Historical Society, Menomonie, WI.................................1609

East Jordan Portside Art & Historical Museum, East Jordan, MI.......................739

Fisher Museum of Forestry, Petersham, MA.................................702

Forest Capital State Museum, Perry, FL......337

The Guest House Museum, Fort Bragg, CA.................................95

Heritage House Museum of Montgomery County, Mount Ida, AR......................64

Hoo-Hoo International Forestry Museum, Gurdon, AR.................................59

Iron County Museum, Caspian, MI.............731

Lake County Historical Society, Two Harbors, MN.................................794

Louisville Slugger Museum & Factory, Louisville, KY.................................577

Marinette County Historical Museum, Marinette, WI.................................1607

Menominee County Heritage Museum, Menominee, MI.................................754

Merrill Historical Museum, Merrill, WI.....1609

Midland County Historical Society, Midland, MI.................................755

Miracle of America Museum Inc., Polson, MT.................................852

Mississippi Agriculture & Forestry/National Agricultural Aviation Museum, Jackson, MS.................................802

Nici Self Museum, Centennial, WY...........1630

North Carolina Museum of Forestry, Whiteville, NC.................................1122

Old Town Hall Museum, Fifield, WI.........1597

PALCO, Scotia, CA.................................186

Patten Lumbermen's Museum, Inc., Patten, ME.................................618

Paul Bunyan Logging Camp Museum, Eau Claire, WI.................................1596

Pennsylvania Lumber Museum, Galeton, PA.................................1254

Port Gamble Historic Museum, Port Gamble, WA.................................1562

Rangeley Lakes Region Logging Museum, Rangeley, ME......................620

Rhinelander Logging Museum, Rhinelander, WI.................................1620

Riverside Museum, La Crosse, WI............1603

Samoa Cookhouse & Logging Museum, Samoa, CA.................................155

Southern Forest Heritage Museum, Long Leaf, LA.................................591

Umpqua Discovery Center, Reedsport, OR.................................1234

Washburn Historical Museum & Cultural Center, Inc. aka Washburn Cultural Center, Washburn, WI.................................1625

Mappariums

Historical Society of the Tonawandas, Inc., Tonawanda, NY.................................1078

Jay I. Kislak Foundation, Miami Lakes, FL.................................327

Museum of Surveying, Lansing, MI...........750

Pioneer Auto Trails Historical Society (PATHS), Tucson, AZ.................................50

Mining Museums

Alabama Mining Museum, Dora, AL..............7

Alpine County Museum, Markleeville, CA.................................124

Argo Gold Mine & Mill Museum, Idaho Springs, CO.................................223

Arizona Mining and Mineral Museum, Phoenix, AZ.................................39

Aspen Historical Society, Aspen, CO...........202

Baxter Springs Heritage Center and Museum, Baxter Springs, KS.................533

Big Thunder Gold Mine, Keystone, SD.....1349

Bisbee Mining & Historical Museum, Bisbee, AZ.................................30

Black Hills Mining Museum, Lead, SD.....1350

Bob Campbell Geology Museum, Clemson, SC.................................1328

Bodie State Historic Park, Bridgeport, CA.................................79

Brimstone Museum, Sulphur, LA.................602

Butte County Pioneer Memorial Museum, Oroville, CA.................................136

California State Mining & Mineral Museum, Mariposa, CA.................................124

The Central Museum, Central, AK...............23

Colfax County Society of Art, History and Archaeology, Raton, NM.................945

Comer Museum, Morgantown, WV...........1585

Coppertown U.S.A., Calumet, MI..............731

Creede Underground Mining Museum, Creede, CO.................................208

Curry Historical Society Museum, Gold Beach, OR.................................1225

Cuyuna Range Historical Society & Museum, Crosby, MN 772

Dahlonega Gold Museum State Historic Site, Dahlonega, GA..............369

Eckley Miners' Village, Eckley, PA..............1251
Elberton Granite Museum & Exhibit, Elberton, GA..............371

Folsom History Museum, Folsom, CA..........95
Fort Wilkins Historic Complex, Copper Harbor, MI..............733
Frankfort Area Historical Museum, West Frankfort, IL..............464
Franklin Mineral Museum, Franklin, NJ.....904

Galena Mining & Historical Museum, Galena, KS..............541
Grand Encampment Museum, Inc., Encampment, WY 1632
Grant County Historical Museum, Canyon City, OR 1221
Groveland Yosemite Gateway Museum, Groveland, CA..............101

Heritage House Museum of Montgomery County, Mount Ida, AR..............64
Heritage Museum & Gallery, Leadville, CO..............226
The Heritage Museum & Underhill Museum, Idaho Springs, CO..............223
Homestake Gold Mine Visitor Center, Lead, SD 1351
Huerfano County Historical Society, including The Walsenburg Mining Museum & Ft. Francisco Museum of La Veta, Walsenburg, CO..............234

Idaho Museum of Mining and Geology, Boise, ID..............404
Iron County Museum, Caspian, MI..............731
Iron Mountain Iron Mine, Vulcan, MI 766
Ironwood Area Historical Museum, Ironwood, MI..............747
Ironworld Discovery Center, Chisholm, MN..............771

Jerome State Historic Park, Jerome, AZ 36
Juneau-Douglas City Museum, Juneau, AK..............26

Kentucky Coal Mining Museum, Benham, KY..............565
Klondike Gold Rush National Historical Park, Seattle, WA 1566

Lafayette Miners Museum, Lafayette, CO ...224
Leadville National Mining Hall of Fame & Museum, Leadville, CO..............226
Luzerne County Historical Society, Wilkes-Barre, PA..............1307

Matchless Mine Museum (Leadville Assembly), Leadville, CO..............226
Mineral County Museum & Historical Society, Superior, MT 854
Miners Foundry Cultural Center, Nevada City, CA..............129
Minnesota Museum of Mining, Chisholm, MN..............771
Museum of Anthracite Mining, Weatherly, PA 1307

Nevada County Historical Society, Inc., Nevada City, CA..............130
New Almaden Quicksilver Mining Museum, San Jose, CA..............172
Nici Self Museum, Centennial, WY..........1630

Old New-Gate Prison and Copper Mine, East Granby, CT..............238

Pioneer Museum & The Big Stampede, Fairbanks, AK..............24

Pioneer Tunnel Coal Mine & Steam Train, Ashland, PA 1241
Platteville Mining Museum, Platteville, WI 1617
Plumas-Eureka State Park, Blairsden, CA......78
Plymouth Historical Society, Inc., Plymouth, PA..............1295

Raton Museum, Raton, NM..............945
Reed Gold Mine State Historic Site, Midland, NC..............1111
Rock Springs Historical Museum, Rock Springs, WY..............1638

Shakespeare Ghost Town, Lordsburg, NM...942
Silver City Museum, Silver City, NM..........951
Slate Valley Museum, Granville, NY 996
Sterling Hill Mining Museum, Inc., Ogdensburg, NJ..............918

Telluride Historical Museum, Telluride, CO..............233
Tintic Mining Museum, Eureka, UT 1464
Tri-State Mineral Museum, Joplin, MO 820
Turquoise Museum, Albuquerque, NM 936

Underground Gold Miners Museum, Alleghany, CA..............70

Vermont Marble Museum, Proctor, VT......1485
Victor Heritage Museum, Victor, MT..........854

Wallace District Mining Museum, Wallace, ID..............410
Weinman Mineral Museum, White, GA.......391
Western Mining & Railroad Museum, Helper, UT..............1466
Western Museum of Mining & Industry, Colorado Springs, CO..............208
Whiskeytown Unit, Whiskeytown-Shasta-Trinity National Recreation Area, Whiskeytown, CA........198
World Museum of Mining, Butte, MT 843

Money and Numismatics Museums

American Numismatic Association Money Museum, Colorado Springs, CO..............206
The American Numismatic Society, New York, NY..............1020
Archives of J.S.G. Boggs, Brandon, FL.......298

Farmers Bank (The Petersburg Museums), Petersburg, VA..............1525

The Higgins Museum, Okoboji, IA 525

IMF Center, Washington, DC 281

Museum of American Finance, New York, NY..............1031

Squished Penny Museum, Washington, DC..............291

U.S. Army Finance Corps Museum, Fort Jackson, SC..............1333
U.S. Mint-Philadelphia, Philadelphia, PA...1289

Wooden Nickel Historical Museum, San Antonio, TX..............1452

Musical Instruments Museums

Alabama Music Hall of Fame, Tuscumbia, AL..............20
American Classical Music Hall of Fame and Museum, Cincinnati, OH 1148
The American Jazz Museum, Kansas City, MO..............820
America's National Music Museum, Vermillion, SD..............1358

Bagpipe Music Museum, Manchester, NH...891
The Band Museum, Pine Bluff, AR..............66

Conklin Reed Organ & History Museum, Hanover, MI..............745

Delta Blues Museum, Clarksdale, MS..........799

Experience Music Project, Seattle, WA......1565

Festival-Institute, James Dick Foundation, Round Top, TX..............1446
Fostoria Area Historical Museum, Fostoria, OH..............1164
French Cable Station Museum in Orleans, Orleans, MA..............701

Georgia Music Hall of Fame and Museum, Macon, GA..............377
Graceland, Memphis, TN..............1373

Hancock Historical Society, Hancock, NH..............888
Huntington Beach International Surfing Museum, Huntington Beach, CA.............104

John Philip Sousa Museum, Champaign, IL..............416
Johnson Victrola Museum, Dover, DE.........270

Kenneth G. Fiske Museum of The Claremont Colleges, Claremont, CA 85

Lentz Center for Asian Culture, Lincoln, NE..............865
Liberace Museum & Foundation, Las Vegas, NV..............879
Light Crust Doughboys Hall of Fame & Museum - Governor Jim Hogg City Park, Quitman, TX 1444

Museum of Fife and Drum, Ivoryton, CT....246
Museum of Making Music, Carlsbad, CA 81
The Music House Museum, Acme, MI 722
Musical Box Society International, Houston, TX..............1429
Musical Wonder House, Wiscasset, ME......626

Nethercutt Collection, Sylmar, CA 190
New Braunfels Museum of Art & Music, New Braunfels, TX..............1440

Pablo Casals Museum, Old San Juan, PR..1641
Percussive Arts Society Museum, Lawton, OK..............1204

Rebel State Historic Site & Louisiana Country Music Museum, Marthaville, LA..............592
The Rock and Roll Hall of Fame and Museum, Cleveland, OH..............1155

The Schubert Club Museum of Musical Instruments, Saint Paul, MN..............792
STAX Museum of American Soul Music, Memphis, TN..............1376
Stearns Collection of Musical Instruments, Ann Arbor, MI..............725

Texas Music Museum, Austin, TX 1392

Wheels O' Time Museum, Peoria, IL..........451

Yale University Collection of Musical Instruments, New Haven, CT..............255

Philatelic Museums

The Calvin Coolidge Memorial Foundation, Inc., Plymouth, VT 1484

Lawrence L. Lee Scouting Museum, Manchester, NH..............891

National Postal Museum, Smithsonian Institution, Washington, DC..............287

Spellman Museum of Stamps and Postal History, Weston, MA..............719

Photography Museums

Photography Museums–Continued

Albany Regional Museum, Albany, OR 1217
The Albin O. Kuhn Library & Gallery,
  University of Maryland-Baltimore
  County, Baltimore, MD 628
Aperture Foundation, New York, NY 1020
Archives of J.S.G. Boggs, Brandon, FL......298
Aspen Historical Society, Aspen, CO 202
Associated American Jewish Museums,
  Pittsburgh, PA 1290

Baldwin Photo Gallery, Murfreesboro,
  TN 1376
Brooks Academy Museum, Harwich, MA ...686
Burke County Historical Powers Lake
  Complex, Powers Lake, ND 1136

Cazenovia College - Art & Design
  Gallery, Cazenovia, NY 976
The Center for Civil War Photography,
  Gettysburg, PA 1255
Center for Creative Photography, Tucson,
  AZ 48
Center for Photographic Arts, Carmel,
  CA 81
Center for Photography at Woodstock,
  Woodstock, NY 1086
The Central Museum, Central, AK 23
Civil War Life - The Soldier's Museum,
  Fredericksburg, VA 1505
Clifton Community Historical Society,
  Clifton, KS 535
Custer Battlefield Museum, Garryowen,
  MT 847
Czech Center New York, New York, NY 1024

Danvers Archival Center, Danvers, MA.......678
Dishman Art Museum, Beaumont, TX 1394

East Hillsborough Historical Society, Inc.,
  Plant City, FL 337

Fossil Museum, Fossil, OR 1224

Griffin Museum of Photography,
  Winchester, MA 720

Hampton History Museum, Hampton, VA .1509
Hancock Historical Society, Hancock,
  NH 888
Harry Ransom Center at the University
  of Texas at Austin, Austin, TX 1390
Historical Society of Oak Park & River
  Forest, Oak Park, IL 448

International Center of Photography, New
  York, NY 1028
Iowa Great Lakes Maritime Museum,
  Arnolds Park, IA 505

Japanese American National Museum,
  Los Angeles, CA 117

The Light Factory - Museum of
  Photography & Film, Charlotte, NC......1095
Lou Holtz/Upper Ohio Valley Hall of
  Fame, East Liverpool, OH 1163

The Magic Lantern Castle Museum, San
  Antonio, TX 1448
Manhattan Arts Center, Manhattan, KS........551
Mary McLeod Bethune Council House
  National Historic Site, Washington,
  DC 283
Museum of Photographic Arts, San
  Diego, CA 158
Museum of the Southern Jewish
  Experience, Jackson, MS 803

National Academy of Sciences,
  Washington, DC 283
Northeast Document Conservation
  Center, Andover, MA 660

O. Winston Link Museum, Roanoke, VA...1535

Palm Beach Photographic Centre, Delray
  Beach, FL 305
Photographic Archives, University of
  Louisville Libraries, Louisville, KY 578
Photographic Resource Center, Boston,
  MA 669
Project Art-University of Iowa and
  Clinics, Iowa City, IA 520

Ripley's Believe It or Not!, Key West,
  FL 319

Safe Haven Museum and Education
  Center, Oswego, NY 1048
Searchlight Historic Museum & Mining
  Park, Searchlight, NV 882
The Simon Paneak Memorial Museum,
  Anaktuvuk Pass, AK 21
Southeast Museum of Photography,
  Daytona Beach, FL 303

UCR/California Museum of Photography,
  Riverside, CA 150

Visual Arts Museum, New York, NY 1040

Washakie Museum, Worland, WY 1639
Washburn Historical Museum & Cultural
  Center, Inc. aka Washburn Cultural
  Center, Washburn, WI 1625

Religious Museums

American Catholic Historical Society,
  Philadelphia, PA 1276
American Jewish Historical Society, New
  York, NY 1019
Archives - Archdiocese of St. Paul and
  Minneapolis, Saint Paul, MN 789
Archives Museum, Temple Mickve Israel,
  Savannah, GA 384
The Arthur J. Moore Methodist Museum,
  Saint Simons Island, GA 383
Associated American Jewish Museums,
  Pittsburgh, PA 1290

Baker University, William A. Quayle
  Bible Collection, Baldwin City, KS........533
Barratt's Chapel and Museum, Frederica,
  DE 270
Beehive House, Salt Lake City, UT 1470
The Benjamin & Dr. Edgar R. Cofeld
  Judaic Museum of Temple Beth Zion,
  Buffalo, NY 971
Bernard Judaica Museum, Congregation
  Emanu-El of the City of New York,
  New York, NY 1021
Beth Ahabah Museum & Archives,
  Richmond, VA 1528
Biblical Arts Center, Dallas, TX 1404
Biblical Resource Center & Museum,
  Collierville, TN 1364
Billy Graham Center Museum, Wheaton,
  IL 465
Bob Jones University Museum & Gallery,
  Inc., Greenville, SC 1333
Boston Center for Jewish Heritage,
  Boston, MA 663
The Bowne House Historical Society,
  Flushing, NY 990

Cathedral Cultural Center, Omaha, NE 870
The Cathedral of St. John the Divine,
  New York, NY 1022
Catholic Historical Society of the
  Roanoke Valley, Roanoke, VA 1535
Coeur d'Alenes Old Mission State Park,
  Cataldo, ID 405
Columbus Chapel, Boal Mansion
  Museum, Boalsburg, PA 1244
Community of Christ, Independence, MO ...817
Concordia Historical Institute, Saint
  Louis, MO 832
Cumberland Presbyterian Church
  Birthplace Shrine, Burns, TN 1360

Eldridge Street Project, New York, NY 1025
Enfield Shaker Museum, Enfield, NH 887
Ephrata Cloister, Ephrata, PA 1251

First Church of Christ Unitarian,
  Lancaster, MA 688
Friends (Quaker) Meeting House, Mount
  Pleasant, OH 1177

Gadsden Museum, Mesilla, NM 943
Glencairn Museum: Academy of the New
  Church, Bryn Athyn, PA 1244
Grand River Museum, Lemmon, SD 1351
Gustav Jeeninga Museum of Bible and
  Near Eastern Studies, Anderson, IN 467

Hill Cumorah Visitors Center & Historic
  Sites, Palmyra, NY 1050
Historic Bethabara Park, Winston-Salem,
  NC 1125
Historic Preservation Association of
  Bourbon County, Inc., Fort Scott, KS 540
Holyland Exhibition, Los Angeles, CA 116

Immaculate Conception Catholic Church,
  Natchitoches, LA 593
International Gospel Music Hall of Fame
  & Museum, Detroit, MI 737

Jane L. and Robert H. Weiner Judaic
  Museum, Rockville, MD 651
The Jewish Museum, New York, NY 1029
Jewish Museum of Maryland, Baltimore,
  MD 633
The Joseph A. Callaway Archaeological
  Museum, Louisville, KY 576
Judah L. Magnes Museum, Berkeley, CA......76
Judaica Museum of Central Synagogue,
  New York, NY 1029
The Judaica Museum of the Hebrew
  Home at Riverdale, Riverdale, NY 1057

Kateri Galleries, The National Shrine of
  the North American Martyrs,
  Auriesville, NY 959
Kirtland Temple Historic Center,
  Kirtland, OH 1170
Knights of Columbus Museum, New
  Haven, CT 253
Koreshan State Historic Site, Estero, FL....306

Liberty Jail Historic Site, Liberty, MO 826
Living Bible Museum, Mansfield, OH 1173
Longyear Museum, Chestnut Hill, MA 675
Lovely Lane Museum, Baltimore, MD 634
Loyola University Museum of Art,
  Chicago, IL 423
Luckhard Museum - The Indian Mission,
  Sebewaing, MI 764
Lutheran Heritage Center & Museum of
  the Perry County Lutheran Historical
  Society, Altenburg, MO 810

Mennonite Heritage Center, Harleysville,
  PA 1258
Mennonite Library and Archives, North
  Newton, KS 554
Mission Nuestra Senora de la Soledad,
  Soledad, CA 187
Mission San Antonio de Padua, Jolon,
  CA 105
Mission San Carlos Borromeo Del Rio
  Carmelo, Carmel, CA 81
Mission San Luis Obispo de Tolosa, San
  Luis Obispo, CA 174
Mission San Miguel, San Miguel, CA 175
Mission Santa Clara de Asis, Santa Clara,
  CA 181
Mission Santa Cruz, Santa Cruz, CA 182
Mississippi Baptist Historical
  Commission, Clinton, MS 799
Moravian Historical Society, Nazareth,
  PA 1273
Moravian Museum of Bethlehem, Inc.,
  Bethlehem, PA 1242

Mormon Visitors Center, Independence, MO..818
Museum of Ancient Artifacts, Las Vegas, NV..879
Museum of Church History and Art, Salt Lake City, UT..............................1471
Museum of Contemporary Religious Art (MOCRA)-St. Louis University, Saint Louis, MO..835
Museum of Earth and Life History, Lynchburg, VA.......................................1515
Museum of Great Christian Preachers & Ministries, Orange Park, FL.............331
Museum of Religious Arts, Logan, IA........522
Museum of Russian Culture, San Francisco, CA..167
The Museum of the Alphabet, Waxhaw, NC...1121
Museum of the Southern Jewish Experience, Jackson, MS.......................803
Museum of Woodcarving, Shell Lake, WI.1621

National Liberty Museum, Philadelphia, PA..1284
National Museum of American Jewish History, Philadelphia, PA 1284
The National Museum of Catholic Art & History, New York, NY......................1034
Native American Exhibit, National Kateri Shrine, Fonda, NY..........................991
Nebraska Conference United Methodist Historical Center, Lincoln, NE 866

Ohef Sholom Temple Archives, Norfolk, VA...1523
Old Cathedral Museum, Saint Louis, MO....836
Old St. Ferdinand's Shrine, Florissant, MO...815
Old St. Hilary's Church Museum & St. Hilary's Preserve, Tiburon, CA..............192
Oroville Chinese Temple, Oroville, CA.......136

Peter Whitmer Sr. Home and Visitors Center, Waterloo, NY.........................1083
Philadelphia Museum of Judaica/Congregation Rodeph Shalom, Philadelphia, PA 1286
Pohick Episcopal Church, Lorton, VA.......1514
Pope John Paul II Cultural Center, Washington, DC..................................289
Presbyterian Historical Society, Philadelphia, PA 1286
Presbyterian Historical Society (Montreat), Montreat, NC.....................1111

Romanian Ethnic Art Museum, Cleveland, OH.......................................1156
Rose Lawn Museum, Cartersville, GA........368
Rothko Chapel, Houston, TX.....................1429

St. George's United Methodist Church, Philadelphia, PA 1287
St. John's Episcopal Church, Richmond, VA..1531
St. Photios Greek Orthodox National Shrine, Saint Augustine, FL.............340
The Salvation Army Southern Historical Center & Museum, Atlanta, GA 363
San Gabriel Mission Museum, San Gabriel, CA..171
San Miguel Mission Church, Santa Fe, NM...950
Santa Barbara Mission Museum, Santa Barbara, CA..179
Santa Ysabel Asistencia, Santa Ysabel, CA...185
Santuario de Nuestra Senora de Guadalupe, Santa Fe, NM......................950
Schoenbrunn Village State Memorial, New Philadelphia, OH......................1177
Scotland Heritage Chapel & Museum, Scotland, SD..1355
1719 Hans Herr House & Museum, Willow Street, PA..................................1308

Shaker Museum, New Gloucester, ME 615
Sherwin Miller Museum of Jewish Art, Tulsa, OK...1216
Siegfried H. Horn Archaeological Museum, Berrien Springs, MI 729
Siskin Museum of Religious and Ceremonial Art, Chattanooga, TN 1362
Southern Baptist Historical Library and Archives, Nashville, TN.........................1380
Spertus Museum, Chicago, IL 427
Sylvia Plotkin Judaica Museum of Congregation Beth Israel, Scottsdale, AZ 44

The Temple Museum of Religious Art, Cleveland, OH 1156
Teutopolis Monastery Museum, Teutopolis, IL...461
Texas Baptist Historical Center Museum, Brenham, TX......................................1397
Thomas L. Kane Memorial Chapel, Kane, PA..1264
Tome Parish Museum, Tome, NM................953
Trinity Museum of the Parish of Trinity Church, New York, NY.........................1040

Union for Reform Judaism, New York, NY..1040
Upper Room Chapel Museum, Nashville, TN...1381

Waldensian Heritage Museum, Valdese, NC...1121
Washington National Cathedral, Washington, DC..................................294
Wings of Love, Clinton, MI.......................732
WordSpring Discovery Center, Orlando, FL..333
World Methodist Museum, Lake Junaluska, NC...1109

Yeshiva University Museum at the Center for Jewish History, New York, NY........1041

Scouting Museums

Canby Historical Society, Canby, OR 1221
Central States Scout Museum, Larned, KS..547

Las Vegas International Scouting Museum, Las Vegas, NV 879
Lawrence L. Lee Scouting Museum, Manchester, NH.......................................891

National Scouting Museum, Irving, TX 1430
North Star Museum of Boy Scouting and Girl Scouting, North Saint Paul, MN 785

Otis Chidester Scout Museum of Southern Arizona, Tucson, AZ..................50
Ottawa Scouting Museum, Ottawa, IL 449

World of Scouting Museum, Valley Forge, PA..1304

Sports Museums

ASA National Softball Hall of Fame and Museum Complex, Oklahoma City, OK..1207
Aiken Thoroughbred Racing Hall of Fame and Museum, Aiken, SC 1320
Alabama Sports Hall of Fame, Birmingham, AL..4
Alumni Center - Husky Heritage Sports Museum, Storrs, CT.........................261
The American Museum of Fly Fishing, Manchester, VT 1481
American Quarter Horse Hall of Fame & Museum, Amarillo, TX 1386
American Sport Art Museum and Archives, Daphne, AL................................7
American Water Ski Educational Foundation, Polk City, FL.....................337

Babe Didrikson Zaharias Museum, Beaumont, TX 1394
The Babe Ruth Museum and Sports Legends at Camden Yards, Baltimore, MD..629
Backing Up Classics Auto Museum, Concord, NC...1097
Bob Feller Museum, Van Meter, IA.............529
B's Ballpark Museum, Centennial, CO 205

California Surf Museum, Oceanside, CA.....135
College Football Hall of Fame, South Bend, IN...499
Colorado Ski Museum-Ski & Snowboard Hall of Fame, Vail, CO 234

Darlington Raceway Stock Car Museum, NMPA Hall of Fame, Darlington, SC....1331
Don Garlits Museum of Drag Racing Inc., Ocala, FL...330

Eastern Museum of Motor Racing, York Springs, PA..1309
Golf Museum, Newport News, VA.............1519
Green Bay Packers Hall of Fame, Green Bay, WI..1598
Greyhound Hall of Fame, Abilene, KS 531

Hall of Fame & Classic Car Museum, Weedsport, NY...1084
The Harness Racing Museum and Hall of Fame, Goshen, NY.................................995
Huntington Beach International Surfing Museum, Huntington Beach, CA.............104
Hydroplane & Raceboat Museum, Kent, WA...1557

Indiana Basketball Hall of Fame, New Castle, IN...494
Indiana Football Hall of Fame, Richmond, IN..497
International Bowling Museum and Hall of Fame, Saint Louis, MO.....................833
International Motor Racing Research Center at Watkins Glen, Watkins Glen, NY..1084
International Motorsports Hall of Fame and Museum, Lincoln, AL 13
International Swimming Hall of Fame, Inc., Fort Lauderdale, FL.........................307
International Tennis Hall of Fame & Museum, Newport, RI............................1313

Jack Nicklaus Museum, Columbus, OH.....1158

Kansas Sports Hall of Fame, Wichita, KS ...562
Kentucky Derby Museum, Louisville, KY...576

The Lacrosse Museum & National Hall of Fame/US Lacrosse, Baltimore, MD 633
Legends of the Game Baseball Museum and Learning Center, Arlington, TX......1388
Louisville Slugger Museum & Factory, Louisville, KY...577

Michigan Sports Hall of Fame, Detroit, MI...737
Minnesota Amateur Baseball Hall of Fame, Saint Cloud, MN 788
Mississippi Sports Hall of Fame & Museum, Jackson, MS 803
Motorcycle Hall of Fame Museum, Pickerington, OH.....................................1182
Museum of Family Camping, Allenstown, NH...883
Museum of Yachting, Newport, RI.............1314

Naismith Memorial Basketball Hall of Fame, Springfield, MA...........................710
National Art Museum of Sport, Inc., Indianapolis, IN......................................485
National Baseball Hall of Fame and Museum, Inc., Cooperstown, NY...........981
National Football Museum, Inc., Canton, OH..1145

Sports Museums–Continued

National Fresh Water Fishing Hall of
Fame, Hayward, WI 1600
National Italian American Sports Hall of
Fame, Chicago, IL...............................425
National Museum of Polo and Hall of
Fame, Inc., Lake Worth, FL..................320
National Museum of Racing and Hall of
Fame, Saratoga Springs, NY.................1065
National Museum of Roller Skating,
Lincoln, NE 866
National Museum of the Morgan Horse,
Shelburne, VT 1487
The National Soccer Hall of Fame,
Oneonta, NY 1046
National Sprint Car Hall of Fame &
Museum, Knoxville, IA........................521
National Steeplechase Museum, Camden,
SC 1323
National Wrestling Hall of Fame,
Stillwater, OK 1214
NCAA Hall of Champions, Indianapolis,
IN 486
Negro Leagues Baseball Museum, Kansas
City, MO 822
New England Ski Museum, Franconia,
NH 888
The New Hampshire Snowmobile
Museum, Allenstown, NH.....................883
North Carolina Auto Racing Hall of
Fame, Mooresville, NC........................1111

Oklahoma Sports Museum, Guthrie, OK ..1202
Oregon Sports Hall of Fame & Museum,
Inc., Portland, OR..............................1232

Paul W. Bryant Museum, Tuscaloosa, AL......19
Peter J. McGovern Little League
Museum, South Williamsport, PA.........1301
Pro Rodeo Hall of Fame & Museum of
the American Cowboy, Colorado
Springs, CO 207

Richard Petty Museum, Randleman, NC....1117
Roger Maris Museum, Fargo, ND 1131

St. Louis Cardinals Hall of Fame
Museum, Saint Louis, MO....................836
Saints Hall of Fame Museum, Kenner,
LA 589
San Diego Hall of Champions Sports
Museum, San Diego, CA......................159
Sanford Museum, Sanford, FL..................343
Schwartz Collection of Skiing Heritage,
Tiburon, CA 192
Snowmobile Hall of Fame and Museum,
Saint Germain, WI.............................1620
South Carolina Tennis Hall of Fame,
Belton, SC..1321
South Dakota Amateur Baseball Hall of
Fame, Lake Norden, SD.......................1350
The Sports Museum, Boston, MA...............669

Ted Williams Museum and Hitters Hall
of Fame, Hernando, FL........................312
Texas Sports Hall of Fame, Waco, TX.......1459

U.S. Bicycling Hall of Fame, Somerville,
NJ...924
United States Golf Association Museum
& Archives, Far Hills, NJ.....................903
United States Hockey Hall of Fame,
Eveleth, MN......................................774
University of Kentucky Basketball
Museum, Lexington, KY.......................574
U.S. National Ski Hall of Fame &
Museum, Inc., Ishpeming, MI...............747
USA Weightlifting Hall of Fame, York,
PA 1309

Vermont Ski Museum, Stowe, VT.............1488
Virginia Sports Hall of Fame,
Portsmouth, VA.................................1526

Western Skisport Museum, Donner Pass,
CA 91
World Figure Skating Museum & Hall of
Fame, Colorado Springs, CO.................208
World Golf Hall of Fame, Saint
Augustine, FL 340

Yogi Berra Museum and Learning Center,
Little Falls, NJ...................................910

Technology Museums

A.W.A. Electronic-Communication
Museum, Bloomfield, NY 963
Adler Planetarium & Astronomy
Museum, Chicago, IL...........................417
Adventure Science Center, Nashville, TN..1377
American Computer Museum, Bozeman,
MT..842
American Maple Museum, Croghan, NY.....983
American Museum of Radio and
Electricity, Bellingham, WA.................1548
American Museum of Science & Energy,
Oak Ridge, TN 1382
American Precision Museum Association,
Inc., Windsor, VT...............................1490
Anderson/Abruzzo Albuquerque
International Balloon Museum,
Albuquerque, NM...............................933
Apple Farm Mill House, San Luis
Obispo, CA 174
Argo Gold Mine & Mill Museum, Idaho
Springs, CO 223
Arkansas Museum of Natural Resources,
Smackover, AR...................................68
The Atomic Testing Museum, Las Vegas,
NV...878

The Bakken Library and Museum,
Minneapolis, MN................................781
Baltimore Museum of Industry,
Baltimore, MD...................................630
Buffalo Museum of Science, Buffalo, NY ...972
Burwell-Morgan Mill, Millwood, VA.........1518

COSI Columbus, Columbus, OH...............1157
CTS Turner Museum, Elkhart, IN 474
California Science Center, Los Angeles,
CA...113
Carnegie Museums of Pittsburgh
(Carnegie Institute), Pittsburgh, PA.......1291
Carnegie Science Center, Pittsburgh, PA....1291
Catawba Science Center, Hickory, NC.......1106
Columbia River Exhibition of History,
Science and Technology, Richland,
WA 1564
Comer Museum, Morgantown, WV 1585
Computer History Museum, Mountain
View, CA 129

Dayton History at Carillon Park, Dayton,
OH 1161
Discovery Place, Inc., Charlotte, NC.........1094
Discovery Science Center, Fort Collins,
CO...216
Discovery World - The James Lovell
Museum of Science, Economics and
Technology, Milwaukee, WI 1610
Don Harrington Discovery Center,
Amarillo, TX 1387

East Texas Oil Museum at Kilgore
College, Kilgore, TX............................1432
Eli Whitney Museum, Inc., Hamden, CT....244
Essex Shipbuilding Museum, Essex, MA 681
Explora, Albuquerque, NM 933

Frank H. Woods Telephone Museum,
Lincoln, NE 865
The Franklin Institute, Philadelphia, PA....1280
Frontiers of Flight Museum, Dallas, TX 1406

George Westinghouse Museum,
Wilmerding, PA 1308

Georgia Rural Telephone Museum,
Leslie, GA...376
Glenn L. Martin Maryland Aviation
Museum, Baltimore, MD......................632
Golden Gate Railroad Museum, San
Francisco, CA....................................166
Great Lakes Science Center, Cleveland,
OH 1154

The Hagley Museum and Library,
Wilmington, DE.................................273
Hammel Museum, Socorro, NM.................951
Hammond Museum of Bells, Eureka
Springs, AR.......................................57
Hanford Mills Museum, East Meredith,
NY...987
Harold Warp Pioneer Village Foundation,
Minden, NE 868
Healdton Oil Museum, Healdton, OK........1202
HealthSpace Cleveland, Cleveland, OH 1154
Herschell Carrousel Factory Museum,
North Tonawanda, NY.........................1043
Hesston Steam Museum, LaPorte, IN 487
The Hicksville Gregory Museum,
Hicksville, NY 998
Hiller Aviation Institute, San Carlos, CA.....155
Historical Electronics Museum,
Linthicum, MD..................................648
Horseless Carriage Foundation &
Automotive Research Library, La
Mesa, CA 107

Impression 5 Science Center, Lansing,
MI...750
Intel Museum, Santa Clara, CA.................181
International Spy Museum, Washington,
DC...281
Interurban Railway Station Museum,
Plano, TX 1444
Intrepid Sea-Air-Space Museum, New
York, NY...1028

Jefferson Telephone Museum, Jefferson,
IA..521
Jericho Historical Society, Jericho
Corners, VT 1480
John Rivers Communications Museum,
Charleston, SC...................................1325
Johnson Victrola Museum, Dover, DE.........270

Kalamazoo Valley Museum, Kalamazoo,
MI...749

Lake Shore Railway Museum, North
East, PA..1274
Lakeview Museum of Arts and Sciences,
Peoria, IL..450
Liberty Science Center, Jersey City, NJ.......909
Long Island Museum of Science and
Technology, Garden City, NY................993
Louisville Science Center, Louisville, KY...577
Lowell National Historical Park, Lowell,
MA 691

MIT Museum, Cambridge, MA..................674
The Magic Lantern Castle Museum, San
Antonio, TX......................................1448
Maitland Historical Museums, Maitland,
FL...322
The Mary Brogan Museum of Art and
Science, Tallahassee, FL.......................347
Maryland Science Center, Baltimore, MD ...634
McWane Science Center, Birmingham,
AL..5
Mercer Museum of the Bucks County
Historical Society, Doylestown, PA.........1250
Mid-America Science Museum, Hot
Springs, AR.......................................60
Mid-America Windmill Museum,
Kendallville, IN..................................486
Milton J. Rubenstein Museum of Science
& Technology, Syracuse, NY................1076
Montshire Museum of Science, Inc.,
Norwich, VT......................................1483

The Movie Museum, Owosso, MI................759
Museum of Anthracite Mining,
    Weatherly, PA 1307
Museum of Flying, Santa Monica, CA 183
The Museum of Man in the Sea, Inc.,
    Panama City Beach, FL 335
Museum of Radio & Technology, Inc.,
    Huntington, WV 1583
Museum of Robotics, Orinda, CA................136
Museum of Science, Boston, MA................667
Museum of Science and Industry,
    Chicago, IL..425
Museum of Surveying, Lansing, MI............750
The Museum of the Alphabet, Waxhaw,
    NC...1121
Museum of the Moving Image, Astoria,
    NY..958

NASA Glenn Research Center's Visitor
    Center, Cleveland, OH 1155
National Atomic Museum, Albuquerque,
    NM...934
National Automotive & Truck Museum
    of the United States, Inc. (NATMUS),
    Auburn, IN...468
National Building Museum, Washington,
    DC..284
National Canal Museum, Hugh Moore
    Historical Park and Museums, Easton,
    PA...1250
National Italian American Sports Hall of
    Fame, Chicago, IL.....................................425
National Museum of American History,
    Washington, DC...285
National Museum of Roller Skating,
    Lincoln, NE..866
National Museum of the United States
    Air Force, Wright-Patterson Air Force
    Base, OH..1193
National Packard Museum, Warren, OH 1189
The National Science Center's Fort
    Discovery, Augusta, GA............................366
Nauticus, The National Maritime Center,
    Norfolk, VA...1522
Naval Undersea Museum, Keyport, WA....1557
Neil Armstrong Air & Space Museum,
    Wapakoneta, OH......................................1189
New Britain Industrial Museum, New
    Britain, CT..251
New England Wireless & Steam Museum
    Inc., East Greenwich, RI 1311
New Mexico Museum of Space History,
    Alamogordo, NM......................................932
New York Hall of Science, Flushing
    Meadows, NY..990
New York Power Authority-Niagara
    Power Project Visitors' Center,
    Lewiston, NY...1009
North Anna Nuclear Information Center,
    Mineral, VA..1518

Ocean Star Offshore Drilling Rig &
    Museum, Galveston, TX 1421
Odyssey Maritime Discovery Center,
    Seattle, WA...1567
Omniplex Science Museum, Oklahoma
    City, OK..1210
Oregon Air & Space Museum, Eugene,
    OR..1224
Oregon Museum of Science and Industry,
    Portland, OR..1231
Orlando Science Center, Inc., Orlando,
    FL..332
Outagamie Museum, Appleton, WI 1589
Owls Head Transportation Museum, Owls
    Head, ME...617

Pacific Science Center, Seattle, WA 1568
Paper Discovery Center, Appleton, WI 1590
Pavek Museum of Broadcasting, St.
    Louis Park, MN...794
The Petroleum Museum, Midland, TX.......1439
Pima Air & Space Museum, Tucson, AZ.......50

Platen Press Printing Museum, Zion, IL 467
Radio & Television Museum, Bowie, MD...638
Regional Science & Discovery Center,
    Horseheads, NY...999
Reuben H. Fleet Science Center, San
    Diego, CA...158
Rhinebeck Aerodrome Museum,
    Rhinebeck, NY...1056
Robert C. Williams American Museum of
    Papermaking at Georgia Tech, Atlanta,
    GA..363

San Francisco Bay Model Visitor Center,
    Sausalito, CA...186
Sci-Tech Center of Northern New York,
    Watertown, NY...1084
Science Center of Connecticut, West
    Hartford, CT...265
Science Center of Iowa, Des Moines, IA.....515
Science Discovery Center of Oneonta,
    Oneonta, NY...1046
The Science Fiction Museum and Hall of
    Fame, Seattle, WA...................................1568
The Science Museum of Minnesota, Saint
    Paul, MN..792
Science Museum of Virginia, Richmond,
    VA..1531
Science Spectrum, Lubbock, TX 1435
Sciencenter, Ithaca, NY..............................1004
Scitrek, The Science and Technology
    Museum of Atlanta, Valdosta, GA...........389
Seashore Trolley Museum,
    Kennebunkport, ME...................................613
The Skyscraper Museum, New York, NY..1038
Slate Valley Museum, Granville, NY 996
Sloane-Stanley Museum and Kent
    Furnace, Kent, CT......................................247
Sloss Furnaces National Historic
    Landmark, Birmingham, AL 5
Sony Wonder Technology Lab, New
    York, NY...1039
South Coast Railroad Museum at Goleta
    Depot, Goleta, CA.....................................100
South Florida Science Museum, West
    Palm Beach, FL...353
Southwest Museum of Engineering,
    Communications and Computation,
    Glendale, AZ...35
Southwest Museum of Science and
    Technology, The Science Place & TI
    Founders IMAX Theater, Dallas, TX 1407
Space Center Houston, Houston, TX.........1429
Spartanburg Science Center, Spartanburg,
    SC..1342
State Capital Publishing Museum,
    Guthrie, OK..1202
Steam Railroading Institute, Owosso, MI 759
Stevens County Gas and Historical
    Museum, Hugoton, KS...............................544

The Tech Museum of Innovation, San
    Jose, CA..173
The Telephone Museum, Ellsworth, ME......610
Tennessee Valley Railroad Museum Inc.,
    Chattanooga, TN......................................1363
Texas Air Museum, Slaton, TX 1453
Texas Energy Museum, Beaumont, TX......1395
Titan Missile Museum, Green Valley, AZ......36
Towe Auto Museum, Sacramento, CA 154

U.S. Army Aviation Museum, Fort
    Rucker, AL...10
U.S. Patent and Trademark Office -
    Museum, Alexandria, VA 1494
The U.S. Space & Rocket Center,
    Huntsville, AL 12

Virginia Air & Space Center, Hampton,
    VA 1510

Warhawk Air Museum, Nampa, ID..............408
Western Historic Radio Museum, Virginia
    City, NV...882

Western Museum of Mining & Industry,
    Colorado Springs, CO 208
Westport Maritime Museum, Westport,
    WA 1578
White 1 Foundation, Kissimmee, FL...........319
The Wine Museum of Greyton H. Taylor,
    Hammondsport, NY...................................997

Zeum, San Francisco, CA 170

Theatre Museums

American Museum of Magic & Lund
    Memorial Library, Inc., Marshall, MI 754
The Arts & Science Center for Southeast
    Arkansas, Pine Bluff, AR 65

Bread & Puppet Museum, Glover, VT.......1479

Center for Puppetry Arts, Atlanta, GA 359
Central City Opera House Association,
    Central City, CO..205
City Stage Company, Boston, MA 665

Hampden-Booth Theatre Library at the
    Players, New York, NY.............................1027
Harry Ransom Center at the University
    of Texas at Austin, Austin, TX 1390
Hocking Valley Museum of Theatrical
    History, Inc., Nelsonville, OH................1177
The Houdini Museum & Theater,
    Scranton, PA..1298

The Jimmy Stewart Museum, Indiana, PA.1262
John and Mable Ringling Museum of Art,
    Sarasota, FL...344

Korner's Folly, Kernersville, NC................1108

Manhattan Arts Center, Manhattan, KS........551
Mario Lanza Institute/Museum,
    Philadelphia, PA......................................1282
Midwest Old Settlers & Threshers
    Association, Inc., Mount Pleasant, IA.....524

The New York Public Library, Astor,
    Lenox and Tilden Foundations, New
    York, NY...1036
The New York Public Library for the
    Performing Arts, New York, NY 1036

Oz Museum, Wamego, KS...........................560

Rocky Mount Arts Center, Rocky Mount,
    NC..1117
The Rose Museum at Carnegie Hall, New
    York, NY...1038

Strasenburgh Planetarium/Rochester
    Museum & Science Center, Rochester,
    NY...1060

Tabor Opera House Museum, Leadville,
    CO..226

Vent Haven Museum, Fort Mitchell, KY 568

Toy and Doll Museums

America's Ice Cream & Dairy Museum,
    Medina, OH...1175
Angels Attic Museum, Santa Monica, CA ...183
Arizona Doll and Toy Museum, Phoenix,
    AZ...39

The Ballard Institute & Museum of
    Puppetry, Storrs, CT.................................261
Bethlehem Historical Association,
    Selkirk, NY..1068
Buccleuch Mansion, New Brunswick, NJ....915
Burlingame Museum of Pez & Classic
    Toy Museum, Burlingame, CA..................80

CHTJ Southard House Museum,
    Brunswick, ME...607
Center for Puppetry Arts, Atlanta, GA 359

Toy and Doll Museums–Continued

The Children's Toy & Doll Museum, Marietta, OH 1174

Crossroads of America, Bethlehem, NH 883

Dancing Bear Folk Center, Thermopolis, WY 1639

Deer Park Escondido Winery & Auto Museum, Escondido, CA 93

Delaware Toy and Miniature Museum, Wilmington, DE 273

Denver Museum of Miniatures, Dolls and Toys, Denver, CO 211

Dolls at Home Museum, Spearfish, SD 1357

Eliza Cruce Hall Doll Collection, Ardmore, OK 1196

The Enchanted Mansion, A Doll Museum, Baton Rouge, LA 585

Enchanted World Doll Museum, Mitchell, SD 1352

Eugene Field House and St. Louis Toy Museum, Saint Louis, MO 833

Gadsden Museum, Mesilla, NM 943

Gay Nineties Button and Doll Museum, Eureka Springs, AR 57

Grier Musser Museum, Los Angeles, CA 115

Hartmann Model R.R. & Toy Museum, Intervale, NH 889

Hawaii Loves Barbie Dolls Museum, Kailua, HI 399

Hazel Kibler Museum, Girard, PA 1256

Helen Moe Antique Doll Museum, Paso Robles, CA 141

House of a Thousand Dolls, Loma, MT 851

Hurricane Valley Heritage Park Museum, Hurricane, UT 1466

The Ida Dennie Willis Museum of Miniatures, Dolls, and Toys, Tulsa, OK 1215

Ipswich Historical Society and Museum, Ipswich, MA 688

Kruger Street Toy & Train Museum, Wheeling, WV 1588

Lincoln County Historical Society, Lincoln, KS 549

Lux Center for the Arts, Lincoln, NE 866

Matchbox Road Museum, Newfield, NJ 917

Medina Railroad Museum, Medina, NY 1014

Medora Doll House, Medora, ND 1134

Milan Historical Museum, Inc., Milan, OH 1176

The Museum of Miniature Houses and Other Collections, Inc., Carmel, IN 471

National Farm Toy Museum, Dyersville, IA 517

The National Toy Train Museum, Strasburg, PA 1301

Newell Museum, Newell, SD 1352

The Official Marx Toy Museum, Moundsville, WV 1585

Oz Museum, Wamego, KS 560

Patee House Museum, Saint Joseph, MO 831

Pauline E. Glidden Toy Museum, Ashland, NH 883

The Prairie Museum of Art & History, Colby, KS 535

Rosalie Whyel Museum of Doll Art, Bellevue, WA 1548

Sturdivant Hall, Selma, AL 18

Stutsman County Memorial Museum, Jamestown, ND 1133

Tinkertown Museum, Sandia Park, NM 947

Town of Yorktown Museum, Yorktown Heights, NY 1087

Toy & Miniature Museum of Kansas City, Kansas City, MO 823

Trainland U.S.A., Colfax, IA 511

Washburn Historical Museum & Cultural Center, Inc. aka Washburn Cultural Center, Washburn, WI 1625

Washington Doll's House and Toy Museum, Washington, DC 294

Webster House Museum, Elkhorn, WI 1596

Wenham Museum, Wenham, MA 717

World's Largest Toy Museum and Harold Bell Wright, Branson, MO 811

Yesterday's Children Antique Doll & Toy Museum, Vicksburg, MS 809

Yesteryears Doll Museum, Sandwich, MA 708

Transportation Museums

AT & SF Depot, Alden, KS 532

Age of Steam Railroad Museum, Dallas, TX 1404

The Agricultural Memories Museum, Penn Yan, NY 1052

The Air Museum - Planes of Fame, Chino, CA 84

Airline History Museum, Kansas City, MO 820

Allegheny Portage Railroad National Historic Site and Johnstown Flood National Memorial, Gallitzin, PA 1255

America On Wheels, Inc., Allentown, PA ..1239

American Airlines C.R. Smith Museum, Fort Worth, TX 1416

American Merchant Marine Museum, Kings Point, NY 1007

America's Ice Cream & Dairy Museum, Medina, OH 1175

Arizona Railway Museum, Chandler, AZ 31

Arkansas Railroad Museum, Pine Bluff, AR 65

Ashland Railroad Station Museum, Ashland, NH 883

Auburn Cord Duesenberg Museum, Auburn, IN 468

Automobile Driving Museum, Los Angeles, CA 112

Automotive Hall of Fame, Inc., Dearborn, MI 733

Aviation Museum of Kentucky Inc., Lexington, KY 572

B&O Railroad Museum: Ellicott City Station, Ellicott City, MD 643

Backing Up Classics Auto Museum, Concord, NC 1097

Baltimore & Ohio Railroad Museum, Baltimore, MD 629

Baltimore Civil War Museum, Baltimore, MD 629

Baltimore Streetcar Museum, Inc., Baltimore, MD 631

Barber Vintage Motorsports Museum, Leeds, AL 12

Belair Stable Museum, Bowie, MD 638

Benjy's Harley-Davidson, Huntington, WV 1583

Berkshire Scenic Railway Museum, Inc., Lenox, MA 689

Best Friend of Charleston, Charleston, SC 1324

BG John C.L. Scribner Texas Military Forces Museum, Austin, TX 1389

The Bicycle Museum of America, New Bremen, OH 1177

Blackhawk Museum (Behring-Hofmann Educational Institute, Inc.), Danville, CA 89

Bluegrass Railroad Museum, Versailles, KY 584

Bluemont Historical Railroad Junction, Arlington, VA 1495

Bolin Wildlife Exhibit & Antique Collection, McKinney, TX 1437

Boothbay Railway Village, Boothbay, ME...607

Bowie Railroad Station and Huntington Museum, Bowie, MD 638

Boyertown Museum of Historic Vehicles, Boyertown, PA 1244

Bradford Ohio Railroad Museum, Bradford, OH 1143

Branchville Railroad Shrine and Museum, Inc., Branchville, SC 1322

Branigan Cultural Center, Las Cruces, NM 940

The Bruce Weiner Microcar Museum, Madison, GA 378

Brunswick Railroad Museum and C&O Canal Visitors Center, Brunswick, MD ...639

Buffalo County Historical Society, Kearney, NE 863

Burlington-Rock Island Railroad and Historical Museum, Teague, TX 1454

C. Grier Beam Truck Museum, Cherryville, NC 1096

Caldwell County Railroad Museum, Princeton, KY 583

California State Railroad Museum, Sacramento, CA 152

Camp Five Museum Foundation, Inc., Laona, WI 1604

Canton Classic Car Museum, Canton, OH.1145

Carriage House Museum, Colorado Springs, CO 206

Casey Jones Home and Railroad Museum, Jackson, TN 1367

Catawissa Railroad Co., Catawissa, PA 1246

Central Florida Railroad Museum, Winter Garden, FL 354

Central Texas Museum of Automotive History, Rosanky, TX 1446

Cheyenne Frontier Days Old West Museum, Cheyenne, WY 1630

Chittenango Landing Canal Boat Museum, Chittenango, NY 978

Choctaw County Historical Society, Hugo, OK 1203

Cimarron Valley Railroad Museum, Cushing, OK 1199

Classic Cars International, Salt Lake City, UT 1471

Clovis Depot Model Train Museum, Clovis, NM 939

Cole Land Transportation Museum, Bangor, ME 604

Collis P. Huntington Railroad Historical Society, Inc., Huntington, WV 1583

Colorado Railroad Museum, Golden, CO 220

Conneaut Railroad Museum, Conneaut, OH 1159

Connecticut Fire Museum, East Windsor, CT 239

Connecticut Trolley Museum, East Windsor, CT 239

Conway Scenic Railroad, Inc., North Conway, NH 892

Cookeville Depot Museum, Cookeville, TN 1364

Crawford Auto-Aviation Museum, Cleveland, OH 1154

Dakota Territory Air Museum, Minot, ND.1134

Danbury Railway Museum, Danbury, CT 238

Dayton Historical Depot Society, Dayton, WA 1552

Dayton History at Carillon Park, Dayton, OH 1161

Deer Park Escondido Winery & Auto Museum, Escondido, CA 93

Delaware and Hudson Canal Historical Society and Museum, High Falls, NY.....998

The Dennison Railroad Depot Museum,
Dennison, OH 1162
Dixie Gun Works' Old Car Museum,
Union City, TN 1384
Dows Depot Welcome Center, Dows, IA 516
Dunedin Historical Society & Museum,
Dunedin, FL 305

EAA AirVenture Museum, Oshkosh, WI ...1616
East Troy Electric Railroad Museum,
East Troy, WI 1595
El Dorado County Historical Museum,
Placerville, CA 142
End-O-Line Railroad Park & Museum,
Currie, MN..772
Erie Canal Village, Rome, NY 1061
Estes-Winn Antique Automobile
Museum, Asheville, NC 1089

Fantasy of Flight, Polk City, FL 337
Florida Gulf Coast Railroad Museum,
Parrish, FL 335
Forney Museum of Transportation,
Denver, CO 212
Fort Smith Trolley Museum, Fort Smith,
AR 58
Four Wheel Drive Foundation,
Clintonville, WI 1594
Fox Lake Historical Museum, Inc., Fox
Lake, WI 1598
Fox River Trolley Museum/Fox River
Trolley Association, South Elgin, IL 457
The Frick Art & Historical Center,
Pittsburgh, PA 1292

Galveston Railroad Museum, Galveston,
TX 1421
Gilmore Car Museum, Hickory Corners,
MI 746
Glenn L. Martin Maryland Aviation
Museum, Baltimore, MD 632
Gold Coast Railroad Museum, Inc.,
Miami, FL 323
The Golden Age of Trucking Museum,
Middlebury, CT 249
Golden Spike National Historic Site,
Brigham City, UT 1463
Golden State Model Railroad Museum,
Point Richmond, CA 143
Good Old Days Vintage Motorcar
Museum, Inc., Hardy, AR 59
Graceland, Memphis, TN 1373
Grand Encampment Museum, Inc.,
Encampment, WY 1632
The Great Overland Station, Topeka, KS 559
Great Plains Transportation Museum,
Wichita, KS 561
Great Smoky Mountains Heritage Center,
Townsend, TN 1384

H.H. Franklin Foundation, Tucson, AZ 49
Hagerstown Roundhouse Museum,
Hagerstown, MD 646
Hall of Fame & Classic Car Museum,
Weedsport, NY 1084
Harold Warp Pioneer Village Foundation,
Minden, NE 868
Hartung's Auto and License Plate
Museum, Glenview, IL 438
Hays Antique Truck Museum, Woodland,
CA 199
Heart of Dixie Railroad Museum, Calera,
AL 6
Heritage Square Museum, Los Angeles,
CA 116
Hesston Steam Museum, LaPorte, IN 487
Hiller Aviation Institute, San Carlos, CA 155
Historic Auto Attractions, Roscoe, IL 456
Horseless Carriage Foundation &
Automotive Research Library, La
Mesa, CA 107

Illinois Railway Museum, Union, IL............461

Indiana Transportation Museum,
Noblesville, IN....................................495
Indianapolis Motor Speedway Hall of
Fame Museum, Indianapolis, IN.............484
Interurban Railway Station Museum,
Plano, TX 1444
Iowa Aviation Museum, Greenfield, IA........519
Iowa Railroad Historical Society, Boone,
IA 506
Iron Mission State Park & Museum,
Cedar City, UT 1464
Ironwood Area Historical Museum,
Ironwood, MI 747

Justice Brothers Racing Museum, Duarte,
CA 91

Kalamazoo Aviation History Museum,
Kalamazoo, MI 748
Kate Shelley Railroad Museum, Boone,
IA 506
Kentucky Railway Museum, Inc., New
Haven, KY 580

La Porte County Historical Society
Museum, La Porte, IN..........................487
Lake Shore Railway Museum, North
East, PA 1274
Lake Superior Railroad Museum, Duluth,
MN 773
Lake Waccamaw Depot Museum, Lake
Waccamaw, NC 1109
Larz Anderson Auto Museum, Brookline,
MA 671
Laws Railroad Museum and Historical
Site, Bishop, CA 78
Layland Museum, Cleburne, TX 1400
Linden Railroad Museum, Linden, IN..........488
Long Island Museum of American Art,
History & Carriages, Stony Brook,
NY 1075
Los Angeles Maritime Museum, San
Pedro, CA 176

Mac's Antique Car Museum, Tulsa, OK 1215
Medina Railroad Museum, Medina, NY 1014
Michigan Transit Museum, Inc., Mount
Clemens, MI 756
Mid-Continent Railway Museum, North
Freedom, WI 1615
Midwest Old Settlers & Threshers
Association, Inc., Mount Pleasant, IA 524
Mifflinburg Buggy Museum Association,
Inc., Mifflinburg, PA 1271
The Millionaires' Cars & Disney
Collection, Saint Ignace, MI 763
Minnesota Transportation Museum, Inc.,
Saint Paul, MN 792
Minnesota's Machinery Museum, Hanley
Falls, MN 777
Miracle of America Museum Inc., Polson,
MT..852
Monticello Railway Museum, Monticello,
IL..445
Motion Unlimited Museum & Classic
Car Lot, Rapid City, SD 1355
Motorcycle Hall of Fame Museum,
Pickerington, OH 1182
Museum of Alaska Transportation &
Industry, Inc., Wasilla, AK 29
Museum of Automobile Art and Design,
Syracuse, NY 1076
The Museum of Automobiles, Morrilton,
AR 64
The Museum of Bus Transportation, Inc.,
Hershey, PA 1261
Museum of Transportation, Saint Louis,
MO..835
Museum of Yachting, Newport, RI............1314

The National Agricultural Center & Hall
of Fame, Bonner Springs, KS 534
National Automobile Museum (The
Harrah Collection), Reno, NV 881

National Automotive & Truck Museum
of the United States, Inc. (NATMUS),
Auburn, IN...468
National Canal Museum, Hugh Moore
Historical Park and Museums, Easton,
PA 1250
National Capital Trolley Museum, Silver
Spring, MD 654
National Corvette Museum, Bowling
Green, KY 566
National Motorcycle Museum, Anamosa,
IA 505
National New York Central Railroad
Museum, Elkhart, IN 475
National Packard Museum, Warren, OH 1189
National Railroad Museum, Green Bay,
WI 1599
National Road/Zane Grey Museum,
Norwich, OH....................................1180
Nethercutt Collection, Sylmar, CA 190
Nevada State Railroad Museum, Carson
City, NV 876
New England Air Museum of the
Connecticut Aeronautical Historical
Association, Inc., Windsor Locks, CT 267
New York Museum of Transportation,
West Henrietta, NY 1084
New York Transit Museum, Brooklyn
Heights, NY 970
Newark Valley Depot Museum, Newark
Valley, NY 1042
Nici Self Museum, Centennial, WY 1630
Niles Depot Museum, Fremont, CA 96
North Alabama Railroad Museum,
Huntsville, AL 12
North Carolina Transportation Museum,
Spencer, NC 1120
North Dakota State Railroad Museum,
Mandan, ND 1134
North Lee County Historic Center and
Santa Fe Depot Museum Complex,
Fort Madison, IA 518
Northeast Texas Rural Heritage Museum,
Pittsburg, TX 1443
Northern Pacific Railway Museum,
Toppenish, WA 1575
The Northwest Carriage Museum,
Raymond, WA 1564
Northwest Railway Museum,
Snoqualmie, WA 1570
Norwood Historical Association and
Museum, Norwood, NY 1044

Oakfield Railroad Museum, Oakfield, ME ...616
Odyssey Maritime Discovery Center,
Seattle, WA 1567
Ohio Railway Museum, Worthington, OH .1192
Oklahoma Railway Museum, Oklahoma
City, OK 1210
Oklahoma Route 66 Museum, Clinton,
OK..1198
The Old Depot Railroad Museum,
Dassel, MN 772
Old Dominion Railway Museum,
Richmond, VA 1531
Olympic Flight Museum, Olympia, WA 1560
Orange Empire Railway Museum, Perris,
CA 141
Oregon Air & Space Museum, Eugene,
OR 1224
Oregon Electric Railway Historical
Society, Inc., Salem, OR 1236
Otero Museum Association, La Junta, CO ...224
Owls Head Transportation Museum, Owls
Head, ME 617
Ozaukee County Pioneer Village,
Saukville, WI 1620

Pacific Aerospace Museum, Honolulu, HI ...397
Pacific Northwest Truck Museum,
Brooks, OR 1220
Pate Museum of Transportation, Cresson,
TX 1403

Transportation Museums–Continued

Patee House Museum, Saint Joseph, MO 831
Pedaling History Bicycle Museum,
  Orchard Park, NY.....................................1047
Pennsylvania Trolley Museum,
  Washington, PA 1305
Petersen Automotive Museum, Los
  Angeles, CA..121
Photomobile Model Museum, Woodstock,
  CT...268
Piccadilly Museum of Transportation
  Memorabilia and Advertising Art,
  Butte, MT..843
Pikes Peak Hill Climb Educational
  Museum, Colorado Springs, CO.............207
Pioneer Auto Museum, Murdo, SD 1352
Pioneer Auto Trails Historical Society
  (PATHS), Tucson, AZ................................50
Pioneer Museum of Motorcycles &
  Conference Center, Tacoma, WA...........1574
Piper Aviation Museum Foundation, Lock
  Haven, PA..1269
The Portal of the Folded Wings Shrine to
  Aviation and Museum, North
  Hollywood, CA...131
Portholes Into the Past, Medina, OH.........1176
Portola Railroad Museum, Portola, CA.......144

R.E. Olds Transportation Museum,
  Lansing, MI..751
Railroad and Heritage Museum Inc.,
  Temple, TX..1454
Railroad Museum of Minot, Minot, ND.....1135
Railroad Museum of Pennsylvania,
  Strasburg, PA...1302
Railroaders Memorial Museum, Altoona,
  PA...1240
The Railway Exposition Co., Inc.,
  Covington, KY..567
Railway Museum of San Angelo, San
  Angelo, TX...1447
Railways to Yesterday, Inc., Rockhill
  Furnace, PA..1297
Reading Railroad Heritage Museum,
  Reading, PA...1296
Rhinebeck Aerodrome Museum,
  Rhinebeck, NY...1056
River Heritage Museum, Paducah, KY 582
Roaring Twenties Antique Car Museum,
  Hood, VA...1511
Rockhill Trolley Museum, Rockhill
  Furnace, PA..1297
Roscoe Village Foundation, Coshocton,
  OH..1159

Salamanca Rail Museum, Salamanca, NY.1063
San Diego Automotive Museum, San
  Diego, CA...159
San Diego Model Railroad Museum, Inc.,
  San Diego, CA..159
Sandown Historical Society and Museum,
  Sandown, NH..896
Sarasota Classic Car Museum, Sarasota,
  FL...345
Saratoga Automobile Museum, Saratoga
  Springs, NY...1065
Seashore Trolley Museum,
  Kennebunkport, ME.................................613
Sheboygan County Historical Museum,
  Sheboygan, WI..1621
Shelby American Collection, Boulder, CO...203
Shore Line Trolley Museum, East Haven,
  CT...239
Sloan Museum, Flint, MI............................742
Smoky Mountain Trains, Bryson City,
  NC...1092
The South Carolina Railroad Museum,
  Winnsboro, SC...1343
South Coast Railroad Museum at Goleta
  Depot, Goleta, CA.....................................100
South Florida Railway Museum,
  Deerfield Beach, FL..................................304

Southeastern Railway Museum, Duluth,
  GA..371
Southern California Chapter Railway &
  Locomotive Historical Society,
  Pomona, CA...143
Southern Museum of Flight, Birmingham,
  AL...6
Stanley Museum, Estes Park, CO................215
Stanley Museum, Inc., Kingfield, ME.........613
Star Cars Museum, Gatlinburg, TN...........1365
Steam Railroading Institute, Owosso, MI 759
Steamship William G. Mather Museum,
  Cleveland, OH...1156
Steamtown National Historic Site,
  Scranton, PA..1299
Studebaker National Museum, Inc., South
  Bend, IN...500
Swigart Museum, Huntingdon, PA............1262

Tallahassee Automobile Museum,
  Tallahassee, FL...348
Tennessee Central Railway Museum,
  Nashville, TN...1380
Tennessee Valley Railroad Museum Inc.,
  Chattanooga, TN......................................1363
Tex Ark Antique Auto Museum,
  Texarkana, AR..69
Texas Transportation Museum, San
  Antonio, TX...1451
Thrasher Carriage Museum, Frostburg,
  MD..645
Tooele County Railroad Museum, Tooele,
  UT..1475
Towe Auto Museum, Sacramento, CA 154
Town of Yorktown Museum, Yorktown
  Heights, NY...1087
Travel Town Museum, Los Angeles, CA 121
Tri-County Historical Society &
  Museum, Inc., Herington, KS...................544
Trolley Museum of New York, Kingston,
  NY...1008
Trust for the Preservation of Maine
  Industrial History and Technology
  d/b/a Maine Narrow Gauge Railroad
  Co. & Museum, Portland, ME..................620
Tupelo Automobile Museum, Tupelo, MS ...809

Union Pacific Railroad Museum, Council
  Bluffs, IA...512
U.S. Army Transportation Museum, Fort
  Eustis, VA..1504

The Vestal Museum, Vestal, NY................1081
Vintage Flying Museum, Fort Worth, TX ..1419
Virginia Museum of Transportation, Inc.,
  Roanoke, VA..1536
Volo Antique Auto Museum and Village,
  Volo, IL..463

Wabash Frisco and Pacific Association,
  Inc., Glencoe, MO....................................816
Wade House Stagecoach Inn & Wesley
  Jung Carriage Museum State Historic
  Site, Greenbush, WI................................1599
Walter P. Chrysler Museum, Auburn
  Hills, MI..726
Warther Museum Inc., Dover, OH.............1163
Waterfront Museum, Brooklyn, NY 970
Wedell-Williams Memorial Aviation
  Museum, Patterson, LA............................599
Wells Auto Museum, Wells, ME 625
West Chicago City Museum, West
  Chicago, IL..464
West Florida Railroad Museum, Milton,
  FL...327
West Virginia Northern Community
  College Alumni Association Museum,
  Wheeling, WV...1588
Western Mining & Railroad Museum,
  Helper, UT...1466
Western Museum of Flight, Hawthorne,
  CA..101
Western North Carolina Air Museum,
  Hendersonville, NC.................................1105

The Western Railway Museum, Suisun
  City, CA...189
Western Reserve Historical Society,
  Cleveland, OH...1156
Wheels O' Time Museum, Peoria, IL..........451
Wheels of Yesterday, Ocean City, MD........650
Wheels Through Time Museum, Inc.,
  Maggie Valley, NC..................................1110
Whippany Railway Museum, Whippany,
  NJ...930
Whitewater Canal State Historic Site,
  Metamora, IN...490
Wilmington Railroad Museum,
  Wilmington, NC......................................1124
Wings Over Miami Museum, Inc.,
  Miami, FL..326
Wiscasset, Waterville & Farmington
  Railway Museum, Alna, ME....................603
Wisconsin Automotive Museum,
  Hartford, WI..1600

Typography Museums

Baker University, William A. Quayle
  Bible Collection, Baldwin City, KS.........533

The International Printing Museum,
  Carson, CA..82

La Casa Del Libro, San Juan, PR.............1642

Village Museums

Anasazi State Park Museum, Boulder, UT.1463
Appomattox Court House National
  Historical Park, Appomattox, VA 1495
Arrow Rock State Historic Site, Arrow
  Rock, MO...810
Au Glaize Village, Defiance, OH..............1162
Aztec Museum and Pioneer Village,
  Aztec, NM...936

Barton County Historical Museum &
  Village, Great Bend, KS..........................542
Batsto Village, Hammonton, NJ.................907
Big Horn County Historical Museum,
  Hardin, MT..849
Buffalo County Historical Society,
  Kearney, NE..863

CHTJ Southard House Museum,
  Brunswick, ME..607
Cades Cove Visitor Center and Open-Air
  Museum, Townsend, TN..........................1384
Canterbury Shaker Village, Inc.,
  Canterbury, NH..883
Cashmere Museum & Pioneer Village,
  Cashmere, WA...1550
Cass County Historical Society at
  Bonanzaville, West Fargo, ND................1137
Castleton Historical Society, Castleton,
  VT..1478
Century Village Museum, Burton, OH.......1144
Chickasaw County Historical Society
  Bradford Pioneer Village Museum,
  Nashua, IA...525
Chippewa County Historical Society,
  Montevideo, MN......................................783
Clewiston Museum, Inc., Clewiston, FL......300
Colonel Allensworth State Historic Park,
  Allensworth, CA..70
The Colonial Spanish Quarter Museum,
  Saint Augustine, FL.................................338
Conner Prairie, Fishers, IN.......................476
Cracker Country, Tampa, FL.....................348

Dallas Heritage Village at Old City Park,
  Dallas, TX...1405
Daniels County Museum and Pioneer
  Town, Scobey, MT...................................853
Dennys River Historical Society,
  Dennysville, ME......................................609
Divide County Historical Society
  Museum, Crosby, ND...............................1129

East Jersey Olde Towne, Piscataway, NJ ,....921
Eckley Miners' Village, Eckley, PA............1251
Empire Area Heritage Group, Empire, MI...740
Enfield Shaker Museum, Enfield, NH 887
Ephrata Cloister, Ephrata, PA 1251

The Farm, Sturgeon Bay, WI......................1623
The Farmers' Museum, Inc.,
    Cooperstown, NY 980
Fort Delaware Museum of Colonial
    History, Narrowsburg, NY....................1017
Fort Dodge & Frontier Village, Fort
    Dodge, IA..518
Fort Walla Walla Museum, Walla Walla,
    WA 1576
Frontier Village Association, Inc.,
    Jamestown, ND 1133
Furnace Town Living Heritage Museum,
    Snow Hill, MD..654

General Jacob Brown Historical Society,
    Brownville, NY 971
Geographical Center Historical Museum,
    Rugby, ND 1136
Glenn H. Curtiss Museum,
    Hammondsport, NY...............................997

Hale Farm and Village, Bath, OH 1141
Hancock Shaker Village, Inc., Pittsfield,
    MA 703
Har-Ber Village, Grove, OK 1202
Harrimans Falls Educational Centre and
    Museum, Bath, NH................................883
Helvetia Museum, Helvetia, WV 1582
The Henry Ford, Dearborn, MI 733
Heritage Hill State Historical Park, Green
    Bay, WI 1599
Heritage Village, Mountain Lake, MN 785
Heritage Village Museum, Woodville, TX .1462
Hettinger County Historical Society,
    Regent, ND 1136
Historic Deerfield, Inc., Deerfield, MA 679
Historic Fallsington, Inc., Fallsington, PA .1253
Historic Gardner's Basin, Atlantic City,
    NJ 898
Historic Sauder Village, Archbold, OH 1140
Historic Schaefferstown, Inc.,
    Schaefferstown, PA..............................1297
Historic Southwest Ohio, Inc.,
    Sharonville, OH 1185
Historic Westville, Inc., Lumpkin, GA.........376

Illinois and Michigan Canal
    Commissioners Office Museum,
    Lockport, IL...443

Jimmie Rodgers Museum, Meridian, MS.....805

Kern County Museum, Bakersfield, CA.........73
Kingman Tavern Historical Museum,
    Cummington, MA...................................678

La Purisima Mission State Historic Park,
    Lompoc, CA 109
Lakewood's Heritage Center, Lakewood,
    CO...225
Lexington County Museum, Lexington,
    SC...1336
Lincoln's New Salem State Historic Site,
    Petersburg, IL..451
Lisle Station Museum, Lisle, IL 443
Log Cabin Village, Fort Worth, TX............1417
The Lyons Redstone Museum, Lyons, CO...227

Mason County Historical Society/Historic
    White Pine Village, Ludington, MI 751
Mechanicsburg Museum Association,
    Mechanicsburg, PA..............................1270
Midway Village & Museum Center,
    Rockford, IL...455
Mill Race Historical Village, Northville,
    MI..758

Mississippi Agriculture &
    Forestry/National Agricultural Aviation
    Museum, Jackson, MS 802
Missouri Town 1855, Lee's Summit, MO....825
Museum of Appalachia, Clinton, TN..........1363
Museum of the Berkeley Springs,
    Berkeley Springs, WV...........................1580
Museum Village, Monroe, NY...................1015

Nassau County, Division of Museum
    Services, Department of Recreation,
    Parks & Museums, East Meadow, NY 987
Navarro County Historical Society,
    Pioneer Village, Corsicana, TX..............1402
New Jersey Office of Historic Sites,
    Trenton, NJ..927
Northport Historical Society Museum,
    Northport, NY.......................................1044

Oak Creek Historical Society-Pioneer
    Village, Oak Creek, WI..........................1615
Ohio Historical Society, Columbus, OH....1158
Old Bethpage Village Restoration, Old
    Bethpage, NY.......................................1045
Old Cowtown Museum, Wichita, KS...........562
Old Economy Village, Ambridge, PA.........1240
Old Falls Village, Menomonee Falls, WI...1609
Old Salem Inc., Winston-Salem, NC.........1126
Old Sturbridge Village, Sturbridge, MA......713
Old World Wisconsin, Eagle, WI...............1595
Orangetown Historical Museum and
    Archives, Pearl River, NY 1051
Oysterponds Historical Society: The
    Museum of Orient and East Marion
    History, Orient, NY 1047
Ozaukee County Pioneer Village,
    Saukville, WI..1620

Pella Historical Village, Pella, IA................526
Pioneer Auto Museum, Murdo, SD 1352
Pioneer Settlement for the Creative Arts,
    Barberville, FL..295
Pioneer Town, Wimberley, TX...................1462
Pioneer Village, Rison, AR 67
Pioneer Village, Farmington, UT...............1465
Pioneer Village & Virgil Grissom
    Memorial at Spring Mill State Park,
    Mitchell, IN..491
Prairie Village, Madison, SD.....................1351

Red Barn Museum, Morristown, NY 1016
Rochester Hills Museum at Van Hoosen
    Farm, Rochester Hills, MI 762
Roscoe Village Foundation, Coshocton,
    OH...1159

The Schuette Biermann Farmhouse
    Museum, Elk Grove Village, IL 432
Sea Cliff Village Museum, Sea Cliff, NY ..1068
Seabrook Village, Midway, GA 380
Senator John Heinz Pittsburgh Regional
    History Center, Pittsburgh, PA..............1294
Shaker Village of Pleasant Hill,
    Harrodsburg, KY 571
Shoal Creek Living History Museum,
    Kansas City, MO...................................822
Silt Historical Society, Silt, CO 232
South Park City Museum, Fairplay, CO......215
Storrowton Village Museum, West
    Springfield, MA......................................718
Stuhr Museum of the Prairie Pioneer,
    Grand Island, NE...................................862
Swiss Historical Village, New Glarus, WI.1615

Tinley Park Historical Society, Tinley
    Park, IL..461
Troy Museum & Historic Village, Troy,
    MI..765

Union County Historical Complex,
    Creston, IA..512

The Vestal Museum, Vestal, NY.................1081

The Vinalhaven Historical Society
    Museum, Vinalhaven, ME......................624
Volo Antique Auto Museum and Village,
    Volo, IL..463

Wade House Stagecoach Inn & Wesley
    Jung Carriage Museum State Historic
    Site, Greenbush, WI.............................1599
West Overton Museums, Scottdale, PA.......1298
West Virginia State Farm Museum, Point
    Pleasant, WV..1586
Winedale, Center for American History,
    University of Texas at Austin, Round
    Top, TX..1446
World Museum of Mining, Butte, MT.........843

Zoar State Memorial, Zoar, OH.................1194

Wax Museums

Buckhorn Saloon & Museum, San
    Antonio, TX..1448

Holiday World/Splashin' Safari, Santa
    Claus, IN...498
Hollywood Wax Museum, Branson, MO 811
Hollywood Wax Museum, Inc.,
    Hollywood, CA.......................................103
House of Frankenstein Wax Museum,
    Lake George, NY 1008

John Brown Wax Museum Inc., Harpers
    Ferry, WV 1582

Living Bible Museum, Mansfield, OH 1173

Madame-Tussaud's Wax Museum, Las
    Vegas, Las Vegas, NV..........................879
Mammoth Cave Wax Museum, Cave
    City, KY 566
Musee Conti Wax Museum, New
    Orleans, LA 597

The National Great Blacks in Wax
    Museum, Inc., Baltimore, MD................635
National Presidential Wax Museum,
    Keystone, SD.......................................1350

Old West Wax Museum, Thermopolis,
    WY 1639

Potter's Wax Museum, Saint Augustine,
    FL...339

Ripley's Believe It or Not!, Key West,
    FL...319
Ripley's Believe It or Not! Museum,
    Orlando, FL 332

Wax Museum at Fisherman's Wharf, San
    Francisco, CA 170

Whaling Museums

Cold Spring Harbor Whaling Museum,
    Cold Spring Harbor, NY 979

East Hampton Town Marine Museum,
    Amagansett, NY 957

Leaming's Run Garden & Colonial Farm,
    Swainton, NJ...926

Nantucket Historical Association,
    Nantucket, MA 696
New Bedford Whaling Museum, New
    Bedford, MA..696

Sag Harbor Whaling & Historical
    Museum, Sag Harbor, NY.....................1063

Whalers Village Museum, Lahaina, HI 401

Woodcarving Museums

Alaska Indian Arts, Inc., Haines, AK 24
Atlantic Wildfowl Heritage Museum,
    Virginia Beach, VA...............................1541

Index to
Institutions by Collection From Volume One

List of Collections

ANTHROPOLOGY AND ARCHAEOLOGICAL COLLECTIONS

Archaeological...189
Ethnological/Ethnographical.....................202
Folk Culture..210
Physical Anthropology................................218

ART COLLECTIONS

Archaeological/Ethnographical...................220
Audiovisual and Film..................................226
Costumes and Textiles.................................234
Decorative Arts..255
Paintings..270
Photographs..299
Prints, Drawings, Graphic Arts..................334
Sculpture..355

HISTORICAL COLLECTIONS

Communication Artifacts.............................369

Distribution and Transportation Artifacts.....................385
Furnishings...399
Personal Artifacts..429
Recreational Artifacts..................................464
Structures..480
Tools and Equipment for Communication..............504
Tools and Equipment for Materials.............520
Tools and Equipment for Science and Technology.................541

NATURAL COLLECTIONS

Botanical (Living)..554
Botanical (Nonliving)..................................560
Geological..564
Paleontological..571
Zoological (Living).....................................575
Zoological (Nonliving).................................579

Index to
Institutions by Collection From Volume One

List of Collections

ANTHROPOLOGY AND ARCHAEOLOGICAL COLLECTIONS

Archaeological

A.D. German Warehouse, Designed By Frank Lloyd Wright, Richland Center, WI 1620

A.R. Bowman Memorial Museum, Prineville, OR 1234

A:shiwi A:wan Museum and Heritage Center, Zuni, NM 954

Abbe Museum, Bar Harbor, ME................605

Adams Old Stone Grist Mill, Bellows Falls, VT 1476

Adan E. Treganza Anthropology Museum, Dept. of Anthropology, San Francisco State University, San Francisco, CA 162

Adirondack History Center, Elizabethtown, NY 987

Agate Fossil Beds National Monument, Harrison, NE................................862

Agua Caliente Cultural Museum, Palm Springs, CA 138

Ah-Tah-Thi-Ki Museum at Okalee, Hollywood, FL................................312

Aiken County Historical Museum, Aiken, SC 1320

Alabama Department of Archives & History, Montgomery, AL 15

Alabama Museum of Natural History, Tuscaloosa, AL................................19

The Alamo, San Antonio, TX 1447

Alaska Heritage Museum at Wells Fargo, Anchorage, AK................................21

Alaska Museum of Natural History, Anchorage, AK................................21

Albinger Archeological Museum, Ventura, CA 194

Alden House Historic Site, Duxbury, MA ...680

Alexander Brest Museum and Gallery, Jacksonville, FL................................313

Alexandria Archaeology Museum, Alexandria, VA 1491

Alexandria Black History Resource Center, Alexandria, VA 1491

Allegheny Portage Railroad National Historic Site and Johnstown Flood National Memorial, Gallitzin, PA 1255

Allen County Museum, Lima, OH 1172

Allison-Antrim Museum, Inc., Greencastle, PA................................1257

Alpine County Museum, Markleeville, CA..124

Alutiiq Museum and Archaeological Repository, Kodiak, AK................26

Amador County Museum, Jackson, CA 105

Amelia Island Museum of History, Fernandina Beach, FL 306

American Association for State and Local History, Nashville, TN................1377

American Museum of Natural History, New York, NY................................1019

The American Numismatic Society, New York, NY................................1020

America's Stonehenge, North Salem, NH 893

The Amerind Foundation, Inc., Dragoon, AZ..32

Amherst County Museum & Historical Society, Amherst, VA 1495

Amory Regional Museum, Amory, MS........797

Amy B.H. Greenwell Ethnobotanical Garden, Captain Cook, HI................392

Anasazi Heritage Center, Dolores, CO.........214

Anasazi State Park Museum, Boulder, UT.1463

Andersonville National Historic Site, Andersonville, GA 355

Andrew County Museum & Historical Society, Savannah, MO................838

Andrew Johnson National Historic Site, Greeneville, TN................................1366

Androscoggin Historical Society, Auburn, ME................................603

Angel Mounds State Historic Site, Evansville, IN................................475

Angels Attic Museum, Santa Monica, CA ...183

Animas Museum, Durango, CO................214

Anna Bemis Palmer Museum, York, NE......875

Annie E. Woodman Institute Museum, Dover, NH................................886

Annie Riggs Memorial Museum, Fort Stockton, TX................................1415

Anniston Museum of Natural History, Anniston, AL 3

Anson County Historical Society, Inc., Wadesboro, NC................................1121

Antelope Valley Indian Museum, Lancaster, CA 108

The Anthropology Museum, DeKalb, IL......429

Anthropology Museum, University of San Diego, San Diego, CA 155

Anthropology Teaching Museum, California State University, Fullerton, Fullerton, CA 98

Anza-Borrego Desert State Park, Borrego Springs, CA................................79

Apostles Islands National Lakeshore, Bayfield, WI................................1591

Appomattox Court House National Historical Park, Appomattox, VA 1495

Aptucxet Trading Post Museum, Bourne, MA 670

APVA Preservation Virginia, Richmond, VA 1528

Arcadia Township Historical Commission, Arcadia, MI................726

Archer County Museum, Archer City, TX.1387

Arches National Park Visitor Center, Moab, UT................................1467

Argo Gold Mine & Mill Museum, Idaho Springs, CO 223

Arizona Historical Society-Fort Lowell Museum, Tucson, AZ................47

Arizona Historical Society Museum - Downtown, Tucson, AZ 47

Arizona State Capitol Museum, Phoenix, AZ..39

Arizona State Museum, Tucson, AZ............48

Arizona State Parks Board, Phoenix, AZ.......39

Arizona State University Museum of Anthropology, Tempe, AZ................46

Arkansas Post Museum, Gillett, AR............58

Arkansas Post National Memorial, Gillett, AR..58

Arkansas Tech University Museum of Prehistory and History, Russellville, AR..67

Arlington House, The Robert E. Lee Memorial, Arlington, VA................1495

The Arms Family Museum of Local History, Youngstown, OH................1193

Arrow Rock State Historic Site, Arrow Rock, MO................................810

Art Museum of The University of Memphis, Memphis, TN................1372

Artesia Historical Museum & Art Center, Artesia, NM................................936

Arthur Ross Gallery, University of Pennsylvania, Philadelphia, PA................1276

Ash Hollow State Historical Park, Lewellen, NE................................864

Ashland, The Henry Clay Estate, Lexington, KY................................572

Ashton Villa & The Heritage Visitor Center, Galveston, TX................1420

Asian Arts & Culture Center, Towson University, Towson, MD................655

Association for the Preservation of Tennessee Antiquities, Nashville, TN....1377

Ataloa Lodge Museum, Muskogee, OK.....1205

Atchison County Historical Society, Atchison, KS................................533

Atlantic Heritage Center, Somers Point, NJ..924

Attmore-Oliver House, New Bern, NC.......1112

Audubon Canyon Ranch, Stinson Beach, CA..188

Audubon County Historical Society, Exira, IA................................517

Auglaize County Historical Society, Saint Marys, OH 1184

Augusta Museum of History, Augusta, GA..364

Aurora Fossil Museum, Aurora, NC..........1091

Aurora History Museum, Aurora, CO..........202

Avery Research Center for African American History & Culture, Charleston, SC................................1323

Aztalan Museum, Jefferson, WI................1601

Aztec Ruins National Monument, Aztec, NM..937

Bacon's Castle, Surry County, VA..............1540

The Bade Institute of Biblical Archaeology and The Howell Bible Collection, Berkeley, CA 75

Bailey House Museum - Maui Historical Society, Wailuku, HI................402

Baldwin Historical Society and Museum, Baldwin, NY................................960

Baltimore Public Works Museum, Inc., Baltimore, MD................................630

Balzekas Museum of Lithuanian Culture, Chicago, IL................................418

Bandelier National Monument, Los Alamos, NM................................942

Baranov Museum, Kodiak, AK................26

The Bartlett Museum, Amesbury, MA 657

Barton County Historical Museum & Village, Great Bend, KS................542

Bartram's Garden, Philadelphia, PA 1277

Batsto Village, Hammonton, NJ................907

Battleground Historical Society, Englishtown, NJ................................903

Battleship Texas State Historic Site, La Porte, TX................................1433

Bay Area Museum, Seabrook, TX..............1452

Bear Butte State Park Visitors Center, Sturgis, SD................................1358

Bear Mountain Trailside Museums and Zoo, Bear Mountain, NY................961

The Beaufort Arsenal, Beaufort, SC...........1321

Beauvoir, The Jefferson Davis Home and Presidential Library, Biloxi, MS 798

Beaver Island Historical Society, Beaver Island, MI................................728

Beaverhead County Museum, Dillon, MT ...845

Bedford Historical Society Museum and Library, Bedford, OH 1142

Behringer-Crawford Museum, Covington, KY..567

Bell County Museum, Belton, TX.............1395

Belle Grove Plantation, Middletown, VA...1517

Belle Meade Plantation, Nashville, TN......1377

The Benjamin Banneker Park & Museum, Baltimore, MD................631

Benson Memorial Museum, Malheur National Wildlife Refuge, Princeton, OR..1233

Bentonville Battlefield State Historic Site, Four Oaks, NC................................1102

Bent's Old Fort National Historic Site, La Junta, CO................................224

Berea College Burroughs Geological Museum, Berea, KY................565

Bergen Museum of Art & Science, Paramus, NJ................................919

Berkeley County Museum & Heritage Center, Moncks Corner, SC................1336

Berkeley Plantation, Charles City, VA 1498

Berlin Art and Historical Collections, Berlin, MA................................662

Bernard Historical Society and Museum, Delton, MI................................734

Archaeological–Continued

Besh-Ba-Gowah Archaeological Park, Globe, AZ 35
Besser Museum for Northeast Michigan, Alpena, MI 723
Betts House Research Center, Cincinnati, OH 1148
Beyer Home, Oconto County Historical Society Museum, Oconto, WI 1616
Biblical Resource Center & Museum, Collierville, TN 1364
Biedenharn Museum & Gardens, Monroe, LA 592
Big Bend National Park, Big Bend, TX 1396
Big Bone Lick State Park Museum, Union, KY 584
Big Cypress National Preserve, Ochopee, FL 330
Big Hole National Battlefield, Wisdom, MT 855
Billings Curation Center, Billings, MT 841
Biscayne National Park, Homestead, FL 313
Bishop Hill State Historic Site, Bishop Hill, IL 413
Bishop Museum, Honolulu, HI 394
Blackwater Draw Museum, Portales, NM 944
Blaine County Historical Museum, Hailey, ID 406
Blount Mansion, Knoxville, TN 1369
Blue Hills Trailside Museum, Milton, MA 695
Blue Licks Battlefield Museum, Mount Olivet, KY 580
B'nai B'rith Klutznick National Jewish Museum, Washington, DC 277
Bob Jones University Museum & Gallery, Inc., Greenville, SC 1333
Bolduc House Museum, Sainte Genevieve, MO 837
Booker T. Washington National Monument, Hardy, VA 1510
Boone County Historical Center, Boone, IA 506
Boone's Lick State Historic Site, Boonesboro, MO 811
Boonsborough Museum of History, Boonsboro, MD 637
Boonshoft Museum of Discovery, Dayton, OH 1160
Bosque Memorial Museum, Clifton, TX 1400
Boston National Historical Park, Boston, MA 664
Botanical Museum of Harvard University, Cambridge, MA 672
Bowers Museum, Santa Ana, CA 177
Boyhood Home of President Woodrow Wilson, Augusta, GA 365
Brasstown Bald Visitor Center, Hiawassee, GA 374
Brazoria County Historical Museum, Angleton, TX 1387
Brazos Valley Museum of Natural History, Bryan, TX 1398
Brazosport Museum of Natural Science, Clute, TX 1400
Brec's Magnolia Mound Plantation, Baton Rouge, LA 585
Brevard Museum of History & Science, Cocoa, FL 300
Bridge Hampton Historical Society, Bridgehampton, NY 964
Brooklyn Children's Museum, Brooklyn, NY 968
The Broome County Historical Society, Binghamton, NY 962
Broward County Historical Commission, Fort Lauderdale, FL 307
Bruce Museum, Greenwich, CT 243
Brucemore, Cedar Rapids, IA 509
Brunswick Town/Fort Anderson State Historic Site, Winnabow, NC 1124

Bucks County Civil War Library & Museum, Doylestown, PA 1249
Buffalo and Erie County Historical Society, Buffalo, NY 972
Buffalo Museum of Science, Buffalo, NY 972
Buffalo National River, Harrison, AR 59
Buffalo Trails Museum, Epping, ND 1130
Bulloch Hall, Roswell, GA 382
Bulow Plantation Ruins Historic State Park, Bunnell, FL 298
Bunker Hill Museum, Charlestown, MA 675
Burke Museum of Natural History and Culture, Seattle, WA 1565
Burlington Historical Museum, Burlington, MA 672
Burnside Plantation, Inc., Bethlehem, PA 1242
Burpee Museum of Natural History, Rockford, IL 454
Burritt on the Mountain-A Living Museum, Huntsville, AL 11
Burrowes Mansion Museum, Matawan, NJ 911

C.E. Smith Museum of Anthropology, Hayward, CA 101
C.H. Nash Museum-Chucalissa Archaeological Museum, Memphis, TN 1372
CSS Neuse State Historic Site and Gov. Richard Caswell Memorial, Kinston, NC 1108
Caddoan Mounds State Historic Site, Cherokee County, TX 1399
Caguana Indian Ceremonial Park & Museum, Utuado, PR 1644
Cahokia Courthouse State Historic Site, Cahokia, IL 415
Cahokia Mounds State Historic Site, Collinsville, IL 428
Calaveras County Museum, San Andreas, CA 155
Calhoun County Museum, Port Lavaca, TX 1444
Calhoun County Museum & Cultural Center, Saint Matthews, SC 1341
California Museum of Ancient Art, Beverly Hills, CA 78
California State Indian Museum, Sacramento, CA 151
Calkins Nature Area/Field Museum, Iowa Falls, IA 521
Calusa Nature Center and Planetarium, Fort Myers, FL 308
Cambridge Museum, Cambridge, NE 858
Camden Archives & Museum, Camden, SC 1322
Camden County Historical Society, Camden, NJ 899
Campbell County Rockpile Museum, Gillette, WY 1633
Campus Martius Museum, Marietta, OH 1173
Canby Historical Society, Canby, OR 1221
Canterbury Shaker Village, Inc., Canterbury, NH 883
Canyon de Chelly National Monument, Chinle, AZ 31
Caparra Museum and Historic Park, Guaynabo, PR 1641
Cape Cod Museum of Natural History, Inc., Brewster, MA 670
Cape Cod National Seashore, Wellfleet, MA 717
Cape Fear Museum of History and Science, Wilmington, NC 1123
Capitol Reef National Park Visitor Center, Torrey, UT 1475
Capitol Visitors Center, a Division of the State Preservation Board, Austin, TX 1389
Carlsbad Caverns National Park, Carlsbad, NM 937
Carlsbad Museum & Art Center, Carlsbad, NM 938

Carlyle House Historic Park, Alexandria, VA 1492
Carnegie Museum of Natural History, Pittsburgh, PA 1291
Carnton Plantation, Franklin, TN 1365
Carroll County Historical Museum, Delphi, IN 474
Carson County Square House Museum, Panhandle, TX 1442
Carter County Museum, Ekalaka, MT 846
Carter's Grove, Williamsburg, VA 1544
Casa Grande Ruins National Monument, Coolidge, AZ 31
Casa Grande Valley Historical Society & Museum, Casa Grande, AZ 30
Cashmere Museum & Pioneer Village, Cashmere, WA 1550
Castle Museum of Saginaw County History, Saginaw, MI 762
Catalina Island Museum Society, Inc., Avalon, CA 73
Cave Creek Museum, Cave Creek, AZ 31
Cedar Breaks National Monument, Cedar City, UT 1464
Cedar Key Historical Society Museum, Cedar Key, FL 298
Cedar Key Museum State Park, Cedar Key, FL 299
The Centennial Museum at the University of Texas at El Paso, TX 1411
Center for American Archaeology, Kampsville, IL 440
The Center for Western Studies, Sioux Falls, SD 1356
Center of Southwest Studies/Fort Lewis College, Durango, CO 214
Central Iowa Art Association, Marshalltown, IA 523
Central Missouri State University Archives and Museum, Warrensburg, MO 839
Central Nevada Museum & Historical Society, Tonopah, NV 882
Centre County Historical Society, State College, PA 1301
Chaco Culture National Historical Park, Nageezi, NM 943
Champion Mill State Historical Park, Champion, NE 859
Chandler Museum, Chandler, AZ 31
Channel Islands National Park, Robert J. Lagomarsino Visitor Center, Ventura, CA 194
Charles A. Lindbergh Historic Site, Little Falls, MN 779
Charles H. Wright Museum of African American History, Detroit, MI 735
Charles Pinckney National Historic Site, Mount Pleasant, SC 1337
Charles Towne Landing State Historic Site, Charleston, SC 1324
The Charleston Museum, Charleston, SC 1324
Charlotte County Historical Center, Charlotte Harbor, FL 299
Charlotte Museum of History and Hezekiah Alexander Homesite, Charlotte, NC 1094
Chattahoochee River National Recreation Area, Atlanta, GA 359
Chattanooga Regional History Museum, Chattanooga, TN 1361
Chautauqua County Historical Society, McClurg Museum, Westfield, NY 1086
Chemung Valley History Museum, Elmira, NY 988
Chenango County Historical Society Museum, Norwich, NY 1044
Cherokee County Historical Museum, Inc., Murphy, NC 1112
Cherokee National Museum, Park Hill, OK 1211
Cherry County Historical Society, Valentine, NE 874

Chesapeake and Ohio Canal National Historical Park, Hagerstown, MD............646
Chester County Historical Society Museum, Chester, SC............................1327
Chesterfield County Museum, Chesterfield, VA.......................................1501
Chickamauga-Chattanooga National Military Park, Fort Oglethorpe, GA 372
Chickasaw National Recreation Area, Sulphur, OK...................................1214
Chieftains Museum, Rome, GA..............381
Children's Discovery Museum of the Desert, Rancho Mirage, CA.....................145
Children's Museum/Detroit Public Schools, Detroit, MI...............................735
Children's Museum, Inc., Boca Raton, FL...296
The Children's Museum of Portsmouth, Portsmouth, NH..894
The Children's Museum of Rose Hill Manor Park, Frederick, MD.....................644
Chimney Point State Historic Site, Addison, VT..1475
Chinese American Museum, Los Angeles, CA..114
Chinese House/O.R. & N. Museum & St. Peter's Catholic Church, Echo, OR.......1222
Chippewa Nature Center, Midland, MI.....755
Chiricahua National Monument, Willcox, AZ..53
Chisholm Trail Museum, Wellington, KS 561
Chittenango Landing Canal Boat Museum, Chittenango, NY.....................978
Choctaw County Historical Society, Hugo, OK..1203
Christiansted National Historic Site, Saint Croix, VI...1644
Churchill County Museum and Archives, Fallon, NV..877
Cincinnati Museum Center at Union Terminal, Cincinnati, OH.......................1149
City Museum, Saint Louis, MO...............832
City of Fort Walton Beach Heritage Park & Cultural Center, Fort Walton Beach, FL...310
Clark County Historical Museum, Vancouver, WA..1576
Clark County Historical Society - Heritage Center of Clark County, Springfield, OH..1186
Clark County Museum, Henderson, NV 878
Clark Hotel Museum, Van Horn, TX 1457
Clarke County Historical Association, Inc., Berryville, VA 1496
Clarke Historical Museum, Eureka, CA.........94
Clarke House Museum, Chicago, IL.............420
Clarksville-Montgomery County Museum dba Customs House Museum & Cultural Center, Clarksville, TN............1363
Clausen Memorial Museum, Petersburg, AK..27
Clay County Historical Museum, Liberty, MO..826
Clermont State Historic Site, Clermont, NY..979
The Cleveland Museum of Art, Cleveland, OH 1152
The Cleveland Museum of Natural History, Cleveland, OH 1153
Cliff Dwellings Museum, Manitou Springs, CO 227
Cliffs of the Neuse State Park, Seven Springs, NC..1119
Clinton County Historical Association & Museum, Plattsburgh, NY.....................1052
Cliveden of the National Trust, Philadelphia, PA..1278
Coastal Discovery Museum, Hilton Head Island, SC..1335
Coastal Heritage Museum, Crystal River, FL...301
Cobb Institute of Archaeology, Mississippi State University, MS............805

The Coffey County Historical Museum, Burlington, KS..534
Colfax County Society of Art, History and Archaeology, Raton, NM.................945
College of Eastern Utah Prehistoric Museum, Price, UT...............................1469
College Park Aviation Museum, College Park, MD 641
Collier County Museum, Naples, FL............328
Collingwood Library and Museum on Americanism, Alexandria, VA............1492
Colonel Davenport Historical Foundation, Rock Island, IL...453
Colonel William Jones State Historic Site/Lincoln State Park & Colonel Jones Home, Lincoln City, IN............488
Colonial Industrial Quarter, Bethlehem, PA...1242
Colonial National Historical Park: Jamestown & Yorktown, Yorktown, VA...1546
Colonial Pemaquid, New Harbor, ME..........615
The Colonial Spanish Quarter Museum, Saint Augustine, FL.....................................338
Colonial Williamsburg, Williamsburg, VA .1544
Colorado Historical Society, Denver, CO.....210
Colorado National Monument, Fruita, CO...218
Colorado River Indian Tribes Museum, Parker, AZ..38
Colorado Springs Museum, Colorado Springs, CO.....................................206
Columbia Gorge Discovery Center and Wasco County Museum, The Dalles, OR...1237
Columbia Gorge Interpretive Center Museum, Stevenson, WA.......................1572
Columbia River Exhibition of History, Science and Technology, Richland, WA...1564
Columbia State Historic Park, Columbia, CA..87
The Columbus Museum, Columbus, GA 368
Comanche Crossing Historical Society & Museum, Strasburg, CO.....................233
Command Museum, Marine Corps Recruit Depot, San Diego, San Diego, CA..156
The Commonwealth Museum, Boston, MA...665
Commonwealth of the Northern Mariana Islands Museum of History and Culture, Saipan, MP..............................1640
Community Historical Museum, Maxwell, IA...523
Concord Museum, Concord, MA.................676
Confederated Tribes of Grand Ronde Cultural Resources Department, Grand Ronde, OR..1225
Congaree National Park, Hopkins, SC 1336
Connecticut State Museum of Natural History and Connecticut Archaeology Center, Storrs, CT.....................................261
Coolspring Power Museum, Coolspring, PA...1248
Copia: The American Center for Wine, Food & the Arts, Napa, CA.....................129
The Corning Museum of Glass, Corning, NY...981
Coronado-Quivira Museum, Lyons, KS 550
Coronado State Monument, Bernalillo, NM...937
Corpus Christi Museum of Science and History, Corpus Christi, TX.................1401
Cottonlandia Museum, Greenwood, MS 800
Courthouse Square Association, Charlotte, MI...731
The Cowley County Historical Society, Winfield, KS..564
Cracker Trail Museum, Zolfo Springs, FL...355
Crailo State Historic Site, Rensselaer, NY.1056
Cranbrook Institute of Science, Bloomfield Hills, MI.................................730
Crane Point, Marathon, FL 323

Craters of the Moon National Monument, Arco, ID...403
Crazy Mountain Museum, Big Timber, MT...841
Creation Evidence Museum, Glen Rose, TX...1422
Creation Museum, Petersburg, KY..............583
Creek Council House Museum, Okmulgee, OK...1211
Crockett County Museum, Ozona, TX.......1442
Crockett Tavern Museum, Morristown, TN...1376
Crook County Museum & Art Gallery, Sundance, WY.....................................1638
Crosby County Pioneer Memorial Museum, Crosbyton, TX.....................1403
Crow Canyon Archaeological Center, Cortez, CO..208
Crow Wing County Historical Society, Brainerd, MN.....................................769
Crowley Museum & Nature Center, Sarasota, FL..344
Crown Point State Historic Site, Crown Point, NY..984
Crystal River State Archaeological Site, Crystal River, FL...302
Cullman County Museum, Cullman, AL.........6
Cultural Museum, Nashville, TN................1378
Cumberland County Historical Society, Greenwich, NJ.....................................905
Cumberland Gap National Historical Park, Middlesboro, KY.............................580
Cumberland Island National Seashore, Saint Marys, GA...382
The Curious Kids' Museum, Saint Joseph, MI..763
Custer Battlefield Museum, Garryowen, MT...847
Custer County 1881 Courthouse Museum, Custer, SD..1345
Cuyahoga Valley National Park, Brecksville, OH.....................................1144

DAAP Galleries, Cincinnati, OH................1150
Dakota County Historical Society, South Saint Paul, MN...793
Dakotaland Museum, Huron, SD................1348
Dallas Museum of Natural History, Dallas, TX..1406
Dan O'Laurie Museum of Moab, Moab, UT...1467
Dana Adobe, Nipomo, CA............................130
Daniels County Museum and Pioneer Town, Scobey, MT...853
Danvers Historical Society, Danvers, MA....678
Darnall's Chance House Museum, M-NCPPC, Upper Marlboro, MD...........655
Davenport House Museum, Savannah, GA...384
The Davistown Museum, Liberty, ME.........614
Dawes County Historical Society Museum, Chadron, NE.........................859
Dead Horse Point State Park, Moab, UT ...1467
Dearborn Historical Museum, Dearborn, MI...733
Death Valley National Park Visitor Center and Museums, Death Valley, CA.........91
Decatur House Museum, Washington, DC...277
Dedham Historical Society Museum, Dedham, MA..679
Deer Valley Rock Art Center, Glendale, AZ..35
Deere & Company, Administrative Center, Moline, IL.....................................445
Delaware Archaeology Museum, Dover, DE...269
Delaware County Institute of Science, Media, PA..1270
Delaware Division of Historical & Cultural Affairs, Dover, DE.................269
Delaware Nature Society, Hockessin, DE ...271
Deming Luna Mimbres Museum, Deming, NM...939

Archaeological–Continued

Denali National Park and Preserve, Denali Park, AK..................23

Denver Museum of Nature & Science, Denver, CO..................211

Department of Historic Resources, Richmond, VA..................1529

Deschutes County Historical Society, Bend, OR..................1220

DeSoto National Memorial, Bradenton, FL..................297

Devils Tower Visitor Center, Devils Tower, WY..................1631

DeWitt Stetten, Jr., Museum of Medical Research, Bethesda, MD..................637

Dickson Mounds Museum, Lewistown, IL..................442

Diego Sepulveda Adobe Estancia, Costa Mesa, CA..................87

Dinosaur Gardens, LLC, Ossineke, MI..................759

The Dinosaur Museum, Blanding, UT..................1463

Dinosaur Walk Museum, Pigeon Forge, TN..................1383

The Discovery Center, Fresno, CA..................96

Discovery Place, Inc., Charlotte, NC..................1094

Donald G. Trayser Memorial Museum/Barnstable County Customs House, Barnstable, MA..................661

Donner Memorial State Park and Emigrant Trail Museum, Truckee, CA....192

Douglas County Historical Society, Superior, WI..................1624

Douglas County Historical Society - Carson Valley Museum & Cultural Center, Gardnerville, NV..................877

Douglas County Historical Society - Genoa Courthouse Museum, Genoa, NV..................877

Douglas County Museum of History and Natural History, Roseburg, OR..................1234

Drayton Hall, Charleston, SC..................1325

Drew County Historical Museum, Monticello, AR..................64

Drummond Island Historical Museum, Drummond Island, MI..................739

Dry Falls Interpretive Center, Coulee City, WA..................1551

Dublin-Laurens Museum, Dublin, GA..................370

Duke Homestead State Historic Site, Durham, NC..................1098

Durham Center Museum/Research Library, East Durham, NY..................985

Durham Historic Association Museum, Durham, NH..................886

Dutchess County Historical Society, Poughkeepsie, NY..................1054

Dyckman Farmhouse Museum and Park, New York, NY..................1025

Eagle Tavern Museum, Watkinsville, GA....391

EarlyWorks Museums, Huntsville, AL..................11

Earth & Mineral Sciences Museum and Art Gallery, University Park, PA..................1303

East Hampton Town Marine Museum, Amagansett, NY..................957

East Lyme Historical Society/Thomas Lee House, Niantic, CT..................256

Eastern Arizona Museum and Historical Society of Graham County Inc., Pima, AZ..................42

Edgar Allan Poe Museum, Richmond, VA.1529

Edge of the Cedars State Park Museum, Blanding, UT..................1463

Edwin Wolters Memorial Museum, Shiner, TX..................1453

Effigy Mounds National Monument, Harpers Ferry, IA..................519

Ehrhart Museum, Antwerp, OH..................1139

El Morro National Monument, Ramah, NM..................945

El Museo Del Barrio, New York, NY..................1025

El Paso Museum of Archaeology, El Paso, TX..................1411

El Pueblo Historical Monument, Los Angeles, CA..................114

Elder Art Gallery, Nebraska Wesleyan University, Lincoln, NE..................865

Elgin Public Museum, Elgin, IL..................432

Ellis County Museum, Inc., Waxahachie, TX..................1460

Elsing Museum, Tulsa, OK..................1215

Emporia State University Johnston Geology Museum, Emporia, KS..................538

Environmental Education Center, Somerset County Park Commission, Basking Ridge, NJ..................898

Ephrata Cloister, Ephrata, PA..................1251

The Esther Thomas Atkinson Museum, Hampden-Sydney, VA..................1509

Etowah Indian Mounds Historical Site, Cartersville, GA..................367

Eugene O'Neill National Historic Site, Danville, CA..................89

Everglades National Park, Homestead, FL...313

Explorium of Lexington, Lexington, KY..................572

Fairfax County Park Authority, Resource Management Division, Fairfax, VA..................1503

Fairfax Museum & Visitor Center, Fairfax, VA..................1503

Fairfield County Museum, Winnsboro, SC..................1343

Fairfield Historical Society, Fairfield, CT..................241

Fall River County Historical Museum, Hot Springs, SD..................1348

Falls of the Ohio State Park, Clarksville, IN..................472

Faninadahen Kosas Guahan-Guam Museum, Hagatna, GU..................1640

Faulkner County Museum, Conway, AR..................56

Faust Park-Thornhill Historic Site & 19th Century Village, Chesterfield, MO..................812

Favell Museum Inc., Klamath Falls, OR....1227

Fayette County Museum, Washington Court House, OH..................1190

Fayette Historic State Park, Garden, MI..................742

Fayetteville Museum of Art, Fayetteville, NC..................1100

Felix Valle State Historic Site, Sainte Genevieve, MO..................837

Fernbank Museum of Natural History, Atlanta, GA..................359

Fick Fossil & History Museum, Oakley, KS..................554

Fiedler Memorial Museum, Seguin, TX..................1452

Field Museum of Natural History, Chicago, IL..................420

Fillmore Historical Museum, Inc., Fillmore, CA..................95

Finney County Kansas Historical Society, Inc., Garden City, KS..................541

First Landing State Park, Virginia Beach, VA..................1542

Flint House, Scotia, NY..................1068

Flint Ridge State Memorial Museum, Glenford, OH..................1166

Florence Griswold Museum, Old Lyme, CT..................258

Florence Hawley Ellis Museum of Anthropology and Ruth Hall Museum of Paleontology, Abiquiu, NM..................931

Florence Museum of Art, Science & History and the Florence Railroad Museum, Florence, SC..................1332

Florence Price Pioneer Museum, Florence, CO..................216

Florida Museum of Natural History, Gainesville, FL..................310

Florissant Fossil Beds National Monument, Florissant, CO..................216

Flowerdew Hundred Foundation, Hopewell, VA..................1511

The Fluvanna County Historical Society Old Stone Jail Museum, Palmyra, VA...1524

Folsom Museum, Inc., Folsom, NM..................939

Fontenelle Nature Association, Bellevue, NE..................857

Ford County Historical Society, Paxton, IL..................450

Forest Park Museum and Arboretum, Perry, IA..................527

Fort Abraham Lincoln State Park, Mandan, ND..................1134

Fort Ancient Museum, Oregonia, OH..................1181

The Fort at No. 4 Living History Museum, Charlestown, NH..................884

Fort Atkinson State Historical Park, Fort Calhoun, NE..................860

Fort Boonesborough Museum, Richmond, KY..................583

Fort Bowie National Historic Site, Bowie, AZ..................30

Fort Bridger State Museum, Fort Bridger, WY..................1632

Fort Buford State Historic Site, Williston, ND..................1137

Fort Caspar Museum, Casper, WY..................1629

Fort Clark Trading Post State Historic Site, Center, ND..................1129

Fort Clatsop National Memorial, Astoria, OR..................1218

Fort Collins Museum, Fort Collins, CO..................217

Fort Concho National Historic Landmark, San Angelo, TX..................1447

Fort Crawford Museum, Prairie du Chien, WI..................1618

Fort Dalles Museum/Anderson Homestead, The Dalles, OR..................1237

Fort Davidson State Historic Site, Pilot Knob, MO..................828

Fort Davis National Historic Site, Fort Davis, TX..................1414

Fort de Chartres State Historic Site & Museum, Prairie du Rocher, IL..................451

Fort Dobbs State Historic Site, Statesville, NC..................1120

Fort Dodge & Frontier Village, Fort Dodge, IA..................518

Fort Fetterman State Historic Site, Douglas, WY..................1631

Fort Fisher State Historic Site, Kure Beach, NC..................1108

Fort Frederica National Monument, Saint Simons Island, GA..................383

Fort Frederick State Park, Big Pool, MD.....637

Fort Garland Museum, Fort Garland, CO....217

Fort Gibson Historic Site, Fort Gibson, OK..................1200

Fort Harker Museum Complex, Kanopolis, KS..................546

Fort Hartsuff State Historical Park, Burwell, NE..................858

Fort Hays State Historic Site, Hays, KS......543

Fort Henrietta Interpretive Park, Echo, OR..................1223

Fort Kearney Museum, Kearney, NE..................863

Fort Kearny State Historical Park, Kearney, NE..................864

Fort King George Historic Site, Darien, GA..................370

Fort Laramie National Historic Site, Fort Laramie, WY..................1633

Fort Larned National Historic Site, Larned, KS..................547

Fort Laurens State Memorial, Bolivar, OH..................1143

Fort Leaton State Historical Site, Presidio, TX..................1444

Fort Ligonier Association, Ligonier, PA.....1269

Fort MacArthur Museum, San Pedro, CA....176

Fort Matanzas National Monument, Saint Augustine, FL..................339

Fort McHenry National Monument and Historic Shrine, Baltimore, MD..................632

Fort McKavett State Historical Site, Fort McKavett, TX..................1415

Fort Mifflin, Philadelphia, PA 1279
Fort Morgan Museum, Fort Morgan, CO.....218
Fort Morris State Historic Site, Midway,
   GA 379
Fort Necessity National Battlefield,
   Farmington, PA 1253
Fort Nisqually Living History Museum,
   Tacoma, WA 1573
Fort Okanogan Interpretive Center,
   Brewster, WA..1550
Fort Osage National Historic Landmark,
   Sibley, MO..838
Fort Phil Kearny, Banner, WY...................1628
The Fort Pitt Block House, Pittsburgh,
   PA 1292
Fort Pitt Museum, Pittsburgh, PA 1292
Fort Plain Museum, Fort Plain, NY 991
Fort Pulaski National Monument,
   Savannah, GA..385
Fort Raleigh National Historic Site,
   Manteo, NC..1110
Fort Recovery Museum, Fort Recovery,
   OH 1164
Fort Robinson Museum, Crawford, NE.......860
Fort Roosevelt Natural Science and
   History Museum, Hanford, CA....................101
Fort St. Jean Baptiste State Historic Site,
   Natchitoches, LA 593
Fort St. Joseph Museum, Niles, MI.............758
Fort Scott National Historic Site, Fort
   Scott, KS...540
Fort Selden State Monument, Radium
   Springs, NM..945
Fort Sill National Historic Landmark,
   Fort Sill, OK...1201
Fort Sisseton State Historic Park, Lake
   City, SD..1350
Fort Smith National Historic Site, Fort
   Smith, AR...58
Fort Spokane Visitor Center and
   Museum, Davenport, WA...........................1552
Fort Stanwix National Monument, Rome,
   NY 1061
Fort Sumter National Monument,
   Sullivan's Island, SC 1342
Fort Tejon State Historic Park, Lebec,
   CA 108
Fort Ticonderoga, Ticonderoga, NY 1078
Fort Towson Historic Site, Fort Towson,
   OK 1201
Fort Uncompahgre Living History
   Museum, Delta, CO.....................................209
Fort Union Trading Post National
   Historic Site, Williston, ND 1138
Fort Vancouver National Historic Site,
   Vancouver, WA..1576
Fort Vasquez Museum, Platteville, CO 230
Fort Verde State Historic Park, Camp
   Verde, AZ..30
Fort Washita, Durant, OK 1199
Fort Wilkins Historic Complex, Copper
   Harbor, MI..733
Fort William Henry Museum, Lake
   George, NY..1008
Fort Worth Museum of Science and
   History, Fort Worth, TX 1417
Fort Yargo State Park, Winder, GA 391
Forts Folle Avoine Historic Park,
   Danbury, WI...1594
Foundation For Historic Christ Church,
   Inc., Irvington, VA...................................1511
Fountain Rock Nature Center,
   Walkersville, MD..656
Fox Island Historical Society, Fox Island,
   WA 1554
Fox Lake Historical Museum, Inc., Fox
   Lake, WI...1598
Francisco Fort Museum, La Veta, CO.........224
Frank H. McClung Museum, Knoxville,
   TN 1370
Fred Dana Marsh Museum, Ormond
   Beach, FL..333

Frederick Douglass National Historic
   Site, Washington, DC 279
Fredericksburg & Spotsylvania National
   Military Park, Fredericksburg, VA.........1506
Freeport Historical Society, Freeport, ME....611
Freestone County Historical Museum,
   Fairfield, TX..1413
Fremont County Pioneer Museum,
   Lander, WY..1635
French Azilum, Inc., Towanda, PA.............1303
The French Legation Museum, Austin,
   TX 1390
Fresno Metropolitan Museum, Fresno,
   CA 97
Friends of Arrow Rock, Inc., Arrow
   Rock, MO 811
The Friends of the Caleb Pusey House,
   Inc., Upland, PA......................................1304
Friendship Hill National Historic Site,
   Point Marion, PA......................................1295
Frisco Native American Museum and
   Natural History Center, Frisco, NC 1102
Frontier Army Museum, Fort
   Leavenworth, KS...539
Frontier Historical Society and Museum,
   Glenwood Springs, CO................................219
Frontier Museum, Williston, ND 1138
Fruitlands Museums, Harvard, MA 686
Fulton County Museum, Groversville,
   NY 996
Furnace Town Living Heritage Museum,
   Snow Hill, MD..654
Furnas-Gosper Historical Society &
   Museum, Arapahoe, NE 856

Gadsby's Tavern Museum, Alexandria,
   VA 1492
Gadsden Museum, Mesilla, NM 943
Gadsden Museum of Art, Gadsden, AL 10
Galloway House and Village - Blakely
   Museum, Fond du Lac, WI........................1597
Galveston County Historical Museum,
   Galveston, TX...1420
Garfield Farm Museum, LaFox, IL 441
Garnavillo Historical Museum,
   Garnavillo, IA 518
Gateway NRA, Sandy Hook Unit, Fort
   Hancock, NJ..904
General Adam Stephen House,
   Martinsburg, WV......................................1584
General Daniel Bissell House, Saint
   Louis, MO...833
General Sterling Price Museum,
   Keytesville, MO..824
General Wait House, Waitsfield, VT...........1489
The George D. and Harriet W. Cornell
   Fine Arts Museum, Winter Park, FL 354
George Washington Birthplace National
   Monument, Colonial Beach, VA 1502
George Washington Carver Museum,
   Tuskegee Institute, AL.................................20
George Washington Carver National
   Monument, Diamond, MO.........................814
George Washington's Ferry Farm,
   Stafford County, VA 1537
George Washington's Fredericksburg
   Foundation, Historic Kenmore &
   Washington's Ferry Farm,
   Fredericksburg, VA...................................1506
Georgia Capitol Museum, Atlanta, GA 360
Georgia Museum of Natural History,
   Athens, GA...356
Georgia Salzburger Society Museum,
   Rincon, GA...381
Geronimo Springs Museum, Truth or
   Consequences, NM......................................953
Gilcrease Museum, Tulsa, OK 1215
Gilman Museum, Hellertown, PA..............1260
Glacier National Park Museum, West
   Glacier, MT...854
Gloucester County Historical Society,
   Woodbury, NJ..931

Gnadenhutten Historical Park & Museum,
   Gnadenhutten, OH 1167
The Godwin-Ternbach Museum,
   Flushing, NY 990
Golden Ball Tavern Museum, Weston,
   MA 718
Golden Gate National Recreation Area,
   San Francisco, CA......................................165
Golden Pioneer Museum, Golden, CO.........220
Golden Spike National Historic Site,
   Brigham City, UT......................................1463
Goliad State Park, Goliad, TX....................1423
Gomez Foundation for Mill House,
   Marlboro, NY 1014
Goodhue County Historical Society, Red
   Wing, MN..787
Goodnow Museum State Historic Site,
   Manhattan, KS..550
Governor John Sevier Memorial
   Association, Knoxville, TN.......................1370
Governor Printz Park, Essington, PA 1253
Graeme Park, Horsham, PA 1261
Graham Cave State Park, Montgomery
   City, MO...827
Graham County Historical Society,
   Thatcher, AZ...46
Grand Canyon National Park Museum
   Collection, Grand Canyon National
   Park, AZ..36
Grand Encampment Museum, Inc.,
   Encampment, WY.....................................1632
Grand Gulf Military Park, Port Gibson,
   MS 807
Grand Portage National Monument,
   Grand Marais, MN 776
Grand River Museum, Lemmon, SD..........1351
Grand Village of the Natchez Indians,
   Natchez, MS 805
Grant County Historical Museum,
   Canyon City, OR 1221
Grant County Historical Society, Elbow
   Lake, MN..774
Grant-Kohrs Ranch National Historic
   Site, Deer Lodge, MT..................................845
Grave Creek Mound Archaeology
   Complex, Moundsville, WV 1585
Graves Museum of Archaeology and
   Natural History, Dania Beach, FL...........302
Great Basin National Park, Baker, NV........875
Great Sand Dunes National Monument
   and Preserve, Mosca, CO...........................229
Great Smoky Mountains Heritage Center,
   Townsend, TN...1384
Green River Valley Museum, Big Piney,
   WY 1629
Greene County Historical Museum,
   Waynesburg, PA...1306
Greenfield Historical Society, Greenfield,
   WI 1599
Greenwood County Historical Society,
   Eureka, KS..539
Greybull Museum, Greybull, WY 1634
Guadalupe Mountains National Park, Salt
   Flat, TX..1447
Guilford Courthouse National Military
   Park, Greensboro, NC 1104
Gulf Coast Exploreum Science Center,
   Mobile, AL..13
Gulf Islands National Seashore, Gulf
   Breeze, FL...312
Gustav Jeeninga Museum of Bible and
   Near Eastern Studies, Anderson, IN....467
Gwinnett County Parks & Recreation
   Outdoor Interpretive Section,
   Lawrenceville, GA.......................................375
Gwinnett Historical Society,
   Lawrenceville, GA.......................................376

H. Earl Clack Museum, Havre, MT 849
H.G. Albee Memorial Museum,
   Estherville, IA..517
Haffenreffer Museum of Anthropology,
   Brown University, Bristol, RI 1310

Archaeological–Continued

The Haggin Museum, Stockton, CA 189
The Hall of Fame for Great Americans,
  Bronx, NY 966
Hamilton Township Historical Society -
  John Abbott II House, Hamilton, NJ.......906
Hamline University Galleries, Department
  of Studio Arts & Art History, Saint
  Paul, MN 790
Hammond-Harwood House Association,
  Annapolis, MD 628
Hampson Archeological Museum State
  Park, Wilson, AR 70
Hampton County Historical Museum,
  Hampton, SC 1334
Hampton History Museum, Hampton, VA .1509
Hampton Plantation State Historic Site,
  McClellanville, SC 1336
Hampton Roads Naval Museum, Norfolk,
  VA 1521
Hana Cultural Center, Hana, Maui, HI.........392
Hancock House, Hancock's Bridge, NJ.......907
Hannah Lindahl Children's Museum,
  Mishawaka, IN 491
Harbour House Museum, Crystal Falls,
  MI...733
Hardin County Historical Museums, Inc.,
  Kenton, OH 1170
Harney County Historical Museum,
  Burns, OR 1221
Harpers Ferry National Historical Park,
  Harpers Ferry, WV 1582
Harrisonburg-Rockingham Historical
  Society, Dayton, VA 1503
Harvard University Semitic Museum,
  Cambridge, MA 673
Haskell County Historical Society,
  Sublette, KS 558
Hattiesburg Area Historical Society and
  HAHS Museum, Hattiesburg, MS 801
Haverhill Historical Society, Haverhill,
  MA 686
Hawaii Maritime Center, Honolulu, HI.......395
Hawaii Volcanoes National Park, Kilauea
  Visitor Center, Hawaii Volcanoes
  National Park, HI...........................393
Hawks Nest State Park, Ansted, WV 1579
Headwaters Heritage Museum, Three
  Forks, MT..................................854
Heard Natural Science Museum and
  Wildlife Sanctuary, Inc., McKinney,
  TX 1437
Heisey Museum, Clinton County
  Historical Society, Lock Haven, PA 1269
Hellenic Museum & Cultural Center,
  Chicago, IL 421
Hemet Museum, Hemet, CA.....................103
Henrico County Historic Preservation &
  Museum Services, Richmond, VA 1529
Henry Whitfield State Historical
  Museum, Guilford, CT 243
The Heritage Center, Pine Ridge, SD.........1354
Heritage Center Museum, Berryville, AR 55
Heritage-Hjemkomst Interpretive Center,
  Moorhead, MN 784
Heritage Library Museum, Anchorage,
  AK 22
Heritage Museum & Potton House, Big
  Spring, TX 1396
Heritage Museum Foundation of Tate
  County, Inc., Senatobia, MS 808
Heritage Museum of Northwest Florida,
  Valparaiso, FL.............................352
Heritage of the Americas Museum, El
  Cajon, CA 92
The Hermitage: Home of President
  Andrew Jackson, Hermitage, TN...........1367
Hernando Heritage Museum, Brooksville,
  FL...298
Herrett Center for Arts & Science,
  Faulkner Planetarium and Centennial
  Observatory, Twin Falls, ID.................410

Hershey Museum, Hershey, PA 1261
Hibbing Historical Society and Museum,
  Hibbing, MN 778
Higgins Armory Museum, Worcester, MA...721
High Desert Museum, Bend, OR 1220
High Plains Museum, Goodland, KS............542
Hillwood Art Museum, Brookville, NY 971
The Hispanic Society of America, New
  York, NY 1027
Historic Annapolis Foundation,
  Annapolis, MD 628
Historic Bethabara Park, Winston-Salem,
  NC 1125
Historic Brattonsville, McConnells, SC......1336
Historic Camden Revolutionary War Site,
  Camden, SC 1323
Historic Columbia Foundation, Columbia,
  SC 1329
Historic Crab Orchard Museum &
  Pioneer Park, Inc., Tazewell, VA 1541
Historic Deerfield, Inc., Deerfield, MA......679
Historic Fallsington, Inc., Fallsington, PA .1253
Historic Fort Snelling, Saint Paul, MN 790
Historic Halifax State Historic Site,
  Halifax, NC...............................1105
Historic Hope Foundation, Inc., Windsor,
  NC 1124
Historic House Trust of New York City,
  New York, NY 1027
Historic Indian Agency House, Portage,
  WI 1618
Historic Jamestowne, Jamestown, VA 1512
Historic Langhorne Association,
  Langhorne, PA 1267
Historic Latta Plantation, Huntersville,
  NC 1107
Historic London Town and Gardens,
  Edgewater, MD 642
Historic New Harmony, New Harmony,
  IN 494
Historic Pensacola Village, Pensacola, FL ...335
Historic Price House, Woodruff, SC...........1343
Historic Prophetstown, Battle Ground, IN ...468
Historic Richmond Town, Staten Island,
  NY 1072
Historic Rosedale, Charlotte, NC..............1095
Historic St. Mary's City, Saint Mary's
  City, MD 652
Historic Schaefferstown, Inc.,
  Schaefferstown, PA 1297
Historic Shepherdstown Museum,
  Shepherdstown, WV 1586
Historic Smithfield, Blacksburg, VA...........1497
Historic Spanish Point, Osprey, FL.............333
Historic Speedwell, Morristown, NJ............913
Historic Walnford, Upper Freehold Twp.,
  NJ 929
Historical and Genealogical Society of
  Somerset County, Somerset, PA 1300
Historical Museum-Archival Center,
  Mission Hills, CA...........................126
Historical Museum of Bay County, Bay
  City, MI...................................727
Historical Museum of Southern Florida,
  Miami, FL 324
Historical Natural History & Library
  Society of Natick dba Natick
  Historical Society, South Natick, MA 709
Historical Resources and Museum
  Services, Little Rock, AR....................62
Historical Society of Berks County,
  Reading, PA 1296
Historical Society of Glastonbury,
  Glastonbury, CT 242
Historical Society of Greater Port
  Jefferson, Port Jefferson, NY 1053
Historical Society of Old Yarmouth,
  Yarmouth Port, MA 722
Historical Society of Princeton,
  Princeton, NJ 921
Historical Society of Quaker Hill &
  Pawling, Pawling, NY 1051

Historical Society of Rockland County,
  New City, NY..............................1017
Historical Society of the Phoenixville
  Area, Phoenixville, PA 1290
The Historical Society of the Town of
  Warwick, Warwick, NY 1082
The Historical Society of Trappe,
  Collegeville, Perkiomen Valley, Inc.,
  Trappe, PA 1303
The Historical Society, serving Sleepy
  Hollow and Tarrytown, Tarrytown, NY.1078
The History Center, Cedar Rapids, IA 509
The History Center in Tompkins County,
  Ithaca, NY................................1003
Hixon House, La Crosse, WI.................1603
Hoard Historical Museum and National
  Dairy Shrine's Visitors Center, Fort
  Atkinson, WI 1598
Hodgden House Museum Complex,
  Ellsworth, KS..............................538
Hollenberg Station State Historic Site,
  Hanover, KS................................543
Holocaust Museum Houston, Houston,
  TX 1426
Homolovi Ruins State Park, Winslow, AZ.....53
Hood Museum of Art, Hanover, NH 888
Hoopa Valley Tribal Museum, Hoopa,
  CA 103
Hope Lodge and Mather Mill, Fort
  Washington, PA 1254
Hopewell Culture National Historical
  Park, Chillicothe, OH 1147
Hopewell Furnace National Historic Site,
  Elverson, PA 1251
Hopsewee Plantation, Georgetown, SC 1333
Horseshoe Bend National Military Park,
  Daviston, AL................................7
Hot Springs County Museum and
  Cultural Center, Thermopolis, WY 1639
The House of the Seven Gables, Salem,
  MA 706
Houston Museum of Natural Science,
  Houston, TX 1427
Howard County Historical Society,
  Ellicott City, MD 643
Howland House, Plymouth, MA..............703
The Hubbard Museum of the American
  West, Ruidoso Downs, NM..................946
Hubbell Trading Post National Historic
  Site, Ganado, AZ 34
Hudson Museum, The University of
  Maine, Orono, ME 617
The Huguenot Historical Society, New
  Paltz, NY 1017
Hui No'eau Visual Arts Center,
  Makawao, Maui, HI 401
Hulihee Palace, Kailua-Kona, HI..............399
Humboldt Redwoods State Park Visitor
  Center, Weott, CA 197
Huntingdon County Historical Society,
  Huntingdon, PA 1262
Hutchinson County Museum, Borger, TX..1397
Hyrum City Museum, Hyrum, UT 1466

ICR Museum of Creation & Earth
  History, Santee, CA 185
Idaho Museum of Natural History,
  Pocatello, ID 408
Idaho State Historical Museum, Boise, ID...404
Illinois and Michigan Canal
  Commissioners Office Museum,
  Lockport, IL 443
Illinois State Museum, Springfield, IL 458
IMA - Indianapolis Museum of Art,
  Indianapolis, IN 483
The Imaginarium Science Discovery
  Center, Anchorage, AK 22
Imperial Calcasieu Museum, Inc., Lake
  Charles, LA 590
Independence National Historical Park,
  Philadelphia, PA 1281
Indian City U.S.A., Anadarko, OK............1195

Indian Museum of Lake County, Ohio, Willoughby, OH......................................1191
Indiana Dunes National Lakeshore, Porter, IN...496
Indiana State Museum, Indianapolis, IN 484
The Institute For American Indian Studies (IAIS), Washington Green, CT ...263
Institute of American Indian Arts Museum, Santa Fe, NM 947
Iraan Museum, Iraan, TX............................1430
Iris & B. Gerald Cantor Center for Visual Arts at Stanford University, Stanford, CA...188
Iron & Steel Museum of Alabama, Tannehill Ironworks Historical State Park, McCalla, AL.....................................13
Iron Hill Museum, Newark, DE 272
Iroquois County Historical Society, Watseka, IL...463
Isabel Anderson Comer Museum & Arts Center, Sylacauga, AL..............................18
Island County Historical Society Museum, Coupeville, WA.....................1551
Isle Royale National Park, Houghton, MI....747

J.J. Jackson Memorial Museum, Weaverville, CA...................................197
J.L. Scott Marine Education Center and Aquarium, Gulf Coast Research Laboratory College of Marine Sciences, The U. of Southern Mississippi, Biloxi, MS.........................798
J.M. Davis Arms & Historical Museum, Claremore, OK....................................1198
Jackson County Historical Museum & Research Library, Maquoketa, IA.............522
Jackson Hole Historical Society and Museum, Jackson, WY..........................1634
James E. Lewis Museum of Art, Morgan State University, Baltimore, MD.............633
James Madison's Montpelier, Montpelier Station, VA..1518
Jamestown Settlement, Yorktown Victory Center, The Jamestown-Yorktown Foundation, Williamsburg, VA...............1545
Jane L. and Robert H. Weiner Judaic Museum, Rockville, MD.........................651
Jarrell Plantation Georgia State Historic Site, Juliette, GA..................................374
Jay I. Kislak Foundation, Miami Lakes, FL...327
Jean Lafitte National Historical Park & Preserve, New Orleans, LA 596
Jeffers Petroglyphs Historic Site, Comfrey, MN...771
Jefferson County Historical Society, Watertown, NY..................................1083
Jefferson National Expansion Memorial, Saint Louis, MO....................................833
Jefferson Patterson Park & Museum, Saint Leonard, MD...............................651
Jekyll Island Museum, Jekyll Island, GA 374
Jemez State Monument, Jemez Springs, NM...940
Jensen Arctic Museum, Monmouth, OR ...1228
Jerome Ford Nature Center, Alexandria, VA...1493
Jesse Peter Museum, Santa Rosa, CA..........184
Jim Gatchell Memorial Museum, Buffalo, WY...1629
John and Mable Ringling Museum of Art, Sarasota, FL..344
John Deere Historic Site, Dixon, IL.............431
John E. Conner Museum, Kingsville, TX ..1432
John Hutchings Museum of Natural History, Lehi, UT 1466
John Jay Homestead State Historic Site, Katonah, NY.......................................1006
John Muir National Historic Site, Martinez, CA..124
John Sydnor's 1847 Powhatan House, Galveston, TX.....................................1421

John Wesley Powell Memorial Museum, Page, AZ..37
Johnson Hall State Historic Site, Johnstown, NY.....................................1005
Johnson-Humrickhouse Museum, Coshocton, OH.....................................1159
Johnstown Area Heritage Association, Johnstown, PA...................................1263
Johnstown Historical Society, Johnstown, NY...1005
Jonathan Hager House & Museum, Hagerstown, MD.....................................646
The Joseph A. Callaway Archaeological Museum, Louisville, KY..........................576
Joseph Moore Museum, Richmond, IN........497
Joseph Smith Historic Site, Nauvoo, IL........447
Joshua Tree National Park, Oasis Visitor Center, Twentynine Palms, CA..............193
The Journey Museum, Rapid City, SD.......1354
Judaica Museum of Central Synagogue, New York, NY.....................................1029
Jurupa Mountains Cultural Center, Riverside, CA..149

Ka-Do-Ha Indian Village Museum, Murfreesboro, AR.....................................65
Kalamazoo Valley Museum, Kalamazoo, MI...749
Kalaupapa National Historical Park, Kalaupapa, HI..400
Kandiyohi County Historical Society, Willmar, MN..796
Kankakee County Museum, Kankakee, IL...441
Kauai Museum, Lihue, HI............................401
Kearney Mansion Museum, Fresno, CA 97
Kelsey Museum of Archaeology, Ann Arbor, MI..724
Kenosha Public Museum, Kenosha, WI.....1602
The Kentucky Library & Museum, Bowling Green, KY.................................565
Ker Place, Onancock, VA 1523
King Manor, Jamaica, NY 1004
Kingman Museum, Battle Creek, MI 727
Kings Mountain National Military Park, Blacksburg, SC....................................1322
Kingsley Plantation, Jacksonville, FL 315
Kit Carson Historical Society, Kit Carson, CO...223
Kittery Historical & Naval Museum, Kittery, ME...613
Kittson County History Center Museum, Lake Bronson, MN..................................778
Klamath County Museum, Klamath Falls, OR...1227
Klein Museum, Mobridge, SD...................1352
Kline Creek Farm, Winfield, IL...................466
Klondike Gold Rush National Historical Park, Skagway, AK......................................28
Klyne Esopus Museum, Ulster Park, NY...1079
Knife River Indian Villages National Historic Site, Stanton, ND.....................1136
Knox County Historical Society Museum, Edina, MO..814
Knox Headquarters State Historic Site, Vails Gate, NY.....................................1080
Kolomoki Mounds State Park Museum, Blakely, GA...366
Koochiching County Historical Museum, International Falls, MN............................778
Koshare Indian Museum, Inc., La Junta, CO...224

L.C. Bates Museum, Hinckley, ME.............612
La Porte County Historical Society Museum, La Porte, IN.............................487
La Puente Valley Historical Society City Hall, LaPuente, CA...................................107
La Purisima Mission State Historic Park, Lompoc, CA..109
LaBelle Heritage Museum, LaBelle, FL 319
Lafayette Natural History Museum and Planetarium, Lafayette, LA.....................589
LaGrange Plantation, Cambridge, MD.........639

The Lake Champlain Maritime Museum, Vergennes, VT..................................1488
Lake County Historic Courthouse Museum, Lakeport, CA...........................108
Lake County Historical Museum, Tavares, FL...351
Lake County Historical Society, Kirtland Hills, OH..1170
Lake Forest-Lake Bluff Historical Society, Lake Forest, IL........................441
Lake George Historical Association Museum, Lake George, NY..................1008
Lake Guernsey Museum-Guernsey State Park, Guernsey, WY.............................1634
Lake Hopatcong Historical Museum, Landing, NJ...909
Lake Jackson Historical Museum, Lake Jackson, TX......................................1433
Lake Mead National Recreation Area, Boulder City, NV.................................875
Lake Meredith Aquatic and Wildlife Museum, Fritch, TX.............................1420
Lake of the Red Cedars Museum, Cedar Lake, IN...472
Lake of the Woods County Museum, Baudette, MN..768
Lake Perris Regional Indian Museum (Home of the Wind), Perris, CA.............141
Lake Wales Depot Museum & Cultural Center, Lake Wales, FL........................320
Lakeview Museum of Arts and Sciences, Peoria, IL..450
The LaPointe-Krebs House & Old Spanish Fort Museum, Pascagoula, MS...807
LaSalle County Historical Society Museum, Utica, IL....................................462
Lassen Historical Museum, Susanville, CA...190
Latvian Museum, Rockville, MD................651
The Laurel Museum, Laurel, MD................648
Lava Beds National Monument, Tulelake, CA...193
Lawrence County Historical and Genealogical Society, Bedford, IN..........469
Leelanau Historical Museum, Leland, MI....751
Lehigh County Historical Society, Allentown, PA....................................1239
Lewis and Clark Visitor Center, Yankton, SD...1360
Libby Museum, Wolfeboro, NH..................897
Liberty County Museum, Chester, MT........844
Lincoln Boyhood National Memorial, Lincoln City, IN..................................488
Lincoln Home National Historic Site, Springfield, IL.......................................459
Lincoln State Monument, Lincoln, NM 941
Linn County Historical Museum and Moyer House, Brownsville, OR.............1220
Linn County Museum/Geneaology Library, Pleasanton, KS.........................556
Little Bighorn Battlefield National Monument, Crow Agency, MT...............844
Little Compton Historical Society, Little Compton, RI.....................................1312
The Living Word National Bible Museum, Aledo, TX..............................1386
Locust Creek Covered Bridge State Historic Site, Laclede, MO 825
Locust Grove, Louisville, KY.....................577
The Log House Museum of the Historical Society of Columbiana-Fairfield Township, Columbiana, OH.................1157
Logan Museum of Anthropology, Beloit, WI...1592
Loggerhead Marinelife Center, Juno Beach, FL...316
Lompoc Museum, Lompoc, CA..................109
Long Island Culture History Lab & Museum, Commack, NY........................980
Longfellow National Historic Site, Cambridge, MA....................................673
Longmont Museum, Longmont, CO............227

Archaeological–Continued

Lopez Island Historical Museum, Lopez Island, WA 1558

Los Alamos Historical Museum, Los Alamos, NM 942

Lost City Museum, Overton, NV 880

Lou Holtz/Upper Ohio Valley Hall of Fame, East Liverpool, OH 1163

Louden-Henritze Archaeology Museum, Trinidad, CO 234

Loudoun Museum, Inc., Leesburg, VA.......1512

Louisiana State Exhibit Museum, Shreveport, LA 600

Louisiana State Oil & Gas Museum, Oil City, LA 599

Louisiana Tech Museum, Ruston, LA 600

Louisville Science Center, Louisville, KY ...577

Lovely Lane Museum, Baltimore, MD 634

Lovettsville Historical Society Museum, Lovettsville, VA....................1514

Lowell National Historical Park, Lowell, MA 691

Lower East Side Tenement Museum, New York, NY....................1029

Lowndes County Historical Society and Museum, Valdosta, GA 389

Loxahatchee River Historical Society, Jupiter, FL....................316

Luckhard Museum - The Indian Mission, Sebewaing, MI....................764

Lummis Home: El Alisal, Los Angeles, CA 119

Lutz Children's Museum, Manchester, CT...248

Luzerne County Historical Society, Wilkes-Barre, PA 1307

Lyman Museum, Hilo, HI 393

Lynden Pioneer Museum, Lynden, WA......1559

The Lyons Redstone Museum, Lyons, CO...227

Mabee Farm Historic Site, Rotterdam Junction, NY 1062

MacCallum More Museum and Gardens, Chase City, VA 1500

Mackinac Island State Park Commission-Mackinac State Historic Parks, Mackinaw City, MI 752

Mackinac State Historic Parks-Colonial Michilimackinac & Old Mackinac Point Lighthouse, Mackinaw City, MI 752

Mackinac State Historic Parks-Fort Mackinac & Mackinac Island State Park, Mackinac Island, MI....................752

Mackinac State Historic Parks-Historic Mill Creek, Mackinaw City, MI 753

Madeline Island Historical Museum, La Pointe, WI....................1603

Madison County Historical Society-Cottage Lawn, Oneida, NY 1045

Maidu Interpretive Center, Roseville, CA....151

Maine State Museum, Augusta, ME............604

Makoshika Dinosaur Museum, Glendive, MT....................848

Malheur Historical Project, Stonehouse Museum, Vale, OR....................1238

Malki Museum, Banning, CA....................74

Mammoth Cave National Park, Mammoth Cave, KY 579

Mammoth Site of Hot Springs, Inc., Hot Springs, SD....................1348

Manassas Museum System, Manassas, VA....................1516

Manassas National Battlefield Park, Manassas, VA 1516

Manchester Historic Association Millyard Museum, Manchester, NH....................891

Maramec Museum, The James Foundation, Saint James, MO.................830

Marble Historical Society, Marble, CO 228

Mardi Gras Museum, Biloxi, MS 798

Marfa and Presidio County Museum, Marfa, TX....................1436

Marias Museum of History and Art, Shelby, MT....................853

Marin Museum of the American Indian, Novato, CA....................131

The Marion County Historical Society Museum, Marion, OH 1174

Maritime & Seafood Industry Museum, Biloxi, MS....................798

Maritime Museum - Cohasset Historical Society, Cohasset, MA 676

Marlboro County Historical Museum, Bennettsville, SC....................1322

Marshall Gold Discovery State Historic Park, Coloma, CA 86

Martha's Vineyard Museum, Edgartown, MA....................681

Martin County Historical Museum, Stanton, TX....................1453

Martin County Museum, Shoals, IN............499

Mary Ball Washington Museum & Library, Inc., Lancaster, VA....................1512

The Mary Brogan Museum of Art and Science, Tallahassee, FL 347

Maryhill Museum of Art, Goldendale, WA....................1556

Maryland Science Center, Baltimore, MD ...634

Mashantucket Pequot Museum and Research Center, Mashantucket, CT........248

Masonic Grand Lodge Library and Museum of Texas, Waco, TX 1459

Massacre Rocks State Park, American Falls, ID....................402

Matagorda County Museum, Bay City, TX....................1393

Maturango Museum of the Indian Wells Valley, Ridgecrest, CA 148

Maxwell Museum of Anthropology, Albuquerque, NM....................934

Mayborn Museum Complex, Waco, TX.....1459

McCone County Museum, Circle, MT........844

McLarty Treasure Museum, Vero Beach, FL....................352

McLean-Alanreed Area Museum, McLean, TX....................1438

McLean County Historical Society Museum, Washburn, ND 1137

McLean County Museum of History, Bloomington, IL ,....................414

McNamara House Museum, Victoria, TX..1457

McWane Science Center, Birmingham, AL....................5

Meade County Historical Society Museum, Meade, KS....................552

Meadows Museum of Art of Centenary College, Shreveport, LA....................601

Mechanicsburg Museum Association, Mechanicsburg, PA....................1270

Medina County Historical Society, The John Smart House, Medina, OH....................1175

Meeteetse Museum District, Meeteetse, WY....................1636

Meigs County Museum, Pomeroy, OH....1183

Mel Fisher Maritime Heritage Society, Key West, FL....................318

Mendocino County Museum, Willits, CA....198

Mendocino Historical Research, Inc./Kelley House Museum, Mendocino, CA....................125

Mercer County Historical Museum, The Riley Home, Celina, OH....................1146

Mercer Museum of the Bucks County Historical Society, Doylestown, PA.......1250

Meriwether Lewis National Monument, Hohenwald, TN....................1367

Merritt Museum of Anthropology, Oakland, CA....................133

Mesa Southwest Museum, Mesa, AZ.........37

Mesa Verde National Park Museum, Mesa Verde National Park, CO...............228

Mexican Fine Arts Center Museum, Chicago, IL....................424

Miami County Museum, Peru, IN 496

Michael C. Carlos Museum, Atlanta, GA 361

The Michigan State University Museum, East Lansing, MI 740

Midland County Historical Museum, Midland, TX....................1438

Milam County Museum and Annex, Cameron, TX....................1399

Milan Historical Museum, Inc., Milan, OH....................1176

Millerton Courthouse, Friant, CA.................98

Mills County Historical Society and Museum, Glenwood, IA....................519

Milton Historical Museum, Milton, VT 1482

Milwaukee Public Museum, Milwaukee, WI....................1612

Minnesota Historical Society, Saint Paul, MN....................791

Minute Man National Historical Park, Concord, MA....................676

Mission San Antonio de Padua, Jolon, CA....................105

Mission San Diego de Alcala, San Diego, CA....................157

Mission San Juan Capistrano Museum, San Juan Capistrano, CA 173

Mission San Luis Rey Museum, Oceanside, CA....................135

Mississippi County Historical Society, Charleston, MO....................812

Mississippi River Museum at Mud Island River Park, Memphis, TN....................1375

Missouri Historical Society, Saint Louis, MO....................835

The Mitchell Museum of the American Indian, Evanston, IL....................435

Moanalua Gardens Foundation, Honolulu, HI....................397

Moccasin Lake Nature Park, An Environmental & Energy Education Center, Clearwater, FL 299

Modoc County Historical Museum, Alturas, CA....................70

Mohave Museum of History and Arts, Kingman, AZ....................36

Mohonk Preserve, Inc., Gardiner, NY 993

Monmouth County Historical Association, Freehold, NJ....................905

Monocacy National Battlefield, Frederick, MD....................644

Monroe County Heritage Museum, Monroeville, AL....................15

Monroe County Historical Museum, Monroe, MI....................756

Montezuma Castle National Monument, Camp Verde, AZ....................30

Montgomery Zoo, Montgomery, AL 17

Monticello, Home of Thomas Jefferson, Thomas Jefferson Foundation, Inc., Charlottesville, VA 1499

Montpelier Mansion, Laurel, MD....................648

Montrose County Historical Museum, Montrose, CO 228

Moore County Historical Museum, Dumas, TX....................1410

The Moore-Youse Home Museum, Muncie, IN....................492

Mormon Station State Historic Park, Genoa, NV....................877

Morris-Jumel Mansion, New York, NY 1030

Morristown National Historical Park, Morristown, NJ....................914

Morrow Mountain State Park, Albemarle, NC....................1088

Morven Museum & Garden, Princeton, NJ....................922

Moses Lake Museum & Art Center, Moses Lake, WA....................1559

Moundbuilders State Memorial & Museum, Newark, OH....................1178

Moundville Archaeological Park, Moundville, AL....................17

Mount Clare Museum House, Baltimore, MD....................635

Mount Independence Historic Site, Orwell, VT...1484
Mt. Rainier National Park, Ashford, WA ...1547
Mount Vernon Ladies' Association, Mount Vernon, VA...................................1518
Mountain Heritage Center, Cullowhee, NC...1097
Mulberry Phospate Museum, Mulberry, FL...327
Murfreesboro Historical Association, Murfreesboro, NC....................................1112
Museo de Arte de Ponce (The Luis A. Ferre Foundation, Inc.), Ponce, PR ...1642
Museo de Las Americas, San Juan, PR......1642
Museo Fuerte Conde de Mirasol de Vieques, Vieques, PR 1644
Museum and Arts Center in the Sequim Dungeness Valley, Sequim, WA.............1570
Museum at Southwestern Michigan College, Dowagiac, MI 738
Museum of Afro-American History, Boston, MA 667
Museum of Ancient Artifacts, Las Vegas, NV...879
Museum of Anthropology, Highland Heights, KY 571
Museum of Anthropology, Winston-Salem, NC...............................1125
Museum of Anthropology, Pullman, WA ...1563
Museum of Anthropology, Chico, CA............83
Museum of Anthropology, University of Denver, Denver, CO.................................213
Museum of Anthropology, University of Missouri, Columbia, MO 813
Museum of Appalachia, Clinton, TN.........1363
Museum of Archaeology & Material Culture, Cedar Crest, NM.......................938
Museum of Art and Archaeology, University of Missouri - Columbia, Columbia, MO...813
Museum of Arts and Sciences, Macon, GA...378
The Museum of Arts and Sciences, Inc. and Center for Florida History, Daytona Beach, FL...............................303
Museum of Cultural & Natural History, Mount Pleasant, MI.................................757
Museum of Discovery and Science, Fort Lauderdale, FL...307
Museum of Discovery: Arkansas Museum of Science and History, Little Rock, AR...62
Museum of Florida History, Tallahassee, FL...348
Museum of Funeral Customs, Springfield, IL...459
Museum of History & Art, Ontario, Ontario, CA 136
Museum of History, Anthropology and Art, San Juan, PR.................................1643
Museum of Idaho, Idaho Falls, ID 406
Museum of Indian Arts & Culture/Laboratory of Anthropology, Santa Fe, NM..948
Museum of Indian Culture, Allentown, PA...1239
The Museum of Man in the Sea, Inc., Panama City Beach, FL 335
The Museum of Mobile, Mobile, AL 14
Museum of Natural History and Planetarium, Providence, RI...................1317
Museum of Natural Science, Baton Rouge, LA..587
Museum of New Mexico, Santa Fe, NM 949
Museum of Northern Arizona, Flagstaff, AZ..33
Museum of Peoples and Cultures, Provo, UT...1470
Museum of Primitive Art and Culture, Peace Dale, RI..1316
Museum of Rim Country Archaeology, Payson, AZ...38

Museum of San Diego History and Research Library, San Diego, CA 158
Museum of San Rafael, Castle Dale, UT...1464
Museum of Science, Boston, MA.................667
Museum of Science & History of Jacksonville, Jacksonville, FL..................315
Museum of Seminole County History, Sanford, FL...343
Museum of Texas Tech University, Lubbock, TX.......................................1435
Museum of the Albemarle, Elizabeth City, NC...1099
Museum of the Aleutians, Unalaska, AK 28
Museum of the Arkansas Grand Prairie, Stuttgart, AR...69
Museum of the Big Bend, Alpine, TX 1386
Museum of the Cape Fear Historical Complex, Fayetteville, NC.....................1101
Museum of the Cherokee Indian, Cherokee, NC.......................................1096
Museum of the Great Plains, Lawton, OK.1204
Museum of the Gulf Coast, Port Arthur, TX...1444
Museum of the Islands, Pine Island Center, FL...337
Museum of the Llano Estacado, Plainview, TX.......................................1443
Museum of the Middle Appalachians, Saltville, VA.......................................1536
Museum of the Red River, Idabel, OK 1203
Museum of the Rockies, Bozeman, MT.......842
Museum of the Southwest, Midland, TX ...1439
Museum of the Waxhaws & Andrew Jackson Memorial, Waxhaw, NC...........1122
Museum of West Louisiana, Leesville, LA...591
Museum of Western Colorado, Grand Junction, CO...220
Museum of World Treasures, Wichita, KS...562
Museum on Main: A History Museum for West Georgia, LaGrange, GA 375
Mystic Aquarium & Institute for Exploration, Mystic, CT...........................250

Nashville Zoo at Grassmere, Nashville, TN...1379
Nassau County, Division of Museum Services, Department of Recreation, Parks & Museums, East Meadow, NY 987
Natchez Trace Parkway, Tupelo, MS...........808
National Capital Parks-East, Washington, DC..284
National Geographic Museum at Explorers Hall, Washington, DC..............285
National Historic Oregon Trail Interpretive Center, Baker City, OR 1219
National Museum of Funeral History, Houston, TX...1429
National Museum of Natural History, Washington, DC...................................286
National Museum of the American Indian, Washington, DC 286
National Museum of the American Indian, Smithsonian Institution, New York, NY...1034
National Park Service, Washington, DC.......287
National Park Service-Great Falls Park, McLean, VA.......................................1517
National Park Service Museum Resource Center, Landover, MD............................648
National Tropical Botanical Garden, Kalaheo, HI...399
National Trust for Historic Preservation, Washington, DC...................................288
Native American Exhibit, National Kateri Shrine, Fonda, NY...............................991
Native American Heritage Museum at Highland Mission State Historic Site, Highland, KS...544
Native American Museum, Terre Haute, IN...500
Native American Resource Center, Pembroke, NC......................................1114

The Natural History Museum, Santa Maria, CA...182
Natural History Museum of Los Angeles County, Los Angeles, CA.......................120
Natural History Museum of Western Wyoming College, Rock Springs, WY ..1638
The Natural Science Center of Greensboro, Inc., Greensboro, NC.........1104
Nauvoo Historical Society Museum, Nauvoo, IL...447
Navajo Nation Museum, Window Rock, AZ..53
Navajo National Monument, Tonalea, AZ......47
Nebraska Prairie Museum of the Phelps County Historical Society, Holdrege, NE...863
Nebraska State Historical Society's Museum of Nebraska History, Lincoln, NE...866
Neenah Historical Society, Hiram Smith, Neenah's Heritage Park, Octagon House & Ward House, Neenah, WI.......1614
The Nelson-Atkins Museum of Art, Kansas City, MO 822
Nelson Pioneer Farm and Museum, Oskaloosa, IA 526
Netherland Inn House Museum & Boatyard Complex, Kingsport, TN........1368
Neuberger Museum of Art, Purchase College, State University of New York, Purchase, NY..............................1056
Nevada Historical Society, Reno, NV 881
Nevada State Museum, Carson City, NV 876
Neversink Valley Area Museum, Cuddebackville, NY 984
Neville Public Museum of Brown County, Green Bay, WI.........................1599
New Bedford Whaling Museum, New Bedford, MA...696
New Britain Youth Museum at Hungerford Park, Kensington, CT...........247
New Castle Historical Society - Horace Greeley House, Chappaqua, NY.............977
New England Wireless & Steam Museum Inc., East Greenwich, RI......................1311
New Harmony State Historic Site/Historic New Harmony, New Harmony, IN...494
The New Jersey Museum of Agriculture, North Brunswick, NJ..............................917
New Jersey Office of Historic Sites, Trenton, NJ...927
New Jersey State Museum, Trenton, NJ 927
New London Public Museum, New London, WI...1615
New Windsor Cantonment State Historic Site and National Purple Heart Hall of Honor, Vails Gate, NY 1080
The New York Historical Society, New York, NY...1035
The New York Public Library, Astor, Lenox and Tilden Foundations, New York, NY...1036
New York State Bureau of Historic Sites, Waterford, NY..1082
New York State Museum, Albany, NY.........955
New York State Office of Parks, Recreation & Historic Preservation, Albany, NY...955
Newell Museum, Newell, SD 1352
Newport Historical Society & The Museum of Newport History, Newport, RI...1315
Newtown History Center, Stephens City, VA...1538
Nez Perce National Historical Park, Spalding, ID...409
Ninety Six National Historic Site, Ninety Six, SC...1338
Nishna Heritage Museum, Oakland, IA 525
No Man's Land Historical Society, Goodwell, OK...1201

Archaeological–Continued

Noah Webster House/West Hartford Historical Society, West Hartford, CT 265

Nobleboro Historical Society, Nobleboro, ME.................616

Nobles County Historical Society, Worthington, MN.................797

Nohwike Bagowa, The White Mountain Apache Cultural Center and Museum, Fort Apache, AZ.................34

North Carolina Office of Archives and History, Raleigh, NC 1116

North Cascades National Park Service Complex, Marblemount, WA 1559

North Haven Historical Society, North Haven, CT.................257

North House Museum, Lewisburg, WV 1584

The North Museum of Natural History & Science, Lancaster, PA 1266

Northampton County Historical and Genealogical Society, Easton, PA 1250

Northeast Texas Rural Heritage Museum, Pittsburg, TX.................1443

Northeastern Nevada Museum, Elko, NV 876

Northern Indiana Center for History, South Bend, IN.................499

The Northern Maine Museum of Science, University of Maine, Presque Isle, ME...620

The Northumberland County Historical Society, Sunbury, PA.................1302

Northwestern Oklahoma State University Museum, Alva, OK.................1195

Nowetah's American Indian Museum & Store, New Portland, ME.................615

The Nylander Museum of Natural History, Caribou, ME.................609

The Oaks House Museum, Jackson, MS.....804

Ocean County Historical Museum, Toms River, NJ.................926

Ocmulgee National Monument, Macon, GA.................378

The Octagon, Washington, DC.................288

Ogden Union Station Museums, Ogden, UT.................1468

Ohio Historical Society, Columbus, OH.....1158

Oklahoma Historical Society, Oklahoma City, OK.................1209

Oktibbeha County Heritage Museum, Starkville, MS.................808

Old Barracks Museum, Trenton, NJ.................927

Old Castle Museum, Baldwin City, KS.......533

Old Court House Museum-Eva Whitaker Davis Memorial, Vicksburg, MS.................809

Old Dorchester State Historic Site, Summerville, SC.................1342

Old Exchange & Provost Dungeon, Charleston, SC.................1326

Old Fort Harrod State Park Mansion Museum, Harrodsburg, KY.................570

Old Fort House Museum, Fort Edward, NY.................991

Old Fort Jackson, Savannah, GA.................385

Old Fort Johnson, Fort Johnson, NY.................991

Old Fort Niagara, Youngstown, NY.................1088

Old Fort Western, Augusta, ME.................604

Old Independence Regional Museum, Batesville, AR.................54

Old Jail Museum, Albion, IN.................467

The Old Jail Museum, Crawfordsville, IN...473

The Old Jail Museum, Warrenton, VA.................1543

Old Lincoln County Courthouse Museum, Lincoln, NM.................942

Old Log Jail and Chapel Museums, Greenfield, IN.................480

Old Mill Museum, Cimarron, NM.................938

Old New-Gate Prison and Copper Mine, East Granby, CT.................238

Old St. Ferdinand's Shrine, Florissant, MO.................815

Old Salem Inc., Winston-Salem, NC.........1126

Old Santee Canal Park, Moncks Corner, SC.................1337

The Old Schwamb Mill, Arlington, MA.....660

Old Stone Fort Museum Complex, Schoharie, NY.................1067

Old Sturbridge Village, Sturbridge, MA.......713

Old Town San Diego State Historic Park, San Diego, CA.................158

Old Trail Museum, Choteau, MT.................844

Old West Museum, Wimberley, TX.................1462

Oldest House Museum Complex, Saint Augustine, FL.................339

Oliver Kelley Farm, Elk River, MN.................774

Oneida County Historical Society, Utica, NY.................1080

Onondaga Historical Association Museum & Research Center, Syracuse, NY.........1077

Onslow County Museum, Richlands, NC...1117

Ontario County Historical Society, Canandaigua, NY.................975

Ontonagon County Historical Society Museum, Ontonagon, MI.................758

Orange County Regional History Center, Orlando, FL.................331

Orcas Island Historical Museum, Orcas Island, WA.................1560

Oregon Coast History Center, Newport, OR.................1229

Oregon-Jerusalem Historical Museum, Oregon, OH.................1181

Oregon Museum of Science and Industry, Portland, OR.................1231

Organ Pipe Cactus National Monument Museum, Ajo, AZ.................29

Oriental Institute Museum, University of Chicago, Chicago, IL.................426

Oriskany Battlefield State Historic Site, Oriskany, NY.................1047

Osage Village State Historic Site, Lamar, MO.................825

Oscar Getz Museum of Whiskey History And The Bardstown Historical Museum, Bardstown, KY.................565

Overfield Tavern Museum, Troy, OH.................1188

Overland Trail Museum, Sterling, CO.........232

Owensboro Area Museum of Science & History, Owensboro, KY.................581

The Oyster and Maritime Museum of Chincoteague, Chincoteague, VA.................1501

Oysterponds Historical Society: The Museum of Orient and East Marion History, Orient, NY.................1047

Ozark National Scenic Riverways, Van Buren, MO.................839

Pacific Grove Museum of Natural History, Pacific Grove, CA.................137

Pacific Science Center, Seattle, WA.................1568

Padre Island National Seashore, Corpus Christi, TX.................1402

Painted Post - Erwin Museum at the Depot, Painted Post, NY.................1050

Palace of the Governors/New Mexico History Museum, Santa Fe, NM.................949

PALCO, Scotia, CA.................186

Panhandle-Plains Historical Museum, Canyon, TX.................1399

Paris-Henry County Heritage Center, Paris, TN.................1382

Parks, Recreation & Historic Sites Division, Georgia Dept. of Natural Resources, Atlanta, GA.................362

Parris Island Museum, Parris Island, SC....1338

Passaic County Historical Society & Lambert Castle Museum, Paterson, NJ ...920

The Paterson Museum, Paterson, NJ.................920

Paul H. Karshner Memorial Museum, Puyallup, WA.................1564

Pawnee Indian Village State Historic Site, Republic, KS.................556

Paynes Creek Historic State Park, Bowling Green, FL.................297

Pea Ridge National Military Park, Garfield, AR.................58

Peabody Museum of Archaeology & Ethnology, Cambridge, MA.................674

Peabody Museum of Natural History, New Haven, CT.................253

Pecos National Historical Park, Pecos, NM.................944

Pembina State Museum, Pembina, ND.......1135

Pembroke Historical Society, Inc., Pembroke, MA.................701

The Pena-Peck House, Saint Augustine, FL.................339

Pendleton District Agricultural Museum, Pendleton, SC.................1339

Pendleton District Historical, Recreational and Tourism Commission, Pendleton, SC.................1339

Pennsylvania Historical & Museum Commission, Harrisburg, PA.................1259

Pensacola Historical Society Museum, Pensacola, FL.................336

Perryville Battlefield Museum, Perryville, KY.................582

Petaluma Adobe State Historic Park, Petaluma, CA.................142

Peter Wentz Farmstead, Worcester, PA.......1308

Peter Yegen Jr. Yellowstone County Museum, Billings, MT.................841

Petersburg National Battlefield, Petersburg, VA.................1525

Petrified Forest National Park, Petrified Forest National Park, AZ.................38

Pettis County Historical Society, Sedalia, MO.................838

Philipse Manor Hall State Historic Site, Yonkers, NY.................1087

Phillips County Museum, Helena, AR.........59

Philmont Museums, Cimarron, NM.............938

Phoebe Apperson Hearst Museum of Anthropology, Berkeley, CA.................77

Piatt Castles, West Liberty, OH.................1190

Pickens County Museum of Art & History, Pickens, SC.................1340

Pike County Historical Society, Milford, PA.................1272

Pilgrim Hall Museum, Plymouth, MA.........703

Pimeria Alta Historical Society, Nogales, AZ.................37

Pinal County Historical Society and Museum, Florence, AZ.................34

Pink Palace Family of Museums, Memphis, TN.................1375

Pinson Mounds State Archaeological Area, Pinson, TN.................1383

Pioneer Heritage Center, LSU-Shreveport, Shreveport, LA.................601

Pioneer-Krier Museum, Ashland, KS.........532

Pioneer Trails Regional Museum, Bowman, ND.................1129

Pioneer Village, Rison, AR.................67

Pipestone National Monument, Pipestone, MN.................787

Piqua Historical Area State Memorial, Piqua, OH.................1182

Pithole Visitor Center, Pleasantville, PA 1295

Placer County Museums, Auburn, CA 72

Plains Conservation Center, Aurora, CO......202

Plainsman Museum, Aurora, NE.................856

Please Touch Museum, Philadelphia, PA ...1286

Plimoth Plantation Inc., Plymouth, MA.......703

Plum Grove Historic Home, Iowa City, IA.................520

Plumas County Museum, Quincy, CA.........144

Pocahontas County Museum, Marlinton, WV.................1584

Point Reyes National Seashore, Point Reyes, CA.................143

Polk County Historical Society, Des Moines, IA.................515

Polk County Memorial Museum, Livingston, TX.................1434

Polk County Museum, Balsam Lake, WI...1590

Ponce DeLeon Inlet Lighthouse
Preservation Association, Inc., Ponce
Inlet, FL 337

Pony Express Museum, Saint Joseph,
MO 831

Pope County Historical Society,
Glenwood, MN 776

Port Huron Museum, Port Huron, MI 761

Port Townsend Marine Science Center,
Port Townsend, WA 1562

Portage County Historical Society,
Ravenna, OH 1183

Post Rock Museum, La Crosse, KS 547

Potter County Historical Society,
Coudersport, PA 1248

Pound Ridge Society/Museum, Pound
Ridge, NY 1055

Powder Magazine, Charleston, SC 1326

Powell County Museum, Deer Lodge,
MT 845

Pratt County Historical Society Museum,
Pratt, KS 556

Pratt Museum, Homer, AK 25

The Pratt Museum of Natural History,
Amherst, MA 659

The Prehistoric Life Museum, Evanston,
IL 435

Presidio La Bahia, Goliad, TX 1423

Prince William Forest Park Visitor
Center, Triangle, VA 1541

Princeton University Art Museum,
Princeton, NJ 922

Providence Canyon State Park, Lumpkin,
GA 377

Prudence Crandall Museum, Canterbury,
CT 237

Pueblo County Historical Society
Museum and Edward H. Broadhead
Library, Pueblo, CO 230

Pueblo Grande Museum and
Archaeological Park, Phoenix, AZ 42

Putnam Museum of History & Natural
Science, Davenport, IA 513

Putney Historical Society, Putney, VT 1485

Puukohola Heiau National Historic Site,
Kamuela, HI 400

The Quincy Museum, Quincy, IL 452

R.P. Strathearn Historical Park and
Museum, Simi Valley, CA 187

Railroad House Historical Association
Museum, Sanford, NC 1119

Ralph Milliken Museum, Los Banos, CA 122

Ramsey House Museum Plantation,
Knoxville, TN 1371

Rancho Los Cerritos Historic Site, Long
Beach, CA 111

Rankin Museum, Rankin, TX 1445

Rankin Museum, Inc., Ellerbe, NC 1100

The Raymond M. Alf Museum of
Paleontology, Claremont, CA 86

Red Clay State Historic Park, Cleveland,
TN 1363

Red River Valley Museum, Vernon, TX......1457

Red Rock Museum, Church Rock, NM 938

Redwood National and State Parks,
Crescent City, CA 88

Reed Gold Mine State Historic Site,
Midland, NC 1111

Renfrew Museum & Park, Waynesboro,
PA 1306

Reshaw Exhibit, Evansville, WY 1632

Reuel B. Pritchett Museum, Bridgewater,
VA 1497

Rice County Museum of History,
Faribault, MN 775

The Rice Museum, Georgetown, SC 1333

Richland County Historical Museum,
Wahpeton, ND 1137

Riley House Museum of African
American History & Culture,
Tallahassee, FL 348

Rim Country Museum, Payson, AZ............38

Rimrocker Historical Museum of West
Montrose County, Naturita, CO 229

Rio Grande Valley Museum, Harlingen,
TX 1423

Rip Van Winkle Gardens on Jefferson
Island, New Iberia, LA 593

River Museum, Wellsville, OH 1190

Riversdale House Mansion, Riverdale
Park, MD 651

Riverside Museum, La Crosse, WI 1603

Riverside, The Farnsley-Moremen
Landing, Louisville, KY 579

Riverton Museum, Riverton, WY 1637

Robbins Museum of Archaeology,
Middleborough, MA 694

Roberson Museum and Science Center,
Binghamton, NY 962

Robert Hull Fleming Museum,
Burlington, VT 1478

Robert S. Kerr Museum, Poteau, OK.........1212

Robert S. Peabody Museum of
Archaeology, Andover, MA 660

Robert Toombs House, Washington, GA.....391

Roberts County Museum, Miami, TX........1438

Rochester Hills Museum at Van Hoosen
Farm, Rochester Hills, MI 762

Rochester Museum & Science Center,
Rochester, NY 1059

Rock County Historical Society,
Janesville, WI 1601

Rock Creek Nature Center, Washington,
DC 290

Rockwoods Reservation, Wildwood, MO 840

Rocky Ford Historical Museum, Rocky
Ford, CO 231

Rocky Mountain National Park, Estes
Park, CO 215

Rocky Reach Dam, Wenatchee, WA 1577

Rodef Shalom Biblical Botanical Garden,
Pittsburgh, PA 1294

Rome Area History Museum, Rome, GA 382

Rome Historical Society Museum, Rome,
NY 1061

Roniger Memorial Museum, Cottonwood
Falls, KS 536

The Root House Museum, Marietta, GA 379

Rose Hill Plantation State Historic Site,
Union, SC 1343

Roseau County Historical Museum and
Interpretive Center, Roseau, MN 788

Rosicrucian Egyptian Museum, San Jose,
CA 172

Roslyn Landmark Society, Roslyn, NY......1061

Rotary Nature Center, Oakland, CA 134

Royal Gorge Regional Museum &
History Center, Canon City, CO 205

Royalton Historical Society, Royalton,
VT 1486

Ruggles House Society, Columbia Falls,
ME 609

Runestone Museum, Alexandria, MN 767

Rural Farming & Agriculture Museum,
Warner, OK 1216

Russell Cave National Monument,
Bridgeport, AL 6

The Rye Historical Society and Square
House Museum, Rye, NY 1062

Sackets Harbor Battlefield State Historic
Site, Sackets Harbor, NY 1062

Saco Museum, Saco, ME 621

Sacramento Archives and Museum
Collection Center, Sacramento, CA 153

Safety Harbor Museum of Regional
History, Safety Harbor, FL 338

Saguache County Museum, Saguache,
CO 231

St. Augustine Lighthouse & Museum,
Inc., Saint Augustine, FL 340

St. Charles Heritage Center, Saint
Charles, IL 457

St. Clements Island and Piney Point
Museums, Colton's Point, MD 641

St. Francis County Museum, Forrest City,
AR 57

St. John's Church and Parish Museum,
Hampton, VA 1510

St. Joseph Museum Inc., Saint Joseph,
MO 831

St. Louis Science Center, Saint Louis,
MO 836

St. Petersburg Museum of History, Saint
Petersburg, FL 342

St. Photios Greek Orthodox National
Shrine, Saint Augustine, FL 340

St. Simons Island Lighthouse Museum,
Saint Simons Island, GA 383

Ste. Genevieve Museum, Sainte
Genevieve, MO 838

Salem County Historical Society, Salem,
NJ 924

Salem Maritime National Historic Site,
Salem, MA 707

The Salem Museum, Salem, VA 1536

Salida Museum, Salida, CO 232

Salinas Pueblo Missions National
Monument, Mountainair, NM 943

Sam Noble Oklahoma Museum of
Natural History, Norman, OK 1206

Samuel Dorsky Museum of Art, State
University of New York at New Paltz,
New Paltz, NY 1018

San Antonio Missions National Historical
Park, San Antonio, TX 1449

San Antonio Museum of Art, San
Antonio, TX 1450

San Bernardino County Museum,
Redlands, CA 147

San Diego Archaeological Center,
Escondido, CA 93

San Diego Museum of Man, San Diego,
CA 160

San Dieguito Heritage Museum,
Encinitas, CA 92

San Jacinto Museum, San Jacinto, CA.........171

San Jacinto Museum of History
Association, La Porte, TX 1433

San Juan County Archaeological
Research Center and Library at the
Salmon Ruin/San Juan County
Museum Association, Bloomfield, NM ...937

San Juan Island National Historical Park,
Friday Harbor, WA 1555

San Juan National Historic Site, San
Juan, PR 1643

San Marcos de Apalache Historic State
Park, Saint Marks, FL 340

San Mateo County Historical Association
and Museum, Redwood City, CA 147

San Miguel Mission Church, Santa Fe,
NM 950

Sanchez Adobe Historic Site, Pacifica,
CA 138

Sandwich Glass Museum, Sandwich, MA ...708

Sandwich Historical Society, Sandwich,
IL 457

Sanford Museum and Planetarium,
Cherokee, IA 510

Sanilac County Historical Museum and
Village, Port Sanilac, MI 761

The Santa Barbara Historical Museum,
Santa Barbara, CA 179

Santa Barbara Maritime Museum, Santa
Barbara, CA 179

Santa Barbara Museum of Natural
History, Santa Barbara, CA 179

Santa Barbara Trust for Historic
Preservation, Santa Barbara, CA 180

Santa Cruz Museum of Natural History,
Santa Cruz, CA 182

Santa Fe Trail Center, Larned, KS 547

Archaeological–Continued

Santa Monica Mountains National
  Recreation Area, Thousand Oaks, CA.....191
Santa Ynez Valley Historical Society,
  Santa Ynez, CA 185
Saratoga Museum, Saratoga, WY 1638
Saratoga National Historical Park,
  Stillwater, NY 1075
Sarpy County Historical Museum,
  Bellevue, NE......................................857
Saugus Iron Works National Historic
  Site, Saugus, MA................................708
Sauk County Historical Museum,
  Baraboo, WI......................................1591
Saunders County Historical Complex,
  Wahoo, NE..874
Scantic Academy Museum, East Windsor
  Historical Society, Inc., East Windsor,
  CT 239
The Schein-Joseph International Museum
  of Ceramic Art, Alfred, NY 956
Schiele Museum of Natural History and
  Lynn Planetarium, Gastonia, NC 1102
Schifferstadt Architectural Museum,
  Frederick, MD 644
Schingoethe Center for Native American
  Cultures, Aurora, IL.............................412
Schoenbrunn Village State Memorial,
  New Philadelphia, OH...........................1177
School of American Research, Indian
  Arts Research Center, Santa Fe, NM 950
Schuyler County Historical Society, Inc.,
  Montour Falls, NY 1015
Sci-Tech Center of Northern New York,
  Watertown, NY 1084
The Science Center of Pinellas County,
  Saint Petersburg, FL............................342
Science Museum of Long Island,
  Manhasset, NY 1013
The Science Museum of Minnesota, Saint
  Paul, MN...792
Scituate Historical Society, Scituate, MA 708
Sciworks, Winston-Salem, NC.....................1126
Scotchtown, Beaverdam, VA.......................1496
Scotts Bluff National Monument, Gering,
  NE...861
Seminole Canyon State Park and Historic
  Site, Comstock, TX 1401
Seminole Nation Museum, Wewoka, OK...1217
Senate House State Historic Site,
  Kingston, NY......................................1008
Senator John Heinz Pittsburgh Regional
  History Center, Pittsburgh, PA...............1294
Seneca-Iroquois National Museum,
  Salamanca, NY 1063
Sequoia and Kings Canyon National
  Parks, Three Rivers, CA 191
Sequoyah Cabin, Sallisaw, OK 1213
Serpent Mound Museum, Peebles, OH.......1182
Serra Museum/San Diego Historical
  Society, San Diego, CA 161
The 1719 William Trent House Museum,
  Trenton, NJ.......................................928
1797 Ezekiel Harris House, Augusta, GA....366
1761 Pownalborough Courthouse,
  Dresden, ME.......................................610
The Shadows-on-the-Teche, New Iberia,
  LA 593
Shako:wi Cultural Center, Oneida, NY 1046
Sharlot Hall Museum, Prescott, AZ..............43
Shasta College Museum & Research
  Center, Redding, CA.............................146
Shasta State Historic Park, Shasta, CA 186
Sheldon Peck Homestead, Lombard, IL.......444
Sherburne History Center, Becker, MN.......768
Sherwin Miller Museum of Jewish Art,
  Tulsa, OK..1216
Sherwood Forest Plantation, Charles City,
  VA 1498
Shiloh Museum of Ozark History,
  Springdale, AR.....................................68

Shiloh National Military Park &
  Cemetery, Shiloh, TN...........................1384
Shirley Plantation, Charles City, VA 1498
Sidney Historical Association, Sidney,
  NY...1069
Siegfried H. Horn Archaeological
  Museum, Berrien Springs, MI 729
Sierra Mono Indian Museum, North Fork,
  CA...131
Silver River Museum & Environmental
  Education Center, Ocala, FL....................330
The Simon Paneak Memorial Museum,
  Anaktuvuk Pass, AK 21
Siskiyou County Museum, Yreka, CA 200
Sitka National Historical Park, Sitka, AK......28
Skirball Cultural Center, Los Angeles,
  CA 121
Skirball Museum Cincinnati Hebrew
  Union College-Jewish Institute of
  Religion, Cincinnati, OH........................1151
Sky City Cultural Center, Pueblo of
  Acoma, NM 944
Slater Mill Historic Site, Pawtucket, RI.....1315
Sleeping Bear Dunes National Lakeshore,
  Empire, MI...741
Smith County Historical Society, Tyler,
  TX..1456
Smithtown Historical Society, Smithtown,
  NY...1070
Smoki Museum - American Indian Art &
  Culture, Prescott, AZ.............................43
Smyth County Museum, Marion, VA.........1516
Snake River Heritage Center, Weiser, ID.....410
Snyder Museum & Creative Arts Center,
  Bastrop, LA..585
Somerset Historical Center, Somerset, PA .1300
Somerset Place State Historic Site,
  Creswell, NC 1097
Somervell County Historical Museum,
  Glen Rose, TX.....................................1423
Sonoma County Museum, Santa Rosa,
  CA...185
South Boston-Halifax County Museum of
  Fine Arts & History, South Boston,
  VA 1536
South Carolina Department of Archives
  & History, Columbia, SC........................1330
South Carolina Department of Parks,
  Recreation and Tourism, Columbia,
  SC...1330
South Carolina Institute of Archaeology
  & Anthropology, Columbia, SC..............1330
South Charleston Museum, South
  Charleston, WV 1586
South County Historical Society, Arroyo
  Grande, CA...72
South Dakota State Historical Society,
  Pierre, SD...1353
South Florida Museum, Bishop
  Planetarium & Parker Manatee
  Aquarium, Bradenton, FL 297
South Florida Science Museum, West
  Palm Beach, FL....................................353
South Pass City State Historic Site, South
  Pass City, WY.....................................1638
South Shore Natural Science Center, Inc.,
  Norwell, MA.......................................700
South Texas Museum, Alice, TX.................1386
Southampton Historical Museum,
  Southampton, NY 1070
Southeast Missouri Regional Museum,
  Cape Girardeau, MO 812
Southern Oregon Historical Society,
  Jacksonville, OR...................................1226
Southern Ute Cultural Center and
  Museum, Ignacio, CO 223
Southold Indian Museum, Southold, NY ...1071
Southwest Florida Museum of History,
  Fort Myers, FL.....................................309
Southwest Museum, Los Angeles, CA 121
Space Farms Zoological Park and
  Museum, Sussex, NJ 925

Spartanburg County Regional Museum of
  History, Spartanburg, SC........................1341
Spartanburg Science Center, Spartanburg,
  SC...1342
Spencer-Peirce-Little Farm, Newbury,
  MA...697
Spirit of '76 Museum, Wellington, OH......1190
Spiro Mounds Archaeological Center,
  Spiro, OK...1214
Spokane House Interpretive Center, Nine
  Mile Falls, WA 1559
Springfield Museums - Springfield
  Science Museum, Springfield, MA 711
Springs Museum, Springs, PA 1301
Stagecoach Inn Museum Complex,
  Newbury Park, CA................................130
Stamford Museum & Nature Center,
  Stamford, CT......................................261
Stanley-Whitman House, Farmington,
  Farmington, CT...................................241
Stanton House, Clinton, CT.......................237
Star of the Republic Museum,
  Washington, TX...................................1460
Starved Rock State Park, Utica, IL 462
State Historical Society of North Dakota,
  Bismarck, ND 1128
The State Museum of Pennsylvania,
  Harrisburg, PA....................................1259
State of Illinois-Historic Preservation
  Agency, Historic Sites Division,
  Springfield, IL.....................................460
Staten Island Historical Society, Staten
  Island, NY..1074
Staten Island Institute of Arts & Sciences
  (SIIAS), Staten Island, NY 1074
Statue of Liberty National Monument &
  Ellis Island Immigration Museum,
  New York, NY 1039
The Steamboat Arabia Museum, Kansas
  City, MO..822
Steamboat Bertrand Collection, Missouri
  Valley, IA 524
The Stephens Museum, Fayette, MO 815
Stephenville Museum, Stephenville, TX 1454
Sterling-Rock Falls Historical Society
  Museum, Sterling, IL 461
Stewart M. Lord Memorial Historical
  Society, Inc., Burlington, ME 608
Stockbridge Library Historical Collection,
  Stockbridge, MA 713
Stone Fort Museum, Nacogdoches, TX......1440
The Stone House Museum, Belchertown,
  MA...662
The Stone Museum, Monroe Township,
  NJ 912
Stones River National Battlefield,
  Murfreesboro, TN 1377
Stonewall Jackson Museum at Hupp's
  Hill, Strasburg, VA 1539
Stony Point Battlefield State Historic
  Site, Stony Point, NY 1075
Strawbery Banke Museum, Portsmouth,
  NH...895
Stuart Heritage Museum, Stuart, FL...........346
Stuart House City Museum, Mackinac
  Island, MI...752
Sunnyside Historical Museum,
  Sunnyside, WA 1572
Sunset Crater Volcano National
  Monument, Flagstaff, AZ 33
SunWatch Indian Village/Archaeological
  Park, Dayton, OH 1162
Superstition Mountain Lost Dutchman
  Museum, Apache Junction, AZ..................30
Suquamish Museum, Poulsbo, WA.............1563
Sussex County Historical Society,
  Newton, NJ...917
Sutter's Fort State Historic Park,
  Sacramento, CA...................................153
Sweet Briar Museum, Sweet Briar, VA......1540
Swenson Memorial Museum of Stephens
  County, Breckenridge, TX......................1397

Switzerland County Historical Museum, Vevay, IN 502

T Rex Museum, Tucson, AZ............................50
Tallahassee Museum, Tallahassee, FL 348
Tamastslikt Cultural Institute, Pendleton, OR...1230
Tampa Bay History Center, Inc., Tampa, FL..350
Tannenbaum Historic Park, Greensboro, NC...1104
Tantaquidgeon Indian Museum, Uncasville, CT...263
Ted Smallwood's Store, Inc., Chokoloskee, FL.......................................299
Temecula Valley Museum, Temecula, CA....191
Ten Broeck Mansion - Albany County Historical Association, Albany, NY 956
Tennessee Historical Commission, Nashville, TN.......................................1380
Tennessee Historical Society, Nashville, TN...1380
Tennessee State Museum, Nashville, TN ...1381
Tennessee Valley Art Center, Tuscumbia, AL...20
Territorial Capital-Lane Museum, Lecompton, KS.....................................549
Texarkana Museums System, Texarkana, TX...1455
Texas Historical Commission, Austin, TX .1391
Texas Parks and Wildlife Department, Austin, TX..1392
The Texas Zoo, Victoria, TX 1457
Theodore Roosevelt National Park-Visitor Center, Medora, ND 1134
Thomas Clarke House/Princeton Battlefield State Park, Princeton, NJ 922
Thomas E. McMillan Museum, Brewton, AL...6
Thomas Jefferson's Poplar Forest, Forest, VA..1504
The Thomas T. Taber Museum of the Lycoming County Historical Society, Williamsport, PA.................................1308
The Thoreau Institute at Walden Woods, Lincoln, MA...691
Three Village Historical Society, Setauket, NY...1069
Thronateeska Heritage Foundation, Inc., Albany, GA...355
Tillamook County Pioneer Museum, Tillamook, OR..1237
Timexpo Museum, Waterbury, CT...............264
Timucuan Ecological and Historic Preserve and Fort Caroline National Memorial, Jacksonville, FL.................315
Tinley Park Historical Society, Tinley Park, IL..461
Tioga County Historical Society Museum, Owego, NY.............................1048
Tioga Point Museum, Athens, PA..............1241
Tippecanoe Battlefield, Battle Ground, IN ...468
Tippecanoe County Historical Association, Lafayette, IN......................487
Tipton County Museum, Veteran's Memorial & Nature Center, Covington, TN.......................................1364
Tipton-Haynes Historic Site, Johnson City, TN...1368
The Toledo Zoo, Toledo, OH.....................1187
Tolland Historical Society - Tolland County Jail and Warden's Home Museum, Tolland, CT.............................262
Toltec Mounds Archeological State Park, Scott, AR..68
Tombstone Courthouse State Historic Park, Tombstone, AZ.............................46
Tonto National Monument, Roosevelt, AZ...43
Torpedo Factory Art Center, Alexandria, VA..1494
Town Creek Indian Mound State Historic Site, Mount Gilead, NC......................1111

Trailside Nature Center, Cincinnati, OH 1151
Trailside Nature Museum, Cross River, NY..983
Traveler's Rest State Historic Site, Toccoa, GA..389
Travellers Rest Plantation & Museum, Nashville, TN..1381
Treasures of the Sea Exhibit, Georgetown, DE.......................................271
Tri-County Historical Society & Museum, Inc., Herington, KS.................544
Triangle Tattoo & Museum, Fort Bragg, CA...95
The Trout Gallery, Carlisle, PA 1245
Tryon Palace Historic Sites and Gardens, New Bern, NC..1112
T.T. Wentworth, Jr. Florida State Museum, Pensacola, FL 336
Tubac Presidio State Historic Park, Tubac, AZ...47
Tubman African-American Museum, Macon, GA..378
Tucumcari Historical Research Institute, Tucumcari, NM......................................953
Tulare County Museum at Mooney Grove Park, Visalia, CA......................................195
Tularosa Basin Historical Society Museum, Alamogordo, NM 932
Tulsa Zoo & Living Museum, Tulsa, OK ..1216
Tumacacori National Historical Park, Tumacacori, AZ.......................................52
Tunica-Biloxi Native American Museum, Marksville, LA.......................................591
Turabo University, Gurabo, PR..................1641
The Turner Museum, Sarasota, FL...............345

UCLA Fowler Museum of Cultural History, Los Angeles, CA.......................122
UCR/California Museum of Photography, Riverside, CA...150
UNLV Marjorie Barrick Museum, Las Vegas, NV...880
U.S. Navy Museum, Washington, DC.........292
Ulster County Historical Society, Marbletown, NY....................................1013
Umpqua Discovery Center, Reedsport, OR..1234
Union County Heritage Museum, New Albany, MS...806
University Art Gallery, University of Pittsburgh, Pittsburgh, PA 1294
University Museum, Carbondale, IL 415
The University Museum, Edwardsville, IL..432
University Museum & Historic Houses, The University of Mississippi, Oxford, MS..806
The University Museum Collections, Fayetteville, AR..57
University Museum, New Mexico State University, Las Cruces, NM....................941
University of Alaska Museum of the North, Fairbanks, AK..............................24
University of Colorado Museum, Boulder, CO...203
University of Iowa Museum of Natural History, Iowa City, IA..........................520
The University of Michigan Exhibit Museum of Natural History, Ann Arbor, MI...725
University of Michigan Museum of Anthropology, Ann Arbor, MI................725
University of Nebraska State Museum, Lincoln, NE..867
University of Northern Iowa Museums & Collections, Cedar Falls, IA..................508
University of Oregon Museum of Natural and Cultural History, Eugene, OR 1224
University of Pennsylvania Museum of Archaeology and Anthropology, Philadelphia, PA 1288
University of Wisconsin-Madison Arboretum, Madison, WI 1605

University of Wyoming Anthropology Museum, Laramie, WY 1636
Upham Mansion, Marshfield, WI 1608
Upper Musselshell Historical Society, Harlowton, MT......................................849
Upstate History Alliance, Oneonta, NY 1046
USS Arizona Memorial, Honolulu, HI 398
Utah Field House of Natural History State Park, Vernal, UT 1475
Utah Museum of Natural History, Salt Lake City, UT...1473
Utah State University's Museum of Anthropology, Logan, UT 1467

Valentown Museum, Victor, NY................1081
Valley Community Historical Society, Inc., Valley, NE.......................................874
Valley County Pioneer Museum, Glasgow, MT..847
Valley Forge National Historical Park, King of Prussia, PA...............................1264
Van Buren County Historical Society, Keosauqua, IA..521
Van Meter State Park, Miami, MO..............827
Van Wyck Homestead Museum, Fishkill, NY...989
Vann House, Chatsworth, GA......................368
Verde Historical Society, Clemenceau Heritage Museum, Cottonwood, AZ..........32
Vermont Historical Society Museum, Montpelier, VT......................................1482
Victor Valley Museum & Art Gallery, Apple Valley, CA.......................................71
Village of Elsah Museum, Elsah, IL 433
The Vinalhaven Historical Society Museum, Vinalhaven, ME......................624
Virgin Islands National Park, St. John, VI.1644
Virginia Aquarium & Marine Science Center, Virginia Beach, VA...................1542
Virginia Association of Museums, Richmond, VA......................................1532
Virginia Museum of Natural History, Martinsville, VA 1516
Vista Historical Museum, Vista, CA............196
The Voas Nature Area/Voas Museum, Minburn, IA..523

W.H. Over Museum, Vermillion, SD..........1358
Wabasha County Museum, Wabasha County Historical Society at Reads Landing, Reads Landing, MN.................787
Wade House Stagecoach Inn & Wesley Jung Carriage Museum State Historic Site, Greenbush, WI 1599
Wagner Free Institute of Science, Philadelphia, PA 1289
Wahkiakum County Historical Museum, Cathlamet, WA.....................................1550
Waimea Arboretum and Botanical Garden in Waimea Valley Audubon Center, Haleiwa, HI...392
Wakefield Museum Association, Wakefield, KS...560
Walney Visitor Center-At Ellanor C. Lawrence Park, Chantilly, VA..............1498
Walnut Canyon National Monument, Flagstaff, AZ...34
Walter B. Jacobs Memorial Nature Park, Shreveport, LA..602
Walters Art Museum, Baltimore, MD..........636
Wanapum Dam Heritage Center, Beverly, WA..1549
War in the Pacific National Historical Park, Piti, GU......................................1640
Warner House, Portsmouth, NH 895
Warren County Historical Society Museum, Lebanon, OH 1171
Washakie Museum, Worland, WY..............1639
Washington & Jefferson College - Olin Fine Arts Center, Washington, PA 1305
Washington County Historical Society Inc., West Bend, WI...............................1627

Archaeological–Continued

Washington Oaks Gardens State Park,
Palm Coast, FL............334

Washington State Capital Museum and
Outreach Center, Olympia, WA............1560

Washington State Historical Society,
Tacoma, WA 1574

Watermen's Museum, Yorktown, VA............1547

Watertown Historical Society, Inc.,
Watertown, CT............264

Watkins Woolen Mill State Historic Site
& Park, Lawson, MO............825

Watson-Curtze Mansion, Erie, PA............1253

Wayne County Historical Society,
Wooster, OH............1192

Wayne County Historical Society,
Honesdale, PA............1261

Wayne State University Museum of
Anthropology, Detroit, MI............738

Weems-Botts Museum, Dumfries, VA............1503

Wells County Historical Museum,
Bluffton, IN............470

Wenatchee Valley Museum and Cultural
Center, Wenatchee, WA............1577

West of the Pecos Museum, Pecos, TX............1443

West Virginia State Museum, Charleston,
WV............1581

Western Archeological & Conservation
Center, Tucson, AZ............52

Western Hotel/Museum, Lancaster, CA............108

Western New Mexico University
Museum, Silver City, NM............951

Westport Historical Society, Westport, CT...266

Wharton County Historical Museum,
Wharton, TX............1461

Whiskeytown Unit,
Whiskeytown-Shasta-Trinity National
Recreation Area, Whiskeytown, CA............198

White County Historical Society, Carmi,
IL............415

White County Historical Society
Museum, Monticello, IN............491

White Deer Land Museum, Pampa, TX............1442

White Sands National Monument,
Alamogordo, NM............932

Whitewater Canal State Historic Site,
Metamora, IN............490

Whitley County Historical Museum,
Columbia City, IN............472

Whitman Mission National Historic Site,
Walla Walla, WA............1577

Wickliffe Mounds State Historic Site,
Wickliffe, KY............584

Wildlife Museum at Petaluma High
School, Petaluma, CA............142

Wildlife Prairie State Park, Hanna City,
IL............439

William Henry Harrison Mansion,
Grouseland, Vincennes, IN............503

William Otis Sawtelle Collections and
Research Center, Bar Harbor, ME............606

William Pryor Letchworth Museum,
Castile, NY............976

William S. Webb Museum of
Anthropology, Lexington, KY............575

William Weston Clarke Emison Museum
of Art, Greencastle, IN............479

William Whitley House State Historic
Site, Stanford, KY............584

Williams County Historical Museum,
Montpelier, OH............1177

Wilson Czech Opera House Corporation,
Foundation, Inc. & House of
Memories Museum, Wilson, KS............564

Wilson's Creek National Battlefield,
Republic, MO............829

Wing Luke Asian Museum, Seattle, WA....1569

Winnebago Area Museum, Winnebago,
MN............797

Winnie Davis Museum of History,
Gaffney, SC............1333

Winona County Historical Museum,
Winona, MN............797

Wisconsin Historical Museum, Madison,
WI............1606

Wisconsin Maritime Museum,
Manitowoc, WI............1607

Witte Museum, San Antonio, TX............1451

Wood County Historical Center and
Museum, Bowling Green, OH............1143

Woodruff Museum of Indian Artifacts,
Bridgeton, NJ............898

Woolaroc Museum, Bartlesville, OK............1197

The Works: Ohio Center for History, Art
& Technology, Newark, OH............1179

World Forestry Center, Portland, OR............1233

World Museum of Mining, Butte, MT............843

Wormsloe State Historic Site, Savannah,
GA............387

Worthington Historical Society,
Worthington, OH............1192

Wray Museum, Wray, CO............235

Wriston Art Center Galleries, Appleton,
WI............1590

Wupatki National Monument, Flagstaff,
AZ............34

Wyandotte County Museum, Bonner
Springs, KS............534

Wyoming Pioneer Memorial Museum,
Douglas, WY............1632

Wyoming Territorial Prison State Historic
Site, Laramie, WY............1636

The Yager Museum of Art & Culture,
Oneonta, NY............1046

Yellowstone Gateway Museum of Park
County, Livingston, MT............850

Yellowstone National Park, Gardiner, MT...847

Yeshiva University Museum at the Center
for Jewish History, New York, NY............1041

Yorktown Historical Museum, Yorktown,
TX............1462

The Yosemite Museum, National Park
Service, Yosemite National Park, CA............199

Young at Art Children's Museum, Davie,
FL............302

Youth Science Institute, San Jose, CA............173

Ziibiwing Center of Anishinabe Culture
& Lifeways, Mount Pleasant, MI............757

Zion Human History Museum,
Springdale, UT............1474

Ethnological/Ethnographical

Abbe Museum, Bar Harbor, ME............605

Adams State College Luther Bean
Museum, Alamosa, CO............201

Adventure Science Center, Nashville, TN...1377

African American Historical Museum &
Cultural Center of Iowa, Cedar
Rapids, IA............508

The African American Museum in
Philadelphia, Philadelphia, PA............1275

Afro-American Cultural Center,
Charlotte, NC............1094

Agate Fossil Beds National Monument,
Harrison, NE............862

Agua Caliente Cultural Museum, Palm
Springs, CA............138

Ah-Tah-Thi-Ki Museum, Big Cypress
Seminole Indian Reservation, FL............295

Ah-Tah-Thi-Ki Museum at Okalee,
Hollywood, FL............312

Akta Lakota Museum and Cultural
Center, Chamberlain, SD............1345

Akwesasne Museum, Hogansburg, NY............998

Alabama Center for Traditional Culture,
Montgomery, AL............15

Alabama Museum of Natural History,
Tuscaloosa, AL............19

Alaska Heritage Museum at Wells Fargo,
Anchorage, AK............21

Alaska Indian Arts, Inc., Haines, AK............24

Alaska Museum of Natural History,
Anchorage, AK............21

Alaska Native Heritage Center,
Anchorage, AK............22

Alaska State Museum, Juneau, AK............25

Albany Civil Rights Movement Museum
at Old Mt. Zion Church, Albany, GA............355

Albany Museum of Art, Albany, GA............355

Alcatraz Island, San Francisco, CA............163

Alpine County Museum, Markleeville,
CA............124

Alutiiq Museum and Archaeological
Repository, Kodiak, AK............26

Amana Heritage Museum, Amana, IA............504

American Catholic Historical Society,
Philadelphia, PA............1276

American Hungarian Foundation/Museum
of the American Hungarian
Foundation, New Brunswick, NJ............915

American Museum of Asmat Art, Saint
Paul, MN............789

American Museum of Natural History,
New York, NY............1019

American Numismatic Association
Money Museum, Colorado Springs,
CO............206

America's Black Holocaust Museum,
Milwaukee, WI............1610

America's National Music Museum,
Vermillion, SD............1358

America's Stonehenge, North Salem, NH....893

The Amerind Foundation, Inc., Dragoon,
AZ............32

Anadarko Heritage Museum, Anadarko,
OK............1195

Anchorage Museum at Rasmuson Center,
Anchorage, AK............22

Angel Mounds State Historic Site,
Evansville, IN............475

Animas Museum, Durango, CO............214

Anniston Museum of Natural History,
Anniston, AL............3

Antelope Valley Indian Museum,
Lancaster, CA............108

The Anthropology Museum, DeKalb, IL......429

Anthropology Museum, University of San
Diego, San Diego, CA............155

Anthropology Teaching Museum,
California State University, Fullerton,
Fullerton, CA............98

Anti-Saloon League Museum,
Westerville, OH............1190

Anza-Borrego Desert State Park, Borrego
Springs, CA............79

The Appaloosa Museum and Heritage
Center, Moscow, ID............407

Appomattox Court House National
Historical Park, Appomattox, VA............1495

Arab American National Museum,
Dearborn, MI............733

Archer County Museum, Archer City, TX.1387

Archives Museum, Temple Mickve Israel,
Savannah, GA............384

Arizona Jewish Historical Society,
Phoenix, AZ............39

Arizona Military Museum, Phoenix, AZ............39

Arizona State Capitol Museum, Phoenix,
AZ............39

Arizona State Museum, Tucson, AZ............48

Arizona State University Museum of
Anthropology, Tempe, AZ............46

Arkansas Post National Memorial, Gillett,
AR............58

Arkansas State University Museum,
Jonesboro, AR............60

Armenian Library and Museum of
America, Watertown, MA............716

Art Museum of The University of
Memphis, Memphis, TN............1372

Arthur Ross Gallery, University of
Pennsylvania, Philadelphia, PA............1276

Ashland, The Henry Clay Estate,
Lexington, KY............572

Asian American Arts Centre, New York, NY ...1021

Asian Arts & Culture Center, Towson University, Towson, MD ...655

Associated American Jewish Museums, Pittsburgh, PA ...1290

The Association for Gravestone Studies, Greenfield, MA ...685

Ataloa Lodge Museum, Muskogee, OK ...1205

Audubon Canyon Ranch, Stinson Beach, CA ...188

Augusta Museum of History, Augusta, GA ...364

Aztec Ruins National Monument, Aztec, NM ...937

Bagpipe Music Museum, Manchester, NH ...891

Bale Grist Mill State Historic Park, Calistoga, CA ...80

Balzekas Museum of Lithuanian Culture, Chicago, IL ...418

Bandelier National Monument, Los Alamos, NM ...942

Bannock County Historical Museum, Pocatello, ID ...408

Baranov Museum, Kodiak, AK ...26

Bayard Cutting Arboretum, Great River, NY ...996

The Bead Museum, Glendale, AZ ...35

Beaverhead County Museum, Dillon, MT ...845

Becker County Historical Society, Detroit Lakes, MN ...772

Belle Grove Plantation, Middletown, VA ...1517

Berea College Burroughs Geological Museum, Berea, KY ...565

Berea College, Doris Ulmann Galleries, Berea, KY ...565

Berkshire Museum, Pittsfield, MA ...702

Berman Museum of World History, Anniston, AL ...3

Big Cypress National Preserve, Ochopee, FL ...330

Big Hole National Battlefield, Wisdom, MT ...855

Big Thunder Gold Mine, Keystone, SD ...1349

Billings Curation Center, Billings, MT ...841

Bily Clock Museum/Antonin Dvorak Exhibit, Spillville, IA ...528

Bishop Hill State Historic Site, Bishop Hill, IL ...413

Bishop Museum, Honolulu, HI ...394

Black American West Museum & Heritage Center, Denver, CO ...209

Black Hawk State Historic Site: Hauberg Indian Museum, Rock Island, IL ...453

Black Hills Reptile Gardens, Inc., Rapid City, SD ...1354

Black Kettle Museum, Cheyenne, OK ...1198

Blackwater Draw Museum, Portales, NM ...944

Blue Earth County Historical Society, Mankato, MN ...780

Boca Raton Museum of Art, Boca Raton, FL ...296

Bodie State Historic Park, Bridgeport, CA ...79

Bonner County Historical Museum, Sandpoint, ID ...409

Boone County Heritage Museum, Harrison, AR ...59

Boone County Historical Center, Boone, IA ...506

Boonsborough Museum of History, Boonsboro, MD ...637

Boonshoft Museum of Discovery, Dayton, OH ...1160

Boston Childrens Museum, Boston, MA ...664

Bowers Museum, Santa Ana, CA ...177

Brazos Valley Museum of Natural History, Bryan, TX ...1398

The Bronx County Historical Society, Bronx, NY ...964

The Bronx Museum of the Arts, Bronx, NY ...965

Brooklyn Children's Museum, Brooklyn, NY ...968

Brown County Historical Society, New Ulm, MN ...785

Bruce Museum, Greenwich, CT ...243

Buffalo and Erie County Historical Society, Buffalo, NY ...972

Buffalo Bill Museum & Grave, Golden, CO ...219

Buffalo Museum of Science, Buffalo, NY ...972

Burke Museum of Natural History and Culture, Seattle, WA ...1565

Burpee Museum of Natural History, Rockford, IL ...454

Bushwhacker Museum, Nevada, MO ...828

C.E. Smith Museum of Anthropology, Hayward, CA ...101

C.H. Nash Museum-Chucalissa Archaeological Museum, Memphis, TN ...1372

C.M. Russell Museum, Great Falls, MT ...848

CWU Anthropology Department, Ellensburg, WA ...1553

Caguana Indian Ceremonial Park & Museum, Utuado, PR ...1644

Calaveras County Museum, San Andreas, CA ...155

California Academy of Sciences, San Francisco, CA ...163

California State Indian Museum, Sacramento, CA ...151

Calkins Nature Area/Field Museum, Iowa Falls, IA ...521

Camden County Historical Society, Camden, NJ ...899

Canyon de Chelly National Monument, Chinle, AZ ...31

Cape Cod Museum of Natural History, Inc., Brewster, MA ...670

Carlsbad Museum & Art Center, Carlsbad, NM ...938

Carlton County Historical Society, Cloquet, MN ...771

Carnegie Museum of Natural History, Pittsburgh, PA ...1291

Carpenter Home Museum and Gallery, Cle Elum, WA ...1551

Carter County Museum, Ekalaka, MT ...846

Casa Adobe de San Rafael, Glendale, CA ...100

Casa Grande Ruins National Monument, Coolidge, AZ ...31

Castine Scientific Society, Castine, ME ...609

Cathedral Cultural Center, Omaha, NE ...870

The Centennial Museum at the University of Texas at El Paso, El Paso, TX ...1411

Center for Latino Arts & Culture, New Brunswick, NJ ...915

Center of Southwest Studies/Fort Lewis College, Durango, CO ...214

Central High School National Historic Site, Little Rock, AR ...61

Central Missouri State University Archives and Museum, Warrensburg, MO ...839

Central Texas Area Museum, Inc., Salado, TX ...1447

Chaco Culture National Historical Park, Nageezi, NM ...943

Charles H. Wright Museum of African American History, Detroit, MI ...735

Charlotte Museum of History and Hezekiah Alexander Homesite, Charlotte, NC ...1094

Chatillon-DeMenil Mansion, Saint Louis, MO ...832

Cheraw Lyceum Museum, Cheraw, SC ...1327

Cherry County Historical Society, Valentine, NE ...874

Chickasaw National Recreation Area, Sulphur, OK ...1214

Chico Museum, Chico, CA ...83

Chief Plenty Coups Museum, Pryor, MT ...852

Chieftains Museum, Rome, GA ...381

Children's Museum at La Habra, La Habra, CA ...106

Children's Museum/Detroit Public Schools, Detroit, MI ...735

Children's Museum of History, Natural History and Science at Utica, New York, Utica, NY ...1079

Children's Museum of Oak Ridge, Inc., Oak Ridge, TN ...1382

The Children's Museum of Rose Hill Manor Park, Frederick, MD ...644

Children's Museum of Southeastern Connecticut, Niantic, CT ...256

Children's Museum of the Arts, New York, NY ...1022

Chinese American Museum, Los Angeles, CA ...114

Chinese House/O.R. & N. Museum & St. Peter's Catholic Church, Echo, OR ...1222

Chippewa Valley Museum, Inc., Eau Claire, WI ...1595

Chiricahua National Monument, Willcox, AZ ...53

Chisholm Trail Historical Museum, Waurika, OK ...1216

Chisholm Trail Museum, Kingfisher, OK ...1203

Churchill County Museum and Archives, Fallon, NV ...877

Cincinnati Museum Center at Union Terminal, Cincinnati, OH ...1149

City of Fort Walton Beach Heritage Park & Cultural Center, Fort Walton Beach, FL ...310

Clark County Museum, Henderson, NV ...878

Clarke Historical Museum, Eureka, CA ...94

Clausen Memorial Museum, Petersburg, AK ...27

Clearwater Historical Museum, Orofino, ID ...408

The Cleveland Museum of Art, Cleveland, OH ...1152

The Cleveland Museum of Natural History, Cleveland, OH ...1153

Coeur d'Alenes Old Mission State Park, Cataldo, ID ...405

Collier County Museum, Naples, FL ...328

Colonel Allensworth State Historic Park, Allensworth, CA ...70

The Colonial Spanish Quarter Museum, Saint Augustine, FL ...338

Colonial Williamsburg, Williamsburg, VA ...1544

Colorado Historical Society, Denver, CO ...210

Colorado River Indian Tribes Museum, Parker, AZ ...38

Colorado Springs Fine Arts Center (Taylor Museum), Colorado Springs, CO ...206

Colorado Springs Museum, Colorado Springs, CO ...206

Colton Area Museum, Colton, CA ...87

Columbia Gorge Discovery Center and Wasco County Museum, The Dalles, OR ...1237

Columbia River Exhibition of History, Science and Technology, Richland, WA ...1564

Commonwealth of the Northern Mariana Islands Museum of History and Culture, Saipan, MP ...1640

Community Memorial Museum of Sutter County, Yuba City, CA ...200

Concordia Historical Institute, Saint Louis, MO ...832

Confederated Tribes and Bands of the Yakama Indian Nation - Cultural Heritage Center Museum, Toppenish, WA ...1575

Confederated Tribes of Grand Ronde Cultural Resources Department, Grand Ronde, OR ...1225

Ethnological/Ethnographical–Continued

Connecticut State Museum of Natural
  History and Connecticut Archaeology
  Center, Storrs, CT.............................261
Conner Prairie, Fishers, IN 476
Corpus Christi Museum of Science and
  History, Corpus Christi, TX 1401
The Cowley County Historical Society,
  Winfield, KS...................................564
Cowlitz County Historical Museum,
  Kelso, WA.....................................1557
Cranbrook Institute of Science,
  Bloomfield Hills, MI 730
Cranbury Historical & Preservation
  Society, Cranbury, NJ 902
Creative Arts Center, Pontiac, MI...............760
Creek Council House Museum,
  Okmulgee, OK.................................1211
Crispus Attucks Center Museum,
  Indianapolis, IN...............................482
Crystal Caverns at Hupp's Hill,
  Strasburg, VA.................................1538
Culinary Archives & Museum, Johnson
  & Wales University, Providence, RI......1316
Cultural Museum, Nashville, TN..............1378
Custer Battlefield Museum, Garryowen,
  MT..847

DAAP Galleries, Cincinnati, OH...............1150
Dacotah Prairie Museum, Aberdeen, SD....1344
Dakota Discovery Museum, Mitchell, SD..1352
Dakota Territorial Museum, Yankton, SD..1359
Dana Adobe, Nipomo, CA 130
De Saisset Museum, Santa Clara, CA..........180
Deer Valley Rock Art Center, Glendale,
  AZ..35
Delaware Archaeology Museum, Dover,
  DE...269
Denali National Park and Preserve,
  Denali Park, AK................................23
Denison Museum, Granville, OH 1167
Denver Museum of Miniatures, Dolls and
  Toys, Denver, CO.............................211
Denver Museum of Nature & Science,
  Denver, CO...................................211
Desert Caballeros Western Museum,
  Wickenburg, AZ................................53
DeSoto National Memorial, Bradenton,
  FL...297
Devils Tower Visitor Center, Devils
  Tower, WY....................................1631
Diego Sepulveda Adobe Estancia, Costa
  Mesa, CA......................................87
Disciples of Christ Historical Society,
  Nashville, TN.................................1378
The Discovery Center of the Southern
  Tier, Binghamton, NY 962
Douglas County Historical Society -
  Carson Valley Museum & Cultural
  Center, Gardnerville, NV 877
Douglas County Historical Society -
  Genoa Courthouse Museum, Genoa,
  NV..877
Dubois Museum, Dubois, WY.................1632
Duluth Children's Museum, Duluth, MN.....772
Dunbar House State Memorial, Dayton,
  OH...1161

E.M. Violette Museum, Kirksville, MO 824
East Brunswick Museum Corporation,
  East Brunswick, NJ 902
Eastern California Museum,
  Independence, CA..............................104
Edge of the Cedars State Park Museum,
  Blanding, UT.................................1463
Effie Yeaw Nature Center, Carmichael,
  CA...82
Effigy Mounds National Monument,
  Harpers Ferry, IA..............................519
Eiteljorg Museum of American Indians
  and Western Art, Indianapolis, IN 482

El Dorado Nature Center, Long Beach,
  CA..110
El Museo Latino, Omaha, NE 870
El Paso Museum of Archaeology, El
  Paso, TX......................................1411
Elgin Area Historical Society, Elgin, IL.......432
Elgin Public Museum, Elgin, IL.................432
Elverhoj Museum of History and Art,
  Solvang, CA...................................187
Environmental Education Center,
  Somerset County Park Commission,
  Basking Ridge, NJ.............................898
Erie County History Center & Cashier's
  House, Erie, PA 1252
Estelle H. Womack Museum of Natural
  History, Danville, VA 1503
Ethnic Heritage Museum, Rockford, IL.......455
Everglades National Park, Homestead, FL...313
Everhart Museum: Natural History,
  Science and Art, Scranton, PA..............1298
Explorit Science Center, Davis, CA 89
Explorium of Lexington, Lexington, KY 572

Fairbanks Museum and Planetarium,
  Saint Johnsbury, VT...........................1486
Fairfield County Museum, Winnsboro,
  SC..1343
Faninadahen Kosas Guahan-Guam
  Museum, Hagatna, GU.........................1640
Faust Park Foundation, Chesterfield, MO....812
Favell Museum Inc., Klamath Falls, OR....1227
Fayetteville Museum of Art, Fayetteville,
  NC..1100
Fernbank Museum of Natural History,
  Atlanta, GA...................................359
The Finley House, Wayne, PA...................1306
Firelands Historical Society Museum,
  Norwalk, OH..................................1180
First Landing State Park, Virginia Beach,
  VA..1542
Flathead Indian Museum, Saint Ignatius,
  MT..853
Florence Hawley Ellis Museum of
  Anthropology and Ruth Hall Museum
  of Paleontology, Abiquiu, NM...............931
Florida Museum of Natural History,
  Gainesville, FL................................310
Flowerdew Hundred Foundation,
  Hopewell, VA.................................1511
Folk Art Society of America, Richmond,
  VA..1529
Folsom History Museum, Folsom, CA...........95
Fonthill Museum of the Bucks County
  Historical Society, Doylestown, PA.......1249
Ford House Visitor Center and Museum,
  Mendocino, CA................................125
Forest Park Museum and Arboretum,
  Perry, IA.....................................527
Foresthill Divide Museum, Foresthill, CA.....95
Fort Abraham Lincoln State Park,
  Mandan, ND..................................1134
Fort Ancient Museum, Oregonia, OH.........1181
The Fort at No. 4 Living History
  Museum, Charlestown, NH....................884
Fort Caspar Museum, Casper, WY.............1629
Fort Clatsop National Memorial, Astoria,
  OR...1218
Fort Dalles Museum/Anderson
  Homestead, The Dalles, OR.................1237
Fort Davidson State Historic Site, Pilot
  Knob, MO.....................................828
Fort de Chartres State Historic Site &
  Museum, Prairie du Rocher, IL..............451
Fort Henrietta Interpretive Park, Echo,
  OR...1223
Fort Kearny State Historical Park,
  Kearney, NE..................................864
Fort Lauderdale Historical Society, Fort
  Lauderdale, FL................................307
Fort Leaton State Historical Site,
  Presidio, TX..................................1444
Fort Nisqually Living History Museum,
  Tacoma, WA..................................1573

Fort Payne Depot Museum, Fort Payne,
  AL...10
Fort Pitt Museum, Pittsburgh, PA.............1292
Fort St. Jean Baptiste State Historic Site,
  Natchitoches, LA..............................593
Fort Sill National Historic Landmark,
  Fort Sill, OK.................................1201
Fort Tejon State Historic Park, Lebec,
  CA..108
Fort Vasquez Museum, Platteville, CO 230
Fort Worth Museum of Science and
  History, Fort Worth, TX 1417
Forts Folle Avoine Historic Park,
  Danbury, WI..................................1594
Fortuna Depot Museum, Fortuna, CA...........96
Foundation For Historic Christ Church,
  Inc., Irvington, VA............................1511
Four Rivers Cultural Center & Museum,
  Ontario, OR..................................1229
Fox Island Historical Society, Fox Island,
  WA...1554
Frank H. McClung Museum, Knoxville,
  TN..1370
Franklin County Historical Museum,
  Mount Vernon, TX 1440
Franklin County Historical Museum,
  Pasco, WA....................................1561
Freeport Arts Center, Freeport, IL...............435
Fremont County Pioneer Museum,
  Lander, WY...................................1635
Fresno Metropolitan Museum, Fresno,
  CA...97
Frisco Native American Museum and
  Natural History Center, Frisco, NC 1102
Fruitlands Museums, Harvard, MA..............686

Ganondagan State Historic Site, Victor,
  NY..1081
Garibaldi and Meucci Museum, Staten
  Island, NY....................................1072
Gatekeeper's Museum & Marion
  Steinbach Indian Basket Museum,
  Tahoe City, CA................................190
Gem County Historical Society and
  Museum, Emmett, ID..........................405
The George D. and Harriet W. Cornell
  Fine Arts Museum, Winter Park, FL.......354
George I. Ashby Memorial Museum,
  Copper Center, AK.............................23
Georgia Music Hall of Fame and
  Museum, Macon, GA..........................377
Georgia Southern University Museum,
  Statesboro, GA................................387
Gilcrease Museum, Tulsa, OK..................1215
Gillespie County Historical Society,
  Fredericksburg, TX...........................1419
Golden Pioneer Museum, Golden, CO.........220
Goliad State Park, Goliad, TX..................1423
Gomez Foundation for Mill House,
  Marlboro, NY.................................1014
Governor Bent Museum, Taos, NM 952
Grace Hudson Museum & Sun House,
  Ukiah, CA....................................193
Graham County Historical Society,
  Thatcher, AZ...................................46
Grand Canyon National Park Museum
  Collection, Grand Canyon National
  Park, AZ......................................36
Grand County Museum, Hot Sulphur
  Springs, CO...................................222
Grand Encampment Museum, Inc.,
  Encampment, WY 1632
Grand Forks County Historical Society,
  Grand Forks, ND..............................1132
Grand Portage National Monument,
  Grand Marais, MN.............................776
Grand River Museum, Lemmon, SD..........1351
Grand Teton National Park, Colter Bay
  Indian Arts Museum, Colter Bay
  Village, WY...................................1631
Grand Traverse Heritage Center, Traverse
  City, MI......................................765

Graves Museum of Archaeology and Natural History, Dania Beach, FL 302

Great Plains Zoo & Delbridge Museum, Sioux Falls, SD...............................1356

Great Sand Dunes National Monument and Preserve, Mosca, CO...................229

Great Smoky Mountains Heritage Center, Townsend, TN..........................1384

The Greenburgh Nature Center, Scarsdale, NY.................................1066

Grout Museum District: Grout Museum of History and Science, Bluedorn Science Imaginarium, Rensselaer Russell House Museum, Snowden House, Waterloo, IA.......................529

Guadalupe Mountains National Park, Salt Flat, TX....................................1447

Guilford Courthouse National Military Park, Greensboro, NC...................1104

Gunn Memorial Library and Museum, Washington, CT...........................263

Gunnison Museum of Natural History, Pawling, NY.................................1051

Haffenreffer Museum of Anthropology, Brown University, Bristol, RI...............1310

The Haggin Museum, Stockton, CA 189

Hallockville Museum Farm, Riverhead, NY.................................1057

Hamline University Galleries, Department of Studio Arts & Art History, Saint Paul, MN.....................................790

Hampton University Museum, Hampton, VA.....................................1509

Hancock House, Hancock's Bridge, NJ........907

Harbour House Museum, Crystal Falls, MI.....................................733

Hardin County Historical Museums, Inc., Kenton, OH................................1170

Harold L. Lyon Arboretum, Honolulu, HI ...395

Harrison Museum of African-American Culture, Roanoke, VA...................1535

Harvard University Semitic Museum, Cambridge, MA...........................673

Haskell County Historical Society, Sublette, KS................................558

Hastings Museum, Hastings, NE.................863

Hawks Inn Historical Society, Inc., Delafield, WI...............................1595

Heard Museum, Phoenix, AZ.......................40

Held-Poage Memorial Home and Research Library, Ukiah, CA.................193

Helen Louise Allen Textile Collection, Madison, WI.................................1605

Hemet Museum, Hemet, CA.......................103

Hennepin History Museum, Minneapolis, MN.....................................782

The Heritage Center, Pine Ridge, SD.........1354

Heritage-Hjemkomst Interpretive Center, Moorhead, MN...............................784

Heritage Library Museum, Anchorage, AK.....................................22

Heritage Museums & Gardens, Sandwich, MA.....................................707

Herrett Center for Arts & Science, Faulkner Planetarium and Centennial Observatory, Twin Falls, ID....................410

Hettinger County Historical Society, Regent, ND.................................1136

Hi-Desert Nature Museum, Yucca Valley, CA.....................................201

Hibbing Historical Society and Museum, Hibbing, MN...............................778

Higgins Armory Museum, Worcester, MA...721

High Desert Museum, Bend, OR...............1220

Hillwood Art Museum, Brookville, NY.......971

Hinckley Fire Museum, Hinckley, MN........778

Historic Charlton Park Village and Museum, Hastings, MI...........................745

Historic Fort Snelling, Saint Paul, MN.......790

Historic Hermann Museum, Hermann, MO.....................................817

Historic Hope Foundation, Inc., Windsor, NC.....................................1124

Historic Lincoln, Lincoln, NM....................941

Historic Oakland Cemetery, Atlanta, GA 360

Historic Prophetstown, Battle Ground, IN 468

Historic Stagville, Durham, NC.................1098

Historical and Genealogical Society of Somerset County, Somerset, PA 1300

Historical Natural History & Library Society of Natick dba Natick Historical Society, South Natick, MA 709

The Historical Society of Dauphin County, Harrisburg, PA 1258

Historical Society of Fort Washington, Fort Washington, PA 1254

Historical Society of St. Marys and Benzinger Township, Saint Marys, PA..1297

The Historical Society of Trappe, Collegeville, Perkiomen Valley, Inc., Trappe, PA.................................1303

The History Place, Morehead City, NC......1111

Hiwan Homestead Museum, Evergreen, CO.....................................215

Hixon House, La Crosse, WI....................1603

The Holland Museum, Holland, MI 746

Holocaust Museum Houston, Houston, TX.....................................1426

Homolovi Ruins State Park, Winslow, AZ.....53

Hood Museum of Art, Hanover, NH 888

Hoopa Valley Tribal Museum, Hoopa, CA.....................................103

Horseshoe Bend National Military Park, Daviston, AL...................................7

Housatonic Museum of Art, Bridgeport, CT.....................................236

Houston Museum of Natural Science, Houston, TX...............................1427

The Hubbard Museum of the American West, Ruidoso Downs, NM.................946

Hubbell Trading Post National Historic Site, Ganado, AZ.............................34

Hudson Museum, The University of Maine, Orono, ME.........................617

The Huguenot Historical Society, New Paltz, NY.................................1017

Hulihee Palace, Kailua-Kona, HI.................399

Humboldt Redwoods State Park Visitor Center, Weott, CA...........................197

Hutchinson County Museum, Borger, TX..1397

Idaho Museum of Natural History, Pocatello, ID...............................408

Idaho State Historical Museum, Boise, ID...404

Illinois State Museum, Springfield, IL 458

Immigration Museum of New Americans Post WWII, San Diego, CA....................156

Imperial Calcasieu Museum, Inc., Lake Charles, LA.................................590

Indian Museum of Lake County, Ohio, Willoughby, OH...........................1191

Indian Pueblo Cultural Center, Albuquerque, NM.........................933

The Institute For American Indian Studies (IAIS), Washington Green, CT ...263

Institute of American Indian Arts Museum, Santa Fe, NM.........................947

The Interchurch Center, New York, NY.....1027

International Bluegrass Music Museum, Owensboro, KY...........................581

International Museum of Art and Science, McAllen, TX...............................1437

International Museum of Cultures, Dallas, TX.....................................1406

Iolani Palace, Honolulu, HI 396

Iron County Museum, Caspian, MI.............731

Iron Hill Museum, Newark, DE 272

Ironwood Area Historical Museum, Ironwood, MI..............................747

Iroquois Indian Museum, Howes Cave, NY.....................................999

Isabel Miller Museum/Sitka Historical Society, Sitka, AK............................27

Isanti County Historical Society, Cambridge, MN...........................770

Island County Historical Society Museum, Coupeville, WA...................1551

Isle Royale National Park, Houghton, MI....747

Italian American Museum, New York, NY.....................................1028

JFK Special Warfare Museum, Fort Bragg, NC.................................1101

Jackson Hole Historical Society and Museum, Jackson, WY.......................1634

Jacques Marchais Museum of Tibetan Art, Staten Island, NY.......................1072

Japanese American National Museum, Los Angeles, CA...........................117

Jean Lafitte National Historical Park & Preserve, New Orleans, LA.................596

Jefferson County Historical Society Museum, Port Townsend, WA 1562

Jefferson County Museum, Charles Town, WV.....................................1580

Jefferson National Expansion Memorial, Saint Louis, MO...........................833

Jemez State Monument, Jemez Springs, NM.....................................940

Jensen Arctic Museum, Monmouth, OR 1228

Jesse Peter Museum, Santa Rosa, CA..........184

The Jewish Museum, New York, NY..........1029

Jewish Museum of Florida, Miami Beach, FL.................................326

Jewish Museum of Maryland, Baltimore, MD.....................................633

John Burroughs Association, Inc., West Park, NY.................................1085

John E. Conner Museum, Kingsville, TX ..1432

John Muir National Historic Site, Martinez, CA...............................124

The Johns Hopkins University Archaeological Collection, Baltimore, MD.....................................633

Johnson-Humrickhouse Museum, Coshocton, OH...........................1159

Joseph Moore Museum, Richmond, IN........497

Joshua Tree National Park, Oasis Visitor Center, Twentynine Palms, CA...............193

Joslyn Art Museum, Omaha, NE.................871

The Judaica Museum of the Hebrew Home at Riverdale, Riverdale, NY........1057

Julia A. Purnell Museum, Snow Hill, MD...654

Julian H. Sleeper House, Saint Paul, MN 790

Juneau-Douglas City Museum, Juneau, AK.....................................26

Kalamazoo Valley Museum, Kalamazoo, MI.....................................749

Kandiyohi County Historical Society, Willmar, MN...............................796

Kauai Museum, Lihue, HI 401

Kauffman Museum, North Newton, KS.......553

Kaw Mission State Historic Site, Council Grove, KS.................................536

Kearney Mansion Museum, Fresno, CA 97

Kelsey Museum of Archaeology, Ann Arbor, MI.................................724

Kenosha Public Museum, Kenosha, WI.....1602

Kent State University, School of Art Galleries, Kent, OH.......................1169

Ker Place, Onancock, VA.........................1523

Kern County Museum, Bakersfield, CA........73

King Kamehameha V-Judiciary History Center, Honolulu, HI.......................397

Kingman Museum, Battle Creek, MI 727

Kingsley Plantation, Jacksonville, FL 315

Kit Carson Home & Museum, Inc., Taos, NM.....................................952

Klein Museum, Mobridge, SD...................1352

Klondike Gold Rush National Historical Park, Seattle, WA...........................1566

Kluge-Ruhe Aboriginal Art Collection at the University of Virginia, Charlottesville, VA.......................1499

Klyne Esopus Museum, Ulster Park, NY...1079

Ethnological/Ethnographical–Continued

Knife River Indian Villages National Historic Site, Stanton, ND....................1136
Koochiching County Historical Museum, International Falls, MN 778
Koshare Indian Museum, Inc., La Junta, CO 224
The Kurdish Museum, Brooklyn, NY 969

La Puente Valley Historical Society City Hall, LaPuente, CA 107
The Lackawanna Historical Society at the Catlin House, Scranton, PA.................1298
Lahaina Restoration Foundation, Lahaina, HI 400
Lake County Discovery Museum, Wauconda, IL 463
Lake County Historic Courthouse Museum, Lakeport, CA 108
Lake County Historical Museum, Tavares, FL 351
Lake Guernsey Museum-Guernsey State Park, Guernsey, WY 1634
Lake Perris Regional Indian Museum (Home of the Wind), Perris, CA..............141
Lakeview Museum of Arts and Sciences, Peoria, IL 450
Lamar Dodd Art Center, LaGrange College, LaGrange, GA...........................375
Lancaster Historical Society, Lancaster, NH 890
Lars Noak Blacksmith Shop, Larsson/Ostlund Log Home & One-Room Capitol School, New Sweden, ME...616
Latvian Museum, Rockville, MD 651
Lava Beds National Monument, Tulelake, CA 193
Leelanau Historical Museum, Leland, MI....751
Lehigh University Art Galleries/Museum Operations, Bethlehem, PA.................1242
Lesbian Herstory Educational Foundation, Inc. aka Lesbian Herstory Archives, Brooklyn, NY 969
Lewis County Historical Museum, Chehalis, WA 1550
Library of Congress, Washington, DC 282
Lillian and Albert Small Jewish Museum, Washington, DC..........................282
Lincoln County Historical Society, Lincoln, KS..549
Lincoln Park Historical Museum, Lincoln Park, MI 751
The Lincoln-Tallman Restorations, Janesville, WI 1601
The Lithuanian Museum, Chicago, IL.........423
Little Bighorn Battlefield National Monument, Crow Agency, MT.............844
The Living Desert, Palm Desert, CA 138
Living Desert Zoo and Gardens State Park, Carlsbad, NM 938
Logan Museum of Anthropology, Beloit, WI 1592
Lois E. Woods Museum, Norfolk, VA........1522
Lompoc Museum, Lompoc, CA 109
Long Island Culture History Lab & Museum, Commack, NY........................980
Los Alamos Historical Museum, Los Alamos, NM 942
Lost City Museum, Overton, NV 880
Louisiana State Oil & Gas Museum, Oil City, LA 599
Louisiana Tech Museum, Ruston, LA 600
Louisville Science Center, Louisville, KY ...577
Lovely Lane Museum, Baltimore, MD 634
Lower East Side Tenement Museum, New York, NY 1029
Lutheran Heritage Center & Museum of the Perry County Lutheran Historical Society, Altenburg, MO...........................810
Lutz Children's Museum, Manchester, CT...248
Lynden Pioneer Museum, Lynden, WA......1559

Macalester College Art Gallery, Janet Wallace Fine Arts Center, Saint Paul, MN 790
MacCallum More Museum and Gardens, Chase City, VA 1500
The Madam Brett Homestead, Beacon, NY 961
Madeline Island Historical Museum, La Pointe, WI 1603
Madison County Historical Society-Cottage Lawn, Oneida, NY 1045
Maidu Interpretive Center, Roseville, CA....151
Maine Historical Society, Portland, ME.......619
Malki Museum, Banning, CA 74
Manassas Museum System, Manassas, VA 1516
Marathon County Historical Society, Wausau, WI...1626
Marin Museum of the American Indian, Novato, CA 131
Mariposa Museum & World Culture Center, Peterborough, NH 893
Marlboro Historical Society, Marlboro, VT 1481
Martha's Vineyard Museum, Edgartown, MA 681
Martin and Osa Johnson Safari Museum, Inc., Chanute, KS 535
Mary Vagle Museum & Nature Center, Fontana, CA 95
Maryhill Museum of Art, Goldendale, WA 1556
Mashantucket Pequot Museum and Research Center, Mashantucket, CT........248
Maturango Museum of the Indian Wells Valley, Ridgecrest, CA 148
Maxwell Museum of Anthropology, Albuquerque, NM 934
Mayborn Museum Complex, Waco, TX.....1459
McLean County Historical Society Museum, Washburn, ND 1137
McPherson County Old Mill Museum and Park, Lindsborg, KS 550
Meadows Museum of Art of Centenary College, Shreveport, LA...........................601
Medina County Historical Society, The John Smart House, Medina, OH............1175
Mel Fisher Maritime Heritage Society, Key West, FL 318
Melrose Plantation Home Complex, Melrose, LA 592
Mendocino County Museum, Willits, CA ...198
Mennonite Library and Archives, North Newton, KS 554
Mercer County Historical Museum, The Riley Home, Celina, OH 1146
Mercer Museum of the Bucks County Historical Society, Doylestown, PA.......1250
Mesa Southwest Museum, Mesa, AZ.............37
Mesa Verde National Park Museum, Mesa Verde National Park, CO...............228
Mexic-Arte Museum, Austin, TX ,.............1391
Michael C. Carlos Museum, Atlanta, GA 361
Michigan Maritime Museum, South Haven, MI 764
The Michigan State University Museum, East Lansing, MI 740
Mid-America All Indian Center, Wichita, KS 562
Mille Lacs Indian Museum, Onamia, MN ...786
Millicent Rogers Museum of Northern New Mexico, Taos, NM......................952
Milwaukee Public Museum, Milwaukee, WI 1612
Missouri Historical Society, Saint Louis, MO 835
The Mitchell Museum of the American Indian, Evanston, IL 435
Mizel Museum, Denver, CO 213
Moanalua Gardens Foundation, Honolulu, HI 397
Montana Historical Society, Helena, MT 849

Montana Museum of Art and Culture, Missoula, MT................................852
Monterey State Historic Park, Monterey, CA 128
Moravian Historical Society, Nazareth, PA 1273
The Morikami Museum and Japanese Gardens, Delray Beach, FL......................305
Morro Bay State Park Museum of Natural History, Morro Bay, CA 129
Moses Lake Museum & Art Center, Moses Lake, WA 1559
Mt. Rainier National Park, Ashford, WA ...1547
Murrell Home, Park Hill, OK.............1211
Museo Fuerte Conde de Mirasol de Vieques, Vieques, PR...........................1644
The Museum, Greenwood, SC................1334
Museum and Arts Center in the Sequim Dungeness Valley, Sequim, WA.............1570
The Museum at Warm Springs, Warm Springs, OR 1238
Museum, Mission San Juan Bautista, San Juan Bautista, CA...........................173
The Museum of African Culture, Portland, ME................................619
Museum of Afro-American History, Boston, MA 667
Museum of Anthropology, Highland Heights, KY 571
Museum of Anthropology, Winston-Salem, NC...1125
Museum of Anthropology, Pullman, WA ...1563
Museum of Anthropology, Chico, CA............83
Museum of Anthropology, University of Denver, Denver, CO...........................213
Museum of Anthropology, University of Missouri, Columbia, MO 813
Museum of Arts and Sciences, Macon, GA 378
Museum of Cultural & Natural History, Mount Pleasant, MI...........................757
Museum of Discovery: Arkansas Museum of Science and History, Little Rock, AR 62
Museum of History, Anthropology and Art, San Juan, PR...1643
Museum of Indian Arts & Culture/Laboratory of Anthropology, Santa Fe, NM................................948
Museum of International Folk Art, Santa Fe, NM 948
Museum of Jewish Heritage-A Living Memorial to the Holocaust, New York, NY 1032
The Museum of Mobile, Mobile, AL.............14
The Museum of Natural History, Stevens Point, WI 1622
Museum of Natural History and Planetarium, Providence, RI.................1317
Museum of Natural Science, Baton Rouge, LA 587
Museum of New Mexico, Santa Fe, NM 949
Museum of Northern Arizona, Flagstaff, AZ 33
Museum of Peoples and Cultures, Provo, UT 1470
Museum of Primitive Art and Culture, Peace Dale, RI...1316
Museum of Rim Country Archaeology, Payson, AZ 38
Museum of Russian Culture, San Francisco, CA 167
Museum of Science, Boston, MA................667
Museum of Science & History of Jacksonville, Jacksonville, FL.................315
Museum of South Texas History, Edinburg, TX 1410
Museum of Texas Tech University, Lubbock, TX 1435
Museum of the Aleutians, Unalaska, AK 28
The Museum of the Alphabet, Waxhaw, NC 1121
Museum of the Big Bend, Alpine, TX 1386

Museum of the Fur Trade, Chadron, NE......859
Museum of the Great Plains, Lawton, OK.1204
Museum of the Plains Indian, Browning,
   MT..................843
Museum of the Red River, Idabel, OK 1203
Museum of the Rockies, Bozeman, MT.......842
Museum of Western Colorado, Grand
   Junction, CO..................220
Museum of Yarmouth History, Yarmouth,
   ME..................626
Museum of York County, Rock Hill, SC ...1340

Nanticoke Indian Museum, Millsboro,
   DE..................271
Napa Valley Museum, Yountville, CA 200
Nassau County, Division of Museum
   Services, Department of Recreation,
   Parks & Museums, East Meadow, NY....987
Natchez Trace Parkway, Tupelo, MS...........808
National Civil Rights Museum, Memphis,
   TN..................1375
National Czech & Slovak Museum &
   Library, Cedar Rapids, IA..................509
National Geographic Museum at
   Explorers Hall, Washington, DC...........285
National Italian American Sports Hall of
   Fame, Chicago, IL..................425
National Museum of Dance & Hall of
   Fame, Saratoga Springs, NY..................1065
National Museum of Funeral History,
   Houston, TX..................1429
National Museum of Natural History,
   Washington, DC..................286
National Museum of the American
   Indian, Smithsonian Institution, New
   York, NY..................1034
National Park Service, Washington, DC.......287
National Temple Hill Association, Inc.,
   New Windsor, NY..................1018
National Tropical Botanical Garden,
   Kalaheo, HI..................399
National Yiddish Book Center, Amherst,
   MA..................659
Native American Heritage Museum at
   Highland Mission State Historic Site,
   Highland, KS..................544
Native American Museum, Terre Haute,
   IN..................500
Native American Resource Center,
   Pembroke, NC..................1114
Natural History Museum of Los Angeles
   County, Los Angeles, CA..................120
Natural History Museum of Western
   Wyoming College, Rock Springs, WY..1638
The Nature Museum at Grafton, Grafton,
   VT..................1479
Navajo Nation Museum, Window Rock,
   AZ..................53
Nebraska Prairie Museum of the Phelps
   County Historical Society, Holdrege,
   NE..................863
Nebraska State Historical Society's
   Museum of Nebraska History, Lincoln,
   NE..................866
Nevada County Historical Society, Inc.,
   Nevada City, CA..................130
Nevada Historical Society, Reno, NV 881
Neville Public Museum of Brown
   County, Green Bay, WI..................1599
New Britain Youth Museum, New
   Britain, CT..................252
New Castle Historical Society - Horace
   Greeley House, Chappaqua, NY.............977
New Jersey State Museum, Trenton, NJ 927
New London Public Museum, New
   London, WI..................1615
New Mexico Farm & Ranch Heritage
   Museum, Las Cruces, NM..................940
New Orleans Museum of Art, New
   Orleans, LA..................597
New Orleans Pharmacy Museum, New
   Orleans, LA..................597

New Visions Gallery, Inc., Marshfield,
   WI..................1608
New World Art Center/T.F. Chen Cultural
   Center, New York, NY..................1035
The New York Public Library for the
   Performing Arts, New York, NY 1036
New York State Museum, Albany, NY.........955
The Newark Museum, Newark, NJ..............916
Nez Perce National Historical Park,
   Spalding, ID..................409
Nici Self Museum, Centennial, WY...........1630
Nicollet County Historical Society, Saint
   Peter, MN..................793
Ninety Six National Historic Site, Ninety
   Six, SC..................1338
Nohwike Bagowa, The White Mountain
   Apache Cultural Center and Museum,
   Fort Apache, AZ..................34
Nordic Heritage Museum, Seattle, WA 1567
North Carolina A&T State University
   Galleries, Greensboro, NC..................1104
The North Museum of Natural History &
   Science, Lancaster, PA..................1266
Northeast Georgia History Center at
   Brenau University, Gainesville, GA 373
Northeastern Nevada Museum, Elko, NV....876
Northern Indiana Center for History,
   South Bend, IN..................499
Northwest Art Center, Minot, ND 1134
Northwest Museum of Arts & Culture
   (Eastern Washington State Historical
   Society), Spokane, WA..................1571
Norwegian-American Historical
   Association, Northfield, MN..................786

Oakland Museum of California, Oakland,
   CA..................134
Occoneechee State Park, Clarksville, VA...1501
Ocmulgee National Monument, Macon,
   GA..................378
Oklahoma Historical Society, Oklahoma
   City, OK..................1209
Oklahoma Museum of History, Oklahoma
   City, OK..................1210
Oktibbeha County Heritage Museum,
   Starkville, MS..................808
Olana State Historic Site, Hudson, NY 1000
Old Castle Museum, Baldwin City, KS.......533
Old Fort Meade Museum and Historic
   Research Association, Fort Meade, SD.1347
Old Greer County Museum & Hall of
   Fame, Mangum, OK..................1204
The Old Jail Museum, Warrenton, VA........1543
Oldest House Museum Complex, Saint
   Augustine, FL..................339
Olympic National Park Visitor Center,
   Port Angeles, WA..................1561
Omniplex Science Museum, Oklahoma
   City, OK..................1210
Oneida Nation Museum, De Pere, WI........1594
Opelousas Museum and Interpretive
   Center, Opelousas, LA..................599
Orange County Regional History Center,
   Orlando, FL..................331
Orcas Island Historical Museum, Orcas
   Island, WA..................1560
Oregon Coast History Center, Newport,
   OR..................1229
Oregon Historical Society, Portland, OR....1231
Oregon Museum of Science and Industry,
   Portland, OR..................1231
Oriental Institute Museum, University of
   Chicago, Chicago, IL..................426
Orma J. Smith Museum of Natural
   History, Caldwell, ID..................405
Oshkosh Public Museum, Oshkosh, WI.....1616
Ottawa County Historical Museum, Port
   Clinton, OH..................1183
Oxford Library Museum, Oxford, MA.......701
Oysterponds Historical Society: The
   Museum of Orient and East Marion
   History, Orient, NY..................1047

The Ozark Folk Center, Mountain View,
   AR..................65
Pacific County Historical Museum, South
   Bend, WA..................1571
Pacific Grove Museum of Natural
   History, Pacific Grove, CA..................137
Pacific Science Center, Seattle, WA 1568
Painted Post - Erwin Museum at the
   Depot, Painted Post, NY..................1050
Palace of the Governors/New Mexico
   History Museum, Santa Fe, NM.............949
PALCO, Scotia, CA..................186
Palm Beach Zoo at Dreher Park, West
   Palm Beach, FL..................353
Palo Alto Junior Museum and Zoo, Palo
   Alto, CA..................139
Pamunkey Indian Museum, King
   William, VA..................1512
Panhandle-Plains Historical Museum,
   Canyon, TX..................1399
The Pardee Home Museum, Oakland, CA...134
Paul H. Karshner Memorial Museum,
   Puyallup, WA..................1564
Paunsaugunt Wildlife Museum, Bryce,
   UT..................1464
Pawnee Indian Village State Historic Site,
   Republic, KS..................556
Peabody Museum of Archaeology &
   Ethnology, Cambridge, MA..................674
Peabody Museum of Natural History,
   New Haven, CT..................253
The Peace Museum, Chicago, IL..................426
Peaks of Otter Visitor Center, Bedford,
   VA..................1496
The Peary-MacMillan Arctic Museum,
   Brunswick, ME..................608
The Peggy Notebaert Nature Museum,
   Chicago, IL..................426
Pella Historical Village, Pella, IA..................526
Pember Museum of Natural History,
   Granville, NY..................995
Pembina State Museum, Pembina, ND.......1135
The Pena-Peck House, Saint Augustine,
   FL..................339
Pennyroyal Area Museum, Hopkinsville,
   KY..................572
Peoria Historical Society, Peoria, IL 451
Petaluma Adobe State Historic Park,
   Petaluma, CA..................142
Peter Yegen Jr. Yellowstone County
   Museum, Billings, MT..................841
Petrified Forest National Park, Petrified
   Forest National Park, AZ..................38
Petterson Museum of Intercultural Art,
   Claremont, CA..................85
Pettis County Historical Society, Sedalia,
   MO..................838
Philipse Manor Hall State Historic Site,
   Yonkers, NY..................1087
Phillips County Museum, Helena, AR..........59
The Phillips Museum of Art, Franklin &
   Marshall College, Lancaster, PA...........1267
Philmont Museums, Cimarron, NM.............938
Phoebe Apperson Hearst Museum of
   Anthropology, Berkeley, CA..................77
Phoenix Museum of History, Phoenix,
   AZ..................41
Pinnacles National Monument, Paicines,
   CA..................138
Pipestone County Historical Museum,
   Pipestone, MN..................786
Pipestone National Monument, Pipestone,
   MN..................787
Placer County Museums, Auburn, CA 72
Plains Indians and Pioneers Museum,
   Woodward, OK..................1217
Plantation Historical Museum, Plantation,
   FL..................337
Plimoth Plantation Inc., Plymouth, MA 703
Plymouth Historical Society, Inc.,
   Plymouth, PA..................1295

Ethnological/Ethnographical–Continued

Point Reyes National Seashore, Point Reyes, CA 143

Pointe Coupee Museum, New Roads, LA....599

Polish Museum of America, Chicago, IL.....426

Polynesian Cultural Center, Laie, HI............401

Pope County Historical Society, Glenwood, MN 776

Port Huron Museum, Port Huron, MI 761

Portage County Historical Society, Ravenna, OH 1183

Potter County Historical Society, Coudersport, PA 1248

Pratt Museum, Homer, AK 25

The Pratt Museum of Natural History, Amherst, MA 659

Presbyterian Historical Society (Montreat), Montreat, NC......................1111

Prince William Forest Park Visitor Center, Triangle, VA..............................1541

Public Museum of West Michigan, Grand Rapids, MI 744

Pueblo County Historical Society Museum and Edward H. Broadhead Library, Pueblo, CO 230

Pueblo Grande Museum and Archaeological Park, Phoenix, AZ.............42

Pueblo of Pojoaque, Poeh Museum, Santa Fe, NM 949

Putnam Museum of History & Natural Science, Davenport, IA 513

Putney Historical Society, Putney, VT 1485

Queens Botanical Garden, Flushing, NY 990

The Quincy Museum, Quincy, IL 452

Ravalli County Museum/Bitter Root Valley Historical Society, Hamilton, MT...848

Reading Public Museum, Reading, PA.......1296

Red Earth Museum, Oklahoma City, OK...1210

Red River Valley Museum, Vernon, TX.....1457

Red Rock Museum, Church Rock, NM 938

Republic County Historical Society Museum, Belleville, KS 534

Rhode Island Black Heritage Society, Providence, RI 1318

Rhode Island Historical Society, Providence, RI 1318

Riverside Metropolitan Museum, Riverside, CA...150

Riverton Museum, Riverton, WY 1637

Robbins Museum of Archaeology, Middleborough, MA 694

Robert C. Williams American Museum of Papermaking at Georgia Tech, Atlanta, GA..363

Robert Hull Fleming Museum, Burlington, VT 1478

Robert Newell House, DAR Museum, Saint Paul, OR 1235

Robert S. Peabody Museum of Archaeology, Andover, MA 660

Robert V. Fullerton Art Museum, California State University, San Bernardino, San Bernardino, CA.............155

Rochester Hills Museum at Van Hoosen Farm, Rochester Hills, MI 762

Rochester Museum & Science Center, Rochester, NY...1059

Rock County Historical Society, Janesville, WI 1601

Rockwoods Reservation, Wildwood, MO 840

Rocky Ford Historical Museum, Rocky Ford, CO 231

Rodef Shalom Biblical Botanical Garden, Pittsburgh, PA...1294

Rose Center Museum, Morristown, TN 1376

Rosemount Museum, Pueblo, CO.................230

Rosicrucian Egyptian Museum, San Jose, CA..172

Roswell Museum and Art Center, Roswell, NM...946

Royal Gorge Regional Museum & History Center, Canon City, CO..............205

Rural Life Museum & Windrush Gardens, Baton Rouge, LA..................587

Sacramento Archives and Museum Collection Center, Sacramento, CA.........153

St. Albans Historical Museum, Saint Albans, VT..1486

St. Clements Island and Piney Point Museums, Colton's Point, MD................641

St. Joseph Museum Inc., Saint Joseph, MO...831

The St. Louis County Historical Society, Duluth, MN..773

St. Louis Science Center, Saint Louis, MO...836

St. Petersburg Museum of History, Saint Petersburg, FL 342

St. Photios Greek Orthodox National Shrine, Saint Augustine, FL....................340

Sainte Marie among the Iroquois, Liverpool, NY..1010

The Salgo Trust for Education, Port Washington, NY 1054

Salinas Pueblo Missions National Monument, Mountainair, NM 943

Sam Houston Memorial Museum, Huntsville, TX 1430

Sam Noble Oklahoma Museum of Natural History, Norman, OK..................1206

San Antonio Missions National Historical Park, San Antonio, TX 1449

San Antonio Museum of Art, San Antonio, TX..1450

San Bernardino County Museum, Redlands, CA...147

San Diego Archaeological Center, Escondido, CA..93

San Diego Museum of Man, San Diego, CA..160

San Joaquin County Historical Society & Museum, Lodi, CA 109

San Juan County Archaeological Research Center and Library at the Salmon Ruin/San Juan County Museum Association, Bloomfield, NM ...937

San Lorenzo Valley Museum, Boulder Creek, CA...79

Santa Barbara Botanic Garden, Santa Barbara, CA...178

Santa Barbara Maritime Museum, Santa Barbara, CA...179

Santa Barbara Museum of Natural History, Santa Barbara, CA.......................179

Santa Cruz Museum of Natural History, Santa Cruz, CA..182

Santa Fe Trail Center, Larned, KS 547

Santa Monica Mountains National Recreation Area, Thousand Oaks, CA.....191

Saunders County Historical Complex, Wahoo, NE...874

The Schein-Joseph International Museum of Ceramic Art, Alfred, NY 956

Schiele Museum of Natural History and Lynn Planetarium, Gastonia, NC 1102

Schifferstadt Architectural Museum, Frederick, MD..644

Schingoethe Center for Native American Cultures, Aurora, IL 412

Schoenbrunn Village State Memorial, New Philadelphia, OH...............................1177

The Schomburg Center for Research in Black Culture, New York, NY...............1038

School of American Research, Indian Arts Research Center, Santa Fe, NM 950

The Science Museum of Minnesota, Saint Paul, MN..792

The Scottish Tartans Museum, Franklin, NC...1102

Seabrook Village, Midway, GA 380

Seminole Nation Museum, Wewoka, OK...1217

Sequoyah Cabin, Sallisaw, OK 1213

Serra Museum/San Diego Historical Society, San Diego, CA 161

Shako:wi Cultural Center, Oneida, NY 1046

Sharlot Hall Museum, Prescott, AZ.............43

Sheldon Jackson Museum, Sitka, AK............27

Sheldon Museum and Cultural Center, Inc., Haines, AK...25

Sheppard Fine Arts Gallery, Reno, NV 881

Sherwin Miller Museum of Jewish Art, Tulsa, OK...1216

Shimmin Tveit Museum, Forbes, ND.........1131

Shoshone Bannock Tribal Museum, Fort Hall, ID 406

Shoshone County Mining and Smelting Museum d/b/a The Staff House Museum, Kellogg, ID..................................406

Shoshone Tribal Cultural Center, Fort Washakie, WY..1633

Sibley House Historic Site, Mendota, MN...780

Siegfried H. Horn Archaeological Museum, Berrien Springs, MI 729

Sierra Mono Indian Museum, North Fork, CA..131

The Simon Paneak Memorial Museum, Anaktuvuk Pass, AK.....................................21

Sioux City Public Museum, Sioux City, IA 528

Sioux Indian Museum, Rapid City, SD 1355

Siouxland Heritage Museums, Sioux Falls, SD...1357

Siskiyou County Museum, Yreka, CA 200

Sitka National Historical Park, Sitka, AK......28

Six Nations Indian Museum, Onchiota, NY 1045

Skagit County Historical Museum, La Conner, WA 1557

Skagway Museum & Archives, Skagway, AK..28

Skirball Cultural Center, Los Angeles, CA..121

Skirball Museum Cincinnati Hebrew Union College-Jewish Institute of Religion, Cincinnati, OH......................1151

Sky City Cultural Center, Pueblo of Acoma, NM 944

Smithsonian Institution, Washington, DC.....290

Smoki Museum - American Indian Art & Culture, Prescott, AZ.................................43

Sod House Museum, Aline, OK 1195

Somerset Historical Center, Somerset, PA .1300

Sonoma County Museum, Santa Rosa, CA..185

Sonoma State Historic Park, Sonoma, CA...188

Sosa-Carrillo-Fremont House Museum, Tucson, AZ...50

Sotterley Plantation, Hollywood, MD 647

South Carolina Department of Parks, Recreation and Tourism, Columbia, SC..1330

South Carolina Institute of Archaeology & Anthropology, Columbia, SC.............1330

South Charleston Museum, South Charleston, WV 1586

South Dakota State Historical Society, Pierre, SD..1353

South Florida Museum, Bishop Planetarium & Parker Manatee Aquarium, Bradenton, FL 297

Southdown Plantation House/The Terrebonne Museum, Houma, LA 589

Southern Plains Indian Museum, Anadarko, OK 1196

Southern Ute Cultural Center and Museum, Ignacio, CO 223

Southern Vermont Natural History Museum, West Marlboro, VT...............1489

Southold Indian Museum, Southold, NY ...1071

Southwest Museum, Los Angeles, CA.........121

Spertus Museum, Chicago, IL 427

Spiro Mounds Archaeological Center, Spiro, OK..................1214
Spotsylvania Historical Association and Museum, Spotsylvania, VA...................1537
Springfield Museums - Springfield Science Museum, Springfield, MA..........711
Spurlock Museum, University of Illinois at Urbana-Champaign, Urbana, IL...........462
Stagecoach Inn Museum Complex, Newbury Park, CA.........................130
Stamford Museum & Nature Center, Stamford, CT.................................261
Star Eco Station, Culver City, CA.................88
State Historical Society of Iowa, Des Moines, IA.....................................515
State Historical Society of North Dakota, Bismarck, ND.....................................1128
State of Illinois-Historic Preservation Agency, Historic Sites Division, Springfield, IL.......................................460
Stearns Collection of Musical Instruments, Ann Arbor, MI....................725
Stearns History Museum, Saint Cloud, MN..788
Stephens African-American Museum, Shreveport, LA.................................602
The Stephens Museum, Fayette, MO..........815
Stepping Stones Museum for Children, Norwalk, CT...257
Stones River National Battlefield, Murfreesboro, TN................................1377
Stonewall House, Rocky Mount, NC.........1118
Stoughton Historical Society, Stoughton, MA..713
Stuhr Museum of the Prairie Pioneer, Grand Island, NE....................................862
Suffolk County Historical Society, Riverhead, NY......................................1057
Suffolk County Vanderbilt Museum, Centerport, NY......................................977
Sullivan Museum and History Center, Northfield, VT......................................1483
Sunset Crater Volcano National Monument, Flagstaff, AZ............................33
SunWatch Indian Village/Archaeological Park, Dayton, OH.................................1162
Sutter's Fort State Historic Park, Sacramento, CA.....................................153
Sweetwater County Historical Museum, Green River, WY....................................1633

T Rex Museum, Tucson, AZ.........................50
Tamastslikt Cultural Institute, Pendleton, OR...1230
Tampa Bay History Center, Inc., Tampa, FL..350
Tampa's Lowry Park Zoo, Tampa, FL.........350
Taos Historic Museums, Taos, NM..............953
Tarpon Springs Cultural Center, Tarpon Springs, FL...351
Temecula Valley Museum, Temecula, CA....191
Tennessee Historical Society, Nashville, TN..1380
Terwilliger Museum, Waterloo, NY............1083
Texas Music Museum, Austin, TX.............1392
Texas Ranger Hall of Fame and Museum, Waco, TX.......................................1459
Texas State Museum of Asian Cultures & Educational Center, Corpus Christi, TX..1402
The Textile Museum, Washington, DC.........291
Three Valley Museum, Durant, OK..........1200
Three Village Historical Society, Setauket, NY......................................1069
Timexpo Museum, Waterbury, CT................264
Timucuan Ecological and Historic Preserve and Fort Caroline National Memorial, Jacksonville, FL.....................315
Tioga Point Museum, Athens, PA..............1241
The Toledo Zoo, Toledo, OH......................1187
Tonto National Monument, Roosevelt, AZ...43
Totem Heritage Center, Ketchikan, AK.........26

Tougaloo College, Tougaloo, MS.................808
Trailside Nature Museum, Cross River, NY..983
Triangle Tattoo & Museum, Fort Bragg, CA...95
The Trout Gallery, Carlisle, PA.................1245
Tubac Presidio State Historic Park, Tubac, AZ...47
Tubman African-American Museum, Macon, GA...378
Tucker Tower Nature Center, Ardmore, OK..1196
Tucson Botanical Gardens, Tucson, AZ.........51
Tulare County Museum at Mooney Grove Park, Visalia, CA...................................195
Tulsa Zoo & Living Museum, Tulsa, OK..1216
Tumacacori National Historical Park, Tumacacori, AZ...52
Turabo University, Gurabo, PR..................1641
Turtle Bay Exploration Park, Redding, CA...146
Turtle Mountain Chippewa Historical Society, Belcourt, ND............................1127

UCLA Fowler Museum of Cultural History, Los Angeles, CA.......................122
UCR/California Museum of Photography, Riverside, CA...150
UNLV Marjorie Barrick Museum, Las Vegas, NV...880
Ukrainian-American Museum & Archives, Warren, MI...........................766
Ukrainian Museum-Archives, Inc., Cleveland, OH.......................................1156
Ukrainian National Museum, Inc., Chicago, IL...428
Union County Heritage Museum, New Albany, MS...806
Union for Reform Judaism, New York, NY..1040
Union Station Kansas City, Inc., Kansas City, MO...823
United States Botanic Garden, Washington, DC.....................................292
United States Department of the Interior Museum, Washington, DC.....................293
University Art Museum, Santa Barbara, Santa Barbara, CA...................................180
University Galleries, Clarion, PA...............1247
University Museum, Carbondale, IL............415
The University Museum, Edwardsville, IL..432
University Museum & Historic Houses, The University of Mississippi, Oxford, MS..806
The University Museum Collections, Fayetteville, AR...57
University Museum, New Mexico State University, Las Cruces, NM....................941
University of Alaska Museum of the North, Fairbanks, AK.................................24
University of Colorado Museum, Boulder, CO...203
University of Iowa Museum of Natural History, Iowa City, IA...........................520
The University of Michigan Exhibit Museum of Natural History, Ann Arbor, MI..725
University of Michigan Museum of Anthropology, Ann Arbor, MI.................725
University of Nebraska State Museum, Lincoln, NE..867
University of Northern Iowa Museums & Collections, Cedar Falls, IA....................508
University of Oregon Museum of Natural and Cultural History, Eugene, OR.........1224
University of Pennsylvania Museum of Archaeology and Anthropology, Philadelphia, PA...................................1288
University of Washington Botanic Garden, Seattle, WA.................................1569
University of Wyoming Anthropology Museum, Laramie, WY...........................1636

University Saint Thomas Art History, Saint Paul, MN.......................................792
Utah Field House of Natural History State Park, Vernal, UT..........................1475
Utah Museum of Natural History, Salt Lake City, UT..1473
Utah State University's Museum of Anthropology, Logan, UT.....................1467
Ute Indian Museum/Montrose Visitor Center, Montrose, CO.............................228

The Valdez Museum & Historical Archive Association, Inc., Valdez, AK......29
Valentine Richmond History Center, Richmond, VA.....................................1532
Vann House, Chatsworth, GA....................368
Venango Museum of Art, Science & Industry, Oil City, PA...........................1274
Victor Valley Museum & Art Gallery, Apple Valley, CA......................................71
Virgin Islands National Park, St. John, VI.1644

W.H. Over Museum, Vermillion, SD..........1358
Waikiki Aquarium, Honolulu, HI................399
Waimea Arboretum and Botanical Garden in Waimea Valley Audubon Center, Haleiwa, HI...392
Walnut Canyon National Monument, Flagstaff, AZ..34
Wanapum Dam Heritage Center, Beverly, WA..1549
War in the Pacific National Historical Park, Piti, GU...1640
Washburn County Historical Society Museum, Shell Lake, WI.......................1621
Washington County Historical Society, Portland, OR...1233
Washington Irving Trail Museum, Ripley, OK..1213
Washington State Historical Society, Tacoma, WA...1574
Waukesha County Museum, Waukesha, WI..1625
Wayne State University Museum of Anthropology, Detroit, MI.....................738
Welsh-American Heritage Museum, Oak Hill, OH...1180
Wenatchee Valley Museum and Cultural Center, Wenatchee, WA.........................1577
West Milford Museum, West Milford, NJ....930
Western Archeological & Conservation Center, Tucson, AZ...52
The Whale Museum, Friday Harbor, WA...1555
Whatcom Museum of History and Art, Bellingham, WA.....................................1549
The Wheelwright Museum of the American Indian, Santa Fe, NM..............950
White Hall State Historic Site, Richmond, KY...583
White River Valley Museum, Auburn, WA..1547
Whitewater Canal State Historic Site, Metamora, IN...490
Whitingham Historical Museum, Whitingham, VT......................................1490
Whitman Mission National Historic Site, Walla Walla, WA....................................1577
Wickliffe Mounds State Historic Site, Wickliffe, KY...584
Wilbur D. May Museum, Reno, NV...........882
Wilderness Road Regional Museum, Newbern, VA...1519
William Hammond Mathers Museum, Bloomington, IN.....................................470
William McKinley Presidential Library & Museum, Canton, OH...........................1146
William Pryor Letchworth Museum, Castile, NY...976
William S. Webb Museum of Anthropology, Lexington, KY...............575
William Weston Clarke Emison Museum of Art, Greencastle, IN..........................479

Ethnological/Ethnographical–Continued

Windham Textile and History Museum (The Mill Museum), Willimantic, CT 267

Wings of Love, Clinton, MI 732

Winnebago Area Museum, Winnebago, MN 797

Wisconsin Historical Museum, Madison, WI 1606

Wisconsin National Guard Museum, Camp Douglas, WI 1593

Witte Museum, San Antonio, TX 1451

Woodruff Museum of Indian Artifacts, Bridgeton, NJ 898

Woolaroc Museum, Bartlesville, OK 1197

WordSpring Discovery Center, Orlando, FL 333

World Museum of Mining, Butte, MT 843

World Museum of Natural History, Riverside, CA 150

Wormsloe State Historic Site, Savannah, GA 387

Wounded Knee Museum, Wall, SD 1358

Wrangell Museum, Wrangell, AK 29

Wriston Art Center Galleries, Appleton, WI 1590

Wupatki National Monument, Flagstaff, AZ 34

Wyoming State Museum, Cheyenne, WY ..1631

The Yager Museum of Art & Culture, Oneonta, NY 1046

Yeshiva University Museum at the Center for Jewish History, New York, NY 1041

Yolo County Historical Museum, Woodland, CA 199

York W. Bailey Museum at Penn Center, Saint Helena Island, SC 1340

The Yosemite Museum, National Park Service, Yosemite National Park, CA 199

Ypsilanti Historical Museum, Ypsilanti, MI 767

Ziibiwing Center of Anishinabe Culture & Lifeways, Mount Pleasant, MI 757

Zimmer Children's Museum, Los Angeles, CA 122

Folk Culture

The A.D. Buck Museum of Natural History & Science, Tonkawa, OK 1215

A:shiwi A:wan Museum and Heritage Center, Zuni, NM 954

Abraham Lincoln Birthplace National Historic Site, Hodgenville, KY 571

Adams Museum & House, Deadwood, SD 1346

Adams State College Luther Bean Museum, Alamosa, CO 201

Adan E. Treganza Anthropology Museum, Dept. of Anthropology, San Francisco State University, San Francisco, CA 162

African American Museum, Cleveland, OH 1152

African American Museum, Dallas, TX 1403

African-American Museum and Library at Oakland, Oakland, CA 132

African Art Museum of the S.M.A. Fathers, Tenafly, NJ 926

Afro-American Cultural Center, Charlotte, NC 1094

Agrirama, Georgia's Living History Museum & Village, Tifton, GA 388

Ah-Tah-Thi-Ki Museum, Big Cypress Seminole Indian Reservation, FL 295

Akwesasne Museum, Hogansburg, NY 998

Alamo Township Museum-John E. Gray Memorial Museum, Kalamazoo, MI 748

Alaska Indian Arts, Inc., Haines, AK 24

Albany Civil Rights Movement Museum at Old Mt. Zion Church, Albany, GA 355

Alden House Historic Site, Duxbury, MA ...680

Alexandria Museum of Art, Alexandria, LA 584

Allen County Historical Society, Iola, KS ...545

Alling Coverlet Museum, Palmyra, NY 1050

Alton Museum of History and Art, Inc., Alton, IL 410

Alutiiq Museum and Archaeological Repository, Kodiak, AK 26

Amana Heritage Museum, Amana, IA 504

American Classical Music Hall of Fame and Museum, Cincinnati, OH 1148

American Historical Society of Germans from Russia, Lincoln, NE 865

American Hungarian Foundation/Museum of the American Hungarian Foundation, New Brunswick, NJ 915

American Museum of Straw Art, Long Beach, CA 110

American Swedish Institute, Minneapolis, MN 781

America's National Music Museum, Vermillion, SD 1358

America's Stonehenge, North Salem, NH 893

Anderson Gallery, School of the Arts, Virginia Commonwealth University, Richmond, VA 1528

Andrew County Museum & Historical Society, Savannah, MO 838

Angels Attic Museum, Santa Monica, CA ...183

Annie Riggs Memorial Museum, Fort Stockton, TX 1415

Antelope Valley Indian Museum, Lancaster, CA 108

The Anthropology Museum, DeKalb, IL 429

The Antiquarian and Landmarks Society, Inc., Hartford, CT 244

The Appalachian Trail Conservancy, Harpers Ferry, WV 1581

Appleton Museum of Art, Ocala, FL 330

Arab American National Museum, Dearborn, MI 733

Arizona Historical Society Pioneer Museum, Flagstaff, AZ 32

Arizona State Museum, Tucson, AZ 48

Arizona State University Museum of Anthropology, Tempe, AZ 46

Arkansas Historic Wine Museum, Paris, AR 65

Arkansas Museum of Natural Resources, Smackover, AR 68

Armenian Library and Museum of America, Watertown, MA 716

Arrowmont School of Arts & Crafts, Gatlinburg, TN 1365

Art Museum of Southeast Texas, Beaumont, TX 1393

Arthur Ross Gallery, University of Pennsylvania, Philadelphia, PA 1276

Ash Lawn-Highland, Charlottesville, VA ...1498

Ashland Historical Society Museum, Ashland, WI 1590

Asian American Arts Centre, New York, NY 1021

Asian Art Museum of San Francisco, Chong-Moon Lee Center for Asian Art and Culture, San Francisco, CA 163

Asian Arts & Culture Center, Towson University, Towson, MD 655

The Association for Gravestone Studies, Greenfield, MA 685

Association for the Preservation of Tennessee Antiquities, Nashville, TN 1377

Atlanta College of Art, Atlanta, GA 358

Atlanta Historical Society, Atlanta, GA 358

Atwater Kent Museum of Philadelphia, Philadelphia, PA 1276

Audubon House & Tropical Gardens, Key West, FL 317

Avery County Museum, Newland, NC 1113

Avery Research Center for African American History & Culture, Charleston, SC 1323

Aztalan Museum, Jefferson, WI 1601

The Babe Ruth Museum and Sports Legends at Camden Yards, Baltimore, MD 629

Baca House, Trinidad History Museum, Trinidad, CO 233

Bailey House Museum - Maui Historical Society, Wailuku, HI 402

Baldwin Historical Society and Museum, Baldwin, NY 960

Balzekas Museum of Lithuanian Culture, Chicago, IL 418

The Band Museum, Pine Bluff, AR 66

Baranov Museum, Kodiak, AK 26

Barataria Preserve, Jean Lafitte National Historical Park and Preserve, Marrero, LA 591

The Barnacle Historic State Park, Coconut Grove, FL 300

Barrington Living History Farm, Washington, TX 1460

Bartow History Center, Cartersville, GA 367

Batsto Village, Hammonton, NJ 907

Baxter Springs Heritage Center and Museum, Baxter Springs, KS 533

The Bead Museum, Glendale, AZ 35

Beaufort Historic Site, Beaufort, NC 1091

Beaver Island Historical Society, Beaver Island, MI 728

Beck Cultural Exchange Center, Knoxville, TN 1369

Belhaven Memorial Museum, Inc., Belhaven, NC 1092

Belle Grove Plantation, Middletown, VA ...1517

Bennington Battlefield State Historic Site, Walloomsac, NY 1081

Benton County Historical Museum, Prosser, WA 1563

Bernard Historical Society and Museum, Delton, MI 734

Bethel Historical Society Regional History Center, Bethel, ME 606

Big Thicket National Preserve, Kountze, TX 1432

Big Timbers Museum, Lamar, CO 225

Biltmore Homespun Shops - Grovewood Gallery, Asheville, NC 1089

Bily Clock Museum/Antonin Dvorak Exhibit, Spillville, IA 528

Bishop Hill Heritage Museum, Bishop Hill, IL 413

Bishop Hill State Historic Site, Bishop Hill, IL 413

Bishop Museum, Honolulu, HI 394

Black American West Museum & Heritage Center, Denver, CO 209

Black Heritage Museum, Miami, FL 323

Blacksmith Shop Museum, Dover-Foxcroft, ME 610

Blue Hills Trailside Museum, Milton, MA 695

Blue Ridge Institute and Museum, Ferrum, VA 1504

B'nai B'rith Klutznick National Jewish Museum, Washington, DC 277

Bodie Island Visitor Center, South Nags Head, NC 1120

Bolinas Museum, Bolinas, CA 79

Bosque Memorial Museum, Clifton, TX 1400

Boston Childrens Museum, Boston, MA 664

Boston Fire Museum, Boston, MA 664

Boulder City/Hoover Dam Museum, Boulder City, NV 875

Branigan Cultural Center, Las Cruces, NM 940

Bread & Puppet Museum, Glover, VT 1479

Bridgton Historical Society, Bridgton, ME 607

Brigham City Museum-Gallery, Brigham City, UT 1463

Brigham Young's Winter Home, Saint George, UT 1470

The Bronx County Historical Society, Bronx, NY 964
The Bronx Museum of the Arts, Bronx, NY 965
Brookings County Historical Society Museum, Volga, SD..............1358
Brooklyn Children's Museum, Brooklyn, NY..............968
Brown County Historical Society Pioneer Museum, Nashville, IN 493
Brush Country Museum, Cotulla, TX 1403
Buchanan Center for the Arts, Monmouth, IL..............445
Bucks County Civil War Library & Museum, Doylestown, PA..............1249
Bucksport Historical Society, Inc., Bucksport, ME..............608
Burlington Historical Museum, Burlington, MA 672
Burnham Tavern, Machias, ME 614
Burpee Museum of Natural History, Rockford, IL..............454
Burrowes Mansion Museum, Matawan, NJ..............911
Byron Historical Museum, Byron, NY..........974

CHTJ Southard House Museum, Brunswick, ME..............607
Cabin Nature Center, Wood Dale, IL 466
Cabrillo National Monument, San Diego, CA..............156
Cahokia Courthouse State Historic Site, Cahokia, IL..............415
Calaveras County Museum, San Andreas, CA..............155
Calhoun County Museum, Port Lavaca, TX..............1444
Calhoun County Museum & Cultural Center, Saint Matthews, SC 1341
California Heritage Museum, Santa Monica, CA..............183
California Route 66 Museum, Victorville, CA..............195
California Surf Museum, Oceanside, CA......135
Call of the Wild Museum, Gaylord, MI......742
Calvert Marine Museum, Solomons, MD 654
Camden County Historical Society, Camden, NJ..............899
Campbell County Rockpile Museum, Gillette, WY..............1633
Canadian County Historical Museum, El Reno, OK..............1200
Canal Fulton Heritage Society, Canal Fulton, OH..............1145
Canterbury Shaker Village, Inc., Canterbury, NH..............883
Canyon de Chelly National Monument, Chinle, AZ 31
Cape Cod Museum of Natural History, Inc., Brewster, MA..............670
Capitol Reef National Park Visitor Center, Torrey, UT..............1475
Carlsbad Museum & Art Center, Carlsbad, NM..............938
Carnegie Center for Art & History, New Albany, IN 493
Carpenter Home Museum and Gallery, Cle Elum, WA..............1551
Carroll Reece Museum, Johnson City, TN.1367
Cartoon Art Museum, San Francisco, CA....164
Cary Cottage, Cincinnati, OH..............1148
Casa Blanca Museum, San Juan, PR..........1642
Cascade County Historical Society Museum, Great Falls, MT..............848
Cass County Historical Society at Bonanzaville, West Fargo, ND..............1137
Casteel-Linn House and Museum, Princeton, MO..............829
Castellani Art Museum of Niagara University, Niagara University, NY.......1043
Catawba County Museum of History, Newton, NC..............1113
Cathedral Cultural Center, Omaha, NE........870

Cedar Key Historical Society Museum, Cedar Key, FL..............298
Center for Agricultural Science and Heritage, Indianapolis, IN..............481
Center for American Music, Pittsburgh, PA..............1291
Center for Puppetry Arts, Atlanta, GA 359
The Center for Western Studies, Sioux Falls, SD..............1356
Center for Wooden Boats, Seattle, WA 1565
Center of Southwest Studies/Fort Lewis College, Durango, CO..............214
Central Montana Historical Association, Inc. Museum, Lewistown, MT..............850
Chancellor Robert R. Livingston Masonic Library & Museum, New York, NY......1022
Chandler Museum, Chandler, AZ 31
Charlotte Museum of History and Hezekiah Alexander Homesite, Charlotte, NC..............1094
Chase County Historical Society, Inc., Cottonwood Falls, KS..............536
Chase Home Museum of Utah Folk Arts, Salt Lake City, UT 1470
The Chelmsford Historical Society, Inc., South Chelmsford, MA..............709
Chemung Valley History Museum, Elmira, NY..............988
Chesapeake and Ohio Canal National Historical Park, Hagerstown, MD..............646
Chesapeake Bay Maritime Museum, Saint Michaels, MD..............652
Chesterfield County Museum, Chesterfield, VA..............1501
Chicago Children's Museum, Chicago, IL....419
Chicago History Museum, Chicago, IL........419
The Chief John Ross House, Rossville, GA..............382
Children's Discovery Museum of North San Diego, Carlsbad, CA..............81
Children's Hands-On Museum (CHOM), Tuscaloosa, AL 19
The Children's Museum, Seattle, WA 1565
Children's Museum at La Habra, La Habra, CA..............106
Children's Museum/Detroit Public Schools, Detroit, MI..............735
Children's Museum, Inc., Boca Raton, FL...296
Children's Museum of History, Natural History and Science at Utica, New York, Utica, NY..............1079
Children's Museum of Oak Ridge, Inc., Oak Ridge, TN 1382
Children's Museum of Pittsburgh, Pittsburgh, PA..............1291
The Children's Museum of Rose Hill Manor Park, Frederick, MD..............644
Children's Museum of the Arts, New York, NY..............1022
The Children's Toy & Doll Museum, Marietta, OH..............1174
Chippewa Nature Center, Midland, MI........755
Chippewa Valley Museum, Inc., Eau Claire, WI..............1595
Chisholm Trail Historical Museum, Waurika, OK..............1216
Cincinnati Museum Center at Union Terminal, Cincinnati, OH..............1149
City Museum, Saint Louis, MO..............832
City of Las Vegas Museum and Rough Rider Memorial Collection, Las Vegas, NM..............941
Clark County Historical Museum, Vancouver, WA..............1576
Clark County Museum, Marshall, IL............444
Clark County Museum, Henderson, NV 878
Clarke House Museum, Chicago, IL 420
Clay County Historical Museum, Liberty, MO..............826
Clay County Historical Society Museum and Archives, Moorhead, MN..............784
Clearwater Historical Museum, Orofino, ID..............408

The Cleveland Museum of Art, Cleveland, OH..............1152
Cleveland State University Art Gallery, Cleveland, OH..............1153
Cliffs of the Neuse State Park, Seven Springs, NC..............1119
Clinton Academy, East Hampton, NY..........985
Cloud County Historical Society Museum, Concordia, KS..............536
Coal Miners' Museum/Van Lear Historical Society, Inc., Van Lear, KY 584
Coarsegold Historic Museum, Coarsegold, CA..............86
Codington County Heritage Museum, Watertown, SD..............1359
The Coffey County Historical Museum, Burlington, KS..............534
Coggeshall Farm Museum, Bristol, RI.......1310
College Football Hall of Fame, South Bend, IN..............499
Collinsville Depot Museum, Collinsville, OK..............1198
Colonel Davenport Historical Foundation, Rock Island, IL..............453
Colorado Springs Fine Arts Center (Taylor Museum), Colorado Springs, CO..............206
Colorado Springs Museum, Colorado Springs, CO..............206
Columbia State Historic Park, Columbia, CA..............87
The Commonwealth Museum, Boston, MA..............665
Community of Christ, Independence, MO ...817
Confederated Tribes and Bands of the Yakama Indian Nation - Cultural Heritage Center Museum, Toppenish, WA..............1575
Connecticut River Museum, Essex, CT........239
Conner Prairie, Fishers, IN 476
Constitution Convention Museum State Park, Port St. Joe, FL..............338
Copia: The American Center for Wine, Food & the Arts, Napa, CA..............129
Copper Village Museum & Arts Center of Deer Lodge County, Anaconda, MT.......840
Country Music Hall of Fame and Museum, Country Music Foundation, Nashville, TN..............1378
Cracker Country, Tampa, FL..............348
Craft and Folk Art Museum - CAFAM, Los Angeles, CA..............114
Crafts Museum, Mequon, WI 1609
Craftsmen's Guild of Mississippi, Jackson, MS..............802
Cragfont-Historic Cragfont, Inc., Castalian Springs, TN 1360
Crane Point, Marathon, FL..............323
Crawford W. Long Museum, Jefferson, GA..............374
Creative Photographic Art Center of Maine, Lewiston, ME..............614
Creek Council House Museum, Okmulgee, OK..............1211
Croatian Heritage Museum & Library, Eastlake, OH..............1163
Crockett Tavern Museum, Morristown, TN..............1376
Crossman Gallery, UW-Whitewater, Whitewater, WI..............1628
Culinary Archives & Museum, Johnson & Wales University, Providence, RI......1316
Cultural Museum, Nashville, TN..............1378
Cumberland County Historical Society, The Hamilton Library and The Two Mile House, Carlisle, PA..............1245
Cumberland Gap National Historical Park, Middlesboro, KY..............580
Cupola House, Egg Harbor, WI..............1596
The Curious Kids' Museum, Saint Joseph, MI..............763
The Custom House Maritime Museum, Newburyport, MA..............697

Folk Culture–Continued

Cuyuna Range Historical Society &
  Museum, Crosby, MN 772

DAAP Galleries, Cincinnati, OH 1150
DAR John Strong Mansion Museum,
  Addison, VT 1475
D.R. Barker Historical Museum,
  Fredonia, NY 992
D. Ralph Hostetter Museum of Natural
  History, Harrisonburg, VA......................1510
Dakotaland Museum, Huron, SD.................1348
Dal-Paso Museum, Lamesa, TX 1433
The Danbury Museum & Historical
  Society, Danbury, CT 238
Dancing Bear Folk Center, Thermopolis,
  WY 1639
The Danish Immigrant Museum, Elk
  Horn, IA..517
Daughters of Utah Pioneers Pioneer
  Memorial Museum & International
  Society Daughters of Utah Pioneers,
  Salt Lake City, UT 1471
David Crockett Cabin, Rutherford, TN 1383
Davidson County Historical Museum,
  Lexington, NC 1109
Dayton Historical Depot Society, Dayton,
  WA 1552
Deer Valley Rock Art Center, Glendale,
  AZ 35
Degrazia Gallery In The Sun, Tucson, AZ....48
Del Norte County Historical Society,
  Crescent City, CA....................................87
Delaware Agricultural Museum and
  Village, Dover, DE 269
Delaware and Hudson Canal Historical
  Society and Museum, High Falls, NY.....998
Delta Blues Museum, Clarksdale, MS..........799
Denton County Historical Museum, Inc.
  and Texas Heritage Center, Denton,
  TX 1409
Denver Museum of Miniatures, Dolls and
  Toys, Denver, CO 211
The Depot Museum Complex,
  Henderson, TX.......................................1424
The Design Center at Philadelphia
  University, Philadelphia, PA 1278
Deutschheim State Historic Site,
  Hermann, MO...817
Dewey Hotel Museum, Dewey, OK 1199
DeWitt County Historical Museum,
  Cuero, TX..1403
Diggs Gallery at Winston-Salem State
  University, Winston-Salem, NC 1125
Disney's Animal Kingdom Theme Park,
  Bay Lake, FL...295
Dr. Increase Mathews House, Zanesville,
  OH 1194
Dr Pepper Museum and Free Enterprise
  Institute, Waco, TX................................1458
Dr. William Robinson Plantation, Clark,
  NJ 901
Dog Mushing Museum, Fairbanks, AK.........24
Donald G. Trayser Memorial
  Museum/Barnstable County Customs
  House, Barnstable, MA 661
Douglas County Historical Society -
  Carson Valley Museum & Cultural
  Center, Gardnerville, NV 877
Douglas County Historical Society -
  Genoa Courthouse Museum, Genoa,
  NV 877
Douglas County Museum Complex,
  Armour, SD..1344
Downieville Museum, Downieville, CA 91
Dubois Museum, Dubois, WY 1632
Duluth Children's Museum, Duluth, MN....772
Dunn County Historical Society,
  Menomonie, WI.....................................1609

Early American Museum, Mahomet, IL.......444
EarlyWorks Museums, Huntsville, AL 11

East Hampton Historical Society, Inc.,
  East Hampton, NY 985
East Jersey Olde Towne, Piscataway, NJ 921
East Tennessee Historical Society,
  Knoxville, TN...1369
East Texas Oil Museum at Kilgore
  College, Kilgore, TX...............................1432
East-West Center, Honolulu, HI...................394
ECHO at the Leahy Center for Lake
  Champlain, Burlington, VT....................1478
1859 Jail, Marshal's Home & Museum,
  Independence, MO...................................817
Eiteljorg Museum of American Indians
  and Western Art, Indianapolis, IN 482
El Camino Real International Heritage
  Center, San Antonio, NM.......................947
El Museo Del Barrio, New York, NY 1025
El Museo Latino, Omaha, NE 870
El Pueblo History Museum, Pueblo, CO.....230
El Rancho de Las Golondrinas Museum,
  Santa Fe, NM..947
Ellis County Historical Society, Hays, KS...543
Elverhoj Museum of History and Art,
  Solvang, CA 187
Emmett Kelly Historical Museum, Sedan,
  KS 558
Epcot at Walt Disney World Resort, Lake
  Buena Vista, FL 319
The Erlander Home Museum, Rockford,
  IL 454
Esther M. Klein Art Gallery at University
  City Science Center, Philadelphia, PA...1279
The Ethel Wright Mohamed Stitchery
  Museum, Belzoni, MS 798
Ethnic Heritage Museum, Rockford, IL 455
Eubie Blake National Jazz Institute and
  Cultural Center, Baltimore, MD 632
Exploris, Raleigh, NC 1115
Explorium of Lexington, Lexington, KY 572

Fairfield County Museum, Winnsboro,
  SC 1343
Fairview Museum of History & Art,
  Fairview, UT..1465
Faninadahen Kosas Guahan-Guam
  Museum, Hagatna, GU............................1640
Farmers Branch Historical Park, Farmers
  Branch, TX..1413
Farragut Folklife Museum, Farragut, TN ...1364
Farrar-Mansur House & Old Mill
  Museum, Weston, VT.............................1490
Faulkner County Museum, Conway, AR........56
Faust Park Foundation, Chesterfield, MO 812
Faust Park-Thornhill Historic Site & 19th
  Century Village, Chesterfield, MO 812
Fayette Art Museum, Fayette, AL..................9
Fayette County Helpers Club &
  Historical Society, West Union, IA..........530
Fayette Historic State Park, Garden, MI 742
Fenton History Center-Museum &
  Library, Jamestown, NY........................1005
Fifth Maine Regiment Museum, Peaks
  Island, ME 618
First Territorial Capitol of Kansas, Fort
  Riley, KS...540
Fleming Historical Society, Fleming, CO 216
Florence Ranch Homestead, Mesquite,
  TX 1438
Florida Agricultural Museum, Palm
  Coast, FL 334
Folk Art Society of America, Richmond,
  VA 1529
Folsom History Museum, Folsom, CA..........95
Fort Abraham Lincoln State Park,
  Mandan, ND..1134
Fort Atkinson State Historical Park, Fort
  Calhoun, NE...860
Fort Bliss Museum, Fort Bliss, TX 1413
Fort Croghan Museum, Burnet, TX............1398
Fort Crook Historical Museum, Fall
  River Mills, CA 94
Fort Dalles Museum/Anderson
  Homestead, The Dalles, OR...................1237

Fort Davidson State Historic Site, Pilot
  Knob, MO...828
Fort de Chartres State Historic Site &
  Museum, Prairie du Rocher, IL 451
Fort Frederick State Park, Big Pool, MD.....637
Fort Garland Museum, Fort Garland, CO 217
Fort Hill (The John C. Calhoun House),
  Clemson, SC 1328
Fort Inglish, Bonham, TX..........................1396
Fort Kearny State Historical Park,
  Kearney, NE..864
Fort Leaton State Historical Site,
  Presidio, TX...1444
Fort Morris State Historic Site, Midway,
  GA 379
Fort Nashborough, Nashville, TN..............1379
Fort Okanogan Interpretive Center,
  Brewster, WA 1550
Fort Plain Museum, Fort Plain, NY 991
Fort St. Jean Baptiste State Historic Site,
  Natchitoches, LA 593
Fossil Museum, Fossil, OR 1224
Fostoria Area Historical Museum,
  Fostoria, OH...1164
Four Mile Historic Park, Denver, CO 212
Four Rivers Cultural Center & Museum,
  Ontario, OR...1229
The Foxfire Museum & Heritage Center,
  Mountain City, GA 380
Franklin County Old Jail Museum,
  Winchester, TN......................................1385
Freestone County Historical Museum,
  Fairfield, TX..1413
Fresno Flats Historical Park, Oakhurst,
  CA 132
Frontier Culture Museum, Staunton, VA....1537
Frontier Gateway Museum, Glendive,
  MT 847
Frontier Times Museum, Bandera, TX.......1393
Fulton County Historical Society
  Museum, Rochester, IN...........................498

Gadsden Museum, Mesilla, NM 943
Garfield Farm Museum, LaFox, IL 441
Garnavillo Historical Museum,
  Garnavillo, IA 518
Gateway to the Panhandle, Gate, OK.........1201
General Daniel Bissell House, Saint
  Louis, MO...833
General Wait House, Waitsfield, VT...........1489
Geographical Center Historical Museum,
  Rugby, ND...1136
Georgia Music Hall of Fame and
  Museum, Macon, GA 377
Georgia Southern University Museum,
  Statesboro, GA..387
Georgia's Old Capital Museum,
  Milledgeville, GA 380
Gilcrease Museum, Tulsa, OK 1215
Glove Museum, New York, NY 1026
Gnadenhutten Historical Park & Museum,
  Gnadenhutten, OH.................................1167
Gold Coast Railroad Museum, Inc.,
  Miami, FL...323
Goliad State Park, Goliad, TX...................1423
Gomez Foundation for Mill House,
  Marlboro, NY...1014
Goschenhoppen Folklife Library and
  Museum, Green Lane, PA.......................1257
Governor John Sevier Memorial
  Association, Knoxville, TN.....................1370
The Governor's Mansion, Frankfort, KY 569
Graham County Historical Society,
  Thatcher, AZ..46
Grand Forks County Historical Society,
  Grand Forks, ND....................................1132
The Grand River Historical Society &
  Museum, Chillicothe, MO.......................813
Grant County Museum, Medford, OK.........1205
Grant County Museum & Historic
  Society, Hyannis, NE...............................863
Grants Pass Museum of Art, Grants Pass,
  OR...1225

Granville County Historical Society
Museum, Oxford, NC 1114
Great Harbor Maritime Museum,
Northeast Harbor, ME 616
Great Sand Dunes National Monument
and Preserve, Mosca, CO.......................229
Green Hill Art Gallery, Greensboro, NC 1103
Guilford Courthouse National Military
Park, Greensboro, NC 1104
Gunnison County Pioneer and Historical
Society, Gunnison, CO 222
Gunnison Museum of Natural History,
Pawling, NY 1051
Gwinnett Historical Society,
Lawrenceville, GA...............................376
Gwinnett History Museum,
Lawrenceville, GA...............................376

H.G. Albee Memorial Museum,
Estherville, IA......................................517
Hahns Peak Area Historical Society and
School House, Clark, CO..........................205
The Hall of Fame for Great Americans,
Bronx, NY 966
Hallockville Museum Farm, Riverhead,
NY...1057
Hamilton Van Wagoner Museum, Clifton,
NJ 901
Hamline University Galleries, Department
of Studio Arts & Art History, Saint
Paul, MN...790
Hampton County Historical Museum,
Hampton, SC 1334
Hana Cultural Center, Hana, Maui, HI.........392
Hancock Shaker Village, Inc., Pittsfield,
MA...703
The Handweaving Museum & Arts
Center, Clayton, NY..............................978
Hannah Lindahl Children's Museum,
Mishawaka, IN......................................491
Hanover House, Clemson, SC 1328
Harding Museum, Franklin, OH 1164
The Harness Racing Museum and Hall of
Fame, Goshen, NY.................................995
Harrisonburg-Rockingham Historical
Society, Dayton, VA..............................1503
The Harwood Museum of Art of the
University of New Mexico, Taos, NM 952
Hatteras Island Visitor Center, Buxton,
NC...1093
Hattiesburg Area Historical Society and
HAHS Museum, Hattiesburg, MS 801
Hatton-Eielson Museum & Historical
Association, Hatton, ND 1132
Haverford Township Historical Society,
Havertown, PA....................................1260
Havre de Grace Decoy Museum, Havre
de Grace, MD......................................647
Hawaii Maritime Center, Honolulu, HI.......395
Hawaii's Plantation Village, Waipahu, HI 402
Hawks Inn Historical Society, Inc.,
Delafield, WI 1595
Heard Museum, Phoenix, AZ.......................40
Heisey Museum, Clinton County
Historical Society, Lock Haven, PA 1269
Helen Louise Allen Textile Collection,
Madison, WI..1605
Helvetia Museum, Helvetia, WV.................1582
Henrico County Historic Preservation &
Museum Services, Richmond, VA 1529
Henry Ford Estate-Fair Lane, Dearborn,
MI..734
The Heritage Center, Pine Ridge, SD.........1354
Heritage Center Museum, Berryville, AR 55
Heritage Center of Lancaster County,
Inc., Lancaster, PA...............................1265
Heritage Farmstead Museum, Plano, TX ...1444
Heritage Hall Museum & Archives,
Freeman, SD.......................................1347
Heritage-Hjemkomst Interpretive Center,
Moorhead, MN....................................784
Heritage House Museum of Montgomery
County, Mount Ida, AR 64

The Heritage Museum at Falfurrias, Inc.,
Falfurrias, TX 1413
Heritage Museum Foundation of Tate
County, Inc., Senatobia, MS 808
The Heritage Museum of Fine Arts for
Youth, Detroit, MI................................736
Heritage Museum of Northwest Florida,
Valparaiso, FL......................................352
Hernando Heritage Museum, Brooksville,
FL..298
Hershey Museum, Hershey, PA 1261
Hettinger County Historical Society,
Regent, ND...1136
Hibbing Historical Society and Museum,
Hibbing, MN.......................................778
Hiddenite Center, Inc., Hiddenite, NC........1106
The High Museum of Art, Atlanta, GA........360
Highland County Museum and Heritage
Center, McDowell, VA 1517
Highland Maple Museum, Monterey, VA...1518
Highlands Museum & Discovery Center,
Ashland, KY..564
Hillsboro Area Historical Society,
Hillsboro, WI......................................1600
Hillsboro Museums, Hillsboro, KS...............544
Hillwood Art Museum, Brookville, NY 971
Hinckley Fire Museum, Hinckley, MN.........778
Hinsdale Historical Society, Hinsdale, IL 440
Historic Bethabara Park, Winston-Salem,
NC...1125
Historic Bowens Mills & Pioneer Park,
Middleville, MI....................................754
Historic Carson House, Marion, NC...........1110
Historic Crab Orchard Museum &
Pioneer Park, Inc., Tazewell, VA 1541
Historic Deerfield, Inc., Deerfield, MA.......679
Historic Fort Snelling, Saint Paul, MN 790
Historic Hermann Museum, Hermann,
MO..817
Historic Landmarks Foundation of
Indiana, Indianapolis, IN........................482
Historic Latta Plantation, Huntersville,
NC...1107
Historic Palmyra's Print Shop, Palmyra,
NY...1050
Historic Palmyra's - Wm. Phelps General
Store, Palmyra, NY...............................1050
Historic Prophetstown, Battle Ground, IN ...468
Historic Schaefferstown, Inc.,
Schaefferstown, PA..............................1297
Historic Southwest Ohio, Inc.,
Sharonville, OH...................................1185
Historic Stagville, Durham, NC..................1098
Historic Westville, Inc., Lumpkin, GA.........376
Historical and Genealogical Society of
Somerset County, Somerset, PA 1300
The Historical Museum at St. Gertrude,
Cottonwood, ID...................................405
Historical Museum of Southern Florida,
Miami, FL...324
Historical Society of Rockland County,
New City, NY......................................1017
Historical Society of Saratoga Springs,
Saratoga Springs, NY............................1064
Historical Society of Stanton County
Museums at Stanton and Pilger, Pilger,
NE 872
Historical Society of the Town of
Clarence, Clarence, NY.........................978
The History Center, Fort Wayne, IN 477
The History Place, Morehead City, NC......1111
Hoard Historical Museum and National
Dairy Shrine's Visitors Center, Fort
Atkinson, WI......................................1598
Holmes County Historical Society,
Millersburg, OH..................................1176
Homestead National Monument of
America, Beatrice, NE 857
Hoopa Valley Tribal Museum, Hoopa,
CA...103
Hornby Museum, Hornby, NY....................999

Hot Spring County Museum - The Boyle
House/1876 Log Cabin, Malvern, AR.......63
House of Wickersham State Historical
Site, Juneau, AK 25
Huddleston Farmhouse Inn Museum,
Cambridge City, IN...............................471
Hudson Museum, The University of
Maine, Orono, ME 617
Humpback Rocks Mountain Farm &
Visitor Center, Waynesboro, VA 1544
The 100th Meridian Museum, Cozad, NE ...859
Hungarian Folk-Art Museum, Port
Orange, FL...338
Huntington Beach International Surfing
Museum, Huntington Beach, CA.............104
Hutchinson Art Center, Hutchinson, KS......545

Ilwaco Heritage Museum, Ilwaco, WA.......1556
IMA - Indianapolis Museum of Art,
Indianapolis, IN....................................483
Immaculate Conception Catholic Church,
Natchitoches, LA..................................593
Immigration Museum of New Americans
Post WWII, San Diego, CA....................156
Imperial Calcasieu Museum, Inc., Lake
Charles, LA..590
Indian City U.S.A., Anadarko, OK.............1195
Indian King Tavern Museum,
Haddonfield, NJ...................................906
Indian Springs State Park Museum,
Flovilla, GA...372
International Bluegrass Music Museum,
Owensboro, KY....................................581
International Bowling Museum and Hall
of Fame, Saint Louis, MO 833
International Institute of Metropolitan
Detroit, Detroit, MI..............................737
International Museum of Cultures, Dallas,
TX...1406
Iosco County Historical Museum, East
Tawas, MI...740
Irish American Heritage Museum,
Albany, NY..954
Iron Mission State Park & Museum,
Cedar City, UT....................................1464
Ironworld Discovery Center, Chisholm,
MN..771
Iroquois Indian Museum, Howes Cave,
NY...999
Isanti County Historical Society,
Cambridge, MN...................................770
Isla Center For the Arts at the University
of Guam, Mangilao, GU 1640
Italian American Museum, New York,
NY...1028

J.W. Parmley Historical Home Society,
Ipswich, SD 1349
Jackson County Historical Museum,
Lakefield, MN.....................................778
Jackson Hole Historical Society and
Museum, Jackson, WY..........................1634
Jacob Hamblin Home, Santa Clara, UT 1474
Jacques Marchais Museum of Tibetan
Art, Staten Island, NY...........................1072
Jail Museum, Neligh, NE...........................869
James W. Dillon House Museum, Dillon,
SC..1331
Japan Society Gallery, New York, NY 1028
Japanese Cultural Center of Hawaii,
Honolulu, HI..397
Jarrell Plantation Georgia State Historic
Site, Juliette, GA 374
Jean P. Haydon Museum, Pago Pago, AS ..1640
Jefferson County Historical Society
Museum, Port Townsend, WA 1562
Jefferson Patterson Park & Museum,
Saint Leonard, MD...............................651
The Jewish Museum, New York, NY.........1029
Jewish Museum of Florida, Miami
Beach, FL..326
Jewish Museum of Maryland, Baltimore,
MD..633

Folk Culture–Continued

Jimmie Rodgers Museum, Meridian, MS.....805
Joachim Regional Museum, Dickinson,
    ND...1130
John E. Conner Museum, Kingsville, TX ..1432
John G. Neihardt State Historic Site,
    Bancroft, NE..856
John Hutchings Museum of Natural
    History, Lehi, UT 1466
John Rivers Communications Museum,
    Charleston, SC...1325
Johnson County Historical Society, Inc.,
    Tecumseh, NE...873
Johnson Ferry House Museum, Titusville,
    NJ...926
Johnson Hall State Historic Site,
    Johnstown, NY..1005
Judah L. Magnes Museum, Berkeley, CA......76
Judaica Museum of Central Synagogue,
    New York, NY..1029
Julia A. Purnell Museum, Snow Hill, MD...654
Junction City Historical Society, Junction
    City, OR..1226

The Kate Chopin House & Bayou Folk
    Museum, Cloutierville, LA.........................588
Kauai Museum, Lihue, HI...........................401
Kauffman Museum, North Newton, KS.......553
Kearney County Historical Museum,
    Minden, NE...868
Kearney Mansion Museum, Fresno, CA 97
Kemerer Museum of Decorative Arts,
    Bethlehem, PA...1242
Kenosha Public Museum, Kenosha, WI.....1602
The Kentucky Folk Art Center,
    Morehead, KY...580
Kentucky Historical Society, Frankfort,
    KY...569
The Kentucky Library & Museum,
    Bowling Green, KY.....................................565
Ker Place, Onancock, VA...........................1523
King Saddlery Museum, Sheridan, WY.....1638
Kitt Peak National Observatory, Tucson,
    AZ...49
Klyne Esopus Museum, Ulster Park, NY...1079
Knight Museum, Alliance, NE.....................855
Knoxville Public Library, Knoxville, PA...1265
Koshare Indian Museum, Inc., La Junta,
    CO...224
The Kurdish Museum, Brooklyn, NY..........969

La Raza/Galeria Posada, Sacramento, CA ...153
LaBelle Heritage Museum, LaBelle, FL......319
The Lace Museum, Sunnyvale, CA..............190
Lacey Historical Society, Forked River,
    NJ...904
The Lackawanna Historical Society at the
    Catlin House, Scranton, PA.......................1298
Lafayette Natural History Museum and
    Planetarium, Lafayette, LA.........................589
Lake City Columbia County Historical
    Museum, Inc., Lake City, FL.......................319
Lake County Discovery Museum,
    Wauconda, IL...463
Lake County Historical Museum,
    Tavares, FL...351
Lake George Historical Association
    Museum, Lake George, NY........................1008
Lake Waccamaw Depot Museum, Lake
    Waccamaw, NC...1109
Lamar Dodd Art Center, LaGrange
    College, LaGrange, GA................................375
Land of the Yankee Fork Historic
    Association Museum, Stanley, ID................410
Landis Valley Museum, Lancaster, PA.......1266
Langlade County Historical Society
    Museum, Antigo, WI..................................1589
Laramie Plains Museum, Laramie, WY.....1635
Lars Noak Blacksmith Shop,
    Larsson/Ostlund Log Home &
    One-Room Capitol School, New
    Sweden, ME..616

Latvian Museum, Rockville, MD................651
Laura Ingalls Wilder Museum and Tourist
    Center, Walnut Grove, MN.........................795
Laura Ingalls Wilder Park & Museum,
    Inc., Burr Oak, IA.......................................507
Lawrence County Historical and
    Genealogical Society, Bedford, IN.............469
Lawrence Heritage State Park, Lawrence,
    MA..689
The Leffingwell House Museum,
    Norwich, CT...258
Lesbian Herstory Educational Foundation,
    Inc. aka Lesbian Herstory Archives,
    Brooklyn, NY..969
Leverett Historical Society, Leverett, MA....689
Lexington County Museum, Lexington,
    SC..1336
Library of Congress, Washington, DC.........282
Library of the Supreme Council, 33
    Degrees, Washington, DC............................282
Lillian and Albert Small Jewish Museum,
    Washington, DC...282
Lincoln Boyhood National Memorial,
    Lincoln City, IN..488
Lincoln County Museum, Hugo, CO............222
Lincoln Park Historical Museum, Lincoln
    Park, MI..751
The Lincoln-Tallman Restorations,
    Janesville, WI..1601
The Little Brick House, Vandalia, IL...........462
Locust Creek Covered Bridge State
    Historic Site, Laclede, MO.........................825
Lois E. Woods Museum, Norfolk, VA.........1522
Longfellow Evangeline State Historic
    Site, Saint Martinville, LA..........................600
Longfellow's Wayside Inn, Sudbury, MA ...714
Longhorn Museum, Pleasanton, TX...........1444
Los Angeles County Museum of Art, Los
    Angeles, CA..118
Loudoun Museum, Inc., Leesburg, VA.......1512
The Louisiana Cotton Museum, Lake
    Providence, LA...590
Loveland Museum Gallery, Loveland, CO...227
Lovely Lane Museum, Baltimore, MD.........634
Lowell Area Historical Museum, Lowell,
    MI...751
Lowell's Boat Shop, Amesbury, MA............658
Loxahatchee River Historical Society,
    Jupiter, FL..316
Lubeznik Center for the Arts, Michigan
    City, IN..490
Luckhard Museum - The Indian Mission,
    Sebewaing, MI..764
Luis Munoz Rivera Library & Museum,
    Barranquitas, PR.......................................1641
Lum & Abner Museum & Jot 'Em Down
    Store, Pine Ridge, AR...................................66
Lutheran Heritage Center & Museum of
    the Perry County Lutheran Historical
    Society, Altenburg, MO...............................810
Lutz Children's Museum, Manchester, CT...248
Lyman Museum, Hilo, HI.............................393
Lyon County Historical Society and
    Museum, Emporia, KS.................................538

Madeline Island Historical Museum, La
    Pointe, WI...1603
Madison County Historical
    Society-Cottage Lawn, Oneida, NY.........1045
Madison Museum of Fine Art, Madison,
    GA..378
Manatee Village Historical Park,
    Bradenton, FL..297
Maramec Museum, The James
    Foundation, Saint James, MO.....................830
Marias Museum of History and Art,
    Shelby, MT...853
Marin Museum of the American Indian,
    Novato, CA...131
Marinette County Historical Museum,
    Marinette, WI..1607
Marion County Historical Society, Salem,
    OR...1236

Mariposa Museum & World Culture
    Center, Peterborough, NH..........................893
Marlboro Historical Society, Marlboro,
    VT...1481
Marshall County Historical Society
    Museum, Warren, MN.................................795
Martin County Historical Museum,
    Stanton, TX...1453
Mary Ball Washington Museum &
    Library, Inc., Lancaster, VA.....................1512
The Mary Brogan Museum of Art and
    Science, Tallahassee, FL.............................347
Maryland Historical Society, Baltimore,
    MD..634
Matagorda County Museum, Bay City,
    TX...1393
Matchless Mine Museum (Leadville
    Assembly), Leadville, CO............................226
Mathias Ham House Historic Site,
    Dubuque, IA..516
Maxwell Museum of Anthropology,
    Albuquerque, NM.......................................934
Mc Cook County Historical Society and
    Museum, Salem, SD...................................1355
McConnell Mansion, Moscow, ID...............407
McDowell House Museum, Danville, KY ...567
McIntosh County Historical Society,
    Ashley, ND..1127
McMinn County Living Heritage
    Museum, Athens, TN.................................1360
McPherson County Old Mill Museum
    and Park, Lindsborg, KS.............................550
Memoryville USA, Inc., Rolla, MO.............829
Mendocino County Museum, Willits, CA....198
Mennello Museum of American Art,
    Orlando, FL..331
Mennonite Heritage Center, Harleysville,
    PA...1258
Menominee County Heritage Museum,
    Menominee, MI...754
Mercer Museum of the Bucks County
    Historical Society, Doylestown, PA.......1250
Meridian Museum of Art, Meridian, MS....805
Meriwether Lewis Dredge Museum,
    Brownville, NE..858
Merritt Museum of Anthropology,
    Oakland, CA...133
Metamora Courthouse Historic Site,
    Metamora, IL...444
Mexic-Arte Museum, Austin, TX..............1391
Mexican Fine Arts Center Museum,
    Chicago, IL...424
Michie Tavern ca. 1784, Charlottesville,
    VA...1499
The Michigan State University Museum,
    East Lansing, MI...740
Mid-America All Indian Center, Wichita,
    KS...562
Mid-Hudson Children's Museum,
    Poughkeepsie, NY.....................................1055
Middlebury Historical Society, Wyoming,
    NY...1087
Middleton Historical Society - Lura
    Woodside Watkins Museum,
    Middleton, MA..694
Middletown Valley Historical Society,
    Middletown, MD..649
Milam County Museum and Annex,
    Cameron, TX...1399
Miles B. Carpenter Museum, Waverly,
    VA...1543
Millicent Rogers Museum of Northern
    New Mexico, Taos, NM...............................952
Mingei International Museum, San
    Diego, CA...157
Minnesota Historical Society, Saint Paul,
    MN..791
Mission Cultural Center for Latino Arts,
    San Francisco, CA.......................................166
Mission Houses Museum, Honolulu, HI......397
Mission Inn Foundation/Museum,
    Riverside, CA...149

Mission Mill Museum Association, Salem, OR..1236
Mission San Juan Capistrano Museum, San Juan Capistrano, CA 173
Mission San Miguel, San Miguel, CA 175
Mississippi Agriculture & Forestry/National Agricultural Aviation Museum, Jackson, MS 802
Mississippi Crafts Center, Ridgeland, MS ...807
Mizel Museum, Denver, CO 213
Mohonk Preserve, Inc., Gardiner, NY 993
Mondak Heritage Center, Sidney, MT..........853
Monroe County Heritage Museum, Monroeville, AL 15
Monroe County Local History Room & Library, Sparta, WI..................................1622
Montgomery Museum & Lewis Miller Regional Art Center, Christiansburg, VA..1501
Montrose County Historical Museum, Montrose, CO 228
Moravian Historical Society, Nazareth, PA..1273
Moravian Museum of Bethlehem, Inc., Bethlehem, PA 1242
Morgan Row Museum and Harrodsburg-Mercer County Research Library, Harrodsburg, KY 570
The Morikami Museum and Japanese Gardens, Delray Beach, FL......................305
Morris-Butler House Museum, Indianapolis, IN 485
Motown Historical Museum, Detroit, MI.....737
Mountain Farm Museum-Great Smoky Mountains National Park, Cherokee, NC..1096
Mountain Gateway Museum, Old Fort, NC..1113
Mountain Heritage Center, Cullowhee, NC..1097
Mountain Life Museum, London, KY..........575
Muckenthaler Cultural Center and Mansion Museum, Fullerton, CA 99
Mulford Farm, East Hampton, NY 986
Museo de las Americas, Denver, CO 213
Museo de Las Americas, San Juan, PR......1642
Museo Fuerte Conde de Mirasol de Vieques, Vieques, PR 1644
Museum at Southwestern Michigan College, Dowagiac, MI 738
The Museum of African Culture, Portland, ME..619
Museum of Afro-American History, Boston, MA 667
Museum of Ancient Artifacts, Las Vegas, NV..879
Museum of Anthropology, Highland Heights, KY...571
Museum of Anthropology, University of Denver, Denver, CO 213
Museum of Appalachia, Clinton, TN..........1363
Museum of Art & History at Weston, Weston, CT...266
The Museum of Arts and Sciences, Inc. and Center for Florida History, Daytona Beach, FL...................................303
Museum of Carousel Art & History, Sandusky, OH 1185
Museum of Chinese in the Americas, New York, NY...1032
Museum of Craft and Folk Art, San Francisco, CA...167
Museum of Florida History, Tallahassee, FL..348
Museum of Funeral Customs, Springfield, IL..459
Museum of History, Anthropology and Art, San Juan, PR....................................1643
Museum of Indian Culture, Allentown, PA..1239
Museum of International Folk Art, Santa Fe, NM..948
Museum of New Mexico, Santa Fe, NM 949

Museum of Peoples and Cultures, Provo, UT..1470
Museum of Primitive Art and Culture, Peace Dale, RI...1316
Museum of Science & History of Jacksonville, Jacksonville, FL.................315
Museum of Seminole County History, Sanford, FL...343
Museum of South Texas History, Edinburg, TX...1410
Museum of the Albemarle, Elizabeth City, NC...1099
The Museum of the Alphabet, Waxhaw, NC..1121
Museum of the American Quilter's Society (MAQS), Paducah, KY 581
Museum of the Berkeley Springs, Berkeley Springs, WV.........................1580
Museum of the Cape Fear Historical Complex, Fayetteville, NC....................1101
Museum of the Cherokee Strip, Enid, OK.1200
Museum of the Hudson Highlands, Cornwall-on-Hudson, NY 982
Museum of the Islands, Pine Island Center, FL..337
Museum of the Plains Indian, Browning, MT..843
Museum of the Puerto Rican Family of the 19th Century, San Juan, PR.............1643
Museum of the Waxhaws & Andrew Jackson Memorial, Waxhaw, NC...........1122
The Museum of Western Art, Kerrville, TX..1431
Musselshell Valley Historical Museum, Roundup, MT..853

Nantucket Lightship Basket Museum, Nantucket, MA 696
Nathaniel W. Faison Home and Museum, La Grange, TX...1432
National Art Museum of Sport, Inc., Indianapolis, IN 485
National Christmas Center, Paradise, PA ...1275
National Czech & Slovak Museum & Library, Cedar Rapids, IA.......................509
National Geographic Museum at Explorers Hall, Washington, DC..............285
The National Great Blacks in Wax Museum, Inc., Baltimore, MD.................635
National Historic Oregon Trail Interpretive Center, Baker City, OR 1219
The National Soccer Hall of Fame, Oneonta, NY...1046
National Steinbeck Center, Salinas, CA 154
Native American Heritage Museum at Highland Mission State Historic Site, Highland, KS 544
Nauvoo Historical Society Museum, Nauvoo, IL..447
Nebraska State Historical Society's Museum of Nebraska History, Lincoln, NE..866
Nevada State Museum, Las Vegas, Las Vegas, NV...880
New Bedford Whaling Museum, New Bedford, MA...696
The New Berlin Historical Society, New Berlin, WI...1614
New Braunfels Conservation Society, New Braunfels, TX 1440
The New England Carousel Museum, Bristol, CT...236
New England Maple Museum, Pittsford, VT..1484
New London Public Museum, New London, WI...1615
New Mexico Farm & Ranch Heritage Museum, Las Cruces, NM.....................940
New Orleans Museum of Art, New Orleans, LA 597
New Orleans Pharmacy Museum, New Orleans, LA 597

New Sweden Historical Society, New Sweden, ME..616
The New York Public Library for the Performing Arts, New York, NY 1036
New York State Historical Association/Fenimore Art Museum, Cooperstown, NY.....................................981
Newaygo County Museum, Newaygo, MI...758
Nici Self Museum, Centennial, WY...........1630
Nixon Presidential Materials Staff, College Park, MD......................................641
Nordic Heritage Museum, Seattle, WA 1567
North Carolina Museum of Forestry, Whiteville, NC...1122
North Carolina Museum of History, Raleigh, NC...1115
North Carolina Pottery Center, Seagrove, NC..1119
North Castle Historical Society, Armonk, NY..958
North Tonawanda History Museum, North Tonawanda, NY 1043
Northeast Georgia History Center at Brenau University, Gainesville, GA 373
Northeast Louisiana Delta African American Heritage Museum, Monroe, LA..592
Northeast Texas Rural Heritage Museum, Pittsburg, TX...1443
Northeastern Nevada Museum, Elko, NV 876
Northern Indiana Center for History, South Bend, IN...499
Northfield Historical Society Museum, Northfield, MN...785
Norwood Historical Association and Museum, Norwood, NY.........................1044
Nowata County Historical Society Museum, Nowata, OK..................................1207
The Noyes Museum of Art, Oceanville, NJ..918

O. Henry Museum, Austin, TX..................1391
The Oaks House Museum, Jackson, MS......804
Oatland Island Education Center, Savannah, GA...385
Ocean City Life-Saving Station Museum, Ocean City, MD......................................650
Ogden Union Station Museums, Ogden, UT..1468
Ohr-O'Keefe Museum of Art, Biloxi, MS ...799
Oklahoma Historical Society, Oklahoma City, OK...1209
Old Bethpage Village Restoration, Old Bethpage, NY...1045
Old Castle Museum, Baldwin City, KS........533
The Old Courthouse Heritage Museum, Inverness, FL...313
Old Economy Village, Ambridge, PA.........1240
Old Fort Bissell, Phillipsburg, KS...............555
Old Fort House Museum, Fort Edward, NY..991
The Old Hoxie House, Sandwich, MA 708
The Old Jail Museum, Crawfordsville, IN...473
The Old Jail Museum, Warrenton, VA 1543
Old Lighthouse Museum, Stonington, CT....261
Old Mill Museum, Cimarron, NM...............938
Old St. Ferdinand's Shrine, Florissant, MO..815
Old State House, Hartford, CT 245
Old State House Museum, Little Rock, AR..63
The Old Tavern Museum, Tuscaloosa, AL.....19
Old Town Museum, Old Town, ME.............617
Old World Wisconsin, Eagle, WI...............1595
Old York Historical Society, York, ME........626
The Oliver Tucker Museum, Beverly, OH .1142
Omniplex Science Museum, Oklahoma City, OK...1210
Oneida County Historical Society, Utica, NY..1080
Opelousas Museum and Interpretive Center, Opelousas, LA 599

Folk Culture–Continued

Orange County Historical Museum, Hillsborough, NC......1107

Orcas Island Historical Museum, Orcas Island, WA......1560

Oregon-Jerusalem Historical Museum, Oregon, OH......1181

Oregon Trail Regional Museum, Baker City, OR......1219

Orleans County Historical Society & The Old Stone House Museum, Brownington, VT......1477

Oroville Chinese Temple, Oroville, CA......136

Oscar Getz Museum of Whiskey History And The Bardstown Historical Museum, Bardstown, KY......565

Overland Trail Museum, Sterling, CO......232

Overstreet-Kerr Historical Farm, Keota, OK......1203

The Ozark Folk Center, Mountain View, AR......65

Ozark National Scenic Riverways, Van Buren, MO......839

Pacific Asia Museum, Pasadena, CA......140

Palm Beach Zoo at Dreher Park, West Palm Beach, FL......353

Paper Airplane Museum and the Tin Can Man of Maui, Kahului Central Maui, HI......399

Paris-Henry County Heritage Center, Paris, TN......1382

Parishville Museum, Parishville, NY......1050

Parks, Recreation & Historic Sites Division, Georgia Dept. of Natural Resources, Atlanta, GA......362

Pasadena Museum of History, Pasadena, CA......140

Patten Lumbermen's Museum, Inc., Patten, ME......618

Paul H. Karshner Memorial Museum, Puyallup, WA......1564

Pawnee Indian Village State Historic Site, Republic, KS......556

Paynes Creek Historic State Park, Bowling Green, FL......297

Peabody Museum of Archaeology & Ethnology, Cambridge, MA......674

The Pearl S. Buck House, Perkasie, PA......1275

The Pearson Museum, Springfield, IL......460

Peel Mansion Museum & Historic Gardens, Bentonville, AR......55

The Peggy Notebaert Nature Museum, Chicago, IL......426

Pendarvis State Historic Site, Mineral Point, WI......1614

Pennsylvania German Cultural Heritage Center at Kutztown University, Kutztown, PA......1265

Pennyroyal Area Museum, Hopkinsville, KY......572

Penobscot Marine Museum, Searsport, ME......622

Peter Conser House, Heavener, OK......1202

Peter Wentz Farmstead, Worcester, PA......1308

Peter Yegen Jr. Yellowstone County Museum, Billings, MT......841

Petterson Museum of Intercultural Art, Claremont, CA......85

Philadelphia Mummers Museum, Philadelphia, PA......1285

Philip and Muriel Berman Museum of Art at Ursinus College, Collegeville, PA......1247

The Phillips Museum of Art, Franklin & Marshall College, Lancaster, PA......1267

Phoebe Apperson Hearst Museum of Anthropology, Berkeley, CA......77

Pickens County Museum of Art & History, Pickens, SC......1340

Pioneer Corner Museum, New Holstein, WI......1615

Pioneer Heritage Center, LSU-Shreveport, Shreveport, LA......601

The Pioneer Memorial Association of Fenton and Mundy Townships, Fenton, MI......741

Pioneer Museum, Watford City, ND......1137

Pioneer Museum, Wild Rose, WI......1628

Pioneer Museum & The Big Stampede, Fairbanks, AK......24

Pioneer Museum - Martin County Historical Society, Fairmont, MN......775

Pioneer Settlement for the Creative Arts, Barberville, FL......295

Pioneer Village, Farmington, UT......1465

Pioneer Village & Virgil Grissom Memorial at Spring Mill State Park, Mitchell, IN......491

Pioneers, Trail Drivers and Texas Rangers Memorial Museum, San Antonio, TX......1449

Placer County Museums, Auburn, CA......72

Plains Indians and Pioneers Museum, Woodward, OK......1217

Plainsman Museum, Aurora, NE......856

Plantation Historical Museum, Plantation, FL......337

Plaza de La Raza, Inc. & Boathouse Gallery, Los Angeles, CA......121

Plimoth Plantation Inc., Plymouth, MA......703

Pointe Coupee Museum, New Roads, LA......599

Polish American Museum; Port Washington, NY......1054

Polish Heritage Center, Ashton, NE......856

Polish Museum of America, Chicago, IL......426

Polk County Historical Museum, Bartow, FL......295

The Polk County Historical Society, Cedartown, GA......368

Ponce DeLeon Inlet Lighthouse Preservation Association, Inc., Ponce Inlet, FL......337

Pope County Historical Society, Glenwood, MN......776

Popular Arts Museum, San Juan, PR......1643

Portage County Historical Society, Ravenna, OH......1183

Porter Thermometer Museum, Onset, MA......700

Portland Children's Museum, Portland, OR......1233

Portland Museum, Louisville, KY......578

Postville Courthouse State Historic Site, Lincoln, IL......442

Potter County Historical Society, Coudersport, PA......1248

Powell County Museum, Deer Lodge, MT......845

Prairie Village, Madison, SD......1351

Praters Mill Foundation, Varnell, GA......390

Pratt County Historical Society Museum, Pratt, KS......556

President James K. Polk State Historic Site, Pineville, NC......1114

Putnam Cottage, Greenwich, CT......243

Putney Historical Society, Putney, VT......1485

The Quincy Museum, Quincy, IL......452

The Ralph Foster Museum, Point Lookout, MO......828

Ramsey House Museum Plantation, Knoxville, TN......1371

Rangeley Lakes Region Logging Museum, Rangeley, ME......620

Ravalli County Museum/Bitter Root Valley Historical Society, Hamilton, MT......848

Reading Historical Society Museum, Reading, OH......1184

Reading Public Museum, Reading, PA......1296

Rebel State Historic Site & Louisiana Country Music Museum, Marthaville, LA......592

Red Butte Garden & Arboretum, Salt Lake City, UT......1472

Reese Bullen Gallery, Arcata, CA......72

Refugio County Museum, Refugio, TX......1445

Reginald F. Lewis Museum of Maryland African American History and Culture, Baltimore, MD......636

Remick Country Doctor Museum and Farm, Tamworth, NH......896

Reno County Museum, Hutchinson, KS......545

Republic County Historical Society Museum, Belleville, KS......534

Reuel B. Pritchett Museum, Bridgewater, VA......1497

Rhode Island Black Heritage Society, Providence, RI......1318

Rice County Museum of History, Faribault, MN......775

Richland County Museum, Lexington, OH......1172

Riddick's Folly, Suffolk, VA......1539

Rikard's Mill Historical Park, Beatrice, AL......3

Rim Country Museum, Payson, AZ......38

Rio Grande Valley Museum, Harlingen, TX......1423

Ripley's Believe It or Not!, Key West, FL......319

River Heritage Museum, Paducah, KY......582

Roaring Twenties Antique Car Museum, Hood, VA......1511

Roberson Museum and Science Center, Binghamton, NY......962

Rocky Mount Museum, Piney Flats, TN......1383

Rocky Mountain Quilt Museum, Golden, CO......220

Romanian Ethnic Art Museum, Cleveland, OH......1156

Rome Area History Museum, Rome, GA......382

Ronald Reagan Boyhood Home, Dixon, IL......431

Rosalie Whyel Museum of Doll Art, Bellevue, WA......1548

Rose Center Museum, Morristown, TN......1376

Rosemount Museum, Pueblo, CO......230

Roswell Museum and Art Center, Roswell, NM......946

Rowley Historical Society, Rowley, MA......706

Royal Gorge Regional Museum & History Center, Canon City, CO......205

Rural Life Museum & Windrush Gardens, Baton Rouge, LA......587

S.C.R.A.P. Gallery, Indio, CA......104

Saco Museum, Saco, ME......621

Saguache County Museum, Saguache, CO......231

St. Augustine Lighthouse & Museum, Inc., Saint Augustine, FL......340

St. Charles Heritage Center, Saint Charles, IL......457

St. Petersburg Museum of History, Saint Petersburg, FL......342

St. Photios Greek Orthodox National Shrine, Saint Augustine, FL......340

St. Simons Island Lighthouse Museum, Saint Simons Island, GA......383

Ste. Genevieve Museum, Sainte Genevieve, MO......838

Salem Historical Society and Museum, Salem, OH......1184

The Salgo Trust for Education, Port Washington, NY......1054

The Salvation Army Southern Historical Center & Museum, Atlanta, GA......363

San Antonio Missions National Historical Park, San Antonio, TX......1449

San Antonio Museum of Art, San Antonio, TX......1450

San Diego Archaeological Center, Escondido, CA......93

San Diego Model Railroad Museum, Inc., San Diego, CA......159

San Diego Museum of Man, San Diego, CA.................160

San Dieguito Heritage Museum, Encinitas, CA.................92

San Fernando Valley Historical Society, Inc., Mission Hills, CA.................126

San Francisco Maritime National Historical Park, San Francisco, CA.................169

San Juan County Archaeological Research Center and Library at the Salmon Ruin/San Juan County Museum Association, Bloomfield, NM...937

San Juan County Historical Society Museum, Silverton, CO.................232

Sanborn Area Historical Society, Sanborn, NY.................1064

Sand Springs Cultural & Historical Museum, Sand Springs, OK.................1213

Sandown Historical Society and Museum, Sandown, NH.................896

Sandwich Historical Society, Center Sandwich, NH.................884

Sandy Spring Museum, Sandy Spring, MD.................653

Sapulpa Historical Museum, Sapulpa, OK.1213

Schifferstadt Architectural Museum, Frederick, MD.................644

Schingoethe Center for Native American Cultures, Aurora, IL.................412

Schoenbrunn Village State Memorial, New Philadelphia, OH.................1177

Schoharie Colonial Heritage Association, Schoharie, NY.................1067

The Schomburg Center for Research in Black Culture, New York, NY.................1038

School of American Research, Indian Arts Research Center, Santa Fe, NM......950

School of Nations Museum, Elsah, IL.........433

The Schuette Biermann Farmhouse Museum, Elk Grove Village, IL.................432

The Schuylkill Center for Environmental Education, Philadelphia, PA.................1288

The Science Museum of Minnesota, Saint Paul, MN.................792

1719 Hans Herr House & Museum, Willow Street, PA.................1308

Seward County Historical Society Museum, Goehner, NE.................861

Shaker Heritage Society, Albany, NY.........956

Shaker Museum at South Union, South Union, KY.................583

Shaker Village of Pleasant Hill, Harrodsburg, KY.................571

Shako:wi Cultural Center, Oneida, NY......1046

Sharpsteen Museum, Calistoga, CA.................80

Sheldon Jackson Museum, Sitka, AK.............27

Shelter House Society, Emmaus, PA.........1251

Sheppard Fine Arts Gallery, Reno, NV........881

Shiloh Museum of Ozark History, Springdale, AR.................68

Shoshone Tribal Cultural Center, Fort Washakie, WY.................1633

Siegfried H. Horn Archaeological Museum, Berrien Springs, MI.................729

Silt Historical Society, Silt, CO.................232

Silver Cliff Museum, Silver Cliff, CO.........232

Silver River Museum & Environmental Education Center, Ocala, FL.................330

The Skinner Museum of Mount Holyoke College, South Hadley, MA.................709

Skirball Cultural Center, Los Angeles, CA.................121

Skirball Museum Cincinnati Hebrew Union College-Jewish Institute of Religion, Cincinnati, OH.................1151

Slate Valley Museum, Granville, NY.........996

Slifer House, Lewisburg, PA.................1268

Smith Robertson Museum & Cultural Center, Jackson, MS.................804

Smith-Zimmermann Heritage Museum, Madison, SD.................1351

Smithsonian Institution, Washington, DC.....290

Smokey Bear Museum, Capitan, NM.........937

Smoki Museum - American Indian Art & Culture, Prescott, AZ.................43

Smyth County Museum, Marion, VA.........1516

Snake River Heritage Center, Weiser, ID....410

Sod House Museum, Aline, OK.................1195

SoDus Bay Historical Society, Sodus Point, NY.................1070

Somerset Historical Center, Somerset, PA .1300

Somerset Place State Historic Site, Creswell, NC.................1097

South Bannock County Historical Center, Lava Hot Springs, ID.................407

South Carolina Artisans Center, Walterboro, SC.................1343

The South Carolina Botanical Garden, Clemson, SC.................1328

South Carolina Department of Parks, Recreation and Tourism, Columbia, SC.................1330

South Charleston Museum, South Charleston, WV.................1586

South County Museum Inc., Narragansett, RI.................1313

South Dakota Hall of Fame, Chamberlain, SD.................1345

South Hero Bicentennial Museum, South Hero, VT.................1487

South Park City Museum, Fairplay, CO.......215

South Texas Museum, Alice, TX.................1386

Southdown Plantation House/The Terrebonne Museum, Houma, LA.................589

Southeast Missouri Regional Museum, Cape Girardeau, MO.................812

Southern Arts Federation, Atlanta, GA.........363

Southern Highland Craft Guild at the Folk Art Center, Asheville, NC.................1090

Southern Museum of Flight, Birmingham, AL.................6

Southern Plains Indian Museum, Anadarko, OK.................1196

Southern Ute Cultural Center and Museum, Ignacio, CO.................223

Southwest Museum, Los Angeles, CA.........121

Spertus Museum, Chicago, IL.................427

SPJST Library Archives & Museum, Temple, TX.................1455

Springfield Museums - Springfield Science Museum, Springfield, MA.........711

Springs Museum, Springs, PA.................1301

Spurlock Museum, University of Illinois at Urbana-Champaign, Urbana, IL.................462

Stanly County Historic Preservation Commission and Museum, Albemarle, NC.................1088

Staten Island Children's Museum, Staten Island, NY.................1073

Statue of Liberty National Monument & Ellis Island Immigration Museum, New York, NY.................1039

Stearns Collection of Musical Instruments, Ann Arbor, MI.................725

Stearns History Museum, Saint Cloud, MN.................788

Steele County Historical Society, Hope, ND.................1133

Steilacoom Historical Museum Association, Steilacoom, WA.................1572

Stephen C. Foster State Park, Fargo, GA.....371

Stephen Foster Folk Culture Center State Park, White Springs, FL.................354

Stephens African-American Museum, Shreveport, LA.................602

Stephens County Historical Society and Museum, Duncan, OK.................1199

The Stephens Museum, Fayette, MO.........815

Stephenville Museum, Stephenville, TX.....1454

Stepping Stones Museum for Children, Norwalk, CT.................257

Sterling Historical Society and Little Red Schoolhouse Museum, Sterling, NY......1074

Stevens County Historical Society Museum, Morris, MN.................784

Stockholm Historical Society Museum, Stockholm, ME.................623

Stonewall Jackson Museum at Hupp's Hill, Strasburg, VA.................1539

Storrowton Village Museum, West Springfield, MA.................718

Stoughton Historical Society, Stoughton, MA.................713

Strasburg Museum, Strasburg, VA.................1539

Stuart House City Museum, Mackinac Island, MI.................752

Stutsman County Memorial Museum, Jamestown, ND.................1133

Sunnyside Historical Museum, Sunnyside, WA.................1572

SunWatch Indian Village/Archaeological Park, Dayton, OH.................1162

Susquehanna Museum of Havre de Grace Inc. at the Lock House, Havre de Grace, MD.................647

Sussex County Historical Society, Newton, NJ.................917

Sutter's Fort State Historic Park, Sacramento, CA.................153

Swedish American Museum Association of Chicago, Chicago, IL.................428

Switzerland County Historical Museum, Vevay, IN.................502

T.J. Elder Community Center, Sandersville, GA.................384

Tampa Bay History Center, Inc., Tampa, FL.................350

Tampa's Lowry Park Zoo, Tampa, FL.........350

Tannenbaum Historic Park, Greensboro, NC.................1104

Tante Blanche Museum, Madawaska, ME...614

Tarble Arts Center, Eastern Illinois University, Charleston, IL.................417

Tarpon Springs Cultural Center, Tarpon Springs, FL.................351

The Teddy Bear Museum of Naples, Naples, FL.................328

The Temple Judea Museum of Reform Congregation Keneseth Israel, Elkins Park, PA.................1251

The Temple Museum of Religious Art, Cleveland, OH.................1156

Tennessee Historical Society, Nashville, TN.................1380

Tennessee State Museum, Nashville, TN ...1381

Terrace Gallery-City of Orlando, Orlando, FL.................332

Texas Music Museum, Austin, TX.................1392

Texas Ranger Hall of Fame and Museum, Waco, TX.................1459

Texas State Museum of Asian Cultures & Educational Center, Corpus Christi, TX.................1402

This Is The Place Heritage Park, Salt Lake City, UT.................1472

Thousand Islands Museum, Clayton, NY....979

Tinkertown Museum, Sandia Park, NM.......947

Top of Oklahoma Historical Museum, Blackwell, OK.................1197

Trailside Nature Museum, Cross River, NY.................983

Tread of Pioneers Museum, Steamboat Springs, CO.................232

Triangle Tattoo & Museum, Fort Bragg, CA.................95

Troutdale Historical Society, Troutdale, OR.................1237

Troy Museum & Historic Village, Troy, MI.................765

Tsa Mo Ga Memorial Museum, Plains, TX.................1443

Tubac Presidio State Historic Park, Tubac, AZ.................47

Tuckerton Seaport, Tuckerton, NJ.................928

Folk Culture—Continued

Tumacacori National Historical Park, Tumacacori, AZ..............52

Tunica-Biloxi Native American Museum, Marksville, LA..............591

Turtle Mountain Chippewa Historical Society, Belcourt, ND..............1127

Twin Falls State Park & Museum, Mullens, WV..............1585

UCLA Fowler Museum of Cultural History, Los Angeles, CA..............122

UCR/California Museum of Photography, Riverside, CA..............150

USDA Forest Service - Land Between the Lakes, Golden Pond, KY..............570

Ukrainian-American Museum & Archives, Warren, MI..............766

The Ukrainian Museum, New York, NY....1040

Ukrainian Museum-Archives, Inc., Cleveland, OH..............1156

Ukrainian National Museum, Inc., Chicago, IL..............428

Ulster County Historical Society, Marbletown, NY..............1013

Uncle Remus Museum, Eatonton, GA..............371

Union County Heritage Museum, New Albany, MS..............806

Union County Historical Society, Lewisburg, PA..............1268

Union County Historical Society Museum, Blairsville, GA..............366

University Museum, Carbondale, IL..............415

The University Museum, Edwardsville, IL..............432

The University Museum, Indiana, PA..............1263

University Museum & Historic Houses, The University of Mississippi, Oxford, MS..............806

University Museum, New Mexico State University, Las Cruces, NM..............941

The University of Michigan Exhibit Museum of Natural History, Ann Arbor, MI..............725

University of Oregon Museum of Natural and Cultural History, Eugene, OR..............1224

The University of South Carolina McKissick Museum, Columbia, SC..............1331

UTSA's Institute of Texan Cultures, San Antonio, TX..............1451

Valley Art Center, Inc., Clarkston, WA..............1551

Valley Community Historical Society, Inc., Valley, NE..............874

Venango Museum of Art, Science & Industry, Oil City, PA..............1274

Vermont Folklife Center, Middlebury, VT..............1482

Vesterheim Norwegian-American Museum, Decorah, IA..............513

Victor Heritage Museum, Victor, MT..............854

Virgin Islands National Park, St. John, VI..............1644

Virginia Baptist Historical Society, Richmond, VA..............1532

Vista Historical Museum, Vista, CA..............196

W.H. Over Museum, Vermillion, SD..............1358

Waldensian Heritage Museum, Valdese, NC..............1121

The Walker African American Museum & Research Center, Las Vegas, NV..............880

The Ward Museum of Wildfowl Art, Salisbury University, Salisbury, MD..............653

Ward W. O'Hara Agricultural Museum, Auburn, NY..............959

Washington County Fair Farm Museum, Greenwich, NY..............996

Washington County Historical Association, Fort Calhoun, NE..............860

Washington County Rural Heritage Museum, Boonsboro, MD..............637

Washington Historical Museum, Washington, GA..............391

Waterford Historical Museum and Cultural Center, Inc., Waterford, NY..............1083

Waterloo Area Historical Society, Grass Lake, MI..............744

Waterloo Center for the Arts, Waterloo, IA..............529

Watermen's Museum, Yorktown, VA..............1547

Watts Towers Arts Center, Los Angeles, CA..............122

Wauconda Township Historical Society, Wauconda, IL..............463

Wayne County Historical Museum, Richmond, IN..............497

Wayne State University Museum of Anthropology, Detroit, MI..............738

Wells County Museum, Fessenden, ND..............1131

Wenham Museum, Wenham, MA..............717

Weslaco Museum, Weslaco, TX..............1461

West Baton Rouge Museum, Port Allen, LA..............599

West Pasco Historical Society Museum and Library, New Port Richey, FL..............329

Western Michigan University Richmond Center for Visual Arts School of Art, Kalamazoo, MI..............749

Western Mining & Railroad Museum, Helper, UT..............1466

The Whale Museum, Friday Harbor, WA..............1555

Wharton County Historical Museum, Wharton, TX..............1461

Wheat Ridge Historic Park, Wheat Ridge, CO..............235

The Wheelwright Museum of the American Indian, Santa Fe, NM..............950

Whitehead Memorial Museum, Del Rio, TX..............1409

Whitingham Historical Museum, Whitingham, VT..............1490

Wickliffe Mounds State Historic Site, Wickliffe, KY..............584

Wilber Czech Museum, Wilber, NE..............875

Wilbur D. May Museum, Reno, NV..............882

Wilkinson County Museum, Woodville, MS..............810

William Brewster Nickerson Memorial Room, Cape Cod Community College, West Barnstable, MA..............717

William Hammond Mathers Museum, Bloomington, IN..............470

William S. Hart County Park & Museum, Newhall, CA..............130

William Weston Clarke Emison Museum of Art, Greencastle, IN..............479

William Whitley House State Historic Site, Stanford, KY..............584

Williamson County Historical Society, Marion, IL..............444

Wilson County Historical Society Museum, Fredonia, KS..............540

Wilson Czech Opera House Corporation, Foundation, Inc. & House of Memories Museum, Wilson, KS..............564

Windham Textile and History Museum (The Mill Museum), Willimantic, CT..............267

Winedale, Center for American History, University of Texas at Austin, Round Top, TX..............1446

Woldumar Nature Center, Lansing, MI..............751

Woodbine International Fire Museum, Woodbine, GA..............392

Woodstock Museum of Shenandoah County, Inc., Woodstock, VA..............1546

World Kite Museum & Hall of Fame, Long Beach, WA..............1558

World Museum of Mining, Butte, MT..............843

World O' Tools Museum, Waverly, TN..............1385

Wormsloe State Historic Site, Savannah, GA..............387

Worthington Historical Society, Worthington, OH..............1192

Wrather West Kentucky Museum, Murray, KY..............580

Wray Museum, Wray, CO..............235

Wright County Historical Society, Buffalo, MN..............770

The Wyckoff Farmhouse Museum, Brooklyn, NY..............970

Wyoming Territorial Prison State Historic Site, Laramie, WY..............1636

The Yager Museum of Art & Culture, Oneonta, NY..............1046

Ybor City Museum State Park, Tampa, FL..............351

Yellow Medicine County Historical Society and Museum, Granite Falls, MN..............777

Yeshiva University Museum at the Center for Jewish History, New York, NY..............1041

York W. Bailey Museum at Penn Center, Saint Helena Island, SC..............1340

Yucaipa Valley Historical Society Museum, Yucaipa, CA..............201

Zippo/Case Visitors Center, Bradford, PA..1244

Physical Anthropology

Alabama Museum of Natural History, Tuscaloosa, AL..............19

Alaska Museum of Natural History, Anchorage, AK..............21

Alfred B. Maclay State Gardens, Tallahassee, FL..............346

Alutiiq Museum and Archaeological Repository, Kodiak, AK..............26

American Museum of Natural History, New York, NY..............1019

America's Stonehenge, North Salem, NH....893

Anasazi Heritage Center, Dolores, CO..............214

The Anthropology Museum, DeKalb, IL..............429

Anthropology Museum, University of San Diego, San Diego, CA..............155

Appomattox Court House National Historical Park, Appomattox, VA..............1495

Arizona State Museum, Tucson, AZ..............48

Arizona State University Museum of Anthropology, Tempe, AZ..............46

The Bead Museum, Glendale, AZ..............35

Belvedere-Tiburon Landmarks Society, Tiburon, CA..............192

Biscayne National Park, Homestead, FL..............313

Black American West Museum & Heritage Center, Denver, CO..............209

Buena Vista Museum of Natural History, Bakersfield, CA..............73

C.E. Smith Museum of Anthropology, Hayward, CA..............101

C.H. Nash Museum-Chucalissa Archaeological Museum, Memphis, TN..............1372

Call of the Wild Museum, Gaylord, MI..............742

Canyon de Chelly National Monument, Chinle, AZ..............31

Cape Cod Museum of Natural History, Inc., Brewster, MA..............670

Central Iowa Art Association, Marshalltown, IA..............523

The Central Museum, Central, AK..............23

Chief Plenty Coups Museum, Pryor, MT..............852

Children's Museum, Inc., Boca Raton, FL....296

Children's Museum of Southeastern Connecticut, Niantic, CT..............256

Clearfield County Historical Society, Clearfield, PA..............1247

The Cleveland Museum of Natural History, Cleveland, OH..............1153

Coastal Discovery Museum, Hilton Head Island, SC..............1335

The Colonial Spanish Quarter Museum, Saint Augustine, FL..............338

Columbia Gorge Interpretive Center Museum, Stevenson, WA..............1572

Community Historical Museum, Maxwell, IA..............523

Cranbrook Institute of Science, Bloomfield Hills, MI 730

Dakota Zoo, Bismarck, ND......................1128
Dana Adobe, Nipomo, CA 130
De Smet Depot Museum, De Smet, SD....1346
Denver Museum of Nature & Science, Denver, CO..211
The Discovery Center of the Southern Tier, Binghamton, NY 962
Discovery Science Center, Fort Collins, CO..216
Dr. Increase Mathews House, Zanesville, OH..1194
Dubois Museum, Dubois, WY..................1632
Duncan Cottage Museum, Metlakatla, AK.....27
Dunn County Historical Society, Menomonie, WI....................................1609

EdVenture, Inc., Columbia, SC...............1329
Effigy Mounds National Monument, Harpers Ferry, IA..............................519
Elgin Public Museum, Elgin, IL..................432

Favell Museum Inc., Klamath Falls, OR....1227
Florida Museum of Natural History, Gainesville, FL......................................310
Fort de Chartres State Historic Site & Museum, Prairie du Rocher, IL 451
Fort Matanzas National Monument, Saint Augustine, FL......................................339
Frank H. McClung Museum, Knoxville, TN..1370
Fresno Flats Historical Park, Oakhurst, CA..132
The Friends of the Caleb Pusey House, Inc., Upland, PA..................................1304

The Genealogical Society of Pennsylvania, Philadelphia, PA........1280
Gomez Foundation for Mill House, Marlboro, NY....................................1014
Graves Museum of Archaeology and Natural History, Dania Beach, FL 302
Great Sand Dunes National Monument and Preserve, Mosca, CO....................229
Groton Historical Society, Groton, MA........685
Gwinnett County Parks & Recreation Outdoor Interpretive Section, Lawrenceville, GA................................375

H. Earl Clack Museum, Havre, MT 849
Hamline University Galleries, Department of Studio Arts & Art History, Saint Paul, MN..790
Hampson Archeological Museum State Park, Wilson, AR..................................70
Handwerker Gallery, Ithaca, NY 1003
Hawaii's Plantation Village, Waipahu, HI....402
The Health Adventure, Asheville, NC........1090
HealthSpace Cleveland, Cleveland, OH 1154
Heard Natural Science Museum and Wildlife Sanctuary, Inc., McKinney, TX..1437
Heartland, The California Museum of the Heart, Rancho Mirage, CA 145
Heritage of the Americas Museum, El Cajon, CA..92
Hi-Desert Nature Museum, Yucca Valley, CA..201
Hibbing Historical Society and Museum, Hibbing, MN..778
Historic Fort Snelling, Saint Paul, MN........790
Historic St. Mary's City, Saint Mary's City, MD..652
The History Center, Fort Wayne, IN 477
House of Wickersham State Historical Site, Juneau, AK..................................25
Huntington Museum of Art, Inc., Huntington, WV 1583

Idaho Museum of Natural History, Pocatello, ID..408

International Museum of Surgical Science, Chicago, IL 422
Iowa Masonic Library and Museum, Cedar Rapids, IA..................................509
Italian American Museum, New York, NY..1028

Jefferson Patterson Park & Museum, Saint Leonard, MD..................................651

Kansas Learning Center for Health, Halstead, KS..542

Lake County Historical Museum, Tavares, FL..351
Lake Tahoe Historical Society & Museum, South Lake Tahoe, CA.............188
Laramie Plains Museum, Laramie, WY 1635
Libby Museum, Wolfeboro, NH 897
Logan Museum of Anthropology, Beloit, WI..1592
Louisiana Tech Museum, Ruston, LA.........600

MacCallum More Museum and Gardens, Chase City, VA 1500
Maxwell Museum of Anthropology, Albuquerque, NM..................................934
Mel Fisher Maritime Heritage Society, Key West, FL..318
Meriwether Lewis Dredge Museum, Brownville, NE..858
Merritt Museum of Anthropology, Oakland, CA..133
Miami Museum of Science & Planetarium, Miami, FL..........................325
Mission San Juan Capistrano Museum, San Juan Capistrano, CA 173
Museo de Las Americas, San Juan, PR....1642
Museo Fuerte Conde de Mirasol de Vieques, Vieques, PR............................1644
Museum of Anthropology, Highland Heights, KY..571
Museum of Anthropology, University of Denver, Denver, CO....................213
Museum of Earth and Life History, Lynchburg, VA..................................1515
Museum of Peoples and Cultures, Provo, UT..1470
Museum of Rim Country Archaeology, Payson, AZ..38
Museum of Seminole County History, Sanford, FL..343
The Museum of the Alphabet, Waxhaw, NC..1121
Museum of the City of New York, New York, NY..1033
Museum of the Great Plains, Lawton, OK.1204
Museum of the Islands, Pine Island Center, FL..337
Museum of World Treasures, Wichita, KS...562
Mutter Museum, College of Physicians of Philadelphia, Philadelphia, PA 1283

National Museum of Health and Medicine, Washington, DC 286
National Museum of Natural History, Washington, DC..286
Nevada State Museum, Carson City, NV 876
New Castle Historical Society - Horace Greeley House, Chappaqua, NY 977
North Carolina A&T State University Galleries, Greensboro, NC....................1104
North Lee County Historic Center and Santa Fe Depot Museum Complex, Fort Madison, IA..................................518
The North Museum of Natural History & Science, Lancaster, PA 1266

Ocracoke Island Visitor Center, Ocracoke, NC..1113
Ojai Valley Historical Society and Museum, Ojai, CA..................................135
Oklahoma Museum of History, Oklahoma City, OK..1210

Old Trail Museum, Choteau, MT 844
Oregon Museum of Science and Industry, Portland, OR..1231
Orpheum Children's Science Museum, Champaign, IL..417
Osage County Historical Society Museum, Pawhuska, OK......................1211

Pacific Science Center, Seattle, WA 1568
Pawnee Indian Village State Historic Site, Republic, KS..556
Peabody Museum of Archaeology & Ethnology, Cambridge, MA 674
Peabody Museum of Natural History, New Haven, CT..253
The Peggy Notebaert Nature Museum, Chicago, IL..426
Pember Museum of Natural History, Granville, NY..995
The Pena-Peck House, Saint Augustine, FL..339
Petrified Forest National Park, Petrified Forest National Park, AZ 38
Phoebe Apperson Hearst Museum of Anthropology, Berkeley, CA....................77
Pioneer Village, Farmington, UT..............1465
Plains Conservation Center, Aurora, CO......202
Pope County Historical Society, Glenwood, MN..776
Port Townsend Marine Science Center, Port Townsend, WA............................1562
Pueblo Grande Museum and Archaeological Park, Phoenix, AZ............42
Pueblo of Pojoaque, Poeh Museum, Santa Fe, NM..949

Reading Public Museum, Reading, PA.......1296
Red River Historical Society Museum, Clay City, KY..566
River Heritage Museum, Paducah, KY 582
Robert Crown Center for Health Education, Hinsdale, IL............................440
Robert S. Peabody Museum of Archaeology, Andover, MA....................660

St. Louis Science Center, Saint Louis, MO..836
San Diego Archaeological Center, Escondido, CA..93
San Diego Museum of Man, San Diego, CA..160
San Gabriel Mission Museum, San Gabriel, CA..171
San Jacinto Museum, San Jacinto, CA.........171
Sanchez Adobe Historic Site, Pacifica, CA..138
Sandown Historical Society and Museum, Sandown, NH..896
Santa Barbara Museum of Natural History, Santa Barbara, CA....................179
Saratoga Museum, Saratoga, WY..............1638
Saunders County Historical Complex, Wahoo, NE..874
The Science Museum of Minnesota, Saint Paul, MN..792
Sciworks, Winston-Salem, NC..................1126
Shorter Mansion Museum, Eufaula, AL...........8
South Carolina Aquarium, Charleston, SC.1326
South Carolina Institute of Archaeology & Anthropology, Columbia, SC................1330
Southern Ute Cultural Center and Museum, Ignacio, CO 223
Steuben Memorial State Historic Site, Remsen, NY..1056
Stewart M. Lord Memorial Historical Society, Inc., Burlington, ME 608
Stockholm Historical Society Museum, Stockholm, ME..623
Stoughton Historical Society, Stoughton, WI..1623
SunWatch Indian Village/Archaeological Park, Dayton, OH..................................1162

Physical Anthropology–Continued

Tampa Bay History Center, Inc., Tampa, FL 350

Tonto National Monument, Roosevelt, AZ 43

Triangle Tattoo & Museum, Fort Bragg, CA 95

Tunica-Biloxi Native American Museum, Marksville, LA 591

Turabo University, Gurabo, PR 1641

UCLA Fowler Museum of Cultural History, Los Angeles, CA 122

UCR/California Museum of Photography, Riverside, CA 150

The University Museum Collections, Fayetteville, AR 57

University of Iowa Museum of Natural History, Iowa City, IA 520

The University of Michigan Exhibit Museum of Natural History, Ann Arbor, MI 725

University of Michigan Museum of Anthropology, Ann Arbor, MI 725

University of Nebraska State Museum, Lincoln, NE 867

University of Oregon Museum of Natural and Cultural History, Eugene, OR 1224

University of Pennsylvania Museum of Archaeology and Anthropology, Philadelphia, PA 1288

University of Wyoming Anthropology Museum, Laramie, WY 1636

Utah State University's Museum of Anthropology, Logan, UT 1467

Virgin Islands National Park, St. John, VI 1644

Washakie Museum, Worland, WY 1639

Watson-Curtze Mansion, Erie, PA 1253

Wells County Museum, Fessenden, ND 1131

West Rock Nature Center, New Haven, CT 254

White County Historical Society, Carmi, IL 415

Whitingham Historical Museum, Whitingham, VT 1490

Wickliffe Mounds State Historic Site, Wickliffe, KY 584

Wildlife Museum at Petaluma High School, Petaluma, CA 142

Wildlife Prairie State Park, Hanna City, IL 439

William Hammond Mathers Museum, Bloomington, IN 470

William S. Webb Museum of Anthropology, Lexington, KY 575

Zion Human History Museum, Springdale, UT 1474

ART COLLECTIONS

Archaeological/Ethnographical

Abbe Museum, Bar Harbor, ME 605

Adams County Historical Society Museum, Brighton, CO 204

Adams National Historical Park, Quincy, MA 704

Adams National Historical Park-John Adams and John Quincy Adams Birthplaces, Quincy, MA 704

Adan E. Treganza Anthropology Museum, Dept. of Anthropology, San Francisco State University, San Francisco, CA 162

African Art Museum of the S.M.A. Fathers, Tenafly, NJ 926

Afro-American Cultural Center, Charlotte, NC 1094

Agate Fossil Beds National Monument, Harrison, NE 862

Agua Caliente Cultural Museum, Palm Springs, CA 138

Akwesasne Museum, Hogansburg, NY 998

Alabama Department of Archives & History, Montgomery, AL 15

Alabama Museum of Natural History, Tuscaloosa, AL 19

The Alamo, San Antonio, TX 1447

Alamo Township Museum-John E. Gray Memorial Museum, Kalamazoo, MI 748

Alaska State Museum, Juneau, AK 25

Albany Museum of Art, Albany, GA 355

Albion College Department of Art and Art History, Albion, MI 722

Alexander Brest Museum and Gallery, Jacksonville, FL 313

Alice C. Sabatini Gallery-Topeka and Shawnee County Public Library, Topeka, KS 558

Alutiiq Museum and Archaeological Repository, Kodiak, AK 26

American Folk Art Museum, New York, NY 1018

American Museum of Asmat Art, Saint Paul, MN 789

The American Numismatic Society, New York, NY 1020

American Quarter Horse Hall of Fame & Museum, Amarillo, TX 1386

America's Stonehenge, North Salem, NH 893

Amory Regional Museum, Amory, MS 797

Anacortes Museum, Anacortes, WA 1547

Anchorage Museum at Rasmuson Center, Anchorage, AK 22

Andrew J. Blackbird Museum, Harbor Springs, MI 745

Angel Mounds State Historic Site, Evansville, IN 475

Animas Museum, Durango, CO 214

Ann Arbor Art Center, Ann Arbor, MI 724

Antelope Valley Indian Museum, Lancaster, CA 108

Anza-Borrego Desert State Park, Borrego Springs, CA 79

Appleton Museum of Art, Ocala, FL 330

Archer County Museum, Archer City, TX 1387

Arizona State Museum, Tucson, AZ 48

Arkansas Historic Wine Museum, Paris, AR 65

Arnot Art Museum, Elmira, NY 987

Art and Culture Center of Hollywood, Hollywood, FL 312

The Art Gallery at the University of Maryland, College Park, College Park, MD 640

The Art Gallery, University of New Hampshire, Durham, NH 886

Art In Embassies Program, U.S. Department of State, Washington, DC 276

The Art Institute of Chicago, Chicago, IL 418

The Arthur J. Moore Methodist Museum, Saint Simons Island, GA 383

Arthur M. Sackler Gallery, Washington, DC 276

Arthur Ross Gallery, University of Pennsylvania, Philadelphia, PA 1276

Arts Consortium of Cincinnati's African American Museum, Cincinnati, OH 1148

Ash Lawn-Highland, Charlottesville, VA 1498

Asian Art Museum of San Francisco, Chong-Moon Lee Center for Asian Art and Culture, San Francisco, CA 163

The Association for Gravestone Studies, Greenfield, MA 685

Ataloa Lodge Museum, Muskogee, OK 1205

Atlanta College of Art, Atlanta, GA 358

The Avon Historical Society, Inc., Avon, CT 235

Aztec Museum and Pioneer Village, Aztec, NM 936

The Bade Institute of Biblical Archaeology and The Howell Bible Collection, Berkeley, CA 75

Bailey House Museum - Maui Historical Society, Wailuku, HI 402

Ball State University Museum of Art, Muncie, IN 492

Baltimore Civil War Museum, Baltimore, MD 629

The Baltimore Museum of Art, Baltimore, MD 630

Baltimore Public Works Museum, Inc., Baltimore, MD 630

Balzekas Museum of Lithuanian Culture, Chicago, IL 418

Barnwell County Museum, Barnwell, SC 1321

The Bartlett Museum, Amesbury, MA 657

Bates College Museum of Art, Lewiston, ME 613

The Bead Museum, Glendale, AZ 35

Beard Gallery, Norton, MA 700

Beaverhead County Museum, Dillon, MT 845

Becker County Historical Society, Detroit Lakes, MN 772

Bedford Historical Society Museum and Library, Bedford, OH 1142

Bellamy Mansion Museum of History and Design Arts, Wilmington, NC 1122

Belle Meade Plantation, Nashville, TN 1377

Ben Shahn Galleries at William Paterson University of New Jersey, Wayne, NJ 929

Benedicta Arts Center, Saint Joseph, MN 789

The Benjamin Banneker Park & Museum, Baltimore, MD 631

Berea College Burroughs Geological Museum, Berea, KY 565

Berea College, Doris Ulmann Galleries, Berea, KY 565

Bernard Historical Society and Museum, Delton, MI 734

Besh-Ba-Gowah Archaeological Park, Globe, AZ 35

Betts House Research Center, Cincinnati, OH 1148

Biblical Arts Center, Dallas, TX 1404

Birger Sandzen Memorial Gallery, Lindsborg, KS 549

Birmingham Museum of Art, Birmingham, AL 5

Biscayne National Park, Homestead, FL 313

Bishop Museum, Honolulu, HI 394

Black Hills Mining Museum, Lead, SD 1350

Black Hills Reptile Gardens, Inc., Rapid City, SD 1354

Blithewold Mansion, Gardens & Arboretum, Bristol, RI 1310

Bloomfield Academy Museum, Bloomfield, NY 963

Blount-Bridgers House/Hobson Pittman Memorial Gallery, Tarboro, NC 1121

Boca Raton Museum of Art, Boca Raton, FL 296

Boehm Gallery, San Marcos, CA 174

Boise Art Museum, Boise, ID 403

Bolduc House Museum, Sainte Genevieve, MO 837

Bolton Historical Society, Inc., Bolton, MA 663

Bonnet House Museum & Gardens, Fort Lauderdale, FL 306

Boone County Historical Center, Boone, IA 506

Boot Hill Museum, Inc., Dodge City, KS 536

Booth Western Art Museum, Cartersville, GA 367

Bowdoin College Museum of Art, Brunswick, ME 607

Bowers Museum, Santa Ana, CA 177

The Bowne House Historical Society, Flushing, NY 990

Bradford Brinton Memorial & Museum, Big Horn, WY 1628

Bradford Historical Society Inc., Bradford, VT 1477

Brenau University Galleries, Brenau University, Gainesville, GA 373

The Bronx Museum of the Arts, Bronx, NY......................................965

Brookings County Historical Society Museum, Volga, SD...............1358

Brooklyn Children's Museum, Brooklyn, NY......................................968

Brooklyn Museum, Brooklyn, NY..............968

Brunswick Town/Fort Anderson State Historic Site, Winnabow, NC......1124

Buffalo Bill Historical Center, Cody, WY..1631

Bunker Hill Museum, Charlestown, MA......675

Burke Museum of Natural History and Culture, Seattle, WA.........1565

Bushy Run Battlefield, Jeannette, PA.........1263

C.H. Nash Museum-Chucalissa Archaeological Museum, Memphis, TN...1372

Caguana Indian Ceremonial Park & Museum, Utuado, PR.............1644

Calhoun County Museum & Cultural Center, Saint Matthews, SC.................1341

California Museum of Ancient Art, Beverly Hills, CA..........................78

California State Indian Museum, Sacramento, CA...........................151

Canyon de Chelly National Monument, Chinle, AZ...................................31

Caparra Museum and Historic Park, Guaynabo, PR............................1641

Capitol Reef National Park Visitor Center, Torrey, UT..................1475

Carleton College Art Gallery, Northfield, MN...785

Carlsbad Museum & Art Center, Carlsbad, NM............................938

Caryl House and Fisher Barn, Dover, MA...680

Casteel-Linn House and Museum, Princeton, MO.............................829

Cedar Key Historical Society Museum, Cedar Key, FL...........................298

Cedar Key Museum State Park, Cedar Key, FL.......................................299

Center of Southwest Studies/Fort Lewis College, Durango, CO.............214

The Central Museum, Central, AK.................23

Chamizal National Memorial, El Paso, TX...1411

Channel Islands National Park, Robert J. Lagomarsino Visitor Center, Ventura, CA...194

Charles H. Wright Museum of African American History, Detroit, MI.........735

Chautauqua County Historical Society, McClurg Museum, Westfield, NY 1086

Chazen Museum of Art, Madison, WI....1604

Cheraw Lyceum Museum, Cheraw, SC......1327

Cherokee County Historical Museum, Inc., Murphy, NC..........................1112

Chico Museum, Chico, CA.........................83

Chief Oshkosh Native American Arts, Egg Harbor, WI...........................1596

Chieftains Museum, Rome, GA.................381

The Children's Museum, Seattle, WA 1565

The Children's Museum, Inc., Bloomsburg, PA............................1243

Children's Museum of Southeastern Connecticut, Niantic, CT...............256

Chimney Point State Historic Site, Addison, VT...............................1475

Chinese Culture Center of San Francisco, San Francisco, CA.........................164

Chinqua-Penn Plantation, Reidsville, NC...1117

Christiansted National Historic Site, Saint Croix, VI.....................................1644

Cincinnati Art Museum, Cincinnati, OH...1148

City Museum, Saint Louis, MO.................832

City of Bowie Museums, Bowie, MD.........638

Clearwater Historical Museum, Orofino, ID..408

The Cleveland Museum of Art, Cleveland, OH..........................1152

Cleveland State University Art Gallery, Cleveland, OH.........................1153

Cliffs of the Neuse State Park, Seven Springs, NC.............................1119

Cliveden of the National Trust, Philadelphia, PA........................1278

Coal Miners' Museum/Van Lear Historical Society, Inc., Van Lear, KY 584

The College of Wooster Art Museum, Wooster, OH.............................1192

Colonial Pemaquid, New Harbor, ME.........615

Colorado Springs Fine Arts Center (Taylor Museum), Colorado Springs, CO...206

Columbia Gorge Discovery Center and Wasco County Museum, The Dalles, OR...1237

Command Museum, Marine Corps Recruit Depot, San Diego, San Diego, CA...156

Commonwealth of the Northern Mariana Islands Museum of History and Culture, Saipan, MP...............1640

Confederated Tribes and Bands of the Yakama Indian Nation - Cultural Heritage Center Museum, Toppenish, WA...1575

Confederated Tribes of Grand Ronde Cultural Resources Department, Grand Ronde, OR........................1225

Connecticut State Museum of Natural History and Connecticut Archaeology Center, Storrs, CT.....................261

Conner Prairie, Fishers, IN....................476

The Contemporary Arts Center, Cincinnati, OH..........................1150

Coronado State Monument, Bernalillo, NM...937

Cowlitz County Historical Museum, Kelso, WA..................................1557

Creek Council House Museum, Okmulgee, OK..........................1211

Croatian Heritage Museum & Library, Eastlake, OH.............................1163

Crosby County Pioneer Memorial Museum, Crosbyton, TX.................1403

Crow Wing County Historical Society, Brainerd, MN.............................769

Cultural Museum, Nashville, TN.............1378

Cumberland County Historical Society, The Hamilton Library and The Two Mile House, Carlisle, PA.................1245

Cummer Museum of Art and Gardens, Jacksonville, FL..........................314

Curfman Gallery & Duhesa Lounge, Fort Collins, CO...............................216

The Custom House Maritime Museum, Newburyport, MA.......................697

Dallas Museum of Art, Dallas, TX.............1405

Danforth Museum of Art, Framingham, MA...683

The David Davis Mansion, Bloomington, IL..413

Davis Art Gallery, Columbia, MO.............813

Davis Museum and Cultural Center, Wellesley, MA............................716

Dayton Art Institute, Dayton, OH.............1161

De Saisset Museum, Santa Clara, CA.........180

Deaf Smith County Museum, Hereford, TX...1424

Dedham Historical Society Museum, Dedham, MA..............................679

Deer Valley Rock Art Center, Glendale, AZ..35

Delta Blues Museum, Clarksdale, MS.........799

Denison Museum, Granville, OH.............1167

Denver Art Museum, Denver, CO.............210

Department of Historic Resources, Richmond, VA.............................1529

DePree Art Center & Gallery, Holland, MI...746

Des Moines Art Center, Des Moines, IA 514

Deschutes County Historical Society, Bend, OR....................................1220

DeSoto National Memorial, Bradenton, FL..297

The Detroit Institute of Arts, Detroit, MI....736

Detroit Zoo, Royal Oak, MI.....................762

Dickson Mounds Museum, Lewistown, IL..442

The Discovery Center of the Southern Tier, Binghamton, NY.................962

The Douglas F. Cooley Memorial Art Gallery, Reed College, Portland, OR.....1231

Drayton Hall, Charleston, SC.................1325

Duluth Art Institute, Duluth, MN.............772

Dumbarton Oaks Research Library & Collections, Washington, DC.................278

Eagle Tavern Museum, Watkinsville, GA 391

East Brunswick Museum Corporation, East Brunswick, NJ.......................902

Eastern California Museum, Independence, CA...........................104

Eastside Heritage Center, Bellevue, WA 1548

Edge of the Cedars State Park Museum, Blanding, UT..............................1463

Eiteljorg Museum of American Indians and Western Art, Indianapolis, IN.........482

El Museo Del Barrio, New York, NY.........1025

El Museo Latino, Omaha, NE.....................870

The Emerson Gallery, Clinton, NY.............979

Environmental Education Center, Somerset County Park Commission, Basking Ridge, NJ.......................898

Epcot at Walt Disney World Resort, Lake Buena Vista, FL...........................319

Essex Historical Society, Inc., Essex, CT 240

Etowah Indian Mounds Historical Site, Cartersville, GA..........................367

Eubie Blake National Jazz Institute and Cultural Center, Baltimore, MD.............632

Everhart Museum: Natural History, Science and Art, Scranton, PA.................1298

Faulconer Gallery at Grinnell College, Grinnell, IA................................519

Favell Museum Inc., Klamath Falls, OR....1227

Fayette County Helpers Club & Historical Society, West Union, IA.........530

Fernbank Museum of Natural History, Atlanta, GA...............................359

Fine Arts Collection, Luther College, Decorah, IA...............................513

Firelands Historical Society Museum, Norwalk, OH..............................1180

The Fisk University Galleries, Nashville, TN..1379

Flint Institute of Arts, Flint, MI.................741

Flint Ridge State Memorial Museum, Glenford, OH.............................1166

Florence Hawley Ellis Museum of Anthropology and Ruth Hall Museum of Paleontology, Abiquiu, NM.................931

Florence Museum of Art, Science & History and the Florence Railroad Museum, Florence, SC.................1332

Florida State University Museum of Fine Arts, Tallahassee, FL......................347

Folsom Museum, Inc., Folsom, NM.............939

Ford County Historical Society, Paxton, IL..450

The Forges and Manor of Ringwood, Ringwood, NJ.............................923

Fort Benton Museum of the Upper Missouri, Fort Benton, MT.................846

Fort Hartsuff State Historical Park, Burwell, NE...............................858

Fort Henrietta Interpretive Park, Echo, OR...1223

Archaeological/Ethnographical–Continued

Fort King George Historic Site, Darien, GA.................370

Fort Klock Historic Restoration, Saint Johnsville, NY.................1063

Fort Leaton State Historical Site, Presidio, TX.................1444

Fort McAllister, Richmond Hill, GA.............381

Fort Payne Depot Museum, Fort Payne, AL.................10

Fort Raleigh National Historic Site, Manteo, NC.................1110

Fort Sill National Historic Landmark, Fort Sill, OK.................1201

Fort Vasquez Museum, Platteville, CO.........230

Four Rivers Cultural Center & Museum, Ontario, OR.................1229

Fox Lake Historical Museum, Inc., Fox Lake, WI.................1598

Frances Young Tang Teaching Museum and Art Gallery, Saratoga Springs, NY .1064

Franklin D. Roosevelt Presidential Library-Museum, Hyde Park, NY.........1002

Fraunces Tavern Museum, New York, NY.................1025

Frederick Douglass National Historic Site, Washington, DC.................279

Frederick R. Weisman Art Museum, Minneapolis, MN.................781

Freeport Arts Center, Freeport, IL.................435

Freer Gallery of Art, Washington, DC.........279

French Art Colony, Gallipolis, OH.............1165

Fresno Art Museum, Fresno, CA.................97

Fruitlands Museums, Harvard, MA.............686

Fulton County Museum, Groversville, NY.................996

Galena-Jo Daviess County Historical Society & Museum, Galena, IL.............436

Galeria, Orchard Lake, MI.................759

Garnavillo Historical Museum, Garnavillo, IA.................518

Gatekeeper's Museum & Marion Steinbach Indian Basket Museum, Tahoe City, CA.................190

Gateway to the Panhandle, Gate, OK.........1201

General Patton Memorial Museum, Chiriaco Summit, CA.................84

General Wait House, Waitsfield, VT...........1489

The George D. and Harriet W. Cornell Fine Arts Museum, Winter Park, FL.......354

Georgia Museum of Art, University of Georgia, Athens, GA.................356

Georgia Salzburger Society Museum, Rincon, GA.................381

The Georgian Museum, Lancaster, OH......1171

Glencairn Museum: Academy of the New Church, Bryn Athyn, PA.................1244

The Godwin-Ternbach Museum, Flushing, NY.................990

Golden Ball Tavern Museum, Weston, MA.................718

Golden Pioneer Museum, Golden, CO.........220

Goliad State Park, Goliad, TX.................1423

Grand Teton National Park, Colter Bay Indian Arts Museum, Colter Bay Village, WY.................1631

Grant County Museum & Historic Society, Hyannis, NE.................863

Greene County Historical Society, Xenia, OH.................1193

Grey Art Gallery, New York University Art Collection, New York, NY.............1026

Guilford College Art Gallery, Greensboro, NC.................1103

Gustav Jeeninga Museum of Bible and Near Eastern Studies, Anderson, IN.......467

Haffenreffer Museum of Anthropology, Brown University, Bristol, RI.................1310

The Hall of Fame for Great Americans, Bronx, NY.................966

Hallie Ford Museum of Art, Salem, OR 1235

Hamline University Galleries, Department of Studio Arts & Art History, Saint Paul, MN.................790

Hammond-Harwood House Association, Annapolis, MD.................628

Hampden-Booth Theatre Library at the Players, New York, NY.................1027

Handwerker Gallery, Ithaca, NY.................1003

Hanover Historical Society Museum, Hanover, VA.................1510

Harney County Historical Museum, Burns, OR.................1221

Hastings Museum, Hastings, NE.................863

Hatton Gallery, Colorado State University, Fort Collins, CO.................217

Hawaii Maritime Center, Honolulu, HI........395

Headley-Whitney Museum, Lexington, KY.................573

Heard Museum, Phoenix, AZ.................40

Hearst Art Gallery, St. Mary's College, Moraga, CA.................128

Held-Poage Memorial Home and Research Library, Ukiah, CA.................193

Helen Louise Allen Textile Collection, Madison, WI.................1605

Henry County Museum and Cultural Arts Center, Clinton, MO.................813

Herbert F. Johnson Museum of Art, Ithaca, NY.................1003

Heritage Library Museum, Anchorage, AK.................22

Heritage Station, Umatilla County Historical Society Museum, Pendleton, OR.................1230

Hershey Museum, Hershey, PA.................1261

Hiddenite Center, Inc., Hiddenite, NC.......1106

Higgins Armory Museum, Worcester, MA...721

High Cliff Historical Society & General Store Museum, Sherwood, WI.................1622

Hillwood Art Museum, Brookville, NY.......971

The Hispanic Society of America, New York, NY.................1027

Historic Brattonsville, McConnells, SC......1336

Historic House Trust of New York City, New York, NY.................1027

Historic Indian Agency House, Portage, WI.................1618

Historic London Town and Gardens, Edgewater, MD.................642

Historic Northampton, Northampton, MA....699

Historical Natural History & Library Society of Natick dba Natick Historical Society, South Natick, MA 709

Historical Society of Berks County, Reading, PA.................1296

Historical Society of Glastonbury, Glastonbury, CT.................242

Historical Society of Saratoga Springs, Saratoga Springs, NY.................1064

Hiwan Homestead Museum, Evergreen, CO.................215

Hoard Historical Museum and National Dairy Shrine's Visitors Center, Fort Atkinson, WI.................1598

Hofstra Museum, Hempstead, NY.................997

Honolulu Academy of Arts, Honolulu, HI ...395

Hopsewee Plantation, Georgetown, SC......1333

Hotel de Paris Museum, Georgetown, CO...219

Housatonic Museum of Art, Bridgeport, CT.................236

House of Wickersham State Historical Site, Juneau, AK.................25

Houston Museum of Natural Science, Houston, TX.................1427

Huntington Museum of Art, Inc., Huntington, WV.................1583

Huntsville Museum of Art, Huntsville, AL.................12

Hutchinson County Museum, Borger, TX..1397

The Hyland House, Guilford, CT.................243

Illinois State Museum, Chicago Gallery, Chicago, IL.................422

Immaculate Conception Catholic Church, Natchitoches, LA.................593

Indian Pueblo Cultural Center, Albuquerque, NM.................933

Indiana University Art Museum, Bloomington, IN.................469

The Institute For American Indian Studies (IAIS), Washington Green, CT ...263

International Museum of the Horse, Lexington, KY.................573

Iowa Masonic Library and Museum, Cedar Rapids, IA.................509

Iraan Museum, Iraan, TX.................1430

Iris & B. Gerald Cantor Center for Visual Arts at Stanford University, Stanford, CA.................188

Iroquois Indian Museum, Howes Cave, NY.................999

Isabel Anderson Comer Museum & Arts Center, Sylacauga, AL.................18

Isla Center For the Arts at the University of Guam, Mangilao, GU.................1640

Italian American Museum, New York, NY.................1028

Jackson Hole Historical Society and Museum, Jackson, WY.................1634

Jacques Marchais Museum of Tibetan Art, Staten Island, NY.................1072

James Madison's Montpelier, Montpelier Station, VA.................1518

Jay I. Kislak Foundation, Miami Lakes, FL.................327

Jersey City Museum, Jersey City, NJ.........908

Jesse Peter Museum, Santa Rosa, CA.........184

Jewish Museum of Maryland, Baltimore, MD.................633

The John Nicholas Brown Center for the Study of American Civilization, Providence, RI.................1317

John Wesley Powell Memorial Museum, Page, AZ.................37

Johnson Hall State Historic Site, Johnstown, NY.................1005

Jordan Schnitzer Museum of Art, Eugene, OR.................1223

Judah L. Magnes Museum, Berkeley, CA......76

Judaica Museum of Central Synagogue, New York, NY.................1029

Juniata County Historical Society, Mifflintown, PA.................1271

Ka-Do-Ha Indian Village Museum, Murfreesboro, AR.................65

The Kansas African American Museum, Wichita, KS.................561

Kansas Museum of History, Topeka, KS 559

Kelsey Museum of Archaeology, Ann Arbor, MI.................724

Kennedy Museum of Art, Athens, OH 1140

Kent State University, School of Art Galleries, Kent, OH.................1169

Keweenaw County Historical Society, Eagle Harbor, MI.................739

King Kamehameha V-Judiciary History Center, Honolulu, HI.................397

Kingman County Historical Museum, Kingman, KS.................547

Kittery Historical & Naval Museum, Kittery, ME.................613

Kiwanis Van Slyke Museum Foundation Inc., Caldwell, ID.................404

Klein Museum, Mobridge, SD.................1352

Kolomoki Mounds State Park Museum, Blakely, GA.................366

Krannert Art Museum and Kinkead Pavilion, Champaign, IL.................416

L.C. Bates Museum, Hinckley, ME.............612

Lafayette Miners Museum, Lafayette, CO...224

Lahaina Restoration Foundation, Lahaina, HI 400
Lake County Historical Museum, Tavares, FL 351
Lake Perris Regional Indian Museum (Home of the Wind), Perris, CA..............141
Lake Tahoe Historical Society & Museum, South Lake Tahoe, CA..............188
Lamar Dodd Art Center, LaGrange College, LaGrange, GA........................375
Lane Place, Crawfordsville, IN....................473
Latvian Museum, Rockville, MD 651
Lauren Rogers Museum of Art, Laurel, MS 804
Legends of New Mexico Museum, Algodones, NM 936
Lemhi County Historical Museum, Salmon, ID 409
Lentz Center for Asian Culture, Lincoln, NE 865
Lexington County Museum, Lexington, SC 1336
Liberty County Museum, Chester, MT........844
Liberty Village Arts Center & Gallery, Chester, MT 844
Library of Congress, Washington, DC 282
Library of the Supreme Council, 33 Degrees, Washington, DC.......................282
Lincoln State Monument, Lincoln, NM 941
Locust Creek Covered Bridge State Historic Site, Laclede, MO 825
Long Island Culture History Lab & Museum, Commack, NY...........................980
Longwood Center for the Visual Arts, Farmville, VA 1504
Lopez Island Historical Museum, Lopez Island, WA 1558
Lore Degenstein Gallery, Selinsgrove, PA .1299
Los Angeles County Museum of Art, Los Angeles, CA 118
Lou Holtz/Upper Ohio Valley Hall of Fame, East Liverpool, OH 1163
Louisiana Art & Science Museum - Irene W. Pennington Planetarium, Baton Rouge, LA 586
Lowe Art Museum, University of Miami, Coral Gables, FL 301
Loyola University Museum of Art, Chicago, IL 423
The Luther W. Brady Art Gallery, Washington, DC...282
Lynden Pioneer Museum, Lynden, WA.......1559
The Lyons Redstone Museum, Lyons, CO...227

Mabee Farm Historic Site, Rotterdam Junction, NY..1062
Mabee-Gerrer Museum of Art, Shawnee, OK..1213
Madison Museum of Fine Art, Madison, GA..378
Manitowoc County Historical Society, Manitowoc, WI......................................1607
Marin History Museum, San Rafael, CA.....177
Mariposa Museum & World Culture Center, Peterborough, NH.........................893
Maritime Museum - Cohasset Historical Society, Cohasset, MA 676
Martin and Osa Johnson Safari Museum, Inc., Chanute, KS.....................................535
Martin County Museum, Shoals, IN............499
Marxhausen Art Gallery, Seward, NE 873
Mary and Leigh Block Museum of Art, Northwestern University, Evanston, IL ...434
Mary Ball Washington Museum & Library, Inc., Lancaster, VA 1512
Mashantucket Pequot Museum and Research Center, Mashantucket, CT........248
Mattapoisett Museum and Carriage House, Mattapoisett, MA 693
Maxwell Museum of Anthropology, Albuquerque, NM..934
Mechanicsburg Museum Association, Mechanicsburg, PA..................................1270

The Menil Collection, Houston, TX...........1428
Meridian Museum of Art, Meridian, MS 805
Merritt Museum of Anthropology, Oakland, CA 133
Mesa Southwest Museum, Mesa, AZ...........37
The Metropolitan Museum of Art, New York, NY 1030
The Mexican Museum, San Francisco, CA 166
Miami County Museum, Peru, IN...............496
Miami University Art Museum, Oxford, OH..1181
Michael C. Carlos Museum, Atlanta, GA 361
Michelson Museum of Art, Marshall, TX ..1436
Mid-Hudson Children's Museum, Poughkeepsie, NY...1055
Mildred Lane Kemper Art Museum, Saint Louis, MO 834
Millicent Rogers Museum of Northern New Mexico, Taos, NM..........................952
Mingei International Museum, San Diego, CA 157
Minneapolis Institute of Arts, Minneapolis, MN...782
Mission Houses Museum, Honolulu, HI 397
Mission San Diego de Alcala, San Diego, CA 157
Mission San Juan Capistrano Museum, San Juan Capistrano, CA 173
Mississippi Agriculture & Forestry/National Agricultural Aviation Museum, Jackson, MS 802
Mississippi Crafts Center, Ridgeland, MS ...807
Mississippi Museum of Art, Jackson, MS....802
Mississippi River Museum at Mud Island River Park, Memphis, TN.......................1375
Mizel Museum, Denver, CO 213
Mobile Museum of Art, Mobile, AL 14
Monroe County Historical Association/Stroud Mansion, Stroudsburg, PA...1302
Montclair Art Museum, Montclair, NJ 912
Monterey Bay Aquarium, Monterey, CA 127
Monterey Museum of Art, Monterey, CA 128
Monticello, Home of Thomas Jefferson, Thomas Jefferson Foundation, Inc., Charlottesville, VA 1499
Moody County Museum, Flandreau, SD....1347
Moores Creek National Battlefield, Currie, NC 1097
The Morikami Museum and Japanese Gardens, Delray Beach, FL.........................305
Moundbuilders State Memorial & Museum, Newark, OH...........................1178
Mount Clare Museum House, Baltimore, MD..635
Mount Pleasant Historical Society, Mount Pleasant, OH 1177
Mt. Rainier National Park, Ashford, WA ...1547
Murrell Home, Park Hill, OK 1211
Museo de las Americas, Denver, CO 213
Museo Fuerte Conde de Mirasol de Vieques, Vieques, PR.........................1644
Museo ItaloAmericano, San Francisco, CA 167
The Museum, Greenwood, SC...................1334
The Museum at Warm Springs, Warm Springs, OR 1238
Museum of American Architecture and Decorative Arts, Houston, TX 1428
Museum of Anthropology, Highland Heights, KY 571
Museum of Anthropology, Winston-Salem, NC................................1125
Museum of Anthropology, University of Denver, Denver, CO.........................213
Museum of Art and Archaeology, University of Missouri - Columbia, Columbia, MO 813
Museum of Art/Fort Lauderdale, Fort Lauderdale, FL...307

Museum of Art, Rhode Island School of Design, Providence, RI..........................1317
The Museum of Arts and Sciences, Inc. and Center for Florida History, Daytona Beach, FL 303
Museum of Central Connecticut State University, New Britain, CT..................251
Museum of Chinese in the Americas, New York, NY...1032
Museum of Craft and Folk Art, San Francisco, CA 167
The Museum of Fine Arts, Houston, Houston, TX 1428
Museum of Fine Arts of St. Petersburg, Florida, Saint Petersburg, FL 341
Museum of Indian Arts & Culture/Laboratory of Anthropology, Santa Fe, NM...948
Museum of Indian Culture, Allentown, PA..1239
Museum of Northern Arizona, Flagstaff, AZ..33
Museum of Peoples and Cultures, Provo, UT..1470
Museum of Primitive Art and Culture, Peace Dale, RI...1316
Museum of Rim Country Archaeology, Payson, AZ 38
Museum of the Fur Trade, Chadron, NE......859
Museum of the Red River, Idabel, OK 1203
Museum of the Southwest, Midland, TX ...1439
Museum of the Waxhaws & Andrew Jackson Memorial, Waxhaw, NC..........1122
Muskegon County Museum, Muskegon, MI..757
Mystic Aquarium & Institute for Exploration, Mystic, CT........................250

NIU Art Museum, DeKalb, IL....................429
Napa Valley Museum, Yountville, CA 200
Naples Museum of Art and the Philharmonic Center for the Arts Galleries, Naples, FL...............................328
Nasher Museum of Art at Duke University, Durham, NC.........................1099
Nathaniel W. Faison Home and Museum, La Grange, TX...1432
National Capital Parks-East, Washington, DC..284
National Cowboy & Western Heritage Museum, Oklahoma City, OK 1208
National Infantry Museum, Fort Benning, GA..372
National Museum of Natural History, Washington, DC...286
National Museum of the American Indian, Smithsonian Institution, New York, NY...1034
Native American Heritage Museum at Highland Mission State Historic Site, Highland, KS...544
Native American Museum, Terre Haute, IN..500
Native American Resource Center, Pembroke, NC...1114
Natural Center for the American Revolution, Wayne, PA 1306
Natural History Museum of Los Angeles County, Los Angeles, CA........................120
Navajo Nation Museum, Window Rock, AZ..53
Nebraska State Historical Society's Museum of Nebraska History, Lincoln, NE..866
The Nelson-Atkins Museum of Art, Kansas City, MO...822
Nevada County Historical Society, Inc., Nevada City, CA...130
New Britain Youth Museum at Hungerford Park, Kensington, CT..........247
New London County Historical Society, New London, CT...255

Archaeological/Ethnographical–Continued

New Orleans Museum of Art, New Orleans, LA 597
New Orleans Pharmacy Museum, New Orleans, LA 597
New Visions Gallery, Inc., Marshfield, WI 1608
The New York Botanical Garden, Bronx, NY 966
The Newark Museum, Newark, NJ 916
Nohwike Bagowa, The White Mountain Apache Cultural Center and Museum, Fort Apache, AZ 34
North Carolina A&T State University Galleries, Greensboro, NC 1104
North Carolina Maritime Museum, Beaufort, NC 1091
North Carolina Pottery Center, Seagrove, NC 1119
Northampton County Historical and Genealogical Society, Easton, PA 1250
Northeast Georgia History Center at Brenau University, Gainesville, GA 373
The Northumberland County Historical Society, Sunbury, PA 1302
Notah Dineh Museum, Cortez, CO 208
The Nylander Museum of Natural History, Caribou, ME 609

Oakland University Art Gallery, Rochester, MI 761
Ocmulgee National Monument, Macon, GA 378
The Octagon Center for the Arts, Ames, IA 505
Ohr-O'Keefe Museum of Art, Biloxi, MS ...799
Oklahoma Museum of History, Oklahoma City, OK 1210
Oklahoma Route 66 Museum, Clinton, OK 1198
Old Barracks Museum, Trenton, NJ 927
Old Castle Museum, Baldwin City, KS 533
Old Dorchester State Historic Site, Summerville, SC 1342
Old Fort Bissell, Phillipsburg, KS 555
The Old Jail Art Center, Albany, TX 1385
Old Lighthouse Museum, Michigan City, IN 491
Old Lighthouse Museum, Stonington, CT 261
Old Log Jail and Chapel Museums, Greenfield, IN 480
Old Mill Museum, El Molino Viejo - Old Mill Foundation, San Marino, CA 175
Old Mission Santa Ines, Solvang, CA 187
Old Town Museum, Old Town, ME 617
Olde Colonial Courthouse, Tales of Cape Cod, Inc., Barnstable, MA 661
Oregon Coast History Center, Newport, OR 1229
Oregon Zoo, Portland, OR 1232
Oriental Institute Museum, University of Chicago, Chicago, IL 426
Orland Historical Society, Orland, ME 617
Orlando Museum of Art, Orlando, FL 332
Our House State Memorial, Gallipolis, OH 1165
Owensboro Museum of Fine Art, Inc., Owensboro, KY 581

P.H. Sullivan Museum and Genealogy Library, Zionsville, IN 504
Pacific Asia Museum, Pasadena, CA 140
Pacific Grove Museum of Natural History, Pacific Grove, CA 137
Pacific University Museum, Forest Grove, OR 1224
The Pardee Home Museum, Oakland, CA ...134
Parris Island Museum, Parris Island, SC ...1338
The Parthenon, Nashville, TN 1379
Paul and Lulu Hilliard University Art Museum, University of Louisiana at Lafayette, Lafayette, LA 590

Peabody Essex Museum, Salem, MA 706
The Peary-MacMillan Arctic Museum, Brunswick, ME 608
Pecos National Historical Park, Pecos, NM 944
The Pena-Peck House, Saint Augustine, FL 339
Pence Gallery, Davis, CA 90
Pensacola Museum of Art, Pensacola, FL ...336
Peoria Historical Society, Peoria, IL 451
Petaluma Adobe State Historic Park, Petaluma, CA 142
Peter Yegen Jr. Yellowstone County Museum, Billings, MT 841
Petterson Museum of Intercultural Art, Claremont, CA 85
The Philbrook Museum of Art, Inc., Tulsa, OK 1215
Phillips County Museum, Helena, AR 59
Phoenix Museum of History, Phoenix, AZ 41
Pickens County Museum of Art & History, Pickens, SC 1340
The Picker Art Gallery, Hamilton, NY 997
The Pierpont Morgan Library, New York, NY 1037
Pierre Menard Home State Historic Site, Ellis Grove, IL 433
Pike County Historical Society, Milford, PA 1272
Pilgrim Hall Museum, Plymouth, MA 703
Pimeria Alta Historical Society, Nogales, AZ 37
Pioneer Museum of Alabama, Troy, AL 18
Pipestone County Historical Museum, Pipestone, MN 786
Pipestone National Monument, Pipestone, MN 787
Plimoth Plantation Inc., Plymouth, MA 703
Polk County Memorial Museum, Livingston, TX 1434
Polk Museum of Art, Lakeland, FL 321
Pomona College Museum of Art, Claremont, CA 85
Pope County Historical Society, Glenwood, MN 776
Porterville Historical Museum, Porterville, CA 144
Portland Art Museum, Portland, OR 1232
Portsmouth Athenaeum, Portsmouth, NH 894
Pound Ridge Society/Museum, Pound Ridge, NY 1055
Presbyterian Historical Society (Montreat), Montreat, NC 1111
Presidio La Bahia, Goliad, TX 1423
Prestwould Foundation, Clarksville, VA 1501
Princeton University Art Museum, Princeton, NJ 922
Pueblo Grande Museum and Archaeological Park, Phoenix, AZ 42
Pueblo of Pojoaque, Poeh Museum, Santa Fe, NM 949
Purdue University Galleries, West Lafayette, IN 503

Racine Art Museum (RAM), Racine, WI ...1619
Radford University Art Museum, Radford, VA 1527
Ralston Historical Association, John Ralston Museum, Mendham, NJ 911
Rankin Museum, Inc., Ellerbe, NC 1100
The Ray Drew Gallery-New Mexico Highlands University, Las Vegas, NM 941
Raynham Hall Museum, Oyster Bay, NY ..1049
Red Earth Museum, Oklahoma City, OK ...1210
Red Rock Museum, Church Rock, NM 938
Redington Museum, Waterville, ME 625
The Regina A. Quick Center for the Arts, Saint Bonaventure, NY 1063
Rim Country Museum, Payson, AZ 38
Rimrocker Historical Museum of West Montrose County, Naturita, CO 229

Riverside Museum, La Crosse, WI 1603
Robbins Museum of Archaeology, Middleborough, MA 694
Robert Hull Fleming Museum, Burlington, VT 1478
Robert Newell House, DAR Museum, Saint Paul, OR 1235
Robert V. Fullerton Art Museum, California State University, San Bernardino, San Bernardino, CA 155
Rock County Historical Society, Janesville, WI 1601
Rockwell Museum of Western Art, Corning, NY 982
Rodgers Tavern, Perryville, MD 650
Roland Gibson Gallery, Potsdam, NY 1054
Ronald Reagan Presidential Library and Museum, Simi Valley, CA 187
Rosemount Museum, Pueblo, CO 230
Rosenberg Gallery, Goucher College, Baltimore, MD 636
Rosicrucian Egyptian Museum, San Jose, CA 172
Roslyn Landmark Society, Roslyn, NY 1061
Roswell Museum and Art Center, Roswell, NM 946
Russell County Historical Society/Fossil Station Museum, Russell, KS 556
Ruth Chandler Williamson Gallery, Scripps College, Claremont, CA 86

Sacajawea Interpretive Center, Pasco, WA.1561
Safety Harbor Museum of Regional History, Safety Harbor, FL 338
Saginaw Art Museum, Saginaw, MI 763
St. Clements Island and Piney Point Museums, Colton's Point, MD 641
The Saint Louis Art Museum, Saint Louis, MO 836
Salinas Pueblo Missions National Monument, Mountainair, NM 943
Salisbury House Foundation, Des Moines, IA 515
Samuel Dorsky Museum of Art, State University of New York at New Paltz, New Paltz, NY 1018
Samuel P. Harn Museum of Art, Gainesville, FL 311
San Antonio Missions National Historical Park, San Antonio, TX 1449
San Antonio Museum of Art, San Antonio, TX 1450
San Diego Museum of Man, San Diego, CA 160
San Joaquin County Historical Society & Museum, Lodi, CA 109
Santa Barbara Museum of Art, Santa Barbara, CA 179
Santa Monica Mountains National Recreation Area, Thousand Oaks, CA 191
Saratoga County Historical Society, Brookside Museum, Ballston Spa, NY 960
Saratoga Museum, Saratoga, WY 1638
Sauk Prairie Area Historical Society, Inc., Prairie du Sac, WI 1619
Sawin Memorial Building, Dover, MA 680
Scantic Academy Museum, East Windsor Historical Society, Inc., East Windsor, CT 239
The Schein-Joseph International Museum of Ceramic Art, Alfred, NY 956
Schingoethe Center for Native American Cultures, Aurora, IL 412
Schmucker Art Gallery, Gettysburg, PA 1256
Schneider Museum of Art, Ashland, OR ...1217
Schoharie Colonial Heritage Association, Schoharie, NY 1067
School of American Research, Indian Arts Research Center, Santa Fe, NM 950
Schuyler County Historical Society, Inc., Montour Falls, NY 1015
Science Museum of Long Island, Manhasset, NY 1013

The Science Museum of Minnesota, Saint
  Paul, MN..792
Scotchtown, Beaverdam, VA.....................1496
Scotts Bluff National Monument, Gering,
  NE..861
Seattle Art Museum, Seattle, WA..............1568
Seattle Asian Art Museum, Seattle, WA.......1569
Seminole Canyon State Park and Historic
  Site, Comstock, TX.............................1401
Seminole Nation Museum, Wewoka, OK...1217
Senator John Heinz Pittsburgh Regional
  History Center, Pittsburgh, PA.............1294
Seneca-Iroquois National Museum,
  Salamanca, NY..................................1063
Shako:wi Cultural Center, Oneida, NY......1046
Shasta College Museum & Research
  Center, Redding, CA...........................146
Shasta State Historic Park, Shasta, CA........186
Sheehan Gallery at Whitman College,
  Walla Walla, WA................................1577
Sherwin Miller Museum of Jewish Art,
  Tulsa, OK..1216
Sibley House Historic Site, Mendota, MN...780
Sidney Historical Association, Sidney,
  NY...1069
Siegfried H. Horn Archaeological
  Museum, Berrien Springs, MI................729
Sierra Mono Indian Museum, North Fork,
  CA...131
The Simon Paneak Memorial Museum,
  Anaktuvuk Pass, AK..............................21
Siskin Museum of Religious and
  Ceremonial Art, Chattanooga, TN.........1362
Skirball Cultural Center, Los Angeles,
  CA..121
Skirball Museum Cincinnati Hebrew
  Union College-Jewish Institute of
  Religion, Cincinnati, OH.....................1151
The Slater Memorial Museum - Norwich
  Free Academy, Norwich, CT..................258
Smith-Zimmermann Heritage Museum,
  Madison, SD.....................................1351
Smith's Fort Plantation, Surry, VA............1540
Smoki Museum - American Indian Art &
  Culture, Prescott, AZ............................43
The Snite Museum of Art, University of
  Notre Dame, Notre Dame, IN................495
Snyder Museum & Creative Arts Center,
  Bastrop, LA......................................585
Sophienburg Museum & Archives Inc.,
  New Braunfels, TX..............................1440
Sotterley Plantation, Hollywood, MD.........647
South Charleston Museum, South
  Charleston, WV.................................1586
Southern Ohio Museum, Portsmouth, OH..1183
Southern Plains Indian Museum,
  Anadarko, OK...................................1196
Southold Indian Museum, Southold, NY...1071
Southwest Museum, Los Angeles, CA.........121
Spartanburg Science Center, Spartanburg,
  SC...1342
The Speed Art Museum, Louisville, KY......579
Spertus Museum, Chicago, IL..................427
Spiro Mounds Archaeological Center,
  Spiro, OK..1214
Springfield Art Museum, Springfield, MO...839
Springfield Museums - Springfield
  Science Museum, Springfield, MA.........711
Stark Museum of Art, Orange, TX.............1441
Staten Island Historical Society, Staten
  Island, NY.......................................1074
The Stephens Museum, Fayette, MO.........815
Stonewall Jackson House, Lexington, VA...1514
The Stowitts Museum & Library, Pacific
  Grove, CA..137
Stratford, Robert E. Lee Memorial
  Association, Inc., Stratford, VA.............1539
SUArt Galleries - Syracuse University,
  Syracuse, NY....................................1077
SunWatch Indian Village/Archaeological
  Park, Dayton, OH...............................1162

Tallahassee Museum, Tallahassee, FL..........348
Tama County Historical Museum, Toledo,
  IA...528
Tamastslikt Cultural Institute, Pendleton,
  OR...1230
Tampa Museum of Art, Tampa, FL.............350
Tampa's Lowry Park Zoo, Tampa, FL.........350
Telluride Historical Museum, Telluride,
  CO..233
The Temple Judea Museum of Reform
  Congregation Keneseth Israel, Elkins
  Park, PA...1251
The Temple Museum of Religious Art,
  Cleveland, OH..................................1156
Tenino Depot Museum, Tenino, WA..........1575
Texarkana Museums System, Texarkana,
  TX...1455
Texas Maritime Museum, Rockport, TX...1446
Texas Parks and Wildlife Department,
  Austin, TX.......................................1392
The Texas Zoo, Victoria, TX.....................1457
The Textile Museum, Washington, DC.........291
Thomas J. Walsh Art Gallery, Quick
  Center for the Arts at Fairfield
  University, Fairfield, CT........................241
Thomasville Cultural Center, Inc.,
  Thomasville, GA..................................388
Thornton W. Burgess Museum,
  Sandwich, MA....................................708
Tinker Swiss Cottage Museum, Rockford,
  IL...456
Tinley Park Historical Society, Tinley
  Park, IL..461
Tippecanoe Battlefield, Battle Ground, IN...468
Tippecanoe County Historical
  Association, Lafayette, IN......................487
The Toledo Zoo, Toledo, OH....................1187
Tongass Historical Museum, Ketchikan,
  AK...26
Tougaloo College, Tougaloo, MS...............808
Treasures of the Sea Exhibit,
  Georgetown, DE..................................271
Triton Museum of Art, Santa Clara, CA......181
The Trout Gallery, Carlisle, PA.................1245
Tubman African-American Museum,
  Macon, GA..378
Tuck Museum, Hampton, NH....................888
Tucson Museum of Art & Historic Block,
  Tucson, AZ...51
Tucumcari Historical Research Institute,
  Tucumcari, NM...................................953
Tufts University Art Gallery, Medford,
  MA..694
Tulsa Zoo & Living Museum, Tulsa, OK..1216
Turabo University, Gurabo, PR.................1641
Turtle Bay Exploration Park, Redding,
  CA...146
Tweed Museum of Art, Duluth, MN...........774

UCLA Fowler Museum of Cultural
  History, Los Angeles, CA......................122
UNLV Marjorie Barrick Museum, Las
  Vegas, NV..880
The Ukrainian Museum, New York, NY....1040
University Art Galleries, Vermillion, SD...1358
University Art Galleries, Murray State
  University, Murray, KY.........................580
University Art Gallery, University of the
  South, Sewanee, TN............................1384
The University Museum, Edwardsville,
  IL...432
The University Museum, Indiana, PA........1263
University Museum, New Mexico State
  University, Las Cruces, NM...................941
University Museums, University of
  Delaware, Newark, DE..........................272
University of Iowa Museum of Art, Iowa
  City, IA..520
University of Kentucky Art Museum,
  Lexington, KY....................................574
University of Michigan Museum of
  Anthropology, Ann Arbor, MI................725

The University of Michigan Museum of
  Art, Ann Arbor, MI..............................726
University of Missouri-Kansas City
  Gallery of Art, Kansas City, MO.............823
University of Nebraska State Museum,
  Lincoln, NE.......................................867
University of Oregon Museum of Natural
  and Cultural History, Eugene, OR.........1224
University of Pennsylvania Museum of
  Archaeology and Anthropology,
  Philadelphia, PA................................1288
University of Richmond Museums,
  Richmond, VA....................................1532
University of Virginia Art Museum,
  Charlottesville, VA..............................1500
University of Wyoming Anthropology
  Museum, Laramie, WY.........................1636
University of Wyoming Art Museum,
  Laramie, WY.....................................1636
Utah Field House of Natural History
  State Park, Vernal, UT.........................1475
Utah Museum of Fine Arts, Salt Lake
  City, UT...1472
Ute Indian Museum/Montrose Visitor
  Center, Montrose, CO...........................228

Valdosta State University Fine Arts
  Gallery, Valdosta, GA...........................389
Valentown Museum, Victor, NY...............1081
Van Meter State Park, Miami, MO.............827
Vanderbilt University Fine Arts Gallery,
  Nashville, TN....................................1381
Varner-Hogg Plantation State Historic
  Site, West Columbia, TX.....................1461
Virginia Museum of Natural History,
  Martinsville, VA.................................1516

Wabaunsee County Historical Museum,
  Alma, KS..532
The Wagnalls Memorial, Lithopolis, OH...1172
Waimea Arboretum and Botanical Garden
  in Waimea Valley Audubon Center,
  Haleiwa, HI.......................................392
Walnut Canyon National Monument,
  Flagstaff, AZ.......................................34
Walters Art Museum, Baltimore, MD.........636
Wanapum Dam Heritage Center, Beverly,
  WA...1549
Warren County Historical Society,
  Warren, PA.......................................1304
Washington Crossing Historic Park,
  Washington Crossing, PA......................1305
Washington Historical Museum,
  Washington, GA...................................391
Washington's Headquarters State Historic
  Site, Newburgh, NY............................1042
Watts Towers Arts Center, Los Angeles,
  CA..122
Wayland Historical Society, Wayland,
  MA..716
Wellington B. Gray Gallery, Greenville,
  NC...1105
Western Colorado Center for the Arts,
  Grand Junction, CO.............................221
Western Hotel/Museum, Lancaster, CA.......108
Western New Mexico University
  Museum, Silver City, NM......................951
Whiskeytown Unit,
  Whiskeytown-Shasta-Trinity National
  Recreation Area, Whiskeytown, CA........198
Wickersham House Museum
  (Tanana-Yukon Historical Society),
  Fairbanks, AK......................................24
Wickliffe Mounds State Historic Site,
  Wickliffe, KY.....................................584
Wilderness Road Regional Museum,
  Newbern, VA.....................................1519
William Weston Clarke Emison Museum
  of Art, Greencastle, IN.........................479
Williams College Museum of Art,
  Williamstown, MA...............................719
Wing Luke Asian Museum, Seattle, WA....1569

Archaeological/Ethnographical–Continued

Wise County Heritage Museum, Decatur,
  TX..1408
Wiseman & FireHouse Galleries, Rogue
  Community College, Grants Pass, OR ..1225
Woodlawn Plantation Museum,
  Alexandria, VA 1494
Woolaroc Museum, Bartlesville, OK 1197
Worcester Art Museum, Worcester, MA.......721
World Erotic Art Museum, Miami Beach,
  FL...327
World Forestry Center, Portland, OR 1233
World Golf Hall of Fame, Saint
  Augustine, FL 340
Wormsloe State Historic Site, Savannah,
  GA..387
Wriston Art Center Galleries, Appleton,
  WI...1590
Wyoming Pioneer Memorial Museum,
  Douglas, WY..1632

The Yager Museum of Art & Culture,
  Oneonta, NY..1046
Yale University Art Gallery, New Haven,
  CT...254
Ybor City Museum State Park, Tampa,
  FL...351
Yellowstone Gateway Museum of Park
  County, Livingston, MT...........................850
Yolo County Historical Museum,
  Woodland, CA..199
Youth Science Institute, San Jose, CA 173

Zanesville Art Center, Zanesville, OH........1194
Zelienople Historical Society, Zelienople,
  PA..1309

Audiovisual and Film

A.K.C. Museum of The Dog, Saint
  Louis, MO...831
A.R. Bowman Memorial Museum,
  Prineville, OR..1234
A.W.A. Electronic-Communication
  Museum, Bloomfield, NY.........................963
Abilene Zoological Gardens, Abilene, TX .1385
Abington Art Center, Jenkintown, PA 1263
Abraham Lincoln Birthplace National
  Historic Site, Hodgenville, KY................571
Academy Hall Museum of the Rocky
  Hill Historical Society, Inc., Rocky
  Hill, CT..259
Adan E. Treganza Anthropology
  Museum, Dept. of Anthropology, San
  Francisco State University, San
  Francisco, CA..162
The Adirondack Museum, Blue Mountain
  Lake, NY...963
Admiral Nimitz National Museum of the
  Pacific War, Fredericksburg, TX............1419
The African American Museum in
  Philadelphia, Philadelphia, PA..............1275
Ah-Tah-Thi-Ki Museum at Okalee,
  Hollywood, FL...312
Air Mobility Command Museum, Dover
  AFB, DE..270
Air Victory Museum, Inc., Lumberton,
  NJ..910
Airline History Museum, Kansas City,
  MO..820
Ak-Sar-Ben Aquarium Outdoor Education
  Center, Gretna, NE..................................862
Alabama Jazz Hall of Fame,
  Birmingham, AL...4
Alabama Mining Museum, Dora, AL...............7
Alabama River Museum, Finchburg, AL 9
Alabama Sports Hall of Fame,
  Birmingham, AL...4
The Alamo, San Antonio, TX 1447
Alamo Township Museum-John E. Gray
  Memorial Museum, Kalamazoo, MI.......748
Alaska Aviation Heritage Museum,
  Anchorage, AK..21

Alcatraz Island, San Francisco, CA..............163
Alger County Heritage Center, Munising,
  MI..757
Alice Austen House Museum, Staten
  Island, NY...1072
Allison-Antrim Museum, Inc.,
  Greencastle, PA.....................................1257
Alumni Center - Husky Heritage Sports
  Museum, Storrs, CT.................................261
Alutiiq Museum and Archaeological
  Repository, Kodiak, AK.............................26
Amelia Earhart Birthplace Museum,
  Atchison, KS..532
American Airlines C.R. Smith Museum,
  Fort Worth, TX.......................................1416
American Classical Music Hall of Fame
  and Museum, Cincinnati, OH 1148
American Clock and Watch Museum,
  Inc., Bristol, CT......................................236
The American Film Institute, Washington,
  DC..275
American Folk Art Museum, New York,
  NY..1018
The American Jazz Museum, Kansas
  City, MO..820
American Jewish Historical Society, New
  York, NY..1019
American Labor Museum, Botto House
  National Landmark, Haledon, NJ 906
American Museum of Asmat Art, Saint
  Paul, MN...789
The American Museum of Fly Fishing,
  Manchester, VT......................................1481
American Museum of Nursing, Tempe,
  AZ..45
American Quarter Horse Hall of Fame &
  Museum, Amarillo, TX 1386
American Red Cross Visitors Center and
  Gift Shop, Washington, DC 275
American Royal Museum & Visitors
  Center, Kansas City, MO 820
American Saddlebred Museum,
  Lexington, KY..572
American Sport Art Museum and
  Archives, Daphne, AL.................................7
American Swedish Historical Foundation
  & Museum, Philadelphia, PA.................1276
American Visionary Art Museum,
  Baltimore, MD...629
American Water Ski Educational
  Foundation, Polk City, FL.......................337
American Wings Air Museum, Blaine,
  MN..769
America's Ice Cream & Dairy Museum,
  Medina, OH...1175
Americas Society, New York, NY 1020
America's Stonehenge, North Salem, NH 893
Amory Regional Museum, Amory, MS........797
Anderson/Abruzzo Albuquerque
  International Balloon Museum,
  Albuquerque, NM....................................933
Andover Historical Society, Andover, MA...660
The Andy Warhol Museum, Pittsburgh,
  PA..1290
Ano Nuevo State Reserve, Pescadero, CA...141
Anthology Film Archives, New York, NY.1020
The Appalachian Trail Conservancy,
  Harpers Ferry, WV 1581
Arab American National Museum,
  Dearborn, MI..733
ARC Gallery (Artists, Residents of
  Chicago), Chicago, IL.............................417
Arcadia Township Historical
  Commission, Arcadia, MI........................726
Archives Museum, Temple Mickve Israel,
  Savannah, GA...384
Arizona Historical Society Museum at
  Papago Park, Tempe, AZ...........................45
Arizona Jewish Historical Society,
  Phoenix, AZ..39
Arizona State University Art Museum,
  Tempe, AZ...45

Ark-La-Tex Antique & Classic Vehicle
  Museum, Shreveport, LA.........................600
Arkansas Air Museum, Fayetteville, AR........57
Arkansas Country Doctor Museum,
  Lincoln, AR...61
Arkansas Museum of Natural Resources,
  Smackover, AR..68
Arkansas Post National Memorial, Gillett,
  AR..58
Arlington Arts Center, Arlington, VA.........1495
Arlington Museum of Art, Arlington, TX ..1387
Armstrong Browning Library, Waco, TX...1458
Art Association of Randolph County,
  Inc., Union City, IN.................................501
The Art Center at Fuller Lodge, Los
  Alamos, NM..942
The Art Gallery, John C. Calhoun State
  Community College, Decatur, AL 7
Arthur D. Feiro Marine Life Center c/o
  Peninsula College, Port Angeles, WA ...1561
The Arthur J. Moore Methodist Museum,
  Saint Simons Island, GA.........................383
Arts Consortium of Cincinnati's African
  American Museum, Cincinnati, OH 1148
Asheville Art Museum, Asheville, NC.......1088
Asian American Arts Centre, New York,
  NY..1021
Aspen Historical Society, Aspen, CO..........202
Association for the Preservation of
  Tennessee Antiquities, Nashville, TN 1377
Astronaut Memorial Planetarium and
  Observatory, Cocoa, FL 300
The Atlanta Cyclorama, Atlanta, GA...........358
Atlantic Heritage Center, Somers Point,
  NJ..924
The Atomic Testing Museum, Las Vegas,
  NV...878
Attleboro Arts Museum, Attleboro, MA.......661
Auburn Cord Duesenberg Museum,
  Auburn, IN..468
Austin Museum of Art - Downtown,
  Austin, TX...1388
Avery County Museum, Newland, NC.......1113

Babe Didrikson Zaharias Museum,
  Beaumont, TX..1394
The Babe Ruth Museum and Sports
  Legends at Camden Yards, Baltimore,
  MD..629
Badger Mine and Museum, Shullsburg,
  WI..1622
Baker-Cederberg Museum & Archives,
  Rochester, NY..1058
Bale Grist Mill State Historic Park,
  Calistoga, CA..80
Baltimore & Ohio Railroad Museum,
  Baltimore, MD...629
Baltimore Maritime Museum, Baltimore,
  MD..630
Baltimore Museum of Industry,
  Baltimore, MD...630
Baltimore Public Works Museum, Inc.,
  Baltimore, MD...630
Balzekas Museum of Lithuanian Culture,
  Chicago, IL..418
Bandon Historical Society Museum,
  Bandon, OR...1219
Barataria Preserve, Jean Lafitte National
  Historical Park and Preserve, Marrero,
  LA..591
Barnes County Historical Museum,
  Valley City, ND......................................1136
Barton Museum, Wilson, NC....................1124
Battleship New Jersey Museum &
  Memorial, Camden, NJ 899
Baxter Springs Heritage Center and
  Museum, Baxter Springs, KS..................533
Bay View Historical Museum, Bay View,
  MI..728
Beacon Historical Society, Beacon, NY.......960
Beck Cultural Exchange Center,
  Knoxville, TN..1369
Beehive House, Salt Lake City, UT 1470

Belle Isle Nature Zoo, Detroit, MI 735

The Benjamin Banneker Park & Museum, Baltimore, MD 631

Bennett Place State Historic Site, Durham, NC...1098

Benton County Historical Museum, Prosser, WA 1563

Bergen Museum of Art & Science, Paramus, NJ 919

Berkeley Plantation, Charles City, VA 1498

Beth Ahabah Museum & Archives, Richmond, VA 1528

Bexley Historical Society, Bexley, OH.......1143

Biblical Arts Center, Dallas, TX................1404

Big Springs Museum, Caledonia, NY 974

Big Timbers Museum, Lamar, CO 225

Birch Aquarium at Scripps, Scripps Institution of Oceanography, University of California, San Diego, La Jolla, CA..106

Birger Sandzen Memorial Gallery, Lindsborg, KS...549

Birmingham Civil Rights Institute, Birmingham, AL...4

Bishop Museum, Honolulu, HI....................394

Black Arts National Diaspora Museum, New Orleans, LA......................................594

Black Mountain College Museum & Arts Center, Asheville, NC.............................1089

Blue and Gray Museum, Fitzgerald, GA......371

Blue Ridge Institute and Museum, Ferrum, VA...1504

B'nai B'rith Klutznick National Jewish Museum, Washington, DC 277

Boston Fire Museum, Boston, MA...............664

Boston National Historical Park, Boston, MA...664

Boulder Museum of Contemporary Art, Boulder, CO..203

Boys Town Hall of History & Father Flanagan House, Boys Town, NE............858

Bradford Historical Society Inc., Bradford, VT...1477

Bread & Puppet Museum, Glover, VT.......1479

Brec's Magnolia Mound Plantation, Baton Rouge, LA......................................585

Briar Bush Nature Center, Abington, PA ...1238

Brimstone Museum, Sulphur, LA................602

Bromfield Art Gallery, Boston, MA 665

The Bronx County Historical Society, Bronx, NY...964

Brooklyn Children's Museum, Brooklyn, NY...968

Brueckner Museum of Starr Commonwealth, Albion, MI......................723

Brunswick Railroad Museum and C&O Canal Visitors Center, Brunswick, MD ...639

Buchanan Center for the Arts, Monmouth, IL...445

Buena Park Historical Society, Buena Park, CA..80

Buffalo Bill Cody Homestead, Princeton, IA...527

Buffalo Bill Museum & Grave, Golden, CO..219

Bunker Hill Museum, Charlestown, MA.......675

Burrowes Mansion Museum, Matawan, NJ..911

Bushy Run Battlefield, Jeannette, PA 1263

Byers-Evans House Museum, Denver, CO..209

COSI Toledo, Toledo, OH........................1187

Calhoun County Museum, Rockwell City, IA...527

California African-American Museum, Los Angeles, CA......................................113

California Center for the Arts, Escondido, Escondido, CA..93

California Surf Museum, Oceanside, CA.....135

Call of the Wild Museum, Gaylord, MI.......742

Calusa Nature Center and Planetarium, Fort Myers, FL...308

Calvin Coolidge Presidential Library & Museum, Northampton, MA....................699

Camp Five Museum Foundation, Inc., Laona, WI...1604

Camp Moore Cemetery and Museum, Tangipahoa, LA......................................603

Camp 6 Logging Museum, Tacoma, WA ...1572

The Camron-Stanford House Preservation Association, Oakland, CA........................133

Canal Fulton Heritage Society, Canal Fulton, OH...1145

Canton Classic Car Museum, Canton, OH.1145

The Canton Museum of Art, Canton, OH ..1145

Cape Cod Museum of Art, Dennis, MA 680

Capitol Visitors Center, a Division of the State Preservation Board, Austin, TX....1389

Captain George Flavel House Museum, Astoria, OR...1218

Carnegie Center for Art & History, New Albany, IN...493

Carroll Mansion Museum Home of Leavenworth County Historical Society, Leavenworth, KS 549

Cartoon Art Museum, San Francisco, CA....164

Casa Navarro State Historical Park, San Antonio, TX..1448

Casemate Museum, Fort Monroe, VA 1505

Cass County Historical Society, Logansport, IN.......................................489

Catholic Historical Society of the Roanoke Valley, Roanoke, VA 1535

Catskill Fly Fishing Center & Museum, Livingston Manor, NY...........................1010

Cattle Raisers Museum, Fort Worth, TX....1416

Cayuga-Owasco Lakes Historical Society, Moravia, NY...1015

Cazenovia College - Art & Design Gallery, Cazenovia, NY..........................976

Cedar Falls Historical Society, Cedar Falls, IA...507

Cedar Key Historical Society Museum, Cedar Key, FL...298

Center for American History, Austin, TX...1390

Center for American Music, Pittsburgh, PA...1291

The Center for Civil War Photography, Gettysburg, PA.....................................1255

Center for Curatorial Studies, Annandale-on-Hudson, NY......................958

Center for Exploratory and Perceptual Art, Buffalo, NY......................................973

Center for Photography at Woodstock, Woodstock, NY 1086

Center for Puppetry Arts, Atlanta, GA 359

Center on Contemporary Art, Seattle, WA.1565

Centerville - Washington Township Historical Society & Asahel Wright Community Center, Centerville, OH 1146

Central Park Conservancy, New York, NY...1022

Cernan Earth & Space Center, River Grove, IL...453

Charles B. Goddard Center for Visual and Performing Arts, Ardmore, OK.......1196

Charles H. Wright Museum of African American History, Detroit, MI................735

Charles M. Schulz Museum and Research Center, Santa Rosa, CA.........................184

Charles Towne Landing State Historic Site, Charleston, SC.................................1324

Charleston Library Society, Charleston, SC..1324

Chattanooga African Museum/Bessie Smith Hall, Chattanooga, TN.................1360

Cherokee Courthouse Visitors Information Center & Museum, Gore, OK...1201

Cherokee Strip Museum, Alva, OK............1195

The Chicago Athenaeum: Museum of Architecture and Design, Galena, IL........436

Chicago Zoological Park (Brookfield Zoo), Brookfield, IL 414

The Children's Museum, Seattle, WA 1565

Chinati Foundation, Marfa, TX 1436

Christiansted National Historic Site, Saint Croix, VI...1644

Cincinnati Fire Museum, Cincinnati, OH...1149

Circus World Museum, Baraboo, WI 1591

City of Wayne Historical Museum, Wayne, MI...766

Clark County Museum, Marshall, IL...........444

Clear Lake Area Historical Museum, Clear Lake, WI......................................1594

Clearwater Historical Museum, Orofino, ID..408

Cleveland State University Art Gallery, Cleveland, OH......................................1153

Clewiston Museum, Inc., Clewiston, FL......300

Cliffs of the Neuse State Park, Seven Springs, NC..1119

Clifton Community Historical Society, Clifton, KS...535

Cloud County Historical Society Museum, Concordia, KS.........................536

Cokato Museum & Akerlund Photography Studio, Cokato, MN...........771

The College Art Gallery, Ewing, NJ 903

College Football Hall of Fame, South Bend, IN..499

Collis P. Huntington Railroad Historical Society, Inc., Huntington, WV...............1583

Colorado River Indian Tribes Museum, Parker, AZ..38

Colorado Ski Museum-Ski & Snowboard Hall of Fame, Vail, CO...........................234

Columbia River Exhibition of History, Science and Technology, Richland, WA...1564

Command Museum, Marine Corps Recruit Depot, San Diego, San Diego, CA..156

Computer History Museum, Mountain View, CA...129

Concord Historical Society, Warner Museum, Springville, NY.......................1071

Concordia Historical Institute, Saint Louis, MO..832

Confederate Museum, New Orleans, LA 594

Contemporary Art Museum St. Louis, Saint Louis, MO......................................832

The Contemporary Arts Center, Cincinnati, OH.....................................1150

Copia: The American Center for Wine, Food & the Arts, Napa, CA....................129

Country Music Hall of Fame and Museum, Country Music Foundation, Nashville, TN..1378

The Cowley County Historical Society, Winfield, KS...564

Cowpens National Battlefield, Chesnee, SC..1327

Crater Lake National Park, Crater Lake, OR..1222

Crawford W. Long Museum, Jefferson, GA...374

Creative Photographic Art Center of Maine, Lewiston, ME...............................614

Croatian Heritage Museum & Library, Eastlake, OH..1163

Crockett Tavern Museum, Morristown, TN..1376

Crook County Museum & Art Gallery, Sundance, WY.......................................1638

Crossroads of America, Bethlehem, NH 883

Crown Point State Historic Site, Crown Point, NY..984

Crystal Rice Plantation, Crowley, LA 588

Czech Center New York, New York, NY...1024

Dade Battlefield Historic State Park, Bushnell, FL...298

Dahlonega Gold Museum State Historic Site, Dahlonega, GA.................................369

Dakota Zoo, Bismarck, ND......................1128

Audiovisual and Film—Continued

The Dallas Center for Contemporary Art
- The Dallas Contemporary, Dallas,
TX 1404
Dallas Museum of Art, Dallas, TX.............1405
The Dan Quayle Center & Museum,
Huntington, IN...481
The Dana-Thomas House State Historic
Site, Springfield, IL.................................458
Darlington Raceway Stock Car Museum,
NMPA Hall of Fame, Darlington, SC....1331
De Graaf Nature Center, Holland, MI.........746
De Saisset Museum, Santa Clara, CA..........180
Deaf Smith County Museum, Hereford,
TX 1424
DeCordova Museum and Sculpture Park,
Lincoln, MA...690
Deerfield Beach Historical Society,
Deerfield Beach, FL.................................304
Degrazia Gallery In The Sun, Tucson, AZ.....48
Delta Cultural Center, Helena, AR 59
Delta Music Museum, Ferriday, LA.............588
Denali National Park and Preserve,
Denali Park, AK...23
Denver Firefighters Museum, Denver, CO...211
The Detroit Institute of Arts, Detroit, MI.....736
Detroit Zoo, Royal Oak, MI 762
Devils Tower Visitor Center, Devils
Tower, WY..1631
DeWitt Stetten, Jr., Museum of Medical
Research, Bethesda, MD..........................637
Dia:Beacon, Riggio Galleries, Beacon,
NY...960
Dia: Chelsea, New York, NY.......................1024
Dr Pepper Museum and Free Enterprise
Institute, Waco, TX.................................1458
Don F. Pratt Memorial Museum, Fort
Campbell, KY...568
Don Harrington Discovery Center,
Amarillo, TX 1387
Door County Historical Museum,
Sturgeon Bay, WI....................................1623
Drake Well Museum, Titusville, PA 1303
Drew County Historical Museum,
Monticello, AR...64
Drummond Island Historical Museum,
Drummond Island, MI.............................739
Dry Falls Interpretive Center, Coulee
City, WA...1551
Duluth Art Institute, Duluth, MN 772
Dusable Museum of African-American
History, Inc., Chicago, IL........................420
Dutchess County Historical Society,
Poughkeepsie, NY....................................1054
Dwight D. Eisenhower Library-Museum,
Abilene, KS..531

EAA AirVenture Museum, Oshkosh, WI....1616
East Texas Oil Museum at Kilgore
College, Kilgore, TX................................1432
Edgar Allan Poe Cottage, Bronx, NY 965
Edgar County Historical Museum, Paris,
IL...449
Edmonds Art Festival Museum,
Edmonds, WA...1553
Edward H. White II Memorial Museum,
Brooks Air Force Base, TX 1397
Egan Maritime Foundation, Nantucket,
MA...695
Eisenhower Birthplace State Historical
Site, Denison, TX....................................1409
El Museo Del Barrio, New York, NY 1025
El Museo Latino, Omaha, NE 870
Elbert Hubbard-Roycroft Museum, East
Aurora, NY...985
Elberton Granite Museum & Exhibit,
Elberton, GA..371
Elwood Haynes Museum, Kokomo, IN.......486
Environmental Education Center,
Somerset County Park Commission,
Basking Ridge, NJ....................................898
Ernie Pyle State Historic Site, Dana, IN.....473

Essex Shipbuilding Museum, Essex, MA 681
Ethnic Heritage Museum, Rockford, IL........455
Eubie Blake National Jazz Institute and
Cultural Center, Baltimore, MD 632
Evergreen Aviation Museum,
McMinnville, OR.....................................1228
Everson Museum of Art, Syracuse, NY.....1076
Experience Music Project, Seattle, WA......1565
Exploris, Raleigh, NC..................................1115

The Fabric Workshop and Museum,
Philadelphia, PA 1279
Fargo Air Museum, Fargo, ND..................1130
Fayette County Helpers Club &
Historical Society, West Union, IA..........530
Fayetteville Museum of Art, Fayetteville,
NC...1100
Feet First: The Scholl Story, Rosalind
Franklin University, North Chicago, IL...448
Fenton Glass Museum, Williamstown,
WV..1589
Fillmore Historical Museum, Inc.,
Fillmore, CA..95
Fine Arts Center for New River Valley,
Pulaski, VA..1526
Fire Museum of Maryland, Inc.,
Lutherville, MD...649
Fire Museum of Memphis, Memphis, TN..1373
1st Cavalry Division Museum, Fort
Hood, TX..1414
The First Division Museum at Cantigny,
Wheaton, IL..465
The Flag House and Star-Spangled
Banner Museum, Baltimore, MD............632
Flandrau Science Center and Planetarium,
Tucson, AZ...49
Flint Institute of Arts, Flint, MI.................741
Flint Ridge State Memorial Museum,
Glenford, OH...1166
Florence Griswold Museum, Old Lyme,
CT...258
Florida Holocaust Museum, Saint
Petersburg, FL..341
Folger Shakespeare Library, Washington,
DC...278
Folk Art Society of America, Richmond,
VA...1529
Folsom History Museum, Folsom, CA...........95
Ford House Visitor Center and Museum,
Mendocino, CA..125
Fort Abraham Lincoln State Park,
Mandan, ND...1134
The Fort at No. 4 Living History
Museum, Charlestown, NH......................884
Fort Bliss Museum, Fort Bliss, TX 1413
Fort Christmas Historical Park,
Christmas, FL...299
Fort Crawford Museum, Prairie du Chien,
WI...1618
Fort Davis National Historic Site, Fort
Davis, TX...1414
Fort Hartsuff State Historical Park,
Burwell, NE..858
Fort Kearney Museum, Kearney, NE 863
Fort King George Historic Site, Darien,
GA...370
Fort Leaton State Historical Site,
Presidio, TX...1444
Fort MacArthur Museum, San Pedro, CA....176
Fort McAllister, Richmond Hill, GA............381
Fort Ontario State Historic Site, Oswego,
NY...1048
Fort Raleigh National Historic Site,
Manteo, NC..1110
Fort Selden State Monument, Radium
Springs, NM...945
Fort Sidney Museum & Post
Commander's Home, Sidney, NE............873
Fort Sisseton State Historical Park, Lake
City, SD..1350
Forts Folle Avoine Historic Park,
Danbury, WI...1594

45th Infantry Division Museum,
Oklahoma City, OK.................................1207
Foster Gallery, University of
Wisconsin-Eau Claire, Eau Claire, WI..1596
Fountain Rock Nature Center,
Walkersville, MD......................................656
Frances Young Tang Teaching Museum
and Art Gallery, Saratoga Springs, NY .1064
Franklin Furnace Archive, Inc., Brooklyn,
NY...969
Frederick Douglass National Historic
Site, Washington, DC...............................279
Freedman Gallery-Albright College,
Reading, PA...1296
Freeport Historical Society, Freeport, ME....611
French Art Colony, Gallipolis, OH 1165
The French Legation Museum, Austin,
TX...1390
The Friends of Lucy Hayes Heritage
Center, Chillicothe, OH..........................1147

Gallery of Contemporary Art, University
of Colorado, Colorado Springs,
Colorado Springs, CO.............................207
Gatekeeper's Museum & Marion
Steinbach Indian Basket Museum,
Tahoe City, CA..190
Geddes Historic District Village, Geddes,
SD...1347
General Crook House Museum and
Library/Archives Center, Omaha, NE......870
The General Douglas L. McBride
Museum, New Mexico Military
Institute, Roswell, NM.............................945
The George Bush Presidential Library
and Museum, College Station, TX 1400
George C. Marshall Museum, Lexington,
VA...1513
George Eastman House/International
Museum of Photography and Film,
Rochester, NY..1058
George Meany Memorial Archives, Silver
Spring, MD...654
Georgia Aquarium, Atlanta, GA 360
Georgia Music Hall of Fame and
Museum, Macon, GA...............................377
Georgia Salzburger Society Museum,
Rincon, GA...381
Germantown Historical Society,
Philadelphia, PA......................................1280
Gig Harbor Peninsula Historical Society,
Gig Harbor, WA.......................................1555
The Gilbert Stuart Birthplace and
Museum, Saunderstown, RI.....................1319
Glenn L. Martin Maryland Aviation
Museum, Baltimore, MD..........................632
Gnadenhutten Historical Park & Museum,
Gnadenhutten, OH...................................1167
Gold Coast Railroad Museum, Inc.,
Miami, FL...323
Golden Spike National Historic Site,
Brigham City, UT....................................1463
Gone With The Wind Movie Museum,
Marietta, GA..379
Governor's Mansion State Historic Park,
Sacramento, CA..152
Graceland, Memphis, TN 1373
Grand Rapids Art Museum, Grand
Rapids, MI...743
Grand Traverse Heritage Center, Traverse
City, MI..765
Grant County Historical Museum,
Ephrata, WA...1553
Grant County Museum aka Historic
Adobe Museum, Ulysses, KS..................560
Gravette Historical Museum, Gravette,
AR...59
Graycliff Conservancy, Derby, NY 984
Great Harbor Maritime Museum,
Northeast Harbor, ME..............................616
Great Lakes Naval Memorial and
Museum, Muskegon, MI..........................757
The Great Overland Station, Topeka, KS....559

Great Sand Dunes National Monument and Preserve, Mosca, CO 229
Greeley History Museum, Greeley, CO........221
Green Bay Packers Hall of Fame, Green Bay, WI...1598
Greybull Museum, Greybull, WY 1634
Grier Musser Museum, Los Angeles, CA 115
Groveland Yosemite Gateway Museum, Groveland, CA...101
Guadalupe Mountains National Park, Salt Flat, TX...1447
Gulf Coast Exploreum Science Center, Mobile, AL...13

H.E.A.R.T.S. Veterans Museum of Texas, Huntsville, TX.......................................1430
H. Earl Clack Museum, Havre, MT 849
Haas-Lilienthal House, San Francisco, CA..166
Halifax Historical Museum, Daytona Beach, FL...303
Hamilton Van Wagoner Museum, Clifton, NJ..901
Hampton Roads Naval Museum, Norfolk, VA...1521
Hanby House, Westerville, OH 1191
The Harness Racing Museum and Hall of Fame, Goshen, NY.................................995
Harpers Ferry Center, Harpers Ferry, WV .1582
Harry Ransom Center at the University of Texas at Austin, Austin, TX 1390
Harry S. Truman Library-Museum, Independence, MO.....................................818
Harry S. Truman Little White House Museum, Key West, FL.........................317
Harvey County Historical Society, Newton, KS...553
Hatton Gallery, Colorado State University, Fort Collins, CO.................217
Hawaii Maritime Center, Honolulu, HI........395
Heard Museum, Phoenix, AZ........................40
Heart of West Texas Museum, Colorado City, TX...1401
Hellenic Museum & Cultural Center, Chicago, IL..421
The Hemingway Museum and The Ernest Hemingway Birthplace, Oak Park, IL 448
Henry Art Gallery, Seattle, WA 1566
Herbert F. Johnson Museum of Art, Ithaca, NY...1003
Herbert Hoover Presidential Library-Museum, West Branch, IA..........530
Heritage Center Museum, Berryville, AR 55
The Heritage Museum, Baltimore, MD.......632
The Heritage Museum of Fine Arts for Youth, Detroit, MI.................................736
Heritage Preservation, Washington, DC 280
Heritage Square Museum, Ontario, NY 1047
Hibel Museum of Art, Jupiter, FL...............316
The High Museum of Art, Atlanta, GA.......360
Highlands Center for Natural History, Prescott, AZ...42
Highlands Hammock State Park/Civilian Conservation Corps Museum, Sebring, FL..346
Hiller Aviation Institute, San Carlos, CA 155
Hiram Blauvelt Art Museum, Oradell, NJ....919
The Hispanic Society of America, New York, NY...1027
Historic Edenton State Historic Site, Edenton, NC...1099
Historic Halifax State Historic Site, Halifax, NC...1105
Historic Landmarks Foundation of Indiana, Indianapolis, IN.........................482
Historic Langhorne Association, Langhorne, PA......................................1267
Historic Pullman Foundation, Chicago, IL...421
Historical Museum of Bay County, Bay City, MI...727
Historical Society of Brookfield, Brookfield Center, VT............................1477

The Historical Society of Dauphin County, Harrisburg, PA 1258
Historical Society of Palm Beach County, Palm Beach, FL.......................334
Historical Society of St. Marys and Benzinger Township, Saint Marys, PA ..1297
Historical Society of the Phoenixville Area, Phoenixville, PA 1290
The History Center, Cedar Rapids, IA 509
Hollywood Guinness World of Records Museum, Hollywood, CA 103
Hollywood Heritage Museum, Hollywood, CA...103
Hollywood History Museum, Hollywood, CA..103
Holocaust Memorial Center, Farmington Hills, MI..741
Holocaust Memorial Resource and Education Center of Florida, Inc., Maitland, FL...322
Holocaust Museum Houston, Houston, TX..1426
Holocaust Museum of Southwest Florida, Naples, FL...328
Holy Trinity (Old Swedes) Church & Hendrickson House Museum, Wilmington, DE.....................................274
Home of Franklin D. Roosevelt National Historic Site, Hyde Park, NY 1002
Homestead National Monument of America, Beatrice, NE...........................857
Honolulu Academy of Arts, Honolulu, HI ...395
Hood Museum of Art, Hanover, NH...........888
Hoopa Valley Tribal Museum, Hoopa, CA..103
Hoover Historical Center, North Canton, OH..1179
The Houdini Museum & Theater, Scranton, PA...1298
Houghton County Historical Museum Society, Lake Linden, MI.......................749
House of Broadcasting Radio & Television Museum, Scottsdale, AZ 44
House of the Temple, Washington, DC 280
Hudson River Maritime Museum, Kingston, NY......................................1007
Hulihee Palace, Kailua-Kona, HI.................399
Humboldt Redwoods State Park Visitor Center, Weott, CA 197
The Humphrey Forum, Minneapolis, MN....782
Hungarian Folk-Art Museum, Port Orange, FL...338
Huntington Beach International Surfing Museum, Huntington Beach, CA.............104
Huron City Museums, Port Austin, MI.......761
Hutchinson County Museum, Borger, TX ..1397
Hyde Park Art Center, Chicago, IL 421
Hydroplane & Raceboat Museum, Kent, WA...1557

IMF Center, Washington, DC 281
Indian Hill Historical Society, Cincinnati, OH...1150
Indian Museum of Lake County, Ohio, Willoughby, OH.................................1191
Indiana Basketball Hall of Fame, New Castle, IN...494
Indiana Historical Society, Indianapolis, IN...483
Indiana War Memorials, Indianapolis, IN 484
Inland Seas Maritime Museum, Vermilion, OH...1189
Institute of American Indian Arts Museum, Santa Fe, NM..........................947
Institute of Contemporary Art, University of Pennsylvania, Philadelphia, PA 1282
Interlaken Historical Society, Interlaken, NY...1002
International Bluegrass Music Museum, Owensboro, KY......................................581
International Bowling Museum and Hall of Fame, Saint Louis, MO 833

International Center of Photography, New York, NY...1028
International Gospel Music Hall of Fame & Museum, Detroit, MI...........................737
International Motor Racing Research Center at Watkins Glen, Watkins Glen, NY...1084
International Museum of Cultures, Dallas, TX..1406
International Museum of the Horse, Lexington, KY...573
International Swimming Hall of Fame, Inc., Fort Lauderdale, FL........................307
International Tennis Hall of Fame & Museum, Newport, RI.........................1313
International UFO Museum and Research Center, Roswell, NM................................946
International Women's Air and Space Museum, Inc., Cleveland, OH................1155
Irish American Heritage Museum, Albany, NY...954
Ironworld Discovery Center, Chisholm, MN..771
Iroquois Indian Museum, Howes Cave, NY...999
Isanti County Historical Society, Cambridge, MN.......................................770
Ischua Valley Historical Society, Inc., Franklinville, NY.....................................992

J.E. Reeves Home & Museum, Dover, OH..1163
J.L. Scott Marine Education Center and Aquarium, Gulf Coast Research Laboratory College of Marine Sciences, The U. of Southern Mississippi, Biloxi, MS............................798
Jackson County Historical Museum, Lakefield, MN...778
Jacksonville Maritime Museum Society, Jacksonville, FL..314
James A. McFaul Environmental Center of Bergen County, Wyckoff, NJ.............931
James S. Copley Library, La Jolla, CA........106
James W. Dillon House Museum, Dillon, SC..1331
Japanese American National Museum, Los Angeles, CA.......................................117
Jarrell Plantation Georgia State Historic Site, Juliette, GA 374
The Jefferson County Historical Assoc., Steubenville, OH..1186
Jericho Historical Society, Jericho Corners, VT......................................1480
Jesse James Farm & Museum, Kearney, MO..823
The Jewish Museum, New York, NY.........1029
Jewish Museum of Florida, Miami Beach, FL...326
Jewish Museum of Maryland, Baltimore, MD..633
Jim Crow Museum - Ferris State University, Big Rapids, MI 729
Jimmy Carter National Historic Site, Plains, GA...381
The Jimmy Stewart Museum, Indiana, PA.1262
John F. Kennedy Presidential Library & Museum, Boston, MA.............................666
John G. Neihardt State Historic Site, Bancroft, NE...856
John Hutchings Museum of Natural History, Lehi, UT.....................................1466
The John Nicholas Brown Center for the Study of American Civilization, Providence, RI.......................................1317
John Rivers Communications Museum, Charleston, SC.....................................1325
Johnson County Community College, Gallery of Art, Overland Park, KS.........555
Johnstown Flood National Memorial, South Fork, PA.....................................1300
Joliet Area Historical Museum, Joliet, IL 440
Judah L. Magnes Museum, Berkeley, CA......76

Audiovisual and Film–Continued

Judy Garland Museum, Grand Rapids, MN 777

Kalamazoo Aviation History Museum, Kalamazoo, MI 748

Kansas Aviation Museum, Wichita, KS 562

Kansas Department of Wildlife & Parks, Pratt, KS 556

Karl E. Mundt Historical & Educational Foundation, Madison, SD 1351

Kate Shelley Railroad Museum, Boone, IA 506

Kellogg's Cereal City USA, Battle Creek, MI 727

Kenilworth Aquatic Gardens, Washington, DC 281

Kennesaw Mountain National Battlefield Park, Kennesaw, GA 374

Kentucky Derby Museum, Louisville, KY ...576

Kentucky Military History Museum, Frankfort, KY 569

Kentucky Railway Museum, Inc., New Haven, KY 580

King Kamehameha V-Judiciary History Center, Honolulu, HI 397

Kirby Science Discovery Center at the Washington Pavilion, Sioux Falls, SD ...1356

Klondike Gold Rush National Historical Park, Seattle, WA 1566

Knights of Columbus Museum, New Haven, CT 253

Knox County Museum, Benjamin, TX 1395

Kolomoki Mounds State Park Museum, Blakely, GA 366

Korean War Veterans National Museum & Library, Rantoul, IL 453

The Kurdish Museum, Brooklyn, NY 969

La Puente Valley Historical Society City Hall, LaPuente, CA 107

LACE (Los Angeles Contemporary Exhibitions), Los Angeles, CA 117

The Lace Museum, Sunnyvale, CA 190

The Lackawanna Historical Society at the Catlin House, Scranton, PA 1298

The Lacrosse Museum & National Hall of Fame/US Lacrosse, Baltimore, MD 633

Lafayette Miners Museum, Lafayette, CO ...224

Lahaina Restoration Foundation, Lahaina, HI 400

Lake County Historic Courthouse Museum, Lakeport, CA 108

Lake Hopatcong Historical Museum, Landing, NJ 909

Lake Jackson Historical Museum, Lake Jackson, TX 1433

Lake Meredith Aquatic and Wildlife Museum, Fritch, TX 1420

Lake Shore Railway Museum, North East, PA 1274

Lake Tahoe Historical Society & Museum, South Lake Tahoe, CA 188

Land of the Yankee Fork Historic Association Museum, Stanley, ID 410

Larchmont Historical Society, Mamaroneck, NY 1013

Lars Noak Blacksmith Shop, Larsson/Ostlund Log Home & One-Room Capitol School, New Sweden, ME 616

Las Cabezas de San Juan Nature Reserve (El Faro), Fajardo, PR 1641

Las Vegas Art Museum, Las Vegas, NV 879

Latvian Museum, Rockville, MD 651

Lauder Museum - Amityville Historical Society, Amityville, NY 957

The Laurel Museum, Laurel, MD 648

Laurence C. Jones Museum, Piney Woods, MS 807

Lawrence Heritage State Park, Lawrence, MA 689

Le Sueur Museum, Le Sueur, MN 779

Lea County Cowboy Hall of Fame and Western Heritage Center, Hobbs, NM 940

Legends of New Mexico Museum, Algodones, NM 936

Legends of the Game Baseball Museum and Learning Center, Arlington, TX 1388

Lesbian Herstory Educational Foundation, Inc. aka Lesbian Herstory Archives, Brooklyn, NY 969

Lewis County Historical Society Museum, Lowville, NY 1012

Liberace Museum & Foundation, Las Vegas, NV 879

Liberty Jail Historic Site, Liberty, MO 826

Library of Congress, Washington, DC 282

Library of the Supreme Council, 33 Degrees, Washington, DC 282

The Light Factory - Museum of Photography & Film, Charlotte, NC 1095

Lillian and Albert Small Jewish Museum, Washington, DC 282

The Lincoln Museum, Fort Wayne, IN 478

Lincoln Park Historical Museum, Lincoln Park, MI 751

Lincoln's New Salem State Historic Site, Petersburg, IL 451

Linn County Historical Museum and Moyer House, Brownsville, OR 1220

Little White Schoolhouse, Ripon, WI 1620

The Living Arts and Science Center, Inc., Lexington, KY 573

Logoly State Park, McNeil, AR 64

Lone Star Flight Museum/Texas Aviation Hall of Fame, Galveston, TX 1421

Long Island Culture History Lab & Museum, Commack, NY 980

Longwood Gardens, Kennett Square, PA ...1264

The Los Angeles Art Association/Gallery 825, Los Angeles, CA 117

Los Angeles Maritime Museum, San Pedro, CA 176

Los Angeles Museum of the Holocaust, Los Angeles, CA 118

Los Angeles Police Historical Society & Museum, Los Angeles, CA 119

Lou Holtz/Upper Ohio Valley Hall of Fame, East Liverpool, OH 1163

Louisiana State Museum, New Orleans, LA 596

Louisiana's Old State Capitol, Political History Museum, Baton Rouge, LA 587

Louisville Slugger Museum & Factory, Louisville, KY 577

Lowell Area Historical Museum, Lowell, MI 751

Lowell Observatory, Flagstaff, AZ 33

Loxahatchee River Historical Society, Jupiter, FL 316

Lucy-Desi Museum, Jamestown, NY 1005

Lutheran Heritage Center & Museum of the Perry County Lutheran Historical Society, Altenburg, MO 810

Luzerne County Historical Society, Wilkes-Barre, PA 1307

Lynchburg Museum System, Lynchburg, VA 1515

Lyndon Baines Johnson Library and Museum, Austin, TX 1391

MIT Museum, Cambridge, MA 674

Madison County Historical Society-Cottage Lawn, Oneida, NY 1045

Madison Museum of Contemporary Art, Madison, WI 1605

Madison Museum of Fine Art, Madison, GA 378

The Magic Lantern Castle Museum, San Antonio, TX 1448

Maine Maritime Museum, Bath, ME 606

Malki Museum, Banning, CA 74

Manassas Museum System, Manassas, VA 1516

Marathon County Historical Society, Wausau, WI 1626

Mardi Gras Museum, Kenner, LA 589

The Margaret Mitchell House & Museum, Atlanta, GA 361

Marias Museum of History and Art, Shelby, MT 853

The Marine Museum at Fall River, Inc., Fall River, MA 682

Mario Lanza Institute/Museum, Philadelphia, PA 1282

Maritime Museum at Historic Coast Guard Station, Saint Simons Island, GA 383

Maritime Museum of Monterey, Monterey, CA 127

Martin and Osa Johnson Safari Museum, Inc., Chanute, KS 535

Martinez Museum, Martinez, CA 124

Marvin Newton House, Brookfield, VT 1477

The Mary Baker Eddy Library for the Betterment of Humanity, Boston, MA 666

Mary McLeod Bethune Council House National Historic Site, Washington, DC 283

MASS MoCA, North Adams, MA 698

Matchless Mine Museum (Leadville Assembly), Leadville, CO 226

The Mattatuck Museum Arts and History Center, Waterbury, CT 264

Mattress Factory, Ltd., Pittsburgh, PA 1293

May Natural History Museum and Museum of Space Exploration, Colorado Springs, CO 207

McDonald's #1 Store Museum, Des Plaines, IL 431

Meadow Brook Hall, Rochester, MI 761

Mechanicsburg Museum Association, Mechanicsburg, PA 1270

Meigs County Museum, Pomeroy, OH 1183

Memphis Brooks Museum of Art, Memphis, TN 1374

Mendocino County Museum, Willits, CA 198

Mennonite Library and Archives, North Newton, KS 554

The Metropolitan Museum of Art, New York, NY 1030

Metropolitan State College of Denver/Center for Visual Art, Denver, CO 212

Mexic-Arte Museum, Austin, TX 1391

Miami Art Museum, Miami, FL 324

Miami-Dade College Kendall Campus Art Gallery, Miami, FL 324

Michigan Maritime Museum, South Haven, MI 764

Michigan Transit Museum, Inc., Mount Clemens, MI 756

Mid-America Air Museum, Liberal, KS 549

Mid-Hudson Children's Museum, Poughkeepsie, NY 1055

Midland County Historical Museum, Midland, TX 1438

Midwest Old Settlers & Threshers Association, Inc., Mount Pleasant, IA 524

Mighty Eighth Air Force Museum, Pooler, GA 381

Military Veterans Museum, Inc., Oshkosh, WI 1616

Mille Lacs Indian Museum, Onamia, MN ...786

Mingei International Museum, San Diego, CA 157

Minnesota Air National Guard Historical Foundation, Inc., Saint Paul, MN 790

Minnesota Historical Society, Saint Paul, MN 791

Minute Man National Historical Park, Concord, MA 676

Mississippi Baptist Historical Commission, Clinton, MS 799

Mississippi River Museum at Mud Island River Park, Memphis, TN 1375

Mississippi University for Women, Archives and Museum, Columbus, MS...800

Missoula Art Museum, Missoula, MT.........851

Modern Art Museum of Fort Worth, Fort Worth, TX................1418

Monocacy National Battlefield, Frederick, MD................644

Monroe County Heritage Museum, Monroeville, AL................15

Montauk Point Lighthouse Museum, Montauk, NY................1015

Monterey Bay Aquarium, Monterey, CA.....127

Monterey History and Art Association, Monterey, CA................127

Montgomery Zoo, Montgomery, AL..............17

Moores Creek National Battlefield, Currie, NC................1097

Morehead Planetarium and Science Center, Chapel Hill, NC................1093

Moriarty Historical Museum, Moriarty, NM................943

Mormon Visitors Center, Independence, MO................818

Morris Museum of Art, Augusta, GA...........365

Mote Marine Laboratory/Aquarium, Sarasota, FL................345

Motorcycle Hall of Fame Museum, Pickerington, OH................1182

Motown Historical Museum, Detroit, MI.....737

Motts Military Museum, Groveport, OH.......1167

Mount Rushmore National Memorial, Keystone, SD................1350

The Movie Museum, Owosso, MI................759

Murrell Home, Park Hill, OK................1211

Museo de Las Americas, San Juan, PR.......1642

Museo Fuerte Conde de Mirasol de Vieques, Vieques, PR................1644

Museum and Arts Center in the Sequim Dungeness Valley, Sequim, WA.............1570

The Museum of African Culture, Portland, ME................619

Museum of Alaska Transportation & Industry, Inc., Wasilla, AK................29

The Museum of American Illustration at the Society of Illustrators, New York, NY................1031

Museum of Ancient Artifacts, Las Vegas, NV................879

Museum of Art and History at the McPherson Center, Santa Cruz, CA........182

Museum of Art/Fort Lauderdale, Fort Lauderdale, FL................307

Museum of Astrogeology, Meteor Crater, Winslow, AZ................53

Museum of Chinese in the Americas, New York, NY................1032

Museum of Contemporary Art Cleveland, Cleveland, OH................1155

Museum of Contemporary Art (MoCA), North Miami, FL................329

The Museum of Contemporary Art of Georgia (MOCA GA), Atlanta, GA.........362

Museum of Contemporary Art of Puerto Rico, Santurce, PR................1644

Museum of Contemporary Art San Diego, La Jolla, CA................106

Museum of Contemporary Art San Diego - Downtown, San Diego, CA................157

Museum of Contemporary Religious Art (MOCRA)-St. Louis University, Saint Louis, MO................835

Museum of Cosmetology, Chicago, IL.........425

Museum of Fife and Drum, Ivoryton, CT....246

The Museum of Fine Arts, Houston, Houston, TX................1428

The Museum of Flight, Seattle, WA...........1567

Museum of Flying, Santa Monica, CA........183

Museum of Jewish Heritage-A Living Memorial to the Holocaust, New York, NY................1032

The Museum of Man in the Sea, Inc., Panama City Beach, FL................335

The Museum of Modern Art, New York, NY................1033

Museum of Natural History, Marshall, MN................780

Museum of Northwest Art, La Conner, WA................1557

The Museum of Nursing History, Inc., Philadelphia, PA................1283

Museum of Photographic Arts, San Diego, CA................158

Museum of Robotics, Orinda, CA................136

Museum of Rural Life, Denton, MD............642

Museum of San Diego History and Research Library, San Diego, CA...........158

The Museum of Southern History, Sugarland, TX................1454

The Museum of Television & Radio, New York, NY................1033

The Museum of Television & Radio, Beverly Hills, CA................78

The Museum of the Alphabet, Waxhaw, NC................1121

Museum of the Arkansas Grand Prairie, Stuttgart, AR................69

Museum of the Berkeley Springs, Berkeley Springs, WV................1580

Museum of the Cherokee Indian, Cherokee, NC................1096

Museum of the Cherokee Strip, Enid, OK.1200

Museum of the City of New York, New York, NY................1033

Museum of the Jimmy Carter Library, Atlanta, GA................362

Museum of the Moving Image, Astoria, NY................958

Museum of the National Center of Afro-American Artists, Roxbury, MA.....706

Museum of the Plains Indian, Browning, MT................843

Museum of the Southern Jewish Experience, Jackson, MS................803

Museum of the Waxhaws & Andrew Jackson Memorial, Waxhaw, NC...........1122

Museum of Tolerance, Los Angeles, CA.....120

Museum of Transportation, Saint Louis, MO................835

Museum of Women's History, Billings, MT................841

Museum of Yachting, Newport, RI.............1314

Mystic Seaport - The Museum of America and the Sea, Mystic, CT...........251

NASA Glenn Research Center's Visitor Center, Cleveland, OH................1155

Nantucket Historical Association, Nantucket, MA................696

Naper Settlement, Naperville, IL................447

NASA Kennedy Space Center, Merritt Island, FL................323

National Afro-American Museum & Cultural Center, Wilberforce, OH.........1191

The National Agricultural Center & Hall of Fame, Bonner Springs, KS................534

National Air and Space Museum, Washington, DC................283

National Archives and Records Administration, Washington, DC.............284

National Baseball Hall of Fame and Museum, Inc., Cooperstown, NY...........981

The National Border Patrol Museum and Memorial Library, El Paso, TX...........1412

National Canal Museum, Hugh Moore Historical Park and Museums, Easton, PA................1250

National Civil Rights Museum, Memphis, TN................1375

National Corvette Museum, Bowling Green, KY................566

National First Ladies' Library, Canton, OH................1145

National Football Museum, Inc., Canton, OH................1145

National Geographic Museum at Explorers Hall, Washington, DC.............285

National Hispanic Cultural Center, Art Museum, Albuquerque, NM................935

National Italian American Sports Hall of Fame, Chicago, IL................425

National Liberty Museum, Philadelphia, PA................1284

National Medal of Honor Museum of Military History, Chattanooga, TN........1362

National Museum of African Art, Smithsonian Institution, Washington, DC................285

National Museum of American Jewish Military History, Washington, DC...........286

The National Museum of Communications, Richardson, TX.........1445

National Museum of Dance & Hall of Fame, Saratoga Springs, NY................1065

National Museum of Health and Medicine, Washington, DC................286

National Museum of Industrial History, Bethlehem, PA................1243

National Museum of Natural History, Washington, DC................286

National Museum of Naval Aviation, Pensacola, FL................336

National Museum of Patriotism, Atlanta, GA................362

National Museum of Polo and Hall of Fame, Inc., Lake Worth, FL................320

National Museum of Racing and Hall of Fame, Saratoga Springs, NY................1065

National Museum of Roller Skating, Lincoln, NE................866

National Museum of the American Indian, Washington, DC................286

National Museum of the American Indian, Smithsonian Institution, New York, NY................1034

National Museum of the Morgan Horse, Shelburne, VT................1487

National Museum of the United States Air Force, Wright-Patterson Air Force Base, OH................1193

National Museum of Wildlife Art, Jackson, WY................1634

National Museum of Women in the Arts, Washington, DC................287

National Ornamental Metal Museum, Memphis, TN................1375

National Postal Museum, Smithsonian Institution, Washington, DC................287

National Railroad Museum, Green Bay, WI................1599

National Scouting Museum, Irving, TX.....1430

National Soaring Museum, Elmira, NY.......988

The National Soccer Hall of Fame, Oneonta, NY................1046

National Sprint Car Hall of Fame & Museum, Knoxville, IA................521

National Steeplechase Museum, Camden, SC................1323

National Steinbeck Center, Salinas, CA.......154

National Temple Hill Association, Inc., New Windsor, NY................1018

National Voting Rights Museum and Institute, Selma, AL................18

National Warplane Museum, Horseheads, NY................999

The National World War II Museum, New Orleans, LA................597

National Wrestling Hall of Fame, Stillwater, OK................1214

Native American Resource Center, Pembroke, NC................1114

Naugatuck Historical Society, Naugatuck, CT................251

The Nelson-Atkins Museum of Art, Kansas City, MO................822

Nevada Historical Society, Reno, NV.........881

New Braunfels Museum of Art & Music, New Braunfels, TX................1440

Audiovisual and Film–Continued

New Castle Historical Society - Horace
    Greeley House, Chappaqua, NY 977
New England Fire and History Museum,
    Brewster, MA 670
New England Ski Museum, Franconia,
    NH 888
New Jersey Naval Museum, Hackensack,
    NJ 905
New Jersey State Police Museum, West
    Trenton, NJ 930
The New Museum of Contemporary Art,
    New York, NY 1035
New Sweden Historical Society, New
    Sweden, ME 616
New York City Fire Museum, New York,
    NY 1035
New York City Police Museum, New
    York, NY 1035
The New York Public Library for the
    Performing Arts, New York, NY 1036
Newseum, Washington, DC 288
Nez Perce National Historical Park,
    Spalding, ID 409
Niagara Gorge Discovery Center, Niagara
    Falls, NY 1042
Nicollet County Historical Society, Saint
    Peter, MN 793
North Alabama Railroad Museum,
    Huntsville, AL 12
North Carolina Aquarium at Fort Fisher,
    Kure Beach, NC 1109
North Carolina Auto Racing Hall of
    Fame, Mooresville, NC 1111
North Carolina Transportation Museum,
    Spencer, NC 1120
North Carolina Zoological Park,
    Asheboro, NC 1088
North Dakota Museum of Art, Grand
    Forks, ND 1132
North Star Museum of Boy Scouting and
    Girl Scouting, North Saint Paul, MN 785
North Tonawanda History Museum,
    North Tonawanda, NY 1043
Northeast Louisiana Delta African
    American Heritage Museum, Monroe,
    LA 592
Northeast Oakland Historical Museum,
    Oxford, MI 759
Northeastern Nevada Museum, Elko, NV 876
Northfield Historical Society Museum,
    Northfield, MN 785
Novato History Museum, Novato, CA 132

O. Henry Museum, Austin, TX..............1391
O. Winston Link Museum, Roanoke, VA..1535
Ocean City Life-Saving Station Museum,
    Ocean City, MD 650
Ocean County Historical Museum, Toms
    River, NJ 926
Odyssey Maritime Discovery Center,
    Seattle, WA 1567
The Ogden Museum of Southern Art,
    University of New Orleans, New
    Orleans, LA 598
Ohef Sholom Temple Archives, Norfolk,
    VA 1523
Oklahoma City Museum of Art,
    Oklahoma City, OK 1208
Oklahoma Historical Society, Oklahoma
    City, OK 1209
Oklahoma Museum of History, Oklahoma
    City, OK 1210
Oklahoma Route 66 Museum, Clinton,
    OK 1198
Oklahoma Territorial Museum, Guthrie,
    OK 1202
Old Conway Homestead Complex and
    Museum, Camden, ME....................608
Old Fort Bissell Museum, Phillipsburg, KS .555
Old Fort Meade Museum and Historic
    Research Association, Fort Meade, SD .1347

Old Manchester Museum, Manchester,
    CT 248
Old Market House State Historic Site,
    Galena, IL 436
The Old Schwamb Mill, Arlington, MA 660
Old State House Museum, Little Rock,
    AR 63
Olde Colonial Courthouse, Tales of Cape
    Cod, Inc., Barnstable, MA 661
Oldham County History Center, La
    Grange, KY 572
Oneida Nation Museum, De Pere, WI........1594
Opelousas Museum and Interpretive
    Center, Opelousas, LA 599
Orange County Museum of Art, Newport
    Beach, CA 130
Orange County Regional History Center,
    Orlando, FL 331
Oregon Electric Railway Historical
    Society, Inc., Salem, OR 1236
Oregon Historical Society, Portland, OR....1231
Oregon-Jerusalem Historical Museum,
    Oregon, OH 1181
Osage Nation Tribal Museum, Pawhuska,
    OK 1212
Oscar Getz Museum of Whiskey History
    And The Bardstown Historical
    Museum, Bardstown, KY 565
Ossining Historical Society Museum,
    Ossining, NY 1047
Otis Chidester Scout Museum of
    Southern Arizona, Tucson, AZ 50
Ottawa Scouting Museum, Ottawa, IL 449
Owens Community College/Walter E.
    Terhune Gallery, Perrysburg, OH........1182
Oz Museum, Wamego, KS 560
The Ozark Folk Center, Mountain View,
    AR 65

The P.T. Boat Museum & Library,
    Germantown, TN 1365
Pablo Casals Museum, Old San Juan, PR..1641
Pacific Aviation Museum - Pearl Harbor,
    Honolulu, HI 397
Pacific Northwest Truck Museum,
    Brooks, OR 1220
Painted Post - Erwin Museum at the
    Depot, Painted Post, NY 1050
Pajaro Valley Historical Association,
    Watsonville, CA 196
PALCO, Scotia, CA 186
Palos Verdes Art Center, Rancho Palos
    Verdes, CA 145
Paper Airplane Museum and the Tin Can
    Man of Maui, Kahului Central Maui,
    HI 399
Paper Discovery Center, Appleton, WI 1590
Parishville Museum, Parishville, NY.........1050
Parris Island Museum, Parris Island, SC....1338
Pascack Historical Society, Park Ridge,
    NJ 920
Paul and Lulu Hilliard University Art
    Museum, University of Louisiana at
    Lafayette, Lafayette, LA 590
Paul Bunyan Logging Camp Museum,
    Eau Claire, WI 1596
Paul W. Bryant Museum, Tuscaloosa, AL......19
The Peary-MacMillan Arctic Museum,
    Brunswick, ME 608
The Peekskill Museum, Peekskill, NY.......1051
Pendleton District Historical, Recreational
    and Tourism Commission, Pendleton,
    SC 1339
Pennsylvania Federation of Museums and
    Historical Organizations, Harrisburg,
    PA 1259
Pennsylvania Trolley Museum,
    Washington, PA 1305
Petaluma Adobe State Historic Park,
    Petaluma, CA 142
Petrified Creatures Museum of Natural
    History, Richfield Springs, NY 1057

Philadelphia Mummers Museum,
    Philadelphia, PA 1285
Philmont Museums, Cimarron, NM...........938
Phoebe Apperson Hearst Museum of
    Anthropology, Berkeley, CA 77
Piatt Castles, West Liberty, OH 1190
The Picker Art Gallery, Hamilton, NY......997
Piedmont Environmental Center, High
    Point, NC 1107
Pierre Menard Home State Historic Site,
    Ellis Grove, IL 433
Pima Air & Space Museum, Tucson, AZ.......50
Pimeria Alta Historical Society, Nogales,
    AZ 37
Pine Bluff/Jefferson County Historical
    Museum, Pine Bluff, AR 66
Pioneer-Krier Museum, Ashland, KS 532
Pioneer Museum - Martin County
    Historical Society, Fairmont, MN 775
Piper Aviation Museum Foundation, Lock
    Haven, PA 1269
Pipestone National Monument, Pipestone,
    MN 787
Pittsburgh Center for the Arts, Pittsburgh,
    PA 1293
Pittsford Historical Society Museum,
    Pittsford, VT 1484
Planetarium at the Reading Public
    Museum, Reading, PA 1296
Polish Heritage Center, Ashton, NE 856
Portland Museum, Louisville, KY 578
Potter's Wax Museum, Saint Augustine,
    FL 339
Prairie Grove Battlefield State Park,
    Prairie Grove, AR 66
President James K. Polk State Historic
    Site, Pineville, NC 1114
Presidential Pet Museum, Lothian, MD 649
Presidio La Bahia, Goliad, TX 1423
Pro Rodeo Hall of Fame & Museum of
    the American Cowboy, Colorado
    Springs, CO 207
Promont House Museum, Milford, OH 1176
Providence Canyon State Park, Lumpkin,
    GA 377
Provisions Library, Washington, DC 289
Public Library of Charlotte and
    Mecklenburg County, Charlotte, NC 1096
Pueblo of Pojoaque, Poeh Museum, Santa
    Fe, NM 949

QCC Art Gallery, Bayside, NY 960
Queen Mary Museum, Long Beach, CA 111
Queens Historical Society, Flushing, NY 990
Queens Museum of Art, Queens, NY.........1056
Quoddy Maritime Museum, Eastport, ME ...610

RV/MH Heritage Foundation, Inc.,
    Elkhart, IN 475
Railroad Museum of Pennsylvania,
    Strasburg, PA 1302
Rattlesnake Museum (American
    International), Albuquerque, NM 935
Ravalli County Museum/Bitter Root
    Valley Historical Society, Hamilton,
    MT 848
The Ray Drew Gallery-New Mexico
    Highlands University, Las Vegas, NM 941
Reading Historical Society Museum,
    Reading, OH 1184
Redington Museum, Waterville, ME 625
Redwood County Historical Society,
    Redwood Falls, MN 787
Reese Bullen Gallery, Arcata, CA 72
Refugio County Museum, Refugio, TX 1445
Reginald F. Lewis Museum of Maryland
    African American History and Culture,
    Baltimore, MD 636
Rehoboth Art League, Inc., Rehoboth
    Beach, DE 272
Reitz Home Museum, Evansville, IN 476
Richard L. Nelson Gallery & The Fine
    Arts Collection, UC Davis, Davis, CA......90

Richard Petty Museum, Randleman, NC....1117
Ripley's Believe It or Not!, Key West,
    FL...319
Ripley's Believe It or Not! Museum,
    Atlantic City, NJ..898
River Heritage Museum, Paducah, KY 582
Robert C. Williams American Museum of
    Papermaking at Georgia Tech, Atlanta,
    GA...363
Robert Louis Stevenson Memorial
    Cottage, Saranac Lake, NY....................1064
Rock Island County Historical Society,
    Moline, IL..445
Rockhill Trolley Museum, Rockhill
    Furnace, PA...1297
Roger Tory Peterson Institute of Natural
    History, Jamestown, NY...........................1005
Rome Historical Society Museum, Rome,
    NY..1061
Ronald Reagan Presidential Library and
    Museum, Simi Valley, CA..........................187
Roosevelt Campobello International Park
    Commission, Lubec, ME............................614
The Rose Art Museum, Waltham, MA........715
Roswell Museum and Art Center,
    Roswell, NM..946
Russell County Historical Society/Fossil
    Station Museum, Russell, KS 556
Ruth Chandler Williamson Gallery,
    Scripps College, Claremont, CA................86

S.C. Tobacco Museum, Mullins, SC...........1337
Sacramento Archives and Museum
    Collection Center, Sacramento, CA.........153
Safe Haven Museum and Education
    Center, Oswego, NY................................1048
Sahuaro Ranch Historical Area, Glendale,
    AZ...35
St. Albans Historical Museum, Saint
    Albans, VT..1486
St. John's Northwestern Military
    Academy Archives & Museum,
    Delafield, WI...1595
St. Photios Greek Orthodox National
    Shrine, Saint Augustine, FL.....................340
Saints Hall of Fame Museum, Kenner,
    LA..589
Salamanca Rail Museum, Salamanca, NY.1063
Salem Witch Museum, Salem, MA 707
Salida Museum, Salida, CO.........................232
Salina Art Center, Salina, KS 557
Salinas Pueblo Missions National
    Monument, Mountainair, NM..................943
Salvador Dali Museum, Saint Petersburg,
    FL..342
The Salvation Army Southern Historical
    Center & Museum, Atlanta, GA 363
Samuel Cupples House of Saint Louis
    University, Saint Louis, MO......................837
Samuel Dorsky Museum of Art, State
    University of New York at New Paltz,
    New Paltz, NY...1018
San Antonio Missions National Historical
    Park, San Antonio, TX.............................1449
San Diego Air & Space Museum, San
    Diego, CA...159
San Diego Automotive Museum, San
    Diego, CA...159
San Diego Hall of Champions Sports
    Museum, San Diego, CA 159
San Francisco Museum of Modern Art,
    San Francisco, CA.....................................169
San Jose State University Art Galleries,
    San Jose, CA..173
Sand Springs Cultural & Historical
    Museum, Sand Springs, OK.....................1213
Santa Barbara Maritime Museum, Santa
    Barbara, CA..179
Santa Monica Museum of Art, Santa
    Monica, CA...183
Sarasota Classic Car Museum, Sarasota,
    FL..345

Sauk Prairie Area Historical Society, Inc.,
    Prairie du Sac, WI....................................1619
Savannah College of Art and Design
    Galleries, Savannah, GA 386
Savannah History Museum, Savannah,
    GA...386
Scarfone/Hartley Gallery, Tampa, FL.........349
The Scarsdale Historical Society,
    Scarsdale, NY..1066
Schenectady Museum and Suits-Bueche
    Planetarium, Schenectady, NY................1067
Schmidt House Museum & Research
    Library, Grants Pass, OR 1225
Schmucker Art Gallery, Gettysburg, PA.....1256
The Schomburg Center for Research in
    Black Culture, New York, NY 1038
School of the Art Institute of Chicago,
    Gallery 2, Chicago, IL 427
Schuyler County Historical Society, Inc.,
    Montour Falls, NY 1015
The Schuylkill Center for Environmental
    Education, Philadelphia, PA 1288
Sci-Tech Center of Northern New York,
    Watertown, NY 1084
The Science Fiction Museum and Hall of
    Fame, Seattle, WA 1568
Scituate Maritime and Irish Mossing
    Museum, Scituate, MA..............................709
Scotia-Glenville Children's Museum,
    Scotia, NY...1068
Scottsdale Museum of Contemporary Art,
    Scottsdale, AZ..44
Senator George Norris State Historic Site,
    McCook, NE..868
Sequoia and Kings Canyon National
    Parks, Three Rivers, CA 191
Shelby American Collection, Boulder, CO...203
Sheldon Memorial Art Gallery and
    Sculpture Garden/University of
    Nebraska-Lincoln, Lincoln, NE 867
Sheppard Fine Arts Gallery, Reno, NV 881
Sherwood-Davidson House, Newark, OH ..1178
Ships of the Sea Maritime
    Museum/William Scarbrough House,
    Savannah, GA 386
Shoshone Tribal Cultural Center, Fort
    Washakie, WY 1633
Sidney Historical Association, Sidney,
    NY..1069
Silent Wings Museum, Lubbock, TX 1435
Simsbury Historical Society, Phelps
    Tavern, Museum & Homestead,
    Simsbury, CT..260
Sinclair Lewis House Museum &
    Interpretive Center/Museum, Sauk
    Centre, MN...793
The Sixth Floor Museum at Dealey
    Plaza, Dallas, TX.....................................1407
The Skyscraper Museum, New York, NY..1038
Slidell Museum, Slidell, LA 602
Snake River Heritage Center, Weiser, ID.....410
Snoqualmie Valley Historical Museum,
    North Bend, WA.......................................1559
Snowmobile Hall of Fame and Museum,
    Saint Germain, WI...................................1620
Snug Harbor Cultural Center - Visitors'
    Center and Newhouse Center for
    Contemporary Art, Staten Island, NY ...1073
SoDus Bay Historical Society, Sodus
    Point, NY..1070
Soldiers National Museum, Gettysburg,
    PA..1256
Solomon R. Guggenheim Museum, New
    York, NY...1038
Sony Wonder Technology Lab, New
    York, NY...1039
Sophienburg Museum & Archives Inc.,
    New Braunfels, TX...................................1440
Sosa-Carrillo-Fremont House Museum,
    Tucson, AZ...50
Sotterley Plantation, Hollywood, MD 647
South Carolina Aquarium, Charleston, SC.1326

South Carolina Artisans Center,
    Walterboro, SC 1343
South Dakota Hall of Fame,
    Chamberlain, SD 1345
South Milwaukee Historical Society
    Museum, South Milwaukee, WI 1622
South Pass City State Historic Site, South
    Pass City, WY...1638
Space Center Houston, Houston, TX.........1429
The SPAM Museum, Austin, MN.................768
The Sports Museum, Boston, MA.................669
Stanwood Wildlife Sanctuary, Ellsworth,
    ME...610
Stanzel Model Aircraft Museum,
    Schulenburg, TX.......................................1452
Star Eco Station, Culver City, CA..................88
Statue of Liberty National Monument &
    Ellis Island Immigration Museum,
    New York, NY..1039
STAX Museum of American Soul Music,
    Memphis, TN...1376
Sterling Historical Society and Little Red
    Schoolhouse Museum, Sterling, NY......1074
Stoughton Historical Society, Stoughton,
    MA...713
The Stowitts Museum & Library, Pacific
    Grove, CA...137
Strategic Air & Space Museum, Ashland,
    NE...856
Stutsman County Memorial Museum,
    Jamestown, ND...1133
SUArt Galleries - Syracuse University,
    Syracuse, NY...1077
Suffolk County Vanderbilt Museum,
    Centerport, NY...977
Sugarlands Visitor Center, Gatlinburg, TN.1365
Sullivan Museum and History Center,
    Northfield, VT...1483
Sun Prairie Historical Library &
    Museum, Sun Prairie, WI........................1624
Sunnyvale Historical Museum,
    Sunnyvale, CA..190
The Supreme Court of the United States,
    Washington, DC...291
Suquamish Museum, Poulsbo, WA.............1563
Surratt House Museum, Clinton, MD..........640
Swiss Historical Village, New Glarus, WI.1615

Tante Blanche Museum, Madawaska, ME ...614
Taos County Historical Society, Inc.,
    Taos, NM...953
Tappantown Historical Society, Tappan,
    NY..1077
Tarpon Springs Cultural Center, Tarpon
    Springs, FL...351
Taube Museum of Art, Minot, ND 1135
Ted Smallwood's Store, Inc.,
    Chokoloskee, FL...299
Telfair Museum of Art, Savannah, GA 386
Tenino Depot Museum, Tenino, WA 1575
Terrace Gallery-City of Orlando,
    Orlando, FL..332
Terrace Hill Historic Site and Governor's
    Mansion, Des Moines, IA.........................516
Texas Air Museum, Slaton, TX...................1453
Texas Cowboy Hall of Fame, Fort Worth,
    TX 1418
Texas Energy Museum, Beaumont, TX....1395
Texas Music Museum, Austin, TX.............1392
Texas Seaport Museum, Galveston, TX.....1422
Texas Sports Hall of Fame, Waco, TX......1459
Theodore Roosevelt Birthplace National
    Historic Site, New York, NY 1040
Thetford Historical Society Library and
    Museum, Thetford, VT............................1488
This Is The Place Heritage Park, Salt
    Lake City, UT..1472
Thomas Edison House, Louisville, KY........579
Thomasville Cultural Center, Inc.,
    Thomasville, GA...388
Thornton W. Burgess Museum,
    Sandwich, MA..708
Three Rivers Museum, Muskogee, OK......1205

Audiovisual and Film–Continued

Tile Heritage Foundation, Healdsburg, CA................102

Tillamook Naval Air Station Museum, Tillamook, OR................1237

Tom Mix Museum, Dewey, OK................1199

Top of Oklahoma Historical Museum, Blackwell, OK................1197

Town of Yorktown Museum, Yorktown Heights, NY................1087

Trailside Nature Museum, Cross River, NY................983

Tri-County Historical Society & Museum, Inc., Herington, KS................544

Tu-Endie-Wei State Park, Point Pleasant, WV................1586

Turabo University, Gurabo, PR................1641

Twinsburg Historical Society, Twinsburg, OH................1188

Umlauf Sculpture Garden & Museum, Austin, TX................1392

Umpqua Discovery Center, Reedsport, OR................1234

Union Station Kansas City, Inc., Kansas City, MO................823

United States Golf Association Museum & Archives, Far Hills, NJ................903

United States Hockey Hall of Fame, Eveleth, MN................774

United States Holocaust Memorial Museum, Washington, DC................293

University Galleries, Florida Atlantic University, Boca Raton, FL................296

University of Alaska Museum of the North, Fairbanks, AK................24

University of California Berkeley Art Museum and Pacific Film Archive, Berkeley, CA................77

University of Kentucky Basketball Museum, Lexington, KY................574

University of Missouri-Kansas City Gallery of Art, Kansas City, MO................823

University Saint Thomas Art History, Saint Paul, MN................792

Upham Mansion, Marshfield, WI................1608

Urban Institute for Contemporary Arts, Grand Rapids, MI................744

U.S. Air Force Academy Visitor Center, USAF Academy, CO................234

U.S. Army Air Defense Artillery Museum, Fort Bliss, TX................1414

U.S. Army Finance Corps Museum, Fort Jackson, SC................1333

U.S. Army Signal Corps Museum, Fort Gordon, GA................372

U.S. Army Transportation Museum, Fort Eustis, VA................1504

U.S. Army Women's Museum, Fort Lee, VA................1505

U.S. Cavalry Museum, Fort Riley, KS................540

U.S. National Ski Hall of Fame & Museum, Inc., Ishpeming, MI................747

U.S. Navy Seabee Museum, Port Hueneme, CA................143

U.S. Patent and Trademark Office - Museum, Alexandria, VA................1494

The U.S. Space & Rocket Center, Huntsville, AL................12

USS Arizona Memorial, Honolulu, HI................398

USS Bowfin Submarine Museum & Park, Honolulu, HI................398

USS Lexington Museum on the Bay, Corpus Christi, TX................1402

Vacaville Museum, Vacaville, CA................194

Valentine-Varian House/Museum of Bronx History, Bronx, NY................967

Valley County Pioneer Museum, Glasgow, MT................847

Venango Museum of Art, Science & Industry, Oil City, PA................1274

Vermont Folklife Center, Middlebury, VT................1482

Vermont Historical Society Museum, Montpelier, VT................1482

Vermont Marble Museum, Proctor, VT................1485

Vermont Ski Museum, Stowe, VT................1488

Vernon County Historical Museum, Viroqua, WI................1625

Vero Beach Museum of Art, Inc., Vero Beach, FL................352

Veterans Memorial Museum, Laurel, MS................804

Vicksburg Battlefield Museum, Vicksburg, MS................809

Vietnam Era Educational Center, Holmdel, NJ................908

Viking Union Gallery, Bellingham, WA................1549

Village Historical Society, Inc., Harrison, OH................1168

The Vinalhaven Historical Society Museum, Vinalhaven, ME................624

Virginia Aquarium & Marine Science Center, Virginia Beach, VA................1542

Virginia Beach Maritime Museum, Inc./The Old Coast Guard Station, Virginia Beach, VA................1543

Virginia Holocaust Museum, Richmond, VA................1533

Virginia Museum of Transportation, Inc., Roanoke, VA................1536

Virginia War Memorial, Richmond, VA................1534

Visual Arts Museum, New York, NY................1040

Wabaunsee County Historical Museum, Alma, KS................532

Waikiki Aquarium, Honolulu, HI................399

The Walker African American Museum & Research Center, Las Vegas, NV................880

Walker Art Center, Minneapolis, MN................783

Wallace District Mining Museum, Wallace, ID................410

The Waltham Museum, Waltham, MA................716

War in the Pacific National Historical Park, Piti, GU................1640

The Ward Museum of Wildfowl Art, Salisbury University, Salisbury, MD................653

Warsaw Historical Museum, Warsaw, NY................1082

Washington County Historical Society, Portland, OR................1233

Washington Museum & Tourist Center, Washington, LA................603

Waterford Historical Museum and Cultural Center, Inc., Waterford, NY................1083

Watermen's Museum, Yorktown, VA................1547

Watervliet Arsenal's Museum of the Big Guns, Watervliet, NY................1084

Watts Towers Arts Center, Los Angeles, CA................122

Wells County Museum, Fessenden, ND................1131

Wendell Gilley Museum, Southwest Harbor, ME................623

West River Museum Society, Philip, SD................1353

Western Aerospace Museum, Oakland, CA................134

Western Heritage Center, Billings, MT................841

Western Michigan University Richmond Center for Visual Arts School of Art, Kalamazoo, MI................749

Western New Mexico University Museum, Silver City, NM................951

Weston Woods Institute, Weston, CT................266

The Wetlands Institute, Stone Harbor, NJ................925

Wexner Center for the Arts, Columbus, OH................1159

The Whale Museum, Friday Harbor, WA................1555

Wheels Through Time Museum, Inc., Maggie Valley, NC................1110

The Wheelwright Museum of the American Indian, Santa Fe, NM................950

Whitney Museum of American Art, New York, NY................1041

Whittier Home Association, Amesbury, MA................658

Wilber Czech Museum, Wilber, NE................875

Wilder Memorial Museum, Strawberry Point, IA................528

Wildlife Experience Museum, Parker, CO................229

Wildling Art Museum, Los Olivos, CA................123

Will Rogers Memorial Museum, Claremore, OK................1198

Willa Cather Pioneer Memorial and Educational Foundation, Red Cloud, NE................872

The William Breman Jewish Heritage Museum, Atlanta, GA................364

William J. Clinton Presidential Library & Museum, Little Rock, AR................63

William Otis Sawtelle Collections and Research Center, Bar Harbor, ME................606

Williams College Museum of Art, Williamstown, MA................719

Wing Haven Garden and Bird Sanctuary, Charlotte, NC................1096

Wings Over Miami Museum, Inc., Miami, FL................326

Wisconsin Maritime Museum, Manitowoc, WI................1607

Wisconsin National Guard Museum, Camp Douglas, WI................1593

Women's History Museum, West Liberty, WV................1587

Wood Library-Museum of Anesthesiology, Park Ridge, IL................450

Worcester County Horticultural Society/Tower Hill Botanic Garden, Boylston, MA................670

The Works: Ohio Center for History, Art & Technology, Newark, OH................1179

World Figure Skating Museum & Hall of Fame, Colorado Springs, CO................208

World Forestry Center, Portland, OR................1233

World Kite Museum & Hall of Fame, Long Beach, WA................1558

World's Largest Toy Museum and Harold Bell Wright, Branson, MO................811

World's Smallest Museum, Superior, AZ................45

Wright Museum, Wolfeboro, NH................897

Yankee Air Force, Inc. (Yankee Air Museum), Ypsilanti, MI................766

Ybor City Museum State Park, Tampa, FL................351

Yerba Buena Center for the Arts, San Francisco, CA................170

Yogi Berra Museum and Learning Center, Little Falls, NJ................910

York W. Bailey Museum at Penn Center, Saint Helena Island, SC................1340

The Yosemite Museum, National Park Service, Yosemite National Park, CA................199

Zeum, San Francisco, CA................170

Ziibiwing Center of Anishinabe Culture & Lifeways, Mount Pleasant, MI................757

Costumes and Textiles

A.R. Mitchell Museum, Trinidad, CO................233

Abby Aldrich Rockefeller Folk Art Museum, Williamsburg, VA................1544

Abington Art Center, Jenkintown, PA................1263

Abraham Lincoln Library & Museum, Lincoln Memorial University, Harrogate, TN................1366

Academy Hall Museum of the Rocky Hill Historical Society, Inc., Rocky Hill, CT................259

Ace of Clubs House, Texarkana, TX................1455

Adam Thoroughgood House, Virginia Beach, VA................1541

Adams County Historical Museum, Decatur, IN................474

Adams County Historical Society, Gettysburg, PA................1255

Adams County Historical Society Museum, Brighton, CO................204

Adams Museum & House, Deadwood, SD................1346

Adan E. Treganza Anthropology Museum, Dept. of Anthropology, San Francisco State University, San Francisco, CA 162

The Adirondack Museum, Blue Mountain Lake, NY 963

Admiral Nimitz National Museum of the Pacific War, Fredericksburg, TX 1419

Adsmore Museum, Princeton, KY 583

The African American Museum in Philadelphia, Philadelphia, PA 1275

African Art Museum of Maryland, Columbia, MD 641

African Art Museum of the S.M.A. Fathers, Tenafly, NJ 926

Agecroft Hall, Richmond, VA 1527

Agricultural and Industrial Museum, York County Heritage Trust, York, PA 1309

Ah-Tah-Thi-Ki Museum, Big Cypress Seminole Indian Reservation, FL 295

Ah-Tah-Thi-Ki Museum at Okalee, Hollywood, FL 312

Aiken County Historical Museum, Aiken, SC 1320

Aiken Thoroughbred Racing Hall of Fame and Museum, Aiken, SC 1320

Airmen Memorial Museum, Suitland, MD 655

Alamo Township Museum-John E. Gray Memorial Museum, Kalamazoo, MI 748

Alaska Aviation Heritage Museum, Anchorage, AK 21

Alaska Indian Arts, Inc., Haines, AK 24

Alaska Native Heritage Center, Anchorage, AK 22

Alaska State Museum, Juneau, AK 25

Albany Institute of History & Art, Albany, NY 954

Albany Museum of Art, Albany, GA 355

Albion Academy Historical Museum, Edgerton, WI 1596

Alden Historical Society, Inc., Alden, NY ...956

Alexandre Mouton House/Lafayette Museum, Lafayette, LA 589

Alger County Heritage Center, Munising, MI 757

Alice C. Sabatini Gallery-Topeka and Shawnee County Public Library, Topeka, KS 558

The Alice T. Miner Colonial Collection, Chazy, NY 977

Aliceville Museum, Aliceville, AL 3

Allaire Village Inc., Farmingdale, NJ 903

Allegany County Historical Society, Inc., Cumberland, MD 641

Allen County Museum, Lima, OH 1172

Allen Memorial Art Museum, Oberlin, OH 1180

Allentown Art Museum, Allentown, PA 1239

Alling Coverlet Museum, Palmyra, NY 1050

Allison-Antrim Museum, Inc., Greencastle, PA 1257

Almond Historical Society/Hagadorn House Museum, Almond, NY 957

Alton Museum of History and Art, Inc., Alton, IL 410

Amador County Museum, Jackson, CA 105

Amana Heritage Museum, Amana, IA 504

Amarillo Museum of Art, Amarillo, TX 1386

Amelia Island Museum of History, Fernandina Beach, FL 306

American Airlines C.R. Smith Museum, Fort Worth, TX 1416

American Airpower Heritage Museum, Inc. & Commemorative Air Force Headquarters, Midland, TX 1438

American Folk Art Museum, New York, NY 1018

American Independence Museum, Exeter, NH 887

The American Jazz Museum, Kansas City, MO 820

American Jewish Historical Society, New York, NY 1019

American Labor Museum, Botto House National Landmark, Haledon, NJ 906

American Museum of Asmat Art, Saint Paul, MN 789

American Museum of Magic & Lund Memorial Library, Inc., Marshall, MI 754

American Museum of Nursing, Tempe, AZ 45

American Museum of Straw Art, Long Beach, CA 110

American Red Cross Visitors Center and Gift Shop, Washington, DC 275

American Royal Museum & Visitors Center, Kansas City, MO 820

American Swedish Historical Foundation & Museum, Philadelphia, PA 1276

American Swedish Institute, Minneapolis, MN 781

American Textile History Museum, Lowell, MA 691

American Visionary Art Museum, Baltimore, MD 629

American Water Ski Educational Foundation, Polk City, FL 337

Americas Society, New York, NY 1020

Amherst County Museum & Historical Society, Amherst, VA 1495

Amherst History Museum at the Strong House - Amherst Historical Society, Amherst, MA 658

Amherst Museum, Amherst, NY 957

Amity and Woodbridge Historical Society, Woodbridge, CT 268

Amory Regional Museum, Amory, MS 797

Amos Herr House Foundation and Historic Society, Landisville, PA 1267

Anadarko Heritage Museum, Anadarko, OK 1195

Anaheim Museum, Anaheim, CA 71

Ancient and Honorable Artillery Company, Boston, MA 663

Anderson County Museum, Anderson, SC.1321

Anderson Gallery, School of the Arts, Virginia Commonwealth University, Richmond, VA 1528

Andover Historical Society, Andover, MA ...660

Andrew County Museum & Historical Society, Savannah, MO 838

Andrew J. Blackbird Museum, Harbor Springs, MI 745

Andrew Low House, Savannah, GA 384

Androscoggin Historical Society, Auburn, ME 603

Anna Bemis Palmer Museum, York, NE 875

Annie E. Woodman Institute Museum, Dover, NH 886

Annie Riggs Memorial Museum, Fort Stockton, TX 1415

Anoka County Historical Society, Anoka, MN 767

The Anthropology Museum, DeKalb, IL 429

Anthropology Museum, University of San Diego, San Diego, CA 155

The Apple Trees Museum, Burlington, IA ...506

Appleton Museum of Art, Ocala, FL 330

Appomattox Court House National Historical Park, Appomattox, VA 1495

APVA's John Marshall House, Richmond, VA 1528

Arbor Lodge State Historical Park, Nebraska City, NE 868

Archives Museum, Temple Mickve Israel, Savannah, GA 384

Archives of J.S.G. Boggs, Brandon, FL 298

Arizona Historical Society Museum, Tucson, AZ 47

Arizona Historical Society Museum at Papago Park, Tempe, AZ 45

Arizona Historical Society Museum - Downtown, Tucson, AZ 47

Arizona Historical Society Pioneer Museum, Flagstaff, AZ 32

Arizona Military Museum, Phoenix, AZ 39

Arizona State Capitol Museum, Phoenix, AZ 39

Arizona State Museum, Tucson, AZ 48

Arizona State Parks Board, Phoenix, AZ 39

Arizona State University Museum of Anthropology, Tempe, AZ 46

Ark-La-Tex Antique & Classic Vehicle Museum, Shreveport, LA 600

Arkansas Country Doctor Museum, Lincoln, AR 61

Arkansas Post Museum, Gillett, AR 58

Arkansas State University Museum, Jonesboro, AR 60

Arkansas Tech University Museum of Prehistory and History, Russellville, AR 67

Arlington Historical Museum, Arlington, VA 1495

The Arlington Historical Society, Arlington, MA 660

Arlington House, The Robert E. Lee Memorial, Arlington, VA 1495

Armenian Library and Museum of America, Watertown, MA 716

Armstrong Browning Library, Waco, TX ...1458

Arrow Rock State Historic Site, Arrow Rock, MO 810

Art Association of Randolph County, Inc., Union City, IN 501

The Art Center at Fuller Lodge, Los Alamos, NM 942

Art Center of Battle Creek, Battle Creek, MI 726

Art Complex Museum, Duxbury, MA 680

The Art Gallery, Lower Columbia College Fine Arts Gallery, Longview, WA 1558

Art In Embassies Program, U.S. Department of State, Washington, DC 276

The Art Institute of Chicago, Chicago, IL ...418

Art Museum of The University of Memphis, Memphis, TN 1372

Artesia Historical Museum & Art Center, Artesia, NM 936

The Arthur J. Moore Methodist Museum, Saint Simons Island, GA 383

Arthur M. Sackler Gallery, Washington, DC 276

Arthur Ross Gallery, University of Pennsylvania, Philadelphia, PA 1276

Artillery Company of Newport Military Museum, Newport, RI 1313

Artisans Center of Virginia, Waynesboro, VA 1543

Arts Consortium of Cincinnati's African American Museum, Cincinnati, OH 1148

Ash Lawn-Highland, Charlottesville, VA ...1498

Ashland Historical Society Museum, Ashland, WI 1590

Ashland, The Henry Clay Estate, Lexington, KY 572

Ashtabula County Historical Society, Geneva-on-the-Lake, OH 1166

Ashton Villa & The Heritage Visitor Center, Galveston, TX 1420

Asian Art Museum of San Francisco, Chong-Moon Lee Center for Asian Art and Culture, San Francisco, CA 163

Asian Arts & Culture Center, Towson University, Towson, MD 655

Association for the Preservation of Tennessee Antiquities, Nashville, TN ...1377

Astor House Museum, Golden, CO 219

Astors' Beechwood Mansion - Living History Museum, Newport, RI 1313

Ataloa Lodge Museum, Muskogee, OK 1205

Atchison County Historical Society, Atchison, KS 533

Atlanta Historical Society, Atlanta, GA 358

Costumes and Textiles—Continued

Atlantic City Historical Museum, Atlantic City, NJ 897

Atlantic Heritage Center, Somers Point, NJ 924

Attleboro Arts Museum, Attleboro, MA.......661

Attmore-Oliver House, New Bern, NC.......1112

Atwater Kent Museum of Philadelphia, Philadelphia, PA 1276

Atwood House Museum, Home of Chatham Historical Society, Chatham, MA 675

Audie Murphy/American Cotton Museum, Inc, Greenville, TX 1423

Audrain Historical Museum, Graceland, Mexico, MO.......827

Audubon County Historical Society, Exira, IA 517

Aurora Historical Society, Aurora, IL.......411

Aurora Historical Society, Aurora, OH.......1140

Aurora History Museum, Aurora, CO 202

Aurora Public Art Commission, Aurora, IL.......411

The Avon Historical Society, Inc., Avon, CT 235

Aztalan Museum, Jefferson, WI.......1601

Aztec Museum and Pioneer Village, Aztec, NM 936

Babe Didrikson Zaharias Museum, Beaumont, TX 1394

The Babe Ruth Museum and Sports Legends at Camden Yards, Baltimore, MD.......629

Bailey House Museum - Maui Historical Society, Wailuku, HI.......402

Baker-Cederberg Museum & Archives, Rochester, NY.......1058

Baldwin-Reynolds House Museum, Meadville, PA 1270

The Ballard Institute & Museum of Puppetry, Storrs, CT 261

Baltimore County Historical Society, Cockeysville, MD.......640

Baltimore Maritime Museum, Baltimore, MD.......630

The Baltimore Museum of Art, Baltimore, MD.......630

Balzekas Museum of Lithuanian Culture, Chicago, IL.......418

Bandon Historical Society Museum, Bandon, OR.......1219

Bangor Museum & Center for History, Bangor, ME.......604

Banning Residence Museum, Wilmington, CA.......198

Baranov Museum, Kodiak, AK.......26

The Barbara Fritchie House, Frederick, MD.......644

The Bare Cove Fire Museum, Hingham, MA.......687

The Barnacle Historic State Park, Coconut Grove, FL.......300

Barnard's Mill Art Museum, Glen Rose, TX.......1422

Barnes County Historical Museum, Valley City, ND.......1136

Barnes Museum, Southington, CT.......260

The Barnum Museum, Bridgeport, CT.......235

Barnwell County Museum, Barnwell, SC..1321

Barratt's Chapel and Museum, Frederica, DE.......270

Barre Historical Society, Inc., Barre, MA...662

Bartlesville Area History Museum, Bartlesville, OK.......1196

The Bartlett Museum, Amesbury, MA 657

Barton County Historical Museum & Village, Great Bend, KS.......542

Barton Museum, Wilson, NC.......1124

Bartow History Center, Cartersville, GA 367

Bass Museum of Art, Miami Beach, FL 326

Bates-Scofield Homestead, The Darien Historical Society, Darien, CT 238

Battle of Lexington State Historic Site, Lexington, MO.......826

The Battles Museums of Rural Life, Girard, PA.......1256

Battleship North Carolina, Wilmington, NC.......1122

Battleship Texas State Historic Site, La Porte, TX.......1433

Baxter Springs Heritage Center and Museum, Baxter Springs, KS.......533

Bay Area Museum, Seabrook, TX.......1452

Bay View Historical Museum, Bay View, MI.......728

Beard Gallery, Norton, MA 700

Beauchamp Newman Museum, Elizabeth, WV.......1581

The Beaufort Arsenal, Beaufort, SC.......1321

Beaufort Historic Site, Beaufort, NC.......1091

Beauvais Heritage Center, Clark, SD 1345

Beauvoir, The Jefferson Davis Home and Presidential Library, Biloxi, MS.......798

Beaverhead County Museum, Dillon, MT ...845

Becker County Historical Society, Detroit Lakes, MN.......772

Bedford Historical Society Museum and Library, Bedford, OH 1142

Bedingfield Inn Museum, Lumpkin, GA.......376

Beehive House, Salt Lake City, UT.......1470

Behringer-Crawford Museum, Covington, KY.......567

Belcourt Castle, Newport, RI.......1313

Belding Museum, Belding, MI.......728

Belhaven Memorial Museum, Inc., Belhaven, NC.......1092

The Belknap Mill Society, Laconia, NH.......890

Bell County Museum, Belton, TX.......1395

Belle Grove Plantation, Middletown, VA...1517

Belle Meade Plantation, Nashville, TN 1377

Bellflower Historical and Genealogical Society, Bellflower, IL.......413

Bellport-Brookhaven Historical Society and Museum, Bellport, NY.......961

Belmont County Victorian Mansion Museum, Barnesville, OH.......1141

Beloit Historical Society, Beloit, WI.......1592

Beltrami County History Center, Bemidji, MN.......768

Bement-Billings Farmstead, Newark Valley, NY.......1041

Benedicta Arts Center, Saint Joseph, MN 789

Benjamin Harrison Presidential Site, Indianapolis, IN.......481

Bennett Place State Historic Site, Durham, NC.......1098

Bennington Battlefield State Historic Site, Walloomsac, NY.......1081

The Bennington Museum, Bennington, VT.......1476

Benton County Historical Museum, Prosser, WA.......1563

Benzie Area Historical Museum, Benzonia, MI.......729

Berea College, Doris Ulmann Galleries, Berea, KY.......565

Bergen Museum of Local History, Bergen, NY.......962

Berkshire County Historical Society, Inc. - Arrowhead, Pittsfield, MA.......702

Berlin Art and Historical Collections, Berlin, MA.......662

Berman Museum of World History, Anniston, AL 3

Bernard Historical Society and Museum, Delton, MI.......734

Bernard Judaica Museum, Congregation Emanu-El of the City of New York, New York, NY.......1021

Bernheim Arboretum and Research Forest, Clermont, KY.......567

Berrien County Historical Association, Berrien Springs, MI.......729

Besser Museum for Northeast Michigan, Alpena, MI.......723

Bethel Historical Society Regional History Center, Bethel, ME.......606

Betsy Ross House and Flag Museum, Philadelphia, PA.......1277

Beverly Historical Society and Museum, Beverly, MA 662

Bexley Historical Society, Bexley, OH.......1143

The Bidwell House Museum, Monterey, MA.......695

Big Springs Museum, Caledonia, NY 974

Big Timbers Museum, Lamar, CO 225

Bigelow House Museum, Olympia, WA 1560

Biltmore Estate, Asheville, NC.......1089

Birger Sandzen Memorial Gallery, Lindsborg, KS.......549

Birmingham Civil Rights Institute, Birmingham, AL.......4

Birmingham Museum of Art, Birmingham, AL.......5

Bisbee Mining & Historical Museum, Bisbee, AZ.......30

Bishop Hill Heritage Museum, Bishop Hill, IL.......413

Bishop Museum, Honolulu, HI.......394

The Black Fashion Museum, Washington, DC.......277

Black Heritage Museum, Miami, FL.......323

Black Hills Mining Museum, Lead, SD.......1350

Black Kettle Museum, Cheyenne, OK.......1198

Black River Academy Museum, Ludlow, VT.......1480

Black River Historical Society of Lorain, Lorain, OH.......1172

Blackberry Farm's Pioneer Village, Aurora, IL.......411

Blackman House Museum, Snohomish, WA.......1570

Blaine County Historical Museum, Hailey, ID.......406

Blanden Memorial Art Museum, Fort Dodge, IA.......518

Blithewold Mansion, Gardens & Arboretum, Bristol, RI.......1310

Bloomfield Academy Museum, Bloomfield, NY.......963

Blount-Bridgers House/Hobson Pittman Memorial Gallery, Tarboro, NC.......1121

Blount Mansion, Knoxville, TN.......1369

Blue Earth County Historical Society, Mankato, MN.......780

Bluff Hall Antebellum Home and Museum, Demopolis, AL.......7

B'nai B'rith Klutznick National Jewish Museum, Washington, DC.......277

Bob Jones University Museum & Gallery, Inc., Greenville, SC.......1333

Boehm Gallery, San Marcos, CA.......174

Bolduc House Museum, Sainte Genevieve, MO.......837

Bolton Historical Society, Inc., Bolton, MA.......663

Boone County Historical Museum, Belvidere, IL.......413

Boonsborough Museum of History, Boonsboro, MD.......637

Boonshoft Museum of Discovery, Dayton, OH.......1160

The Boorman House - The Juneau County Historical Society, Mauston, WI.......1608

Boot Hill Museum, Inc., Dodge City, KS 536

Bosque Memorial Museum, Clifton, TX.......1400

Boston Childrens Museum, Boston, MA.......664

Boston National Historical Park, Boston, MA.......664

Boulder History Museum, Boulder, CO 202

Boundary County Historical Society, Bonners Ferry, ID.......404

Bowers Museum, Santa Ana, CA 177
Bradford Historical Society Inc.,
    Bradford, VT 1477
Bragg-Mitchell Mansion, Mobile, AL 13
Braintree Historical Society, Inc.,
    Braintree, MA 670
Brand Library & Art Center, Glendale,
    CA 100
Branigan Cultural Center, Las Cruces,
    NM 940
Brazoria County Historical Museum,
    Angleton, TX 1387
Bread & Puppet Museum, Glover, VT 1479
Brec's Magnolia Mound Plantation,
    Baton Rouge, LA 585
Brick Store Museum, Kennebunk, ME 612
Bridge Hampton Historical Society,
    Bridgehampton, NY 964
Bridgton Historical Society, Bridgton,
    ME 607
Bronck Museum, Coxsackie, NY 983
Brookings County Historical Society
    Museum, Volga, SD........................1358
Brooklyn Children's Museum, Brooklyn,
    NY 968
The Brooklyn Historical Society,
    Brooklyn, NY 968
Brooklyn Historical Society, Brooklyn,
    OH...1144
Brooklyn Museum, Brooklyn, NY 968
Brooks Academy Museum, Harwich, MA ...686
The Broome County Historical Society,
    Binghamton, NY 962
Brown County Historical Society, New
    Ulm, MN 785
Brown County Historical Society Pioneer
    Museum, Nashville, IN 493
Brownville Historical Society Museum,
    Brownville, NE 858
Bruce Museum, Greenwich, CT 243
Brueckner Museum of Starr
    Commonwealth, Albion, MI................723
Brunswick Railroad Museum and C&O
    Canal Visitors Center, Brunswick, MD ...639
Buccleuch Mansion, New Brunswick, NJ....915
Buchanan Center for the Arts,
    Monmouth, IL 445
Bucks County Civil War Library &
    Museum, Doylestown, PA 1249
Bucksport Historical Society, Inc.,
    Bucksport, ME 608
Buechel Memorial Lakota Museum, Saint
    Francis, SD 1355
Buena Park Historical Society, Buena
    Park, CA 80
Buffalo and Erie County Historical
    Society, Buffalo, NY 972
Buffalo Bill Museum & Grave, Golden,
    CO..219
Buffalo Trails Museum, Epping, ND 1130
Bunker Hill Museum, Charlestown, MA......675
Bureau County Historical Society
    Museum, Princeton, IL......................452
The Burgwin-Wright Museum,
    Wilmington, NC..............................1123
Burlington County Historical Society,
    Burlington, NJ 898
Burlington Historical Museum,
    Burlington, MA 672
Burnham Tavern, Machias, ME 614
Burritt on the Mountain-A Living
    Museum, Huntsville, AL 11
Burrowes Mansion Museum, Matawan,
    NJ 911
Burt County Museum, Tekamah, NE 873
Bushwhacker Museum, Nevada, MO 828
Bushy Run Battlefield, Jeannette, PA 1263
Butler County History Center & Kansas
    Oil Museum, El Dorado, KS 537
Butler County Museum, Hamilton, OH......1168
Butte County Pioneer Memorial Museum,
    Oroville, CA 136

Butte-Silver Bow Arts Chateau, Butte,
    MT..843
Byron Historical Museum, Byron, NY.........974

C.F. Lott Historic Home, Oroville, CA 136
CHTJ Southard House Museum,
    Brunswick, ME 607
Cabot Historical Society, Cabot, VT 1478
Calaveras County Museum, San Andreas,
    CA 155
Calhoun County Museum, Rockwell City,
    IA 527
California African-American Museum,
    Los Angeles, CA..............................113
California Center for the Arts, Escondido,
    Escondido, CA 93
California Historical Society, San
    Francisco, CA 163
California State Indian Museum,
    Sacramento, CA 151
California State Railroad Museum,
    Sacramento, CA 152
California Surf Museum, Oceanside, CA 135
Call of the Wild Museum, Gaylord, MI.......742
Calumet County Historical Society, Inc.,
    New Holstein, WI 1615
Calvin Coolidge Historic Site, Plymouth
    Notch, VT 1484
Cambridge Historical Society,
    Cambridge, MA 672
Camden County Historical Society,
    Camden, NJ 899
Camp Five Museum Foundation, Inc.,
    Laona, WI 1604
Campbell County Rockpile Museum,
    Gillette, WY 1633
Campbell House Museum, Saint Louis,
    MO 832
Campus Martius Museum, Marietta, OH ...1173
Canaan Historical Society, Inc., Canaan,
    NY 974
Canadian County Historical Museum, El
    Reno, OK 1200
Canal Fulton Heritage Society, Canal
    Fulton, OH 1145
Cannon Falls Area Historical Museum,
    Cannon Falls, MN 770
Canton Classic Car Museum, Canton, OH.1145
The Canton Museum of Art, Canton, OH..1145
Cape Ann Historical Museum,
    Gloucester, MA...............................684
Cape Fear Museum of History and
    Science, Wilmington, NC..................1123
Capitol Visitors Center, a Division of the
    State Preservation Board, Austin, TX....1389
Capitola Historical Museum, Capitola,
    CA 81
Captain Forbes House Museum, Milton,
    MA 695
Captain George Flavel House Museum,
    Astoria, OR 1218
Captain John Wilson House, Cohasset,
    MA 676
Captain Nathaniel B. Palmer House -
    Home of the Discoverer of Antarctica,
    Stonington, CT 261
Caramoor Center for Music & the Arts,
    Inc., Katonah, NY 1006
Carleton College Art Gallery, Northfield,
    MN 785
Carpenter Home Museum and Gallery,
    Cle Elum, WA 1551
Carroll Mansion Museum Home of
    Leavenworth County Historical
    Society, Leavenworth, KS 549
Carroll Reece Museum, Johnson City, TN.1367
Carson County Square House Museum,
    Panhandle, TX 1442
The Carter House Association, Inc.,
    Franklin, TN 1365
Cary Cottage, Cincinnati, OH.................1148
Caryl House and Fisher Barn, Dover, MA...680
Casa Adobe de San Rafael, Glendale, CA...100

Cascade County Historical Society
    Museum, Great Falls, MT....................848
Casemate Museum, Fort Monroe, VA 1505
Cass County Historical Society,
    Logansport, IN................................489
Cass County Historical Society at
    Bonanzaville, West Fargo, ND.............1137
Cass County Historical Society Museum,
    Plattsmouth, NE..............................872
Cass County Museum & Pioneer School,
    Walker, MN 795
The Castle, Marietta, OH 1174
Castle Museum of Saginaw County
    History, Saginaw, MI.........................762
The Casto House and Northfield
    Museum, Northfield, NJ 917
Cathedral Cultural Center, Omaha, NE 870
The Cathedral of St. John the Divine,
    New York, NY 1022
Catholic Historical Society of the
    Roanoke Valley, Roanoke, VA 1535
Catskill Fly Fishing Center & Museum,
    Livingston Manor, NY 1010
Cattle Raisers Museum, Fort Worth, TX....1416
Cayuga-Owasco Lakes Historical Society,
    Moravia, NY 1015
Cedar Falls Historical Society, Cedar
    Falls, IA 507
Cedar Grove Historical Society, Cedar
    Grove, NJ......................................901
Cedar Key Historical Society Museum,
    Cedar Key, FL 298
Cedar Rapids Museum of Art, Cedar
    Rapids, IA 509
Centennial Village Museum, Greeley, CO ...221
Center for History, Wheaton, IL 465
The Center for Western Studies, Sioux
    Falls, SD 1356
Center of Southwest Studies/Fort Lewis
    College, Durango, CO 214
Centerville Historical Museum,
    Centerville, MA 675
Centerville - Washington Township
    Historical Society & Asahel Wright
    Community Center, Centerville, OH 1146
Centerville - Washington Township
    Historical Society & Walton House
    Museum, Centerville, OH 1147
Central City Opera House Association,
    Central City, CO..............................205
Central Missouri State University
    Archives and Museum, Warrensburg,
    MO 839
Central Montana Historical Association,
    Inc. Museum, Lewistown, MT...............850
The Central Museum, Central, AK.............23
Centre County Library and Historical
    Museum, Bellefonte, PA 1241
Centre Hill Museum (The Petersburg
    Museums), Petersburg, VA..................1524
Century Village Museum, Burton, OH......1144
Chagrin Falls Historical Society, Chagrin
    Falls, OH.......................................1147
Champaign County Historical Museum,
    Champaign, IL.................................416
Champaign County Historical Museum,
    Urbana, OH...................................1188
Chancellor Robert R. Livingston Masonic
    Library & Museum, New York, NY......1022
Charles A. Lindbergh Historic Site, Little
    Falls, MN 779
Charles A. Weyerhaeuser Memorial
    Museum, Little Falls, MN....................779
The Charles Hosmer Morse Museum of
    American Art, Winter Park, FL 354
Charles M. Schulz Museum and Research
    Center, Santa Rosa, CA.....................184
The Charleston Museum, Charleston, SC ..1324
Charlotte County Historical Center,
    Charlotte Harbor, FL 299
Chase Home Museum of Utah Folk Arts,
    Salt Lake City, UT 1470

Costumes and Textiles—Continued

Chatillon-DeMenil Mansion, Saint Louis, MO..............832

Chattanooga African Museum/Bessie Smith Hall, Chattanooga, TN..............1360

Chattanooga Regional History Museum, Chattanooga, TN..............1361

Chautauqua County Historical Society, McClurg Museum, Westfield, NY..........1086

Cheekwood-Tennessee Botanical Garden & Museum of Art, Nashville, TN..............1378

The Chelmsford Historical Society, Inc., South Chelmsford, MA..............709

Chemung Valley History Museum, Elmira, NY..............988

Chenango County Historical Society Museum, Norwich, NY..............1044

Cherokee County Historical Museum, Inc., Murphy, NC..............1112

Cherokee Courthouse Visitors Information Center & Museum, Gore, OK..............1201

Cherokee National Museum, Park Hill, OK..............1211

Cherokee Strip Land Rush Museum, Arkansas City, KS..............532

Cherry County Historical Society, Valentine, NE..............874

Cherry Valley Museum, Cherry Valley, NY..............978

The Chesapeake Beach Railway Museum, Chesapeake Beach, MD..............639

Chester County Historical Society, West Chester, PA..............1307

Chester County Historical Society Museum, Chester, SC..............1327

Chesterfield County Museum, Chesterfield, VA..............1501

Cheyenne Frontier Days Old West Museum, Cheyenne, WY..............1630

The Chicago Athenaeum: Museum of Architecture and Design, Galena, IL..............436

Chicago Cultural Center, Chicago, IL..........419

Chickasaw Council House Museum, Tishomingo, OK..............1214

Chickasaw County Historical Society Bradford Pioneer Village Museum, Nashua, IA..............525

Chieftains Museum, Rome, GA..............381

Children's Discovery Museum of North San Diego, Carlsbad, CA..............81

The Children's Museum, Seattle, WA..........1565

Children's Museum/Detroit Public Schools, Detroit, MI..............735

Children's Museum, Inc., Boca Raton, FL...296

The Children's Museum of Indianapolis, Indianapolis, IN..............481

Children's Museum of Oak Ridge, Inc., Oak Ridge, TN..............1382

The Children's Museum of Portsmouth, Portsmouth, NH..............894

The Children's Museum of Rose Hill Manor Park, Frederick, MD..............644

The Children's Museum of Science and Technology, Troy, NY..............1079

Children's Museum of Tacoma, Tacoma, WA..............1573

Chinese American Museum, Los Angeles, CA..............114

Chinese Culture Center of San Francisco, San Francisco, CA..............164

Chippewa County Historical Society, Montevideo, MN..............783

Chisholm Trail Museum, Wellington, KS....561

Choctaw County Historical Society, Hugo, OK..............1203

Cincinnati Art Museum, Cincinnati, OH....1148

Cincinnati Fire Museum, Cincinnati, OH...1149

Circus City Festival Museum, Peru, IN..............495

Circus World Museum, Baraboo, WI.........1591

The Citadel Archives & Museum, Charleston, SC..............1324

City Island Nautical Museum, Bronx, NY...965

City of Burlington Historical Society, Burlington, NJ..............899

City of Las Vegas Museum and Rough Rider Memorial Collection, Las Vegas, NM..............941

City of Wayne Historical Museum, Wayne, MI..............766

City Stage Company, Boston, MA..............665

Civil War Museum of Lonejack, Jackson County, Lone Jack, MO..............826

Clallam County Historical Society, Port Angeles, WA..............1561

Clarion County Historical Society, Sutton-Ditz House Museum, Clarion, PA..............1247

Clark Atlanta University Art Galleries, Atlanta, GA..............359

Clark County Historical Museum, Vancouver, WA..............1576

Clark County Museum, Marshall, IL..............444

Clark County Museum, Henderson, NV..............878

Clarke County Historical Association, Inc., Berryville, VA..............1496

Clarke Historical Museum, Eureka, CA.........94

Clarke House Museum, Chicago, IL..............420

Clarkson Historical Museum, Clarkson, NE..............859

Clay County Historical Museum, Liberty, MO..............826

Clay County Historical Society Museum and Archives, Moorhead, MN..............784

Cleveland Artists Foundation at Beck Center for the Arts, Lakewood, OH..............1170

The Cleveland Museum of Art, Cleveland, OH..............1152

Cleveland State University Art Gallery, Cleveland, OH..............1153

Clewiston Museum, Inc., Clewiston, FL..............300

Cliffs of the Neuse State Park, Seven Springs, NC..............1119

Clifton Community Historical Society, Clifton, KS..............535

Clinton Academy, East Hampton, NY..........985

Clinton County Historical Association & Museum, Plattsburgh, NY..............1052

Clinton County Historical Society, Wilmington, OH..............1191

Clinton County Historical Society Paine-Gillam-Scott Museum, Saint Johns, MI..............763

Cliveden of the National Trust, Philadelphia, PA..............1278

The Cloisters, New York, NY..............1023

Cloud County Historical Society Museum, Concordia, KS..............536

Clough-Hanson Gallery, Rhodes College, Memphis, TN..............1372

Coachella Valley Museum and Cultural Center, Indio, CA..............104

Coastal Discovery Museum, Hilton Head Island, SC..............1335

Coeur d'Alenes Old Mission State Park, Cataldo, ID..............405

The Coffey County Historical Museum, Burlington, KS..............534

Coggeshall Farm Museum, Bristol, RI..............1310

Colby College Museum of Art, Waterville, ME..............624

Cole County Historical Museum, Jefferson City, MO..............819

The Coleman House Museum and Brown County Historical Society, Ainsworth, NE..............855

Colesville & Windsor Museum at St. Luke's Church, Harpursville, NY..............997

The Coley Homestead & Barn Museum, Weston, CT..............265

College Football Hall of Fame, South Bend, IN..............499

College Park Aviation Museum, College Park, MD..............641

Colleton Museum, Walterboro, SC..............1343

Collin County Historical Society, Inc. & History Museum, McKinney, TX..........1437

Colonial Williamsburg, Williamsburg, VA.1544

Colorado Historical Society, Denver, CO.....210

Colorado River Indian Tribes Museum, Parker, AZ..............38

Colorado Ski Museum-Ski & Snowboard Hall of Fame, Vail, CO..............234

Colorado Springs Fine Arts Center (Taylor Museum), Colorado Springs, CO..............206

Colorado Springs Museum, Colorado Springs, CO..............206

Colton Area Museum, Colton, CA..............87

Columbia County Historical and Genealogical Society, Bloomsburg, PA.1243

Columbia County Historical Society, Inc., Kinderhook, NY..............1007

Columbia Fire Department Museum, Columbia, SC..............1328

Columbia Museum of Art, Columbia, SC..1329

Columbia State Historic Park, Columbia, CA..............87

Columbus-Belmont Civil War Museum, Columbus, KY..............567

The Columbus Museum, Columbus, GA....368

Comanche Crossing Historical Society & Museum, Strasburg, CO..............233

Command Museum, Marine Corps Recruit Depot, San Diego, San Diego, CA..............156

Community Historical Museum, Maxwell, IA..............523

Community Memorial Museum of Sutter County, Yuba City, CA..............200

Compass Inn Museum, Laughlintown, PA.1267

Concord Historical Society, Warner Museum, Springville, NY..............1071

Concord Museum, Concord, MA..............676

Concordia Historical Institute, Saint Louis, MO..............832

Confederate Memorial Hall-Bleak House, Knoxville, TN..............1369

Conklin Reed Organ & History Museum, Hanover, MI..............745

Connecticut Historical Society, Hartford, CT..............244

Conner Prairie, Fishers, IN..............476

Conrad Mansion National Historic Site Museum, Kalispell, MT..............850

Constitution Island Association, West Point, NY..............1085

Constitution Square State Historic Site, Danville, KY..............567

The Contemporary Arts Center, Cincinnati, OH..............1150

Contemporary Crafts Museum & Gallery, Portland, OR..............1230

Cook County Historical Museum, Grand Marais, MN..............776

Cooper-Hewitt National Design Museum, Smithsonian Institution, New York, NY..............1023

Coos Historical & Maritime Museum, North Bend, OR..............1229

Copper Range Historical Museum, South Range, MI..............764

Copper Village Museum & Arts Center of Deer Lodge County, Anaconda, MT........840

Copshaholm House Museum & Historic Oliver Gardens, South Bend, IN..............499

Coronado National Memorial, Hereford, AZ..............36

Corry Area Historical Society, Corry, PA...1248

Cortland County Historical Society, Cortland, NY..............982

Cottage Grove Museum & Annex, Cottage Grove, OR..............1222

Cottonwood County Historical Society, Windom, MN..............796

Country Music Hall of Fame and Museum, Country Music Foundation, Nashville, TN..............1378

Courthouse Square Association, Charlotte, MI 731

Cow Neck Peninsula Historical Society Sands-Willets House, Port Washington, NY 1053

The Cowley County Historical Society, Winfield, KS 564

Cowlitz County Historical Museum, Kelso, WA............1557

Cozens Ranch Museum, Fraser, CO............218

Cradle of Aviation Museum, Garden City, NY............992

Craft and Folk Art Museum - CAFAM, Los Angeles, CA............114

Craftsmen's Guild of Mississippi, Jackson, MS............802

Cramer-Kenyon Heritage Home, Yankton, SD............1359

Cranbrook Art Museum, Bloomfield Hills, MI............730

Cranbury Historical & Preservation Society, Cranbury, NJ............902

Cranford Historical Society, Cranford, NJ ...902

Cravens House, Lookout Mountain, TN ...1371

Crawford W. Long Museum, Jefferson, GA............374

Creek Council House Museum, Okmulgee, OK............1211

Crestline Shunk Museum, Crestline, OH ...1160

Croatian Heritage Museum & Library, Eastlake, OH............1163

Crocker House, Mount Clemens, MI............756

Crockett Tavern Museum, Morristown, TN............1376

Crook County Museum & Art Gallery, Sundance, WY............1638

Crosby County Pioneer Memorial Museum, Crosbyton, TX............1403

Crossroads Museum, Corinth, MS............800

Crow Wing County Historical Society, Brainerd, MN............769

Crystal Rice Plantation, Crowley, LA 588

Culbertson Mansion State Historic Site, New Albany, IN............493

Culbertson Museum, Culbertson, MT............845

Culinary Archives & Museum, Johnson & Wales University, Providence, RI......1316

Cultural Museum, Nashville, TN............1378

Cumberland County Historical Society, Greenwich, NJ............905

Cumberland County Historical Society, The Hamilton Library and The Two Mile House, Carlisle, PA............1245

Cuneo Museum & Gardens, Vernon Hills, IL............463

Cupertino Historical Society & Museum, Cupertino, CA............88

The Curious Kids' Museum, Saint Joseph, MI............763

The Currier Museum of Art, Manchester, NH............891

DAAP Galleries, Cincinnati, OH............1150

DAR John Strong Mansion Museum, Addison, VT............1475

D.R. Barker Historical Museum, Fredonia, NY............992

Dacotah Prairie Museum, Aberdeen, SD....1344

Dakotaland Museum, Huron, SD............1348

Dal-Paso Museum, Lamesa, TX............1433

Dallam-Hartley XIT Museum, Dalhart, TX............1403

Dallas Heritage Village at Old City Park, Dallas, TX............1405

Dallas Historical Society, Dallas, TX............1405

Dallas Museum of Art, Dallas, TX............1405

The Dan Quayle Center & Museum, Huntington, IN............481

The Danbury Museum & Historical Society, Danbury, CT............238

Dancing Bear Folk Center, Thermopolis, WY............1639

Daniel Boone Home and Boonesfield Village, Lindenwood University, Defiance, MO............814

Danvers Historical Society, Danvers, MA....678

Danville Museum of Fine Arts & History, Danville, VA............1502

Darlington Raceway Stock Car Museum, NMPA Hall of Fame, Darlington, SC....1331

Daughters of the American Revolution Museum, Washington, DC 277

Daughters of Utah Pioneers Pioneer Memorial Museum & International Society Daughters of Utah Pioneers, Salt Lake City, UT 1471

Davenport House Museum, Savannah, GA............384

David Bradford House, Washington, PA 1305

David Conklin Farmhouse, Huntington, NY............1000

The David Davis Mansion, Bloomington, IL............413

Davidson County Historical Museum, Lexington, NC............1109

Dawes County Historical Society Museum, Chadron, NE............859

Dawson County Historical Museum, Lexington, NE............864

Dawson Springs Museum and Art Center, Inc., Dawson Springs, KY............568

Dayton Art Institute, Dayton, OH............1161

Dayton Historical Depot Society, Dayton, WA............1552

De Graaf Nature Center, Holland, MI............746

De Saisset Museum, Santa Clara, CA............180

Deaf Smith County Museum, Hereford, TX............1424

Dearborn Historical Museum, Dearborn, MI............733

Dedham Historical Society Museum, Dedham, MA............679

Deer Isle-Stonington Historical Society, Deer Isle, ME............609

Deerfield Beach Historical Society, Deerfield Beach, FL............304

DeKalb History Center Museum, Decatur, GA............370

Delaware Agricultural Museum and Village, Dover, DE............269

Delaware Division of Historical & Cultural Affairs, Dover, DE............269

Delta Blues Museum, Clarksdale, MS............799

Delta County Museum, Delta, CO............209

Delta Music Museum, Ferriday, LA............588

Deming Luna Mimbres Museum, Deming, NM............939

Denison Museum, Granville, OH 1167

The Dennison Railroad Depot Museum, Dennison, OH 1162

Dennys River Historical Society, Dennysville, ME............609

Denver Art Museum, Denver, CO............210

Denver Museum of Miniatures, Dolls and Toys, Denver, CO............211

Depot Museum & Fort Sedgwick Museum, Julesburg, CO............223

Depot Park Museum, Sonoma, CA............187

Depreciation Lands Museum, Allison Park, PA............1240

Des Plaines History Center, Des Plaines, IL............430

Deschutes County Historical Society, Bend, OR............1220

Desert Caballeros Western Museum, Wickenburg, AZ............53

Desha County Museum, Dumas, AR............56

The Design Center at Philadelphia University, Philadelphia, PA 1278

Detroit Historical Society, Detroit, MI............735

The Detroit Institute of Arts, Detroit, MI.....736

Detroit Zoo, Royal Oak, MI............762

Deutschheim State Historic Site, Hermann, MO............817

Dewey Hotel Museum, Dewey, OK............1199

DeWitt County Historical Museum, Cuero, TX............1403

DeWitt Wallace Decorative Arts Museum, Williamsburg, VA............1545

Dexter Area Historical Society & Museum, Dexter, MI............738

Dey Mansion/Washington's Headquarters Museum, Wayne, NJ............929

Dickinson County Heritage Center, Abilene, KS............531

Dinsmore Homestead Foundation, Burlington, KY............566

The Discovery Center of the Southern Tier, Binghamton, NY............962

Dr. Daniel W. Kissam House, Huntington, NY............1000

Dr. Increase Mathews House, Zanesville, OH............1194

Dr. William Robinson Plantation, Clark, NJ............901

Dodge County Historical Society Museum, Beaver Dam, WI............1591

Don F. Pratt Memorial Museum, Fort Campbell, KY............568

Dorothea B. Hoover Historical Museum, Joplin, MO............819

Douglas County Museum Complex, Armour, SD............1344

Douglass Historical Museum, Douglass, KS............537

The Downers Grove Park District Museum, Downers Grove, IL............431

Downieville Museum, Downieville, CA 91

Drew County Historical Museum, Monticello, AR............64

Drum Barracks Civil War Museum, Wilmington, CA............198

Drummond Home, Hominy, OK............1203

Duke Homestead State Historic Site, Durham, NC............1098

Duluth Art Institute, Duluth, MN 772

Duluth Children's Museum, Duluth, MN.....772

Dumbarton Oaks Research Library & Collections, Washington, DC............278

Dunbar House State Memorial, Dayton, OH............1161

Dundee Township Historical Society, Inc., Dundee, IL............431

Dundy County Historical Society, Benkelman, NE............857

DuPage County Historical Museum, Wheaton, IL............465

Durham Center Museum/Research Library, East Durham, NY............985

Dutchess County Historical Society, Poughkeepsie, NY............1054

Duxbury Rural and Historical Society, Inc., Duxbury, MA............681

Dwight D. Eisenhower Library-Museum, Abilene, KS............531

Dyckman Farmhouse Museum and Park, New York, NY............1025

E. St. Julien Cox House, Saint Peter, MN ...792

Eagle Tavern Museum, Watkinsville, GA 391

East Brunswick Museum Corporation, East Brunswick, NJ............902

East Jordan Portside Art & Historical Museum, East Jordan, MI............739

East Texas Oil Museum at Kilgore College, Kilgore, TX............1432

East-West Center, Honolulu, HI............394

Eastside Heritage Center, Bellevue, WA 1548

The Ebenezer Maxwell Mansion, Inc., Philadelphia, PA............1278

Edgar Allan Poe Cottage, Bronx, NY 965

Edge of the Cedars State Park Museum, Blanding, UT............1463

Edisto Island Historic Preservation Society Museum, Edisto Island, SC 1332

Edmonds Art Festival Museum, Edmonds, WA............1553

Costumes and Textiles–Continued

Edmonds South Snohomish County
  Historical Society, Inc., Edmonds, WA .1553
Edsel & Eleanor Ford House, Grosse
  Pointe Shores, MI...................745
Egan Maritime Foundation, Nantucket,
  MA...................695
1859 Jail, Marshal's Home & Museum,
  Independence, MO...................817
Eiteljorg Museum of American Indians
  and Western Art, Indianapolis, IN...........482
El Museo Latino, Omaha, NE...................870
El Paso Museum of History, El Paso, TX..1412
Eldridge Street Project, New York, NY 1025
Elgin Area Historical Society, Elgin, IL.......432
Elizabeth Sage Historic Costume
  Collection, Bloomington, IN...................469
Elkhart County Historical Museum,
  Bristol, IN...................471
Ella Sharp Museum, Jackson, MI...............748
Elliott Museum, Stuart, FL...................346
Ellis County Historical Society, Hays, KS...543
Ellis County Museum, Inc., Waxahachie,
  TX...................1460
Ellwood House Museum, DeKalb, IL.........429
Elmhurst Historical Museum, Elmhurst,
  IL...................433
Elverhoj Museum of History and Art,
  Solvang, CA...................187
Emil A. Blackmore Museum of The
  American Legion, Indianapolis, IN.........482
Emily Dickinson Museum: The
  Homestead and The Evergreens,
  Amherst, MA...................658
Emmett Kelly Historical Museum, Sedan,
  KS...................558
Empire State Aerosciences Museum,
  Glenville, NY...................995
Enchanted World Doll Museum, Mitchell,
  SD...................1352
Enfield Shaker Museum, Enfield, NH.........887
Epcot at Walt Disney World Resort, Lake
  Buena Vista, FL...................319
Ephraim Historical Foundation, Ephraim,
  WI...................1597
Erie Canal Museum, Syracuse, NY...........1076
Erie Canal Village, Rome, NY...................1061
Erie County History Center & Cashier's
  House, Erie, PA...................1252
The Erlander Home Museum, Rockford,
  IL...................454
Ernie Pyle State Historic Site, Dana, IN......473
Estes Park Museum, Estes Park, CO............215
The Esther Thomas Atkinson Museum,
  Hampden-Sydney, VA...................1509
Ethnic Heritage Museum, Rockford, IL.......455
Eubie Blake National Jazz Institute and
  Cultural Center, Baltimore, MD............632
Eugene Field House and St. Louis Toy
  Museum, Saint Louis, MO...................833
Eureka School House, Springfield, VT......1487
Eustis Historical Museum & Preservation
  Society, Inc., Eustis, FL...................306
Evanston Historical Society and Charles
  Gates Dawes House, Evanston, IL..........434
Evergreen Aviation Museum,
  McMinnville, OR...................1228
Evergreen House, The Johns Hopkins
  University, Baltimore, MD...................632
Experience Music Project, Seattle, WA...1565
Exploris, Raleigh, NC...................1115
Ezra Meeker Mansion, Puyallup, WA........1564

The Fabric Workshop and Museum,
  Philadelphia, PA...................1279
Fairbanks House, Dedham, MA...................679
Fairfax County Park Authority, Resource
  Management Division, Fairfax, VA.......1503
Fairfield County Museum, Winnsboro,
  SC...................1343
Fairfield Historical Society, Fairfield, CT...241
Fairport Historical Museum, Fairport, NY...989

Fairport Marine Museum, Fairport
  Harbor, OH...................1164
Fairview Museum of History & Art,
  Fairview, UT...................1465
Faith Trumbull Chapter, Daughters of the
  American Revolution, Inc., Museum
  and Chapter House, Norwich, CT.........258
Fall River County Historical Museum,
  Hot Springs, SD...................1348
Fall River Historical Society Museum,
  Fall River, MA...................682
Falls Village-Canaan Historical Society,
  Falls Village, CT...................241
Falmouth Historical Society, Falmouth,
  MA...................682
Family Museum, Bettendorf, IA...................505
Farmers Branch Historical Park, Farmers
  Branch, TX...................1413
The Farmers' Museum, Inc.,
  Cooperstown, NY...................980
Farmington Museum, Farmington, NM........939
Farrar-Mansur House & Old Mill
  Museum, Weston, VT...................1490
The Fashion Institute of Design &
  Merchandising/FIDM Museum &
  Galleries, Los Angeles, CA...................114
Favell Museum Inc., Klamath Falls, OR....1227
Fayette Heritage Museum & Archives, La
  Grange, TX...................1432
Fenton History Center-Museum &
  Library, Jamestown, NY...................1005
Fernbank Museum of Natural History,
  Atlanta, GA...................359
Festival-Institute, James Dick Foundation,
  Round Top, TX...................1446
Fifth Maine Regiment Museum, Peaks
  Island, ME...................618
Fillmore Historical Museum, Inc.,
  Fillmore, CA...................95
Filoli Center, Woodside, CA...................199
Fine Arts Center for New River Valley,
  Pulaski, VA...................1526
The Fine Arts Museums of San
  Francisco, de Young Museum, San
  Francisco, CA...................165
The Fine Arts Museums of San
  Francisco, Legion of Honor, San
  Francisco, CA...................165
Fire Museum of Maryland, Inc.,
  Lutherville, MD...................649
Fire Museum of Texas, Beaumont, TX......1394
Firelands Historical Society Museum,
  Norwalk, OH...................1180
1st Cavalry Division Museum, Fort
  Hood, TX...................1414
The First Division Museum at Cantigny,
  Wheaton, IL...................465
First White House of the Confederacy,
  Montgomery, AL...................16
The Fisk University Galleries, Nashville,
  TN...................1379
The Five Civilized Tribes Museum,
  Muskogee, OK...................1205
The Flag House and Star-Spangled
  Banner Museum, Baltimore, MD............632
Flagler Museum, Palm Beach, FL.................333
Flaten Art Museum of St. Olaf College,
  Northfield, MN...................785
Fleming Historical Society, Fleming, CO....216
Flint Institute of Arts, Flint, MI...................741
Florence Hawley Ellis Museum of
  Anthropology and Ruth Hall Museum
  of Paleontology, Abiquiu, NM...................931
The Florence McLeod Hazard Museum,
  Columbus, MS...................800
Florence Museum of Art, Science &
  History and the Florence Railroad
  Museum, Florence, SC...................1332
Florewood State Park, Greenwood, MS......801
Florida Holocaust Museum, Saint
  Petersburg, FL...................341
Florissant Valley Historical Society,
  Florissant, MO...................815

Folger Shakespeare Library, Washington,
  DC...................278
Folsom History Museum, Folsom, CA...........95
The Folsom House Museum, Taylors
  Falls, MN...................794
Fonthill Museum of the Bucks County
  Historical Society, Doylestown, PA.......1249
The Forges and Manor of Ringwood,
  Ringwood, NJ...................923
Forney Museum of Transportation,
  Denver, CO...................212
The Fort at No. 4 Living History
  Museum, Charlestown, NH...................884
Fort Bedford Museum, Bedford, PA...........1241
Fort Bend Museum Association,
  Richmond, TX...................1445
Fort Benton Museum of the Upper
  Missouri, Fort Benton, MT...................846
Fort Bliss Museum, Fort Bliss, TX 1413
Fort Boonesborough Museum, Richmond,
  KY...................583
Fort Caspar Museum, Casper, WY.............1629
Fort Christmas Historical Park,
  Christmas, FL...................299
Fort Collins Museum, Fort Collins, CO......217
Fort Croghan Museum, Burnet, TX...........1398
Fort Crook Historical Museum, Fall
  River Mills, CA...................94
Fort Davis National Historic Site, Fort
  Davis, TX...................1414
Fort Delaware Society, Delaware City,
  DE...................268
Fort Dix Museum, Fort Dix, NJ.................904
Fort George G. Meade Museum, Fort
  Meade, MD...................643
Fort Harker Museum Complex,
  Kanopolis, KS...................546
Fort Hunter Mansion & Park, Harrisburg,
  PA...................1258
Fort Klock Historic Restoration, Saint
  Johnsville, NY...................1063
Fort Lauderdale Historical Society, Fort
  Lauderdale, FL...................307
Fort MacArthur Museum, San Pedro, CA...176
Fort McAllister, Richmond Hill, GA...........381
Fort McHenry National Monument and
  Historic Shrine, Baltimore, MD.............632
Fort Mifflin, Philadelphia, PA...................1279
Fort Morgan Museum, Fort Morgan, CO.....218
Fort Necessity National Battlefield,
  Farmington, PA...................1253
Fort Okanogan Interpretive Center,
  Brewster, WA...................1550
Fort Ontario State Historic Site, Oswego,
  NY...................1048
Fort Payne Depot Museum, Fort Payne,
  AL...................10
Fort Plain Museum, Fort Plain, NY.............991
Fort St. Joseph Museum, Niles, MI.............758
Fort Scott National Historic Site, Fort
  Scott, KS...................540
Fort Selden State Monument, Radium
  Springs, NM...................945
Fort Sidney Museum & Post
  Commander's Home, Sidney, NE...........873
Fort Sill National Historic Landmark,
  Fort Sill, OK...................1201
Fort Smith Museum of History, Fort
  Smith, AR...................58
Fort Ticonderoga, Ticonderoga, NY...........1078
Fort Totten State Historic Site, Fort
  Totten, ND...................1131
Fort Vasquez Museum, Platteville, CO........230
Fort Verde State Historic Park, Camp
  Verde, AZ...................30
Fort Ward Museum and Historic Site,
  Alexandria, VA...................1492
Fort Wayne Museum of Art, Fort Wayne,
  IN...................477
45th Infantry Division Museum,
  Oklahoma City, OK...................1207
Fossil Country Museum, Kemmerer, WY ..1635

Fostoria Area Historical Museum, Fostoria, OH 1164

Four Rivers Cultural Center & Museum, Ontario, OR 1229

Framingham Historical Society & Museum, Framingham, MA 683

Frances Willard House Museum, Evanston, IL 434

Francisco Fort Museum, La Veta, CO 224

Franconia Heritage Museum, Franconia, NH 888

Frank H. McClung Museum, Knoxville, TN 1370

Frank Lloyd Wright's Pope-Leighey House, Alexandria, VA 1492

Frankfort Area Historical Museum, West Frankfort, IL 464

Franklin County Historical Museum, Pasco, WA 1561

Franklin County Seminary and Museum, Brookville, IN 471

Franklin D. Roosevelt Presidential Library-Museum, Hyde Park, NY 1002

Fraternal Order of Alaska State Troopers Museum, Anchorage, AK 22

Frederick R. Weisman Museum of Art, Malibu, CA 123

Freeport Arts Center, Freeport, IL 435

Freer Gallery of Art, Washington, DC 279

French Art Colony, Gallipolis, OH 1165

The French Legation Museum, Austin, TX 1390

Fresno Flats Historical Park, Oakhurst, CA 132

The Frick Art & Historical Center, Pittsburgh, PA 1292

Friends of Firemen's Museum, New Bern, NC 1112

The Friends of Peace Church, Camp Hill, PA 1245

Frisco Historic Park & Museum, Frisco, CO 218

Frisco Native American Museum and Natural History Center, Frisco, NC 1102

Frontier Museum, Williston, ND 1138

The Fullerton Arboretum, Fullerton, CA 98

Fulton County Historical Museum, Wauseon, OH 1190

Fulton County Historical Society Museum, Rochester, IN 498

Fulton County Museum, Groversville, NY 996

Fulton Mansion State Historic Site, Rockport, TX 1446

Furnas-Gosper Historical Society & Museum, Arapahoe, NE 856

Gage County Historical Society and Museum, Beatrice, NE 857

Galerie Trinitas, Great Falls, MT 848

Gallery on the York - Yorktown Arts Foundation, Yorktown, VA 1547

Gallier House, New Orleans, LA 595

Galveston County Historical Museum, Galveston, TX 1420

Galveston Historical Foundation, Inc., Galveston, TX 1421

Gardner House Museum, Albion, MI 723

Garnavillo Historical Museum, Garnavillo, IA 518

Gaston County Museum of Art and History, Dallas, NC 1097

Gatekeeper's Museum & Marion Steinbach Indian Basket Museum, Tahoe City, CA 190

Gates Mills Historical Society, Gates Mills, OH 1166

Gateway to the Panhandle, Gate, OK 1201

Gathland State Park, Boonsboro, MD 637

Gay Nineties Button and Doll Museum, Eureka Springs, AR 57

Geddes Historic District Village, Geddes, SD 1347

General Adam Stephen House, Martinsburg, WV 1584

General Crook House Museum and Library/Archives Center, Omaha, NE 870

General Douglas MacArthur Memorial, Norfolk, VA 1521

General John J. Pershing Boyhood Home State Historic Site, Laclede, MO 824

General Lew Wallace Study & Museum, Crawfordsville, IN 473

General Patton Memorial Museum, Chiriaco Summit, CA 84

General Wait House, Waitsfield, VT 1489

Geneva Historical Society & Prouty-Chew House & Museum, Geneva, NY 994

Geneva Historical Society & Rose Hill Mansion, Geneva, NY 994

The George Bush Presidential Library and Museum, College Station, TX 1400

George C. Marshall Museum, Lexington, VA 1513

George Washington Carver Museum, Tuskegee Institute, AL 20

George Washington's Fredericksburg Foundation, Historic Kenmore & Washington's Ferry Farm, Fredericksburg, VA 1506

Georgia Capitol Museum, Atlanta, GA 360

Georgia Museum of Art, University of Georgia, Athens, GA 356

Georgia Music Hall of Fame and Museum, Macon, GA 377

The Georgian Museum, Lancaster, OH 1171

Georgia's Old Capital Museum, Milledgeville, GA 380

Georgia's Stone Mountain Park, Stone Mountain, GA 387

Gerald R. Ford Presidential Museum, Grand Rapids, MI 743

Germantown Historical Society, Philadelphia, PA 1280

The Gibson Society, Inc. dba Gibson House Museum, Boston, MA 665

Gila County Historical Museum, Globe, AZ 35

The Gilbert Stuart Birthplace and Museum, Saunderstown, RI 1319

Gilpin History Museum, Central City, CO 205

Glencairn Museum: Academy of the New Church, Bryn Athyn, PA 1244

Glendower State Memorial, Lebanon, OH 1171

Glenview Area Historical Society, Glenview, IL 438

Gloucester County Historical Society, Woodbury, NJ 931

Glove Museum, New York, NY 1026

The Godwin-Ternbach Museum, Flushing, NY 990

Gold Coast Railroad Museum, Inc., Miami, FL 323

Golden Pioneer Museum, Golden, CO 220

The Goldstein Museum of Design, Saint Paul, MN 789

Goliad State Park, Goliad, TX 1423

Gone With The Wind Movie Museum, Marietta, GA 379

Goodhue County Historical Society, Red Wing, MN 787

Goodman Museum, Tyler, TX 1456

Goodnow Museum State Historic Site, Manhattan, KS 550

Gore Place, Waltham, MA 715

Goschenhoppen Folklife Library and Museum, Green Lane, PA 1257

Goshen Historical Society, Goshen, CT 242

Gouverneur Historical Association, Gouverneur, NY 995

Governor John Sevier Memorial Association, Knoxville, TN 1370

Governor Seay Mansion, Kingfisher, OK 1204

Governor's Mansion State Historic Park, Sacramento, CA 152

Grace Hudson Museum & Sun House, Ukiah, CA 193

Graceland, Memphis, TN 1373

Grafton Historical Society, Grafton, VT 1479

Graham County Historical Society, Thatcher, AZ 46

Grand Army of the Republic Civil War Museum, Philadelphia, PA 1281

Grand County Museum, Hot Sulphur Springs, CO 222

Grand Gulf Military Park, Port Gibson, MS 807

Grand Lake Area Historical Society, Grand Lake, CO 221

Grand Lodge AF&AM of Virginia - Allen E. Roberts Masonic Library and Museum, Richmond, VA 1529

The Grand River Historical Society & Museum, Chillicothe, MO 813

Grand Teton National Park, Colter Bay Indian Arts Museum, Colter Bay Village, WY 1631

The Granger Homestead Society, Inc., Canandaigua, NY 975

Grant County Historical Museum, Ephrata, WA 1553

Grant County Historical Society, Elbow Lake, MN 774

Grant County Museum aka Historic Adobe Museum, Ulysses, KS 560

Grant County Museum & Historic Society, Hyannis, NE 863

Grant-Kohrs Ranch National Historic Site, Deer Lodge, MT 845

Grants Pass Museum of Art, Grants Pass, OR 1225

Granville Historical Society Museum, Granville, OH 1167

Graycliff Conservancy, Derby, NY 984

Great Lakes Naval Memorial and Museum, Muskegon, MI 757

Great Sand Dunes National Monument and Preserve, Mosca, CO 229

Greater Hazleton Historical Society, Hazleton, PA 1260

Greater Loveland Historical Society Museum, Loveland, OH 1173

Greenbelt Museum, Greenbelt, MD 646

Greene County Historical Society, Xenia, OH 1193

Greensboro Historical Museum, Inc., Greensboro, NC 1103

Greenwood County Historical Society, Eureka, KS 539

Gresham History Museum, Gresham, OR 1226

Grey Art Gallery, New York University Art Collection, New York, NY 1026

Grier Musser Museum, Los Angeles, CA 115

Grissom Air Museum, Peru, IN 496

Grosse Ile Historical Society, Grosse Ile, MI 745

Groton Historical Society, Groton, MA 685

Guernsey County Museum, Cambridge, OH 1144

Gunn Memorial Library and Museum, Washington, CT 263

Gunnison County Pioneer and Historical Society, Gunnison, CO 222

Gustafson Gallery/Design & Merchandising, Fort Collins, CO 217

Gwinnett History Museum, Lawrenceville, GA 376

H. Earl Clack Museum, Havre, MT 849

Haas-Lilienthal House, San Francisco, CA 166

Haffenreffer Museum of Anthropology, Brown University, Bristol, RI 1310

The Haggin Museum, Stockton, CA 189

The Hagley Museum and Library, Wilmington, DE 273

Hahns Peak Area Historical Society and School House, Clark, CO 205

Costumes and Textiles–Continued

Haines Museum, Waukegan Historical
Society, Waukegan, IL.............................463

Halifax Historical Museum, Daytona
Beach, FL...303

Hallie Ford Museum of Art, Salem, OR 1235

Hamilton Township Historical Society -
John Abbott II House, Hamilton, NJ.......906

Hamilton Van Wagoner Museum, Clifton,
NJ...901

Hampton History Museum, Hampton, VA .1509

Hampton University Museum, Hampton,
VA...1509

Hanby House, Westerville, OH.................1191

Hancock Historical Museum, Findlay,
OH...1164

Hancock Historical Society, Hancock,
NH...888

Hancock Shaker Village, Inc., Pittsfield,
MA...703

The Handweaving Museum & Arts
Center, Clayton, NY................................978

Handwerker Gallery, Ithaca, NY...............1003

Hannah Lindahl Children's Museum,
Mishawaka, IN..491

Hanover House, Clemson, SC...................1328

Har-Ber Village, Grove, OK.....................1202

Harbor Defense Museum, Brooklyn, NY....969

Harbour House Museum, Crystal Falls,
MI...733

Harding Museum, Franklin, OH................1164

Harlan-Lincoln House, Mount Pleasant,
IA..524

The Harness Racing Museum and Hall of
Fame, Goshen, NY..................................995

Harold Warp Pioneer Village Foundation,
Minden, NE...868

Harper City Historical Society, Harper,
KS...543

Harriet Beecher Stowe Center, Hartford,
CT...245

Harrison County Historical Museum,
Marshall, TX..1436

Harry S. Truman Library-Museum,
Independence, MO..................................818

Hartsville Museum, Hartsville, SC............1335

Harvard Historical Society, Still River,
MA...711

Harvey County Historical Society,
Newton, KS...553

Hastings Museum, Hastings, NE...............863

Hatton-Eielson Museum & Historical
Association, Hatton, ND.........................1132

Haverford Township Historical Society,
Havertown, PA.......................................1260

Haverhill Historical Society, Haverhill,
MA...686

Havre de Grace Decoy Museum, Havre
de Grace, MD..647

Hawaii's Plantation Village, Waipahu, HI...402

Hawks Inn Historical Society, Inc.,
Delafield, WI...1595

Hayden Museum of American Art, Paris,
TX...1442

Headley-Whitney Museum, Lexington,
KY...573

Headwaters Heritage Museum, Three
Forks, MT...854

Heard Museum, Phoenix, AZ.......................40

Hearst Castle, San Simeon, CA..................177

Hearthstone Historic House Museum,
Appleton, WI...1589

Held-Poage Memorial Home and
Research Library, Ukiah, CA...................193

Helen Louise Allen Textile Collection,
Madison, WI..1605

Hellenic Museum & Cultural Center,
Chicago, IL..421

Hennepin History Museum, Minneapolis,
MN..782

Henrico County Historic Preservation &
Museum Services, Richmond, VA..........1529

Henry Art Gallery, Seattle, WA...............1566

Henry County Historical Society, New
Castle, IN...494

Henry County Museum and Cultural Arts
Center, Clinton, MO...............................813

The Henry Ford, Dearborn, MI.................733

The Henry Sheldon Museum of Vermont
History, Middlebury, VT........................1481

Herbert Hoover Presidential
Library-Museum, West Branch, IA.........530

Heritage Farmstead Museum, Plano, TX...1444

Heritage Hall Museum & Archives,
Freeman, SD...1347

Heritage Hill State Historical Park, Green
Bay, WI..1599

Heritage-Hjemkomst Interpretive Center,
Moorhead, MN..784

Heritage House Museum of Montgomery
County, Mount Ida, AR.............................64

Heritage House of Orange County
Association Inc., Orange, TX.................1441

The Heritage Museum, Astoria, OR.........1218

The Heritage Museum & Underhill
Museum, Idaho Springs, CO...................223

The Heritage Museum of Fine Arts for
Youth, Detroit, MI.................................736

Heritage of the Americas Museum, El
Cajon, CA...92

The Heritage Society, Houston, TX..........1426

Heritage Square Museum, Ontario, NY....1047

Heritage Square Museum, Los Angeles,
CA...116

Heritage Station, Umatilla County
Historical Society Museum, Pendleton,
OR...1230

Heritage Village Museum, Woodville, TX .1462

Herkimer County Historical Society,
Herkimer, NY..998

Hermann-Grima/Gallier Historic Houses,
New Orleans, LA.....................................595

The Hermitage, Ho-Ho-Kus, NJ................907

The Hermitage Foundation, Norfolk, VA...1521

The Hermitage: Home of President
Andrew Jackson, Hermitage, TN...........1367

Hernando Heritage Museum, Brooksville,
FL...298

Herrett Center for Arts & Science,
Faulkner Planetarium and Centennial
Observatory, Twin Falls, ID....................410

Hershey Museum, Hershey, PA................1261

Hettinger County Historical Society,
Regent, ND...1136

The Hickories Museum of the Lorain
County Historical Society, Elyria, OH ..1163

Hickory Grove Rural School Museum,
Ogden, IA..525

The High Museum of Art, Atlanta, GA........360

High Plains Museum, Goodland, KS...........542

High Point Museum & Historical Park,
High Point, NC.......................................1106

Highland County Museum and Heritage
Center, McDowell, VA...........................1517

Highland House Museum, Hillsboro, OH ..1168

Highland Park Historical Society,
Highland Park, IL...................................439

Highlands Art League, Sebring, FL...........345

Highlands Center for Natural History,
Prescott, AZ..42

Highlands Hammock State Park/Civilian
Conservation Corps Museum, Sebring,
FL...346

Highlands Museum & Discovery Center,
Ashland, KY..564

The Hill Country Museum, Kerrville, TX..1431

Hill-Stead Museum, Farmington, CT.........241

Hillforest House Museum, Aurora, IN........468

Hillwood Art Museum, Brookville, NY.......971

Hillwood Museum & Gardens,
Washington, DC......................................280

Hinckley Fire Museum, Hinckley, MN........778

Hinsdale Historical Society, Hinsdale, IL 440

The Hispanic Society of America, New
York, NY..1027

Historic Arkansas Museum, Little Rock,
AR...62

Historic Auto Attractions, Roscoe, IL..........456

Historic Carson House, Marion, NC..........1110

Historic Cherry Hill, Albany, NY..............954

Historic Costume & Textiles Collection,
Columbus, OH..1158

Historic Crab Orchard Museum &
Pioneer Park, Inc., Tazewell, VA...........1541

Historic Deepwood Estate, Salem, OR......1235

Historic Deerfield, Inc., Deerfield, MA......679

Historic Edenton State Historic Site,
Edenton, NC...1099

Historic General Dodge House, Council
Bluffs, IA..512

Historic Georgetown Inc., Georgetown,
CO...218

Historic Governors' Mansion, Cheyenne,
WY...1630

Historic Halifax State Historic Site,
Halifax, NC..1105

Historic Hermann Museum, Hermann,
MO...817

Historic Homes Foundation, Inc.,
Louisville, KY..576

Historic Hope Foundation, Inc., Windsor,
NC...1124

Historic House Trust of New York City,
New York, NY..1027

Historic Hudson Valley, Tarrytown, NY.....1077

Historic Jefferson College, Washington,
MS...810

Historic Landmarks Foundation of
Indiana, Indianapolis, IN.........................482

Historic Langhorne Association,
Langhorne, PA.......................................1267

Historic Latta Plantation, Huntersville,
NC...1107

Historic London Town and Gardens,
Edgewater, MD.......................................642

Historic Northampton, Northampton, MA....699

Historic Occoquan, Inc., Occoquan, VA.....1523

Historic Palmyra's Print Shop, Palmyra,
NY...1050

Historic Palmyra's - Wm. Phelps General
Store, Palmyra, NY...............................1050

Historic Pensacola Village, Pensacola, FL ...335

Historic Preservation Association of
Bourbon County, Inc., Fort Scott, KS.....540

Historic Richmond Town, Staten Island,
NY...1072

Historic Rosedale, Charlotte, NC..............1095

Historic Schaefferstown, Inc.,
Schaefferstown, PA...............................1297

Historic Shepherdstown Museum,
Shepherdstown, WV...............................1586

Historic Smithfield, Blacksburg, VA.........1497

Historic Southwest Ohio, Inc.,
Sharonville, OH.....................................1185

Historic Waco Foundation, Waco, TX........1459

Historical and Genealogical Society of
Indiana County, Indiana, PA.................1262

Historical and Genealogical Society of
Somerset County, Somerset, PA............1300

Historical Center for Southeast New
Mexico, Roswell, NM.............................946

The Historical Museum at St. Gertrude,
Cottonwood, ID.......................................405

Historical Museum of Bay County, Bay
City, MI..727

Historical Museum of Southern Florida,
Miami, FL..324

Historical Natural History & Library
Society of Natick dba Natick
Historical Society, South Natick, MA.....709

Historical Shrine Foundation of San
Diego County, San Diego, CA.................156

Historical Society of Berks County,
Reading, PA...1296

Historical Society of Bloomfield New Jersey, Bloomfield, NJ..............................898
Historical Society of Brookfield, Brookfield Center, VT..................1477
Historical Society of Carroll County, Westminster, MD..............................656
The Historical Society of Dauphin County, Harrisburg, PA 1258
Historical Society of Delaware, Wilmington, DE..............................274
Historical Society of Fort Washington, Fort Washington, PA 1254
The Historical Society of Frederick County, Inc., Frederick, MD..............644
Historical Society of Glastonbury, Glastonbury, CT..............................242
Historical Society of Greater Port Jefferson, Port Jefferson, NY.................1053
Historical Society of Greenfield, Greenfield, MA..............................685
Historical Society of Haddonfield, Haddonfield, NJ..............................905
Historical Society of Kent County, Inc., Chestertown, MD..............................640
Historical Society of Middletown and the Wallkill Precinct, Inc., Middletown, NY..............................1014
Historical Society of Newburgh Bay & the Highlands - David Crawford House, Newburgh, NY 1042
Historical Society of Oak Park & River Forest, Oak Park, IL..........................448
Historical Society of Ocean Grove, New Jersey, Ocean Grove, NJ..............918
Historical Society of Old Newbury, Cushing House Museum, Newburyport, MA..............................698
Historical Society of Old Yarmouth, Yarmouth Port, MA..............................722
Historical Society of Princeton, Princeton, NJ..............................921
Historical Society of Quincy and Adams County, Quincy, IL..............................452
Historical Society of Rockland County, New City, NY..............................1017
Historical Society of St. Marys and Benzinger Township, Saint Marys, PA..1297
Historical Society of Santuit and Cotuit, Cotuit, MA..............................677
Historical Society of Saratoga Springs, Saratoga Springs, NY..............................1064
Historical Society of Stanton County Museums at Stanton and Pilger, Pilger, NE..............................872
Historical Society of Talbot County, Easton, MD..............................642
Historical Society of the Cocalico Valley, Ephrata, PA..............................1252
Historical Society of the Tonawandas, Inc., Tonawanda, NY..............................1078
Historical Society of Wells and Ogunquit, Wells, ME..............................625
Historical Society Porter County Old Jail Museum, Valparaiso, IN..............................502
The Historical Society, serving Sleepy Hollow and Tarrytown, Tarrytown, NY.1078
The History Center, Fort Wayne, IN 477
The History Center in Tompkins County, Ithaca, NY..............................1003
The History Place, Morehead City, NC 1111
History San Jose, San Jose, CA..............................171
Hixon House, La Crosse, WI..............................1603
Hoard Historical Museum and National Dairy Shrine's Visitors Center, Fort Atkinson, WI 1598
Hobart Historical Society Museum, Hobart, IN..............................480
Hodgden House Museum Complex, Ellsworth, KS..............................538
The Holland Museum, Holland, MI 746
Holly History Center & Hutchinson House Museum, Waupaca, WI..............1626

Hollywood Heritage Museum, Hollywood, CA..............................103
Holmes County Historical Society, Millersburg, OH..............................1176
Holter Museum of Art, Helena, MT............849
Home of Franklin D. Roosevelt National Historic Site, Hyde Park, NY..........1002
Home of Stone (The Mueller-Schmidt House 1881), a Ford County Museum, curated by Ford County Historic Society, Dodge City, KS 537
Home Sweet Home Museum, East Hampton, NY..............................986
Homesteader Museum, Powell, WY..........1637
Honolulu Academy of Arts, Honolulu, HI ...395
Honolulu House Museum, Marshall, MI......754
Honolulu Police Department Law Enforcement Museum, Honolulu, HI......396
Hood Museum of Art, Hanover, NH............888
Hood River County Historical Museum, Hood River, OR..............................1226
Hoover Historical Center, North Canton, OH..............................1179
Hopewell Furnace National Historic Site, Elverson, PA..............................1251
Hopewell Museum, Paris, KY..............................582
Hopewell Museum, Hopewell, NJ..............908
Hornby Museum, Hornby, NY..............................999
Hot Spring County Museum - The Boyle House/1876 Log Cabin, Malvern, AR.......63
Hotel de Paris Museum, Georgetown, CO...219
House of Broadcasting Radio & Television Museum, Scottsdale, AZ..........44
House of the Temple, Washington, DC........280
Howard County Center of African American Culture, Columbia, MD...........641
Howard County Historical Museum, Kokomo, IN..............................486
Howard County Historical Society, Ellicott City, MD..............................643
Howland House, Plymouth, MA..............................703
The Hoyt Institute of Fine Arts, New Castle, PA..............................1273
Huddleston Farmhouse Inn Museum, Cambridge City, IN 471
Hudson Library and Historical Society, Hudson, OH..............................1168
The Hudson River Museum, Yonkers, NY.1087
Huerfano County Historical Society, including The Walsenburg Mining Museum & Ft. Francisco Museum of La Veta, Walsenburg, CO..............................234
Hulihee Palace, Kailua-Kona, HI..............................399
Humboldt Arts Council/Morris Graves Museum of Art, Eureka, CA..............................94
Humpback Rocks Mountain Farm & Visitor Center, Waynesboro, VA 1544
The 100th Meridian Museum, Cozad, NE ...859
Hungarian Folk-Art Museum, Port Orange, FL..............................338
Huntingdon County Historical Society, Huntingdon, PA 1262
Huntington County Historical Society Museum, Huntington, IN..............................481
Huntington Museum of Art, Inc., Huntington, WV..............................1583
Huntsville Museum of Art, Huntsville, AL..............................12
Huron City Museums, Port Austin, MI 761
Hurst Ranch Historical Foundation, West Covina, CA..............................197
Hutchinson Art Center, Hutchinson, KS.......545
The Hyde Collection, Glens Falls, NY 994
The Hyland House, Guilford, CT..............................243
Hyser Rivers Museum, Belmont, MI............728

Idaho State Historical Museum, Boise, ID...404
Illinois Citizen Soldier Museum, Galesburg, IL..............................437
Illinois State Museum, Springfield, IL 458
Ilwaco Heritage Museum, Ilwaco, WA.......1556
IMA - Indianapolis Museum of Art, Indianapolis, IN 483

Immaculate Conception Catholic Church, Natchitoches, LA..............................593
Imperial Calcasieu Museum, Inc., Lake Charles, LA..............................590
Indian King Tavern Museum, Haddonfield, NJ..............................906
Indian Pueblo Cultural Center, Albuquerque, NM..............................933
Indiana Basketball Hall of Fame, New Castle, IN..............................494
Indiana Dunes National Lakeshore, Porter, IN..............................496
Indiana State Museum, Indianapolis, IN 484
Indiana University Art Museum, Bloomington, IN..............................469
Indiana War Memorials, Indianapolis, IN 484
Institute of American Indian Arts Museum, Santa Fe, NM 947
Interlaken Historical Society, Interlaken, NY..............................1002
International Bluegrass Music Museum, Owensboro, KY..............................581
International Bowling Museum and Hall of Fame, Saint Louis, MO..............................833
The International Clown Hall of Fame & Research Center, Inc., Milwaukee, WI..1611
International Institute of Metropolitan Detroit, Detroit, MI..............................737
International Linen Registry Museum, Tulsa, OK..............................1215
International Motor Racing Research Center at Watkins Glen, Watkins Glen, NY..............................1084
International Museum of Art and Science, McAllen, TX..............................1437
International Museum of Cultures, Dallas, TX..............................1406
International Museum of the Horse, Lexington, KY..............................573
International Swimming Hall of Fame, Inc., Fort Lauderdale, FL..............................307
International Tennis Hall of Fame & Museum, Newport, RI..............................1313
International Women's Air and Space Museum, Inc., Cleveland, OH..............1155
Iolani Palace, Honolulu, HI..............................396
Iowa Masonic Library and Museum, Cedar Rapids, IA..............................509
Ipswich Historical Society and Museum, Ipswich, MA..............................688
Iredell Museum of Arts & Heritage, Statesville, NC..............................1120
Iris & B. Gerald Cantor Art Gallery-College of the Holy Cross, Worcester, MA..............................721
Iron County Museum, Caspian, MI..............731
Iroquois County Historical Society, Watseka, IL..............................463
Iroquois Indian Museum, Howes Cave, NY..............................999
Isaac Winslow House, Marshfield, MA........693
Isabel Anderson Comer Museum & Arts Center, Sylacauga, AL..............................18
Isabella Stewart Gardner Museum, Boston, MA..............................666
Isanti County Historical Society, Cambridge, MN..............................770
Ischua Valley Historical Society, Inc., Franklinville, NY..............................992
Isla Center For the Arts at the University of Guam, Mangilao, GU..............................1640
Island County Historical Society Museum, Coupeville, WA..............................1551
Issaquah History Museum, Issaquah, WA..1557
Italian American Museum, New York, NY..............................1028

J.E. Reeves Home & Museum, Dover, OH..............................1163
JFK Special Warfare Museum, Fort Bragg, NC..............................1101
Jackson County Historical Society, Black River Falls, WI..............................1592

Costumes and Textiles—Continued

Jacksonport State Park, Jacksonport, AR 60

Jacques Marchais Museum of Tibetan Art, Staten Island, NY............................1072

Jail Museum, Neligh, NE..............................869

James Buchanan Foundation for the Preservation of Wheatland, Lancaster, PA..1266

The James Madison Museum, Orange, VA..1524

James Monroe Museum and Memorial Library, Fredericksburg, VA.................1507

James S. Copley Library, La Jolla, CA 106

James W. Dillon House Museum, Dillon, SC..1331

Jamestown Settlement, Yorktown Victory Center, The Jamestown-Yorktown Foundation, Williamsburg, VA..............1545

Japan Society Gallery, New York, NY 1028

Japanese American National Museum, Los Angeles, CA....................................117

Japanese Cultural Center of Hawaii, Honolulu, HI..397

Jarrell Plantation Georgia State Historic Site, Juliette, GA....................................374

Jeane Dixon Museum and Library, Strasburg, VA.....................................1538

Jeanerette Bicentennial Park and Museum, Jeanerette, LA......................589

Jefferson Barracks Historic Site, Saint Louis, MO...833

The Jefferson County Historical Assoc., Steubenville, OH................................1186

Jefferson County Historical Society, Watertown, NY...................................1083

Jefferson County Museum, Charles Town, WV...1580

Jefferson Historical Society and Museum, Jefferson, TX.......................................1431

Jemez State Monument, Jemez Springs, NM...940

Jennings-Brown House Female Academy, Bennettsville, SC................................1322

Jersey City Museum, Jersey City, NJ...........908

Jesse James Farm & Museum, Kearney, MO...823

Jesse Peter Museum, Santa Rosa, CA 184

Jewell County Historical Museum, Mankato, KS...552

The Jewish Museum, New York, NY.......1029

Jewish Museum of Florida, Miami Beach, FL...326

Jim Crow Museum - Ferris State University, Big Rapids, MI....................729

Jimmie Rodgers Museum, Meridian, MS.....805

The Jimmy Stewart Museum, Indiana, PA.1262

Joachim Regional Museum, Dickinson, ND..1130

John and Mable Ringling Museum of Art, Sarasota, FL...344

John Burroughs Association, Inc., West Park, NY...1085

John F. Kennedy Presidential Library & Museum, Boston, MA.............................666

John Hutchings Museum of Natural History, Lehi, UT...................................1466

John James Audubon Museum, Henderson, KY......................................571

John Michael Kohler Arts Center, Sheboygan, WI...................................1621

John Muir National Historic Site, Martinez, CA...124

John Nance Garner Museum, Uvalde, TX .1457

John Paul Jones House Museum, Portsmouth, NH....................................894

John Rains House, Rancho Cucamonga, CA...145

John Sydnor's 1847 Powhatan House, Galveston, TX.....................................1421

John Wesley Powell Memorial Museum, Page, AZ..37

John Wornall House Museum, Kansas City, MO...821

Johnson County Historical Society, Coralville, IA......................................511

Johnson County Historical Society Museum, Warrensburg, MO.................840

Johnson County Museum of History, Franklin, IN...478

Johnson-Humrickhouse Museum, Coshocton, OH...................................1159

Johnstown Area Heritage Association, Johnstown, PA....................................1263

Joliet Area Historical Museum, Joliet, IL 440

Jonathan Hager House & Museum, Hagerstown, MD................................646

Jonesborough-Washington County History Museum, Jonesborough, TN...............1368

Jordan Schnitzer Museum of Art, Eugene, OR...1223

Joseph Smith Historic Site, Nauvoo, IL.......447

Judah L. Magnes Museum, Berkeley, CA......76

The Judah P. Benjamin Confederate Memorial at Gamble Plantation Historic State Park, Ellenton, FL.............306

Judaica Museum of Central Synagogue, New York, NY.....................................1029

Judith Basin County Museum, Stanford, MT...853

Judy Garland Museum, Grand Rapids, MN...777

Julia A. Purnell Museum, Snow Hill, MD ...654

Juliette Gordon Low Birthplace, Savannah, GA......................................385

Junction City Historical Society, Junction City, OR...1226

Jundt Art Museum, Spokane, WA 1571

Juniata County Historical Society, Mifflintown, PA...................................1271

Justin Smith Morrill Homestead, Strafford, VT.....................................1488

Kalamazoo Valley Museum, Kalamazoo, MI...749

Kankakee County Museum, Kankakee, IL...441

Kansas Museum of History, Topeka, KS 559

Katherine Dunham Dynamic Museum, East Saint Louis, IL..............................431

Kauai Museum, Lihue, HI 401

Kearney County Historical Museum, Minden, NE..868

Kearney Mansion Museum, Fresno, CA 97

The Kearny Cottage, Perth Amboy, NJ........921

Keeler Tavern Museum, Ridgefield, CT.......259

Kell House Museum, Wichita Falls, TX 1461

Kellogg Historical Society, Kellogg, IA......521

Kelly-Griggs House Museum, Red Bluff, CA...146

Kelsey Museum of Archaeology, Ann Arbor, MI..724

Kelton House Museum & Garden, Columbus, OH...................................1158

Kemerer Museum of Decorative Arts, Bethlehem, PA...................................1242

The Kenilworth Historical Society, Kenilworth, IL......................................441

Kennebunkport Historical Society, Kennebunkport, ME.............................612

Kennedy Museum of Art, Athens, OH 1140

Kennesaw Mountain National Battlefield Park, Kennesaw, GA.............................374

Kensington Mansion, Eastover, SC 1332

Kent-Delord House Museum, Plattsburgh, NY..1052

Kent State University Museum, Kent, OH.1169

Kentucky Derby Museum, Louisville, KY...576

Kentucky Gateway Museum Center, Maysville, KY......................................579

Kentucky Historical Society, Frankfort, KY...569

The Kentucky Library & Museum, Bowling Green, KY..............................565

Kentucky Military History Museum, Frankfort, KY.......................................569

Kern County Museum, Bakersfield, CA.........73

Kewaunee County Historical Museum, Kewaunee, WI....................................1602

Keyport Historical Society-Steamboat Dock Museum, Keyport, NJ...................909

Keystone Area Historical Society, Keystone, SD....................................1350

Kimberly Crest House & Gardens, Redlands, CA..147

King Manor, Jamaica, NY 1004

Kingman Tavern Historical Museum, Cummington, MA.................................678

Kit Carson Historical Society, Kit Carson, CO...223

Kitsap County Historical Society Museum, Bremerton, WA.....................1549

Klickitat County Historical Society, Goldendale, WA.................................1555

Knight Museum, Alliance, NE....................855

Knights of Columbus Museum, New Haven, CT...253

Knott House Museum, Tallahassee, FL........347

Knox Headquarters State Historic Site, Vails Gate, NY...................................1080

Knudt Salle Log Cabin, Adams, ND 1127

Kohl Children's Museum of Greater Chicago, Glenview, IL 438

Koochiching County Historical Museum, International Falls, MN 778

Korean War Veterans National Museum & Library, Rantoul, IL 453

Koshare Indian Museum, Inc., La Junta, CO...224

Kuhlmann King Historical House and Museum, Boerne, TX............................1396

The Kurdish Museum, Brooklyn, NY 969

La Porte County Historical Society Museum, La Porte, IN............................487

La Puente Valley Historical Society City Hall, LaPuente, CA...............................107

The Lace Museum, Sunnyvale, CA..............190

Lacey Historical Society, Forked River, NJ...904

The Lacrosse Museum & National Hall of Fame/US Lacrosse, Baltimore, MD 633

Lafayette Miners Museum, Lafayette, CO 224

Lafayette Natural History Museum and Planetarium, Lafayette, LA....................589

Lagrange County Historical Society, Inc., Lagrange, IN...488

Lahaina Restoration Foundation, Lahaina, HI...400

Lake County Historical Museum, Tavares, FL...351

Lake County Historical Society, Kirtland Hills, OH..1170

Lake George Historical Association Museum, Lake George, NY.................1008

Lake Jackson Historical Museum, Lake Jackson, TX.......................................1433

Lake of the Red Cedars Museum, Cedar Lake, IN...472

Lake of the Woods County Museum, Baudette, MN......................................768

Lake Tahoe Historical Society & Museum, South Lake Tahoe, CA..........188

Lake Wales Depot Museum & Cultural Center, Lake Wales, FL............................320

Lakeview Museum of Arts and Sciences, Peoria, IL..450

Lancaster County Historical Society, Lancaster, PA.......................................1266

Land of the Yankee Fork Historic Association Museum, Stanley, ID...........410

Landis Valley Museum, Lancaster, PA 1266

The Landmark Society of Western New York, Rochester, NY............................1058

Lane County Historical Museum, Dighton, KS...536

Langlade County Historical Society Museum, Antigo, WI............................1589

Lapham-Patterson House, Thomasville, GA.................388
Laramie Plains Museum, Laramie, WY.....1635
Larchmont Historical Society, Mamaroneck, NY.................1013
LaSalle County Historical Society Museum, Utica, IL.................462
Latvian Folk Art Museum, Chicago, IL.......423
Latvian Museum, Rockville, MD.................651
Lauder Museum - Amityville Historical Society, Amityville, NY.................957
Laura Ingalls Wilder Museum and Tourist Center, Walnut Grove, MN.................795
Laura Ingalls Wilder Park & Museum, Inc., Burr Oak, IA.................507
Laurel Arts, Somerset, PA.................1300
The Laurel Museum, Laurel, MD.................648
Laurence C. Jones Museum, Piney Woods, MS.................807
Lawrence County Gray House Museum, Ironton, OH.................1169
Lawrence County Historical and Genealogical Society, Bedford, IN.........469
Laws Railroad Museum and Historical Site, Bishop, CA.................78
Layland Museum, Cleburne, TX.................1400
Lea County Cowboy Hall of Fame and Western Heritage Center, Hobbs, NM.....940
The Lebanon County Historical Society, Lebanon, PA.................1268
Lee-Fendall House Museum and Garden, Alexandria, VA.................1493
Leelanau Historical Museum, Leland, MI....751
Lefferts Historic House, Brooklyn, NY........969
Legends of New Mexico Museum, Algodones, NM.................936
Lemhi County Historical Museum, Salmon, ID.................409
Lemon Hill Mansion, Philadelphia, PA......1282
Lentz Center for Asian Culture, Lincoln, NE.................865
LeRoy House & JELL-O Gallery, LeRoy, NY.................1009
Lesbian Herstory Educational Foundation, Inc. aka Lesbian Herstory Archives, Brooklyn, NY.................969
Leverett Historical Society, Leverett, MA....689
Levi Coffin House, Fountain City, IN.........478
Levine Museum of the New South, Charlotte, NC.................1095
Lewis County Historical Society Museum, Lowville, NY.................1012
Lexington County Museum, Lexington, SC.................1336
Lexington Historical Society, Lexington, MA.................689
Liberace Museum & Foundation, Las Vegas, NV.................879
Liberty Hall Historic Center, Lamoni, IA....522
Liberty Hall Historic Site, Frankfort, KY....569
Libertyville-Mundelein Historical Society, Inc., Libertyville, IL.................442
Library of the Supreme Council, 33 Degrees, Washington, DC.................282
Licking County Historical Society, Newark, OH.................1178
Lillian and Albert Small Jewish Museum, Washington, DC.................282
Lincoln County Historical Museum, Davenport, WA.................1552
Lincoln County Historical Society, Lincoln, KS.................549
Lincoln County Historical Society, North Platte, NE.................869
Lincoln County Museum, Hugo, CO.................222
Lincoln County Pioneer Museum, Hendricks, MN.................778
The Lincoln Museum, Fort Wayne, IN........478
Lincoln Parish Museum & Historical Society, Ruston, LA.................600
Lincoln's New Salem State Historic Site, Petersburg, IL.................451

Linn County Historical Museum and Moyer House, Brownsville, OR.............1220
Lisbon Historical Society, Lisbon, OH.......1172
Lisle Station Museum, Lisle, IL.................443
Litchfield Historical Society and Museum, Litchfield, CT.................247
Little Bighorn Battlefield National Monument, Crow Agency, MT.................844
The Little Brick House, Vandalia, IL.........462
Little Compton Historical Society, Little Compton, RI.................1312
Little White Schoolhouse, Ripon, WI.........1620
Littleton Historical Museum, Littleton, CO.................227
Livingston County Historical Society Museum, Geneseo, NY.................993
Livingston Depot Center, Livingston, MT...850
Locust Grove, Louisville, KY.................577
Locust Grove, The Samuel Morse Historic Site, Poughkeepsie, NY.............1055
Locust Lawn and Terwilliger House, Gardiner, NY.................993
Logan County Museum, Paris, AR.................65
Lois E. Woods Museum, Norfolk, VA.........1522
Lombard Historical Museum, Lombard, IL.................443
Lompoc Valley Historical Society, Inc., Lompoc, CA.................110
Lone Star Flight Museum/Texas Aviation Hall of Fame, Galveston, TX.................1421
Long Island Museum of American Art, History & Carriages, Stony Brook, NY.................1075
Longfellow Evangeline State Historic Site, Saint Martinville, LA.................600
Longfellow National Historic Site, Cambridge, MA.................673
Longfellow's Wayside Inn, Sudbury, MA....714
Longhorn Museum, Pleasanton, TX.................1444
LongHouse Reserve, East Hampton, NY.....986
Longue Vue House & Gardens, New Orleans, LA.................596
Longyear Museum, Chestnut Hill, MA.........675
Lopez Island Historical Museum, Lopez Island, WA.................1558
Lorenzo State Historic Site, Cazenovia, NY.................976
Los Alamos Historical Museum, Los Alamos, NM.................942
Los Altos History Museum aka Association of the Los Altos Historical Museum, Los Altos, CA.................112
The Los Angeles County Arboretum & Botanic Garden, Arcadia, CA.................71
Los Angeles County Museum of Art, Los Angeles, CA.................118
Los Angeles Maritime Museum, San Pedro, CA.................176
Los Angeles Museum of the Holocaust, Los Angeles, CA.................118
Los Angeles Police Historical Society & Museum, Los Angeles, CA.................119
Los Nogales Museum, Seguin, TX.................1452
Loudoun Museum, Inc., Leesburg, VA.......1512
Louis H. & Lena Firn Grover Museum, Shelbyville, IN.................498
Louisiana Art & Science Museum - Irene W. Pennington Planetarium, Baton Rouge, LA.................586
The Louisiana Cotton Museum, Lake Providence, LA.................590
Louisiana's Old State Capitol, Political History Museum, Baton Rouge, LA.......587
Loveland Museum Gallery, Loveland, CO...227
Lovely Lane Museum, Baltimore, MD.........634
Lovettsville Historical Society Museum, Lovettsville, VA.................1514
Lowe Art Museum, University of Miami, Coral Gables, FL.................301
Lower Cape Fear Historical Society, Inc., Wilmington, NC.................1123

Lower White River Museum, Des Arc, AR.................56
Lowndes County Historical Society and Museum, Valdosta, GA.................389
Loxahatchee River Historical Society, Jupiter, FL.................316
Loyola University Museum of Art, Chicago, IL.................423
Luckhard Museum - The Indian Mission, Sebewaing, MI.................764
Lucretia Vaile Museum, Palmer Lake, CO.................229
Lucy-Desi Museum, Jamestown, NY.........1005
The Lyceum, Alexandria's History Museum, Alexandria, VA.................1493
Lyman Allyn Art Museum, New London, CT.................255
Lyman Museum, Hilo, HI.................393
Lynchburg Museum System, Lynchburg, VA.................1515
Lyndhurst, Tarrytown, NY.................1078
Lynnhaven House, Virginia Beach, VA.......1542
Lyon County Historical Society and Museum, Emporia, KS.................538
The Lyons Redstone Museum, Lyons, CO...227
Mabee Farm Historic Site, Rotterdam Junction, NY.................1062
Mabel Hartzell Historical Home, Alliance, OH.................1139
Mabry-Hazen House, Knoxville, TN.........1371
Macculloch Hall Historical Museum & Gardens, Morristown, NJ.................913
Macon County Historical Society Museum Complex, Decatur, IL.................430
The Madam Brett Homestead, Beacon, NY.................961
Madeline Island Historical Museum, La Pointe, WI.................1603
Madera County Museum, Madera, CA.........123
Madison County Historical Society-Cottage Lawn, Oneida, NY.......1045
Madison Historical Society, Madison, CT....247
Madison Museum of Fine Art, Madison, GA.................378
Magevney House, Memphis, TN.................1373
Maggie L. Walker National Historic Site, Richmond, VA.................1530
Magnolia Grove-Historic House Museum, Greensboro, AL.................10
Magnolia Manor, Cairo, IL.................415
Magoffin Home State Historic Site, El Paso, TX.................1412
Maine Historical Society, Portland, ME.......619
Maine State Museum, Augusta, ME.............604
Maitland Historical Museums, Maitland, FL.................322
The Major General Frederick Funston Boyhood Home and Museum, Iola, KS.................546
Major John Bradford House, Kingston, MA.................688
Malheur Historical Project, Stonehouse Museum, Vale, OR.................1238
Mallory-Neely House, Memphis, TN.........1373
Mamie Doud Eisenhower Birthplace, Boone, IA.................506
Manassas Museum System, Manassas, VA.................1516
Manchester Historic Association Millyard Museum, Manchester, NH.................891
Manchester Historical Society, Manchester, MA.................692
Manitowoc County Historical Society, Manitowoc, WI.................1607
Mansfield Historical Society Museum, Storrs, CT.................261
Mansfield Township Historical Society (1849 Georgetown School/Museum), Columbus, NJ.................902
Manship House Museum, Jackson, MS.......802
Marathon County Historical Society, Wausau, WI.................1626

Costumes and Textiles–Continued

Marblehead Museum & Historical Society, Marblehead, MA..........................693

Marcella Sembrich Opera Museum, Bolton Landing, NY.............................963

Marcellus Historical Society, Marcellus, NY..1013

March Field Air Museum, Riverside, CA 149

Mardi Gras Museum, Kenner, LA.................589

Margaret Harwell Art Museum, Poplar Bluff, MO...829

The Margaret Mitchell House & Museum, Atlanta, GA..........................361

Mariani Gallery, University of Northern Colorado, Greeley, CO.......................221

Marianna-Lee County Museum Assoc. Inc., Marianna, AR...............................64

Marias Museum of History and Art, Shelby, MT.....................................853

Maridon Museum, Butler, PA.................1245

Marietta House Museum, Glenn Dale, MD..645

Marietta Museum of History, Marietta, GA..379

Marin History Museum, San Rafael, CA 177

Marinette County Historical Museum, Marinette, WI...1607

Mario Lanza Institute/Museum, Philadelphia, PA.................................1282

The Marion County Historical Society Museum, Marion, OH.......................1174

Marion Public Library Museum, Marion, IN...490

Mariposa Museum & World Culture Center, Peterborough, NH.................893

Maritime Museum of Monterey, Monterey, CA.......................................127

Marjorie Kinnan Rawlings Historic State Park, Cross Creek, FL.......................301

The Mark Twain House & Museum, Hartford, CT...245

Marland's Grand Home, Ponca City, OK...1212

Marlboro County Historical Museum, Bennettsville, SC.................................1322

Marlboro Historical Society, Marlboro, VT...1481

Marquette County Historical Society, Westfield, WI.......................................1627

Marquette County History Museum, Marquette, MI...753

Marshall County Historical Museum, Plymouth, IN...496

Marshall County Historical Museum, Holly Springs, MS.................................801

Martin and Osa Johnson Safari Museum, Inc., Chanute, KS.................................535

Martin County Historical Museum, Stanton, TX...1453

Martin County Museum, Shoals, IN.............499

The Martin D'Arcy Museum of Art: The Loyola University Museum of Medieval, Renaissance and Baroque Art, Chicago, IL..................................424

Marvin Newton House, Brookfield, VT 1477

Mary Aaron Memorial Museum, Marysville, CA.......................................125

Mary Ball Washington Museum & Library, Inc., Lancaster, VA.................1512

Mary McLeod Bethune Council House National Historic Site, Washington, DC...283

Maryhill Museum of Art, Goldendale, WA...1556

Maryland Historical Society, Baltimore, MD...634

Mashantucket Pequot Museum and Research Center, Mashantucket, CT........248

Mason County Museum, Mason, TX 1437

The Masonic Library and Museum of Pennsylvania, Philadelphia, PA.............1283

The Massillon Museum, Massillon, OH.....1175

Mathias Ham House Historic Site, Dubuque, IA...516

Mattapoisett Museum and Carriage House, Mattapoisett, MA.......................693

Matthews Museum of Maine Heritage, Union, ME...624

Maxwell Museum of Anthropology, Albuquerque, NM...............................934

May Museum & Farmville Heritage Center, Farmville, NC.............................1100

Mayville Area Museum of History and Genealogy, Mayville, MI.......................754

Mazomanie Historical Society, Mazomanie, WI.......................................1608

Mc Cook County Historical Society and Museum, Salem, SD.............................1355

McCallum Museum, Sibley, IA.................527

McCook House, Civil War Museum, Carrollton, OH...1146

McCoy House, Lewistown, PA..................1269

McHenry County Historical Society and Museum, Union, IL.............................461

McHenry Museum, Modesto, CA................126

McIntosh County Historical Society, Ashley, ND...1127

McLarty Treasure Museum, Vero Beach, FL...352

McLean-Alanreed Area Museum, McLean, TX...1438

McLean County Museum of History, Bloomington, IL...414

McMinn County Living Heritage Museum, Athens, TN.............................1360

McMullen Museum of Art, Boston College, Chestnut Hill, MA.................675

McNamara House Museum, Victoria, TX...1457

McPherson Museum & Arts Foundation, McPherson, KS...552

McWethy Hall, Luce Gallery, Cornell College, Mount Vernon, IA.................524

Meadow Brook Hall, Rochester, MI............761

Meadowlands Museum, Rutherford, NJ.......923

Meagher County Historical Association Castle Museum, White Sulphur Springs, MT...855

Mecosta County Historical Museum, Big Rapids, MI...729

Medina County Historical Society, The John Smart House, Medina, OH............1175

Meeker Home Museum, Greeley, CO 222

Meeteetse Museum District, Meeteetse, WY...1636

Meigs County Museum, Pomeroy, OH.......1183

Mellette House, Watertown, SD.................1359

Melrose Plantation Home Complex, Melrose, LA...592

Memorial Art Gallery of the University of Rochester, Rochester, NY.................1059

Memoryville USA, Inc., Rolla, MO.............829

Memphis College of Art, Memphis, TN 1374

Mendocino County Museum, Willits, CA....198

Mendocino Historical Research, Inc./Kelley House Museum, Mendocino, CA...125

Mennonite Heritage Center, Harleysville, PA...1258

Mennonite Heritage Museum, Goessel, KS...542

Mercer Museum of the Bucks County Historical Society, Doylestown, PA.......1250

Merchant's House Museum, New York, NY...1029

Metamora Courthouse Historic Site, Metamora, IL...444

The Metropolitan Museum of Art, New York, NY...1030

Metropolitan State College of Denver/Center for Visual Art, Denver, CO...212

Meux Home Museum, Fresno, CA................98

Mexic-Arte Museum, Austin, TX...............1391

Mexican Fine Arts Center Museum, Chicago, IL...424

The Mexican Museum, San Francisco, CA...166

Miami Children's Museum, Miami, FL........324

Miami University Art Museum, Oxford, OH...1181

Michigan Historical Museum, Michigan Historical Center, Lansing, MI.............750

Michigan Maritime Museum, South Haven, MI...764

The Michigan State University Museum, East Lansing, MI.......................................740

Mid-America Air Museum, Liberal, KS.......549

Mid-America All Indian Center, Wichita, KS...562

Mid-Atlantic Center for the Arts/Emlen Physick Estate/Cape May Lighthouse, Cape May, NJ...900

Mid-Hudson Children's Museum, Poughkeepsie, NY.................................1055

Middleborough Historical Association, Inc., Middleborough, MA.................694

Middlebury Historical Society, Wyoming, NY...1087

Middlesex County Historical Society, Middletown, CT...249

Middletown Valley Historical Society, Middletown, MD.......................................649

Midland County Historical Museum, Midland, TX...1438

Midway Village & Museum Center, Rockford, IL...455

Midwest Museum of American Art, Elkhart, IN...474

Midwest Old Settlers & Threshers Association, Inc., Mount Pleasant, IA.....524

Mifflinburg Buggy Museum Association, Inc., Mifflinburg, PA...............................1271

Mighty Eighth Air Force Museum, Pooler, GA...381

Milam County Museum and Annex, Cameron, TX...1399

Milan Historical Museum, Inc., Milan, OH...1176

Milford Historical Museum, Milford, MI....756

Milford Historical Society, Milford, CT.......250

Milford Museum, Milford, DE.................271

Military Museum of Southern New England, Danbury, CT.............................238

Mill Race Historical Village, Northville, MI...758

Millard Fillmore House, East Aurora, NY ...985

Miller-Cory House Museum, Westfield, NJ...930

Millicent Rogers Museum of Northern New Mexico, Taos, NM.........................952

Mills College Art Museum, Oakland, CA....133

Milton Historical Museum, Milton, VT 1482

Milton House Museum Historic Site, Milton, WI...1610

Milwaukee County Historical Society, Milwaukee, WI.......................................1611

Mingei International Museum, San Diego, CA...157

Minneapolis Institute of Arts, Minneapolis, MN.......................................782

Minnesota Historical Society, Saint Paul, MN...791

Mint Museum of Art, Charlotte, NC..........1095

Miramont Castle Museum, Manitou Springs, CO...228

Mission Houses Museum, Honolulu, HI 397

Mission Inn Foundation/Museum, Riverside, CA...149

Mission Mill Museum Association, Salem, OR...1236

Mission San Juan Capistrano Museum, San Juan Capistrano, CA.........................173

Mission San Luis Rey Museum, Oceanside, CA...135

Mission San Miguel, San Miguel, CA 175

Mission Santa Cruz, Santa Cruz, CA 182
Mississippi Agriculture &
   Forestry/National Agricultural Aviation
   Museum, Jackson, MS 802
Mississippi County Historical Society,
   Charleston, MO 812
Mississippi Governor's Mansion,
   Jackson, MS..802
Mississippi Museum of Art, Jackson, MS...802
Mississippi River Museum at Mud Island
   River Park, Memphis, TN 1375
Mississippi Society Daughters of the
   American Revolution Rosalie House
   Museum, Natchez, MS 805
Mississippi University for Women,
   Archives and Museum, Columbus, MS...800
Missoula Art Museum, Missoula, MT.........851
Missouri Historical Society, Saint Louis,
   MO..835
Mitchell County Historical Museum,
   Osage, IA 526
The Mitchell Museum of the American
   Indian, Evanston, IL 435
Mizel Museum, Denver, CO 213
Mobile Medical Museum, Mobile, AL...........14
Mobile Museum of Art, Mobile, AL 14
Moffatt-Ladd House and Garden,
   Portsmouth, NH 894
Molly Brown House Museum, Denver,
   CO...213
Mondak Heritage Center, Sidney, MT.........853
Monmouth County Historical Association,
   Freehold, NJ...905
Monroe County Historical
   Association/Stroud Mansion,
   Stroudsburg, PA 1302
Monroe County Historical Museum,
   Monroe, MI...756
Monroe County Historical Society,
   Bloomington, IN.......................................469
Monroe Historical Society, Monroe, CT 250
Montana Historical Society, Helena, MT 849
Montana Museum of Art and Culture,
   Missoula, MT..852
Montauk, Clermont, IA 511
Montclair Art Museum, Montclair, NJ 912
Montclair Historical Society, Montclair,
   NJ..912
Monterey History and Art Association,
   Monterey, CA 127
Monterey Museum of Art, Monterey, CA 128
Monterey State Historic Park, Monterey,
   CA...128
The Montgomery County Historical
   Society, Dayton, OH 1161
The Montgomery County Historical
   Society, Inc., Rockville, MD....................651
Montgomery Museum & Lewis Miller
   Regional Art Center, Christiansburg,
   VA..1501
Monticello, Home of Thomas Jefferson,
   Thomas Jefferson Foundation, Inc.,
   Charlottesville, VA 1499
Montpelier-The General Henry Knox
   Museum, Thomaston, ME.........................624
Montville Township Historical Museum,
   Montville, NJ..912
Moody County Museum, Flandreau, SD....1347
The Moody Mansion Museum,
   Galveston, TX..1421
Moore County Art Association, Dumas,
   TX..1410
Moravian Historical Society, Nazareth,
   PA..1273
Moravian Museum of Bethlehem, Inc.,
   Bethlehem, PA 1242
Mordecai Historic Park, Raleigh, NC.........1115
Morgan Row Museum and
   Harrodsburg-Mercer County Research
   Library, Harrodsburg, KY 570
Moriarty Historical Museum, Moriarty,
   NM..943

The Morikami Museum and Japanese
   Gardens, Delray Beach, FL......................305
Morris County Historical Society (Acorn
   Hall House Museum), Morristown, NJ ...914
The Morris Museum, Morristown, NJ..........914
Morrison's Heritage Museum, Morrison,
   IL..446
Morristown National Historical Park,
   Morristown, NJ...914
Morton Grove Historical
   Museum/Haupt-Yehl House, Morton
   Grove, IL..446
Morton House Museum, Benton Harbor,
   MI..728
Morven Park, Leesburg, VA.......................1512
Moss Mansion Historic House Museum,
   Billings, MT 841
Motorcycle Hall of Fame Museum,
   Pickerington, OH.....................................1182
Motown Historical Museum, Detroit, MI.....737
Motts Military Museum, Groveport, OH.....1167
Mount Clare Museum House, Baltimore,
   MD..635
Mount Desert Island Historical Society,
   Mount Desert, ME....................................615
Mount Dora Center for the Arts, Mount
   Dora, FL...327
Mount Mary College Historic Costume
   Collection, Milwaukee, WI 1613
Mount Pleasant Historical Society, Mount
   Pleasant, OH...1177
Mount Prospect Historical Society
   Museums, Mount Prospect, IL.................446
Mount Vernon Ladies' Association,
   Mount Vernon, VA..................................1518
The Movie Museum, Owosso, MI...............759
Mulford Farm, East Hampton, NY..............986
Murfreesboro Historical Association,
   Murfreesboro, NC...................................1112
Murray-Lindsay Mansion, Lindsay, OK.....1204
Muscatine Art Center, Muscatine, IA 524
Museo de Las Americas, San Juan, PR......1642
The Museum, Greenwood, SC....................1334
The Museum at the Fashion Institute of
   Technology, New York, NY 1031
The Museum at Warm Springs, Warm
   Springs, OR...1238
The Museum for African Art, Long
   Island City, NY..1011
The Museum of African Culture,
   Portland, ME..619
Museum of American Presidents,
   Strasburg, VA..1539
Museum of Anthropology, Chico, CA............83
Museum of Anthropology, University of
   Denver, Denver, CO.................................213
Museum of Appalachia, Clinton, TN..........1363
Museum of Art and Archaeology,
   University of Missouri - Columbia,
   Columbia, MO..813
Museum of Art and History at the
   McPherson Center, Santa Cruz, CA 182
Museum of Art/Fort Lauderdale, Fort
   Lauderdale, FL...307
Museum of Art, Rhode Island School of
   Design, Providence, RI...........................1317
The Museum of Arts and Sciences, Inc.
   and Center for Florida History,
   Daytona Beach, FL...................................303
Museum of Chicot County Arkansas,
   Lake Village, AR..61
Museum of Chinese in the Americas,
   New York, NY...1032
Museum of Church History and Art, Salt
   Lake City, UT..1471
Museum of Contemporary Religious Art
   (MOCRA)-St. Louis University, Saint
   Louis, MO..835
Museum of Cosmetology, Chicago, IL.........425
Museum of Craft and Folk Art, San
   Francisco, CA...167
Museum of Early Southern Decorative
   Arts (MESDA), Winston-Salem, NC.....1125

Museum of Fine Arts, Boston, MA.............667
The Museum of Fine Arts, Houston,
   Houston, TX..1428
The Museum of Flight, Seattle, WA...........1567
Museum of Florida History, Tallahassee,
   FL..348
Museum of Funeral Customs, Springfield,
   IL..459
Museum of Great Christian Preachers &
   Ministries, Orange Park, FL.....................331
Museum of History & Art, Ontario,
   Ontario, CA...136
Museum of History & Industry
   (MOHAI), Seattle, WA............................1567
Museum of Indian Arts &
   Culture/Laboratory of Anthropology,
   Santa Fe, NM..948
Museum of International Folk Art, Santa
   Fe, NM..948
The Museum of Mobile, Mobile, AL.............14
Museum of Nebraska Art, Kearney, NE......864
Museum of New Mexico, Santa Fe, NM 949
Museum of North Idaho, Coeur d'Alene,
   ID..405
The Museum of Nursing History, Inc.,
   Philadelphia, PA 1283
Museum of Religious Arts, Logan, IA.........522
Museum of San Diego History and
   Research Library, San Diego, CA 158
Museum of South Texas History,
   Edinburg, TX...1410
The Museum of Southern History,
   Sugarland, TX..1454
Museum of Spanish Colonial Art -
   MoSCA, Santa Fe, NM.............................949
The Museum of Television & Radio,
   New York, NY...1033
The Museum of the Alphabet, Waxhaw,
   NC..1121
Museum of the American Quilter's
   Society (MAQS), Paducah, KY...............581
Museum of the Arkansas Grand Prairie,
   Stuttgart, AR..69
Museum of the Bedford Historical
   Society, Bedford, NY...............................961
Museum of the Cape Fear Historical
   Complex, Fayetteville, NC.....................1101
Museum of the Cherokee Indian,
   Cherokee, NC..1096
Museum of the City of Lake Worth, Lake
   Worth, FL...320
Museum of the City of New York, New
   York, NY...1033
The Museum of the Confederacy,
   Richmond, VA...1531
Museum of the Fur Trade, Chadron, NE......859
Museum of the Gulf Coast, Port Arthur,
   TX..1444
Museum of the Jimmy Carter Library,
   Atlanta, GA...362
Museum of the Moving Image, Astoria,
   NY..958
Museum of the National Center of
   Afro-American Artists, Roxbury, MA 706
Museum of the Northern Great Plains,
   Fort Benton, MT.......................................846
Museum of the Plains Indian, Browning,
   MT..843
Museum of the Red River, Idabel, OK.......1203
Museum of the Rockies, Bozeman, MT.......842
Museum of the Southern Jewish
   Experience, Jackson, MS 803
Museum of the Southwest, Midland, TX...1439
Museum of the Waxhaws & Andrew
   Jackson Memorial, Waxhaw, NC...........1122
Museum of the Weston Historical
   Society, Inc., Weston, MA 718
Museum of Yachting, Newport, RI.............1314
Museum of Yarmouth History, Yarmouth,
   ME..626
Museum on Main: A History Museum for
   West Georgia, LaGrange, GA...................375

Costumes and Textiles–Continued

Museum Village, Monroe, NY 1015
Muskogee War Memorial Park &
 Military Museum, Muskogee, OK 1205
Musselshell Valley Historical Museum,
 Roundup, MT 853

NASA Glenn Research Center's Visitor
 Center, Cleveland, OH 1155
Nanticoke Indian Museum, Millsboro,
 DE 271
Nantucket Historical Association,
 Nantucket, MA 696
Napa Valley Museum, Yountville, CA 200
Naples Museum of Art and the
 Philharmonic Center for the Arts
 Galleries, Naples, FL 328
Napoleonic Society of America, Inc.,
 Clearwater, FL 300
Narcissa Prentiss House, Prattsburgh, NY . 1055
Narragansett Historical Society,
 Templeton, MA 714
Nasher Museum of Art at Duke
 University, Durham, NC 1099
Nathan Denison Advocates, Forty Fort,
 PA 1254
National Afro-American Museum &
 Cultural Center, Wilberforce, OH 1191
National Air and Space Museum,
 Washington, DC 283
National Baseball Hall of Fame and
 Museum, Inc., Cooperstown, NY 981
National Capital Parks-East, Washington,
 DC 284
National Civil Rights Museum, Memphis,
 TN 1375
National Civil War Naval Museum at
 Port Columbus, Columbus, GA 369
National Cowboy & Western Heritage
 Museum, Oklahoma City, OK 1208
National Cowgirl Museum and Hall of
 Fame, Fort Worth, TX 1418
National Czech & Slovak Museum &
 Library, Cedar Rapids, IA 509
National First Ladies' Library, Canton,
 OH 1145
National Football Museum, Inc., Canton,
 OH 1145
National Frontier Trails Museum,
 Independence, MO 818
The National Great Blacks in Wax
 Museum, Inc., Baltimore, MD 635
National Heritage Museum, Lexington,
 MA 690
National Hispanic Cultural Center, Art
 Museum, Albuquerque, NM 935
National Infantry Museum, Fort Benning,
 GA 372
National Medal of Honor Museum of
 Military History, Chattanooga, TN 1362
National Museum of African Art,
 Smithsonian Institution, Washington,
 DC 285
National Museum of American History,
 Washington, DC 285
National Museum of American Jewish
 Military History, Washington, DC 286
The National Museum of Catholic Art &
 History, New York, NY 1034
National Museum of Dance & Hall of
 Fame, Saratoga Springs, NY 1065
National Museum of Natural History,
 Washington, DC 286
National Museum of Polo and Hall of
 Fame, Inc., Lake Worth, FL 320
National Museum of Racing and Hall of
 Fame, Saratoga Springs, NY 1065
National Museum of Roller Skating,
 Lincoln, NE 866
National Museum of the American
 Indian, Washington, DC 286

National Museum of the American
 Indian, Smithsonian Institution, New
 York, NY 1034
National Museum of the United States
 Air Force, Wright-Patterson Air Force
 Base, OH 1193
National Park Service Museum Resource
 Center, Landover, MD 648
National Postal Museum, Smithsonian
 Institution, Washington, DC 287
National Scouting Museum, Irving, TX 1430
The National Soccer Hall of Fame,
 Oneonta, NY 1046
National Steinbeck Center, Salinas, CA 154
National Warplane Museum, Horseheads,
 NY 999
National World War I Museum at Liberty
 Memorial, Kansas City, MO 822
The National World War II Museum,
 New Orleans, LA 597
National Wrestling Hall of Fame,
 Stillwater, OK 1214
Native American Heritage Museum at
 Highland Mission State Historic Site,
 Highland, KS 544
Natural Center for the American
 Revolution, Wayne, PA 1306
Naumkeag, Stockbridge, MA 712
Nauvoo Historical Society Museum,
 Nauvoo, IL 447
Navajo Nation Museum, Window Rock,
 AZ 53
Naval War College Museum, Newport,
 RI 1314
Navarro County Historical Society,
 Pioneer Village, Corsicana, TX 1402
Nebraska Prairie Museum of the Phelps
 County Historical Society, Holdrege,
 NE 863
Nebraska State Capitol, Lincoln, NE 866
Nebraska State Historical Society's
 Museum of Nebraska History, Lincoln,
 NE 866
Neenah Historical Society, Hiram Smith,
 Neenah's Heritage Park, Octagon
 House & Ward House, Neenah, WI 1614
Neill-Cochran Museum House, Austin,
 TX 1391
Neill Museum, Fort Davis, TX 1414
The Nelson-Atkins Museum of Art,
 Kansas City, MO 822
Netherland Inn House Museum &
 Boatyard Complex, Kingsport, TN 1368
Nevada County Historical Society, Inc.,
 Nevada City, CA 130
Nevada State Museum, Carson City, NV 876
Neville Public Museum of Brown
 County, Green Bay, WI 1599
The New Berlin Historical Society, New
 Berlin, WI 1614
New Britain Youth Museum, New
 Britain, CT 252
New Canaan Historical Society, New
 Canaan, CT 252
New Castle Historical Society, New
 Castle, DE 272
New Castle Historical Society - Horace
 Greeley House, Chappaqua, NY 977
New England Fire and History Museum,
 Brewster, MA 670
New England Quilt Museum, Lowell,
 MA 692
New England Ski Museum, Franconia,
 NH 888
New Hampshire Antiquarian Society,
 Hopkinton, NH 889
New Hampshire Farm Museum, Inc.,
 Milton, NH 892
New Hampshire Historical Society,
 Concord, NH 885
New Harmony State Historic
 Site/Historic New Harmony, New
 Harmony, IN 494

The New Jersey Children's Museum,
 Paramus, NJ 919
The New Jersey Historical Society,
 Newark, NJ 916
New Jersey State Museum, Trenton, NJ 927
New London County Historical Society,
 New London, CT 255
New London Historical Society, New
 London, NH 892
New London Public Museum, New
 London, WI 1615
New Market Battlefield State Historical
 Park, New Market, VA 1519
New Mexico Farm & Ranch Heritage
 Museum, Las Cruces, NM 940
The New Milford Historical Society, New
 Milford, CT 256
New Orleans Fire Dept. Museum &
 Educational Center, New Orleans, LA 597
New Richmond Preservation Society,
 New Richmond, WI 1615
New Sweden Historical Society, New
 Sweden, ME 616
New York City Fire Museum, New York,
 NY 1035
The New York Public Library for the
 Performing Arts, New York, NY 1036
New York State Historical
 Association/Fenimore Art Museum,
 Cooperstown, NY 981
New York State Military Museum and
 Veterans Research Center, Saratoga
 Springs, NY 1065
The Newark Museum, Newark, NJ 916
Newaygo County Museum, Newaygo, MI ... 758
Newcomb Art Gallery, New Orleans, LA 598
Newell Museum, Newell, SD 1352
Newport Historical Society & The
 Museum of Newport History,
 Newport, RI 1315
The Newton History Museum at The
 Jackson Homestead, Newton, MA 698
Newtown History Center, Stephens City,
 VA 1538
Nez Perce County Museum, Lewiston, ID ... 407
The Niagara County Historical Center
 and Niagara County Genealogical
 Society, Lockport, NY 1010
Nici Self Museum, Centennial, WY 1630
Nicollet County Historical Society, Saint
 Peter, MN 793
Nishna Heritage Museum, Oakland, IA 525
Nixon Presidential Materials Staff,
 College Park, MD 641
Noah Webster House/West Hartford
 Historical Society, West Hartford, CT 265
Nohwike Bagowa, The White Mountain
 Apache Cultural Center and Museum,
 Fort Apache, AZ 34
Nordic Heritage Museum, Seattle, WA 1567
Norfolk Historical Museum, Norfolk, CT ... 257
Norfolk Historical Society, Norfolk, VA ... 1522
Norman #1 Oil Well Museum, Neodesha,
 KS 553
North Andover Historical Society, North
 Andover, MA 698
North Carolina A&T State University
 Galleries, Greensboro, NC 1104
North Carolina Museum of History,
 Raleigh, NC 1115
North Carolina State University Gallery
 of Art & Design, Raleigh, NC 1116
North Country Museum of Arts, Park
 Rapids, MN 786
North Dakota Museum of Art, Grand
 Forks, ND 1132
North Haven Historical Society, North
 Haven, CT 257
North Platte Valley Museum, Gering, NE ... 861
North Star Museum of Boy Scouting and
 Girl Scouting, North Saint Paul, MN 785
North Tonawanda History Museum,
 North Tonawanda, NY 1043

Northampton County Historical and Genealogical Society, Easton, PA 1250
Northborough Historical Society, Inc., Northborough, MA 700
Northeast Classic Car Museum, Norwich, NY 1044
Northeast Louisiana Delta African American Heritage Museum, Monroe, LA 592
Northeast Texas Rural Heritage Museum, Pittsburg, TX 1443
Northeastern Nevada Museum, Elko, NV 876
Northern Kentucky University Art Galleries, Highland Heights, KY 571
Northern Pacific Railway Museum, Toppenish, WA 1575
Northfield Historical Society Museum, Northfield, MN 785
Northport Historical Society Museum, Northport, NY 1044
The Northumberland County Historical Society, Sunbury, PA 1302
Northwest Museum of Arts & Culture (Eastern Washington State Historical Society), Spokane, WA 1571
Norwich Historical Society, Norwich, VT .1484
Novato History Museum, Novato, CA 132
Nowetah's American Indian Museum & Store, New Portland, ME 615
Noyes House Museum, Morrisville, VT 1483
The Noyes Museum of Art, Oceanville, NJ 918

Oakland County Pioneer and Historical Society, Pontiac, MI 760
Oaklands Historic House Museum, Murfreesboro, TN 1376
Oakley Park, UDC Shrine, Edgefield, SC ..1332
The Oaks House Museum, Jackson, MS 804
Oatland Island Education Center, Savannah, GA 385
Oberlin Heritage Center, Oberlin, OH 1180
Ocean City Historical Museum, Inc., Ocean City, NJ 918
Ocean City Life-Saving Station Museum, Ocean City, MD 650
Ocean County Historical Museum, Toms River, NJ 926
The Octagon Center for the Arts, Ames, IA 505
The Octagon House, Hudson, WI 1600
The Ogden Museum of Southern Art, University of New Orleans, New Orleans, LA 598
Ohef Sholom Temple Archives, Norfolk, VA 1523
Ohio Historical Society, Columbus, OH 1158
Ojai Valley Historical Society and Museum, Ojai, CA 135
Oklahoma Museum of History, Oklahoma City, OK 1210
Oktibbeha County Heritage Museum, Starkville, MS 808
Olana State Historic Site, Hudson, NY 1000
Old Bohemia Historical Society, Warwick, MD 656
Old Brutus Historical Society, Inc., Weedsport, NY 1084
Old Castle Museum, Baldwin City, KS 533
Old Colony Historical Society, Taunton, MA 714
Old Conway Homestead Complex and Museum, Camden, ME 608
Old Court House Museum-Eva Whitaker Davis Memorial, Vicksburg, MS 809
Old Economy Village, Ambridge, PA 1240
Old Exchange & Provost Dungeon, Charleston, SC 1326
Old Falls Village, Menomonee Falls, WI ..1609
Old Fort Johnson, Fort Johnson, NY 991
Old Fort Meade Museum and Historic Research Association, Fort Meade, SD .1347

The Old Guard Museum, Fort Myer, VA ...1505
Old Independence Regional Museum, Batesville, AR 54
Old Iron County Courthouse Museum, Hurley, WI 1601
Old Jail Museum, Albion, IN 467
The Old Jail Museum, Crawfordsville, IN ...473
Old Lighthouse Museum, Michigan City, IN 491
Old Lincoln County Courthouse Museum, Lincoln, NM 942
Old Manchester Museum, Manchester, CT 248
Old Mission Santa Ines, Solvang, CA 187
Old Ordinary House Museum, Hingham, MA 687
Old St. Ferdinand's Shrine, Florissant, MO 815
Old State House Museum, Little Rock, AR 63
Old State House-The Bostonian Society, Boston, MA 668
Old Stone Fort Museum Complex, Schoharie, NY 1067
Old Stone House Museum, Windsor, NY ..1086
Old Sturbridge Village, Sturbridge, MA 713
Old Town Hall Museum, Fifield, WI 1597
Old Town Museum, Old Town, ME 617
Old Trail Museum, Choteau, MT 844
Old Westbury Gardens, Old Westbury, NY 1045
Old World Wisconsin, Eagle, WI 1595
Old York Historical Society, York, ME 626
Oldest Stone House Museum, Lakewood, OH 1170
Oldham County History Center, La Grange, KY 572
The Oliver Tucker Museum, Beverly, OH .1142
Olmsted County Historical Society, Rochester, MN 788
103rd Ohio Volunteer Infantry Civil War Museum, Sheffield Lake, OH 1185
Oneida Community Mansion House, Oneida, NY 1046
Oneida Nation Museum, De Pere, WI 1594
Onondaga Historical Association Museum & Research Center, Syracuse, NY 1077
Onslow County Museum, Richlands, NC ...1117
Ontario County Historical Society, Canandaigua, NY 975
Opelousas Museum and Interpretive Center, Opelousas, LA 599
Orange County Historical Museum, Hillsborough, NC 1107
Orange County Regional History Center, Orlando, FL 331
Orchard Park Historical Society, Orchard Park, NY 1047
Oregon Coast History Center, Newport, OR 1229
Oregon Historical Society, Portland, OR 1231
Oregon-Jerusalem Historical Museum, Oregon, OH 1181
Oriental Institute Museum, University of Chicago, Chicago, IL 426
Orland Historical Society, Orland, ME 617
Oroville Chinese Temple, Oroville, CA 136
Osage Nation Tribal Museum, Pawhuska, OK 1212
Osborn-Jackson House, East Hampton, NY 986
Oshkosh Public Museum, Oshkosh, WI 1616
Osterville Historical Society, Inc., Osterville, MA 701
Ottawa Scouting Museum, Ottawa, IL 449
Ouachita County Historical Society, Camden, AR 55
Our House State Memorial, Gallipolis, OH 1165
Overland Trail Museum, Sterling, CO 232
Owatonna Arts Center, Owatonna, MN 786

Owens Community College/Walter E. Terhune Gallery, Perrysburg, OH 1182
Owensboro Area Museum of Science & History, Owensboro, KY 581
Owensboro Museum of Fine Art, Inc., Owensboro, KY 581
Owls Head Transportation Museum, Owls Head, ME 617
Oysterponds Historical Society: The Museum of Orient and East Marion History, Orient, NY 1047
The Ozark Folk Center, Mountain View, AR 65

P.H. Sullivan Museum and Genealogy Library, Zionsville, IN 504
Pacific Asia Museum, Pasadena, CA 140
Pacific Aviation Museum - Pearl Harbor, Honolulu, HI 397
Pacific Grove Art Center Associates, Inc., Pacific Grove, CA 137
Packwood House Museum, Lewisburg, PA 1268
Paine Art Center and Gardens, Oshkosh, WI 1617
Painted Post - Erwin Museum at the Depot, Painted Post, NY 1050
Pajaro Valley Historical Association, Watsonville, CA 196
Palmer Museum, Jewell, KS 546
Pamplin Historical Park and The National Museum of the Civil War Soldier, Petersburg, VA 1525
Panhandle-Plains Historical Museum, Canyon, TX 1399
Paris-Henry County Heritage Center, Paris, TN 1382
Parishville Museum, Parishville, NY 1050
Park City Historical Society & Museum, Park City, UT 1468
The Park-McCullough House, North Bennington, VT 1483
Parks, Recreation & Historic Sites Division, Georgia Dept. of Natural Resources, Atlanta, GA 362
Parris Island Museum, Parris Island, SC 1338
The Parry Mansion Museum, New Hope, PA 1273
Parson Fisher House, Blue Hill, ME 606
Parsonsfield-Porter Historical Society, Porter, ME 618
Pasadena Museum of History, Pasadena, CA 140
Pascack Historical Society, Park Ridge, NJ 920
Passaic County Historical Society & Lambert Castle Museum, Paterson, NJ ..920
Patterson Inn Museum/Corning - Painted Post Historical Society, Corning, NY 982
Paul and Lulu Hilliard University Art Museum, University of Louisiana at Lafayette, Lafayette, LA 590
Paul Bunyan Logging Camp Museum, Eau Claire, WI 1596
Paul W. Bryant Museum, Tuscaloosa, AL 19
Pawnee Bill Ranch and Museum, Pawnee, OK 1212
Pawnee City Historical Society & Museum, Pawnee City, NE 871
Peabody Essex Museum, Salem, MA 706
Peabody Museum of Archaeology & Ethnology, Cambridge, MA 674
The Pearl S. Buck House, Perkasie, PA 1275
The Pearson Museum, Springfield, IL 460
The Peekskill Museum, Peekskill, NY 1051
Pejepscot Historical Society, Brunswick, ME 608
Pella Historical Village, Pella, IA 526
The Pena-Peck House, Saint Augustine, FL 339
Pendleton District Historical, Recreational and Tourism Commission, Pendleton, SC 1339

Costumes and Textiles–Continued

Pendleton Historic Foundation, Pendleton, SC 1339

Pennsylvania Anthracite Heritage Museum, Scranton, PA 1299

Pennsylvania German Cultural Heritage Center at Kutztown University, Kutztown, PA....................................1265

Pennsylvania Trolley Museum, Washington, PA...................................1305

Pennypacker Mills, Schwenksville, PA 1297

Pensacola Historical Society Museum, Pensacola, FL...336

Peoria Historical Society, Peoria, IL 451

Perkins County Historical Society, Grant, NE 862

Perryville Battlefield Museum, Perryville, KY 582

Petaluma Adobe State Historic Park, Petaluma, CA 142

Peter Rice Homestead, Home of Marlborough Historical Society, Inc., Marlboro, MA..693

Peter Wentz Farmstead, Worcester, PA.......1308

Peter Yegen Jr. Yellowstone County Museum, Billings, MT 841

Peterborough Historical Society, Peterborough, NH...................................893

Petersham Historical Society, Inc., Petersham, MA 702

Pettaquamscutt Historical Society, Kingston, RI...1312

Petterson Museum of Intercultural Art, Claremont, CA...85

Pettis County Historical Society, Sedalia, MO 838

Philadelphia Mummers Museum, Philadelphia, PA 1285

Philadelphia Museum of Art, Philadelphia, PA 1285

Philadelphia Society for the Preservation of Landmarks, Philadelphia, PA 1286

The Philbrook Museum of Art, Inc., Tulsa, OK..1215

Phillips County Museum, Helena, AR............59

Phoebe Apperson Hearst Museum of Anthropology, Berkeley, CA 77

Phoenix Art Museum, Phoenix, AZ...............41

Phoenix Museum of History, Phoenix, AZ 41

Piatt County Museum, Monticello, IL..........446

The Picker Art Gallery, Hamilton, NY.........997

Pierre Menard Home State Historic Site, Ellis Grove, IL...433

Pike County Historical Society, Milford, PA 1272

Pilgrim Hall Museum, Plymouth, MA 703

Pinal County Historical Society and Museum, Florence, AZ...........................34

Pine Bluff/Jefferson County Historical Museum, Pine Bluff, AR...........................66

Pioneer Arizona Living History Village & Museum, Phoenix, AZ.............................41

Pioneer Corner Museum, New Holstein, WI 1615

Pioneer Heritage Center, LSU-Shreveport, Shreveport, LA...601

The Pioneer Memorial Association of Fenton and Mundy Townships, Fenton, MI..741

Pioneer Museum, Watford City, ND...........1137

Pioneer Museum, Wild Rose, WI 1628

Pioneer Museum - Martin County Historical Society, Fairmont, MN..........775

Pioneer Museum of Alabama, Troy, AL.........18

Pioneer Settlement for the Creative Arts, Barberville, FL...295

Pioneer Village, Farmington, UT...............1465

Pioneer Village & Virgil Grissom Memorial at Spring Mill State Park, Mitchell, IN...491

Pioneer Woman Statue & Museum, Ponca City, OK....................................1212

Pioneers, Trail Drivers and Texas Rangers Memorial Museum, San Antonio, TX...1449

Piper Aviation Museum Foundation, Lock Haven, PA...1269

Pipestone County Historical Museum, Pipestone, MN...786

Pipestone National Monument, Pipestone, MN 787

Pitot House Museum, New Orleans, LA......598

Pittock Mansion, Portland, OR 1232

Pittsford Historical Society Museum, Pittsford, VT..1484

Placer County Museums, Auburn, CA 72

Plains Indians and Pioneers Museum, Woodward, OK.......................................1217

Plainsman Museum, Aurora, NE 856

Plantation Agriculture Museum, Scott, AR...67

Please Touch Museum, Philadelphia, PA ...1286

Plimoth Plantation Inc., Plymouth, MA 703

Plumas County Museum, Quincy, CA..........144

Plymouth Antiquarian Society, Plymouth, MA 704

Plymouth Historical Museum, Plymouth, MI 760

Pocahontas County Iowa Historical Society Museum, Laurens, IA 522

Point of Honor, Lynchburg, VA.................1515

Pointe Coupee Museum, New Roads, LA....599

Polish American Museum, Port Washington, NY 1054

Polish Heritage Center, Ashton, NE 856

Polish Museum of America, Chicago, IL.....426

Polk County Historical Museum, Bartow, FL...295

The Polk County Historical Society, Cedartown, GA.......................................368

Polk County Historical Society, Crookston, MN.......................................771

Polk County Memorial Museum, Livingston, TX.....................................1434

Polk Museum of Art, Lakeland, FL............321

Pope County Historical Society, Glenwood, MN.......................................776

Popular Arts Museum, San Juan, PR..........1643

Port Gamble Historic Museum, Port Gamble, WA...1562

Portage County Historical Society, Stevens Point, WI................................1623

Porter-Phelps-Huntington Foundation, Inc., Hadley, MA...................................685

Porterville Historical Museum, Porterville, CA...144

Portland Children's Museum, Portland, OR 1233

Portland Museum, Louisville, KY 578

Potsdam Public Museum, Potsdam, NY.....1054

Potts Inn Museum, Pottsville, AR.................66

Pound Ridge Society/Museum, Pound Ridge, NY...1055

Powers Museum, Carthage, MO 812

Prairie Village, Madison, SD 1351

Pratt Building - Cohasset Historical Society, Cohasset, MA 676

The Preservation Society of Newport County/The Newport Mansions, Newport, RI...1315

Presque Isle County Historical Museum, Rogers City, MI.......................................762

Princeton University Art Museum, Princeton, NJ...922

Pro Rodeo Hall of Fame & Museum of the American Cowboy, Colorado Springs, CO...207

Promont House Museum, Milford, OH 1176

Proprietary House, The Royal Governor's Mansion, Perth Amboy, NJ....................921

Public Museum of West Michigan, Grand Rapids, MI...744

Pueblo County Historical Society Museum and Edward H. Broadhead Library, Pueblo, CO 230

Puget Sound Coast Artillery Museum at Fort Worden, Port Townsend, WA.........1562

Purdue University Galleries, West Lafayette, IN...503

Putnam Cottage, Greenwich, CT 243

Putnam County Historical Society & Foundry School Museum, Cold Spring, NY...979

Putnam County Historical Society Museum, Kalida, OH.............................1169

Putnam Museum of History & Natural Science, Davenport, IA 513

Putney Historical Society, Putney, VT 1485

Queen Emma Summer Palace, Honolulu, HI 398

Queens Historical Society, Flushing, NY.....990

The Quilters Hall of Fame, Inc., Marion, IN 490

The Quincy Museum, Quincy, IL................452

Radford University Art Museum, Radford, VA..1527

Railroad and Heritage Museum Inc., Temple, TX..1454

Ralls Historical Museum, Ralls, TX..........1445

The Ralph Foster Museum, Point Lookout, MO...828

Ralph Waldo Emerson House, Concord, MA 677

Ramapogue Historical Society, West Springfield, MA.......................................718

Ramsey House Museum Plantation, Knoxville, TN.......................................1371

Rancho La Patera - The Stow House G.V.H.S., Goleta, CA 100

Rancho Los Cerritos Historic Site, Long Beach, CA..111

Randolph County Historical Museum, Winchester, IN...503

Randolph Historical Society, Inc., Randolph, VT..1485

Rankin Museum, Rankin, TX....................1445

Ransom County Historical Society, Fort Ransom, ND...1131

Rattlesnake Museum (American International), Albuquerque, NM.............935

The Ray Drew Gallery-New Mexico Highlands University, Las Vegas, NM 941

Raynham Hall Museum, Oyster Bay, NY.,1049

Readsboro Historical Society, Readsboro, VT 1486

Rebel State Historic Site & Louisiana Country Music Museum, Marthaville, LA 592

Red Mill Museum Village, Clinton, NJ........901

Red Rock Museum, Church Rock, NM 938

Redington Museum, Waterville, ME 625

Reese Bullen Gallery, Arcata, CA 72

Reginald F. Lewis Museum of Maryland African American History and Culture, Baltimore, MD...636

Rehoboth Art League, Inc., Rehoboth Beach, DE..272

Reitz Home Museum, Evansville, IN...........476

Remick Country Doctor Museum and Farm, Tamworth, NH.............................896

Reno County Museum, Hutchinson, KS 545

Rensselaer County Historical Society, Troy, NY...1079

Renton Historical Society and Museum, Renton, WA...1564

Reuel B. Pritchett Museum, Bridgewater, VA 1497

Reverend Dan Foster House, Museum of the Weathersfield Historical Society, Weathersfield, VT................................1489

Reynolda House Museum of American Art, Winston-Salem, NC 1126

Rhode Island Historical Society, Providence, RI 1318

Rice County Museum of History, Faribault, MN 775

Richard Salter Storrs House, Longmeadow, MA 691

Richards DAR House Museum, Mobile, AL 15

Richardson-Bates House Museum, Oswego, NY 1048

Richland County Historical Museum, Wahpeton, ND 1137

Richland County Museum, Lexington, OH 1172

Riddick's Folly, Suffolk, VA 1539

Rifle Creek Museum, Rifle, CO 231

Riley County Historical Museum, Manhattan, KS 551

Ripley's Believe It or Not!, Key West, FL 319

Rising Sun Tavern, Fredericksburg, VA 1507

Riverdale House Mansion, Riverdale Park, MD 651

Riverside Museum, La Crosse, WI 1603

Riverview at Hobson Grove, Bowling Green, KY 566

Roanoke Island Festival Park; Homeport of the "Elizabeth II", Manteo, NC 1110

Robbins Hunter Museum, Avery-Downer House, Granville, OH 1167

Robbins Museum of Archaeology, Middleborough, MA 694

Roberson Museum and Science Center, Binghamton, NY 962

Robert Hull Fleming Museum, Burlington, VT 1478

Robert Louis Stevenson House, Monterey, CA 128

Robert Newell House, DAR Museum, Saint Paul, OR 1235

Robert R. McCormick Museum at Cantigny, Wheaton, IL 465

Robert Toombs House, Washington, GA 391

Robert V. Fullerton Art Museum, California State University, San Bernardino, San Bernardino, CA 155

Rochester Historical Society, Rochester, NY 1059

Rochester Museum & Science Center, Rochester, NY 1059

Rock County Historical Society, Janesville, WI 1601

Rock Island County Historical Society, Moline, IL 445

Rockingham, Kingston, NJ 909

Rockingham Free Public Library and Museum, Bellows Falls, VT 1476

Rockwell Museum of Western Art, Corning, NY 982

Rockwood Park, Wilmington, DE 274

Rocky Mount Arts Center, Rocky Mount, NC 1117

Rocky Mount Museum, Piney Flats, TN 1383

Rocky Mountain Quilt Museum, Golden, CO 220

Rocky Reach Dam, Wenatchee, WA 1577

Rogers Historical Museum, Rogers, AR 67

Rokeby (Ancestral Estate of Rowland Evans Robinson), Ferrisburgh, VT 1479

Rollo Jamison Museum, Platteville, WI 1617

Romanian Ethnic Art Museum, Cleveland, OH 1156

Rome Area History Museum, Rome, GA 382

Ronald Reagan Presidential Library and Museum, Simi Valley, CA 187

The Root House Museum, Marietta, GA 379

Rosalie House, Eureka Springs, AR 57

Rosalie Whyel Museum of Doll Art, Bellevue, WA 1548

Roscoe Village Foundation, Coshocton, OH 1159

Rose Center Museum, Morristown, TN 1376

Rose Hill Museum, Bay Village, OH 1141

Rose Hill Plantation State Historic Site, Union, SC 1343

Rose Lawn Museum, Cartersville, GA 368

Roseau County Historical Museum and Interpretive Center, Roseau, MN 788

Rosebud County Pioneer Museum, Forsyth, MT 846

Roseland Cottage, Woodstock, CT 268

Rosemont Plantation, Woodville, MS 810

Rosemount Museum, Pueblo, CO 230

Rosenbach Museum & Library, Philadelphia, PA 1287

Rosenberg Library, Galveston, TX 1422

Roslyn Landmark Society, Roslyn, NY 1061

Ross County Historical Society, Inc., Chillicothe, OH 1147

Roswell Museum and Art Center, Roswell, NM 946

The Rotch-Jones-Duff House & Garden Museum, Inc., New Bedford, MA 697

The Rotunda, University of Virginia, Charlottesville, VA 1500

Rowan Museum, Inc., Salisbury, NC 1118

Rowley Historical Society, Rowley, MA 706

The Roy Rogers-Dale Evans Museum and Theater, Branson, MO 811

Rusk County Historical Society, Ladysmith, WI 1604

Russell County Historical Society/Fossil Station Museum, Russell, KS 556

Ruth Chandler Williamson Gallery, Scripps College, Claremont, CA 86

The Rye Historical Society and Square House Museum, Rye, NY 1062

Saco Museum, Saco, ME 621

Safety Harbor Museum of Regional History, Safety Harbor, FL 338

Safford House Historic House Museum, Tarpon Springs, FL 351

Sahuaro Ranch Historical Area, Glendale, AZ 35

St. Albans Historical Museum, Saint Albans, VT 1486

St. Charles County Historical Society, Inc., Saint Charles, MO 830

St. Charles Heritage Center, Saint Charles, IL 457

St. Clair County Historical Society, Belleville, IL 412

St. John's Northwestern Military Academy Archives & Museum, Delafield, WI 1595

St. Lawrence County Historical Association - Silas Wright House, Canton, NY 975

The Saint Louis Art Museum, Saint Louis, MO 836

St. Louis Cardinals Hall of Fame Museum, Saint Louis, MO 836

St. Paul Museum, Randleman, NC 1117

Ste. Genevieve Museum, Sainte Genevieve, MO 838

Salamanca Rail Museum, Salamanca, NY .1063

Salem Art Association-Bush House Museum and Bush Barn Art Center, Salem, OR 1236

Salem County Historical Society, Salem, NJ 924

Salem Historical Society and Museum, Salem, OH 1184

The Salem Museum, Salem, VA 1536

Salisbury House Foundation, Des Moines, IA 515

Salmon Brook Historical Society, Inc., Granby, CT 242

Salvador Dali Museum, Saint Petersburg, FL 342

The Salvation Army Southern Historical Center & Museum, Atlanta, GA 363

Sam Bell Maxey House State Historic Site, Paris, TX 1442

Sam Houston Regional Library & Research Center, Liberty, TX 1434

Sam Noble Oklahoma Museum of Natural History, Norman, OK 1206

Sam Rayburn House Museum, Bonham, TX 1397

Samek Art Gallery, Lewisburg, PA 1268

Samuel Cupples House of Saint Louis University, Saint Louis, MO 837

San Antonio Conservation Society, San Antonio, TX 1449

San Antonio Missions National Historical Park, San Antonio, TX 1449

San Buenaventura Mission Museum, Ventura, CA 195

San Diego Air & Space Museum, San Diego, CA 159

San Diego Automotive Museum, San Diego, CA 159

San Diego Model Railroad Museum, Inc., San Diego, CA 159

San Diego Museum of Man, San Diego, CA 160

San Gabriel Mission Museum, San Gabriel, CA 171

San Jacinto Museum of History Association, La Porte, TX 1433

San Joaquin County Historical Society & Museum, Lodi, CA 109

San Jose Museum of Quilts & Textiles, San Jose, CA 172

San Juan Bautista State Historic Park, San Juan Bautista, CA 173

San Juan Historical Society, Friday Harbor, WA 1555

San Luis Obispo County Historical Museum, San Luis Obispo, CA 174

San Mateo County Historical Association and Museum, Redwood City, CA 147

Sanborn Area Historical Society, Sanborn, NY 1064

Sandown Historical Society and Museum, Sandown, NH 896

Sandusky Library Follett House Museum, Sandusky, OH 1185

Sandwich Glass Museum, Sandwich, MA ...708

Sandwich Historical Society, Center Sandwich, NH 884

Sandy Spring Museum, Sandy Spring, MD 653

Sanford Museum, Sanford, FL 343

Sanford Museum and Planetarium, Cherokee, IA 510

Sanilac County Historical Museum and Village, Port Sanilac, MI 761

The Santa Barbara Historical Museum, Santa Barbara, CA 179

Santa Barbara Museum of Art, Santa Barbara, CA 179

Santa Cruz Art League, Inc., Santa Cruz, CA 182

Santa Maria Valley Historical Museum, Santa Maria, CA 183

Santa Ynez Valley Historical Society, Santa Ynez, CA 185

Sapulpa Historical Museum, Sapulpa, OK.1213

Sarah A. Mooney Memorial Museum, Lemoore, CA 109

Saratoga County Historical Society, Brookside Museum, Ballston Spa, NY 960

Saratoga Museum, Saratoga, WY 1638

Satterlee Clark House, Horicon, WI 1600

Sauk County Historical Museum, Baraboo, WI 1591

Saunders County Historical Complex, Wahoo, NE 874

Saunders Memorial Museum, Berryville, AR 55

Savannah College of Art and Design Galleries, Savannah, GA 386

Sawin Memorial Building, Dover, MA 680

Sayville Historical Society, Sayville, NY ...1066

Scalamandre, Long Island City, NY 1011

Costumes and Textiles—Continued

Scantic Academy Museum, East Windsor Historical Society, Inc., East Windsor, CT 239

Scarborough Historical Museum, Scarborough, ME 621

The Scarsdale Historical Society, Scarsdale, NY 1066

Schenectady County Historical Society, Schenectady, NY 1067

Schenectady Museum and Suits-Bueche Planetarium, Schenectady, NY 1067

Schingoethe Center for Native American Cultures, Aurora, IL 412

Schminck Memorial Museum, Lakeview, OR 1227

Schmucker Art Gallery, Gettysburg, PA 1256

Schoharie Colonial Heritage Association, Schoharie, NY 1067

Scholte House Museum, Pella, IA 527

School of American Research, Indian Arts Research Center, Santa Fe, NM 950

School of Nations Museum, Elsah, IL 433

Schoolcraft County Historical Society, Manistique, MI 753

Schoolhouse Museum of the Ridgewood Historical Society, Inc., Ridgewood, NJ 923

The Schuette Biermann Farmhouse Museum, Elk Grove Village, IL 432

Schuyler-Hamilton House, Morristown, NJ 914

Schwenkfelder Library & Heritage Center, Pennsburg, PA 1275

The Science Fiction Museum and Hall of Fame, Seattle, WA 1568

The Science Museum of Minnesota, Saint Paul, MN 792

Scituate Historical Society, Scituate, MA 708

Scotchtown, Beaverdam, VA 1496

Scotia-Glenville Children's Museum, Scotia, NY 1068

Scurry County Museum, Snyder, TX 1453

Sea Cliff Village Museum, Sea Cliff, NY ..1068

Seattle Art Museum, Seattle, WA 1568

Seattle Asian Art Museum, Seattle, WA.....1569

The Seay House, Spartanburg, SC 1341

Sedgwick-Brooklin Historical Society, Sedgwick, ME 622

Senate House State Historic Site, Kingston, NY 1008

Senator George Norris State Historic Site, McCook, NE 868

Senator John Heinz Pittsburgh Regional History Center, Pittsburgh, PA 1294

Seneca County Museum, Tiffin, OH 1186

Seneca Falls Historical Society, Seneca Falls, NY 1069

1797 Ezekiel Harris House, Augusta, GA....366

1768 Jeremiah Lee Mansion, Marblehead, MA 693

1761 Pownalborough Courthouse, Dresden, ME 610

The Sevier County Historical Museum, De Queen, AR 56

Sewall-Belmont House and Museum, Washington, DC 290

Seward County Historical Society Museum, Goehner, NE 861

Seward House, Auburn, NY 959

The Shadows-on-the-Teche, New Iberia, LA 593

Shaftsbury Historical Society, Shaftsbury, VT 1487

Shaker Heritage Society, Albany, NY 956

Shaker Historical Society, Shaker Heights, OH 1185

Shaker Museum, New Gloucester, ME 615

The Shaker Museum and Library, Old Chatham, NY 1045

Shako:wi Cultural Center, Oneida, NY 1046

Shandy Hall, Geneva, OH 1166

Sharlot Hall Museum, Prescott, AZ 43

Sharon Historical Society, Sharon, CT 260

Sharpsteen Museum, Calistoga, CA 80

Shawano County Historical Society, Inc., Shawano, WI 1621

Shelburne Museum, Inc., Shelburne, VT ...1487

Sheldon Memorial Art Gallery and Sculpture Garden/University of Nebraska-Lincoln, Lincoln, NE 867

Shelter Island Historical Society, Shelter Island, NY 1069

Sherwin Miller Museum of Jewish Art, Tulsa, OK 1216

Sherwood Forest Plantation, Charles City, VA 1498

Shippensburg University Fashion Archives and Museum, Shippensburg, PA 1300

Shoal Creek Living History Museum, Kansas City, MO 822

Shorter Mansion Museum, Eufaula, AL 8

Shortgrass Country Museum Society, Sayre, OK 1213

Shoshone County Mining and Smelting Museum d/b/a The Staff House Museum, Kellogg, ID 406

Sibley County Historical Museum, Henderson, MN 777

Sibley House Historic Site, Mendota, MN...780

Sidney Historical Association, Sidney, NY 1069

Silent Wings Museum, Lubbock, TX 1435

Siloam Springs Museum, Siloam Springs, AR 68

Silt Historical Society, Silt, CO 232

Silver Cliff Museum, Silver Cliff, CO.........232

Silvercreek Museum, Freeport, IL 435

Simsbury Historical Society, Phelps Tavern, Museum & Homestead, Simsbury, CT 260

Sioux City Public Museum, Sioux City, IA 528

Sioux Empire Medical Museum, Sioux Falls, SD 1356

Sioux Indian Museum, Rapid City, SD 1355

Sitka National Historical Park, Sitka, AK 28

Skirball Museum Cincinnati Hebrew Union College-Jewish Institute of Religion, Cincinnati, OH 1151

Slate Valley Museum, Granville, NY 996

The Slater Memorial Museum - Norwich Free Academy, Norwich, CT 258

Slater Mill Historic Site, Pawtucket, RI.....1315

Slidell Museum, Slidell, LA 602

Slifer House, Lewisburg, PA 1268

Sloan Museum, Flint, MI 742

Smith-McDowell House Museum, Asheville, NC 1090

Smith-Zimmermann Heritage Museum, Madison, SD 1351

Smithtown Historical Society, Smithtown, NY 1070

Smoki Museum - American Indian Art & Culture, Prescott, AZ 43

Smoky Hill Museum, Salina, KS 557

Smyth County Museum, Marion, VA 1516

Snake River Heritage Center, Weiser, ID.....410

The Snite Museum of Art, University of Notre Dame, Notre Dame, IN 495

Snoqualmie Valley Historical Museum, North Bend, WA 1559

The Snyder County Historical Society, Middleburg, PA 1271

Snyder Museum & Creative Arts Center, Bastrop, LA 585

The Society of California Pioneers, San Francisco, CA 170

The Society of the Cincinnati at Anderson House, Washington, DC 291

The Society of the Four Arts, Palm Beach, FL 334

Soldiers & Sailors Memorial Building, Huntington, NY 1001

Somers Historical Society, Somers, NY 1070

The Somerset County Historical Society, Inc., Princess Anne, MD 650

Sonnenberg Gardens & Mansion State Historic Park, Canandaigua, NY 975

Sonoma State Historic Park, Sonoma, CA...188

Sophienburg Museum & Archives Inc., New Braunfels, TX 1440

Sosa-Carrillo-Fremont House Museum, Tucson, AZ 50

South Boston-Halifax County Museum of Fine Arts & History, South Boston, VA 1536

South Carolina Artisans Center, Walterboro, SC 1343

South Carolina Confederate Relic Room and Museum, Columbia, SC 1330

South Charleston Museum, South Charleston, WV 1586

South County Museum Inc., Narragansett, RI 1313

South Dakota Hall of Fame, Chamberlain, SD 1345

South Dakota State Historical Society, Pierre, SD 1353

South Hero Bicentennial Museum, South Hero, VT 1487

South Holland Historical Society, South Holland, IL 457

South Milwaukee Historical Society Museum, South Milwaukee, WI 1622

South Pass City State Historic Site, South Pass City, WY 1638

South Sutton Old Store Museum, South Sutton, NH 896

South Texas Museum, Alice, TX 1386

Southampton Historical Museum, Southampton, NY 1070

Southeast Missouri Regional Museum, Cape Girardeau, MO 812

Southeast Museum Association, Inc., Brewster, NY 964

Southern Oregon Historical Society, Jacksonville, OR 1226

Southern Ute Cultural Center and Museum, Ignacio, CO 223

Southold Historical Society and Museum, Southold, NY 1071

Southwest Florida Museum of History, Fort Myers, FL 309

Southwest Museum, Los Angeles, CA 121

Southwest Virginia Museum Historical State Park, Big Stone Gap, VA 1497

Space Center Houston, Houston, TX...........1429

Spartanburg County Regional Museum of History, Spartanburg, SC 1341

Spencer Museum of Art, The University of Kansas, Lawrence, KS 548

Spertus Museum, Chicago, IL 427

SPJST Library Archives & Museum, Temple, TX 1455

The Sports Museum, Boston, MA 669

Spring Street Historical Museum, Shreveport, LA 602

Springfield Art & Historical Society - Miller Art Center, Springfield, VT.........1488

Springfield Art Association, Springfield, IL 460

Springfield Museum of Art, Springfield, OH 1186

Springfield Museum of Old Domestic Life, High Point, NC 1107

Springfield Museums - Springfield Science Museum, Springfield, MA 711

Spurlock Museum, University of Illinois at Urbana-Champaign, Urbana, IL...........462

Staatsburgh State Historic Site, Staatsburg, NY 1071

Stagecoach Inn Museum Complex, Newbury Park, CA 130

Stamford Historical Society, Inc., Stamford, CT 260

Stamford Museum & Nature Center, Stamford, CT 261

Stan Hywet Hall and Gardens, Inc., Akron, OH 1139

Stanley-Whitman House, Farmington, Farmington, CT 241

Stanly County Historic Preservation Commission and Museum, Albemarle, NC 1088

Stanton House, Clinton, CT 237

Stanwood Wildlife Sanctuary, Ellsworth, ME 610

Star of the Republic Museum, Washington, TX 1460

State Historical Society of Iowa, Des Moines, IA 515

State Historical Society of North Dakota, Bismarck, ND 1128

Staten Island Historical Society, Staten Island, NY 1074

Stauth Memorial Museum, Montezuma, KS 553

STAX Museum of American Soul Music, Memphis, TN 1376

The Steamboat Arabia Museum, Kansas City, MO 822

Steamship Keewatin, Douglas, MI 738

Steele County Historical Society, Hope, ND 1133

Steilacoom Historical Museum Association, Steilacoom, WA 1572

The Stephen Phillips House, Salem, MA 707

Stephenson County Historical Society, Freeport, IL 436

Stepping Stones Museum for Children, Norwalk, CT 257

Steppingstone Museum, Havre de Grace, MD 647

Sterling Historical Society and Little Red Schoolhouse Museum, Sterling, NY 1074

The Stevens-Coolidge Place, a property of The Trustees of Reservations, North Andover, MA 698

Stevens Museum, Salem, IN 498

Stewart M. Lord Memorial Historical Society, Inc., Burlington, ME 608

Stockholm Historical Society Museum, Stockholm, ME 623

Stone Fort Museum, Nacogdoches, TX 1440

Stonewall House, Rocky Mount, NC 1118

Stonewall Jackson House, Lexington, VA 1514

Stonewall Jackson Museum at Hupp's Hill, Strasburg, VA 1539

Stoughton Historical Society, Stoughton, MA 713

The Stowitts Museum & Library, Pacific Grove, CA 137

Stranahan House, Inc., Fort Lauderdale, FL 308

Strasburg Museum, Strasburg, VA 1539

Strater Hotel, Durango, CO 214

The Stratford Historical Society & Catherine B. Mitchell Museum, Stratford, CT 262

Stratford, Robert E. Lee Memorial Association, Inc., Stratford, VA 1539

Strawbery Banke Museum, Portsmouth, NH 895

Strong - National Museum of Play, Rochester, NY 1060

Stuart Heritage Museum, Stuart, FL 346

The Studio Museum in Harlem, New York, NY 1040

Stuhr Museum of the Prairie Pioneer, Grand Island, NE 862

SUArt Galleries - Syracuse University, Syracuse, NY 1077

Suffolk County Historical Society, Riverhead, NY 1057

Sullivan County Historical Society, Inc., Hurleyville, NY 1001

Sullivan Museum and History Center, Northfield, VT 1483

Summit Historical Society, Breckenridge, CO 204

The Sumter County Museum, Sumter, SC 1342

Sun Gallery, Hayward, CA 102

Sun Prairie Historical Library & Museum, Sun Prairie, WI 1624

Sunnyside Historical Museum, Sunnyside, WA 1572

SunWatch Indian Village/Archaeological Park, Dayton, OH 1162

The Supreme Court of the United States, Washington, DC 291

Surratt House Museum, Clinton, MD 640

Susan B. Anthony House, Rochester, NY 1060

Susquehanna County Historical Society & Free Library Association, Montrose, PA 1272

Swampscott Historical Society (John Humphrey House), Swampscott, MA 714

Swedish American Museum Association of Chicago, Chicago, IL 428

Sweet Briar Museum, Sweet Briar, VA 1540

Swenson Memorial Museum of Stephens County, Breckenridge, TX 1397

Swift County Historical Society, Benson, MN 769

Swisher County Archives and Museum Association, Tulia, TX 1456

Swiss Historical Village, New Glarus, WI 1615

Switzerland County Historical Museum, Vevay, IN 502

T.C. Steele State Historic Site, Nashville, IN 493

The Taft Museum of Art, Cincinnati, OH 1151

Tallahassee Museum, Tallahassee, FL 348

Tamastslikt Cultural Institute, Pendleton, OR 1230

Tante Blanche Museum, Madawaska, ME 614

Tappantown Historical Society, Tappan, NY 1077

Tarpon Springs Area Historical Society - Depot Museum, Tarpon Springs, FL 351

Tarpon Springs Cultural Center, Tarpon Springs, FL 351

Tate House Museum, Portland, ME 620

Telfair Museum of Art, Savannah, GA 386

Telluride Historical Museum, Telluride, CO 233

Temecula Valley Museum, Temecula, CA 191

Tempe Historical Museum, Tempe, AZ 46

Temperance Tavern, Newcomerstown, OH 1179

The Temple Judea Museum of Reform Congregation Keneseth Israel, Elkins Park, PA 1251

The Temple Museum of Religious Art, Cleveland, OH 1156

Ten Broeck Mansion - Albany County Historical Association, Albany, NY 956

Tenino Depot Museum, Tenino, WA 1575

Tennessee Museum of Aviation, Sevierville, TN 1383

Tennessee State Museum, Nashville, TN 1381

Terrace Gallery-City of Orlando, Orlando, FL 332

Terrace Hill Historic Site and Governor's Mansion, Des Moines, IA 516

Terwilliger Museum, Waterloo, NY 1083

Teutopolis Monastery Museum, Teutopolis, IL 461

Texas Air Museum, Slaton, TX 1453

Texas Parks and Wildlife Department, Austin, TX 1392

Texas State Museum of Asian Cultures & Educational Center, Corpus Christi, TX 1402

The Textile Museum, Washington, DC 291

Theodore Roosevelt Birthplace National Historic Site, New York, NY 1040

Theodore Roosevelt Inaugural National Historic Site, Buffalo, NY 973

Theodore Roosevelt National Park-Visitor Center, Medora, ND 1134

Thetford Historical Society Library and Museum, Thetford, VT 1488

Third Cavalry Museum, Fort Carson, CO 216

This Is The Place Heritage Park, Salt Lake City, UT 1472

Thomas Clarke House/Princeton Battlefield State Park, Princeton, NJ 922

The Thomas Griswold House and Museum, Guilford, CT 243

The Thomas T. Taber Museum of the Lycoming County Historical Society, Williamsport, PA 1308

Thomas Warne Historical Museum & Library, Old Bridge, NJ 918

Thronateeska Heritage Foundation, Inc., Albany, GA 355

Tinker Swiss Cottage Museum, Rockford, IL 456

Tinley Park Historical Society, Tinley Park, IL 461

Tioga County Historical Society Museum, Owego, NY 1048

Tippecanoe County Historical Association, Lafayette, IN 487

Tobacco Farm Life Museum, Inc., Kenly, NC 1107

Tolland Historical Society - Tolland County Jail and Warden's Home Museum, Tolland, CT 262

Tom Mix Museum, Dewey, OK 1199

Top of Oklahoma Historical Museum, Blackwell, OK 1197

Towe Auto Museum, Sacramento, CA 154

Town of Manlius Historical Society with Museum, Manlius, NY 1013

Town of Yorktown Museum, Yorktown Heights, NY 1087

Traill County Historical Society, Hillsboro, ND 1132

The Trammell & Margaret Crow Collection of Asian Art, Dallas, TX 1408

Traveler's Rest State Historic Site, Toccoa, GA 389

Travellers Rest Plantation & Museum, Nashville, TN 1381

Trenton City Museum, Trenton, NJ 928

Trenton Historical Museum, Trenton, MI 765

Tri-County Historical Society & Museum, Inc., Herington, KS 544

Triangle Tattoo & Museum, Fort Bragg, CA 95

Trinity Museum of the Parish of Trinity Church, New York, NY 1040

The Trout Gallery, Carlisle, PA 1245

Troutdale Historical Society, Troutdale, OR 1237

Troy Museum & Historic Village, Troy, MI 765

Tsa Mo Ga Memorial Museum, Plains, TX 1443

Tuck Museum, Hampton, NH 888

Tucson Museum of Art & Historic Block, Tucson, AZ 51

Tulare County Museum at Mooney Grove Park, Visalia, CA 195

Tularosa Basin Historical Society Museum, Alamogordo, NM 932

Tunica-Biloxi Native American Museum, Marksville, LA 591

The Turner Museum, Sarasota, FL 345

Turtle Bay Exploration Park, Redding, CA 146

Tuskegee Institute National Historic Site, Tuskegee Institute, AL 21

Twin Falls County Historical Museum, Filer, ID 405

Twinsburg Historical Society, Twinsburg, OH 1188

Costumes and Textiles—Continued

UCLA Fowler Museum of Cultural History, Los Angeles, CA 122
UNLV Marjorie Barrick Museum, Las Vegas, NV....................................880
U.S. Navy Museum, Washington, DC..........292
Ukrainian-American Museum & Archives, Warren, MI......................766
The Ukrainian Museum, New York, NY....1040
Ukrainian Museum-Archives, Inc., Cleveland, OH 1156
Ukrainian National Museum, Inc., Chicago, IL..................................428
Ulster County Historical Society, Marbletown, NY.....................1013
Ulysses S. Grant Cottage State Historic Site, Wilton, NY.......................1086
Umpqua Discovery Center, Reedsport, OR....................................1234
Union County Museum, Union, OR...........1238
Union Mills Homestead & Grist Mill, Westminster, MD......................656
Union Station Kansas City, Inc., Kansas City, MO..................................823
United States Golf Association Museum & Archives, Far Hills, NJ 903
United States Hockey Hall of Fame, Eveleth, MN................................774
United States Holocaust Memorial Museum, Washington, DC 293
University Art Galleries, Murray State University, Murray, KY.....................580
University Art Gallery, Indiana State University, Terre Haute, IN......................501
University Art Gallery, University of the South, Sewanee, TN......................1384
University Galleries, Clarion, PA 1247
The University Museum Collections, Fayetteville, AR......................57
University Museum, New Mexico State University, Las Cruces, NM.................941
University of Arizona Student Union Galleries, Tucson, AZ..........................52
University of Arkansas at Little Rock Art Department Gallery I & II & III, Little Rock, AR................................63
University of Michigan Museum of Anthropology, Ann Arbor, MI.................725
The University of Michigan Museum of Art, Ann Arbor, MI......................726
University of Missouri-Kansas City Gallery of Art, Kansas City, MO............823
University of Oregon Museum of Natural and Cultural History, Eugene, OR........1224
The University of South Carolina McKissick Museum, Columbia, SC.......1331
University Saint Thomas Art History, Saint Paul, MN................................792
Upper Musselshell Historical Society, Harlowton, MT............................849
Upper Room Chapel Museum, Nashville, TN....................................1381
U.S. Army Center of Military History, Museum Division, Fort McNair, DC.......275
U.S. Army Chaplain Museum, Fort Jackson, SC..................................1332
U.S. Army Finance Corps Museum, Fort Jackson, SC..................................1333
U.S. Army Transportation Museum, Fort Eustis, VA..................................1504
U.S. Army Women's Museum, Fort Lee, VA 1505
U.S. Capitol Historical Society, Washington, DC................................293
U.S. Cavalry Museum, Fort Riley, KS........540
U.S. Coast Guard Museum, New London, CT....................................255
U.S. Grant's Home State Historic Site, Galena, IL..................................436
U.S. National Ski Hall of Fame & Museum, Inc., Ishpeming, MI.................747
USS Arizona Memorial, Honolulu, HI.........398

USS Bowfin Submarine Museum & Park, Honolulu, HI................................398
USS Lexington Museum on the Bay, Corpus Christi, TX 1402
USS Radford National Naval Museum, Newcomerstown, OH..........................1179
Utah Museum of Fine Arts, Salt Lake City, UT................................1472
Utah State Historical Society, Salt Lake City, UT................................1473
Utica Museum, Utica, MT 854

Valdosta State University Fine Arts Gallery, Valdosta, GA.....................389
Valentine Richmond History Center, Richmond, VA................................1532
Vallejo Naval & Historical Museum, Vallejo, CA..................................194
Van Buren County Historical Society, Keosauqua, IA................................521
Van Wyck Homestead Museum, Fishkill, NY..................................989
Vanderbilt University Fine Arts Gallery, Nashville, TN................................1381
Vann House, Chatsworth, GA....................368
Varner-Hogg Plantation State Historic Site, West Columbia, TX 1461
Verde Historical Society, Clemenceau Heritage Museum, Cottonwood, AZ..........32
Vermilion County Museum Society, Danville, IL................................429
Vermont Historical Society Museum, Montpelier, VT................................1482
Vermont Ski Museum, Stowe, VT..............1488
The Vermont State House, Montpelier, VT..................................1483
Vernon County Historical Museum, Viroqua, WI................................1625
The Vestal Museum, Vestal, NY.................1081
Vesterheim Norwegian-American Museum, Decorah, IA..........................513
Victoria Mansion, Portland, ME..................620
Viking Union Gallery, Bellingham, WA.....1549
Vikingsholm, Tahoma, CA........................191
Village Historical Society, Inc., Harrison, OH..................................1168
Village of Elsah Museum, Elsah, IL 433
The Vinalhaven Historical Society Museum, Vinalhaven, ME.......................624
Virginia City J. Spencer Watkins Memorial Museum, Virginia City, MT....854
Virginia Museum of Fine Arts, Richmond, VA................................1533
Virginia Museum of Transportation, Inc., Roanoke, VA................................1536
Virginia Sports Hall of Fame, Portsmouth, VA................................1526
Vista Historical Museum, Vista, CA.............196
Visual Arts Center of Northwest Florida, Panama City, FL................................334
Visual Arts Museum, New York, NY.........1040
Vizcaya Museum and Gardens, Miami, FL..................................326
VSA Arts of Georgia - Arts for All Gallery, Atlanta, GA........................364

The W.H. Stark House, Orange, TX...........1442
Wade House Stagecoach Inn & Wesley Jung Carriage Museum State Historic Site, Greenbush, WI 1599
Wadsworth Atheneum Museum of Art, Hartford, CT................................246
Wailoa Center for Culture and Arts, Hilo, HI..................................393
Wakefield Historical Society, Wakefield, MA..................................715
Waldensian Heritage Museum, Valdese, NC..................................1121
Wallingford Historical Society, Inc., Wallingford, CT................................263
Walnut Grove Plantation, Roebuck, SC 1340
Walters Art Museum, Baltimore, MD..........636

Waltham Historical Society, Waltham, MA....................................716
The Waltham Museum, Waltham, MA.........716
Wapello County Historical Museum, Ottumwa, IA................................526
War in the Pacific National Historical Park, Piti, GU................................1640
Warner House, Portsmouth, NH 895
Warren County Historical Society, Warren, PA................................1304
Warren County Historical Society Museum, Lebanon, OH......................1171
Warrick County Museum, Inc., Boonville, IN..................................470
Washakie Museum, Worland, WY.............1639
Washburn County Historical Society Museum, Shell Lake, WI.....................1621
Washington County Historical Association, Fort Calhoun, NE..............860
Washington County Historical Society, Washington, KS................................560
Washington County Historical Society, Portland, OR................................1233
Washington County Historical Society, Washington, PA................................1305
Washington County Historical Society and Miller House Museum, Hagerstown, MD................................646
Washington County Historical Society Inc., West Bend, WI........................1627
Washington County Historical Society Warden's House Museum, Stillwater, MN..................................794
Washington Historical Museum, Washington, GA................................391
Washington Museum & Tourist Center, Washington, LA................................603
Washington National Cathedral, Washington, DC................................294
Washington State Historical Society, Tacoma, WA 1574
Washington's Headquarters State Historic Site, Newburgh, NY.......................1042
Washington's Lands Museum & Sayre Log House, Ravenswood, WV..............1586
Waterford Historical Museum and Cultural Center, Inc., Waterford, NY.....1083
Waterloo Area Historical Society, Grass Lake, MI..................................744
Watertown Historical Society, Inc., Watertown, CT................................264
Watkins Community Museum of History, Lawrence, KS................................548
Watson-Curtze Mansion, Erie, PA 1253
Wauconda Township Historical Society, Wauconda, IL................................463
Waukesha County Museum, Waukesha, WI..................................1625
Wayland Historical Society, Wayland, MA..................................716
Wayne County Historical Museum, Richmond, IN................................497
Wayne County Historical Society, Lyons, NY..................................1012
Wayne County Historical Society, Wooster, OH................................1192
Wayne County Historical Society, Honesdale, PA................................1261
Webb House Museum, Newark, OH 1179
Webster House Museum, Elkhorn, WI.......1596
Wellesley Historical Society, Inc., Wellesley Hills, MA........................717
Wellington B. Gray Gallery, Greenville, NC..................................1105
Wells County Historical Museum, Bluffton, IN................................470
Wenatchee Valley Museum and Cultural Center, Wenatchee, WA........................1577
Wenham Museum, Wenham, MA.............717
West Allis Historical Society Museum, West Allis, WI................................1626
West Baton Rouge Museum, Port Allen, LA..................................599

West Chicago City Museum, West Chicago, IL 464
West Pasco Historical Society Museum and Library, New Port Richey, FL 329
West Point Museum, West Point, NY 1085
West Valley Art Museum, Surprise, AZ 45
Western Colorado Center for the Arts, Grand Junction, CO 221
Western Heritage Center, Billings, MT 841
Western Hotel/Museum, Lancaster, CA........108
Western Kentucky University Gallery, Bowling Green, KY..................566
Western Michigan University Richmond Center for Visual Arts School of Art, Kalamazoo, MI 749
Western New Mexico University Museum, Silver City, NM 951
Western Reserve Historical Society, Cleveland, OH 1156
Western Rhode Island Civic Historical Society, Coventry, RI 1311
Westminster Historical Society, Westminster, VT 1490
Westport Historical Society, Westport, CT ...266
The Wethersfield Historical Society, Wethersfield, CT 266
Wexford County Historical Society & Museum, Cadillac, MI..................731
The Whale Museum, Friday Harbor, WA...1555
Whatcom Museum of History and Art, Bellingham, WA..................1549
Wheels O' Time Museum, Peoria, IL............451
Wheels Through Time Museum, Inc., Maggie Valley, NC 1110
The Wheelwright Museum of the American Indian, Santa Fe, NM..............950
White County Historical Society Museum, Monticello, IN 491
White Hall State Historic Site, Richmond, KY..................583
Whitehead Memorial Museum, Del Rio, TX 1409
Whitewater Historical Museum, Whitewater, WI 1628
Whitley County Historical Museum, Columbia City, IN 472
Whittier Home Association, Amesbury, MA 658
Wichita-Sedgwick County Historical Museum Association, Wichita, KS 563
Wickersham House Museum (Tanana-Yukon Historical Society), Fairbanks, AK..................24
Wilber Czech Museum, Wilber, NE 875
Wilbur D. May Museum, Reno, NV 882
Wilbur Wright Birthplace & Interpretive Center, Hagerstown, IN..................480
Wilderness Road Regional Museum, Newbern, VA 1519
Will Rogers State Historic Park, Pacific Palisades, CA..................137
Willa Cather Pioneer Memorial and Educational Foundation, Red Cloud, NE 872
Willard House and Clock Museum, Inc., Grafton, MA 685
The William Breman Jewish Heritage Museum, Atlanta, GA..................364
William Clark Market House Museum, Paducah, KY..................582
William Cullen Bryant Homestead, Cummington, MA..................678
William Hammond Mathers Museum, Bloomington, IN..................470
William Heath Davis House Museum administered by Gaslamp Quarter Historical Foundation, San Diego, CA....162
William Henry Harrison Mansion, Grouseland, Vincennes, IN..................503
William J. Clinton Presidential Library & Museum, Little Rock, AR..................63
William King Regional Arts Center, Abingdon, VA..................1491

William McKinley Presidential Library & Museum, Canton, OH..................1146
William Otis Sawtelle Collections and Research Center, Bar Harbor, ME..........606
William S. Hart County Park & Museum, Newhall, CA..................130
William Weston Clarke Emison Museum of Art, Greencastle, IN..................479
Williams College Museum of Art, Williamstown, MA..................719
Williamson County Historical Society, Marion, IL..................444
Willowbrook Museum Village, Newfield, ME..................616
Wilmette Historical Museum, Wilmette, IL..................466
Wilson Historical Museum, Wilson, NY....1086
Wilton Historical Museums, Wilton, CT......267
Wilton House Museum, Richmond, VA.....1534
Winchendon Historical Society, Inc., Winchendon, MA..................720
Winchester-Frederick County Historical Society, Inc., Winchester, VA..................1546
Windham Textile and History Museum (The Mill Museum), Willimantic, CT 267
Winedale, Center for American History, University of Texas at Austin, Round Top, TX..................1446
Wing Luke Asian Museum, Seattle, WA...1569
Winnetka Historical Society, Winnetka, IL..................466
Winterthur Museum & Country Estate, Winterthur, DE..................274
Wisconsin Historical Museum, Madison, WI..................1606
Wiseman & FireHouse Galleries, Rogue Community College, Grants Pass, OR ..1225
Wistariahurst Museum, Holyoke, MA..........687
Witte Museum, San Antonio, TX 1451
Wolcott House Museum Complex, Maumee, OH..................1175
Wolfeboro Historical Society, Wolfeboro, NH..................897
Woodbine International Fire Museum, Woodbine, GA..................392
Woodburn Historic House, Pendleton, SC .1339
Woodlawn Museum/The Black House, Ellsworth, ME..................610
Woodlawn Plantation Museum, Alexandria, VA..................1494
Woodmere Art Museum, Philadelphia, PA.1289
Woodrow Wilson House, Washington, DC..................294
Woodrow Wilson Presidential Library at His Birthplace, Staunton, VA..................1537
Woodson County Historical Society, Yates Center, KS..................564
Woodstock Historical Society, Inc., Woodstock, CT..................268
Woodstock Historical Society, Inc., Woodstock, VT..................1491
Woolaroc Museum, Bartlesville, OK..........1197
Working Men's Institute, New Harmony, IN..................495
World Figure Skating Museum & Hall of Fame, Colorado Springs, CO..................208
Wright Museum, Wolfeboro, NH..................897
Wright Museum of Art, Beloit College, Beloit, WI..................1592
Wright's Ferry Mansion, Columbia, PA 1248
Wupatki National Monument, Flagstaff, AZ..................34
Wyandotte County Museum, Bonner Springs, KS..................534
The Wyckoff Farmhouse Museum, Brooklyn, NY..................970
The Wyman Tavern, Keene, NH..................890
Wyoming Pioneer Memorial Museum, Douglas, WY..................1632
Wyoming State Museum, Cheyenne, WY..1631

Yakima Valley Museum and Historical Association, Yakima, WA..................1579

Yates County Genealogical and Historical Society and Oliver House Museum and L. Caroline Underwood Museum, Penn Yan, NY..................1052
Ybor City Museum State Park, Tampa, FL..................351
Yellow Medicine County Historical Society and Museum, Granite Falls, MN..................777
Yellowstone Art Museum, Billings, MT.......842
Yellowstone Gateway Museum of Park County, Livingston, MT..................850
Yeshiva University Museum at the Center for Jewish History, New York, NY........1041
Yolo County Historical Museum, Woodland, CA..................199
Yorktown Historical Museum, Yorktown, TX..................1462
Ypsilanti Historical Museum, Ypsilanti, MI..................767
Yuma Crossing State Historic Park, Yuma, AZ..................54

Z. Taylor Brown-Sarah Dorsey House, Midland, TX..................1439
Zalud House, Porterville, CA..................144
Zanesville Art Center, Zanesville, OH........1194
Zebulon B. Vance Birthplace State Historic Site, Weaverville, NC..................1122
Zelienople Historical Society, Zelienople, PA..................1309
Ziibiwing Center of Anishinabe Culture & Lifeways, Mount Pleasant, MI 757
Zoar State Memorial, Zoar, OH..................1194

Decorative Arts

A.K.C. Museum of The Dog, Saint Louis, MO..................831
Abington Art Center, Jenkintown, PA 1263
Ace of Clubs House, Texarkana, TX............1455
Ackland Art Museum, Chapel Hill, NC 1093
Adam Thoroughgood House, Virginia Beach, VA..................1541
Adams Museum & House, Deadwood, SD..................1346
Adams National Historical Park, Quincy, MA..................704
Adan E. Treganza Anthropology Museum, Dept. of Anthropology, San Francisco State University, San Francisco, CA..................162
Addison Gallery of American Art, Andover, MA..................659
Admiral Nimitz National Museum of the Pacific War, Fredericksburg, TX....1419
Adsmore Museum, Princeton, KY..................583
African Art Museum of the S.M.A. Fathers, Tenafly, NJ..................926
Alaska Museum of Natural History, Anchorage, AK..................21
Albany Institute of History & Art, Albany, NY..................954
Albany Museum of Art, Albany, GA............355
Albion Academy Historical Museum, Edgerton, WI..................1596
Albion College Department of Art and Art History, Albion, MI..................722
The Albrecht-Kemper Museum of Art, Saint Joseph, MO..................830
Albuquerque Museum, Albuquerque, NM....932
Alden B. Dow Museum of Science and Art of the Midland Center for the Arts, Midland, MI..................755
Alexander Brest Museum and Gallery, Jacksonville, FL..................313
Alexander Ramsey House, Minnesota Historical Society, Saint Paul, MN..........789
Alice Austen House Museum, Staten Island, NY..................1072
Alice C. Sabatini Gallery-Topeka and Shawnee County Public Library, Topeka, KS..................558

Decorative Arts—Continued

The Alice T. Miner Colonial Collection, Chazy, NY 977

Allaire Village Inc., Farmingdale, NJ 903

Allegheny Highlands Arts & Crafts Center, Inc., Clifton Forge, VA 1501

Allegheny Portage Railroad National Historic Site and Johnstown Flood National Memorial, Gallitzin, PA 1255

Allen County Museum, Lima, OH 1172

Allen R. Hite Art Institute, Louisville, KY.........575

Allentown Art Museum, Allentown, PA 1239

Alva deMars Megan Chapel Art Center, Manchester, NH.........891

Amelia Earhart Birthplace Museum, Atchison, KS.........532

American Academy of Arts and Letters, New York, NY.........1018

American Catholic Historical Society, Philadelphia, PA 1276

American Craft Museum, New York, NY ..1018

American Folk Art Museum, New York, NY.........1018

American Hungarian Foundation/Museum of the American Hungarian Foundation, New Brunswick, NJ 915

American Independence Museum, Exeter, NH.........887

American Jewish Historical Society, New York, NY.........1019

American Labor Museum, Botto House National Landmark, Haledon, NJ 906

American Museum of Asmat Art, Saint Paul, MN 789

The American Museum of Fly Fishing, Manchester, VT 1481

American Museum of Straw Art, Long Beach, CA 110

American Numismatic Association Money Museum, Colorado Springs, CO.........206

American Swedish Historical Foundation & Museum, Philadelphia, PA 1276

American Swedish Institute, Minneapolis, MN.........781

American Visionary Art Museum, Baltimore, MD.........629

America's Ice Cream & Dairy Museum, Medina, OH 1175

America's National Music Museum, Vermillion, SD.........1358

Amherst County Museum & Historical Society, Amherst, VA 1495

Amherst History Museum at the Strong House - Amherst Historical Society, Amherst, MA.........658

Amherst Museum, Amherst, NY 957

Amity and Woodbridge Historical Society, Woodbridge, CT 268

Amory Regional Museum, Amory, MS.........797

Anderson/Abruzzo Albuquerque International Balloon Museum, Albuquerque, NM.........933

Anderson County Historical Museum, Garnett, KS.........541

Andover Historical Society, Andover, MA..660

Andrew County Museum & Historical Society, Savannah, MO.........838

Andrew J. Blackbird Museum, Harbor Springs, MI.........745

Andrew Low House, Savannah, GA 384

Angels Attic Museum, Santa Monica, CA ...183

Anoka County Historical Society, Anoka, MN.........767

The Antiquarian and Landmarks Society, Inc., Hartford, CT.........244

Appalachian Center For Craft, Smithville, TN 1384

The Apple Trees Museum, Burlington, IA..506

Appleton Museum of Art, Ocala, FL.........330

APVA's John Marshall House, Richmond, VA 1528

Arab American National Museum, Dearborn, MI.........733

Arbor Lodge State Historical Park, Nebraska City, NE.........868

Archives Museum, Temple Mickve Israel, Savannah, GA.........384

Archives of J.S.G. Boggs, Brandon, FL....298

Arizona State Parks Board, Phoenix, AZ 39

Arizona State University Art Museum, Tempe, AZ.........45

The Arkansas Arts Center, Little Rock, AR.........61

Arkansas State University Museum, Jonesboro, AR.........60

Arlington, Birmingham, AL.........4

The Arlington Historical Society, Arlington, MA 660

Arlington House, The Robert E. Lee Memorial, Arlington, VA.........1495

Armenian Library and Museum of America, Watertown, MA 716

Arnot Art Museum, Elmira, NY 987

Arrowmont School of Arts & Crafts, Gatlinburg, TN.........1365

Art Association of Randolph County, Inc., Union City, IN.........501

The Art Center at Fuller Lodge, Los Alamos, NM 942

Art Center of Battle Creek, Battle Creek, MI.........726

Art Center Sarasota, Inc, Sarasota, FL.........343

Art Complex Museum, Duxbury, MA.........680

The Art Institute of Chicago, Chicago, IL ...418

Art Museum of Greater Lafayette, Lafayette, IN.........487

Art Museum of The University of Memphis, Memphis, TN 1372

Art Museum of Western Virginia, Roanoke, VA.........1534

The Art Studio, Inc., Beaumont, TX 1393

The Arthur J. Moore Methodist Museum, Saint Simons Island, GA.........383

Arthur M. Sackler Gallery, Washington, DC.........276

Arthur Ross Gallery, University of Pennsylvania, Philadelphia, PA.........1276

Ash Lawn-Highland, Charlottesville, VA ...1498

Asheville Art Museum, Asheville, NC 1088

Ashton Villa & The Heritage Visitor Center, Galveston, TX.........1420

Asian Art Museum of San Francisco, Chong-Moon Lee Center for Asian Art and Culture, San Francisco, CA 163

Asian Arts & Culture Center, Towson University, Towson, MD 655

Association for the Preservation of Tennessee Antiquities, Nashville, TN 1377

Astor House Museum, Golden, CO.........219

The Athenaeum of Philadelphia, Philadelphia, PA.........1276

Atlanta Historical Society, Atlanta, GA.........358

Atlantic Wildfowl Heritage Museum, Virginia Beach, VA.........1541

Attleboro Arts Museum, Attleboro, MA.......661

Atwater Kent Museum of Philadelphia, Philadelphia, PA.........1276

Atwood House Museum, Home of Chatham Historical Society, Chatham, MA.........675

Audrain Historical Museum, Graceland, Mexico, MO.........827

Audubon County Historical Society, Exira, IA.........517

Audubon House & Tropical Gardens, Key West, FL.........317

Augustana College Art Museum, Rock Island, IL.........453

Aurora Historical Society, Aurora, IL.........411

Aurora Historical Society, Aurora, OH.......1140

Aurora Public Art Commission, Aurora, IL.........411

Autry National Center of the American West, Los Angeles, CA 112

The AXA Gallery, New York, NY.........1021

Bailey House Museum - Maui Historical Society, Wailuku, HI 402

Ball State University Museum of Art, Muncie, IN.........492

Baltimore County Historical Society, Cockeysville, MD.........640

The Baltimore Museum of Art, Baltimore, MD.........630

Bangor Museum & Center for History, Bangor, ME.........604

Banning Residence Museum, Wilmington, CA 198

The Bard Graduate Center for Studies in the Decorative Arts, Design, & Culture, New York, NY.........1021

Barnes Foundation, Merion, PA.........1271

Barnes Museum, Southington, CT.........260

The Barnum Museum, Bridgeport, CT.........235

Barnwell County Museum, Barnwell, SC ..1321

Barrett House, Forest Hall, New Ipswich, NH.........892

Bartholomew County Historical Society, Columbus, IN.........472

Barton Museum, Wilson, NC.........1124

Bartow-Pell Mansion Museum, Carriage House & Gardens, Bronx, NY.........964

Bass Museum of Art, Miami Beach, FL 326

Bassett Hall, Williamsburg, VA.........1544

Bates-Scofield Homestead, The Darien Historical Society, Darien, CT.........238

Batsto Village, Hammonton, NJ 907

Battle of Lexington State Historic Site, Lexington, MO.........826

Baum Gallery of Fine Art, University of Central Arkansas, Conway, AR.........56

Baycrafters, Inc., Bay Village, OH 1141

Bayou Bend Collection and Gardens, Houston, TX.........1425

The Bead Museum, Glendale, AZ.........35

Beard Gallery, Norton, MA 700

Beauchamp Newman Museum, Elizabeth, WV.........1581

Beauport, Sleeper-McCann House, Gloucester, MA.........684

Beauvoir, The Jefferson Davis Home and Presidential Library, Biloxi, MS 798

Bedingfield Inn Museum, Lumpkin, GA.....376

Beehive House, Salt Lake City, UT 1470

Behringer-Crawford Museum, Covington, KY.........567

Belair Mansion, Bowie, MD.........638

Belcourt Castle, Newport, RI.........1313

Belle Grove Plantation, Middletown, VA....1517

Belle Meade Plantation, Nashville, TN 1377

Bellflower Historical and Genealogical Society, Bellflower, IL.........413

Bellingrath Gardens & Home, Theodore, AL.........18

Ben Shahn Galleries at William Paterson University of New Jersey, Wayne, NJ 929

Benjamin Harrison Presidential Site, Indianapolis, IN 481

Bennington Battlefield State Historic Site, Walloomsac, NY.........1081

The Bennington Museum, Bennington, VT.........1476

Berea College, Doris Ulmann Galleries, Berea, KY.........565

Bergen Museum of Art & Science, Paramus, NJ.........919

Bergen Museum of Local History, Bergen, NY.........962

Bergstrom-Mahler Museum, Neenah, WI...1614

Berkeley Plantation, Charles City, VA 1498

Berkshire County Historical Society, Inc. - Arrowhead, Pittsfield, MA.........702

Berlin Art and Historical Collections, Berlin, MA......662
Bernard Judaica Museum, Congregation Emanu-El of the City of New York, New York, NY......1021
Bethel Historical Society Regional History Center, Bethel, ME......606
Bethlehem Historical Association, Selkirk, NY......1068
Betsey Williams Cottage, Providence, RI..1316
Betsy Ross House and Flag Museum, Philadelphia, PA......1277
Beverly Historical Society and Museum, Beverly, MA......662
Bicentennial Art Center & Museum, Paris, IL......449
The Bidwell House Museum, Monterey, MA......695
Biedenharn Museum & Gardens, Monroe, LA......592
Bigelow House Museum, Olympia, WA......1560
Biggs Museum of American Art, Dover, DE......269
Biltmore Estate, Asheville, NC......1089
Biltmore Homespun Shops - Grovewood Gallery, Asheville, NC......1089
Birger Sandzen Memorial Gallery, Lindsborg, KS......549
Birks Museum, Decatur, IL......430
Birmingham Museum of Art, Birmingham, AL......5
Bishop Hill State Historic Site, Bishop Hill, IL......413
Black Heritage Museum, Miami, FL......323
Blackberry Farm's Pioneer Village, Aurora, IL......411
Blackhawk Museum (Behring-Hofmann Educational Institute, Inc.), Danville, CA......89
Blackman House Museum, Snohomish, WA......1570
Blair Museum of Lithophanes, Toledo, OH......1187
Blanton Museum of Art, Austin, TX......1389
Bloomfield Academy Museum, Bloomfield, NY......963
Blount-Bridgers House/Hobson Pittman Memorial Gallery, Tarboro, NC......1121
Blount County Memorial Museum, Oneonta, AL......17
Blue Earth County Historical Society, Mankato, MN......780
Blue Ridge Institute and Museum, Ferrum, VA......1504
Bluff Hall Antebellum Home and Museum, Demopolis, AL......7
Bob Jones University Museum & Gallery, Inc., Greenville, SC......1333
Boca Raton Historical Society, Boca Raton, FL......296
Boca Raton Museum of Art, Boca Raton, FL......296
Boehm Gallery, San Marcos, CA......174
Boise Art Museum, Boise, ID......403
Bolduc House Museum, Sainte Genevieve, MO......837
Bolton Historical Society, Inc., Bolton, MA......663
Bonnet House Museum & Gardens, Fort Lauderdale, FL......306
The Boorman House - The Juneau County Historical Society, Mauston, WI......1608
Boot Hill Museum, Inc., Dodge City, KS....536
Boscobel, Garrison, NY......993
Boston Athenaeum Library, Boston, MA......663
Bowdoin College Museum of Art, Brunswick, ME......607
The Bowne House Historical Society, Flushing, NY......990
Boyhood Home of President Woodrow Wilson, Augusta, GA......365

Bradford Brinton Memorial & Museum, Big Horn, WY......1628
Bradford Historical Society Inc., Bradford, VT......1477
Brand Library & Art Center, Glendale, CA......100
Bread & Puppet Museum, Glover, VT......1479
Brec's Magnolia Mound Plantation, Baton Rouge, LA......585
Brevard Museum of Art and Science, Inc., Melbourne, FL......323
Brick Store Museum, Kennebunk, ME......612
Bridge Hampton Historical Society, Bridgehampton, NY......964
Bridgton Historical Society, Bridgton, ME......607
Brooklyn Children's Museum, Brooklyn, NY......968
The Brooklyn Historical Society, Brooklyn, NY......968
Brooklyn Museum, Brooklyn, NY......968
The Broome County Historical Society, Binghamton, NY......962
Broward County Historical Commission, Fort Lauderdale, FL......307
Brown County Historical Society, New Ulm, MN......785
Brownsville Museum of Fine Art - Brownsville Art League, Brownsville, TX......1398
Brownville Historical Society Museum, Brownville, NE......858
Bruce Museum, Greenwich, CT......243
Brucemore, Cedar Rapids, IA......509
Brueckner Museum of Starr Commonwealth, Albion, MI......723
Brunnier Art Museum, Ames, IA......504
Buccleuch Mansion, New Brunswick, NJ....915
Buchanan Center for the Arts, Monmouth, IL......445
Buechel Memorial Lakota Museum, Saint Francis, SD......1355
Bulloch Hall, Roswell, GA......382
Burchfield-Penney Art Center, Buffalo, NY......973
Bureau County Historical Society Museum, Princeton, IL......452
Burlington County Historical Society, Burlington, NJ......898
Burnham Tavern, Machias, ME......614
Butler County Museum, Hamilton, OH......1168
Butte-Silver Bow Arts Chateau, Butte, MT......843
Byers-Evans House Museum, Denver, CO......209

Cahoon Museum of American Art, Cotuit, MA......677
California African-American Museum, Los Angeles, CA......113
California Center for the Arts, Escondido, Escondido, CA......93
California Heritage Museum, Santa Monica, CA......183
California Historical Society, San Francisco, CA......163
California State Capitol Museum, Sacramento, CA......151
Cambridge Historical Society, Cambridge, MA......672
Cambridge Museum, Cambridge, NE......858
Campus Martius Museum, Marietta, OH......1173
Canterbury Shaker Village, Inc., Canterbury, NH......883
The Canton Museum of Art, Canton, OH..1145
Cape Ann Historical Museum, Gloucester, MA......684
Cape Cod Museum of Art, Dennis, MA......680
Cape May County Historical Museum and Genealogical Society, Cape May Court House, NJ......900
Capitola Historical Museum, Capitola, CA......81

Cappon & Settlers House Museums, Holland, MI......746
Captain Forbes House Museum, Milton, MA......695
Captain John Wilson House, Cohasset, MA......676
Captain Nathaniel B. Palmer House - Home of the Discoverer of Antarctica, Stonington, CT......261
Caramoor Center for Music & the Arts, Inc., Katonah, NY......1006
Carleton College Art Gallery, Northfield, MN......785
Carnegie Center for Art & History, New Albany, IN......493
Carnton Plantation, Franklin, TN......1365
The Carter House Association, Inc., Franklin, TN......1365
Caryl House and Fisher Barn, Dover, MA...680
Casa Adobe de San Rafael, Glendale, CA...100
The Casa del Herrero Foundation, Santa Barbara, CA......178
Cass County Historical Society Museum, Plattsmouth, NE......872
Castleton Historical Society, Castleton, VT......1478
Catalina Island Museum Society, Inc., Avalon, CA......73
Cedar Rapids Museum of Art, Cedar Rapids, IA......509
Centennial Village Museum, Greeley, CO...221
The Center for Western Studies, Sioux Falls, SD......1356
Centerville Historical Museum, Centerville, MA......675
Centerville - Washington Township Historical Society & Asahel Wright Community Center, Centerville, OH......1146
Centerville - Washington Township Historical Society & Walton House Museum, Centerville, OH......1147
Central City Opera House Association, Central City, CO......205
Central Park Conservancy, New York, NY......1022
Centre County Library and Historical Museum, Bellefonte, PA......1241
Centre Hill Museum (The Petersburg Museums), Petersburg, VA......1524
Century Village Museum, Burton, OH......1144
Champaign County Historical Museum, Champaign, IL......416
Chancellor Robert R. Livingston Masonic Library & Museum, New York, NY......1022
Chandler Museum, Chandler, AZ......31
Charles A. Grignon Mansion, Kaukauna, WI......1601
Charles A. Weyerhaeuser Memorial Museum, Little Falls, MN......779
Charles Allis Art Museum, Milwaukee, WI......1610
The Charles Hosmer Morse Museum of American Art, Winter Park, FL......354
Chase Home Museum of Utah Folk Arts, Salt Lake City, UT......1470
Chatillon-DeMenil Mansion, Saint Louis, MO......832
Chattahoochee Valley Art Museum, LaGrange, GA......375
Chautauqua County Historical Society, McClurg Museum, Westfield, NY......1086
Chazen Museum of Art, Madison, WI......1604
Cheekwood-Tennessee Botanical Garden & Museum of Art, Nashville, TN......1378
Cheraw Lyceum Museum, Cheraw, SC......1327
Cherry County Historical Society, Valentine, NE......874
Cherry Valley Museum, Cherry Valley, NY......978
Chester Art Guild, Chester, VT......1478
Chester County Historical Society, West Chester, PA......1307

Decorative Arts–Continued

Chesterfield County Museum, Chesterfield, VA 1501

Chesterwood, Stockbridge, MA 711

Chetopa Historical Museum, Chetopa, KS...535

The Chicago Athenaeum: Museum of Architecture and Design, Galena, IL 436

Chicago Botanic Garden, Glencoe, IL 438

Chicago Children's Museum, Chicago, IL....419

Chicago Cultural Center, Chicago, IL 419

Chicago History Museum, Chicago, IL........419

Chicago Zoological Park (Brookfield Zoo), Brookfield, IL 414

Chief Plenty Coups Museum, Pryor, MT.....852

Children's Museum/Detroit Public Schools, Detroit, MI 735

The Children's Museum of Indianapolis, Indianapolis, IN 481

Children's Museum of Los Angeles, Van Nuys, CA 194

The Children's Museum of Portsmouth, Portsmouth, NH 894

Children's Museum of Tacoma, Tacoma, WA 1573

Chimney Point State Historic Site, Addison, VT 1475

Chinese American Museum, Los Angeles, CA 114

Chinese Culture Center of San Francisco, San Francisco, CA 164

Chinese Joss House Museum, Evanston, WY 1632

Chinqua-Penn Plantation, Reidsville, NC...1117

Chrysler Museum of Art, Norfolk, VA.......1521

Church-Waddel-Brumby House Museum & Athens Welcome Center, Athens, GA 356

Cigna Museum and Art Collection, Philadelphia, PA 1277

Cincinnati Art Museum, Cincinnati, OH ...1148

City Island Nautical Museum, Bronx, NY...965

City Museum, Saint Louis, MO..................832

City of Bowie Museums, Bowie, MD..........638

Clara Barton National Historic Site, Glen Echo, MD 645

Clarion County Historical Society, Sutton-Ditz House Museum, Clarion, PA 1247

Clarke Historical Museum, Eureka, CA 94

Clarke House Museum, Chicago, IL 420

Clermont State Historic Site, Clermont, NY 979

Cleveland Artists Foundation at Beck Center for the Arts, Lakewood, OH 1170

The Cleveland Museum of Art, Cleveland, OH 1152

Cleveland State University Art Gallery, Cleveland, OH 1153

Clinton Academy, East Hampton, NY..........985

Clinton County Historical Society, Wilmington, OH 1191

Cliveden of the National Trust, Philadelphia, PA 1278

The Cloisters, New York, NY 1023

Clough-Hanson Gallery, Rhodes College, Memphis, TN 1372

Coachella Valley Museum and Cultural Center, Indio, CA 104

Coal Miners' Museum/Van Lear Historical Society, Inc., Van Lear, KY 584

Coastal Discovery Museum, Hilton Head Island, SC 1335

Coe Hall, Oyster Bay, NY 1049

Coffin House, Newbury, MA 697

Colby College Museum of Art, Waterville, ME.......................................624

College Park Aviation Museum, College Park, MD 641

Colonial Industrial Quarter, Bethlehem, PA 1242

Colonial National Historical Park: Jamestown & Yorktown, Yorktown, VA 1546

Colonial Williamsburg, Williamsburg, VA .1544

Colorado Historical Society, Denver, CO.....210

Colorado Springs Museum, Colorado Springs, CO 206

Columbia County Historical Society, Inc., Kinderhook, NY 1007

Columbia Gorge Discovery Center and Wasco County Museum, The Dalles, OR 1237

Columbia Museum of Art, Columbia, SC..1329

The Columbian Theatre, Museum & Art Center, Wamego, KS 560

Columbus Chapel, Boal Mansion Museum, Boalsburg, PA 1244

The Columbus Museum, Columbus, GA 368

Columbus Museum of Art, Columbus, OH 1157

The Commonwealth Museum, Boston, MA 665

Community Council for the Arts, Kinston, NC 1108

Community Memorial Museum of Sutter County, Yuba City, CA 200

Concord Art Association, Concord, MA 676

Concord Museum, Concord, MA..................676

Confederate Memorial Hall-Bleak House, Knoxville, TN 1369

Conklin Reed Organ & History Museum, Hanover, MI 745

Connecticut Audubon Birdcraft Museum, Fairfield, CT..240

Connecticut Historical Society, Hartford, CT 244

Conrad Mansion National Historic Site Museum, Kalispell, MT 850

Constitution Island Association, West Point, NY 1085

The Contemporary Arts Center, Cincinnati, OH 1150

Contemporary Crafts Museum & Gallery, Portland, OR 1230

Cooper-Hewitt National Design Museum, Smithsonian Institution, New York, NY 1023

Coos Art Museum, Coos Bay, OR.............1222

Coos Historical & Maritime Museum, North Bend, OR 1229

Copia: The American Center for Wine, Food & the Arts, Napa, CA 129

Copshaholm House Museum & Historic Oliver Gardens, South Bend, IN.............499

The Corcoran Gallery of Art, Washington, DC.....................................277

The Corning Museum of Glass, Corning, NY 981

Coronado State Monument, Bernalillo, NM 937

Cortland County Historical Society, Cortland, NY 982

Cow Neck Peninsula Historical Society Sands-Willets House, Port Washington, NY 1053

Cracker Trail Museum, Zolfo Springs, FL...355

Craft Alliance, Saint Louis, MO..................833

Craft and Folk Art Museum - CAFAM, Los Angeles, CA 114

Craftsmen's Guild of Mississippi, Jackson, MS 802

Cranbrook Art Museum, Bloomfield Hills, MI 730

Cranbrook House and Gardens Auxiliary, Bloomfield Hills, MI 730

Cranbury Historical & Preservation Society, Cranbury, NJ 902

Cravens House, Lookout Mountain, TN 1371

Crawford County Historical Museum, Pittsburg, KS 556

Crescent Bend/The Armstrong-Lockett House and The William P. Toms Memorial Gardens, Knoxville, TN 1369

Crocker Art Museum, Sacramento, CA........152

Crocker House, Mount Clemens, MI...........756

Crook County Museum & Art Gallery, Sundance, WY 1638

Crow Wing County Historical Society, Brainerd, MN.......................................769

Crowley Art Association & Gallery, Crowley, LA 588

Culbertson Mansion State Historic Site, New Albany, IN 493

Culbertson Museum, Culbertson, MT 845

Cumberland Island National Seashore, Saint Marys, GA 382

Cummer Museum of Art and Gardens, Jacksonville, FL 314

Cuneo Museum & Gardens, Vernon Hills, IL 463

Cupola House, Egg Harbor, WI.................1596

The Currier Museum of Art, Manchester, NH 891

DAAP Galleries, Cincinnati, OH 1150

DAR John Strong Mansion Museum, Addison, VT 1475

D.R. Barker Historical Museum, Fredonia, NY 992

Dahesh Museum of Art, New York, NY ...1024

The Dallas Center for Contemporary Art - The Dallas Contemporary, Dallas, TX 1404

Dallas Heritage Village at Old City Park, Dallas, TX 1405

Dallas Museum of Art, Dallas, TX............1405

Dalton Galleries, Decatur, GA 370

The Dana-Thomas House State Historic Site, Springfield, IL 458

The Danbury Museum & Historical Society, Danbury, CT 238

Danforth Museum of Art, Framingham, MA 683

Daniel Boone Home and Boonesfield Village, Lindenwood University, Defiance, MO...814

Danvers Historical Society, Danvers, MA....678

Danville Museum of Fine Arts & History, Danville, VA 1502

Daughters of the American Revolution Museum, Washington, DC 277

Daughters of Utah Pioneers Pioneer Memorial Museum & International Society Daughters of Utah Pioneers, Salt Lake City, UT 1471

Daum Museum of Contemporary Art, Sedalia, MO...838

Daura Gallery, Lynchburg, VA..................1515

Davenport House Museum, Savannah, GA 384

David Conklin Farmhouse, Huntington, NY 1000

The David Davis Mansion, Bloomington, IL 413

David Strawn Art Gallery, Jacksonville, IL 440

Davis Museum and Cultural Center, Wellesley, MA 716

Dawson Springs Museum and Art Center, Inc., Dawson Springs, KY 568

Dayton Art Institute, Dayton, OH..............1161

Dayton Historical Depot Society, Dayton, WA 1552

De Saisset Museum, Santa Clara, CA 180

De Smet Depot Museum, De Smet, SD.....1346

Dearborn Historical Museum, Dearborn, MI 733

Decatur House Museum, Washington, DC...277

The Decorative Arts Center of Ohio, Lancaster, OH 1171

Decorative Arts Collection, Inc. Museum of Decorative Painting, Wichita, KS 561

Dedham Historical Society Museum, Dedham, MA 679

Degenhart Paperweight & Glass Museum, Inc., Cambridge, OH 1144

The DeLand Museum of Art, De Land, FL ...303
Delaware Art Museum, Wilmington, DE 273
Delaware Division of Historical & Cultural Affairs, Dover, DE 269
Deming Luna Mimbres Museum, Deming, NM ...939
Denison Museum, Granville, OH ...1167
Dennys River Historical Society, Dennysville, ME ...609
Denver Art Museum, Denver, CO ...210
Denver Museum of Miniatures, Dolls and Toys, Denver, CO ...211
Department of the Treasury, Washington, DC ...278
DePree Art Center & Gallery, Holland, MI ...746
The Detroit Institute of Arts, Detroit, MI ...736
Detroit Zoo, Royal Oak, MI ...762
Deutschheim State Historic Site, Hermann, MO ...817
Dewey Hotel Museum, Dewey, OK ...1199
DeWitt Wallace Decorative Arts Museum, Williamsburg, VA ...1545
Dey Mansion/Washington's Headquarters Museum, Wayne, NJ ...929
Dinsmore Homestead Foundation, Burlington, KY ...566
Diplomatic Reception Rooms, Department of State, Washington, DC 278
The Discovery Museum, Inc., Bridgeport, CT ...236
The Dixon Gallery and Gardens, Memphis, TN ...1372
Dr. Daniel W. Kissam House, Huntington, NY ...1000
Dodge County Historical Society Museum, Beaver Dam, WI ...1591
Donkey Milk House, Historic Home, Key West, FL ...317
Dorothea B. Hoover Historical Museum, Joplin, MO ...819
The Downers Grove Park District Museum, Downers Grove, IL ...431
Drayton Hall, Charleston, SC ...1325
Drummond Home, Hominy, OK ...1203
Dublin-Laurens Museum, Dublin, GA ...370
Dubuque Museum of Art, Dubuque, IA ...516
Duluth Art Institute, Duluth, MN ...772
Dumbarton House, Washington, DC ...278
Dumbarton Oaks Research Library & Collections, Washington, DC ...278
The Duncan Gallery of Art, De Land, FL ...304
Dusable Museum of African-American History, Inc., Chicago, IL ...420
Duxbury Rural and Historical Society, Inc., Duxbury, MA ...681
Dwight D. Eisenhower Library-Museum, Abilene, KS ...531
Dyckman Farmhouse Museum and Park, New York, NY ...1025

East Hampton Historical Society, Inc., East Hampton, NY ...985
East Hampton Town Marine Museum, Amagansett, NY ...957
East Jersey Olde Towne, Piscataway, NJ ...921
East-West Center, Honolulu, HI ...394
Eastchester Historical Society - 1835 Marble Schoolhouse, Bronxville, NY ...967
The Ebenezer Maxwell Mansion, Inc., Philadelphia, PA ...1278
Edison National Historic Site, West Orange, NJ ...930
Edsel & Eleanor Ford House, Grosse Pointe Shores, MI ...745
Edward-Dean Museum and Gardens, Cherry Valley, CA ...82
Egan Maritime Foundation, Nantucket, MA ...695
The 1890 House-Museum & Center for Arts, Cortland, NY ...983

Eisenhower National Historic Site, Gettysburg, PA ...1255
El Paso Museum of History, El Paso, TX ..1412
El Rancho de Las Golondrinas Museum, Santa Fe, NM ...947
Elbert Hubbard-Roycroft Museum, East Aurora, NY ...985
Eldridge Street Project, New York, NY ...1025
Elizabeth Myers Mitchell Art Gallery at St. John's College, Annapolis, MD ...627
Elliott Museum, Stuart, FL ...346
Ellis County Museum, Inc., Waxahachie, TX ...1460
Ellwood House Museum, DeKalb, IL ...429
Elmhurst Art Museum, Elmhurst, IL ...433
Elverhoj Museum of History and Art, Solvang, CA ...187
Emily Dickinson Museum: The Homestead and The Evergreens, Amherst, MA ...658
The Endowment Fund of the Phi Kappa Psi Fraternity-Heritage Hall, Indianapolis, IN ...482
Éphrata Cloister, Ephrata, PA ...1251
Erie Art Museum, Erie, PA ...1252
Erie County History Center & Cashier's House, Erie, PA ...1252
The Esther Thomas Atkinson Museum, Hampden-Sydney, VA ...1509
Ethnic Heritage Museum, Rockford, IL ...455
Eugene Field House and St. Louis Toy Museum, Saint Louis, MO ...833
Eureka School House, Springfield, VT ...1487
Eustis Historical Museum & Preservation Society, Inc., Eustis, FL ...306
Evanston Historical Society and Charles Gates Dawes House, Evanston, IL ...434
Evergreen House, The Johns Hopkins University, Baltimore, MD ...632
Everhart Museum: Natural History, Science and Art, Scranton, PA ...1298
Exploris, Raleigh, NC ...1115

The Fabric Workshop and Museum, Philadelphia, PA ...1279
Fairfax Museum & Visitor Center, Fairfax, VA ...1503
Fairfield County Museum, Winnsboro, SC ...1343
Fairfield Historical Society, Fairfield, CT ...241
Fall River County Historical Museum, Hot Springs, SD ...1348
Fall River Historical Society Museum, Fall River, MA ...682
Fallingwater, Mill Run, PA ...1272
Farmamerica, The Minnesota Agricultural Interpretive Center, Waseca, MN ...796
The Farmers' Museum, Inc., Cooperstown, NY ...980
Farmington Historic Home, Louisville, KY ...575
Farragut Folklife Museum, Farragut, TN ...1364
Farrar-Mansur House & Old Mill Museum, Weston, VT ...1490
Faulkner County Museum, Conway, AR ...56
Favell Museum Inc., Klamath Falls, OR ...1227
Fayette Art Museum, Fayette, AL ...9
Federal Hall National Memorial, New York, NY ...1025
Fenton History Center-Museum & Library, Jamestown, NY ...1005
Festival-Institute, James Dick Foundation, Round Top, TX ...1446
Fick Fossil & History Museum, Oakley, KS ...554
Filoli Center, Woodside, CA ...199
The Filson Historical Society, Inc., Louisville, KY ...576
Fine Arts Center for New River Valley, Pulaski, VA ...1526
Fine Arts Collection, Luther College, Decorah, IA ...513

The Fine Arts Museums of San Francisco, de Young Museum, San Francisco, CA ...165
The Fine Arts Museums of San Francisco, Legion of Honor, San Francisco, CA ...165
Firehouse Art Gallery, Nassau Community College, Garden City, NY ...992
Firelands Historical Society Museum, Norwalk, OH ...1180
First White House of the Confederacy, Montgomery, AL ...16
Fisher Gallery, University of Southern California, Los Angeles, CA ...115
The Fisk University Galleries, Nashville, TN ...1379
Fitchburg Art Museum, Fitchburg, MA ...683
The Five Civilized Tribes Museum, Muskogee, OK ...1205
Flagler Museum, Palm Beach, FL ...333
Flaten Art Museum of St. Olaf College, Northfield, MN ...785
Flint Institute of Arts, Flint, MI ...741
Florence Griswold Museum, Old Lyme, CT ...258
The Florence McLeod Hazard Museum, Columbus, MS ...800
Florence Museum of Art, Science & History and the Florence Railroad Museum, Florence, SC ...1332
Florewood State Park, Greenwood, MS ...801
Florida State University Museum of Fine Arts, Tallahassee, FL ...347
The Fluvanna County Historical Society Old Stone Jail Museum, Palmyra, VA ...1524
Folger Shakespeare Library, Washington, DC ...278
The Folsom House Museum, Taylors Falls, MN ...794
Fonthill Museum of the Bucks County Historical Society, Doylestown, PA ...1249
Ford's Theatre National Historic Site (Lincoln Museum), Washington, DC ...279
Forest Lawn Museum, Glendale, CA ...100
The Forges and Manor of Ringwood, Ringwood, NJ ...923
Fort Bend Museum Association, Richmond, TX ...1445
Fort Benton Museum of the Upper Missouri, Fort Benton, MT ...846
Fort Collins Museum, Fort Collins, CO ...217
Fort Concho National Historic Landmark, San Angelo, TX ...1447
Fort Crawford Museum, Prairie du Chien, WI ...1618
Fort Davis National Historic Site, Fort Davis, TX ...1414
Fort Dix Museum, Fort Dix, NJ ...904
Fort Hartsuff State Historical Park, Burwell, NE ...858
Fort Hunter Mansion & Park, Harrisburg, PA ...1258
Fort Lauderdale Historical Society, Fort Lauderdale, FL ...307
Fort St. Joseph Museum, Niles, MI ...758
Fort Scott National Historic Site, Fort Scott, KS ...540
Fort Smith Art Center, Fort Smith, AR ...57
Fort Ward Museum and Historic Site, Alexandria, VA ...1492
45th Infantry Division Museum, Oklahoma City, OK ...1207
Foster Gallery, University of Wisconsin-Eau Claire, Eau Claire, WI ..1596
Fosterfields Living Historical Farm, Morristown, NJ ...913
Framingham Historical Society & Museum, Framingham, MA ...683
Frances Willard House Museum, Evanston, IL ...434
Frances Young Tang Teaching Museum and Art Gallery, Saratoga Springs, NY .1064

Decorative Arts—Continued

Frank Chiarenza Museum of Glass, Meriden, CT................................248

Frank H. McClung Museum, Knoxville, TN...1370

Frank Lloyd Wright Home and Studio, Oak Park, IL.................................448

Frank Lloyd Wright's Pope-Leighey House, Alexandria, VA.................1492

Franklin County Old Jail Museum, Winchester, TN.................................1385

Franklin D. Roosevelt Presidential Library-Museum, Hyde Park, NY 1002

Fraunces Tavern Museum, New York, NY...1025

Fred Dana Marsh Museum, Ormond Beach, FL..333

Frederic Remington Art Museum, Ogdensburg, NY...............................1044

Frederick C. Robie House, Chicago, IL.......420

Frederick R. Weisman Art Museum, Minneapolis, MN................................781

Frederick R. Weisman Museum of Art, Malibu, CA..123

Fredericksburg Area Museum & Cultural Center, Inc., Fredericksburg, VA............1506

Freeport Arts Center, Freeport, IL 435

Freeport Historical Society, Freeport, ME......611

Freer Gallery of Art, Washington, DC 279

French Art Colony, Gallipolis, OH.............1165

French Azilum, Inc., Towanda, PA.............1303

The French Legation Museum, Austin, TX..1390

Fresno Flats Historical Park, Oakhurst, CA...132

Fresno Metropolitan Museum, Fresno, CA..97

The Frick Art & Historical Center, Pittsburgh, PA.......................................1292

The Frick Collection, New York, NY.........1025

Friends of Historic Kingston, Fred J. Johnston House Museum, Kingston, NY..1007

Friendship Firehouse, Alexandria, VA........1492

Frisco Native American Museum and Natural History Center, Frisco, NC 1102

Frontier Times Museum, Bandera, TX.......1393

Fruitlands Museums, Harvard, MA.............686

The Fullerton Arboretum, Fullerton, CA........98

Fulton County Historical Museum, Wauseon, OH.......................................1190

Fulton Mansion State Historic Site, Rockport, TX...1446

Gadsden Museum of Art, Gadsden, AL 10

Gaineswood, Demopolis, AL 7

Gallery on the York - Yorktown Arts Foundation, Yorktown, VA.................1547

Gallier House, New Orleans, LA.................595

Galloway House and Village - Blakely Museum, Fond du Lac, WI...................1597

Galveston Historical Foundation, Inc., Galveston, TX..1421

Gamble House, Pasadena, CA 140

Gari Melchers Home and Studio, Fredericksburg, VA................................1506

Gaston County Museum of Art and History, Dallas, NC..............................1097

Gene Stratton-Porter State Historic Site, Rome City, IN..498

General Crook House Museum and Library/Archives Center, Omaha, NE......870

General Daniel Bissell House, Saint Louis, MO..833

General Douglas MacArthur Memorial, Norfolk, VA...1521

Geneva Historical Society & Prouty-Chew House & Museum, Geneva, NY..994

Geneva Historical Society & Rose Hill Mansion, Geneva, NY............................994

The George D. and Harriet W. Cornell Fine Arts Museum, Winter Park, FL.......354

George Washington Birthplace National Monument, Colonial Beach, VA............1502

George Washington Carver Museum, Tuskegee Institute, AL...........................20

George Washington's Fredericksburg Foundation, Historic Kenmore & Washington's Ferry Farm, Fredericksburg, VA................................1506

Georgetown University Art Collection, Washington, DC....................................279

Georgia Historical Society, Savannah, GA...385

Georgia Museum of Art, University of Georgia, Athens, GA.............................356

The Georgian Museum, Lancaster, OH......1171

Georgia's Stone Mountain Park, Stone Mountain, GA...387

Germantown Historical Society, Philadelphia, PA...................................1280

Gibbes Museum of Art, Charleston, SC.....1325

The Gibson Society, Inc. dba Gibson House Museum, Boston, MA.................665

Gilmer Arts and Heritage Association, Ellijay, GA..371

Gilmore Car Museum, Hickory Corners, MI...746

Glencairn Museum: Academy of the New Church, Bryn Athyn, PA 1244

Glendower State Memorial, Lebanon, OH.1171

Glensheen Historic Estate, Duluth, MN......773

Glessner House Museum, Chicago, IL.........421

Gloucester County Historical Society, Woodbury, NJ...931

Glove Museum, New York, NY 1026

The Godwin-Ternbach Museum, Flushing, NY...990

Golden Ball Tavern Museum, Weston, MA...718

Golden Gate Railroad Museum, San Francisco, CA...166

The Goldstein Museum of Design, Saint Paul, MN...789

Goliad State Park, Goliad, TX...................1423

Gomez Foundation for Mill House, Marlboro, NY..1014

Goodhue County Historical Society, Red Wing, MN..787

Goodnow Museum State Historic Site, Manhattan, KS..550

Gore Place, Waltham, MA...........................715

Gorgas House, Tuscaloosa, AL......................19

Goschenhoppen Folklife Library and Museum, Green Lane, PA.....................1257

Goshen Historical Society, Goshen, CT.......242

Governor Henry Lippitt House Museum, Providence, RI.......................................1316

Governor Ross Plantation, Seaford, DE.......272

The Governor's Mansion, Frankfort, KY 569

Graceland, Memphis, TN...........................1373

The Gracie Mansion Conservancy, New York, NY...1026

Grand Forks County Historical Society, Grand Forks, ND....................................1132

Grand Lodge AF&AM of Virginia - Allen E. Roberts Masonic Library and Museum, Richmond, VA.....................1529

Grand Rapids Art Museum, Grand Rapids, MI...743

Grand Teton National Park, Colter Bay Indian Arts Museum, Colter Bay Village, WY...1631

Grand Traverse Heritage Center, Traverse City, MI...765

The Granger Homestead Society, Inc., Canandaigua, NY.....................................975

Granville County Historical Society Museum, Oxford, NC..........................1114

Graycliff Conservancy, Derby, NY.............984

Great Sand Dunes National Monument and Preserve, Mosca, CO.......................229

The Greenburgh Nature Center, Scarsdale, NY...1066

Greene County Historical Society, Xenia, OH...1193

Greensboro Historical Museum, Inc., Greensboro, NC....................................1103

Grevemberg House Museum, Franklin, LA...588

Grey Art Gallery, New York University Art Collection, New York, NY 1026

Grier Musser Museum, Los Angeles, CA 115

Gropius House, Lincoln, MA.......................690

Groton Historical Society, Groton, MA........685

Guilford Courthouse National Military Park, Greensboro, NC...........................1104

Gulf Coast Museum of Art, Inc., Largo, FL..321

Gunston Hall Plantation, Mason Neck, VA...1517

Haas-Lilienthal House, San Francisco, CA..166

Hacienda Buena Vista, Ponce, PR.............1642

Hackley & Hume Historic Site, Muskegon, MI..757

The Haggin Museum, Stockton, CA...........189

The Hagley Museum and Library, Wilmington, DE....................................273

Hahns Peak Area Historical Society and School House, Clark, CO......................205

Haines Museum, Waukegan Historical Society, Waukegan, IL............................463

Hale Farm and Village, Bath, OH 1141

Hallie Ford Museum of Art, Salem, OR 1235

Hamilton House, South Berwick, ME.........622

Hamline University Galleries, Department of Studio Arts & Art History, Saint Paul, MN..790

Hammond-Harwood House Association, Annapolis, MD..628

Hammond Museum and Japanese Stroll Garden, North Salem, NY....................1043

Hampton History Museum, Hampton, VA .1509

Hampton National Historic Site, Towson, MD...655

Hanby House, Westerville, OH..................1191

Hancock Historical Museum, Findlay, OH...1164

Hancock Historical Society, Hancock, NH...888

Hanover House, Clemson, SC....................1328

Harbour House Museum, Crystal Falls, MI...733

Harney County Historical Museum, Burns, OR...1221

Harpers Ferry Center, Harpers Ferry, WV .1582

Harriet Beecher Stowe Center, Hartford, CT...245

Harrison House, Branford, CT.....................235

Harry S. Truman Library-Museum, Independence, MO..................................818

Harvard Historical Society, Still River, MA...711

Harvard University Art Museums, Cambridge, MA.....................................672

The Harwood Museum of Art of the University of New Mexico, Taos, NM....952

Hastings Museum, Hastings, NE.................863

Hawaii's Plantation Village, Waipahu, HI....402

Hawks Inn Historical Society, Inc., Delafield, WI...1595

Hay House Museum, Macon, GA 377

Hayden Museum of American Art, Paris, TX...1442

Headley-Whitney Museum, Lexington, KY...573

Healdton Oil Museum, Healdton, OK........1202

Healy House-Dexter Cabin, Leadville, CO...225

Heard Museum, Phoenix, AZ.......................40

Hearst Castle, San Simeon, CA..................177

Hearthstone Historic House Museum, Appleton, WI...1589

Heckscher Museum of Art, Huntington, NY..............1000
Helena Gallery, Helena, MT..........849
Hellenic Museum & Cultural Center, Chicago, IL..........421
Hennepin History Museum, Minneapolis, MN..........782
Henry B. Plant Museum, Tampa, FL..........349
Henry County Museum and Cultural Arts Center, Clinton, MO..........813
The Henry Sheldon Museum of Vermont History, Middlebury, VT..........1481
Herbert Hoover Presidential Library-Museum, West Branch, IA..........530
Heritage Center Museum, Berryville, AR..........55
Heritage Center of Lancaster County, Inc., Lancaster, PA..........1265
Heritage Hill State Historical Park, Green Bay, WI..........1599
Heritage of the Americas Museum, El Cajon, CA..........92
The Heritage Society, Houston, TX..........1426
Hermann-Grima/Gallier Historic Houses, New Orleans, LA..........595
The Hermitage, Ho-Ho-Kus, NJ..........907
The Hermitage Foundation, Norfolk, VA..........1521
The Hermitage: Home of President Andrew Jackson, Hermitage, TN..........1367
Herrett Center for Arts & Science, Faulkner Planetarium and Centennial Observatory, Twin Falls, ID..........410
Hershey Museum, Hershey, PA..........1261
Hibel Museum of Art, Jupiter, FL..........316
The Hickory Museum of Art, Hickory, NC..........1106
Higgins Armory Museum, Worcester, MA..........721
The High Museum of Art, Atlanta, GA..........360
High Point Museum & Historical Park, High Point, NC..........1106
Highland Park Historical Society, Highland Park, IL..........439
Highlands Art League, Sebring, FL..........345
Hill-Stead Museum, Farmington, CT..........241
Hillforest House Museum, Aurora, IN..........468
Hills and Dales Estate, LaGrange, GA..........375
Hillstrom Museum of Art, Saint Peter, MN..........793
Hillwood Museum & Gardens, Washington, DC..........280
The Hispanic Society of America, New York, NY..........1027
Historic Annapolis Foundation, Annapolis, MD..........628
Historic Arkansas Museum, Little Rock, AR..........62
Historic Bath State Historic Site, Bath, NC..........1091
Historic Bethabara Park, Winston-Salem, NC..........1125
Historic Brattonsville, McConnells, SC..........1336
Historic Camden Revolutionary War Site, Camden, SC..........1323
Historic Charleston Foundation, Charleston, SC..........1325
Historic Cherry Hill, Albany, NY..........954
Historic Columbia Foundation, Columbia, SC..........1329
Historic Crab Orchard Museum & Pioneer Park, Inc., Tazewell, VA..........1541
Historic Deepwood Estate, Salem, OR..........1235
Historic Deerfield, Inc., Deerfield, MA..........679
Historic Edenton State Historic Site, Edenton, NC..........1099
Historic General Dodge House, Council Bluffs, IA..........512
Historic Georgetown Inc., Georgetown, CO..........218
Historic Governors' Mansion, Cheyenne, WY..........1630
Historic Halifax State Historic Site, Halifax, NC..........1105

Historic Hermann Museum, Hermann, MO..........817
Historic Homes Foundation, Inc., Louisville, KY..........576
Historic Hope Foundation, Inc., Windsor, NC..........1124
Historic House Trust of New York City, New York, NY..........1027
Historic Hudson Valley, Tarrytown, NY..........1077
Historic Indian Agency House, Portage, WI..........1618
Historic Jefferson College, Washington, MS..........810
Historic Landmarks Foundation of Indiana, Indianapolis, IN..........482
Historic Langhorne Association, Langhorne, PA..........1267
Historic Latta Plantation, Huntersville, NC..........1107
Historic Lincoln, Lincoln, NM..........941
Historic London Town and Gardens, Edgewater, MD..........642
Historic Mann House, Concord, MI..........732
Historic Mobile Preservation Society, Mobile, AL..........14
Historic New England, Boston, MA..........665
Historic New England/Cogswells Grant, Essex, MA..........682
The Historic New Orleans Collection, New Orleans, LA..........595
Historic Northampton, Northampton, MA..........699
Historic Preservation Association of Bourbon County, Inc., Fort Scott, KS..........540
Historic Price House, Woodruff, SC..........1343
Historic Renville Preservation Commission, Renville, MN..........787
Historic Richmond Town, Staten Island, NY..........1072
Historic St. Mary's City, Saint Mary's City, MD..........652
Historic Sauder Village, Archbold, OH..........1140
Historic Schaefferstown, Inc., Schaefferstown, PA..........1297
Historic Southwest Ohio, Inc., Sharonville, OH..........1185
Historic Stagville, Durham, NC..........1098
Historic Waco Foundation, Waco, TX..........1459
Historic Walnford, Upper Freehold Twp., NJ..........929
Historic Westville, Inc., Lumpkin, GA..........376
Historical and Genealogical Society of Somerset County, Somerset, PA..........1300
Historical Society of Berks County, Reading, PA..........1296
Historical Society of Bloomfield New Jersey, Bloomfield, NJ..........898
Historical Society of Cheshire County, Keene, NH..........890
The Historical Society of Dauphin County, Harrisburg, PA..........1258
Historical Society of Delaware, Wilmington, DE..........274
The Historical Society of Frederick County, Inc., Frederick, MD..........644
Historical Society of Haddonfield, Haddonfield, NJ..........905
Historical Society of Kent County, Inc., Chestertown, MD..........640
Historical Society of Newburgh Bay & the Highlands - David Crawford House, Newburgh, NY..........1042
Historical Society of Old Yarmouth, Yarmouth Port, MA..........722
Historical Society of Princeton, Princeton, NJ..........921
Historical Society of Quincy and Adams County, Quincy, IL..........452
Historical Society of St. Marys and Benzinger Township, Saint Marys, PA..........1297
Historical Society of Saratoga Springs, Saratoga Springs, NY..........1064
Historical Society of Talbot County, Easton, MD..........642

Historical Society of the Town of Greenwich Inc. aka Bush-Holley Historic Site, Cos Cob, CT..........237
Historical Society of Wells and Ogunquit, Wells, ME..........625
Historical Society Porter County Old Jail Museum, Valparaiso, IN..........502
History San Jose, San Jose, CA..........171
Hiwan Homestead Museum, Evergreen, CO..........215
Hixon House, La Crosse, WI..........1603
The Holland Museum, Holland, MI..........746
Holmes County Historical Society, Millersburg, OH..........1176
Holter Museum of Art, Helena, MT..........849
Home of Franklin D. Roosevelt National Historic Site, Hyde Park, NY..........1002
Homewood House Museum, Baltimore, MD..........633
Honolulu Academy of Arts, Honolulu, HI..........395
Honolulu House Museum, Marshall, MI..........754
Hood Museum of Art, Hanover, NH..........888
Hoosier Salon Gallery, Indianapolis, IN..........483
Hope Lodge and Mather Mill, Fort Washington, PA..........1254
Hopewell Museum, Paris, KY..........582
Hopewell Museum, Hopewell, NJ..........908
Hopsewee Plantation, Georgetown, SC..........1333
Horatio Colony House Museum & Nature Preserve, Keene, NH..........890
Hotel de Paris Museum, Georgetown, CO..........219
The House of the Seven Gables, Salem, MA..........706
House of the Temple, Washington, DC..........280
House of Wickersham State Historical Site, Juneau, AK..........25
Houston Center for Contemporary Craft, Houston, TX..........1426
Houston Museum of Decorative Arts, Chattanooga, TN..........1362
Howard County Historical Museum, Kokomo, IN..........486
Howard University Museum, Moorland Spingarn Research Center, Washington, DC..........281
The Hoyt Institute of Fine Arts, New Castle, PA..........1273
The Hubbard Museum of the American West, Ruidoso Downs, NM..........946
The Hudson River Museum, Yonkers, NY..........1087
Hui No'eau Visual Arts Center, Makawao, Maui, HI..........401
Humboldt Arts Council/Morris Graves Museum of Art, Eureka, CA..........94
The 100th Meridian Museum, Cozad, NE..........859
Hunt-Morgan House, Lexington, KY..........573
Hunter House Victorian Museum, Norfolk, VA..........1522
Hunter Museum of American Art, Chattanooga, TN..........1362
Huntington Library, Art Collections, and Botanical Gardens, San Marino, CA..........174
Huntington Museum of Art, Inc., Huntington, WV..........1583
Huntsville Museum of Art, Huntsville, AL..........12
Huron City Museums, Port Austin, MI..........761
Hurricane Valley Heritage Park Museum, Hurricane, UT..........1466
Hus Var Fine Art, Buffalo, NY..........973
Hutchinson County Museum, Borger, TX..........1397
The Hyde Collection, Glens Falls, NY..........994
Hyde Hall, Inc., Cooperstown, NY..........980
The Hyland House, Guilford, CT..........243

Illinois State Museum, Springfield, IL..........458
Illinois State Museum, Chicago Gallery, Chicago, IL..........422
Illinois State Museum/Lockport Gallery, Lockport, IL..........443
IMA - Indianapolis Museum of Art, Indianapolis, IN..........483

Decorative Arts–Continued

Independence National Historical Park, Philadelphia, PA 1281
Independence Seaport Museum, Philadelphia, PA 1281
Indian Arts and Crafts Board, Washington, DC 281
Indian City U.S.A., Anadarko, OK 1195
Indian King Tavern Museum, Haddonfield, NJ 906
Indiana State Museum, Indianapolis, IN 484
Indiana University Art Museum, Bloomington, IN 469
International Institute of Metropolitan Detroit, Detroit, MI 737
International Museum of Art and Science, McAllen, TX 1437
International Swimming Hall of Fame, Inc., Fort Lauderdale, FL 307
Iolani Palace, Honolulu, HI 396
Iowa Masonic Library and Museum, Cedar Rapids, IA 509
Ipswich Historical Society and Museum, Ipswich, MA 688
Iraan Museum, Iraan, TX 1430
Iris & B. Gerald Cantor Center for Visual Arts at Stanford University, Stanford, CA 188
Iroquois County Historical Society, Watseka, IL 463
Iroquois Indian Museum, Howes Cave, NY 999
Isabella Stewart Gardner Museum, Boston, MA 666
Isla Center For the Arts at the University of Guam, Mangilao, GU 1640
Islesford Historical Museum, Islesford, ME 612
Italian American Museum, New York, NY 1028

The J. Paul Getty Museum, Los Angeles, CA 116
J. Wayne Stark University Center Galleries, College Station, TX 1401
Jackson County Historical Museum, Lakefield, MN 778
Jacques Marchais Museum of Tibetan Art, Staten Island, NY 1072
James A. Garfield National Historic Site, Mentor, OH 1176
James A. Michener Art Museum, Doylestown, PA 1249
James Buchanan Foundation for the Preservation of Wheatland, Lancaster, PA 1266
James E. Lewis Museum of Art, Morgan State University, Baltimore, MD 633
James J. Hill House, Saint Paul, MN 790
James Madison's Montpelier, Montpelier Station, VA 1518
James Monroe Museum and Memorial Library, Fredericksburg, VA 1507
James S. Copley Library, La Jolla, CA 106
Jane Voorhees Zimmerli Art Museum, New Brunswick, NJ 915
Japan Society Gallery, New York, NY 1028
Japanese Cultural Center of Hawaii, Honolulu, HI 397
Jeane Dixon Museum and Library, Strasburg, VA 1538
Jeff Matthews Memorial Museum, Galax, VA 1508
The Jefferson County Historical Assoc., Steubenville, OH 1186
Jefferson County Historical Society, Watertown, NY 1083
Jefferson County Museum, Charles Town, WV 1580
Jekyll Island Museum, Jekyll Island, GA 374
Jensen Arctic Museum, Monmouth, OR 1228
Jersey City Museum, Jersey City, NJ 908

The Jewish Museum, New York, NY 1029
Jewish Museum of Maryland, Baltimore, MD 633
Jim Crow Museum - Ferris State University, Big Rapids, MI 729
John A. Logan College Museum, Carterville, IL 416
John and Mable Ringling Museum of Art, Sarasota, FL 344
John Jay Homestead State Historic Site, Katonah, NY 1006
John Michael Kohler Arts Center, Sheboygan, WI 1621
John Nance Garner Museum, Uvalde, TX .1457
The John Nicholas Brown Center for the Study of American Civilization, Providence, RI 1317
John Paul Jones House Museum, Portsmouth, NH 894
John Rains House, Rancho Cucamonga, CA 145
John Stark Edwards House, Warren, OH ...1189
John Sydnor's 1847 Powhatan House, Galveston, TX 1421
John Wornall House Museum, Kansas City, MO 821
Johnson County Community College, Gallery of Art, Overland Park, KS 555
Johnson Hall State Historic Site, Johnstown, NY 1005
Johnson-Humrickhouse Museum, Coshocton, OH 1159
Johnstown Area Heritage Association, Johnstown, PA 1263
Joliet Area Historical Museum, Joliet, IL 440
Jordan Schnitzer Museum of Art, Eugene, OR 1223
Joseph Priestley House, Northumberland, PA 1274
Josiah Quincy House, Quincy, MA 705
Joslyn Art Museum, Omaha, NE 871
Judah L. Magnes Museum, Berkeley, CA 76
The Judah P. Benjamin Confederate Memorial at Gamble Plantation Historic State Park, Ellenton, FL 306
Judaica Museum of Central Synagogue, New York, NY 1029
The Judaica Museum of the Hebrew Home at Riverdale, Riverdale, NY 1057
Judith Basin County Museum, Stanford, MT 853
Julian H. Sleeper House, Saint Paul, MN 790
Juliette Gordon Low Birthplace, Savannah, GA 385

Kalamazoo Valley Museum, Kalamazoo, MI 749
Kaminski House Museum, Georgetown, SC 1333
Kankakee County Museum, Kankakee, IL ...441
The Kansas African American Museum, Wichita, KS 561
Kansas Museum of History, Topeka, KS 559
Katonah Museum of Art, Katonah, NY 1006
Kauffman Museum, North Newton, KS 553
The Kearny Cottage, Perth Amboy, NJ 921
Keeler Tavern Museum, Ridgefield, CT 259
Kell House Museum, Wichita Falls, TX 1461
Kelton House Museum & Garden, Columbus, OH 1158
Kemerer Museum of Decorative Arts, Bethlehem, PA 1242
Kennebunkport Historical Society, Kennebunkport, ME 612
Kenosha Public Museum, Kenosha, WI 1602
Kensington Mansion, Eastover, SC 1332
Kent-Delord House Museum, Plattsburgh, NY 1052
Kent State University Museum, Kent, OH.1169
Kent State University, School of Art Galleries, Kent, OH 1169
The Kentucky Folk Art Center, Morehead, KY 580

Kentucky Gateway Museum Center, Maysville, KY 579
Kentucky Historical Society, Frankfort, KY 569
The Kentucky Library & Museum, Bowling Green, KY 565
Kentucky Museum of Art and Craft, Louisville, KY 577
Keweenaw County Historical Society, Eagle Harbor, MI 739
Kidspace Children's Museum, Pasadena, CA 140
Kimball House Museum, Battle Creek, MI 727
Kimbell Art Museum, Fort Worth, TX 1417
Kimberly Crest House & Gardens, Redlands, CA 147
King Manor, Jamaica, NY 1004
King Saddlery Museum, Sheridan, WY 1638
Kirkland Museum of Fine & Decorative Art, Denver, CO 212
Kittery Historical & Naval Museum, Kittery, ME 613
Klemm Gallery, Adrian, MI 722
Kline Creek Farm, Winfield, IL 466
Knights of Columbus Museum, New Haven, CT 253
Knott House Museum, Tallahassee, FL 347
Knox Headquarters State Historic Site, Vails Gate, NY 1080
Knoxville Museum of Art, Knoxville, TN .1370
Korner's Folly, Kernersville, NC 1108
Krannert Art Museum and Kinkead Pavilion, Champaign, IL 416
Kresge Art Museum, East Lansing, MI 739
The Kurdish Museum, Brooklyn, NY 969

La Casa Del Libro, San Juan, PR 1642
La Porte County Historical Society Museum, La Porte, IN 487
La Raza/Galeria Posada, Sacramento, CA ...153
La Salle University Art Museum, Philadelphia, PA 1282
The Lace Museum, Sunnyvale, CA 190
The Lackawanna Historical Society at the Catlin House, Scranton, PA 1298
Ladew Topiary Gardens, Monkton, MD 649
Lafayette College Art Gallery, Williams Center for the Arts, Easton, PA 1250
Lake George Historical Association Museum, Lake George, NY 1008
Lake Wales Depot Museum & Cultural Center, Lake Wales, FL 320
Lakeview Museum of Arts and Sciences, Peoria, IL 450
Lakewood's Heritage Center, Lakewood, CO 225
Lamar Dodd Art Center, LaGrange College, LaGrange, GA 375
Lancaster County Historical Society, Lancaster, PA 1266
The Landmark Society of Western New York, Rochester, NY 1058
Landmarks Foundation/Old Alabama Town, Montgomery, AL 16
Lanier Mansion State Historic Site, Madison, IN 489
Lansing Art Gallery, Lansing, MI 750
Lanterman House, La Canada Flintridge, CA 105
Lapham-Patterson House, Thomasville, GA 388
Larchmont Historical Society, Mamaroneck, NY 1013
Larson Museum and Gallery, Yakima, WA 1578
Las Vegas Art Museum, Las Vegas, NV 879
Latvian Museum, Rockville, MD 651
The Laurel Museum, Laurel, MD 648
Lauren Rogers Museum of Art, Laurel, MS 804
Laurence C. Jones Museum, Piney Woods, MS 807

Lea County Cowboy Hall of Fame and
Western Heritage Center, Hobbs, NM 940
The Lebanon County Historical Society,
Lebanon, PA 1268
Lee-Fendall House Museum and Garden,
Alexandria, VA 1493
Lefferts Historic House, Brooklyn, NY 969
The Leffingwell House Museum,
Norwich, CT 258
Legends of New Mexico Museum,
Algodones, NM 936
Leigh Yawkey Woodson Art Museum,
Wausau, WI 1626
Lemon Hill Mansion, Philadelphia, PA 1282
Lentz Center for Asian Culture, Lincoln,
NE 865
LeRoy House & JELL-O Gallery, LeRoy,
NY 1009
Lesbian Herstory Educational Foundation,
Inc. aka Lesbian Herstory Archives,
Brooklyn, NY 969
Levere Memorial Temple, Evanston, IL 434
Lewes Historical Society, Lewes, DE 271
Lexington Historical Society, Lexington,
MA 689
Liberace Museum & Foundation, Las
Vegas, NV 879
Liberty Hall Historic Center, Lamoni, IA 522
Liberty Hall Historic Site, Frankfort, KY 569
Liberty Village Arts Center & Gallery,
Chester, MT 844
Libertyville-Mundelein Historical Society,
Inc., Libertyville, IL 442
Library Company of Philadelphia,
Philadelphia, PA 1282
Library of the Supreme Council, 33
Degrees, Washington, DC 282
Licking County Arts, Newark, OH 1178
Licking County Historical Society,
Newark, OH 1178
Life on the Ohio River History Museum,
Vevay, IN 502
Lightner Museum, Saint Augustine, FL 339
Limberlost State Historic Site, Geneva,
IN 479
The Lincoln-Tallman Restorations,
Janesville, WI 1601
Litchfield Historical Society and
Museum, Litchfield, CT 247
The Lithuanian Museum, Chicago, IL 423
The Little Cowboy Bar & Museum,
Fromberg, MT 847
Little White House Historic Site, Warm
Springs, GA 390
Livingston County Historical Society
Museum, Geneseo, NY 993
Lizzadro Museum of Lapidary Art,
Elmhurst, IL 433
Lockwood-Mathews Mansion Museum,
Norwalk, CT 257
Locust Grove, Louisville, KY 577
Locust Grove, The Samuel Morse
Historic Site, Poughkeepsie, NY 1055
Locust Lawn and Terwilliger House,
Gardiner, NY 993
Logan County Historical Society
Museum, Bellefontaine, OH 1142
Lois E. Woods Museum, Norfolk, VA 1522
Long Beach Museum of Art, Long
Beach, CA 111
Long Island Museum of American Art,
History & Carriages, Stony Brook,
NY 1075
Longboat Key Center for the Arts,
Longboat Key, FL 322
Longfellow National Historic Site,
Cambridge, MA 673
Longfellow's Wayside Inn, Sudbury, MA 714
LongHouse Reserve, East Hampton, NY 986
Longue Vue House & Gardens, New
Orleans, LA 596

Longview Museum of Fine Arts,
Longview, TX 1434
Longwood Center for the Visual Arts,
Farmville, VA 1504
Longyear Museum, Chestnut Hill, MA 675
Lorenzo State Historic Site, Cazenovia,
NY 976
Los Altos History Museum aka
Association of the Los Altos Historical
Museum, Los Altos, CA 112
Los Angeles County Museum of Art, Los
Angeles, CA 118
Los Angeles Maritime Museum, San
Pedro, CA 176
Loudoun Museum, Inc., Leesburg, VA 1512
Louis E. May Museum, Fremont, NE 861
Louise Wells Cameron Art Museum,
Wilmington, NC 1123
Louisiana Art & Science Museum - Irene
W. Pennington Planetarium, Baton
Rouge, LA 586
Louisiana State Museum, New Orleans,
LA 596
Louisiana State University Museum of
Art, Baton Rouge, LA 586
Louisiana's Old State Capitol, Political
History Museum, Baton Rouge, LA 587
Lowe Art Museum, University of Miami,
Coral Gables, FL 301
Lower Cape Fear Historical Society, Inc.,
Wilmington, NC 1123
Loyola University Museum of Art,
Chicago, IL 423
Luckhard Museum - The Indian Mission,
Sebewaing, MI 764
Luther Burbank Home & Gardens, Santa
Rosa, CA 184
Lutheran Heritage Center & Museum of
the Perry County Lutheran Historical
Society, Altenburg, MO 810
Lux Center for the Arts, Lincoln, NE 866
Luzerne County Historical Society,
Wilkes-Barre, PA 1307
The Lyceum, Alexandria's History
Museum, Alexandria, VA 1493
Lyman Allyn Art Museum, New London,
CT 255
Lynchburg Museum System, Lynchburg,
VA 1515
Lyndhurst, Tarrytown, NY 1078
Lyndon Baines Johnson Library and
Museum, Austin, TX 1391
Lynn Museum & Historical Society,
Lynn, MA 692

MSC Forsyth Center Galleries, Texas
A&M University, College Station, TX ..1401
Mabry-Hazen House, Knoxville, TN 1371
Macculloch Hall Historical Museum &
Gardens, Morristown, NJ 913
Mackinac Island State Park
Commission-Mackinac State Historic
Parks, Mackinaw City, MI 752
Mackinac State Historic Parks-Colonial
Michilimackinac & Old Mackinac
Point Lighthouse, Mackinaw City, MI 752
Mackinac State Historic Parks-Fort
Mackinac & Mackinac Island State
Park, Mackinac Island, MI 752
Macon County Historical Society
Museum Complex, Decatur, IL 430
Madison-Morgan Cultural Center,
Madison, GA 378
Madison Museum of Fine Art, Madison,
GA 378
Magevney House, Memphis, TN 1373
Maggie L. Walker National Historic Site,
Richmond, VA 1530
Magnolia Grove-Historic House Museum,
Greensboro, AL 10
Magnolia Manor, Cairo, IL 415
Magnolia Plantation and Gardens,
Charleston, SC 1326

Magoffin Home State Historic Site, El
Paso, TX 1412
Maine Historical Society, Portland, ME 619
Maine Maritime Museum, Bath, ME 606
Maitland Art Center, Maitland, FL 322
Maitland Historical Museums, Maitland,
FL 322
Mallory-Neely House, Memphis, TN 1373
Manchester Historic Association Millyard
Museum, Manchester, NH 891
Manhattan Arts Center, Manhattan, KS 551
The Mansfield Art Center, Mansfield, OH .1173
Mansfield Historical Society Museum,
Storrs, CT 261
Manship House Museum, Jackson, MS 802
Marathon County Historical Society,
Wausau, WI 1626
Marblehead Arts Association - King
Hooper Mansion, Marblehead, MA 693
Marblehead Museum & Historical
Society, Marblehead, MA 693
Marcella Sembrich Opera Museum,
Bolton Landing, NY 963
Marianna Kistler Beach Museum of Art
at Kansas State University, Manhattan,
KS 551
Maridon Museum, Butler, PA 1245
Marietta House Museum, Glenn Dale,
MD 645
The Mariners' Museum, Newport News,
VA 1519
Mariposa Museum & World Culture
Center, Peterborough, NH 893
Maritime Museum - Cohasset Historical
Society, Cohasset, MA 676
Maritime Museum of Monterey,
Monterey, CA 127
Marjorie Kinnan Rawlings Historic State
Park, Cross Creek, FL 301
The Mark Twain House & Museum,
Hartford, CT 245
Marlboro County Historical Museum,
Bennettsville, SC 1322
Marlboro Historical Society, Marlboro,
VT 1481
Marrett House, Standish, ME 623
The Marston House/San Diego Historical
Society, San Diego, CA 157
Martha's Vineyard Museum, Edgartown,
MA 681
The Martin D'Arcy Museum of Art: The
Loyola University Museum of
Medieval, Renaissance and Baroque
Art, Chicago, IL 424
Martin Van Buren National Historic Site,
Kinderhook, NY 1007
Marvin Samson Center for History of
Pharmacy/USP Museum, Philadelphia,
PA 1283
Marxhausen Art Gallery, Seward, NE 873
Mary Ball Washington Museum &
Library, Inc., Lancaster, VA 1512
Mary McLeod Bethune Council House
National Historic Site, Washington,
DC 283
Mary Washington House, Fredericksburg,
VA 1507
Maryhill Museum of Art, Goldendale,
WA 1556
Maryland Historical Society, Baltimore,
MD 634
Maryland State Archives, Annapolis, MD ...628
Marywood University Art Galleries
(Suraci Gallery and Mahady Gallery),
Scranton, PA 1298
The Masonic Library and Museum of
Pennsylvania, Philadelphia, PA 1283
The Massillon Museum, Massillon, OH 1175
Mathias Ham House Historic Site,
Dubuque, IA 516
The Mattatuck Museum Arts and History
Center, Waterbury, CT 264

Decorative Arts—Continued

Matthews Museum of Maine Heritage, Union, ME 624

May Natural History Museum and Museum of Space Exploration, Colorado Springs, CO 207

Maymont, Richmond, VA 1530

McConaghy House, Hayward, CA 102

McCook House, Civil War Museum, Carrollton, OH 1146

McCoy House, Lewistown, PA 1269

McDowell House Museum, Danville, KY ...567

McLean County Museum of History, Bloomington, IL 414

McMinn County Living Heritage Museum, Athens, TN 1360

McMullen Museum of Art, Boston College, Chestnut Hill, MA 675

McNamara House Museum, Victoria, TX ..1457

McNay Art Museum, San Antonio, TX 1448

McPherson Museum & Arts Foundation, McPherson, KS 552

McWethy Hall, Luce Gallery, Cornell College, Mount Vernon, IA 524

Mead Art Museum, Amherst, MA 658

Meadow Brook Hall, Rochester, MI 761

Mecosta County Historical Museum, Big Rapids, MI 729

Medina County Historical Society, The John Smart House, Medina, OH 1175

Meigs County Museum, Pomeroy, OH 1183

Mellette House, Watertown, SD 1359

Melton Art Reference Library, Oklahoma City, OK 1208

Memorial Art Gallery of the University of Rochester, Rochester, NY 1059

Memphis Botanic Garden, Goldsmith Civic Garden Center, Memphis, TN 1374

Memphis Brooks Museum of Art, Memphis, TN 1374

Memphis College of Art, Memphis, TN 1374

Mennello Museum of American Art, Orlando, FL 331

Mennonite Heritage Museum, Goessel, KS 542

Merced County Courthouse Museum, Merced, CA 125

Merchant's House Museum, New York, NY 1029

Meriden Historical Society, Inc., Meriden, CT 249

Meridian Museum of Art, Meridian, MS 805

Merritt Museum of Anthropology, Oakland, CA 133

Merwin House, Tranquility, Stockbridge, MA 712

The Metropolitan Museum of Art, New York, NY 1030

Metropolitan State College of Denver/Center for Visual Art, Denver, CO 212

Mexic-Arte Museum, Austin, TX 1391

The Mexican Museum, San Francisco, CA 166

Miami County Museum, Peru, IN 496

Miami University Art Museum, Oxford, OH 1181

Michigan Historical Museum, Michigan Historical Center, Lansing, MI 750

The Michigan State University Museum, East Lansing, MI 740

Mid-America All Indian Center, Wichita, KS 562

Mid-Atlantic Center for the Arts/Emlen Physick Estate/Cape May Lighthouse, Cape May, NJ 900

Mid-Continent Railway Museum, North Freedom, WI 1615

Middleton Place Foundation, Charleston, SC 1326

Midland County Historical Society, Midland, MI 755

Midwest Museum of American Art, Elkhart, IN 474

Mifflinburg Buggy Museum Association, Inc., Mifflinburg, PA 1271

Milford Historical Society, Milford, CT 250

Millicent Rogers Museum of Northern New Mexico, Taos, NM 952

Mills College Art Museum, Oakland, CA 133

Milwaukee Art Museum, Milwaukee, WI ..1611

Milwaukee Public Museum, Milwaukee, WI 1612

Minneapolis Institute of Arts, Minneapolis, MN 782

Minnesota Historical Society, Saint Paul, MN 791

Mint Museum of Art, Charlotte, NC 1095

Mint Museum of Craft + Design, Charlotte, NC 1096

Mission Inn Foundation/Museum, Riverside, CA 149

Mission San Diego de Alcala, San Diego, CA 157

Mission San Luis Rey Museum, Oceanside, CA 135

Mission San Miguel, San Miguel, CA 175

Mississippi Crafts Center, Ridgeland, MS ...807

Mississippi Governor's Mansion, Jackson, MS 802

Mississippi Museum of Art, Jackson, MS 802

Mississippi Society Daughters of the American Revolution Rosalie House Museum, Natchez, MS 805

Missoula Art Museum, Missoula, MT 851

Missouri Historical Society, Saint Louis, MO 835

Mobile Museum of Art, Mobile, AL 14

Moffatt-Ladd House and Garden, Portsmouth, NH 894

Mohave Museum of History and Arts, Kingman, AZ 36

Molly Brown House Museum, Denver, CO 213

Monmouth County Historical Association, Freehold, NJ 905

Monroe County Historical Association/Stroud Mansion, Stroudsburg, PA 1302

Montalvo Arts Center, Saratoga, CA 185

Montana Historical Society, Helena, MT 849

Montauk, Clermont, IA 511

Montclair Historical Society, Montclair, NJ 912

Monterey Museum of Art, Monterey, CA 128

The Montgomery County Historical Society, Dayton, OH 1161

The Montgomery County Historical Society, Inc., Rockville, MD 651

Montgomery Museum of Fine Arts, Montgomery, AL 16

Monticello, Home of Thomas Jefferson, Thomas Jefferson Foundation, Inc., Charlottesville, VA 1499

Montpelier Mansion, Laurel, MD 648

Montpelier-The General Henry Knox Museum, Thomaston, ME 624

The Moody Mansion Museum, Galveston, TX 1421

Moore County Art Association, Dumas, TX 1410

The Moore-Youse Home Museum, Muncie, IN 492

Moravian Museum of Bethlehem, Inc., Bethlehem, PA 1242

Morris-Butler House Museum, Indianapolis, IN 485

Morris County Historical Society (Acorn Hall House Museum), Morristown, NJ ...914

Morris-Jumel Mansion, New York, NY 1030

The Morris Museum, Morristown, NJ 914

Morris Museum of Art, Augusta, GA 365

Morristown National Historical Park, Morristown, NJ 914

Morven Museum & Garden, Princeton, NJ 922

Morven Park, Leesburg, VA 1512

Moses Myers House, Norfolk, VA 1522

Moundbuilders State Memorial & Museum, Newark, OH 1178

Mount Clare Museum House, Baltimore, MD 635

Mount Desert Island Historical Society, Mount Desert, ME 615

Mount Dora Center for the Arts, Mount Dora, FL 327

Mount Holyoke College Art Museum, South Hadley, MA 709

Mount Vernon Hotel Museum & Garden, New York, NY 1031

Mount Vernon Ladies' Association, Mount Vernon, VA 1518

Muckenthaler Cultural Center and Mansion Museum, Fullerton, CA 99

Mulford Farm, East Hampton, NY 986

Munson-Williams-Proctor Arts Institute Museum of Art, Utica, NY 1079

Murfreesboro Historical Association, Murfreesboro, NC 1112

Murray-Lindsay Mansion, Lindsay, OK 1204

Murrell Home, Park Hill, OK 1211

Muscatine Art Center, Muscatine, IA 524

Museo de Arte de Ponce (The Luis A. Ferre Foundation, Inc.), Ponce, PR 1642

Museo de las Americas, Denver, CO 213

Museo ItaloAmericano, San Francisco, CA 167

The Museum of African Culture, Portland, ME 619

Museum of American Architecture and Decorative Arts, Houston, TX 1428

Museum of American Glass at Wheaton Village, Millville, NJ 911

Museum of Ancient Artifacts, Las Vegas, NV 879

Museum of Art and Archaeology, University of Missouri - Columbia, Columbia, MO 813

Museum of Art and History at the McPherson Center, Santa Cruz, CA 182

Museum of Art & History at Weston, Weston, CT 266

Museum of Art/Fort Lauderdale, Fort Lauderdale, FL 307

Museum of Art, Rhode Island School of Design, Providence, RI 1317

Museum of Arts & Design, New York, NY 1032

Museum of Arts and Sciences, Macon, GA 378

Museum of Astrogeology, Meteor Crater, Winslow, AZ 53

Museum of Carousel Art & History, Sandusky, OH 1185

Museum of Ceramics, East Liverpool, OH 1163

Museum of Church History and Art, Salt Lake City, UT 1471

Museum of Contemporary Religious Art (MOCRA)-St. Louis University, Saint Louis, MO 835

Museum of Craft and Folk Art, San Francisco, CA 167

Museum of Early Southern Decorative Arts (MESDA), Winston-Salem, NC 1125

Museum of Fine Arts, Boston, MA 667

The Museum of Fine Arts, Houston, Houston, TX 1428

Museum of Fine Arts of St. Petersburg, Florida, Saint Petersburg, FL 341

Museum of Florida History, Tallahassee, FL 348

Museum of History & Industry (MOHAI), Seattle, WA 1567

Museum of International Folk Art, Santa Fe, NM 948

Museum of Jewish Heritage-A Living Memorial to the Holocaust, New York, NY.............................1032
Museum of Lifestyle & Fashion History, Delray Beach, FL 305
The Museum of Mobile, Mobile, AL 14
Museum of Nebraska Art, Kearney, NE.......864
Museum of North Idaho, Coeur d'Alene, ID 405
The Museum of Printing History, Houston, TX................................1428
The Museum of Russian Art, Minneapolis, MN.............................783
Museum of San Diego History and Research Library, San Diego, CA 158
Museum of Spanish Colonial Art - MoSCA, Santa Fe, NM...........................949
Museum of Texas Tech University, Lubbock, TX...............................1435
Museum of the Albemarle, Elizabeth City, NC.................................1099
Museum of the American Philosophical Society, Philadelphia, PA 1283
Museum of the Bedford Historical Society, Bedford, NY 961
Museum of the Cherokee Indian, Cherokee, NC.............................1096
Museum of the City of New York, New York, NY.................................1033
The Museum of the Confederacy, Richmond, VA..............................1531
Museum of the Gulf Coast, Port Arthur, TX 1444
Museum of the National Center of Afro-American Artists, Roxbury, MA 706
Museum of the Northern Great Plains, Fort Benton, MT.............................846
Museum of the Puerto Rican Family of the 19th Century, San Juan, PR 1643
Museum of the Weston Historical Society, Inc., Weston, MA 718
Museum of Yarmouth History, Yarmouth, ME................................626
Musical Box Society International, Houston, TX..............................1429
Muskegon County Museum, Muskegon, MI................................757
Muskegon Museum of Art, Muskegon, MI................................758

Nantucket Historical Association, Nantucket, MA 696
Nantucket Lightship Basket Museum, Nantucket, MA 696
Naomi Wood Collection at Woodford Mansion, Philadelphia, PA 1284
Naper Settlement, Naperville, IL.................447
Naples Museum of Art and the Philharmonic Center for the Arts Galleries, Naples, FL............................328
Napoleonic Society of America, Inc., Clearwater, FL 300
Narragansett Historical Society, Templeton, MA 714
Nassau County, Division of Museum Services, Department of Recreation, Parks & Museums, East Meadow, NY....987
National Academy of Sciences, Washington, DC..............................283
National Afro-American Museum & Cultural Center, Wilberforce, OH 1191
National Arts Club, New York, NY............1034
National Baseball Hall of Fame and Museum, Inc., Cooperstown, NY 981
National Christmas Center, Paradise, PA ...1275
National Civil War Naval Museum at Port Columbus, Columbus, GA 369
National Cowgirl Museum and Hall of Fame, Fort Worth, TX.......................1418
National Czech & Slovak Museum & Library, Cedar Rapids, IA.......................509
National Gallery of Art, Washington, DC...285

The National Great Blacks in Wax Museum, Inc., Baltimore, MD.................635
National Heritage Museum, Lexington, MA................................690
National Hispanic Cultural Center, Art Museum, Albuquerque, NM.....................935
National Museum of American Illustration, Newport, RI 1314
The National Museum of Catholic Art & History, New York, NY......................1034
National Museum of Polo and Hall of Fame, Inc., Lake Worth, FL....................320
National Museum of Racing and Hall of Fame, Saratoga Springs, NY.................1065
National Museum of Roller Skating, Lincoln, NE.................................866
National Museum of the American Indian, Smithsonian Institution, New York, NY.................................1034
National Museum of Women in the Arts, Washington, DC............................287
National Ornamental Metal Museum, Memphis, TN............................1375
National Park Service Museum Resource Center, Landover, MD............................648
National Road/Zane Grey Museum, Norwich, OH............................1180
National Scouting Museum, Irving, TX 1430
National Society of the Children of the American Revolution Museum, Washington, DC............................287
National Society of the Sons of the American Revolution, Louisville, KY 578
National Trust for Historic Preservation, Washington, DC............................288
Natural Center for the American Revolution, Wayne, PA.......................1306
Naumkeag, Stockbridge, MA..................712
Nebraska State Capitol, Lincoln, NE...........866
Neill-Cochran Museum House, Austin, TX................................1391
The Nelson-Atkins Museum of Art, Kansas City, MO 822
Nemours Mansion and Gardens, Wilmington, DE..............................274
The Neustadt Collection of Tiffany Glass, Long Island City, NY 1011
Nevada Historical Society, Reno, NV 881
Nevada State Museum, Carson City, NV.....876
New Bedford Whaling Museum, New Bedford, MA..............................696
New Braunfels Conservation Society, New Braunfels, TX 1440
New Castle Historical Society, New Castle, DE.................................272
The New England Carousel Museum, Bristol, CT.................................236
New England Quilt Museum, Lowell, MA................................692
New Hampshire Historical Society, Concord, NH.................................885
New Hampshire Institute of Art, Manchester, NH..............................892
New Harmony State Historic Site/Historic New Harmony, New Harmony, IN..............................494
New Haven Colony Historical Society, New Haven, CT..............................253
The New Jersey Historical Society, Newark, NJ.................................916
New Jersey Office of Historic Sites, Trenton, NJ.................................927
New Jersey State Museum, Trenton, NJ 927
New London County Historical Society, New London, CT..............................255
The New Milford Historical Society, New Milford, CT..............................256
The New Museum of Contemporary Art, New York, NY..............................1035
New Orleans Museum of Art, New Orleans, LA.................................597
New Visions Gallery, Inc., Marshfield, WI 1608

New York City Fire Museum, New York, NY................................1035
The New York Historical Society, New York, NY................................1035
New York State Bureau of Historic Sites, Waterford, NY.................................1082
New York State Historical Association/Fenimore Art Museum, Cooperstown, NY............................981
New York State Museum, Albany, NY........955
New York State Office of Parks, Recreation & Historic Preservation, Albany, NY.................................955
The Newark Museum, Newark, NJ..............916
Newcomb Art Gallery, New Orleans, LA 598
Newport Historical Society & The Museum of Newport History, Newport, RI.................................1315
Newport Restoration Foundation, Newport, RI.................................1315
The Niagara County Historical Center and Niagara County Genealogical Society, Lockport, NY.......................1010
Nichols House Museum, Boston, MA..........668
Nici Self Museum, Centennial, WY...........1630
Nickels-Sortwell House, Wiscasset, ME 626
Nixon Presidential Materials Staff, College Park, MD..............................641
Noah Webster House/West Hartford Historical Society, West Hartford, CT.....265
Nordic Heritage Museum, Seattle, WA 1567
Norfolk History Museum, Norfolk, VA......1523
The Norman Cleveland County Historical Museum, Norman, OK..............................1206
Norman R. Eppink Art Gallery, Emporia State University, Emporia, KS.................539
North Carolina Museum of History, Raleigh, NC.................................1115
North Carolina Office of Archives and History, Raleigh, NC 1116
North Carolina Pottery Center, Seagrove, NC.................................1119
North Carolina State University Gallery of Art & Design, Raleigh, NC 1116
North Dakota Museum of Art, Grand Forks, ND.................................1132
North House Museum, Lewisburg, WV 1584
Northampton County Historical and Genealogical Society, Easton, PA 1250
Northeast Georgia History Center at Brenau University, Gainesville, GA 373
Northeast Texas Rural Heritage Museum, Pittsburg, TX.................................1443
Northern Kentucky University Art Galleries, Highland Heights, KY 571
Northfield Historical Society Museum, Northfield, MN.................................785
The Northumberland County Historical Society, Sunbury, PA 1302
Northwest Art Center, Minot, ND 1134
Northwest Museum of Arts & Culture (Eastern Washington State Historical Society), Spokane, WA..........................1571
Norwich Historical Society, Norwich, VT .1484
Nowetah's American Indian Museum & Store, New Portland, ME.......................615
The Noyes Museum of Art, Oceanville, NJ................................918

Oak Hill and The Martha Berry Museum, Rome, GA.................................382
Oakland County Pioneer and Historical Society, Pontiac, MI.......................760
Oakland Museum of California, Oakland, CA................................134
Oaklands Historic House Museum, Murfreesboro, TN..............................1376
Oakley Park, UDC Shrine, Edgefield, SC..1332
The Oaks House Museum, Jackson, MS......804
Oatlands, Leesburg, VA.........................1512
Oberlin Heritage Center, Oberlin, OH........1180
The Octagon, Washington, DC 288
Octagon House, San Francisco, CA 168

Decorative Arts–Continued

Ogden Union Station Museums, Ogden,
  UT 1468
Ohio Historical Society, Columbus, OH 1158
Ohio River Museum, Marietta, OH 1174
Ohr-O'Keefe Museum of Art, Biloxi, MS ...799
Ojai Valley Historical Society and
  Museum, Ojai, CA 135
Oklahoma Historical Society, Oklahoma
  City, OK 1209
Oktibbeha County Heritage Museum,
  Starkville, MS 808
Olana State Historic Site, Hudson, NY 1000
Old Barracks Museum, Trenton, NJ 927
Old Bethpage Village Restoration, Old
  Bethpage, NY 1045
Old Colony Historical Society, Taunton,
  MA 714
Old Economy Village, Ambridge, PA 1240
Old Falls Village, Menomonee Falls, WI ...1609
Old Fort Harrod State Park Mansion
  Museum, Harrodsburg, KY 570
Old Fort House Museum, Fort Edward,
  NY 991
Old Fort Western, Augusta, ME 604
The Old Jail Art Center, Albany, TX 1385
Old Lighthouse Museum, Stonington, CT 261
Old Market House State Historic Site,
  Galena, IL 436
Old Mission Santa Ines, Solvang, CA 187
Old Ordinary House Museum, Hingham,
  MA 687
Old Salem Inc., Winston-Salem, NC 1126
Old State House, Hartford, CT 245
Old State House Museum, Little Rock,
  AR 63
Old State House-The Bostonian Society,
  Boston, MA 668
Old Sturbridge Village, Sturbridge, MA 713
Old Town Hall Museum, Fifield, WI 1597
Old Washington Historic State Park,
  Washington, AR 69
Old West Museum, Wimberley, TX 1462
Old Westbury Gardens, Old Westbury,
  NY 1045
Old York Historical Society, York, ME 626
Olmsted County Historical Society,
  Rochester, MN 788
103rd Ohio Volunteer Infantry Civil War
  Museum, Sheffield Lake, OH 1185
Onondaga Historical Association Museum
  & Research Center, Syracuse, NY 1077
Orange County Historical Museum,
  Hillsborough, NC 1107
Orchard House, Concord, MA 677
Oregon Coast History Center, Newport,
  OR 1229
Orleans County Historical Society & The
  Old Stone House Museum,
  Brownington, VT 1477
Oroville Chinese Temple, Oroville, CA 136
Osage Nation Tribal Museum, Pawhuska,
  OK 1212
Osborn-Jackson House, East Hampton,
  NY 986
Oshkosh Public Museum, Oshkosh, WI 1616
Osterville Historical Society, Inc.,
  Osterville, MA 701
Ouachita County Historical Society,
  Camden, AR 55
Owatonna Arts Center, Owatonna, MN 786
Owensboro Museum of Fine Art, Inc.,
  Owensboro, KY 581
Oxford Museum, Inc., Oxford, MD 650
Oyster Bay Historical Society, Oyster
  Bay, NY 1049
Oysterponds Historical Society: The
  Museum of Orient and East Marion
  History, Orient, NY 1047

P.H. Sullivan Museum and Genealogy
  Library, Zionsville, IN 504

Pacific Asia Museum, Pasadena, CA 140
Pacific Grove Art Center Associates, Inc.,
  Pacific Grove, CA 137
Pacific University Museum, Forest
  Grove, OR 1224
Packwood House Museum, Lewisburg,
  PA 1268
Paine Art Center and Gardens, Oshkosh,
  WI 1617
Palmer Museum of Art, The Pennsylvania
  State University, University Park, PA 1304
Palos Verdes Art Center, Rancho Palos
  Verdes, CA 145
Paper Airplane Museum and the Tin Can
  Man of Maui, Kahului Central Maui,
  HI 399
Paper Discovery Center, Appleton, WI 1590
The Pardee Home Museum, Oakland, CA ...134
The Park-McCullough House, North
  Bennington, VT 1483
Parker Tavern, Reading, MA 705
Parks, Recreation & Historic Sites
  Division, Georgia Dept. of Natural
  Resources, Atlanta, GA 362
The Parry Mansion Museum, New Hope,
  PA 1273
Parson Fisher House, Blue Hill, ME 606
Parsonsfield-Porter Historical Society,
  Porter, ME 618
Pasadena Museum of History, Pasadena,
  CA 140
Passaic County Historical Society &
  Lambert Castle Museum, Paterson, NJ ...920
The Patrick & Beatrice Haggerty
  Museum of Art, Milwaukee, WI 1613
Patterson Homestead, Dayton, OH 1161
Paul and Lulu Hilliard University Art
  Museum, University of Louisiana at
  Lafayette, Lafayette, LA 590
Paul W. Bryant Museum, Tuscaloosa, AL 19
Peabody Essex Museum, Salem, MA 706
The Peace Museum, Chicago, IL 426
The Pearl S. Buck House, Perkasie, PA 1275
Pebble Hill Plantation, Thomasville, GA 388
The Peekskill Museum, Peekskill, NY 1051
Peel Mansion Museum & Historic
  Gardens, Bentonville, AR 55
Pejepscot Historical Society, Brunswick,
  ME 608
The Pena-Peck House, Saint Augustine,
  FL 339
Pendleton Historic Foundation,
  Pendleton, SC 1339
Pennsbury Manor, Morrisville, PA 1272
Pennsylvania Anthracite Heritage
  Museum, Scranton, PA 1299
Pennsylvania German Cultural Heritage
  Center at Kutztown University,
  Kutztown, PA 1265
Pennypacker Mills, Schwenksville, PA 1297
Pensacola Historical Society Museum,
  Pensacola, FL 336
The Peoria Art Guild, Peoria, IL 451
Petaluma Adobe State Historic Park,
  Petaluma, CA 142
Peter Wentz Farmstead, Worcester, PA 1308
Peterborough Historical Society,
  Peterborough, NH 893
Petersburg Area Art League, Petersburg,
  VA 1525
Petersham Historical Society, Inc.,
  Petersham, MA 702
Pettaquamscutt Historical Society,
  Kingston, RI 1312
Petterson Museum of Intercultural Art,
  Claremont, CA 85
Pewabic Pottery, Detroit, MI 737
Philadelphia Mummers Museum,
  Philadelphia, PA 1285
Philadelphia Museum of Art,
  Philadelphia, PA 1285

Philadelphia Society for the Preservation
  of Landmarks, Philadelphia, PA 1286
The Philbrook Museum of Art, Inc.,
  Tulsa, OK 1215
Phillips County Museum, Helena, AR 59
The Phillips Museum of Art, Franklin &
  Marshall College, Lancaster, PA 1267
Phoebe Apperson Hearst Museum of
  Anthropology, Berkeley, CA 77
Phoenix Art Museum, Phoenix, AZ 41
Phoenix Museum of History, Phoenix,
  AZ 41
Piatt County Museum, Monticello, IL 446
The Picker Art Gallery, Hamilton, NY 997
The Pierpont Morgan Library, New York,
  NY 1037
Pierre Menard Home State Historic Site,
  Ellis Grove, IL 433
Pilgrim Hall Museum, Plymouth, MA 703
Pilgrim Monument and Provincetown
  Museum, Provincetown, MA 704
Pioneer Arizona Living History Village &
  Museum, Phoenix, AZ 41
Pitot House Museum, New Orleans, LA 598
Pittock Mansion, Portland, OR 1232
Plains Art Museum, Fargo, ND 1130
Plainsman Museum, Aurora, NE 856
Plantation Agriculture Museum, Scott,
  AR 67
Plattsburgh State Art Museum S.U.N.Y.,
  Plattsburgh, NY 1053
Plimoth Plantation Inc., Plymouth, MA 703
Plymouth Antiquarian Society, Plymouth,
  MA 704
Point of Honor, Lynchburg, VA 1515
Polish American Museum, Port
  Washington, NY 1054
Polish Museum of America, Chicago, IL 426
The Polk County Historical Society,
  Cedartown, GA 368
Polk County Memorial Museum,
  Livingston, TX 1434
Polk County Memorial Museum,
  Livingston, TX 1434
Polk Museum of Art, Lakeland, FL 321
Popular Arts Museum, San Juan, PR 1643
Port Huron Museum, Port Huron, MI 761
Porter-Phelps-Huntington Foundation,
  Inc., Hadley, MA 685
Porter Thermometer Museum, Onset, MA ...700
Porterville Historical Museum,
  Porterville, CA 144
Portland Art Museum, Portland, OR 1232
Portland Children's Museum, Portland,
  OR 1233
Portland Museum of Art, Portland, ME 619
Potsdam Public Museum, Potsdam, NY 1054
Pound Ridge Society/Museum, Pound
  Ridge, NY 1055
Powers Museum, Carthage, MO 812
Praters Mill Foundation, Varnell, GA 390
Pratt Building - Cohasset Historical
  Society, Cohasset, MA 676
Pratt Manhattan Gallery, New York, NY ...1037
The Preservation Society of Newport
  County/The Newport Mansions,
  Newport, RI 1315
Presidential Pet Museum, Lothian, MD 649
Price Tower Arts Center, Bartlesville, OK .1197
Princeton University Art Museum,
  Princeton, NJ 922
Public Museum of West Michigan, Grand
  Rapids, MI 744
Pueblo of Pojoaque, Poeh Museum, Santa
  Fe, NM 949
Purdue University Galleries, West
  Lafayette, IN 503
Putnam Cottage, Greenwich, CT 243
Putnam County Historical Society &
  Foundry School Museum, Cold
  Spring, NY 979
Putney Historical Society, Putney, VT 1485

Queen Emma Summer Palace, Honolulu, HI 398

Queen Mary Museum, Long Beach, CA 111

The R.W. Norton Art Gallery, Shreveport, LA 601

Racine Art Museum (RAM), Racine, WI...1619

Radford University Art Museum, Radford, VA 1527

Rahr West Art Museum, Manitowoc, WI...1607

Ramapogue Historical Society, West Springfield, MA 718

Ramsey House Museum Plantation, Knoxville, TN 1371

Rancho Los Alamitos, Long Beach, CA 111

Randall Library, Stow, MA 713

Randolph County Historical Museum, Winchester, IN 503

Rankin Museum, Inc., Ellerbe, NC............1100

Rawls Museum Arts, Courtland, VA 1502

The Ray Drew Gallery-New Mexico Highlands University, Las Vegas, NM 941

Raynham Hall Museum, Oyster Bay, NY ..1049

The Reader's Digest Association, Inc., Pleasantville, NY 1053

Reading Public Museum, Reading, PA.......1296

Red Hill-Patrick Henry National Memorial, Brookneal, VA 1498

Red Mill Museum Village, Clinton, NJ.......901

Red Rock Museum, Church Rock, NM 938

Redwood Library and Athenaeum, Newport, RI 1315

Reese Bullen Gallery, Arcata, CA 72

The Reeves Center, Washington and Lee University, Lexington, VA 1513

The Regina A. Quick Center for the Arts, Saint Bonaventure, NY 1063

Rehoboth Art League, Inc., Rehoboth Beach, DE............272

Reitz Home Museum, Evansville, IN...........476

Renfrew Museum & Park, Waynesboro, PA............1306

Rensselaer County Historical Society, Troy, NY............1079

Reynolda House Museum of American Art, Winston-Salem, NC............1126

Rhode Island Historical Society, Providence, RI 1318

Richard Sparrow House Inc., Plymouth, MA............704

Richmond Art Museum, Richmond, IN.......497

Riley County Historical Museum, Manhattan, KS............551

Rip Van Winkle Gardens on Jefferson Island, New Iberia, LA............593

Rising Sun Tavern, Fredericksburg, VA 1507

Riversdale House Mansion, Riverdale Park, MD............651

Riverside Metropolitan Museum, Riverside, CA............150

Riverside Museum, La Crosse, WI............1603

Riverside, The Farnsley-Moremen Landing, Louisville, KY............579

Riverview at Hobson Grove, Bowling Green, KY............566

Robbins Hunter Museum, Avery-Downer House, Granville, OH............1167

Roberson Museum and Science Center, Binghamton, NY............962

Robert C. Williams American Museum of Papermaking at Georgia Tech, Atlanta, GA............363

Robert Hull Fleming Museum, Burlington, VT............1478

Robert Newell House, DAR Museum, Saint Paul, OR............1235

Robert R. McCormick Museum at Cantigny, Wheaton, IL 465

Robert V. Fullerton Art Museum, California State University, San Bernardino, San Bernardino, CA............155

Roberts County Museum, Miami, TX........1438

Rochester Museum & Science Center, Rochester, NY............1059

Rock County Historical Society, Janesville, WI 1601

Rock Island County Historical Society, Moline, IL............445

Rockbridge Historical Society, Lexington, VA 1513

Rockford Art Museum, Rockford, IL............455

Rockingham Free Public Library and Museum, Bellows Falls, VT............1476

Rockwell Museum of Western Art, Corning, NY 982

Rocky Mount Arts Center, Rocky Mount, NC............1117

Rocky Mount Museum, Piney Flats, TN....1383

Rocky Mountain Quilt Museum, Golden, CO............220

Rokeby (Ancestral Estate of Rowland Evans Robinson), Ferrisburgh, VT 1479

Ronald Reagan Presidential Library and Museum, Simi Valley, CA............187

Rosalie House, Eureka Springs, AR 57

Roscoe Village Foundation, Coshocton, OH............1159

Rose Hill Plantation State Historic Site, Union, SC............1343

Rose Lawn Museum, Cartersville, GA........368

Roseland Cottage, Woodstock, CT 268

Rosemont Plantation, Woodville, MS........810

Rosemount Museum, Pueblo, CO............230

Rosenbach Museum & Library, Philadelphia, PA 1287

Rosenberg Gallery, Goucher College, Baltimore, MD............636

Rosenberg Library, Galveston, TX 1422

Roslyn Landmark Society, Roslyn, NY......1061

Ross County Historical Society, Inc., Chillicothe, OH............1147

The Rotch-Jones-Duff House & Garden Museum, Inc., New Bedford, MA............697

Rowan Museum, Inc., Salisbury, NC..........1118

The Rubelle & Norman Schafler Gallery, Brooklyn, NY 970

Rundlet-May House, Portsmouth, NH........895

Russell County Historical Society/Fossil Station Museum, Russell, KS............556

Ruth and Charles Gilb Arcadia Historical Museum, Arcadia, CA............71

The Ruth & Sherman Lee Institute for Japanese Art, Hanford, CA............101

Ruth Chandler Williamson Gallery, Scripps College, Claremont, CA............86

Ruthmere Museum, Elkhart, IN............475

Ryerss Museum & Library, Philadelphia, PA 1287

Sackets Harbor Battlefield State Historic Site, Sackets Harbor, NY............1062

Saco Museum, Saco, ME............621

Safety Harbor Museum of Regional History, Safety Harbor, FL............338

Safford House Historic House Museum, Tarpon Springs, FL............351

Sag Harbor Whaling & Historical Museum, Sag Harbor, NY............1063

Sagamore Hill National Historic Site, Oyster Bay, NY 1049

Saginaw Art Museum, Saginaw, MI............763

Saint-Gaudens National Historic Site, Cornish, NH............885

St. James' House, Fredericksburg, VA 1507

Saint Joseph's University - University Gallery - Boland Hall, Philadelphia, PA............1288

St. Lawrence County Historical Association - Silas Wright House, Canton, NY............975

The Saint Louis Art Museum, Saint Louis, MO............836

St. Simons Island Lighthouse Museum, Saint Simons Island, GA............383

Salem Art Association-Bush House Museum and Bush Barn Art Center, Salem, OR............1236

Salem County Historical Society, Salem, NJ............924

Salem Historical Society and Museum, Salem, OH............1184

The Salgo Trust for Education, Port Washington, NY 1054

Salisbury House Foundation, Des Moines, IA............515

Salmon Brook Historical Society, Inc., Granby, CT 242

Sam Bell Maxey House State Historic Site, Paris, TX 1442

Sam Houston Regional Library & Research Center, Liberty, TX............1434

Sam Noble Oklahoma Museum of Natural History, Norman, OK............1206

Samek Art Gallery, Lewisburg, PA............1268

Samuel Cupples House of Saint Louis University, Saint Louis, MO............837

San Antonio Conservation Society, San Antonio, TX............1449

San Antonio Museum of Art, San Antonio, TX............1450

San Diego Automotive Museum, San Diego, CA............159

San Diego Museum of Art, San Diego, CA............160

San Fernando Valley Historical Society, Inc., Mission Hills, CA 126

San Francisco Maritime National Historical Park, San Francisco, CA.........169

San Francisco Museum of Modern Art, San Francisco, CA............169

San Jacinto Museum of History Association, La Porte, TX............1433

San Jose Museum of Quilts & Textiles, San Jose, CA............172

Sand Springs Cultural & Historical Museum, Sand Springs, OK............1213

Sandwich Glass Museum, Sandwich, MA ...708

Sandwich Historical Society, Center Sandwich, NH............884

Sandy Spring Museum, Sandy Spring, MD............653

Sanford Museum, Sanford, FL............343

The Santa Barbara Historical Museum, Santa Barbara, CA............179

Santa Barbara Museum of Art, Santa Barbara, CA............179

Sappington House Museum, Crestwood, MO............814

Sapulpa Historical Museum, Sapulpa, OK.1213

Sarah Orne Jewett House, South Berwick, ME............622

Sarasota Classic Car Museum, Sarasota, FL............345

The Sargent House Museum, Gloucester, MA............684

Saunders County Historical Complex, Wahoo, NE............874

Saunders Memorial Museum, Berryville, AR............55

Sautee-Nacoochee Center, Sautee, GA........384

Savannah College of Art and Design Galleries, Savannah, GA 386

Sawin Memorial Building, Dover, MA 680

Sayward-Wheeler House, York Harbor, ME............627

Scarborough Historical Museum, Scarborough, ME............621

The Scarsdale Historical Society, Scarsdale, NY............1066

The Schein-Joseph International Museum of Ceramic Art, Alfred, NY 956

Schenectady County Historical Society, Schenectady, NY............1067

Schingoethe Center for Native American Cultures, Aurora, IL 412

School of Nations Museum, Elsah, IL 433

Decorative Arts–Continued

The Schuette Biermann Farmhouse Museum, Elk Grove Village, IL 432

Schuyler Mansion State Historic Site, Albany, NY 955

Schwenkfelder Library & Heritage Center, Pennsburg, PA...........................1275

Scituate Historical Society, Scituate, MA 708

Scotchtown, Beaverdam, VA.........................1496

Scotland Heritage Chapel & Museum, Scotland, SD...............1355

Scottsdale Museum of Contemporary Art, Scottsdale, AZ...........................44

Scurry County Museum, Snyder, TX 1453

Seattle Art Museum, Seattle, WA 1568

Seattle Asian Art Museum, Seattle, WA....1569

The Seay House, Spartanburg, SC..............1341

Sedgwick-Brooklin Historical Society, Sedgwick, ME...............622

Senate House State Historic Site, Kingston, NY..............1008

Senator George Baldwin Hotel, Klamath Falls, OR..............1227

Senator George Norris State Historic Site, McCook, NE...............868

Senator John Heinz Pittsburgh Regional History Center, Pittsburgh, PA..............1294

Seneca Falls Historical Society, Seneca Falls, NY..............1069

Sequoyah Cabin, Sallisaw, OK 1213

Serra Museum/San Diego Historical Society, San Diego, CA 161

The 1719 William Trent House Museum, Trenton, NJ..............928

1768 Jeremiah Lee Mansion, Marblehead, MA..............693

1761 Pownalborough Courthouse, Dresden, ME..............610

The Sevier County Historical Museum, De Queen, AR 56

Seward County Historical Society Museum, Goehner, NE..............861

Seward House, Auburn, NY..............959

The Shadows-on-the-Teche, New Iberia, LA..............593

Shaftsbury Historical Society, Shaftsbury, VT..............1487

Shaker Heritage Society, Albany, NY 956

The Shaker Museum and Library, Old Chatham, NY..............1045

Shaker Museum at South Union, South Union, KY..............583

Shandy Hall, Geneva, OH..............1166

Sharlot Hall Museum, Prescott, AZ..............43

The Sharon Arts Center, Inc., Sharon, NH..896

Sharon Historical Society, Sharon, CT.........260

Sharpsteen Museum, Calistoga, CA 80

Shelburne Museum, Inc., Shelburne, VT ...1487

Sheldon Memorial Art Gallery and Sculpture Garden/University of Nebraska-Lincoln, Lincoln, NE 867

Shelter Island Historical Society, Shelter Island, NY..............1069

Sherwin Miller Museum of Jewish Art, Tulsa, OK..............1216

Sherwood Forest Plantation, Charles City, VA..............1498

Shirley-Eustis House, Boston, MA..............669

Shirley Plantation, Charles City, VA 1498

Shoal Creek Living History Museum, Kansas City, MO..............822

Shortgrass Country Museum Society, Sayre, OK 1213

Siegfried H. Horn Archaeological Museum, Berrien Springs, MI 729

Simsbury Historical Society, Phelps Tavern, Museum & Homestead, Simsbury, CT..............260

Sioux City Public Museum, Sioux City, IA..............528

Sioux Indian Museum, Rapid City, SD......1355

Skirball Cultural Center, Los Angeles, CA..............121

Skirball Museum Cincinnati Hebrew Union College-Jewish Institute of Religion, Cincinnati, OH..............1151

The Skyscraper Museum, New York, NY..1038

The Slater Memorial Museum - Norwich Free Academy, Norwich, CT 258

Slater Mill Historic Site, Pawtucket, RI.....1315

Slifer House, Lewisburg, PA..............1268

Sloan Museum, Flint, MI..............742

The Smart Museum of Art, Chicago, IL 427

Smith College Museum of Art, Northampton, MA 700

Smith's Fort Plantation, Surry, VA..............1540

Smithtown Historical Society, Smithtown, NY..............1070

Smyth County Museum, Marion, VA..............1516

Snake River Heritage Center, Weiser, ID.....410

The Snite Museum of Art, University of Notre Dame, Notre Dame, IN..............495

Society for Contemporary Craft, Pittsburgh, PA..............1294

Society for the Preservation of Long Island Antiquities, Cold Spring Harbor, NY..............980

The Society of California Pioneers, San Francisco, CA..............170

The Society of the Four Arts, Palm Beach, FL..............334

Soldiers & Sailors Memorial Building, Huntington, NY..............1001

Somers Historical Society, Somers, NY.....1070

Sonnenberg Gardens & Mansion State Historic Park, Canandaigua, NY..............975

Sonoma State Historic Park, Sonoma, CA...188

Sotterley Plantation, Hollywood, MD 647

South Carolina Artisans Center, Walterboro, SC..............1343

South Carolina Department of Parks, Recreation and Tourism, Columbia, SC..............1330

South Carolina State Museum, Columbia, SC..............1331

South Dakota Art Museum, Brookings, SD..............1344

South Dakota State Historical Society, Pierre, SD..............1353

South Park City Museum, Fairplay, CO.......215

South Street Seaport Museum, New York, NY..............1039

Southampton Historical Museum, Southampton, NY..............1070

Southdown Plantation House/The Terrebonne Museum, Houma, LA 589

Southeast Missouri Regional Museum, Cape Girardeau, MO 812

Southeastern Architectural Archive, New Orleans, LA..............598

Southern Arts Federation, Atlanta, GA.........363

Southern Highland Craft Guild at the Folk Art Center, Asheville, NC..............1090

Southern Illinois Art & Artisans Center, Whittington, IL..............466

Southern Ohio Museum, Portsmouth, OH..1183

Southern Plains Indian Museum, Anadarko, OK..............1196

Southold Historical Society and Museum, Southold, NY..............1071

Southwest Museum, Los Angeles, CA 121

Space Farms Zoological Park and Museum, Sussex, NJ..............925

Spanish Governor's Palace, San Antonio, TX..............1450

Spartanburg County Museum of Art, Spartanburg, SC..............1341

Spartanburg County Regional Museum of History, Spartanburg, SC..............1341

The Speed Art Museum, Louisville, KY.....579

Spencer Museum of Art, The University of Kansas, Lawrence, KS..............548

Spertus Museum, Chicago, IL..............427

Spiers Gallery, Brevard, NC 1092

SPJST Library Archives & Museum, Temple, TX..............1455

Spring Street Historical Museum, Shreveport, LA..............602

Springfield Art Association, Springfield, IL..............460

Springfield Art Museum, Springfield, MO ...839

Springfield Museum of Art, Springfield, OH..............1186

Springfield Museums - Connecticut Valley Historical Museum, Springfield, MA..............710

Springfield Museums - George Walter Vincent Smith Art Museum, Springfield, MA..............710

Springfield Museums - Museum of Fine Arts, Springfield, MA..............711

Staatsburgh State Historic Site, Staatsburg, NY..............1071

Stamford Historical Society, Inc., Stamford, CT..............260

Stan Hywet Hall and Gardens, Inc., Akron, OH..............1139

Stark Museum of Art, Orange, TX..............1441

State Capitol, Hartford, Conn., Hartford, CT..............246

State of Illinois-Historic Preservation Agency, Historic Sites Division, Springfield, IL..............460

Staten Island Historical Society, Staten Island, NY..............1074

Staten Island Institute of Arts & Sciences (SIIAS), Staten Island, NY..............1074

Stauth Memorial Museum, Montezuma, KS..............553

Stephen Foster Folk Culture Center State Park, White Springs, FL..............354

The Stephen Girard Collection, Philadelphia, PA..............1288

The Stephen Phillips House, Salem, MA.....707

Sterling and Francine Clark Art Institute, Williamstown, MA..............719

Sterling Historical Society and Little Red Schoolhouse Museum, Sterling, NY......1074

The Stevens-Coolidge Place, a property of The Trustees of Reservations, North Andover, MA..............698

Steves Homestead, San Antonio, TX..........1450

The Stickley Museum at Craftsman Farms, Parsippany, NJ..............920

Stockbridge Library Historical Collection, Stockbridge, MA..............713

Stonewall House, Rocky Mount, NC..........1118

The Stowitts Museum & Library, Pacific Grove, CA..............137

Stranahan House, Inc., Fort Lauderdale, FL..............308

The Stratford Historical Society & Catherine B. Mitchell Museum, Stratford, CT..............262

Stratford, Robert E. Lee Memorial Association, Inc., Stratford, VA..............1539

Strawbery Banke Museum, Portsmouth, NH..............895

Stuart Heritage Museum, Stuart, FL............346

Studio San Giuseppe Art Gallery, Cincinnati, OH..............1151

Stuhr Museum of the Prairie Pioneer, Grand Island, NE..............862

SUArt Galleries - Syracuse University, Syracuse, NY..............1077

Suffolk County Historical Society, Riverhead, NY..............1057

Suffolk County Vanderbilt Museum, Centerport, NY..............977

Summit County Historical Society, Akron, OH..............1139

Sun Gallery, Hayward, CA 102

SunWatch Indian Village/Archaeological Park, Dayton, OH..............1162

The Supreme Court of the United States, Washington, DC..............291

Swampscott Historical Society (John Humphrey House), Swampscott, MA......714
Sweet Briar Museum, Sweet Briar, VA......1540
Switzerland County Historical Museum, Vevay, IN......502
Sylvia Plotkin Judaica Museum of Congregation Beth Israel, Scottsdale, AZ......44

T.C. Steele State Historic Site, Nashville, IN......493
Tacoma Art Museum, Tacoma, WA......1574
The Taft Museum of Art, Cincinnati, OH..1151
Tall Grass Arts Association, Park Forest, IL......449
Tamastslikt Cultural Institute, Pendleton, OR......1230
Tampa's Lowry Park Zoo, Tampa, FL......350
Taos Historic Museums, Taos, NM......953
Tarpon Springs Area Historical Society - Depot Museum, Tarpon Springs, FL......351
Tate House Museum, Portland, ME......620
Taube Museum of Art, Minot, ND......1135
Telfair Museum of Art, Savannah, GA......386
The Temple Museum of Religious Art, Cleveland, OH......1156
Ten Broeck Mansion - Albany County Historical Association, Albany, NY......956
Tennessee Historical Society, Nashville, TN......1380
Tennessee State Museum, Nashville, TN...1381
Terrace Gallery-City of Orlando, Orlando, FL......332
Terrace Hill Historic Site and Governor's Mansion, Des Moines, IA......516
Texarkana Museums System, Texarkana, TX......1455
Texas Governor's Mansion, Austin, TX......1391
Texas Parks and Wildlife Department, Austin, TX......1392
Texas State Museum of Asian Cultures & Educational Center, Corpus Christi, TX......1402
Theodore Roosevelt Birthplace National Historic Site, New York, NY......1040
Theodore Roosevelt Inaugural National Historic Site, Buffalo, NY......973
Thetford Historical Society Library and Museum, Thetford, VT......1488
The Thomas T. Taber Museum of the Lycoming County Historial Society, Williamsport, PA......1308
Thomasville Cultural Center, Inc., Thomasville, GA......388
Thorne-Sagendorph Art Gallery, Keene, NH......890
Thousand Islands Museum, Clayton, NY.....979
Tile Heritage Foundation, Healdsburg, CA......102
Timken Museum of Art, San Diego, CA.....162
Tinker Swiss Cottage Museum, Rockford, IL......456
Tippecanoe County Historical Association, Lafayette, IN......487
Tohono Chul Park Inc., Tucson, AZ......51
The Toledo Museum of Art, Toledo, OH...1187
Torpedo Factory Art Center, Alexandria, VA......1494
Torrington Historical Society, Inc., Torrington, CT......263
Toy & Miniature Museum of Kansas City, Kansas City, MO......823
Traill County Historical Society, Hillsboro, ND......1132
Trailside Nature Museum, Cross River, NY......983
The Trammell & Margaret Crow Collection of Asian Art, Dallas, TX......1408
Travellers Rest Plantation & Museum, Nashville, TN......1381
Tread of Pioneers Museum, Steamboat Springs, CO......232
Trenton City Museum, Trenton, NJ......928

Triangle Tattoo & Museum, Fort Bragg, CA......95
Trinity Museum of the Parish of Trinity Church, New York, NY......1040
Triton Museum of Art, Santa Clara, CA......181
The Trout Gallery, Carlisle, PA......1245
Troy-Hayner Cultural Center, Troy, OH.....1188
The Trustees of Reservations, Beverly, MA......662
Tryon Palace Historic Sites and Gardens, New Bern, NC......1112
Tu-Endie-Wei State Park, Point Pleasant, WV......1586
Tubman African-American Museum, Macon, GA......378
Tucson Museum of Art & Historic Block, Tucson, AZ......51
Tudor Place Foundation, Inc., Washington, DC......292
The Turner Museum, Sarasota, FL......345
Turquoise Museum, Albuquerque, NM......936
Tuskegee Institute National Historic Site, Tuskegee Institute, AL......21
Tyler Museum of Art, Tyler, TX......1456

Ukrainian-American Museum & Archives, Warren, MI......766
The Ukrainian Museum, New York, NY.....1040
Ukrainian Museum-Archives, Inc., Cleveland, OH......1156
Ulster County Historical Society, Marbletown, NY......1013
Ulysses S. Grant Cottage State Historic Site, Wilton, NY......1086
Union County Historical Complex, Creston, IA......512
Union Mills Homestead & Grist Mill, Westminster, MD......656
United States Capitol, Washington, DC......293
United States Golf Association Museum & Archives, Far Hills, NJ......903
United States Hockey Hall of Fame, Eveleth, MN......774
United States Senate Commission on Art, Washington, DC......293
University Art Galleries, Murray State University, Murray, KY......580
University Art Gallery, University of Pittsburgh, Pittsburgh, PA......1294
University Art Gallery, University of the South, Sewanee, TN......1384
University Art Museum, Binghamton, NY...963
University Art Museum, Santa Barbara, Santa Barbara, CA......180
University Art Museum, The University of New Mexico, Albuquerque, NM......936
University Galleries, Clarion, PA......1247
The University Museum, Edwardsville, IL......432
The University Museum, Indiana, PA......1263
University Museum & Historic Houses, The University of Mississippi, Oxford, MS......806
University Museum, New Mexico State University, Las Cruces, NM......941
University of Arizona Student Union Galleries, Tucson, AZ......52
University of Arkansas at Little Rock Art Department Gallery I & II & III, Little Rock, AR......63
University of Iowa Museum of Art, Iowa City, IA......520
University of Kentucky Art Museum, Lexington, KY......574
The University of Michigan Museum of Art, Ann Arbor, MI......726
University of Richmond Museums, Richmond, VA......1532
The University of South Carolina McKissick Museum, Columbia, SC......1331
University of Wyoming Art Museum, Laramie, WY......1636

University Saint Thomas Art History, Saint Paul, MN......792
Upper Room Chapel Museum, Nashville, TN......1381
U.S. Army Women's Museum, Fort Lee, VA......1505
U.S. Grant's Home State Historic Site, Galena, IL......436
USS Constitution Museum, Boston, MA.....669
USS Lexington Museum on the Bay, Corpus Christi, TX......1402
Utah Museum of Fine Arts, Salt Lake City, UT......1472

Vacaville Museum, Vacaville, CA......194
Valdosta State University Fine Arts Gallery, Valdosta, GA......389
Valentine Richmond History Center, Richmond, VA......1532
Valentine-Varian House/Museum of Bronx History, Bronx, NY......967
Valentown Museum, Victor, NY......1081
Van Cortlandt House Museum, Bronx, NY......967
Vanderbilt Mansion National Historic Site, Hyde Park, NY......1002
Vanderbilt University Fine Arts Gallery, Nashville, TN......1381
Vann House, Chatsworth, GA......368
Varner-Hogg Plantation State Historic Site, West Columbia, TX......1461
Ventura County Maritime Museum, Inc., Oxnard, CA......137
The Verdier House, Beaufort, SC......1321
Vermilion County Museum Society, Danville, IL......429
Vermont Historical Society Museum, Montpelier, VT......1482
The Vermont State House, Montpelier, VT......1483
Vesterheim Norwegian-American Museum, Decorah, IA......513
Victoria Mansion, Portland, ME......620
Vikingsholm, Tahoma, CA......191
Villa Louis Historic Site, Prairie du Chien, WI......1619
Villa Montezuma Museum/San Diego Historical Society, San Diego, CA......162
Villa Terrace Decorative Arts Museum, Milwaukee, WI......1613
Village Historical Society, Inc., Harrison, OH......1168
Virginia Historical Society, Richmond, VA......1533
Virginia Museum of Fine Arts, Richmond, VA......1533
Visual Arts Center of Northwest Florida, Panama City, FL......334
Vizcaya Museum and Gardens, Miami, FL......326

W.C. Handy Home Museum and Library, Florence, AL......9
The W.H. Stark House, Orange, TX......1442
Wade House Stagecoach Inn & Wesley Jung Carriage Museum State Historic Site, Greenbush, WI......1599
Wadsworth Atheneum Museum of Art, Hartford, CT......246
Wailoa Center for Culture and Arts, Hilo, HI......393
The Walker African American Museum & Research Center, Las Vegas, NV......880
The Walker Art Collection of the Garnett Public Library, Garnett, KS......541
Walnut Grove Plantation, Roebuck, SC.....1340
Walter Anderson Museum of Art, Ocean Springs, MS......806
Walter Reed Birthplace, Gloucester County, VA......1508
Walters Art Museum, Baltimore, MD......636
The Ward Museum of Wildfowl Art, Salisbury University, Salisbury, MD......653

Decorative Arts—Continued

Warner House, Portsmouth, NH 895

Warren County Historical Society, Warren, PA 1304

Warren County Historical Society Museum, Lebanon, OH 1171

Warther Museum Inc., Dover, OH 1163

Washburn County Historical Society Museum, Shell Lake, WI 1621

Washington County Historical Society, Portland, OR 1233

Washington County Historical Society, Washington, PA 1305

Washington County Historical Society and Miller House Museum, Hagerstown, MD 646

Washington County Museum of Fine Arts, Hagerstown, MD 647

Washington Crossing Historic Park, Washington Crossing, PA 1305

Washington Historical Museum, Washington, GA 391

Washington National Cathedral, Washington, DC 294

Washington State Historical Society, Tacoma, WA 1574

Washington's Headquarters State Historic Site, Newburgh, NY 1042

Waterford Historical Museum and Cultural Center, Inc., Waterford, NY.....1083

Waterloo Area Historical Society, Grass Lake, MI 744

Waterloo Center for the Arts, Waterloo, IA 529

Watkins Woolen Mill State Historic Site & Park, Lawson, MO 825

Watson-Curtze Mansion, Erie, PA 1253

Waveland State Historic Site, Lexington, KY 574

Wayne County Historical Museum, Richmond, IN 497

The Webb-Deane-Stevens Museum, Wethersfield, CT 266

Webb House Museum, Newark, OH 1179

Webster House Museum, Elkhorn, WI.......1596

Weems-Botts Museum, Dumfries, VA........1503

Weir Farm National Historic Site, Wilton, CT 267

Wellesley Historical Society, Inc., Wellesley Hills, MA 717

Wenatchee Valley Museum and Cultural Center, Wenatchee, WA 1577

West Allis Historical Society Museum, West Allis, WI 1626

West Baton Rouge Museum, Port Allen, LA 599

West Bend Art Museum, West Bend, WI...1627

West Chicago City Museum, West Chicago, IL 464

Western Colorado Center for the Arts, Grand Junction, CO 221

Western Heritage Center, Billings, MT.......841

Western Michigan University Richmond Center for Visual Arts School of Art, Kalamazoo, MI 749

Western Reserve Historical Society, Cleveland, OH 1156

Westminster Historical Society, Westminster, VT 1490

Westmoreland Museum of American Art, Greensburg, PA 1257

Westport Historical Society, Westport, CT...266

The Wethersfield Historical Society, Wethersfield, CT 266

The Whale Museum, Friday Harbor, WA...1555

Wharton County Historical Museum, Wharton, TX 1461

The Wharton Esherick Museum, Malvern, PA 1269

Wheels Through Time Museum, Inc., Maggie Valley, NC 1110

The Wheelwright Museum of the American Indian, Santa Fe, NM 950

Whistler House Museum of Art, Lowell, MA 692

White Hall State Historic Site, Richmond, KY 583

The White House, Washington, DC.............294

Whittier Home Association, Amesbury, MA 658

Wichita Art Museum, Wichita, KS 563

Wichita Center for the Arts, Wichita, KS.....563

Wichita-Sedgwick County Historical Museum Association, Wichita, KS 563

Wickersham House Museum (Tanana-Yukon Historical Society), Fairbanks, AK 24

Widener Gallery, Austin Arts Center, Trinity College, Hartford, CT 246

Wilber Czech Museum, Wilber, NE 875

Wilbur D. May Museum, Reno, NV 882

Wilkinson County Museum, Woodville, MS 810

Willard House and Clock Museum, Inc., Grafton, MA 685

William Holmes McGuffey Museum, Oxford, OH 1181

William J. Clinton Presidential Library & Museum, Little Rock, AR 63

William King Regional Arts Center, Abingdon, VA 1491

William S. Hart County Park & Museum, Newhall, CA 130

William Whitley House State Historic Site, Stanford, KY 584

Williams College Museum of Art, Williamstown, MA 719

Willowbrook Museum Village, Newfield, ME 616

Wilson Czech Opera House Corporation, Foundation, Inc. & House of Memories Museum, Wilson, KS 564

Wilson Historical Museum, Wilson, NY....1086

Wilton Historical Museums, Wilton, CT.....267

Wilton House Museum, Richmond, VA 1534

Winchester-Frederick County Historical Society, Inc., Winchester, VA 1546

Winedale, Center for American History, University of Texas at Austin, Round Top, TX 1446

Wing Luke Asian Museum, Seattle, WA....1569

Wings Over The Rockies Air & Space Museum, Denver, CO 213

Winslow Crocker House, Yarmouth Port, MA 722

Winterthur Museum & Country Estate, Winterthur, DE 274

Wiregrass Museum of Art, Dothan, AL 8

Wisconsin Historical Museum, Madison, WI 1606

The Wisconsin Union Galleries, University of Wisconsin-Madison, Madison, WI 1606

Wisconsin Veterans Museum-King, King, WI 1602

Wistariahurst Museum, Holyoke, MA 687

Witte Museum, San Antonio, TX 1451

Wolcott House Museum Complex, Maumee, OH 1175

Wolf House Museum, Manhattan, KS..........552

Wolfeboro Historical Society, Wolfeboro, NH 897

The Wolfsonian - Florida International University, Miami Beach, FL..................327

Wood County Historical Center and Museum, Bowling Green, OH 1143

Woodlawn Museum/The Black House, Ellsworth, ME 610

Woodlawn Plantation Museum, Alexandria, VA 1494

Woodmere Art Museum, Philadelphia, PA.1289

Woodrow Wilson House, Washington, DC 294

Woodstock Artists Association, Woodstock, NY 1087

Woodstock Historical Society, Inc., Woodstock, VT 1491

Worcester Art Museum, Worcester, MA.......721

Workman & Temple Family Homestead Museum, City of Industry, CA 85

World Erotic Art Museum, Miami Beach, FL 327

World Figure Skating Museum & Hall of Fame, Colorado Springs, CO 208

World Golf Hall of Fame, Saint Augustine, FL 340

World Kite Museum & Hall of Fame, Long Beach, WA 1558

The World Organization of China Painters, Oklahoma City, OK..............1211

Wright Museum of Art, Beloit College, Beloit, WI 1592

Wright's Ferry Mansion, Columbia, PA ..1248

The Wyman Tavern, Keene, NH..................890

Yale University Art Gallery, New Haven, CT 254

Yankee Air Force, Inc. (Yankee Air Museum), Ypsilanti, MI 766

Yates County Genealogical and Historical Society and Oliver House Museum and L. Caroline Underwood Museum, Penn Yan, NY 1052

Ybor City Museum State Park, Tampa, FL 351

Yellowstone Art Museum, Billings, MT.......842

Yeshiva University Museum at the Center for Jewish History, New York, NY........1041

Yolo County Historical Museum, Woodland, CA 199

York County Heritage Trust, Museum & Library, York, PA 1309

York W. Bailey Museum at Penn Center, Saint Helena Island, SC 1340

Ypsilanti Historical Museum, Ypsilanti, MI 767

Yuma Art Center Museum - Yuma Fine Arts, Yuma, AZ 54

Zalud House, Porterville, CA......................144

Zanesville Art Center, Zanesville, OH........1194

Zeum, San Francisco, CA 170

Ziibiwing Center of Anishinabe Culture & Lifeways, Mount Pleasant, MI 757

Zippo/Case Visitors Center, Bradford, PA..1244

Zoar State Memorial, Zoar, OH..................1194

Paintings

A.D. German Warehouse, Designed By Frank Lloyd Wright, Richland Center, WI 1620

A.K.C. Museum of The Dog, Saint Louis, MO..831

A.L. Fetterman Educational Museum, Fort Valley, GA......................................372

The APEX Museum, Atlanta, GA 357

A.R. Mitchell Museum, Trinidad, CO..........233

ASA National Softball Hall of Fame and Museum Complex, Oklahoma City, OK..1207

A:shiwi A:wan Museum and Heritage Center, Zuni, NM 954

Abby Aldrich Rockefeller Folk Art Museum, Williamsburg, VA 1544

Abilene Zoological Gardens, Abilene, TX.1385

Abington Art Center, Jenkintown, PA 1263

Abraham Lincoln Library & Museum, Lincoln Memorial University, Harrogate, TN 1366

Academy Art Museum, Easton, MD 642

Ace of Clubs House, Texarkana, TX..........1455

Ackland Art Museum, Chapel Hill, NC.....1093

Adair County Historical Society, Inc., Kirksville, MO 824

Adams County Historical Society Museum, Brighton, CO 204

Adams Museum & House, Deadwood, SD 1346

Adams National Historical Park, Quincy, MA 704

Adams State College Luther Bean Museum, Alamosa, CO 201

Addison Gallery of American Art, Andover, MA 659

The Adirondack Museum, Blue Mountain Lake, NY 963

Adler Planetarium & Astronomy Museum, Chicago, IL 417

Admiral Nimitz National Museum of the Pacific War, Fredericksburg, TX 1419

African American Museum, Dallas, TX 1403

The African American Museum in Philadelphia, Philadelphia, PA 1275

African American Museum of the Arts, De Land, FL 303

Afro-American Cultural Center, Charlotte, NC 1094

Agecroft Hall, Richmond, VA 1527

Ah-Tah-Thi-Ki Museum, Big Cypress Seminole Indian Reservation, FL 295

Ah-Tah-Thi-Ki Museum at Okalee, Hollywood, FL 312

Aiken Center for the Arts, Aiken, SC 1320

Aiken Thoroughbred Racing Hall of Fame and Museum, Aiken, SC 1320

Air Force Flight Test Center Museum, Edwards AFB, CA 92

Airmen Memorial Museum, Suitland, MD 655

Akron Art Museum, Akron, OH 1138

Akta Lakota Museum and Cultural Center, Chamberlain, SD 1345

Akwesasne Museum, Hogansburg, NY 998

Alabama Artist's Gallery, Montgomery, AL 15

Alabama Department of Archives & History, Montgomery, AL 15

Alabama Mining Museum, Dora, AL 7

Alachua County Historic Trust: Matheson Museum, Inc., Gainesville, FL 310

The Alamo, San Antonio, TX 1447

Alamo Township Museum-John E. Gray Memorial Museum, Kalamazoo, MI 748

Alaska Aviation Heritage Museum, Anchorage, AK 21

Alaska Heritage Museum at Wells Fargo, Anchorage, AK 21

Alaska State Museum, Juneau, AK 25

Albany Historical Society, Inc., Sabetha, KS 557

Albany Institute of History & Art, Albany, NY 954

Albany Museum of Art, Albany, GA 355

Albin Polasek Museum and Sculpture Gardens, Winter Park, FL 354

Albion Academy Historical Museum, Edgerton, WI 1596

Albion College Department of Art and Art History, Albion, MI 722

The Albrecht-Kemper Museum of Art, Saint Joseph, MO 830

Albright-Knox Art Gallery, Buffalo, NY 971

Albuquerque Museum, Albuquerque, NM 932

Alden B. Dow Museum of Science and Art of the Midland Center for the Arts, Midland, MI 755

Alden Historical Society, Inc., Alden, NY ...956

The Aldrich Contemporary Art Museum, Ridgefield, CT 259

Alexander Brest Museum and Gallery, Jacksonville, FL 313

Alexander House, Port Edwards, WI 1618

Alexandre Mouton House/Lafayette Museum, Lafayette, LA 589

Alexandria Museum of Art, Alexandria, LA 584

Alger County Heritage Center, Munising, MI 757

Alice C. Sabatini Gallery-Topeka and Shawnee County Public Library, Topeka, KS 558

Alice Moseley Folk Art and Antique Museum, Bay Saint Louis, MS 798

The Alice T. Miner Colonial Collection, Chazy, NY 977

Aliceville Museum, Aliceville, AL 3

Aljira, A Center for Contemporary Art, Newark, NJ 916

Allaire Village Inc., Farmingdale, NJ 903

Allegan County Historical Society and Old Jail Museum, Allegan, MI 723

Allegany County Historical Society, Inc., Cumberland, MD 641

Allegheny College Art Galleries (Bowman, Penelec & Megahan Galleries), Meadville, PA 1270

Allegheny Portage Railroad National Historic Site and Johnstown Flood National Memorial, Gallitzin, PA 1255

Allen Memorial Art Museum, Oberlin, OH 1180

Allen R. Hite Art Institute, Louisville, KY 575

Allentown Art Museum, Allentown, PA 1239

Allied Arts Council of Yakima Valley Gallery, Yakima, WA 1578

Allison-Antrim Museum, Inc., Greencastle, PA 1257

Almond Historical Society/Hagadorn House Museum, Almond, NY 957

Alpine County Museum, Markleeville, CA 124

Altama Museum of Art & History, Vidalia, GA 390

Alternative Museum, New York, NY 1018

Alton Museum of History and Art, Inc., Alton, IL 410

Alva deMars Megan Chapel Art Center, Manchester, NH 891

Amador County Museum, Jackson, CA 105

Amarillo Museum of Art, Amarillo, TX 1386

Amazement Square, The Rightmire Children's Museum, Lynchburg, VA 1514

Amelia Earhart Birthplace Museum, Atchison, KS 532

Amelia Island Museum of History, Fernandina Beach, FL 306

American Academy of Arts and Letters, New York, NY 1018

American Airlines C.R. Smith Museum, Fort Worth, TX 1416

American Airpower Heritage Museum, Inc. & Commemorative Air Force Headquarters, Midland, TX 1438

American Baptist Historical Society, Rochester, NY 1058

American Catholic Historical Society, Philadelphia, PA 1276

American Clock and Watch Museum, Inc., Bristol, CT 236

American Folk Art Museum, New York, NY 1018

American Independence Museum, Exeter, NH 887

American Irish Historical Society, New York, NY 1019

American Jewish Historical Society, New York, NY 1019

American Merchant Marine Museum, Kings Point, NY 1007

The American Museum of Fly Fishing, Manchester, VT 1481

American Museum of Nursing, Tempe, AZ 45

American Quarter Horse Hall of Fame & Museum, Amarillo, TX 1386

American Red Cross Visitors Center and Gift Shop, Washington, DC 275

American Royal Museum & Visitors Center, Kansas City, MO 820

American Saddlebred Horse Museum, Mexico, MO 827

American Saddlebred Museum, Lexington, KY 572

American Sport Art Museum and Archives, Daphne, AL 7

American Swedish Historical Foundation & Museum, Philadelphia, PA 1276

American Swedish Institute, Minneapolis, MN 781

American Textile History Museum, Lowell, MA 691

American University Museum at The Katzen Arts Center, Washington, DC 275

American Visionary Art Museum, Baltimore, MD 629

American Water Ski Educational Foundation, Polk City, FL 337

America's Ice Cream & Dairy Museum, Medina, OH 1175

Americas Society, New York, NY 1020

The Amerind Foundation, Inc., Dragoon, AZ 32

Amherst History Museum at the Strong House - Amherst Historical Society, Amherst, MA 658

Amity and Woodbridge Historical Society, Woodbridge, CT 268

Amon Carter Museum, Fort Worth, TX 1416

Amory Regional Museum, Amory, MS 797

Anadarko Heritage Museum, Anadarko, OK 1195

Anaheim Museum, Anaheim, CA 71

Anchorage Museum at Rasmuson Center, Anchorage, AK 22

Ancient and Honorable Artillery Company, Boston, MA 663

Ancient Spanish Monastery of St. Bernard de Clairvaux Cloisters, North Miami Beach, FL 329

Anderson/Abruzzo Albuquerque International Balloon Museum, Albuquerque, NM 933

Anderson County Arts Center, Anderson, SC 1320

Anderson County Historical Museum, Garnett, KS 541

Anderson County Museum, Anderson, SC.1321

Anderson Fine Arts Center, Anderson, IN ...467

Anderson Gallery - Drake University, Des Moines, IA 514

Anderson Gallery, School of the Arts, Virginia Commonwealth University, Richmond, VA 1528

Anderson Museum of Contemporary Art, Roswell, NM 945

Anderson Ranch Arts Center & Museum, Snowmass Village, CO 232

Andover Historical Society, Andover, MA...660

Andrew J. Blackbird Museum, Harbor Springs, MI 745

Andrew Low House, Savannah, GA 384

The Andy Warhol Museum, Pittsburgh, PA 1290

Angels Gate Cultural Center, San Pedro, CA 176

Anita S. Wooten Gallery at Valencia Community College East Campus, Orlando, FL 331

Anna Lamar Switzer Center for Visual Arts, Pensacola, FL 335

Annie E. Woodman Institute Museum, Dover, NH 886

Annmary Brown Memorial, Providence, RI 1316

Anson County Historical Society, Inc., Wadesboro, NC 1121

Antelope Valley California Poppy Reserve, Lancaster, CA 108

Antelope Valley Indian Museum, Lancaster, CA 108

Paintings–Continued

Antietam National Battlefield-Visitor Center, Sharpsburg, MD 653

The Antiquarian and Landmarks Society, Inc., Hartford, CT 244

The Antique Boat Museum, Clayton, NY 978

The Appaloosa Museum and Heritage Center, Moscow, ID.........................407

Appleton Art Center, Appleton, WI 1589

Appleton Museum of Art, Ocala, FL...........330

APVA's John Marshall House, Richmond, VA 1528

Arbor Lodge State Historical Park, Nebraska City, NE 868

ARC Gallery (Artists, Residents of Chicago), Chicago, IL 417

Arcadia Township Historical Commission, Arcadia, MI 726

Arcadia University Art Gallery, Glenside, PA.........................1256

The Archer Gallery, Vancouver, WA 1576

Archives Museum, Temple Mickve Israel, Savannah, GA.........................384

Archives of J.S.G. Boggs, Brandon, FL....298

Arizona Museum For Youth, Mesa, AZ 37

Arizona State Capitol Museum, Phoenix, AZ 39

Arizona State Museum, Tucson, AZ..............48

Arizona State University Art Museum, Tempe, AZ 45

Ark-La-Tex Antique & Classic Vehicle Museum, Shreveport, LA.........................600

The Arkansas Arts Center, Little Rock, AR.........................61

Arkansas Country Doctor Museum, Lincoln, AR.........................61

Arkansas Museum of Natural Resources, Smackover, AR.........................68

Arkansas River Valley Arts Center, Russellville, AR 67

Arkansas State University Art Gallery, Jonesboro, AR.........................60

Arkansas Tech University Museum of Prehistory and History, Russellville, AR.........................67

Arlington, Birmingham, AL.........................4

Arlington Arts Center, Arlington, VA 1495

The Arlington Historical Society, Arlington, MA 660

Arlington House, The Robert E. Lee Memorial, Arlington, VA.........................1495

Arlington Museum of Art, Arlington, TX ..1387

Armenian Library and Museum of America, Watertown, MA 716

The Armory Art Center, West Palm Beach, FL.........................353

Armstrong Browning Library, Waco, TX ...1458

Arnot Art Museum, Elmira, NY 987

Arrow Rock State Historic Site, Arrow Rock, MO 810

Arrowmont School of Arts & Crafts, Gatlinburg, TN.........................1365

Art and Culture Center of Hollywood, Hollywood, FL.........................312

Art Association of Harrisburg, Harrisburg, PA 1258

Art Association of Henry County, Inc., New Castle, IN.........................494

Art Association of Randolph County, Inc., Union City, IN.........................501

The Art Center at Fuller Lodge, Los Alamos, NM 942

Art Center In Hargate, St. Paul's School, Concord, NH.........................884

Art Center Manatee, Bradenton, FL 297

Art Center of Battle Creek, Battle Creek, MI.........................726

Art Center Sarasota, Inc, Sarasota, FL....343

Art Center Waco, Waco, TX 1458

Art Complex Museum, Duxbury, MA..........680

Art Galleries, California State University, Northridge, Northridge, CA 131

The Art Gallery at the University of Maryland, College Park, College Park, MD 640

Art Gallery at the University of New England, Portland, ME.........................618

The Art Gallery, John C. Calhoun State Community College, Decatur, AL 7

The Art Gallery, Lower Columbia College Fine Arts Gallery, Longview, WA 1558

Art Gallery Marist College, Poughkeepsie, NY 1054

The Art Gallery, University of New Hampshire, Durham, NH 886

Art Guild of Burlington, Inc., Burlington, IA 507

The Art Gym, Marylhurst, OR.........................1228

Art In Embassies Program, U.S. Department of State, Washington, DC 276

The Art Institute of Boston Main Gallery, Boston, MA 663

The Art Institute of Chicago, Chicago, IL ...418

Art League of Houston, Houston, TX.........1425

Art Museum of Greater Lafayette, Lafayette, IN.........................487

Art Museum of South Texas, Corpus Christi, TX 1401

Art Museum of Southeast Texas, Beaumont, TX 1393

Art Museum of the Americas, Oas, Washington, DC.........................276

Art Museum of The University of Memphis, Memphis, TN 1372

Art Museum of Western Virginia, Roanoke, VA.........................1534

ART Station, Stone Mountain, GA..............387

ArtCenter/South Florida, Miami Beach, FL.........................326

Arte Americas, Fresno, CA.........................96

Arthur A. Houghton Jr. Gallery & The Great Hall Gallery, New York, NY 1020

The Arthur J. Moore Methodist Museum, Saint Simons Island, GA.........................383

Arthur M. Sackler Gallery, Washington, DC.........................276

Arthur Ross Gallery, University of Pennsylvania, Philadelphia, PA.........................1276

Artillery Company of Newport Military Museum, Newport, RI.........................1313

Artists Association of Nantucket, Nantucket, MA 695

Artlink, Fort Wayne, IN 477

Artmobile, Newtown, PA.........................1274

Artpace San Antonio, San Antonio, TX 1448

Artrain USA, Ann Arbor, MI.........................724

The Arts & Science Center for Southeast Arkansas, Pine Bluff, AR.........................65

The Arts Center, Jamestown, ND 1133

Arts Center at Okaloosa-Walton College, Niceville, FL.........................329

The Arts Center in Orange, Orange, VA 1524

The Arts Centre, Inc., Martinsburg, WV 1584

Arts Consortium of Cincinnati's African American Museum, Cincinnati, OH 1148

Arts Council of Fayetteville/Cumberland County, Fayetteville, NC.........................1100

Arts Council of Moore County - Campbell House, Southern Pines, NC...1120

Arts Council of Wayne County, Goldsboro, NC.........................1102

Artspace, Raleigh, NC.........................1114

ARTSplace, Grand Forks, ND 1131

Arvada Center for the Arts and Humanities, Arvada, CO.........................201

Ash Hollow State Historical Park, Lewellen, NE.........................864

Ash Lawn-Highland, Charlottesville, VA ...1498

The Ashby-Hodge Gallery of American Art, Central Methodist University, Fayette, MO.........................815

Asheville Art Museum, Asheville, NC.......1088

Ashland Historical Society, Ashland, MA....661

Ashland, The Henry Clay Estate, Lexington, KY.........................572

Ashtabula Arts Center, Ashtabula, OH 1140

Asia Society Museum, New York, NY.......1020

Asian American Arts Centre, New York, NY.........................1021

Asian Art Museum of San Francisco, Chong-Moon Lee Center for Asian Art and Culture, San Francisco, CA 163

Asian Arts & Culture Center, Towson University, Towson, MD 655

Associated Artists of Pittsburgh, Pittsburgh, PA 1290

Association for the Preservation of Tennessee Antiquities, Nashville, TN 1377

Astors' Beechwood Mansion - Living History Museum, Newport, RI.........................1313

The Athenaeum of Philadelphia, Philadelphia, PA 1276

Atlanta Botanical Garden, Atlanta, GA 357

Atlanta College of Art, Atlanta, GA............358

The Atlanta Cyclorama, Atlanta, GA...........358

Atlantic Heritage Center, Somers Point, NJ 924

Atlantic Wildfowl Heritage Museum, Virginia Beach, VA.........................1541

Atrium Gallery Ltd., Saint Louis, MO.........832

Attleboro Arts Museum, Attleboro, MA.......661

Atwater Kent Museum of Philadelphia, Philadelphia, PA 1276

Atwood House Museum, Home of Chatham Historical Society, Chatham, MA 675

Audrain Historical Museum, Graceland, Mexico, MO.........................827

Audubon House & Tropical Gardens, Key West, FL.........................317

Audubon Society of New Hampshire, Concord, NH.........................884

Audubon Society of Rhode Island, Smithfield, RI.........................1319

Augustana College Art Museum, Rock Island, IL.........................453

Aurora Historical Society, Aurora, IL.........411

Aurora Historical Society, Aurora, OH.......1140

Aurora Historical Society, Inc., East Aurora, NY.........................984

Aurora Public Art Commission, Aurora, IL.........................411

Austin Museum of Art - Downtown, Austin, TX.........................1388

Autry National Center of the American West, Los Angeles, CA 112

Avery Research Center for African American History & Culture, Charleston, SC.........................1323

Aviation Museum of Kentucky Inc., Lexington, KY.........................572

The AXA Gallery, New York, NY.........1021

Babe Didrikson Zaharias Museum, Beaumont, TX 1394

Bailey House Museum - Maui Historical Society, Wailuku, HI.........................402

Bakersfield Museum of Art, Bakersfield, CA.........................73

Baldwin Historical Society and Museum, Baldwin, NY.........................960

Baldwin-Reynolds House Museum, Meadville, PA.........................1270

Ball State University Museum of Art, Muncie, IN.........................492

Baltimore & Ohio Railroad Museum, Baltimore, MD.........................629

The Baltimore Museum of Art, Baltimore, MD.........................630

Balzekas Museum of Lithuanian Culture, Chicago, IL.........................418

Bandelier National Monument, Los Alamos, NM.........................942

Bangor Museum & Center for History, Bangor, ME..............604

Banner County Historical Society, Harrisburg, NE..............862

Baranov Museum, Kodiak, AK..............26

The Barbara Fritchie House, Frederick, MD..............644

Barbed Wire Museum, La Crosse, KS..........547

Barker Mansion, Michigan City, IN..............490

Barnard's Mill Art Museum, Glen Rose, TX..............1422

Barnes Foundation, Merion, PA..............1271

Barnes Museum, Southington, CT..............260

The Barnsdall Junior Arts Center & Barnsdall Art Center, Los Angeles, CA..............113

The Barnum Museum, Bridgeport, CT..........235

Barnwell County Museum, Barnwell, SC..1321

Barratt's Chapel and Museum, Frederica, DE..............270

Barrington Living History Farm, Washington, TX..............1460

Barron Arts Center & Museum, Woodbridge, NJ..............931

Bartholomew County Historical Society, Columbus, IN..............472

Bartlett Arboretum & Gardens, Stamford, CT..............260

Barton Museum, Wilson, NC..............1124

Bartow-Pell Mansion Museum, Carriage House & Gardens, Bronx, NY..............964

Bass Museum of Art, Miami Beach, FL......326

Bassett Hall, Williamsburg, VA..............1544

Bates College Museum of Art, Lewiston, ME..............613

Bates-Scofield Homestead, The Darien Historical Society, Darien, CT..............238

The Battles Museums of Rural Life, Girard, PA..............1256

Battleship North Carolina, Wilmington, NC..............1122

Baum Gallery of Fine Art, University of Central Arkansas, Conway, AR..............56

Baxter Springs Heritage Center and Museum, Baxter Springs, KS..............533

Bay Area Museum, Seabrook, TX..............1452

Baycrafters, Inc., Bay Village, OH..............1141

Bayou Bend Collection and Gardens, Houston, TX..............1425

Beall Center for Art and Technology, Irvine, CA..............104

Beard Gallery, Norton, MA..............700

Beau Fort Plantation Home, Bermuda, LA..............587

Beaufort Historic Site, Beaufort, NC..........1091

Beaumont Art League, Beaumont, TX......1394

Beauvoir, The Jefferson Davis Home and Presidential Library, Biloxi, MS..............798

Beck Cultural Exchange Center, Knoxville, TN..............1369

Bedford Gallery at the Dean Lesher Regional Center for the Arts, Walnut Creek, CA..............196

Bedford Historical Society Museum and Library, Bedford, OH..............1142

Bedingfield Inn Museum, Lumpkin, GA......376

Beehive House, Salt Lake City, UT..........1470

Behringer-Crawford Museum, Covington, KY..............567

Belair Mansion, Bowie, MD..............638

Belair Stable Museum, Bowie, MD..............638

Belcourt Castle, Newport, RI..............1313

Belding Museum, Belding, MI..............728

Bellagio Gallery of Fine Arts, Las Vegas, NV..............878

Belle Grove Plantation, Middletown, VA...1517

Belle Meade Plantation, Nashville, TN......1377

Bellport-Brookhaven Historical Society and Museum, Bellport, NY..............961

Belskie Museum of Art & Science, Closter, NJ..............902

Belvedere-Tiburon Landmarks Society, Tiburon, CA..............192

Bement-Billings Farmstead, Newark Valley, NY..............1041

Ben Maltz Gallery at OTIS College of Art and Design, Los Angeles, CA..........113

Ben Shahn Galleries at William Paterson University of New Jersey, Wayne, NJ.....929

Benedicta Arts Center, Saint Joseph, MN....789

Benicia Historical Museum, Benicia, CA......74

The Benjamin Banneker Park & Museum, Baltimore, MD..............631

Benjamin Harrison Presidential Site, Indianapolis, IN..............481

Bennington Center for the Natural & Cultural Arts, Bennington, VT..............1476

Bennington Covered Bridge Museum, Bennington, VT..............1476

The Bennington Museum, Bennington, VT..............1476

Benton County Historical Museum, Philomath, OR..............1230

Benton County Historical Museum, Prosser, WA..............1563

Berea College, Doris Ulmann Galleries, Berea, KY..............565

Bergen County Historical Society, River Edge, NJ..............923

Bergen Museum of Art & Science, Paramus, NJ..............919

Berkeley Art Center, Berkeley, CA..............75

Berkeley County Museum & Heritage Center, Moncks Corner, SC..............1336

Berkeley Plantation, Charles City, VA......1498

Berkshire Artisans/Lichtenstein Center for the Arts, Pittsfield, MA..............702

Berlin Art and Historical Collections, Berlin, MA..............662

Bernheim Arboretum and Research Forest, Clermont, KY..............567

Besser Museum for Northeast Michigan, Alpena, MI..............723

Beth Ahabah Museum & Archives, Richmond, VA..............1528

Bethel Historical Society Regional History Center, Bethel, ME..............606

Bethlehem Historical Association, Selkirk, NY..............1068

Betsy Ross House and Flag Museum, Philadelphia, PA..............1277

Beverly Historical Society and Museum, Beverly, MA..............662

Bexley Historical Society, Bexley, OH.......1143

BG John C.L. Scribner Texas Military Forces Museum, Austin, TX..............1389

Biblical Arts Center, Dallas, TX..............1404

Bicentennial Art Center & Museum, Paris, IL..............449

Bigelow House Museum, Olympia, WA...1560

Biggs Museum of American Art, Dover, DE..............269

Billy Graham Center Museum, Wheaton, IL..............465

Billy Sunday Home Museum and Visitors Center, Winona Lake, IN..............504

Billy the Kid Museum, Fort Sumner, NM...939

Biltmore Estate, Asheville, NC..............1089

Birger Sandzen Memorial Gallery, Lindsborg, KS..............549

Birmingham Bloomfield Art Center, Birmingham, MI..............730

Birmingham Civil Rights Institute, Birmingham, AL..............4

Birmingham Museum of Art, Birmingham, AL..............5

Bishop Hill State Historic Site, Bishop Hill, IL..............413

Bishop Museum, Honolulu, HI..............394

Black Arts National Diaspora Museum, New Orleans, LA..............594

Black Heritage Museum, Miami, FL............323

Black Kettle Museum, Cheyenne, OK.......1198

Black Mountain College Museum & Arts Center, Asheville, NC..............1089

Black River Academy Museum, Ludlow, VT..............1480

Blackhawk Museum (Behring-Hofmann Educational Institute, Inc.), Danville, CA..............89

Blackman House Museum, Snohomish, WA..............1570

Blaffer Gallery, The Art Museum of the University of Houston, Houston, TX...1425

Blaine County Museum, Chinook, MT.......844

Blanden Memorial Art Museum, Fort Dodge, IA..............518

Blanton Museum of Art, Austin, TX...........1389

Blithewold Mansion, Gardens & Arboretum, Bristol, RI..............1310

Bloomfield Academy Museum, Bloomfield, NY..............963

Bloomington Art Center, Bloomington, MN..............769

Blount-Bridgers House/Hobson Pittman Memorial Gallery, Tarboro, NC..............1121

Blount County Memorial Museum, Oneonta, AL..............17

Blount Mansion, Knoxville, TN..............1369

Blue Star Contemporary Art Center, San Antonio, TX..............1448

Bluff Hall Antebellum Home and Museum, Demopolis, AL..............7

B'nai B'rith Klutznick National Jewish Museum, Washington, DC..............277

Bob Burns Museum & River Valley Museum of Van Buren, Van Buren, AR..............69

Bob Jones University Museum & Gallery, Inc., Greenville, SC..............1333

Bob Rauschenberg Gallery, Edison Community College, Fort Myers, FL......308

Boca Raton Historical Society, Boca Raton, FL..............296

Boca Raton Museum of Art, Boca Raton, FL..............296

Boehm Gallery, San Marcos, CA..............174

Boise Art Museum, Boise, ID..............403

Bolduc House Museum, Sainte Genevieve, MO..............837

Bolin Wildlife Exhibit & Antique Collection, McKinney, TX..............1437

Bolinas Museum, Bolinas, CA..............79

Bolton Historical Society, Inc., Bolton, MA..............663

Booker T. Washington National Monument, Hardy, VA..............1510

The Boorman House - The Juneau County Historical Society, Mauston, WI..............1608

Booth Western Art Museum, Cartersville, GA..............367

Boothbay Region Art Foundation, Inc., Boothbay Harbor, ME..............607

Boscobel, Garrison, NY..............993

Boston Athenaeum Library, Boston, MA.....663

Boston Center for Jewish Heritage, Boston, MA..............663

Boston Fire Museum, Boston, MA..............664

Boston National Historical Park, Boston, MA..............664

Boston Public Library, Boston, MA..............664

Boston University Art Gallery, Boston, MA..............665

Boulder Museum of Contemporary Art, Boulder, CO..............203

Bountiful/Davis Art Center, Bountiful, UT..............1463

Bowdoin College Museum of Art, Brunswick, ME..............607

Bowers Museum, Santa Ana, CA..............177

Bowling Green State University Fine Arts Center Galleries, Bowling Green, OH...1143

The Bowne House Historical Society, Flushing, NY..............990

Paintings—Continued

Boyce Thompson Arboretum, Superior, AZ 44

Boys Town Hall of History & Father Flanagan House, Boys Town, NE 858

Bradford Brinton Memorial & Museum, Big Horn, WY 1628

Bradford Historical Society Inc., Bradford, VT 1477

Bradley Gallery of Art, Plymouth, WI 1617

Bragg-Mitchell Mansion, Mobile, AL 13

Braintree Historical Society, Inc., Braintree, MA 670

Braithwaite Fine Arts Gallery, Cedar City, UT 1464

Brand Library & Art Center, Glendale, CA 100

Brandywine River Museum, Chadds Ford, PA 1246

Branigan Cultural Center, Las Cruces, NM 940

Brattleboro Museum & Art Center, Brattleboro, VT 1477

Brauer Museum of Art, Valparaiso, IN 501

Brazosport Museum of Natural Science, Clute, TX 1400

Bread & Puppet Museum, Glover, VT 1479

Bremerton Naval Museum, Bremerton, WA 1549

Brenau University Galleries, Brenau University, Gainesville, GA 373

Brevard Museum of Art and Science, Inc., Melbourne, FL 323

Brick House, Montgomery, NY 1015

Brick Store Museum, Kennebunk, ME 612

Bridge Hampton Historical Society, Bridgehampton, NY 964

Bridgton Historical Society, Bridgton, ME 607

Brigham City Museum-Gallery, Brigham City, UT 1463

Brimstone Museum, Sulphur, LA 602

Bromfield Art Gallery, Boston, MA 665

Bronck Museum, Coxsackie, NY 983

The Bronx County Historical Society, Bronx, NY 964

The Bronx Museum of the Arts, Bronx, NY 965

Brookings Arts Council, Brookings, SD 1344

Brookings County Historical Society Museum, Volga, SD 1358

The Brooklyn Historical Society, Brooklyn, NY 968

Brooklyn Museum, Brooklyn, NY 968

Brooks Academy Museum, Harwich, MA 686

The Broome County Historical Society, Binghamton, NY 962

Broward County Historical Commission, Fort Lauderdale, FL 307

Brown County Art Gallery and Museum, Nashville, IN 493

Brown County Historical Society, New Ulm, MN 785

Brownsville Museum of Fine Art - Brownsville Art League, Brownsville, TX 1398

Bruce Museum, Greenwich, CT 243

Brucemore, Cedar Rapids, IA 509

Brueckner Museum of Starr Commonwealth, Albion, MI 723

Brunnier Art Museum, Ames, IA 504

Brunswick Railroad Museum and C&O Canal Visitors Center, Brunswick, MD 639

Buccleuch Mansion, New Brunswick, NJ 915

Buchanan Center for the Arts, Monmouth, IL 445

Buckaroo Hall of Fame, Winnemucca, NV 882

Buckhorn Saloon & Museum, San Antonio, TX 1448

Bucks County Civil War Library & Museum, Doylestown, PA 1249

Bucksport Historical Society, Inc., Bucksport, ME 608

Bucyrus Historical Society, Bucyrus, OH 1144

Buechel Memorial Lakota Museum, Saint Francis, SD 1355

Buffalo and Erie County Naval & Military Park, Buffalo, NY 972

Buffalo Bill Cody Homestead, Princeton, IA 527

Buffalo Bill Historical Center, Cody, WY 1631

Buffalo Bill Museum & Grave, Golden, CO 219

Buffalo Gap Historic Village, Buffalo Gap, TX 1398

Buffalo Museum of Science, Buffalo, NY 972

Buffalo National River, Harrison, AR 59

Bunker Hill Museum, Charlestown, MA 675

Burchfield-Penney Art Center, Buffalo, NY 973

Bureau County Historical Society Museum, Princeton, IL 452

The Burgwin-Wright Museum, Wilmington, NC 1123

Burlington Historical Museum, Burlington, MA 672

Burnham Tavern, Machias, ME 614

Burritt on the Mountain-A Living Museum, Huntsville, AL 11

Burrowes Mansion Museum, Matawan, NJ 911

Burt County Museum, Tekamah, NE 873

Bushy Run Battlefield, Jeannette, PA 1263

Butler County History Center & Kansas Oil Museum, El Dorado, KS 537

Butler County Museum, Hamilton, OH 1168

The Butler Institute of American Art, Youngstown, OH 1193

The Butler Institute of American Art - Salem Branch, Salem, OH 1184

Butte County Pioneer Memorial Museum, Oroville, CA 136

Butte-Silver Bow Arts Chateau, Butte, MT 843

Butterfield Trail Historical Museum, Russell Springs, KS 557

Butterfly Lodge Museum, Greer, AZ 36

Byers-Evans House Museum, Denver, CO 209

CFCC Webber Center Gallery, Ocala, FL 330

C.M. Russell Museum, Great Falls, MT 848

CU Art Galleries, Boulder, CO 203

Cabrillo Gallery, Aptos, CA 71

Cabrillo Marine Aquarium, San Pedro, CA 176

Cabrillo National Monument, San Diego, CA 156

Cahoon Museum of American Art, Cotuit, MA 677

Caldwell Arts Council, Lenoir, NC 1109

Calhoun County Museum & Cultural Center, Saint Matthews, SC 1341

California African-American Museum, Los Angeles, CA 113

California Center for the Arts, Escondido, Escondido, CA 93

California Historical Society, San Francisco, CA 163

California Oil Museum, Santa Paula, CA 183

California Route 66 Museum, Victorville, CA 195

California State Capitol Museum, Sacramento, CA 151

California State Indian Museum, Sacramento, CA 151

California State Railroad Museum, Sacramento, CA 152

California State University, Long Beach, University Art Museum, Long Beach, CA 110

Call-Booth House Gallery, Paso Robles, CA 141

Calvert Marine Museum, Solomons, MD 654

Calvin College Center Art Gallery, Grand Rapids, MI 743

Calvin Coolidge Historic Site, Plymouth Notch, VT 1484

Calvin Coolidge Presidential Library & Museum, Northampton, MA 699

Cambridge Historical Society, Cambridge, MA 672

Cambridge Museum, Cambridge, NE 858

Camp 6 Logging Museum, Tacoma, WA 1572

Campbell County Rockpile Museum, Gillette, WY 1633

Campbell House Museum, Saint Louis, MO 832

Campus Martius Museum, Marietta, OH 1173

The Camron-Stanford House Preservation Association, Oakland, CA 133

Canaan Historical Society, Inc., Canaan, NY 974

Canajoharie Library and Art Gallery, Canajoharie, NY 974

Canal Fulton Heritage Society, Canal Fulton, OH 1145

Canby Historical Society, Canby, OR 1221

Cando Arts Center/Gallery, Minot, ND 1134

The Cannon Village Visitor Center, Kannapolis, NC 1107

Canoga-Owensmouth Historical Museum, Canoga Park, CA 81

The Canton Museum of Art, Canton, OH 1145

Canyon de Chelly National Monument, Chinle, AZ 31

Cape Ann Historical Museum, Gloucester, MA 684

Cape Cod Museum of Art, Dennis, MA 680

Cape Fear Museum of History and Science, Wilmington, NC 1123

Capitol Reef National Park Visitor Center, Torrey, UT 1475

Capitola Historical Museum, Capitola, CA 81

Cappon & Settlers House Museums, Holland, MI 746

Captain Forbes House Museum, Milton, MA 695

Captain George Flavel House Museum, Astoria, OR 1218

Captain John Wilson House, Cohasset, MA 676

Captain Nathaniel B. Palmer House - Home of the Discoverer of Antarctica, Stonington, CT 261

Caramoor Center for Music & the Arts, Inc., Katonah, NY 1006

Carbon County Museum, Rawlins, WY 1637

Carleton College Art Gallery, Northfield, MN 785

Carlsbad Museum & Art Center, Carlsbad, NM 938

Carnegie Art Museum, Oxnard, CA 136

Carnegie Center for Art & History, New Albany, IN 493

Carnegie Museum of Art, Pittsburgh, PA 1290

Carnegie Resource Center, Mitchell, SD 1351

Carnton Plantation, Franklin, TN 1365

Carpenter Home Museum and Gallery, Cle Elum, WA 1551

Carpenter Museum, Rehoboth, MA 705

Carroll County Historical Museum, Delphi, IN 474

Carroll Mansion Museum Home of Leavenworth County Historical Society, Leavenworth, KS 549

Carroll Reece Museum, Johnson City, TN 1367

Carry A. Nation Home Memorial, Medicine Lodge, KS 553

Carson County Square House Museum, Panhandle, TX 1442

Cartoon Art Museum, San Francisco, CA 164

Cary Cottage, Cincinnati, OH 1148
CAS Gallery, Union, NJ.............................928
Casa Adobe de San Rafael, Glendale, CA ...100
The Casa del Herrero Foundation, Santa
    Barbara, CA...178
Casa Navarro State Historical Park, San
    Antonio, TX..1448
Casemate Museum, Fort Monroe, VA 1505
Cashmere Museum & Pioneer Village,
    Cashmere, WA.......................................1550
Cass County Historical Society,
    Logansport, IN..489
Cass County Historical Society at
    Bonanzaville, West Fargo, ND..............1137
Casteel-Linn House and Museum,
    Princeton, MO..829
Castellani Art Museum of Niagara
    University, Niagara University, NY 1043
The Castle, Marietta, OH 1174
Castle Air Museum, Atwater, CA 72
Catalina Island Museum Society, Inc.,
    Avalon, CA..73
Cathedral Cultural Center, Omaha, NE 870
The Cathedral of St. John the Divine,
    New York, NY.......................................1022
Catholic Historical Society of the
    Roanoke Valley, Roanoke, VA..............1535
Catskill Fly Fishing Center & Museum,
    Livingston Manor, NY 1010
Cayuga Museum & Case Research Lab
    Museum, Auburn, NY 959
Cayuga-Owasco Lakes Historical Society,
    Moravia, NY..1015
Cazenovia College - Art & Design
    Gallery, Cazenovia, NY 976
CCA Wattis Institute for Contemporary
    Arts, San Francisco, CA..........................164
The CCC Weeks Gallery, Jamestown, NY.1004
Cecelia Coker Bell Gallery, Hartsville,
    SC...1335
Cedar Grove Historical Society, Cedar
    Grove, NJ..901
Cedar Rapids Museum of Art, Cedar
    Rapids, IA..509
Cedarhurst Center for the Arts, Mount
    Vernon, IL..446
Centennial Village Museum, Greeley, CO ...221
Center for American Music, Pittsburgh,
    PA...1291
Center for Curatorial Studies,
    Annandale-on-Hudson, NY 958
Center for the Arts - Dalton Gallery,
    Rock Hill, SC..1340
The Center for Western Studies, Sioux
    Falls, SD...1356
Center Galleries, College for Creative
    Studies, Detroit, MI................................735
Center of Southwest Studies/Fort Lewis
    College, Durango, CO.............................214
Center on Contemporary Art, Seattle, WA.1565
Centerville Historical Museum,
    Centerville, MA......................................675
Centerville - Washington Township
    Historical Society & Asahel Wright
    Community Center, Centerville, OH 1146
Central City Opera House Association,
    Central City, CO.....................................205
Central Iowa Art Association,
    Marshalltown, IA....................................523
Central Montana Historical Association,
    Inc. Museum, Lewistown, MT.................850
The Central Museum, Central, AK................23
Centre County Library and Historical
    Museum, Bellefonte, PA 1241
Centre Hill Museum (The Petersburg
    Museums), Petersburg, VA....................1524
Chaffee Center for the Visual Arts,
    Rutland, VT...1486
Chaffey Community Art Association
    Museum of Art, Rancho Cucamonga,
    CA...145

Champaign County Historical Museum,
    Urbana, OH...1188
Chancellor Robert R. Livingston Masonic
    Library & Museum, New York, NY......1022
Chandler Gallery, Randolph, VT 1485
Chandler Museum, Chandler, AZ 31
Chappell Hill Historical Society Museum,
    Chappell Hill, TX..................................1399
Charles A. Grignon Mansion, Kaukauna,
    WI...1601
Charles Allis Art Museum, Milwaukee,
    WI...1610
Charles B. Goddard Center for Visual
    and Performing Arts, Ardmore, OK.......1196
The Charles Edward Choate Exhibit,
    Sandersville, GA.....................................384
Charles H. MacNider Museum, Mason
    City, IA..523
Charles H. Taylor Arts Center, Hampton,
    VA...1509
Charles H. Wright Museum of African
    American History, Detroit, MI.................735
The Charles Hosmer Morse Museum of
    American Art, Winter Park, FL................354
Charles M. Schulz Museum and Research
    Center, Santa Rosa, CA...........................184
Charles River Museum of Industry,
    Waltham, MA 715
Charlotte and Philip Hanes Art Gallery,
    Wake Forest University,
    Winston-Salem, NC...............................1124
Chatillon-DeMenil Mansion, Saint Louis,
    MO...832
Chattahoochee Valley Art Museum,
    LaGrange, GA...375
Chattanooga African Museum/Bessie
    Smith Hall, Chattanooga, TN.................1360
Chazen Museum of Art, Madison, WI 1604
Cheekwood-Tennessee Botanical Garden
    & Museum of Art, Nashville, TN..........1378
Chemung Valley History Museum,
    Elmira, NY..988
Chenango County Historical Society
    Museum, Norwich, NY 1044
Cheney Homestead, Manchester, CT...........248
Cherokee County Historical Museum,
    Inc., Murphy, NC..................................1112
Cherokee Courthouse Visitors
    Information Center & Museum, Gore,
    OK..1201
Cherokee National Museum, Park Hill,
    OK..1211
Cherokee Strip Land Rush Museum,
    Arkansas City, KS...................................532
Cherry Valley Museum, Cherry Valley,
    NY..978
Chesapeake Bay Maritime Museum, Saint
    Michaels, MD...652
Chester Art Guild, Chester, VT 1478
Chester County Historical Society, West
    Chester, PA 1307
Chesterwood, Stockbridge, MA 711
Chetopa Historical Museum, Chetopa, KS...535
Cheyenne Frontier Days Old West
    Museum, Cheyenne, WY 1630
The Chicago Athenaeum: Museum of
    Architecture and Design, Galena, IL.......436
Chicago Botanic Garden, Glencoe, IL.........438
Chicago Children's Museum, Chicago, IL...419
Chicago Cultural Center, Chicago, IL..........419
Chicago History Museum, Chicago, IL........419
Chicago Public Library, Chicago, IL...........419
Chicago Zoological Park (Brookfield
    Zoo), Brookfield, IL................................414
Chickasaw Council House Museum,
    Tishomingo, OK....................................1214
Chief Plenty Coups Museum, Pryor, MT.....852
The Children's Museum, Seattle, WA 1565
Children's Museum at La Habra, La
    Habra, CA...106
The Children's Museum, Inc.,
    Bloomsburg, PA....................................1243

The Children's Museum of Indianapolis,
    Indianapolis, IN 481
Children's Museum of Los Angeles, Van
    Nuys, CA..194
Children's Museum of Pittsburgh,
    Pittsburgh, PA.......................................1291
Children's Museum of the Arts, New
    York, NY...1022
Childress County Heritage Museum,
    Childress, TX..1400
China Institute Gallery, China Institute In
    America, New York, NY 1023
Chinati Foundation, Marfa, TX 1436
Chinese Culture Center of San Francisco,
    San Francisco, CA...................................164
Chinqua-Penn Plantation, Reidsville, NC...1117
Chisholm Trail Heritage Center, Duncan,
    OK..1199
Chisholm Trail Historical Museum,
    Waurika, OK..1216
Chisholm Trail Museum, Wellington, KS 561
Chisholm Trail Museum, Kingfisher, OK...1203
Chittenango Landing Canal Boat
    Museum, Chittenango, NY.......................978
Choctaw County Historical Society,
    Hugo, OK..1203
The Christian C. Sanderson Museum,
    Chadds Ford, PA...................................1246
Chrysler Museum of Art, Norfolk, VA.......1521
Church-Waddel-Brumby House Museum
    & Athens Welcome Center, Athens,
    GA...356
Cigna Museum and Art Collection,
    Philadelphia, PA....................................1277
Cincinnati Art Galleries, Cincinnati, OH....1148
Cincinnati Art Museum, Cincinnati, OH 1148
Cincinnati Museum Center at Union
    Terminal, Cincinnati, OH.......................1149
Circus City Festival Museum, Peru, IN 495
Circus World Museum, Baraboo, WI 1591
City Arts Center, Oklahoma City, OK........1207
City County Pioneer Museum,
    Sweetwater, TX.....................................1454
City Hall Council Chamber Gallery,
    Charleston, SC......................................1324
City Island Nautical Museum, Bronx, NY ...965
City of Bowie Museums, Bowie, MD..........638
City of Burlington Historical Society,
    Burlington, NJ..899
City of Las Cruces Museum System, Las
    Cruces, NM..940
Civil War and Underground Railroad
    Museum of Philadelphia, Philadelphia,
    PA...1278
Civil War Museum of Lonejack, Jackson
    County, Lone Jack, MO 826
Clark Atlanta University Art Galleries,
    Atlanta, GA..359
Clark County Historical Museum,
    Vancouver, WA.....................................1576
Clark Hotel Museum, Van Horn, TX 1457
Clark Humanities Museum-Study,
    Claremont, CA...85
Clarke County Historical Association,
    Inc., Berryville, VA 1496
Clark's Fork Valley Museum, Fromberg,
    MT...846
Clarkson Historical Museum, Clarkson,
    NE...859
Clarksville-Montgomery County Museum
    dba Customs House Museum &
    Cultural Center, Clarksville, TN 1363
Clay Center for Arts & Sciences West
    Virginia, Charleston, WV......................1580
The Clell and Ruth Gannon Gallery at
    Bismarck State College, Bismarck,
    ND...1128
Clermont State Historic Site, Clermont,
    NY..979
Cleveland Artists Foundation at Beck
    Center for the Arts, Lakewood, OH 1170
The Cleveland Museum of Art,
    Cleveland, OH.......................................1152

Paintings–Continued

Cleveland State University Art Gallery, Cleveland, OH 1153

Clifton Community Historical Society, Clifton, KS 535

Clinton Academy, East Hampton, NY 985

Clinton County Historical Society, Wilmington, OH 1191

Clinton County Historical Society Paine-Gillam-Scott Museum, Saint Johns, MI 763

Clinton County Museum, Frankfort, IN 478

Cliveden of the National Trust, Philadelphia, PA 1278

The Cloisters, New York, NY 1023

Clough-Hanson Gallery, Rhodes College, Memphis, TN 1372

Clymer Museum of Art, Ellensburg, WA ...1553

Coachella Valley Museum and Cultural Center, Indio, CA 104

Coal Miners' Museum/Van Lear Historical Society, Inc., Van Lear, KY 584

Codington County Heritage Museum, Watertown, SD 1359

Coe Hall, Oyster Bay, NY 1049

Coeur d'Alenes Old Mission State Park, Cataldo, ID 405

Cokato Museum & Akerlund Photography Studio, Cokato, MN 771

Coke Hallowell Center for River Studies, Fresno, CA 96

Colby College Museum of Art, Waterville, ME 624

Cold Spring Harbor Whaling Museum, Cold Spring Harbor, NY 979

The Coleman House Museum and Brown County Historical Society, Ainsworth, NE 855

Colesville & Windsor Museum at St. Luke's Church, Harpursville, NY 997

The Coley Homestead & Barn Museum, Weston, CT 265

Colfax County Society of Art, History and Archaeology, Raton, NM 945

The College Art Gallery, Ewing, NJ 903

College Football Hall of Fame, South Bend, IN 499

College of Eastern Utah Art Gallery, Gallery East, Price, UT 1469

College of the Redwoods Art Gallery, Eureka, CA 94

College Park Aviation Museum, College Park, MD 641

Collin County Historical Society, Inc. & History Museum, McKinney, TX 1437

Collingsworth County Museum, Wellington, TX 1460

Collinsville Depot Museum, Collinsville, OK 1198

Colonial National Historical Park: Jamestown & Yorktown, Yorktown, VA 1546

The Colonial Spanish Quarter Museum, Saint Augustine, FL 338

Colonial Williamsburg, Williamsburg, VA .1544

Colorado Gallery of the Arts/Araphoe Community College, Littleton, CO 226

Colorado River Indian Tribes Museum, Parker, AZ 38

Colorado Ski Museum-Ski & Snowboard Hall of Fame, Vail, CO 234

Colorado Springs Fine Arts Center (Taylor Museum), Colorado Springs, CO 206

Colorado Springs Museum, Colorado Springs, CO 206

Colton Hall Museum, Monterey, CA 127

Columbia Gorge Discovery Center and Wasco County Museum, The Dalles, OR 1237

Columbia Museum of Art, Columbia, SC ..1329

Columbia River Exhibition of History, Science and Technology, Richland, WA 1564

Columbia River Maritime Museum, Astoria, OR 1218

The Columbian Theatre, Museum & Art Center, Wamego, KS 560

Columbus-Belmont Civil War Museum, Columbus, KY 567

Columbus Chapel, Boal Mansion Museum, Boalsburg, PA 1244

Columbus Cultural Arts Center, Columbus, OH 1157

The Columbus Museum, Columbus, GA 368

Columbus Museum of Art, Columbus, OH 1157

Columbus Museum of Art and Design, Columbus, IN 473

Combat Air Museum, Inc., Topeka, KS 559

Command Museum, Marine Corps Recruit Depot, San Diego, San Diego, CA 156

The Commonwealth Museum, Boston, MA 665

Community Council for the Arts, Kinston, NC 1108

Community Fine Arts Center, Rock Springs, WY 1637

Community of Christ, Independence, MO ...817

Compton Art Collection, Upland, IN, ...501

Concord Art Association, Concord, MA 676

Concord Historical Society, Warner Museum, Springville, NY 1071

Concordia Historical Institute, Saint Louis, MO 832

Concordia University-Wisconsin, Art Gallery, Mequon, WI 1609

Conejo Valley Art Museum, Thousand Oaks, CA 191

Confederate Memorial Hall-Bleak House, Knoxville, TN 1369

Confederate Museum, New Orleans, LA ,....594

Confederated Tribes and Bands of the Yakama Indian Nation - Cultural Heritage Center Museum, Toppenish, WA 1575

Connecticut Audubon Center at Fairfield, Fairfield, CT 240

Connecticut Historical Society, Hartford, CT 244

Connecticut River Museum, Essex, CT 239

Connecticut State Museum of Natural History and Connecticut Archaeology Center, Storrs, CT 261

Constitution Island Association, West Point, NY 1085

Constitution Square State Historic Site, Danville, KY 567

Contemporary Art Center of Virginia, Virginia Beach, VA 1542

Contemporary Art Museum, Raleigh, NC ..1114

Contemporary Art Museum St. Louis, Saint Louis, MO 832

The Contemporary Arts Center, Cincinnati, OH 1150

Contemporary Arts Museum Houston, Houston, TX 1426

The Contemporary Museum, Honolulu, HI 394

The Contemporary Museum at First Hawaiian Center, Honolulu, HI 394

Coos Art Museum, Coos Bay, OR 1222

Coos Historical & Maritime Museum, North Bend, OR 1229

Copia: The American Center for Wine, Food & the Arts, Napa, CA 129

Copper Range Historical Museum, South Range, MI 764

Copshaholm House Museum & Historic Oliver Gardens, South Bend, IN 499

Coral Springs Museum of Art, Coral Springs, FL 301

Corbin Art Center, Spokane, WA 1571

The Corcoran Gallery of Art, Washington, DC 277

Cordova Historical Museum, Cordova, AK 23

Corita Art Center, Los Angeles, CA 114

Cornell Museum of Art & History, Delray Beach, FL 304

Cornish Colony Museum, Windsor, VT 1490

Coronado National Memorial, Hereford, AZ 36

Corpus Christi Museum of Science and History, Corpus Christi, TX 1401

Cortland County Historical Society, Cortland, NY 982

Cottage Grove Museum & Annex, Cottage Grove, OR 1222

Cottonwood County Historical Society, Windom, MN 796

The Country Doctor Museum, Bailey, NC.1091

Coutts Memorial Museum of Art, Inc., El Dorado, KS 537

Cow Neck Peninsula Historical Society Sands-Willets House, Port Washington, NY 1053

Cowpens National Battlefield, Chesnee, SC 1327

Cracker Country, Tampa, FL 348

Cracker Trail Museum, Zolfo Springs, FL...355

Cradle of Aviation Museum, Garden City, NY 992

Cragfont-Historic Cragfont, Inc., Castalian Springs, TN 1360

Cramer-Kenyon Heritage Home, Yankton, SD 1359

Cranbrook Art Museum, Bloomfield Hills, MI 730

Cranbrook House and Gardens Auxiliary, Bloomfield Hills, MI 730

Crater Lake National Park, Crater Lake, OR 1222

Crazy Mountain Museum, Big Timber, MT 841

Creative Arts Guild, Dalton, GA 370

Creek Council House Museum, Okmulgee, OK 1211

Crescent Bend/The Armstrong-Lockett House and The William P. Toms Memorial Gardens, Knoxville, TN 1369

Cress Gallery of Art, Chattanooga, TN 1361

Crestline Shunk Museum, Crestline, OH ...1160

Cripple Creek District Museum, Inc., Cripple Creek, CO 209

Croatian Heritage Museum & Library, Eastlake, OH 1163

Crocker Art Museum, Sacramento, CA 152

Crocker House, Mount Clemens, MI...........756

Crook County Museum & Art Gallery, Sundance, WY 1638

Crooked Tree Arts Center, Petoskey, MI......760

Crossman Gallery, UW-Whitewater, Whitewater, WI 1628

Crossroads Museum, Corinth, MS 800

Crow Wing County Historical Society, Brainerd, MN 769

Crowder College-Longwell Museum & Camp Crowder Collection, Neosho, MO 828

Crowley Art Association & Gallery, Crowley, LA 588

Crystal Rice Plantation, Crowley, LA 588

Culbertson Mansion State Historic Site, New Albany, IN 493

Cumberland County Historical Society, Greenwich, NJ 905

Cumberland County Historical Society, The Hamilton Library and The Two Mile House, Carlisle, PA 1245

Cumberland Island National Seashore, Saint Marys, GA 382

Cummer Museum of Art and Gardens, Jacksonville, FL 314

Cuneo Museum & Gardens, Vernon Hills, IL 463

Cupola House, Egg Harbor, WI..................1596
Curfman Gallery & Duhesa Lounge, Fort
    Collins, CO...216
The Currier Museum of Art, Manchester,
    NH...891
Curwood Castle, Owosso, MI....................759
Custer Battlefield Museum, Garryowen,
    MT...847
Custer County Art & Heritage Center,
    Miles City, MT..851
Custer County 1881 Courthouse Museum,
    Custer, SD..1345
The Custom House Maritime Museum,
    Newburyport, MA.....................................697
Cy Twombly Gallery, Houston, TX............1426
Czech Center New York, New York, NY,...1024

DAAP Galleries, Cincinnati, OH................1150
DAR John Strong Mansion Museum,
    Addison, VT...1475
D.R. Barker Historical Museum,
    Fredonia, NY...992
Dacotah Prairie Museum, Aberdeen, SD....1344
Dade Battlefield Historic State Park,
    Bushnell, FL..298
Dahesh Museum of Art, New York, NY....1024
Dahl Arts Center, Rapid City, SD..............1354
Dakota Discovery Museum, Mitchell, SD.1352
Dakota Sunset Museum, Gettysburg, SD..1348
Dakota Territorial Museum, Yankton, SD..1359
Dakota Territory Air Museum, Minot, ND.1134
Dallam-Hartley XIT Museum, Dalhart,
    TX...1403
The Dallas Center for Contemporary Art
    - The Dallas Contemporary, Dallas,
    TX...1404
Dallas Historical Society, Dallas, TX.........1405
Dallas Holocaust Museum, Dallas, TX......1405
Dallas Museum of Art, Dallas, TX.............1405
The Dalles Art Association, The Dalles,
    OR..1237
Dallidet Adobe and Gardens, San Luis
    Obispo, CA...174
Dalton Galleries, Decatur, GA......................370
The Danbury Museum & Historical
    Society, Danbury, CT................................238
Dane G. Hansen Memorial Museum,
    Logan, KS...550
Danforth Museum of Art, Framingham,
    MA...683
Daniel Boone Home and Boonesfield
    Village, Lindenwood University,
    Defiance, MO..814
The Danish Immigrant Museum, Elk
    Horn, IA..517
Danville Museum of Fine Arts & History,
    Danville, VA..1502
DAR Van Bunschooten Museum, Sussex,
    NJ..925
Daughters of the American Revolution
    Museum, Washington, DC.........................277
Daughters of Utah Pioneers Pioneer
    Memorial Museum & International
    Society Daughters of Utah Pioneers,
    Salt Lake City, UT..................................1471
Daum Museum of Contemporary Art,
    Sedalia, MO..838
Daura Gallery, Lynchburg, VA..................1515
Davenport House Museum, Savannah,
    GA...384
David Conklin Farmhouse, Huntington,
    NY...1000
David Strawn Art Gallery, Jacksonville,
    IL...440
David Winton Bell Gallery, Providence,
    RI...1316
Davis Art Center, Davis, CA..........................89
Davis Art Gallery, Columbia, MO...............813
Davis Museum and Cultural Center,
    Wellesley, MA..716
The Davistown Museum, Liberty, ME.........614
Dawes County Historical Society
    Museum, Chadron, NE..............................859

Dayton Art Institute, Dayton, OH..............1161
Dayton Historical Depot Society, Dayton,
    WA..1552
De Saisset Museum, Santa Clara, CA..........180
De Smet Depot Museum, De Smet, SD.....1346
Deaf Smith County Museum, Hereford,
    TX...1424
Dearborn Historical Museum, Dearborn,
    MI..733
Decatur House Museum, Washington, DC...277
Decorative Arts Collection, Inc. Museum
    of Decorative Painting, Wichita, KS........561
DeCordova Museum and Sculpture Park,
    Lincoln, MA..690
Dedham Historical Society Museum,
    Dedham, MA...679
Deer Isle-Stonington Historical Society,
    Deer Isle, ME..609
Deer Park Escondido Winery & Auto
    Museum, Escondido, CA.............................93
Deerfield Beach Historical Society,
    Deerfield Beach, FL..................................304
Degrazia Gallery In The Sun, Tucson, AZ.....48
Deines Cultural Center, Russell, KS............556
Del Norte County Historical Society,
    Crescent City, CA.......................................87
The DeLand Museum of Art, De Land,
    FL..303
Delaware and Hudson Canal Historical
    Society and Museum, High Falls, NY.....998
Delaware Art Museum, Wilmington, DE.....273
Delaware Center for the Contemporary
    Arts, Wilmington, DE................................273
Delaware Division of Historical &
    Cultural Affairs, Dover, DE......................269
Delta Blues Museum, Clarksdale, MS.........799
Deming Luna Mimbres Museum,
    Deming, NM...939
Denali National Park and Preserve,
    Denali Park, AK...23
Denison Museum, Granville, OH...............1167
The Dennison Railroad Depot Museum,
    Dennison, OH..1162
Dennos Museum Center of Northwestern
    Michigan College, Traverse City, MI......765
Denton County Historical Museum, Inc.
    and Texas Heritage Center, Denton,
    TX...1409
Denver Art Museum, Denver, CO..............210
Denver Botanic Gardens, Inc., Denver,
    CO...210
Department of the Treasury, Washington,
    DC...278
DePaul University Art Museum, Chicago,
    IL...420
DePree Art Center & Gallery, Holland,
    MI..746
Des Moines Art Center, Des Moines, IA.....514
Descanso Gardens Guild, Inc., La Canada
    Flintridge, CA...105
Desert Caballeros Western Museum,
    Wickenburg, AZ...53
Desha County Museum, Dumas, AR............56
Detroit Artists Market, Detroit, MI.............735
Detroit Historical Society, Detroit, MI.........735
The Detroit Institute of Arts, Detroit, MI....736
Detroit Zoo, Royal Oak, MI.......................762
Devils Tower Visitor Center, Devils
    Tower, WY..1631
Dewey Hotel Museum, Dewey, OK...........1199
DeWitt County Historical Museum,
    Cuero, TX..1403
DeWitt Stetten, Jr., Museum of Medical
    Research, Bethesda, MD............................637
DeWitt Wallace Decorative Arts Museum,
    Williamsburg, VA....................................1545
Dey Mansion/Washington's Headquarters
    Museum, Wayne, NJ.................................929
Dia:Beacon, Riggio Galleries, Beacon,
    NY...960
Dia: Chelsea, New York, NY....................1024

Diggs Gallery at Winston-Salem State
    University, Winston-Salem, NC.............1125
Dinnerware Contemporary Arts, Tucson,
    AZ...49
Diplomatic Reception Rooms,
    Department of State, Washington, DC....278
The Discovery Museum, Inc., Bridgeport,
    CT...236
Dishman Art Museum, Beaumont, TX.......1394
Dittrick Museum of Medical History,
    Cleveland, OH...1154
The Dixon Gallery and Gardens,
    Memphis, TN...1372
Dr. Daniel W. Kissam House,
    Huntington, NY.......................................1000
Dr. Increase Mathews House, Zanesville,
    OH..1194
Dr Pepper Museum and Free Enterprise
    Institute, Waco, TX.................................1458
Dr. Samuel D. Harris National Museum
    of Dentistry, Baltimore, MD....................631
Dodge County Historical Society,
    Mantorville, MN......................................780
Dodge County Historical Society
    Museum, Beaver Dam, WI.....................1591
Don F. Pratt Memorial Museum, Fort
    Campbell, KY...568
Don Garlits Museum of Drag Racing
    Inc., Ocala, FL..330
Donkey Milk House, Historic Home, Key
    West, FL..317
Donna Beam Fine Art Gallery, UNLV,
    Las Vegas, NV..878
Doric House, Flemington, NJ.....................903
Dossin Great Lakes Museum, Detroit, MI...736
Douglas County Historical Society,
    Superior, WI...1624
The Douglas F. Cooley Memorial Art
    Gallery, Reed College, Portland, OR.....1231
Dowd Fine Arts Gallery, State University
    of New York College at Cortland,
    Cortland, NY..983
Downey Museum of Art, Downey, CA.........91
Dragon Dreams Museum & Gift Shop,
    Chattanooga, TN....................................1362
Drake Well Museum, Titusville, PA...........1303
The Drawing Center, New York, NY.........1024
Drum Barracks Civil War Museum,
    Wilmington, CA..198
Dry Falls Interpretive Center, Coulee
    City, WA...1551
Dublin-Laurens Museum, Dublin, GA.........370
Dubuque Museum of Art, Dubuque, IA.......516
Duluth Art Institute, Duluth, MN...............772
Dumbarton Oaks Research Library &
    Collections, Washington, DC....................278
Duncan Cottage Museum, Metlakatla, AK.....27
The Duncan Gallery of Art, De Land, FL....304
Dupont Gallery, Lexington, VA.................1513
Dusable Museum of African-American
    History, Inc., Chicago, IL..........................420
Dutchess County Historical Society,
    Poughkeepsie, NY...................................1054
Dwight D. Eisenhower Library-Museum,
    Abilene, KS...531
The Dwight Frederick Boyden Gallery,
    Saint Mary's City, MD..............................652
Dyckman Farmhouse Museum and Park,
    New York, NY...1025

EAA AirVenture Museum, Oshkosh, WI....1616
Eagle Rock Art Museum and Education
    Center, Idaho Falls, ID.............................406
Earth & Mineral Sciences Museum and
    Art Gallery, University Park, PA.............1303
East Brunswick Museum Corporation,
    East Brunswick, NJ..................................902
East End Seaport Museum and Marine
    Foundation, Greenport, NY......................996
East Hampton Historical Society, Inc.,
    East Hampton, NY...................................985
East Hawaii Cultural Center, Hilo, HI.........393

Paintings—Continued

East Jordan Portside Art & Historical Museum, East Jordan, MI 739

East Martello Museum, Key West, FL 317

East Tennessee Historical Society, Knoxville, TN 1369

East-West Center, Honolulu, HI 394

Eastern Arizona Museum and Historical Society of Graham County Inc., Pima, AZ 42

Eastern Shore Art Center, Fairhope, AL 9

The Ebenezer Maxwell Mansion, Inc., Philadelphia, PA 1278

Eccles Community Arts Center, Ogden, UT 1467

Edgar Allan Poe Cottage, Bronx, NY 965

Edgar Allan Poe House and Museum, Baltimore, MD 631

Edgar Allan Poe Museum, Richmond, VA.1529

Edgar County Historical Museum, Paris, IL 449

Edison Museum, Beaumont, TX 1394

Edmonds Art Festival Museum, Edmonds, WA 1553

Edsel & Eleanor Ford House, Grosse Pointe Shores, MI 745

Edward-Dean Museum and Gardens, Cherry Valley, CA 82

Edward H. White II Memorial Museum, Brooks Air Force Base, TX 1397

Egan Maritime Foundation, Nantucket, MA 695

Ehrhart Museum, Antwerp, OH 1139

The 1890 House-Museum & Center for Arts, Cortland, NY 983

82nd Airborne Division War Memorial Museum, Fort Bragg, NC 1101

Eisenhower Birthplace State Historical Site, Denison, TX 1409

Eisenhower National Historic Site, Gettysburg, PA 1255

Eiteljorg Museum of American Indians and Western Art, Indianapolis, IN 482

El Museo Del Barrio, New York, NY 1025

El Museo Latino, Omaha, NE 870

El Paso Museum of Art, El Paso, TX 1411

Elbert Hubbard-Roycroft Museum, East Aurora, NY 985

Elder Art Gallery, Nebraska Wesleyan University, Lincoln, NE 865

Elegba Folklore Society Cultural Center, Richmond, VA 1529

Elizabeth Myers Mitchell Art Gallery at St. John's College, Annapolis, MD 627

Elkhart County Historical Museum, Bristol, IN 471

The Ellen Noel Art Museum of the Permian Basin, Odessa, TX 1441

Elliott Museum, Stuart, FL 346

Ellwood House Museum, DeKalb, IL 429

Elmhurst Art Museum, Elmhurst, IL 433

Eloise Pickard Smith Gallery at Cowell College, Santa Cruz, CA 181

Elsing Museum, Tulsa, OK 1215

Elverhoj Museum of History and Art, Solvang, CA 187

The Emerson Gallery, Clinton, NY 979

Emil A. Blackmore Museum of The American Legion, Indianapolis, IN 482

Emily Dickinson Museum: The Homestead and The Evergreens, Amherst, MA 658

Emmett Kelly Historical Museum, Sedan, KS 558

Epcot at Walt Disney World Resort, Lake Buena Vista, FL 319

Ephraim Historical Foundation, Ephraim, WI 1597

Erie Art Museum, Erie, PA 1252

Erie County History Center & Cashier's House, Erie, PA 1252

Erie Maritime Museum, Homeport U.S. Brig Niagara, Erie, PA 1252

The Erlander Home Museum, Rockford, IL 454

Ernest Hemingway House Museum, Key West, FL 317

Essley-Noble Museum: Mercer County Historical Society, Aledo, IL 410

Estes Park Museum, Estes Park, CO 215

The Esther and John Clay Fine Arts Gallery, Cheyenne, WY 1630

Esther M. Klein Art Gallery at University City Science Center, Philadelphia, PA...1279

The Esther Thomas Atkinson Museum, Hampden-Sydney, VA 1509

Ethnic Heritage Museum, Rockford, IL 455

Eubie Blake National Jazz Institute and Cultural Center, Baltimore, MD 632

Eugene V. Debs Home, Terre Haute, IN 500

Euphrat Museum of Art, Cupertino, CA 89

Eureka Pioneer Museum of McPherson County, Inc., Eureka, SD 1346

Eureka School House, Springfield, VT 1487

Eustis Historical Museum & Preservation Society, Inc., Eustis, FL 306

Evanston Art Center, Evanston, IL 434

Evanston Historical Society and Charles Gates Dawes House, Evanston, IL 434

Evansville Museum of Arts History & Science, Evansville, IN 475

Everglades National Park, Homestead, FL...313

Evergreen Aviation Museum, McMinnville, OR 1228

Evergreen Galleries, Olympia, WA 1560

Evergreen House, The Johns Hopkins University, Baltimore, MD 632

Everson Museum of Art, Syracuse, NY 1076

The Exploratorium, San Francisco, CA........164

Explorit Science Center, Davis, CA 89

Ezra and Cecile Zilkha Gallery, Middletown, CT 249

The Fabric Workshop and Museum, Philadelphia, PA 1279

Fairbanks House, Dedham, MA 679

Fairfax County Park Authority, Resource Management Division, Fairfax, VA 1503

Fairfield Art Association, Fairfield, IA 518

Fairfield County Museum, Winnsboro, SC 1343

Fairfield Historical Society, Fairfield, CT 241

Fairport Marine Museum, Fairport Harbor, OH 1164

Fairview Museum of History & Art, Fairview, UT 1465

Faith Trumbull Chapter, Daughters of the American Revolution, Inc., Museum and Chapter House, Norwich, CT 258

Fall River County Historical Museum, Hot Springs, SD 1348

Fall River Historical Society Museum, Fall River, MA 682

Fallingwater, Mill Run, PA 1272

Falmouth Historical Society, Falmouth, MA 682

Faninadahen Kosas Guahan-Guam Museum, Hagatna, GU 1640

Fargo Air Museum, Fargo, ND 1130

The Farmers' Museum, Inc., Cooperstown, NY 980

Farrar-Mansur House & Old Mill Museum, Weston, VT 1490

FASNY Museum of Fire Fighting, Hudson, NY 1000

Faulconer Gallery at Grinnell College, Grinnell, IA 519

Faulkner County Museum, Conway, AR 56

Favell Museum Inc., Klamath Falls, OR....1227

Fayette Art Museum, Fayette, AL 9

Fayette County Museum, Washington Court House, OH 1190

Fayetteville Museum of Art, Fayetteville, NC 1100

Federal Hall National Memorial, New York, NY 1025

Federal Reserve Board, Washington, DC.....278

Felix Valle State Historic Site, Sainte Genevieve, MO 837

Fender Museum of Music and the Arts, Corona, CA 87

Festival-Institute, James Dick Foundation, Round Top, TX 1446

Fick Fossil & History Museum, Oakley, KS 554

Figge Art Museum, Davenport, IA 512

Filoli Center, Woodside, CA 199

The Filson Historical Society, Inc., Louisville, KY 576

Finch Lane Gallery, Salt Lake City, UT 1471

Fine Arts Center at Miriam Hall, Anna Maria College, Paxton, MA 701

Fine Arts Center for New River Valley, Pulaski, VA 1526

Fine Arts Collection, Luther College, Decorah, IA 513

The Fine Arts Museums of San Francisco, de Young Museum, San Francisco, CA 165

The Fine Arts Museums of San Francisco, Legion of Honor, San Francisco, CA 165

Fire Museum of Maryland, Inc., Lutherville, MD 649

Fire Museum of Memphis, Memphis, TN..1373

Firehouse Art Center, Norman, OK 1206

Firehouse Art Gallery, Nassau Community College, Garden City, NY ...992

The Firehouse Gallery, Burlington, VT......1478

Firelands Historical Society Museum, Norwalk, OH 1180

Fireman's Hall Museum, Philadelphia, PA.1279

1st Cavalry Division Museum, Fort Hood, TX 1414

The First Division Museum at Cantigny, Wheaton, IL 465

First White House of the Confederacy, Montgomery, AL 16

Fisher Gallery, University of Southern California, Los Angeles, CA 115

The Fisk University Galleries, Nashville, TN 1379

Fitchburg Art Museum, Fitchburg, MA........683

The Five Civilized Tribes Museum, Muskogee, OK 1205

The Flag House and Star-Spangled Banner Museum, Baltimore, MD 632

Flagler Museum, Palm Beach, FL 333

Flandrau Science Center and Planetarium, Tucson, AZ 49

Flaten Art Museum of St. Olaf College, Northfield, MN 785

Fleischer Museum, Scottsdale, AZ 43

Fleming Historical Society, Fleming, CO 216

Flint House, Scotia, NY 1068

Flint Institute of Arts, Flint, MI 741

Florence Griswold Museum, Old Lyme, CT 258

Florence Museum of Art, Science & History and the Florence Railroad Museum, Florence, SC 1332

Florewood State Park, Greenwood, MS 801

Florida Air Museum At Sun'n Fun, Lakeland, FL 321

Florida Community College, Kent Campus Museum/Gallery, Jacksonville, FL 314

Florida Gulf Coast University Art Gallery, Fort Myers, FL 309

Florida Holocaust Museum, Saint Petersburg, FL 341

Florida State University Museum of Fine Arts, Tallahassee, FL 347

Flowerdew Hundred Foundation, Hopewell, VA 1511

Folger Shakespeare Library, Washington, DC...................278

The Folsom House Museum, Taylors Falls, MN...................794

Folsom Museum, Inc., Folsom, NM............939

Fondo Del Sol Visual Arts & Media Center/El Museo de Culturas y Herencias Americanas/MOCHA, Washington, DC...................279

Foothills Art Center, Golden, CO.................220

Ford's Theatre National Historic Site (Lincoln Museum), Washington, DC.......279

Forest Lawn Museum, Glendale, CA...........100

The Forges and Manor of Ringwood, Ringwood, NJ...................923

Forney Museum of Transportation, Denver, CO...................212

Fort Abraham Lincoln State Park, Mandan, ND...................1134

Fort Bend Museum Association, Richmond, TX...................1445

Fort Benton Museum of the Upper Missouri, Fort Benton, MT...................846

Fort Bliss Museum, Fort Bliss, TX............1413

Fort Caspar Museum, Casper, WY.............1629

Fort Clatsop National Memorial, Astoria, OR...................1218

Fort Collins Museum of Contemporary Art, Fort Collins, CO...................217

Fort Crawford Museum, Prairie du Chien, WI...................1618

Fort Davis National Historic Site, Fort Davis, TX...................1414

Fort Delaware Society, Delaware City, DE...................268

Fort Douglas Military Museum, Fort Douglas, UT...................1465

Fort Frederick State Park, Big Pool, MD.....637

Fort George G. Meade Museum, Fort Meade, MD...................643

Fort Harker Museum Complex, Kanopolis, KS...................546

Fort Hill (The John C. Calhoun House), Clemson, SC...................1328

Fort Ligonier Association, Ligonier, PA.....1269

Fort McAllister, Richmond Hill, GA............381

Fort Mifflin, Philadelphia, PA...................1279

Fort Phil Kearny, Banner, WY...................1628

The Fort Pitt Block House, Pittsburgh, PA...................1292

Fort Plain Museum, Fort Plain, NY.............991

Fort Polk Museum Activity, Fort Polk, LA...................588

Fort Sam Houston Museum, Fort Sam Houston, TX...................1415

Fort Scott National Historic Site, Fort Scott, KS...................540

Fort Sill National Historic Landmark, Fort Sill, OK...................1201

Fort Sisseton State Historic Park, Lake City, SD...................1350

Fort Smith Art Center, Fort Smith, AR..........57

Fort Union National Monument, Watrous, NM...................954

Fort Vasquez Museum, Platteville, CO.........230

Fort Walton Beach Art Museum, Fort Walton Beach, FL...................310

Fort Wayne Museum of Art, Fort Wayne, IN...................477

Fort Worth Zoological Park, Fort Worth, TX...................1417

Forts Folle Avoine Historic Park, Danbury, WI...................1594

45th Infantry Division Museum, Oklahoma City, OK...................1207

Fossil Museum, Fossil, OR...................1224

Foster Gallery, University of Wisconsin-Eau Claire, Eau Claire, WI..1596

Foster-Tanner Fine Arts Gallery, Tallahassee, FL...................347

Framingham Historical Society & Museum, Framingham, MA...................683

The Frances Lehman Loeb Art Center, Poughkeepsie, NY...................1055

Frances Willard House Museum, Evanston, IL...................434

Frances Young Tang Teaching Museum and Art Gallery, Saratoga Springs, NY .1064

Francis Colburn Gallery, Burlington, VT...1478

Francis Land House Historic Site, Virginia Beach, VA...................1542

Francis McCray Gallery, Silver City, NM....951

Franconia Heritage Museum, Franconia, NH...................888

Frank Lloyd Wright Home and Studio, Oak Park, IL...................448

Frank Phillips Home, Bartlesville, OK.......1197

Frankfort Area Historical Museum, West Frankfort, IL...................464

Franklin County Seminary and Museum, Brookville, IN...................471

Franklin D. Roosevelt Presidential Library-Museum, Hyde Park, NY.........1002

Franklin Furnace Archive, Inc., Brooklyn, NY...................969

Franklin G. Burroughs-Simeon B. Chapin Art Museum, Myrtle Beach, SC...........1338

The Franklin Pierce Homestead, Hillsborough, NH...................889

Fraunces Tavern Museum, New York, NY...................1025

Fred Dana Marsh Museum, Ormond Beach, FL...................333

Fred Harman Art Museum, Pagosa Springs, CO...................229

The Fred Jones Jr. Museum of Art, Norman, OK...................1206

Fred Wolf, Jr. Gallery/Klein Branch Jewish Community Center, Philadelphia, PA...................1280

Frederic Remington Art Museum, Ogdensburg, NY...................1044

Frederick C. Robie House, Chicago, IL.......420

Frederick Douglass National Historic Site, Washington, DC...................279

Frederick R. Weisman Art Museum, Minneapolis, MN...................781

Frederick R. Weisman Museum of Art, Malibu, CA...................123

Fredericksburg Area Museum & Cultural Center, Inc., Fredericksburg, VA...........1506

Freedman Gallery-Albright College, Reading, PA...................1296

Freeport Arts Center, Freeport, IL...............435

Freeport Historical Society, Freeport, ME....611

Freer Gallery of Art, Washington, DC.........279

French Art Colony, Gallipolis, OH.............1165

The French Legation Museum, Austin, TX...................1390

Fresno Art Museum, Fresno, CA...................97

Fresno Flats Historical Park, Oakhurst, CA...................132

Fresno Metropolitan Museum, Fresno, CA...................97

The Frick Art & Historical Center, Pittsburgh, PA...................1292

The Frick Collection, New York, NY.........1025

Friends of Firemen's Museum, New Bern, NC...................1112

Friends of Historic Kingston, Fred J. Johnston House Museum, Kingston, NY...................1007

Frisco Historic Park & Museum, Frisco, CO...................218

Frisco Native American Museum and Natural History Center, Frisco, NC.......1102

Frist Center for the Visual Arts, Nashville, TN...................1379

Frontier Historical Society and Museum, Glenwood Springs, CO...................219

Fruitlands Museums, Harvard, MA.............686

Frye Art Museum, Seattle, WA...................1566

Fulton County Museum, Groversville, NY...................996

Gadsby's Tavern Museum, Alexandria, VA...................1492

Gadsden Arts Center, Quincy, FL...................338

Gadsden Museum, Mesilla, NM...................943

Gadsden Museum of Art, Gadsden, AL.........10

Gaineswood, Demopolis, AL...................7

Galena-Jo Daviess County Historical Society & Museum, Galena, IL...................436

Galena Mining & Historical Museum, Galena, KS...................541

Galeria, Orchard Lake, MI...................759

Galerie Trinitas, Great Falls, MT...................848

Galesburg Civic Art Center, Galesburg, IL...................437

The Gallery at UTA, Arlington, TX...........1387

Gallery 510 Arts Guild, Decatur, IL.............430

Gallery North, Setauket, NY...................1069

Gallery of Contemporary Art, University of Colorado, Colorado Springs, Colorado Springs, CO...................207

Gallery of Henry Street Settlement/Abrons Arts Center, New York, NY...................1026

Gallery on the York - Yorktown Arts Foundation, Yorktown, VA...................1547

Gallery '76, Wenatchee, WA...................1577

Gallier House, New Orleans, LA...................595

Galloping Road Compound & Poker Alley; Harbor Ranch, Dripping Springs, TX...................1410

Galloway House and Village - Blakely Museum, Fond du Lac, WI...................1597

Garden Grove Historical Society, Garden Grove, CA...................99

Gardiner Art Gallery, Stillwater, OK.........1214

The Gardner Museum, Inc., Gardner, MA ...684

Gari Melchers Home and Studio, Fredericksburg, VA...................1506

Garibaldi and Meucci Museum, Staten Island, NY...................1072

Garnavillo Historical Museum, Garnavillo, IA...................518

Garrison Art Center, Garrison, NY...................993

Gary's Gallery, Bismarck, ND...................1128

Gates Mills Historical Society, Gates Mills, OH...................1166

Geddes Historic District Village, Geddes, SD...................1347

General Adam Stephen House, Martinsburg, WV...................1584

General Daniel Bissell House, Saint Louis, MO...................833

The General Douglas L. McBride Museum, New Mexico Military Institute, Roswell, NM...................945

General Douglas MacArthur Memorial, Norfolk, VA...................1521

General Jacob Brown Historical Society, Brownville, NY...................971

General Lew Wallace Study & Museum, Crawfordsville, IN...................473

General Wait House, Waitsfield, VT...........1489

Genesee Country Village & Museum, Mumford, NY...................1016

Geneva Historical Society & Prouty-Chew House & Museum, Geneva, NY...................994

Geneva Historical Society & Rose Hill Mansion, Geneva, NY...................994

George A. Spiva Center for the Arts, Joplin, MO...................820

The George Bush Presidential Library and Museum, College Station, TX.........1400

George C. Marshall Museum, Lexington, VA...................1513

The George D. and Harriet W. Cornell Fine Arts Museum, Winter Park, FL.......354

George J. Doizaki Gallery, Los Angeles, CA...................115

George Washington Carver Museum, Tuskegee Institute, AL...................20

Paintings–Continued

George Washington Carver National Monument, Diamond, MO 814

George Washington Masonic National Memorial, Alexandria, VA 1493

George Washington's Ferry Farm, Stafford County, VA 1537

George Washington's Fredericksburg Foundation, Historic Kenmore & Washington's Ferry Farm, Fredericksburg, VA 1506

George Westinghouse Museum, Wilmerding, PA 1308

Georgetown University Art Collection, Washington, DC..................279

Georgia Capitol Museum, Atlanta, GA 360

Georgia Historical Society, Savannah, GA...385

Georgia Museum of Art, University of Georgia, Athens, GA 356

Georgia O'Keeffe Museum, Santa Fe, NM 947

Georgia Salzburger Society Museum, Rincon, GA 381

Georgia State University School of Art & Design Gallery, Atlanta, GA 360

The Georgian Museum, Lancaster, OH 1171

Georgia's Old Capital Museum, Milledgeville, GA..................380

Gerald R. Ford Presidential Museum, Grand Rapids, MI 743

Geronimo Springs Museum, Truth or Consequences, NM 953

Gertrude Herbert Institute of Art, Augusta, GA 365

Gibbes Museum of Art, Charleston, SC.....1325

The Gibson Society, Inc. dba Gibson House Museum, Boston, MA..................665

The Gilbert Stuart Birthplace and Museum, Saunderstown, RI 1319

Gilcrease Museum, Tulsa, OK 1215

Gilmer Arts and Heritage Association, Ellijay, GA..................371

Glendower State Memorial, Lebanon, OH.1171

Glenn L. Martin Maryland Aviation Museum, Baltimore, MD 632

Glensheen Historic Estate, Duluth, MN 773

The Glynn Art Association, Inc., Saint Simons Island, GA 383

The Godwin-Ternbach Museum, Flushing, NY 990

The Golden Age of Trucking Museum, Middlebury, CT 249

Golden Gate National Recreation Area, San Francisco, CA..................165

The Goldie Paley Gallery at Moore College of Art and Design, Philadelphia, PA 1281

Goodman Museum, Tyler, TX 1456

Goodyear World of Rubber Museum, Akron, OH 1139

Gore Place, Waltham, MA 715

Gorgas House, Tuscaloosa, AL..................19

Goschenhoppen Folklife Library and Museum, Green Lane, PA 1257

Goshen Historical Society, Goshen, CT 242

Gouverneur Historical Association, Gouverneur, NY 995

Governor Bent Museum, Taos, NM 952

Governor Henry Lippitt House Museum, Providence, RI 1316

Governor Ross Plantation, Seaford, DE 272

Governor Seay Mansion, Kingfisher, OK...1204

The Governor's Mansion, Frankfort, KY 569

Governor's Mansion, Columbia, SC 1329

Grace Armantrout Museum, George West, TX 1422

Grace Hudson Museum & Sun House, Ukiah, CA..................193

The Grace Museum, Abilene, TX..................1385

Graceland, Memphis, TN 1373

The Gracie Mansion Conservancy, New York, NY..................1026

Graeme Park, Horsham, PA 1261

Grafton Historical Society, Grafton, VT.....1479

Grand Army of the Republic Civil War Museum, Philadelphia, PA 1281

Grand Lodge AF&AM of Virginia - Allen E. Roberts Masonic Library and Museum, Richmond, VA..................1529

Grand Rapids Art Museum, Grand Rapids, MI..................743

The Grand River Historical Society & Museum, Chillicothe, MO..................813

The Granger Homestead Society, Inc., Canandaigua, NY..................975

Grant County Historical Museum, Canyon City, OR 1221

Grant County Historical Museum, Ephrata, WA..................1553

Grant County Museum, Medford, OK.......1205

Grant County Museum aka Historic Adobe Museum, Ulysses, KS 560

Grant County Museum & Historic Society, Hyannis, NE 863

Grant-Humphreys Mansion, Denver, CO 212

Grant-Kohrs Ranch National Historic Site, Deer Lodge, MT 845

Grants Pass Museum of Art, Grants Pass, OR..................1225

Granville County Historical Society Museum, Oxford, NC..................1114

Grass Valley Museum, Grass Valley, CA 100

Graue Mill and Museum, Oak Brook, IL.....448

Grave Creek Mound Archaeology Complex, Moundsville, WV 1585

Great Basin National Park, Baker, NV.........875

Great Lakes Naval Memorial and Museum, Muskegon, MI..................757

Great Plains Art Museum, Lincoln, NE 865

Great Smoky Mountains Heritage Center, Townsend, TN 1384

The Greater Reston Arts Center (GRACE), Reston, VA 1527

Green Bay Packers Hall of Fame, Green Bay, WI..................1598

Green Hill Art Gallery, Greensboro, NC....1103

Greenbelt Museum, Greenbelt, MD..................646

The Greenburgh Nature Center, Scarsdale, NY 1066

Greene County Historical Society, Xenia, OH..................1193

Greensboro Artists' League, Greensboro, NC..................1103

Greenville County Museum of Art, Greenville, SC 1334

Greenville Museum of Art, Inc., Greenville, NC..................1105

Gregory Kondos Gallery, Sacramento, CA..................152

Grey Art Gallery, New York University Art Collection, New York, NY 1026

Grier Musser Museum, Los Angeles, CA 115

Grissom Air Museum, Peru, IN 496

Gropius House, Lincoln, MA..................690

Grossmont College Hyde Art Gallery, El Cajon, CA..................92

Groton Historical Society, Groton, MA........685

Groveland Yosemite Gateway Museum, Groveland, CA..................101

Guernsey County Museum, Cambridge, OH..................1144

Guggenheim Hermitage Museum, Las Vegas, NV..................878

Guild Hall Museum, East Hampton, NY 986

Guilford College Art Gallery, Greensboro, NC..................1103

Guilford Courthouse National Military Park, Greensboro, NC 1104

Gulf Beach Art Center, Indian Rocks Beach, FL..................313

Gulf Coast Museum of Art, Inc., Largo, FL..................321

GumTree Museum of Art, Tupelo, MS 808

Gunston Hall Plantation, Mason Neck, VA..................1517

Haas-Lilienthal House, San Francisco, CA..................166

Habitot Children's Museum, Berkeley, CA..................75

The Haggin Museum, Stockton, CA 189

The Hagley Museum and Library, Wilmington, DE..................273

Hagood-Mauldin House and Irma Morris Museum of Fine Arts, Pickens, SC....1340

Hahns Peak Area Historical Society and School House, Clark, CO..................205

Hallie Ford Museum of Art, Salem, OR 1235

Halsey Institute of Contemporary Art at the College of Charleston, Charleston, SC..................1325

Hamilton Township Historical Society - John Abbott II House, Hamilton, NJ.......906

Hamline University Galleries, Department of Studio Arts & Art History, Saint Paul, MN..................790

Hammer Museum, Los Angeles, CA...........115

Hammond Castle Museum, Gloucester, MA..................684

Hammond-Harwood House Association, Annapolis, MD 628

Hammond Museum and Japanese Stroll Garden, North Salem, NY..................1043

Hampton County Historical Museum, Hampton, SC 1334

Hampton National Historic Site, Towson, MD..................655

Hampton University Museum, Hampton, VA..................1509

Hanby House, Westerville, OH..................1191

Hancock Historical Society, Hancock, NH..................888

Hancock Memorial Museum, Los Angeles, CA..................116

Hancock Shaker Village, Inc., Pittsfield, MA..................703

Handwerker Gallery, Ithaca, NY 1003

Hank Williams Museum, Montgomery, AL..................16

Hannah Lindahl Children's Museum, Mishawaka, IN..................491

Hanover House, Clemson, SC 1328

Har-Ber Village, Grove, OK 1202

Harbor Defense Museum, Brooklyn, NY.....969

Harding Home and Museum, Marion, OH.1174

Harding Museum, Franklin, OH 1164

Harlan-Lincoln House, Mount Pleasant, IA..................524

Harlow Gallery, Kennebec Valley Art Association, Hallowell, ME 611

The Harness Racing Museum and Hall of Fame, Goshen, NY..................995

Harney County Historical Museum, Burns, OR..................1221

Harold Warp Pioneer Village Foundation, Minden, NE 868

Harper City Historical Society, Harper, KS..................543

Harriet Beecher Stowe Center, Hartford, CT..................245

Harrison County Historical Museum, Marshall, TX..................1436

Harrison Museum of African-American Culture, Roanoke, VA 1535

Harry Ransom Center at the University of Texas at Austin, Austin, TX 1390

Harry S. Truman Library-Museum, Independence, MO..................818

Harvard Historical Society, Still River, MA..................711

Harvard University Art Museums, Cambridge, MA 672

Harvey Cushing/John Hay Whitney Medical Library, New Haven, CT..................253

The Harwood Museum of Art of the University of New Mexico, Taos, NM 952
Hattiesburg Area Historical Society and HAHS Museum, Hattiesburg, MS 801
Hatton Gallery, Colorado State University, Fort Collins, CO 217
Haverhill Historical Society, Haverhill, MA 686
Hawaii Maritime Center, Honolulu, HI 395
Hawaii Pacific University Gallery, Honolulu, HI...395
Hawaii State Foundation on Culture & the Arts and Hawaii State Art Museum, Honolulu, HI.............................395
Hawaii Volcanoes National Park, Kilauea Visitor Center, Hawaii Volcanoes National Park, HI...............................393
Hay House Museum, Macon, GA 377
Hayden Museum of American Art, Paris, TX 1442
Hayward Area Historical Society, Hayward, CA 102
Healdton Oil Museum, Healdton, OK 1202
Heard Museum, Phoenix, AZ.........................40
Hearst Art Gallery, St. Mary's College, Moraga, CA 128
Hearst Castle, San Simeon, CA 177
Heart of West Texas Museum, Colorado City, TX 1401
Hearthstone Historic House Museum, Appleton, WI 1589
Heckscher Museum of Art, Huntington, NY 1000
Heisey Museum, Clinton County Historical Society, Lock Haven, PA 1269
Held-Poage Memorial Home and Research Library, Ukiah, CA...................193
Helena Gallery, Helena, MT 849
Hellenic Museum & Cultural Center, Chicago, IL..421
The Hemingway Museum and The Ernest Hemingway Birthplace, Oak Park, IL 448
Henrico County Historic Preservation & Museum Services, Richmond, VA 1529
Henry Art Gallery, Seattle, WA 1566
Henry B. Plant Museum, Tampa, FL.............349
Henry County Historical Society, New Castle, IN 494
Henry County Museum and Cultural Arts Center, Clinton, MO..............................813
Henry Ford Estate-Fair Lane, Dearborn, MI 734
The Henry Sheldon Museum of Vermont History, Middlebury, VT....................1481
Herbert F. Johnson Museum of Art, Ithaca, NY..1003
Herbert Hoover Presidential Library-Museum, West Branch, IA..........530
Hereford Inlet Lighthouse, North Wildwood, NJ..917
The Heritage Center, Pine Ridge, SD.........1354
Heritage Center of Lancaster County, Inc., Lancaster, PA.................................1265
Heritage Conservancy, Doylestown, PA 1249
Heritage Hill State Historical Park, Green Bay, WI...1599
Heritage Library Museum, Anchorage, AK...22
The Heritage Museum, Baltimore, MD........632
The Heritage Museum, Astoria, OR 1218
Heritage Museum Foundation of Tate County, Inc., Senatobia, MS 808
The Heritage Museum of Fine Arts for Youth, Detroit, MI.................................736
Heritage Museums & Gardens, Sandwich, MA 707
The Heritage Society, Houston, TX............1426
Hermann-Grima/Gallier Historic Houses, New Orleans, LA..595
The Hermitage, Ho-Ho-Kus, NJ 907
The Hermitage Foundation, Norfolk, VA ...1521

The Hermitage: Home of President Andrew Jackson, Hermitage, TN...........1367
Hernando Heritage Museum, Brooksville, FL...298
Herreshoff Marine Museum/America's Cup Hall of Fame, Bristol, RI 1311
Herrett Center for Arts & Science, Faulkner Planetarium and Centennial Observatory, Twin Falls, ID....................410
Hettinger County Historical Society, Regent, ND...1136
Hi-Desert Nature Museum, Yucca Valley, CA..201
Hibel Museum of Art, Jupiter, FL 316
The Hickory Museum of Art, Hickory, NC...1106
Hiddenite Center, Inc., Hiddenite, NC........1106
Higgins Armory Museum, Worcester, MA ...721
Higgins Art Gallery - Cape Cod Community College, West Barnstable, MA...717
High Cliff Historical Society & General Store Museum, Sherwood, WI...............1622
The High Museum of Art, Atlanta, GA.......360
Highland House Museum, Hillsboro, OH ..1168
Highland Park Historical Society, Highland Park, IL..439
Highlands Art League, Sebring, FL..............345
Hill Aerospace Museum, Hill Air Force Base, UT..1466
Hill Cumorah Visitors Center & Historic Sites, Palmyra, NY....................................1050
Hill-Stead Museum, Farmington, CT 241
Hillforest House Museum, Aurora, IN 468
Hills and Dales Estate, LaGrange, GA.........375
Hillstrom Museum of Art, Saint Peter, MN...793
Hillwood Art Museum, Brookville, NY 971
Hillwood Museum & Gardens, Washington, DC,..280
Hinckley Fire Museum, Hinckley, MN 778
Hiram Blauvelt Art Museum, Oradell, NJ....919
Hirshhorn Museum and Sculpture Garden, Smithsonian Institution, Washington, DC...280
The Hispanic Society of America, New York, NY...1027
Historic Arkansas Museum, Little Rock, AR..62
Historic Bowens Mills & Pioneer Park, Middleville, MI..754
Historic Brattonsville, McConnells, SC......1336
Historic Camden Revolutionary War Site, Camden, SC...1323
Historic Charleston Foundation, Charleston, SC..1325
Historic Cherry Hill, Albany, NY 954
Historic Columbia Foundation, Columbia, SC..1329
Historic Columbus Foundation, Inc., Columbus, GA..369
Historic Deerfield, Inc., Deerfield, MA........679
Historic Edenton State Historic Site, Edenton, NC..1099
Historic Fallsington, Inc., Fallsington, PA .1253
Historic Gardner's Basin, Atlantic City, NJ..898
Historic General Dodge House, Council Bluffs, IA...512
Historic Georgetown Inc., Georgetown, CO..218
Historic Governors' Mansion, Cheyenne, WY...1630
Historic Hermann Museum, Hermann, MO..817
Historic Hope Foundation, Inc., Windsor, NC...1124
Historic House Trust of New York City, New York, NY...1027
Historic Hudson Valley, Tarrytown, NY.....1077
Historic Landmarks Foundation of Indiana, Indianapolis, IN........................482

Historic Mobile Preservation Society, Mobile, AL...14
Historic New England/Cogswells Grant, Essex, MA..682
Historic New Harmony, New Harmony, IN..494
The Historic New Orleans Collection, New Orleans, LA..595
Historic Northampton, Northampton, MA....699
Historic Palmyra's Print Shop, Palmyra, NY..1050
Historic Palmyra's - Wm. Phelps General Store, Palmyra, NY.................................1050
Historic Price House, Woodruff, SC...........1343
Historic Prophetstown, Battle Ground, IN ...468
Historic Renville Preservation Commission, Renville, MN.........................787
Historic Richmond Town, Staten Island, NY..1072
Historic Shepherdstown Museum, Shepherdstown, WV...............................1586
Historic Southwest Ohio, Inc., Sharonville, OH..1185
Historic Speedwell, Morristown, NJ.............913
Historic Westville, Inc., Lumpkin, GA.........376
Historical and Genealogical Society of Indiana County, Indiana, PA.................1262
Historical Shrine Foundation of San Diego County, San Diego, CA.................156
Historical Society of Berks County, Reading, PA...1296
Historical Society of Bloomfield New Jersey, Bloomfield, NJ..............................898
Historical Society of Carroll County, Westminster, MD..656
Historical Society of Cecil County, Elton, MD...643
Historical Society of Cheshire County, Keene, NH..890
Historical Society of Columbia County, Saint Helens, OR......................................1234
The Historical Society of Dauphin County, Harrisburg, PA 1258
Historical Society of Delaware, Wilmington, DE.......................................274
The Historical Society of Frederick County, Inc., Frederick, MD 644
Historical Society of Garden County, Oshkosh, NE..871
Historical Society of Glastonbury, Glastonbury, CT..242
Historical Society of Greater Port Jefferson, Port Jefferson, NY 1053
Historical Society of Greenfield, Greenfield, MA..685
Historical Society of Kent County, Inc., Chestertown, MD..640
Historical Society of Millersburg & Upper Paxton Township Museum, Millersburg, PA.......................................1272
Historical Society of Newburgh Bay & the Highlands - David Crawford House, Newburgh, NY.............................1042
Historical Society of Oak Park & River Forest, Oak Park, IL................................448
Historical Society of Ocean Grove, New Jersey, Ocean Grove, NJ...........................918
Historical Society of Old Yarmouth, Yarmouth Port, MA..722
Historical Society of Palm Beach County, Palm Beach, FL............................334
Historical Society of Quincy and Adams County, Quincy, IL....................................452
Historical Society of Rockland County, New City, NY..1017
Historical Society of St. Marys and Benzinger Township, Saint Marys, PA ..1297
Historical Society of Saratoga Springs, Saratoga Springs, NY...............................1064
Historical Society of Stanton County Museums at Stanton and Pilger, Pilger, NE...872

Paintings—Continued

Historical Society of the Town of
    Greenwich Inc. aka Bush-Holley
    Historic Site, Cos Cob, CT 237
Historical Society of Wells and Ogunquit,
    Wells, ME...625
The Historical Society, serving Sleepy
    Hollow and Tarrytown, Tarrytown, NY.1078
History and Traditions Museum,
    Lackland Air Force Base, TX 1433
The History Center in Tompkins County,
    Ithaca, NY...1003
History of Medicine Collections,
    Durham, NC.......................................1098
History San Jose, San Jose, CA...................171
Hockaday Museum of Art, Kalispell, MT....850
Hodgden House Museum Complex,
    Ellsworth, KS.....................................538
Hofstra Museum, Hempstead, NY...............997
Holland Area Arts Council, Holland, MI 746
The Holland Museum, Holland, MI 746
Hollins University Eleanor D. Wilson
    Museum, Roanoke, VA 1535
Holocaust Museum Houston, Houston,
    TX...1426
Holter Museum of Art, Helena, MT............849
Holy Trinity (Old Swedes) Church &
    Hendrickson House Museum,
    Wilmington, DE..................................274
Holyland Exhibition, Los Angeles, CA 116
Home of Franklin D. Roosevelt National
    Historic Site, Hyde Park, NY 1002
Homestead National Monument of
    America, Beatrice, NE.........................857
Homesteader Museum, Powell, WY............1637
Honeywell Center, Wabash, IN....................503
Honolulu Academy of Arts, Honolulu, HI ...395
Honolulu House Museum, Marshall, MI......754
Honolulu Police Department Law
    Enforcement Museum, Honolulu, HI....396
Hood Museum of Art, Hanover, NH 888
Hood River County Historical Museum,
    Hood River, OR..................................1226
Hoosier Salon Gallery, Indianapolis, IN.......483
Hope Lodge and Mather Mill, Fort
    Washington, PA 1254
Hopewell Furnace National Historic Site,
    Elverson, PA......................................1251
Hopewell Museum, Paris, KY.....................582
Hopewell Museum, Hopewell, NJ................908
Horatio Colony House Museum & Nature
    Preserve, Keene, NH 890
Hot Spring County Museum - The Boyle
    House/1876 Log Cabin, Malvern, AR 63
Hot Springs County Museum and
    Cultural Center, Thermopolis, WY 1639
Hotel de Paris Museum, Georgetown, CO...219
Housatonic Museum of Art, Bridgeport,
    CT...236
The House of the Seven Gables, Salem,
    MA..706
House of the Temple, Washington, DC........280
Houston Zoo, Inc., Houston, TX 1427
Howard County Historical Museum,
    Kokomo, IN..486
Howard County Historical Society,
    Ellicott City, MD................................643
Howard-Dickinson House Museum,
    Henderson, TX....................................1424
Howard Steamboat Museum and
    Mansion, Jeffersonville, IN 486
Howard University Gallery of Art,
    Washington, DC..................................281
Howard University Museum, Moorland
    Spingarn Research Center,
    Washington, DC..................................281
Howard Weeden House Museum,
    Huntsville, AL......................................11
The Hoyt Institute of Fine Arts, New
    Castle, PA 1273
Hoyt Sherman Place, Des Moines, IA.........514

The Hubbard Museum of the American
    West, Ruidoso Downs, NM....................946
Hubbell Trading Post National Historic
    Site, Ganado, AZ 34
Hudson Library and Historical Society,
    Hudson, OH.......................................1168
Hudson River Maritime Museum,
    Kingston, NY......................................1007
The Hudson River Museum, Yonkers, NY.1087
The Huguenot Historical Society, New
    Paltz, NY...1017
Hui No'eau Visual Arts Center,
    Makawao, Maui, HI 401
Humboldt Arts Council/Morris Graves
    Museum of Art, Eureka, CA 94
Humboldt Historical Museum, Humboldt,
    KS...544
The 100th Meridian Museum, Cozad, NE ...859
Hunt Institute for Botanical
    Documentation, Pittsburgh, PA 1292
Hunt-Morgan House, Lexington, KY 573
Hunter College Art Galleries, New York,
    NY...1027
Hunter House Victorian Museum,
    Norfolk, VA 1522
Hunter Museum of American Art,
    Chattanooga, TN.................................1362
Huntingdon County Historical Society,
    Huntingdon, PA 1262
Huntington Beach International Surfing
    Museum, Huntington Beach, CA.............104
Huntington County Historical Society
    Museum, Huntington, IN 481
Huntington Library, Art Collections, and
    Botanical Gardens, San Marino, CA 174
Huntington Museum of Art, Inc.,
    Huntington, WV..................................1583
Huntington Sewing & Trade School,
    Huntington, NY...................................1001
Huntsville Museum of Art, Huntsville,
    AL..12
Huron City Museums, Port Austin, MI 761
Hurricane Valley Heritage Park Museum,
    Hurricane, UT.....................................1466
Hus Var Fine Art, Buffalo, NY 973
Hutchinson Art Center, Hutchinson, KS......545
Hutchinson County Museum, Borger, TX..1397
The Hyde Collection, Glens Falls, NY 994
Hyde Hall, Inc., Cooperstown, NY 980
Hyde Park Art Center, Chicago, IL 421
The Hyland House, Guilford, CT................243

IUPUI Cultural Arts Gallery,
    Indianapolis, IN 483
Ida Goodstein Visual Arts Center, Casper,
    WY..1629
Illinois State Museum, Springfield, IL 458
Illinois State Museum, Chicago Gallery,
    Chicago, IL...422
Illinois State Museum/Lockport Gallery,
    Lockport, IL..443
Ilwaco Heritage Museum, Ilwaco, WA.......1556
IMA - Indianapolis Museum of Art,
    Indianapolis, IN 483
Immaculate Conception Catholic Church,
    Natchitoches, LA.................................593
Imperial Calcasieu Museum, Inc., Lake
    Charles, LA..590
Independence Historical Museum,
    Independence, KS................................545
Independence National Historical Park,
    Philadelphia, PA 1281
Independence Seaport Museum,
    Philadelphia, PA 1281
Indian Arts and Crafts Board,
    Washington, DC..................................281
Indian City U.S.A., Anadarko, OK 1195
Indian King Tavern Museum,
    Haddonfield, NJ..................................906
Indian Museum of North America at
    Crazy Horse Memorial, Crazy Horse,
    SD 1345

Indian Pueblo Cultural Center,
    Albuquerque, NM...............................933
Indiana Historical Society, Indianapolis,
    IN 483
Indiana Medical History Museum,
    Indianapolis, IN..................................484
Indiana State Museum, Indianapolis, IN 484
Indiana University Art Museum,
    Bloomington, IN.................................469
Indiana University Kokomo Art Gallery,
    Kokomo, IN..486
Indiana War Memorials, Indianapolis, IN 484
Indianapolis Art Center, Indianapolis, IN.....484
Indianapolis Museum of Contemporary
    Art, Indianapolis, IN...........................485
Inland Seas Maritime Museum,
    Vermilion, OH....................................1189
The Institute For American Indian
    Studies (IAIS), Washington Green, CT ...263
Institute of American Indian Arts
    Museum, Santa Fe, NM 947
The Institute of Contemporary Art,
    Boston, MA..666
Institute of Contemporary Art at Maine
    College of Art (ICA at MECA),
    Portland, ME......................................619
Institute of Contemporary Art, University
    of Pennsylvania, Philadelphia, PA 1282
Institute of Visual Arts, University of
    Wisconsin-Milwaukee, Milwaukee, WI.1611
The Interchurch Center, New York, NY....1027
International Bowling Museum and Hall
    of Fame, Saint Louis, MO 833
International Children's Art Museum, San
    Francisco, CA.....................................166
The International Clown Hall of Fame &
    Research Center, Inc., Milwaukee, WI..1611
International Images, Ltd., Sewickley, PA .1299
International Motor Racing Research
    Center at Watkins Glen, Watkins Glen,
    NY...1084
International Museum of Art and Science,
    McAllen, TX.......................................1437
International Museum of Surgical
    Science, Chicago, IL............................422
International Swimming Hall of Fame,
    Inc., Fort Lauderdale, FL......................307
International UFO Museum and Research
    Center, Roswell, NM...........................946
International Wildlife Museum, Tucson,
    AZ..49
International Women's Air and Space
    Museum, Inc., Cleveland, OH...............1155
Intuit: The Center for Intuitive and
    Outsider Art, Chicago, IL......................422
Iolani Palace, Honolulu, HI 396
Iowa Aviation Museum, Greenfield, IA........519
Iowa Masonic Library and Museum,
    Cedar Rapids, IA.................................509
Ipswich Historical Society and Museum,
    Ipswich, MA.......................................688
Iredell Museum of Arts & Heritage,
    Statesville, NC....................................1120
Irene Cullis Gallery, Greensboro College,
    Greensboro, NC..................................1104
Iris & B. Gerald Cantor Art
    Gallery-College of the Holy Cross,
    Worcester, MA....................................721
Iris & B. Gerald Cantor Center for Visual
    Arts at Stanford University, Stanford,
    CA...188
Irish American Heritage Museum,
    Albany, NY...954
Iron County Museum, Caspian, MI............731
Iroquois County Historical Society,
    Watseka, IL..463
Iroquois Indian Museum, Howes Cave,
    NY...999
Irvine Fine Arts Center, Irvine, CA.............105
The Irvine Museum, Irvine, CA..................105
Isaac Farrar Mansion, Bangor, ME.............604
Isaac Winslow House, Marshfield, MA........693

Isabel Anderson Comer Museum & Arts
    Center, Sylacauga, AL..................18
Isabel Miller Museum/Sitka Historical
    Society, Sitka, AK.......................27
Isabella Stewart Gardner Museum,
    Boston, MA...............................666
Isla Center For the Arts at the University
    of Guam, Mangilao, GU................1640
Island Museum of Art, Westcott Bay
    Institute, Friday Harbor, WA..........1554
Islesford Historical Museum, Islesford,
    ME..612
Islip Art Museum, East Islip, NY.........986

J.L. Scott Marine Education Center and
    Aquarium, Gulf Coast Research
    Laboratory College of Marine
    Sciences, The U. of Southern
    Mississippi, Biloxi, MS................798
The J. Paul Getty Museum, Los Angeles,
    CA..116
J. Wayne Stark University Center
    Galleries, College Station, TX........1401
Jackson County Historical Museum,
    Lakefield, MN...........................778
Jacksonville Museum of Modern Art,
    Jacksonville, FL........................314
Jacqueline Casey Hudgens Center for the
    Arts, Duluth, GA........................371
Jacques Marchais Museum of Tibetan
    Art, Staten Island, NY.................1072
Jaffrey Civic Center, Jaffrey, NH........889
Jail Museum, Neligh, NE..................869
Jamaica Center for Arts & Learning
    (JCAL), Jamaica, NY...................1004
James A. Garfield National Historic Site,
    Mentor, OH.............................1176
James A. Michener Art Museum,
    Doylestown, PA.........................1249
James & Meryl Hearst Center for the
    Arts and Sculpture Garden, Cedar
    Falls, IA................................508
James E. Lewis Museum of Art, Morgan
    State University, Baltimore, MD.......633
James Ford Bell Museum of Natural
    History, Minneapolis, MN..............782
James J. Hill House, Saint Paul, MN......790
James Monroe Museum and Memorial
    Library, Fredericksburg, VA...........1507
James Prendergast Library Association,
    Art Gallery, Jamestown, NY...........1005
James S. Copley Library, La Jolla, CA....106
James W. Dillon House Museum, Dillon,
    SC.......................................1331
James Whitcomb Riley Museum Home,
    Indianapolis, IN........................485
Jamestown Settlement, Yorktown Victory
    Center, The Jamestown-Yorktown
    Foundation, Williamsburg, VA.........1545
Jane Addams Hull-House Museum,
    University of Illinois Chicago,
    Chicago, IL.............................422
Jane Voorhees Zimmerli Art Museum,
    New Brunswick, NJ.....................915
Janet Turner Print Museum, Chico, CA....83
Japan Society Gallery, New York, NY....1028
Japanese American National Museum,
    Los Angeles, CA........................117
Japanese Cultural Center of Hawaii,
    Honolulu, HI............................397
Jasper Rand Art Museum, at Westfield
    Athenaeum, Westfield, MA.............718
Jean P. Haydon Museum, Pago Pago, AS..1640
Jeane Dixon Museum and Library,
    Strasburg, VA...........................1538
Jeff Matthews Memorial Museum, Galax,
    VA.......................................1508
Jefferson Barracks Historic Site, Saint
    Louis, MO..............................833
Jefferson County Historical Society,
    Watertown, NY..........................1083

Jefferson County Historical Society and
    Farnsworth TV Pioneer Museum,
    Rigby, ID...............................409
Jefferson County Historical Society
    Museum, Port Townsend, WA..........1562
Jefferson Historical Society and Museum,
    Jefferson, TX...........................1431
Jefferson National Expansion Memorial,
    Saint Louis, MO........................833
Jensen Arctic Museum, Monmouth, OR....1228
Jerome State Historic Park, Jerome, AZ....36
Jersey City Museum, Jersey City, NJ......908
Jesse James Home Museum, Saint
    Joseph, MO.............................830
Jesse Peter Museum, Santa Rosa, CA.....184
The Jewish Museum, New York, NY.......1029
Jim Gatchell Memorial Museum, Buffalo,
    WY......................................1629
Jim Powers Junk Art Museum, Gage, OK.1201
Jim Savage Western Art and Gift Gallery
    and Memorial Studio, Sioux Falls, SD.1356
Jimmie Rodgers Museum, Meridian, MS....805
Joachim Regional Museum, Dickinson,
    ND......................................1130
John A. Logan College Museum,
    Carterville, IL.........................416
John and Mable Ringling Museum of Art,
    Sarasota, FL............................344
John Burroughs Association, Inc., West
    Park, NY...............................1085
John F. Kennedy Presidential Library &
    Museum, Boston, MA...................666
John Furlong Gallery, Menomonie, WI....1609
John G. Neihardt State Historic Site,
    Bancroft, NE............................856
John James Audubon Center at Mill
    Grove, Audubon, PA....................1241
John James Audubon Museum,
    Henderson, KY..........................571
John Jay Homestead State Historic Site,
    Katonah, NY...........................1006
John Marlor Arts Center, Milledgeville,
    GA......................................380
John Michael Kohler Arts Center,
    Sheboygan, WI.........................1621
John Nance Garner Museum, Uvalde, TX.1457
The John Nicholas Brown Center for the
    Study of American Civilization,
    Providence, RI.........................1317
John Paul Jones House Museum,
    Portsmouth, NH........................894
John Slade Ely House, New Haven, CT...253
John Stark Edwards House, Warren, OH..1189
John Wesley Powell Museum, Green
    River, UT...............................1466
John Wornall House Museum, Kansas
    City, MO................................821
Johnson County Community College,
    Gallery of Art, Overland Park, KS.....555
Johnson County Museum of History,
    Franklin, IN............................478
Johnson Hall State Historic Site,
    Johnstown, NY.........................1005
Johnson Victrola Museum, Dover, DE....270
Johnstown Historical Society, Johnstown,
    NY......................................1005
Jonathan Hager House & Museum,
    Hagerstown, MD........................646
Jonson Gallery of the University of New
    Mexico Art Museum, Albuquerque,
    NM.....................................933
Jordan Schnitzer Museum of Art, Eugene,
    OR.....................................1223
Joseloff Gallery, Hartford Art School,
    University of Hartford, West Hartford,
    CT......................................264
Joseph Smith Historic Site, Nauvoo, IL..447
Joslyn Art Museum, Omaha, NE..........871
The Journey Museum, Rapid City, SD....1354
Judah L. Magnes Museum, Berkeley, CA..76
Judaica Museum of Central Synagogue,
    New York, NY..........................1029

The Judaica Museum of the Hebrew
    Home at Riverdale, Riverdale, NY.....1057
Judith Basin County Museum, Stanford,
    MT......................................853
Judy Garland Museum, Grand Rapids,
    MN.....................................777
Jule Collins Smith Museum of Fine Art,
    Auburn, AL...............................3
Juliette Gordon Low Birthplace,
    Savannah, GA...........................385
Jundt Art Museum, Spokane, WA........1571
Juneteenth Creative Cultural Center &
    Museum, Saginaw, MI...................762
Juniata College Museum of Art,
    Huntingdon, PA........................1262
Juniata County Historical Society,
    Mifflintown, PA........................1271
Justice Brothers Racing Museum, Duarte,
    CA.......................................91
Justin Smith Morrill Homestead,
    Strafford, VT...........................1488

Kalamazoo Aviation History Museum,
    Kalamazoo, MI..........................748
Kalamazoo Institute of Arts, Kalamazoo,
    MI.......................................748
Kalamazoo Valley Museum, Kalamazoo,
    MI.......................................749
Kaleidoscope, Kansas City, MO...........821
Kalkaska County Historical Museum,
    Kalkaska, MI............................749
Kaminski House Museum, Georgetown,
    SC......................................1333
The Kansas African American Museum,
    Wichita, KS.............................561
Kansas Aviation Museum, Wichita, KS....562
Kansas Department of Wildlife & Parks,
    Pratt, KS...............................556
Kansas Museum of History, Topeka, KS..559
Karl C. Harrison Museum of George
    Washington, Columbiana, AL.............6
Karl Drerup Fine Arts Gallery at
    Plymouth State University, Plymouth,
    NH.....................................893
Kateri Galleries, The National Shrine of
    the North American Martyrs,
    Auriesville, NY..........................959
Katherine Dunham Dynamic Museum,
    East Saint Louis, IL....................431
Katherine Nash Gallery, Minneapolis,
    MN.....................................782
Katonah Museum of Art, Katonah, NY...1006
Kauai Museum, Lihue, HI................401
Kearney County Historical Museum,
    Minden, NE.............................868
The Kearny Cottage, Perth Amboy, NJ...921
Kelly-Griggs House Museum, Red Bluff,
    CA......................................146
Kelton House Museum & Garden,
    Columbus, OH.........................1158
Kemerer Museum of Decorative Arts,
    Bethlehem, PA.........................1242
Kemp Center for the Arts, Wichita Falls,
    TX.....................................1461
Kemper Museum of Contemporary Art,
    Kansas City, MO........................821
Kenilworth Aquatic Gardens, Washington,
    DC......................................281
Kennebunkport Historical Society,
    Kennebunkport, ME.....................612
Kennedy Art Center Gallery at Holy
    Names University, Oakland, CA.........133
Kennedy-Douglass Center for the Arts,
    Florence, AL..............................9
Kennedy Museum of Art, Athens, OH...1140
Kennesaw Mountain National Battlefield
    Park, Kennesaw, GA.....................374
Kenosha County Historical Society and
    Museum, Inc., Kenosha, WI............1602
Kenosha Public Museum, Kenosha, WI...1602
The Kent Art Association, Kent, CT......247
Kent-Delord House Museum, Plattsburgh,
    NY.....................................1052

Paintings—Continued

Kent State University Museum, Kent, OH.1169
Kent State University, School of Art
  Galleries, Kent, OH..................................1169
The Kentuck Museum Association/Art
  Center/Festival of the Arts, Northport,
  AL..17
Kentucky Derby Museum, Louisville, KY...576
The Kentucky Folk Art Center,
  Morehead, KY...580
Kentucky Gateway Museum Center,
  Maysville, KY...579
Kentucky Historical Society, Frankfort,
  KY...569
The Kentucky Library & Museum,
  Bowling Green, KY...................................565
Kentucky State Capitol, Frankfort, KY.........569
Key West Museum of Art and History,
  Key West, FL..318
Keyport Historical Society-Steamboat
  Dock Museum, Keyport, NJ......................909
Kid City - The Children's Museum of
  Tampa, Tampa, FL....................................349
Kimbell Art Museum, Fort Worth, TX.......1417
Kimberly Crest House & Gardens,
  Redlands, CA..147
King Kamehameha V-Judiciary History
  Center, Honolulu, HI.................................397
King Manor, Jamaica, NY.............................1004
Kings Mountain National Military Park,
  Blacksburg, SC..1322
Kingwood Center, Mansfield, OH...............1173
Kipp Gallery at Indiana University of
  Pennsylvania, Indiana, PA.......................1262
Kirkland Arts Center, Kirkland, WA...........1557
Kirkland Fine Arts Center-Perkinson
  Gallery, Decatur, IL..................................430
Kirkland Museum of Fine & Decorative
  Art, Denver, CO.......................................212
Kirtland Temple Historic Center,
  Kirtland, OH...1170
Kittery Historical & Naval Museum,
  Kittery, ME...613
Kittredge Gallery, University of Puget
  Sound Art Dept., Tacoma, WA.................1573
Kittson County History Center Museum,
  Lake Bronson, MN....................................778
Klein Museum, Mobridge, SD.....................1352
Klemm Gallery, Adrian, MI..........................722
Kluge-Ruhe Aboriginal Art Collection at
  the University of Virginia,
  Charlottesville, VA..................................1499
Knights of Columbus Museum, New
  Haven, CT...253
Knox Headquarters State Historic Site,
  Vails Gate, NY..1080
Knoxville Museum of Art, Knoxville, TN.1370
Koester House Museum, Marysville, KS.....552
Kohl Children's Museum of Greater
  Chicago, Glenview, IL..............................438
Kokomo Art Association Art Center,
  Kokomo, IN..487
Koochiching County Historical Museum,
  International Falls, MN..............................778
Korean War Veterans National Museum
  & Library, Rantoul, IL..............................453
Koreshan State Historic Site, Estero, FL......306
Korner's Folly, Kernersville, NC.................1108
Koshare Indian Museum, Inc., La Junta,
  CO...224
Koucky Gallery, Bokeelia, FL......................297
Krannert Art Museum and Kinkead
  Pavilion, Champaign, IL...........................416
The Kreeger Museum, Washington, DC......281
Krempp Gallery, Jasper, IN...........................486
Kresge Art Museum, East Lansing, MI........739
Kuhlmann King Historical House and
  Museum, Boerne, TX...............................1396

L.C. Bates Museum, Hinckley, ME..............612
L.D. "Brink" Brinkman Foundation,
  Kerrville, TX..1431

L.H. Bailey Hortorium, Ithaca, NY............1003
La Miranda, Monterey, CA............................127
La Purisima Mission State Historic Park,
  Lompoc, CA..109
La Raza/Galeria Posada, Sacramento, CA...153
La Salle University Art Museum,
  Philadelphia, PA......................................1282
LaBelle Heritage Museum, LaBelle, FL.......319
Lac Qui Parle County Historical Society,
  Madison, MN..779
Lacey Historical Society, Forked River,
  NJ..904
The Lackawanna Historical Society at the
  Catlin House, Scranton, PA.....................1298
The Lacrosse Museum & National Hall
  of Fame/US Lacrosse, Baltimore, MD....633
Ladew Topiary Gardens, Monkton, MD......649
Lafayette College Art Gallery, Williams
  Center for the Arts, Easton, PA...............1250
LaGrange Plantation, Cambridge, MD.........639
Laguna Art Museum, Laguna Beach, CA....107
Lahaina Restoration Foundation, Lahaina,
  HI..400
The Lake Champlain Maritime Museum,
  Vergennes, VT...1488
Lake County Historical Society, Two
  Harbors, MN...794
Lake George Historical Association
  Museum, Lake George, NY.....................1008
Lake Guernsey Museum-Guernsey State
  Park, Guernsey, WY................................1634
Lake Jackson Historical Museum, Lake
  Jackson, TX..1433
Lake Wales Depot Museum & Cultural
  Center, Lake Wales, FL............................320
Lakes Art Center, Okoboji, IA......................525
Lakeview Museum of Arts and Sciences,
  Peoria, IL..450
Lamar Dodd Art Center, LaGrange
  College, LaGrange, GA............................375
The Lamont Gallery, Exeter, NH..................888
Lancaster County Historical Society,
  Lancaster, PA..1266
Lancaster Museum of Art, Lancaster, PA...1266
The Landmark Society of Western New
  York, Rochester, NY...............................1058
Lane Community College Art Gallery,
  Eugene, OR..1223
Lane Place, Crawfordsville, IN....................473
Lanier Mansion State Historic Site,
  Madison, IN...489
Lansing Art Gallery, Lansing, MI................750
Laramie Plains Museum, Laramie, WY.....1635
Larchmont Historical Society,
  Mamaroneck, NY....................................1013
Laredo Center for the Arts, Laredo, TX.....1434
Larson Museum and Gallery, Yakima,
  WA...1578
Las Vegas Art Museum, Las Vegas, NV......879
Las Vegas Natural History Museum, Las
  Vegas, NV...879
LaSalle County Historical Society
  Museum, Utica, IL....................................462
Latitudes Gallery, Bismarck, ND................1128
Lauder Museum - Amityville Historical
  Society, Amityville, NY...........................957
Laumeier Sculpture Park & Museum,
  Saint Louis, MO.......................................834
Laura A. Sprague Art Gallery, Joliet, IL......440
Laurel Arts, Somerset, PA...........................1300
Lauren Rogers Museum of Art, Laurel,
  MS..804
Laurence C. Jones Museum, Piney
  Woods, MS...807
Law Enforcement Memorial Association,
  Inc., Roselle, IL..456
Lawrence County Gray House Museum,
  Ironton, OH...1169
Lawrence Heritage State Park, Lawrence,
  MA...689
Laws Railroad Museum and Historical
  Site, Bishop, CA.......................................78

Le Sueur Museum, Le Sueur, MN...............779
Lea County Cowboy Hall of Fame and
  Western Heritage Center, Hobbs, NM.....940
Leanin' Tree Museum of Western Art,
  Boulder, CO...203
The Lebanon County Historical Society,
  Lebanon, PA..1268
Lee Chapel and Museum, Lexington, VA..1513
Lee-Fendall House Museum and Garden,
  Alexandria, VA.......................................1493
Leedel Moorehead-Graham Fine Arts
  Gallery, Pine Bluff, AR............................66
Leelanau Historical Museum, Leland, MI....751
The Leffingwell House Museum,
  Norwich, CT..258
Legends of the Game Baseball Museum
  and Learning Center, Arlington, TX.......1388
Lehigh University Art Galleries/Museum
  Operations, Bethlehem, PA.....................1242
Lehman College Art Gallery, Bronx, NY.....966
Leigh Yawkey Woodson Art Museum,
  Wausau, WI...1626
Lemon Hill Mansion, Philadelphia, PA.....1282
LeMoyne Art Foundation, Inc.,
  Tallahassee, FL.......................................347
Lentz Center for Asian Culture, Lincoln,
  NE..865
LeRoy House & JELL-O Gallery, LeRoy,
  NY..1009
Lesbian Herstory Educational Foundation,
  Inc. aka Lesbian Herstory Archives,
  Brooklyn, NY...969
Leslie Powell Foundation and Gallery,
  Lawton, OK...1204
Levere Memorial Temple, Evanston, IL......434
Levi Coffin House, Fountain City, IN..........478
Lewes Historical Society, Lewes, DE..........271
Lewistown Art Center, Lewistown, MT......850
Lexington Historical Society, Lexington,
  MA...689
Libby Museum, Wolfeboro, NH..................897
Liberty Hall Historic Center, Lamoni, IA...522
Liberty Hall Historic Site, Frankfort, KY...569
Liberty Jail Historic Site, Liberty, MO........826
Liberty Village Arts Center & Gallery,
  Chester, MT...844
Library Company of Philadelphia,
  Philadelphia, PA......................................1282
Library of the Supreme Council, 33
  Degrees, Washington, DC........................282
The Library of Virginia, Richmond, VA....1530
Licking County Arts, Newark, OH.............1178
Life on the Ohio River History Museum,
  Vevay, IN...502
Lighthouse Center for the Arts, Tequesta,
  FL...351
Lightner Museum, Saint Augustine, FL.......339
Lilian Fendig Art Gallery, Rensselaer, IN...497
Lincoln County Historical Society,
  Lincoln, KS..549
Lincoln Herdon Law Offices State
  Historic Site, Springfield, IL...................458
Lincoln Memorial Shrine, Redlands, CA.....147
The Lincoln Museum, Fort Wayne, IN........478
Lincoln Parish Museum & Historical
  Society, Ruston, LA.................................600
The Lincoln-Tallman Restorations,
  Janesville, WI...1601
Linn County Museum/Geneaology
  Library, Pleasanton, KS...........................556
The Lion and Lamb Peace Arts Center,
  Bluffton, OH...1143
Litchfield Historical Society and
  Museum, Litchfield, CT...........................247
Little Bighorn Battlefield National
  Monument, Crow Agency, MT.................844
The Little Brick House, Vandalia, IL...........462
Little Compton Historical Society, Little
  Compton, RI...1312
The Little Cowboy Bar & Museum,
  Fromberg, MT..847

Little Falls Historical Society Museum, Little Falls, NY..1009
Little Log Church & Museum, Yachats, OR..1238
Little White House Historic Site, Warm Springs, GA..390
Little White Schoolhouse, Ripon, WI.........1620
Littleton Historical Museum, Littleton, CO...227
The Living Arts and Science Center, Inc., Lexington, KY.....................................573
Living Bible Museum, Mansfield, OH.......1173
Livingston Depot Center, Livingston, MT...850
Lockwood-Mathews Mansion Museum, Norwalk, CT.......................................257
Locust Grove, Louisville, KY......................577
Locust Grove, The Samuel Morse Historic Site, Poughkeepsie, NY...........1055
Locust Lawn and Terwilliger House, Gardiner, NY..993
Logan County Historical Society Museum, Bellefontaine, OH.................1142
Lois E. Woods Museum, Norfolk, VA........1522
Lompoc Valley Historical Society, Inc., Lompoc, CA..110
Lone Star Flight Museum/Texas Aviation Hall of Fame, Galveston, TX.................1421
Long Beach Museum of Art, Long Beach, CA..111
Long Island Museum of American Art, History & Carriages, Stony Brook, NY..1075
Longboat Key Center for the Arts, Longboat Key, FL.................................322
Longfellow National Historic Site, Cambridge, MA.....................................673
Longfellow's Wayside Inn, Sudbury, MA....714
Longue Vue House & Gardens, New Orleans, LA...596
Longview Museum of Fine Arts, Longview, TX...1434
Longwood Center for the Visual Arts, Farmville, VA.......................................1504
Longyear Museum, Chestnut Hill, MA........675
Lore Degenstein Gallery, Selinsgrove, PA.1299
Lorenzo State Historic Site, Cazenovia, NY..976
Los Alamos Historical Museum, Los Alamos, NM..942
Los Altos History Museum aka Association of the Los Altos Historical Museum, Los Altos, CA....................112
The Los Angeles Art Association/Gallery 825, Los Angeles, CA............................117
Los Angeles County Museum of Art, Los Angeles, CA..118
Los Angeles Maritime Museum, San Pedro, CA..176
Los Angeles Municipal Art Gallery - Barnsdall Art Park, Los Angeles, CA......118
Los Angeles Museum of the Holocaust, Los Angeles, CA....................................118
Los Medanos College Art Gallery, Pittsburg, CA..142
Lou Holtz/Upper Ohio Valley Hall of Fame, East Liverpool, OH.....................1163
Loudoun Museum, Inc., Leesburg, VA.......1512
Louie-Meager Art Gallery, Fremont, CA.......96
Louisburg College Art Gallery, Louisburg, NC..1109
Louise Wells Cameron Art Museum, Wilmington, NC.....................................1123
Louisiana Art & Science Museum - Irene W. Pennington Planetarium, Baton Rouge, LA..586
Louisiana Naval War Memorial/U.S.S. Kidd, Baton Rouge, LA.........................586
Louisiana State Exhibit Museum, Shreveport, LA.......................................600
Louisiana State Museum, New Orleans, LA..596
Louisiana State University Museum of Art, Baton Rouge, LA............................586

Louisiana's Old State Capitol, Political History Museum, Baton Rouge, LA........587
Louisville Slugger Museum & Factory, Louisville, KY...577
Loveland Museum Gallery, Loveland, CO...227
Lovely Lane Museum, Baltimore, MD........634
Lowe Art Museum, University of Miami, Coral Gables, FL....................................301
Lowell Observatory, Flagstaff, AZ................33
Lowell Telecommunications Corp., Lowell, MA..691
Lower Cape Fear Historical Society, Inc., Wilmington, NC.....................................1123
Lower Rio Grande Valley Nature Center, Weslaco, TX...1460
Loyola University Museum of Art, Chicago, IL..423
Lubeznik Center for the Arts, Michigan City, IN..490
Lucy Craft Laney Museum of Black History and Conference Center, Augusta, GA..365
Luis Munoz Rivera Library & Museum, Barranquitas, PR...................................1641
Luther Burbank Home & Gardens, Santa Rosa, CA..184
The Luther W. Brady Art Gallery, Washington, DC....................................282
Luzerne County Historical Society, Wilkes-Barre, PA...................................1307
The Lyceum, Alexandria's History Museum, Alexandria, VA......................1493
Lyman Allyn Art Museum, New London, CT..255
Lyman Museum, Hilo, HI.............................393
Lynchburg Museum System, Lynchburg, VA..1515
Lyndhurst, Tarrytown, NY...........................1078
Lyndon Baines Johnson Library and Museum, Austin, TX..............................1391
The Lyons Redstone Museum, Lyons, CO...227

MIT-List Visual Arts Center, Cambridge, MA..673
MIT Museum, Cambridge, MA....................674
M. Louise Aughinbaugh Gallery at Messiah College, Grantham, PA.............1257
MSC Forsyth Center Galleries, Texas A&M University, College Station, TX..1401
Mabee-Gerrer Museum of Art, Shawnee, OK..1213
Mabry-Hazen House, Knoxville, TN..........1371
Macalester College Art Gallery, Janet Wallace Fine Arts Center, Saint Paul, MN..790
Macculloch Hall Historical Museum & Gardens, Morristown, NJ........................913
MacDonald Art Gallery, Dallas, PA...........1249
Macon County Historical Society Museum Complex, Decatur, IL..............430
Mac's Antique Car Museum, Tulsa, OK....1215
Madeline Island Historical Museum, La Pointe, WI...1603
Madera County Museum, Madera, CA........123
MADI Museum, Dallas, TX........................1407
Madison Museum of Contemporary Art, Madison, WI...1605
Madison Museum of Fine Art, Madison, GA..378
Magevney House, Memphis, TN.................1373
The Magic Lantern Castle Museum, San Antonio, TX...1448
Magnolia Grove-Historic House Museum, Greensboro, AL.......................................10
Magnolia Manor, Cairo, IL...........................415
Magnolia Plantation and Gardens, Charleston, SC.....................................1326
Magoffin Home State Historic Site, El Paso, TX...1412
Maier Museum of Art, Randolph-Macon Woman's College, Lynchburg, VA.........1515
Maine Art Gallery, Wiscasset, ME..............626
Maine Historical Society, Portland, ME......619

Maine Lighthouse Museum, Rockland, ME..621
Maine Maritime Museum, Bath, ME...........606
Maine State Museum, Augusta, ME............604
Maitland Art Center, Maitland, FL...............322
Maitland Historical Museums, Maitland, FL..322
The Major General Frederick Funston Boyhood Home and Museum, Iola, KS..546
Malabar Farm State Park, Lucas, OH........1173
Malden Public Library, Malden, MA..........692
Mallory-Neely House, Memphis, TN.........1373
Mamie Doud Eisenhower Birthplace, Boone, IA..506
Manassas National Battlefield Park, Manassas, VA.......................................1516
Manchester Historic Association Millyard Museum, Manchester, NH.....................891
Mandeville Gallery, Union College, Schenectady, NY...................................1067
Manhattan Arts Center, Manhattan, KS........551
The Mansfield Art Center, Mansfield, OH .1173
Mansfield Township Historical Society (1849 Georgetown School/Museum), Columbus, NJ...902
Maramec Museum, The James Foundation, Saint James, MO.................830
Marblehead Arts Association - King Hooper Mansion, Marblehead, MA.........693
Marblehead Museum & Historical Society, Marblehead, MA........................693
Marcella Sembrich Opera Museum, Bolton Landing, NY................................963
Marcellus Historical Society, Marcellus, NY..1013
March Field Air Museum, Riverside, CA....149
Margaret Fort Trahern Gallery, Clarksville, TN.......................................1363
Margaret Harwell Art Museum, Poplar Bluff, MO..829
The Margaret Mitchell House & Museum, Atlanta, GA...........................361
Mariani Gallery, University of Northern Colorado, Greeley, CO.........................221
Marianna Kistler Beach Museum of Art at Kansas State University, Manhattan, KS..551
Marias Museum of History and Art, Shelby, MT..853
Maridon Museum, Butler, PA.....................1245
Marietta/Cobb Museum of Art, Marietta, GA..379
Marin History Museum, San Rafael, CA.....177
The Marine Museum at Fall River, Inc., Fall River, MA.......................................682
The Mariners' Museum, Newport News, VA..1519
Mario Lanza Institute/Museum, Philadelphia, PA...................................1282
Marion Public Library Museum, Marion, IN..490
Mariposa Museum & World Culture Center, Peterborough, NH......................893
Maritime & Seafood Industry Museum, Biloxi, MS..798
Maritime and Yachting Museum of the Treasure Coast, Stuart, FL.....................346
Maritime Industry Museum at Fort Schuyler, Bronx, NY.............................966
Maritime Museum of Monterey, Monterey, CA.......................................127
Maritime Museum of San Diego, San Diego, CA..157
Marjorie Kinnan Rawlings Historic State Park, Cross Creek, FL.........................301
Mark Twain Birthplace State Historic Site, Florida, MO......................................815
Mark Twain Home and Museum, Hannibal, MO.......................................816
The Mark Twain House & Museum, Hartford, CT.......................................245

Paintings–Continued

Marquette County Historical Society, Westfield, WI 1627
Marquette County History Museum, Marquette, MI..................753
Marshall County Historical Museum, Holly Springs, MS..................801
Marshall M. Fredericks Sculpture Museum, University Center, MI 766
The Marston House/San Diego Historical Society, San Diego, CA 157
Martha's Vineyard Museum, Edgartown, MA..................681
Martin and Osa Johnson Safari Museum, Inc., Chanute, KS 535
Martin Art Gallery, Allentown, PA ..1239
Martin County Museum, Shoals, IN ..499
The Martin D'Arcy Museum of Art: The Loyola University Museum of Medieval, Renaissance and Baroque Art, Chicago, IL..................424
The Mary Baker Eddy Library for the Betterment of Humanity, Boston, MA.....666
Mary Baldwin College/Hunt Gallery, Staunton, VA..................1537
The Mary Brogan Museum of Art and Science, Tallahassee, FL 347
Mary McLeod Bethune Council House National Historic Site, Washington, DC..................283
Mary Porter Sesnon Art Gallery, Santa Cruz, CA..................181
Mary Todd Lincoln House, Lexington, KY..................574
Maryhill Museum of Art, Goldendale, WA..................1556
Maryland Art Place, Baltimore, MD 634
Maryland Historical Society, Baltimore, MD..................634
The Maryland Institute, College of Art: Decker, Meyerhoff and Pinkard Galleries, Baltimore, MD..................634
Maryland State Archives, Annapolis, MD....628
Maryville University - Morton J. May Foundation Gallery, Saint Louis, MO 834
Mashantucket Pequot Museum and Research Center, Mashantucket, CT........248
Masonic Grand Lodge Library and Museum of Texas, Waco, TX 1459
The Masonic Library and Museum of Pennsylvania, Philadelphia, PA..............1283
MASS MoCA, North Adams, MA 698
Massachusetts Historical Society, Boston, MA..................667
Massee Lane Gardens, Home of American Camellia Society, Fort Valley, GA..................373
Masur Museum of Art, Monroe, LA 592
Matchless Mine Museum (Leadville Assembly), Leadville, CO..................226
Mathias Ham House Historic Site, Dubuque, IA..................516
Mattapoisett Museum and Carriage House, Mattapoisett, MA 693
The Mattatuck Museum Arts and History Center, Waterbury, CT..................264
Maturango Museum of the Indian Wells Valley, Ridgecrest, CA..................148
Maude I. Kerns Art Center, Eugene, OR ...1223
Maui Arts and Cultural Center, Kahului, Maui, HI..................399
Maxwell Museum of Anthropology, Albuquerque, NM..................934
The May Gallery, Patron's Lounge, Beaver Creek, CO..................202
Maymont, Richmond, VA 1530
Mayville Historical Society, Inc., Mayville, WI..................1608
MCAD Gallery, Minneapolis, MN 782
McCarthy Arts Center Gallery, Colchester, VT..................1479
McConnell Mansion, Moscow, ID..............407

McCook House, Civil War Museum, Carrollton, OH..................1146
McCormick Gallery, Midland, TX..............1438
McDowell House Museum, Danville, KY ...567
McGuffey Art Center, Charlottesville, VA .1499
McHenry Museum, Modesto, CA..................126
McLarty Treasure Museum, Vero Beach, FL..................352
McLean County Arts Center, Bloomington, IL..................414
McLean County Historical Society Museum, Washburn, ND 1137
McLean County Museum of History, Bloomington, IL..................414
McMinn County Living Heritage Museum, Athens, TN..................1360
McMullen Museum of Art, Boston College, Chestnut Hill, MA..................675
McNamara House Museum, Victoria, TX ..1457
McNay Art Museum, San Antonio, TX......1448
McPherson Museum & Arts Foundation, McPherson, KS..................552
McWethy Hall, Luce Gallery, Cornell College, Mount Vernon, IA.......524
Mead Art Museum, Amherst, MA.......658
Meadow Brook Hall, Rochester, MI............761
Meadow Garden Museum, Augusta, GA......365
Meadows Museum, Dallas, TX 1407
Meadows Museum of Art of Centenary College, Shreveport, LA..................601
Meagher County Historical Association Castle Museum, White Sulphur Springs, MT..................855
Mecosta County Historical Museum, Big Rapids, MI..................729
Meeker Home Museum, Greeley, CO 222
Meeteetse Museum District, Meeteetse, WY..................1636
Melrose Plantation Home Complex, Melrose, LA..................592
Melton Art Reference Library, Oklahoma City, OK..................1208
Mem-Erie Historical Museum, Erie, KS......539
Memorial Art Gallery of the University of Rochester, Rochester, NY..................1059
Memorial Hall Museum, Pocumtuck Valley Memorial Assoc., Deerfield, MA..................679
Memorial Union Art Gallery, Davis, CA 90
Memorial Union Gallery, Fargo, ND..........1130
Memoryville USA, Inc., Rolla, MO 829
Memphis Botanic Garden, Goldsmith Civic Garden Center, Memphis, TN......1374
Memphis Brooks Museum of Art, Memphis, TN..................1374
Memphis College of Art, Memphis, TN 1374
The Menczer Museum of Medicine & Dentistry, Hartford, CT..................245
Mendocino County Museum, Willits, CA ...198
The Menil Collection, Houston, TX...........1428
Mennello Museum of American Art, Orlando, FL..................331
Mennonite Library and Archives, North Newton, KS..................554
Menominee County Heritage Museum, Menominee, MI..................754
Mercer Museum of the Bucks County Historical Society, Doylestown, PA.......1250
Meridian Museum of Art, Meridian, MS 805
The Merrick Art Gallery, New Brighton, PA..................1273
Merrill Historical Museum, Merrill, WI.....1609
Merritt Museum of Anthropology, Oakland, CA..................133
Mesa Southwest Museum, Mesa, AZ.............37
Mesa Verde National Park Museum, Mesa Verde National Park, CO..................228
Mesalands Community College's Dinosaur Museum, Tucumcari, NM 953
Metamora Museum of Ethnographic Art, Metamora, IN..................490

The Metropolitan Museum of Art, New York, NY..................1030
Metropolitan State College of Denver/Center for Visual Art, Denver, CO..................212
Meux Home Museum, Fresno, CA..................98
Mexic-Arte Museum, Austin, TX 1391
Mexican Fine Arts Center Museum, Chicago, IL..................424
The Mexican Museum, San Francisco, CA..................166
Miami Art Museum, Miami, FL..................324
Miami County Museum, Peru, IN 496
Miami-Dade College Kendall Campus Art Gallery, Miami, FL..................324
Miami University Art Museum, Oxford, OH..................1181
Michael C. Rockefeller Arts Center Gallery, Fredonia, NY..................992
Michelson Museum of Art, Marshall, TX ..1436
Michigan Maritime Museum, South Haven, MI..................764
Michigan Transit Museum, Inc., Mount Clemens, MI..................756
Mid-America Air Museum, Liberal, KS.......549
Mid-America All Indian Center, Wichita, KS..................562
Middleborough Historical Association, Inc., Middleborough, MA..................694
Middlebury College Museum of Art, Middlebury, VT..................1482
Middlebury Historical Society, Wyoming, NY..................1087
Middlesex Canal Collection, Lowell, MA...691
Middleton Place Foundation, Charleston, SC..................1326
Middletown Valley Historical Society, Middletown, MD..................649
Midwest Museum of American Art, Elkhart, IN..................474
Mighty Eighth Air Force Museum, Pooler, GA..................381
Milan Historical Museum, Inc., Milan, OH..................1176
Mildred Lane Kemper Art Museum, Saint Louis, MO..................834
Miles B. Carpenter Museum, Waverly, VA..................1543
Milford Historical Society, Milford, CT......250
Milford Museum, Milford, DE 271
Military Museum of Southern New England, Danbury, CT..................238
Military Veterans Museum, Inc., Oshkosh, WI..................1616
Miller Art Museum, Sturgeon Bay, WI......1623
Millicent Rogers Museum of Northern New Mexico, Taos, NM..................952
Milliken Gallery, Converse College, Spartanburg, SC..................1341
Mills College Art Museum, Oakland, CA....133
Milton Art Museum, Canton, MA..................674
Milwaukee Art Museum, Milwaukee, WI ..1611
Mingei International Museum, San Diego, CA..................157
The Minna Anthony Common Nature Center at Wellesley State Park, Fineview, NY..................989
Minneapolis Institute of Arts, Minneapolis, MN..................782
Minnesota Historical Society, Saint Paul, MN..................791
Minnesota Landscape Arboretum, University of Minnesota, Chaska, MN....770
Minnesota Museum of American Art, Saint Paul, MN..................791
Minnesota State Capitol Historic Site, Saint Paul, MN..................791
Minnesota's Machinery Museum, Hanley Falls, MN..................777
Minnetrista, Muncie, IN..................492
Mint Museum of Art, Charlotte, NC..........1095

Minute Man National Historical Park, Concord, MA 676
Miramont Castle Museum, Manitou Springs, CO 228
Miriam & Ira D. Wallach Art Gallery, New York, NY 1030
Mission Cultural Center for Latino Arts, San Francisco, CA 166
Mission Houses Museum, Honolulu, HI 397
Mission Inn Foundation/Museum, Riverside, CA 149
Mission San Antonio de Padua, Jolon, CA 105
Mission San Diego de Alcala, San Diego, CA 157
Mission San Francisco de Asis (Mission Dolores), San Francisco, CA 167
Mission San Luis Rey Museum, Oceanside, CA 135
Mission San Miguel, San Miguel, CA 175
Mission Santa Cruz, Santa Cruz, CA 182
Mississippi Governor's Mansion, Jackson, MS 802
Mississippi Museum of Art, Jackson, MS....802
Mississippi Society Daughters of the American Revolution Rosalie House Museum, Natchez, MS 805
Missoula Art Museum, Missoula, MT.........851
Missouri Historical Society, Saint Louis, MO 835
The Mitchell Museum of the American Indian, Evanston, IL 435
Mizel Museum, Denver, CO 213
Mobile Medical Museum, Mobile, AL...........14
Mobile Museum of Art, Mobile, AL 14
Modern Art Museum of Fort Worth, Fort Worth, TX 1418
Modoc County Historical Museum, Alturas, CA 70
Moffatt-Ladd House and Garden, Portsmouth, NH 894
Mohave Museum of History and Arts, Kingman, AZ 36
Molly Brown House Museum, Denver, CO 213
Mondak Heritage Center, Sidney, MT.........853
The Monhegan Museum, Monhegan, ME....615
Monmouth County Historical Association, Freehold, NJ 905
Monongalia Arts Center, Morgantown, WV 1585
Monroe Community College, Mercer Gallery, Rochester, NY 1059
Monroe Historical Society, Monroe, CT......250
Montague Museum & Historical Association, Montague, MI 756
Montana Historical Society, Helena, MT.....849
Montana Museum of Art and Culture, Missoula, MT 852
Montauk, Clermont, IA 511
Montauk Point Lighthouse Museum, Montauk, NY 1015
Montclair Art Museum, Montclair, NJ 912
Montclair Historical Society, Montclair, NJ 912
Montclair State University Art Galleries, Upper Montclair, NJ 929
Monterey Bay Aquarium, Monterey, CA 127
Monterey History and Art Association, Monterey, CA 127
Monterey Museum of Art, Monterey, CA 128
Monterey State Historic Park, Monterey, CA 128
The Montgomery County Historical Society, Dayton, OH 1161
The Montgomery County Historical Society, Inc., Rockville, MD 651
Montgomery Museum & Lewis Miller Regional Art Center, Christiansburg, VA 1501
Montgomery Museum of Fine Arts, Montgomery, AL 16

Monticello, Home of Thomas Jefferson, Thomas Jefferson Foundation, Inc., Charlottesville, VA 1499
Montpelier Mansion, Laurel, MD 648
Montpelier-The General Henry Knox Museum, Thomaston, ME 624
Moody-Bradley House Restoration Foundation, Fairfield, TX 1413
Moore County Art Association, Dumas, TX 1410
Moore County Historical Museum, Dumas, TX 1410
Moores Creek National Battlefield, Currie, NC 1097
The Moore-Youse Home Museum, Muncie, IN 492
Moosehead Marine Museum, Greenville, ME 611
Moravian Historical Society, Nazareth, PA 1273
Moravian Museum of Bethlehem, Inc., Bethlehem, PA 1242
Mordecai Historic Park, Raleigh, NC.........1115
Morehead Planetarium and Science Center, Chapel Hill, NC 1093
Morgan Row Museum and Harrodsburg-Mercer County Research Library, Harrodsburg, KY 570
Mormon Visitors Center, Independence, MO 818
Morris-Butler House Museum, Indianapolis, IN 485
Morris County Historical Society (Acorn Hall House Museum), Morristown, NJ ...914
Morris-Jumel Mansion, New York, NY 1030
The Morris Museum, Morristown, NJ..........914
Morris Museum of Art, Augusta, GA.........365
Morristown National Historical Park, Morristown, NJ 914
Morven Museum & Garden, Princeton, NJ 922
Morven Park, Leesburg, VA 1512
Moses Myers House, Norfolk, VA 1522
Moss Mansion Historic House Museum, Billings, MT 841
Motorcycle Hall of Fame Museum, Pickerington, OH 1182
Mount Clare Museum House, Baltimore, MD 635
Mount Desert Island Historical Society, Mount Desert, ME 615
Mount Dora Center for the Arts, Mount Dora, FL 327
Mount Holyoke College Art Museum, South Hadley, MA 709
Mt. Kearsarge Indian Museum, Warner, NH 897
Mount Prospect Historical Society Museums, Mount Prospect, IL 446
Mount Vernon Ladies' Association, Mount Vernon, VA 1518
The Muchnic Gallery, Atchison, KS.............533
Muckenthaler Cultural Center and Mansion Museum, Fullerton, CA 99
Mulvane Art Museum, Topeka, KS 559
Munson-Williams-Proctor Arts Institute Museum of Art, Utica, NY 1079
Murfreesboro Historical Association, Murfreesboro, NC 1112
The Murie Museum, Kelly, WY 1634
Murray-Lindsay Mansion, Lindsay, OK 1204
Murrell Home, Park Hill, OK 1211
Muscarelle Museum of Art, Williamsburg, VA 1545
Muscatine Art Center, Muscatine, IA 524
Museo de Arte de Ponce (The Luis A. Ferre Foundation, Inc.), Ponce, PR 1642
Museo de las Americas, Denver, CO 213
Museo Del Nino, San Juan, PR 1643
Museo ItaloAmericano, San Francisco, CA 167
The Museum, Greenwood, SC 1334

Museum and Arts Center in the Sequim Dungeness Valley, Sequim, WA 1570
The Museum at Warm Springs, Warm Springs, OR 1238
The Museum for African Art, Long Island City, NY 1011
Museum in the Community, Hurricane, WV 1583
Museum NECCA at New England Center for Contemporary Art, Inc., Brooklyn, CT 237
The Museum of African American Art, Los Angeles, CA 119
The Museum of African Culture, Portland, ME 619
Museum of Afro-American History, Boston, MA 667
Museum of American Architecture and Decorative Arts, Houston, TX 1428
The Museum of American Illustration at the Society of Illustrators, New York, NY 1031
Museum of American Presidents, Strasburg, VA 1539
Museum of Ancient Artifacts, Las Vegas, NV 879
Museum of Anthropology, University of Missouri, Columbia, MO 813
Museum of Art, Pullman, WA 1563
Museum of Art and Archaeology, University of Missouri - Columbia, Columbia, MO 813
Museum of Art and History at the McPherson Center, Santa Cruz, CA 182
Museum of Art & History at Weston, Weston, CT 266
Museum of Art at Brigham Young University, Provo, UT 1469
Museum of Art/Fort Lauderdale, Fort Lauderdale, FL 307
Museum of Art of Puerto Rico, Santurce, PR 1643
Museum of Art, Rhode Island School of Design, Providence, RI 1317
Museum of Arts and Sciences, Macon, GA 378
The Museum of Arts and Sciences, Inc. and Center for Florida History, Daytona Beach, FL 303
Museum of Astrogeology, Meteor Crater, Winslow, AZ 53
Museum of Automobile Art and Design, Syracuse, NY 1076
Museum of Aviation at Robins Air Force Base, GA, Warner Robins, GA 390
Museum of Bad Art, Dedham, MA 679
Museum of Biblical Art, New York, NY ...1032
Museum of Ceramics, East Liverpool, OH 1163
Museum of Chicot County Arkansas, Lake Village, AR 61
Museum of Church History and Art, Salt Lake City, UT 1471
Museum of Connecticut History, Hartford, CT 245
Museum of Contemporary Art, Chicago, IL 424
Museum of Contemporary Art, Denver, CO 213
Museum of Contemporary Art Cleveland, Cleveland, OH 1155
The Museum of Contemporary Art, Los Angeles, Los Angeles, CA 119
Museum of Contemporary Art (MoCA), North Miami, FL 329
The Museum of Contemporary Art of Georgia (MOCA GA), Atlanta, GA.........362
Museum of Contemporary Art of Puerto Rico, Santurce, PR 1644
Museum of Contemporary Art San Diego, La Jolla, CA 106
Museum of Contemporary Art San Diego - Downtown, San Diego, CA 157

Paintings–Continued

Museum of Contemporary Religious Art (MOCRA)-St. Louis University, Saint Louis, MO 835

Museum of Craft and Folk Art, San Francisco, CA 167

Museum of Design Atlanta, Atlanta, GA 362

Museum of Early Southern Decorative Arts (MESDA), Winston-Salem, NC 1125

The Museum of East Texas, Lufkin, TX....1436

Museum of Fine Arts, Boston, MA..........667

Museum of Fine Arts, Santa Fe, NM..........948

The Museum of Fine Arts, Houston, Houston, TX 1428

Museum of Fine Arts of St. Petersburg, Florida, Saint Petersburg, FL 341

The Museum of Flight, Seattle, WA..........1567

Museum of Florida History, Tallahassee, FL..............348

Museum of Flying, Santa Monica, CA 183

Museum of Great Christian Preachers & Ministries, Orange Park, FL..........331

Museum of History & Art, Ontario, Ontario, CA 136

Museum of History & Industry (MOHAI), Seattle, WA..........1567

Museum of History, Anthropology and Art, San Juan, PR..............1643

Museum of Indian Arts & Culture/Laboratory of Anthropology, Santa Fe, NM..............948

Museum of International Folk Art, Santa Fe, NM..............948

Museum of Latin American Art, Long Beach, CA..............111

The Museum of Man in the Sea, Inc., Panama City Beach, FL 335

The Museum of Mobile, Mobile, AL..........14

The Museum of Modern Art, New York, NY..............1033

Museum of Nebraska Art, Kearney, NE......864

Museum of New Mexico, Santa Fe, NM 949

Museum of Northern Arizona, Flagstaff, AZ..............33

Museum of Northwest Art, La Conner, WA..............1557

The Museum of Outdoor Arts, Englewood, CO..............214

Museum of Overbeck Art Pottery, Cambridge City, IN..............471

Museum of Primitive Art and Culture, Peace Dale, RI..............1316

Museum of Religious Arts, Logan, IA.........522

The Museum of Russian Art, Minneapolis, MN..............783

Museum of San Diego History and Research Library, San Diego, CA 158

Museum of Science, Boston, MA..............667

Museum of Southern History, Jacksonville, FL..............315

The Museum of Southern History, Sugarland, TX..............1454

Museum of Spanish Colonial Art - MoSCA, Santa Fe, NM..............949

Museum of Texas Tech University, Lubbock, TX..............1435

Museum of the African Diaspora, San Francisco, CA..............167

Museum of the American Philosophical Society, Philadelphia, PA..............1283

Museum of the Big Bend, Alpine, TX.......1386

Museum of the City of New York, New York, NY..............1033

The Museum of the Confederacy, Richmond, VA..............1531

Museum of the Hudson Highlands, Cornwall-on-Hudson, NY..............982

Museum of the Jimmy Carter Library, Atlanta, GA..............362

Museum of the Mountain Man, Pinedale, WY..............1637

Museum of the National Center of Afro-American Artists, Roxbury, MA 706

Museum of the Northern Great Plains, Fort Benton, MT..............846

Museum of the Plains Indian, Browning, MT..............843

Museum of the Rockies, Bozeman, MT.....842

Museum of the Southern Jewish Experience, Jackson, MS..............803

Museum of the Southwest, Midland, TX...1439

Museum of the Waxhaws & Andrew Jackson Memorial, Waxhaw, NC..........1122

Museum of the Weston Historical Society, Inc., Weston, MA..............718

Museum of Transportation, Saint Louis, MO..............835

Museum of Utah Art & History, Salt Lake City, UT..............1471

Museum of West Louisiana, Leesville, LA..............591

The Museum of Western Art, Kerrville, TX..............1431

Museum of Western Colorado, Grand Junction, CO..............220

Museum of Woodcarving, Shell Lake, WI.1621

Museum of World Cultures/University of North Carolina at Wilmington, Wilmington, NC..............1123

Museum of Yachting, Newport, RI..........1314

Museum of York County, Rock Hill, SC...1340

Museums of Los Gatos, Los Gatos, CA.....123

The Museums of Oglebay Institute - Mansion Museum & Glass Museum, Wheeling, WV..............1588

Muskegon Museum of Art, Muskegon, MI..............758

Musselshell Valley Historical Museum, Roundup, MT..............853

Mutter Museum, College of Physicians of Philadelphia, Philadelphia, PA..............1283

My Old Kentucky Home State Park, Bardstown, KY..............564

Mystic Arts Center, Mystic, CT..............250

Mystic Seaport - The Museum of America and the Sea, Mystic, CT..........251

NAU Art Museum, Flagstaff, AZ..............33

NCCU Art Museum, Durham, NC..............1099

Nantucket Historical Association, Nantucket, MA..............696

Naomi Wood Collection at Woodford Mansion, Philadelphia, PA..............1284

Napa Valley Museum, Yountville, CA.........200

Naples Museum of Art and the Philharmonic Center for the Arts Galleries, Naples, FL..............328

Napoleonic Society of America, Inc., Clearwater, FL..............300

Narragansett Historical Society, Templeton, MA..............714

Nasher Museum of Art at Duke University, Durham, NC..............1099

Nasher Sculpture Center, Dallas, TX..........1407

Nassau County, Division of Museum Services, Department of Recreation, Parks & Museums, East Meadow, NY....987

Nassau County Museum of Art, Roslyn Harbor, NY..............1062

Nathan Denison Advocates, Forty Fort, PA..............1254

Nathaniel W. Faison Home and Museum, La Grange, TX..............1432

National Academy Museum and School of Fine Arts, New York, NY..............1033

National Academy of Sciences, Washington, DC..............283

National Afro-American Museum & Cultural Center, Wilberforce, OH..........1191

The National Agricultural Center & Hall of Fame, Bonner Springs, KS..............534

National Air and Space Museum, Washington, DC..............283

National Art Museum of Sport, Inc., Indianapolis, IN..............485

National Arts Club, New York, NY..........1034

National Baseball Hall of Fame and Museum, Inc., Cooperstown, NY.........981

National Bighorn Sheep Interpretive Center, Dubois, WY..............1632

The National Border Patrol Museum and Memorial Library, El Paso, TX..........1412

National Buffalo Museum, Jamestown, ND..............1133

National Building Museum, Washington, DC..............284

National Capital Parks-East, Washington, DC..............284

National Civil Rights Museum, Memphis, TN..............1375

National Civil War Naval Museum at Port Columbus, Columbus, GA..............369

National Cowboy & Western Heritage Museum, Oklahoma City, OK..............1208

National Cowgirl Museum and Hall of Fame, Fort Worth, TX..............1418

National Czech & Slovak Museum & Library, Cedar Rapids, IA..............509

National Fresh Water Fishing Hall of Fame, Hayward, WI..............1600

National Gallery of Art, Washington, DC....285

National Geographic Museum at Explorers Hall, Washington, DC..............285

National Heritage Museum, Lexington, MA..............690

National Hispanic Cultural Center, Art Museum, Albuquerque, NM..............935

National Infantry Museum, Fort Benning, GA..............372

National Liberty Museum, Philadelphia, PA..............1284

National Medal of Honor Museum of Military History, Chattanooga, TN........1362

National Mississippi River Museum & Aquarium, Dubuque, IA..............516

National Museum of African Art, Smithsonian Institution, Washington, DC..............285

National Museum of American Illustration, Newport, RI..............1314

The National Museum of Catholic Art & History, New York, NY..............1034

National Museum of Dance & Hall of Fame, Saratoga Springs, NY..............1065

National Museum of Health and Medicine, Washington, DC..............286

National Museum of Naval Aviation, Pensacola, FL..............336

National Museum of Polo and Hall of Fame, Inc., Lake Worth, FL..............320

National Museum of Racing and Hall of Fame, Saratoga Springs, NY..............1065

National Museum of the American Indian, Washington, DC..............286

National Museum of the American Indian, Smithsonian Institution, New York, NY..............1034

National Museum of the Morgan Horse, Shelburne, VT..............1487

National Museum of the United States Air Force, Wright-Patterson Air Force Base, OH..............1193

National Museum of Wildlife Art, Jackson, WY..............1634

National Museum of Women in the Arts, Washington, DC..............287

National New York Central Railroad Museum, Elkhart, IN..............475

National Park Service, Washington, DC.......287

National Park Service-Great Falls Park, McLean, VA..............1517

National Park Service Museum Resource Center, Landover, MD..............648

National Portrait Gallery, Washington, DC..............287

National Postal Museum, Smithsonian
  Institution, Washington, DC 287
National Railroad Museum, Green Bay,
  WI 1599
National Railroad Museum and Hall of
  Fame, Inc., Hamlet, NC 1105
National Scouting Museum, Irving, TX 1430
The National Soccer Hall of Fame,
  Oneonta, NY 1046
National Society of the Sons of the
  American Revolution, Louisville, KY 578
National Steeplechase Museum, Camden,
  SC 1323
National Steinbeck Center, Salinas, CA 154
National Tropical Botanical Garden,
  Kalaheo, HI..399
National Trust for Historic Preservation,
  Washington, DC..288
National Vietnam Veterans Art Museum,
  Chicago, IL..425
The National World War II Museum,
  New Orleans, LA..597
National Wrestling Hall of Fame,
  Stillwater, OK 1214
Native American Exhibit, National Kateri
  Shrine, Fonda, NY 991
Native American Resource Center,
  Pembroke, NC 1114
Natural Center for the American
  Revolution, Wayne, PA 1306
Naugatuck Historical Society, Naugatuck,
  CT 251
Naumkeag, Stockbridge, MA 712
Navajo Nation Museum, Window Rock,
  AZ 53
Naval War College Museum, Newport,
  RI 1314
Navarro County Historical Society,
  Pioneer Village, Corsicana, TX 1402
Nave Museum, Victoria, TX 1457
Nebraska State Capitol, Lincoln, NE............866
Neill-Cochran Museum House, Austin,
  TX 1391
The Nelson-Atkins Museum of Art,
  Kansas City, MO 822
Nemours Mansion and Gardens,
  Wilmington, DE...274
Netherland Inn House Museum &
  Boatyard Complex, Kingsport, TN 1368
Neuberger Museum of Art, Purchase
  College, State University of New
  York, Purchase, NY 1056
Nevada Historical Society, Reno, NV 881
Nevada Museum of Art, Reno, NV..............881
Neville Public Museum of Brown
  County, Green Bay, WI 1599
New Bedford Whaling Museum, New
  Bedford, MA..696
New Britain Museum of American Art,
  Inc., New Britain, CT................................251
New Castle Historical Society, New
  Castle, DE...272
New Castle Historical Society - Horace
  Greeley House, Chappaqua, NY 977
New England College Gallery, Henniker,
  NH...889
New England Fire and History Museum,
  Brewster, MA...670
New England Maple Museum, Pittsford,
  VT..1484
New England Ski Museum, Franconia,
  NH..888
New Hampshire Antiquarian Society,
  Hopkinton, NH 889
New Hampshire Farm Museum, Inc.,
  Milton, NH...892
New Hampshire Historical Society,
  Concord, NH..885
New Hampshire Institute of Art,
  Manchester, NH..892
New Harmony Gallery of Contemporary
  Art, New Harmony, IN..............................494

New Harmony State Historic
  Site/Historic New Harmony, New
  Harmony, IN..494
New Haven Colony Historical Society,
  New Haven, CT..253
The New Jersey Historical Society,
  Newark, NJ..916
The New Jersey Museum of Agriculture,
  North Brunswick, NJ..................................917
New Jersey Naval Museum, Hackensack,
  NJ 905
New Jersey Office of Historic Sites,
  Trenton, NJ..927
New Jersey State House, Trenton, NJ 927
New Jersey State Museum, Trenton, NJ 927
New London County Historical Society,
  New London, CT..255
New Market Battlefield State Historical
  Park, New Market, VA 1519
New Mexico Farm & Ranch Heritage
  Museum, Las Cruces, NM..........................940
New Mexico State Fair Fine Arts Gallery,
  Albuquerque, NM......................................935
The New Milford Historical Society, New
  Milford, CT..256
The New Museum of Contemporary Art,
  New York, NY..1035
New Orleans Museum of Art, New
  Orleans, LA...597
New Visions Gallery, Inc., Marshfield,
  WI...1608
New World Art Center/T.F. Chen Cultural
  Center, New York, NY 1035
New York City Fire Museum, New York,
  NY...1035
The New York Historical Society, New
  York, NY..1035
New York State Bureau of Historic Sites,
  Waterford, NY 1082
New York State Historical
  Association/Fenimore Art Museum,
  Cooperstown, NY 981
New York State Military Museum and
  Veterans Research Center, Saratoga
  Springs, NY...1065
New York State Office of Parks,
  Recreation & Historic Preservation,
  Albany, NY..955
The New York Studio School of
  Drawing, Painting & Sculpture, New
  York, NY..1036
The Newark Museum, Newark, NJ 916
Newark Valley Depot Museum, Newark
  Valley, NY...1042
Newcomb Art Gallery, New Orleans, LA 598
Newport Art Museum, Newport, RI...........1314
Newport Historical Society & The
  Museum of Newport History,
  Newport, RI...1315
Newport Restoration Foundation,
  Newport, RI...1315
The Newsome House Museum &
  Cultural Center, Newport News, VA 1520
The Newton History Museum at The
  Jackson Homestead, Newton, MA...........698
Newtown Historic Association, Newtown,
  PA..1274
Newtown History Center, Stephens City,
  VA..1538
Nez Perce County Museum, Lewiston, ID...407
Nez Perce National Historical Park,
  Spalding, ID...409
Nicholas Roerich Museum, New York,
  NY..1037
Nicolaysen Art Museum and Discovery
  Center, Casper, WY...................................1629
Nicollet County Historical Society, Saint
  Peter, MN..793
Ninety Six National Historic Site, Ninety
  Six, SC..1338
Nita Stewart Haley Memorial Library &
  J. Evetts Haley History Center,
  Midland, TX 1439

Nixon Presidential Materials Staff,
  College Park, MD......................................641
Noah Webster House/West Hartford
  Historical Society, West Hartford, CT.....265
Noank Historical Society, Inc., Noank,
  CT..256
The Noble Maritime Collection, Staten
  Island, NY...1073
Nohwike Bagowa, The White Mountain
  Apache Cultural Center and Museum,
  Fort Apache, AZ..34
Nora Eccles Harrison Museum of Art,
  Logan, UT...1466
Nordic Heritage Museum, Seattle, WA 1567
Norfolk History Museum, Norfolk, VA......1523
The Norman Cleveland County Historical
  Museum, Norman, OK...............................1206
Norman #1 Oil Well Museum, Neodesha,
  KS..553
Norman R. Eppink Art Gallery, Emporia
  State University, Emporia, KS....................539
Norman Rockwell Museum, Stockbridge,
  MA...712
North Alabama Railroad Museum,
  Huntsville, AL..12
North Carolina A&T State University
  Galleries, Greensboro, NC 1104
North Carolina Aquarium at Fort Fisher,
  Kure Beach, NC 1109
North Carolina Maritime Museum,
  Beaufort, NC..1091
North Carolina Museum of Art, Raleigh,
  NC..1115
North Carolina Museum of History,
  Raleigh, NC...1115
North Carolina Office of Archives and
  History, Raleigh, NC 1116
North Carolina Zoological Park,
  Asheboro, NC...1088
North Country Museum of Arts, Park
  Rapids, MN..786
North Dakota Museum of Art, Grand
  Forks, ND..1132
North Florida Community College Art
  Gallery, Madison, FL.................................322
North Michigan University DeVos Art
  Museum, Marquette, MI.............................754
North Plainfield Exempt Firemen's
  Association, North Plainfield, NJ..............917
North Seattle Community College Art
  Gallery, Seattle, WA 1567
The North Shore Arts Association,
  Gloucester, MA..684
Northampton County Historical and
  Genealogical Society, Easton, PA 1250
Northborough Historical Society, Inc.,
  Northborough, MA 700
Northeast Georgia History Center at
  Brenau University, Gainesville, GA 373
Northeast Louisiana Delta African
  American Heritage Museum, Monroe,
  LA..592
Northeast Oakland Historical Museum,
  Oxford, MI...759
Northeast Texas Rural Heritage Museum,
  Pittsburg, TX...1443
Northern Galleries, Aberdeen, SD 1344
Northern Kentucky University Art
  Galleries, Highland Heights, KY 571
Northern Pacific Railway Museum,
  Toppenish, WA 1575
Northfield Historical Society Museum,
  Northfield, MN...785
The Northumberland County Historical
  Society, Sunbury, PA.................................1302
Northwest Art Center, Minot, ND 1134
Northwest Museum of Arts & Culture
  (Eastern Washington State Historical
  Society), Spokane, WA..............................1571
Northwest Railway Museum,
  Snoqualmie, WA..1570
Norton Museum of Art, West Palm
  Beach, FL...353

Paintings–Continued

Norton Simon Museum, Pasadena, CA 140

Norwich Historical Society, Norwich, VT .1484

Norwood Historical Association and
  Museum, Norwood, NY 1044

The Noyes Museum of Art, Oceanville,
  NJ 918

The Nylander Museum of Natural
  History, Caribou, ME 609

Oak Hill and The Martha Berry Museum,
  Rome, GA 382

The Oak Park Conservatory, Oak Park,
  IL 449

Oak Ridge Art Center, Oak Ridge, TN 1382

Oakdale Museum, Oakdale, CA 132

Oakland Museum of California, Oakland,
  CA 134

Oakland University Art Gallery,
  Rochester, MI 761

Oaklands Historic House Museum,
  Murfreesboro, TN 1376

Oakley Park, UDC Shrine, Edgefield, SC ..1332

The Oaks House Museum, Jackson, MS 804

Oatlands, Leesburg, VA 1512

Oberlin Heritage Center, Oberlin, OH 1180

Ocean County Historical Museum, Toms
  River, NJ 926

The Octagon, Washington, DC 288

Octagon House, San Francisco, CA 168

Office of Cultural Affairs & Museum
  Programs at Salisbury University,
  Salisbury, MD 652

The Ogden Museum of Southern Art,
  University of New Orleans, New
  Orleans, LA 598

Ogden Union Station Museums, Ogden,
  UT 1468

Oglethorpe University Museum of Art,
  Atlanta, GA 362

Ogunquit Museum of American Art,
  Ogunquit, ME 617

Ohio River Museum, Marietta, OH 1174

Ohio University Art Gallery, Athens, OH ..1140

Ohr-O'Keefe Museum of Art, Biloxi, MS ...799

Ohrmann Museum and Gallery,
  Drummond, MT 846

Ojai Valley Historical Society and
  Museum, Ojai, CA 135

Okefenokee Heritage Center, Waycross,
  GA 391

Oklahoma City Museum of Art,
  Oklahoma City, OK 1208

Oklahoma Firefighters Museum,
  Oklahoma City, OK 1209

Oklahoma Forest Heritage Center,
  Broken Bow, OK 1197

Oklahoma Heritage Association,
  Oklahoma City, OK 1209

Oklahoma Visual Arts Coalition,
  Oklahoma City, OK 1210

Olana State Historic Site, Hudson, NY 1000

Olbrich Botanical Gardens, Madison, WI ..1605

Old Barracks Museum, Trenton, NJ 927

Old Bohemia Historical Society,
  Warwick, MD 656

Old Brutus Historical Society, Inc.,
  Weedsport, NY 1084

Old Cathedral Museum, Saint Louis, MO....836

Old Church Cultural Center School of
  Art, Demarest, NJ 902

Old Colony Historical Society, Taunton,
  MA 714

Old Conway Homestead Complex and
  Museum, Camden, ME 608

Old Dominion University - University
  Gallery, Norfolk, VA 1523

Old Exchange & Provost Dungeon,
  Charleston, SC 1326

Old Falls Village, Menomonee Falls, WI...1609

The Old Governor's Mansion, Frankfort,
  KY 570

The Old Jail Art Center, Albany, TX 1385

Old Lighthouse Museum, Michigan City,
  IN 491

Old Lighthouse Museum, Stonington, CT....261

Old Lincoln County Courthouse Museum,
  Lincoln, NM 942

Old Manchester Museum, Manchester,
  CT 248

Old Mill Museum, Cimarron, NM............938

Old Mill Museum, El Molino Viejo - Old
  Mill Foundation, San Marino, CA...........175

Old Mission Santa Ines, Solvang, CA.........187

Old Ordinary House Museum, Hingham,
  MA 687

Old St. Ferdinand's Shrine, Florissant,
  MO 815

The Old Schwamb Mill, Arlington, MA 660

Old South Meeting House, Boston, MA 668

Old State Capitol, Springfield, IL 459

Old State House, Hartford, CT 245

Old State House-The Bostonian Society,
  Boston, MA 668

Old Sturbridge Village, Sturbridge, MA.......713

Old Town Hall Museum, Fifield, WI...........1597

Old Town Museum, Old Town, ME............617

Old West Museum, Wimberley, TX............1462

Old Westbury Gardens, Old Westbury,
  NY 1045

Old York Historical Society, York, ME 626

Oldest House Museum Complex, Saint
  Augustine, FL 339

The Oldest House Museum/Wrecker's
  Museum, Key West, FL 318

The Oliver Tucker Museum, Beverly, OH .1142

Olympic Flight Museum, Olympia, WA 1560

Omniplex Science Museum, Oklahoma
  City, OK 1210

103rd Ohio Volunteer Infantry Civil War
  Museum, Sheffield Lake, OH 1185

Oneida Community Mansion House,
  Oneida, NY 1046

Oneida County Historical Society, Utica,
  NY 1080

Oneida Nation Museum, De Pere, WI.......1594

Onondaga Historical Association Museum
  & Research Center, Syracuse, NY.........1077

Orange County Museum of Art, Newport
  Beach, CA 130

Orchard House, Concord, MA 677

Oregon Historical Society, Portland, OR....1231

Oregon Military Museum, Clackamas,
  OR 1221

Oregon State University Memorial Union
  Concourse Gallery, Corvallis, OR 1222

Oregon Trail Museum, Gering, NE 861

Oregon Zoo, Portland, OR 1232

Orlando Museum of Art, Orlando, FL.........332

Orleans County Historical Society & The
  Old Stone House Museum,
  Brownington, VT 1477

Orma J. Smith Museum of Natural
  History, Caldwell, ID 405

Ormond Memorial Art Museum &
  Garden, Ormond Beach, FL..................333

Osage County Historical Society
  Museum, Pawhuska, OK 1211

Osage Nation Tribal Museum, Pawhuska,
  OK 1212

Osborn-Jackson House, East Hampton,
  NY 986

Oscar Getz Museum of Whiskey History
  And The Bardstown Historical
  Museum, Bardstown, KY 565

Osceola Center for the Arts, Kissimmee,
  FL 319

Oshkosh Public Museum, Oshkosh, WI.....1616

Ossining Historical Society Museum,
  Ossining, NY 1047

Osterville Historical Society, Inc.,
  Osterville, MA 701

Oswego Historical Museum, Inc.,
  Oswego, KS 555

Otero Museum Association, La Junta, CO...224

Ouachita County Historical Society,
  Camden, AR 55

Our House State Memorial, Gallipolis,
  OH 1165

Owatonna Arts Center, Owatonna, MN........786

Owens Community College/Walter E.
  Terhune Gallery, Perrysburg, OH..........1182

Owensboro Museum of Fine Art, Inc.,
  Owensboro, KY 581

Owls Head Transportation Museum, Owls
  Head, ME 617

Oxford Museum, Inc., Oxford, MD............650

Oysterponds Historical Society: The
  Museum of Orient and East Marion
  History, Orient, NY 1047

The Ozark Folk Center, Mountain View,
  AR 65

P. Buckley Moss Museum, Waynesboro,
  VA 1544

P.S. 1 Contemporary Art Center, Long
  Island City, NY 1011

The P.T. Boat Museum & Library,
  Germantown, TN 1365

Pacem in Terris, Warwick, NY 1082

Pacific Asia Museum, Pasadena, CA............140

Pacific Aviation Museum - Pearl Harbor,
  Honolulu, HI 397

Pacific Coast Air Museum, Santa Rosa,
  CA 184

Pacific Grove Art Center Associates, Inc.,
  Pacific Grove, CA 137

Pacific Lutheran University Art Galleries,
  Tacoma, WA 1574

Pacific University Museum, Forest
  Grove, OR 1224

Packwood House Museum, Lewisburg,
  PA 1268

Paine Art Center and Gardens, Oshkosh,
  WI 1617

Painted Bride Art Center, Philadelphia,
  PA 1284

Painted Post - Erwin Museum at the
  Depot, Painted Post, NY 1050

Pajaro Valley Historical Association,
  Watsonville, CA 196

The Palette & Chisel, Chicago, IL 426

Palm Beach Institute of Contemporary
  Art, Lake Worth, FL 320

Palm Springs Art Museum, Palm Springs,
  CA 139

Palmer Museum of Art, The Pennsylvania
  State University, University Park, PA...1304

Palo Alto Art Center, Palo Alto, CA............139

Palos Verdes Art Center, Rancho Palos
  Verdes, CA 145

Panhandle-Plains Historical Museum,
  Canyon, TX 1399

Paper Discovery Center, Appleton, WI 1590

The Pardee Home Museum, Oakland, CA....134

Paris Gibson Square Museum of Art,
  Great Falls, MT 848

Parishville Museum, Parishville, NY..........1050

The Park-McCullough House, North
  Bennington, VT 1483

Parker-O'Malley Air Museum, Ghent,
  NY 994

Parker Tavern, Reading, MA 705

Parkersburg Art Center, Parkersburg, WV .1586

Parkland College Art Gallery,
  Champaign, IL 417

Parris Island Museum, Parris Island, SC....1338

The Parrish Art Museum, Southampton,
  NY 1070

Parrot Jungle Island, Miami, FL...............325

The Parry Mansion Museum, New Hope,
  PA 1273

Parson Fisher House, Blue Hill, ME..........606

The Parthenon, Nashville, TN 1379

Pasadena Museum of California Art,
  Pasadena, CA 140

Pasadena Museum of History, Pasadena,
    CA 140
Passaic County Community College,
    Paterson, NJ 920
Passaic County Historical Society &
    Lambert Castle Museum, Paterson, NJ ...920
Patee House Museum, Saint Joseph, MO 831
The Paterson Museum, Paterson, NJ 920
The Patricia & Phillip Frost Art Museum,
    Miami, FL 325
The Patrick & Beatrice Haggerty
    Museum of Art, Milwaukee, WI 1613
Patten Lumbermen's Museum, Inc.,
    Patten, ME 618
Patterson Homestead, Dayton, OH 1161
Patton Museum of Cavalry and Armor,
    Fort Knox, KY 568
Paul and Lulu Hilliard University Art
    Museum, University of Louisiana at
    Lafayette, Lafayette, LA 590
Paul Robeson Art Gallery, Newark, NJ 917
Paul Robeson Cultural and Performing
    Arts Center, Wilberforce, OH 1191
Paul W. Bryant Museum, Tuscaloosa, AL 19
Paunsaugunt Wildlife Museum, Bryce,
    UT 1464
Pawnee Bill Ranch and Museum,
    Pawnee, OK 1212
Pawnee Indian Village State Historic Site,
    Republic, KS 556
Paynes Creek Historic State Park,
    Bowling Green, FL 297
Pea Ridge National Military Park,
    Garfield, AR 58
Peabody Essex Museum, Salem, MA 706
Peabody Museum of Archaeology &
    Ethnology, Cambridge, MA 674
The Peace Museum, Chicago, IL 426
Pearce Collections Museum, Corsicana,
    TX 1402
The Pearl S. Buck House, Perkasie, PA 1275
Pebble Hill Plantation, Thomasville, GA 388
Pecos National Historical Park, Pecos,
    NM 944
The Peekskill Museum, Peekskill, NY 1051
Pejepscot Historical Society, Brunswick,
    ME 608
Pelham Art Center, Pelham, NY 1052
The Pena-Peck House, Saint Augustine,
    FL 339
Pence Gallery, Davis, CA 90
Pendleton Historic Foundation,
    Pendleton, SC 1339
Peninsula Fine Arts Center, Newport
    News, VA 1520
Peninsula Museum of Art, Belmont, CA........74
Pennsylvania Academy of the Fine Arts,
    Philadelphia, PA 1284
Pennsylvania German Cultural Heritage
    Center at Kutztown University,
    Kutztown, PA 1265
Pennsylvania Historical & Museum
    Commission, Harrisburg, PA 1259
Penobscot Marine Museum, Searsport,
    ME 622
Pensacola Historical Society Museum,
    Pensacola, FL 336
Pensacola Museum of Art, Pensacola, FL....336
The Peoria Art Guild, Peoria, IL 451
Peoria Historical Society, Peoria, IL 451
Perkins Center for the Arts, Moorestown,
    NJ 912
Perry's Victory & International Peace
    Memorial, Put-in-Bay, OH 1183
Perspective Gallery, Blacksburg, VA 1497
Peter Whitmer Sr. Home and Visitors
    Center, Waterloo, NY 1083
Peter Yegen Jr. Yellowstone County
    Museum, Billings, MT 841
Peterborough Historical Society,
    Peterborough, NH 893

Petersburg Area Art League, Petersburg,
    VA 1525
Petersburg Regional Art Center,
    Petersburg, VA 1525
Petersham Historical Society, Inc.,
    Petersham, MA 702
Peterson Air & Space Museum, Peterson
    Air Force Base, CO 229
Petrified Creatures Museum of Natural
    History, Richfield Springs, NY 1057
Petrified Forest National Park, Petrified
    Forest National Park, AZ 38
The Petroleum Museum, Midland, TX 1439
Pettaquamscutt Historical Society,
    Kingston, RI 1312
The Philadelphia Art Alliance,
    Philadelphia, PA 1285
Philadelphia Mummers Museum,
    Philadelphia, PA 1285
Philadelphia Museum of Art,
    Philadelphia, PA 1285
Philadelphia Society for the Preservation
    of Landmarks, Philadelphia, PA 1286
The Philbrook Museum of Art, Inc.,
    Tulsa, OK 1215
Philip and Muriel Berman Museum of
    Art at Ursinus College, Collegeville,
    PA 1247
Philipse Manor Hall State Historic Site,
    Yonkers, NY 1087
The Phillips Collection, Washington, DC.....289
Phillips County Museum, Helena, AR............59
Phillips Historical Society, Phillips, ME 618
The Phillips Museum of Art, Franklin &
    Marshall College, Lancaster, PA 1267
Philmont Museums, Cimarron, NM.............938
Phippen Museum, Prescott, AZ 42
Phoebe Apperson Hearst Museum of
    Anthropology, Berkeley, CA 77
Phoenix Art Museum, Phoenix, AZ..............41
Phoenix Museum of History, Phoenix,
    AZ 41
Photographic Investments Gallery,
    Atlanta, GA 363
Piatt Castles, West Liberty, OH 1190
Pickens County Museum of Art &
    History, Pickens, SC 1340
The Picker Art Gallery, Hamilton, NY.........997
Piedmont Arts Association, Martinsville,
    VA 1516
The Pierce Manse/New Hampshire
    Political Library, Concord, NH 885
The Pierpont Morgan Library, New York,
    NY 1037
Pierre Menard Home State Historic Site,
    Ellis Grove, IL 433
Pierrepont Museum, Canton, NY 975
Pike County Historical Society, Milford,
    PA 1272
Pilgrim Hall Museum, Plymouth, MA 703
Pilgrim Monument and Provincetown
    Museum, Provincetown, MA 704
Pima Air & Space Museum, Tucson, AZ.......50
Pimeria Alta Historical Society, Nogales,
    AZ 37
Pioneer Arizona Living History Village &
    Museum, Phoenix, AZ........................41
Pioneer Museum & The Big Stampede,
    Fairbanks, AK 24
Pioneer Museum and Vereins Kirche,
    Fredericksburg, TX 1419
Pioneer Museum of Alabama, Troy, AL.........18
Pioneer Village, Farmington, UT 1465
Piper Aviation Museum Foundation, Lock
    Haven, PA 1269
Pipestone National Monument, Pipestone,
    MN 787
Piqua Historical Area State Memorial,
    Piqua, OH 1182
Pitot House Museum, New Orleans, LA......598
Pittock Mansion, Portland, OR 1232

Pittsburgh Center for the Arts, Pittsburgh,
    PA 1293
Pittsford Historical Society Museum,
    Pittsford, VT 1484
Placer County Museums, Auburn, CA 72
Plains Art Museum, Fargo, ND 1130
Plains Indians and Pioneers Museum,
    Woodward, OK 1217
Plainsman Museum, Aurora, NE 856
Plantation Agriculture Museum, Scott,
    AR 67
Plantation Historical Museum, Plantation,
    FL 337
Plattsburgh State Art Museum S.U.N.Y.,
    Plattsburgh, NY 1053
Plaza de La Raza, Inc. & Boathouse
    Gallery, Los Angeles, CA 121
Plumas County Museum, Quincy, CA.........144
Plymouth Antiquarian Society, Plymouth,
    MA 704
Pocahontas County Iowa Historical
    Society Museum, Laurens, IA 522
Polish American Museum, Port
    Washington, NY 1054
Polish Heritage Center, Ashton, NE 856
Polish Museum of America, Chicago, IL.....426
Polk County Heritage Gallery, Des
    Moines, IA 515
Polk County Historical Society,
    Crookston, MN 771
Polk Museum of Art, Lakeland, FL.............321
Pomerene Center for the Arts, Coshocton,
    OH 1159
Pomona College Museum of Art,
    Claremont, CA 85
Ponca City Art Center, Ponca City, OK 1212
Pony Express Museum, Saint Joseph,
    MO 831
Pope John Paul II Cultural Center,
    Washington, DC 289
Port Angeles Fine Arts Center &
    Webster's Woods Art Park, Port
    Angeles, WA 1561
Port Gamble Historic Museum, Port
    Gamble, WA 1562
Port Huron Museum, Port Huron, MI 761
Portage County Historical Society,
    Ravenna, OH 1183
Porter-Phelps-Huntington Foundation,
    Inc., Hadley, MA 685
Portholes Into the Past, Medina, OH 1176
Portland Art Museum, Portland, OR 1232
Portland Museum of Art, Portland, ME 619
Portland State University Galleries,
    Portland, OR 1233
Portsmouth Athenaeum, Portsmouth, NH.....894
Portsmouth Museum of Military History
    Inc., Portsmouth, VA 1526
Pottsgrove Manor, Pottstown, PA 1295
Prairie Village, Madison, SD 1351
Praters Mill Foundation, Varnell, GA...........390
Pratt Building - Cohasset Historical
    Society, Cohasset, MA 676
Pratt Manhattan Gallery, New York, NY ...1037
Pratt Museum, Homer, AK 25
The Preservation Society of Newport
    County/The Newport Mansions,
    Newport, RI 1315
Presidential Pet Museum, Lothian, MD 649
President's Cottage Museum-The
    Greenbrier, White Sulphur Springs,
    WV 1588
Presidio La Bahia, Goliad, TX 1423
Price Tower Arts Center, Bartlesville, OK .1197
Princeton University Art Museum,
    Princeton, NJ 922
Pro Rodeo Hall of Fame & Museum of
    the American Cowboy, Colorado
    Springs, CO 207
Project Art-University of Iowa and
    Clinics, Iowa City, IA 520
Promont House Museum, Milford, OH 1176

Paintings–Continued

Proprietary House, The Royal Governor's Mansion, Perth Amboy, NJ 921

Providence Canyon State Park, Lumpkin, GA...377

Provincetown Art Association and Museum, Provincetown, MA 704

Prudence Crandall Museum, Canterbury, CT..237

Pueblo Art Guild and Gallery, Pueblo, CO..230

Pueblo County Historical Society Museum and Edward H. Broadhead Library, Pueblo, CO 230

Pueblo Weisbrod Aircraft Museum, Pueblo, CO...230

Pump House Regional Arts Center, La Crosse, WI...1603

Purdue University Galleries, West Lafayette, IN...503

Putnam Cottage, Greenwich, CT.......243

Putnam County Historical Society & Foundry School Museum, Cold Spring, NY.......................................979

Putnam County Historical Society Museum, Kalida, OH............................1169

Putnam County Museum, Greencastle, IN...479

Putney Historical Society, Putney, VT 1485

Puukohola Heiau National Historic Site, Kamuela, HI.......................................400

QCC Art Gallery, Bayside, NY 960

Quartersaw Gallery, Portland, OR 1233

Queen Emma Summer Palace, Honolulu, HI..398

Queen Mary Museum, Long Beach, CA......111

Queens Historical Society, Flushing, NY.....990

Queens Library Gallery, Jamaica, NY........1004

Queens Museum of Art, Queens, NY.........1056

Quincy Art Center, Quincy, IL...............452

The Quincy Museum, Quincy, IL.................452

Quinlan Visual Arts Center, Gainesville, GA..374

R.S. Barnwell Memorial Garden and Art Center, Shreveport, LA 601

The R.W. Norton Art Gallery, Shreveport, LA...601

Racine Art Museum (RAM), Racine, WI...1619

Radford University Art Museum, Radford, VA.....................................1527

Rahr West Art Museum, Manitowoc, WI...1607

Railroad House Historical Association Museum, Sanford, NC..........................1119

Railroad Museum of Pennsylvania, Strasburg, PA 1302

The Ralph Foster Museum, Point Lookout, MO....................................828

Ralph Waldo Emerson House, Concord, MA..677

Ramapogue Historical Society, West Springfield, MA 718

Rancho La Patera - The Stow House G.V.H.S., Goleta, CA 100

Randall Library, Stow, MA......................713

Randolph County Historical Museum, Winchester, IN.......................................503

Randolph Historical Society, Inc., Randolph, VT 1485

Rangeley Lakes Region Logging Museum, Rangeley, ME......................620

Rankin Museum, Rankin, TX.....................1445

Ransom County Historical Society, Fort Ransom, ND 1131

Ransom Visual Arts Center, Saint Petersburg, FL.....................................342

Raton Museum, Raton, NM......................945

Rattlesnake Museum (American International), Albuquerque, NM.............935

Rawls Museum Arts, Courtland, VA 1502

The Ray Drew Gallery-New Mexico Highlands University, Las Vegas, NM 941

Raynham Hall Museum, Oyster Bay, NY..1049

The Reader's Digest Association, Inc., Pleasantville, NY.....................................1053

Reading Public Museum, Reading, PA.......1296

Red Earth Museum, Oklahoma City, OK...1210

Red Hill-Patrick Henry National Memorial, Brookneal, VA 1498

Red River Valley Museum, Vernon, TX....1457

Red Rock Museum, Church Rock, NM 938

Redington Museum, Waterville, ME 625

Redwood Library and Athenaeum, Newport, RI.......................................1315

Reedville Fishermen's Museum, Reedville, VA.....................................1527

Reese Bullen Gallery, Arcata, CA 72

The Reeves Center, Washington and Lee University, Lexington, VA.....................1513

Reeves-Reed Arboretum, Summit, NJ.........925

The Regina A. Quick Center for the Arts, Saint Bonaventure, NY 1063

Regina Gouger Miller Gallery, Pittsburgh, PA...1294

Reginald F. Lewis Museum of Maryland African American History and Culture, Baltimore, MD...636

Rehoboth Art League, Inc., Rehoboth Beach, DE...272

Reitz Home Museum, Evansville, IN...........476

Remington Firearms Museum and Country Store, Ilion, NY 1002

Renaissance Gallery, Northport, AL 17

The Renaissance Society at The University of Chicago, Chicago, IL.........427

Rensselaer County Historical Society, Troy, NY...1079

Renville County Historical Society, Inc., Mohall, ND..1135

Renwick Gallery of the Smithsonian American Art Museum, Washington, DC..290

Reverend Dan Foster House, Museum of the Weathersfield Historical Society, Weathersfield, VT 1489

Reynolda House Museum of American Art, Winston-Salem, NC 1126

Rhode Island Historical Society, Providence, RI....................................1318

Rice County Museum of History, Faribault, MN.....................................775

The Rice Museum, Georgetown, SC 1333

Rice University Art Gallery, Houston, TX.1429

Richard E. Peeler Art Center, Greencastle, IN.....................................479

Richard L. Nelson Gallery & The Fine Arts Collection, UC Davis, Davis, CA.......90

Richard Petty Museum, Randleman, NC...1117

Richard Salter Storrs House, Longmeadow, MA.................................691

Richards DAR House Museum, Mobile, AL...15

Richmond Art Center, Richmond, CA..........148

Richmond Art Museum, Richmond, IN........497

Riddick's Folly, Suffolk, VA 1539

Riley House Museum of African American History & Culture, Tallahassee, FL...................................348

Rimrocker Historical Museum of West Montrose County, Naturita, CO.............229

Rip Van Winkle Gardens on Jefferson Island, New Iberia, LA..........................593

Ripley County, Indiana, Historical Society Museum, Versailles, IN..............502

Ripley's Believe It or Not!, Key West, FL...319

River Heritage Museum, Paducah, KY 582

River Museum, Wellsville, OH 1190

Riversdale House Mansion, Riverdale Park, MD...651

Riverside Art Museum, Riverside, CA........149

Riverside Community College Art Gallery, Riverside, CA 149

Riverview at Hobson Grove, Bowling Green, KY..566

Robbins Hunter Museum, Avery-Downer House, Granville, OH..............................1167

Robbins Museum of Archaeology, Middleborough, MA...............................694

Roberson Museum and Science Center, Binghamton, NY....................................962

Robert E. Wilson Gallery, Huntington, IN...481

Robert Else Gallery, Sacramento, CA 153

Robert Hull Fleming Museum, Burlington, VT.....................................1478

Robert Louis Stevenson House, Monterey, CA.....................................128

Robert Louis Stevenson Memorial Cottage, Saranac Lake, NY...................1064

Robert Louis Stevenson Silverado Museum, Saint Helena, CA 154

Robert R. McCormick Museum at Cantigny, Wheaton, IL.........................465

Robert T. Wright Community Gallery of Art, Grayslake, IL....................................439

Robert V. Fullerton Art Museum, California State University, San Bernardino, San Bernardino, CA.............155

Roberts County Museum, Miami, TX........1438

Rochester Art Center, Rochester, MN 788

Rochester Historical Society, Rochester, NY..1059

Rock House Museum, Wytheville, VA.......1546

Rock Island County Historical Society, Moline, IL...445

Rockbridge Historical Society, Lexington, VA...1513

Rockford Art Museum, Rockford, IL...........455

Rockford College Art Gallery/Clark Arts Center, Rockford, IL 455

Rockingham, Kingston, NJ......................909

Rockport Art Association, Rockport, MA 705

Rockwell Museum of Western Art, Corning, NY 982

Rockwood Park, Wilmington, DE...............274

Rocky Mount Arts Center, Rocky Mount, NC...1117

Rocky Mountain College of Art + Design Galleries, Lakewood, CO.......................225

Rocky Mountain National Park, Estes Park, CO...215

Rocky Reach Dam, Wenatchee, WA 1577

Rodgers Tavern, Perryville, MD.................650

Roger Tory Peterson Institute of Natural History, Jamestown, NY.......................1005

Rogers House Museum Gallery, Ellsworth, KS.....................................538

Rokeby (Ancestral Estate of Rowland Evans Robinson), Ferrisburgh, VT 1479

Roland Gibson Gallery, Potsdam, NY........1054

Romanian Ethnic Art Museum, Cleveland, OH.....................................1156

Rome Art and Community Center, Rome, NY...1061

Ronald Reagan Presidential Library and Museum, Simi Valley, CA.......................187

Roniger Memorial Museum, Cottonwood Falls, KS...536

Roosevelt Campobello International Park Commission, Lubec, ME.......................614

Rosalie House, Eureka Springs, AR 57

Roscoe Village Foundation, Coshocton, OH..1159

The Rose Art Museum, Waltham, MA.........715

Rose Hill Museum, Bay Village, OH..........1141

Rose Hill Plantation State Historic Site, Union, SC...1343

Rose Lawn Museum, Cartersville, GA.........368

Roseland Cottage, Woodstock, CT..............268

Rosemont Plantation, Woodville, MS..........810

Rosemount Museum, Pueblo, CO...............230

Rosenbach Museum & Library, Philadelphia, PA 1287

Rosenberg Gallery, Goucher College, Baltimore, MD.....................................636

Rosenberg Library, Galveston, TX 1422
Rosenthal Gallery of Art, Caldwell, ID........405
Ross County Historical Society, Inc.,
    Chillicothe, OH.................................1147
Roswell Museum and Art Center,
    Roswell, NM....................................946
Roswell Visual Arts Center & Gallery,
    Roswell, GA....................................382
The Rotch-Jones-Duff House & Garden
    Museum, Inc., New Bedford, MA..........697
Rothko Chapel, Houston, TX....................1429
The Rotunda, University of Virginia,
    Charlottesville, VA.............................1500
Rowan Museum, Inc., Salisbury, NC.........1118
The Roy Rogers-Dale Evans Museum
    and Theater, Branson, MO.....................811
Royall House Association, Medford, MA 694
The Rubelle & Norman Schafler Gallery,
    Brooklyn, NY...................................970
Rudolph E. Lee Gallery, Clemson, SC.......1328
Rumford Historical Association, North
    Woburn, MA....................................699
Rural Life Museum & Windrush
    Gardens, Baton Rouge, LA.....................587
Rushmore Borglum Story, Keystone, SD...1350
Russell County Historical Society/Fossil
    Station Museum, Russell, KS 556
Ruth and Charles Gilb Arcadia Historical
    Museum, Arcadia, CA..........................71
The Ruth & Sherman Lee Institute for
    Japanese Art, Hanford, CA 101
Ruth Chandler Williamson Gallery,
    Scripps College, Claremont, CA...............86
Ruth Eckerd Hall, Clearwater, FL 300
Ruthmere Museum, Elkhart, IN 475
Ryerss Museum & Library, Philadelphia,
    PA...1287

SITE Santa Fe, Santa Fe, NM 950
S.S. Meteor Maritime Museum, Superior,
    WI...1624
Saco Museum, Saco, ME..........................621
Safe Haven Museum and Education
    Center, Oswego, NY 1048
Safford House Historic House Museum,
    Tarpon Springs, FL.............................351
Sag Harbor Whaling & Historical
    Museum, Sag Harbor, NY.....................1063
Sagamore Hill National Historic Site,
    Oyster Bay, NY 1049
Saginaw Art Museum, Saginaw, MI.............763
Sahuaro Ranch Historical Area, Glendale,
    AZ...35
St. Charles County Historical Society,
    Inc., Saint Charles, MO.......................830
St. Clements Island and Piney Point
    Museums, Colton's Point, MD................641
Saint-Gaudens National Historic Site,
    Cornish, NH....................................885
St. George Art Museum, Saint George,
    UT...1470
St. George's United Methodist Church,
    Philadelphia, PA...............................1287
St. James' House, Fredericksburg, VA 1507
St. Johnsbury Athenaeum, Saint
    Johnsbury, VT..................................1487
Saint Joseph College Art Gallery, West
    Hartford, CT....................................265
Saint Joseph's University - University
    Gallery - Boland Hall, Philadelphia,
    PA...1288
St. Lawrence County Historical
    Association - Silas Wright House,
    Canton, NY......................................975
St. Lawrence University - Richard F.
    Brush Art Gallery and Permanent
    Collection, Canton, NY........................976
The Saint Louis Art Museum, Saint
    Louis, MO......................................836
St. Louis Artists' Guild, Saint Louis, MO....836
The St. Louis County Historical Society,
    Duluth, MN.....................................773

St. Lucie County Historical Museum,
    Fort Pierce, FL.................................309
St. Marys Submarine Museum, Saint
    Marys, GA......................................382
St. Paul Museum, Randleman, NC 1117
St. Photios Greek Orthodox National
    Shrine, Saint Augustine, FL...................340
Salem Art Association-Bush House
    Museum and Bush Barn Art Center,
    Salem, OR......................................1236
Salem County Historical Society, Salem,
    NJ...924
The Salem Museum, Salem, VA.................1536
The Salgo Trust for Education, Port
    Washington, NY 1054
Salida Museum, Salida, CO.......................232
Salina Art Center, Salina, KS.....................557
Saline County Historical Society, Inc.,
    Dorchester, NE 860
Salmagundi Museum of American Art,
    New York, NY..................................1038
Salmon Brook Historical Society, Inc.,
    Granby, CT......................................242
Salt Lake Art Center, Salt Lake City, UT ..1472
Salvador Dali Museum, Saint Petersburg,
    FL..342
Sam Bell Maxey House State Historic
    Site, Paris, TX 1442
Sam Houston Regional Library &
    Research Center, Liberty, TX.................1434
Sam Rayburn House Museum, Bonham,
    TX...1397
The Sam Rayburn Library and Museum,
    a Division of the Center for American
    History of the University of Texas at
    Austin, Bonham, TX...........................1397
Samek Art Gallery, Lewisburg, PA.............1268
Samuel Cupples House of Saint Louis
    University, Saint Louis, MO...................837
Samuel Dorsky Museum of Art, State
    University of New York at New Paltz,
    New Paltz, NY.................................1018
Samuel P. Harn Museum of Art,
    Gainesville, FL.................................311
Samuel S. Fleisher Art Memorial,
    Philadelphia, PA 1288
San Angelo Museum of Fine Arts, San
    Angelo, TX.....................................1447
San Antonio Art League Museum, San
    Antonio, TX....................................1449
San Antonio Museum of Art, San
    Antonio, TX....................................1450
San Buenaventura Mission Museum,
    Ventura, CA....................................195
San Diego Air & Space Museum, San
    Diego, CA......................................159
San Diego Automotive Museum, San
    Diego, CA......................................159
San Diego Hall of Champions Sports
    Museum, San Diego, CA 159
San Diego Museum of Art, San Diego,
    CA...160
San Diego Museum of Man, San Diego,
    CA...160
San Fernando Mission, Mission Hills, CA...126
San Francisco African American
    Historical and Cultural Society, Inc.,
    San Francisco, CA.............................168
San Francisco Art Institute - Walter &
    McBean Galleries, San Francisco, CA 168
San Francisco Maritime National
    Historical Park, San Francisco, CA.........169
San Francisco Museum of Modern Art,
    San Francisco, CA.............................169
San Gabriel Mission Museum, San
    Gabriel, CA....................................171
San Jacinto Museum of History
    Association, La Porte, TX.....................1433
San Jose Museum of Art, San Jose, CA 172
San Jose State University Art Galleries,
    San Jose, CA...................................173
San Juan Bautista State Historic Park,
    San Juan Bautista, CA.........................173

San Miguel Mission Church, Santa Fe,
    NM..950
Sand Springs Cultural & Historical
    Museum, Sand Springs, OK..................1213
The Sandor Teszler Library, Spartanburg,
    SC...1341
Sandusky Library Follett House Museum,
    Sandusky, OH..................................1185
Sandwich Glass Museum, Sandwich, MA ...708
Sandwich Historical Society, Center
    Sandwich, NH..................................884
Sandy Bay Historical Society &
    Museums, Inc., Rockport, MA...............705
Sandy Spring Museum, Sandy Spring,
    MD..653
Sanford Museum, Sanford, FL....................343
Sangre de Cristo Arts Center & Buell
    Children's Museum, Pueblo, CO 231
Sanilac County Historical Museum and
    Village, Port Sanilac, MI......................761
Santa Ana College Art Gallery, Santa
    Ana, CA..178
The Santa Barbara Historical Museum,
    Santa Barbara, CA.............................179
Santa Barbara Maritime Museum, Santa
    Barbara, CA....................................179
Santa Barbara Museum of Art, Santa
    Barbara, CA....................................179
Santa Cruz Art League, Inc., Santa Cruz,
    CA...182
Santa Fe Gallery, Gainesville, FL................311
Santa Fe Trail Museum, Ingalls, KS 545
Santa Maria Museum of Flight, Inc.,
    Santa Maria, CA...............................183
Santa Monica Museum of Art, Santa
    Monica, CA....................................183
Santa Rosa Jr. College Art Gallery, Santa
    Rosa, CA..184
Santuario de Nuestra Senora de
    Guadalupe, Santa Fe, NM.....................950
Sapulpa Historical Museum, Sapulpa, OK.1213
Sarah Campbell Blaffer Foundation,
    Houston, TX....................................1429
Sarah Moody Gallery of Art, The
    University of Alabama, Tuscaloosa,
    AL...20
Saratoga County Historical Society,
    Brookside Museum, Ballston Spa, NY....960
The Sargent House Museum, Gloucester,
    MA..684
Satwiwa Native American Indian Culture
    Center, Thousand Oaks, CA..................191
Sauk County Historical Museum,
    Baraboo, WI....................................1591
Sauk Prairie Area Historical Society, Inc.,
    Prairie du Sac, WI.............................1619
Saunders Memorial Museum, Berryville,
    AR...55
Sautee-Nacoochee Center, Sautee, GA.........384
Savannah College of Art and Design
    Galleries, Savannah, GA......................386
Sawhill Gallery, James Madison
    University, Harrisonburg, VA.................1511
Sawin Memorial Building, Dover, MA 680
Sayward-Wheeler House, York Harbor,
    ME..627
SCAD Museum of Art, Savannah, GA 386
Scantic Academy Museum, East Windsor
    Historical Society, Inc., East Windsor,
    CT...239
Scarborough Historical Museum,
    Scarborough, ME..............................621
Scarfone/Hartley Gallery, Tampa, FL...........349
The Scarsdale Historical Society,
    Scarsdale, NY..................................1066
Schedel Arboretum & Gardens, Elmore,
    OH...1163
Schenectady County Historical Society,
    Schenectady, NY 1067
The Schick Art Gallery, Skidmore
    College, Saratoga Springs, NY.............1065
Schingoethe Center for Native American
    Cultures, Aurora, IL 412

Paintings–Continued

Schminck Memorial Museum, Lakeview,
  OR 1227
Schmucker Art Gallery, Gettysburg, PA 1256
Schneider Museum of Art, Ashland, OR 1217
Scholte House Museum, Pella, IA 527
The Schomburg Center for Research in
  Black Culture, New York, NY 1038
School of American Research, Indian
  Arts Research Center, Santa Fe, NM 950
School of Fine Arts Gallery, Indiana
  University, Bloomington, IN 470
The Schuette Biermann Farmhouse
  Museum, Elk Grove Village, IL 432
The Schumacher Gallery, Capital
  University, Columbus, OH 1159
Schuyler-Hamilton House, Morristown,
  NJ 914
Schuyler Mansion State Historic Site,
  Albany, NY 955
The Schuylkill Center for Environmental
  Education, Philadelphia, PA 1288
Schweinfurth Memorial Art Center,
  Auburn, NY 959
Schwenkfelder Library & Heritage
  Center, Pennsburg, PA 1275
Science Museum of Western Virginia,
  Roanoke, VA 1535
Scituate Historical Society, Scituate, MA 708
Scotchtown, Beaverdam, VA 1496
Scotts Bluff National Monument, Gering,
  NE 861
Scottsdale Museum of Contemporary Art,
  Scottsdale, AZ 44
Scranton Museum of Art, Scranton, PA 1299
Seagraves-Loop Museum and Art Center
  Inc., Seagraves, TX 1452
Seattle Art Museum, Seattle, WA 1568
Seattle Asian Art Museum, Seattle, WA 1569
Second Street Gallery, Charlottesville, VA.1500
Sedgwick-Brooklin Historical Society,
  Sedgwick, ME 622
Sedona Arts Center, Inc., Sedona, AZ 44
Seippel Homestead and Center for the
  Arts, Beaver Dam, WI 1592
Seminole Nation Museum, Wewoka, OK ...1217
Senate House State Historic Site,
  Kingston, NY 1008
Senator George Baldwin Hotel, Klamath
  Falls, OR 1227
Senator George Norris State Historic Site,
  McCook, NE 868
Senator John Heinz Pittsburgh Regional
  History Center, Pittsburgh, PA 1294
Seneca County Museum, Tiffin, OH 1186
Seneca Falls Historical Society, Seneca
  Falls, NY 1069
Seneca-Iroquois National Museum,
  Salamanca, NY 1063
Sequoia and Kings Canyon National
  Parks, Three Rivers, CA 191
Sequoyah Cabin, Sallisaw, OK 1213
1797 Ezekiel Harris House, Augusta, GA ...366
1768 Jeremiah Lee Mansion, Marblehead,
  MA 693
The Sevier County Historical Museum,
  De Queen, AR 56
Sewall-Belmont House and Museum,
  Washington, DC 290
Seward House, Auburn, NY 959
Seward Museum, Seward, AK 27
The Shadows-on-the-Teche, New Iberia,
  LA 593
Shaftsbury Historical Society, Shaftsbury,
  VT 1487
Shaker Historical Society, Shaker
  Heights, OH 1185
Shandy Hall, Geneva, OH 1166
The Sharon Arts Center, Inc., Sharon, NH ...896
Sharpsteen Museum, Calistoga, CA 80

Shasta College Museum & Research
  Center, Redding, CA 146
Shasta State Historic Park, Shasta, CA 186
Sheboygan County Historical Museum,
  Sheboygan, WI 1621
Sheehan Gallery at Whitman College,
  Walla Walla, WA 1577
Shelburne Museum, Inc., Shelburne, VT ...1487
Sheldon Memorial Art Gallery and
  Sculpture Garden/University of
  Nebraska-Lincoln, Lincoln, NE 867
Sheldon Peck Homestead, Lombard, IL 444
Shelter House Society, Emmaus, PA 1251
Shelter Island Historical Society, Shelter
  Island, NY 1069
Shemer Art Center & Museum, Phoenix,
  AZ 42
Sheppard Fine Arts Gallery, Reno, NV 881
Sherman Indian Museum, Riverside, CA 150
Sherwin Miller Museum of Jewish Art,
  Tulsa, OK 1216
Sherwood-Davidson House, Newark, OH ..1178
Sherwood Forest Plantation, Charles City,
  VA 1498
Ships of the Sea Maritime
  Museum/William Scarbrough House,
  Savannah, GA 386
Shirley-Eustis House, Boston, MA 669
Shirley Plantation, Charles City, VA 1498
Shoal Creek Living History Museum,
  Kansas City, MO 822
Shortgrass Country Museum Society,
  Sayre, OK 1213
Sibley House Historic Site, Mendota, MN...780
Sid Richardson Museum, Fort Worth, TX..1418
Sidney Historical Association, Sidney,
  NY 1069
Sidney Mishkin Gallery of Baruch
  College, New York, NY 1038
Siege Museum (The Petersburg
  Museums), Petersburg, VA 1525
Siegfried H. Horn Archaeological
  Museum, Berrien Springs, MI 729
Sierra Mono Indian Museum, North Fork,
  CA 131
Silver Cliff Museum, Silver Cliff, CO 232
Simpson College/Farnham Galleries,
  Indianola, IA 519
Simsbury Historical Society, Phelps
  Tavern, Museum & Homestead,
  Simsbury, CT 260
Sioux City Art Center, Sioux City, IA 527
Sioux Indian Museum, Rapid City, SD 1355
Siouxland Heritage Museums, Sioux
  Falls, SD 1357
Siskin Museum of Religious and
  Ceremonial Art, Chattanooga, TN 1362
Sisson Museum, Mount Shasta, CA 129
Skirball Cultural Center, Los Angeles,
  CA 121
Skirball Museum Cincinnati Hebrew
  Union College-Jewish Institute of
  Religion, Cincinnati, OH 1151
Slate Valley Museum, Granville, NY 996
The Slater Memorial Museum - Norwich
  Free Academy, Norwich, CT 258
Slater Mill Historic Site, Pawtucket, RI 1315
Slidell Cultural Center, Slidell, LA 602
Slifer House, Lewisburg, PA 1268
Sloane-Stanley Museum and Kent
  Furnace, Kent, CT 247
Slocumb Galleries, Johnson City, TN 1368
The Smart Museum of Art, Chicago, IL 427
Smith College Museum of Art,
  Northampton, MA 700
Smith County Historical Society, Tyler,
  TX 1456
Smithsonian American Art Museum,
  Washington, DC 290
Smithsonian Institution, Washington, DC 290
Smithtown Historical Society, Smithtown,
  NY 1070

Smoki Museum - American Indian Art &
  Culture, Prescott, AZ 43
Smyrna Museum, Smyrna, DE 272
The Snite Museum of Art, University of
  Notre Dame, Notre Dame, IN 495
Snug Harbor Cultural Center - Visitors'
  Center and Newhouse Center for
  Contemporary Art, Staten Island, NY ...1073
Snyder Museum & Creative Arts Center,
  Bastrop, LA 585
Society for the Preservation of Long
  Island Antiquities, Cold Spring
  Harbor, NY 980
The Society of California Pioneers, San
  Francisco, CA 170
The Society of the Cincinnati at
  Anderson House, Washington, DC 291
The Society of the Four Arts, Palm
  Beach, FL 334
Sod House Museum, Gothenburg, NE 862
Soldiers & Sailors Memorial Building,
  Huntington, NY 1001
Solomon R. Guggenheim Museum, New
  York, NY 1038
Somers Historical Society, Somers, NY 1070
The Somerset County Historical Society,
  Inc., Princess Anne, MD 650
The Somerville Museum, Somerville,
  MA 709
Sonoma County Museum, Santa Rosa,
  CA 185
Sonoma State Historic Park, Sonoma, CA...188
Sonoma Valley Museum of Art, Sonoma,
  CA 188
Sordoni Art Gallery, Wilkes-Barre, PA 1307
Sotterley Plantation, Hollywood, MD 647
South Arkansas Arts Center, El Dorado,
  AR 56
South Bannock County Historical Center,
  Lava Hot Springs, ID 407
South Bend Regional Museum of Art,
  South Bend, IN 500
South Carolina Artisans Center,
  Walterboro, SC 1343
South Carolina Confederate Relic Room
  and Museum, Columbia, SC 1330
South Carolina Department of Parks,
  Recreation and Tourism, Columbia,
  SC 1330
South Carolina Historical Society,
  Charleston, SC 1327
South Carolina State Museum, Columbia,
  SC 1331
South Carolina Tennis Hall of Fame,
  Belton, SC 1321
South Dakota Art Museum, Brookings,
  SD 1344
South Dakota Hall of Fame,
  Chamberlain, SD 1345
South Florida Community College
  Museum of Florida Art and Culture,
  Avon Park, FL 295
South Milwaukee Historical Society
  Museum, South Milwaukee, WI 1622
South Seattle Community College Art
  Gallery, West Seattle, WA 1578
South Shore Arts, Munster, IN 493
Southampton Historical Museum,
  Southampton, NY 1070
Southdown Plantation House/The
  Terrebonne Museum, Houma, LA 589
Southeast Missouri Regional Museum,
  Cape Girardeau, MO 812
Southeastern Center for Contemporary
  Art, Winston-Salem, NC 1126
Southern Alleghenies Museum of Art,
  Loretto, PA 1269
Southern Alleghenies Museum of Art at
  Johnstown, Johnstown, PA 1264
Southern Baptist Historical Library and
  Archives, Nashville, TN 1380
Southern Forest World, Waycross, GA 391

Southern Museum of Flight, Birmingham, AL..6
Southern Ohio Museum, Portsmouth, OH..1183
Southern Plains Indian Museum, Anadarko, OK..1196
Southern Ute Cultural Center and Museum, Ignacio, CO 223
Southern Vermont Art Center, Manchester, VT 1481
Southold Historical Society and Museum, Southold, NY..1071
Southwest Museum, Los Angeles, CA 121
Southwest Virginia Museum Historical State Park, Big Stone Gap, VA.............1497
Space Center Houston, Houston, TX.........1429
Spanish Governor's Palace, San Antonio, TX..1450
The Spanish Institute, New York, NY........1039
Spartanburg County Museum of Art, Spartanburg, SC..1341
Spartanburg County Regional Museum of History, Spartanburg, SC.........................1341
The Speed Art Museum, Louisville, KY......579
Spelman College Museum of Fine Art, Atlanta, GA..363
Spencer Museum of Art, The University of Kansas, Lawrence, KS.....................548
Spertus Museum, Chicago, IL 427
Spiers Gallery, Brevard, NC 1092
Spirit Square Center for Arts and Education, Charlotte, NC 1096
Spiro Mounds Archaeological Center, Spiro, OK..1214
Spokane Arts Commission-Chase Gallery, Spokane, WA 1572
Spokane Falls Community College Fine Art Gallery, Spokane, WA.....................1572
The Sports Museum, Boston, MA 669
Spring Grove Hospital Center, Alumni Museum, Catonsville, MD 639
Spring Street Historical Museum, Shreveport, LA 602
Spring Valley Community Historical Society, Inc., Spring Valley, MN 794
Springfield Art & Historical Society - Miller Art Center, Springfield, VT.........1488
Springfield Art Association, Springfield, IL..460
Springfield Art Museum, Springfield, MO ...839
Springfield Museum of Art, Springfield, OH..1186
Springfield Museums - Connecticut Valley Historical Museum, Springfield, MA..710
Springfield Museums - George Walter Vincent Smith Art Museum, Springfield, MA.....................710
Springfield Museums - Museum of Fine Arts, Springfield, MA.........................711
Springville Museum of Art, Springville, UT..1474
Spruill Gallery, Atlanta, GA.....................364
Staatsburgh State Historic Site, Staatsburg, NY..1071
Stafford County Historical Society Museum, Stafford, KS............................558
Stamford Historical Society, Inc., Stamford, CT..260
Stamford Museum & Nature Center, Stamford, CT..261
Stan Hywet Hall and Gardens, Inc., Akron, OH..1139
Stanlee & Gerald Rubin Center for the Visual Arts, University of Texas, El Paso, El Paso, TX..1413
Stanley Museum, Inc., Kingfield, ME.........613
Stanley-Whitman House, Farmington, Farmington, CT..241
Stanwood Wildlife Sanctuary, Ellsworth, ME..610
Stark Museum of Art, Orange, TX.............1441

State Historical Society of Missouri, Columbia, MO..814
The State House Museum, Dover, DE 270
The State Museum of Pennsylvania, Harrisburg, PA 1259
State of Illinois-Historic Preservation Agency, Historic Sites Division, Springfield, IL..460
Staten Island Historical Society, Staten Island, NY..1074
Staten Island Institute of Arts & Sciences (SIIAS), Staten Island, NY............1074
Statue of Liberty National Monument & Ellis Island Immigration Museum, New York, NY..1039
Staunton Augusta Art Center, Staunton, VA..1537
Steamship Keewatin, Douglas, MI 738
Stedman Gallery, Camden, NJ 900
Steffen Thomas Museum and Archives, Buckhead, GA..367
Stengel-True Museum, Marion, OH 1174
The Stephen Phillips House, Salem, MA.....707
Stephens African-American Museum, Shreveport, LA 602
Sterling and Francine Clark Art Institute, Williamstown, MA 719
Sterling Historical Society and Little Red Schoolhouse Museum, Sterling, NY......1074
Stillman Art Gallery, Tuscaloosa, AL.............20
Stockbridge Library Historical Collection, Stockbridge, MA..713
Stone House Gallery, Fredonia, KS.............540
Stonewall House, Rocky Mount, NC..........1118
Stonewall Jackson House, Lexington, VA...1514
Stoughton Historical Society, Stoughton, MA..713
The Stowitts Museum & Library, Pacific Grove, CA..137
Strategic Air & Space Museum, Ashland, NE..856
Strater Hotel, Durango, CO 214
The Stratford Historical Society & Catherine B. Mitchell Museum, Stratford, CT..262
Stratford, Robert E. Lee Memorial Association, Inc., Stratford, VA...............1539
Strawbery Banke Museum, Portsmouth, NH..895
Strong - National Museum of Play, Rochester, NY..1060
Stuart Heritage Museum, Stuart, FL.............346
The Studio Museum in Harlem, New York, NY..1040
Studio San Giuseppe Art Gallery, Cincinnati, OH..1151
Sturdivant Hall, Selma, AL............................18
Sturgis Library, Barnstable, MA....................662
SUArt Galleries - Syracuse University, Syracuse, NY..1077
Suffolk County Vanderbilt Museum, Centerport, NY..977
The Suffolk Museum, Suffolk, VA.............1540
Suffolk Resolves House, Milton, MA..........695
Sugarlands Visitor Center, Gatlinburg, TN.1365
Sullivan Museum and History Center, Northfield, VT 1483
SullivanMunce Cultural Center, Zionsville, IN..504
Sumter Gallery of Art, Sumter, SC............1342
Sun Gallery, Hayward, CA 102
Sunnyside Historical Museum, Sunnyside, WA..1572
The Supreme Court of the United States, Washington, DC..291
Susan B. Anthony House, Rochester, NY ..1060
Sushi Performance and Visual Art, San Diego, CA..161
Susquehanna County Historical Society & Free Library Association, Montrose, PA..1272

Susquehanna Museum of Havre de Grace Inc. at the Lock House, Havre de Grace, MD..647
Sutton County Historical Society - Miers Home Museum, Sonora, TX.................1453
Suzanne H. Arnold Art Gallery, Lebanon Valley College, Annville, PA.............1241
Swampscott Historical Society (John Humphrey House), Swampscott, MA......714
Sweet Briar College Art Gallery, Sweet Briar, VA..1540
Sweet Briar Museum, Sweet Briar, VA......1540
Swigart Museum, Huntingdon, PA 1262
Switzerland County Historical Museum, Vevay, IN..502
Swope Art Museum, Terre Haute, IN...........501
Sylvia Plotkin Judaica Museum of Congregation Beth Israel, Scottsdale, AZ..44

T.B. Ferguson Home, Watonga, OK...........1216
T.C. Steele State Historic Site, Nashville, IN..493
T Rex Museum, Tucson, AZ............................50
T.W. Wood Gallery & Arts Center, Montpelier, VT..1482
Table Rock Historical Society and Museums, Table Rock, NE....................873
Tabor Opera House Museum, Leadville, CO..226
Tacoma Art Museum, Tacoma, WA...........1574
The Taft Museum of Art, Cincinnati, OH ..1151
Talkeetna Historical Society and Museum, Talkeetna, AK............................28
Tall Grass Arts Association, Park Forest, IL..449
Tampa Museum of Art, Tampa, FL 350
Taos Historic Museums, Taos, NM 953
Tappantown Historical Society, Tappan, NY..1077
Tarble Arts Center, Eastern Illinois University, Charleston, IL....................417
Tarpon Springs Area Historical Society - Depot Museum, Tarpon Springs, FL....351
Tarpon Springs Cultural Center, Tarpon Springs, FL..351
Tarpon Springs Heritage Museum, Tarpon Springs, FL..351
Taube Museum of Art, Minot, ND 1135
The Teddy Bear Museum of Naples, Naples, FL..328
Telfair Museum of Art, Savannah, GA 386
Temple Gallery, Tyler School of Art of Temple University, Philadelphia, PA 1288
The Temple Judea Museum of Reform Congregation Keneseth Israel, Elkins Park, PA..1251
The Temple Museum of Religious Art, Cleveland, OH..1156
Ten Broeck Mansion - Albany County Historical Association, Albany, NY.........956
Tennessee Historical Society, Nashville, TN..1380
Tennessee State Museum, Nashville, TN....1381
Tennessee Valley Art Center, Tuscumbia, AL..20
Terrace Gallery-City of Orlando, Orlando, FL..332
Terrace Hill Historic Site and Governor's Mansion, Des Moines, IA....................516
Territorial Capital-Lane Museum, Lecompton, KS..549
Territorial Statehouse State Park & Museum, Fillmore, UT....................1465
Terwilliger Museum, Waterloo, NY...........1083
Teutopolis Monastery Museum, Teutopolis, IL..461
Texas Air Museum, Slaton, TX 1453
Texas Maritime Museum, Rockport, TX....1446
Texas Ranger Hall of Fame and Museum, Waco, TX..1459
Texas Seaport Museum, Galveston, TX 1422

Paintings—Continued

Texas State Museum of Asian Cultures &
   Educational Center, Corpus Christi,
   TX 1402
Texas Woman's University Art Galleries,
   Denton, TX 1409
Theodore Roosevelt Birthplace National
   Historic Site, New York, NY 1040
Theodore Roosevelt Inaugural National
   Historic Site, Buffalo, NY 973
Theodore Roosevelt National Park-Visitor
   Center, Medora, ND 1134
Thetford Historical Society Library and
   Museum, Thetford, VT 1488
This Century Art Gallery, Williamsburg,
   VA 1545
Thomas Center Galleries, Gainesville, FL ...311
Thomas Edison Birthplace Museum,
   Milan, OH 1176
Thomas Hart Benton Home and Studio
   State Historic Site, Kansas City, MO 823
Thomas J. Walsh Art Gallery, Quick
   Center for the Arts at Fairfield
   University, Fairfield, CT 241
Thomas Kinkade Museum, Morgan Hill,
   CA 129
Thomas L. Kane Memorial Chapel, Kane,
   PA 1264
Thomas Whaley House Museum, San
   Diego, CA 161
Thomaston Historical Society,
   Thomaston, ME 624
Thomasville Cultural Center, Inc.,
   Thomasville, GA 388
Thorne-Sagendorph Art Gallery, Keene,
   NH 890
Thornhill Gallery at Avila University,
   Kansas City, MO 823
Thornton W. Burgess Museum,
   Sandwich, MA 708
Thousand Islands Museum, Clayton, NY ...979
Thunderbird Foundation for the Arts,
   Mount Carmel, UT 1467
Tillamook County Pioneer Museum,
   Tillamook, OR 1237
Timken Museum of Art, San Diego, CA 162
Tinker Swiss Cottage Museum, Rockford,
   IL 456
Tioga County Historical Society
   Museum, Owego, NY 1048
Tioga Point Museum, Athens, PA 1241
Tippecanoe County Historical
   Association, Lafayette, IN 487
Tohono Chul Park Inc., Tucson, AZ 51
The Toledo Museum of Art, Toledo, OH ...1187
Tolland Historical Society - Tolland
   County Jail and Warden's Home
   Museum, Tolland, CT 262
Tome Parish Museum, Tome, NM 953
Tongass Historical Museum, Ketchikan,
   AK 26
Top of Oklahoma Historical Museum,
   Blackwell, OK 1197
Toppenish Museum, Toppenish, WA 1575
Torpedo Factory Art Center, Alexandria,
   VA 1494
Torrance Art Museum, Torrance, CA 192
Tougaloo College, Tougaloo, MS 808
Tower Fine Arts Gallery (SUNY
   Brockport), Brockport, NY 964
Town of Manlius Historical Society with
   Museum, Manlius, NY 1013
Town of Yorktown Museum, Yorktown
   Heights, NY 1087
Trail End State Historic Site, Sheridan,
   WY 1638
The Trammell & Margaret Crow
   Collection of Asian Art, Dallas, TX 1408
Travellers Rest Plantation & Museum,
   Nashville, TN 1381
Tread of Pioneers Museum, Steamboat
   Springs, CO 232

Trenton City Museum, Trenton, NJ 928
Trenton Historical Museum, Trenton, MI 765
Tri-State University, General Lewis B.
   Hershey Museum, Angola, IN 468
Trinity Museum of the Parish of Trinity
   Church, New York, NY 1040
Triton Museum of Art, Santa Clara, CA 181
The Trout Gallery, Carlisle, PA 1245
Troy Museum & Historic Village, Troy,
   MI 765
The Trustees of Reservations, Beverly,
   MA 662
Tryon Palace Historic Sites and Gardens,
   New Bern, NC 1112
Tsa Mo Ga Memorial Museum, Plains,
   TX 1443
T.T. Wentworth, Jr. Florida State
   Museum, Pensacola, FL 336
Tu-Endie-Wei State Park, Point Pleasant,
   WV 1586
Tubac Center of the Arts, Tubac, AZ 47
Tubman African-American Museum,
   Macon, GA 378
Tuck Museum, Hampton, NH 888
Tucson Museum of Art & Historic Block,
   Tucson, AZ 51
Tudor Place Foundation, Inc.,
   Washington, DC 292
Tufts University Art Gallery, Medford,
   MA 694
Turabo University, Gurabo, PR 1641
Turquoise Museum, Albuquerque, NM 936
Turtle Bay Exploration Park, Redding,
   CA 146
Turtle Mountain Chippewa Historical
   Society, Belcourt, ND 1127
Tuskegee Institute National Historic Site,
   Tuskegee Institute, AL 21
Tweed Museum of Art, Duluth, MN 774
Tyler Art Gallery, Oswego, NY 1048
Tyler Museum of Art, Tyler, TX 1456

USM Art Gallery, Gorham, ME 611
U.S. Navy Museum, Washington, DC 292
UWM Union-Art Gallery, Milwaukee, WI.1613
Ukrainian-American Museum &
   Archives, Warren, MI 766
Ukrainian Institute of Modern Art,
   Chicago, IL 428
The Ukrainian Museum, New York, NY 1040
Ukrainian Museum-Archives, Inc.,
   Cleveland, OH 1156
Ulrich Museum of Art, Wichita, KS 563
Ulster County Historical Society,
   Marbletown, NY 1013
Umlauf Sculpture Garden & Museum,
   Austin, TX 1392
Uncle Remus Museum, Eatonton, GA 371
UNI Gallery of Art, University of
   Northern Iowa, Cedar Falls, IA 508
Union County Historical Society
   Museum, Blairsville, GA 366
United States Army Heritage and
   Education Center - Army Heritage
   Museum, Carlisle, PA 1246
The United States Army Quartermaster
   Museum, Fort Lee, VA 1505
United States Capitol, Washington, DC 293
United States Department of the Interior
   Museum, Washington, DC 293
United States Golf Association Museum
   & Archives, Far Hills, NJ 903
United States Hockey Hall of Fame,
   Eveleth, MN 774
United States Holocaust Memorial
   Museum, Washington, DC 293
United States Marine Corps Air-Ground
   Museum, Quantico, VA 1526
United States Naval Academy Museum,
   Annapolis, MD 628
United States Senate Commission on Art,
   Washington, DC 293
University Art Galleries, Vermillion, SD....1358

University Art Galleries, Murray State
   University, Murray, KY 580
University Art Gallery, CSU Dominguez
   Hills, Carson, CA 82
University Art Gallery, Indiana State
   University, Terre Haute, IN 501
University Art Gallery, New Mexico
   State University, Las Cruces, NM 941
University Art Gallery, Sonoma State
   University, Rohnert Park, CA 151
University Art Gallery, State University
   of New York at Stony Brook, Stony
   Brook, NY 1075
University Art Gallery, Texas Christian
   University, Fort Worth, TX 1418
University Art Gallery, University of
   California, San Diego, La Jolla, CA........107
University Art Gallery, University of
   Massachusetts Dartmouth, New
   Bedford, MA 697
University Art Gallery, University of
   Pittsburgh, Pittsburgh, PA 1294
University Art Gallery, University of the
   South, Sewanee, TN 1384
University Art Museum, Binghamton, NY...963
University Art Museum, Santa Barbara,
   Santa Barbara, CA 180
University Art Museum, The University
   of New Mexico, Albuquerque, NM 936
University Art Museum, University at
   Albany, Albany, NY 956
University at Buffalo Art Galleries,
   Buffalo, NY 974
University Galleries, Clarion, PA 1247
University Galleries, Florida Atlantic
   University, Boca Raton, FL 296
University Gallery, Gainesville, FL 312
University Gallery, University of
   Massachusetts at Amherst, Amherst,
   MA 659
University Museum, Carbondale, IL 415
The University Museum, Edwardsville,
   IL 432
The University Museum, Indiana, PA 1263
University Museum, Martin, TN 1371
University Museum & Historic Houses,
   The University of Mississippi, Oxford,
   MS 806
University Museums, University of
   Delaware, Newark, DE 272
University of Alaska Museum of the
   North, Fairbanks, AK 24
The University of Arizona Museum of
   Art, Tucson, AZ 52
University of Arizona Student Union
   Galleries, Tucson, AZ 52
University of Arkansas at Little Rock Art
   Department Gallery I & II & III,
   Little Rock, AR 63
University of California Berkeley Art
   Museum and Pacific Film Archive,
   Berkeley, CA 77
University of Central Florida Art Gallery,
   Orlando, FL 332
University of Colorado Museum,
   Boulder, CO 203
University of Denver, School of Art &
   Art History, Victoria H. Myhren
   Gallery, Denver, CO 213
University of Hawaii Art Gallery,
   Honolulu, HI 398
University of Iowa Museum of Art, Iowa
   City, IA 520
University of Kansas Medical Center,
   Clendening History of Medicine
   Library and Museum, Kansas City, KS...546
University of Kentucky Art Museum,
   Lexington, KY 574
University of Maine Museum of Art,
   Bangor, ME 605
University of Mary Washington Galleries,
   Fredericksburg, VA 1507

The University of Michigan Museum of Art, Ann Arbor, MI 726
University of Missouri-Kansas City Gallery of Art, Kansas City, MO............823
The University of Montana-Western Art Gallery & Museum, Dillon, MT.............846
University of North Texas Art Gallery, Denton, TX 1409
University of Rhode Island Fine Arts Center Galleries, Kingston, RI..............1312
University of Richmond Museums, Richmond, VA 1532
The University of South Carolina McKissick Museum, Columbia, SC.......1331
University of South Florida Contemporary Art Museum, Tampa, FL...350
The University of Texas at San Antonio, Art Gallery, San Antonio, TX 1451
The University of the Arts - Rosenwald-Wolf Gallery, Philadelphia, PA...1289
University of Virginia Art Museum, Charlottesville, VA 1500
University of West Florida Art Gallery, Pensacola, FL...............................336
University of Wyoming Art Museum, Laramie, WY 1636
University Saint Thomas Art History, Saint Paul, MN 792
Upper Room Chapel Museum, Nashville, TN...1381
Upton Red Onion Museum, Upton, WY 1639
Urban Institute for Contemporary Arts, Grand Rapids, MI...........................744
U.S. Army Air Defense Artillery Museum, Fort Bliss, TX.................1414
U.S. Army Center of Military History, Museum Division, Fort McNair, DC.......275
U.S. Army Finance Corps Museum, Fort Jackson, SC...............................1333
U.S. Army Medical Department Museum, Fort Sam Houston, TX 1415
U.S. Army Ordnance Museum, Aberdeen Proving Ground, MD.......................627
U.S. Army Signal Corps Museum, Fort Gordon, GA 372
U.S. Army Transportation Museum, Fort Eustis, VA...............................1504
U.S. Army Women's Museum, Fort Lee, VA..1505
U.S. Cavalry Museum, Fort Riley, KS.........540
U.S. Coast Guard Museum, New London, CT......................................255
U.S. Grant's Home State Historic Site, Galena, IL.....................................436
U.S. Navy Memorial Foundation and Naval Heritage Center, Washington, DC..294
U.S. Navy Seabee Museum, Port Hueneme, CA 143
The U.S. Space & Rocket Center, Huntsville, AL 12
USS Arizona Memorial, Honolulu, HI.........398
USS Bowfin Submarine Museum & Park, Honolulu, HI......................................398
USS Constellation Museum, Baltimore, MD...636
USS Constitution Museum, Boston, MA 669
USS Lexington Museum on the Bay, Corpus Christi, TX 1402
Utah Field House of Natural History State Park, Vernal, UT 1475
Utah Museum of Fine Arts, Salt Lake City, UT..1472
Utah State Historical Society, Salt Lake City, UT..1473

Vacaville Museum, Vacaville, CA 194
Vachel Lindsay Home State Historic Site, Springfield, IL..................................460
The Valdez Museum & Historical Archive Association, Inc., Valdez, AK 29

Valdosta State University Fine Arts Gallery, Valdosta, GA.......................389
Valentine-Varian House/Museum of Bronx History, Bronx, NY 967
Valley Art Center, Inc., Clarkston, WA 1551
Valley County Pioneer Museum, Glasgow, MT..847
Van Cortlandt House Museum, Bronx, NY......................................967
Van Every/Smith Galleries, Davidson, NC......................................1098
Van Wyck Homestead Museum, Fishkill, NY......................................989
Vanderbilt Mansion National Historic Site, Hyde Park, NY..........................1002
Vanderbilt University Fine Arts Gallery, Nashville, TN.....................................1381
Varner-Hogg Plantation State Historic Site, West Columbia, TX 1461
Vashon Maury Island Heritage Association, Vashon, WA 1576
Venango Museum of Art, Science & Industry, Oil City, PA.........................1274
Ventura County Maritime Museum, Inc., Oxnard, CA...137
Ventura County Museum of History & Art, Ventura, CA...............................195
Vermont Historical Society Museum, Montpelier, VT.....................................1482
The Vermont State House, Montpelier, VT..1483
Vero Beach Museum of Art, Inc., Vero Beach, FL...352
Vesterheim Norwegian-American Museum, Decorah, IA 513
Vicksburg Battlefield Museum, Vicksburg, MS....................................809
Victor Heritage Museum, Victor, MT..........854
Victor Valley Museum & Art Gallery, Apple Valley, CA.....................................71
Victoria Mansion, Portland, ME 620
Viking Union Gallery, Bellingham, WA.....1549
Villa Louis Historic Site, Prairie du Chien, WI...1619
Villa Terrace Decorative Arts Museum, Milwaukee, WI.....................................1613
Village Gallery, La Jolla, CA.......................107
Village Historical Society, Inc., Harrison, OH...1168
Village of Elsah Museum, Elsah, IL 433
Virginia Air & Space Center, Hampton, VA..1510
Virginia Baptist Historical Society, Richmond, VA 1532
Virginia Historical Society, Richmond, VA..1533
Virginia Holocaust Museum, Richmond, VA..1533
Virginia Military Institute Museum, Lexington, VA.....................................1514
Virginia Museum of Fine Arts, Richmond, VA 1533
The Virginia War Museum, Newport News, VA...1520
Visual Arts Center at the Washington Pavilion, Sioux Falls, SD 1357
Visual Arts Center of New Jersey, Summit, NJ...925
Visual Arts Center of Northwest Florida, Panama City, FL.......................334
Visual Arts Museum, New York, NY..........1040
Vizcaya Museum and Gardens, Miami, FL..326
The von Liebig Art Center, Naples, FL 328
VSA Arts of Georgia - Arts for All Gallery, Atlanta, GA..................................364

WARM (Women's Art Registry of Minnesota), Saint Paul, MN...................792
W.C. Handy Home Museum and Library, Florence, AL...9
The W.H. Stark House, Orange, TX...........1442

Wabasha County Museum, Wabasha County Historical Society at Reads Landing, Reads Landing, MN.................787
Wabaunsee County Historical Museum, Alma, KS...532
Wadsworth Atheneum Museum of Art, Hartford, CT......................................246
The Wagnalls Memorial, Lithopolis, OH ...1172
Waikiki Aquarium, Honolulu, HI.................399
Wailoa Center for Culture and Arts, Hilo, HI...393
Wake Forest College Birthplace Society, Inc., Wake Forest, NC.............................1121
Wakefield Historical Society, Wakefield, MA......................................715
The Walker African American Museum & Research Center, Las Vegas, NV...........880
Walker Art Center, Minneapolis, MN...........783
The Walker Art Collection of the Garnett Public Library, Garnett, KS 541
Wallace District Mining Museum, Wallace, ID...410
Wallingford Historical Society, Inc., Wallingford, CT......................................263
Walnut Grove Plantation, Roebuck, SC 1340
Walter Anderson Museum of Art, Ocean Springs, MS...806
Walter E. Heller Nature Center, Highland Park, IL...439
Walter Elwood Museum, Amsterdam, NY ...957
Walter P. Chrysler Boyhood Home and Museum, Ellis, KS.........................538
Walters Art Museum, Baltimore, MD..........636
Ward County Historical Society, Minot, ND......................................1135
The Ward Museum of Wildfowl Art, Salisbury University, Salisbury, MD 653
Warner House, Portsmouth, NH 895
Warren County Historical Society Museum, Lebanon, OH 1171
Warsaw Historical Museum, Warsaw, NY .1082
Warwick Museum of Art, Warwick, RI......1320
Washburn County Historical Society Museum, Shell Lake, WI....................1621
Washburn Historical Museum & Cultural Center, Inc. aka Washburn Cultural Center, Washburn, WI 1625
Washington & Jefferson College - Olin Fine Arts Center, Washington, PA 1305
Washington County Historical Society, Washington, PA 1305
Washington County Museum of Fine Arts, Hagerstown, MD 647
Washington Crossing Historic Park, Washington Crossing, PA.....................1305
Washington Historical Museum, Washington, GA 391
Washington Pavilion of Arts and Science, Sioux Falls, SD...1357
Washington State Historical Society, Tacoma, WA 1574
Washington's Headquarters State Historic Site, Newburgh, NY 1042
Waterford Historical Museum and Cultural Center, Inc., Waterford, NY...1083
Waterloo Center for the Arts, Waterloo, IA......................................529
Watermen's Museum, Yorktown, VA.........1547
Watervliet Arsenal's Museum of the Big Guns, Watervliet, NY.............................1084
Waterworks Visual Arts Center, Salisbury, NC......................................1118
Watkins Institute, Nashville, TN.................1381
Watkins Woolen Mill State Historic Site & Park, Lawson, MO.............................825
Watson-Curtze Mansion, Erie, PA 1253
Watts Towers Arts Center, Los Angeles, CA......................................122
Wayland Historical Society, Wayland, MA......................................716
Wayne Center for the Arts, Wooster, OH ...1192

Paintings—Continued

Wayne County Historical Museum, Richmond, IN 497

Wayne County Historical Society, Lyons, NY 1012

Wayne County Historical Society, Wooster, OH 1192

Wayne County Historical Society, Honesdale, PA 1261

Wayne State University Art Galleries, Detroit, MI 738

Weatherspoon Art Museum, Greensboro, NC 1104

The Webb-Deane-Stevens Museum, Wethersfield, CT 266

Webb House Museum, Newark, OH 1179

Webster House Museum, Elkhorn, WI 1596

Weir Farm National Historic Site, Wilton, CT 267

Welder Wildlife Foundation & Refuge, Sinton, TX 1453

Wellesley Historical Society, Inc., Wellesley Hills, MA 717

Wellfleet Historical Society Museum, Wellfleet, MA 717

Wellington B. Gray Gallery, Greenville, NC 1105

Wells County Museum, Fessenden, ND 1131

Wells Fargo History Museum, Phoenix, AZ 42

Wentworth-Coolidge Mansion, Portsmouth, NH 895

Wentworth Gardner & Tobias Lear Houses Association, Portsmouth, NH ...895

West Baton Rouge Museum, Port Allen, LA 599

West Bend Art Museum, West Bend, WI ...1627

West Point Museum, West Point, NY 1085

West River Museum Society, Philip, SD ...1353

West Valley Art Museum, Surprise, AZ 45

West Virginia Independence Hall, Wheeling, WV 1588

West Virginia State Museum, Charleston, WV 1581

West Virginia University-Mesaros Galleries, Morgantown, WV 1585

Western Heritage Center, Billings, MT 841

Western Illinois University Art Gallery, Macomb, IL 444

Western Kentucky University Gallery, Bowling Green, KY 566

Western Michigan University Richmond Center for Visual Arts School of Art, Kalamazoo, MI 749

Western Museum of Mining & Industry, Colorado Springs, CO 208

Western Reserve Historical Society, Cleveland, OH 1156

Western Springs Historical Society, Western Springs, IL 464

Westmoreland Museum of American Art, Greensburg, PA 1257

The Wetlands Institute, Stone Harbor, NJ 925

Wexford County Historical Society & Museum, Cadillac, MI 731

Wexner Center for the Arts, Columbus, OH 1159

The Wharton Esherick Museum, Malvern, PA 1269

Whatcom Museum of History and Art, Bellingham, WA 1549

Wheeler Historic Farm, Salt Lake City, UT 1474

Wheels Through Time Museum, Inc., Maggie Valley, NC 1110

The Wheelwright Museum of the American Indian, Santa Fe, NM 950

Whistler House Museum of Art, Lowell, MA 692

White Deer Land Museum, Pampa, TX ...1442

White Hall State Historic Site, Richmond, KY 583

The White House, Washington, DC 294

Whitney Museum of American Art, New York, NY 1041

Whittier Home Association, Amesbury, MA 658

Wichita Art Museum, Wichita, KS 563

Wichita Center for the Arts, Wichita, KS.....563

Wichita Falls Museum and Art Center, Wichita Falls, TX 1461

Widener Gallery, Austin Arts Center, Trinity College, Hartford, CT 246

Widener University Art Collection and Gallery, Chester, PA 1247

The Wiegand Gallery, Belmont, CA 74

Wignall Museum/Gallery, Rancho Cucamonga, CA 145

Wilbur D. May Museum, Reno, NV 882

Wilder Memorial Museum, Strawberry Point, IA 528

Wilderness Road Regional Museum, Newbern, VA 1519

Wildlife Experience Museum, Parker, CO ...229

Wildling Art Museum, Los Olivos, CA 123

Wilhelm Reich Museum - Orgonon, Rangeley, ME 621

Wilkes Art Gallery, North Wilkesboro, NC 1113

Wilkinson County Museum, Woodville, MS 810

Will Rogers Memorial Museum, Claremore, OK 1198

Will Rogers State Historic Park, Pacific Palisades, CA 137

Willa Cather Pioneer Memorial and Educational Foundation, Red Cloud, NE 872

Willard House and Clock Museum, Inc., Grafton, MA 685

William A. Farnsworth Library and Art Museum, Inc. d/b/a Farnsworth Art Museum, Rockland, ME 621

The William Benton Museum of Art, Storrs, CT 262

William Bonifas Fine Arts Center, Escanaba, MI 741

William Cullen Bryant Homestead, Cummington, MA 678

William Henry Harrison Mansion, Grouseland, Vincennes, IN 503

William Holmes McGuffey Museum, Oxford, OH 1181

William J. Clinton Presidential Library & Museum, Little Rock, AR 63

William King Regional Arts Center, Abingdon, VA 1491

William Otis Sawtelle Collections and Research Center, Bar Harbor, ME 606

William Pryor Letchworth Museum, Castile, NY 976

William S. Hart County Park & Museum, Newhall, CA 130

William Weston Clarke Emison Museum of Art, Greencastle, IN 479

Williams College Museum of Art, Williamstown, MA 719

Wilson Czech Opera House Corporation, Foundation, Inc. & House of Memories Museum, Wilson, KS 564

Wilson Galleries, Anderson, IN 467

Wilson Historical Museum, Wilson, NY 1086

Wilson's Creek National Battlefield, Republic, MO 829

Wilton House Museum, Richmond, VA 1534

Winchendon Historical Society, Inc., Winchendon, MA 720

Winchester-Frederick County Historical Society, Inc., Winchester, VA 1546

The Wine Museum of Greyton H. Taylor, Hammondsport, NY 997

Winedale, Center for American History, University of Texas at Austin, Round Top, TX 1446

Wing Luke Asian Museum, Seattle, WA ...1569

Winston Churchill Memorial and Library, Fulton, MO 816

Winterset Art Center, Winterset, IA 531

Winterthur Museum & Country Estate, Winterthur, DE 274

Wiregrass Museum of Art, Dothan, AL 8

Wisconsin Fine Arts Association, Inc., Cedarburg, WI 1594

Wisconsin Historical Museum, Madison, WI 1606

Wisconsin Maritime Museum, Manitowoc, WI 1607

The Wisconsin Union Galleries, University of Wisconsin-Madison, Madison, WI 1606

Wisconsin Veterans Museum-King, King, WI 1602

Wisconsin Veterans Museum-Madison, Madison, WI 1606

Wise County Heritage Museum, Decatur, TX 1408

Wiseman & FireHouse Galleries, Rogue Community College, Grants Pass, OR ..1225

Witte Museum, San Antonio, TX 1451

Witter Gallery, Storm Lake, IA 528

Wolcott House Museum Complex, Maumee, OH 1175

Wolf Point Area Historical Society, Inc., Wolf Point, MT 855

Wolfeboro Historical Society, Wolfeboro, NH 897

The Wolfsonian - Florida International University, Miami Beach, FL 327

Wood County Historical Center and Museum, Bowling Green, OH 1143

Wood Library-Museum of Anesthesiology, Park Ridge, IL 450

Wood Street Galleries, Pittsburgh, PA 1295

Woodbine International Fire Museum, Woodbine, GA 392

Woodford County Historical Society Museum, Versailles, KY 584

Woodlawn Museum/The Black House, Ellsworth, ME 610

Woodlawn Plantation Museum, Alexandria, VA 1494

Woodmere Art Museum, Philadelphia, PA.1289

Woodrow Wilson House, Washington, DC 294

Woodrow Wilson Presidential Library at His Birthplace, Staunton, VA 1537

Woodstock Artists Association, Woodstock, NY 1087

Woodstock Historical Society, Bryant Pond, ME 608

Woodstock Historical Society, Inc., Woodstock, VT 1491

Woodstock Museum of Shenandoah County, Inc., Woodstock, VA 1546

Woolaroc Museum, Bartlesville, OK 1197

Worcester Art Museum, Worcester, MA 721

Worcester Center for Crafts, Worcester, MA 721

Worcester County Horticultural Society/Tower Hill Botanic Garden, Boylston, MA 670

Working Men's Institute, New Harmony, IN 495

World Erotic Art Museum, Miami Beach, FL 327

World Figure Skating Museum & Hall of Fame, Colorado Springs, CO 208

World Golf Hall of Fame, Saint Augustine, FL 340

World Methodist Museum, Lake Junaluska, NC 1109

World Museum of Mining, Butte, MT 843

World O' Tools Museum, Waverly, TN 1385

World of Wings Pigeon Center, Oklahoma City, OK 1211

World's Largest Toy Museum and Harold Bell Wright, Branson, MO 811

Wrangell Museum, Wrangell, AK 29

Wrather West Kentucky Museum, Murray, KY 580
Wright Brothers National Memorial, Kill Devil Hills, NC 1108
Wright County Historical Society, Buffalo, MN 770
Wright Museum of Art, Beloit College, Beloit, WI 1592
Wright State University Art Galleries, Dayton, OH 1162
Wriston Art Center Galleries, Appleton, WI 1590
Wyandot County Historical Society, Upper Sandusky, OH 1188
The Wyman Tavern, Keene, NH 890
Wyoming Arts Council Gallery, Cheyenne, WY 1630
Wyoming Pioneer Memorial Museum, Douglas, WY 1632
Wyoming State Museum, Cheyenne, WY ..1631

Xavier University Art Gallery, Cincinnati, OH 1152
Xochipilli Art Gallery, Birmingham, MI 730

The Yager Museum of Art & Culture, Oneonta, NY 1046
Yale Center for British Art, New Haven, CT 254
Yale University Art Gallery, New Haven, CT 254
Yeiser Art Center, Paducah, KY 582
Yellowstone Art Museum, Billings, MT 842
Yellowstone National Park, Gardiner, MT ...847
Yeshiva University Museum at the Center for Jewish History, New York, NY 1041
Yogi Berra Museum and Learning Center, Little Falls, NJ 910
Yolo County Historical Museum, Woodland, CA 199
The Yosemite Museum, National Park Service, Yosemite National Park, CA 199
Young at Art Children's Museum, Davie, FL 302
Ypsilanti Historical Museum, Ypsilanti, MI 767
Yuma Art Center Museum - Yuma Fine Arts, Yuma, AZ 54
Yuma Crossing State Historic Park, Yuma, AZ 54
Yuma Territorial Prison State Historic Park, Yuma, AZ 54

Zabriskie Gallery, New York, NY 1041
Zado Gallery, Portland, OR 1233
ZAM - Zigler Art Museum, Jennings, LA ...589
Zane Grey Museum, Lackawaxen, PA 1265
Zanesville Art Center, Zanesville, OH 1194
Zelienople Historical Society, Zelienople, PA 1309
Zenith Gallery, Washington, DC 294
Zeum, San Francisco, CA 170
Ziibiwing Center of Anishinabe Culture & Lifeways, Mount Pleasant, MI 757
Zion Human History Museum, Springdale, UT 1474
Zora Neale Hurston National Museum of Fine Arts, Eatonville, FL 305

Photographs

The A.D. Buck Museum of Natural History & Science, Tonkawa, OK 1215
A.D. German Warehouse, Designed By Frank Lloyd Wright, Richland Center, WI 1620
A.K.C. Museum of The Dog, Saint Louis, MO 831
A.R. Bowman Memorial Museum, Prineville, OR 1234
A.R. Mitchell Museum, Trinidad, CO 233
ASA National Softball Hall of Fame and Museum Complex, Oklahoma City, OK 1207

A:shiwi A:wan Museum and Heritage Center, Zuni, NM 954
Aberdeen Museum of History, Aberdeen, WA 1547
Abilene Zoological Gardens, Abilene, TX .1385
Abington Art Center, Jenkintown, PA 1263
Abraham Lincoln Birthplace National Historic Site, Hodgenville, KY 571
Abraham Lincoln Library & Museum, Lincoln Memorial University, Harrogate, TN 1366
Abraham Lincoln Presidential Library & Museum, Springfield, IL 458
Academy Art Museum, Easton, MD 642
Academy Hall Museum of the Rocky Hill Historical Society, Inc., Rocky Hill, CT 259
Ace of Clubs House, Texarkana, TX 1455
Ackland Art Museum, Chapel Hill, NC 1093
Adair County Historical Society, Inc., Kirksville, MO 824
Adams County Historical Museum, Decatur, IN 474
Adams County Historical Society Museum, Brighton, CO 204
Adams Museum & House, Deadwood, SD 1346
Adams National Historical Park, Quincy, MA 704
Adams State College Luther Bean Museum, Alamosa, CO 201
Adan E. Treganza Anthropology Museum, Dept. of Anthropology, San Francisco State University, San Francisco, CA 162
Addison Gallery of American Art, Andover, MA 659
Adirondack History Center, Elizabethtown, NY 987
The Adirondack Museum, Blue Mountain Lake, NY 963
Adler Planetarium & Astronomy Museum, Chicago, IL 417
Admiral Nimitz National Museum of the Pacific War, Fredericksburg, TX 1419
African American Museum, Cleveland, OH 1152
African American Museum, Dallas, TX 1403
The African American Museum in Philadelphia, Philadelphia, PA 1275
African American Museum of the Arts, De Land, FL 303
African Art Museum of the S.M.A. Fathers, Tenafly, NJ 926
Afro-American Cultural Center, Charlotte, NC 1094
Afro American Historical Association of Fauquier County, The Plains, VA 1541
Agate Fossil Beds National Monument, Harrison, NE 862
Agricultural and Industrial Museum, York County Heritage Trust, York, PA 1309
Ah-Tah-Thi-Ki Museum at Okalee, Hollywood, FL 312
Aiken Thoroughbred Racing Hall of Fame and Museum, Aiken, SC 1320
Air Force Flight Test Center Museum, Edwards AFB, CA 92
Air Mobility Command Museum, Dover AFB, DE 270
Air Victory Museum, Inc., Lumberton, NJ 910
The Airborne & Special Operations Museum, Fayetteville, NC 1100
Airline History Museum, Kansas City, MO 820
Airmen Memorial Museum, Suitland, MD 655
Akron Art Museum, Akron, OH 1138
Akron Zoological Park, Akron, OH 1138
Akta Lakota Museum and Cultural Center, Chamberlain, SD 1345
Akwesasne Museum, Hogansburg, NY 998

Alabama Department of Archives & History, Montgomery, AL 15
Alabama Jazz Hall of Fame, Birmingham, AL 4
Alabama Mining Museum, Dora, AL 7
Alabama Museum of Natural History, Tuscaloosa, AL 19
Alabama Museum of the Health Sciences, Birmingham, AL 4
Alabama River Museum, Finchburg, AL 9
Alabama Sports Hall of Fame, Birmingham, AL 4
Alabama Women's Hall of Fame, Marion, AL 13
Alachua County Historic Trust: Matheson Museum, Inc., Gainesville, FL 310
The Alamo, San Antonio, TX 1447
Alamo Township Museum-John E. Gray Memorial Museum, Kalamazoo, MI 748
Alan Short Gallery, Stockton, CA 189
Alaska Aviation Heritage Museum, Anchorage, AK 21
Alaska Museum of Natural History, Anchorage, AK 21
Alaska Native Heritage Center, Anchorage, AK 22
Albany Civil Rights Movement Museum at Old Mt. Zion Church, Albany, GA 355
Albany Historical Society, Inc., Sabetha, KS 557
Albany Institute of History & Art, Albany, NY 954
Albany Museum of Art, Albany, GA 355
Albany Regional Museum, Albany, OR 1217
The Albin O. Kuhn Library & Gallery, University of Maryland-Baltimore County, Baltimore, MD 628
Albion Academy Historical Museum, Edgerton, WI 1596
Albion College Department of Art and Art History, Albion, MI 722
The Albrecht-Kemper Museum of Art, Saint Joseph, MO 830
Albright-Knox Art Gallery, Buffalo, NY 971
Alden B. Dow Museum of Science and Art of the Midland Center for the Arts, Midland, MI 755
Alden Historical Society, Inc., Alden, NY ...956
Alden House Historic Site, Duxbury, MA ...680
Alexander & Baldwin Sugar Museum, Puunene, HI 401
Alexander Brest Museum and Gallery, Jacksonville, FL 313
Alexandre Mouton House/Lafayette Museum, Lafayette, LA 589
Alexandria Black History Resource Center, Alexandria, VA 1491
Alexandria Museum of Art, Alexandria, LA 584
Alger County Heritage Center, Munising, MI 757
Alice Austen House Museum, Staten Island, NY 1072
Alice C. Sabatini Gallery-Topeka and Shawnee County Public Library, Topeka, KS 558
Aliceville Museum, Aliceville, AL 3
Allan Shivers Museum, Woodville, TX 1462
Allegan County Historical Society and Old Jail Museum, Allegan, MI 723
Allegheny College Art Galleries (Bowman, Penelec & Megahan Galleries), Meadville, PA 1270
Allen County Historical Society, Iola, KS ...545
Allen County Museum, Lima, OH 1172
Allen Memorial Art Museum, Oberlin, OH 1180
Allentown Art Museum, Allentown, PA 1239
Allied Arts Council of Yakima Valley Gallery, Yakima, WA 1578
Allison-Antrim Museum, Inc., Greencastle, PA 1257

Photographs–Continued

Almond Historical Society/Hagadorn House Museum, Almond, NY..................957

Alpine County Museum, Markleeville, CA..................124

Altama Museum of Art & History, Vidalia, GA..................390

Alton Museum of History and Art, Inc., Alton, IL..................410

Alumni Center - Husky Heritage Sports Museum, Storrs, CT..................261

Alutiiq Museum and Archaeological Repository, Kodiak, AK..................26

Alva deMars Megan Chapel Art Center, Manchester, NH..................891

Amador County Museum, Jackson, CA...105

Amana Heritage Museum, Amana, IA..................504

Amarillo Museum of Art, Amarillo, TX....1386

Amelia Earhart Birthplace Museum, Atchison, KS..................532

Amelia Island Museum of History, Fernandina Beach, FL..................306

American Airlines C.R. Smith Museum, Fort Worth, TX..................1416

American Antiquarian Society, Worcester, MA..................720

American Baptist Historical Society, Rochester, NY..................1058

American Catholic Historical Society, Philadelphia, PA..................1276

American Clock and Watch Museum, Inc., Bristol, CT..................236

American Folk Art Museum, New York, NY..................1018

American Historical Society of Germans from Russia, Lincoln, NE..................865

American Hungarian Foundation/Museum of the American Hungarian Foundation, New Brunswick, NJ..................915

American Independence Museum, Exeter, NH..................887

American Jewish Historical Society, New York, NY..................1019

American Labor Museum, Botto House National Landmark, Haledon, NJ..................906

American Maple Museum, Croghan, NY.....983

American Merchant Marine Museum, Kings Point, NY..................1007

American Museum of Asmat Art, Saint Paul, MN..................789

The American Museum of Fly Fishing, Manchester, VT..................1481

American Museum of Magic & Lund Memorial Library, Inc., Marshall, MI.....754

American Museum of Nursing, Tempe, AZ..................45

American Museum of Radio and Electricity, Bellingham, WA..................1548

American Numismatic Association Money Museum, Colorado Springs, CO..................206

American Printing House for the Blind, Callahan Museum, Louisville, KY..................575

American Quarter Horse Hall of Fame & Museum, Amarillo, TX..................1386

American Red Cross Visitors Center and Gift Shop, Washington, DC..................275

American Royal Museum & Visitors Center, Kansas City, MO..................820

American Saddlebred Horse Museum, Mexico, MO..................827

American Saddlebred Museum, Lexington, KY..................572

American Sign Museum, Cincinnati, OH...1148

American Sport Art Museum and Archives, Daphne, AL..................7

American Swedish Historical Foundation & Museum, Philadelphia, PA..................1276

American Swedish Institute, Minneapolis, MN..................781

American Textile History Museum, Lowell, MA..................691

American Truck Historical Society, Kansas City, MO..................820

American Visionary Art Museum, Baltimore, MD..................629

American Watchmakers-Clockmakers Institute, Harrison, OH..................1168

American Water Ski Educational Foundation, Polk City, FL..................337

American Wings Air Museum, Blaine, MN..................769

America's Ice Cream & Dairy Museum, Medina, OH..................1175

Americas Society, New York, NY..................1020

America's Stonehenge, North Salem, NH....893

Amherst County Museum & Historical Society, Amherst, VA..................1495

Amherst History Museum at the Strong House - Amherst Historical Society, Amherst, MA..................658

Amherst Museum, Amherst, NY..................957

Amity and Woodbridge Historical Society, Woodbridge, CT..................268

Amon Carter Museum, Fort Worth, TX.....1416

Amory Regional Museum, Amory, MS.......797

Anacortes Museum, Anacortes, WA..................1547

Anadarko Heritage Museum, Anadarko, OK..................1195

Anaheim Museum, Anaheim, CA..................71

Ancient and Honorable Artillery Company, Boston, MA..................663

Anderson/Abruzzo Albuquerque International Balloon Museum, Albuquerque, NM..................933

Anderson County Historical Museum, Garnett, KS..................541

Anderson County Museum, Anderson, SC.1321

Anderson Fine Arts Center, Anderson, IN...467

Anderson Gallery, School of the Arts, Virginia Commonwealth University, Richmond, VA..................1528

Anderson Museum of Contemporary Art, Roswell, NM..................945

Andover Historical Society, Andover, MA...660

Andrew County Museum & Historical Society, Savannah, MO..................838

Andrew J. Blackbird Museum, Harbor Springs, MI..................745

Androscoggin Historical Society, Auburn, ME..................603

The Andy Warhol Museum, Pittsburgh, PA..................1290

Animas Museum, Durango, CO..................214

Anita S. Wooten Gallery at Valencia Community College East Campus, Orlando, FL..................331

Anna Bemis Palmer Museum, York, NE......875

Anna Lamar Switzer Center for Visual Arts, Pensacola, FL..................335

Anna Miller Museum, Newcastle, WY..................1637

Annie E. Woodman Institute Museum, Dover, NH..................886

Annie Riggs Memorial Museum, Fort Stockton, TX..................1415

Ano Nuevo State Reserve, Pescadero, CA,..141

The Ansel Adams Gallery, Yosemite, CA ...199

Antelope Valley African American Museum, Lancaster, CA..................108

Antelope Valley Indian Museum, Lancaster, CA..................108

Anthology Film Archives, New York, NY.1020

Antietam National Battlefield-Visitor Center, Sharpsburg, MD..................653

The Antiquarian and Landmarks Society, Inc., Hartford, CT..................244

The Antique Boat Museum, Clayton, NY....978

Aperture Foundation, New York, NY..................1020

Apostles Islands National Lakeshore, Bayfield, WI..................1591

The Appalachian Trail Conservancy, Harpers Ferry, WV..................1581

The Appaloosa Museum and Heritage Center, Moscow, ID..................407

Appleton Museum of Art, Ocala, FL..................330

Appomattox Court House National Historical Park, Appomattox, VA..................1495

APVA's John Marshall House, Richmond, VA..................1528

Arbor Lodge State Historical Park, Nebraska City, NE..................868

ARC Gallery (Artists, Residents of Chicago), Chicago, IL..................417

Arcade Historical Society, Arcade, NY........958

Arcadia Township Historical Commission, Arcadia, MI..................726

Archer County Museum, Archer City, TX.1387

Archives Museum, Temple Mickve Israel, Savannah, GA..................384

Archives of J.S.G. Boggs, Brandon, FL......298

Argo Gold Mine & Mill Museum, Idaho Springs, CO..................223

Arizona Historical Society Museum, Tucson, AZ..................47

Arizona Historical Society Museum at Papago Park, Tempe, AZ..................45

Arizona Historical Society Museum - Downtown, Tucson, AZ..................47

Arizona Historical Society Pioneer Museum, Flagstaff, AZ..................32

Arizona Historical Society-Yuma: Sarguinetti House Museum and Garden, Yuma, AZ..................54

Arizona Jewish Historical Society, Phoenix, AZ..................39

Arizona Military Museum, Phoenix, AZ.......39

Arizona State Museum, Tucson, AZ..................48

Arizona State Parks Board, Phoenix, AZ.......39

Arizona Zoological Society, dba the Phoenix Zoo, Phoenix, AZ..................40

Ark-La-Tex Antique & Classic Vehicle Museum, Shreveport, LA..................600

Arkansas Air Museum, Fayetteville, AR........57

The Arkansas Arts Center, Little Rock, AR..................61

Arkansas Country Doctor Museum, Lincoln, AR..................61

Arkansas Historic Wine Museum, Paris, AR..................65

Arkansas Museum of Natural Resources, Smackover, AR..................68

Arkansas Post Museum, Gillett, AR..................58

Arkansas River Valley Arts Center, Russellville, AR..................67

Arkansas State University Art Gallery, Jonesboro, AR..................60

Arkansas State University Museum, Jonesboro, AR..................60

Arkansas Tech University Museum of Prehistory and History, Russellville, AR..................67

Arlington Arts Center, Arlington, VA.........1495

Arlington Heights Historical Museum, Arlington Heights, IL..................411

Arlington Historical Museum, Arlington, VA..................1495

The Arlington Historical Society, Arlington, MA..................660

Arlington House, The Robert E. Lee Memorial, Arlington, VA..................1495

Arlington Museum of Art, Arlington, TX ..1387

Armenian Library and Museum of America, Watertown, MA..................716

Armstrong Browning Library, Waco, TX...1458

Art and Culture Center of Hollywood, Hollywood, FL..................312

Art Association of Henry County, Inc., New Castle, IN..................494

Art Association of Randolph County, Inc., Union City, IN..................501

The Art Center at Fuller Lodge, Los Alamos, NM..................942

Art Center In Hargate, St. Paul's School, Concord, NH..................884

Art Center of Battle Creek, Battle Creek, MI..................726

Art Center Sarasota, Inc, Sarasota, FL 343
Art Center Waco, Waco, TX 1458
Art Complex Museum, Duxbury, MA 680
The Art Gallery at the University of
  Maryland, College Park, College Park,
  MD 640
Art Gallery at the University of New
  England, Portland, ME 618
The Art Gallery, John C. Calhoun State
  Community College, Decatur, AL 7
Art Gallery Marist College,
  Poughkeepsie, NY 1054
The Art Gallery, University of New
  Hampshire, Durham, NH 886
Art Guild of Burlington, Inc., Burlington,
  IA 507
Art In Embassies Program, U.S.
  Department of State, Washington, DC 276
The Art Institute of Chicago, Chicago, IL ...418
Art Museum of Greater Lafayette,
  Lafayette, IN 487
Art Museum of South Texas, Corpus
  Christi, TX 1401
Art Museum of Southeast Texas,
  Beaumont, TX 1393
Art Museum of Western Virginia,
  Roanoke, VA 1534
ART Station, Stone Mountain, GA 387
Artesia Historical Museum & Art Center,
  Artesia, NM 936
Arthur A. Houghton Jr. Gallery & The
  Great Hall Gallery, New York, NY 1020
Arthur D. Feiro Marine Life Center c/o
  Peninsula College, Port Angeles, WA ...1561
The Arthur J. Moore Methodist Museum,
  Saint Simons Island, GA 383
Arthur M. Sackler Gallery, Washington,
  DC 276
Arthur Ross Gallery, University of
  Pennsylvania, Philadelphia, PA 1276
Arthurdale Heritage, Inc., Arthurdale,
  WV 1579
Artillery Company of Newport Military
  Museum, Newport, RI 1313
The Arts & Science Center for Southeast
  Arkansas, Pine Bluff, AR 65
Arts Consortium of Cincinnati's African
  American Museum, Cincinnati, OH 1148
Arts Council of Moore County -
  Campbell House, Southern Pines, NC ...1120
ARTSplace, Grand Forks, ND 1131
Arvada Center for the Arts and
  Humanities, Arvada, CO 201
Ash Hollow State Historical Park,
  Lewellen, NE 864
The Ashby-Hodge Gallery of American
  Art, Central Methodist University,
  Fayette, MO 815
Asheville Art Museum, Asheville, NC 1088
Ashland Historical Society, Ashland, MA ...661
Ashland Historical Society Museum,
  Ashland, WI 1590
Ashland, The Henry Clay Estate,
  Lexington, KY 572
Ashtabula County Historical Society,
  Geneva-on-the-Lake, OH 1166
Asian American Arts Centre, New York,
  NY 1021
Asian Art Museum of San Francisco,
  Chong-Moon Lee Center for Asian Art
  and Culture, San Francisco, CA 163
Aspen Historical Society, Aspen, CO 202
Associated Artists of Pittsburgh,
  Pittsburgh, PA 1290
The Association for Gravestone Studies,
  Greenfield, MA 685
Association for the Preservation of
  Tennessee Antiquities, Nashville, TN 1377
Astor House Museum, Golden, CO 219
Atchison County Historical Society,
  Atchison, KS 533
The Athenaeum of Philadelphia,
  Philadelphia, PA 1276

Atlanta College of Art, Atlanta, GA 358
The Atlanta Cyclorama, Atlanta, GA 358
Atlanta Historical Society, Atlanta, GA 358
Atlantic Center for the Arts, Inc., New
  Smyrna Beach, FL 329
Atlantic City Historical Museum, Atlantic
  City, NJ 897
Atlantic Heritage Center, Somers Point,
  NJ 924
Atlantic Wildfowl Heritage Museum,
  Virginia Beach, VA 1541
Atrium Gallery Ltd., Saint Louis, MO 832
Attleboro Area Industrial Museum, Inc.,
  Attleboro, MA 661
Attleboro Arts Museum, Attleboro, MA 661
Attmore-Oliver House, New Bern, NC 1112
Atwood House Museum, Home of
  Chatham Historical Society, Chatham,
  MA 675
Auburn Cord Duesenberg Museum,
  Auburn, IN 468
Audrain Historical Museum, Graceland,
  Mexico, MO 827
Audubon County Historical Society,
  Exira, IA 517
Audubon House & Tropical Gardens,
  Key West, FL 317
Audubon Society of Rhode Island,
  Smithfield, RI 1319
Auglaize County Historical Society, Saint
  Marys, OH 1184
Augusta Historical Museum &
  Genealogy, Augusta, KS 533
Augustana College Art Museum, Rock
  Island, IL 453
Aurora Historical Society, Aurora, IL 411
Aurora Historical Society, Aurora, OH 1140
Aurora Historical Society, Inc., East
  Aurora, NY 984
Aurora Regional Fire Museum, Aurora,
  IL 411
Austin History Center, Austin, TX 1388
Austin Museum of Art - Downtown,
  Austin, TX 1388
Automobile Driving Museum, Los
  Angeles, CA 112
Ava Gardner Museum, Smithfield, NC 1119
Avery County Museum, Newland, NC 1113
Aviation Hall of Fame and Museum of
  New Jersey, Teterboro, NJ 926
The Avon Historical Society, Inc., Avon,
  CT 235
Awbury Arboretum, Philadelphia, PA 1277
Aztalan Museum, Jefferson, WI 1601
Aztec Museum and Pioneer Village,
  Aztec, NM 936

Babe Didrikson Zaharias Museum,
  Beaumont, TX 1394
The Babe Ruth Museum and Sports
  Legends at Camden Yards, Baltimore,
  MD 629
Backing Up Classics Auto Museum,
  Concord, NC 1097
Badger Mine and Museum, Shullsburg,
  WI 1622
Bailey House Museum - Maui Historical
  Society, Wailuku, HI 402
Baker-Cederberg Museum & Archives,
  Rochester, NY 1058
Bakersfield Museum of Art, Bakersfield,
  CA 73
Baldwin Photo Gallery, Murfreesboro,
  TN 1376
Baldwin-Reynolds House Museum,
  Meadville, PA 1270
Bale Grist Mill State Historic Park,
  Calistoga, CA 80
Ball State University Museum of Art,
  Muncie, IN 492
Baltimore & Ohio Railroad Museum,
  Baltimore, MD 629

Baltimore County Historical Society,
  Cockeysville, MD 640
Baltimore Maritime Museum, Baltimore,
  MD 630
The Baltimore Museum of Art,
  Baltimore, MD 630
Baltimore Museum of Industry,
  Baltimore, MD 630
Baltimore Public Works Museum, Inc.,
  Baltimore, MD 630
Balzekas Museum of Lithuanian Culture,
  Chicago, IL 418
Bandelier National Monument, Los
  Alamos, NM 942
Bandon Historical Society Museum,
  Bandon, OR 1219
Bangor Museum & Center for History,
  Bangor, ME 604
Banning Residence Museum,
  Wilmington, CA 198
Bannock County Historical Museum,
  Pocatello, ID 408
Bar Harbor Historical Society, Bar
  Harbor, ME 605
Baranov Museum, Kodiak, AK 26
Barbed Wire Museum, La Crosse, KS 547
The Bare Cove Fire Museum, Hingham,
  MA 687
The Barker Character, Comic and
  Cartoon Museum, Cheshire, CT 237
The Barnacle Historic State Park,
  Coconut Grove, FL 300
Barnes County Historical Museum,
  Valley City, ND 1136
Barnes Foundation, Merion, PA 1271
Barnes Museum, Southington, CT 260
The Barnum Museum, Bridgeport, CT 235
Barnwell County Museum, Barnwell, SC ..1321
Barratt's Chapel and Museum, Frederica,
  DE 270
Barre Historical Society, Inc., Barre, MA 662
Barron County Historical Society's
  Pioneer Village Museum, Cameron,
  WI 1593
Barstow Route 66 Mother Road Museum,
  Barstow, CA 74
Bartholomew County Historical Society,
  Columbus, IN 472
Bartlesville Area History Museum,
  Bartlesville, OK 1196
Barton County Historical Museum &
  Village, Great Bend, KS 542
Barton Museum, Wilson, NC 1124
Bass Museum of Art, Miami Beach, FL 326
Batavia Depot Museum, Batavia, IL 412
Bates College Museum of Art, Lewiston,
  ME 613
Bates-Scofield Homestead, The Darien
  Historical Society, Darien, CT 238
Battles for Chattanooga Museum,
  Lookout Mountain, TN 1371
The Battles Museums of Rural Life,
  Girard, PA 1256
Battleship North Carolina, Wilmington,
  NC 1122
Battleship South Dakota Memorial, Sioux
  Falls, SD 1356
Battleship Texas State Historic Site, La
  Porte, TX 1433
Baum Gallery of Fine Art, University of
  Central Arkansas, Conway, AR 56
Bay Area Discovery Museum, Sausalito,
  CA 186
Bay Area Museum, Seabrook, TX 1452
Bay of Pigs Museum & Library, Miami,
  FL 323
Bay View Historical Museum, Bay View,
  MI 728
Baycrafters, Inc., Bay Village, OH 1141
Beacon Historical Society, Beacon, NY 960
Beatty Museum and Historical Society,
  Beatty, NV 875

Photographs—Continued

The Beaufort Arsenal, Beaufort, SC 1321
Beaumont Art League, Beaumont, TX 1394
Beauvoir, The Jefferson Davis Home and
  Presidential Library, Biloxi, MS 798
Beaver Island Historical Society, Beaver
  Island, MI...728
Beaverhead County Museum, Dillon, MT ...845
Beck Cultural Exchange Center,
  Knoxville, TN.......................................1369
Becker County Historical Society, Detroit
  Lakes, MN..772
Bedford Historical Society Museum and
  Library, Bedford, OH 1142
Beehive House, Salt Lake City, UT 1470
Beith House Museum, Saint Charles, IL 456
Belair Mansion, Bowie, MD.......................638
Belair Stable Museum, Bowie, MD.............638
Belding Museum, Belding, MI 728
Belhaven Memorial Museum, Inc.,
  Belhaven, NC.......................................1092
Bell County Museum, Belton, TX 1395
Bella Vista Historical Museum, Bella
  Vista, AR...55
Bellamy Mansion Museum of History
  and Design Arts, Wilmington, NC 1122
Bellevue Arts Museum, Bellevue, WA 1548
Bellflower Historical and Genealogical
  Society, Bellflower, IL............................413
Bellingrath Gardens & Home, Theodore,
  AL...18
Bellport-Brookhaven Historical Society
  and Museum, Bellport, NY 961
Beloit Historical Society, Beloit, WI 1592
Belvedere-Tiburon Landmarks Society,
  Tiburon, CA..192
Bement-Billings Farmstead, Newark
  Valley, NY..1041
Benedicta Arts Center, Saint Joseph, MN 789
The Benjamin Banneker Park &
  Museum, Baltimore, MD 631
Benjamin Harrison Presidential Site,
  Indianapolis, IN 481
Bennett Place State Historic Site,
  Durham, NC...1098
The Bennett School, West Des Moines,
  IA...530
Bennington Battlefield State Historic Site,
  Walloomsac, NY...................................1081
Bennington Covered Bridge Museum,
  Bennington, VT 1476
The Bennington Museum, Bennington,
  VT...1476
Benton County Historical Museum,
  Prosser, WA...1563
Benzie Area Historical Museum,
  Benzonia, MI...729
Berea College Burroughs Geological
  Museum, Berea, KY...............................565
Berea College, Doris Ulmann Galleries,
  Berea, KY...565
Bergen County Historical Society, River
  Edge, NJ..923
Bergen Museum of Art & Science,
  Paramus, NJ..919
Bergen Museum of Local History,
  Bergen, NY...962
Berkshire Artisans/Lichtenstein Center for
  the Arts, Pittsfield, MA 702
Berkshire County Historical Society, Inc.
  - Arrowhead, Pittsfield, MA...................702
Berkshire Scenic Railway Museum, Inc.,
  Lenox, MA..689
Berlin Art and Historical Collections,
  Berlin, MA..662
Berman Museum of World History,
  Anniston, AL...3
Bernard Historical Society and Museum,
  Delton, MI..734
Bernheim Arboretum and Research
  Forest, Clermont, KY.............................567

Berrien County Historical Association,
  Berrien Springs, MI...............................729
The Berry Botanic Garden, Portland, OR ..1230
Best Friend of Charleston, Charleston,
  SC...1324
Beth Ahabah Museum & Archives,
  Richmond, VA......................................1528
Bethel Historical Society Regional
  History Center, Bethel, ME....................606
Bethlehem Historical Association,
  Selkirk, NY...1068
Betsy Ross House and Flag Museum,
  Philadelphia, PA...................................1277
Beverly Historical Society and Museum,
  Beverly, MA..662
Bexley Historical Society, Bexley, OH......1143
BG John C.L. Scribner Texas Military
  Forces Museum, Austin, TX...................1389
Biblical Arts Center, Dallas, TX................1404
Bicentennial Art Center & Museum,
  Paris, IL...449
Big Bend National Park, Big Bend, TX......1396
Big Hole National Battlefield, Wisdom,
  MT...855
Big Horn County Historical Museum,
  Hardin, MT...849
Big Springs Museum, Caledonia, NY..........974
Big Thicket National Preserve, Kountze,
  TX...1432
Big Thunder Gold Mine, Keystone, SD.....1349
Big Timbers Museum, Lamar, CO 225
Bigelow House Museum, Olympia, WA.....1560
Billy the Kid Museum, Fort Sumner, NM ...939
Biltmore Homespun Shops - Grovewood
  Gallery, Asheville, NC 1089
Birch Aquarium at Scripps, Scripps
  Institution of Oceanography,
  University of California, San Diego,
  La Jolla, CA..106
Birger Sandzen Memorial Gallery,
  Lindsborg, KS.......................................549
Birmingham Civil Rights Institute,
  Birmingham, AL......................................4
Birmingham Museum of Art,
  Birmingham, AL......................................5
Birthplace of John Wayne, Winterset, IA.....530
Bisbee Mining & Historical Museum,
  Bisbee, AZ...30
Biscayne National Park, Homestead, FL......313
Bishop Hill Heritage Museum, Bishop
  Hill, IL...413
Bishop Museum, Honolulu, HI...................394
Black American West Museum &
  Heritage Center, Denver, CO 209
Black Arts National Diaspora Museum,
  New Orleans, LA....................................594
Black Heritage Museum, Miami, FL...........323
Black Hills Mining Museum, Lead, SD.....1350
Black History Museum and Cultural
  Center, Richmond, VA 1528
Black Kettle Museum, Cheyenne, OK 1198
Black Mountain College Museum & Arts
  Center, Asheville, NC............................1089
Black River Academy Museum, Ludlow,
  VT...1480
Black River Historical Society of Lorain,
  Lorain, OH...1172
Blackhawk Museum (Behring-Hofmann
  Educational Institute, Inc.), Danville,
  CA..89
Blackman House Museum, Snohomish,
  WA..1570
Blaine County Historical Museum,
  Hailey, ID...406
Blaine County Museum, Chinook, MT........844
Blanden Memorial Art Museum, Fort
  Dodge, IA...518
Bloomfield Academy Museum,
  Bloomfield, NY......................................963
Blount-Bridgers House/Hobson Pittman
  Memorial Gallery, Tarboro, NC.............1121

Blount County Memorial Museum,
  Oneonta, AL...17
Blount Mansion, Knoxville, TN 1369
Blue and Gray Museum, Fitzgerald, GA......371
Blue Earth County Historical Society,
  Mankato, MN..780
Blue Ridge Institute and Museum,
  Ferrum, VA...1504
B'nai B'rith Klutznick National Jewish
  Museum, Washington, DC 277
Bob Burns Museum & River Valley
  Museum of Van Buren, Van Buren,
  AR..69
Bob Feller Museum, Van Meter, IA............529
Boca Raton Historical Society, Boca
  Raton, FL..296
Boca Raton Museum of Art, Boca Raton,
  FL..296
Bodie State Historic Park, Bridgeport,
  CA..79
Boerner Botanical Gardens, Hales
  Corners, WI..1600
Boise Art Museum, Boise, ID....................403
Bolinas Museum, Bolinas, CA.....................79
Bolton Hall Historical Museum, Tujunga,
  CA..193
Bolton Historical Society, Inc., Bolton,
  MA...663
Bonnet House Museum & Gardens, Fort
  Lauderdale, FL......................................306
Booker T. Washington National
  Monument, Hardy, VA 1510
Boone County Heritage Museum,
  Harrison, AR...59
Boone County Historical Museum,
  Belvidere, IL..413
The Boorman House - The Juneau
  County Historical Society, Mauston,
  WI...1608
Boot Hill Museum, Inc., Dodge City, KS 536
Boothbay Region Art Foundation, Inc.,
  Boothbay Harbor, ME.............................607
Boston Athenaeum Library, Boston, MA 663
Boston Center for Jewish Heritage,
  Boston, MA...663
Boston Fire Museum, Boston, MA.............664
Boston National Historical Park, Boston,
  MA...664
Boston Public Library, Boston, MA 664
Boston University Art Gallery, Boston,
  MA...665
Botetourt County Historical Society,
  Fincastle, VA...1504
Bottineau County Historical Museum,
  Bottineau, ND.......................................1129
Boulder City/Hoover Dam Museum,
  Boulder City, NV...................................875
Boulder History Museum, Boulder, CO 202
Boulder Museum of Contemporary Art,
  Boulder, CO..203
Boundary County Historical Society,
  Bonners Ferry, ID..................................404
Bowdoin College Museum of Art,
  Brunswick, ME......................................607
Bowers Museum, Santa Ana, CA...............177
Bowie Heritage Children's Museum &
  Welcome Center, Bowie, MD.................638
Bowie Railroad Station and Huntington
  Museum, Bowie, MD.............................638
Boys Town Hall of History & Father
  Flanagan House, Boys Town, NE............858
Bradford Brinton Memorial & Museum,
  Big Horn, WY.......................................1628
Bradford Historical Society Inc.,
  Bradford, VT...1477
Bragg-Mitchell Mansion, Mobile, AL 13
Braintree Historical Society, Inc.,
  Braintree, MA.......................................670
Braithwaite Fine Arts Gallery, Cedar
  City, UT...1464
Brand Library & Art Center, Glendale,
  CA..100

Branigan Cultural Center, Las Cruces, NM..............940

Brattleboro Museum & Art Center, Brattleboro, VT..............1477

Brauer Museum of Art, Valparaiso, IN........501

Brazoria County Historical Museum, Angleton, TX..............1387

Bread & Puppet Museum, Glover, VT.......1479

Bremerton Naval Museum, Bremerton, WA..............1549

Brenau University Galleries, Brenau University, Gainesville, GA..............373

Brevard Museum of Art and Science, Inc., Melbourne, FL..............323

Brick Store Museum, Kennebunk, ME........612

Bridge Hampton Historical Society, Bridgehampton, NY..............964

Bridgton Historical Society, Bridgton, ME..............607

Brimstone Museum, Sulphur, LA..............602

Brockton Fire Museum, Brockton, MA........671

Bromfield Art Gallery, Boston, MA..............665

The Bronx County Historical Society, Bronx, NY..............964

The Bronx Museum of the Arts, Bronx, NY..............965

Brookings County Historical Society Museum, Volga, SD..............1358

Brookline Historical Society, Brookline, MA..............671

Brooklyn Museum, Brooklyn, NY..............968

Brooks Academy Museum, Harwich, MA...686

The Broome County Historical Society, Binghamton, NY..............962

Broward County Historical Commission, Fort Lauderdale, FL..............307

Brown County Historical Society, New Ulm, MN..............785

Brown County Historical Society Pioneer Museum, Nashville, IN..............493

Brownsville Museum of Fine Art - Brownsville Art League, Brownsville, TX..............1398

Brownville Historical Society Museum, Brownville, NE..............858

Bruce Museum, Greenwich, CT..............243

Brucemore, Cedar Rapids, IA..............509

Brueckner Museum of Starr Commonwealth, Albion, MI..............723

Brunswick Railroad Museum and C&O Canal Visitors Center, Brunswick, MD ...639

B's Ballpark Museum, Centennial, CO........205

Buccleuch Mansion, New Brunswick, NJ...915

Buchanan Center for the Arts, Monmouth, IL..............445

Bucks County Civil War Library & Museum, Doylestown, PA..............1249

Bucksport Historical Society, Inc., Bucksport, ME..............608

Buddy Holly Center, Lubbock, TX..............1435

Buechel Memorial Lakota Museum, Saint Francis, SD..............1355

Buehler Challenger & Science Center, Paramus, NJ..............919

Buena Park Historical Society, Buena Park, CA..............80

Buena Vista Heritage Museum, Buena Vista, CO..............204

Buffalo and Erie County Historical Society, Buffalo, NY..............972

Buffalo and Erie County Naval & Military Park, Buffalo, NY..............972

Buffalo Bill Museum & Grave, Golden, CO..............219

Buffalo Bill Ranch State Historical Park, North Platte, NE..............869

Buffalo County Historical Society, Kearney, NE..............863

Buffalo Museum of Science, Buffalo, NY ...972

Buffalo National River, Harrison, AR..............59

Buffalo Soldiers National Museum, Houston, TX..............1425

Buffalo Trails Museum, Epping, ND..........1130

Bunker Hill Museum, Charlestown, MA......675

Burchfield-Penney Art Center, Buffalo, NY..............973

Bureau County Historical Society Museum, Princeton, IL..............452

Burleson County Historical Museum, Caldwell, TX..............1399

Burlington County Historical Society, Burlington, NJ..............898

Burlington Historical Museum, Burlington, MA..............672

Burritt on the Mountain-A Living Museum, Huntsville, AL..............11

Burrowes Mansion Museum, Matawan, NJ..............911

Burt County Museum, Tekamah, NE..........873

Bushwhacker Museum, Nevada, MO..........828

The Butler Institute of American Art, Youngstown, OH..............1193

Butte County Pioneer Memorial Museum, Oroville, CA..............136

Butterfield Trail Historical Museum, Russell Springs, KS..............557

CFCC Webber Center Gallery, Ocala, FL....330

CHTJ Southard House Museum, Brunswick, ME..............607

C.M. Russell Museum, Great Falls, MT......848

CU Art Galleries, Boulder, CO..............203

Cabot Historical Society, Cabot, VT..........1478

Cabrillo Gallery, Aptos, CA..............71

Cabrillo National Monument, San Diego, CA..............156

Calaveras County Archives, San Andreas, CA..............155

Calaveras County Museum, San Andreas, CA..............155

Calhoun County Museum, Rockwell City, IA..............527

Calhoun County Museum, Port Lavaca, TX..............1444

Calhoun County Museum & Cultural Center, Saint Matthews, SC..............1341

Calico Ghost Town and the Lane House & Museum, Yermo, CA..............199

California Academy of Sciences, San Francisco, CA..............163

California African-American Museum, Los Angeles, CA..............113

California Center for the Arts, Escondido, Escondido, CA..............93

California Heritage Museum, Santa Monica, CA..............183

California Historical Society, San Francisco, CA..............163

California History Center & Foundation, Cupertino, CA..............88

California Indian Museum & Cultural Center, Santa Rosa, CA..............184

The California Memorial and Museum, Clovis, CA..............86

California Oil Museum, Santa Paula, CA....183

California Route 66 Museum, Victorville, CA..............195

California State Capitol Museum, Sacramento, CA..............151

California State Indian Museum, Sacramento, CA..............151

The California State Military Museum, Sacramento, CA..............151

California State Railroad Museum, Sacramento, CA..............152

California State University, Long Beach, University Art Museum, Long Beach, CA..............110

California Surf Museum, Oceanside, CA.....135

Call of the Wild Museum, Gaylord, MI.......742

Calumet County Historical Society, Inc., New Holstein, WI..............1615

Calvert Marine Museum, Solomons, MD....654

Calvin College Center Art Gallery, Grand Rapids, MI..............743

The Calvin Coolidge Memorial Foundation, Inc., Plymouth, VT............1484

Calvin Coolidge Presidential Library & Museum, Northampton, MA..............699

Cambridge Historical Society, Cambridge, MA..............672

Cambridge Museum, Cambridge, NE..........858

Camden Archives & Museum, Camden, SC..............1322

Camden County Historical Society, Camden, NJ..............899

Camp Atterbury Museum, Edinburgh, IN ...474

Camp Five Museum Foundation, Inc., Laona, WI..............1604

Camp Moore Cemetery and Museum, Tangipahoa, LA..............603

Camp 6 Logging Museum, Tacoma, WA ...1572

Campbell County Rockpile Museum, Gillette, WY..............1633

Campbell House Museum, Saint Louis, MO..............832

Campus Martius Museum, Marietta, OH ...1173

The Camron-Stanford House Preservation Association, Oakland, CA..............133

Canaan Historical Society, Inc., Canaan, NY..............974

Canadian County Historical Museum, El Reno, OK..............1200

Canal Fulton Heritage Society, Canal Fulton, OH..............1145

Canby Historical Society, Canby, OR........1221

Caney Valley Historical Society, Caney, KS..............534

Cannon Falls Area Historical Museum, Cannon Falls, MN..............770

The Cannon Village Visitor Center, Kannapolis, NC..............1107

Canoga-Owensmouth Historical Museum, Canoga Park, CA..............81

Canterbury Shaker Village, Inc., Canterbury, NH..............883

Canton Classic Car Museum, Canton, OH.1145

Canton Historical Society, Canton, MA......674

The Canton Museum of Art, Canton, OH ..1145

Canyon County Historical Society & Museum, Nampa, ID..............408

Cape Ann Historical Museum, Gloucester, MA..............684

The Cape Cod Maritime Museum, Hyannis, MA..............688

Cape Cod Museum of Art, Dennis, MA......680

Cape Cod National Seashore, Wellfleet, MA..............717

Cape Fear Museum of History and Science, Wilmington, NC..............1123

Cape May County Historical Museum and Genealogical Society, Cape May Court House, NJ..............900

Capitol Reef National Park Visitor Center, Torrey, UT..............1475

Capitol Visitors Center, a Division of the State Preservation Board, Austin, TX....1389

Capitola Historical Museum, Capitola, CA..............81

Cappon & Settlers House Museums, Holland, MI..............746

Captain Forbes House Museum, Milton, MA..............695

Captain George Flavel House Museum, Astoria, OR..............1218

Captain John Mullan Museum, Mullan, ID..............407

Captain Nathaniel B. Palmer House - Home of the Discoverer of Antarctica, Stonington, CT..............261

Captain Salem Avery House Museum, Shady Side Rural Heritage Society, Inc., Shady Side, MD..............653

Caramoor Center for Music & the Arts, Inc., Katonah, NY..............1006

Carbon County Museum, Rawlins, WY.....1637

Carleton College Art Gallery, Northfield, MN..............785

Photographs—Continued

Carlsbad Caverns National Park, Carlsbad, NM......937
Carlsbad Museum & Art Center, Carlsbad, NM......938
Carnegie Art Museum, Oxnard, CA......136
Carnegie Center for Art & History, New Albany, IN......493
Carnegie Museum of Art, Pittsburgh, PA......1290
Carnton Plantation, Franklin, TN......1365
Carpenter Home Museum and Gallery, Cle Elum, WA......1551
Carriage and Western Art Museum, Santa Barbara, CA......178
Carroll County Historical Museum, Delphi, IN......474
Carry A. Nation Home Memorial, Medicine Lodge, KS......553
Carson County Square House Museum, Panhandle, TX......1442
The Carter House Association, Inc., Franklin, TN......1365
CAS Gallery, Union, NJ......928
Casa Adobe de San Rafael, Glendale, CA......100
Casa de Rancho Cucamonga, Rancho Cucamonga, CA......144
Casa Grande Valley Historical Society & Museum, Casa Grande, AZ......30
Casa Navarro State Historical Park, San Antonio, TX......1448
Cascade County Historical Society Museum, Great Falls, MT......848
Casemate Museum, Fort Monroe, VA......1505
Cass County Historical Society, Logansport, IN......489
Cass County Historical Society at Bonanzaville, West Fargo, ND......1137
Cass County Historical Society Museum, Plattsmouth, NE......872
Cass County Museum & Pioneer School, Walker, MN......795
Cassia County Museum, Burley, ID......404
Castellani Art Museum of Niagara University, Niagara University, NY......1043
The Castle, Marietta, OH......1174
The Casto House and Northfield Museum, Northfield, NJ......917
Cathedral Cultural Center, Omaha, NE......870
The Cathedral of St. John the Divine, New York, NY......1022
Catholic Historical Society of the Roanoke Valley, Roanoke, VA......1535
Catskill Fly Fishing Center & Museum, Livingston Manor, NY......1010
Cattle Raisers Museum, Fort Worth, TX......1416
Cayuga-Owasco Lakes Historical Society, Moravia, NY......1015
Cazenovia College - Art & Design Gallery, Cazenovia, NY......976
Cedar Falls Historical Society, Cedar Falls, IA......507
Cedar Grove Historical Society, Cedar Grove, NJ......901
Cedar Key Historical Society Museum, Cedar Key, FL......298
Cedar Rapids Museum of Art, Cedar Rapids, IA......509
Cedarhurst Center for the Arts, Mount Vernon, IL......446
Centennial Village Museum, Greeley, CO......221
Center for Agricultural Science and Heritage, Indianapolis, IN......481
Center for American History, Austin, TX......1390
Center for American Music, Pittsburgh, PA......1291
The Center for Civil War Photography, Gettysburg, PA......1255
Center for Creative Photography, Tucson, AZ......48
Center for Curatorial Studies, Annandale-on-Hudson, NY......958

Center for Exploratory and Perceptual Art, Buffalo, NY......973
Center for History, Wheaton, IL......465
Center for Photographic Arts, Carmel, CA......81
Center for Photography at Woodstock, Woodstock, NY......1086
Center for Puppetry Arts, Atlanta, GA......359
The Center for Western Studies, Sioux Falls, SD......1356
Center of Southwest Studies/Fort Lewis College, Durango, CO......214
Center on Contemporary Art, Seattle, WA......1565
Centerville Historical Museum, Centerville, MA......675
Centerville - Washington Township Historical Society & Asahel Wright Community Center, Centerville, OH......1146
Centerville - Washington Township Historical Society & Walton House Museum, Centerville, OH......1147
Central City Opera House Association, Central City, CO......205
Central Delta Depot Museum, Brinkley, AR......55
Central High School National Historic Site, Little Rock, AR......61
Central Missouri State University Archives and Museum, Warrensburg, MO......839
Central Montana Historical Association, Inc. Museum, Lewistown, MT......850
The Central Museum, Central, AK......23
Central Nevada Museum & Historical Society, Tonopah, NV......882
Central Park Conservancy, New York, NY......1022
Centre County Historical Society, State College, PA......1301
Centre County Library and Historical Museum, Bellefonte, PA......1241
Centre Hill Museum (The Petersburg Museums), Petersburg, VA......1524
Chaffee Center for the Visual Arts, Rutland, VT......1486
Chagrin Falls Historical Society, Chagrin Falls, OH......1147
Champaign County Historical Museum, Urbana, OH......1188
Chandler Museum, Chandler, AZ......31
Chapin Library of Rare Books, Williamstown, MA......719
The Chapman Historical Museum, Glens Falls, NY......994
Chappell Hill Historical Society Museum, Chappell Hill, TX......1399
Charles A. Grignon Mansion, Kaukauna, WI......1601
Charles A. Lindbergh Historic Site, Little Falls, MN......779
Charles A. Weyerhaeuser Memorial Museum, Little Falls, MN......779
Charles B. Goddard Center for Visual and Performing Arts, Ardmore, OK......1196
The Charles Edward Choate Exhibit, Sandersville, GA......384
Charles H. MacNider Museum, Mason City, IA......523
Charles H. Taylor Arts Center, Hampton, VA......1509
Charles H. Wright Museum of African American History, Detroit, MI......735
The Charles Hosmer Morse Museum of American Art, Winter Park, FL......354
Charles M. Schulz Museum and Research Center, Santa Rosa, CA......184
Charles River Museum of Industry, Waltham, MA......715
The Charleston Museum, Charleston, SC......1324
Chase County Historical Society, Inc., Cottonwood Falls, KS......536
Chattahoochee Valley Art Museum, LaGrange, GA......375

Chattanooga African Museum/Bessie Smith Hall, Chattanooga, TN......1360
Chattanooga Regional History Museum, Chattanooga, TN......1361
Chautauqua County Historical Society, McClurg Museum, Westfield, NY......1086
Chazen Museum of Art, Madison, WI......1604
Cheboygan County Historical Museum Complex, Cheboygan, MI......732
Cheekwood-Tennessee Botanical Garden & Museum of Art, Nashville, TN......1378
The Chelmsford Historical Society, Inc., South Chelmsford, MA......709
Chemung Valley History Museum, Elmira, NY......988
Chenango County Historical Society Museum, Norwich, NY......1044
Cheraw Lyceum Museum, Cheraw, SC......1327
Cherokee County Historical Museum, Inc., Murphy, NC......1112
Cherokee Courthouse Visitors Information Center & Museum, Gore, OK......1201
Cherokee National Museum, Park Hill, OK......1211
Cherokee Strip Land Rush Museum, Arkansas City, KS......532
Cherokee Strip Museum and Henry S. Johnston Library, Perry, OK......1212
Cherry County Historical Society, Valentine, NE......874
Cherry Valley Museum, Cherry Valley, NY......978
Chesapeake and Ohio Canal National Historical Park, Hagerstown, MD......646
Chesapeake Bay Maritime Museum, Saint Michaels, MD......652
The Chesapeake Beach Railway Museum, Chesapeake Beach, MD......639
Chester Art Guild, Chester, VT......1478
Chester County Historical Society, West Chester, PA......1307
Chester County Historical Society Museum, Chester, SC......1327
The Chester Gould-Dick Tracy Museum, Woodstock, IL......467
Chesterfield County Museum, Chesterfield, VA......1501
Chesterwood, Stockbridge, MA......711
Cheyenne Frontier Days Old West Museum, Cheyenne, WY......1630
Chicago Botanic Garden, Glencoe, IL......438
Chicago Cultural Center, Chicago, IL......419
Chicago History Museum, Chicago, IL......419
Chicago Public Library, Chicago, IL......419
Chicago Zoological Park (Brookfield Zoo), Brookfield, IL......414
Chickamauga-Chattanooga National Military Park, Fort Oglethorpe, GA......372
Chico Museum, Chico, CA......83
The Chief John Ross House, Rossville, GA......382
Chief Plenty Coups Museum, Pryor, MT......852
Chieftains Museum, Rome, GA......381
The Children's Museum, Seattle, WA......1565
Children's Museum at La Habra, La Habra, CA......106
The Children's Museum, Inc., Bloomsburg, PA......1243
The Children's Museum of Indianapolis, Indianapolis, IN......481
Children's Museum of Los Angeles, Van Nuys, CA......194
Children's Museum of Oak Ridge, Inc., Oak Ridge, TN......1382
Children's Museum of Pittsburgh, Pittsburgh, PA......1291
Children's Museum of the Native American, New York, NY......1023
Childress County Heritage Museum, Childress, TX......1400

Chimney Point State Historic Site, Addison, VT 1475

China Institute Gallery, China Institute In America, New York, NY 1023

Chinati Foundation, Marfa, TX 1436

Chinese American Museum, Los Angeles, CA 114

Chinese Culture Center of San Francisco, San Francisco, CA 164

Chinese Joss House Museum, Evanston, WY 1632

Chino's Old Schoolhouse Museum, Chino, CA 84

Chippewa County Historical Society, Montevideo, MN 783

Chippewa Valley Museum, Inc., Eau Claire, WI 1595

Chisholm Trail Heritage Center, Duncan, OK 1199

Chisholm Trail Museum, Wellington, KS 561

Chittenango Landing Canal Boat Museum, Chittenango, NY 978

Chrysler Museum of Art, Norfolk, VA 1521

Churchill County Museum and Archives, Fallon, NV 877

Cigna Museum and Art Collection, Philadelphia, PA 1277

Cincinnati Art Museum, Cincinnati, OH 1148

Cincinnati Fire Museum, Cincinnati, OH ...1149

Cincinnati Museum Center at Union Terminal, Cincinnati, OH 1149

Circus City Festival Museum, Peru, IN 495

Circus World Museum, Baraboo, WI 1591

The Citadel Archives & Museum, Charleston, SC 1324

City County Pioneer Museum, Sweetwater, TX 1454

City Island Nautical Museum, Bronx, NY ...965

City of Bowie Museums, Bowie, MD 638

City of Las Cruces Museum System, Las Cruces, NM 940

City of Las Vegas Museum and Rough Rider Memorial Collection, Las Vegas, NM 941

Civil War and Underground Railroad Museum of Philadelphia, Philadelphia, PA 1278

Civil War Museum of Lonejack, Jackson County, Lone Jack, MO 826

Clallam County Historical Society, Port Angeles, WA 1561

Clara Barton National Historic Site, Glen Echo, MD 645

Clarion County Historical Society, Sutton-Ditz House Museum, Clarion, PA 1247

Clark Atlanta University Art Galleries, Atlanta, GA 359

Clark County Historical Museum, Vancouver, WA 1576

Clark County Museum, Marshall, IL 444

Clark County Museum, Henderson, NV 878

Clark Humanities Museum-Study, Claremont, CA 85

Clarke County Historical Association, Inc., Berryville, VA 1496

Clarke Historical Museum, Eureka, CA 94

Clark's Fork Valley Museum, Fromberg, MT 846

Clausen Memorial Museum, Petersburg, AK 27

Clay Center for Arts & Sciences West Virginia, Charleston, WV 1580

Clay County Historical Museum, Liberty, MO 826

Cle Elum Telephone Museum, Cle Elum, WA 1551

Clearfield County Historical Society, Clearfield, PA 1247

Clearwater County Historical Society, Shevlin, MN 793

Cleo Redd Fisher Museum, Loudonville, OH 1172

Cleveland Artists Foundation at Beck Center for the Arts, Lakewood, OH 1170

The Cleveland Museum of Art, Cleveland, OH 1152

Cleveland State University Art Gallery, Cleveland, OH 1153

Clewiston Museum, Inc., Clewiston, FL 300

Cliffs of the Neuse State Park, Seven Springs, NC 1119

Clifton Community Historical Society, Clifton, KS 535

Clinton Academy, East Hampton, NY 985

Clinton County Historical Society Paine-Gillam-Scott Museum, Saint Johns, MI 763

Clinton County Museum, Frankfort, IN 478

Cliveden of the National Trust, Philadelphia, PA 1278

Cloud County Historical Society Museum, Concordia, KS 536

Clough-Hanson Gallery, Rhodes College, Memphis, TN 1372

Clovis Big Dry Creek Historical Museum, Clovis, CA 86

Coachella Valley Museum and Cultural Center, Indio, CA 104

Coal Miners' Museum/Van Lear Historical Society, Inc., Van Lear, KY 584

Coarsegold Historic Museum, Coarsegold, CA 86

Coastal Discovery Museum, Hilton Head Island, SC 1335

Codington County Heritage Museum, Watertown, SD 1359

Coe Hall, Oyster Bay, NY 1049

The Coffey County Historical Museum, Burlington, KS 534

Cokato Museum & Akerlund Photography Studio, Cokato, MN 771

Coke Hallowell Center for River Studies, Fresno, CA 96

Colby College Museum of Art, Waterville, ME 624

Cole County Historical Museum, Jefferson City, MO 819

Cole Land Transportation Museum, Bangor, ME 604

The Coleman House Museum and Brown County Historical Society, Ainsworth, NE 855

Colesville & Windsor Museum at St. Luke's Church, Harpursville, NY 997

The Coley Homestead & Barn Museum, Weston, CT 265

Colfax County Society of Art, History and Archaeology, Raton, NM 945

The Collectors Club, Inc., New York, NY .1023

The College Art Gallery, Ewing, NJ 903

College Football Hall of Fame, South Bend, IN 499

College of the Redwoods Art Gallery, Eureka, CA 94

College Park Aviation Museum, College Park, MD 641

Colleton Museum, Walterboro, SC 1343

Collier County Museum, Naples, FL 328

Collin County Farm Museum, McKinney, TX 1437

Collinsville Depot Museum, Collinsville, OK 1198

Collis P. Huntington Railroad Historical Society, Inc., Huntington, WV 1583

Colonial Industrial Quarter, Bethlehem, PA 1242

Colorado Historical Society, Denver, CO 210

Colorado National Monument, Fruita, CO ...218

Colorado Railroad Museum, Golden, CO 220

Colorado River Indian Tribes Museum, Parker, AZ 38

Colorado Ski Museum-Ski & Snowboard Hall of Fame, Vail, CO 234

Colorado Springs Fine Arts Center (Taylor Museum), Colorado Springs, CO 206

Colorado Springs Museum, Colorado Springs, CO 206

Colton Area Museum, Colton, CA 87

Colton Hall Museum, Monterey, CA 127

Columbia County Historical and Genealogical Society, Bloomsburg, PA .1243

Columbia Fire Department Museum, Columbia, SC 1328

Columbia Gorge Discovery Center and Wasco County Museum, The Dalles, OR 1237

Columbia Museum of Art, Columbia, SC ..1329

Columbia River Exhibition of History, Science and Technology, Richland, WA 1564

Columbia River Maritime Museum, Astoria, OR 1218

Columbia State Historic Park, Columbia, CA 87

The Columbus Museum, Columbus, GA 368

Columbus Museum of Art, Columbus, OH 1157

Columbus Museum of Art and Design, Columbus, IN 473

Comanche Crossing Historical Society & Museum, Strasburg, CO 233

Combat Air Museum, Inc., Topeka, KS 559

Comer Museum, Morgantown, WV 1585

Command Museum, Marine Corps Recruit Depot, San Diego, San Diego, CA 156

Communal Agriculture Museum, South Amana, IA 528

Community Council for the Arts, Kinston, NC 1108

Community Fine Arts Center, Rock Springs, WY 1637

Community Historical Museum, Maxwell, IA 523

Community Memorial Museum of Sutter County, Yuba City, CA 200

Community of Christ, Independence, MO ...817

Concord Historical Society, Warner Museum, Springville, NY 1071

Concordia Historical Institute, Saint Louis, MO 832

Confederate Memorial Museum, Atoka, OK 1196

Confederate Memorial State Historic Site, Higginsville, MO 817

Confederated Tribes of Grand Ronde Cultural Resources Department, Grand Ronde, OR 1225

Conklin Reed Organ & History Museum, Hanover, MI 745

Connecticut Audubon Birdcraft Museum, Fairfield, CT 240

Connecticut Audubon Center at Fairfield, Fairfield, CT 240

Connecticut Historical Society, Hartford, CT 244

Connecticut State Museum of Natural History and Connecticut Archaeology Center, Storrs, CT 261

Connecticut Trolley Museum, East Windsor, CT 239

Conner Prairie, Fishers, IN 476

Conrad Mansion National Historic Site Museum, Kalispell, MT 850

Constitution Square State Historic Site, Danville, KY 567

Contemporary Art Museum St. Louis, Saint Louis, MO 832

The Contemporary Arts Center, Cincinnati, OH 1150

The Contemporary Jewish Museum, San Francisco, CA 164

The Contemporary Museum, Honolulu, HI 394

Photographs—Continued

The Contemporary Museum at First Hawaiian Center, Honolulu, HI 394
Conway Scenic Railroad, Inc., North Conway, NH 892
Cook County Historical Museum, Grand Marais, MN 776
Cookeville Depot Museum, Cookeville, TN 1364
Coos Art Museum, Coos Bay, OR..............1222
Coos Historical & Maritime Museum, North Bend, OR.................................1229
Copia: The American Center for Wine, Food & the Arts, Napa, CA 129
Copper Range Historical Museum, South Range, MI 764
Copper Village Museum & Arts Center of Deer Lodge County, Anaconda, MT........840
Copshaholm House Museum & Historic Oliver Gardens, South Bend, IN..............499
Coral Springs Museum of Art, Coral Springs, FL 301
The Corcoran Gallery of Art, Washington, DC.................................277
Cordell Hull Birthplace & Museum State Historic Park, Byrdstown, TN 1360
Cordova Historical Museum, Cordova, AK 23
Cornell Museum of Art & History, Delray Beach, FL 304
Coronado-Quivira Museum, Lyons, KS 550
Corpus Christi Museum of Science and History, Corpus Christi, TX 1401
Corry Area Historical Society, Corry, PA...1248
Cortland County Historical Society, Cortland, NY 982
Cottage Grove Museum & Annex, Cottage Grove, OR 1222
Cottonlandia Museum, Greenwood, MS 800
Cottonwood County Historical Society, Windom, MN 796
Country Music Hall of Fame and Museum, Country Music Foundation, Nashville, TN......................................1378
County Center Historical Society, Wabasso, MN 795
Coutts Memorial Museum of Art, Inc., El Dorado, KS 537
Cow Neck Peninsula Historical Society Sands-Willets House, Port Washington, NY 1053
The Cowley County Historical Society, Winfield, KS 564
Cowlitz County Historical Museum, Kelso, WA.......................................1557
Cozens Ranch Museum, Fraser, CO.........218
Cramer-Kenyon Heritage Home, Yankton, SD 1359
Cranbrook Art Museum, Bloomfield Hills, MI.......................................730
Cranbury Historical & Preservation Society, Cranbury, NJ.............................902
Cranford Historical Society, Cranford, NJ ...902
Crater Lake National Park, Crater Lake, OR..1222
Cravens House, Lookout Mountain, TN 1371
Crawford W. Long Museum, Jefferson, GA.......................................374
Crazy Mountain Museum, Big Timber, MT.......................................841
Creative Arts Guild, Dalton, GA 370
Creative Photographic Art Center of Maine, Lewiston, ME.............................614
Creek Council House Museum, Okmulgee, OK.......................................1211
Crescent Bend/The Armstrong-Lockett House and The William P. Toms Memorial Gardens, Knoxville, TN........1369
Cress Gallery of Art, Chattanooga, TN 1361
Crested Butte Mountain Heritage Museum, Crested Butte, CO 208
Crestline Shunk Museum, Crestline, OH ...1160

Crispus Attucks Center Museum, Indianapolis, IN 482
Croatian Heritage Museum & Library, Eastlake, OH..1163
Crocker Art Museum, Sacramento, CA........152
Crocker House, Mount Clemens, MI............756
Crook County Museum & Art Gallery, Sundance, WY.......................................1638
Crosby County Pioneer Memorial Museum, Crosbyton, TX 1403
Crossroads Museum, Corinth, MS...............800
Crossroads of America, Bethlehem, NH 883
Crowley Art Association & Gallery, Crowley, LA 588
Crystal Lake Falls Historical Association, Barton, VT.......................................1476
Crystal Rice Plantation, Crowley, LA 588
Culbertson Mansion State Historic Site, New Albany, IN......................................493
Cumberland County Historical Society, Greenwich, NJ.......................................905
Cumberland County Historical Society, The Hamilton Library and The Two Mile House, Carlisle, PA......................1245
Cumberland Island National Seashore, Saint Marys, GA......................................382
Cummer Museum of Art and Gardens, Jacksonville, FL......................................314
Cupertino Historical Society & Museum, Cupertino, CA..88
Curfman Gallery & Duhesa Lounge, Fort Collins, CO.......................................216
The Currier Museum of Art, Manchester, NH.......................................891
Curwood Castle, Owosso, MI.....................759
Custer Battlefield Museum, Garryowen, MT.......................................847
Custer County Art & Heritage Center, Miles City, MT......................................851
Custer County 1881 Courthouse Museum, Custer, SD.......................................1345
Custer State Park, Custer, SD...................1346
The Custom House Maritime Museum, Newburyport, MA 697
Cuyahoga Valley National Park, Brecksville, OH......................................1144
Czech Center New York, New York, NY...1024

DAAP Galleries, Cincinnati, OH................1150
D.C. Booth Historic National Fish Hatchery, Spearfish, SD 1357
D.R. Barker Historical Museum, Fredonia, NY 992
Dacotah Prairie Museum, Aberdeen, SD....1344
Dahl Arts Center, Rapid City, SD...............1354
Dahlonega Gold Museum State Historic Site, Dahlonega, GA................................369
Dakota Sunset Museum, Gettysburg, SD...1348
Dakota Territorial Museum, Yankton, SD...1359
Dakota Territory Air Museum, Minot, ND.1134
Dal-Paso Museum, Lamesa, TX 1433
Dallam-Hartley XIT Museum, Dalhart, TX.......................................1403
The Dallas Center for Contemporary Art - The Dallas Contemporary, Dallas, TX.......................................1404
Dallas Firefighter's Museum, Inc., Dallas, TX.......................................1404
Dallas Historical Society, Dallas, TX.........1405
Dallas Holocaust Museum, Dallas, TX 1405
Dallas Museum of Art, Dallas, TX............1405
Dalton Defenders Museum, Coffeyville, KS.......................................535
The Dan Quayle Center & Museum, Huntington, IN......................................481
Dana Adobe, Nipomo, CA............................130
The Dana-Thomas House State Historic Site, Springfield, IL................................458
The Danbury Museum & Historical Society, Danbury, CT................................238
Dancing Bear Folk Center, Thermopolis, WY.......................................1639

Danforth Museum of Art, Framingham, MA.......................................683
Daniel Boone Home and Boonesfield Village, Lindenwood University, Defiance, MO.......................................814
Danvers Archival Center, Danvers, MA........678
Danville Museum of Fine Arts & History, Danville, VA.......................................1502
Darlington Raceway Stock Car Museum, NMPA Hall of Fame, Darlington, SC...1331
Daughters of Utah Pioneers Pioneer Memorial Museum & International Society Daughters of Utah Pioneers, Salt Lake City, UT................................1471
Daum Museum of Contemporary Art, Sedalia, MO.......................................838
Daura Gallery, Lynchburg, VA...................1515
Davenport House Museum, Savannah, GA.......................................384
David Bradford House, Washington, PA 1305
David Conklin Farmhouse, Huntington, NY.......................................1000
The David Davis Mansion, Bloomington, IL.......................................413
David Winton Bell Gallery, Providence, RI.......................................1316
Davidson County Historical Museum, Lexington, NC......................................1109
Davis Art Center, Davis, CA 89
Davis Art Gallery, Columbia, MO...............813
Davis Museum and Cultural Center, Wellesley, MA 716
Davison Art Center, Wesleyan University, Middletown, CT......................................249
The Davistown Museum, Liberty, ME.........614
The Dawes Arboretum, Newark, OH 1177
Dawes County Historical Society Museum, Chadron, NE.............................859
Dawson County Historical Museum, Lexington, NE.......................................864
Dawson Springs Museum and Art Center, Inc., Dawson Springs, KY 568
Dayton Art Institute, Dayton, OH..............1161
Dayton Historical Depot Society, Dayton, WA.......................................1552
De Saisset Museum, Santa Clara, CA 180
De Smet Depot Museum, De Smet, SD.....1346
Deaf Smith County Museum, Hereford, TX.......................................1424
Dearborn Historical Museum, Dearborn, MI.......................................733
Decatur House Museum, Washington, DC...277
DeCordova Museum and Sculpture Park, Lincoln, MA.......................................690
Dedham Historical Society Museum, Dedham, MA.......................................679
Deer Isle-Stonington Historical Society, Deer Isle, ME.......................................609
Deer Park Escondido Winery & Auto Museum, Escondido, CA 93
Deerfield Beach Historical Society, Deerfield Beach, FL...............................304
Degrazia Gallery In The Sun, Tucson, AZ.....48
Deines Cultural Center, Russell, KS............556
DeKalb History Center Museum, Decatur, GA.......................................370
Del Norte County Historical Society, Crescent City, CA......................................87
The DeLand Museum of Art, De Land, FL.......................................303
Delaware Agricultural Museum and Village, Dover, DE.......................................269
Delaware Art Museum, Wilmington, DE 273
Delaware Center for the Contemporary Arts, Wilmington, DE................................273
Delaware Visitor's Center, Dover, DE..........270
Delta Blues Museum, Clarksdale, MS..........799
Delta County Museum, Delta, CO................209
Delta Cultural Center, Helena, AR 59
Delta Music Museum, Ferriday, LA.............588
Deming Luna Mimbres Museum, Deming, NM.......................................939

Denali National Park and Preserve, Denali Park, AK 23
The Dennison Railroad Depot Museum, Dennison, OH 1162
Dennos Museum Center of Northwestern Michigan College, Traverse City, MI 765
Dennys River Historical Society, Dennysville, ME 609
Denton County Historical Museum, Inc. and Texas Heritage Center, Denton, TX 1409
Denver Art Museum, Denver, CO 210
Denver Firefighters Museum, Denver, CO ...211
Department of the Treasury, Washington, DC 278
DePaul University Art Museum, Chicago, IL 420
Depot Museum & Fort Sedgwick Museum, Julesburg, CO 223
Depot Park Museum, Sonoma, CA 187
Depreciation Lands Museum, Allison Park, PA 1240
Des Moines Art Center, Des Moines, IA 514
Des Plaines History Center, Des Plaines, IL 430
Descanso Gardens Guild, Inc., La Canada Flintridge, CA 105
Deschutes County Historical Society, Bend, OR 1220
Desert Caballeros Western Museum, Wickenburg, AZ 53
Detroit Artists Market, Detroit, MI..............735
The Detroit Institute of Arts, Detroit, MI.....736
Detroit Zoo, Royal Oak, MI 762
Devils Tower Visitor Center, Devils Tower, WY..................1631
Dewey Hotel Museum, Dewey, OK 1199
DeWitt County Historical Museum, Cuero, TX..................1403
DeWitt Stetten, Jr., Museum of Medical Research, Bethesda, MD 637
Dexter Area Historical Society & Museum, Dexter, MI 738
Dexter Historical Society Campus, Dexter, ME 609
Dey Mansion/Washington's Headquarters Museum, Wayne, NJ 929
Dia:Beacon, Riggio Galleries, Beacon, NY..................960
Dia: Chelsea, New York, NY..................1024
Dickinson County Heritage Center, Abilene, KS 531
Diggs Gallery at Winston-Salem State University, Winston-Salem, NC 1125
Dinsmore Homestead Foundation, Burlington, KY 566
The Discovery Center of the Southern Tier, Binghamton, NY 962
Dishman Art Museum, Beaumont, TX 1394
Dittrick Museum of Medical History, Cleveland, OH 1154
Dr. Daniel W. Kissam House, Huntington, NY 1000
Dr Pepper Museum and Free Enterprise Institute, Waco, TX..................1458
Dodge County Historical Society Museum, Beaver Dam, WI 1591
Dog Mushing Museum, Fairbanks, AK..........24
Don F. Pratt Memorial Museum, Fort Campbell, KY 568
Don Garlits Museum of Drag Racing Inc., Ocala, FL..................330
Donna Beam Fine Art Gallery, UNLV, Las Vegas, NV..................878
Donner Memorial State Park and Emigrant Trail Museum, Truckee, CA 192
Door County Historical Museum, Sturgeon Bay, WI 1623
Door County Maritime Museum (at Sturgeon Bay), Sturgeon Bay, WI 1623
Dorothea B. Hoover Historical Museum, Joplin, MO..................819

Dossin Great Lakes Museum, Detroit, MI ...736
Douglas County Historical Society, Superior, WI..................1624
Douglas County Museum Complex, Armour, SD..................1344
The Douglas F. Cooley Memorial Art Gallery, Reed College, Portland, OR.....1231
Douglass Historical Museum, Douglass, KS 537
Dowd Fine Arts Gallery, State University of New York College at Cortland, Cortland, NY 983
The Downers Grove Park District Museum, Downers Grove, IL 431
Downey Museum of Art, Downey, CA 91
Downieville Museum, Downieville, CA 91
Downing Planetarium, Fresno, CA..................96
Drake Well Museum, Titusville, PA 1303
Drew County Historical Museum, Monticello, AR..................64
Drum Barracks Civil War Museum, Wilmington, CA 198
Drummond Home, Hominy, OK..................1203
Drummond Island Historical Museum, Drummond Island, MI..................739
Dublin-Laurens Museum, Dublin, GA 370
Dubois Museum, Dubois, WY..................1632
Dubuque Museum of Art, Dubuque, IA.....516
Dugger Coal Museum, Dugger, IN..................474
Duke Homestead State Historic Site, Durham, NC..................1098
Duluth Art Institute, Duluth, MN 772
Dunbar House State Memorial, Dayton, OH..................1161
The Duncan Gallery of Art, De Land, FL....304
Dundee Township Historical Society, Inc., Dundee, IL..................431
Dundy County Historical Society, Benkelman, NE..................857
Dunedin Historical Society & Museum, Dunedin, FL..................305
Dunklin County Museum, Inc., Kennett, MO 824
Dunn County Historical Society, Menomonie, WI..................1609
DuPage County Historical Museum, Wheaton, IL 465
Durham Center Museum/Research Library, East Durham, NY 985
Durham Western Heritage Museum, Omaha, NE 870
Dusable Museum of African-American History, Inc., Chicago, IL..................420
Dutchess County Historical Society, Poughkeepsie, NY 1054
Duxbury Rural and Historical Society, Inc., Duxbury, MA 681
Dwight D. Eisenhower Library-Museum, Abilene, KS 531
The Dwight Frederick Boyden Gallery, Saint Mary's City, MD..................652
Dyckman Farmhouse Museum and Park, New York, NY 1025

E. St. Julien Cox House, Saint Peter, MN ...792
EAA AirVenture Museum, Oshkosh, WI....1616
Eagle Bluff Lighthouse, Fish Creek, WI....1597
Eagle Historical Society & Museums, Eagle, AK..................23
Eagle Rock Art Museum and Education Center, Idaho Falls, ID..................406
Earth & Mineral Sciences Museum and Art Gallery, University Park, PA 1303
East Brunswick Museum Corporation, East Brunswick, NJ 902
East Contra Costa Museum, Brentwood, CA..................79
East End Seaport Museum and Marine Foundation, Greenport, NY..................996
East Hampton Historical Society, Inc., East Hampton, NY 985
East Hampton Town Marine Museum, Amagansett, NY 957

East Jersey Olde Towne, Piscataway, NJ 921
East Texas Oil Museum at Kilgore College, Kilgore, TX..................1432
East-West Center, Honolulu, HI..................394
Eastchester Historical Society - 1835 Marble Schoolhouse, Bronxville, NY......967
Eastern Arizona Museum and Historical Society of Graham County Inc., Pima, AZ..................42
Eastern Museum of Motor Racing, York Springs, PA..................1309
Eastern Shore Art Center, Fairhope, AL...........9
Eastside Heritage Center, Bellevue, WA 1548
Eccles Community Arts Center, Ogden, UT..................1467
Edgar Allan Poe Cottage, Bronx, NY 965
Edgar Allan Poe House and Museum, Baltimore, MD..................631
Edgar Allan Poe Museum, Richmond, VA.1529
Edgar County Historical Museum, Paris, IL..................449
Edison & Ford Winter Estates, Fort Myers, FL..................308
Edisto Island Historic Preservation Society Museum, Edisto Island, SC 1332
Edmond Historical Society Museum, Edmond, OK..................1200
Edmonds Art Festival Museum, Edmonds, WA..................1553
Edmonds South Snohomish County Historical Society, Inc., Edmonds, WA .1553
Edward H. White II Memorial Museum, Brooks Air Force Base, TX 1397
Edwards County Historical Museum, Kinsley, KS 547
Effie Yeaw Nature Center, Carmichael, CA..................82
Egan Maritime Foundation, Nantucket, MA..................695
Ehrhart Museum, Antwerp, OH..................1139
The 1811 Old Lincoln County Jail and Lincoln County Museum, Wiscasset, ME..................625
The 1890 House-Museum & Center for Arts, Cortland, NY 983
82nd Airborne Division War Memorial Museum, Fort Bragg, NC..................1101
Eisenhower Birthplace State Historical Site, Denison, TX 1409
Eiteljorg Museum of American Indians and Western Art, Indianapolis, IN 482
El Camino Real International Heritage Center, San Antonio, NM..................947
El Dorado Nature Center, Long Beach, CA..................110
El Monte Historical Society Museum, El Monte, CA..................92
El Museo Del Barrio, New York, NY 1025
El Museo Latino, Omaha, NE..................870
El Paso Holocaust Museum & Study Center, El Paso, TX..................1411
El Paso Museum of Art, El Paso, TX 1411
El Pueblo Historical Monument, Los Angeles, CA..................114
Elbert Hubbard-Roycroft Museum, East Aurora, NY..................985
Elberton Granite Museum & Exhibit, Elberton, GA..................371
Elder Art Gallery, Nebraska Wesleyan University, Lincoln, NE 865
Eleanor Roosevelt National Historic Site, Hyde Park, NY..................1002
Elfreth's Alley Association, Philadelphia, PA..................1279
Elgin Area Historical Society, Elgin, IL.......432
Elisabet Ney Museum, Austin, TX.............1390
Elizabeth Myers Mitchell Art Gallery at St. John's College, Annapolis, MD.........627
Elkhart County Historical Museum, Bristol, IN..................471
Elkhorn Valley Museum & Research Center, Norfolk, NE 869

Photographs–Continued

The Ellen Noel Art Museum of the Permian Basin, Odessa, TX 1441
Ellis County Historical Society, Hays, KS...543
Ellis County Museum, Inc., Waxahachie, TX 1460
Ellwood House Museum, DeKalb, IL 429
Elmhurst Art Museum, Elmhurst, IL............433
Elmhurst Historical Museum, Elmhurst, IL..433
Eloise Pickard Smith Gallery at Cowell College, Santa Cruz, CA.........................181
Elverhoj Museum of History and Art, Solvang, CA..187
The Emerson Gallery, Clinton, NY 979
Emil A. Blackmore Museum of The American Legion, Indianapolis, IN 482
Emily Dickinson Museum: The Homestead and The Evergreens, Amherst, MA.....................................658
Emmett Kelly Historical Museum, Sedan, KS...558
Empire State Aerosciences Museum, Glenville, NY..995
Enchanted World Doll Museum, Mitchell, SD..1352
Enfield Historical Society Museum, Enfield Center, NH................................887
Enfield Shaker Museum, Enfield, NH 887
Enlisted Heritage Hall, Maxwell AFB - Gunter Annex, AL..................................13
Enos Mills Cabin Museum & Gallery, Estes Park, CO.......................................215
Ephraim Historical Foundation, Ephraim, WI..1597
Erie Art Museum, Erie, PA 1252
Erie Canal Museum, Syracuse, NY 1076
Erie Canal Village, Rome, NY 1061
Erie County History Center & Cashier's House, Erie, PA.......................................1252
Erie Maritime Museum, Homeport U.S. Brig Niagara, Erie, PA 1252
The Erlander Home Museum, Rockford, IL..454
Ernest Hemingway House Museum, Key West, FL..317
Ernie Pyle State Historic Site, Dana, IN 473
Erskine Caldwell Birthplace Museum, Moreland, GA.......................................380
Escondido History Center, Escondido, CA..93
Essex Historical Society, Inc., Essex, CT 240
Essex Shipbuilding Museum, Essex, MA 681
Essley-Noble Museum: Mercer County Historical Society, Aledo, IL...................410
Estes Park Museum, Estes Park, CO..........215
Esther M. Klein Art Gallery at University City Science Center, Philadelphia, PA...1279
Ethnic Heritage Museum, Rockford, IL.......455
Eubie Blake National Jazz Institute and Cultural Center, Baltimore, MD 632
Eugene O'Neill National Historic Site, Danville, CA..89
Eugene V. Debs Home, Terre Haute, IN 500
Euphrat Museum of Art, Cupertino, CA 89
Eureka Fire Museum, Milltown, NJ 911
Eureka Pioneer Museum of McPherson County, Inc., Eureka, SD 1346
Eureka School House, Springfield, VT 1487
Eustis Historical Museum & Preservation Society, Inc., Eustis, FL 306
Evanston Historical Society and Charles Gates Dawes House, Evanston, IL 434
Evansville Museum of Arts History & Science, Evansville, IN 475
Everglades National Park, Homestead, FL...313
Evergreen Aviation Museum, McMinnville, OR..................................1228
Evergreen Galleries, Olympia, WA............1560
Everson Museum of Art, Syracuse, NY 1076

Excelsior-Lake Minnetonka Historical Society, Excelsior, MN.......................775
Experience Music Project, Seattle, WA......1565
Exploris, Raleigh, NC..................................1115
Ezra Meeker Mansion, Puyallup, WA 1564

The Fabric Workshop and Museum, Philadelphia, PA 1279
Fairbanks Museum and Planetarium, Saint Johnsbury, VT................................1486
Fairfax Museum & Visitor Center, Fairfax, VA..1503
Fairfield Historical Society, Fairfield, CT 241
Fairlawn Mansion & Museum, Superior, WI..1624
Fairmount Historical Museum & Gift Shop, Fairmount, IN.................................476
Fairport Historical Museum, Fairport, NY...989
Fairport Marine Museum, Fairport Harbor, OH...1164
Fall River County Historical Museum, Hot Springs, SD...................................1348
Fall River Historical Society Museum, Fall River, MA.....................................682
Fallingwater, Mill Run, PA 1272
Falls of the Ohio State Park, Clarksville, IN..472
Falls Village-Canaan Historical Society, Falls Village, CT..241
Falmouth Historical Society, Falmouth, MA..682
Family Museum, Bettendorf, IA 505
Faninadahen Kosas Guahan-Guam Museum, Hagatna, GU............................1640
Fargo Air Museum, Fargo, ND 1130
Farmamerica, The Minnesota Agricultural Interpretive Center, Waseca, MN.............796
Farmers Branch Historical Park, Farmers Branch, TX 1413
Farmington Museum, Farmington, NM.......939
Farrar-Mansur House & Old Mill Museum, Weston, VT...............................1490
FASNY Museum of Fire Fighting, Hudson, NY.......................................1000
Faulconer Gallery at Grinnell College, Grinnell, IA......................................519
Faulkner County Museum, Conway, AR........56
Favell Museum Inc., Klamath Falls, OR....1227
Fayette Art Museum, Fayette, AL 9
Fayette County Helpers Club & Historical Society, West Union, IA.........530
Fayette County Museum, Washington Court House, OH....................................1190
Fayette Heritage Museum & Archives, La Grange, TX...1432
Fayette Historic State Park, Garden, MI 742
Fayetteville Museum of Art, Fayetteville, NC..1100
Federal Hall National Memorial, New York, NY..1025
Feet First: The Scholl Story, Rosalind Franklin University, North Chicago, IL...448
Fenton History Center-Museum & Library, Jamestown, NY.......................1005
Fernbank Museum of Natural History, Atlanta, GA......................................359
Festival-Institute, James Dick Foundation, Round Top, TX...............................1446
Fick Fossil & History Museum, Oakley, KS...554
Fifth Maine Regiment Museum, Peaks Island, ME..618
Figge Art Museum, Davenport, IA 512
Fillmore Historical Museum, Inc., Fillmore, CA..95
The Filson Historical Society, Inc., Louisville, KY...576
Finch Lane Gallery, Salt Lake City, UT 1471
Fine Arts Center at Miriam Hall, Anna Maria College, Paxton, MA...................701
Fine Arts Center for New River Valley, Pulaski, VA..1526

Fine Arts Collection, Luther College, Decorah, IA...513
The Fine Arts Museums of San Francisco, Legion of Honor, San Francisco, CA...165
The Finley House, Wayne, PA....................1306
Finney County Kansas Historical Society, Inc., Garden City, KS............................541
Fire Museum of Maryland, Inc., Lutherville, MD..................................649
Fire Museum of Memphis, Memphis, TN..1373
Fire Museum of Missouri, Willow Springs, MO..840
Fire Museum of Texas, Beaumont, TX 1394
Firehouse Art Gallery, Nassau Community College, Garden City, NY ...992
The Firehouse Gallery, Burlington, VT......1478
Firehouse Museum, San Diego, CA.............156
Fireman's Hall Museum, Philadelphia, PA.1279
1st Cavalry Division Museum, Fort Hood, TX..1414
First Consolidated School in Minnesota, Saum, MN.......................................793
The First Division Museum at Cantigny, Wheaton, IL...465
First Territorial Capitol of Kansas, Fort Riley, KS...540
First White House of the Confederacy, Montgomery, AL..................................16
Fisher Gallery, University of Southern California, Los Angeles, CA..................115
The Fishermen's Museum, New Harbor, ME..615
The Fisk University Galleries, Nashville, TN..1379
Fitchburg Art Museum, Fitchburg, MA........683
Fitchburg Historical Society, Fitchburg, MA..683
The Five Civilized Tribes Museum, Muskogee, OK..1205
Flandrau Science Center and Planetarium, Tucson, AZ...49
Fleming Historical Society, Fleming, CO 216
Flint House, Scotia, NY 1068
Flint Institute of Arts, Flint, MI.................741
Florence Griswold Museum, Old Lyme, CT..258
Florence Price Pioneer Museum, Florence, CO...216
Florence Ranch Homestead, Mesquite, TX..1438
Florewood State Park, Greenwood, MS 801
Florida Agricultural Museum, Palm Coast, FL...334
Florida Air Museum At Sun'n Fun, Lakeland, FL...321
Florida Holocaust Museum, Saint Petersburg, FL.......................................341
The Florida International Museum, Saint Petersburg, FL.......................................341
Florida State University Museum of Fine Arts, Tallahassee, FL............................347
Floyd County Historical Museum, Charles City, IA....................................510
The Fluvanna County Historical Society Old Stone Jail Museum, Palmyra, VA...1524
Flying Heritage Collection, Arlington, WA 1547
Folger Shakespeare Library, Washington, DC..278
Folk Art Society of America, Richmond, VA..1529
The Folsom House Museum, Taylors Falls, MN..794
Ford County Historical Society, Paxton, IL..450
Ford's Theatre National Historic Site (Lincoln Museum), Washington, DC.......279
Forest Lawn Museum, Glendale, CA..........100
Foresthill Divide Museum, Foresthill, CA....95
Fort Abraham Lincoln State Park, Mandan, ND...1134

Fort Belknap Museum and Archives, Inc., Newcastle, TX 1441
Fort Bend Museum Association, Richmond, TX 1445
Fort Benton Museum of the Upper Missouri, Fort Benton, MT 846
Fort Bliss Museum, Fort Bliss, TX 1413
Fort Boonesborough Museum, Richmond, KY 583
Fort Building, Fort Bragg, CA 95
Fort Caspar Museum, Casper, WY 1629
Fort Christmas Historical Park, Christmas, FL 299
Fort Concho National Historic Landmark, San Angelo, TX 1447
Fort Crawford Museum, Prairie du Chien, WI 1618
Fort Crook Historical Museum, Fall River Mills, CA 94
Fort Dalles Museum/Anderson Homestead, The Dalles, OR............1237
Fort Davis National Historic Site, Fort Davis, TX............1414
Fort de Chartres State Historic Site & Museum, Prairie du Rocher, IL 451
Fort Delaware Society, Delaware City, DE 268
Fort Dix Museum, Fort Dix, NJ 904
Fort Douglas Military Museum, Fort Douglas, UT............1465
Fort Fisher State Historic Site, Kure Beach, NC............1108
Fort Frederica National Monument, Saint Simons Island, GA 383
Fort Frederick State Park, Big Pool, MD....637
Fort Garland Museum, Fort Garland, CO 217
Fort George G. Meade Museum, Fort Meade, MD............643
Fort Gibson Historic Site, Fort Gibson, OK............1200
Fort Harker Museum Complex, Kanopolis, KS............546
Fort Hunter Mansion & Park, Harrisburg, PA............1258
Fort King George Historic Site, Darien, GA............370
Fort Knox State Historic Site, Prospect, ME............620
Fort Lauderdale Historical Society, Fort Lauderdale, FL............307
Fort Lewis Military Museum, Fort Lewis, WA............1554
Fort MacArthur Museum, San Pedro, CA....176
Fort Matanzas National Monument, Saint Augustine, FL............339
Fort McAllister, Richmond Hill, GA............381
Fort McHenry National Monument and Historic Shrine, Baltimore, MD............632
Fort Mifflin, Philadelphia, PA............1279
Fort Morgan Museum, Fort Morgan, CO....218
Fort Niobrara National Wildlife Refuge, Valentine, NE............874
Fort Nisqually Living History Museum, Tacoma, WA............1573
Fort Okanogan Interpretive Center, Brewster, WA............1550
Fort Ontario State Historic Site, Oswego, NY............1048
Fort Payne Depot Museum, Fort Payne, AL............10
Fort Peck Interpretive Center, Fort Peck, MT............846
The Fort Pitt Block House, Pittsburgh, PA............1292
Fort Polk Museum Activity, Fort Polk, LA............588
Fort St. Joseph Museum, Niles, MI............758
Fort Sam Houston Museum, Fort Sam Houston, TX............1415
Fort Scott National Historic Site, Fort Scott, KS............540

Fort Selden State Monument, Radium Springs, NM............945
Fort Sidney Museum & Post Commander's Home, Sidney, NE............873
Fort Sill National Historic Landmark, Fort Sill, OK............1201
Fort Smith Art Center, Fort Smith, AR 57
Fort Smith Museum of History, Fort Smith, AR 58
Fort Spokane Visitor Center and Museum, Davenport, WA............1552
Fort Stewart Museum, Fort Stewart, GA 372
Fort Ticonderoga, Ticonderoga, NY............1078
Fort Totten State Historic Site, Fort Totten, ND............1131
Fort Vasquez Museum, Platteville, CO 230
Fort Verde State Historic Park, Camp Verde, AZ............30
Fort Walla Walla Museum, Walla Walla, WA............1576
Fort Walton Beach Art Museum, Fort Walton Beach, FL............310
Fort Ward Museum and Historic Site, Alexandria, VA............1492
Fort Wayne Firefighters Museum, Fort Wayne, IN............477
Fort Wayne Museum of Art, Fort Wayne, IN............477
Forts Folle Avoine Historic Park, Danbury, WI............1594
45th Infantry Division Museum, Oklahoma City, OK............1207
Fossil Country Museum, Kemmerer, WY ..1635
Fossil Museum, Fossil, OR............1224
Foster Gallery, University of Wisconsin-Eau Claire, Eau Claire, WI..1596
Fosterfields Living Historical Farm, Morristown, NJ............913
Fostoria Area Historical Museum, Fostoria, OH............1164
Foundation For Historic Christ Church, Inc., Irvington, VA............1511
Fountain County War Museum, Inc., Veedersburg, IN............502
Four Rivers Cultural Center & Museum, Ontario, OR............1229
Framingham Historical Society & Museum, Framingham, MA............683
The Frances Lehman Loeb Art Center, Poughkeepsie, NY............1055
Frances Willard House Museum, Evanston, IL............434
Frances Young Tang Teaching Museum and Art Gallery, Saratoga Springs, NY .1064
Francisco Fort Museum, La Veta, CO............224
Franconia Heritage Museum, Franconia, NH............888
Frank Lloyd Wright Home and Studio, Oak Park, IL............448
Frank Lloyd Wright's Pope-Leighey House, Alexandria, VA............1492
Frank Murphy Memorial Museum, Harbor Beach, MI............745
Frankenmuth Historical Museum, Frankenmuth, MI............742
Frankfort Area Historical Museum, West Frankfort, IL............464
Franklin County Historical & Museum Society & House of History, Malone, NY............1012
Franklin County Historical Museum, Pasco, WA............1561
Franklin County Old Jail Museum, Winchester, TN............1385
Franklin County Seminary and Museum, Brookville, IN............471
Franklin D. Roosevelt Presidential Library-Museum, Hyde Park, NY 1002
Franklin Furnace Archive, Inc., Brooklyn, NY............969
Franklin G. Burroughs-Simeon B. Chapin Art Museum, Myrtle Beach, SC............1338
Franklin Historical Society, Franklin, ME....611

Fraternal Order of Alaska State Troopers Museum, Anchorage, AK............22
Fraunces Tavern Museum, New York, NY............1025
Fred Harman Art Museum, Pagosa Springs, CO............229
The Fred Jones Jr. Museum of Art, Norman, OK............1206
Fred Wolf, Jr. Gallery/Klein Branch Jewish Community Center, Philadelphia, PA............1280
Frederic Remington Art Museum, Ogdensburg, NY............1044
Frederick C. Robie House, Chicago, IL.......420
Frederick Douglass National Historic Site, Washington, DC............279
Frederick R. Weisman Art Museum, Minneapolis, MN............781
Frederick R. Weisman Museum of Art, Malibu, CA............123
Fredericksburg Area Museum & Cultural Center, Inc., Fredericksburg, VA............1506
Freedman Gallery-Albright College, Reading, PA............1296
Freeport Arts Center, Freeport, IL 435
Freeport Historical Society, Freeport, ME............611
Freer Gallery of Art, Washington, DC 279
French Art Colony, Gallipolis, OH............1165
French Azilum, Inc., Towanda, PA............1303
Fresno Art Museum, Fresno, CA............97
Fresno Flats Historical Park, Oakhurst, CA............132
Fresno Metropolitan Museum, Fresno, CA............97
Friends of Historic Kingston, Fred J. Johnston House Museum, Kingston, NY............1007
The Friends of Lucy Hayes Heritage Center, Chillicothe, OH............1147
The Friends of Peace Church, Camp Hill, PA............1245
Friendship Fire Company Museum, Woodbury, NJ............931
Friendship Hill National Historic Site, Point Marion, PA............1295
Frisco Historic Park & Museum, Frisco, CO............218
Frisco Native American Museum and Natural History Center, Frisco, NC............1102
Frontier Army Museum, Fort Leavenworth, KS............539
Frontier Gateway Museum, Glendive, MT............847
Frontier Historical Society and Museum, Glenwood Springs, CO............219
Frontier Times Museum, Bandera, TX............1393
Frontiers of Flight Museum, Dallas, TX............1406
Frye Art Museum, Seattle, WA............1566
Fryer Memorial Museum, Munnsville, NY............1017
The Fullerton Arboretum, Fullerton, CA........98
Fulton County Historical Museum, Wauseon, OH............1190
Fulton County Historical Society Museum, Rochester, IN............498
Fulton County Museum, Groversville, NY............996
Furnas-Gosper Historical Society & Museum, Arapahoe, NE............856

Gadsden Museum of Art, Gadsden, AL 10
Gage County Historical Society and Museum, Beatrice, NE............857
Gaineswood, Demopolis, AL............7
Galerie Trinitas, Great Falls, MT............848
Galesburg Civic Art Center, Galesburg, IL............437
Gallery North, Setauket, NY............1069
Gallery of Contemporary Art, University of Colorado, Colorado Springs, Colorado Springs, CO............207

Photographs–Continued

Gallery of Henry Street
  Settlement/Abrons Arts Center, New
  York, NY..1026
Gallery on the York - Yorktown Arts
  Foundation, Yorktown, VA.................1547
Gallery '76, Wenatchee, WA.....................1577
Galloway House and Village - Blakely
  Museum, Fond du Lac, WI..................1597
Galveston County Historical Museum,
  Galveston, TX.....................................1420
Garden Grove Historical Society, Garden
  Grove, CA..99
Garden in the Woods of the New
  England Wild Flower Society,
  Framingham, MA 683
Gardner House Museum, Albion, MI 723
The Gardner Museum, Inc., Gardner, MA ...684
Garfield Farm Museum, LaFox, IL 441
Garnavillo Historical Museum,
  Garnavillo, IA......................................518
Gaston County Museum of Art and
  History, Dallas, NC.............................1097
Gatekeeper's Museum & Marion
  Steinbach Indian Basket Museum,
  Tahoe City, CA....................................190
Gates House, Machiasport Historical
  Society, Machiasport, ME.....................614
Gates Mills Historical Society, Gates
  Mills, OH...1166
Gateway NRA, Sandy Hook Unit, Fort
  Hancock, NJ..904
Gateway to the Panhandle, Gate, OK........1201
Gathland State Park, Boonsboro, MD 637
Geddes Historic District Village, Geddes,
  SD..1347
Gem County Historical Society and
  Museum, Emmett, ID............................405
Gene Autry Oklahoma Museum, Gene
  Autry, OK...1201
Gene Stratton-Porter State Historic Site,
  Rome City, IN......................................498
Genealogy Research Center and Museum,
  Sandersville, GA...................................384
General Adam Stephen House,
  Martinsburg, WV................................1584
General Crook House Museum and
  Library/Archives Center, Omaha, NE......870
The General Douglas L. McBride
  Museum, New Mexico Military
  Institute, Roswell, NM..........................945
General Douglas MacArthur Memorial,
  Norfolk, VA.......................................1521
General Grant National Memorial, New
  York, NY..1026
General John J. Pershing Boyhood Home
  State Historic Site, Laclede, MO............824
General Lew Wallace Study & Museum,
  Crawfordsville, IN................................473
General Patton Memorial Museum,
  Chiriaco Summit, CA..............................84
General Wait House, Waitsfield, VT..........1489
Genesee Country Village & Museum,
  Mumford, NY......................................1016
Geneva Historical Society &
  Prouty-Chew House & Museum,
  Geneva, NY...994
Geographical Center Historical Museum,
  Rugby, ND..1136
George A. Spiva Center for the Arts,
  Joplin, MO...820
The George Bush Presidential Library
  and Museum, College Station, TX 1400
George C. Marshall Museum, Lexington,
  VA...1513
The George D. and Harriet W. Cornell
  Fine Arts Museum, Winter Park, FL 354
George Eastman House/International
  Museum of Photography and Film,
  Rochester, NY....................................1058
George I. Ashby Memorial Museum,
  Copper Center, AK.................................23

George Meany Memorial Archives, Silver
  Spring, MD..654
George Washington Carver Museum,
  Tuskegee Institute, AL...........................20
George Washington Carver Museum and
  Cultural Center, Phoenix, AZ..................40
George Washington Carver National
  Monument, Diamond, MO......................814
George Washington's Ferry Farm,
  Stafford County, VA............................1537
George Washington's Fredericksburg
  Foundation, Historic Kenmore &
  Washington's Ferry Farm,
  Fredericksburg, VA..............................1506
George Westinghouse Museum,
  Wilmerding, PA...................................1308
Georgetown Energy Museum,
  Georgetown, CO...................................218
Georgia Aquarium, Atlanta, GA 360
Georgia Historical Society, Savannah, GA...385
Georgia Museum of Art, University of
  Georgia, Athens, GA.............................356
Georgia Music Hall of Fame and
  Museum, Macon, GA.............................377
Georgia O'Keeffe Museum, Santa Fe,
  NM...947
Georgia Salzburger Society Museum,
  Rincon, GA..381
The Georgian Museum, Lancaster, OH 1171
Georgia's Old Capital Museum,
  Milledgeville, GA.................................380
Georgia's Stone Mountain Park, Stone
  Mountain, GA......................................387
Gerald R. Ford Conservation Center,
  Omaha, NE..871
Gerald R. Ford Presidential Museum,
  Grand Rapids, MI.................................743
German American Heritage Center,
  Davenport, IA......................................513
Germantown Historical Society,
  Philadelphia, PA.................................1280
Gertrude Herbert Institute of Art,
  Augusta, GA..365
Gibbes Museum of Art, Charleston, SC.....1325
The Gibson Society, Inc. dba Gibson
  House Museum, Boston, MA...................665
Gig Harbor Peninsula Historical Society,
  Gig Harbor, WA.................................1555
Gila County Historical Museum, Globe,
  AZ..35
The Gilbert Stuart Birthplace and
  Museum, Saunderstown, RI..................1319
Gillespie County Historical Society,
  Fredericksburg, TX.............................1419
Gilliam County Historical Society -
  Depot Museum Complex, Condon, OR.1222
Gilmer Arts and Heritage Association,
  Ellijay, GA..371
Gilpin History Museum, Central City, CO...205
Glacier National Park Museum, West
  Glacier, MT...854
Glencairn Museum: Academy of the New
  Church, Bryn Athyn, PA......................1244
Glenn L. Martin Maryland Aviation
  Museum, Baltimore, MD.......................632
Glenview Area Historical Society,
  Glenview, IL..438
Gloucester County Historical Society,
  Woodbury, NJ......................................931
The Glynn Art Association, Inc., Saint
  Simons Island, GA...............................383
The Godwin-Ternbach Museum,
  Flushing, NY..990
The Golden Age of Trucking Museum,
  Middlebury, CT....................................249
Golden Gate National Recreation Area,
  San Francisco, CA................................165
Golden Gate Railroad Museum, San
  Francisco, CA......................................166
Golden Pioneer Museum, Golden, CO........220
Golden Spike National Historic Site,
  Brigham City, UT...............................1463

Gone With The Wind Movie Museum,
  Marietta, GA..379
Goochland County Museum & Historical
  Center, Goochland, VA........................1508
Goodhue County Historical Society, Red
  Wing, MN..787
Goodman Museum, Tyler, TX 1456
Goschenhoppen Folklife Library and
  Museum, Green Lane, PA.....................1257
Goshen Historical Society, Goshen, CT 242
Gouverneur Historical Association,
  Gouverneur, NY...................................995
Governor Bent Museum, Taos, NM 952
Governor Henry Lippitt House Museum,
  Providence, RI....................................1316
Governor John Sevier Memorial
  Association, Knoxville, TN...................1370
The Governor's Mansion, Frankfort, KY 569
Governor's Mansion State Historic Park,
  Sacramento, CA...................................152
Grace Hudson Museum & Sun House,
  Ukiah, CA...193
The Grace Museum, Abilene, TX...............1385
Graceland, Memphis, TN.........................1373
Grafton Historical Society, Grafton, VT.....1479
Graham County Historical Society,
  Thatcher, AZ..46
Grand Army of the Republic Civil War
  Museum, Philadelphia, PA...................1281
Grand Canyon National Park Museum
  Collection, Grand Canyon National
  Park, AZ...36
Grand County Museum, Hot Sulphur
  Springs, CO...222
Grand Encampment Museum, Inc.,
  Encampment, WY................................1632
Grand Gulf Military Park, Port Gibson,
  MS..807
Grand Lake Area Historical Society,
  Grand Lake, CO...................................221
Grand Lodge AF&AM of Virginia - Allen
  E. Roberts Masonic Library and
  Museum, Richmond, VA.......................1529
Grand Rapids Art Museum, Grand
  Rapids, MI...743
The Grand River Historical Society &
  Museum, Chillicothe, MO......................813
Grand River Museum, Lemmon, SD..........1351
Grand Traverse Heritage Center, Traverse
  City, MI..765
The Granger Homestead Society, Inc.,
  Canandaigua, NY.................................975
Grant County Historical Museum,
  Canyon City, OR.................................1221
Grant County Historical Museum,
  Ephrata, WA.......................................1553
Grant County Historical Society, Elbow
  Lake, MN..774
Grant County Museum, Medford, OK.......1205
Grant County Museum, Sheridan, AR...........68
Grant County Museum aka Historic
  Adobe Museum, Ulysses, KS.................560
Grant County Museum & Historic
  Society, Hyannis, NE...........................863
Grant-Kohrs Ranch National Historic
  Site, Deer Lodge, MT..........................845
Grant Wood Gallery, Anamosa, IA............505
Grants Pass Museum of Art, Grants Pass,
  OR..1225
Granville County Historical Society
  Museum, Oxford, NC..........................1114
Granville Historical Society Museum,
  Granville, OH.....................................1167
Gravette Historical Museum, Gravette,
  AR..59
Graycliff Conservancy, Derby, NY.............984
Great Basin Historical Society &
  Museum, Delta, UT.............................1464
Great Basin National Park, Baker, NV........875
Great Harbor Maritime Museum,
  Northeast Harbor, ME..........................616

Great Lakes Naval Memorial and
    Museum, Muskegon, MI 757
Great Lakes Naval Museum, Great
    Lakes, IL..439
Great Lakes Shipwreck Museum,
    Paradise, MI..760
The Great Overland Station, Topeka, KS 559
Great Plains Art Museum, Lincoln, NE 865
Great Plains Transportation Museum,
    Wichita, KS..561
Great Sand Dunes National Monument
    and Preserve, Mosca, CO.........................229
Greater Loveland Historical Society
    Museum, Loveland, OH 1173
Greeley History Museum, Greeley, CO........221
Green Bay Packers Hall of Fame, Green
    Bay, WI...1598
Green Hill Art Gallery, Greensboro, NC ...1103
Green Mountain Club, Inc., Waterbury
    Center, VT...1489
Green River Valley Museum, Big Piney,
    WY...1629
Greene County Historical Museum,
    Waynesburg, PA......................................1306
Greenfield Historical Society, Greenfield,
    WI..1599
Greensboro Artists' League, Greensboro,
    NC...1103
Greensboro Historical Museum, Inc.,
    Greensboro, NC......................................1103
Greenwood County Historical Society,
    Eureka, KS..539
Gresham History Museum, Gresham, OR..1226
Grey Art Gallery, New York University
    Art Collection, New York, NY 1026
Greybull Museum, Greybull, WY 1634
Grier Musser Museum, Los Angeles, CA 115
Griffin Museum of Photography,
    Winchester, MA.......................................720
Grissom Air Museum, Peru, IN....................496
Grosse Ile Historical Society, Grosse Ile,
    MI..745
Grossmont College Hyde Art Gallery, El
    Cajon, CA..92
Groton Historical Society, Groton, MA.......685
Groveland Yosemite Gateway Museum,
    Groveland, CA..101
Grunwald Center for the Graphic Arts,
    Hammer Museum, Los Angeles, CA.......115
Guadalupe Mountains National Park, Salt
    Flat, TX...1447
Guernsey County Museum, Cambridge,
    OH..1144
The Guest House Museum, Fort Bragg,
    CA..95
Guild Hall Museum, East Hampton, NY 986
Guilford College Art Gallery,
    Greensboro, NC......................................1103
Guinness World of Records Museum, Las
    Vegas, NV..879
Gulf Coast Museum of Art, Inc., Largo,
    FL...321
Gulf Shores Museum, Gulf Shores, AL 11
GumTree Museum of Art, Tupelo, MS 808
Gunn Memorial Library and Museum,
    Washington, CT..263
Gunnison County Pioneer and Historical
    Society, Gunnison, CO.............................222
Guy B. Woodward Museum, Ramona,
    CA..144
Gwinnett Historical Society,
    Lawrenceville, GA....................................376
Gwinnett History Museum,
    Lawrenceville, GA....................................376

H.E.A.R.T.S. Veterans Museum of Texas,
    Huntsville, TX.......................................1430
Hacienda Buena Vista, Ponce, PR 1642
Hackettstown Historical Society Museum
    & Library, Hackettstown, NJ 905
Haffenreffer Museum of Anthropology,
    Brown University, Bristol, RI 1310

Hagerstown Roundhouse Museum,
    Hagerstown, MD 646
The Hagley Museum and Library,
    Wilmington, DE..273
Hahns Peak Area Historical Society and
    School House, Clark, CO...........................205
Haines Museum, Waukegan Historical
    Society, Waukegan, IL...............................463
Halifax Historical Museum, Daytona
    Beach, FL...303
Hall of Fame & Classic Car Museum,
    Weedsport, NY.......................................1084
Hall of Flame Museum of Firefighting,
    Phoenix, AZ...40
Hallie Ford Museum of Art, Salem, OR 1235
Hamilton Township Historical Society -
    John Abbott II House, Hamilton, NJ 906
Hamilton Van Wagoner Museum, Clifton,
    NJ..901
Hamilton Wood Type Printing Museum,
    Two Rivers, WI......................................1625
Hamline University Galleries, Department
    of Studio Arts & Art History, Saint
    Paul, MN...790
Hammer Museum, Los Angeles, CA...........115
Hammond-Harwood House Association,
    Annapolis, MD 628
Hammond Museum and Japanese Stroll
    Garden, North Salem, NY.......................1043
Hampton County Historical Museum,
    Hampton, SC...1334
Hampton History Museum, Hampton, VA .1509
Hampton National Historic Site, Towson,
    MD..655
Hampton University Museum, Hampton,
    VA...1509
Hana Cultural Center, Hana, Maui, HI........392
Hanby House, Westerville, OH.................1191
Hancock Historical Museum, Findlay,
    OH..1164
Hancock Historical Society, Hancock,
    NH..888
Hancock Shaker Village, Inc., Pittsfield,
    MA..703
The Handweaving Museum & Arts
    Center, Clayton, NY.................................978
Hanford Carnegie Museum, Hanford, CA....101
Hank Williams Museum, Montgomery,
    AL..16
Hanna Basin Museum, Hanna, WY...........1634
Hanover Historical Society Museum,
    Hanover, VA...1510
Hans Christian Andersen Museum,
    Solvang, CA...187
Happy Hollow Park & Zoo, San Jose,
    CA..171
Har-Ber Village, Grove, OK 1202
Harbor Defense Museum, Brooklyn, NY 969
Harbour House Museum, Crystal Falls,
    MI..733
Hardin Planetarium, Bowling Green, KY 565
Harding Museum, Franklin, OH 1164
Hardwick Historical Society, Hardwick,
    MA..686
Harlan-Lincoln House, Mount Pleasant,
    IA..524
The Harness Racing Museum and Hall of
    Fame, Goshen, NY...................................995
Harold M. Freund American Museum of
    Baking, Manhattan, KS 550
Harper City Historical Society, Harper,
    KS...543
Harpers Ferry Center, Harpers Ferry, WV .1582
Harpers Ferry National Historical Park,
    Harpers Ferry, WV 1582
Harriet Beecher Stowe Center, Hartford,
    CT...245
Harrison County Historical Museum,
    Marshall, TX..1436
Harrison House, Branford, CT....................235
Harrison Museum of African-American
    Culture, Roanoke, VA 1535

Harrisonburg-Rockingham Historical
    Society, Dayton, VA 1503
Harry Ransom Center at the University
    of Texas at Austin, Austin, TX 1390
Harry S. Truman Library-Museum,
    Independence, MO....................................818
Harry S. Truman Little White House
    Museum, Key West, FL 317
Hartslog Heritage Museum, Alexandria,
    PA...1239
Hartsville Museum, Hartsville, SC 1335
Harvard Historical Society, Still River,
    MA..711
Harvard University Art Museums,
    Cambridge, MA..672
Harvey County Historical Society,
    Newton, KS..553
Harvey Cushing/John Hay Whitney
    Medical Library, New Haven, CT...........253
Harvey House Museum, Florence, KS 539
The Harwood Museum of Art of the
    University of New Mexico, Taos, NM 952
Haskell County Historical Society,
    Sublette, KS...558
Hathaway Ranch Museum, Santa Fe
    Springs, CA...182
Hattiesburg Area Historical Society and
    HAHS Museum, Hattiesburg, MS 801
Hatton-Eielson Museum & Historical
    Association, Hatton, ND 1132
Hatton Gallery, Colorado State
    University, Fort Collins, CO 217
Haverford Township Historical Society,
    Havertown, PA.......................................1260
Havre de Grace Decoy Museum, Havre
    de Grace, MD...647
Hawaii Maritime Center, Honolulu, HI........395
Hawaii State Foundation on Culture &
    the Arts and Hawaii State Art
    Museum, Honolulu, HI.............................395
Hawaii Volcanoes National Park, Kilauea
    Visitor Center, Hawaii Volcanoes
    National Park, HI.....................................393
Hawaii's Plantation Village, Waipahu, HI 402
Hayden Museum of American Art, Paris,
    TX...1442
Hazel Kibler Museum, Girard, PA 1256
Headwaters Heritage Museum, Three
    Forks, MT..854
Healdton Oil Museum, Healdton, OK........1202
Heard Museum, Phoenix, AZ........................40
Heard Natural Science Museum and
    Wildlife Sanctuary, Inc., McKinney,
    TX...1437
Hearst Art Gallery, St. Mary's College,
    Moraga, CA..128
Heart of West Texas Museum, Colorado
    City, TX...1401
Heckscher Museum of Art, Huntington,
    NY..1000
Heisey Museum, Clinton County
    Historical Society, Lock Haven, PA 1269
Held-Poage Memorial Home and
    Research Library, Ukiah, CA...................193
Hellenic Museum & Cultural Center,
    Chicago, IL..421
Hemet Museum, Hemet, CA.......................103
The Hemingway Museum and The Ernest
    Hemingway Birthplace, Oak Park, IL 448
Henager "Memories and Nostalgia"
    Museum, Buckskin, IN.............................471
Hendricks Hill Museum, Southport, ME......623
Hennepin History Museum, Minneapolis,
    MN...782
Henrico County Historic Preservation &
    Museum Services, Richmond, VA 1529
Henry Art Gallery, Seattle, WA 1566
Henry B. Plant Museum, Tampa, FL...........349
Henry County Historical Society, New
    Castle, IN...494
Henry County Museum and Cultural Arts
    Center, Clinton, MO.................................813
The Henry Ford, Dearborn, MI 733

Photographs–Continued

The Henry Sheldon Museum of Vermont History, Middlebury, VT 1481

Henryetta Territorial Museum, Henryetta, OK...1203

Herbert F. Johnson Museum of Art, Ithaca, NY..1003

Herbert Hoover Presidential Library-Museum, West Branch, IA.........530

Hereford Inlet Lighthouse, North Wildwood, NJ..917

The Heritage Center and Citrus Museum, Vero Beach, FL...352

Heritage Conservancy, Doylestown, PA.....1249

Heritage Farmstead Museum, Plano, TX ...1444

Heritage Hall Museum & Archives, Freeman, SD...1347

Heritage Hill State Historical Park, Green Bay, WI...1599

Heritage-Hjemkomst Interpretive Center, Moorhead, MN 784

Heritage House Museum of Montgomery County, Mount Ida, AR..............................64

Heritage House of Orange County Association Inc., Orange, TX 1441

The Heritage Museum, Baltimore, MD.......632

The Heritage Museum, Astoria, OR...........1218

The Heritage Museum & Underhill Museum, Idaho Springs, CO....................223

The Heritage Museum at Falfurrias, Inc., Falfurrias, TX 1413

Heritage Museum Foundation of Tate County, Inc., Senatobia, MS.....................808

The Heritage Museum of Fine Arts for Youth, Detroit, MI.....................................736

Heritage Museum of Northwest Florida, Valparaiso, FL...352

The Heritage Society, Houston, TX...........1426

Heritage Square Museum, Ontario, NY 1047

Heritage Square Museum, Los Angeles, CA..116

Heritage Station, Umatilla County Historical Society Museum, Pendleton, OR...1230

Heritage Village, Largo, FL 321

Heritage Village, Mountain Lake, MN........785

Herkimer County Historical Society, Herkimer, NY..998

The Hermitage, Ho-Ho-Kus, NJ 907

The Hermitage Foundation, Norfolk, VA...1521

Hernando Heritage Museum, Brooksville, FL..298

Herreshoff Marine Museum/America's Cup Hall of Fame, Bristol, RI 1311

Herrett Center for Arts & Science, Faulkner Planetarium and Centennial Observatory, Twin Falls, ID.....................410

Hettinger County Historical Society, Regent, ND...1136

Hibbing Historical Society and Museum, Hibbing, MN...778

Hibel Museum of Art, Jupiter, FL 316

The Hickories Museum of the Lorain County Historical Society, Elyria, OH ..1163

Hickory Hill, Thomson, GA 388

The Hickory Museum of Art, Hickory, NC...1106

The Hicksville Gregory Museum, Hicksville, NY..998

Hiddenite Center, Inc., Hiddenite, NC........1106

High Cliff Historical Society & General Store Museum, Sherwood, WI................1622

The High Museum of Art, Atlanta, GA.......360

High Plains Museum, Goodland, KS...........542

High Point Museum & Historical Park, High Point, NC......................................1106

Highland County Museum and Heritage Center, McDowell, VA.............................1517

Highland House Museum, Hillsboro, OH ..1168

Highland Park Historical Society, Highland Park, IL..439

Highlands Art League, Sebring, FL..............345

Highlands Center for Natural History, Prescott, AZ..42

Highlands Hammock State Park/Civilian Conservation Corps Museum, Sebring, FL..346

Highlands Museum & Discovery Center, Ashland, KY..564

Hill-Stead Museum, Farmington, CT 241

Hiller Aviation Institute, San Carlos, CA.....155

Hillforest House Museum, Aurora, IN 468

Hillsboro Area Historical Society, Hillsboro, WI...1600

Hillwood Art Museum, Brookville, NY 971

Hillwood Museum & Gardens, Washington, DC.......................................280

Hinsdale Historical Society, Hinsdale, IL 440

The Hispanic Society of America, New York, NY...1027

Historic Auto Attractions, Roscoe, IL 456

Historic Brattonsville, McConnells, SC......1336

Historic Carson House, Marion, NC...........1110

Historic Cherry Hill, Albany, NY 954

Historic Columbus Foundation, Inc., Columbus, GA...369

Historic Deerfield, Inc., Deerfield, MA........679

Historic Edenton State Historic Site, Edenton, NC...1099

Historic General Dodge House, Council Bluffs, IA...512

Historic Georgetown Inc., Georgetown, CO...218

Historic Governors' Mansion, Cheyenne, WY..1630

Historic Hartwood Mansion, Pittsburgh, PA...1292

Historic Hermann Museum, Hermann, MO..817

Historic House Trust of New York City, New York, NY..1027

Historic Hudson Valley, Tarrytown, NY.....1077

Historic Jefferson College, Washington, MS..810

Historic Landmarks Foundation of Indiana, Indianapolis, IN......................482

Historic Langhorne Association, Langhorne, PA.......................................1267

Historic Macon Foundation, Inc. - Sidney Lanier Cottage House Museum, Macon, GA...377

Historic Mobile Preservation Society, Mobile, AL...14

Historic New England, Boston, MA............665

Historic New England/Cogswells Grant, Essex, MA...682

The Historic New Orleans Collection, New Orleans, LA....................................595

Historic Northampton, Northampton, MA....699

Historic Occoquan, Inc., Occoquan, VA....1523

Historic Palmyra's Print Shop, Palmyra, NY...1050

Historic Palmyra's - Wm. Phelps General Store, Palmyra, NY 1050

Historic Pullman Foundation, Chicago, IL...421

Historic Renville Preservation Commission, Renville, MN.....................787

Historic Richmond Town, Staten Island, NY...1072

Historic Shepherdstown Museum, Shepherdstown, WV...............................1586

Historical and Genealogical Society of Indiana County, Indiana, PA 1262

Historical and Genealogical Society of Somerset County, Somerset, PA 1300

Historical and Wildlife Museum, Gridley, CA..101

Historical Center for Southeast New Mexico, Roswell, NM..............................946

The Historical Museum at St. Gertrude, Cottonwood, ID.......................................405

Historical Museum of Southern Florida, Miami, FL..324

Historical Natural History & Library Society of Natick dba Natick Historical Society, South Natick, MA 709

Historical Shrine Foundation of San Diego County, San Diego, CA................156

Historical Society of Berks County, Reading, PA...1296

Historical Society of Bloomfield New Jersey, Bloomfield, NJ.............................898

Historical Society of Brookfield, Brookfield Center, VT............................1477

Historical Society of Carroll County, Westminster, MD...................................656

Historical Society of Cecil County, Elkton, MD...643

Historical Society of Columbia County, Saint Helens, OR....................................1234

The Historical Society of Dauphin County, Harrisburg, PA.............................1258

Historical Society of Delaware, Wilmington, DE......................................274

Historical Society of Fort Washington, Fort Washington, PA...............................1254

The Historical Society of Frederick County, Inc., Frederick, MD....................644

Historical Society of Garden County, Oshkosh, NE..871

Historical Society of Glastonbury, Glastonbury, CT....................................242

Historical Society of Greater Port Jefferson, Port Jefferson, NY 1053

Historical Society of Greenfield, Greenfield, MA.......................................685

Historical Society of Middletown and the Wallkill Precinct, Inc., Middletown, NY...1014

Historical Society of Millersburg & Upper Paxton Township Museum, Millersburg, PA.......................................1272

Historical Society of Newburgh Bay & the Highlands - David Crawford House, Newburgh, NY 1042

Historical Society of Oak Park & River Forest, Oak Park, IL..............................448

Historical Society of Ocean Grove, New Jersey, Ocean Grove, NJ.........................918

Historical Society of Old Yarmouth, Yarmouth Port, MA................................722

Historical Society of Palm Beach County, Palm Beach, FL..334

Historical Society of Pennsylvania, Philadelphia, PA.....................................1281

Historical Society of Princeton, Princeton, NJ...921

Historical Society of Quincy and Adams County, Quincy, IL.................................452

Historical Society of St. Marys and Benzinger Township, Saint Marys, PA..1297

Historical Society of Santuit and Cotuit, Cotuit, MA..677

Historical Society of Saratoga Springs, Saratoga Springs, NY............................1064

Historical Society of Talbot County, Easton, MD...642

Historical Society of the Cocalico Valley, Ephrata, PA...1252

Historical Society of the Phoenixville Area, Phoenixville, PA.............................1290

Historical Society of the Tonawandas, Inc., Tonawanda, NY...............................1078

Historical Society of the Town of Clarence, Clarence, NY............................978

Historical Society of the Town of Greenwich Inc. aka Bush-Holley Historic Site, Cos Cob, CT.......................237

The Historical Society of the Town of Warwick, Warwick, NY 1082

Historical Society of Walden & Wallkill Valley, Walden, NY..................................1081

Historical Society of Wells and Ogunquit, Wells, ME...625

Historical Society Porter County Old Jail Museum, Valparaiso, IN.............................502

The Historical Society, serving Sleepy Hollow and Tarrytown, Tarrytown, NY.1078
History and Traditions Museum, Lackland Air Force Base, TX 1433
The History Center, Fort Wayne, IN 477
The History Center, Cedar Rapids, IA 509
The History Center in Tompkins County, Ithaca, NY...1003
History Museum for Springfield-Greene County, Springfield, MO 839
History Museum of Western Virginia, Roanoke, VA...1535
History of Medicine Collections, Durham, NC..1098
The History Place, Morehead City, NC 1111
Hiwan Homestead Museum, Evergreen, CO 215
Hixon House, La Crosse, WI......................1603
Hobart Historical Society Museum, Hobart, IN...480
Hoboken Historical Museum, Hoboken, NJ 907
Hockaday Museum of Art, Kalispell, MT....850
Hodgden House Museum Complex, Ellsworth, KS..538
Hofstra Museum, Hempstead, NY..............997
Holland Historical Society Museum, Inc., Holland, VT.......................................1480
The Holland Museum, Holland, MI 746
Hollins University Eleanor D. Wilson Museum, Roanoke, VA 1535
Holly History Center & Hutchinson House Museum, Waupaca, WI.............1626
Hollywood Bowl Museum, Los Angeles, CA 116
Hollywood Guinness World of Records Museum, Hollywood, CA 103
Hollywood Heritage Museum, Hollywood, CA...103
Hollywood History Museum, Hollywood, CA...103
Holmes County Historical Society, Millersburg, OH..................................1176
Holocaust Documentation & Education Center, Inc., Hollywood, FL 313
Holocaust Memorial Resource and Education Center of Florida, Inc., Maitland, FL...322
Holocaust Museum Houston, Houston, TX...1426
Holocaust Museum of Southwest Florida, Naples, FL...328
Holt-Atherton Special Collections, Stockton, CA...189
Holter Museum of Art, Helena, MT.............849
Home of Franklin D. Roosevelt National Historic Site, Hyde Park, NY..............1002
Home of Stone (The Mueller-Schmidt House 1881), a Ford County Museum, curated by Ford County Historic Society, Dodge City, KS 537
Homesteader Museum, Powell, WY...........1637
Honeywell Center, Wabash, IN...................503
Honolulu Academy of Arts, Honolulu, HI ...395
Honolulu House Museum, Marshall, MI......754
Honolulu Police Department Law Enforcement Museum, Honolulu, HI.......396
Hood Museum of Art, Hanover, NH 888
Hood River County Historical Museum, Hood River, OR.....................................1226
Hoover Historical Center, North Canton, OH...1179
Hope Historical Society, Hope, NJ..............908
Hope Lodge and Mather Mill, Fort Washington, PA 1254
Hopewell Furnace National Historic Site, Elverson, PA 1251
Hopewell Museum, Paris, KY 582
Hopewell Museum, Hopewell, NJ...............908
Horatio Colony House Museum & Nature Preserve, Keene, NH 890
Hornby Museum, Hornby, NY....................999

Horry County Museum, Conway, SC.........1331
Hose 5 Fire Museum, Bangor, ME..............604
Hot Spring County Museum - The Boyle House/1876 Log Cabin, Malvern, AR.......63
Hot Springs County Museum and Cultural Center, Thermopolis, WY 1639
Hotel de Paris Museum, Georgetown, CO...219
The Houdini Museum & Theater, Scranton, PA...1298
Houghton County Historical Museum Society, Lake Linden, MI.......................749
Housatonic Museum of Art, Bridgeport, CT...236
House of Broadcasting Radio & Television Museum, Scottsdale, AZ 44
House of the Temple, Washington, DC........280
House of Wickersham State Historical Site, Juneau, AK.......................................25
House with the Eye Museum, Leadville, CO..226
Houston Police Museum, Houston, TX......1427
Howard County Center of African American Culture, Columbia, MD..........641
Howard County Historical Museum, Kokomo, IN.......................................486
Howard County Historical Society, Ellicott City, MD..................................643
Howard Steamboat Museum and Mansion, Jeffersonville, IN 486
Howard University Museum, Moorland Spingarn Research Center, Washington, DC...................................281
Howell Living History Farm, Titusville, NJ...926
Howland House, Plymouth, MA..................703
The Hoyt Institute of Fine Arts, New Castle, PA...1273
Hubbell Trading Post National Historic Site, Ganado, AZ......................................34
Huddleston Farmhouse Inn Museum, Cambridge City, IN................................471
Hudson Library and Historical Society, Hudson, OH...1168
Hudson River Maritime Museum, Kingston, NY..1007
The Hudson River Museum, Yonkers, NY.1087
Huerfano County Historical Society, including The Walsenburg Mining Museum & Ft. Francisco Museum of La Veta, Walsenburg, CO.......................234
Hui No'eau Visual Arts Center, Makawao, Maui, HI 401
Hull Lifesaving Museum Inc., the Museum of Boston Harbor Heritage, Hull, MA...687
Humboldt Arts Council/Morris Graves Museum of Art, Eureka, CA....................94
Humboldt Historical Museum, Humboldt, KS...544
Humboldt Redwoods State Park Visitor Center, Weott, CA 197
The Humphrey Forum, Minneapolis, MN....782
The 100th Meridian Museum, Cozad, NE ...859
Hunt Institute for Botanical Documentation, Pittsburgh, PA..............1292
Hunter College Art Galleries, New York, NY...1027
Hunter Museum of American Art, Chattanooga, TN...................................1362
Huntingdon County Historical Society, Huntingdon, PA......................................1262
Huntington County Historical Society Museum, Huntington, IN 481
Huntington Library, Art Collections, and Botanical Gardens, San Marino, CA.......174
Huntington Museum of Art, Inc., Huntington, WV.....................................1583
Huntington Sewing & Trade School, Huntington, NY.......................................1001
Huntsville Museum of Art, Huntsville, AL..12
Hurst Ranch Historical Foundation, West Covina, CA...197

Hus Var Fine Art, Buffalo, NY 973
Hutchinson Art Center, Hutchinson, KS.......545
Hutchinson County Museum, Borger, TX..1397
Hyde Hall, Inc., Cooperstown, NY 980
Hyde Park Art Center, Chicago, IL 421
Hydroplane & Raceboat Museum, Kent, WA...1557
Hyrum City Museum, Hyrum, UT 1466
Hyser Rivers Museum, Belmont, MI...........728

I.P. Stanback Museum & Planetarium, Orangeburg, SC 1338
Ice House Museum, Cedar Falls, IA 508
Ida Goodstein Visual Arts Center, Casper, WY...1629
Idaho Black History Museum, Boise, ID.....403
Idaho Military History Museum, Boise, ID..404
Illinois State Museum, Chicago Gallery, Chicago, IL...422
Illinois State Museum/Lockport Gallery, Lockport, IL...443
IMA - Indianapolis Museum of Art, Indianapolis, IN..................................483
Immaculate Conception Catholic Church, Natchitoches, LA....................................593
Imperial Calcasieu Museum, Inc., Lake Charles, LA...590
Independence Seaport Museum, Philadelphia, PA 1281
Indian City U.S.A., Anadarko, OK.............1195
Indian Hill Historical Society, Cincinnati, OH...1150
Indian Museum of North America at Crazy Horse Memorial, Crazy Horse, SD 1345
Indian Pueblo Cultural Center, Albuquerque, NM....................................933
Indian Springs State Park Museum, Flovilla, GA...372
Indiana Basketball Hall of Fame, New Castle, IN...494
Indiana Dunes National Lakeshore, Porter, IN...496
Indiana Football Hall of Fame, Richmond, IN.......................................497
Indiana Historical Society, Indianapolis, IN 483
Indiana Medical History Museum, Indianapolis, IN..................................484
Indiana State Museum, Indianapolis, IN 484
Indiana University Art Museum, Bloomington, IN....................................469
Indiana War Memorials, Indianapolis, IN 484
Indianapolis Art Center, Indianapolis, IN....484
Inland Seas Maritime Museum, Vermilion, OH..1189
Institute of American Indian Arts Museum, Santa Fe, NM 947
Institute of Contemporary Art, University of Pennsylvania, Philadelphia, PA 1282
Institute of Visual Arts, University of Wisconsin-Milwaukee, Milwaukee, WI.1611
The Interchurch Center, New York, NY.....1027
Interlaken Historical Society, Interlaken, NY...1002
International Bluegrass Music Museum, Owensboro, KY.......................................581
International Bowling Museum and Hall of Fame, Saint Louis, MO.......................833
International Center of Photography, New York, NY...1028
The International Clown Hall of Fame & Research Center, Inc., Milwaukee, WI.1611
International Gospel Music Hall of Fame & Museum, Detroit, MI...........................737
International Institute of Metropolitan Detroit, Detroit, MI 737
International Motor Racing Research Center at Watkins Glen, Watkins Glen, NY...1084
International Museum of Art and Science, McAllen, TX...1437

Photographs—Continued

International Museum of Cultures, Dallas, TX...1406

International Museum of the Horse, Lexington, KY...573

International Peace Garden, Dunseith, ND...1130

International Swimming Hall of Fame, Inc., Fort Lauderdale, FL...307

International Tennis Hall of Fame & Museum, Newport, RI...1313

International UFO Museum and Research Center, Roswell, NM...946

International Women's Air and Space Museum, Inc., Cleveland, OH...1155

Intuit: The Center for Intuitive and Outsider Art, Chicago, IL...422

Iowa Aviation Museum, Greenfield, IA...519

Iowa Department of Natural Resources, Des Moines, IA...515

Iowa Great Lakes Maritime Museum, Arnolds Park, IA...505

Iowa Masonic Library and Museum, Cedar Rapids, IA...509

Iraan Museum, Iraan, TX...1430

Iredell Museum of Arts & Heritage, Statesville, NC...1120

Iris & B. Gerald Cantor Art Gallery-College of the Holy Cross, Worcester, MA...721

Iris & B. Gerald Cantor Center for Visual Arts at Stanford University, Stanford, CA...188

Irish American Heritage Museum, Albany, NY...954

Iron County Museum, Caspian, MI...731

Iron Mission State Park & Museum, Cedar City, UT...1464

Ironwood Area Historical Museum, Ironwood, MI...747

Ironworld Discovery Center, Chisholm, MN...771

Iroquois County Historical Society, Watseka, IL...463

Iroquois Indian Museum, Howes Cave, NY...999

Irvine Fine Arts Center, Irvine, CA...105

Isabel Anderson Comer Museum & Arts Center, Sylacauga, AL...18

Isabel Miller Museum/Sitka Historical Society, Sitka, AK...27

Isamu Noguchi Garden Museum, Long Island City, NY...1010

Isanti County Historical Society, Cambridge, MN...770

Ischua Valley Historical Society, Inc., Franklinville, NY...992

Island County Historical Society Museum, Coupeville, WA...1551

Isle Royale National Park, Houghton, MI...747

Islesford Historical Museum, Islesford, ME...612

Islip Art Museum, East Islip, NY...986

Italian American Museum, New York, NY...1028

Itasca County Historical Society, Grand Rapids, MN...777

JFK Special Warfare Museum, Fort Bragg, NC...1101

J.L. Scott Marine Education Center and Aquarium, Gulf Coast Research Laboratory College of Marine Sciences, The U. of Southern Mississippi, Biloxi, MS...798

The J. Paul Getty Museum, Los Angeles, CA...116

J.W. Parmley Historical Home Society, Ipswich, SD...1349

J. Wayne Stark University Center Galleries, College Station, TX...1401

Jack London State Historic Park, Glen Ellen, CA...99

Jack Nicklaus Museum, Columbus, OH...1158

The Jackson Barracks Military Museum, New Orleans, LA...596

Jackson County Historical Museum, Lakefield, MN...778

Jackson County Historical Society, Black River Falls, WI...1592

Jackson Hole Historical Society and Museum, Jackson, WY...1634

Jacksonport State Park, Jacksonport, AR...60

Jacksonville Fire Museum, Jacksonville, FL...314

Jacksonville Maritime Museum Society, Jacksonville, FL...314

Jacksonville Museum of Modern Art, Jacksonville, FL...314

Jacqueline Casey Hudgens Center for the Arts, Duluth, GA...371

The Jacqueline House African American Museum, Vicksburg, MS...809

Jacques Marchais Museum of Tibetan Art, Staten Island, NY...1072

Jail Museum, Neligh, NE...869

James A. Michener Art Museum, Doylestown, PA...1249

James & Meryl Hearst Center for the Arts and Sculpture Garden, Cedar Falls, IA...508

James Ford Bell Museum of Natural History, Minneapolis, MN...782

The James Madison Museum, Orange, VA...1524

James Madison's Montpelier, Montpelier Station, VA...1518

James S. Copley Library, La Jolla, CA...106

James W. Dillon House Museum, Dillon, SC...1331

Jamestown Fire Department Memorial Museum, Jamestown, RI...1312

Jamestown Museum, Jamestown, RI...1312

Jane Addams Hull-House Museum, University of Illinois Chicago, Chicago, IL...422

Jane Voorhees Zimmerli Art Museum, New Brunswick, NJ...915

Japan Society Gallery, New York, NY...1028

Japanese American National Museum, Los Angeles, CA...117

Jarrell Plantation Georgia State Historic Site, Juliette, GA...374

J.C. Penney Homestead & Historical Foundation, Kemmerer, WY...1635

Jeane Dixon Museum and Library, Strasburg, VA...1538

Jeff Matthews Memorial Museum, Galax, VA...1508

Jefferson Barracks Historic Site, Saint Louis, MO...833

Jefferson County Historical Society, Watertown, NY...1083

Jefferson County Historical Society and Farnsworth TV Pioneer Museum, Rigby, ID...409

Jefferson County Historical Society, Inc., Madison, IN...489

Jefferson County Museum, Charles Town, WV...1580

Jefferson Valley Museum, Whitehall, MT...855

Jekyll Island Museum, Jekyll Island, GA...374

Jemez State Monument, Jemez Springs, NM...940

Jenkins Plantation Museum, Lesage, WV...1584

Jericho Historical Society, Jericho Corners, VT...1480

Jerome County Historical Society, Inc. and Idaho Farm & Ranch Museum, Jerome, ID...406

Jerome State Historic Park, Jerome, AZ...36

Jersey City Museum, Jersey City, NJ...908

Jesse James Farm & Museum, Kearney, MO...823

Jesse James Home Museum, Saint Joseph, MO...830

Jesse Peter Museum, Santa Rosa, CA...184

Jewell County Historical Museum, Mankato, KS...552

The Jewish Museum, New York, NY...1029

Jewish Museum of Florida, Miami Beach, FL...326

Jewish Museum of Maryland, Baltimore, MD...633

Jim Crow Museum - Ferris State University, Big Rapids, MI...729

Jim Thorpe Home, Yale, OK...1217

Jimmy Carter National Historic Site, Plains, GA...381

The Jimmy Stewart Museum, Indiana, PA...1262

Joachim Regional Museum, Dickinson, ND...1130

John A. Logan College Museum, Carterville, IL...416

John and Mable Ringling Museum of Art, Sarasota, FL...344

John Burroughs Association, Inc., West Park, NY...1085

John F. Kennedy Presidential Library & Museum, Boston, MA...666

John Furlong Gallery, Menomonie, WI...1609

John G. Neihardt State Historic Site, Bancroft, NE...856

John Hutchings Museum of Natural History, Lehi, UT...1466

John James Audubon Center at Mill Grove, Audubon, PA...1241

John James Audubon Museum, Henderson, KY...571

John Jay French House, Beaumont Heritage Society, Beaumont, TX...1395

John Michael Kohler Arts Center, Sheboygan, WI...1621

John Muir National Historic Site, Martinez, CA...124

John Nance Garner Museum, Uvalde, TX...1457

The John Nicholas Brown Center for the Study of American Civilization, Providence, RI...1317

John Rains House, Rancho Cucamonga, CA...145

John Stark Edwards House, Warren, OH...1189

John Sydnor's 1847 Powhatan House, Galveston, TX...1421

John Wesley Powell Memorial Museum, Page, AZ...37

Johnson County Community College, Gallery of Art, Overland Park, KS...555

Johnson County Historical Society, Coralville, IA...511

Johnson County Historical Society Museum, Warrensburg, MO...840

Johnson County Museum of History, Franklin, IN...478

Johnson County Museums, Shawnee, KS...558

Johnson Victrola Museum, Dover, DE...270

Johnstown Area Heritage Association, Johnstown, PA...1263

Johnstown Flood National Memorial, South Fork, PA...1300

Johnstown Historical Society, Johnstown, NY...1005

Joliet Area Historical Museum, Joliet, IL...440

Jonesborough-Washington County History Museum, Jonesborough, TN...1368

Jordan Schnitzer Museum of Art, Eugene, OR...1223

Joseloff Gallery, Hartford Art School, University of Hartford, West Hartford, CT...264

Joseph A. Tallman Museum, Cherokee, IA...510

Joseph Smith Historic Site, Nauvoo, IL...447

Joslyn Art Museum, Omaha, NE...871

Judah L. Magnes Museum, Berkeley, CA...76

The Judah P. Benjamin Confederate Memorial at Gamble Plantation Historic State Park, Ellenton, FL..............306

The Judaica Museum of the Hebrew Home at Riverdale, Riverdale, NY........1057

Judith Basin County Museum, Stanford, MT..................853

Judy Garland Museum, Grand Rapids, MN..................777

Jule Collins Smith Museum of Fine Art, Auburn, AL..........3

Junction City Historical Society, Junction City, OR.................1226

Jundt Art Museum, Spokane, WA 1571

Juneteenth Creative Cultural Center & Museum, Saginaw, MI.........762

Juniata College Museum of Art, Huntingdon, PA 1262

Juniata County Historical Society, Mifflintown, PA 1271

Justice Brothers Racing Museum, Duarte, CA..................91

Justin Smith Morrill Homestead, Strafford, VT..................1488

Kalamazoo Aviation History Museum, Kalamazoo, MI..................748

Kalamazoo Institute of Arts, Kalamazoo, MI..................748

Kalamazoo Valley Museum, Kalamazoo, MI..................749

Kalkaska County Historical Museum, Kalkaska, MI..................749

The Kansas African American Museum, Wichita, KS..................561

Kansas Aviation Museum, Wichita, KS........562

Kansas Sports Hall of Fame, Wichita, KS ...562

The Kansas Teachers' Hall of Fame, Dodge City, KS..................537

Karl E. Mundt Historical & Educational Foundation, Madison, SD.................1351

Katherine Dunham Dynamic Museum, East Saint Louis, IL..................431

Katonah Museum of Art, Katonah, NY......1006

Kauai Museum, Lihue, HI 401

Kearney County Historical Museum, Minden, NE..................868

Kearney Mansion Museum, Fresno, CA........97

The Kearny Cottage, Perth Amboy, NJ......921

Keeler Tavern Museum, Ridgefield, CT.......259

Kell House Museum, Wichita Falls, TX 1461

Kelly-Griggs House Museum, Red Bluff, CA..................146

Kelsey Museum of Archaeology, Ann Arbor, MI..................724

The Kelso House Museum, Kent, OH........1169

Kemerer Museum of Decorative Arts, Bethlehem, PA..................1242

The Kemp-McCarthy Memorial Museum of the Rowe Historical Society, Inc., Rowe, MA..................706

Kemper Museum of Contemporary Art, Kansas City, MO..................821

Kenilworth Aquatic Gardens, Washington, DC..................281

The Kenilworth Historical Society, Kenilworth, IL..................441

Kennebunkport Historical Society, Kennebunkport, ME..................612

Kennedy Museum of Art, Athens, OH 1140

Kennesaw Mountain National Battlefield Park, Kennesaw, GA 374

Kenosha Public Museum, Kenosha, WI.....1602

Kensington Mansion, Eastover, SC 1332

Kent-Delord House Museum, Plattsburgh, NY..................1052

Kent Plantation House, Alexandria, LA 585

Kent State University, School of Art Galleries, Kent, OH..................1169

Kentucky Coal Mining Museum, Benham, KY..................565

Kentucky Derby Museum, Louisville, KY...576

Kentucky Gateway Museum Center, Maysville, KY..................579

The Kentucky Library & Museum, Bowling Green, KY..................565

Kentucky Military History Museum, Frankfort, KY..................569

Kentucky Railway Museum, Inc., New Haven, KY..................580

Keokuk River Museum, Keokuk, IA..........521

Kern County Museum, Bakersfield, CA........73

Kewaunee County Historical Museum, Kewaunee, WI..................1602

Keweenaw County Historical Society, Eagle Harbor, MI..................739

Key West Museum of Art and History, Key West, FL..................318

Keyport Historical Society-Steamboat Dock Museum, Keyport, NJ 909

Keystone Area Historical Society, Keystone, SD..................1350

Kimberly Crest House & Gardens, Redlands, CA..................147

Kimble County Historical Museum, Junction, TX..................1431

King Kamehameha V-Judiciary History Center, Honolulu, HI..................397

King Saddlery Museum, Sheridan, WY 1638

Kingman County Historical Museum, Kingman, KS..................547

Kingman Museum, Battle Creek, MI 727

Kings Mountain National Military Park, Blacksburg, SC..................1322

Kingsburg Historical Park, Kingsburg, CA..................105

Kingsley Plantation, Jacksonville, FL 315

Kirtland Temple Historic Center, Kirtland, OH..................1170

Kit Carson Historical Society, Kit Carson, CO..................223

Kit Carson Museum, Las Animas, CO.........225

Kitsap County Historical Society Museum, Bremerton, WA..................1549

Kittery Historical & Naval Museum, Kittery, ME..................613

Kittson County History Center Museum, Lake Bronson, MN..................778

Klein Museum, Mobridge, SD..................1352

Klickitat County Historical Society, Goldendale, WA..................1555

Klondike Gold Rush National Historical Park, Skagway, AK..................28

Klondike Gold Rush National Historical Park, Seattle, WA..................1566

Knight Museum, Alliance, NE..................855

Knights of Columbus Museum, New Haven, CT..................253

Knott House Museum, Tallahassee, FL........347

Knox Headquarters State Historic Site, Vails Gate, NY..................1080

Knoxville Museum of Art, Knoxville, TN .1370

Knoxville Public Library, Knoxville, PA ...1265

Knudt Salle Log Cabin, Adams, ND..........1127

Kodiak Military History Museum, Kodiak, AK..................27

Koochiching County Historical Museum, International Falls, MN..................778

Korean War Veterans National Museum & Library, Rantoul, IL..................453

Koreshan State Historic Site, Estero, FL.......306

Korner's Folly, Kernersville, NC..................1108

Krannert Art Museum and Kinkead Pavilion, Champaign, IL 416

Krempp Gallery, Jasper, IN..................486

Kresge Art Museum, East Lansing, MI........739

Kuhlmann King Historical House and Museum, Boerne, TX..................1396

The Kurdish Museum, Brooklyn, NY 969

Kuser Farm Mansion, Hamilton, NJ............907

L.H. Bailey Hortorium, Ithaca, NY..........1003

La Porte County Historical Society Museum, La Porte, IN..................487

La Puente Valley Historical Society City Hall, LaPuente, CA..................107

La Purisima Mission State Historic Park, Lompoc, CA..................109

La Raza/Galeria Posada, Sacramento, CA ...153

LaBelle Heritage Museum, LaBelle, FL 319

Lac Qui Parle County Historical Society, Madison, MN..................779

The Lace Museum, Sunnyvale, CA..............190

Lacey Historical Society, Forked River, NJ..................904

The Lacrosse Museum & National Hall of Fame/US Lacrosse, Baltimore, MD 633

Ladew Topiary Gardens, Monkton, MD.......649

Lafayette College Art Gallery, Williams Center for the Arts, Easton, PA 1250

Lafayette Miners Museum, Lafayette, CO ...224

Lafayette Natural History Museum and Planetarium, Lafayette, LA 589

Lagrange County Historical Society, Inc., Lagrange, IN..................488

LaGrange Plantation, Cambridge, MD.........639

Laguna Art Museum, Laguna Beach, CA......107

Lahaina Restoration Foundation, Lahaina, HI..................400

The Lake Champlain Maritime Museum, Vergennes, VT..................1488

Lake County Historic Courthouse Museum, Lakeport, CA..................108

Lake County Historical Society, Kirtland Hills, OH..................1170

Lake George Historical Association Museum, Lake George, NY..................1008

Lake Hopatcong Historical Museum, Landing, NJ..................909

Lake Jackson Historical Museum, Lake Jackson, TX..................1433

Lake of the Red Cedars Museum, Cedar Lake, IN..................472

Lake of the Woods County Museum, Baudette, MN..................768

Lake Perris Regional Indian Museum (Home of the Wind), Perris, CA..........141

Lake Shore Railway Museum, North East, PA..................1274

Lake Superior Maritime Visitors Center, Duluth, MN..................773

Lake Tahoe Historical Society & Museum, South Lake Tahoe, CA..............188

Lake Tomahawk Historical Society, Lake Tomahawk, WI..................1604

Lake Wales Depot Museum & Cultural Center, Lake Wales, FL..................320

Lakewood's Heritage Center, Lakewood, CO..................225

Lamar Dodd Art Center, LaGrange College, LaGrange, GA..................375

The Lamont Gallery, Exeter, NH..................888

Lancaster County Historical Society, Lancaster, PA..................1266

Lancaster Museum/Art Gallery, Lancaster, CA..................108

Land of the Yankee Fork Historic Association Museum, Stanley, ID..........410

Landis Valley Museum, Lancaster, PA.......1266

The Landmark Society of Western New York, Rochester, NY..................1058

Lane Community College Art Gallery, Eugene, OR..................1223

Lane County Historical Museum, Dighton, KS..................536

Lane County Historical Society & Museum, Eugene, OR..................1223

Lane Place, Crawfordsville, IN..................473

Langlade County Historical Society Museum, Antigo, WI..................1589

Lansing Art Gallery, Lansing, MI..................750

Laramie Plains Museum, Laramie, WY 1635

Larchmont Historical Society, Mamaroneck, NY..................1013

Photographs–Continued

Lars Noak Blacksmith Shop, Larsson/Ostlund Log Home & One-Room Capitol School, New Sweden, ME.................................616

Larson Museum and Gallery, Yakima, WA..1578

Larz Anderson Auto Museum, Brookline, MA..671

Las Vegas Art Museum, Las Vegas, NV......879

LaSalle County Historical Society Museum, Utica, IL...............................462

Latvian Museum, Rockville, MD.................651

Lauder Museum - Amityville Historical Society, Amityville, NY.....................957

Laumeier Sculpture Park & Museum, Saint Louis, MO...............................834

Laura Ingalls Wilder Museum and Tourist Center, Walnut Grove, MN.....................795

Laurel Arts, Somerset, PA........................1300

The Laurel Museum, Laurel, MD...............648

Lauren Rogers Museum of Art, Laurel, MS..804

Laurence C. Jones Museum, Piney Woods, MS.......................................807

Law Enforcement Memorial Association, Inc., Roselle, IL..............................456

Lawrence County Gray House Museum, Ironton, OH......................................1169

Lawrence County Historical and Genealogical Society, Bedford, IN..........469

Lawrence Heritage State Park, Lawrence, MA..689

Lawrence History Center: Immigrant City Archives & Museum, Lawrence, MA.....689

Laws Railroad Museum and Historical Site, Bishop, CA................................78

Layland Museum, Cleburne, TX...............1400

Le Sueur Museum, Le Sueur, MN..............779

Lea County Cowboy Hall of Fame and Western Heritage Center, Hobbs, NM.....940

Leadville National Mining Hall of Fame & Museum, Leadville, CO.....................226

The Lebanon County Historical Society, Lebanon, PA.......................................1268

Lee Chapel and Museum, Lexington, VA..1513

Lee-Fendall House Museum and Garden, Alexandria, VA...............................1493

Leedel Moorehead-Graham Fine Arts Gallery, Pine Bluff, AR........................66

Leelanau Historical Museum, Leland, MI....751

The Leffingwell House Museum, Norwich, CT......................................258

Legacy Museum of African-American History, Lynchburg, VA.....................1515

Legends of New Mexico Museum, Algodones, NM...............................936

Legends of the Game Baseball Museum and Learning Center, Arlington, TX......1388

Legion of Valor Veterans Museum, Fresno, CA..98

Lehigh University Art Galleries/Museum Operations, Bethlehem, PA.................1242

Lehman College Art Gallery, Bronx, NY.....966

Leigh Yawkey Woodson Art Museum, Wausau, WI......................................1626

Lemhi County Historical Museum, Salmon, ID..409

Lemon Hill Mansion, Philadelphia, PA......1282

Lesbian Herstory Educational Foundation, Inc. aka Lesbian Herstory Archives, Brooklyn, NY.....................................969

Leslie Powell Foundation and Gallery, Lawton, OK.......................................1204

Lesueur County Historical Museum-Chapter 1, Elysian, MN............774

Levere Memorial Temple, Evanston, IL......434

Leverett Historical Society, Leverett, MA....689

Lewes Historical Society, Lewes, DE.........271

Lewis County Historical Museum, Chehalis, WA...................................1550

Lewis County Historical Society Museum, Lowville, NY.......................1012

Lexington County Museum, Lexington, SC..1336

Lexington Historical Society, Lexington, MA..689

Liberace Museum & Foundation, Las Vegas, NV..879

Liberty County Museum, Chester, MT........844

Liberty Hall Historic Center, Lamoni, IA....522

Liberty Hall Historic Site, Frankfort, KY....569

Liberty Jail Historic Site, Liberty, MO.......826

Liberty Science Center, Jersey City, NJ......909

Liberty Village Arts Center & Gallery, Chester, MT..844

Libertyville-Mundelein Historical Society, Inc., Libertyville, IL.............................442

Library Company of Philadelphia, Philadelphia, PA.................................1282

Library of Congress, Washington, DC.........282

Library of the Supreme Council, 33 Degrees, Washington, DC.......................282

The Library of Virginia, Richmond, VA.....1530

Licking County Arts, Newark, OH.............1178

Licking County Historical Society, Newark, OH......................................1178

Life on the Ohio River History Museum, Vevay, IN...502

Light Crust Doughboys Hall of Fame & Museum - Governor Jim Hogg City Park, Quitman, TX................................1444

The Light Factory - Museum of Photography & Film, Charlotte, NC......1095

Lighthouse Center for the Arts, Tequesta, FL..351

Lillian and Albert Small Jewish Museum, Washington, DC.................................282

Limon Heritage Museum, Limon, CO.........226

Lincoln County Historical Museum, Davenport, WA..................................1552

Lincoln County Historical Society, Lincoln, KS......................................549

Lincoln County Historical Society Museum of Pioneer History, Chandler, OK..1197

Lincoln County Museum, Hugo, CO.........222

Lincoln County Pioneer Museum, Hendricks, MN...................................778

Lincoln Fire & Rescue Department Museum, Lincoln, NE...........................866

Lincoln Herdon Law Offices State Historic Site, Springfield, IL....................458

Lincoln Memorial Garden and Nature Center, Springfield, IL..........................459

Lincoln Memorial Shrine, Redlands, CA.....147

The Lincoln Museum, Fort Wayne, IN.......478

Lincoln Parish Museum & Historical Society, Ruston, LA..............................600

Lincoln Park Historical Museum, Lincoln Park, MI..751

The Lincoln-Tallman Restorations, Janesville, WI....................................1601

Lincoln's New Salem State Historic Site, Petersburg, IL......................................451

Linn County Historical Museum and Moyer House, Brownsville, OR..............1220

Linn County Museum/Geneaology Library, Pleasanton, KS......................556

Lisbon Historical Society, Lisbon, OH.......1172

Lisle Station Museum, Lisle, IL.................443

Litchfield Historical Society and Museum, Litchfield, CT........................247

The Lithuanian Museum, Chicago, IL.........423

Little Bighorn Battlefield National Monument, Crow Agency, MT...............844

The Little Brick House, Vandalia, IL..........462

The Little Cowboy Bar & Museum, Fromberg, MT....................................847

Little Falls Historical Society Museum, Little Falls, NY....................................1009

Little Log Church & Museum, Yachats, OR..1238

Little Red Schoolhouse-Living Library, Beloit, KS..534

Little Snake River Museum, Savery, WY..1638

Little White Schoolhouse, Ripon, WI.........1620

Littleton Historical Museum, Littleton, CO..227

The Living Arts and Science Center, Inc., Lexington, KY....................................573

Livingston Depot Center, Livingston, MT...850

Lockehaven Schoolhouse Museum, Enfield, NH..887

Locust Lawn and Terwilliger House, Gardiner, NY......................................993

Log House Museum, Seattle, WA.............1566

Logan County Historical Society Museum, Bellefontaine, OH..................1142

Logan County Museum, Paris, AR.............65

Loghurst Farm Museum, Canfield, OH......1145

Logoly State Park, McNeil, AR..................64

Lone Star Flight Museum/Texas Aviation Hall of Fame, Galveston, TX.................1421

Long Branch Historical Museum, Long Branch, NJ..910

Long Island Museum of American Art, History & Carriages, Stony Brook, NY..1075

Longboat Key Center for the Arts, Longboat Key, FL................................322

Longfellow National Historic Site, Cambridge, MA...................................673

Longfellow's Wayside Inn, Sudbury, MA....714

Longhorn Museum, Pleasanton, TX..........1444

Longmont Museum, Longmont, CO............227

Longue Vue House & Gardens, New Orleans, LA..596

Longview Museum of Fine Arts, Longview, TX......................................1434

Longwood Center for the Visual Arts, Farmville, VA......................................1504

Longwood Gardens, Kennett Square, PA..1264

Longyear Museum, Chestnut Hill, MA........675

Lopez Island Historical Museum, Lopez Island, WA..1558

Lore Degenstein Gallery, Selinsgrove, PA .1299

Lorenzo State Historic Site, Cazenovia, NY..976

Los Altos History Museum aka Association of the Los Altos Historical Museum, Los Altos, CA........................112

The Los Angeles Art Association/Gallery 825, Los Angeles, CA..........................117

Los Angeles (Central) Public Library, Los Angeles, CA......................................117

The Los Angeles County Arboretum & Botanic Garden, Arcadia, CA 71

Los Angeles County Museum of Art, Los Angeles, CA......................................118

Los Angeles Maritime Museum, San Pedro, CA..176

Los Angeles Municipal Art Gallery - Barnsdall Art Park, Los Angeles, CA......118

Los Angeles Museum of the Holocaust, Los Angeles, CA..................................118

Los Angeles Police Historical Society & Museum, Los Angeles, CA....................119

Los Nogales Museum, Seguin, TX............1452

Lost City Museum, Overton, NV................880

Lou Holtz/Upper Ohio Valley Hall of Fame, East Liverpool, OH....................1163

Loudoun Museum, Inc., Leesburg, VA.......1512

Louis H. & Lena Firn Grover Museum, Shelbyville, IN....................................498

Louise Wells Cameron Art Museum, Wilmington, NC..................................1123

Louisiana Arboretum, State Preservation Area, Ville Platte, LA............................603

Louisiana Art & Science Museum - Irene W. Pennington Planetarium, Baton Rouge, LA...586

The Louisiana Cotton Museum, Lake Providence, LA...................................590

Louisiana Marine Fisheries Museum, Lafitte, LA 590
Louisiana Naval War Memorial/U.S.S. Kidd, Baton Rouge, LA 586
Louisiana Political Museum and Hall of Fame, Winnfield, LA 603
Louisiana State Museum, New Orleans, LA 596
Louisiana State Oil & Gas Museum, Oil City, LA 599
Louisiana State University Museum of Art, Baton Rouge, LA 586
Louisiana Tech Museum, Ruston, LA 600
Louisiana's Old State Capitol, Political History Museum, Baton Rouge, LA........587
Louisville Slugger Museum & Factory, Louisville, KY 577
Lovely Lane Museum, Baltimore, MD 634
Lovettsville Historical Society Museum, Lovettsville, VA 1514
Lowe Art Museum, University of Miami, Coral Gables, FL 301
Lowell Area Historical Museum, Lowell, MI 751
Lowell Observatory, Flagstaff, AZ 33
Lowell Telecommunications Corp., Lowell, MA 691
Lower Cape Fear Historical Society, Inc., Wilmington, NC 1123
Lower East Side Tenement Museum, New York, NY 1029
Lower Rio Grande Valley Nature Center, Weslaco, TX 1460
Lower White River Museum, Des Arc, AR 56
Lowndes County Historical Society and Museum, Valdosta, GA 389
Loxahatchee River Historical Society, Jupiter, FL 316
Lubeznik Center for the Arts, Michigan City, IN 490
Lucretia Vaile Museum, Palmer Lake, CO 229
Lucy Craft Laney Museum of Black History and Conference Center, Augusta, GA 365
Lucy-Desi Museum, Jamestown, NY 1005
Luis Munoz Rivera Library & Museum, Barranquitas, PR 1641
Lum & Abner Museum & Jot 'Em Down Store, Pine Ridge, AR 66
Lummis Home: El Alisal, Los Angeles, CA 119
Luther Burbank Home & Gardens, Santa Rosa, CA 184
The Luther W. Brady Art Gallery, Washington, DC 282
Lutheran Heritage Center & Museum of the Perry County Lutheran Historical Society, Altenburg, MO 810
The Lyceum, Alexandria's History Museum, Alexandria, VA 1493
Lyman Allyn Art Museum, New London, CT 255
Lyman Museum, Hilo, HI 393
Lyndon Baines Johnson Library and Museum, Austin, TX 1391
Lynnhaven House, Virginia Beach, VA 1542
Lyon County Historical Society and Museum, Emporia, KS 538
The Lyons Redstone Museum, Lyons, CO...227

MIT-List Visual Arts Center, Cambridge, MA 673
MIT Museum, Cambridge, MA 674
M. Louise Aughinbaugh Gallery at Messiah College, Grantham, PA 1257
Mabee Farm Historic Site, Rotterdam Junction, NY 1062
Mabel Hartzell Historical Home, Alliance, OH 1139
Mabry-Hazen House, Knoxville, TN 1371

Macalester College Art Gallery, Janet Wallace Fine Arts Center, Saint Paul, MN 790
MacArthur Museum of Arkansas Military History, Little Rock, AR 62
MacDonald Art Gallery, Dallas, PA 1249
Mackinac Island State Park Commission-Mackinac State Historic Parks, Mackinaw City, MI 752
Mackinac State Historic Parks-Colonial Michilimackinac & Old Mackinac Point Lighthouse, Mackinaw City, MI 752
Mackinac State Historic Parks-Fort Mackinac & Mackinac Island State Park, Mackinac Island, MI 752
Macon County Historical Society Museum Complex, Decatur, IL 430
Madeline Island Historical Museum, La Pointe, WI 1603
Madera County Museum, Madera, CA 123
Madison Historical Society, Madison, CT....247
Madison-Morgan Cultural Center, Madison, GA 378
Madison Museum of Contemporary Art, Madison, WI 1605
Magevney House, Memphis, TN 1373
The Magic Lantern Castle Museum, San Antonio, TX 1448
Magnolia Grove-Historic House Museum, Greensboro, AL 10
Magoffin Home State Historic Site, El Paso, TX 1412
Mai Wah Society, Butte, MT 843
Maier Museum of Art, Randolph-Macon Woman's College, Lynchburg, VA 1515
Maine Historical Society, Portland, ME 619
Maine Lighthouse Museum, Rockland, ME 621
Maine Maritime Museum, Bath, ME 606
Maine State Museum, Augusta, ME 604
Maitland Art Center, Maitland, FL 322
Maitland Historical Museums, Maitland, FL 322
The Major General Frederick Funston Boyhood Home and Museum, Iola, KS 546
Major John Bradford House, Kingston, MA 688
Malabar Farm State Park, Lucas, OH 1173
Malden Public Library, Malden, MA 692
Malheur Historical Project, Stonehouse Museum, Vale, OR 1238
Malibu Lagoon Museum, Malibu, CA 123
Malki Museum, Banning, CA 74
Mallory-Neely House, Memphis, TN 1373
Maltz Museum of Jewish Heritage, Beachwood, OH 1142
Mamie Doud Eisenhower Birthplace, Boone, IA 506
Mammoth Cave National Park, Mammoth Cave, KY 579
Mammoth Spring State Park, Depot Museum, Mammoth Spring, AR 64
Manassas Museum System, Manassas, VA 1516
Manatee Village Historical Park, Bradenton, FL 297
Manchester Historic Association Millyard Museum, Manchester, NH 891
Manchester Historical Society, Manchester, MA 692
Manhattan Arts Center, Manhattan, KS........551
Manistee County Historical Museum, Manistee, MI 753
Manitowoc County Historical Society, Manitowoc, WI 1607
The Mansfield Art Center, Mansfield, OH .1173
Mansfield Historical Society Museum, Storrs, CT 261
Mansfield Township Historical Society (1849 Georgetown School/Museum), Columbus, NJ 902

Manship House Museum, Jackson, MS........802
Maple Valley Historical Museum, Maple Valley, WA 1559
Maramec Museum, The James Foundation, Saint James, MO 830
Marathon County Historical Society, Wausau, WI 1626
Marblehead Arts Association - King Hooper Mansion, Marblehead, MA 693
Marblehead Museum & Historical Society, Marblehead, MA 693
Marcella Sembrich Opera Museum, Bolton Landing, NY 963
Marcellus Historical Society, Marcellus, NY 1013
March Field Air Museum, Riverside, CA 149
Mardi Gras Museum, Kenner, LA 589
Mardi Gras Museum, Biloxi, MS 798
Marfa and Presidio County Museum, Marfa, TX 1436
Margaret Fort Trahern Gallery, Clarksville, TN 1363
Margaret Harwell Art Museum, Poplar Bluff, MO 829
The Margaret Mitchell House & Museum, Atlanta, GA 361
Mariani Gallery, University of Northern Colorado, Greeley, CO 221
Marianna Kistler Beach Museum of Art at Kansas State University, Manhattan, KS 551
Marias Museum of History and Art, Shelby, MT 853
Marietta/Cobb Museum of Art, Marietta, GA 379
Marietta House Museum, Glenn Dale, MD 645
Marietta Museum of History, Marietta, GA 379
Marilla Historical Society Museum, Marilla, NY 1014
Marin History Museum, San Rafael, CA 177
The Marine Museum at Fall River, Inc., Fall River, MA 682
The Mariners' Museum, Newport News, VA 1519
Marinette County Historical Museum, Marinette, WI 1607
Mario Lanza Institute/Museum, Philadelphia, PA 1282
Marion County Historical Society, Salem, OR 1236
The Marion County Historical Society Museum, Marion, OH 1174
Marion Public Library Museum, Marion, IN 490
Mariposa Museum & World Culture Center, Peterborough, NH 893
Maritime & Seafood Industry Museum, Biloxi, MS 798
Maritime and Yachting Museum of the Treasure Coast, Stuart, FL 346
Maritime Industry Museum at Fort Schuyler, Bronx, NY 966
Maritime Museum at Historic Coast Guard Station, Saint Simons Island, GA 383
Maritime Museum - Cohasset Historical Society, Cohasset, MA 676
Maritime Museum of Monterey, Monterey, CA 127
Maritime Museum of San Diego, San Diego, CA 157
Marjorie Kinnan Rawlings Historic State Park, Cross Creek, FL 301
Mark Twain Home and Museum, Hannibal, MO 816
The Mark Twain House & Museum, Hartford, CT 245
Marlboro County Historical Museum, Bennettsville, SC 1322
Marlboro Historical Society, Marlboro, VT 1481

Photographs–Continued

Marquette County Historical Society, Westfield, WI 1627

Marquette County History Museum, Marquette, MI 753

Marshall County Historical Museum, Plymouth, IN 496

Marshall County Historical Museum, Holly Springs, MS 801

Marshall County Historical Society Museum, Warren, MN 795

Marshall M. Fredericks Sculpture Museum, University Center, MI 766

Marshall Point Lighthouse Museum, Saint George, ME 621

Martin and Osa Johnson Safari Museum, Inc., Chanute, KS 535

Martin County Historical Museum, Stanton, TX 1453

Martin County Museum, Shoals, IN 499

Martinez Museum, Martinez, CA 124

Marvin Newton House, Brookfield, VT 1477

Mary Aaron Memorial Museum, Marysville, CA 125

Mary and Leigh Block Museum of Art, Northwestern University, Evanston, IL ...434

The Mary Baker Eddy Library for the Betterment of Humanity, Boston, MA 666

Mary Baldwin College/Hunt Gallery, Staunton, VA 1537

Mary Ball Washington Museum & Library, Inc., Lancaster, VA 1512

The Mary Brogan Museum of Art and Science, Tallahassee, FL 347

Mary G. Hardin Center for Cultural Arts, Gadsden, AL 10

Mary McLeod Bethune Council House National Historic Site, Washington, DC 283

Mary Porter Sesnon Art Gallery, Santa Cruz, CA 181

Mary Todd Lincoln House, Lexington, KY 574

Maryland Historical Society, Baltimore, MD 634

The Maryland Institute, College of Art: Decker, Meyerhoff and Pinkard Galleries, Baltimore, MD 634

Mashantucket Pequot Museum and Research Center, Mashantucket, CT 248

Masonic Grand Lodge Library and Museum of Texas, Waco, TX 1459

The Masonic Library and Museum of Pennsylvania, Philadelphia, PA 1283

The Massillon Museum, Massillon, OH 1175

Masur Museum of Art, Monroe, LA 592

Matagorda County Museum, Bay City, TX 1393

Mathias Ham House Historic Site, Dubuque, IA 516

Mattapoisett Museum and Carriage House, Mattapoisett, MA 693

Matthews Museum of Maine Heritage, Union, ME 624

Maude I. Kerns Art Center, Eugene, OR ...1223

Maxwell Museum of Anthropology, Albuquerque, NM 934

May Museum & Farmville Heritage Center, Farmville, NC 1100

May Natural History Museum and Museum of Space Exploration, Colorado Springs, CO 207

Maynard Pioneer Museum & Park, Maynard, AR 64

Mayville Area Museum of History and Genealogy, Mayville, MI 754

Mayville Historical Society, Inc., Mayville, WI 1608

Mc Cook County Historical Society and Museum, Salem, SD 1355

McCallum Museum, Sibley, IA 527

McCook House, Civil War Museum, Carrollton, OH 1146

McCormick Gallery, Midland, TX 1438

McDonald's #1 Store Museum, Des Plaines, IL 431

McFarland State Historic Park, Florence, AZ 34

McGuffey Art Center, Charlottesville, VA .1499

McHenry County Historical Society and Museum, Union, IL 461

McHenry Museum, Modesto, CA 126

McIntosh County Historical Society, Ashley, ND 1127

McLean-Alanreed Area Museum, McLean, TX 1438

McLean County Historical Society Museum, Washburn, ND 1137

McMullen Museum of Art, Boston College, Chestnut Hill, MA 675

McNamara House Museum, Victoria, TX .1457

McPherson County Old Mill Museum and Park, Lindsborg, KS 550

McPherson Museum & Arts Foundation, McPherson, KS 552

McWethy Hall, Luce Gallery, Cornell College, Mount Vernon, IA 524

Mead Art Museum, Amherst, MA 658

Meade County Historical Society Museum, Meade, KS 552

Meadow Brook Hall, Rochester, MI 761

Meadowlands Museum, Rutherford, NJ 923

Meadows Museum of Art of Centenary College, Shreveport, LA 601

Meagher County Historical Association Castle Museum, White Sulphur Springs, MT 855

Mechanicsburg Museum Association, Mechanicsburg, PA 1270

Mecosta County Historical Museum, Big Rapids, MI 729

Medicine Bow Museum, Medicine Bow, WY 1636

Medina County Historical Society, The John Smart House, Medina, OH 1175

Meeker County Historical Society Museum & G.A.R. Hall, Litchfield, MN 779

Meigs County Museum, Pomeroy, OH 1183

Mellette House, Watertown, SD 1359

Melrose Plantation Home Complex, Melrose, LA 592

Mem-Erie Historical Museum, Erie, KS 539

The Memorial Day Museum, Waterloo, NY 1083

Memorial Hall Museum, Pocumtuck Valley Memorial Assoc., Deerfield, MA 679

Memorial Union Art Gallery, Davis, CA 90

Memorial Union Gallery, Fargo, ND 1130

Memoryville USA, Inc., Rolla, MO 829

Memphis Brooks Museum of Art, Memphis, TN 1374

Memphis College of Art, Memphis, TN 1374

The Menczer Museum of Medicine & Dentistry, Hartford, CT 245

Mendocino Historical Research, Inc./Kelley House Museum, Mendocino, CA 125

The Menil Collection, Houston, TX 1428

Mennello Museum of American Art, Orlando, FL 331

Mennonite Heritage Center, Harleysville, PA 1258

Mennonite Library and Archives, North Newton, KS 554

Menominee County Heritage Museum, Menominee, MI 754

Merced County Courthouse Museum, Merced, CA 125

Mercer County Historical Museum, The Riley Home, Celina, OH 1146

Meriden Historical Society, Inc., Meriden, CT 249

Meridian Museum of Art, Meridian, MS 805

Meriwether Lewis Dredge Museum, Brownville, NE 858

Meriwether Lewis National Monument, Hohenwald, TN 1367

Merritt Museum of Anthropology, Oakland, CA 133

Mesa Historical Museum, Mesa, AZ 37

Mesa Southwest Museum, Mesa, AZ 37

Mesa Verde National Park Museum, Mesa Verde National Park, CO 228

Metamora Courthouse Historic Site, Metamora, IL 444

The Metropolitan Museum of Art, New York, NY 1030

Metropolitan State College of Denver/Center for Visual Art, Denver, CO 212

Meux Home Museum, Fresno, CA 98

Mexic-Arte Museum, Austin, TX 1391

Mexican Fine Arts Center Museum, Chicago, IL 424

The Mexican Museum, San Francisco, CA 166

Miami Art Museum, Miami, FL 324

Miami County Museum, Peru, IN 496

Miami-Dade College Kendall Campus Art Gallery, Miami, FL 324

Miami University Art Museum, Oxford, OH 1181

Michael C. Carlos Museum, Atlanta, GA ...361

Michael C. Rockefeller Arts Center Gallery, Fredonia, NY 992

Michelson Museum of Art, Marshall, TX .1436

Michigan Maritime Museum, South Haven, MI 764

Michigan Sports Hall of Fame, Detroit, MI 737

Michigan Transit Museum, Inc., Mount Clemens, MI 756

Mid-America Air Museum, Liberal, KS 549

Mid-Continent Railway Museum, North Freedom, WI 1615

Middleborough Historical Association, Inc., Middleborough, MA 694

Middlebury College Museum of Art, Middlebury, VT 1482

Middlebury Historical Society, Wyoming, NY 1087

Middlesex Canal Collection, Lowell, MA....691

Middletown Valley Historical Society, Middletown, MD 649

Midland County Historical Society, Midland, MI 755

Midland Pioneer Museum, Midland, SD....1351

Midway Village & Museum Center, Rockford, IL 455

Midwest Museum of American Art, Elkhart, IN 474

Midwest Old Settlers & Threshers Association, Inc., Mount Pleasant, IA 524

Mifflinburg Buggy Museum Association, Inc., Mifflinburg, PA 1271

Mighty Eighth Air Force Museum, Pooler, GA 381

Milam County Museum and Annex, Cameron, TX 1399

Mildred Lane Kemper Art Museum, Saint Louis, MO 834

Milford Historical Museum, Milford, MI....756

Milford Historical Society, Milford, CT 250

Milford Museum, Milford, DE 271

Military Museum of Southern New England, Danbury, CT 238

Military Veterans Museum, Inc., Oshkosh, WI 1616

Miller Art Museum, Sturgeon Bay, WI 1623

Millicent Rogers Museum of Northern New Mexico, Taos, NM 952

Milliken Gallery, Converse College, Spartanburg, SC.................1341
Mills College Art Museum, Oakland, CA....133
Millville Army Air Field Museum, Millville, NJ.................911
Milton Art Museum, Canton, MA.........674
Milton Historical Museum, Milton, VT.....1482
Milton House Museum Historic Site, Milton, WI.................1610
Milwaukee Art Museum, Milwaukee, WI..1611
Milwaukee County Historical Society, Milwaukee, WI.................1611
Mingei International Museum, San Diego, CA.................157
Minisink Valley Historical Society, Port Jervis, NY.................1053
The Minna Anthony Common Nature Center at Wellesley State Park, Fineview, NY.................989
Minneapolis Institute of Arts, Minneapolis, MN.................782
Minnesota Air National Guard Historical Foundation, Inc., Saint Paul, MN.........790
Minnesota Museum of American Art, Saint Paul, MN.................791
Minnetrista, Muncie, IN.................492
Mint Museum of Art, Charlotte, NC.........1095
Minter Field Air Museum, Shafter, CA.........186
Miracle of America Museum Inc., Polson, MT.................852
Miramont Castle Museum, Manitou Springs, CO.................228
Mission Cultural Center for Latino Arts, San Francisco, CA.................166
Mission Houses Museum, Honolulu, HI.....397
Mission Inn Foundation/Museum, Riverside, CA.................149
Mission San Antonio de Padua, Jolon, CA.................105
Mission San Juan Capistrano Museum, San Juan Capistrano, CA.................173
Mission San Luis Rey Museum, Oceanside, CA.................135
Missisquoi Valley Historical Society, North Troy, VT.................1483
Mississippi Armed Forces Museum, Camp Shelby, MS.................799
Mississippi Baptist Historical Commission, Clinton, MS.................799
Mississippi Entomological Museum, Mississippi State University, MS.........805
Mississippi Museum of Art, Jackson, MS....802
Mississippi River Museum at Mud Island River Park, Memphis, TN.................1375
Mississippi University for Women, Archives and Museum, Columbus, MS...800
Missoula Art Museum, Missoula, MT.........851
Missouri Historical Society, Saint Louis, MO.................835
Mitchell County Historical Museum, Osage, IA.................526
Mizel Museum, Denver, CO.................213
Mobile Medical Museum, Mobile, AL.........14
Mobile Museum of Art, Mobile, AL.........14
Modern Art Museum of Fort Worth, Fort Worth, TX.................1418
Modern Western Museum, Mount Pleasant, TX.................1440
Modoc County Historical Museum, Alturas, CA.................70
Mohave Museum of History and Arts, Kingman, AZ.................36
Mohonk Preserve, Inc., Gardiner, NY.........993
Mojave River Valley Museum, Barstow, CA.................74
Moland House, Warrington, PA.................1305
Molokai Museum and Cultural Center, Kualapuu, HI.................400
The Monhegan Museum, Monhegan, ME....615
Monmouth County Historical Association, Freehold, NJ.................905

Monocacy National Battlefield, Frederick, MD.................644
Monroe Community College, Mercer Gallery, Rochester, NY.................1059
Monroe County Heritage Museum, Monroeville, AL.................15
Monroe County Historical Association/Stroud Mansion, Stroudsburg, PA.................1302
Monroe County Historical Museum, Monroe, MI.................756
Monroe County Historical Society, Bloomington, IN.................469
Monroe County Local History Room & Library, Sparta, WI.................1622
Monroe Historical Society, Monroe, CT.....250
Montague Museum & Historical Association, Montague, MI.................756
Montalvo Arts Center, Saratoga, CA.........185
Montana Historical Society, Helena, MT.....849
Montana Museum of Art and Culture, Missoula, MT.................852
Montauk, Clermont, IA.................511
Montauk Point Lighthouse Museum, Montauk, NY.................1015
Montclair Art Museum, Montclair, NJ.........912
Montclair State University Art Galleries, Upper Montclair, NJ.................929
Monterey Bay Aquarium, Monterey, CA.....127
Monterey History and Art Association, Monterey, CA.................127
Monterey Museum of Art, Monterey, CA....128
The Montgomery County Historical Society, Inc., Rockville, MD.................651
Montgomery Museum & Lewis Miller Regional Art Center, Christiansburg, VA.................1501
Montgomery Museum of Fine Arts, Montgomery, AL.................16
Montgomery Zoo, Montgomery, AL.........17
Monticello, Home of Thomas Jefferson, Thomas Jefferson Foundation, Inc., Charlottesville, VA.................1499
Montrose County Historical Museum, Montrose, CO.................228
Montville Township Historical Museum, Montville, NJ.................912
Moody County Museum, Flandreau, SD....1347
The Moody Mansion Museum, Galveston, TX.................1421
Moore County Art Association, Dumas, TX.................1410
The Moore-Youse Home Museum, Muncie, IN.................492
Moosehead Marine Museum, Greenville, ME.................611
Moravian Historical Society, Nazareth, PA.................1273
Morehead Planetarium and Science Center, Chapel Hill, NC.................1093
Moriarty Historical Museum, Moriarty, NM.................943
The Morikami Museum and Japanese Gardens, Delray Beach, FL.................305
Mormon Station State Historic Park, Genoa, NV.................877
Mormon Visitors Center, Independence, MO.................818
Morris Arboretum of the University of Pennsylvania, Philadelphia, PA.................1283
Morris County Historical Society (Acorn Hall House Museum), Morristown, NJ...914
Morris Museum of Art, Augusta, GA.........365
Morrison's Heritage Museum, Morrison, IL.................446
The Morton Arboretum, Lisle, IL.................443
Morton Grove Historical Museum/Haupt-Yehl House, Morton Grove, IL.................446
Morton House Museum, Benton Harbor, MI.................728
Morven Museum & Garden, Princeton, NJ.................922

Morven Park, Leesburg, VA.................1512
Moss Mansion Historic House Museum, Billings, MT.................841
Mote Marine Laboratory/Aquarium, Sarasota, FL.................345
Motion Unlimited Museum & Classic Car Lot, Rapid City, SD.................1355
Motorcycle Hall of Fame Museum, Pickerington, OH.................1182
Motown Historical Museum, Detroit, MI....737
Motts Military Museum, Groveport, OH....1167
Mount Clare Museum House, Baltimore, MD.................635
Mount Desert Island Historical Society, Mount Desert, ME.................615
Mount Dora Center for the Arts, Mount Dora, FL.................327
Mount Holyoke College Art Museum, South Hadley, MA.................709
Mt. Horeb Area Museum, Mount Horeb, WI.................1614
Mount Pleasant Historical Society, Mount Pleasant, OH.................1177
Mount Prospect Historical Society Museums, Mount Prospect, IL.................446
Mt. Rainier National Park, Ashford, WA...1547
Mount Rushmore National Memorial, Keystone, SD.................1350
Mount Washington Museum and The Weather Discovery Center, North Conway, NH.................893
Mount Wilson Observatory & Museum, Atlanta, GA.................362
Mountain Skies Astronomical Society & Science Center, Lake Arrowhead, CA.....107
The Movie Museum, Owosso, MI.................759
The Muchnic Gallery, Atchison, KS.........533
Mulvane Art Museum, Topeka, KS.........559
Munson-Williams-Proctor Arts Institute Museum of Art, Utica, NY.................1079
Murray-Lindsay Mansion, Lindsay, OK.....1204
Murrell Home, Park Hill, OK.................1211
Muscatine Art Center, Muscatine, IA.........524
Museo de Arte de Ponce (The Luis A. Ferre Foundation, Inc.), Ponce, PR.....1642
Museo de las Americas, Denver, CO.........213
Museo Fuerte Conde de Mirasol de Vieques, Vieques, PR.................1644
Museo ItaloAmericano, San Francisco, CA.................167
The Museum, Greenwood, SC.................1334
Museum & Archives of Georgia Education, Milledgeville, GA.................380
Museum at Southwestern Michigan College, Dowagiac, MI.................738
The Museum at Warm Springs, Warm Springs, OR.................1238
The Museum for African Art, Long Island City, NY.................1011
The Museum of African American Art, Los Angeles, CA.................119
Museum of Afro-American History, Boston, MA.................667
Museum of Alaska Transportation & Industry, Inc., Wasilla, AK.................29
Museum of American Finance, New York, NY.................1031
Museum of American Glass at Wheaton Village, Millville, NJ.................911
The Museum of American Illustration at the Society of Illustrators, New York, NY.................1031
Museum of American Presidents, Strasburg, VA.................1539
Museum of Ancient Artifacts, Las Vegas, NV.................879
Museum of Anthropology, University of Denver, Denver, CO.................213
Museum of Anthropology, University of Missouri, Columbia, MO.................813
Museum of Art and Archaeology, University of Missouri - Columbia, Columbia, MO.................813

Photographs—Continued

Museum of Art and History at the McPherson Center, Santa Cruz, CA 182

Museum of Art at Brigham Young University, Provo, UT 1469

Museum of Art/Fort Lauderdale, Fort Lauderdale, FL................................307

Museum of Art of Puerto Rico, Santurce, PR...1643

Museum of Art, Rhode Island School of Design, Providence, RI....................1317

Museum of Astrogeology, Meteor Crater, Winslow, AZ.......................................53

Museum of Automobile Art and Design, Syracuse, NY.......................................1076

Museum of Aviation at Robins Air Force Base, GA, Warner Robins, GA 390

Museum of Ceramics, East Liverpool, OH..1163

Museum of Chicot County Arkansas, Lake Village, AR..................................61

Museum of Chinese in the Americas, New York, NY.......................................1032

Museum of Colorado Prisons, Canon City, CO...205

Museum of Contemporary Art, Chicago, IL...424

Museum of Contemporary Art, Denver, CO...213

Museum of Contemporary Art Cleveland, Cleveland, OH 1155

The Museum of Contemporary Art, Los Angeles, Los Angeles, CA 119

Museum of Contemporary Art (MoCA), North Miami, FL.............................329

The Museum of Contemporary Art of Georgia (MOCA GA), Atlanta, GA.........362

Museum of Contemporary Art of Puerto Rico, Santurce, PR 1644

Museum of Contemporary Art San Diego, La Jolla, CA...............................106

Museum of Contemporary Art San Diego - Downtown, San Diego, CA...................157

Museum of Contemporary Photography, Columbia College Chicago, Chicago, IL...424

Museum of Contemporary Religious Art (MOCRA)-St. Louis University, Saint Louis, MO.......................................835

Museum of disAbility History, Williamsville, NY...................................1086

Museum of Discovery: Arkansas Museum of Science and History, Little Rock, AR...62

The Museum of East Texas, Lufkin, TX....1436

Museum of Fife and Drum, Ivoryton, CT....246

Museum of Fine Arts, Boston, MA 667

Museum of Fine Arts, Santa Fe, NM 948

The Museum of Fine Arts, Houston, Houston, TX......................................1428

Museum of Fine Arts of St. Petersburg, Florida, Saint Petersburg, FL...................341

The Museum of Flight, Seattle, WA...........1567

Museum of Flying, Santa Monica, CA 183

Museum of Funeral Customs, Springfield, IL...459

Museum of Great Christian Preachers & Ministries, Orange Park, FL...............331

Museum of History & Art, Ontario, Ontario, CA.......................................136

Museum of History & Industry (MOHAI), Seattle, WA.........................1567

Museum of Holography/Chicago, Chicago, IL.....................................425

Museum of Indian Arts & Culture/Laboratory of Anthropology, Santa Fe, NM......................................948

Museum of Lighthouse History, Wells, ME...625

The Museum of Man in the Sea, Inc., Panama City Beach, FL 335

The Museum of Modern Art, New York, NY...1033

Museum of Natural History, Marshall, MN...780

Museum of Nebraska Art, Kearney, NE.......864

Museum of New Mexico, Santa Fe, NM 949

Museum of North Carolina Minerals, Spruce Pine, NC................................1120

Museum of North Idaho, Coeur d'Alene, ID 405

Museum of Northern Arizona, Flagstaff, AZ...33

Museum of Northwest Art, La Conner, WA...1557

The Museum of Outdoor Arts, Englewood, CO...................................214

Museum of Photographic Arts, San Diego, CA.......................................158

The Museum of Printing History, Houston, TX......................................1428

Museum of Religious Arts, Logan, IA 522

Museum of Rural Life, Denton, MD............642

Museum of San Diego History and Research Library, San Diego, CA 158

Museum of Science and Industry, Chicago, IL.....................................425

Museum of South Texas History, Edinburg, TX......................................1410

Museum of Southern History, Jacksonville, FL...................................315

The Museum of Southern History, Sugarland, TX......................................1454

Museum of Southwestern Biology, Albuquerque, NM................................934

Museum of the Albemarle, Elizabeth City, NC.......................................1099

The Museum of the Alphabet, Waxhaw, NC...1121

Museum of the Arkansas Grand Prairie, Stuttgart, AR......................................69

Museum of the Bedford Historical Society, Bedford, NY........................961

Museum of the Cherokee Indian, Cherokee, NC...................................1096

Museum of the Cherokee Strip, Enid, OK.1200

Museum of the City of Lake Worth, Lake Worth, FL.......................................320

Museum of the City of New York, New York, NY.......................................1033

The Museum of the Confederacy, Richmond, VA 1531

Museum of the Gulf Coast, Port Arthur, TX...1444

Museum of the Hudson Highlands, Cornwall-on-Hudson, NY 982

Museum of the Islands, Pine Island Center, FL.......................................337

Museum of the Jimmy Carter Library, Atlanta, GA......................................362

Museum of the Middle Appalachians, Saltville, VA......................................1536

Museum of the Mountain Man, Pinedale, WY...1637

Museum of the Moving Image, Astoria, NY...958

Museum of the National Center of Afro-American Artists, Roxbury, MA 706

Museum of the Northern Great Plains, Fort Benton, MT.................................846

Museum of the Occidental, Buffalo, WY.1629

Museum of the Plains Indian, Browning, MT...843

Museum of the Rockies, Bozeman, MT.......842

Museum of the Southern Jewish Experience, Jackson, MS.........................803

Museum of the Southwest, Midland, TX.....1439

Museum of the Waxhaws & Andrew Jackson Memorial, Waxhaw, NC...........1122

Museum of the Weston Historical Society, Inc., Weston, MA.........................718

Museum of Tolerance, Los Angeles, CA 120

Museum of Transportation, Saint Louis, MO...835

Museum of Vertebrate Zoology, Berkeley, CA...76

Museum of Weapons and Early American History, Saint Augustine, FL.................339

Museum of West Louisiana, Leesville, LA...591

Museum of Women's History, Billings, MT...841

Museum of Woodcarving, Shell Lake, WI.1621

Museum of Work & Culture, Woonsocket, RI...................................1320

Museum of World Cultures/University of North Carolina at Wilmington, Wilmington, NC................................1123

Museum of Yachting, Newport, RI............1314

Museum of Yarmouth History, Yarmouth, ME...626

Museum of York County, Rock Hill, SC ...1340

Museum on Main, Pleasanton, CA..............142

Museum on Main: A History Museum for West Georgia, LaGrange, GA................375

Museums of Los Gatos, Los Gatos, CA 123

The Museums of Oglebay Institute - Mansion Museum & Glass Museum, Wheeling, WV...................................1588

Muskegon County Museum, Muskegon, MI...757

Muskegon Museum of Art, Muskegon, MI...758

Muskogee War Memorial Park & Military Museum, Muskogee, OK.........1205

Musselshell Valley Historical Museum, Roundup, MT....................................853

Mutter Museum, College of Physicians of Philadelphia, Philadelphia, PA..........1283

Mystic Arts Center, Mystic, CT................250

Mystic Seaport - The Museum of America and the Sea, Mystic, CT 251

NIU Art Museum, DeKalb, IL..................429

Nanticoke Indian Museum, Millsboro, DE...271

Nantucket Historical Association, Nantucket, MA...................................696

Nantucket Life-Saving Museum, Nantucket, MA...................................696

Napa Valley Museum, Yountville, CA 200

Naper Settlement, Naperville, IL..................447

Naples Museum of Art and the Philharmonic Center for the Arts Galleries, Naples, FL..........................328

Narcissa Prentiss House, Prattsburgh, NY .1055

Narragansett Historical Society, Templeton, MA...................................714

NASA Kennedy Space Center, Merritt Island, FL.......................................323

Nasher Museum of Art at Duke University, Durham, NC........................1099

Nassau County, Division of Museum Services, Department of Recreation, Parks & Museums, East Meadow, NY....987

Nassau County Museum of Art, Roslyn Harbor, NY......................................1062

Nathan Denison Advocates, Forty Fort, PA...1254

National Academy of Sciences, Washington, DC...................................283

The National African-American Archives and Museum, Mobile, AL 15

National Afro-American Museum & Cultural Center, Wilberforce, OH 1191

National Air and Space Museum, Washington, DC...................................283

National Archives and Records Administration, Washington, DC.............284

National Archives and Records Administration - Mid-Atlantic Region, Philadelphia, PA 1284

National Art Museum of Sport, Inc., Indianapolis, IN................................485

National Baseball Hall of Fame and Museum, Inc., Cooperstown, NY 981

National Bighorn Sheep Interpretive Center, Dubois, WY 1632

National Bird Dog Museum, Grand Junction, TN 1366

The National Border Patrol Museum and Memorial Library, El Paso, TX 1412

National Building Museum, Washington, DC 284

National Canal Museum, Hugh Moore Historical Park and Museums, Easton, PA 1250

National Capital Parks-East, Washington, DC 284

National Ceramic Museum and Heritage Center, Roseville, OH 1184

National Civil Rights Museum, Memphis, TN 1375

The National Civil War Museum, Harrisburg, PA 1258

National Civil War Naval Museum at Port Columbus, Columbus, GA 369

National Corvette Museum, Bowling Green, KY 566

National Cowboy & Western Heritage Museum, Oklahoma City, OK 1208

National Cowgirl Museum and Hall of Fame, Fort Worth, TX 1418

National Cryptologic Museum, Fort Meade, MD 643

National First Ladies' Library, Canton, OH 1145

National Football Museum, Inc., Canton, OH 1145

National Fresh Water Fishing Hall of Fame, Hayward, WI 1600

National Gallery of Art, Washington, DC 285

National Geographic Museum at Explorers Hall, Washington, DC 285

The National Great Blacks in Wax Museum, Inc., Baltimore, MD 635

National Heritage Museum, Lexington, MA 690

National Hispanic Cultural Center, Art Museum, Albuquerque, NM 935

National Historic Oregon Trail Interpretive Center, Baker City, OR 1219

National Infantry Museum, Fort Benning, GA 372

National Italian American Sports Hall of Fame, Chicago, IL 425

National Medal of Honor Museum of Military History, Chattanooga, TN 1362

National Mississippi River Museum & Aquarium, Dubuque, IA 516

National Motorcycle Museum, Anamosa, IA 505

National Museum of African Art, Smithsonian Institution, Washington, DC 285

National Museum of American Jewish Military History, Washington, DC 286

The National Museum of Catholic Art & History, New York, NY 1034

National Museum of Dance & Hall of Fame, Saratoga Springs, NY 1065

National Museum of Health and Medicine, Washington, DC 286

National Museum of Industrial History, Bethlehem, PA 1243

National Museum of Naval Aviation, Pensacola, FL 336

National Museum of Patriotism, Atlanta, GA 362

National Museum of Polo and Hall of Fame, Inc., Lake Worth, FL 320

National Museum of Racing and Hall of Fame, Saratoga Springs, NY 1065

National Museum of Roller Skating, Lincoln, NE 866

National Museum of the American Indian, Washington, DC 286

National Museum of the American Indian, Smithsonian Institution, New York, NY 1034

National Museum of the Morgan Horse, Shelburne, VT 1487

National Museum of the United States Air Force, Wright-Patterson Air Force Base, OH 1193

National Museum of Wildlife Art, Jackson, WY 1634

National Museum of Women in the Arts, Washington, DC 287

National Ornamental Metal Museum, Memphis, TN 1375

National Packard Museum, Warren, OH 1189

National Park Service, Washington, DC......287

National Park Service Museum Resource Center, Landover, MD 648

National Portrait Gallery, Washington, DC 287

National Postal Museum, Smithsonian Institution, Washington, DC 287

National Railroad Museum, Green Bay, WI 1599

National Railroad Museum and Hall of Fame, Inc., Hamlet, NC 1105

National Scouting Museum, Irving, TX 1430

National Shaving And Barbershop Museum, Meriden, CT 249

National Soaring Museum, Elmira, NY 988

The National Soccer Hall of Fame, Oneonta, NY 1046

National Sprint Car Hall of Fame & Museum, Knoxville, IA 521

National Steeplechase Museum, Camden, SC 1323

National Steinbeck Center, Salinas, CA 154

National Tropical Botanical Garden, Kalaheo, HI 399

National Underground Railroad Freedom Center, Cincinnati, OH 1150

National Vietnam Veterans Art Museum, Chicago, IL 425

National Warplane Museum, Horseheads, NY 999

National Women's Hall of Fame, Seneca Falls, NY 1068

National World War I Museum at Liberty Memorial, Kansas City, MO 822

The National World War II Museum, New Orleans, LA 597

National Wrestling Hall of Fame, Stillwater, OK 1214

Native American Exhibit, National Kateri Shrine, Fonda, NY 991

Native American Heritage Museum at Highland Mission State Historic Site, Highland, KS 544

Native American Resource Center, Pembroke, NC 1114

Natural Center for the American Revolution, Wayne, PA 1306

Natural History Museum of Los Angeles County, Los Angeles, CA 120

Naugatuck Historical Society, Naugatuck, CT 251

Navajo Nation Museum, Window Rock, AZ 53

Naval War College Museum, Newport, RI 1314

Navarro County Historical Society, Pioneer Village, Corsicana, TX 1402

Navy UDT-SEAL Museum, Fort Pierce, FL 309

NCAA Hall of Champions, Indianapolis, IN 486

Nebraska Conference United Methodist Historical Center, Lincoln, NE 866

Nebraska State Capitol, Lincoln, NE.............866

Neenah Historical Society, Hiram Smith, Neenah's Heritage Park, Octagon House & Ward House, Neenah, WI.......1614

Negro Leagues Baseball Museum, Kansas City, MO 822

Neill-Cochran Museum House, Austin, TX 1391

Neill Museum, Fort Davis, TX 1414

The Nelson-Atkins Museum of Art, Kansas City, MO 822

Nemours Mansion and Gardens, Wilmington, DE 274

Neuberger Museum of Art, Purchase College, State University of New York, Purchase, NY 1056

Nevada County Depot Museum, Prescott, AR 67

Nevada County Historical Society, Inc., Nevada City, CA 130

Nevada Historical Society, Reno, NV 881

Nevada Museum of Art, Reno, NV 881

Nevada Northern Railway Museum, Ely, NV 876

Nevada State Fire Museum & Comstock Firemen's Museum, Virginia City, NV 882

Nevada State Museum, Carson City, NV 876

Nevada State Museum, Las Vegas, Las Vegas, NV 880

Nevada State Railroad Museum, Carson City, NV 876

Neversink Valley Area Museum, Cuddebackville, NY 984

New Bedford Whaling Museum, New Bedford, MA 696

The New Berlin Historical Society, New Berlin, WI 1614

New Braunfels Museum of Art & Music, New Braunfels, TX 1440

New Canaan Historical Society, New Canaan, CT 252

New Canaan Nature Center, New Canaan, CT 252

New Castle Historical Society, New Castle, DE 272

New Castle Historical Society - Horace Greeley House, Chappaqua, NY 977

New England College Gallery, Henniker, NH 889

New England Maple Museum, Pittsford, VT 1484

New England Pirate Museum, Salem, MA 706

New England Ski Museum, Franconia, NH 888

New Hampshire Antiquarian Society, Hopkinton, NH 889

New Hampshire Farm Museum, Inc., Milton, NH 892

New Hampshire Historical Society, Concord, NH 885

New Hampshire Institute of Art, Manchester, NH 892

New Harmony Gallery of Contemporary Art, New Harmony, IN 494

New Harmony State Historic Site/Historic New Harmony, New Harmony, IN 494

New Hartford Historical Society, Pine Meadow, CT 258

New Haven Colony Historical Society, New Haven, CT 253

New Jersey Botanical Garden at Skylands (NJBG), Ringwood, NJ 923

The New Jersey Historical Society, Newark, NJ 916

The New Jersey Museum of Agriculture, North Brunswick, NJ 917

New Jersey Naval Museum, Hackensack, NJ 905

New Jersey State Museum, Trenton, NJ 927

New Jersey State Police Museum, West Trenton, NJ 930

New London County Historical Society, New London, CT 255

New London Historical Society, New London, NH 892

Photographs—Continued

New London Public Museum, New London, WI 1615

New Market Battlefield State Historical Park, New Market, VA 1519

The New Milford Historical Society, New Milford, CT 256

The New Museum of Contemporary Art, New York, NY 1035

New Orleans Fire Dept. Museum & Educational Center, New Orleans, LA 597

New Orleans Museum of Art, New Orleans, LA 597

New Sweden Historical Society, New Sweden, ME 616

New Visions Gallery, Inc., Marshfield, WI 1608

New Windsor Cantonment State Historic Site and National Purple Heart Hall of Honor, Vails Gate, NY 1080

The New York Botanical Garden, Bronx, NY 966

New York City Fire Museum, New York, NY 1035

New York City Police Museum, New York, NY 1035

The New York Historical Society, New York, NY 1035

New York Museum of Transportation, West Henrietta, NY 1084

The New York Public Library for the Performing Arts, New York, NY 1036

New York State Bureau of Historic Sites, Waterford, NY 1082

New York State Historical Association/Fenimore Art Museum, Cooperstown, NY 981

New York State Military Museum and Veterans Research Center, Saratoga Springs, NY 1065

New York State Office of Parks, Recreation & Historic Preservation, Albany, NY 955

Newark Valley Depot Museum, Newark Valley, NY 1042

Newaygo County Museum, Newaygo, MI ...758

Newcomb Art Gallery, New Orleans, LA 598

Newell Museum, Newell, SD 1352

Newport Art Museum, Newport, RI 1314

Newport Historical Society & The Museum of Newport History, Newport, RI 1315

Newport Restoration Foundation, Newport, RI 1315

Newport State Park, Ellison Bay, WI 1597

Newseum, Washington, DC 288

The Newsome House Museum & Cultural Center, Newport News, VA 1520

The Newton History Museum at The Jackson Homestead, Newton, MA 698

Newtown Historic Association, Newtown, PA 1274

Newtown History Center, Stephens City, VA 1538

Nez Perce County Museum, Lewiston, ID ...407

Nez Perce National Historical Park, Spalding, ID 409

The Niagara County Historical Center and Niagara County Genealogical Society, Lockport, NY 1010

Niagara Gorge Discovery Center, Niagara Falls, NY 1042

Nici Self Museum, Centennial, WY 1630

Nicolaysen Art Museum and Discovery Center, Casper, WY 1629

Nicollet County Historical Society, Saint Peter, MN 793

Niles Depot Museum, Fremont, CA 96

Niles Hotel and Saloon, Alturas, CA 70

Nita Stewart Haley Memorial Library & J. Evetts Haley History Center, Midland, TX 1439

Noah Webster House/West Hartford Historical Society, West Hartford, CT 265

Noank Historical Society, Inc., Noank, CT 256

The Noble Maritime Collection, Staten Island, NY 1073

Nobleboro Historical Society, Nobleboro, ME 616

Nobles County Historical Society, Worthington, MN 797

Nohwike Bagowa, The White Mountain Apache Cultural Center and Museum, Fort Apache, AZ 34

Nora Eccles Harrison Museum of Art, Logan, UT 1466

Nordic Heritage Museum, Seattle, WA 1567

Norfolk Historical Museum, Norfolk, CT 257

Norfolk Historical Society, Norfolk, VA 1522

Norfolk History Museum, Norfolk, VA 1523

The Norman Cleveland County Historical Museum, Norman, OK 1206

Norman #1 Oil Well Museum, Neodesha, KS 553

Norman R. Eppink Art Gallery, Emporia State University, Emporia, KS 539

Norman Rockwell Museum, Stockbridge, MA 712

North Alabama Railroad Museum, Huntsville, AL 12

North Brevard Historical Museum, Titusville, FL 352

North Carolina Aquarium at Fort Fisher, Kure Beach, NC 1109

North Carolina Museum of Forestry, Whiteville, NC 1122

North Carolina Office of Archives and History, Raleigh, NC 1116

North Carolina State University Gallery of Art & Design, Raleigh, NC 1116

North Carolina Transportation Museum, Spencer, NC 1120

North Carolina Zoological Park, Asheboro, NC 1088

North Cascades National Park Service Complex, Marblemount, WA 1559

North Dakota Fishing Hall of Fame and Museum, Garrison, ND 1131

North Dakota Museum of Art, Grand Forks, ND 1132

North Dakota State Railroad Museum, Mandan, ND 1134

North Florida Community College Art Gallery, Madison, FL 322

North Haven Historical Society, North Haven, CT 257

North Plainfield Exempt Firemen's Association, North Plainfield, NJ 917

North Star Museum of Boy Scouting and Girl Scouting, North Saint Paul, MN 785

North Tonawanda History Museum, North Tonawanda, NY 1043

Northampton County Historical and Genealogical Society, Easton, PA 1250

Northborough Historical Society, Inc., Northborough, MA 700

Northeast Document Conservation Center, Andover, MA 660

Northeast Georgia History Center at Brenau University, Gainesville, GA 373

Northeast Texas Rural Heritage Museum, Pittsburg, TX 1443

Northeastern Nevada Museum, Elko, NV 876

Northern Kentucky University Art Galleries, Highland Heights, KY 571

Northern Pacific Railway Museum, Toppenish, WA 1575

Northfield Historical Society Museum, Northfield, MN 785

Northport Historical Society Museum, Northport, NY 1044

The Northumberland County Historical Society, Sunbury, PA 1302

Northwest Art Center, Minot, ND 1134

Northwest Museum of Arts & Culture (Eastern Washington State Historical Society), Spokane, WA 1571

Northwest Railway Museum, Snoqualmie, WA 1570

Northwestern Oklahoma State University Museum, Alva, OK 1195

Norton Museum of Art, West Palm Beach, FL 353

Norton Simon Museum, Pasadena, CA 140

Norwalk Museum, South Norwalk, CT 260

Norwich Historical Society, Norwich, VT .1484

Norwood Historical Association and Museum, Norwood, NY 1044

Novato History Museum, Novato, CA 132

Noyes House Museum, Morrisville, VT 1483

The Noyes Museum of Art, Oceanville, NJ 918

Nutter D. Marvel Museum, Georgetown, DE 271

The Nylander Museum of Natural History, Caribou, ME 609

O. Henry Museum, Austin, TX 1391

O. Winston Link Museum, Roanoke, VA ...1535

Oak Hill and The Martha Berry Museum, Rome, GA 382

The Oak Park Conservatory, Oak Park, IL 449

Oakdale Cowboy Museum, Oakdale, CA 132

Oakdale Museum, Oakdale, CA 132

Oakfield Railroad Museum, Oakfield, ME ...616

Oakland County Pioneer and Historical Society, Pontiac, MI 760

Oakland Museum of California, Oakland, CA 134

Oaklands Historic House Museum, Murfreesboro, TN 1376

Oakley Park, UDC Shrine, Edgefield, SC ..1332

The Oaks House Museum, Jackson, MS 804

Oatlands, Leesburg, VA 1512

Oberlin Heritage Center, Oberlin, OH 1180

Ocean City Historical Museum, Inc., Ocean City, NJ 918

Ocean City Life-Saving Station Museum, Ocean City, MD 650

Ocean County Historical Museum, Toms River, NJ 926

The Octagon, Washington, DC 288

Octave Chanute Aerospace Museum, Rantoul, IL 453

Odyssey Maritime Discovery Center, Seattle, WA 1567

O'Fallon Historical Museum, Baker, MT 840

Office of Cultural Affairs & Museum Programs at Salisbury University, Salisbury, MD 652

The Ogden Museum of Southern Art, University of New Orleans, New Orleans, LA 598

Ogden Union Station Museums, Ogden, UT 1468

Oglethorpe University Museum of Art, Atlanta, GA 362

Ogunquit Museum of American Art, Ogunquit, ME 617

Ohef Sholom Temple Archives, Norfolk, VA 1523

Ohio Historical Society, Columbus, OH 1158

Ohio River Museum, Marietta, OH 1174

Ohr-O'Keefe Museum of Art, Biloxi, MS ...799

Ojai Valley Historical Society and Museum, Ojai, CA 135

Okefenokee Heritage Center, Waycross, GA 391

Oklahoma City Museum of Art, Oklahoma City, OK 1208

Oklahoma Firefighters Museum, Oklahoma City, OK 1209

Oklahoma Forest Heritage Center, Broken Bow, OK 1197

Oklahoma Railway Museum, Oklahoma City, OK 1210

Oklahoma Route 66 Museum, Clinton, OK 1198
Oklahoma Sports Museum, Guthrie, OK ...1202
Oklahoma Territorial Museum, Guthrie, OK 1202
Oktibbeha County Heritage Museum, Starkville, MS 808
Olana State Historic Site, Hudson, NY 1000
Olbrich Botanical Gardens, Madison, WI ..1605
Old Arsenal Powder Magazine Museum, Baton Rouge, LA 587
Old Brutus Historical Society, Inc., Weedsport, NY 1084
Old Castle Museum, Baldwin City, KS........533
Old Cathedral Museum, Saint Louis, MO....836
Old Conway Homestead Complex and Museum, Camden, ME 608
Old Court House Museum-Eva Whitaker Davis Memorial, Vicksburg, MS 809
Old Courthouse Museum, Santa Ana, CA....178
Old Davie School Historical Museum, Davie, FL 302
The Old Depot Railroad Museum, Dassel, MN 772
Old Dominion Railway Museum, Richmond, VA 1531
Old Economy Village, Ambridge, PA.........1240
Old Exchange & Provost Dungeon, Charleston, SC 1326
Old Falls Village, Menomonee Falls, WI..1609
Old Firehouse Museum, Greenville, MS.......800
Old Fort Bissell, Phillipsburg, KS 555
Old Fort Harrod State Park Mansion Museum, Harrodsburg, KY 570
Old Fort Meade Museum and Historic Research Association, Fort Meade, SD.1347
Old Fort Niagara, Youngstown, NY 1088
Old Greer County Museum & Hall of Fame, Mangum, OK...........1204
The Old Guard Museum, Fort Myer, VA...1505
Old Idaho Penitentiary, Boise, ID.................404
Old Independence Regional Museum, Batesville, AR...........54
The Old Jail Art Center, Albany, TX...........1385
Old Jail Museum, Albion, IN...........467
The Old Jail Museum, Crawfordsville, IN...473
The Old Jail Museum, Warrenton, VA 1543
Old Jefferson Town, Oskaloosa, KS 555
Old Lighthouse Museum, Michigan City, IN...........491
Old Lighthouse Museum, Stonington, CT....261
Old Log Jail and Chapel Museums, Greenfield, IN...........480
Old Manchester Museum, Manchester, CT...........248
Old Market House State Historic Site, Galena, IL...........436
Old Mill Museum, Cimarron, NM...........938
Old Mill Museum, El Molino Viejo - Old Mill Foundation, San Marino, CA...........175
Old Prison Museums, Deer Lodge, MT 845
Old St. Ferdinand's Shrine, Florissant, MO...........815
Old Salem Inc., Winston-Salem, NC...........1126
The Old Schwamb Mill, Arlington, MA 660
Old Sod Post Office, Grassy Butte, ND 1132
Old South Meeting House, Boston, MA 668
Old State House-The Bostonian Society, Boston, MA...........668
Old Stone Fort Museum Complex, Schoharie, NY...........1067
Old Stone House Museum, Windsor, NY ..1086
Old Town Hall Museum, Fifield, WI...........1597
Old Town Museum, Burlington, CO 204
Old Trail Museum, Choteau, MT 844
Old West Museum, Wimberley, TX...........1462
Old West Wax Museum, Thermopolis, WY...........1639
Old York Historical Society, York, ME.......626
Old York Road Historical Society, Jenkintown, PA...........1263

Olde Colonial Courthouse, Tales of Cape Cod, Inc., Barnstable, MA 661
Oldest House Museum Complex, Saint Augustine, FL...........339
Oldest Stone House Museum, Lakewood, OH...........1170
Oldham County History Center, La Grange, KY...........572
The Oliver Tucker Museum, Beverly, OH .1142
Olmstead Funeral & Historical Museum, Heber Springs, AR...........59
Olmsted County Historical Society, Rochester, MN...........788
Olympic Flight Museum, Olympia, WA 1560
Omniplex Science Museum, Oklahoma City, OK...........1210
103rd Ohio Volunteer Infantry Civil War Museum, Sheffield Lake, OH...........1185
Oneida Community Mansion House, Oneida, NY...........1046
Oneida County Historical Society, Utica, NY...........1080
Oneida Nation Museum, De Pere, WI........1594
Onondaga Historical Association Museum & Research Center, Syracuse, NY.........1077
Onslow County Museum, Richlands, NC...1117
Ontario County Historical Society, Canandaigua, NY...........975
Ontonagon County Historical Society Museum, Ontonagon, MI...........758
Opelousas Museum and Interpretive Center, Opelousas, LA 599
Orange County Museum of Art, Newport Beach, CA...........130
Orange County Regional History Center, Orlando, FL 331
Orangetown Historical Museum and Archives, Pearl River, NY 1051
Orcas Island Historical Museum, Orcas Island, WA...........1560
Orchard House, Concord, MA...........677
Orchard Park Historical Society, Orchard Park, NY...........1047
Oregon Air & Space Museum, Eugene, OR...........1224
Oregon Electric Railway Historical Society, Inc., Salem, OR...........1236
Oregon Historical Society, Portland, OR....1231
Oregon Military Museum, Clackamas, OR...........1221
Oregon Sports Hall of Fame & Museum, Inc., Portland, OR...........1232
Oregon Zoo, Portland, OR...........1232
Organ Pipe Cactus National Monument Museum, Ajo, AZ...........29
Oriental Institute Museum, University of Chicago, Chicago, IL...........426
Orland Historical Society, Orland, ME 617
Orlando Museum of Art, Orlando, FL.........332
Orleans County Historical Society & The Old Stone House Museum, Brownington, VT...........1477
Ormond Memorial Art Museum & Garden, Ormond Beach, FL...........333
Osage County Historical Society Museum, Pawhuska, OK...........1211
Osage County Historical Society Research Center, Lyndon, KS...........550
Osage Nation Tribal Museum, Pawhuska, OK...........1212
Osborn-Jackson House, East Hampton, NY...........986
Oshkosh Public Museum, Oshkosh, WI.....1616
Ossining Historical Society Museum, Ossining, NY...........1047
Osterville Historical Society, Inc., Osterville, MA...........701
Oswego Historical Museum, Inc., Oswego, KS...........555
Otis Chidester Scout Museum of Southern Arizona, Tucson, AZ...........50
Ottawa County Historical Museum, Port Clinton, OH...........1183

Ottawa Scouting Museum, Ottawa, IL.........449
Ouachita County Historical Society, Camden, AR...........55
Our House State Memorial, Gallipolis, OH...........1165
Overholser Mansion, Oklahoma City, OK .1210
Overland Trail Museum, Sterling, CO.........232
Owatonna Arts Center, Owatonna, MN........786
Owens Community College/Walter E. Terhune Gallery, Perrysburg, OH...........1182
Owensboro Museum of Fine Art, Inc., Owensboro, KY...........581
Owls Head Transportation Museum, Owls Head, ME...........617
Oxford Museum, Inc., Oxford, MD.............650
The Oyster and Maritime Museum of Chincoteague, Chincoteague, VA...........1501
Oyster Bay Historical Society, Oyster Bay, NY...........1049
Oz Museum, Wamego, KS...........560
The Ozark Folk Center, Mountain View, AR...........65
Ozark Heritage Arts Center & Museum, Leslie, AR...........61
Ozark National Scenic Riverways, Van Buren, MO...........839
Ozaukee County Pioneer Village, Saukville, WI...........1620

The P.T. Boat Museum & Library, Germantown, TN...........1365
Pablo Casals Museum, Old San Juan, PR..1641
Pacific Asia Museum, Pasadena, CA...........140
Pacific Aviation Museum - Pearl Harbor, Honolulu, HI...........397
Pacific Grove Art Center Associates, Inc., Pacific Grove, CA...........137
Pacific Grove Museum of Natural History, Pacific Grove, CA...........137
Pacific Northwest Truck Museum, Brooks, OR...........1220
Pacific Tsunami Museum, Hilo, HI 393
Pacific University Museum, Forest Grove, OR...........1224
Padre Island National Seashore, Corpus Christi, TX...........1402
Pajaro Valley Historical Association, Watsonville, CA...........196
Palace of the Governors/New Mexico History Museum, Santa Fe, NM...........949
PALCO, Scotia, CA...........186
Paleontological Research Institution, Ithaca, NY...........1004
Palm Beach Photographic Centre, Delray Beach, FL...........305
Palm Springs Art Museum, Palm Springs, CA...........139
Palmer/Gullickson Octagon Home, West Salem, WI...........1627
Palmer Museum of Art, The Pennsylvania State University, University Park, PA....1304
Palomar Observatory, Palomar Mountain, CA...........139
Palos Verdes Art Center, Rancho Palos Verdes, CA...........145
Panhandle-Plains Historical Museum, Canyon, TX...........1399
Paper Airplane Museum and the Tin Can Man of Maui, Kahului Central Maui, HI...........399
Paper Discovery Center, Appleton, WI 1590
The Pardee Home Museum, Oakland, CA...134
Paris Gibson Square Museum of Art, Great Falls, MT...........848
Paris-Henry County Heritage Center, Paris, TN...........1382
Parishville Museum, Parishville, NY.........1050
Park City Historical Society & Museum, Park City, UT...........1468
The Park-McCullough House, North Bennington, VT...........1483
Parker-O'Malley Air Museum, Ghent, NY...........994

Photographs—Continued

Parkersburg Art Center, Parkersburg, WV .1586
Parkland College Art Gallery,
    Champaign, IL.................................417
Parris Island Museum, Parris Island, SC....1338
The Parrish Art Museum, Southampton,
    NY...1070
The Parry Mansion Museum, New Hope,
    PA...1273
Parsons Historical Commission Museum,
    Parsons, KS..................................555
Parsonsfield-Porter Historical Society,
    Porter, ME...................................618
The Parthenon, Nashville, TN.................1379
Pasadena Museum of California Art,
    Pasadena, CA.................................140
Pasadena Museum of History, Pasadena,
    CA..140
Pascack Historical Society, Park Ridge,
    NJ..920
Passaic County Community College,
    Paterson, NJ.................................920
Passaic County Historical Society &
    Lambert Castle Museum, Paterson, NJ ...920
Patee House Museum, Saint Joseph, MO 831
The Paterson Museum, Paterson, NJ...........920
The Patricia & Phillip Frost Art Museum,
    Miami, FL....................................325
The Patrick & Beatrice Haggerty
    Museum of Art, Milwaukee, WI............1613
Patten Lumbermen's Museum, Inc.,
    Patten, ME...................................618
Patterson Homestead, Dayton, OH.............1161
Patterson Inn Museum/Corning - Painted
    Post Historical Society, Corning, NY......982
Paul and Lulu Hilliard University Art
    Museum, University of Louisiana at
    Lafayette, Lafayette, LA....................590
Paul Bunyan Logging Camp Museum,
    Eau Claire, WI..............................1596
Paul Revere House/Paul Revere
    Memorial Association, Boston, MA........668
Paul Robeson Art Gallery, Newark, NJ.......917
Paul W. Bryant Museum, Tuscaloosa, AL......19
Pawnee Bill Ranch and Museum,
    Pawnee, OK..................................1212
Pawnee City Historical Society &
    Museum, Pawnee City, NE.....................871
Pawnee Indian Village State Historic Site,
    Republic, KS.................................556
Peabody Museum of Archaeology &
    Ethnology, Cambridge, MA....................674
The Peace Museum, Chicago, IL................426
Pearce Collections Museum, Corsicana,
    TX...1402
Pearl S. Buck Birthplace Foundation,
    Hillsboro, WV...............................1582
The Pearl S. Buck House, Perkasie, PA.....1275
Pearson Air Museum, Vancouver, WA 1576
The Pearson Museum, Springfield, IL.........460
The Peary-MacMillan Arctic Museum,
    Brunswick, ME...............................608
Pecos National Historical Park, Pecos,
    NM...944
Pedaling History Bicycle Museum,
    Orchard Park, NY............................1047
The Peekskill Museum, Peekskill, NY.......1051
Peel Mansion Museum & Historic
    Gardens, Bentonville, AR.....................55
Pejepscot Historical Society, Brunswick,
    ME...608
Pence Gallery, Davis, CA......................90
Pendleton District Historical, Recreational
    and Tourism Commission, Pendleton,
    SC..1339
Pendleton Historic Foundation,
    Pendleton, SC...............................1339
Pennsylvania Anthracite Heritage
    Museum, Scranton, PA........................1299
Pennsylvania German Cultural Heritage
    Center at Kutztown University,
    Kutztown, PA................................1265

Pennsylvania Lumber Museum, Galeton,
    PA..1254
Pennsylvania Trolley Museum,
    Washington, PA..............................1305
Penobscot Marine Museum, Searsport,
    ME...622
Pensacola Historical Society Museum,
    Pensacola, FL................................336
The Peoria Art Guild, Peoria, IL..............451
Perkins History Museum, Perkins School
    for the Blind, Watertown, MA................716
Perry's Victory & International Peace
    Memorial, Put-in-Bay, OH....................1183
Petaluma Adobe State Historic Park,
    Petaluma, CA.................................142
Peter Conser House, Heavener, OK...........1202
Peter J. McGovern Little League
    Museum, South Williamsport, PA..........1301
Peter Rice Homestead, Home of
    Marlborough Historical Society, Inc.,
    Marlboro, MA................................693
Peterborough Historical Society,
    Peterborough, NH............................893
Petersburg Area Art League, Petersburg,
    VA..1525
Petersburg National Battlefield,
    Petersburg, VA..............................1525
Petersen Automotive Museum, Los
    Angeles, CA..................................121
Petersham Historical Society, Inc.,
    Petersham, MA...............................702
Peterson Air & Space Museum, Peterson
    Air Force Base, CO..........................229
The Petroleum Museum, Midland, TX.......1439
Pettigrew Home and Museum, Sioux
    Falls, SD...................................1356
Pettis County Historical Society, Sedalia,
    MO..838
Pewabic Pottery, Detroit, MI................737
The Philadelphia Art Alliance,
    Philadelphia, PA............................1285
Philadelphia Mummers Museum,
    Philadelphia, PA............................1285
Philadelphia Museum of Art,
    Philadelphia, PA............................1285
Philipse Manor Hall State Historic Site,
    Yonkers, NY.................................1087
The Phillips Collection, Washington, DC....289
Phillips County Museum, Helena, AR.........59
Phillips County Museum, Holyoke, CO......222
Phillips Historical Society, Phillips, ME.....618
The Phillips Museum of Art, Franklin &
    Marshall College, Lancaster, PA...........1267
Philmont Museums, Cimarron, NM............938
Phippen Museum, Prescott, AZ................42
Phoebe Apperson Hearst Museum of
    Anthropology, Berkeley, CA...................77
Phoenix Museum of History, Phoenix,
    AZ...41
Phoenix Police Museum, Phoenix, AZ..........41
Photographic Archives, Lexington, KY.......574
Photographic Archives, University of
    Louisville Libraries, Louisville, KY.......578
Photographic Investments Gallery,
    Atlanta, GA..................................363
Photographic Resource Center, Boston,
    MA..669
Piatt Castles, West Liberty, OH.............1190
The Picker Art Gallery, Hamilton, NY........997
The Pierce Manse/New Hampshire
    Political Library, Concord, NH.............885
The Pierpont Morgan Library, New York,
    NY..1037
Pierre Menard Home State Historic Site,
    Ellis Grove, IL.............................433
Pike County Historical Society, Milford,
    PA..1272
Pikes Peak Hill Climb Educational
    Museum, Colorado Springs, CO.............207
Pilgrim Hall Museum, Plymouth, MA 703
Pilgrim Monument and Provincetown
    Museum, Provincetown, MA.................704

Pima Air & Space Museum, Tucson, AZ........50
Pimeria Alta Historical Society, Nogales,
    AZ...37
Pinal County Historical Society and
    Museum, Florence, AZ.........................34
Pine Bluff/Jefferson County Historical
    Museum, Pine Bluff, AR.......................66
Pine Lodge (Ehrman Mansion), Tahoma,
    CA..190
Pinnacles National Monument, Paicines,
    CA..138
Pioneer Arizona Living History Village &
    Museum, Phoenix, AZ..........................41
Pioneer Corner Museum, New Holstein,
    WI...1615
Pioneer Heritage Center, Cavalier, ND.......1129
Pioneer Historical Museum of South
    Dakota, Hot Springs, SD....................1348
Pioneer-Krier Museum, Ashland, KS 532
The Pioneer Memorial Association of
    Fenton and Mundy Townships,
    Fenton, MI..................................741
Pioneer Museum, Wild Rose, WI.............1628
Pioneer Museum & The Big Stampede,
    Fairbanks, AK................................24
Pioneer Museum - Martin County
    Historical Society, Fairmont, MN...........775
Pioneer Museum of Alabama, Troy, AL........18
Pioneer Settlement for the Creative Arts,
    Barberville, FL..............................295
Pioneer Village & Virgil Grissom
    Memorial at Spring Mill State Park,
    Mitchell, IN................................491
Pioneer Woman Statue & Museum,
    Ponca City, OK.............................1212
Pioneers Park Nature Center, Lincoln, NE...867
Pioneers, Trail Drivers and Texas
    Rangers Memorial Museum, San
    Antonio, TX................................1449
Piper Aviation Museum Foundation, Lock
    Haven, PA..................................1269
Pipestone County Historical Museum,
    Pipestone, MN...............................786
Pittock Mansion, Portland, OR..............1232
Pittsburgh Center for the Arts, Pittsburgh,
    PA..1293
Pittsford Historical Society Museum,
    Pittsford, VT...............................1484
Placer County Museums, Auburn, CA...........72
Plains Art Museum, Fargo, ND...............1130
Plains Indians and Pioneers Museum,
    Woodward, OK...............................1217
Plainsman Museum, Aurora, NE...............856
Planetarium at the Reading Public
    Museum, Reading, PA........................1296
Plantation Agriculture Museum, Scott,
    AR...67
Plantation Historical Museum, Plantation,
    FL..337
Platt R. Spencer Memorial Archives and
    Special Collections Area, Geneva, OH..1166
Plattsburgh State Art Museum S.U.N.Y.,
    Plattsburgh, NY............................1053
Plaza de La Raza, Inc. & Boathouse
    Gallery, Los Angeles, CA...................121
Plumas County Museum, Quincy, CA..........144
Plumas-Eureka State Park, Blairsden, CA......78
Plymouth Antiquarian Society, Plymouth,
    MA..704
Plymouth Historical Society, Inc.,
    Plymouth, PA...............................1295
Pocahontas County Iowa Historical
    Society Museum, Laurens, IA................522
Point Reyes National Seashore, Point
    Reyes, CA...................................143
Polish American Museum, Port
    Washington, NY.............................1054
Polish Heritage Center, Ashton, NE..........856
Polish Museum of America, Chicago, IL....426
Polk County Heritage Gallery, Des
    Moines, IA..................................515

Polk County Historical Museum, Bartow, FL 295

The Polk County Historical Society, Cedartown, GA 368

Polk County Memorial Museum, Livingston, TX 1434

Polk Museum of Art, Lakeland, FL 321

Pomona College Museum of Art, Claremont, CA 85

Pope County Historical Society, Glenwood, MN 776

Pope John Paul II Cultural Center, Washington, DC 289

Port Angeles Fine Arts Center & Webster's Woods Art Park, Port Angeles, WA 1561

Port Gamble Historic Museum, Port Gamble, WA 1562

Port Huron Museum, Port Huron, MI 761

Port Orford Lifeboat Station, Port Orford, OR 1230

Portage County Historical Society, Ravenna, OH 1183

Portage County Historical Society, Stevens Point, WI 1623

The Portal of the Folded Wings Shrine to Aviation and Museum, North Hollywood, CA 131

Porter-Phelps-Huntington Foundation, Inc., Hadley, MA 685

Porterville Historical Museum, Porterville, CA 144

Portholes Into the Past, Medina, OH 1176

Portland Art Museum, Portland, OR 1232

Portland Harbor Museum, South Portland, ME 623

Portland Museum, Louisville, KY 578

Portland Museum of Art, Portland, ME 619

Portsmouth Athenaeum, Portsmouth, NH 894

Portsmouth Museum of Military History Inc., Portsmouth, VA 1526

Portsmouth Museums, Portsmouth, VA 1526

Postville Courthouse State Historic Site, Lincoln, IL 442

Potsdam Public Museum, Potsdam, NY 1054

Potter County Historical Society, Coudersport, PA 1248

Pound Ridge Society/Museum, Pound Ridge, NY 1055

Powell County Museum, Deer Lodge, MT 845

Powers Museum, Carthage, MO 812

Prairie Village, Madison, SD 1351

Praters Mill Foundation, Varnell, GA 390

Pratt Building - Cohasset Historical Society, Cohasset, MA 676

Pratt Manhattan Gallery, New York, NY 1037

Presbyterian Historical Society, Philadelphia, PA 1286

Presbyterian Historical Society (Montreat), Montreat, NC 1111

Preservation Resource Center, New Orleans, LA 598

The Preservation Society of Newport County/The Newport Mansions, Newport, RI 1315

The Presidential Museum and Leadership Library, Odessa, TX 1441

Presidential Pet Museum, Lothian, MD 649

President's Cottage Museum-The Greenbrier, White Sulphur Springs, WV 1588

Presque Isle County Historical Museum, Rogers City, MI 762

Price Tower Arts Center, Bartlesville, OK 1197

Prince William Forest Park Visitor Center, Triangle, VA 1541

Princeton University Art Museum, Princeton, NJ 922

The Print Center, Philadelphia, PA 1287

Pro Rodeo Hall of Fame & Museum of the American Cowboy, Colorado Springs, CO 207

Project Art-University of Iowa and Clinics, Iowa City, IA 520

Promont House Museum, Milford, OH 1176

Proprietary House, The Royal Governor's Mansion, Perth Amboy, NJ 921

Providence Canyon State Park, Lumpkin, GA 377

Provincetown Art Association and Museum, Provincetown, MA 704

The Public Library of Nashville and Davidson County, Nashville, TN 1380

Pueblo Grande Museum and Archaeological Park, Phoenix, AZ 42

Pueblo of Pojoaque, Poeh Museum, Santa Fe, NM 949

Pueblo Weisbrod Aircraft Museum, Pueblo, CO 230

Puget Sound Coast Artillery Museum at Fort Worden, Port Townsend, WA 1562

Pump House Regional Arts Center, La Crosse, WI 1603

Purdue University Galleries, West Lafayette, IN 503

Putnam Cottage, Greenwich, CT 243

Putnam County Historical Society & Foundry School Museum, Cold Spring, NY 979

Putnam County Historical Society Museum, Kalida, OH 1169

Putnam Museum of History & Natural Science, Davenport, IA 513

Putney Historical Society, Putney, VT 1485

Puukohola Heiau National Historic Site, Kamuela, HI 400

QCC Art Gallery, Bayside, NY 960

Queen Emma Summer Palace, Honolulu, HI 398

Queen Mary Museum, Long Beach, CA 111

Queens County Farm Museum, Floral Park, NY 989

Queens Historical Society, Flushing, NY 990

Queens Museum of Art, Queens, NY 1056

R.P. Strathearn Historical Park and Museum, Simi Valley, CA 187

RV/MH Heritage Foundation, Inc., Elkhart, IN 475

Rachel Carson Homestead, Springdale, PA 1301

Racine Art Museum (RAM), Racine, WI 1619

Radford University Art Museum, Radford, VA 1527

Rahr West Art Museum, Manitowoc, WI 1607

Railroad and Heritage Museum Inc., Temple, TX 1454

Railroad House Historical Association Museum, Sanford, NC 1119

Railroad Museum of Long Island, Riverhead, NY 1057

Railroad Museum of Minot, Minot, ND 1135

Railroad Museum of Pennsylvania, Strasburg, PA 1302

Railway Museum of San Angelo, San Angelo, TX 1447

Railways to Yesterday, Inc., Rockhill Furnace, PA 1297

Raleigh City Museum, Raleigh, NC 1117

Ralls Historical Museum, Ralls, TX 1445

Ralph Mark Gilbert Civil Rights Museum, Savannah, GA 386

Ralph Milliken Museum, Los Banos, CA 122

Ralph Waldo Emerson House, Concord, MA 677

Ralston Historical Association, John Ralston Museum, Mendham, NJ 911

Rancho La Patera - The Stow House G.V.H.S., Goleta, CA 100

Rancho Los Cerritos Historic Site, Long Beach, CA 111

Randolph County Historical Museum, Winchester, IN 503

Randolph Historical Society, Inc., Randolph, VT 1485

Randsburg Desert Museum, Randsburg, CA 146

Rankin Museum, Rankin, TX 1445

Ransom County Historical Society, Fort Ransom, ND 1131

Raton Museum, Raton, NM 945

Rattlesnake Museum (American International), Albuquerque, NM 935

Ravalli County Museum/Bitter Root Valley Historical Society, Hamilton, MT 848

Rawls Museum Arts, Courtland, VA 1502

The Ray Drew Gallery-New Mexico Highlands University, Las Vegas, NM 941

Raynham Hall Museum, Oyster Bay, NY 1049

The Reader's Digest Association, Inc., Pleasantville, NY 1053

Reading Historical Society Museum, Reading, OH 1184

Reading Railroad Heritage Museum, Reading, PA 1296

Readsboro Historical Society, Readsboro, VT 1486

Rebel State Historic Site & Louisiana Country Music Museum, Marthaville, LA 592

Red Earth Museum, Oklahoma City, OK 1210

Red Mill Museum Village, Clinton, NJ 901

Red River Historical Museum, Sherman, TX 1452

Red River Valley Museum, Vernon, TX 1457

Redington Museum, Waterville, ME 625

Redwood County Historical Society, Redwood Falls, MN 787

Redwood National and State Parks, Crescent City, CA 88

Reedville Fishermen's Museum, Reedville, VA 1527

Reese Bullen Gallery, Arcata, CA 72

Reeves-Reed Arboretum, Summit, NJ 925

Refugio County Museum, Refugio, TX 1445

The Regina A. Quick Center for the Arts, Saint Bonaventure, NY 1063

Reginald F. Lewis Museum of Maryland African American History and Culture, Baltimore, MD 636

Reitz Home Museum, Evansville, IN 476

Remick Country Doctor Museum and Farm, Tamworth, NH 896

Remington Firearms Museum and Country Store, Ilion, NY 1002

Renee and Chaim Gross Foundation, New York, NY 1037

Reno County Museum, Hutchinson, KS 545

Rensselaer County Historical Society, Troy, NY 1079

Renton Historical Society and Museum, Renton, WA 1564

Republic County Historical Society Museum, Belleville, KS 534

Reston Museum, Reston, VA 1527

Reuel B. Pritchett Museum, Bridgewater, VA 1497

Reverend Dan Foster House, Museum of the Weathersfield Historical Society, Weathersfield, VT 1489

Reynolda House Museum of American Art, Winston-Salem, NC 1126

Rhinelander Logging Museum, Rhinelander, WI 1620

Rhode Island Historical Society, Providence, RI 1318

Rialto Historical Society, Rialto, CA 148

Rice County Museum of History, Faribault, MN 775

Richard E. Peeler Art Center, Greencastle, IN 479

Photographs—Continued

Richard L. Nelson Gallery & The Fine Arts Collection, UC Davis, Davis, CA......90
Richard Petty Museum, Randleman, NC...1117
Richards DAR House Museum, Mobile, AL 15
Richardson-Bates House Museum, Oswego, NY 1048
Richardson Maritime Museum, Cambridge, MD......639
Richmond Art Museum, Richmond, IN......497
Richmond Museum of History, Richmond, CA......148
Riddick's Folly, Suffolk, VA 1539
Rifle Creek Museum, Rifle, CO......231
Riley House Museum of African American History & Culture, Tallahassee, FL......348
Rimrocker Historical Museum of West Montrose County, Naturita, CO......229
Rio Grande Valley Museum, Harlingen, TX......1423
Rio Vista Museum, Rio Vista, CA 148
Ripley County, Indiana, Historical Society Museum, Versailles, IN......502
Ripley's Believe It or Not!, Key West, FL......319
Ripley's Believe It or Not! Museum, Atlantic City, NJ......898
Ritz Theatre & LaVilla Museum, Jacksonville, FL......315
River Heritage Museum, Paducah, KY 582
River Legacy Living Science Center, Arlington, TX......1388
Riversdale House Mansion, Riverdale Park, MD......651
Riverside Art Museum, Riverside, CA......149
Roanoke Island Festival Park; Homeport of the "Elizabeth II", Manteo, NC......1110
Robbins Hunter Museum, Avery-Downer House, Granville, OH......1167
Robbins Museum of Archaeology, Middleborough, MA......694
Roberson Museum and Science Center, Binghamton, NY......962
Robert A. Bogan Fire Museum, Baton Rouge, LA......587
Robert C. Williams American Museum of Papermaking at Georgia Tech, Atlanta, GA......363
Robert Hull Fleming Museum, Burlington, VT......1478
Robert Louis Stevenson Silverado Museum, Saint Helena, CA......154
Robert R. McCormick Museum at Cantigny, Wheaton, IL......465
Robert S. Kerr Museum, Poteau, OK......1212
Robert S. Peabody Museum of Archaeology, Andover, MA......660
Robert Toombs House, Washington, GA......391
Robert V. Fullerton Art Museum, California State University, San Bernardino, San Bernardino, CA......155
Roberts County Museum, Miami, TX......1438
Rochester Hills Museum at Van Hoosen Farm, Rochester Hills, MI......762
Rochester Historical Society, Rochester, NY......1059
Rock County Historical Society, Janesville, WI......1601
Rock Island Arsenal Museum, Rock Island, IL......454
Rock Island County Historical Society, Moline, IL......445
Rockbridge Historical Society, Lexington, VA......1513
Rockford Art Museum, Rockford, IL......455
Rockford College Art Gallery/Clark Arts Center, Rockford, IL......455
Rockhill Trolley Museum, Rockhill Furnace, PA......1297
Rockport Art Association, Rockport, MA......705

Rockwell Museum of Western Art, Corning, NY......982
Rockwood Park, Wilmington, DE......274
Rockwoods Reservation, Wildwood, MO......840
Rocky Mount Arts Center, Rocky Mount, NC......1117
Rocky Mountain College of Art + Design Galleries, Lakewood, CO......225
Rocky Mountain National Park, Estes Park, CO......215
Rodgers Tavern, Perryville, MD......650
Roger Tory Peterson Institute of Natural History, Jamestown, NY......1005
Rogers Historical Museum, Rogers, AR......67
Rokeby (Ancestral Estate of Rowland Evans Robinson), Ferrisburgh, VT......1479
Roland Gibson Gallery, Potsdam, NY......1054
Romanian Ethnic Art Museum, Cleveland, OH......1156
Rome Area History Museum, Rome, GA......382
Rome Art and Community Center, Rome, NY......1061
Ronald Reagan Presidential Library and Museum, Simi Valley, CA......187
Roosevelt Campobello International Park Commission, Lubec, ME......614
Rosa Ponselle Museum, Meriden, CT......249
Rosalie House, Eureka Springs, AR......57
Roscoe Village Foundation, Coshocton, OH......1159
The Rose Art Museum, Waltham, MA......715
Rose Center Museum, Morristown, TN......1376
Rose Hill Museum, Bay Village, OH......1141
Rose Lawn Museum, Cartersville, GA......368
The Rose Museum at Carnegie Hall, New York, NY......1038
Roseau County Historical Museum and Interpretive Center, Roseau, MN......788
Rosebud County Pioneer Museum, Forsyth, MT......846
Rosemont Plantation, Woodville, MS......810
Rosemount Museum, Pueblo, CO......230
Rosenbach Museum & Library, Philadelphia, PA......1287
Rosenberg Gallery, Goucher College, Baltimore, MD......636
Rosenberg Library, Galveston, TX......1422
Rosenthal Gallery of Art, Caldwell, ID......405
Ross County Historical Society, Inc., Chillicothe, OH......1147
Roswell Museum and Art Center, Roswell, NM......946
Roswell Visual Arts Center & Gallery, Roswell, GA......382
The Rotch-Jones-Duff House & Garden Museum, Inc., New Bedford, MA......697
Rothschild House State Park, Port Townsend, WA......1562
The Rotunda, University of Virginia, Charlottesville, VA......1500
Rowan Museum, Inc., Salisbury, NC......1118
Roxbury Heritage State Park, Roxbury, MA......706
The Roy Rogers-Dale Evans Museum and Theater, Branson, MO......811
Royellou Museum, Mount Dora, FL......327
The Rubelle & Norman Schafler Gallery, Brooklyn, NY......970
Rudolph E. Lee Gallery, Clemson, SC......1328
Rusk County Historical Society, Ladysmith, WI......1604
Russell County Historical Society/Fossil Station Museum, Russell, KS......556
Ruth and Charles Gilb Arcadia Historical Museum, Arcadia, CA......71
Ruth Chandler Williamson Gallery, Scripps College, Claremont, CA......86
Rutherford B. Hayes Presidential Center, Fremont, OH......1165
Rutland Historical Society, Rutland, VT......1486
S.C. Tobacco Museum, Mullins, SC......1337

S.S. Meteor Maritime Museum, Superior, WI......1624
Sackets Harbor Battlefield State Historic Site, Sackets Harbor, NY......1062
Sacramento Archives and Museum Collection Center, Sacramento, CA......153
Safe Haven Museum and Education Center, Oswego, NY......1048
Safety Harbor Museum of Regional History, Safety Harbor, FL......338
Safford House Historic House Museum, Tarpon Springs, FL......351
Sagamore Hill National Historic Site, Oyster Bay, NY......1049
Saginaw Art Museum, Saginaw, MI......763
Saguache County Museum, Saguache, CO......231
Sahuaro Ranch Historical Area, Glendale, AZ......35
St. Albans Historical Museum, Saint Albans, VT......1486
St. Charles County Historical Society, Inc., Saint Charles, MO......830
St. Charles Heritage Center, Saint Charles, IL......457
St. Clair County Historical Society, Belleville, IL......412
St. Francis County Museum, Forrest City, AR......57
Saint-Gaudens National Historic Site, Cornish, NH......885
St. John's Church and Parish Museum, Hampton, VA......1510
St. John's Northwestern Military Academy Archives & Museum, Delafield, WI......1595
St. Johnsbury Athenaeum, Saint Johnsbury, VT......1487
Saint Joseph's University - University Gallery - Boland Hall, Philadelphia, PA......1288
St. Lawrence County Historical Association - Silas Wright House, Canton, NY......975
St. Lawrence University - Richard F. Brush Art Gallery and Permanent Collection, Canton, NY......976
The Saint Louis Art Museum, Saint Louis, MO......836
St. Louis Artists' Guild, Saint Louis, MO......836
St. Louis Cardinals Hall of Fame Museum, Saint Louis, MO......836
St. Lucie County Historical Museum, Fort Pierce, FL......309
St. Marys Submarine Museum, Saint Marys, GA......382
St. Paul Museum, Randleman, NC......1117
St. Photios Greek Orthodox National Shrine, Saint Augustine, FL......340
St. Simons Island Lighthouse Museum, Saint Simons Island, GA......383
Ste. Genevieve Museum, Sainte Genevieve, MO......838
Saints Hall of Fame Museum, Kenner, LA......589
Salem Art Association-Bush House Museum and Bush Barn Art Center, Salem, OR......1236
Salem County Historical Society, Salem, NJ......924
Salem Historical Society and Museum, Salem, OH......1184
Salem Maritime National Historic Site, Salem, MA......707
The Salem Museum, Salem, VA......1536
Salida Museum, Salida, CO......232
Salina Art Center, Salina, KS......557
Salinas Pueblo Missions National Monument, Mountainair, NM......943
Salisbury House Foundation, Des Moines, IA......515
Salmagundi Museum of American Art, New York, NY......1038

Salmon Brook Historical Society, Inc., Granby, CT 242
Salvador Dali Museum, Saint Petersburg, FL 342
The Salvation Army Southern Historical Center & Museum, Atlanta, GA 363
Sam Bell Maxey House State Historic Site, Paris, TX 1442
Sam Brown Log House, Browns Valley, MN 770
Sam Rayburn House Museum, Bonham, TX 1397
Samek Art Gallery, Lewisburg, PA............1268
Samoa Cookhouse & Logging Museum, Samoa, CA......................................155
Samuel Dorsky Museum of Art, State University of New York at New Paltz, New Paltz, NY................................1018
Samuel K. Fox Museum, Dillingham, AK 23
Samuel P. Harn Museum of Art, Gainesville, FL 311
San Antonio Conservation Society, San Antonio, TX 1449
San Antonio Missions National Historical Park, San Antonio, TX 1449
San Antonio Museum of Art, San Antonio, TX 1450
San Benito County Historical Society Museum, Hollister, CA 103
San Buenaventura Mission Museum, Ventura, CA......................................195
San Diego Air & Space Museum, San Diego, CA...159
San Diego Automotive Museum, San Diego, CA...159
San Diego Hall of Champions Sports Museum, San Diego, CA 159
San Diego Model Railroad Museum, Inc., San Diego, CA...............................159
San Diego Museum of Man, San Diego, CA..160
San Diego Zoo, San Diego, CA 161
San Dieguito Heritage Museum, Encinitas, CA......................................92
San Fernando Valley Historical Society, Inc., Mission Hills, CA 126
San Francisco Camerawork, San Francisco, CA.....................................169
San Francisco Maritime National Historical Park, San Francisco, CA 169
San Francisco Museum of Modern Art, San Francisco, CA..............................169
San Gabriel Mission Museum, San Gabriel, CA.......................................171
San Jacinto Museum, San Jacinto, CA.........171
San Jacinto Museum of History Association, La Porte, TX 1433
San Jose Museum of Art, San Jose, CA 172
San Jose State University Art Galleries, San Jose, CA.......................................173
San Juan Historical Society, Friday Harbor, WA......................................1555
San Juan Island National Historical Park, Friday Harbor, WA 1555
San Juan National Historic Site, San Juan, PR...1643
San Luis Obispo County Historical Museum, San Luis Obispo, CA..............174
San Mateo County Historical Association and Museum, Redwood City, CA............147
San Miguel Mission Church, Santa Fe, NM...950
Sanborn Area Historical Society, Sanborn, NY.......................................1064
Sand Springs Cultural & Historical Museum, Sand Springs, OK..................1213
Sandown Historical Society and Museum, Sandown, NH......................................896
Sandusky Library Follett House Museum, Sandusky, OH......................................1185
Sandwich Glass Museum, Sandwich, MA ...708
Sandwich Historical Society, Sandwich, IL...457

Sandwich Historical Society, Center Sandwich, NH................................884
Sandy Bay Historical Society & Museums, Inc., Rockport, MA................705
Sandy Spring Museum, Sandy Spring, MD..653
Sanford Museum, Sanford, FL...................343
Sanford Museum and Planetarium, Cherokee, IA......................................510
Sangre de Cristo Arts Center & Buell Children's Museum, Pueblo, CO 231
Sanilac County Historical Museum and Village, Port Sanilac, MI......................761
Santa Barbara Botanic Garden, Santa Barbara, CA..178
The Santa Barbara Historical Museum, Santa Barbara, CA..............................179
Santa Barbara Maritime Museum, Santa Barbara, CA..179
Santa Barbara Museum of Art, Santa Barbara, CA..179
Santa Cruz Art League, Inc., Santa Cruz, CA..182
Santa Fe Trail Museum, Ingalls, KS 545
Santa Fe Trail Museum/Trinidad History Museum, Trinidad, CO........................234
Santa Maria Museum of Flight, Inc., Santa Maria, CA......................................183
Santa Monica Mountains National Recreation Area, Thousand Oaks, CA.....191
Santa Monica Museum of Art, Santa Monica, CA..183
Santa Ynez Valley Historical Society, Santa Ynez, CA..185
Sapulpa Historical Museum, Sapulpa, OK.1213
Sarah A. Mooney Memorial Museum, Lemoore, CA......................................109
Sarah Moody Gallery of Art, The University of Alabama, Tuscaloosa, AL..20
Sarasota Classic Car Museum, Sarasota, FL..345
Saratoga County Historical Society, Brookside Museum, Ballston Spa, NY....960
Saratoga Museum, Saratoga, WY.............1638
Saratoga National Historical Park, Stillwater, NY......................................1075
Satterlee Clark House, Horicon, WI...........1600
Sauk County Historical Museum, Baraboo, WI......................................1591
Sauk Prairie Area Historical Society, Inc., Prairie du Sac, WI 1619
Saunders County Historical Complex, Wahoo, NE..874
Savannah College of Art and Design Galleries, Savannah, GA 386
Sawin Memorial Building, Dover, MA 680
Sayville Historical Society, Sayville, NY...1066
Sayward-Wheeler House, York Harbor, ME..627
SCAD Museum of Art, Savannah, GA 386
Scantic Academy Museum, East Windsor Historical Society, Inc., East Windsor, CT..239
Scarborough Historical Museum, Scarborough, ME......................................621
Scarfone/Hartley Gallery, Tampa, FL...........349
The Scarsdale Historical Society, Scarsdale, NY......................................1066
Schedel Arboretum & Gardens, Elmore, OH..1163
Schenectady County Historical Society, Schenectady, NY....................................1067
Schenectady Museum and Suits-Bueche Planetarium, Schenectady, NY..............1067
The Schick Art Gallery, Skidmore College, Saratoga Springs, NY..............1065
Schifferstadt Architectural Museum, Frederick, MD 644
Schingoethe Center for Native American Cultures, Aurora, IL............................412
Schmidt House Museum & Research Library, Grants Pass, OR 1225

Schminck Memorial Museum, Lakeview, OR..1227
Schmucker Art Gallery, Gettysburg, PA.....1256
Schneider Museum of Art, Ashland, OR....1217
Scholte House Museum, Pella, IA...............527
The Schomburg Center for Research in Black Culture, New York, NY..............1038
Schoolcraft County Historical Society, Manistique, MI..753
Schoolhouse History & Art Center, Colstrip, MT......................................844
The Schuette Biermann Farmhouse Museum, Elk Grove Village, IL 432
Schwartz Collection of Skiing Heritage, Tiburon, CA..192
Schwenkfelder Library & Heritage Center, Pennsburg, PA............................1275
The Science Center of West Virginia, Bluefield, WV......................................1580
Scituate Historical Society, Scituate, MA 708
Scituate Maritime and Irish Mossing Museum, Scituate, MA..............................709
Scott & Zelda Fitzgerald Museum, Montgomery, AL..17
Scotts Bluff National Monument, Gering, NE...861
Scottsdale Museum of Contemporary Art, Scottsdale, AZ...44
Scottsville Museum, Scottsville, VA...........1536
Scurry County Museum, Snyder, TX 1453
Sea Cliff Village Museum, Sea Cliff, NY ..1068
Seaford Historical Museum, Seaford, NY..1068
Seagraves-Loop Museum and Art Center Inc., Seagraves, TX 1452
Seattle Aquarium, Seattle, WA...................1568
Seattle Art Museum, Seattle, WA...............1568
Seattle Asian Art Museum, Seattle, WA.....1569
Sedgwick-Brooklin Historical Society, Sedgwick, ME..622
Seminole Canyon State Park and Historic Site, Comstock, TX 1401
Senate House State Historic Site, Kingston, NY......................................1008
Senator George Baldwin Hotel, Klamath Falls, OR......................................1227
Senator George Norris State Historic Site, McCook, NE..868
Senator John Heinz Pittsburgh Regional History Center, Pittsburgh, PA..............1294
Seneca County Museum, Tiffin, OH...........1186
Seneca Falls Historical Society, Seneca Falls, NY......................................1069
Seneca-Iroquois National Museum, Salamanca, NY......................................1063
Sequoia and Kings Canyon National Parks, Three Rivers, CA 191
Sequoyah Cabin, Sallisaw, OK 1213
1797 Ezekiel Harris House, Augusta, GA....366
1761 Pownalborough Courthouse, Dresden, ME......................................610
The Sevier County Historical Museum, De Queen, AR..56
Sewall-Belmont House and Museum, Washington, DC......................................290
Seward County Historical Society Museum, Goehner, NE..............................861
Seymour Community Museum, Seymour, WI...1621
The Shadows-on-the-Teche, New Iberia, LA...593
Shaftsbury Historical Society, Shaftsbury, VT...1487
Shaker Heritage Society, Albany, NY 956
Shaker Historical Society, Shaker Heights, OH..1185
The Shaker Museum and Library, Old Chatham, NY......................................1045
Shaker Museum at South Union, South Union, KY..583
Shako:wi Cultural Center, Oneida, NY 1046
Sharlot Hall Museum, Prescott, AZ...............43
The Sharon Arts Center, Inc., Sharon, NH...896

Photographs—Continued

Sharon Historical Society, Sharon, CT........260
Sharpsteen Museum, Calistoga, CA..............80
Shasta College Museum & Research
    Center, Redding, CA 146
Shawano County Historical Society, Inc.,
    Shawano, WI 1621
Shelby American Collection, Boulder, CO...203
Shelby County Museum, Center, TX..........1399
Sheldon Memorial Art Gallery and
    Sculpture Garden/University of
    Nebraska-Lincoln, Lincoln, NE 867
Sheldon Museum and Cultural Center,
    Inc., Haines, AK 25
Shelter Island Historical Society, Shelter
    Island, NY......................................1069
Shemer Art Center & Museum, Phoenix,
    AZ...42
Sheppard Fine Arts Gallery, Reno, NV........881
Sherman Indian Museum, Riverside, CA......150
Sherwin Miller Museum of Jewish Art,
    Tulsa, OK......................................1216
Sherwood-Davidson House, Newark, OH..1178
Shippensburg Historical Society Museum,
    Shippensburg, PA..........................1300
Shoal Creek Living History Museum,
    Kansas City, MO.............................822
Shorter Mansion Museum, Eufaula, AL.........8
Shortgrass Country Museum Society,
    Sayre, OK 1213
Shoshone Bannock Tribal Museum, Fort
    Hall, ID..406
Shoshone County Mining and Smelting
    Museum d/b/a The Staff House
    Museum, Kellogg, ID.......................406
Shoshone Tribal Cultural Center, Fort
    Washakie, WY................................1633
Sibley County Historical Museum,
    Henderson, MN 777
Sidney Historical Association, Sidney,
    NY..1069
Sidney Mishkin Gallery of Baruch
    College, New York, NY.....................1038
Siege Museum (The Petersburg
    Museums), Petersburg, VA................1525
Sierra Mono Indian Museum, North Fork,
    CA...131
Sierra Sacramento Valley Medical
    Society Museum of Medical History,
    Sacramento, CA..............................153
Sieur de Monts Springs Nature Center,
    Bar Harbor, ME...............................605
Silent Wings Museum, Lubbock, TX.........1435
Siloam Springs Museum, Siloam Springs,
    AR..68
Silt Historical Society, Silt, CO................232
Silver City Museum, Silver City, NM.........951
Silver Cliff Museum, Silver Cliff, CO.........232
Silvercreek Museum, Freeport, IL..............435
The Simon Paneak Memorial Museum,
    Anaktuvuk Pass, AK 21
Simsbury Historical Society, Phelps
    Tavern, Museum & Homestead,
    Simsbury, CT..................................260
Sinclair Lewis House Museum &
    Interpretive Center/Museum, Sauk
    Centre, MN....................................793
Sindecuse Museum of Dentistry, Ann
    Arbor, MI.......................................725
Sioux City Art Center, Sioux City, IA 527
Sioux City Public Museum, Sioux City,
    IA...528
Sioux Empire Medical Museum, Sioux
    Falls, SD.......................................1356
Siouxland Heritage Museums, Sioux
    Falls, SD.......................................1357
Sisson Museum, Mount Shasta, CA 129
Sitka National Historical Park, Sitka, AK......28
Skiatook Museum, Skiatook, OK 1214
Skirball Cultural Center, Los Angeles,
    CA...121

Sky City Cultural Center, Pueblo of
    Acoma, NM 944
The Skyscraper Museum, New York, NY..1038
Slate Valley Museum, Granville, NY 996
Slidell Cultural Center, Slidell, LA 602
Slidell Museum, Slidell, LA 602
Sloan Museum, Flint, MI..........................742
Slocumb Galleries, Johnson City, TN........1368
Sloss Furnaces National Historic
    Landmark, Birmingham, AL 5
The Smart Museum of Art, Chicago, IL 427
Smith College Museum of Art,
    Northampton, MA 700
Smith-McDowell House Museum,
    Asheville, NC................................1090
Smith-Zimmermann Heritage Museum,
    Madison, SD.................................1351
Smithsonian American Art Museum,
    Washington, DC..............................290
Smithtown Historical Society, Smithtown,
    NY..1070
Smokey Bear Museum, Capitan, NM..........937
Smoki Museum - American Indian Art &
    Culture, Prescott, AZ........................43
Smoky Hill Museum, Salina, KS................557
Smyth County Museum, Marion, VA........1516
Snake River Heritage Center, Weiser, ID.....410
The Snite Museum of Art, University of
    Notre Dame, Notre Dame, IN.................495
Snoqualmie Valley Historical Museum,
    North Bend, WA.............................1559
Snowmobile Hall of Fame and Museum,
    Saint Germain, WI...........................1620
Snyder Museum & Creative Arts Center,
    Bastrop, LA....................................585
Society for the Preservation of Long
    Island Antiquities, Cold Spring
    Harbor, NY....................................980
The Society of California Pioneers, San
    Francisco, CA.................................170
The Society of the Cincinnati at
    Anderson House, Washington, DC 291
The Society of the Four Arts, Palm
    Beach, FL.......................................334
Sod House Museum, Gothenburg, NE 862
SoDus Bay Historical Society, Sodus
    Point, NY......................................1070
Soldiers' Memorial Military Museum,
    Saint Louis, MO..............................837
Solomon R. Guggenheim Museum, New
    York, NY.......................................1038
Somers Historical Society, Somers, NY.....1070
The Somerset County Historical Society,
    Inc., Princess Anne, MD 650
Somerset Historical Center, Somerset, PA .1300
Somervell County Historical Museum,
    Glen Rose, TX...............................1423
The Somerville Museum, Somerville,
    MA...709
Sonnenberg Gardens & Mansion State
    Historic Park, Canandaigua, NY..............975
Sonoma County Museum, Santa Rosa,
    CA..185
Sonoma State Historic Park, Sonoma, CA...188
Sophienburg Museum & Archives Inc.,
    New Braunfels, TX 1440
Sordoni Art Gallery, Wilkes-Barre, PA.......1307
Sotterley Plantation, Hollywood, MD..........647
South Bannock County Historical Center,
    Lava Hot Springs, ID........................407
South Bend Regional Museum of Art,
    South Bend, IN...............................500
South Boston-Halifax County Museum of
    Fine Arts & History, South Boston,
    VA...1536
South Carolina Aquarium, Charleston, SC.1326
South Carolina Artisans Center,
    Walterboro, SC..............................1343
South Carolina Confederate Relic Room
    and Museum, Columbia, SC.................1330

South Carolina Department of Parks,
    Recreation and Tourism, Columbia,
    SC..1330
South Carolina Historical Society,
    Charleston, SC...............................1327
South Carolina Law Enforcement Officers
    Hall of Fame, Columbia, SC 1330
The South Carolina Railroad Museum,
    Winnsboro, SC...............................1343
South Charleston Museum, South
    Charleston, WV 1586
South County Historical Society, Arroyo
    Grande, CA.....................................72
South Dakota Amateur Baseball Hall of
    Fame, Lake Norden, SD....................1350
South Dakota Art Museum, Brookings,
    SD...1344
South Dakota Hall of Fame,
    Chamberlain, SD.............................1345
South Dakota State Archives, Pierre, SD ...1353
South Dakota State Historical Society,
    Pierre, SD.....................................1353
South Florida Community College
    Museum of Florida Art and Culture,
    Avon Park, FL.................................295
South Hero Bicentennial Museum, South
    Hero, VT.......................................1487
South Holland Historical Society, South
    Holland, IL....................................457
South Milwaukee Historical Society
    Museum, South Milwaukee, WI...........1622
South Park City Museum, Fairplay, CO......215
South River Meeting House, Lynchburg,
    VA...1516
South Shore Arts, Munster, IN 493
South Sutton Old Store Museum, South
    Sutton, NH....................................896
South Texas Museum, Alice, TX...............1386
South Wood County Historical Corp.,
    Wisconsin Rapids, WI......................1628
Southampton Historical Museum,
    Southampton, NY............................1070
Southdown Plantation House/The
    Terrebonne Museum, Houma, LA 589
Southeast Florida Regional Preservation
    Office, Florida Division of Historical
    Resources, Fort Lauderdale, FL..............308
Southeast Museum Association, Inc.,
    Brewster, NY.................................964
Southeast Museum of Photography,
    Daytona Beach, FL..........................303
Southeastern Architectural Archive, New
    Orleans, LA....................................598
Southern Alleghenies Museum of Art,
    Loretto, PA....................................1269
Southern Alleghenies Museum of Art at
    Johnstown, Johnstown, PA.................1264
Southern Arts Federation, Atlanta, GA.......363
Southern Baptist Historical Library and
    Archives, Nashville, TN....................1380
Southern California Chapter Railway &
    Locomotive Historical Society,
    Pomona, CA...................................143
Southern Forest Heritage Museum, Long
    Leaf, LA..591
Southern Forest World, Waycross, GA........391
Southern Museum of Flight, Birmingham,
    AL...6
Southern Ohio Museum, Portsmouth, OH..1183
Southern Oregon Historical Society,
    Jacksonville, OR.............................1226
Southern Plains Indian Museum,
    Anadarko, OK................................1196
Southern Vermont College Art Gallery,
    Bennington, VT...............................1477
Southold Historical Society and Museum,
    Southold, NY.................................1071
Southwest Arkansas Regional Archives
    (SARA), Washington, AR 70
Southwest Florida Museum of History,
    Fort Myers, FL................................309
Southwest Museum, Los Angeles, CA........121

Southwest Virginia Museum Historical State Park, Big Stone Gap, VA 1497
Space Center Houston, Houston, TX 1429
The SPAM Museum, Austin, MN 768
Spartanburg County Museum of Art, Spartanburg, SC 1341
Spartanburg County Regional Museum of History, Spartanburg, SC 1341
The Speed Art Museum, Louisville, KY 579
Spencer Museum of Art, The University of Kansas, Lawrence, KS 548
Spertus Museum, Chicago, IL 427
Spiers Gallery, Brevard, NC 1092
SPJST Library Archives & Museum, Temple, TX 1455
The Sports Museum, Boston, MA 669
Spring Grove Hospital Center, Alumni Museum, Catonsville, MD 639
Spring Street Historical Museum, Shreveport, LA 602
Spring Valley Community Historical Society, Inc., Spring Valley, MN 794
Springfield Art & Historical Society - Miller Art Center, Springfield, VT 1488
Springfield Art Museum, Springfield, MO ...839
Springfield Museum of Art, Springfield, OH 1186
Springfield Museum of Old Domestic Life, High Point, NC 1107
Springfield Museums - Connecticut Valley Historical Museum, Springfield, MA 710
Springs Museum, Springs, PA 1301
Stacy's Tavern Museum and Glen Ellyn Historical Society, Glen Ellyn, IL 437
Stafford County Historical Society Museum, Stafford, KS 558
Stanley Museum, Inc., Kingfield, ME 613
Stanley-Whitman House, Farmington, Farmington, CT 241
Stanly County Historic Preservation Commission and Museum, Albemarle, NC 1088
Stanwood Wildlife Sanctuary, Ellsworth, ME 610
Stanzel Model Aircraft Museum, Schulenburg, TX 1452
Star Eco Station, Culver City, CA 88
Starhill Forest Arboretum, Petersburg, IL 451
State Agricultural Heritage Museum, Brookings, SD 1344
State Historical Society of Missouri, Columbia, MO 814
Staten Island Historical Society, Staten Island, NY 1074
Staten Island Institute of Arts & Sciences (SIIAS), Staten Island, NY 1074
Statue of Liberty National Monument & Ellis Island Immigration Museum, New York, NY 1039
Stauth Memorial Museum, Montezuma, KS 553
STAX Museum of American Soul Music, Memphis, TN 1376
Steamship Keewatin, Douglas, MI 738
Stearns History Museum, Saint Cloud, MN 788
Stedman Gallery, Camden, NJ 900
Steilacoom Historical Museum Association, Steilacoom, WA 1572
The Stephen Phillips House, Salem, MA 707
Stephens County Historical Society and Museum, Duncan, OK 1199
The Stephens Museum, Fayette, MO 815
Stephenson County Historical Society, Freeport, IL 436
Stephenville Museum, Stephenville, TX 1454
Steppingstone Museum, Havre de Grace, MD 647
Sterling and Francine Clark Art Institute, Williamstown, MA 719

Sterling Historical Society and Little Red Schoolhouse Museum, Sterling, NY 1074
Sterling-Rock Falls Historical Society Museum, Sterling, IL 461
The Stevens-Coolidge Place, a property of The Trustees of Reservations, North Andover, MA 698
Stevens Museum, Salem, IN 498
Steves Homestead, San Antonio, TX 1450
Stewart M. Lord Memorial Historical Society, Inc., Burlington, ME 608
Still National Osteopathic Museum, Kirksville, MO 824
Stockbridge Library Historical Collection, Stockbridge, MA 713
Stockholm Historical Society Museum, Stockholm, ME 623
Stones River National Battlefield, Murfreesboro, TN 1377
Stonewall Jackson House, Lexington, VA ..1514
Stoughton Historical Society, Stoughton, MA 713
Stow West School Museum, Stow, MA 713
The Stowitts Museum & Library, Pacific Grove, CA 137
Stranahan House, Inc., Fort Lauderdale, FL 308
Strasburg Museum, Strasburg, VA 1539
Strategic Air & Space Museum, Ashland, NE 856
Strater Hotel, Durango, CO 214
The Stratford Historical Society & Catherine B. Mitchell Museum, Stratford, CT 262
Stratford, Robert E. Lee Memorial Association, Inc., Stratford, VA 1539
Strawbery Banke Museum, Portsmouth, NH 895
Stuart Heritage Museum, Stuart, FL 346
The Studio Museum in Harlem, New York, NY 1040
Stutsman County Memorial Museum, Jamestown, ND 1133
SUArt Galleries - Syracuse University, Syracuse, NY 1077
Sugarlands Visitor Center, Gatlinburg, TN.1365
Sullivan Museum and History Center, Northfield, VT 1483
Summit County Historical Society, Akron, OH 1139
Summit Historical Society, Breckenridge, CO 204
The Sumter County Museum, Sumter, SC.1342
Sun Gallery, Hayward, CA 102
Sun Inn Preservation Association Inc., Bethlehem, PA 1243
Sun Prairie Historical Library & Museum, Sun Prairie, WI 1624
Sunnyside Historical Museum, Sunnyside, WA 1572
Sunnyvale Historical Museum, Sunnyvale, CA 190
The Supreme Court of the United States, Washington, DC 291
Suquamish Museum, Poulsbo, WA 1563
Surratt House Museum, Clinton, MD 640
Susan B. Anthony House, Rochester, NY ..1060
Sushi Performance and Visual Art, San Diego, CA 161
Susquehanna County Historical Society & Free Library Association, Montrose, PA 1272
Sutter's Fort State Historic Park, Sacramento, CA 153
Sutton County Historical Society - Miers Home Museum, Sonora, TX 1453
Swampscott Historical Society (John Humphrey House), Swampscott, MA 714
Swarthout Memorial Museum, La Crosse, WI 1603
Swedish American Museum Association of Chicago, Chicago, IL 428

Sweet Briar Museum, Sweet Briar, VA 1540
Sweetwater County Historical Museum, Green River, WY 1633
Swenson Memorial Museum of Stephens County, Breckenridge, TX 1397
Swift County Historical Society, Benson, MN 769
Swigart Museum, Huntingdon, PA 1262
Swisher County Archives and Museum Association, Tulia, TX 1456
Swiss Historical Village, New Glarus, WI.1615
Switzerland County Historical Museum, Vevay, IN 502

T.B. Ferguson Home, Watonga, OK 1216
T.C. Steele State Historic Site, Nashville, IN 493
T.J. Elder Community Center, Sandersville, GA 384
Table Rock Historical Society and Museums, Table Rock, NE 873
Tacoma Art Museum, Tacoma, WA 1574
Tacoma Public Library/Thomas Handforth Gallery, Tacoma, WA 1574
Talkeetna Historical Society and Museum, Talkeetna, AK 28
Tall Grass Arts Association, Park Forest, IL 449
Tamastslikt Cultural Institute, Pendleton, OR 1230
Tampa Bay History Center, Inc., Tampa, FL 350
Tampa Museum of Art, Tampa, FL 350
Tante Blanche Museum, Madawaska, ME ...614
Taoist Temple and Museum, Hanford, CA...101
Taos County Historical Society, Inc., Taos, NM 953
Taos Historic Museums, Taos, NM 953
Tappantown Historical Society, Tappan, NY 1077
Tarpon Springs Area Historical Society - Depot Museum, Tarpon Springs, FL 351
Tarpon Springs Cultural Center, Tarpon Springs, FL 351
Tarpon Springs Heritage Museum, Tarpon Springs, FL 351
Taube Museum of Art, Minot, ND 1135
The Tech Museum of Innovation, San Jose, CA 173
Ted Smallwood's Store, Inc., Chokoloskee, FL 299
Ted Williams Museum and Hitters Hall of Fame, Hernando, FL 312
Telephone Museum of New Mexico, Albuquerque, NM 935
Telephone Pioneer Museum, Phoenix, AZ 42
Telfair Museum of Art, Savannah, GA 386
Telluride Historical Museum, Telluride, CO 233
Temecula Valley Museum, Temecula, CA ...191
Tempe Historical Museum, Tempe, AZ 46
The Temple Judea Museum of Reform Congregation Keneseth Israel, Elkins Park, PA 1251
Tenino Depot Museum, Tenino, WA 1575
Tennessee Historical Society, Nashville, TN 1380
Tennessee Museum of Aviation, Sevierville, TN 1383
Tennessee State Museum, Nashville, TN ...1381
Tennessee Valley Art Center, Tuscumbia, AL 20
Tennessee Valley Railroad Museum Inc., Chattanooga, TN 1363
Terrace Gallery-City of Orlando, Orlando, FL 332
Terrace Hill Historic Site and Governor's Mansion, Des Moines, IA 516
Territory Town, Okemah, OK 1207
Terwilliger Museum, Waterloo, NY 1083
Teutopolis Monastery Museum, Teutopolis, IL 461

Photographs–Continued

Texarkana Museums System, Texarkana, TX 1455
Texas Air Museum, Slaton, TX 1453
Texas Baptist Historical Center Museum, Brenham, TX 1397
Texas Cowboy Hall of Fame, Fort Worth, TX 1418
Texas Energy Museum, Beaumont, TX......1395
Texas Forestry Museum, Lufkin, TX 1436
Texas Maritime Museum, Rockport, TX 1446
Texas Music Museum, Austin, TX 1392
Texas Parks and Wildlife Department, Austin, TX 1392
Texas Pharmacy Museum, Amarillo, TX ...1387
Texas Prison Museum, Huntsville, TX 1430
Texas Ranger Hall of Fame and Museum, Waco, TX 1459
Texas Sports Hall of Fame, Waco, TX 1459
Texas Transportation Museum, San Antonio, TX 1451
Theodore Roosevelt Birthplace National Historic Site, New York, NY 1040
Theodore Roosevelt Inaugural National Historic Site, Buffalo, NY 973
Theodore Roosevelt National Park-Visitor Center, Medora, ND 1134
Thetford Historical Society Library and Museum, Thetford, VT 1488
Third Cavalry Museum, Fort Carson, CO....216
This Century Art Gallery, Williamsburg, VA 1545
Thomas Clarke House/Princeton Battlefield State Park, Princeton, NJ 922
Thomas E. McMillan Museum, Brewton, AL 6
Thomas Edison Birthplace Museum, Milan, OH 1176
Thomas Edison House, Louisville, KY 579
Thomas-Foreman Home, Muskogee, OK...1205
The Thomas Griswold House and Museum, Guilford, CT 243
Thomas L. Kane Memorial Chapel, Kane, PA 1264
The Thomas T. Taber Museum of the Lycoming County Historial Society, Williamsport, PA 1308
Thomas Warne Historical Museum & Library, Old Bridge, NJ 918
Thomas Whaley House Museum, San Diego, CA 161
Thomaston Historical Society, Thomaston, ME 624
Thorne-Sagendorph Art Gallery, Keene, NH 890
Thornton W. Burgess Museum, Sandwich, MA 708
Thousand Islands Museum, Clayton, NY ...979
Three Rivers Museum, Muskogee, OK......1205
Thronateeska Heritage Foundation, Inc., Albany, GA 355
Thunderbird Foundation for the Arts, Mount Carmel, UT 1467
Tile Heritage Foundation, Healdsburg, CA 102
Tillamook County Pioneer Museum, Tillamook, OR 1237
Tillamook Naval Air Station Museum, Tillamook, OR 1237
Timpanogos Cave National Monument, American Fork, UT 1462
Timucuan Ecological and Historic Preserve and Fort Caroline National Memorial, Jacksonville, FL..................315
Tinker Swiss Cottage Museum, Rockford, IL 456
Tinley Park Historical Society, Tinley Park, IL 461
Tioga County Historical Society Museum, Owego, NY 1048
Tippecanoe County Historical Association, Lafayette, IN.....................487

Tipton County Museum, Veteran's Memorial & Nature Center, Covington, TN 1364
Tobacco Farm Life Museum, Inc., Kenly, NC 1107
Tobias Community Historical Society, Tobias, NE 873
Tohono Chul Park Inc., Tucson, AZ.............51
Toledo Firefighters Museum, Toledo, OH ..1187
The Toledo Museum of Art, Toledo, OH ..1187
The Toledo Zoo, Toledo, OH 1187
Tolland Historical Society - Tolland County Jail and Warden's Home Museum, Tolland, CT 262
Toltec Mounds Archeological State Park, Scott, AR 68
Tom Mix Museum, Dewey, OK...............1199
Tomball Community Museum Center, Tomball, TX 1455
Tombstone Courthouse State Historic Park, Tombstone, AZ 46
Tonto National Monument, Roosevelt, AZ 43
Top of Oklahoma Historical Museum, Blackwell, OK 1197
Toppenish Museum, Toppenish, WA 1575
Torpedo Factory Art Center, Alexandria, VA 1494
Town of Manlius Historical Society with Museum, Manlius, NY 1013
Town of Yorktown Museum, Yorktown Heights, NY 1087
Trail End State Historic Site, Sheridan, WY 1638
Traill County Historical Society, Hillsboro, ND 1132
Trails & Rails Museum, Kearney, NE..........864
Trailside Nature Museum, Cross River, NY 983
Trapper Creek Museum, Trapper Creek, AK 28
Travellers Rest Plantation & Museum, Nashville, TN 1381
Traverse County Historical Society, Wheaton, MN 796
Tread of Pioneers Museum, Steamboat Springs, CO 232
Trenton City Museum, Trenton, NJ............928
Trenton Historical Museum, Trenton, MI....765
Tri-County Historical Society & Museum, Inc., Herington, KS 544
Tri-State Mineral Museum, Joplin, MO 820
Triangle Tattoo & Museum, Fort Bragg, CA 95
Trinity Museum of the Parish of Trinity Church, New York, NY........................1040
Triton Museum of Art, Santa Clara, CA 181
The Trout Gallery, Carlisle, PA 1245
Troutdale Historical Society, Troutdale, OR 1237
Troy Museum & Historic Village, Troy, MI 765
Truckee-Donner Historical Society Jail Museum, Truckee, CA 193
The Trustees of Reservations, Beverly, MA 662
Tsa Mo Ga Memorial Museum, Plains, TX 1443
T.T. Wentworth, Jr. Florida State Museum, Pensacola, FL 336
Tu-Endie-Wei State Park, Point Pleasant, WV 1586
Tubman African-American Museum, Macon, GA 378
Tuckerton Seaport, Tuckerton, NJ 928
Tucson Museum of Art & Historic Block, Tucson, AZ 51
Tucumcari Historical Research Institute, Tucumcari, NM 953
Tudor Place Foundation, Inc., Washington, DC......................................292

Tufts University Art Gallery, Medford, MA 694
Tulare County Museum at Mooney Grove Park, Visalia, CA 195
Tularosa Basin Historical Society Museum, Alamogordo, NM 932
The Turner Museum, Sarasota, FL 345
Turquoise Museum, Albuquerque, NM 936
Turtle Bay Exploration Park, Redding, CA 146
Turtle Mountain Chippewa Historical Society, Belcourt, ND 1127
Tuskegee Institute National Historic Site, Tuskegee Institute, AL 21
Tweed Museum of Art, Duluth, MN 774
Twin Falls County Historical Museum, Filer, ID 405
Twinsburg Historical Society, Twinsburg, OH 1188
Twister the Movie Museum, Wakita, OK...1216
Tybee Island Light Station and Tybee Museum, Tybee Island, GA 389
Tyler Arboretum, Media, PA 1271
Tyler Museum of Art, Tyler, TX...............1456

UCR/California Museum of Photography, Riverside, CA 150
U.S. Bicycling Hall of Fame, Somerville, NJ 924
U.S. Navy Museum, Washington, DC 292
USS Massachusetts Memorial Committee, Inc., Fall River, MA 682
UWM Union-Art Gallery, Milwaukee, WI.1613
Ukrainian-American Museum & Archives, Warren, MI 766
Ukrainian Museum-Archives, Inc., Cleveland, OH 1156
Ukrainian National Museum, Inc., Chicago, IL 428
Ulrich Museum of Art, Wichita, KS............563
Ulysses S. Grant Cottage State Historic Site, Wilton, NY 1086
Umlauf Sculpture Garden & Museum, Austin, TX 1392
Umpqua Discovery Center, Reedsport, OR 1234
Uncle Remus Museum, Eatonton, GA 371
UNI Gallery of Art, University of Northern Iowa, Cedar Falls, IA 508
Union County Heritage Museum, New Albany, MS 806
Union County Historical Complex, Creston, IA 512
Union County Historical Society, Lewisburg, PA 1268
Union County Historical Society Museum, Blairsville, GA 366
Union County Museum, Union, OR 1238
Union Mills Homestead & Grist Mill, Westminster, MD 656
Union Pacific Railroad Museum, Council Bluffs, IA 512
Union Station Kansas City, Inc., Kansas City, MO 823
Unionville Museum, Farmington, CT...........242
The United States Army Quartermaster Museum, Fort Lee, VA 1505
United States Capitol, Washington, DC 293
United States Golf Association Museum & Archives, Far Hills, NJ 903
United States Hockey Hall of Fame, Eveleth, MN 774
United States Holocaust Memorial Museum, Washington, DC 293
United States Marine Corps Air-Ground Museum, Quantico, VA 1526
United States Naval Shipbuilding Museum, Quincy, MA 705
University Art Galleries, Vermillion, SD....1358
University Art Galleries, Murray State University, Murray, KY..........................580
University Art Gallery, Indiana State University, Terre Haute, IN.....................501

University Art Gallery, New Mexico State University, Las Cruces, NM 941
University Art Gallery, Sonoma State University, Rohnert Park, CA 151
University Art Gallery, University of the South, Sewanee, TN 1384
University Art Museum, Binghamton, NY...963
University Art Museum, Santa Barbara, Santa Barbara, CA.........................180
University Art Museum, The University of New Mexico, Albuquerque, NM 936
University Art Museum, University at Albany, Albany, NY..............................956
University Galleries, Clarion, PA 1247
University Galleries, Florida Atlantic University, Boca Raton, FL 296
University Gallery, Gainesville, FL..............312
University Gallery, University of Massachusetts at Amherst, Amherst, MA 659
The University Museum, Edwardsville, IL...432
The University Museum, Indiana, PA 1263
University Museums, University of Delaware, Newark, DE........................272
University of Alaska Museum of the North, Fairbanks, AK 24
University of Arkansas at Little Rock Art Department Gallery I & II & III, Little Rock, AR 63
University of California Berkeley Art Museum and Pacific Film Archive, Berkeley, CA 77
University of Central Florida Art Gallery, Orlando, FL......................................332
University of Colorado Museum, Boulder, CO.....................................203
University of Denver, School of Art & Art History, Victoria H. Myhren Gallery, Denver, CO..................................213
University of Iowa Museum of Art, Iowa City, IA...520
University of Kansas Medical Center, Clendening History of Medicine Library and Museum, Kansas City, KS...546
University of Kentucky Art Museum, Lexington, KY....................................574
University of Kentucky Basketball Museum, Lexington, KY........................574
University of Maine Museum of Art, Bangor, ME......................................605
University of Michigan Museum of Anthropology, Ann Arbor, MI.................725
The University of Michigan Museum of Art, Ann Arbor, MI 726
University of Missouri-Kansas City Gallery of Art, Kansas City, MO............823
The University of Montana-Western Art Gallery & Museum, Dillon, MT.........846
University of North Texas Art Gallery, Denton, TX......................................1409
University of Pennsylvania Museum of Archaeology and Anthropology, Philadelphia, PA..............................1288
University of Rhode Island Fine Arts Center Galleries, Kingston, RI.............1312
University of Richmond Museums, Richmond, VA..................................1532
University of South Florida Contemporary Art Museum, Tampa, FL..350
The University of Texas at San Antonio, Art Gallery, San Antonio, TX.............1451
University of Virginia Art Museum, Charlottesville, VA 1500
University of West Florida Art Gallery, Pensacola, FL....................................336
University of Wyoming Art Museum, Laramie, WY....................................1636
University Saint Thomas Art History, Saint Paul, MN 792
Upper Musselshell Historical Society, Harlowton, MT..................................849

Uppertown Firefighters Museum, Astoria, OR..1219
Upton Red Onion Museum, Upton, WY....1639
Urban Institute for Contemporary Arts, Grand Rapids, MI..............................744
U.S. Army Air Defense Artillery Museum, Fort Bliss, TX.....................1414
U.S. Army Center of Military History, Museum Division, Fort McNair, DC.......275
U.S. Army Chaplain Museum, Fort Jackson, SC...................................1332
U.S. Army Finance Corps Museum, Fort Jackson, SC...................................1333
U.S. Army Medical Department Museum, Fort Sam Houston, TX........................1415
U.S. Army Museum of Hawaii, Fort DeRussy, HI.......................................392
U.S. Army Ordnance Museum, Aberdeen Proving Ground, MD...............................627
U.S. Army Signal Corps Museum, Fort Gordon, GA.....................................372
U.S. Army Transportation Museum, Fort Eustis, VA 1504
U.S. Army Women's Museum, Fort Lee, VA 1505
U.S. Cavalry Museum, Fort Riley, KS.........540
U.S. Coast Guard Museum, New London, CT...255
U.S. Grant's Home State Historic Site, Galena, IL..436
U.S. National Ski Hall of Fame & Museum, Inc., Ishpeming, MI.................747
U.S. Navy Memorial Foundation and Naval Heritage Center, Washington, DC...294
U.S. Navy Seabee Museum, Port Hueneme, CA.......................................143
U.S. Navy Supply Corps Museum, Athens, GA.......................................357
U.S. Patent and Trademark Office - Museum, Alexandria, VA......................1494
The U.S. Space & Rocket Center, Huntsville, AL 12
USA Weightlifting Hall of Fame, York, PA...1309
USS Alabama Battleship Memorial Park, Mobile, AL..15
USS Arizona Memorial, Honolulu, HI 398
USS Bowfin Submarine Museum & Park, Honolulu, HI......................................398
USS Constellation Museum, Baltimore, MD..636
USS Constitution Museum, Boston, MA 669
USS Lexington Museum on the Bay, Corpus Christi, TX...............................1402
USS Radford National Naval Museum, Newcomerstown, OH 1179
Utah Museum of Fine Arts, Salt Lake City, UT 1472
Utica Museum, Utica, MT 854
UTSA's Institute of Texan Cultures, San Antonio, TX.....................................1451

Vacaville Museum, Vacaville, CA 194
The Valdez Museum & Historical Archive Association, Inc., Valdez, AK 29
Valdosta State University Fine Arts Gallery, Valdosta, GA............................389
Valentine Richmond History Center, Richmond, VA 1532
Vallejo Naval & Historical Museum, Vallejo, CA 194
Valley Art Center, Inc., Clarkston, WA 1551
Valley Community Historical Society, Inc., Valley, NE...................................874
Valley County Pioneer Museum, Glasgow, MT....................................847
Valley Forge National Historical Park, King of Prussia, PA...........................1264
Van Buren County Historical Museum, Clinton, AR...55
Van Buren County Historical Society, Keosauqua, IA...................................521

Van Every/Smith Galleries, Davidson, NC..1098
Van Wyck Homestead Museum, Fishkill, NY..989
Vanderbilt Mansion National Historic Site, Hyde Park, NY............................1002
Vann House, Chatsworth, GA.....................368
Varner-Hogg Plantation State Historic Site, West Columbia, TX 1461
Vashon Maury Island Heritage Association, Vashon, WA 1576
Venango Museum of Art, Science & Industry, Oil City, PA.........................1274
Vent Haven Museum, Fort Mitchell, KY 568
Ventura County Maritime Museum, Inc., Oxnard, CA......................................137
Ventura County Museum of History & Art, Ventura, CA 195
Verde Historical Society, Clemenceau Heritage Museum, Cottonwood, AZ..........32
Verendrye Museum, Fort Pierre, SD 1347
Vermilion County Museum Society, Danville, IL....................................429
Vermont Folklife Center, Middlebury, VT .1482
Vermont Marble Museum, Proctor, VT......1485
Vermont Ski Museum, Stowe, VT..............1488
Vernon County Historical Museum, Viroqua, WI....................................1625
Vernon Historians, Inc., Vernon, VT 1489
Vernonia Pioneer Museum, Vernonia, OR..1238
Vero Beach Museum of Art, Inc., Vero Beach, FL.......................................352
The Vestal Museum, Vestal, NY.................1081
Vesterheim Norwegian-American Museum, Decorah, IA 513
Vicksburg Battlefield Museum, Vicksburg, MS.....................................809
Victor Heritage Museum, Victor, MT..........854
Victor Valley Museum & Art Gallery, Apple Valley, CA......................................71
Vietnam Era Educational Center, Holmdel, NJ......................................908
Vietnam War National Museum, Nelson, NE...869
Viking Union Gallery, Bellingham, WA.....1549
Villa Montezuma Museum/San Diego Historical Society, San Diego, CA 162
Village Gallery, La Jolla, CA.....................107
Village of Elsah Museum, Elsah, IL 433
The Vinalhaven Historical Society Museum, Vinalhaven, ME........................624
Virginia Air & Space Center, Hampton, VA..1510
Virginia Baptist Historical Society, Richmond, VA 1532
Virginia Beach Maritime Museum, Inc./The Old Coast Guard Station, Virginia Beach, VA.............................1543
Virginia City J. Spencer Watkins Memorial Museum, Virginia City, MT....854
Virginia Historical Society, Richmond, VA...1533
Virginia Holocaust Museum, Richmond, VA...1533
Virginia Military Institute Museum, Lexington, VA......................................1514
Virginia Museum of Fine Arts, Richmond, VA................................1533
Virginia Museum of Transportation, Inc., Roanoke, VA....................................1536
Virginia War Memorial, Richmond, VA 1534
The Virginia War Museum, Newport News, VA.....................................1520
Vista Historical Museum, Vista, CA...........196
Vista House, Corbett, OR.........................1222
Visual Arts Center at the Washington Pavilion, Sioux Falls, SD.....................1357
Visual Arts Center of New Jersey, Summit, NJ.......................................925
Visual Arts Center of Northwest Florida, Panama City, FL................................334
Visual Arts Museum, New York, NY.........1040

Photographs–Continued

The von Liebig Art Center, Naples, FL 328

W.C. Handy Home Museum and Library, Florence, AL 9
The W.H. Stark House, Orange, TX...........1442
Wabasha County Museum, Wabasha County Historical Society at Reads Landing, Reads Landing, MN.................787
Wade House Stagecoach Inn & Wesley Jung Carriage Museum State Historic Site, Greenbush, WI 1599
Wadsworth Atheneum Museum of Art, Hartford, CT 246
The Wagnalls Memorial, Lithopolis, OH ...1172
Wahkiakum County Historical Museum, Cathlamet, WA..................................1550
Waikiki Aquarium, Honolulu, HI................399
Wailoa Center for Culture and Arts, Hilo, HI 393
Wake Forest College Birthplace Society, Inc., Wake Forest, NC 1121
Wakefield Historical Society, Wakefield, MA..715
Wakefield House Museum, Blue Earth, MN...769
Wakefield Museum Association, Wakefield, KS...................................560
Waldensian Heritage Museum, Valdese, NC..1121
The Walker African American Museum & Research Center, Las Vegas, NV 880
Walker Art Center, Minneapolis, MN...........783
Wallace District Mining Museum, Wallace, ID.......................................410
Wallingford Historical Society, Inc., Wallingford, CT.................................263
Walnut Canyon National Monument, Flagstaff, AZ......................................34
Walt Whitman House Museum and Library, Camden, NJ 900
Walter E. Heller Nature Center, Highland Park, IL......................................439
Walter P. Chrysler Boyhood Home and Museum, Ellis, KS.............................538
Walter Reed Birthplace, Gloucester County, VA 1508
Waltham Historical Society, Waltham, MA..716
The Waltham Museum, Waltham, MA.........716
Wanapum Dam Heritage Center, Beverly, WA..1549
Wantagh Historical & Preservation Society, Wantagh, NY 1081
Wapello County Historical Museum, Ottumwa, IA.......................................526
War Between the States Museum, Florence, SC.....................................1332
Ward County Historical Society, Minot, ND..1135
The Ward Museum of Wildfowl Art, Salisbury University, Salisbury, MD 653
Warren County Historical Society, Warren, PA....................................1304
Warren County Historical Society Museum, Lebanon, OH 1171
Warrick County Museum, Inc., Boonville, IN .,..470
Warwick Museum of Art, Warwick, RI......1320
Washburn County Historical Society Museum, Shell Lake, WI.................1621
Washburn Historical Museum & Cultural Center, Inc. aka Washburn Cultural Center, Washburn, WI 1625
Washington & Jefferson College - Olin Fine Arts Center, Washington, PA 1305
Washington County Historical Association, Fort Calhoun, NE...............860
Washington County Historical Society, Washington, KS..................................560
Washington County Historical Society, Portland, OR 1233

Washington County Historical Society, Washington, PA.................................1305
Washington County Historical Society Inc., West Bend, WI.........................1627
Washington County Historical Society Warden's House Museum, Stillwater, MN..794
Washington County Rural Heritage Museum, Boonsboro, MD.....................637
Washington Crossing Historic Park, Washington Crossing, PA.....................1305
Washington Historical Museum, Washington, GA.................................391
Washington Museum & Tourist Center, Washington, LA.................................603
Washington Oaks Gardens State Park, Palm Coast, FL..................................334
Washington Pavilion of Arts and Science, Sioux Falls, SD.................................1357
Washington State Capital Museum and Outreach Center, Olympia, WA..............1560
Washington State Historical Society, Tacoma, WA....................................1574
Washington's Headquarters State Historic Site, Newburgh, NY 1042
Washington's Lands Museum & Sayre Log House, Ravenswood, WV..............1586
Water Mill Museum, Water Mill, NY 1082
Waterford Historical Museum and Cultural Center, Inc., Waterford, NY.....1083
Waterloo Center for the Arts, Waterloo, IA..529
Watermen's Museum, Yorktown, VA..........1547
Watertown Historical Society, Inc., Watertown, CT.................................264
Watervliet Arsenal's Museum of the Big Guns, Watervliet, NY 1084
Watkins Woolen Mill State Historic Site & Park, Lawson, MO...........................825
Watts Towers Arts Center, Los Angeles, CA...122
Wauconda Township Historical Society, Wauconda, IL...................................463
Waukesha County Museum, Waukesha, WI..1625
Wayland Historical Society, Wayland, MA..716
Wayne County Historical Museum, Richmond, IN 497
Wayne County Historical Society, Lyons, NY..1012
Wayne County Historical Society, Wooster, OH 1192
Weatherspoon Art Museum, Greensboro, NC..1104
Webb House Museum, Newark, OH 1179
Webster House Museum, Elkhorn, WI.......1596
Wedell-Williams Memorial Aviation Museum, Patterson, LA........................599
Weems-Botts Museum, Dumfries, VA.........1503
Weinman Mineral Museum, White, GA.......391
Wellesley Historical Society, Inc., Wellesley Hills, MA..............................717
Wellfleet Historical Society Museum, Wellfleet, MA...................................717
Wells County Historical Museum, Bluffton, IN.....................................470
Wells County Museum, Fessenden, ND 1131
Wells Fargo History Museum, Minneapolis, MN.................................783
Welsh-American Heritage Museum, Oak Hill, OH....................................1180
Wenatchee Valley Museum and Cultural Center, Wenatchee, WA......................1577
Wenham Museum, Wenham, MA................717
Wentworth-Coolidge Mansion, Portsmouth, NH.................................895
Wentworth Gardner & Tobias Lear Houses Association, Portsmouth, NH......895
Weslaco Museum, Weslaco, TX 1461
West Allis Historical Society Museum, West Allis, WI 1626

West Baton Rouge Museum, Port Allen, LA..599
West Chicago City Museum, West Chicago, IL.......................................464
West of the Pecos Museum, Pecos, TX 1443
West Overton Museums, Scottdale, PA......1298
West Pasco Historical Society Museum and Library, New Port Richey, FL 329
West Point Museum, West Point, NY 1085
West River Museum Society, Philip, SD....1353
West Virginia Independence Hall, Wheeling, WV.................................1588
West Virginia Northern Community College Alumni Association Museum, Wheeling, WV.................................1588
West Virginia Penitentiary, Moundsville, WV..1585
West Virginia State Museum, Charleston, WV..1581
West Virginia University-Mesaros Galleries, Morgantown, WV 1585
Westchester County Historical Society, Elmsford, NY....................................988
Western Aerospace Museum, Oakland, CA...134
Western Archeological & Conservation Center, Tucson, AZ................................52
Western Colorado Center for the Arts, Grand Junction, CO...........................221
Western Folklife Center, Elko, NV..............876
Western Heritage Center, Billings, MT........841
Western Historic Radio Museum, Virginia City, NV...882
Western Hotel/Museum, Lancaster, CA........108
Western Illinois University Art Gallery, Macomb, IL......................................444
Western Mining & Railroad Museum, Helper, UT......................................1466
Western Museum of Mining & Industry, Colorado Springs, CO 208
Western New Mexico University Museum, Silver City, NM.....................951
Western North Carolina Air Museum, Hendersonville, NC 1105
Western Reserve Historical Society, Cleveland, OH 1156
Westminster Historical Society, Westminster, VT.................................1490
Westport Historical Society, Westport, CT...266
Westport Maritime Museum, Westport, WA..1578
The Wethersfield Historical Society, Wethersfield, CT.................................266
Wexford County Historical Society & Museum, Cadillac, MI............................731
Wexner Center for the Arts, Columbus, OH..1159
The Whale Museum, Friday Harbor, WA...1555
Whalers Village Museum, Lahaina, HI........401
Whatcom Museum of History and Art, Bellingham, WA...............................1549
Wheeler Historic Farm, Salt Lake City, UT..1474
Wheels O' Time Museum, Peoria, IL...........451
Wheels Through Time Museum, Inc., Maggie Valley, NC 1110
The Wheelwright Museum of the American Indian, Santa Fe, NM.............950
Whiskeytown Unit, Whiskeytown-Shasta-Trinity National Recreation Area, Whiskeytown, CA........198
White County Historical Society, Carmi, IL..415
White County Historical Society Museum, Monticello, IN 491
White Deer Land Museum, Pampa, TX.....1442
The White House, Washington, DC.............294
White Pillars Museum, De Pere Historical Society, De Pere, WI.............1594
White River Valley Museum, Auburn, WA..1547

Whitewater Historical Museum, Whitewater, WI..............................1628

Whitley County Historical Museum, Columbia City, IN................................472

Whitney Museum of American Art, New York, NY.................................1041

Whittier Home Association, Amesbury, MA...658

Wichita Center for the Arts, Wichita, KS.....563

Wichita Falls Museum and Art Center, Wichita Falls, TX...........................1461

Wichita-Sedgwick County Historical Museum Association, Wichita, KS..........563

Wickersham House Museum (Tanana-Yukon Historical Society), Fairbanks, AK...................................24

Wilber Czech Museum, Wilber, NE........875

Wilbur D. May Museum, Reno, NV............882

Wilder Memorial Museum, Strawberry Point, IA...................................528

Wilderness Road Regional Museum, Newbern, VA...........................1519

Wildland Firefighters Museum, Capitan, NM......................................937

Wildlife Experience Museum, Parker, CO ...229

Wildlife Prairie State Park, Hanna City, IL.......................................439

Wildling Art Museum, Los Olivos, CA 123

Wildwood Historical Society, Inc., Wildwood, NJ..............................930

Wilkes Art Gallery, North Wilkesboro, NC....................................1113

Wilkinson County Museum, Woodville, MS......................................810

Will Rogers Memorial Museum, Claremore, OK..............................1198

Will Rogers State Historic Park, Pacific Palisades, CA.............................137

Willa Cather Pioneer Memorial and Educational Foundation, Red Cloud, NE......................................872

Willard House and Clock Museum, Inc., Grafton, MA.................................685

William A. Farnsworth Library and Art Museum, Inc. d/b/a Farnsworth Art Museum, Rockland, ME....................621

The William Benton Museum of Art, Storrs, CT....................................262

The William Breman Jewish Heritage Museum, Atlanta, GA....................364

William Brewster Nickerson Memorial Room, Cape Cod Community College, West Barnstable, MA 717

William Clark Market House Museum, Paducah, KY.................................582

William Cullen Bryant Homestead, Cummington, MA..............................678

William Hammond Mathers Museum, Bloomington, IN.............................470

William Heath Davis House Museum administered by Gaslamp Quarter Historical Foundation, San Diego, CA....162

William J. Clinton Presidential Library & Museum, Little Rock, AR...................63'

William McKinley Presidential Library & Museum, Canton, OH.......................1146

William Otis Sawtelle Collections and Research Center, Bar Harbor, ME...........606

William Pryor Letchworth Museum, Castile, NY....................................976

Williams College Museum of Art, Williamstown, MA...........................719

Williamson County Historical Society, Marion, IL..................................444

Wilmette Historical Museum, Wilmette, IL.......................................466

Wilmington Railroad Museum, Wilmington, NC...........................1124

Wilson's Creek National Battlefield, Republic, MO...............................829

Winchendon Historical Society, Inc., Winchendon, MA............................720

Winchester-Frederick County Historical Society, Inc., Winchester, VA.................1546

Wind Cave National Park, Hot Springs, SD...................................1348

The Wine Museum of Greyton H. Taylor, Hammondsport, NY............................997

Winedale, Center for American History, University of Texas at Austin, Round Top, TX.................................1446

Wing Luke Asian Museum, Seattle, WA...1569

Wings of History Air Museum, San Martin, CA.................................175

Winnebago Area Museum, Winnebago, MN.....................................797

Winnetka Historical Society, Winnetka, IL.......................................466

Wiregrass Museum of Art, Dothan, AL 8

Wisconsin Maritime Museum, Manitowoc, WI................................1607

Wisconsin National Guard Museum, Camp Douglas, WI...........................1593

The Wisconsin Union Galleries, University of Wisconsin-Madison, Madison, WI..............................1606

Wisconsin Veterans Museum-King, King, WI....................................1602

Wisconsin Veterans Museum-Madison, Madison, WI..............................1606

Wise County Heritage Museum, Decatur, TX.....................................1408

Wiseman & FireHouse Galleries, Rogue Community College, Grants Pass, OR ..1225

Wistariahurst Museum, Holyoke, MA..........687

Witte Museum, San Antonio, TX 1451

Wolf Point Area Historical Society, Inc., Wolf Point, MT.............................855

Wolfeboro Historical Society, Wolfeboro, NH....................................897

Women's History Museum, West Liberty, WV...................................1587

Wood County Historical Center and Museum, Bowling Green, OH 1143

Wood Library-Museum of Anesthesiology, Park Ridge, IL...............450

Woodbine International Fire Museum, Woodbine, GA................................392

Woodburn Historic House, Pendleton, SC .1339

Woodford County Historical Society Museum, Versailles, KY....................584

Woodlawn Museum/The Black House, Ellsworth, ME................................610

Woodlawn Plantation Museum, Alexandria, VA..............................1494

Woodmere Art Museum, Philadelphia, PA.1289

Woodrow Wilson House, Washington, DC.......................................294

Woodrow Wilson Presidential Library at His Birthplace, Staunton, VA..............1537

Woodson County Historical Society, Yates Center, KS...........................564

Woodstock Artists Association, Woodstock, NY............................1087

Woodstock Historical Society, Inc., Woodstock, CT...............................268

Woodstock Historical Society, Inc., Woodstock, VT...............................1491

Woodville Museum, Inc., Rogue River, OR.......................................1234

Worcester Art Museum, Worcester, MA........721

Worcester County Horticultural Society/Tower Hill Botanic Garden, Boylston, MA................................670

The Works: Ohio Center for History, Art & Technology, Newark, OH.................1179

World Erotic Art Museum, Miami Beach, FL.......................................327

World Figure Skating Museum & Hall of Fame, Colorado Springs, CO.............208

World Forestry Center, Portland, OR 1233

World Golf Hall of Fame, Saint Augustine, FL.................................340

World Methodist Museum, Lake Junaluska, NC.............................1109

World Museum of Mining, Butte, MT 843

World O' Tools Museum, Waverly, TN......1385

World of Scouting Museum, Valley Forge, PA.................................1304

World of Wings Pigeon Center, Oklahoma City, OK........................1211

World's First Wendy's Restaurant, Columbus, OH................................1159

World's Smallest Museum, Superior, AZ.......45

Wounded Knee Museum, Wall, SD............1358

Wrangell Museum, Wrangell, AK..................29

Wrather West Kentucky Museum, Murray, KY.................................580

Wray Museum, Wray, CO........................235

Wright Brothers National Memorial, Kill Devil Hills, NC..............................1108

Wright County Historical Society, Buffalo, MN................................770

Wright Museum, Wolfeboro, NH.................897

Wright Museum of Art, Beloit College, Beloit, WI..................................1592

Wright State University Art Galleries, Dayton, OH.................................1162

Wupatki National Monument, Flagstaff, AZ......................................34

Wyandot County Historical Society, Upper Sandusky, OH........................1188

Wyandotte County Museum, Bonner Springs, KS.................................534

Wyoming Pioneer Memorial Museum, Douglas, WY...............................1632

Wyoming State Museum, Cheyenne, WY..1631

Wyoming Territorial Prison State Historic Site, Laramie, WY............................1636

Yale Center for British Art, New Haven, CT......................................254

Yale University Art Gallery, New Haven, CT......................................254

Yankee Air Force, Inc. (Yankee Air Museum), Ypsilanti, MI......................766

Yates County Genealogical and Historical Society and Oliver House Museum and L. Caroline Underwood Museum, Penn Yan, NY.............................1052

Yeiser Art Center, Paducah, KY 582

Yellow Medicine County Historical Society and Museum, Granite Falls, MN.....................................777

Yellowstone Art Museum, Billings, MT......842

Yellowstone Gateway Museum of Park County, Livingston, MT.....................850

Yellowstone National Park, Gardiner, MT ...847

Yogi Berra Museum and Learning Center, Little Falls, NJ.............................910

Yolo County Historical Museum, Woodland, CA...............................199

York W. Bailey Museum at Penn Center, Saint Helena Island, SC....................1340

Yorktown Historical Museum, Yorktown, TX.....................................1462

The Yosemite Museum, National Park Service, Yosemite National Park, CA......199

Ypsilanti Historical Museum, Ypsilanti, MI.......................................767

Yucaipa Valley Historical Society Museum, Yucaipa, CA.........................201

Yuma Art Center Museum - Yuma Fine Arts, Yuma, AZ..................................54

Yuma Crossing State Historic Park, Yuma, AZ......................................54

Yuma Territorial Prison State Historic Park, Yuma, AZ.................................54

Zabriskie Gallery, New York, NY 1041

Zalud House, Porterville, CA....................144

Zane Grey Museum, Lackawaxen, PA 1265

Zanesville Art Center, Zanesville, OH......1194

Zelienople Historical Society, Zelienople, PA.......................................1309

Zeum, San Francisco, CA 170

Ziibiwing Center of Anishinabe Culture & Lifeways, Mount Pleasant, MI...........757

Prints, Drawings, Graphic Arts

A.K.C. Museum of The Dog, Saint Louis, MO........831

A.L. Fetterman Educational Museum, Fort Valley, GA........372

The APEX Museum, Atlanta, GA........357

A.R. Mitchell Museum, Trinidad, CO........233

Abby Aldrich Rockefeller Folk Art Museum, Williamsburg, VA........1544

Abilene Zoological Gardens, Abilene, TX.1385

Abington Art Center, Jenkintown, PA........1263

Abraham Lincoln Library & Museum, Lincoln Memorial University, Harrogate, TN........1366

Academy Art Museum, Easton, MD........642

Ackland Art Museum, Chapel Hill, NC.....1093

Adams National Historical Park, Quincy, MA........704

Adams State College Luther Bean Museum, Alamosa, CO........201

Addison Gallery of American Art, Andover, MA........659

African American Museum, Cleveland, OH........1152

African American Museum, Dallas, TX.....1403

The African American Museum in Philadelphia, Philadelphia, PA........1275

Afro-American Cultural Center, Charlotte, NC........1094

Agricultural and Industrial Museum, York County Heritage Trust, York, PA.........1309

Ah-Tah-Thi-Ki Museum, Big Cypress Seminole Indian Reservation, FL........295

Aiken Thoroughbred Racing Hall of Fame and Museum, Aiken, SC........1320

Air Victory Museum, Inc., Lumberton, NJ........910

The Airborne & Special Operations Museum, Fayetteville, NC........1100

Airpower Museum Inc., Ottumwa, IA........526

Akron Art Museum, Akron, OH........1138

Akta Lakota Museum and Cultural Center, Chamberlain, SD........1345

Akwesasne Museum, Hogansburg, NY........998

Alabama River Museum, Finchburg, AL........9

Alachua County Historic Trust: Matheson Museum, Inc., Gainesville, FL........310

The Alamo, San Antonio, TX........1447

Alaska Heritage Museum at Wells Fargo, Anchorage, AK........21

Alaska Indian Arts, Inc., Haines, AK........24

Alaska State Museum, Juneau, AK........25

Albany Institute of History & Art, Albany, NY........954

Albany Museum of Art, Albany, GA........355

Albion College Department of Art and Art History, Albion, MI........722

The Albrecht-Kemper Museum of Art, Saint Joseph, MO........830

Albright-Knox Art Gallery, Buffalo, NY......971

Albuquerque Museum, Albuquerque, NM...932

Alden B. Dow Museum of Science and Art of the Midland Center for the Arts, Midland, MI........755

Alexander Brest Museum and Gallery, Jacksonville, FL........313

Alexandria Museum of Art, Alexandria, LA........584

Alger County Heritage Center, Munising, MI........757

Alice Austen House Museum, Staten Island, NY........1072

Alice C. Sabatini Gallery-Topeka and Shawnee County Public Library, Topeka, KS........558

Alice Moseley Folk Art and Antique Museum, Bay Saint Louis, MS........798

The Alice T. Miner Colonial Collection, Chazy, NY........977

Aliceville Museum, Aliceville, AL........3

Allaire Village Inc., Farmingdale, NJ........903

Allegany County Historical Society, Inc., Cumberland, MD........641

Allegheny College Art Galleries (Bowman, Penelec & Megahan Galleries), Meadville, PA........1270

Allegheny Portage Railroad National Historic Site and Johnstown Flood National Memorial, Gallitzin, PA........1255

Allen Memorial Art Museum, Oberlin, OH........1180

Allen R. Hite Art Institute, Louisville, KY........575

Allentown Art Museum, Allentown, PA........1239

Alpine County Museum, Markleeville, CA........124

Altama Museum of Art & History, Vidalia, GA........390

Alva deMars Megan Chapel Art Center, Manchester, NH........891

Amarillo Museum of Art, Amarillo, TX.....1386

Amelia Earhart Birthplace Museum, Atchison, KS........532

Amelia Island Museum of History, Fernandina Beach, FL........306

America On Wheels, Inc., Allentown, PA..1239

American Academy of Arts and Letters, New York, NY........1018

American Airlines C.R. Smith Museum, Fort Worth, TX........1416

American Antiquarian Society, Worcester, MA........720

American Catholic Historical Society, Philadelphia, PA........1276

American Folk Art Museum, New York, NY........1018

American Hungarian Foundation/Museum of the American Hungarian Foundation, New Brunswick, NJ........915

American Independence Museum, Exeter, NH........887

The American Jazz Museum, Kansas City, MO........820

American Jewish Historical Society, New York, NY........1019

American Merchant Marine Museum, Kings Point, NY........1007

The American Museum of Fly Fishing, Manchester, VT........1481

American Museum of Nursing, Tempe, AZ........45

American Numismatic Association Money Museum, Colorado Springs, CO........206

American Printing House for the Blind, Callahan Museum, Louisville, KY........575

American Quarter Horse Hall of Fame & Museum, Amarillo, TX........1386

American Red Cross Visitors Center and Gift Shop, Washington, DC........275

American Royal Museum & Visitors Center, Kansas City, MO........820

American Saddlebred Horse Museum, Mexico, MO........827

American Saddlebred Museum, Lexington, KY........572

American Sport Art Museum and Archives, Daphne, AL........7

American Swedish Historical Foundation & Museum, Philadelphia, PA........1276

American Swedish Institute, Minneapolis, MN........781

American Textile History Museum, Lowell, MA........691

American University Museum at The Katzen Arts Center, Washington, DC......275

American Visionary Art Museum, Baltimore, MD........629

American Wings Air Museum, Blaine, MN........769

America's Ice Cream & Dairy Museum, Medina, OH........1175

Americas Society, New York, NY........1020

Amity and Woodbridge Historical Society, Woodbridge, CT........268

Amon Carter Museum, Fort Worth, TX.....1416

Amory Regional Museum, Amory, MS........797

Anadarko Heritage Museum, Anadarko, OK........1195

Anaheim Museum, Anaheim, CA........71

Anchorage Museum at Rasmuson Center, Anchorage, AK........22

Ancient and Honorable Artillery Company, Boston, MA........663

Anderson/Abruzzo Albuquerque International Balloon Museum, Albuquerque, NM........933

Anderson Fine Arts Center, Anderson, IN ...467

Anderson Gallery - Drake University, Des Moines, IA........514

Anderson Gallery, School of the Arts, Virginia Commonwealth University, Richmond, VA........1528

Anderson Museum of Contemporary Art, Roswell, NM........945

Andover Historical Society, Andover, MA...660

Andrew County Museum & Historical Society, Savannah, MO........838

Andrew Low House, Savannah, GA........384

The Andy Warhol Museum, Pittsburgh, PA........1290

Anita S. Wooten Gallery at Valencia Community College East Campus, Orlando, FL........331

Anna Lamar Switzer Center for Visual Arts, Pensacola, FL........335

Anniston Museum of Natural History, Anniston, AL........3

Antelope Valley Indian Museum, Lancaster, CA........108

Anthropology Museum, University of San Diego, San Diego, CA........155

The Antiquarian and Landmarks Society, Inc., Hartford, CT........244

The Antique Boat Museum, Clayton, NY ...978

The Appaloosa Museum and Heritage Center, Moscow, ID........407

Appleton Museum of Art, Ocala, FL........330

APVA's John Marshall House, Richmond, VA........1528

Aquarium of Niagara, Niagara Falls, NY ..1042

Arab American National Museum, Dearborn, MI........733

Arbor Lodge State Historical Park, Nebraska City, NE........868

ARC Gallery (Artists, Residents of Chicago), Chicago, IL........417

Arcadia Township Historical Commission, Arcadia, MI........726

Archer County Museum, Archer City, TX.1387

Archives Museum, Temple Mickve Israel, Savannah, GA........384

Archives of J.S.G. Boggs, Brandon, FL........298

Argo Gold Mine & Mill Museum, Idaho Springs, CO........223

Arizona Military Museum, Phoenix, AZ........39

Arizona State Capitol Museum, Phoenix, AZ........39

Arizona State Museum, Tucson, AZ........48

Arizona State Parks Board, Phoenix, AZ........39

Arizona State University Art Museum, Tempe, AZ........45

Ark-La-Tex Antique & Classic Vehicle Museum, Shreveport, LA........600

The Arkansas Arts Center, Little Rock, AR........61

Arkansas Historic Wine Museum, Paris, AR........65

Arkansas Post National Memorial, Gillett, AR........58

Arkansas State University Art Gallery, Jonesboro, AR........60

Arkansas Tech University Museum of Prehistory and History, Russellville, AR........67

Arlington Arts Center, Arlington, VA 1495
Arlington Heights Historical Museum, Arlington Heights, IL 411
The Arlington Historical Society, Arlington, MA 660
Arlington House, The Robert E. Lee Memorial, Arlington, VA.................1495
Arlington Museum of Art, Arlington, TX ..1387
Armenian Library and Museum of America, Watertown, MA 716
Armstrong Browning Library, Waco, TX ..1458
Arnot Art Museum, Elmira, NY 987
Arrow Rock State Historic Site, Arrow Rock, MO.................810
Arrowmont School of Arts & Crafts, Gatlinburg, TN.................1365
Art and Culture Center of Hollywood, Hollywood, FL.................312
Art Association of Harrisburg, Harrisburg, PA.................1258
Art Association of Randolph County, Inc., Union City, IN.................501
The Art Center at Fuller Lodge, Los Alamos, NM.................942
Art Center In Hargate, St. Paul's School, Concord, NH.................884
Art Center of Battle Creek, Battle Creek, MI.................726
Art Center Sarasota, Inc, Sarasota, FL.........343
Art Center Waco, Waco, TX.................1458
Art Complex Museum, Duxbury, MA.........680
The Art Galleries at UAH, Huntsville, AL.................11
The Art Gallery at the University of Maryland, College Park, College Park, MD.................640
Art Gallery at the University of New England, Portland, ME.................618
The Art Gallery, John C. Calhoun State Community College, Decatur, AL.................7
The Art Gallery, Lower Columbia College Fine Arts Gallery, Longview, WA.................1558
The Art Gallery, University of New Hampshire, Durham, NH.................886
Art Guild of Burlington, Inc., Burlington, IA.................507
Art In Embassies Program, U.S. Department of State, Washington, DC 276
The Art Institute of Chicago, Chicago, IL ...418
Art Museum of Greater Lafayette, Lafayette, IN.................487
Art Museum of Southeast Texas, Beaumont, TX.................1393
Art Museum of The University of Memphis, Memphis, TN.................1372
Art Museum of Western Virginia, Roanoke, VA.................1534
Arthouse, Austin, TX.................1388
Arthur A. Houghton Jr. Gallery & The Great Hall Gallery, New York, NY.................1020
The Arthur J. Moore Methodist Museum, Saint Simons Island, GA.................383
Arthur M. Sackler Gallery, Washington, DC.................276
Arthur Ross Gallery, University of Pennsylvania, Philadelphia, PA.................1276
Artillery Company of Newport Military Museum, Newport, RI.................1313
The Arts & Science Center for Southeast Arkansas, Pine Bluff, AR.................65
Arts Club of Washington, Washington, DC.................276
Arts Consortium of Cincinnati's African American Museum, Cincinnati, OH 1148
Arts Council of Moore County - Campbell House, Southern Pines, NC...1120
ARTSplace, Grand Forks, ND.................1131
Arvada Center for the Arts and Humanities, Arvada, CO.................201
The Ashby-Hodge Gallery of American Art, Central Methodist University, Fayette, MO.................815

Asheville Art Museum, Asheville, NC.......1088
Ashtabula Arts Center, Ashtabula, OH.......1140
Asian American Arts Centre, New York, NY.................1021
Asian Art Museum of San Francisco, Chong-Moon Lee Center for Asian Art and Culture, San Francisco, CA.................163
Asian Arts & Culture Center, Towson University, Towson, MD.................655
Associated Artists of Pittsburgh, Pittsburgh, PA.................1290
The Athenaeum of Philadelphia, Philadelphia, PA.................1276
Atlanta College of Art, Atlanta, GA.................358
Atlanta Contemporary Art Center, Atlanta, GA.................358
The Atlanta Cyclorama, Atlanta, GA.................358
Atlantic Center for the Arts, Inc., New Smyrna Beach, FL.................329
Atlantic City Historical Museum, Atlantic City, NJ.................897
Atrium Gallery Ltd., Saint Louis, MO.........832
Attleboro Arts Museum, Attleboro, MA.......661
Atwater Kent Museum of Philadelphia, Philadelphia, PA.................1276
Audrain Historical Museum, Graceland, Mexico, MO.................827
Audubon House & Tropical Gardens, Key West, FL.................317
Audubon Society of New Hampshire, Concord, NH.................884
Audubon Society of Rhode Island, Smithfield, RI.................1319
Audubon State Historic Site, Saint Francisville, LA.................600
Augustana College Art Museum, Rock Island, IL.................453
Aurora Public Art Commission, Aurora, IL.................411
Austin Museum of Art - Downtown, Austin, TX.................1388
Automobile Driving Museum, Los Angeles, CA.................112
Aviation Museum of Kentucky Inc., Lexington, KY.................572
The AXA Gallery, New York, NY.................1021

Baca House, Trinidad History Museum, Trinidad, CO.................233
Badger Mine and Museum, Shullsburg, WI.................1622
Bailey House Museum - Maui Historical Society, Wailuku, HI.................402
Baker University, William A. Quayle Bible Collection, Baldwin City, KS.........533
Bakersfield Museum of Art, Bakersfield, CA.................73
Bale Grist Mill State Historic Park, Calistoga, CA.................80
Ball State University Museum of Art, Muncie, IN.................492
Baltimore & Ohio Railroad Museum, Baltimore, MD.................629
Baltimore Civil War Museum, Baltimore, MD.................629
Baltimore County Historical Society, Cockeysville, MD.................640
The Baltimore Museum of Art, Baltimore, MD.................630
Balzekas Museum of Lithuanian Culture, Chicago, IL.................418
Bandelier National Monument, Los Alamos, NM.................942
Bangor Museum & Center for History, Bangor, ME.................604
Bar Harbor Historical Society, Bar Harbor, ME.................605
The Barker Character, Comic and Cartoon Museum, Cheshire, CT.................237
Barnard's Mill Art Museum, Glen Rose, TX.................1422
Barnes Foundation, Merion, PA.................1271
Barnes Museum, Southington, CT.................260

The Barnum Museum, Bridgeport, CT.........235
Barnwell County Museum, Barnwell, SC ..1321
Barratt's Chapel and Museum, Frederica, DE.................270
Barstow Route 66 Mother Road Museum, Barstow, CA.................74
The Bartlett Museum, Amesbury, MA.........657
Barton Museum, Wilson, NC.................1124
Bass Museum of Art, Miami Beach, FL.......326
Bates College Museum of Art, Lewiston, ME.................613
Battle of Lexington State Historic Site, Lexington, MO.................826
The Battles Museums of Rural Life, Girard, PA.................1256
Battleship North Carolina, Wilmington, NC.................1122
Battleship Texas State Historic Site, La Porte, TX.................1433
Baum Gallery of Fine Art, University of Central Arkansas, Conway, AR.................56
Baycrafters, Inc., Bay Village, OH.................1141
Bayou Bend Collection and Gardens, Houston, TX.................1425
Beard Gallery, Norton, MA.................700
Beaumont Art League, Beaumont, TX.......1394
Beauvoir, The Jefferson Davis Home and Presidential Library, Biloxi, MS.................798
Beaver Island Historical Society, Beaver Island, MI.................728
Beck Cultural Exchange Center, Knoxville, TN.................1369
Beehive House, Salt Lake City, UT.................1470
Belair Mansion, Bowie, MD.................638
Belair Stable Museum, Bowie, MD.................638
Belcourt Castle, Newport, RI.................1313
Bellamy Mansion Museum of History and Design Arts, Wilmington, NC.................1122
Belle Isle Nature Zoo, Detroit, MI.................735
Bellport-Brookhaven Historical Society and Museum, Bellport, NY.................961
Belskie Museum of Art & Science, Closter, NJ.................902
Belvedere-Tiburon Landmarks Society, Tiburon, CA.................192
Bement-Billings Farmstead, Newark Valley, NY.................1041
Ben Shahn Galleries at William Paterson University of New Jersey, Wayne, NJ.....929
Benedicta Arts Center, Saint Joseph, MN 789
The Benjamin & Dr. Edgar R. Cofeld Judaic Museum of Temple Beth Zion, Buffalo, NY.................971
The Benjamin Banneker Park & Museum, Baltimore, MD.................631
Benjamin Harrison Presidential Site, Indianapolis, IN.................481
Bennett Place State Historic Site, Durham, NC.................1098
Bennington Battlefield State Historic Site, Walloomsac, NY.................1081
Benton County Historical Museum, Philomath, OR.................1230
Berea College, Doris Ulmann Galleries, Berea, KY.................565
Bergen Museum of Art & Science, Paramus, NJ.................919
Berkeley County Museum & Heritage Center, Moncks Corner, SC.................1336
Berkeley Plantation, Charles City, VA.................1498
Berkshire Artisans/Lichtenstein Center for the Arts, Pittsfield, MA.................702
Berrien County Historical Association, Berrien Springs, MI.................729
The Berry Botanic Garden, Portland, OR ..1230
Besser Museum for Northeast Michigan, Alpena, MI.................723
Beth Ahabah Museum & Archives, Richmond, VA.................1528
Betsy Ross House and Flag Museum, Philadelphia, PA.................1277

Prints, Drawings, Graphic
Arts—Continued

Betts House Research Center, Cincinnati,
OH 1148
Betty Brinn Children's Museum,
Milwaukee, WI 1610
Beverly Historical Society and Museum,
Beverly, MA 662
Bexley Historical Society, Bexley, OH.......1143
BG John C.L. Scribner Texas Military
Forces Museum, Austin, TX 1389
Biblical Arts Center, Dallas, TX.................1404
Bicentennial Art Center & Museum,
Paris, IL 449
Big Bend National Park, Big Bend, TX.....1396
Big Thicket National Preserve, Kountze,
TX 1432
Big Thunder Gold Mine, Keystone, SD.....1349
Big Timbers Museum, Lamar, CO 225
Biggs Museum of American Art, Dover,
DE 269
Billy the Kid Museum, Fort Sumner, NM ...939
Biltmore Estate, Asheville, NC...................1089
Birger Sandzen Memorial Gallery,
Lindsborg, KS..............................549
Birmingham Botanical Gardens,
Birmingham, AL..............................4
Birmingham Civil Rights Institute,
Birmingham, AL..............................4
Birmingham Museum of Art,
Birmingham, AL..............................5
Birthplace of John Wayne, Winterset, IA.....530
Black Arts National Diaspora Museum,
New Orleans, LA.........................594
Black Heritage Museum, Miami, FL.............323
Black Hills Mining Museum, Lead, SD.....1350
Black History Museum and Cultural
Center, Richmond, VA................1528
Black Mountain College Museum & Arts
Center, Asheville, NC...................1089
Blackhawk Museum (Behring-Hofmann
Educational Institute, Inc.), Danville,
CA 89
Blanden Memorial Art Museum, Fort
Dodge, IA 518
Blanton Museum of Art, Austin, TX..........1389
Blithewold Mansion, Gardens &
Arboretum, Bristol, RI 1310
Bloom Mansion, Trinidad History
Museum, Trinidad, CO................233
Blount-Bridgers House/Hobson Pittman
Memorial Gallery, Tarboro, NC 1121
Blount County Memorial Museum,
Oneonta, AL.................................17
Blount Mansion, Knoxville, TN 1369
Boca Raton Historical Society, Boca
Raton, FL 296
Boca Raton Museum of Art, Boca Raton,
FL 296
Boehm Gallery, San Marcos, CA 174
Boerner Botanical Gardens, Hales
Corners, WI 1600
Boise Art Museum, Boise, ID.....................403
Bolduc House Museum, Sainte
Genevieve, MO............................837
Bolin Wildlife Exhibit & Antique
Collection, McKinney, TX 1437
Bolinas Museum, Bolinas, CA......................79
Bolton Historical Society, Inc., Bolton,
MA 663
Bonnet House Museum & Gardens, Fort
Lauderdale, FL.............................306
Boonsborough Museum of History,
Boonsboro, MD...........................637
The Boorman House - The Juneau
County Historical Society, Mauston,
WI 1608
Booth Western Art Museum, Cartersville,
GA 367
Boothbay Region Art Foundation, Inc.,
Boothbay Harbor, ME 607

Boscobel, Garrison, NY 993
Boston Athenaeum Library, Boston, MA 663
Boston Fire Museum, Boston, MA...............664
Boston National Historical Park, Boston,
MA 664
Boston Public Library, Boston, MA 664
Boston University Art Gallery, Boston,
MA 665
Boulder Museum of Contemporary Art,
Boulder, CO 203
Bowdoin College Museum of Art,
Brunswick, ME 607
Bowie Railroad Station and Huntington
Museum, Bowie, MD 638
Bowling Green State University Fine Arts
Center Galleries, Bowling Green, OH ...1143
Boys Town Hall of History & Father
Flanagan House, Boys Town, NE............858
Bradford Brinton Memorial & Museum,
Big Horn, WY 1628
Bradley Gallery of Art, Plymouth, WI 1617
Braithwaite Fine Arts Gallery, Cedar
City, UT 1464
Brand Library & Art Center, Glendale,
CA 100
Brandywine River Museum, Chadds
Ford, PA 1246
Branigan Cultural Center, Las Cruces,
NM 940
Brattleboro Museum & Art Center,
Brattleboro, VT 1477
Brauer Museum of Art, Valparaiso, IN 501
Brazoria County Historical Museum,
Angleton, TX 1387
Brazos Valley Museum of Natural
History, Bryan, TX 1398
Bread & Puppet Museum, Glover, VT.......1479
Brec's Magnolia Mound Plantation,
Baton Rouge, LA.........................585
Brenau University Galleries, Brenau
University, Gainesville, GA 373
Brevard Museum of Art and Science,
Inc., Melbourne, FL.....................323
Brick House, Montgomery, NY 1015
Bridgton Historical Society, Bridgton,
ME 607
Bromfield Art Gallery, Boston, MA 665
Bronck Museum, Coxsackie, NY 983
The Bronx County Historical Society,
Bronx, NY 964
The Bronx Museum of the Arts, Bronx,
NY 965
Brookings County Historical Society
Museum, Volga, SD.....................1358
The Brooklyn Historical Society,
Brooklyn, NY 968
Brooklyn Museum, Brooklyn, NY...............968
The Broome County Historical Society,
Binghamton, NY..........................962
Brown County Art Gallery and Museum,
Nashville, IN 493
Brown County Historical Society, New
Ulm, MN 785
Brown County Historical Society Pioneer
Museum, Nashville, IN 493
Brownsville Museum of Fine Art -
Brownsville Art League, Brownsville,
TX 1398
Bruce Museum, Greenwich, CT 243
Brueckner Museum of Starr
Commonwealth, Albion, MI.................723
Brunnier Art Museum, Ames, IA.................504
Brunswick Railroad Museum and C&O
Canal Visitors Center, Brunswick, MD ...639
Buckaroo Hall of Fame, Winnemucca,
NV 882
Bucks County Civil War Library &
Museum, Doylestown, PA..............1249
Bucksport Historical Society, Inc.,
Bucksport, ME.............................608
Buechel Memorial Lakota Museum, Saint
Francis, SD 1355

Buffalo and Erie County Naval &
Military Park, Buffalo, NY 972
Buffalo Bill Cody Homestead, Princeton,
IA 527
Buffalo Bill Museum & Grave, Golden,
CO 219
Buffalo Museum of Science, Buffalo, NY ...972
Bulow Plantation Ruins Historic State
Park, Bunnell, FL.........................298
Bunker Hill Museum, Charlestown, MA......675
Burchfield-Penney Art Center, Buffalo,
NY 973
The Burgwin-Wright Museum,
Wilmington, NC..........................1123
Burke Museum of Natural History and
Culture, Seattle, WA...................1565
Burlingame Museum of Pez & Classic
Toy Museum, Burlingame, CA............80
Burlington Historical Museum,
Burlington, MA............................672
Burnham Tavern, Machias, ME...................614
Burrowes Mansion Museum, Matawan,
NJ 911
Bushy Run Battlefield, Jeannette, PA.........1263
The Butler Institute of American Art,
Youngstown, OH........................1193

CFCC Webber Center Gallery, Ocala, FL....330
C.F. Lott Historic Home, Oroville, CA 136
C.M. Russell Museum, Great Falls, MT......848
CU Art Galleries, Boulder, CO...................203
Cable Natural History Museum, Cable,
WI 1593
Cabrillo Gallery, Aptos, CA..........................71
Cabrillo Marine Aquarium, San Pedro,
CA 176
Cabrillo National Monument, San Diego,
CA 156
Cahoon Museum of American Art,
Cotuit, MA...................................677
Calaveras County Museum, San Andreas,
CA 155
Calhoun County Museum & Cultural
Center, Saint Matthews, SC 1341
California African-American Museum,
Los Angeles, CA..........................113
California Center for the Arts, Escondido,
Escondido, CA..............................93
California Historical Society, San
Francisco, CA...............................163
California Route 66 Museum, Victorville,
CA 195
California State Capitol Museum,
Sacramento, CA...........................151
California State Indian Museum,
Sacramento, CA...........................151
California State Railroad Museum,
Sacramento, CA...........................152
California State University, Long Beach,
University Art Museum, Long Beach,
CA 110
California Surf Museum, Oceanside, CA.....135
Calvin College Center Art Gallery, Grand
Rapids, MI...................................743
Cambridge Historical Society,
Cambridge, MA............................672
Camden County Historical Society,
Camden, NJ.................................899
Camp Atterbury Museum, Edinburgh, IN ...474
Camp Five Museum Foundation, Inc.,
Laona, WI.................................1604
Campus Martius Museum, Marietta, OH ...1173
The Camron-Stanford House Preservation
Association, Oakland, CA.....................133
Canajoharie Library and Art Gallery,
Canajoharie, NY..........................974
Canal Fulton Heritage Society, Canal
Fulton, OH................................1145
The Cannon Village Visitor Center,
Kannapolis, NC...........................1107
Canton Classic Car Museum, Canton, OH.1145
The Canton Museum of Art, Canton, OH ..1145

Cape Ann Historical Museum, Gloucester, MA..........684

The Cape Cod Maritime Museum, Hyannis, MA..........688

Cape Cod Museum of Art, Dennis, MA..........680

Capitol Visitors Center, a Division of the State Preservation Board, Austin, TX....1389

Capitola Historical Museum, Capitola, CA..........81

Cappon & Settlers House Museums, Holland, MI..........746

Captain Forbes House Museum, Milton, MA..........695

Captain John Wilson House, Cohasset, MA..........676

Captain Nathaniel B. Palmer House - Home of the Discoverer of Antarctica, Stonington, CT..........261

Carleton College Art Gallery, Northfield, MN..........785

Carlsbad Museum & Art Center, Carlsbad, NM..........938

Carnegie Art Museum, Oxnard, CA..........136

Carnegie Center for Art & History, New Albany, IN..........493

Carnton Plantation, Franklin, TN..........1365

Carpenter Home Museum and Gallery, Cle Elum, WA..........1551

Carroll Reece Museum, Johnson City, TN.1367

The Carter House Association, Inc., Franklin, TN..........1365

Cartoon Art Museum, San Francisco, CA....164

Caryl House and Fisher Barn, Dover, MA....680

CAS Gallery, Union, NJ..........928

Casemate Museum, Fort Monroe, VA..........1505

Castellani Art Museum of Niagara University, Niagara University, NY..........1043

The Castle, Marietta, OH..........1174

Castle Air Museum, Atwater, CA..........72

Cathedral Cultural Center, Omaha, NE..........870

The Cathedral of St. John the Divine, New York, NY..........1022

Catholic Historical Society of the Roanoke Valley, Roanoke, VA..........1535

Catoctin Wildlife Preserve & Zoo, Thurmont, MD..........655

Catskill Fly Fishing Center & Museum, Livingston Manor, NY..........1010

Cayuga Museum & Case Research Lab Museum, Auburn, NY..........959

Cayuga-Owasco Lakes Historical Society, Moravia, NY..........1015

Cazenovia College - Art & Design Gallery, Cazenovia, NY..........976

Cedar Grove Historical Society, Cedar Grove, NJ..........901

Cedar Rapids Museum of Art, Cedar Rapids, IA..........509

Cedarhurst Center for the Arts, Mount Vernon, IL..........446

Centennial Village Museum, Greeley, CO...221

Center for American History, Austin, TX....1390

Center for American Music, Pittsburgh, PA..........1291

Center for Book Arts, New York, NY..........1022

The Center for Civil War Photography, Gettysburg, PA..........1255

Center for Contemporary Printmaking, Norwalk, CT..........257

Center for Curatorial Studies, Annandale-on-Hudson, NY..........958

Center For Maine Contemporary Art, Rockport, ME..........621

Center for the Study of Political Graphics (CSPG), Los Angeles, CA..........113

The Center for Western Studies, Sioux Falls, SD..........1356

Center of Southwest Studies/Fort Lewis College, Durango, CO..........214

Center on Contemporary Art, Seattle, WA.1565

Central Montana Historical Association, Inc. Museum, Lewistown, MT..........850

The Central Museum, Central, AK..........23

Central Park Conservancy, New York, NY..........1022

Centre County Library and Historical Museum, Bellefonte, PA..........1241

Centre Hill Museum (The Petersburg Museums), Petersburg, VA..........1524

Chaffee Center for the Visual Arts, Rutland, VT..........1486

Chancellor Robert R. Livingston Masonic Library & Museum, New York, NY..........1022

Chapin Library of Rare Books, Williamstown, MA..........719

Charles A. Lindbergh Historic Site, Little Falls, MN..........779

Charles Allis Art Museum, Milwaukee, WI..........1610

Charles B. Goddard Center for Visual and Performing Arts, Ardmore, OK..........1196

Charles H. MacNider Museum, Mason City, IA..........523

Charles H. Taylor Arts Center, Hampton, VA..........1509

Charles H. Wright Museum of African American History, Detroit, MI..........735

The Charles Hosmer Morse Museum of American Art, Winter Park, FL..........354

Charles M. Schulz Museum and Research Center, Santa Rosa, CA..........184

Charles River Museum of Industry, Waltham, MA..........715

Charlotte and Philip Hanes Art Gallery, Wake Forest University, Winston-Salem, NC..........1124

Charnley-Persky House Museum, Chicago, IL..........418

Chattahoochee River National Recreation Area, Atlanta, GA..........359

Chattahoochee Valley Art Museum, LaGrange, GA..........375

Chattanooga African Museum/Bessie Smith Hall, Chattanooga, TN..........1360

Chazen Museum of Art, Madison, WI..........1604

Cheekwood-Tennessee Botanical Garden & Museum of Art, Nashville, TN..........1378

Cheney Homestead, Manchester, CT..........248

Cheraw Lyceum Museum, Cheraw, SC..........1327

Cherokee Courthouse Visitors Information Center & Museum, Gore, OK..........1201

Cherokee National Museum, Park Hill, OK..........1211

Cherokee Strip Land Rush Museum, Arkansas City, KS..........532

Cherry County Historical Society, Valentine, NE..........874

Chesapeake Bay Maritime Museum, Saint Michaels, MD..........652

Chester Art Guild, Chester, VT..........1478

Chester County Historical Society, West Chester, PA..........1307

The Chester Gould-Dick Tracy Museum, Woodstock, IL..........467

Chesterwood, Stockbridge, MA..........711

The Chicago Athenaeum: Museum of Architecture and Design, Galena, IL..........436

Chicago Botanic Garden, Glencoe, IL..........438

Chicago Children's Museum, Chicago, IL...419

Chicago Cultural Center, Chicago, IL..........419

Chicago History Museum, Chicago, IL..........419

Chicago Public Library, Chicago, IL..........419

Chicago Zoological Park (Brookfield Zoo), Brookfield, IL..........414

The Chief John Ross House, Rossville, GA..........382

Chief Plenty Coups Museum, Pryor, MT.....852

Chieftains Museum, Rome, GA..........381

Children's Discovery Museum of San Jose, San Jose, CA..........171

The Children's Museum, Seattle, WA..........1565

The Children's Museum, Inc., Bloomsburg, PA..........1243

The Children's Museum of Indianapolis, Indianapolis, IN..........481

Children's Museum of Los Angeles, Van Nuys, CA..........194

Children's Museum of Pittsburgh, Pittsburgh, PA..........1291

The Children's Museum of Rose Hill Manor Park, Frederick, MD..........644

Children's Museum of the Arts, New York, NY..........1022

Chinati Foundation, Marfa, TX..........1436

Chinese Culture Center of San Francisco, San Francisco, CA..........164

Chinqua-Penn Plantation, Reidsville, NC...1117

Chisholm Trail Historical Museum, Waurika, OK..........1216

Chittenango Landing Canal Boat Museum, Chittenango, NY..........978

Choctaw County Historical Society, Hugo, OK..........1203

The Christian C. Sanderson Museum, Chadds Ford, PA..........1246

Christiansted National Historic Site, Saint Croix, VI..........1644

Chrysler Museum of Art, Norfolk, VA..........1521

Chula Vista Nature Center, Chula Vista, CA..........84

Cigna Museum and Art Collection, Philadelphia, PA..........1277

Cincinnati Art Museum, Cincinnati, OH....1148

Cincinnati Fire Museum, Cincinnati, OH....1149

Circus World Museum, Baraboo, WI..........1591

City Arts Center, Oklahoma City, OK..........1207

City Island Nautical Museum, Bronx, NY...965

City of Burlington Historical Society, Burlington, NJ..........899

City of Las Cruces Museum System, Las Cruces, NM..........940

City of Wayne Historical Museum, Wayne, MI..........766

Clark Atlanta University Art Galleries, Atlanta, GA..........359

Clarke House Museum, Chicago, IL..........420

Clark's Fork Valley Museum, Fromberg, MT..........846

Clarkson Historical Museum, Clarkson, NE..........859

Clay Center for Arts & Sciences West Virginia, Charleston, WV..........1580

Clermont State Historic Site, Clermont, NY..........979

Cleveland Artists Foundation at Beck Center for the Arts, Lakewood, OH..........1170

The Cleveland Museum of Art, Cleveland, OH..........1152

Cleveland State University Art Gallery, Cleveland, OH..........1153

Clewiston Museum, Inc., Clewiston, FL..........300

Clinton Academy, East Hampton, NY..........985

The Cloisters, New York, NY..........1023

Cloud County Historical Society Museum, Concordia, KS..........536

Clough-Hanson Gallery, Rhodes College, Memphis, TN..........1372

Clymer Museum of Art, Ellensburg, WA...1553

Coachella Valley Museum and Cultural Center, Indio, CA..........104

Codington County Heritage Museum, Watertown, SD..........1359

Colby College Museum of Art, Waterville, ME..........624

The Coleman House Museum and Brown County Historical Society, Ainsworth, NE..........855

Colfax County Society of Art, History and Archaeology, Raton, NM..........945

The College Art Gallery, Ewing, NJ..........903

College Football Hall of Fame, South Bend, IN..........499

College of Eastern Utah Art Gallery, Gallery East, Price, UT..........1469

Prints, Drawings, Graphic Arts—Continued

College of the Redwoods Art Gallery, Eureka, CA 94

The College of Wooster Art Museum, Wooster, OH 1192

The Colonial Spanish Quarter Museum, Saint Augustine, FL...................................338

Colorado Historical Society, Denver, CO.....210

Colorado Ski Museum-Ski & Snowboard Hall of Fame, Vail, CO 234

Colorado Springs Fine Arts Center (Taylor Museum), Colorado Springs, CO...................................206

Colton Hall Museum, Monterey, CA.......127

Columbia Museum of Art, Columbia, SC ..1329

Columbia River Exhibition of History, Science and Technology, Richland, WA 1564

Columbia River Maritime Museum, Astoria, OR 1218

Columbus-Belmont Civil War Museum, Columbus, KY 567

The Columbus Museum, Columbus, GA 368

Columbus Museum of Art, Columbus, OH...................................1157

Columbus Museum of Art and Design, Columbus, IN...................................473

Combat Air Museum, Inc., Topeka, KS 559

Command Museum, Marine Corps Recruit Depot, San Diego, San Diego, CA...................................156

The Commonwealth Museum, Boston, MA 665

Commonwealth of the Northern Mariana Islands Museum of History and Culture, Saipan, MP 1640

Community Council for the Arts, Kinston, NC 1108

Community Fine Arts Center, Rock Springs, WY 1637

Concord Historical Society, Warner Museum, Springville, NY 1071

Concordia Historical Institute, Saint Louis, MO...................................832

Confederate Memorial Hall-Bleak House, Knoxville, TN 1369

Connecticut Audubon Center at Fairfield, Fairfield, CT...................................240

Connecticut Historical Society, Hartford, CT 244

Constitution Square State Historic Site, Danville, KY...................................567

Contemporary Art Museum St. Louis, Saint Louis, MO 832

The Contemporary Arts Center, Cincinnati, OH 1150

The Contemporary Museum, Honolulu, HI 394

The Contemporary Museum at First Hawaiian Center, Honolulu, HI 394

Conway Scenic Railroad, Inc., North Conway, NH 892

Cookeville Depot Museum, Cookeville, TN 1364

Cooper Regional History Museum, Upland, CA...................................193

Coos Art Museum, Coos Bay, OR...................................1222

Coos Historical & Maritime Museum, North Bend, OR...................................1229

Copia: The American Center for Wine, Food & the Arts, Napa, CA 129

Copper Range Historical Museum, South Range, MI...................................764

Copshaholm House Museum & Historic Oliver Gardens, South Bend, IN...................................499

Coral Springs Museum of Art, Coral Springs, FL 301

The Corcoran Gallery of Art, Washington, DC...................................277

Corita Art Center, Los Angeles, CA...................................114

Cornell Museum of Art & History, Delray Beach, FL 304

Cortland County Historical Society, Cortland, NY 982

Cottonlandia Museum, Greenwood, MS 800

The Country Doctor Museum, Bailey, NC.1091

Coutts Memorial Museum of Art, Inc., El Dorado, KS 537

Craftsmen's Guild of Mississippi, Jackson, MS...................................802

Cranbrook Art Museum, Bloomfield Hills, MI...................................730

Cranbrook House and Gardens Auxiliary, Bloomfield Hills, MI 730

Crater Lake National Park, Crater Lake, OR...................................1222

Crawford W. Long Museum, Jefferson, GA...................................374

Creative Arts Guild, Dalton, GA 370

Creative Photographic Art Center of Maine, Lewiston, ME...................................614

Cress Gallery of Art, Chattanooga, TN.....1361

Cripple Creek District Museum, Inc., Cripple Creek, CO...................................209

Crispus Attucks Center Museum, Indianapolis, IN 482

Croatian Heritage Museum & Library, Eastlake, OH...................................1163

Crocker Art Museum, Sacramento, CA........152

Crook County Museum & Art Gallery, Sundance, WY...................................1638

Crooked Tree Arts Center, Petoskey, MI.....760

Crossman Gallery, UW-Whitewater, Whitewater, WI...................................1628

Crossroads of America, Bethlehem, NH 883

Crowley Art Association & Gallery, Crowley, LA 588

Crown Point State Historic Site, Crown Point, NY 984

Culbertson Museum, Culbertson, MT 845

Culinary Archives & Museum, Johnson & Wales University, Providence, RI......1316

Cumberland County Historical Society, The Hamilton Library and The Two Mile House, Carlisle, PA...................................1245

Cummer Museum of Art and Gardens, Jacksonville, FL...................................314

Cupertino Historical Society & Museum, Cupertino, CA...................................88

Cupola House, Egg Harbor, WI 1596

Curfman Gallery & Duhesa Lounge, Fort Collins, CO...................................216

The Currier Museum of Art, Manchester, NH...................................891

Custer County Art & Heritage Center, Miles City, MT...................................851

The Custom House Maritime Museum, Newburyport, MA 697

Cuyahoga Valley National Park, Brecksville, OH 1144

Czech Center New York, New York, NY...1024

DAAP Galleries, Cincinnati, OH 1150

Dahesh Museum of Art, New York, NY 1024

Dahl Arts Center, Rapid City, SD...................................1354

Dakota Territory Air Museum, Minot, ND.1134

Dakotaland Museum, Huron, SD...................................1348

Dallam-Hartley XIT Museum, Dalhart, TX...................................1403

The Dallas Center for Contemporary Art - The Dallas Contemporary, Dallas, TX...................................1404

Dallas Historical Society, Dallas, TX........1405

Dallas Holocaust Museum, Dallas, TX 1405

Dallas Museum of Art, Dallas, TX.............1405

Dallas Museum of Natural History, Dallas, TX...................................1406

Dalton Galleries, Decatur, GA 370

The Dan Quayle Center & Museum, Huntington, IN...................................481

The Dana-Thomas House State Historic Site, Springfield, IL 458

Dancing Bear Folk Center, Thermopolis, WY...................................1639

Danforth Museum of Art, Framingham, MA...................................683

The Danish Immigrant Museum, Elk Horn, IA...................................517

Danvers Archival Center, Danvers, MA......678

Danville Museum of Fine Arts & History, Danville, VA 1502

Darlington Raceway Stock Car Museum, NMPA Hall of Fame, Darlington, SC....1331

Daughters of the American Revolution Museum, Washington, DC 277

Daum Museum of Contemporary Art, Sedalia, MO...................................838

Daura Gallery, Lynchburg, VA...................................1515

David Bradford House, Washington, PA 1305

The David Davis Mansion, Bloomington, IL...................................413

David Winton Bell Gallery, Providence, RI...................................1316

Davis Art Center, Davis, CA...................................89

Davis Art Gallery, Columbia, MO...............813

Davis Museum and Cultural Center, Wellesley, MA...................................716

Davison Art Center, Wesleyan University, Middletown, CT...................................249

The Davistown Museum, Liberty, ME.........614

Dawes County Historical Society Museum, Chadron, NE...................................859

Dawson Springs Museum and Art Center, Inc., Dawson Springs, KY 568

Dayton Art Institute, Dayton, OH...................................1161

De Saisset Museum, Santa Clara, CA..........180

Decatur House Museum, Washington, DC...277

DeCordova Museum and Sculpture Park, Lincoln, MA...................................690

Dedham Historical Society Museum, Dedham, MA 679

Deer Isle-Stonington Historical Society, Deer Isle, ME...................................609

Deer Park Escondido Winery & Auto Museum, Escondido, CA...................................93

Deerfield Beach Historical Society, Deerfield Beach, FL 304

Degrazia Gallery In The Sun, Tucson, AZ.....48

Deines Cultural Center, Russell, KS.,.........556

The DeLand Museum of Art, De Land, FL...................................303

Delaware Art Museum, Wilmington, DE 273

Delaware Center for the Contemporary Arts, Wilmington, DE...................................273

Delta Blues Museum, Clarksdale, MS.........799

Denison Museum, Granville, OH 1167

The Dennison Railroad Depot Museum, Dennison, OH 1162

Dennos Museum Center of Northwestern Michigan College, Traverse City, MI......765

Dennys River Historical Society, Dennysville, ME...................................609

Denver Art Museum, Denver, CO...................................210

Denver Botanic Gardens, Inc., Denver, CO...................................210

Department of the Treasury, Washington, DC...................................278

DePaul University Art Museum, Chicago, IL...................................420

Depot Museum & Fort Sedgwick Museum, Julesburg, CO...................................223

Depreciation Lands Museum, Allison Park, PA...................................1240

DePree Art Center & Gallery, Holland, MI...................................746

Des Moines Art Center, Des Moines, IA 514

Desert Caballeros Western Museum, Wickenburg, AZ...................................53

Detroit Artists Market, Detroit, MI...............735

The Detroit Institute of Arts, Detroit, MI....736

Detroit Zoo, Royal Oak, MI...................................762

DeWitt Wallace Decorative Arts Museum, Williamsburg, VA 1545

Dey Mansion/Washington's Headquarters
   Museum, Wayne, NJ 929
Dia:Beacon, Riggio Galleries, Beacon,
   NY 960
Dia: Chelsea, New York, NY 1024
Diggs Gallery at Winston-Salem State
   University, Winston-Salem, NC 1125
Dinsmore Homestead Foundation,
   Burlington, KY 566
Diplomatic Reception Rooms,
   Department of State, Washington, DC 278
The Discovery Museum, Inc., Bridgeport,
   CT 236
Dishman Art Museum, Beaumont, TX 1394
The Dixon Gallery and Gardens,
   Memphis, TN..1372
Dr. John Harris Dental Museum,
   Bainbridge, OH 1141
Dr Pepper Museum and Free Enterprise
   Institute, Waco, TX...............................1458
Dr. Samuel D. Harris National Museum
   of Dentistry, Baltimore, MD 631
Dodge County Historical Society
   Museum, Beaver Dam, WI 1591
Dog Mushing Museum, Fairbanks, AK.........24
Don F. Pratt Memorial Museum, Fort
   Campbell, KY 568
Don Garlits Museum of Drag Racing
   Inc., Ocala, FL......................................330
Donkey Milk House, Historic Home, Key
   West, FL...317
Donna Beam Fine Art Gallery, UNLV,
   Las Vegas, NV 878
The Douglas F. Cooley Memorial Art
   Gallery, Reed College, Portland, OR.....1231
Dowd Fine Arts Gallery, State University
   of New York College at Cortland,
   Cortland, NY 983
Downey Museum of Art, Downey, CA..........91
Dragon Dreams Museum & Gift Shop,
   Chattanooga, TN..................................1362
Drew County Historical Museum,
   Monticello, AR 64
Drum Barracks Civil War Museum,
   Wilmington, CA 198
Dublin-Laurens Museum, Dublin, GA 370
Dubuque Museum of Art, Dubuque, IA.......516
Duluth Art Institute, Duluth, MN 772
Duncan Cottage Museum, Metlakatla, AK.....27
The Duncan Gallery of Art, De Land, FL....304
The Dwight Frederick Boyden Gallery,
   Saint Mary's City, MD 652
Dyckman Farmhouse Museum and Park,
   New York, NY......................................1025

E. St. Julien Cox House, Saint Peter, MN ...792
EAA AirVenture Museum, Oshkosh, WI....1616
Earth & Mineral Sciences Museum and
   Art Gallery, University Park, PA 1303
East End Seaport Museum and Marine
   Foundation, Greenport, NY 996
East Hampton Historical Society, Inc.,
   East Hampton, NY 985
East-West Center, Honolulu, HI..................394
Eastern Shore Art Center, Fairhope, AL..........9
Eastern State Penitentiary Historic Site,
   Philadelphia, PA 1278
The Ebenezer Maxwell Mansion, Inc.,
   Philadelphia, PA 1278
Eccles Community Arts Center, Ogden,
   UT 1467
EcoTarium, Worcester, MA.......................720
Edgar Allan Poe Cottage, Bronx, NY 965
Edgar Allan Poe House and Museum,
   Baltimore, MD......................................631
Edgar Allan Poe Museum, Richmond, VA.1529
Edgar County Historical Museum, Paris,
   IL..449
Edisto Island Historic Preservation
   Society Museum, Edisto Island, SC 1332
Edmonds Art Festival Museum,
   Edmonds, WA......................................1553

Edsel & Eleanor Ford House, Grosse
   Pointe Shores, MI..................................745
Edward H. White II Memorial Museum,
   Brooks Air Force Base, TX 1397
Egan Maritime Foundation, Nantucket,
   MA..695
Eisenhower Birthplace State Historical
   Site, Denison, TX 1409
Eiteljorg Museum of American Indians
   and Western Art, Indianapolis, IN 482
El Dorado Nature Center, Long Beach,
   CA 110
El Museo Del Barrio, New York, NY 1025
El Paso Museum of Art, El Paso, TX 1411
El Pueblo Historical Monument, Los
   Angeles, CA..114
Elder Art Gallery, Nebraska Wesleyan
   University, Lincoln, NE 865
Elizabeth Myers Mitchell Art Gallery at
   St. John's College, Annapolis, MD..........627
The Ellen Noel Art Museum of the
   Permian Basin, Odessa, TX 1441
Elliott Museum, Stuart, FL 346
Elmhurst Art Museum, Elmhurst, IL............433
Eloise Pickard Smith Gallery at Cowell
   College, Santa Cruz, CA 181
Elverhoj Museum of History and Art,
   Solvang, CA..187
The Emerson Gallery, Clinton, NY 979
Emil A. Blackmore Museum of The
   American Legion, Indianapolis, IN 482
Emily Dickinson Museum: The
   Homestead and The Evergreens,
   Amherst, MA 658
Empire State Aerosciences Museum,
   Glenville, NY..995
Enlisted Heritage Hall, Maxwell AFB -
   Gunter Annex, AL 13
Epcot at Walt Disney World Resort, Lake
   Buena Vista, FL.....................................319
Ephrata Cloister, Ephrata, PA 1251
The Eric Carle Museum of Picture Book
   Art, Amherst, MA..................................658
Erie Art Museum, Erie, PA 1252
Erie Canal Museum, Syracuse, NY 1076
Erie Maritime Museum, Homeport U.S.
   Brig Niagara, Erie, PA 1252
Ernest Hemingway House Museum, Key
   West, FL...317
Ernie Pyle State Historic Site, Dana, IN......473
Essex Shipbuilding Museum, Essex, MA 681
The Esther and John Clay Fine Arts
   Gallery, Cheyenne, WY........................1630
Esther M. Klein Art Gallery at University
   City Science Center, Philadelphia, PA...1279
The Esther Thomas Atkinson Museum,
   Hampden-Sydney, VA 1509
Ethnic Heritage Museum, Rockford, IL 455
Eubie Blake National Jazz Institute and
   Cultural Center, Baltimore, MD 632
Eugene V. Debs Home, Terre Haute, IN 500
Euphrat Museum of Art, Cupertino, CA 89
Eureka Fire Museum, Milltown, NJ 911
Eureka Pioneer Museum of McPherson
   County, Inc., Eureka, SD 1346
Eureka School House, Springfield, VT 1487
Evansville Museum of Arts History &
   Science, Evansville, IN 475
Everglades National Park, Homestead, FL...313
Evergreen Aviation Museum,
   McMinnville, OR.................................1228
Evergreen Galleries, Olympia, WA............1560
Evergreen House, The Johns Hopkins
   University, Baltimore, MD......................632
Everhart Museum: Natural History,
   Science and Art, Scranton, PA 1298
Everson Museum of Art, Syracuse, NY 1076
Exploration Station - A Children's
   Museum, Bourbonnais, IL......................414
Ezra Meeker Mansion, Puyallup, WA 1564

The Fabric Workshop and Museum,
   Philadelphia, PA 1279

Faith Trumbull Chapter, Daughters of the
   American Revolution, Inc., Museum
   and Chapter House, Norwich, CT 258
Fall River Historical Society Museum,
   Fall River, MA 682
Fallingwater, Mill Run, PA 1272
Faninadahen Kosas Guahan-Guam
   Museum, Hagatna, GU.........................1640
Faulconer Gallery at Grinnell College,
   Grinnell, IA...519
Faulkner County Museum, Conway, AR.......56
Favell Museum Inc., Klamath Falls, OR....1227
Fayette Art Museum, Fayette, AL 9
Fayetteville Museum of Art, Fayetteville,
   NC...1100
Federal Hall National Memorial, New
   York, NY..1025
Federal Reserve Board, Washington, DC 278
Feet First: The Scholl Story, Rosalind
   Franklin University, North Chicago, IL...448
Fender Museum of Music and the Arts,
   Corona, CA..87
Festival-Institute, James Dick Foundation,
   Round Top, TX....................................1446
Figge Art Museum, Davenport, IA 512
Filoli Center, Woodside, CA 199
The Filson Historical Society, Inc.,
   Louisville, KY 576
Fine Arts Center at Miriam Hall, Anna
   Maria College, Paxton, MA 701
Fine Arts Center for New River Valley,
   Pulaski, VA...1526
Fine Arts Collection, Luther College,
   Decorah, IA..513
The Fine Arts Museums of San
   Francisco, Legion of Honor, San
   Francisco, CA 165
Fire Museum of Maryland, Inc.,
   Lutherville, MD.....................................649
Firehouse Art Gallery, Nassau
   Community College, Garden City, NY ...992
Fireman's Hall Museum, Philadelphia, PA.1279
1st Cavalry Division Museum, Fort
   Hood, TX..1414
The First Division Museum at Cantigny,
   Wheaton, IL 465
First White House of the Confederacy,
   Montgomery, AL 16
Fisher Gallery, University of Southern
   California, Los Angeles, CA 115
The Fisk University Galleries, Nashville,
   TN 1379
Fitchburg Art Museum, Fitchburg, MA........683
The Five Civilized Tribes Museum,
   Muskogee, OK....................................1205
The Flag House and Star-Spangled
   Banner Museum, Baltimore, MD.............632
Flagler Museum, Palm Beach, FL................333
Flandrau Science Center and Planetarium,
   Tucson, AZ...49
Flaten Art Museum of St. Olaf College,
   Northfield, MN 785
Fleming Historical Society, Fleming, CO 216
Flint House, Scotia, NY............................1068
Flint Institute of Arts, Flint, MI..................741
Florence Griswold Museum, Old Lyme,
   CT 258
Florewood State Park, Greenwood, MS 801
Florida Air Museum At Sun'n Fun,
   Lakeland, FL...321
Florida Holocaust Museum, Saint
   Petersburg, FL 341
Florida State University Museum of Fine
   Arts, Tallahassee, FL.............................347
Folger Shakespeare Library, Washington,
   DC 278
Folk Art Society of America, Richmond,
   VA...1529
Fonthill Museum of the Bucks County
   Historical Society, Doylestown, PA........1249
Ford's Theatre National Historic Site
   (Lincoln Museum), Washington, DC.......279

Prints, Drawings, Graphic Arts—Continued

Forest Lawn Museum, Glendale, CA 100
The Forges and Manor of Ringwood, Ringwood, NJ.................................923
Fort Benton Museum of the Upper Missouri, Fort Benton, MT.....................846
Fort Dalles Museum/Anderson Homestead, The Dalles, OR..................1237
Fort Davidson State Historic Site, Pilot Knob, MO..828
Fort Davis National Historic Site, Fort Davis, TX...1414
Fort de Chartres State Historic Site & Museum, Prairie du Rocher, IL 451
Fort Delaware Society, Delaware City, DE...268
Fort Dix Museum, Fort Dix, NJ 904
Fort Douglas Military Museum, Fort Douglas, UT..1465
Fort Frederica National Monument, Saint Simons Island, GA 383
Fort George G. Meade Museum, Fort Meade, MD..643
Fort Harker Museum Complex, Kanopolis, KS.......................................546
Fort Kearney Museum, Kearney, NE.........863
Fort Lauderdale Historical Society, Fort Lauderdale, FL.......................................307
Fort MacArthur Museum, San Pedro, CA....176
Fort Matanzas National Monument, Saint Augustine, FL...339
Fort McAllister, Richmond Hill, GA...........381
Fort McHenry National Monument and Historic Shrine, Baltimore, MD.............632
Fort Mifflin, Philadelphia, PA 1279
Fort Morgan Museum, Fort Morgan, CO....218
Fort Okanogan Interpretive Center, Brewster, WA.......................................1550
Fort Ontario State Historic Site, Oswego, NY...1048
Fort Peck Interpretive Center, Fort Peck, MT..846
The Fort Pitt Block House, Pittsburgh, PA..1292
Fort Plain Museum, Fort Plain, NY 991
Fort Polk Museum Activity, Fort Polk, LA...588
Fort Scott National Historic Site, Fort Scott, KS..540
Fort Selden State Monument, Radium Springs, NM.......................................945
Fort Sidney Museum & Post Commander's Home, Sidney, NE............873
Fort Smith Art Center, Fort Smith, AR 57
Fort Ticonderoga, Ticonderoga, NY 1078
Fort Union Trading Post National Historic Site, Williston, ND 1138
Fort Vasquez Museum, Platteville, CO 230
Fort Ward Museum and Historic Site, Alexandria, VA 1492
Fort Wayne Museum of Art, Fort Wayne, IN...477
Foster Gallery, University of Wisconsin-Eau Claire, Eau Claire, WI..1596
Fox Lake Historical Museum, Inc., Fox Lake, WI...1598
Framingham Historical Society & Museum, Framingham, MA.................683
The Frances Lehman Loeb Art Center, Poughkeepsie, NY 1055
Frances Willard House Museum, Evanston, IL..434
Frances Young Tang Teaching Museum and Art Gallery, Saratoga Springs, NY .1064
Francis McCray Gallery, Silver City, NM...951
Franconia Heritage Museum, Franconia, NH...888
Frank H. McClung Museum, Knoxville, TN 1370

Frank Lloyd Wright Home and Studio, Oak Park, IL.................................448
Frank Lloyd Wright's Pope-Leighey House, Alexandria, VA...........................1492
Frank Phillips Home, Bartlesville, OK.......1197
Franklin D. Roosevelt Presidential Library-Museum, Hyde Park, NY 1002
Franklin Furnace Archive, Inc., Brooklyn, NY...969
Franklin G. Burroughs-Simeon B. Chapin Art Museum, Myrtle Beach, SC............1338
Fraternal Order of Alaska State Troopers Museum, Anchorage, AK...................22
Fraunces Tavern Museum, New York, NY..1025
Fred Dana Marsh Museum, Ormond Beach, FL..333
Fred Harman Art Museum, Pagosa Springs, CO..229
The Fred Jones Jr. Museum of Art, Norman, OK.......................................1206
Fred Wolf, Jr. Gallery/Klein Branch Jewish Community Center, Philadelphia, PA 1280
Frederic Remington Art Museum, Ogdensburg, NY 1044
Frederick C. Robie House, Chicago, IL 420
Frederick R. Weisman Art Museum, Minneapolis, MN....................................781
Frederick R. Weisman Museum of Art, Malibu, CA...123
Fredericksburg Area Museum & Cultural Center, Inc., Fredericksburg, VA............1506
Free Library of Philadelphia Rare Book Department, Philadelphia, PA 1280
Freedman Gallery-Albright College, Reading, PA...1296
Freeport Arts Center, Freeport, IL...............435
Freer Gallery of Art, Washington, DC 279
French Art Colony, Gallipolis, OH...............1165
The French Legation Museum, Austin, TX 1390
Fresno Art Museum, Fresno, CA..................97
The Frick Art & Historical Center, Pittsburgh, PA.......................................1292
The Frick Collection, New York, NY.........1025
Friends of Historic Kingston, Fred J. Johnston House Museum, Kingston, NY...1007
Frisco Native American Museum and Natural History Center, Frisco, NC 1102
Frontier Times Museum, Bandera, TX.......1393
Frye Art Museum, Seattle, WA...................1566
Fulton Mansion State Historic Site, Rockport, TX...1446
Furnas-Gosper Historical Society & Museum, Arapahoe, NE 856

Gadsby's Tavern Museum, Alexandria, VA...1492
Gadsden Museum, Mesilla, NM 943
Gadsden Museum of Art, Gadsden, AL 10
Gaineswood, Demopolis, AL........................7
Galesburg Civic Art Center, Galesburg, IL..437
Gallery North, Setauket, NY.......................1069
Gallery of Contemporary Art, University of Colorado, Colorado Springs, Colorado Springs, CO 207
Gallery of Henry Street Settlement/Abrons Arts Center, New York, NY...1026
Gallery on the York - Yorktown Arts Foundation, Yorktown, VA....................1547
Gallery 101, River Falls, WI 1620
Gallery '76, Wenatchee, WA 1577
Gallier House, New Orleans, LA...................595
Galveston County Historical Museum, Galveston, TX...1420
Gardiner Art Gallery, Stillwater, OK..........1214
The Gardner Museum, Inc., Gardner, MA ...684
Gari Melchers Home and Studio, Fredericksburg, VA...............................1506

Garibaldi and Meucci Museum, Staten Island, NY...1072
Gary's Gallery, Bismarck, ND 1128
Gates Mills Historical Society, Gates Mills, OH...1166
Gathland State Park, Boonsboro, MD 637
Geddes Historic District Village, Geddes, SD...1347
Gemological Institute of America Museum, Carlsbad, CA 81
General Adam Stephen House, Martinsburg, WV.....................................1584
General Daniel Bissell House, Saint Louis, MO...833
The General Douglas L. McBride Museum, New Mexico Military Institute, Roswell, NM...........................945
General Douglas MacArthur Memorial, Norfolk, VA..1521
General Wait House, Waitsfield, VT...........1489
Geneva Historical Society & Prouty-Chew House & Museum, Geneva, NY...994
Geneva Historical Society & Rose Hill Mansion, Geneva, NY...............................994
George A. Spiva Center for the Arts, Joplin, MO...820
The George D. and Harriet W. Cornell Fine Arts Museum, Winter Park, FL 354
George I. Ashby Memorial Museum, Copper Center, AK.....................................23
George Meany Memorial Archives, Silver Spring, MD...654
George Washington Carver Museum, Tuskegee Institute, AL...............................20
George Washington Carver National Monument, Diamond, MO.....................814
George Washington's Ferry Farm, Stafford County, VA...............................1537
George Washington's Fredericksburg Foundation, Historic Kenmore & Washington's Ferry Farm, Fredericksburg, VA...............................1506
Georgetown University Art Collection, Washington, DC.......................................279
Georgia Historical Society, Savannah, GA...385
Georgia Museum of Art, University of Georgia, Athens, GA 356
Georgia O'Keeffe Museum, Santa Fe, NM..947
Georgia Salzburger Society Museum, Rincon, GA...381
Georgia's Old Capital Museum, Milledgeville, GA.......................................380
Germantown Historical Society, Philadelphia, PA 1280
Gertrude Herbert Institute of Art, Augusta, GA...365
Gibbes Museum of Art, Charleston, SC.....1325
The Gibson Society, Inc. dba Gibson House Museum, Boston, MA.................665
The Gilbert Stuart Birthplace and Museum, Saunderstown, RI...................1319
Gilcrease Museum, Tulsa, OK....................1215
Gilmer Arts and Heritage Association, Ellijay, GA...371
Glencairn Museum: Academy of the New Church, Bryn Athyn, PA 1244
Glenn L. Martin Maryland Aviation Museum, Baltimore, MD 632
Glessner House Museum, Chicago, IL.........421
The Glynn Art Association, Inc., Saint Simons Island, GA.................................383
Gnadenhutten Historical Park & Museum, Gnadenhutten, OH...............................1167
The Godwin-Ternbach Museum, Flushing, NY...990
Gold Coast Railroad Museum, Inc., Miami, FL...323
The Golden Age of Trucking Museum, Middlebury, CT.......................................249
Golden Gate National Recreation Area, San Francisco, CA.....................................165

The Goldstein Museum of Design, Saint Paul, MN................................789
Gomez Foundation for Mill House, Marlboro, NY...........................1014
Goodnow Museum State Historic Site, Manhattan, KS.............................550
Gorgas House, Tuscaloosa, AL.............19
Goshen Historical Society, Goshen, CT.......242
Governor Bent Museum, Taos, NM.............952
Governor John Sevier Memorial Association, Knoxville, TN................1370
The Governor's Mansion, Frankfort, KY.....569
Grace Hudson Museum & Sun House, Ukiah, CA.............................193
The Grace Museum, Abilene, TX.............1385
Graham County Historical Society, Thatcher, AZ.............................46
Grand Lodge AF&AM of Virginia - Allen E. Roberts Masonic Library and Museum, Richmond, VA.........................1529
Grand Rapids Art Museum, Grand Rapids, MI.............................743
Grant County Museum & Historic Society, Hyannis, NE.............................863
Grant Wood Gallery, Anamosa, IA.............505
Grants Pass Museum of Art, Grants Pass, OR.............................1225
Grave Creek Mound Archaeology Complex, Moundsville, WV.................1585
Great Basin National Park, Baker, NV.........875
Great Lakes Naval Memorial and Museum, Muskegon, MI.............................757
Great Plains Art Museum, Lincoln, NE.......865
The Greater Reston Arts Center (GRACE), Reston, VA.........................1527
Green Bay Packers Hall of Fame, Green Bay, WI.............................1598
Green Hill Art Gallery, Greensboro, NC....1103
Greensboro Artists' League, Greensboro, NC.............................1103
Greenville County Museum of Art, Greenville, SC.............................1334
Greenville Museum of Art, Inc., Greenville, NC.............................1105
Gregory Kondos Gallery, Sacramento, CA.............................152
Grey Art Gallery, New York University Art Collection, New York, NY.............1026
Greyhound Hall of Fame, Abilene, KS.........531
Grier Musser Museum, Los Angeles, CA....115
Grissom Air Museum, Peru, IN...................496
Gropius House, Lincoln, MA...................690
Groton Historical Society, Groton, MA.........685
Grunwald Center for the Graphic Arts, Hammer Museum, Los Angeles, CA.......115
Guadalupe Mountains National Park, Salt Flat, TX.............................1447
Guernsey County Museum, Cambridge, OH.............................1144
Guild Hall Museum, East Hampton, NY.....986
Guilford College Art Gallery, Greensboro, NC.............................1103
Guilford Courthouse National Military Park, Greensboro, NC.............................1104
Gulf Beach Art Center, Indian Rocks Beach, FL.............................313
Gulf Coast Museum of Art, Inc., Largo, FL.............................321
GumTree Museum of Art, Tupelo, MS.........808

Hackettstown Historical Society Museum & Library, Hackettstown, NJ...................905
The Haggin Museum, Stockton, CA...........189
The Hall of Fame for Great Americans, Bronx, NY.............................966
Hall of Flame Museum of Firefighting, Phoenix, AZ.............................40
Hallie Ford Museum of Art, Salem, OR....1235
Hamline University Galleries, Department of Studio Arts & Art History, Saint Paul, MN.............................790
Hammer Museum, Los Angeles, CA...........115

Hampton History Museum, Hampton, VA.1509
Hampton National Historic Site, Towson, MD.............................655
Hampton Roads Naval Museum, Norfolk, VA.............................1521
Hampton University Museum, Hampton, VA.............................1509
Hancock Shaker Village, Inc., Pittsfield, MA.............................703
Handwerker Gallery, Ithaca, NY.............1003
Hanover House, Clemson, SC.............1328
Harbor Defense Museum, Brooklyn, NY.....969
Harlan-Lincoln House, Mount Pleasant, IA.............................524
The Harness Racing Museum and Hall of Fame, Goshen, NY.............................995
Harney County Historical Museum, Burns, OR.............................1221
Harold L. Lyon Arboretum, Honolulu, HI...395
Harold Warp Pioneer Village Foundation, Minden, NE.............................868
Harpers Ferry National Historical Park, Harpers Ferry, WV.............................1582
Harriet Beecher Stowe Center, Hartford, CT.............................245
Harry Ransom Center at the University of Texas at Austin, Austin, TX.............1390
Harry S. Truman Library-Museum, Independence, MO.............................818
Harvard University Art Museums, Cambridge, MA.............................672
Harvey Cushing/John Hay Whitney Medical Library, New Haven, CT...........253
Harvey House Museum, Florence, KS.........539
The Harwood Museum of Art of the University of New Mexico, Taos, NM....952
Hatton Gallery, Colorado State University, Fort Collins, CO...................217
Hawaii Maritime Center, Honolulu, HI.........395
Hawaii State Foundation on Culture & the Arts and Hawaii State Art Museum, Honolulu, HI.............................395
Hayden Museum of American Art, Paris, TX.............................1442
Heard Museum, Phoenix, AZ.............40
Heard Natural Science Museum and Wildlife Sanctuary, Inc., McKinney, TX.............................1437
Hearst Art Gallery, St. Mary's College, Moraga, CA.............................128
Heckscher Museum of Art, Huntington, NY.............................1000
Helen E. Copeland Gallery, Bozeman, MT.............................842
Hellenic Museum & Cultural Center, Chicago, IL.............................421
Helvetia Museum, Helvetia, WV.............1582
The Hemingway Museum and The Ernest Hemingway Birthplace, Oak Park, IL.....448
Henrico County Historic Preservation & Museum Services, Richmond, VA.........1529
Henry Art Gallery, Seattle, WA.............1566
Henry County Museum and Cultural Arts Center, Clinton, MO.............................813
Herbert F. Johnson Museum of Art, Ithaca, NY.............................1003
Herbert Hoover Presidential Library-Museum, West Branch, IA..........530
The Heritage Center, Pine Ridge, SD.........1354
Heritage Center of Lancaster County, Inc., Lancaster, PA.............................1265
Heritage Hill State Historical Park, Green Bay, WI.............................1599
Heritage-Hjemkomst Interpretive Center, Moorhead, MN.............................784
Heritage House of Orange County Association Inc., Orange, TX.............1441
Heritage Library Museum, Anchorage, AK.............................22
The Heritage Museum, Baltimore, MD.........632
The Heritage Museum at Falfurrias, Inc., Falfurrias, TX.............................1413

The Heritage Museum of Fine Arts for Youth, Detroit, MI.............................736
Heritage Museums & Gardens, Sandwich, MA.............................707
Heritage of the Americas Museum, El Cajon, CA.............................92
The Hermitage Foundation, Norfolk, VA...1521
The Hermitage: Home of President Andrew Jackson, Hermitage, TN..........1367
Herreshoff Marine Museum/America's Cup Hall of Fame, Bristol, RI.............1311
Herrett Center for Arts & Science, Faulkner Planetarium and Centennial Observatory, Twin Falls, ID...................410
Hi-Desert Nature Museum, Yucca Valley, CA.............................201
Hibel Museum of Art, Jupiter, FL.............316
The Hickory Museum of Art, Hickory, NC.............................1106
Higgins Art Gallery - Cape Cod Community College, West Barnstable, MA.............................717
High Cliff Historical Society & General Store Museum, Sherwood, WI.............1622
High Desert Museum, Bend, OR.............1220
The High Museum of Art, Atlanta, GA........360
Highland Park Historical Society, Highland Park, IL.............................439
Highlands Art League, Sebring, FL.............345
Hildene, The Lincoln Family Home, Manchester, VT.............................1481
Hill Aerospace Museum, Hill Air Force Base, UT.............................1466
Hill-Stead Museum, Farmington, CT.............241
Hiller Aviation Institute, San Carlos, CA....155
Hillstrom Museum of Art, Saint Peter, MN.............................793
Hillwood Art Museum, Brookville, NY.......971
Hillwood Museum & Gardens, Washington, DC.............................280
Hiram Blauvelt Art Museum, Oradell, NJ....919
Hirshhorn Museum and Sculpture Garden, Smithsonian Institution, Washington, DC.............................280
The Hispanic Society of America, New York, NY.............................1027
Historic Camden Revolutionary War Site, Camden, SC.............................1323
Historic Columbia Foundation, Columbia, SC.............................1329
Historic Columbus Foundation, Inc., Columbus, GA.............................369
Historic Deerfield, Inc., Deerfield, MA........679
Historic Edenton State Historic Site, Edenton, NC.............................1099
Historic General Dodge House, Council Bluffs, IA.............................512
Historic Georgetown Inc., Georgetown, CO.............................218
Historic Governors' Mansion, Cheyenne, WY.............................1630
Historic Halifax State Historic Site, Halifax, NC.............................1105
Historic Hermann Museum, Hermann, MO.............................817
Historic Hope Foundation, Inc., Windsor, NC.............................1124
Historic House Trust of New York City, New York, NY.............................1027
Historic Hudson Valley, Tarrytown, NY.....1077
Historic Indian Agency House, Portage, WI.............................1618
Historic Jefferson College, Washington, MS.............................810
Historic Landmarks Foundation of Indiana, Indianapolis, IN.............................482
Historic New Harmony, New Harmony, IN.............................494
The Historic New Orleans Collection, New Orleans, LA.............................595
Historic Northampton, Northampton, MA...699
Historic Palmyra's Print Shop, Palmyra, NY.............................1050

Prints, Drawings, Graphic
Arts–Continued

Historic Palmyra's - Wm. Phelps General
　Store, Palmyra, NY 1050
Historic Price House, Woodruff, SC...........1343
Historic Prophetstown, Battle Ground, IN ...468
Historic Pullman Foundation, Chicago, IL...421
Historic Richmond Town, Staten Island,
　NY 1072
Historic Schaefferstown, Inc.,
　Schaefferstown, PA 1297
Historic Speedwell, Morristown, NJ............913
Historical Museum of Southern Florida,
　Miami, FL 324
The Historical Society of Frederick
　County, Inc., Frederick, MD 644
Historical Society of Greater Port
　Jefferson, Port Jefferson, NY 1053
Historical Society of Greenfield,
　Greenfield, MA 685
Historical Society of Middletown and the
　Wallkill Precinct, Inc., Middletown,
　NY 1014
Historical Society of Oak Park & River
　Forest, Oak Park, IL 448
Historical Society of Palm Beach County,
　Palm Beach, FL 334
Historical Society of Pennsylvania,
　Philadelphia, PA 1281
Historical Society of Rockland County,
　New City, NY 1017
Historical Society of Saratoga Springs,
　Saratoga Springs, NY 1064
Historical Society of Stanton County
　Museums at Stanton and Pilger, Pilger,
　NE 872
Historical Society of Talbot County,
　Easton, MD 642
Historical Society of the Phoenixville
　Area, Phoenixville, PA 1290
Historical Society of the Town of
　Greenwich Inc. aka Bush-Holley
　Historic Site, Cos Cob, CT 237
Historical Society of Wells and Ogunquit,
　Wells, ME 625
The History Center, Fort Wayne, IN 477
Hockaday Museum of Art, Kalispell, MT....850
Hodgden House Museum Complex,
　Ellsworth, KS 538
Hofstra Museum, Hempstead, NY 997
Hollins University Eleanor D. Wilson
　Museum, Roanoke, VA 1535
Hollywood Guinness World of Records
　Museum, Hollywood, CA 103
Hollywood Heritage Museum,
　Hollywood, CA 103
Holmes County Historical Society,
　Millersburg, OH 1176
Holocaust Documentation & Education
　Center, Inc., Hollywood, FL 313
Holocaust Memorial Resource and
　Education Center of Florida, Inc.,
　Maitland, FL 322
Holocaust Museum Houston, Houston,
　TX 1426
Holter Museum of Art, Helena, MT.............849
Home of Franklin D. Roosevelt National
　Historic Site, Hyde Park, NY 1002
Honolulu Academy of Arts, Honolulu, HI ...395
Hood Museum of Art, Hanover, NH 888
Hoosier Salon Gallery, Indianapolis, IN.......483
Hoover Historical Center, North Canton,
　OH 1179
Hope Lodge and Mather Mill, Fort
　Washington, PA 1254
Horatio Colony House Museum & Nature
　Preserve, Keene, NH 890
Hot Springs National Park Visitor Center,
　Hot Springs, AR 60
Hotel de Paris Museum, Georgetown, CO...219

Housatonic Museum of Art, Bridgeport,
　CT 236
House of Broadcasting Radio &
　Television Museum, Scottsdale, AZ 44
House of the Temple, Washington, DC 280
Houston Zoo, Inc., Houston, TX 1427
Howard County Center of African
　American Culture, Columbia, MD...........641
Howard University Gallery of Art,
　Washington, DC 281
Howard University Museum, Moorland
　Spingarn Research Center,
　Washington, DC 281
The Hoyt Institute of Fine Arts, New
　Castle, PA 1273
The Hubbard Museum of the American
　West, Ruidoso Downs, NM.....................946
Hudson Library and Historical Society,
　Hudson, OH 1168
Hudson River Maritime Museum,
　Kingston, NY 1007
The Hudson River Museum, Yonkers, NY.1087
Hui No'eau Visual Arts Center,
　Makawao, Maui, HI 401
Hull Lifesaving Museum Inc., the
　Museum of Boston Harbor Heritage,
　Hull, MA 687
Humboldt Arts Council/Morris Graves
　Museum of Art, Eureka, CA 94
Humboldt Redwoods State Park Visitor
　Center, Weott, CA 197
The Humphrey Forum, Minneapolis, MN....782
Hunt Institute for Botanical
　Documentation, Pittsburgh, PA 1292
Hunter College Art Galleries, New York,
　NY 1027
Hunterdon Museum of Art, Clinton, NJ.......901
Huntington Beach International Surfing
　Museum, Huntington Beach, CA.............104
Huntington Library, Art Collections, and
　Botanical Gardens, San Marino, CA 174
Huntington Museum of Art, Inc.,
　Huntington, WV 1583
Huntsville Museum of Art, Huntsville,
　AL 12
Hurricane Valley Heritage Park Museum,
　Hurricane, UT 1466
Hus Var Fine Art, Buffalo, NY 973
Hutchinson Art Center, Hutchinson, KS......545
The Hyde Collection, Glens Falls, NY 994
Hyde Park Art Center, Chicago, IL 421
The Hyland House, Guilford, CT 243

Ida Goodstein Visual Arts Center, Casper,
　WY 1629
Illinois Citizen Soldier Museum,
　Galesburg, IL 437
Illinois State Museum, Chicago Gallery,
　Chicago, IL 422
Illinois State Museum/Lockport Gallery,
　Lockport, IL 443
Ilwaco Heritage Museum, Ilwaco, WA......1556
IMA - Indianapolis Museum of Art,
　Indianapolis, IN 483
Immaculate Conception Catholic Church,
　Natchitoches, LA 593
Imperial Calcasieu Museum, Inc., Lake
　Charles, LA 590
Independence Seaport Museum,
　Philadelphia, PA 1281
Indian Arts and Crafts Board,
　Washington, DC 281
Indian Museum of North America at
　Crazy Horse Memorial, Crazy Horse,
　SD 1345
Indian Pueblo Cultural Center,
　Albuquerque, NM 933
Indiana Historical Society, Indianapolis,
　IN 483
Indiana Medical History Museum,
　Indianapolis, IN 484
Indiana University Art Museum,
　Bloomington, IN 469

Indiana War Memorials, Indianapolis, IN 484
Indianapolis Art Center, Indianapolis, IN.....484
Inland Seas Maritime Museum,
　Vermilion, OH..1189
Institute of American Indian Arts
　Museum, Santa Fe, NM 947
Institute of Contemporary Art, University
　of Pennsylvania, Philadelphia, PA 1282
Institute of Visual Arts, University of
　Wisconsin-Milwaukee, Milwaukee, WI.1611
The Interchurch Center, New York, NY.....1027
International Bowling Museum and Hall
　of Fame, Saint Louis, MO 833
The International Clown Hall of Fame &
　Research Center, Inc., Milwaukee, WI..1611
International Motor Racing Research
　Center at Watkins Glen, Watkins Glen,
　NY 1084
International Museum of Art and Science,
　McAllen, TX...1437
International Museum of Surgical
　Science, Chicago, IL 422
International Museum of the Horse,
　Lexington, KY 573
International Print Center New York,
　New York, NY 1028
International Swimming Hall of Fame,
　Inc., Fort Lauderdale, FL 307
International Tennis Hall of Fame &
　Museum, Newport, RI............................1313
International UFO Museum and Research
　Center, Roswell, NM...............................946
International Wildlife Museum, Tucson,
　AZ 49
International Women's Air and Space
　Museum, Inc., Cleveland, OH................1155
Intuit: The Center for Intuitive and
　Outsider Art, Chicago, IL........................422
Iredell Museum of Arts & Heritage,
　Statesville, NC 1120
Iris & B. Gerald Cantor Art
　Gallery-College of the Holy Cross,
　Worcester, MA..721
Iris & B. Gerald Cantor Center for Visual
　Arts at Stanford University, Stanford,
　CA 188
Iron County Museum, Caspian, MI.............731
Iroquois County Historical Society,
　Watseka, IL 463
Iroquois Indian Museum, Howes Cave,
　NY 999
Isaac Farrar Mansion, Bangor, ME..............604
Isabella Stewart Gardner Museum,
　Boston, MA 666
Isamu Noguchi Garden Museum, Long
　Island City, NY 1010
Isla Center For the Arts at the University
　of Guam, Mangilao, GU 1640
Island Museum of Art, Westcott Bay
　Institute, Friday Harbor, WA.................1554
Islip Art Museum, East Islip, NY...............986
Italian American Museum, New York,
　NY 1028

JFK Special Warfare Museum, Fort
　Bragg, NC 1101
The J. Paul Getty Museum, Los Angeles,
　CA 116
J.W. Parmley Historical Home Society,
　Ipswich, SD 1349
J. Wayne Stark University Center
　Galleries, College Station, TX 1401
Jacksonville Museum of Modern Art,
　Jacksonville, FL.......................................314
Jacqueline Casey Hudgens Center for the
　Arts, Duluth, GA 371
James A. Garfield National Historic Site,
　Mentor, OH..1176
James A. Michener Art Museum,
　Doylestown, PA 1249
James & Meryl Hearst Center for the
　Arts and Sculpture Garden, Cedar
　Falls, IA 508

James Buchanan Foundation for the Preservation of Wheatland, Lancaster, PA...................1266

James Ford Bell Museum of Natural History, Minneapolis, MN.....................782

James J. Hill House, Saint Paul, MN...........790

James Madison's Montpelier, Montpelier Station, VA................................1518

James Monroe Museum and Memorial Library, Fredericksburg, VA.............1507

James W. Dillon House Museum, Dillon, SC....................................1331

James Whitcomb Riley Museum Home, Indianapolis, IN.........................485

Jamestown Settlement, Yorktown Victory Center, The Jamestown-Yorktown Foundation, Williamsburg, VA...............1545

Jane Addams Hull-House Museum, University of Illinois Chicago, Chicago, IL...............................422

Jane L. and Robert H. Weiner Judaic Museum, Rockville, MD......................651

Jane Voorhees Zimmerli Art Museum, New Brunswick, NJ.......................915

Janet Turner Print Museum, Chico, CA.........83

Japan Society Gallery, New York, NY.......1028

Japanese American National Museum, Los Angeles, CA..........................117

Jeane Dixon Museum and Library, Strasburg, VA.............................1538

Jeff Matthews Memorial Museum, Galax, VA....................................1508

Jefferson Barracks Historic Site, Saint Louis, MO................................833

The Jefferson County Historical Assoc., Steubenville, OH.........................1186

Jefferson County Museum, Charles Town, WV....................................1580

Jefferson National Expansion Memorial, Saint Louis, MO...........................833

Jensen Arctic Museum, Monmouth, OR....1228

Jerome County Historical Society, Inc. and Idaho Farm & Ranch Museum, Jerome, ID...............................406

Jersey City Museum, Jersey City, NJ...........908

Jesse James Home Museum, Saint Joseph, MO...............................830

Jesse Peter Museum, Santa Rosa, CA..........184

The Jewish Museum, New York, NY.........1029

Jewish Museum of Maryland, Baltimore, MD....................................633

Jim Crow Museum - Ferris State University, Big Rapids, MI..............729

Jim Gatchell Memorial Museum, Buffalo, WY....................................1629

The Jimmy Stewart Museum, Indiana, PA.1262

John A. Logan College Museum, Carterville, IL.............................416

John and Mable Ringling Museum of Art, Sarasota, FL..............................344

John F. Kennedy Presidential Library & Museum, Boston, MA......................666

John Furlong Gallery, Menomonie, WI......1609

John James Audubon Center at Mill Grove, Audubon, PA.....................1241

John James Audubon Museum, Henderson, KY............................571

John Michael Kohler Arts Center, Sheboygan, WI...........................1621

John Paul Jones House Museum, Portsmouth, NH.........................894

The John Q. Adams Center for the History of Otolaryngology - Head and Neck Surgery, Alexandria, VA.............1493

John Slade Ely House, New Haven, CT......253

John Sydnor's 1847 Powhatan House, Galveston, TX............................1421

John Wornall House Museum, Kansas City, MO..................................821

Johnson County Community College, Gallery of Art, Overland Park, KS.........555

Johnson-Humrickhouse Museum, Coshocton, OH............................1159

Johnson Victrola Museum, Dover, DE.........270

Johnstown Historical Society, Johnstown, NY....................................1005

Joliet Area Historical Museum, Joliet, IL....440

Jonson Gallery of the University of New Mexico Art Museum, Albuquerque, NM....................................933

Jordan Schnitzer Museum of Art, Eugene, OR....................................1223

Joseloff Gallery, Hartford Art School, University of Hartford, West Hartford, CT....................................264

Joslyn Art Museum, Omaha, NE.................871

The Journey Museum, Rapid City, SD.......1354

Judah L. Magnes Museum, Berkeley, CA......76

The Judah P. Benjamin Confederate Memorial at Gamble Plantation Historic State Park, Ellenton, FL.............306

Judaica Museum of Central Synagogue, New York, NY.............................1029

The Judaica Museum of the Hebrew Home at Riverdale, Riverdale, NY........1057

Judy Garland Museum, Grand Rapids, MN....................................777

Jule Collins Smith Museum of Fine Art, Auburn, AL................................3

Julian H. Sleeper House, Saint Paul, MN....790

Jundt Art Museum, Spokane, WA 1571

Juneau-Douglas City Museum, Juneau, AK....................................26

Juniata College Museum of Art, Huntingdon, PA 1262

Kala Art Institute Gallery, Berkeley, CA........76

Kalamazoo Aviation History Museum, Kalamazoo, MI...........................748

Kalamazoo Institute of Arts, Kalamazoo, MI....................................748

Kalamazoo Nature Center, Inc., Kalamazoo, MI...........................748

Kalkaska County Historical Museum, Kalkaska, MI.............................749

Kaminski House Museum, Georgetown, SC....................................1333

The Kansas African American Museum, Wichita, KS..............................561

Kansas Aviation Museum, Wichita, KS.......562

Katherine Nash Gallery, Minneapolis, MN....................................782

Katonah Museum of Art, Katonah, NY.....1006

Kauai Museum, Lihue, HI 401

Kearney Mansion Museum, Fresno, CA.......97

Kelly-Griggs House Museum, Red Bluff, CA....................................146

Kemerer Museum of Decorative Arts, Bethlehem, PA...........................1242

Kemper Museum of Contemporary Art, Kansas City, MO..........................821

Kenilworth Aquatic Gardens, Washington, DC....................................281

Kennebunkport Historical Society, Kennebunkport, ME......................612

Kennedy-Douglass Center for the Arts, Florence, AL................................9

Kennedy Museum of Art, Athens, OH......1140

Kennesaw Mountain National Battlefield Park, Kennesaw, GA 374

Kenosha Public Museum, Kenosha, WI.....1602

The Kent Art Association, Kent, CT 247

Kent State University Museum, Kent, OH.1169

Kent State University, School of Art Galleries, Kent, OH........................1169

Kentucky Derby Museum, Louisville, KY...576

The Kentucky Folk Art Center, Morehead, KY............................580

Kentucky Gateway Museum Center, Maysville, KY............................579

Kentucky Historical Society, Frankfort, KY....................................569

Keweenaw County Historical Society, Eagle Harbor, MI.........................739

Key West Museum of Art and History, Key West, FL..............................318

Keystone Area Historical Society, Keystone, SD............................1350

Kimberly Crest House & Gardens, Redlands, CA.............................147

King Manor, Jamaica, NY.......................1004

Kingman Tavern Historical Museum, Cummington, MA........................678

Kirkland Arts Center, Kirkland, WA..........1557

Kirkland Fine Arts Center-Perkinson Gallery, Decatur, IL......................430

Kirkland Museum of Fine & Decorative Art, Denver, CO............................212

Kit Carson Historical Society, Kit Carson, CO..............................223

Kittredge Gallery, University of Puget Sound Art Dept., Tacoma, WA..............1573

Klickitat County Historical Society, Goldendale, WA.........................1555

Knights of Columbus Museum, New Haven, CT...............................253

Knox Headquarters State Historic Site, Vails Gate, NY...........................1080

Knoxville Museum of Art, Knoxville, TN.1370

Kohl Children's Museum of Greater Chicago, Glenview, IL....................438

Korean War Veterans National Museum & Library, Rantoul, IL....................453

Koshare Indian Museum, Inc., La Junta, CO....................................224

Krannert Art Museum and Kinkead Pavilion, Champaign, IL..................416

The Kreeger Museum, Washington, DC.......281

Krempp Gallery, Jasper, IN.......................486

Kresge Art Museum, East Lansing, MI.......739

Kuhlmann King Historical House and Museum, Boerne, TX....................1396

L.C. Bates Museum, Hinckley, ME.............612

L.H. Bailey Hortorium, Ithaca, NY............1003

La Casa Del Libro, San Juan, PR...............1642

La Raza/Galeria Posada, Sacramento, CA...153

La Salle University Art Museum, Philadelphia, PA.........................1282

Laband Art Gallery, Loyola Marymount University, Los Angeles, CA..............117

The Lace Museum, Sunnyvale, CA..............190

Lacey Historical Society, Forked River, NJ....................................904

The Lacrosse Museum & National Hall of Fame/US Lacrosse, Baltimore, MD....633

Lafayette College Art Gallery, Williams Center for the Arts, Easton, PA 1250

Lafayette Miners Museum, Lafayette, CO...224

Lafayette Natural History Museum and Planetarium, Lafayette, LA...............589

Laguna Art Museum, Laguna Beach, CA....107

Lahaina Restoration Foundation, Lahaina, HI....................................400

The Lake Champlain Maritime Museum, Vergennes, VT...........................1488

Lake Guernsey Museum-Guernsey State Park, Guernsey, WY.....................1634

Lake Hopatcong Historical Museum, Landing, NJ..............................909

Lake Perris Regional Indian Museum (Home of the Wind), Perris, CA.............141

Lake Superior Maritime Visitors Center, Duluth, MN..............................773

Lakeview Museum of Arts and Sciences, Peoria, IL................................450

Lamar Dodd Art Center, LaGrange College, LaGrange, GA....................375

Lancaster Museum of Art, Lancaster, PA...1266

The Landmark Society of Western New York, Rochester, NY.....................1058

Lane Community College Art Gallery, Eugene, OR..............................1223

Lanier Mansion State Historic Site, Madison, IN..............................489

Lansing Art Gallery, Lansing, MI...............750

Lapham-Patterson House, Thomasville, GA....................................388

*Prints, Drawings, Graphic
Arts–Continued*

Larchmont Historical Society,
  Mamaroneck, NY 1013
Lars Noak Blacksmith Shop,
  Larsson/Ostlund Log Home &
  One-Room Capitol School, New
  Sweden, ME.................................616
Larson Museum and Gallery, Yakima,
  WA 1578
Larz Anderson Auto Museum, Brookline,
  MA 671
Las Vegas Art Museum, Las Vegas, NV 879
Las Vegas Natural History Museum, Las
  Vegas, NV.....................................879
Latvian Museum, Rockville, MD 651
Laumeier Sculpture Park & Museum,
  Saint Louis, MO 834
Laurel Arts, Somerset, PA......................1300
The Laurel Museum, Laurel, MD.............648
Lauren Rogers Museum of Art, Laurel,
  MS 804
Laurence C. Jones Museum, Piney
  Woods, MS 807
Law Enforcement Memorial Association,
  Inc., Roselle, IL.............................456
Lawrence Heritage State Park, Lawrence,
  MA 689
The Lebanon County Historical Society,
  Lebanon, PA 1268
Leedel Moorehead-Graham Fine Arts
  Gallery, Pine Bluff, AR 66
Legends of New Mexico Museum,
  Algodones, NM 936
Lehigh University Art Galleries/Museum
  Operations, Bethlehem, PA 1242
Lehman College Art Gallery, Bronx, NY 966
Leigh Yawkey Woodson Art Museum,
  Wausau, WI 1626
Lemon Hill Mansion, Philadelphia, PA 1282
LeMoyne Art Foundation, Inc.,
  Tallahassee, FL 347
Lentz Center for Asian Culture, Lincoln,
  NE 865
Lesbian Herstory Educational Foundation,
  Inc. aka Lesbian Herstory Archives,
  Brooklyn, NY 969
Leslie Powell Foundation and Gallery,
  Lawton, OK 1204
Lesueur County Historical
  Museum-Chapter 1, Elysian, MN 774
Levere Memorial Temple, Evanston, IL 434
Lewes Historical Society, Lewes, DE 271
Lewis Ginter Botanical Garden,
  Richmond, VA 1530
Lexington Historical Society, Lexington,
  MA 689
Libby Museum, Wolfeboro, NH 897
Liberty Hall Historic Site, Frankfort, KY 569
Liberty Jail Historic Site, Liberty, MO 826
Liberty Village Arts Center & Gallery,
  Chester, MT 844
Library Company of Philadelphia,
  Philadelphia, PA 1282
Library of Congress, Washington, DC 282
The Library of Virginia, Richmond, VA.....1530
Licking County Arts, Newark, OH.............1178
Life on the Ohio River History Museum,
  Vevay, IN 502
Lighthouse Center for the Arts, Tequesta,
  FL 351
Lilian Fendig Art Gallery, Rensselaer, IN 497
Limon Heritage Museum, Limon, CO.........226
Lincoln Boyhood National Memorial,
  Lincoln City, IN............................488
The Lincoln Museum, Fort Wayne, IN 478
Lincoln State Monument, Lincoln, NM 941
The Lincoln-Tallman Restorations,
  Janesville, WI 1601
The Lion and Lamb Peace Arts Center,
  Bluffton, OH 1143

Lisle Station Museum, Lisle, IL 443
Litchfield Historical Society and
  Museum, Litchfield, CT 247
The Lithuanian Museum, Chicago, IL.........423
Little Bighorn Battlefield National
  Monument, Crow Agency, MT 844
The Little Brick House, Vandalia, IL 462
Little Compton Historical Society, Little
  Compton, RI 1312
The Little Cowboy Bar & Museum,
  Fromberg, MT 847
Little Falls Historical Society Museum,
  Little Falls, NY 1009
Little White House Historic Site, Warm
  Springs, GA 390
Little White Schoolhouse, Ripon, WI.........1620
Littleton Historical Museum, Littleton,
  CO 227
The Living Arts and Science Center, Inc.,
  Lexington, KY 573
The Living Word National Bible
  Museum, Aledo, TX 1386
Livingston Depot Center, Livingston, MT ...850
Locust Grove, The Samuel Morse
  Historic Site, Poughkeepsie, NY 1055
Logan County Historical Society
  Museum, Bellefontaine, OH...............1142
Logoly State Park, McNeil, AR..................64
Lois E. Woods Museum, Norfolk, VA.......1522
Lombard Historical Museum, Lombard,
  IL 443
Lone Star Flight Museum/Texas Aviation
  Hall of Fame, Galveston, TX...............1421
Long Beach Museum of Art, Long
  Beach, CA 111
Long Island Museum of American Art,
  History & Carriages, Stony Brook,
  NY 1075
Longboat Key Center for the Arts,
  Longboat Key, FL 322
Longfellow National Historic Site,
  Cambridge, MA 673
Longfellow's Wayside Inn, Sudbury, MA 714
Longue Vue House & Gardens, New
  Orleans, LA 596
Longview Museum of Fine Arts,
  Longview, TX 1434
Longwood Center for the Visual Arts,
  Farmville, VA 1504
Longyear Museum, Chestnut Hill, MA 675
Lore Degenstein Gallery, Selinsgrove, PA .1299
Los Altos History Museum aka
  Association of the Los Altos Historical
  Museum, Los Altos, CA 112
The Los Angeles Art Association/Gallery
  825, Los Angeles, CA 117
Los Angeles (Central) Public Library, Los
  Angeles, CA 117
Los Angeles County Museum of Art, Los
  Angeles, CA 118
Los Angeles Maritime Museum, San
  Pedro, CA 176
Los Angeles Municipal Art Gallery -
  Barnsdall Art Park, Los Angeles, CA......118
Los Angeles Museum of the Holocaust,
  Los Angeles, CA 118
Los Nogales Museum, Seguin, TX 1452
Lou Holtz/Upper Ohio Valley Hall of
  Fame, East Liverpool, OH 1163
Loudoun Museum, Inc., Leesburg, VA.......1512
Louisburg College Art Gallery,
  Louisburg, NC 1109
Louise Wells Cameron Art Museum,
  Wilmington, NC 1123
Louisiana Art & Science Museum - Irene
  W. Pennington Planetarium, Baton
  Rouge, LA 586
Louisiana State Museum, New Orleans,
  LA 596
Louisiana State University Museum of
  Art, Baton Rouge, LA 586
Louisville Slugger Museum & Factory,
  Louisville, KY 577

Lovely Lane Museum, Baltimore, MD 634
Lovettsville Historical Society Museum,
  Lovettsville, VA 1514
Lowe Art Museum, University of Miami,
  Coral Gables, FL 301
Lowell Observatory, Flagstaff, AZ...............33
Loyola University Museum of Art,
  Chicago, IL 423
Lubeznik Center for the Arts, Michigan
  City, IN 490
Luckhard Museum - The Indian Mission,
  Sebewaing, MI..............................764
Luis Munoz Rivera Library & Museum,
  Barranquitas, PR 1641
The Luther W. Brady Art Gallery,
  Washington, DC............................282
Lux Center for the Arts, Lincoln, NE 866
Luzerne County Historical Society,
  Wilkes-Barre, PA 1307
Lyman Allyn Art Museum, New London,
  CT 255
Lyman Museum, Hilo, HI 393
Lynchburg Museum System, Lynchburg,
  VA 1515
Lyndon Baines Johnson Library and
  Museum, Austin, TX 1391

MIT-List Visual Arts Center, Cambridge,
  MA 673
MIT Museum, Cambridge, MA 674
M. Louise Aughinbaugh Gallery at
  Messiah College, Grantham, PA 1257
Mabee-Gerrer Museum of Art, Shawnee,
  OK 1213
Mabry-Hazen House, Knoxville, TN.........1371
Macalester College Art Gallery, Janet
  Wallace Fine Arts Center, Saint Paul,
  MN 790
Macculloch Hall Historical Museum &
  Gardens, Morristown, NJ 913
Macon County Historical Society
  Museum Complex, Decatur, IL...............430
MADI Museum, Dallas, TX 1407
Madison Museum of Contemporary Art,
  Madison, WI 1605
Madison Museum of Fine Art, Madison,
  GA 378
Maggie L. Walker National Historic Site,
  Richmond, VA 1530
The Magic Lantern Castle Museum, San
  Antonio, TX 1448
Magnolia Grove-Historic House Museum,
  Greensboro, AL..............................10
Magnolia Manor, Cairo, IL......................415
Magnolia Plantation and Gardens,
  Charleston, SC 1326
Maier Museum of Art, Randolph-Macon
  Woman's College, Lynchburg, VA.........1515
Main Art Gallery, California State
  University, Fullerton, Fullerton, CA..........99
Maine Historical Society, Portland, ME........619
Maine Lighthouse Museum, Rockland,
  ME 621
Maitland Art Center, Maitland, FL 322
Malabar Farm State Park, Lucas, OH.........1173
Malden Public Library, Malden, MA 692
Manassas National Battlefield Park,
  Manassas, VA 1516
Manchester Historic Association Millyard
  Museum, Manchester, NH...............891
Manhattan Arts Center, Manhattan, KS.....551
The Mansfield Art Center, Mansfield, OH .1173
Mansfield Township Historical Society
  (1849 Georgetown School/Museum),
  Columbus, NJ 902
Marblehead Arts Association - King
  Hooper Mansion, Marblehead, MA.........693
Marcella Sembrich Opera Museum,
  Bolton Landing, NY 963
Marcellus Historical Society, Marcellus,
  NY 1013
March Field Air Museum, Riverside, CA 149

Margaret Fort Trahern Gallery,
    Clarksville, TN 1363
Margaret Harwell Art Museum, Poplar
    Bluff, MO...829
The Margaret Mitchell House &
    Museum, Atlanta, GA...............................361
Mariani Gallery, University of Northern
    Colorado, Greeley, CO..............................221
Marianna Kistler Beach Museum of Art
    at Kansas State University, Manhattan,
    KS 551
Marias Museum of History and Art,
    Shelby, MT...853
Maridon Museum, Butler, PA 1245
Marietta/Cobb Museum of Art, Marietta,
    GA...379
The Marine Museum at Fall River, Inc.,
    Fall River, MA 682
The Mariners' Museum, Newport News,
    VA...1519
Mario Lanza Institute/Museum,
    Philadelphia, PA 1282
Maritime Industry Museum at Fort
    Schuyler, Bronx, NY..................................966
Maritime Museum - Cohasset Historical
    Society, Cohasset, MA...............................676
Maritime Museum of Monterey,
    Monterey, CA..127
Maritime Museum of San Diego, San
    Diego, CA...157
Marjorie Kinnan Rawlings Historic State
    Park, Cross Creek, FL................................301
Mark Twain Home and Museum,
    Hannibal, MO...816
The Mark Twain House & Museum,
    Hartford, CT...245
Marquette County Historical Society,
    Westfield, WI...1627
Marshall County Historical Museum,
    Plymouth, IN..496
Marshall County Historical Museum,
    Holly Springs, MS.....................................801
Marshall M. Fredericks Sculpture
    Museum, University Center, MI 766
Martin and Osa Johnson Safari Museum,
    Inc., Chanute, KS 535
Martin Art Gallery, Allentown, PA.............1239
Marxhausen Art Gallery, Seward, NE.........873
Mary and Leigh Block Museum of Art,
    Northwestern University, Evanston, IL ...434
Mary Baldwin College/Hunt Gallery,
    Staunton, VA..1537
The Mary Brogan Museum of Art and
    Science, Tallahassee, FL............................347
Mary Porter Sesnon Art Gallery, Santa
    Cruz, CA...181
Maryhill Museum of Art, Goldendale,
    WA..1556
Maryland Historical Society, Baltimore,
    MD...634
The Maryland Institute, College of Art:
    Decker, Meyerhoff and Pinkard
    Galleries, Baltimore, MD...........................634
Maryland State Archives, Annapolis, MD....628
The Masonic Library and Museum of
    Pennsylvania, Philadelphia, PA.................1283
MASS MoCA, North Adams, MA................698
Massachusetts Audubon at Connecticut
    River Valley Sanctuaries,
    Easthampton, MA......................................681
Massachusetts Historical Society, Boston,
    MA...667
Massee Lane Gardens, Home of
    American Camellia Society, Fort
    Valley, GA..373
Masur Museum of Art, Monroe, LA............592
The Mather Homestead Museum, Library
    and Memorial Park, Wellsville, NY 1084
Mattapoisett Museum and Carriage
    House, Mattapoisett, MA............................693
The Mattatuck Museum Arts and History
    Center, Waterbury, CT...............................264
Mattress Factory, Ltd., Pittsburgh, PA........1293

Maturango Museum of the Indian Wells
    Valley, Ridgecrest, CA...............................148
Maude I. Kerns Art Center, Eugene, OR ...1223
May Museum & Farmville Heritage
    Center, Farmville, NC...............................1100
Maymont, Richmond, VA 1530
Mazomanie Historical Society,
    Mazomanie, WI...1608
McCook House, Civil War Museum,
    Carrollton, OH..1146
McCormick Gallery, Midland, TX...............1438
McHenry Museum, Modesto, CA.................126
McLean County Arts Center,
    Bloomington, IL...414
McMullen Museum of Art, Boston
    College, Chestnut Hill, MA.......................675
McNay Art Museum, San Antonio, TX......1448
McWethy Hall, Luce Gallery, Cornell
    College, Mount Vernon, IA........................524
Mead Art Museum, Amherst, MA 658
Meadow Brook Hall, Rochester, MI............761
Meadows Museum, Dallas, TX....................1407
Meadows Museum of Art of Centenary
    College, Shreveport, LA.............................601
Mechanicsburg Museum Association,
    Mechanicsburg, PA....................................1270
Medina Railroad Museum, Medina, NY.....1014
Meeteetse Museum District, Meeteetse,
    WY..1636
Meigs County Museum, Pomeroy, OH.......1183
Mel Fisher Maritime Heritage Society,
    Key West, FL..318
Melton Art Reference Library, Oklahoma
    City, OK...1208
Memorial Art Gallery of the University
    of Rochester, Rochester, NY.....................1059
The Memorial Day Museum, Waterloo,
    NY...1083
Memorial Union Art Gallery, Davis, CA 90
Memorial Union Gallery, Fargo, ND..........1130
Memphis Brooks Museum of Art,
    Memphis, TN..1374
Memphis College of Art, Memphis, TN 1374
The Menczer Museum of Medicine &
    Dentistry, Hartford, CT.............................245
Mendocino Historical Research,
    Inc./Kelley House Museum,
    Mendocino, CA...125
The Menil Collection, Houston, TX..........1428
Mennello Museum of American Art,
    Orlando, FL..331
Mennonite Library and Archives, North
    Newton, KS..554
Menominee County Heritage Museum,
    Menominee, MI...754
Meridian Museum of Art, Meridian, MS 805
Merrill Historical Museum, Merrill, WI.....1609
Merritt Museum of Anthropology,
    Oakland, CA...133
Mesa Southwest Museum, Mesa, AZ.........37
The Metropolitan Museum of Art, New
    York, NY..1030
Metropolitan State College of
    Denver/Center for Visual Art, Denver,
    CO..212
Mexic-Arte Museum, Austin, TX...............1391
Mexican Fine Arts Center Museum,
    Chicago, IL...424
The Mexican Museum, San Francisco,
    CA..166
Miami Art Museum, Miami, FL..................324
Miami-Dade College Kendall Campus
    Art Gallery, Miami, FL.............................324
Miami University Art Museum, Oxford,
    OH...1181
Michael C. Carlos Museum, Atlanta, GA 361
Michael C. Rockefeller Arts Center
    Gallery, Fredonia, NY...............................992
Michelson Museum of Art, Marshall, TX ..1436
Michigan Maritime Museum, South
    Haven, MI..764

Michigan Transit Museum, Inc., Mount
    Clemens, MI...756
Mid-America Air Museum, Liberal, KS.......549
Mid-America All Indian Center, Wichita,
    KS..562
Mid-Continent Railway Museum, North
    Freedom, WI...1615
Middlebury College Museum of Art,
    Middlebury, VT...1482
Middlesex Canal Collection, Lowell, MA....691
Middleton Place Foundation, Charleston,
    SC..1326
Midwest Museum of American Art,
    Elkhart, IN..474
Midwest Old Settlers & Threshers
    Association, Inc., Mount Pleasant, IA 524
Mighty Eighth Air Force Museum,
    Pooler, GA..381
Mildred Lane Kemper Art Museum, Saint
    Louis, MO...834
Milford Museum, Milford, DE.....................271
Military Museum of Southern New
    England, Danbury, CT...............................238
Military Veterans Museum, Inc.,
    Oshkosh, WI...1616
Miller Art Museum, Sturgeon Bay, WI......1623
Millicent Rogers Museum of Northern
    New Mexico, Taos, NM.............................952
Milliken Gallery, Converse College,
    Spartanburg, SC..1341
The Millionaires' Cars & Disney
    Collection, Saint Ignace, MI.....................763
Mills College Art Museum, Oakland, CA....133
Milton Art Museum, Canton, MA...............674
Milwaukee Art Museum, Milwaukee, WI ..1611
Mingei International Museum, San
    Diego, CA...157
The Minna Anthony Common Nature
    Center at Wellesley State Park,
    Fineview, NY..989
Minneapolis Institute of Arts,
    Minneapolis, MN.......................................782
Minnesota Air National Guard Historical
    Foundation, Inc., Saint Paul, MN.............790
Minnesota Museum of American Art,
    Saint Paul, MN...791
Minnesota Transportation Museum, Inc.,
    Saint Paul, MN...792
Mint Museum of Art, Charlotte, NC..........1095
Minute Man National Historical Park,
    Concord, MA...676
Miramont Castle Museum, Manitou
    Springs, CO..228
Mission Cultural Center for Latino Arts,
    San Francisco, CA.....................................166
Mission Houses Museum, Honolulu, HI......397
Mission San Juan Capistrano Museum,
    San Juan Capistrano, CA...........................173
Mission San Miguel, San Miguel, CA.........175
Mississippi Governor's Mansion,
    Jackson, MS..802
Mississippi Museum of Art, Jackson, MS....802
Mississippi Society Daughters of the
    American Revolution Rosalie House
    Museum, Natchez, MS..............................805
Missoula Art Museum, Missoula, MT.........851
Mizel Museum, Denver, CO.......................213
Mobile Museum of Art, Mobile, AL...........14
Moccasin Lake Nature Park, An
    Environmental & Energy Education
    Center, Clearwater, FL..............................299
Modern Art Museum of Fort Worth, Fort
    Worth, TX..1418
Moffatt-Ladd House and Garden,
    Portsmouth, NH...894
Mondak Heritage Center, Sidney, MT.........853
The Monhegan Museum, Monhegan, ME....615
Monmouth County Historical Association,
    Freehold, NJ...905
Monocacy National Battlefield, Frederick,
    MD...644

Prints, Drawings, Graphic
Arts—Continued

Monroe Community College, Mercer
  Gallery, Rochester, NY 1059
Monroe County Heritage Museum,
  Monroeville, AL 15
Montana Museum of Art and Culture,
  Missoula, MT.......................................852
Montauk Point Lighthouse Museum,
  Montauk, NY......................................1015
Montclair Art Museum, Montclair, NJ.........912
Montclair State University Art Galleries,
  Upper Montclair, NJ.............................929
Monterey History and Art Association,
  Monterey, CA 127
Monterey Museum of Art, Monterey, CA....128
Monterey State Historic Park, Monterey,
  CA...128
Montgomery Museum & Lewis Miller
  Regional Art Center, Christiansburg,
  VA 1501
Montgomery Museum of Fine Arts,
  Montgomery, AL 16
Montpelier-The General Henry Knox
  Museum, Thomaston, ME.......................624
Moody County Museum, Flandreau, SD....1347
Moore County Art Association, Dumas,
  TX 1410
Moore County Historical Museum,
  Dumas, TX..1410
Moores Creek National Battlefield,
  Currie, NC 1097
Moosehead Marine Museum, Greenville,
  ME..611
Moravian Historical Society, Nazareth,
  PA 1273
Mordecai Historic Park, Raleigh, NC.........1115
The Morikami Museum and Japanese
  Gardens, Delray Beach, FL.....................305
Morris County Historical Society (Acorn
  Hall House Museum), Morristown, NJ ...914
Morris-Jumel Mansion, New York, NY 1030
The Morris Museum, Morristown, NJ..........914
Morris Museum of Art, Augusta, GA...........365
Morristown National Historical Park,
  Morristown, NJ....................................914
The Morton Arboretum, Lisle, IL................443
Mote Marine Laboratory/Aquarium,
  Sarasota, FL..345
Motorcycle Hall of Fame Museum,
  Pickerington, OH 1182
Motown Historical Museum, Detroit, MI....737
Motts Military Museum, Groveport, OH....1167
Moundbuilders State Memorial &
  Museum, Newark, OH..........................1178
Mount Clare Museum House, Baltimore,
  MD..635
Mount Dora Center for the Arts, Mount
  Dora, FL...327
Mount Holyoke College Art Museum,
  South Hadley, MA................................709
Mount Vernon Hotel Museum & Garden,
  New York, NY....................................1031
Mount Vernon Ladies' Association,
  Mount Vernon, VA..............................1518
Mount Washington Museum and The
  Weather Discovery Center, North
  Conway, NH..893
The Muchnic Gallery, Atchison, KS.............533
Mulvane Art Museum, Topeka, KS 559
Munson-Williams-Proctor Arts Institute
  Museum of Art, Utica, NY 1079
The Murie Museum, Kelly, WY 1634
Murrell Home, Park Hill, OK 1211
Muscarelle Museum of Art,
  Williamsburg, VA................................1545
Muscatine Art Center, Muscatine, IA 524
Museo de Arte de Ponce (The Luis A.
  Ferre Foundation, Inc.), Ponce, PR 1642
Museo de las Americas, Denver, CO 213

Museo Fuerte Conde de Mirasol de
  Vieques, Vieques, PR 1644
Museo ItaloAmericano, San Francisco,
  CA...167
Museum and Arts Center in the Sequim
  Dungeness Valley, Sequim, WA............1570
Museum at Southwestern Michigan
  College, Dowagiac, MI..........................738
The Museum of African American Art,
  Los Angeles, CA...................................119
Museum of Alaska Transportation &
  Industry, Inc., Wasilla, AK.....................29
Museum of American Architecture and
  Decorative Arts, Houston, TX 1428
Museum of American Finance, New
  York, NY..1031
The Museum of American Illustration at
  the Society of Illustrators, New York,
  NY..1031
Museum of American Presidents,
  Strasburg, VA.....................................1539
Museum of Ancient Artifacts, Las Vegas,
  NV..879
Museum of Art, Pullman, WA 1563
Museum of Art and Archaeology,
  University of Missouri - Columbia,
  Columbia, MO.....................................813
Museum of Art and History at the
  McPherson Center, Santa Cruz, CA 182
Museum of Art & History at Weston,
  Weston, CT..266
Museum of Art at Brigham Young
  University, Provo, UT 1469
Museum of Art/Fort Lauderdale, Fort
  Lauderdale, FL.....................................307
Museum of Art of Puerto Rico, Santurce,
  PR...1643
Museum of Art, Rhode Island School of
  Design, Providence, RI.........................1317
Museum of Arts and Sciences, Macon,
  GA..378
The Museum of Arts and Sciences, Inc.
  and Center for Florida History,
  Daytona Beach, FL...............................303
Museum of Astrogeology, Meteor Crater,
  Winslow, AZ...53
Museum of Automobile Art and Design,
  Syracuse, NY 1076
Museum of Central Connecticut State
  University, New Britain, CT...................251
Museum of Chinese in the Americas,
  New York, NY....................................1032
Museum of Church History and Art, Salt
  Lake City, UT....................................1471
Museum of Contemporary Art, Chicago,
  IL..424
Museum of Contemporary Art Cleveland,
  Cleveland, OH....................................1155
The Museum of Contemporary Art, Los
  Angeles, Los Angeles, CA......................119
Museum of Contemporary Art (MoCA),
  North Miami, FL..................................329
The Museum of Contemporary Art of
  Georgia (MOCA GA), Atlanta, GA.........362
Museum of Contemporary Art of Puerto
  Rico, Santurce, PR 1644
Museum of Contemporary Art San Diego,
  La Jolla, CA..106
Museum of Contemporary Art San Diego
  - Downtown, San Diego, CA..................157
Museum of Contemporary Religious Art
  (MOCRA)-St. Louis University, Saint
  Louis, MO...835
The Museum of East Texas, Lufkin, TX....1436
Museum of Fine Arts, Boston, MA.............667
Museum of Fine Arts, Santa Fe, NM..........948
The Museum of Fine Arts, Houston,
  Houston, TX.......................................1428
Museum of Fine Arts of St. Petersburg,
  Florida, Saint Petersburg, FL..................341
The Museum of Flight, Seattle, WA..........1567
Museum of Funeral Customs, Springfield,
  IL..459

Museum of History, Anthropology and
  Art, San Juan, PR...............................1643
Museum of International Folk Art, Santa
  Fe, NM...948
Museum of Latin American Art, Long
  Beach, CA...111
The Museum of Man in the Sea, Inc.,
  Panama City Beach, FL.........................335
The Museum of Modern Art, New York,
  NY..1033
Museum of Nebraska Art, Kearney, NE......864
Museum of New Mexico, Santa Fe, NM.....949
Museum of Northwest Art, La Conner,
  WA 1557
Museum of Northwest Colorado, Craig,
  CO..208
The Museum of Outdoor Arts,
  Englewood, CO....................................214
Museum of Overbeck Art Pottery,
  Cambridge City, IN...............................471
The Museum of Printing History,
  Houston, TX.......................................1428
The Museum of Prints and Printmaking,
  Albany, NY..955
Museum of Robotics, Orinda, CA...............136
The Museum of Russian Art,
  Minneapolis, MN..................................783
Museum of San Diego History and
  Research Library, San Diego, CA 158
The Museum of Southern History,
  Sugarland, TX.....................................1454
The Museum of Television & Radio,
  New York, NY....................................1033
Museum of Texas Tech University,
  Lubbock, TX.......................................1435
Museum of the Albemarle, Elizabeth
  City, NC...1099
Museum of the Berkeley Springs,
  Berkeley Springs, WV..........................1580
Museum of the Cherokee Indian,
  Cherokee, NC.....................................1096
Museum of the City of New York, New
  York, NY..1033
The Museum of the Confederacy,
  Richmond, VA....................................1531
Museum of the Jimmy Carter Library,
  Atlanta, GA...362
Museum of the Mountain Man, Pinedale,
  WY...1637
Museum of the Moving Image, Astoria,
  NY..958
Museum of the National Center of
  Afro-American Artists, Roxbury, MA 706
Museum of the Plains Indian, Browning,
  MT..843
Museum of the Red River, Idabel, OK 1203
Museum of the Southwest, Midland, TX ...1439
Museum of the Waxhaws & Andrew
  Jackson Memorial, Waxhaw, NC...........1122
The Museum of Western Art, Kerrville,
  TX 1431
Museum of Woodcarving, Shell Lake, WI.1621
Museum of World Cultures/University of
  North Carolina at Wilmington,
  Wilmington, NC..................................1123
Museum of Yachting, Newport, RI............1314
Museum of York County, Rock Hill, SC ...1340
Museums of Los Gatos, Los Gatos, CA 123
Muskegon Museum of Art, Muskegon,
  MI..758
Mutter Museum, College of Physicians of
  Philadelphia, Philadelphia, PA..............1283
My Old Kentucky Home State Park,
  Bardstown, KY....................................564
Mystic Arts Center, Mystic, CT..................250

NASA Glenn Research Center's Visitor
  Center, Cleveland, OH 1155
NAU Art Museum, Flagstaff, AZ 33
NIU Art Museum, DeKalb, IL...................429
Naomi Wood Collection at Woodford
  Mansion, Philadelphia, PA...................1284
Napa Valley Museum, Yountville, CA 200

Naples Museum of Art and the Philharmonic Center for the Arts Galleries, Naples, FL..................328

Napoleonic Society of America, Inc., Clearwater, FL.................................300

Narragansett Historical Society, Templeton, MA...........................714

Nasher Museum of Art at Duke University, Durham, NC.....................1099

Nasher Sculpture Center, Dallas, TX..........1407

Nassau County, Division of Museum Services, Department of Recreation, Parks & Museums, East Meadow, NY 987

Nassau County Museum of Art, Roslyn Harbor, NY................................1062

National Academy Museum and School of Fine Arts, New York, NY.................1033

National Academy of Sciences, Washington, DC.............................283

National Afro-American Museum & Cultural Center, Wilberforce, OH..........1191

National Air and Space Museum, Washington, DC............................283

National Archives and Records Administration - Mid-Atlantic Region, Philadelphia, PA 1284

National Art Museum of Sport, Inc., Indianapolis, IN............................485

National Arts Club, New York, NY............1034

National Automotive & Truck Museum of the United States, Inc. (NATMUS), Auburn, IN.................................468

National Baseball Hall of Fame and Museum, Inc., Cooperstown, NY 981

The National Border Patrol Museum and Memorial Library, El Paso, TX 1412

National Building Museum, Washington, DC...284

National Center for Children's Illustrated Literature, Abilene, TX 1385

National Christmas Center, Paradise, PA ...1275

National Civil Rights Museum, Memphis, TN...1375

National Civil War Naval Museum at Port Columbus, Columbus, GA 369

National Cowgirl Museum and Hall of Fame, Fort Worth, TX..........................1418

National Cryptologic Museum, Fort Meade, MD.................................643

National Czech & Slovak Museum & Library, Cedar Rapids, IA.....................509

National First Ladies' Library, Canton, OH...1145

National Fresh Water Fishing Hall of Fame, Hayward, WI 1600

National Gallery of Art, Washington, DC 285

National Geographic Museum at Explorers Hall, Washington, DC.............285

The National Great Blacks in Wax Museum, Inc., Baltimore, MD................635

National Heritage Museum, Lexington, MA...690

National Hispanic Cultural Center, Art Museum, Albuquerque, NM.................935

National Infantry Museum, Fort Benning, GA...372

National Medal of Honor Museum of Military History, Chattanooga, TN........1362

National Mississippi River Museum & Aquarium, Dubuque, IA.........................516

National Museum of African Art, Smithsonian Institution, Washington, DC...285

National Museum of American Illustration, Newport, RI..................1314

National Museum of American Jewish Military History, Washington, DC..........286

The National Museum of Catholic Art & History, New York, NY...................1034

National Museum of Dance & Hall of Fame, Saratoga Springs, NY.................1065

National Museum of Industrial History, Bethlehem, PA............................1243

National Museum of Naval Aviation, Pensacola, FL................................336

National Museum of Polo and Hall of Fame, Inc., Lake Worth, FL.....................320

National Museum of Racing and Hall of Fame, Saratoga Springs, NY.................1065

National Museum of Roller Skating, Lincoln, NE................................866

National Museum of the Morgan Horse, Shelburne, VT................................1487

National Museum of the United States Air Force, Wright-Patterson Air Force Base, OH.................................1193

National Museum of Wildlife Art, Jackson, WY..............................1634

National Museum of Women in the Arts, Washington, DC.............................287

National Museum of Woodcarving, Custer, SD.................................1346

National New York Central Railroad Museum, Elkhart, IN.........................475

National Portrait Gallery, Washington, DC...287

National Postal Museum, Smithsonian Institution, Washington, DC.....................287

National Railroad Museum and Hall of Fame, Inc., Hamlet, NC.........................1105

National Scouting Museum, Irving, TX 1430

National Soaring Museum, Elmira, NY 988

National Society of the Sons of the American Revolution, Louisville, KY 578

National Sprint Car Hall of Fame & Museum, Knoxville, IA.........................521

National Steeplechase Museum, Camden, SC...1323

National Temple Hill Association, Inc., New Windsor, NY.............................1018

National Tropical Botanical Garden, Kalaheo, HI.................................399

National Trust for Historic Preservation, Washington, DC.............................288

National Warplane Museum, Horseheads, NY...999

Native American Heritage Museum at Highland Mission State Historic Site, Highland, KS................................544

Native American Resource Center, Pembroke, NC..............................1114

Natural Center for the American Revolution, Wayne, PA 1306

Naugatuck Historical Society, Naugatuck, CT...251

Navajo Nation Museum, Window Rock, AZ...53

Naval War College Museum, Newport, RI...1314

Nave Museum, Victoria, TX 1457

Nebraska State Capitol, Lincoln, NE............866

Neenah Historical Society, Hiram Smith, Neenah's Heritage Park, Octagon House & Ward House, Neenah, WI...1614

Neill-Cochran Museum House, Austin, TX...1391

The Nelson-Atkins Museum of Art, Kansas City, MO.............................822

Nemours Mansion and Gardens, Wilmington, DE.............................274

Netherland Inn House Museum & Boatyard Complex, Kingsport, TN........1368

Neuberger Museum of Art, Purchase College, State University of New York, Purchase, NY.............................1056

Nevada Historical Society, Reno, NV 881

Nevada Museum of Art, Reno, NV 881

Neville Public Museum of Brown County, Green Bay, WI.........................1599

New Braunfels Conservation Society, New Braunfels, TX 1440

New Britain Museum of American Art, Inc., New Britain, CT.........................251

New Canaan Historical Society, New Canaan, CT................................252

New Castle Historical Society, New Castle, DE.................................272

New Castle Historical Society - Horace Greeley House, Chappaqua, NY.............977

New England College Gallery, Henniker, NH...889

New England Fire and History Museum, Brewster, MA 670

New England Ski Museum, Franconia, NH...888

New Hampshire Farm Museum, Inc., Milton, NH................................892

New Hampshire Historical Society, Concord, NH................................885

New Hampshire Institute of Art, Manchester, NH................................892

New Harmony Gallery of Contemporary Art, New Harmony, IN.........................494

New Harmony State Historic Site/Historic New Harmony, New Harmony, IN................................494

New Haven Colony Historical Society, New Haven, CT................................253

New Jersey Botanical Garden at Skylands (NJBG), Ringwood, NJ.........................923

The New Jersey Historical Society, Newark, NJ................................916

The New Jersey Museum of Agriculture, North Brunswick, NJ.........................917

New Jersey Naval Museum, Hackensack, NJ...905

New London Historical Society, New London, NH................................892

New Market Battlefield State Historical Park, New Market, VA.........................1519

New Mexico Museum of Natural History & Science, Albuquerque, NM.................935

The New Milford Historical Society, New Milford, CT................................256

The New Museum of Contemporary Art, New York, NY................................1035

New Orleans Museum of Art, New Orleans, LA................................597

New Visions Gallery, Inc., Marshfield, WI...1608

New Windsor Cantonment State Historic Site and National Purple Heart Hall of Honor, Vails Gate, NY.........................1080

New World Art Center/T.F. Chen Cultural Center, New York, NY.........................1035

The New York Botanical Garden, Bronx, NY...966

New York City Fire Museum, New York, NY...1035

The New York Historical Society, New York, NY................................1035

The New York Public Library for the Performing Arts, New York, NY...........1036

New York State Bureau of Historic Sites, Waterford, NY................................1082

New York State Historical Association/Fenimore Art Museum, Cooperstown, NY.............................981

New York State Military Museum and Veterans Research Center, Saratoga Springs, NY................................1065

Newark Valley Depot Museum, Newark Valley, NY................................1042

Newcomb Art Gallery, New Orleans, LA 598

Newport Art Museum, Newport, RI...........1314

Newport Historical Society & The Museum of Newport History, Newport, RI................................1315

Newport Restoration Foundation, Newport, RI................................1315

Newseum, Washington, DC 288

The Newsome House Museum & Cultural Center, Newport News, VA 1520

Newtown History Center, Stephens City, VA...1538

Nichols House Museum, Boston, MA.........668

Nicolaysen Art Museum and Discovery Center, Casper, WY.........................1629

Prints, Drawings, Graphic Arts–Continued

Nita Stewart Haley Memorial Library & J. Evetts Haley History Center, Midland, TX 1439

Nixon Presidential Materials Staff, College Park, MD 641

Noah Webster House/West Hartford Historical Society, West Hartford, CT 265

The Noble Maritime Collection, Staten Island, NY 1073

Nora Eccles Harrison Museum of Art, Logan, UT............1466

Norfolk Historical Museum, Norfolk, CT 257

Norfolk Historical Society, Norfolk, VA 1522

Norfolk History Museum, Norfolk, VA 1523

The Norman Cleveland County Historical Museum, Norman, OK 1206

Norman #1 Oil Well Museum, Neodesha, KS 553

Norman R. Eppink Art Gallery, Emporia State University, Emporia, KS 539

Norman Rockwell Museum, Stockbridge, MA 712

Norman Rockwell Museum, Rutland, VT ..1486

North Alabama Railroad Museum, Huntsville, AL 12

North Carolina A&T State University Galleries, Greensboro, NC 1104

North Carolina Aquarium at Fort Fisher, Kure Beach, NC 1109

North Carolina Auto Racing Hall of Fame, Mooresville, NC............1111

North Carolina Maritime Museum, Beaufort, NC............1091

North Carolina Transportation Museum, Spencer, NC 1120

North Country Museum of Arts, Park Rapids, MN............786

The North Dakota Lewis & Clark Interpretive Center, Washburn, ND........1137

North Dakota Museum of Art, Grand Forks, ND 1132

North Florida Community College Art Gallery, Madison, FL 322

The North Shore Arts Association, Gloucester, MA............684

North Star Museum of Boy Scouting and Girl Scouting, North Saint Paul, MN 785

Northampton County Historical and Genealogical Society, Easton, PA 1250

Northborough Historical Society, Inc., Northborough, MA 700

Northeast Document Conservation Center, Andover, MA 660

Northeast Louisiana Delta African American Heritage Museum, Monroe, LA 592

Northern Illinois University Art Gallery in Chicago, Chicago, IL 425

Northern Kentucky University Art Galleries, Highland Heights, KY 571

Northwest Art Center, Minot, ND 1134

Northwest Museum of Arts & Culture (Eastern Washington State Historical Society), Spokane, WA............1571

Northwest Railway Museum, Snoqualmie, WA............1570

Norton Museum of Art, West Palm Beach, FL............353

Norton Simon Museum, Pasadena, CA........140

Norwich Historical Society, Norwich, VT .1484

The Noyes Museum of Art, Oceanville, NJ............918

O. Henry Museum, Austin, TX............1391

Oak Hill and The Martha Berry Museum, Rome, GA 382

The Oak Park Conservatory, Oak Park, IL............449

Oak Ridge Art Center, Oak Ridge, TN 1382

Oakland University Art Gallery, Rochester, MI 761

The Oaks House Museum, Jackson, MS......804

Oatlands, Leesburg, VA............1512

Oberlin Heritage Center, Oberlin, OH........1180

Oceanographic Teaching Station Inc. - Roundhouse Marine Studies Lab & Aquarium, Manhattan Beach, CA............124

The Octagon, Washington, DC............288

O'Fallon Historical Museum, Baker, MT.....840

Office of Cultural Affairs & Museum Programs at Salisbury University, Salisbury, MD 652

The Ogden Museum of Southern Art, University of New Orleans, New Orleans, LA 598

Ogden Union Station Museums, Ogden, UT............1468

Oglethorpe University Museum of Art, Atlanta, GA............362

Ogunquit Museum of American Art, Ogunquit, ME............617

Ohio River Museum, Marietta, OH............1174

Ohr-O'Keefe Museum of Art, Biloxi, MS ...799

Okefenokee Heritage Center, Waycross, GA............391

Oklahoma City Museum of Art, Oklahoma City, OK............1208

Oktibbeha County Heritage Museum, Starkville, MS............808

Olana State Historic Site, Hudson, NY......1000

Olbrich Botanical Gardens, Madison, WI ..1605

Old Barracks Museum, Trenton, NJ............927

Old Bethpage Village Restoration, Old Bethpage, NY 1045

Old Cathedral Museum, Saint Louis, MO....836

The Old Depot Railroad Museum, Dassel, MN 772

Old Dominion University - University Gallery, Norfolk, VA 1523

Old Economy Village, Ambridge, PA.........1240

Old Exchange & Provost Dungeon, Charleston, SC 1326

Old Firehouse Museum, Greenville, MS......800

Old Iron County Courthouse Museum, Hurley, WI 1601

The Old Jail Art Center, Albany, TX..........1385

Old Jefferson Town, Oskaloosa, KS............555

Old New-Gate Prison and Copper Mine, East Granby, CT 238

Old St. Ferdinand's Shrine, Florissant, MO............815

The Old Schwamb Mill, Arlington, MA 660

Old South Meeting House, Boston, MA......668

Old State House Museum, Little Rock, AR............63

Old State House-The Bostonian Society, Boston, MA............668

Old West Museum, Wimberley, TX............1462

Old West Wax Museum, Thermopolis, WY............1639

Old York Historical Society, York, ME........626

Old York Road Historical Society, Jenkintown, PA 1263

Oldest House Museum Complex, Saint Augustine, FL............339

The Oldest House Museum/Wrecker's Museum, Key West, FL............318

The Oliver Tucker Museum, Beverly, OH .1142

Olmsted County Historical Society, Rochester, MN............788

Omniplex Science Museum, Oklahoma City, OK............1210

103rd Ohio Volunteer Infantry Civil War Museum, Sheffield Lake, OH............1185

Oneida Community Mansion House, Oneida, NY............1046

Oneida County Historical Society, Utica, NY............1080

Onondaga Historical Association Museum & Research Center, Syracuse, NY.........1077

Orange County Museum of Art, Newport Beach, CA............130

Orchard House, Concord, MA 677

Oregon Air & Space Museum, Eugene, OR 1224

Oregon State University Memorial Union Concourse Gallery, Corvallis, OR 1222

Oregon Zoo, Portland, OR 1232

Orland Historical Society, Orland, ME........617

Orlando Museum of Art, Orlando, FL..........332

Orleans County Historical Society & The Old Stone House Museum, Brownington, VT............1477

Ormond Memorial Art Museum & Garden, Ormond Beach, FL............333

Osage Nation Tribal Museum, Pawhuska, OK............1212

Osborn-Jackson House, East Hampton, NY............986

Oscar Getz Museum of Whiskey History And The Bardstown Historical Museum, Bardstown, KY............565

Oshkosh Public Museum, Oshkosh, WI......1616

Ossining Historical Society Museum, Ossining, NY............1047

Osterville Historical Society, Inc., Osterville, MA............701

Oswego Historical Museum, Inc., Oswego, KS............555

Ottawa Scouting Museum, Ottawa, IL........449

Our House State Memorial, Gallipolis, OH............1165

Overholser Mansion, Oklahoma City, OK .1210

Owatonna Arts Center, Owatonna, MN.......786

Owens Community College/Walter E. Terhune Gallery, Perrysburg, OH..........1182

Owensboro Museum of Fine Art, Inc., Owensboro, KY............581

Oxford Museum, Inc., Oxford, MD............650

P.H. Sullivan Museum and Genealogy Library, Zionsville, IN............504

The P.T. Boat Museum & Library, Germantown, TN 1365

Pablo Casals Museum, Old San Juan, PR..1641

Pacem in Terris, Warwick, NY 1082

Pacific Asia Museum, Pasadena, CA............140

Pacific Aviation Museum - Pearl Harbor, Honolulu, HI............397

Pacific Coast Air Museum, Santa Rosa, CA............184

Pacific Grove Art Center Associates, Inc., Pacific Grove, CA............137

Pacific University Museum, Forest Grove, OR............1224

Paine Art Center and Gardens, Oshkosh, WI............1617

Palace of the Governors/New Mexico History Museum, Santa Fe, NM............949

The Palette & Chisel, Chicago, IL 426

Palm Springs Art Museum, Palm Springs, CA............139

Palmer Museum of Art, The Pennsylvania State University, University Park, PA....1304

Palo Alto Art Center, Palo Alto, CA 139

Palos Verdes Art Center, Rancho Palos Verdes, CA............145

Pamplin Historical Park and The National Museum of the Civil War Soldier, Petersburg, VA............1525

Paper Discovery Center, Appleton, WI 1590

Paris Gibson Square Museum of Art, Great Falls, MT............848

Paris-Henry County Heritage Center, Paris, TN............1382

Parkersburg Art Center, Parkersburg, WV .1586

Parkland College Art Gallery, Champaign, IL............417

Parris Island Museum, Parris Island, SC....1338

The Parrish Art Museum, Southampton, NY............1070

Parrot Jungle Island, Miami, FL............325

Parson Fisher House, Blue Hill, ME............606

Pasadena Museum of California Art, Pasadena, CA.............140
Pasadena Museum of History, Pasadena, CA.............140
Pascack Historical Society, Park Ridge, NJ.............920
Passaic County Community College, Paterson, NJ.............920
The Paterson Museum, Paterson, NJ.............920
The Patricia & Phillip Frost Art Museum, Miami, FL.............325
The Patrick & Beatrice Haggerty Museum of Art, Milwaukee, WI.............1613
Patterson Homestead, Dayton, OH.............1161
Paul and Lulu Hilliard University Art Museum, University of Louisiana at Lafayette, Lafayette, LA.............590
Paul W. Bryant Museum, Tuscaloosa, AL.............19
Pea Ridge National Military Park, Garfield, AR.............58
Peabody Essex Museum, Salem, MA.............706
Peabody Museum of Archaeology & Ethnology, Cambridge, MA.............674
The Peace Museum, Chicago, IL.............426
Pearson Air Museum, Vancouver, WA.............1576
The Pearson Museum, Springfield, IL.............460
Pebble Hill Plantation, Thomasville, GA.............388
The Peekskill Museum, Peekskill, NY.............1051
The Peggy Notebaert Nature Museum, Chicago, IL.............426
The Pena-Peck House, Saint Augustine, FL.............339
Pence Gallery, Davis, CA.............90
Pendleton Historic Foundation, Pendleton, SC.............1339
Pennsylvania Academy of the Fine Arts, Philadelphia, PA.............1284
Pennsylvania Anthracite Heritage Museum, Scranton, PA.............1299
Pennsylvania German Cultural Heritage Center at Kutztown University, Kutztown, PA.............1265
Pennsylvania Historical & Museum Commission, Harrisburg, PA.............1259
Penobscot Marine Museum, Searsport, ME.............622
Pensacola Museum of Art, Pensacola, FL.............336
The Peoria Art Guild, Peoria, IL.............451
Perry's Victory & International Peace Memorial, Put-in-Bay, OH.............1183
Petersburg Area Art League, Petersburg, VA.............1525
Petersen Automotive Museum, Los Angeles, CA.............121
Petersham Historical Society, Inc., Petersham, MA.............702
Petrified Creatures Museum of Natural History, Richfield Springs, NY.............1057
Petterson Museum of Intercultural Art, Claremont, CA.............85
Pewabic Pottery, Detroit, MI.............737
The Philadelphia Art Alliance, Philadelphia, PA.............1285
Philadelphia Mummers Museum, Philadelphia, PA.............1285
Philadelphia Museum of Art, Philadelphia, PA.............1285
Philadelphia Museum of Judaica/Congregation Rodeph Shalom, Philadelphia, PA.............1286
The Philbrook Museum of Art, Inc., Tulsa, OK.............1215
Philip and Muriel Berman Museum of Art at Ursinus College, Collegeville, PA.............1247
The Phillips Collection, Washington, DC.............289
Phillips County Museum, Helena, AR.............59
Phillips Historical Society, Phillips, ME.............618
The Phillips Museum of Art, Franklin & Marshall College, Lancaster, PA.............1267
Philmont Museums, Cimarron, NM.............938
Phippen Museum, Prescott, AZ.............42

Phoebe Apperson Hearst Museum of Anthropology, Berkeley, CA.............77
Phoenix Art Museum, Phoenix, AZ.............41
Photographic Investments Gallery, Atlanta, GA.............363
Piatt Castles, West Liberty, OH.............1190
Pickens County Museum of Art & History, Pickens, SC.............1340
The Picker Art Gallery, Hamilton, NY.............997
The Pierce Manse/New Hampshire Political Library, Concord, NH.............885
The Pierpont Morgan Library, New York, NY.............1037
Pierre Menard Home State Historic Site, Ellis Grove, IL.............433
Pike County Historical Society, Milford, PA.............1272
Pikes Peak Hill Climb Educational Museum, Colorado Springs, CO.............207
Pilgrim Hall Museum, Plymouth, MA.............703
Pimeria Alta Historical Society, Nogales, AZ.............37
Pioneer Historical Museum of South Dakota, Hot Springs, SD.............1348
Pioneer Museum, Watford City, ND.............1137
Pioneer Museum of Alabama, Troy, AL.............18
Pioneer Town, Wimberley, TX.............1462
Pioneer Village & Virgil Grissom Memorial at Spring Mill State Park, Mitchell, IN.............491
Piper Aviation Museum Foundation, Lock Haven, PA.............1269
Pitot House Museum, New Orleans, LA.............598
Pittock Mansion, Portland, OR.............1232
Pittsburgh Center for the Arts, Pittsburgh, PA.............1293
Plains Art Museum, Fargo, ND.............1130
Plainsman Museum, Aurora, NE.............856
Planetarium at the Reading Public Museum, Reading, PA.............1296
Plantation Agriculture Museum, Scott, AR.............67
Plantation Historical Museum, Plantation, FL.............337
Plattsburgh State Art Museum S.U.N.Y., Plattsburgh, NY.............1053
Plaza de La Raza, Inc. & Boathouse Gallery, Los Angeles, CA.............121
Plymouth Historical Museum, Plymouth, MI.............760
Pocahontas County Iowa Historical Society Museum, Laurens, IA.............522
Point of Honor, Lynchburg, VA.............1515
Polish American Museum, Port Washington, NY.............1054
Polish Museum of America, Chicago, IL.............426
Polk County Heritage Gallery, Des Moines, IA.............515
Polk Museum of Art, Lakeland, FL.............321
Pomona College Museum of Art, Claremont, CA.............85
Port Angeles Fine Arts Center & Webster's Woods Art Park, Port Angeles, WA.............1561
Port Huron Museum, Port Huron, MI.............761
Port Townsend Marine Science Center, Port Townsend, WA.............1562
Portage County Historical Society, Ravenna, OH.............1183
Porter-Phelps-Huntington Foundation, Inc., Hadley, MA.............685
Portland Art Museum, Portland, OR.............1232
Portland Children's Museum, Portland, OR.............1233
Portland Museum of Art, Portland, ME.............619
Portland State University Galleries, Portland, OR.............1233
Portsmouth Athenaeum, Portsmouth, NH.............894
Portsmouth Museum of Military History Inc., Portsmouth, VA.............1526
Postville Courthouse State Historic Site, Lincoln, IL.............442

Pottsgrove Manor, Pottstown, PA.............1295
Prairie Village, Madison, SD.............1351
Praters Mill Foundation, Varnell, GA.............390
Pratt Building - Cohasset Historical Society, Cohasset, MA.............676
Presidential Pet Museum, Lothian, MD.............649
Price Tower Arts Center, Bartlesville, OK.............1197
Princeton University Art Museum, Princeton, NJ.............922
The Print Center, Philadelphia, PA.............1287
Pro Rodeo Hall of Fame & Museum of the American Cowboy, Colorado Springs, CO.............207
Project Art-University of Iowa and Clinics, Iowa City, IA.............520
Promont House Museum, Milford, OH.............1176
Proprietary House, The Royal Governor's Mansion, Perth Amboy, NJ.............921
Provincetown Art Association and Museum, Provincetown, MA.............704
The Public Library of Nashville and Davidson County, Nashville, TN.............1380
Pueblo Weisbrod Aircraft Museum, Pueblo, CO.............230
Puget Sound Coast Artillery Museum at Fort Worden, Port Townsend, WA.............1562
Pump House Regional Arts Center, La Crosse, WI.............1603
Purdue University Galleries, West Lafayette, IN.............503
Putnam Cottage, Greenwich, CT.............243
Putnam County Historical Society & Foundry School Museum, Cold Spring, NY.............979

QCC Art Gallery, Bayside, NY.............960
Queens Museum of Art, Queens, NY.............1056
Quincy Art Center, Quincy, IL.............452
Quoddy Maritime Museum, Eastport, ME.............610

RV/MH Heritage Foundation, Inc., Elkhart, IN.............475
The R.W. Norton Art Gallery, Shreveport, LA.............601
Racine Art Museum (RAM), Racine, WI.............1619
Radford University Art Museum, Radford, VA.............1527
Rahr West Art Museum, Manitowoc, WI.............1607
Railroad House Historical Association Museum, Sanford, NC.............1119
The Ralph Foster Museum, Point Lookout, MO.............828
Ralph Waldo Emerson House, Concord, MA.............677
Rankin Museum, Inc., Ellerbe, NC.............1100
Ransom County Historical Society, Fort Ransom, ND.............1131
Raton Museum, Raton, NM.............945
Rattlesnake Museum (American International), Albuquerque, NM.............935
Rawls Museum Arts, Courtland, VA.............1502
The Ray Drew Gallery-New Mexico Highlands University, Las Vegas, NM.............941
Raynham Hall Museum, Oyster Bay, NY.............1049
The Reader's Digest Association, Inc., Pleasantville, NY.............1053
Reading Historical Society Museum, Reading, OH.............1184
Reading Public Museum, Reading, PA.............1296
Reading Railroad Heritage Museum, Reading, PA.............1296
Red Earth Museum, Oklahoma City, OK.............1210
Red Rock Museum, Church Rock, NM.............938
Redwood National and State Parks, Crescent City, CA.............88
Reedville Fishermen's Museum, Reedville, VA.............1527
Reese Bullen Gallery, Arcata, CA.............72
The Reeves Center, Washington and Lee University, Lexington, VA.............1513
The Regina A. Quick Center for the Arts, Saint Bonaventure, NY.............1063

Prints, Drawings, Graphic Arts—Continued

Rehoboth Art League, Inc., Rehoboth Beach, DE................................272

Remington Firearms Museum and Country Store, Ilion, NY....................1002

Renee and Chaim Gross Foundation, New York, NY..........................1037

Renville County Historical Society, Inc., Mohall, ND..........................1135

Reuel B. Pritchett Museum, Bridgewater, VA....................................1497

Reverend Dan Foster House, Museum of the Weathersfield Historical Society, Weathersfield, VT........................1489

Reynolda House Museum of American Art, Winston-Salem, NC 1126

Richard E. Peeler Art Center, Greencastle, IN..............................479

Richard L. Nelson Gallery & The Fine Arts Collection, UC Davis, Davis, CA......90

Richard Petty Museum, Randleman, NC....1117

Richland County Historical Museum, Wahpeton, ND........................1137

Richmond Art Center, Richmond, CA.........148

Richmond Art Museum, Richmond, IN......497

Richmond National Battlefield Park, Richmond, VA............................1531

Ringling School of Art and Design, Selby Gallery, Sarasota, FL....................345

Ripley County, Indiana, Historical Society Museum, Versailles, IN..............502

Ripley's Believe It or Not!, Key West, FL......................................319

Riverside Art Museum, Riverside, CA.........149

Robbins Hunter Museum, Avery-Downer House, Granville, OH....................1167

Robert E. Wilson Gallery, Huntington, IN...481

Robert Hull Fleming Museum, Burlington, VT..........................1478

Robert Louis Stevenson House, Monterey, CA............................128

Robert Louis Stevenson Memorial Cottage, Saranac Lake, NY.................1064

Robert Louis Stevenson Silverado Museum, Saint Helena, CA 154

Robert R. McCormick Museum at Cantigny, Wheaton, IL 465

Robert V. Fullerton Art Museum, California State University, San Bernardino, San Bernardino, CA.........155

Rock Island County Historical Society, Moline, IL................................445

Rockbridge Historical Society, Lexington, VA....................................1513

Rockford Art Museum, Rockford, IL..........455

Rockford College Art Gallery/Clark Arts Center, Rockford, IL 455

Rockingham, Kingston, NJ 909

Rockport Art Association, Rockport, MA 705

Rockwell Museum of Western Art, Corning, NY............................982

Rocky Mount Arts Center, Rocky Mount, NC..................................1117

Rocky Mountain College of Art + Design Galleries, Lakewood, CO.................225

Rodgers Tavern, Perryville, MD................650

Roger Tory Peterson Institute of Natural History, Jamestown, NY....................1005

Rokeby (Ancestral Estate of Rowland Evans Robinson), Ferrisburgh, VT........1479

Roland Gibson Gallery, Potsdam, NY......1054

Romanian Ethnic Art Museum, Cleveland, OH..........................1156

Rome Art and Community Center, Rome, NY....................................1061

Roosevelt Campobello International Park Commission, Lubec, ME..................614

Rosalie Whyel Museum of Doll Art, Bellevue, WA..........................1548

Roscoe Village Foundation, Coshocton, OH................................1159

The Rose Art Museum, Waltham, MA.........715

Rose Hill Museum, Bay Village, OH 1141

Rosemont Plantation, Woodville, MS..........810

Rosenbach Museum & Library, Philadelphia, PA 1287

Rosenberg Gallery, Goucher College, Baltimore, MD..........................636

Rosenberg Library, Galveston, TX..........1422

Rosenthal Gallery of Art, Caldwell, ID.......405

Roswell Museum and Art Center, Roswell, NM............................946

Roswell Visual Arts Center & Gallery, Roswell, GA............................382

The Roy Rogers-Dale Evans Museum and Theater, Branson, MO 811

Royall House Association, Medford, MA 694

Ruggles House Society, Columbia Falls, ME..................................609

Ruth Chandler Williamson Gallery, Scripps College, Claremont, CA..............86

The Rye Historical Society and Square House Museum, Rye, NY 1062

Ryerss Museum & Library, Philadelphia, PA..................................1287

S.C.R.A.P. Gallery, Indio, CA....................104

Saco Museum, Saco, ME........................621

Sacramento Archives and Museum Collection Center, Sacramento, CA.........153

Safe Haven Museum and Education Center, Oswego, NY....................1048

Saginaw Art Museum, Saginaw, MI............763

Sahuaro Ranch Historical Area, Glendale, AZ....................................35

St. Albans Historical Museum, Saint Albans, VT..............................1486

St. Clair County Historical Society, Belleville, IL............................412

St. Clements Island and Piney Point Museums, Colton's Point, MD.................641

Saint-Gaudens National Historic Site, Cornish, NH............................885

St. George Art Museum, Saint George, UT....................................1470

St. Johnsbury Athenaeum, Saint Johnsbury, VT..........................1487

Saint Joseph College Art Gallery, West Hartford, CT............................265

Saint Joseph's University - University Gallery - Boland Hall, Philadelphia, PA..................................1288

St. Lawrence University - Richard F. Brush Art Gallery and Permanent Collection, Canton, NY....................976

The Saint Louis Art Museum, Saint Louis, MO..............................836

The St. Louis County Historical Society, Duluth, MN............................773

St. Photios Greek Orthodox National Shrine, Saint Augustine, FL.................340

St. Simons Island Lighthouse Museum, Saint Simons Island, GA.................383

Ste. Genevieve Museum, Sainte Genevieve, MO........................838

Salem Art Association-Bush House Museum and Bush Barn Art Center, Salem, OR............................1236

The Salgo Trust for Education, Port Washington, NY 1054

Salina Art Center, Salina, KS 557

Salinas Pueblo Missions National Monument, Mountainair, NM 943

Salisbury House Foundation, Des Moines, IA..............................515

Salmagundi Museum of American Art, New York, NY..........................1038

Salmon Brook Historical Society, Inc., Granby, CT............................242

Salvador Dali Museum, Saint Petersburg, FL....................................342

The Salvation Army Southern Historical Center & Museum, Atlanta, GA..............363

Sam Bell Maxey House State Historic Site, Paris, TX..........................1442

Sam Houston Regional Library & Research Center, Liberty, TX.................1434

Samek Art Gallery, Lewisburg, PA............1268

Samuel Cupples House of Saint Louis University, Saint Louis, MO................837

Samuel Dorsky Museum of Art, State University of New York at New Paltz, New Paltz, NY..........................1018

Samuel P. Harn Museum of Art, Gainesville, FL............................311

San Angelo Museum of Fine Arts, San Angelo, TX............................1447

San Antonio Art League Museum, San Antonio, TX............................1449

San Antonio Museum of Art, San Antonio, TX............................1450

San Buenaventura Mission Museum, Ventura, CA............................195

San Diego Automotive Museum, San Diego, CA..............................159

San Diego Model Railroad Museum, Inc., San Diego, CA..........................159

San Diego Museum of Art, San Diego, CA....................................160

San Diego Museum of Man, San Diego, CA....................................160

San Francisco Museum of Modern Art, San Francisco, CA........................169

San Jose Museum of Art, San Jose, CA 172

San Jose State University Art Galleries, San Jose, CA............................173

San Juan Bautista State Historic Park, San Juan Bautista, CA.....................173

Sand Springs Cultural & Historical Museum, Sand Springs, OK............1213

The Sandor Teszler Library, Spartanburg, SC....................................1341

Sandy Spring Museum, Sandy Spring, MD....................................653

Sangre de Cristo Arts Center & Buell Children's Museum, Pueblo, CO 231

The Santa Barbara Historical Museum, Santa Barbara, CA........................179

Santa Barbara Maritime Museum, Santa Barbara, CA............................179

Santa Barbara Museum of Art, Santa Barbara, CA............................179

Santa Barbara Museum of Natural History, Santa Barbara, CA.....................179

Santa Cruz Art League, Inc., Santa Cruz, CA....................................182

Santa Fe Trail Museum, Ingalls, KS 545

Santa Fe Trail Museum/Trinidad History Museum, Trinidad, CO......................234

Santa Maria Museum of Flight, Inc., Santa Maria, CA..........................183

Santa Monica Museum of Art, Santa Monica, CA............................183

Sarah Campbell Blaffer Foundation, Houston, TX............................1429

Sarah Moody Gallery of Art, The University of Alabama, Tuscaloosa, AL....................................20

Sarasota Classic Car Museum, Sarasota, FL....................................345

Saratoga County Historical Society, Brookside Museum, Ballston Spa, NY....960

Sauk County Historical Museum, Baraboo, WI..............................1591

Sauk Prairie Area Historical Society, Inc., Prairie du Sac, WI..........................1619

Savannah College of Art and Design Galleries, Savannah, GA 386

Sawin Memorial Building, Dover, MA........680

Scarfone/Hartley Gallery, Tampa, FL..........349

The Scarsdale Historical Society, Scarsdale, NY..........................1066

The Schick Art Gallery, Skidmore College, Saratoga Springs, NY.............1065

Schiele Museum of Natural History and Lynn Planetarium, Gastonia, NC 1102

Schingoethe Center for Native American Cultures, Aurora, IL 412

Schmucker Art Gallery, Gettysburg, PA 1256

Schneider Museum of Art, Ashland, OR....1217

Scholte House Museum, Pella, IA...............527

School of American Research, Indian Arts Research Center, Santa Fe, NM 950

The Schumacher Gallery, Capital University, Columbus, OH 1159

Schuyler County Historical Society, Inc., Montour Falls, NY 1015

Schuyler-Hamilton House, Morristown, NJ......................914

The Schuylkill Center for Environmental Education, Philadelphia, PA 1288

Schwartz Collection of Skiing Heritage, Tiburon, CA 192

Schwenkfelder Library & Heritage Center, Pennsburg, PA...................1275

Science Museum of Western Virginia, Roanoke, VA 1535

Sciworks, Winston-Salem, NC..................1126

Scotchtown, Beaverdam, VA......................1496

Scotts Bluff National Monument, Gering, NE......................861

Scottsdale Museum of Contemporary Art, Scottsdale, AZ..................44

Scranton Museum of Art, Scranton, PA 1299

Seattle Aquarium, Seattle, WA..................1568

Seattle Asian Art Museum, Seattle, WA.....1569

Sedgwick-Brooklin Historical Society, Sedgwick, ME..................622

Seminole Nation Museum, Wewoka, OK...1217

Senator George Norris State Historic Site, McCook, NE..................868

Senator John Heinz Pittsburgh Regional History Center, Pittsburgh, PA...............1294

Seneca-Iroquois National Museum, Salamanca, NY 1063

Sequoia and Kings Canyon National Parks, Three Rivers, CA 191

Sequoyah Cabin, Sallisaw, OK 1213

1797 Ezekiel Harris House, Augusta, GA....366

The Sevier County Historical Museum, De Queen, AR 56

Sewall-Belmont House and Museum, Washington, DC...................290

Seward House, Auburn, NY......................959

Shaker Historical Society, Shaker Heights, OH 1185

Shaker Museum, New Gloucester, ME 615

Shako:wi Cultural Center, Oneida, NY 1046

Shandy Hall, Geneva, OH...................1166

The Sharon Arts Center, Inc., Sharon, NH...896

Sharpsteen Museum, Calistoga, CA 80

Sheboygan County Historical Museum, Sheboygan, WI...................1621

Sheehan Gallery at Whitman College, Walla Walla, WA 1577

Shelburne Museum, Inc., Shelburne, VT ...1487

Sheldon Memorial Art Gallery and Sculpture Garden/University of Nebraska-Lincoln, Lincoln, NE 867

Shemer Art Center & Museum, Phoenix, AZ......................42

Sheppard Fine Arts Gallery, Reno, NV 881

Sherwood-Davidson House, Newark, OH ..1178

Sherwood Forest Plantation, Charles City, VA......................1498

Ships of the Sea Maritime Museum/William Scarbrough House, Savannah, GA...................386

Shoreline Historical Museum, Seattle, WA 1569

Shortgrass Country Museum Society, Sayre, OK 1213

Sibley House Historic Site, Mendota, MN...780

Sidney Historical Association, Sidney, NY...................1069

Sidney Mishkin Gallery of Baruch College, New York, NY 1038

Siege Museum (The Petersburg Museums), Petersburg, VA...................1525

Siegfried H. Horn Archaeological Museum, Berrien Springs, MI 729

Sierra Sacramento Valley Medical Society Museum of Medical History, Sacramento, CA...................153

Silvermine Guild Arts Center, New Canaan, CT...................252

The Simon Paneak Memorial Museum, Anaktuvuk Pass, AK 21

Sinclair Lewis House Museum & Interpretive Center/Museum, Sauk Centre, MN...................793

Sindecuse Museum of Dentistry, Ann Arbor, MI...................725

Sioux City Art Center, Sioux City, IA 527

Sioux Indian Museum, Rapid City, SD 1355

Siskin Museum of Religious and Ceremonial Art, Chattanooga, TN 1362

Skirball Cultural Center, Los Angeles, CA...................121

Skirball Museum Cincinnati Hebrew Union College-Jewish Institute of Religion, Cincinnati, OH...................1151

The Skyscraper Museum, New York, NY ..1038

Slate Valley Museum, Granville, NY 996

The Slater Memorial Museum - Norwich Free Academy, Norwich, CT 258

Slater Mill Historic Site, Pawtucket, RI.....1315

Slidell Museum, Slidell, LA 602

Slocumb Galleries, Johnson City, TN.........1368

The Smart Museum of Art, Chicago, IL 427

Smith College Museum of Art, Northampton, MA 700

Smith-Zimmermann Heritage Museum, Madison, SD...................1351

Smithsonian American Art Museum, Washington, DC...................290

The Snite Museum of Art, University of Notre Dame, Notre Dame, IN...................495

Snug Harbor Cultural Center - Visitors' Center and Newhouse Center for Contemporary Art, Staten Island, NY ...1073

Society for the Preservation of Long Island Antiquities, Cold Spring Harbor, NY...................980

The Society of California Pioneers, San Francisco, CA...................170

The Society of the Cincinnati at Anderson House, Washington, DC 291

The Society of the Four Arts, Palm Beach, FL...................334

SoDus Bay Historical Society, Sodus Point, NY...................1070

Solomon R. Guggenheim Museum, New York, NY...................1038

Somers Historical Society, Somers, NY 1070

The Somerset County Historical Society, Inc., Princess Anne, MD...................650

Sonoma County Museum, Santa Rosa, CA...................185

Sordoni Art Gallery, Wilkes-Barre, PA.......1307

Sotterley Plantation, Hollywood, MD 647

South Bannock County Historical Center, Lava Hot Springs, ID...................407

South Bend Regional Museum of Art, South Bend, IN...................500

South Carolina Artisans Center, Walterboro, SC...................1343

South Carolina Department of Parks, Recreation and Tourism, Columbia, SC...................1330

South Carolina State Museum, Columbia, SC...................1331

South County Historical Society, Arroyo Grande, CA...................72

South Dakota Art Museum, Brookings, SD...................1344

South Dakota Hall of Fame, Chamberlain, SD 1345

South Florida Community College Museum of Florida Art and Culture, Avon Park, FL...................295

South Milwaukee Historical Society Museum, South Milwaukee, WI...........1622

South Shore Arts, Munster, IN...................493

South Street Seaport Museum, New York, NY...................1039

Southdown Plantation House/The Terrebonne Museum, Houma, LA 589

Southeast Missouri Regional Museum, Cape Girardeau, MO...................812

Southeast Museum Association, Inc., Brewster, NY...................964

Southeastern Architectural Archive, New Orleans, LA...................598

Southern Alleghenies Museum of Art, Loretto, PA...................1269

Southern Alleghenies Museum of Art at Johnstown, Johnstown, PA...................1264

Southern Arts Federation, Atlanta, GA.........363

Southern California Chapter Railway & Locomotive Historical Society, Pomona, CA...................143

Southern Museum of Flight, Birmingham, AL...................6

Southern Ohio Museum, Portsmouth, OH..1183

Southern Ute Cultural Center and Museum, Ignacio, CO...................223

Southern Vermont Art Center, Manchester, VT...................1481

Southold Historical Society and Museum, Southold, NY...................1071

Southwest Museum, Los Angeles, CA 121

Space Center Houston, Houston, TX..........1429

Spartanburg County Museum of Art, Spartanburg, SC...................1341

Spartanburg County Regional Museum of History, Spartanburg, SC...................1341

The Speed Art Museum, Louisville, KY......579

Spelman College Museum of Fine Art, Atlanta, GA...................363

Spencer Museum of Art, The University of Kansas, Lawrence, KS...................548

Spencer-Peirce-Little Farm, Newbury, MA...................697

Spiers Gallery, Brevard, NC...................1092

SPJST Library Archives & Museum, Temple, TX...................1455

The Sports Museum, Boston, MA...............669

Spring Grove Hospital Center, Alumni Museum, Catonsville, MD...................639

Springfield Art & Historical Society - Miller Art Center, Springfield, VT.........1488

Springfield Art Association, Springfield, IL...................460

Springfield Art Museum, Springfield, MO...839

Springfield Museum of Art, Springfield, OH...................1186

Springfield Museums - Museum of Fine Arts, Springfield, MA...................711

Springs Museum, Springs, PA...................1301

Springville Museum of Art, Springville, UT...................1474

Staatsburgh State Historic Site, Staatsburg, NY...................1071

Stamford Museum & Nature Center, Stamford, CT...................261

Stan Hywet Hall and Gardens, Inc., Akron, OH...................1139

Stanley Museum, Inc., Kingfield, ME..........613

Stanley-Whitman House, Farmington, Farmington, CT...................241

Stanwood Wildlife Sanctuary, Ellsworth, ME...................610

Stark Museum of Art, Orange, TX............1441

Stars and Stripes Museum/Library, Bloomfield, MO...................811

State Historical Society of Missouri, Columbia, MO...................814

State of Illinois-Historic Preservation Agency, Historic Sites Division, Springfield, IL...................460

Prints, Drawings, Graphic Arts–Continued

Staten Island Institute of Arts & Sciences (SIIAS), Staten Island, NY 1074

Stauth Memorial Museum, Montezuma, KS 553

STAX Museum of American Soul Music, Memphis, TN...............................1376

Stedman Gallery, Camden, NJ 900

Steffen Thomas Museum and Archives, Buckhead, GA 367

Steilacoom Historical Museum Association, Steilacoom, WA.................1572

The Stephen Girard Collection, Philadelphia, PA 1288

The Stephen Phillips House, Salem, MA 707

Stepping Stones Museum for Children, Norwalk, CT 257

Sterling and Francine Clark Art Institute, Williamstown, MA 719

Sterling Historical Society and Little Red Schoolhouse Museum, Sterling, NY......1074

The Stevens-Coolidge Place, a property of The Trustees of Reservations, North Andover, MA 698

Stone House Gallery, Fredonia, KS.............540

Stones River National Battlefield, Murfreesboro, TN 1377

Stonewall Jackson House, Lexington, VA..1514

Stony Point Battlefield State Historic Site, Stony Point, NY 1075

Stoughton Historical Society, Stoughton, MA 713

The Stowitts Museum & Library, Pacific Grove, CA 137

Strategic Air & Space Museum, Ashland, NE 856

Strater Hotel, Durango, CO 214

The Stratford Historical Society & Catherine B. Mitchell Museum, Stratford, CT 262

Stratford, Robert E. Lee Memorial Association, Inc., Stratford, VA 1539

Strawbery Banke Museum, Portsmouth, NH 895

Strong - National Museum of Play, Rochester, NY 1060

The Studio Museum in Harlem, New York, NY 1040

Studio San Giuseppe Art Gallery, Cincinnati, OH..................................1151

SUArt Galleries - Syracuse University, Syracuse, NY 1077

Sugarlands Visitor Center, Gatlinburg, TN.1365

Sullivan Museum and History Center, Northfield, VT 1483

SullivanMunce Cultural Center, Zionsville, IN.....................................504

Sumter Gallery of Art, Sumter, SC.............1342

Sun Gallery, Hayward, CA 102

Sunnyside Historical Museum, Sunnyside, WA 1572

The Supreme Court of the United States, Washington, DC...................................291

Susan B. Anthony House, Rochester, NY...1060

Sushi Performance and Visual Art, San Diego, CA 161

Susquehanna County Historical Society & Free Library Association, Montrose, PA 1272

Susquehanna Museum of Havre de Grace Inc. at the Lock House, Havre de Grace, MD 647

Sutter's Fort State Historic Park, Sacramento, CA......................................153

Sutton County Historical Society - Miers Home Museum, Sonora, TX 1453

Suzanne H. Arnold Art Gallery, Lebanon Valley College, Annville, PA 1241

Swampscott Historical Society (John Humphrey House), Swampscott, MA......714

Swedish American Museum Association of Chicago, Chicago, IL.........................428

Sweeney Art Gallery, University of California, Riverside, CA........................150

Sweet Briar College Art Gallery, Sweet Briar, VA 1540

Swiss Historical Village, New Glarus, WI.1615

Swope Art Museum, Terre Haute, IN...........501

Sylvia Plotkin Judaica Museum of Congregation Beth Israel, Scottsdale, AZ 44

T.C. Steele State Historic Site, Nashville, IN 493

T Rex Museum, Tucson, AZ..........................50

T.W. Wood Gallery & Arts Center, Montpelier, VT 1482

Tacoma Art Museum, Tacoma, WA...........1574

The Taft Museum of Art, Cincinnati, OH ..1151

Tall Grass Arts Association, Park Forest, IL 449

Tampa Museum of Art, Tampa, FL 350

Tannenbaum Historic Park, Greensboro, NC 1104

Taos Historic Museums, Taos, NM 953

Tappantown Historical Society, Tappan, NY 1077

Tarble Arts Center, Eastern Illinois University, Charleston, IL......................417

Tarpon Springs Cultural Center, Tarpon Springs, FL 351

Tate House Museum, Portland, ME.............620

Taube Museum of Art, Minot, ND 1135

Ted Smallwood's Store, Inc., Chokoloskee, FL..................................299

Telfair Museum of Art, Savannah, GA 386

The Temple Judea Museum of Reform Congregation Keneseth Israel, Elkins Park, PA 1251

Tennent Art Foundation Gallery, Honolulu, HI.......................................398

Tennessee Agricultural Museum, Nashville, TN....................................1380

Tennessee Historical Society, Nashville, TN 1380

Tennessee Museum of Aviation, Sevierville, TN...................................1383

Tennessee State Museum, Nashville, TN ...1381

Tennessee Valley Art Center, Tuscumbia, AL 20

Terrace Gallery-City of Orlando, Orlando, FL 332

Terrace Hill Historic Site and Governor's Mansion, Des Moines, IA 516

Territorial Capital-Lane Museum, Lecompton, KS...................................549

Texas Air Museum, Slaton, TX 1453

Texas Pharmacy Museum, Amarillo, TX ...1387

Texas Seaport Museum, Galveston, TX 1422

Texas State Museum of Asian Cultures & Educational Center, Corpus Christi, TX 1402

Theodore Roosevelt Birthplace National Historic Site, New York, NY 1040

Theodore Roosevelt Inaugural National Historic Site, Buffalo, NY.....................973

This Century Art Gallery, Williamsburg, VA 1545

Thomas Clarke House/Princeton Battlefield State Park, Princeton, NJ 922

Thomas Edison Birthplace Museum, Milan, OH 1176

Thomas-Foreman Home, Muskogee, OK...1205

The Thomas Griswold House and Museum, Guilford, CT 243

Thomas Hart Benton Home and Studio State Historic Site, Kansas City, MO......823

Thomas J. Walsh Art Gallery, Quick Center for the Arts at Fairfield University, Fairfield, CT 241

Thomas Kinkade Museum, Morgan Hill, CA 129

The Thomas T. Taber Museum of the Lycoming County Historial Society, Williamsport, PA 1308

Thomas Warne Historical Museum & Library, Old Bridge, NJ 918

Thomaston Historical Society, Thomaston, ME 624

Thomasville Cultural Center, Inc., Thomasville, GA 388

Thorne-Sagendorph Art Gallery, Keene, NH 890

Thornton W. Burgess Museum, Sandwich, MA 708

Thunderbird Foundation for the Arts, Mount Carmel, UT 1467

Tile Heritage Foundation, Healdsburg, CA 102

Tinker Swiss Cottage Museum, Rockford, IL 456

Tinkertown Museum, Sandia Park, NM......947

Tobacco Farm Life Museum, Inc., Kenly, NC 1107

Tohono Chul Park Inc., Tucson, AZ.............51

The Toledo Museum of Art, Toledo, OH ..1187

Toltec Mounds Archeological State Park, Scott, AR..68

Tongass Historical Museum, Ketchikan, AK 26

Toppenish Museum, Toppenish, WA 1575

Torpedo Factory Art Center, Alexandria, VA 1494

Tougaloo College, Tougaloo, MS 808

Towe Auto Museum, Sacramento, CA 154

Tower Fine Arts Gallery (SUNY Brockport), Brockport, NY 964

Toy & Miniature Museum of Kansas City, Kansas City, MO 823

Traill County Historical Society, Hillsboro, ND 1132

Trailside Nature Museum, Cross River, NY 983

Tread of Pioneers Museum, Steamboat Springs, CO 232

Trenton City Museum, Trenton, NJ............928

Trenton Historical Museum, Trenton, MI.....765

Trinity Museum of the Parish of Trinity Church, New York, NY 1040

Triton Museum of Art, Santa Clara, CA 181

The Trout Gallery, Carlisle, PA 1245

Tryon Palace Historic Sites and Gardens, New Bern, NC 1112

Tu-Endie-Wei State Park, Point Pleasant, WV 1586

Tubman African-American Museum, Macon, GA 378

Tucson Museum of Art & Historic Block, Tucson, AZ..51

Tudor Place Foundation, Inc., Washington, DC...................................292

Tufts University Art Gallery, Medford, MA 694

Tunica-Biloxi Native American Museum, Marksville, LA.....................................591

Turabo University, Gurabo, PR.................1641

Turquoise Museum, Albuquerque, NM 936

Turtle Bay Exploration Park, Redding, CA 146

Turtle Mountain Chippewa Historical Society, Belcourt, ND...........................1127

Tweed Museum of Art, Duluth, MN 774

Tyler Art Gallery, Oswego, NY 1048

Tyler Museum of Art, Tyler, TX................1456

USM Art Gallery, Gorham, ME...................611

U.S. Navy Museum, Washington, DC...........292

UWM Union-Art Gallery, Milwaukee, WI.1613

Ukrainian-American Museum & Archives, Warren, MI 766

The Ukrainian Museum, New York, NY....1040

Ukrainian Museum-Archives, Inc., Cleveland, OH 1156

Ukrainian National Museum, Inc., Chicago, IL...428

Ulrich Museum of Art, Wichita, KS............563
Ulysses S. Grant Cottage State Historic
   Site, Wilton, NY....................................1086
Umlauf Sculpture Garden & Museum,
   Austin, TX 1392
Uncle Remus Museum, Eatonton, GA 371
UNI Gallery of Art, University of
   Northern Iowa, Cedar Falls, IA 508
Union County Heritage Museum, New
   Albany, MS..806
Union County Historical Society
   Museum, Blairsville, GA 366
United States Army Heritage and
   Education Center - Army Heritage
   Museum, Carlisle, PA............................1246
United States Golf Association Museum
   & Archives, Far Hills, NJ 903
United States Holocaust Memorial
   Museum, Washington, DC 293
United States Marine Corps Air-Ground
   Museum, Quantico, VA 1526
United States Naval Academy Museum,
   Annapolis, MD..628
United States Senate Commission on Art,
   Washington, DC......................................293
University Art Galleries, Vermillion, SD....1358
University Art Galleries, Murray State
   University, Murray, KY............................580
University Art Gallery, Indiana State
   University, Terre Haute, IN......................501
University Art Gallery, New Mexico
   State University, Las Cruces, NM 941
University Art Gallery, Sonoma State
   University, Rohnert Park, CA 151
University Art Gallery, University of
   Pittsburgh, Pittsburgh, PA 1294
University Art Gallery, University of the
   South, Sewanee, TN 1384
University Art Museum, Binghamton, NY...963
University Art Museum, Santa Barbara,
   Santa Barbara, CA..................................180
University Art Museum, The University
   of New Mexico, Albuquerque, NM.........936
University Art Museum, University at
   Albany, Albany, NY 956
University at Buffalo Art Galleries,
   Buffalo, NY 974
University Galleries, Clarion, PA 1247
University Galleries, Florida Atlantic
   University, Boca Raton, FL 296
University Gallery, Gainesville, FL 312
University Gallery, University of
   Massachusetts at Amherst, Amherst,
   MA..659
University Museum, Carbondale, IL 415
The University Museum, Edwardsville,
   IL..432
The University Museum, Indiana, PA 1263
University Museum, Martin, TN 1371
University Museum & Historic Houses,
   The University of Mississippi, Oxford,
   MS..806
University Museums, University of
   Delaware, Newark, DE............................272
The University of Arizona Museum of
   Art, Tucson, AZ 52
University of Arizona Student Union
   Galleries, Tucson, AZ................................52
University of Arkansas at Little Rock Art
   Department Gallery I & II & III,
   Little Rock, AR 63
University of California Berkeley Art
   Museum and Pacific Film Archive,
   Berkeley, CA 77
University of Denver, School of Art &
   Art History, Victoria H. Myhren
   Gallery, Denver, CO 213
University of Iowa Museum of Art, Iowa
   City, IA 520
University of Kansas Medical Center,
   Clendening History of Medicine
   Library and Museum, Kansas City, KS...546

University of Kentucky Art Museum,
   Lexington, KY...574
University of Maine Museum of Art,
   Bangor, ME...605
University of Mary Washington Galleries,
   Fredericksburg, VA................................1507
The University of Michigan Museum of
   Art, Ann Arbor, MI 726
University of Missouri-Kansas City
   Gallery of Art, Kansas City, MO............823
The University of Montana-Western Art
   Gallery & Museum, Dillon, MT............846
University of North Texas Art Gallery,
   Denton, TX..1409
University of Rhode Island Fine Arts
   Center Galleries, Kingston, RI..............1312
University of Richmond Museums,
   Richmond, VA 1532
University of South Florida
   Contemporary Art Museum, Tampa,
   FL...350
The University of Texas at San Antonio,
   Art Gallery, San Antonio, TX...............1451
University of Virginia Art Museum,
   Charlottesville, VA.................................1500
University of West Florida Art Gallery,
   Pensacola, FL..336
University of Wyoming Art Museum,
   Laramie, WY...1636
University Saint Thomas Art History,
   Saint Paul, MN 792
Urban Institute for Contemporary Arts,
   Grand Rapids, MI....................................744
U.S. Army Center of Military History,
   Museum Division, Fort McNair, DC.......275
U.S. Army Chaplain Museum, Fort
   Jackson, SC..1332
U.S. Army Ordnance Museum, Aberdeen
   Proving Ground, MD...............................627
U.S. Army Transportation Museum, Fort
   Eustis, VA 1504
U.S. Army Women's Museum, Fort Lee,
   VA 1505
U.S. Cavalry Museum, Fort Riley, KS 540
U.S. Coast Guard Museum, New London,
   CT...255
U.S. Grant's Home State Historic Site,
   Galena, IL...436
U.S. Naval Museum of Armament &
   Technology, China Lake, CA....................84
U.S. Navy Memorial Foundation and
   Naval Heritage Center, Washington,
   DC...294
USS Arizona Memorial, Honolulu, HI.........398
USS Bowfin Submarine Museum & Park,
   Honolulu, HI...398
USS Constitution Museum, Boston, MA 669
USS Lexington Museum on the Bay,
   Corpus Christi, TX 1402
Utah Museum of Fine Arts, Salt Lake
   City, UT...1472

Vachel Lindsay Home State Historic Site,
   Springfield, IL...460
Valdosta State University Fine Arts
   Gallery, Valdosta, GA..............................389
Valentine Richmond History Center,
   Richmond, VA 1532
Valley Art Center, Inc., Clarkston, WA 1551
Van Cortlandt House Museum, Bronx,
   NY..967
Van Every/Smith Galleries, Davidson,
   NC...1098
Vanderbilt Mansion National Historic
   Site, Hyde Park, NY..............................1002
Vanderbilt University Fine Arts Gallery,
   Nashville, TN...1381
Vann House, Chatsworth, GA.....................368
Varner-Hogg Plantation State Historic
   Site, West Columbia, TX 1461
Vashon Maury Island Heritage
   Association, Vashon, WA 1576

Ventura County Maritime Museum, Inc.,
   Oxnard, CA...137
Ventura County Museum of History &
   Art, Ventura, CA.....................................195
Verde Historical Society, Clemenceau
   Heritage Museum, Cottonwood, AZ..........32
Vermont Historical Society Museum,
   Montpelier, VT......................................1482
Vero Beach Museum of Art, Inc., Vero
   Beach, FL..352
Victor Heritage Museum, Victor, MT..........854
Viking Union Gallery, Bellingham, WA....1549
Villa Louis Historic Site, Prairie du
   Chien, WI..1619
Village Gallery, La Jolla, CA......................107
Village Historical Society, Inc., Harrison,
   OH..1168
Virginia Historical Society, Richmond,
   VA 1533
Virginia Museum of Fine Arts,
   Richmond, VA 1533
Virginia War Memorial, Richmond, VA 1534
Visual Arts Center of New Jersey,
   Summit, NJ..925
Visual Arts Center of Northwest Florida,
   Panama City, FL......................................334
Visual Arts Museum, New York, NY 1040
The von Liebig Art Center, Naples, FL 328
VSA Arts of Georgia - Arts for All
   Gallery, Atlanta, GA................................364
WARM (Women's Art Registry of
   Minnesota), Saint Paul, MN...................792
W.C. Handy Home Museum and Library,
   Florence, AL...9
The W.H. Stark House, Orange, TX...........1442
Wade House Stagecoach Inn & Wesley
   Jung Carriage Museum State Historic
   Site, Greenbush, WI 1599
Wadsworth Atheneum Museum of Art,
   Hartford, CT 246
The Wagnalls Memorial, Lithopolis, OH ...1172
Wagner Free Institute of Science,
   Philadelphia, PA 1289
Wailoa Center for Culture and Arts, Hilo,
   HI 393
Wake Forest College Birthplace Society,
   Inc., Wake Forest, NC...........................1121
The Walker African American Museum &
   Research Center, Las Vegas, NV 880
Walker Art Center, Minneapolis, MN..........783
The Walker Art Collection of the Garnett
   Public Library, Garnett, KS 541
Wallace District Mining Museum,
   Wallace, ID..410
Walnut Grove Plantation, Roebuck, SC 1340
Walter Anderson Museum of Art, Ocean
   Springs, MS...806
Walters Art Museum, Baltimore, MD...........636
The Waltham Museum, Waltham, MA 716
War in the Pacific National Historical
   Park, Piti, GU..1640
The Ward Museum of Wildfowl Art,
   Salisbury University, Salisbury, MD 653
Waring Historical Library, Charleston, SC.1327
Warner House, Portsmouth, NH 895
Warren County Historical Society,
   Warren, PA...1304
Warwick Museum of Art, Warwick, RI......1320
Washakie Museum, Worland, WY 1639
Washington & Jefferson College - Olin
   Fine Arts Center, Washington, PA.........1305
Washington County Museum of Fine
   Arts, Hagerstown, MD 647
Washington Crossing Historic Park,
   Washington Crossing, PA.......................1305
Washington's Headquarters State Historic
   Site, Newburgh, NY 1042
Waterloo Center for the Arts, Waterloo,
   IA 529
Watervliet Arsenal's Museum of the Big
   Guns, Watervliet, NY 1084
Watson-Curtze Mansion, Erie, PA 1253

Zelienople Historical Society, Zelienople,
    PA 1309
Zeum, San Francisco, CA 170
Ziibiwing Center of Anishinabe Culture
    & Lifeways, Mount Pleasant, MI 757

Sculpture

A.K.C. Museum of The Dog, Saint
    Louis, MO..831
A.L. Fetterman Educational Museum,
    Fort Valley, GA 372
The APEX Museum, Atlanta, GA 357
A.R. Mitchell Museum, Trinidad, CO 233
A:shiwi A:wan Museum and Heritage
    Center, Zuni, NM 954
Abby Aldrich Rockefeller Folk Art
    Museum, Williamsburg, VA 1544
Abington Art Center, Jenkintown, PA 1263
Abraham Lincoln Birthplace National
    Historic Site, Hodgenville, KY..............571
Abraham Lincoln Library & Museum,
    Lincoln Memorial University,
    Harrogate, TN 1366
Academy Art Museum, Easton, MD 642
Ackland Art Museum, Chapel Hill, NC 1093
Adair County Historical Society, Inc.,
    Kirksville, MO..................................824
Adams County Historical Society
    Museum, Brighton, CO.......................204
Adams National Historical Park, Quincy,
    MA 704
Adams State College Luther Bean
    Museum, Alamosa, CO 201
Adan E. Treganza Anthropology
    Museum, Dept. of Anthropology, San
    Francisco State University, San
    Francisco, CA 162
Addison Gallery of American Art,
    Andover, MA....................................659
Adler Planetarium & Astronomy
    Museum, Chicago, IL.........................417
Admiral Peary Monument, Cresson, PA.....1248
African American Museum, Dallas, TX 1403
The African American Museum in
    Philadelphia, Philadelphia, PA 1275
African American Museum of the Arts,
    De Land, FL 303
African Art Museum of Maryland,
    Columbia, MD 641
African Art Museum of the S.M.A.
    Fathers, Tenafly, NJ 926
Afro-American Cultural Center,
    Charlotte, NC 1094
Aiken Thoroughbred Racing Hall of
    Fame and Museum, Aiken, SC 1320
The Airborne & Special Operations
    Museum, Fayetteville, NC....................1100
Akron Art Museum, Akron, OH 1138
Akwesasne Museum, Hogansburg, NY 998
Alabama Department of Archives &
    History, Montgomery, AL 15
Alabama Mining Museum, Dora, AL 7
Alabama Sports Hall of Fame,
    Birmingham, AL...................................4
Alamo Township Museum-John E. Gray
    Memorial Museum, Kalamazoo, MI........748
Alaska Indian Arts, Inc., Haines, AK 24
Albany Institute of History & Art,
    Albany, NY.......................................954
Albany Museum of Art, Albany, GA...........355
Albin Polasek Museum and Sculpture
    Gardens, Winter Park, FL 354
Albion College Department of Art and
    Art History, Albion, MI........................722
The Albrecht-Kemper Museum of Art,
    Saint Joseph, MO 830
Albright-Knox Art Gallery, Buffalo, NY 971
Albuquerque Museum, Albuquerque, NM....932
Alden B. Dow Museum of Science and
    Art of the Midland Center for the
    Arts, Midland, MI..............................755

Alexander Brest Museum and Gallery,
    Jacksonville, FL.................................313
Alexandria Museum of Art, Alexandria,
    LA 584
Alice C. Sabatini Gallery-Topeka and
    Shawnee County Public Library,
    Topeka, KS 558
Aliceville Museum, Aliceville, AL 3
Allen Memorial Art Museum, Oberlin,
    OH 1180
Allen R. Hite Art Institute, Louisville,
    KY..575
Allentown Art Museum, Allentown, PA 1239
Altama Museum of Art & History,
    Vidalia, GA 390
Alva deMars Megan Chapel Art Center,
    Manchester, NH.................................891
Amarillo Museum of Art, Amarillo, TX 1386
American Academy of Arts and Letters,
    New York, NY..................................1018
American Catholic Historical Society,
    Philadelphia, PA 1276
American Folk Art Museum, New York,
    NY 1018
American Historical Society of Germans
    from Russia, Lincoln, NE 865
American Hungarian Foundation/Museum
    of the American Hungarian
    Foundation, New Brunswick, NJ 915
American Irish Historical Society, New
    York, NY...1019
American Labor Museum, Botto House
    National Landmark, Haledon, NJ 906
American Merchant Marine Museum,
    Kings Point, NY...............................1007
American Museum of Asmat Art, Saint
    Paul, MN...789
American Museum of Ceramic Art,
    Pomona, CA......................................143
The American Museum of Fly Fishing,
    Manchester, VT 1481
American Numismatic Association
    Money Museum, Colorado Springs,
    CO..206
The American Numismatic Society, New
    York, NY...1020
American Printing House for the Blind,
    Callahan Museum, Louisville, KY 575
American Quarter Horse Hall of Fame &
    Museum, Amarillo, TX 1386
American Red Cross Visitors Center and
    Gift Shop, Washington, DC 275
American Saddlebred Museum,
    Lexington, KY...................................572
American Sport Art Museum and
    Archives, Daphne, AL 7
American Swedish Historical Foundation
    & Museum, Philadelphia, PA................1276
American University Museum at The
    Katzen Arts Center, Washington, DC 275
American Visionary Art Museum,
    Baltimore, MD..................................629
American Water Ski Educational
    Foundation, Polk City, FL....................337
America's Ice Cream & Dairy Museum,
    Medina, OH 1175
Amon Carter Museum, Fort Worth, TX 1416
Amory Regional Museum, Amory, MS........797
Anchorage Museum at Rasmuson Center,
    Anchorage, AK 22
Ancient and Honorable Artillery
    Company, Boston, MA..........................663
Anderson County Arts Center, Anderson,
    SC..1320
Anderson Gallery - Drake University,
    Des Moines, IA 514
Anderson Museum of Contemporary Art,
    Roswell, NM.....................................945
The Andy Warhol Museum, Pittsburgh,
    PA...1290
Anita S. Wooten Gallery at Valencia
    Community College East Campus,
    Orlando, FL 331

Anna Lamar Switzer Center for Visual
    Arts, Pensacola, FL 335
The Appaloosa Museum and Heritage
    Center, Moscow, ID............................407
Appleton Museum of Art, Ocala, FL............330
Arab American National Museum,
    Dearborn, MI....................................733
Arbor Lodge State Historical Park,
    Nebraska City, NE..............................868
ARC Gallery (Artists, Residents of
    Chicago), Chicago, IL 417
Arcadia University Art Gallery, Glenside,
    PA 1256
Archives of J.S.G. Boggs, Brandon, FL........298
Arizona State University Art Museum,
    Tempe, AZ..45
The Arkansas Arts Center, Little Rock,
    AR..61
Arkansas State University Art Gallery,
    Jonesboro, AR.....................................60
Arlington Arts Center, Arlington, VA 1495
Arlington Museum of Art, Arlington, TX ..1387
The Armory Art Center, West Palm
    Beach, FL...353
Armstrong Browning Library, Waco, TX ...1458
Arnot Art Museum, Elmira, NY 987
Arrowmont School of Arts & Crafts,
    Gatlinburg, TN..................................1365
Art and Culture Center of Hollywood,
    Hollywood, FL...................................312
Art Association of Harrisburg,
    Harrisburg, PA 1258
Art Association of Randolph County,
    Inc., Union City, IN............................501
The Art Center at Fuller Lodge, Los
    Alamos, NM 942
Art Center In Hargate, St. Paul's School,
    Concord, NH.....................................884
Art Center of Battle Creek, Battle Creek,
    MI...726
Art Center Sarasota, Inc, Sarasota, FL........343
Art Center Waco, Waco, TX 1458
Art Complex Museum, Duxbury, MA..........680
The Art Gallery at the University of
    Maryland, College Park, College Park,
    MD..640
Art Gallery at the University of New
    England, Portland, ME.........................618
The Art Gallery, John C. Calhoun State
    Community College, Decatur, AL 7
The Art Gallery, Lower Columbia
    College Fine Arts Gallery, Longview,
    WA..1558
Art Gallery Marist College,
    Poughkeepsie, NY 1054
Art Guild of Burlington, Inc., Burlington,
    IA 507
Art In Embassies Program, U.S.
    Department of State, Washington, DC 276
The Art Institute of Chicago, Chicago, IL ...418
Art Museum of South Texas, Corpus
    Christi, TX 1401
Art Museum of Southeast Texas,
    Beaumont, TX 1393
Art Museum of the Americas, Oas,
    Washington, DC 276
Art Museum of Western Virginia,
    Roanoke, VA....................................1534
The Art Studio, Inc., Beaumont, TX 1393
ArtCenter/South Florida, Miami Beach,
    FL...326
Arthur A. Houghton Jr. Gallery & The
    Great Hall Gallery, New York, NY 1020
The Arthur J. Moore Methodist Museum,
    Saint Simons Island, GA......................383
Arthur M. Sackler Gallery, Washington,
    DC..276
Arthur Ross Gallery, University of
    Pennsylvania, Philadelphia, PA..............1276
The Arts & Science Center for Southeast
    Arkansas, Pine Bluff, AR......................65
Arts Consortium of Cincinnati's African
    American Museum, Cincinnati, OH......1148

Sculpture–Continued

Arts Council of Moore County - Campbell House, Southern Pines, NC ...1120

Artspace, Raleigh, NC 1114

Arvada Center for the Arts and Humanities, Arvada, CO 201

The Ashby-Hodge Gallery of American Art, Central Methodist University, Fayette, MO 815

Asheville Art Museum, Asheville, NC 1088

Ashtabula Arts Center, Ashtabula, OH 1140

Asia Society Museum, New York, NY 1020

Asian American Arts Centre, New York, NY 1021

Asian Art Museum of San Francisco, Chong-Moon Lee Center for Asian Art and Culture, San Francisco, CA 163

Asian Arts & Culture Center, Towson University, Towson, MD 655

Aspen Art Museum, Aspen, CO 201

Associated Artists of Pittsburgh, Pittsburgh, PA 1290

Ataloa Lodge Museum, Muskogee, OK 1205

The Athenaeum of Philadelphia, Philadelphia, PA 1276

Atlanta Botanical Garden, Atlanta, GA 357

Atlanta College of Art, Atlanta, GA 358

The Atlanta Cyclorama, Atlanta, GA............358

Atlantic Center for the Arts, Inc., New Smyrna Beach, FL 329

Atlantic Heritage Center, Somers Point, NJ 924

Atrium Gallery Ltd., Saint Louis, MO 832

Attleboro Arts Museum, Attleboro, MA.......661

Audubon Society of New Hampshire, Concord, NH..884

Augustana College Art Museum, Rock Island, IL..453

Aurora Public Art Commission, Aurora, IL..411

Austin Museum of Art - Downtown, Austin, TX...1388

Autry National Center of the American West, Los Angeles, CA 112

The AXA Gallery, New York, NY 1021

Bakersfield Museum of Art, Bakersfield, CA...73

Ball State University Museum of Art, Muncie, IN...492

The Ballard Institute & Museum of Puppetry, Storrs, CT 261

The Baltimore Museum of Art, Baltimore, MD...630

Balzekas Museum of Lithuanian Culture, Chicago, IL..418

Barnard's Mill Art Museum, Glen Rose, TX...1422

Barnes Foundation, Merion, PA..................1271

Barnes Museum, Southington, CT................260

Barton Museum, Wilson, NC......................1124

Bass Museum of Art, Miami Beach, FL 326

Bates College Museum of Art, Lewiston, ME...613

Baum Gallery of Fine Art, University of Central Arkansas, Conway, AR.................56

Baycrafters, Inc., Bay Village, OH 1141

Bayou Bend Collection and Gardens, Houston, TX...1425

Beard Gallery, Norton, MA 700

Beaumont Art League, Beaumont, TX 1394

Beauvoir, The Jefferson Davis Home and Presidential Library, Biloxi, MS 798

Beck Cultural Exchange Center, Knoxville, TN..1369

Beehive House, Salt Lake City, UT 1470

Belair Mansion, Bowie, MD........................638

Belair Stable Museum, Bowie, MD..............638

Belcourt Castle, Newport, RI.....................1313

Bellingrath Gardens & Home, Theodore, AL..18

Bellport-Brookhaven Historical Society and Museum, Bellport, NY....................961

Belskie Museum of Art & Science, Closter, NJ..902

Ben Shahn Galleries at William Paterson University of New Jersey, Wayne, NJ.....929

Benedicta Arts Center, Saint Joseph, MN 789

Bennington Battlefield State Historic Site, Walloomsac, NY.....................................1081

Bennington Center for the Natural & Cultural Arts, Bennington, VT...............1476

The Bennington Museum, Bennington, VT...1476

Berea College, Doris Ulmann Galleries, Berea, KY..565

Bergen County Historical Society, River Edge, NJ..923

Bergen Museum of Art & Science, Paramus, NJ..919

Berkshire Artisans/Lichtenstein Center for the Arts, Pittsfield, MA 702

Berman Museum of World History, Anniston, AL...3

Bernheim Arboretum and Research Forest, Clermont, KY.............................567

Besser Museum for Northeast Michigan, Alpena, MI...723

Beth Ahabah Museum & Archives, Richmond, VA......................................1528

Beverly Historical Society and Museum, Beverly, MA...662

Biblical Arts Center, Dallas, TX................1404

Bicentennial Art Center & Museum, Paris, IL..449

Biedenharn Museum & Gardens, Monroe, LA..592

Biggs Museum of American Art, Dover, DE..269

Biltmore Estate, Asheville, NC..................1089

Biltmore Homespun Shops - Grovewood Gallery, Asheville, NC 1089

Bily Clock Museum/Antonin Dvorak Exhibit, Spillville, IA 528

Birds of Vermont Museum, Huntington, VT...1480

Birger Sandzen Memorial Gallery, Lindsborg, KS...549

Birmingham Bloomfield Art Center, Birmingham, MI.....................................730

Birmingham Botanical Gardens, Birmingham, AL..4

Birmingham Civil Rights Institute, Birmingham, AL..4

Birmingham Museum of Art, Birmingham, AL..5

Birthplace of John Wayne, Winterset, IA.....530

Black Arts National Diaspora Museum, New Orleans, LA.....................................594

Black Heritage Museum, Miami, FL............323

Black Mountain College Museum & Arts Center, Asheville, NC.............................1089

Blackhawk Museum (Behring-Hofmann Educational Institute, Inc.), Danville, CA..89

Blaine County Museum, Chinook, MT 844

Blanden Memorial Art Museum, Fort Dodge, IA...518

Blandford Church & Reception Ctr. (The Petersburg Museums), Petersburg, VA ..1524

Blanton Museum of Art, Austin, TX 1389

Blithewold Mansion, Gardens & Arboretum, Bristol, RI 1310

B'nai B'rith Klutznick National Jewish Museum, Washington, DC 277

Bob Jones University Museum & Gallery, Inc., Greenville, SC.................................1333

Boca Raton Museum of Art, Boca Raton, FL...296

Boehm Gallery, San Marcos, CA.................174

Boerner Botanical Gardens, Hales Corners, WI..1600

Boise Art Museum, Boise, ID......................403

Bonnet House Museum & Gardens, Fort Lauderdale, FL...306

Booker T. Washington National Monument, Hardy, VA 1510

Booth Western Art Museum, Cartersville, GA...367

Boothbay Region Art Foundation, Inc., Boothbay Harbor, ME.............................607

Boston Athenaeum Library, Boston, MA 663

Boston University Art Gallery, Boston, MA...665

Botanica, The Wichita Gardens, Wichita, KS..561

Boulder Museum of Contemporary Art, Boulder, CO..203

Bowdoin College Museum of Art, Brunswick, ME..607

Bowers Museum, Santa Ana, CA 177

Boys Town Hall of History & Father Flanagan House, Boys Town, NE.............858

Bradford Brinton Memorial & Museum, Big Horn, WY...1628

Bragg-Mitchell Mansion, Mobile, AL 13

Braithwaite Fine Arts Gallery, Cedar City, UT..1464

Brand Library & Art Center, Glendale, CA..100

Brandywine River Museum, Chadds Ford, PA..1246

Branigan Cultural Center, Las Cruces, NM...940

Brattleboro Museum & Art Center, Brattleboro, VT......................................1477

Brauer Museum of Art, Valparaiso, IN 501

Bread & Puppet Museum, Glover, VT.......1479

Brenau University Galleries, Brenau University, Gainesville, GA 373

Brevard Museum of Art and Science, Inc., Melbourne, FL.................................323

Bromfield Art Gallery, Boston, MA 665

The Bronx Museum of the Arts, Bronx, NY...965

Brookfield Craft Center, Brookfield, CT 237

Brookgreen Gardens, Murrells Inlet, SC 1337

Brooklyn Children's Museum, Brooklyn, NY...968

Brooklyn Museum, Brooklyn, NY...............968

Brooks Free Library, Harwich, MA..............686

Brown County Art Gallery and Museum, Nashville, IN..493

Brown County Historical Society Pioneer Museum, Nashville, IN...........................493

Brownsville Museum of Fine Art - Brownsville Art League, Brownsville, TX...1398

Brownville Historical Society Museum, Brownville, NE..858

Brueckner Museum of Starr Commonwealth, Albion, MI.......................723

Brunnier Art Museum, Ames, IA................504

Buckaroo Hall of Fame, Winnemucca, NV..882

Buckhorn Saloon & Museum, San Antonio, TX...1448

Bucyrus Historical Society, Bucyrus, OH ..1144

Buffalo Bill Historical Center, Cody, WY..1631

Buffalo Bill Museum & Grave, Golden, CO..219

Buffalo Gap Historic Village, Buffalo Gap, TX...1398

Buffalo Zoological Gardens, Buffalo, NY 972

Bunker Hill Museum, Charlestown, MA......675

Burchfield-Penney Art Center, Buffalo, NY...973

Burlington County Historical Society, Burlington, NJ...898

Burnham Tavern, Machias, ME...................614

Bushy Run Battlefield, Jeannette, PA.........1263

The Butler Institute of American Art, Youngstown, OH....................................1193

Butterfly Lodge Museum, Greer, AZ.............36

CFCC Webber Center Gallery, Ocala, FL 330

C.M. Russell Museum, Great Falls, MT 848

CU Art Galleries, Boulder, CO......................203

Cahoon Museum of American Art,
 Cotuit, MA......................677

California African-American Museum,
 Los Angeles, CA......................113

California Center for the Arts, Escondido,
 Escondido, CA......................93

California Historical Society, San
 Francisco, CA......................163

California Museum of Ancient Art,
 Beverly Hills, CA......................78

California State Indian Museum,
 Sacramento, CA......................151

California State University, Long Beach,
 University Art Museum, Long Beach,
 CA......................110

California Surf Museum, Oceanside, CA.....135

Calvin College Center Art Gallery, Grand
 Rapids, MI......................743

The Camron-Stanford House Preservation
 Association, Oakland, CA......................133

Canajoharie Library and Art Gallery,
 Canajoharie, NY......................974

The Canton Museum of Art, Canton, OH..1145

Cape Ann Historical Museum,
 Gloucester, MA......................684

Cape Cod Museum of Art, Dennis, MA 680

Captain Charles H. Hurley Library,
 Buzzards Bay, MA 672

Caramoor Center for Music & the Arts,
 Inc., Katonah, NY......................1006

Carleton College Art Gallery, Northfield,
 MN......................785

Carlsbad Museum & Art Center,
 Carlsbad, NM......................938

Carnegie Art Museum, Oxnard, CA 136

Carnegie Center for Art & History, New
 Albany, IN......................493

Carnegie Museum of Art, Pittsburgh, PA...1290

Carroll Reece Museum, Johnson City, TN.1367

CAS Gallery, Union, NJ......................928

Casa Adobe de San Rafael, Glendale, CA ...100

Casa Amesti, Monterey, CA......................127

Cass County Historical Society,
 Logansport, IN......................489

Cass County Historical Society at
 Bonanzaville, West Fargo, ND......................1137

Casteel-Linn House and Museum,
 Princeton, MO......................829

Castellani Art Museum of Niagara
 University, Niagara University, NY.......1043

Castillo de San Marcos National
 Monument, Saint Augustine, FL......................338

Cathedral Cultural Center, Omaha, NE 870

The Cathedral of St. John the Divine,
 New York, NY......................1022

Catholic Historical Society of the
 Roanoke Valley, Roanoke, VA 1535

Catskill Fly Fishing Center & Museum,
 Livingston Manor, NY......................1010

Cattle Raisers Museum, Fort Worth, TX...1416

Cazenovia College - Art & Design
 Gallery, Cazenovia, NY......................976

Cedar Rapids Museum of Art, Cedar
 Rapids, IA......................509

Cedarhurst Center for the Arts, Mount
 Vernon, IL......................446

Center for American Music, Pittsburgh,
 PA......................1291

Center for Book Arts, New York, NY........1022

Center for Curatorial Studies,
 Annandale-on-Hudson, NY......................958

Center of Southwest Studies/Fort Lewis
 College, Durango, CO......................214

Center on Contemporary Art, Seattle, WA.1565

Central Park Conservancy, New York,
 NY......................1022

Centre County Library and Historical
 Museum, Bellefonte, PA......................1241

Chaffee Center for the Visual Arts,
 Rutland, VT......................1486

Chaffey Community Art Association
 Museum of Art, Rancho Cucamonga,
 CA......................145

Charles Allis Art Museum, Milwaukee,
 WI......................1610

Charles B. Goddard Center for Visual
 and Performing Arts, Ardmore, OK.......1196

Charles H. MacNider Museum, Mason
 City, IA......................523

Charles H. Taylor Arts Center, Hampton,
 VA......................1509

The Charles Hosmer Morse Museum of
 American Art, Winter Park, FL 354

Charles M. Schulz Museum and Research
 Center, Santa Rosa, CA......................184

Charles Towne Landing State Historic
 Site, Charleston, SC......................1324

Chattahoochee Valley Art Museum,
 LaGrange, GA......................375

Chazen Museum of Art, Madison, WI 1604

Cheekwood-Tennessee Botanical Garden
 & Museum of Art, Nashville, TN..........1378

Cherokee Courthouse Visitors
 Information Center & Museum, Gore,
 OK......................1201

Cherokee National Museum, Park Hill,
 OK......................1211

Chester County Historical Society, West
 Chester, PA......................1307

Chesterwood, Stockbridge, MA......................711

Cheyenne Mountain Zoological Park,
 Colorado Springs, CO......................206

Chicago Botanic Garden, Glencoe, IL..........438

Chicago Children's Museum, Chicago, IL...419

Chicago Cultural Center, Chicago, IL..........419

Chicago Public Library, Chicago, IL............419

Chicago Zoological Park (Brookfield
 Zoo), Brookfield, IL......................414

Chief Plenty Coups Museum, Pryor, MT.....852

The Children's Museum of Indianapolis,
 Indianapolis, IN......................481

Children's Museum of Los Angeles, Van
 Nuys, CA......................194

Children's Museum of Pittsburgh,
 Pittsburgh, PA......................1291

The Children's Museum of Portsmouth,
 Portsmouth, NH......................894

Children's Museum of the Arts, New
 York, NY......................1022

Chinati Foundation, Marfa, TX 1436

Chinese Cultural Garden/Overfelt
 Gardens, San Jose, CA......................171

Chinese Culture Center of San Francisco,
 San Francisco, CA......................164

Chinqua-Penn Plantation, Reidsville, NC...1117

Chisholm Trail Historical Museum,
 Waurika, OK......................1216

Choctaw County Historical Society,
 Hugo, OK......................1203

The Christian C. Sanderson Museum,
 Chadds Ford, PA......................1246

Chrysler Museum of Art, Norfolk, VA.......1521

Chula Vista Nature Center, Chula Vista,
 CA......................84

Cigna Museum and Art Collection,
 Philadelphia, PA......................1277

Cincinnati Art Galleries, Cincinnati, OH...1148

Cincinnati Art Museum, Cincinnati, OH.....1148

Circle Gallery/College of Environment &
 Design - University of Georgia,
 Athens, GA......................356

City Arts Center, Oklahoma City, OK........1207

City Hall Council Chamber Gallery,
 Charleston, SC......................1324

City Museum, Saint Louis, MO......................832

City of Bowie Museums, Bowie, MD..........638

City of Brea Gallery, Brea, CA......................79

Clark Atlanta University Art Galleries,
 Atlanta, GA......................359

Clark Humanities Museum-Study,
 Claremont, CA......................85

Clausen Memorial Museum, Petersburg,
 AK......................27

Clay Center for Arts & Sciences West
 Virginia, Charleston, WV......................1580

Clermont State Historic Site, Clermont,
 NY......................979

Cleveland Artists Foundation at Beck
 Center for the Arts, Lakewood, OH 1170

The Cleveland Museum of Art,
 Cleveland, OH......................1152

Cleveland State University Art Gallery,
 Cleveland, OH......................1153

Clinton County Historical Society,
 Wilmington, OH......................1191

Clinton County Museum, Frankfort, IN 478

Cliveden of the National Trust,
 Philadelphia, PA......................1278

The Cloisters, New York, NY......................1023

Clough-Hanson Gallery, Rhodes College,
 Memphis, TN......................1372

Coeur d'Alenes Old Mission State Park,
 Cataldo, ID......................405

Colby College Museum of Art,
 Waterville, ME......................624

The College Art Gallery, Ewing, NJ 903

College Football Hall of Fame, South
 Bend, IN......................499

College of Eastern Utah Art Gallery,
 Gallery East, Price, UT......................1469

College of the Redwoods Art Gallery,
 Eureka, CA......................94

Colleton Museum, Walterboro, SC............1343

The Colonial Spanish Quarter Museum,
 Saint Augustine, FL......................338

Colorado River Indian Tribes Museum,
 Parker, AZ......................38

Colorado Springs Fine Arts Center
 (Taylor Museum), Colorado Springs,
 CO......................206

Colton Hall Museum, Monterey, CA............127

Columbia Museum of Art, Columbia, SC..1329

Columbus Chapel, Boal Mansion
 Museum, Boalsburg, PA......................1244

The Columbus Museum, Columbus, GA 368

Columbus Museum of Art, Columbus,
 OH......................1157

Columbus Museum of Art and Design,
 Columbus, IN......................473

Command Museum, Marine Corps
 Recruit Depot, San Diego, San Diego,
 CA......................156

The Commonwealth Museum, Boston,
 MA......................665

Community Council for the Arts,
 Kinston, NC......................1108

Community Fine Arts Center, Rock
 Springs, WY......................1637

Compton Art Collection, Upland, IN...........501

Concord Art Association, Concord, MA.......676

Confederate Museum, New Orleans, LA 594

The Conservatory Garden, New York,
 NY......................1023

Constitution Convention Museum State
 Park, Port St. Joe, FL......................338

Contemporary Art Museum St. Louis,
 Saint Louis, MO......................832

The Contemporary Arts Center,
 Cincinnati, OH......................1150

Contemporary Crafts Museum & Gallery,
 Portland, OR......................1230

The Contemporary Jewish Museum, San
 Francisco, CA......................164

The Contemporary Museum, Honolulu,
 HI......................394

Contemporary Museum, Baltimore, MD......631

The Contemporary Museum at First
 Hawaiian Center, Honolulu, HI 394

Coos Art Museum, Coos Bay, OR.............1222

Copia: The American Center for Wine,
 Food & the Arts, Napa, CA......................129

Copshaholm House Museum & Historic
 Oliver Gardens, South Bend, IN............499

Sculpture—Continued

Coral Springs Museum of Art, Coral Springs, FL 301

The Corcoran Gallery of Art, Washington, DC 277

Cornell Museum of Art & History, Delray Beach, FL 304

The Corning Museum of Glass, Corning, NY 981

Cornish Colony Museum, Windsor, VT 1490

Cottonlandia Museum, Greenwood, MS 800

Coutts Memorial Museum of Art, Inc., El Dorado, KS 537

Cozens Ranch Museum, Fraser, CO 218

Craft and Folk Art Museum - CAFAM, Los Angeles, CA 114

Craftsmen's Guild of Mississippi, Jackson, MS 802

Cranbrook Art Museum, Bloomfield Hills, MI 730

Cranbrook House and Gardens Auxiliary, Bloomfield Hills, MI 730

Crater Lake National Park, Crater Lake, OR 1222

Cravens House, Lookout Mountain, TN 1371

Creative Arts Guild, Dalton, GA 370

Cress Gallery of Art, Chattanooga, TN 1361

Crestline Shunk Museum, Crestline, OH ...1160

Cripple Creek District Museum, Inc., Cripple Creek, CO 209

Crispus Attucks Center Museum, Indianapolis, IN 482

Croatian Heritage Museum & Library, Eastlake, OH 1163

Crocker Art Museum, Sacramento, CA 152

Crook County Museum & Art Gallery, Sundance, WY 1638

Crooked Tree Arts Center, Petoskey, MI 760

Cumberland Island National Seashore, Saint Marys, GA 382

Cummer Museum of Art and Gardens, Jacksonville, FL 314

Cuneo Museum & Gardens, Vernon Hills, IL 463

Cupola House, Egg Harbor, WI 1596

Curfman Gallery & Duhesa Lounge, Fort Collins, CO 216

The Currier Museum of Art, Manchester, NH 891

Custer County Art & Heritage Center, Miles City, MT 851

Cy Twombly Gallery, Houston, TX 1426

Cyrus E. Dallin Art Museum, Arlington, MA 660

DAAP Galleries, Cincinnati, OH 1150

Dahesh Museum of Art, New York, NY 1024

Dakota Discovery Museum, Mitchell, SD..1352

Dakota Zoo, Bismarck, ND 1128

The Dallas Center for Contemporary Art - The Dallas Contemporary, Dallas, TX 1404

Dallas Historical Society, Dallas, TX 1405

Dallas Holocaust Museum, Dallas, TX 1405

Dallas Museum of Art, Dallas, TX 1405

Dalton Galleries, Decatur, GA 370

The Dana-Thomas House State Historic Site, Springfield, IL 458

Dane G. Hansen Memorial Museum, Logan, KS 550

Danforth Museum of Art, Framingham, MA 683

The Danish Immigrant Museum, Elk Horn, IA 517

Daum Museum of Contemporary Art, Sedalia, MO 838

Daura Gallery, Lynchburg, VA 1515

David Winton Bell Gallery, Providence, RI 1316

Davis Art Center, Davis, CA 89

Davis Art Gallery, Columbia, MO 813

Davis Museum and Cultural Center, Wellesley, MA 716

The Davistown Museum, Liberty, ME 614

Dayton Art Institute, Dayton, OH 1161

De Saisset Museum, Santa Clara, CA 180

Decatur House Museum, Washington, DC ...277

DeCordova Museum and Sculpture Park, Lincoln, MA 690

Degrazia Gallery In The Sun, Tucson, AZ 48

The DeLand Museum of Art, De Land, FL 303

Delaware Art Museum, Wilmington, DE 273

Delaware Center for the Contemporary Arts, Wilmington, DE 273

Delta Blues Museum, Clarksdale, MS 799

Denison Museum, Granville, OH 1167

Dennos Museum Center of Northwestern Michigan College, Traverse City, MI 765

Denver Art Museum, Denver, CO 210

Denver Botanic Gardens, Inc., Denver, CO 210

Denver Museum of Miniatures, Dolls and Toys, Denver, CO 211

Department of the Treasury, Washington, DC 278

DePaul University Art Museum, Chicago, IL 420

DePree Art Center & Gallery, Holland, MI 746

Des Moines Art Center, Des Moines, IA 514

Des Moines Botanical Center, Des Moines, IA 514

Desert Caballeros Western Museum, Wickenburg, AZ 53

Detroit Artists Market, Detroit, MI 735

The Detroit Institute of Arts, Detroit, MI 736

Detroit Zoo, Royal Oak, MI 762

Dewey Hotel Museum, Dewey, OK 1199

DeWitt Stetten, Jr., Museum of Medical Research, Bethesda, MD 637

Dia:Beacon, Riggio Galleries, Beacon, NY 960

Dia: Chelsea, New York, NY 1024

Diggs Gallery at Winston-Salem State University, Winston-Salem, NC 1125

Dinosaur Gardens, LLC, Ossineke, MI 759

The Dinosaur Museum, Blanding, UT 1463

Diplomatic Reception Rooms, Department of State, Washington, DC 278

The Discovery Museum, Inc., Bridgeport, CT 236

Dishman Art Museum, Beaumont, TX 1394

The Dixon Gallery and Gardens, Memphis, TN 1372

Donald E. Stephens Museum of Hummels, Rosemont, IL 456

Donna Beam Fine Art Gallery, UNLV, Las Vegas, NV 878

The Douglas F. Cooley Memorial Art Gallery, Reed College, Portland, OR 1231

Dow Gardens, Midland, MI 755

Dowd Fine Arts Gallery, State University of New York College at Cortland, Cortland, NY 983

Downey Museum of Art, Downey, CA 91

Dragon Dreams Museum & Gift Shop, Chattanooga, TN 1362

Dubuque Museum of Art, Dubuque, IA 516

Duluth Art Institute, Duluth, MN 772

Dumbarton Oaks Research Library & Collections, Washington, DC 278

The Duncan Gallery of Art, De Land, FL....304

Dusable Museum of African-American History, Inc., Chicago, IL 420

The Dwight Frederick Boyden Gallery, Saint Mary's City, MD 652

Dyckman Farmhouse Museum and Park, New York, NY 1025

Eagle Rock Art Museum and Education Center, Idaho Falls, ID 406

Earl Burns Miller Japanese Garden, Long Beach, CA 110

Earth & Mineral Sciences Museum and Art Gallery, University Park, PA 1303

East-West Center, Honolulu, HI 394

Eastern Shore Art Center, Fairhope, AL 9

The Ebenezer Maxwell Mansion, Inc., Philadelphia, PA 1278

Eccles Community Arts Center, Ogden, UT 1467

Edgar Allan Poe Cottage, Bronx, NY 965

Edgar Allan Poe Museum, Richmond, VA..1529

Edgar County Historical Museum, Paris, IL 449

Edge of the Cedars State Park Museum, Blanding, UT 1463

Edison Museum, Beaumont, TX 1394

Edmonds Art Festival Museum, Edmonds, WA 1553

Edsel & Eleanor Ford House, Grosse Pointe Shores, MI 745

Edward-Dean Museum and Gardens, Cherry Valley, CA 82

Edward H. White II Memorial Museum, Brooks Air Force Base, TX 1397

Egan Maritime Foundation, Nantucket, MA 695

Eisenhower Birthplace State Historical Site, Denison, TX 1409

Eiteljorg Museum of American Indians and Western Art, Indianapolis, IN 482

El Camino Real International Heritage Center, San Antonio, NM 947

El Museo Del Barrio, New York, NY 1025

El Museo Latino, Omaha, NE 870

El Paso Museum of Art, El Paso, TX 1411

El Pueblo Historical Monument, Los Angeles, CA 114

El Rancho de Las Golondrinas Museum, Santa Fe, NM 947

Elbert Hubbard-Roycroft Museum, East Aurora, NY 985

Elberton Granite Museum & Exhibit, Elberton, GA 371

Elder Art Gallery, Nebraska Wesleyan University, Lincoln, NE 865

Elegba Folklore Society Cultural Center, Richmond, VA 1529

Elisabet Ney Museum, Austin, TX 1390

Elizabeth Myers Mitchell Art Gallery at St. John's College, Annapolis, MD 627

The Ellen Noel Art Museum of the Permian Basin, Odessa, TX 1441

Ellwood House Museum, DeKalb, IL 429

Elmhurst Art Museum, Elmhurst, IL 433

Elsing Museum, Tulsa, OK 1215

Elverhoj Museum of History and Art, Solvang, CA 187

The Emerson Gallery, Clinton, NY 979

Epcot at Walt Disney World Resort, Lake Buena Vista, FL 319

Erie Art Museum, Erie, PA 1252

The Esther and John Clay Fine Arts Gallery, Cheyenne, WY 1630

Esther M. Klein Art Gallery at University City Science Center, Philadelphia, PA ...1279

The Esther Thomas Atkinson Museum, Hampden-Sydney, VA 1509

Eubie Blake National Jazz Institute and Cultural Center, Baltimore, MD 632

Eugene V. Debs Home, Terre Haute, IN 500

Eureka Pioneer Museum of McPherson County, Inc., Eureka, SD 1346

Evansville Museum of Arts History & Science, Evansville, IN 475

Evergreen Galleries, Olympia, WA 1560

Evergreen House, The Johns Hopkins University, Baltimore, MD 632

Everhart Museum: Natural History, Science and Art, Scranton, PA 1298

Everson Museum of Art, Syracuse, NY 1076

Exploris, Raleigh, NC 1115

Ezra Meeker Mansion, Puyallup, WA 1564

The Fabric Workshop and Museum,
    Philadelphia, PA 1279
Fairfield Art Association, Fairfield, IA 518
Fairview Museum of History & Art,
    Fairview, UT...1465
Fall River Historical Society Museum,
    Fall River, MA 682
Fallingwater, Mill Run, PA 1272
Faulconer Gallery at Grinnell College,
    Grinnell, IA..519
Favell Museum Inc., Klamath Falls, OR....1227
Fayette Art Museum, Fayette, AL 9
Fayetteville Museum of Art, Fayetteville,
    NC..1100
Federal Hall National Memorial, New
    York, NY...1025
Federal Reserve Board, Washington, DC.....278
Fender Museum of Music and the Arts,
    Corona, CA..87
Festival-Institute, James Dick Foundation,
    Round Top, TX...1446
Fielding L. Wright Art Center, Cleveland,
    MS..799
Figge Art Museum, Davenport, IA..............512
The Filson Historical Society, Inc.,
    Louisville, KY...576
Fine Arts Center for New River Valley,
    Pulaski, VA...1526
Fine Arts Collection, Luther College,
    Decorah, IA..513
The Fine Arts Museums of San
    Francisco, de Young Museum, San
    Francisco, CA...165
The Fine Arts Museums of San
    Francisco, Legion of Honor, San
    Francisco, CA...165
Firehouse Art Gallery, Nassau
    Community College, Garden City, NY ...992
The Firehouse Gallery, Burlington, VT......1478
The First Division Museum at Cantigny,
    Wheaton, IL..465
First White House of the Confederacy,
    Montgomery, AL 16
Fisher Gallery, University of Southern
    California, Los Angeles, CA....................115
The Fisk University Galleries, Nashville,
    TN..1379
Fitchburg Art Museum, Fitchburg, MA.......683
The Five Civilized Tribes Museum,
    Muskogee, OK..1205
Flagler Museum, Palm Beach, FL................333
Flaten Art Museum of St. Olaf College,
    Northfield, MN...785
Fleischer Museum, Scottsdale, AZ 43
Flint Institute of Arts, Flint, MI...................741
Florence Hawley Ellis Museum of
    Anthropology and Ruth Hall Museum
    of Paleontology, Abiquiu, NM.................931
Florida Gulf Coast University Art
    Gallery, Fort Myers, FL............................309
Florida Holocaust Museum, Saint
    Petersburg, FL..341
Florida State University Museum of Fine
    Arts, Tallahassee, FL.................................347
Folger Shakespeare Library, Washington,
    DC...278
Foothills Art Center, Golden, CO 220
Ford's Theatre National Historic Site
    (Lincoln Museum), Washington, DC.......279
Forest Lawn Museum, Glendale, CA 100
The Forges and Manor of Ringwood,
    Ringwood, NJ...923
Fort Christmas Historical Park,
    Christmas, FL...299
Fort Douglas Military Museum, Fort
    Douglas, UT..1465
Fort Frederick State Park, Big Pool, MD....637
Fort Harker Museum Complex,
    Kanopolis, KS..546
Fort McHenry National Monument and
    Historic Shrine, Baltimore, MD..............632

Fort Selden State Monument, Radium
    Springs, NM..945
Fort Smith Art Center, Fort Smith, AR 57
Fort Walton Beach Art Museum, Fort
    Walton Beach, FL......................................310
Fort Ward Museum and Historic Site,
    Alexandria, VA 1492
Fort Wayne Museum of Art, Fort Wayne,
    IN 477
Fort Worth Botanic Garden, Fort Worth,
    TX 1416
45th Infantry Division Museum,
    Oklahoma City, OK..................................1207
Foster Gallery, University of
    Wisconsin-Eau Claire, Eau Claire, WI ..1596
Framingham Historical Society &
    Museum, Framingham, MA........................683
The Frances Lehman Loeb Art Center,
    Poughkeepsie, NY 1055
Frances Willard House Museum,
    Evanston, IL...434
Frances Young Tang Teaching Museum
    and Art Gallery, Saratoga Springs, NY .1064
Francis McCray Gallery, Silver City, NM....951
Frank Lloyd Wright Home and Studio,
    Oak Park, IL...448
Frank Phillips Home, Bartlesville, OK.......1197
Franklin D. Roosevelt Presidential
    Library-Museum, Hyde Park, NY 1002
Franklin G. Burroughs-Simeon B. Chapin
    Art Museum, Myrtle Beach, SC.............1338
Fraternal Order of Alaska State Troopers
    Museum, Anchorage, AK.............................22
Fred Dana Marsh Museum, Ormond
    Beach, FL...333
Fred Harman Art Museum, Pagosa
    Springs, CO...229
The Fred Jones Jr. Museum of Art,
    Norman, OK...1206
Fred Wolf, Jr. Gallery/Klein Branch
    Jewish Community Center,
    Philadelphia, PA.......................................1280
Frederic Remington Art Museum,
    Ogdensburg, NY.......................................1044
Frederick C. Robie House, Chicago, IL.......420
Frederick Douglass National Historic
    Site, Washington, DC................................279
Frederick R. Weisman Art Museum,
    Minneapolis, MN.......................................781
Frederick R. Weisman Museum of Art,
    Malibu, CA..123
Freedman Gallery-Albright College,
    Reading, PA..1296
Freeport Arts Center, Freeport, IL...............435
Freer Gallery of Art, Washington, DC 279
French Art Colony, Gallipolis, OH.............1165
Fresno Art Museum, Fresno, CA....................97
The Frick Art & Historical Center,
    Pittsburgh, PA..1292
The Frick Collection, New York, NY.........1025
Frisco Historic Park & Museum, Frisco,
    CO...218
Frisco Native American Museum and
    Natural History Center, Frisco, NC 1102
Frontier Gateway Museum, Glendive,
    MT...847
Frontier Times Museum, Bandera, TX.......1393
Fruitlands Museums, Harvard, MA 686
Fuller Craft Museum, Brockton, MA 671

Gadsden Arts Center, Quincy, FL.................338
Gadsden Museum of Art, Gadsden, AL 10
Gaineswood, Demopolis, AL 7
Galerie Trinitas, Great Falls, MT.................848
Galesburg Civic Art Center, Galesburg,
    IL..437
Gallery of Contemporary Art, University
    of Colorado, Colorado Springs,
    Colorado Springs, CO...............................207
Gallery of Henry Street
    Settlement/Abrons Arts Center, New
    York, NY...1026

Gallery on the York - Yorktown Arts
    Foundation, Yorktown, VA......................1547
Gallery '76, Wenatchee, WA.......................1577
Gallier House, New Orleans, LA..................595
Galloping Road Compound & Poker
    Alley; Harbor Ranch, Dripping
    Springs, TX..1410
Gardiner Art Gallery, Stillwater, OK..........1214
The Gardner Museum of Architecture &
    Design, Quincy, IL....................................452
General Daniel Bissell House, Saint
    Louis, MO..833
The General Douglas L. McBride
    Museum, New Mexico Military
    Institute, Roswell, NM..............................945
General Grant National Memorial, New
    York, NY...1026
General Lew Wallace Study & Museum,
    Crawfordsville, IN.....................................473
General Patton Memorial Museum,
    Chiriaco Summit, CA..................................84
Genesee Country Village & Museum,
    Mumford, NY...1016
George A. Spiva Center for the Arts,
    Joplin, MO...820
George C. Marshall Museum, Lexington,
    VA...1513
The George D. and Harriet W. Cornell
    Fine Arts Museum, Winter Park, FL 354
George J. Doizaki Gallery, Los Angeles,
    CA..115
George Meany Memorial Archives, Silver
    Spring, MD...654
George Washington Carver Museum,
    Tuskegee Institute, AL................................20
George Washington Carver Museum and
    Cultural Center, Phoenix, AZ.....................40
George Washington Carver National
    Monument, Diamond, MO.........................814
Georgetown University Art Collection,
    Washington, DC...279
Georgia Capitol Museum, Atlanta, GA 360
Georgia Museum of Art, University of
    Georgia, Athens, GA.................................356
The Georgian Museum, Lancaster, OH 1171
Gerald R. Ford Presidential Museum,
    Grand Rapids, MI......................................743
Geronimo Springs Museum, Truth or
    Consequences, NM....................................953
Gertrude Herbert Institute of Art,
    Augusta, GA..365
Gibbes Museum of Art, Charleston, SC.....1325
The Gibson Society, Inc. dba Gibson
    House Museum, Boston, MA.....................665
The Gilbert Stuart Birthplace and
    Museum, Saunderstown, RI.....................1319
Gilcrease Museum, Tulsa, OK.....................1215
Gilmer Arts and Heritage Association,
    Ellijay, GA...371
Glencairn Museum: Academy of the New
    Church, Bryn Athyn, PA..........................1244
Glendower State Memorial, Lebanon, OH.1171
The Glynn Art Association, Inc., Saint
    Simons Island, GA....................................383
The Godwin-Ternbach Museum,
    Flushing, NY..990
Goshen Historical Society, Goshen, CT.......242
The Goudreau Museum of Mathematics
    in Art and Science, aka The Math
    Museum, New Hyde Park, NY...............1017
Governor Henry Lippitt House Museum,
    Providence, RI..1316
The Governor's Mansion, Frankfort, KY 569
The Grace Museum, Abilene, TX................1385
Grand Rapids Art Museum, Grand
    Rapids, MI...743
The Granger Homestead Society, Inc.,
    Canandaigua, NY.......................................975
Grant County Museum & Historic
    Society, Hyannis, NE................................863
Grants Pass Museum of Art, Grants Pass,
    OR...1225
Great Plains Art Museum, Lincoln, NE 865

Sculpture—Continued

The Greater Reston Arts Center
(GRACE), Reston, VA 1527
Green Bay Packers Hall of Fame, Green
Bay, WI 1598
Green Hill Art Gallery, Greensboro, NC 1103
Greenbelt Museum, Greenbelt, MD.............646
Greensboro Artists' League, Greensboro,
NC 1103
Greenville County Museum of Art,
Greenville, SC....................................1334
Greenville Museum of Art, Inc.,
Greenville, NC....................................1105
Grey Art Gallery, New York University
Art Collection, New York, NY 1026
Greyhound Hall of Fame, Abilene, KS 531
Gropius House, Lincoln, MA.......................690
Grossmont College Hyde Art Gallery, El
Cajon, CA...92
Groton Historical Society, Groton, MA.......685
Grounds For Sculpture, Hamilton, NJ..........906
Guild Hall Museum, East Hampton, NY 986
Guilford College Art Gallery,
Greensboro, NC...................................1103
Gulf Beach Art Center, Indian Rocks
Beach, FL..313
Gulf Coast Museum of Art, Inc., Largo,
FL...321
GumTree Museum of Art, Tupelo, MS 808

H.E.A.R.T.S. Veterans Museum of Texas,
Huntsville, TX 1430
H. Earl Clack Museum, Havre, MT.............849
Hacienda Buena Vista, Ponce, PR..............1642
Hakone Gardens, Saratoga, CA 185
The Hall of Fame for Great Americans,
Bronx, NY 966
Hallie Ford Museum of Art, Salem, OR 1235
Hamline University Galleries, Department
of Studio Arts & Art History, Saint
Paul, MN...790
Hammer Museum, Los Angeles, CA.............115
Hammond Museum and Japanese Stroll
Garden, North Salem, NY....................1043
Hampton University Museum, Hampton,
VA 1509
Hana Cultural Center, Hana, Maui, HI........392
Handwerker Gallery, Ithaca, NY 1003
Hanover Historical Society Museum,
Hanover, VA 1510
Harding Home and Museum, Marion, OH.1174
Harlan-Lincoln House, Mount Pleasant,
IA...524
The Harness Racing Museum and Hall of
Fame, Goshen, NY 995
Harold Warp Pioneer Village Foundation,
Minden, NE 868
Harry Ransom Center at the University
of Texas at Austin, Austin, TX 1390
Harry S. Truman Library-Museum,
Independence, MO................................818
Hartsville Museum, Hartsville, SC 1335
Harvard University Art Museums,
Cambridge, MA 672
The Harwood Museum of Art of the
University of New Mexico, Taos, NM 952
Hatton Gallery, Colorado State
University, Fort Collins, CO 217
Havre de Grace Decoy Museum, Havre
de Grace, MD......................................647
Hawaii State Foundation on Culture &
the Arts and Hawaii State Art
Museum, Honolulu, HI.........................395
Hawk Mountain Sanctuary, Kempton, PA..1264
Hay House Museum, Macon, GA 377
Hayden Museum of American Art, Paris,
TX 1442
Heard Museum, Phoenix, AZ........................40
Hearst Art Gallery, St. Mary's College,
Moraga, CA 128
Hearst Castle, San Simeon, CA...................177

Heckscher Museum of Art, Huntington,
NY..1000
Hellenic Museum & Cultural Center,
Chicago, IL 421
The Hemingway Museum and The Ernest
Hemingway Birthplace, Oak Park, IL 448
Henrico County Historic Preservation &
Museum Services, Richmond, VA 1529
Henry Art Gallery, Seattle, WA 1566
Henry B. Plant Museum, Tampa, FL............349
Henry Ford Estate-Fair Lane, Dearborn,
MI...734
Herbert F. Johnson Museum of Art,
Ithaca, NY 1003
Herbert Hoover Presidential
Library-Museum, West Branch, IA.........530
The Heritage Center, Pine Ridge, SD........1354
Heritage Center of Lancaster County,
Inc., Lancaster, PA..............................1265
Heritage Conservancy, Doylestown, PA 1249
Heritage Library Museum, Anchorage,
AK..22
Heritage Museums & Gardens, Sandwich,
MA 707
The Hermitage Foundation, Norfolk, VA ...1521
Herrett Center for Arts & Science,
Faulkner Planetarium and Centennial
Observatory, Twin Falls, ID...................410
Hershey Gardens, Hershey, PA 1260
Hibel Museum of Art, Jupiter, FL 316
The Hickory Museum of Art, Hickory,
NC 1106
Higgins Armory Museum, Worcester, MA...721
Higgins Art Gallery - Cape Cod
Community College, West Barnstable,
MA 717
The High Museum of Art, Atlanta, GA......360
Highland Community College Arboretum,
Freeport, IL...435
Highlands Center for Natural History,
Prescott, AZ..42
Highlands Hammock State Park/Civilian
Conservation Corps Museum, Sebring,
FL...346
Hill Cumorah Visitors Center & Historic
Sites, Palmyra, NY 1050
Hill-Stead Museum, Farmington, CT 241
Hillstrom Museum of Art, Saint Peter,
MN 793
Hillwood Art Museum, Brookville, NY 971
Hillwood Museum & Gardens,
Washington, DC...................................280
Hiram Blauvelt Art Museum, Oradell, NJ....919
Hirshhorn Museum and Sculpture
Garden, Smithsonian Institution,
Washington, DC...................................280
The Hispanic Society of America, New
York, NY...1027
Historic Gardner's Basin, Atlantic City,
NJ...898
Historic General Dodge House, Council
Bluffs, IA..512
Historic Governors' Mansion, Cheyenne,
WY...1630
Historic Hermann Museum, Hermann,
MO...817
Historic Landmarks Foundation of
Indiana, Indianapolis, IN......................482
Historic Oakland Cemetery, Atlanta, GA 360
Historical Society of Carroll County,
Westminster, MD..................................656
Historical Society of Columbia County,
Saint Helens, OR 1234
Historical Society of Ocean Grove, New
Jersey, Ocean Grove, NJ 918
Historical Society of Palm Beach County,
Palm Beach, FL...................................334
Historical Society of Rockland County,
New City, NY 1017
Historical Society of Saratoga Springs,
Saratoga Springs, NY 1064

Historical Society of Stanton County
Museums at Stanton and Pilger, Pilger,
NE..872
Historical Society of the Town of
Greenwich Inc. aka Bush-Holley
Historic Site, Cos Cob, CT 237
History of Medicine Collections,
Durham, NC..1098
Hockaday Museum of Art, Kalispell, MT....850
Hofstra Museum, Hempstead, NY 997
Hollins University Eleanor D. Wilson
Museum, Roanoke, VA 1535
Hollywood Guinness World of Records
Museum, Hollywood, CA 103
Holocaust Documentation & Education
Center, Inc., Hollywood, FL 313
Holocaust Memorial Resource and
Education Center of Florida, Inc.,
Maitland, FL..322
Holocaust Museum Houston, Houston,
TX 1426
Holter Museum of Art, Helena, MT............849
Honeywell Center, Wabash, IN...................503
Honolulu Academy of Arts, Honolulu, HI ...395
Honolulu Botanical Gardens, Honolulu,
HI...396
Hood Museum of Art, Hanover, NH...........888
Hoopa Valley Tribal Museum, Hoopa,
CA..103
Hoosier Salon Gallery, Indianapolis, IN.......483
Horatio Colony House Museum & Nature
Preserve, Keene, NH............................890
Hotel de Paris Museum, Georgetown, CO...219
Housatonic Museum of Art, Bridgeport,
CT..236
House of Wickersham State Historical
Site, Juneau, AK....................................25
Houston Zoo, Inc., Houston, TX 1427
Howard University Gallery of Art,
Washington, DC...................................281
Howard University Museum, Moorland
Spingarn Research Center,
Washington, DC...................................281
The Hoyt Institute of Fine Arts, New
Castle, PA 1273
Hoyt Sherman Place, Des Moines, IA........514
The Hubbard Museum of the American
West, Ruidoso Downs, NM...................946
The Hudson River Museum, Yonkers, NY.1087
Hui No'eau Visual Arts Center,
Makawao, Maui, HI 401
Humboldt Arts Council/Morris Graves
Museum of Art, Eureka, CA...................94
Hunter College Art Galleries, New York,
NY..1027
Hunter Museum of American Art,
Chattanooga, TN.................................1362
Huntington Beach International Surfing
Museum, Huntington Beach, CA.............104
Huntington Library, Art Collections, and
Botanical Gardens, San Marino, CA 174
Huntington Museum of Art, Inc.,
Huntington, WV 1583
Huntsville Museum of Art, Huntsville,
AL..12
Hus Var Fine Art, Buffalo, NY 973
Hutchinson Art Center, Hutchinson, KS.....545
The Hyde Collection, Glens Falls, NY 994
Hyde Park Art Center, Chicago, IL 421

IUPUI Cultural Arts Gallery,
Indianapolis, IN...................................483
Ida Goodstein Visual Arts Center, Casper,
WY...1629
Idaho Botanical Garden, Boise, ID..............403
Illinois State Museum, Chicago Gallery,
Chicago, IL 422
Illinois State Museum/Lockport Gallery,
Lockport, IL...443
IMA - Indianapolis Museum of Art,
Indianapolis, IN...................................483
Immaculate Conception Catholic Church,
Natchitoches, LA..................................593

Indian Arts and Crafts Board, Washington, DC.............................281
Indian City U.S.A., Anadarko, OK.............1195
Indian Museum of North America at Crazy Horse Memorial, Crazy Horse, SD..1345
Indian Pueblo Cultural Center, Albuquerque, NM.............................933
Indiana Historical Society, Indianapolis, IN...483
Indiana University Art Museum, Bloomington, IN.............................469
Indiana War Memorials, Indianapolis, IN 484
Indianapolis Art Center, Indianapolis, IN.....484
Institute of American Indian Arts Museum, Santa Fe, NM.................947
Institute of Contemporary Art, University of Pennsylvania, Philadelphia, PA 1282
Institute of Visual Arts, University of Wisconsin-Milwaukee, Milwaukee, WI.1611
The Interchurch Center, New York, NY.....1027
International Bowling Museum and Hall of Fame, Saint Louis, MO 833
International Institute of Metropolitan Detroit, Detroit, MI...........................737
International Motor Racing Research Center at Watkins Glen, Watkins Glen, NY...1084
International Museum of Art and Science, McAllen, TX.................................1437
International Museum of Cultures, Dallas, TX..1406
International Museum of Surgical Science, Chicago, IL.......................422
International Museum of the Horse, Lexington, KY..............................573
International Sculpture Center, Hamilton, NJ..906
International Swimming Hall of Fame, Inc., Fort Lauderdale, FL.....................307
International Tennis Hall of Fame & Museum, Newport, RI.........................1313
International UFO Museum and Research Center, Roswell, NM.....................946
International Wildlife Museum, Tucson, AZ..49
International Women's Air and Space Museum, Inc., Cleveland, OH..........1155
Intuit: The Center for Intuitive and Outsider Art, Chicago, IL......................422
Iowa Masonic Library and Museum, Cedar Rapids, IA.............................509
Iraan Museum, Iraan, TX...........................1430
Iredell Museum of Arts & Heritage, Statesville, NC............................1120
Iris & B. Gerald Cantor Art Gallery-College of the Holy Cross, Worcester, MA..............................721
Iris & B. Gerald Cantor Center for Visual Arts at Stanford University, Stanford, CA..188
Irish American Heritage Museum, Albany, NY..................................954
Iron County Museum, Caspian, MI.............731
Iroquois Indian Museum, Howes Cave, NY..999
Irving Arts Center, Irving, TX 1430
Isabel Anderson Comer Museum & Arts Center, Sylacauga, AL...............................18
Isabella Stewart Gardner Museum, Boston, MA...............................666
Isamu Noguchi Garden Museum, Long Island City, NY............................1010
Isla Center For the Arts at the University of Guam, Mangilao, GU 1640
Island Museum of Art, Westcott Bay Institute, Friday Harbor, WA............1554
Islip Art Museum, East Islip, NY.................986

J.M. Davis Arms & Historical Museum, Claremore, OK................................1198
The J. Paul Getty Museum, Los Angeles, CA 116

J. Wayne Stark University Center Galleries, College Station, TX 1401
Jack Nicklaus Museum, Columbus, OH.....1158
Jacksonville Museum of Modern Art, Jacksonville, FL...............................314
Jacksonville Zoo and Gardens, Jacksonville, FL...............................315
Jacqueline Casey Hudgens Center for the Arts, Duluth, GA 371
Jacques Marchais Museum of Tibetan Art, Staten Island, NY........................1072
James A. Michener Art Museum, Doylestown, PA 1249
James & Meryl Hearst Center for the Arts and Sculpture Garden, Cedar Falls, IA..508
James E. Lewis Museum of Art, Morgan State University, Baltimore, MD 633
James Ford Bell Museum of Natural History, Minneapolis, MN................782
James Madison's Montpelier, Montpelier Station, VA...............................1518
James Monroe Museum and Memorial Library, Fredericksburg, VA...........1507
James S. Copley Library, La Jolla, CA........106
Jane Voorhees Zimmerli Art Museum, New Brunswick, NJ.......................915
Japan Society Gallery, New York, NY.......1028
Japanese Friendship Garden, San Diego, CA..156
Jeane Dixon Museum and Library, Strasburg, VA..............................1538
Jeff Matthews Memorial Museum, Galax, VA...1508
Jefferson Historical Society and Museum, Jefferson, TX...............................1431
Jekyll Island Museum, Jekyll Island, GA 374
Jesse Peter Museum, Santa Rosa, CA..........184
The Jewish Museum, New York, NY.........1029
Jewish Museum of Maryland, Baltimore, MD..633
Jim Powers Junk Art Museum, Gage, OK.1201
John and Mable Ringling Museum of Art, Sarasota, FL..............................344
John F. Kennedy Presidential Library & Museum, Boston, MA 666
John Furlong Gallery, Menomonie, WI......1609
John Hutchings Museum of Natural History, Lehi, UT..............................1466
John James Audubon Center at Mill Grove, Audubon, PA 1241
John Michael Kohler Arts Center, Sheboygan, WI.............................1621
John Slade Ely House, New Haven, CT.......253
John Stark Edwards House, Warren, OH....1189
John Wesley Powell Museum, Green River, UT..1466
Johnson County Community College, Gallery of Art, Overland Park, KS.......555
Jonson Gallery of the University of New Mexico Art Museum, Albuquerque, NM..933
Jordan Schnitzer Museum of Art, Eugene, OR..1223
Joseloff Gallery, Hartford Art School, University of Hartford, West Hartford, CT..264
The Joseph A. Callaway Archaeological Museum, Louisville, KY..................576
Joseph Smith Historic Site, Nauvoo, IL.......447
Joslyn Art Museum, Omaha, NE.................871
The Journey Museum, Rapid City, SD.......1354
Judah L. Magnes Museum, Berkeley, CA......76
Judaica Museum of Central Synagogue, New York, NY...............................1029
The Judaica Museum of the Hebrew Home at Riverdale, Riverdale, NY........1057
Judy Garland Museum, Grand Rapids, MN..777
Jugville Museum, Grafton, ND.................1131
Jule Collins Smith Museum of Fine Art, Auburn, AL.......................................3

Juliette Gordon Low Birthplace, Savannah, GA................................385
Jundt Art Museum, Spokane, WA 1571
Justin Smith Morrill Homestead, Strafford, VT................................1488

Kalamazoo Aviation History Museum, Kalamazoo, MI............................748
Kalamazoo Institute of Arts, Kalamazoo, MI..748
Kankakee County Museum, Kankakee, IL...441
The Kansas African American Museum, Wichita, KS...............................561
Karl C. Harrison Museum of George Washington, Columbiana, AL........................6
Katherine Nash Gallery, Minneapolis, MN..782
Katonah Museum of Art, Katonah, NY......1006
Kearney Mansion Museum, Fresno, CA........97
The Kearny Cottage, Perth Amboy, NJ.......921
Kelsey Museum of Archaeology, Ann Arbor, MI..................................724
Kemp Center for the Arts, Wichita Falls, TX..1461
Kemper Museum of Contemporary Art, Kansas City, MO.............................821
Kennedy-Douglass Center for the Arts, Florence, AL...9
Kennedy Museum of Art, Athens, OH.......1140
The Kent Art Association, Kent, CT 247
Kent State University, School of Art Galleries, Kent, OH.......................1169
Kentucky Derby Museum, Louisville, KY...576
The Kentucky Folk Art Center, Morehead, KY................................580
Kentucky Military History Museum, Frankfort, KY................................569
Kentucky State Capitol, Frankfort, KY.......569
Kewaunee County Historical Museum, Kewaunee, WI................................1602
Key West Museum of Art and History, Key West, FL................................318
Kimbell Art Museum, Fort Worth, TX.......1417
Kimberly Crest House & Gardens, Redlands, CA...............................147
Kingwood Center, Mansfield, OH 1173
Kirkland Arts Center, Kirkland, WA 1557
Kirkland Fine Arts Center-Perkinson Gallery, Decatur, IL.......................430
Kirkland Museum of Fine & Decorative Art, Denver, CO 212
Klemm Gallery, Adrian, MI........................722
Klondike Gold Rush National Historical Park, Seattle, WA.............................1566
Kluge-Ruhe Aboriginal Art Collection at the University of Virginia, Charlottesville, VA.............................1499
Knights of Columbus Museum, New Haven, CT................................253
Knoxville Museum of Art, Knoxville, TN .1370
Koester House Museum, Marysville, KS 552
Kohl Children's Museum of Greater Chicago, Glenview, IL.........................438
Kokomo Art Association Art Center, Kokomo, IN................................487
Koshare Indian Museum, Inc., La Junta, CO..224
Koucky Gallery, Bokeelia, FL 297
Krannert Art Museum and Kinkead Pavilion, Champaign, IL 416
Krasl Art Center, Saint Joseph, MI.............763
The Kreeger Museum, Washington, DC.......281
Krempp Gallery, Jasper, IN........................486
Kresge Art Museum, East Lansing, MI........739

L.D. "Brink" Brinkman Foundation, Kerrville, TX................................1431
La Salle University Art Museum, Philadelphia, PA 1282
Lacey Historical Society, Forked River, NJ..904
The Lacrosse Museum & National Hall of Fame/US Lacrosse, Baltimore, MD 633

Sculpture–Continued

Ladew Topiary Gardens, Monkton, MD.......649
Lafayette College Art Gallery, Williams
    Center for the Arts, Easton, PA 1250
Laguna Art Museum, Laguna Beach, CA 107
Lakeview Museum of Arts and Sciences,
    Peoria, IL...450
Lamar Dodd Art Center, LaGrange
    College, LaGrange, GA............................375
Lane Community College Art Gallery,
    Eugene, OR..1223
Lane Place, Crawfordsville, IN..................473
Lanier Mansion State Historic Site,
    Madison, IN..489
Lansing Art Gallery, Lansing, MI................750
Laredo Center for the Arts, Laredo, TX....1434
Larson Museum and Gallery, Yakima,
    WA...1578
Las Vegas Art Museum, Las Vegas, NV 879
Las Vegas Natural History Museum, Las
    Vegas, NV...879
Laumeier Sculpture Park & Museum,
    Saint Louis, MO...834
Laurel Arts, Somerset, PA...........................1300
Lauren Rogers Museum of Art, Laurel,
    MS...804
Laurence C. Jones Museum, Piney
    Woods, MS...807
Lea County Cowboy Hall of Fame and
    Western Heritage Center, Hobbs, NM.....940
Leanin' Tree Museum of Western Art,
    Boulder, CO..203
Lee Chapel and Museum, Lexington, VA ..1513
Lehigh University Art Galleries/Museum
    Operations, Bethlehem, PA.....................1242
Lehman College Art Gallery, Bronx, NY.....966
Leigh Yawkey Woodson Art Museum,
    Wausau, WI...1626
LeMoyne Art Foundation, Inc.,
    Tallahassee, FL...347
Lentz Center for Asian Culture, Lincoln,
    NE..865
Leslie Powell Foundation and Gallery,
    Lawton, OK..1204
Levere Memorial Temple, Evanston, IL.......434
Lewis Ginter Botanical Garden,
    Richmond, VA...1530
Libby Museum, Wolfeboro, NH 897
Liberty Jail Historic Site, Liberty, MO 826
Library Company of Philadelphia,
    Philadelphia, PA...1282
Licking County Arts, Newark, OH.............1178
Lighthouse Center for the Arts, Tequesta,
    FL...351
Lightner Museum, Saint Augustine, FL 339
Lincoln Boyhood National Memorial,
    Lincoln City, IN...488
Lincoln County Historical Society, North
    Platte, NE..869
Lincoln Memorial Shrine, Redlands, CA 147
The Lincoln Museum, Fort Wayne, IN 478
The Lithuanian Museum, Chicago, IL..........423
Little Bighorn Battlefield National
    Monument, Crow Agency, MT 844
The Little Cowboy Bar & Museum,
    Fromberg, MT..847
Little Log Church & Museum, Yachats,
    OR...1238
Little White House Historic Site, Warm
    Springs, GA..390
The Living Arts and Science Center, Inc.,
    Lexington, KY..573
Living Bible Museum, Mansfield, OH 1173
Living Memorial Sculpture Garden,
    Weed, CA...197
Lizzadro Museum of Lapidary Art,
    Elmhurst, IL...433
Locust Grove, The Samuel Morse
    Historic Site, Poughkeepsie, NY 1055
Lois E. Woods Museum, Norfolk, VA........1522

Lombard Historical Museum, Lombard,
    IL...443
The London Brass Rubbing Centre in
    Washington D.C., Inc., Gaithersburg,
    MD...645
Longboat Key Center for the Arts,
    Longboat Key, FL.......................................322
Longfellow National Historic Site,
    Cambridge, MA..673
LongHouse Reserve, East Hampton, NY 986
Longue Vue House & Gardens, New
    Orleans, LA..596
Longview Museum of Fine Arts,
    Longview, TX...1434
Longwood Center for the Visual Arts,
    Farmville, VA...1504
Longyear Museum, Chestnut Hill, MA........675
Lore Degenstein Gallery, Selinsgrove, PA .1299
Los Alamos Historical Museum, Los
    Alamos, NM...942
Los Altos History Museum aka
    Association of the Los Altos Historical
    Museum, Los Altos, CA............................112
Los Angeles County Museum of Art, Los
    Angeles, CA...118
Los Angeles Municipal Art Gallery -
    Barnsdall Art Park, Los Angeles, CA......118
Los Angeles Museum of the Holocaust,
    Los Angeles, CA...118
Los Medanos College Art Gallery,
    Pittsburg, CA..142
Lou Holtz/Upper Ohio Valley Hall of
    Fame, East Liverpool, OH 1163
Louisburg College Art Gallery,
    Louisburg, NC..1109
Louise Wells Cameron Art Museum,
    Wilmington, NC...1123
Louisiana Art & Science Museum - Irene
    W. Pennington Planetarium, Baton
    Rouge, LA..586
Louisiana State Museum, New Orleans,
    LA...596
Louisiana State University Museum of
    Art, Baton Rouge, LA................................586
Louisiana Tech Museum, Ruston, LA 600
Louisville Slugger Museum & Factory,
    Louisville, KY..577
Louisville Zoological Garden, Louisville,
    KY..578
Lovely Lane Museum, Baltimore, MD 634
Lowe Art Museum, University of Miami,
    Coral Gables, FL..301
Lower Cape Fear Historical Society, Inc.,
    Wilmington, NC...1123
Loyola University Museum of Art,
    Chicago, IL...423
Lubeznik Center for the Arts, Michigan
    City, IN..490
Lucy Craft Laney Museum of Black
    History and Conference Center,
    Augusta, GA...365
Luis Munoz Rivera Library & Museum,
    Barranquitas, PR..1641
The Luther W. Brady Art Gallery,
    Washington, DC...282
Lyman Allyn Art Museum, New London,
    CT..255
Lyndhurst, Tarrytown, NY 1078
Lyndon Baines Johnson Library and
    Museum, Austin, TX..................................1391

MIT-List Visual Arts Center, Cambridge,
    MA...673
M. Louise Aughinbaugh Gallery at
    Messiah College, Grantham, PA.............1257
Mabee-Gerrer Museum of Art, Shawnee,
    OK..1213
Macalester College Art Gallery, Janet
    Wallace Fine Arts Center, Saint Paul,
    MN...790
MacDonald Art Gallery, Dallas, PA 1249
Madame-Tussaud's Wax Museum, Las
    Vegas, Las Vegas, NV................................879

Madera County Museum, Madera, CA 123
MADI Museum, Dallas, TX 1407
Madison Museum of Contemporary Art,
    Madison, WI...1605
Madison Museum of Fine Art, Madison,
    GA..378
Maggie L. Walker National Historic Site,
    Richmond, VA...1530
The Magic Lantern Castle Museum, San
    Antonio, TX...1448
Magnolia Manor, Cairo, IL.........................415
Magnolia Plantation and Gardens,
    Charleston, SC...1326
Maitland Art Center, Maitland, FL.............322
Malabar Farm State Park, Lucas, OH.........1173
Malden Public Library, Malden, MA 692
Mallory-Neely House, Memphis, TN 1373
Mammoth Cave Wax Museum, Cave
    City, KY...566
Manhattan Arts Center, Manhattan, KS.......551
The Mansfield Art Center, Mansfield, OH .1173
Marblehead Arts Association - King
    Hooper Mansion, Marblehead, MA.........693
Marcella Sembrich Opera Museum,
    Bolton Landing, NY...................................963
March Field Air Museum, Riverside, CA 149
Margaret Fort Trahern Gallery,
    Clarksville, TN 1363
Margaret Harwell Art Museum, Poplar
    Bluff, MO..829
Mariani Gallery, University of Northern
    Colorado, Greeley, CO..............................221
Marianna Kistler Beach Museum of Art
    at Kansas State University, Manhattan,
    KS..551
Maridon Museum, Butler, PA 1245
Marietta/Cobb Museum of Art, Marietta,
    GA..379
Marin History Museum, San Rafael, CA 177
The Mariners' Museum, Newport News,
    VA..1519
Marinette County Historical Museum,
    Marinette, WI...1607
Mario Lanza Institute/Museum,
    Philadelphia, PA...1282
Mariposa Museum & World Culture
    Center, Peterborough, NH 893
Maritime Museum of Monterey,
    Monterey, CA...127
Marjorie McNeely Conservatory at Como
    Park, Saint Paul, MN 790
Mark Twain Birthplace State Historic
    Site, Florida, MO.......................................815
The Mark Twain House & Museum,
    Hartford, CT..245
Marshall M. Fredericks Sculpture
    Museum, University Center, MI 766
Martin and Osa Johnson Safari Museum,
    Inc., Chanute, KS......................................535
The Martin D'Arcy Museum of Art: The
    Loyola University Museum of
    Medieval, Renaissance and Baroque
    Art, Chicago, IL...424
Mary and Leigh Block Museum of Art,
    Northwestern University, Evanston, IL ...434
The Mary Brogan Museum of Art and
    Science, Tallahassee, FL............................347
Mary Porter Sesnon Art Gallery, Santa
    Cruz, CA..181
Maryhill Museum of Art, Goldendale,
    WA...1556
The Maryland Institute, College of Art:
    Decker, Meyerhoff and Pinkard
    Galleries, Baltimore, MD..........................634
Maryland State Archives, Annapolis, MD....628
Marywood University Art Galleries
    (Suraci Gallery and Mahady Gallery),
    Scranton, PA 1298
Masonic Grand Lodge Library and
    Museum of Texas, Waco, TX 1459
The Masonic Library and Museum of
    Pennsylvania, Philadelphia, PA................1283
MASS MoCA, North Adams, MA 698

Massachusetts Historical Society, Boston, MA......667
Masur Museum of Art, Monroe, LA......592
The Mattatuck Museum Arts and History Center, Waterbury, CT......264
Maude I. Kerns Art Center, Eugene, OR...1223
Maui Arts and Cultural Center, Kahului, Maui, HI......399
Maui Okinawa Cultural Center, Waiehu, HI......402
Maymont, Richmond, VA......1530
MCAD Gallery, Minneapolis, MN......782
McCook House, Civil War Museum, Carrollton, OH......1146
McCormick Gallery, Midland, TX......1438
McGuffey Art Center, Charlottesville, VA.1499
McLarty Treasure Museum, Vero Beach, FL......352
McLean County Arts Center, Bloomington, IL......414
McMullen Museum of Art, Boston College, Chestnut Hill, MA......675
McNay Art Museum, San Antonio, TX......1448
McWethy Hall, Luce Gallery, Cornell College, Mount Vernon, IA......524
Mead Art Museum, Amherst, MA......658
Meadow Brook Hall, Rochester, MI......761
Meadows Museum, Dallas, TX......1407
Meadows Museum of Art of Centenary College, Shreveport, LA......601
Memorial Art Gallery of the University of Rochester, Rochester, NY......1059
Memorial Union Art Gallery, Davis, CA......90
Memorial Union Gallery, Fargo, ND......1130
Memphis Botanic Garden, Goldsmith Civic Garden Center, Memphis, TN......1374
Memphis Brooks Museum of Art, Memphis, TN......1374
Memphis College of Art, Memphis, TN....1374
The Menil Collection, Houston, TX......1428
Mennello Museum of American Art, Orlando, FL......331
Meridian Museum of Art, Meridian, MS.....805
Merrill Historical Museum, Merrill, WI.....1609
Merritt Museum of Anthropology, Oakland, CA......133
Mesalands Community College's Dinosaur Museum, Tucumcari, NM......953
Metamora Museum of Ethnographic Art, Metamora, IN......490
The Metropolitan Museum of Art, New York, NY......1030
Metropolitan State College of Denver/Center for Visual Art, Denver, CO......212
Mexic-Arte Museum, Austin, TX......1391
The Mexican Museum, San Francisco, CA......166
Miami Art Museum, Miami, FL......324
Miami-Dade College Kendall Campus Art Gallery, Miami, FL......324
Miami University Art Museum, Oxford, OH......1181
Michael C. Rockefeller Arts Center Gallery, Fredonia, NY......992
Michelson Museum of Art, Marshall, TX..1436
Middlebury College Museum of Art, Middlebury, VT......1482
Midwest Museum of American Art, Elkhart, IN......474
Mighty Eighth Air Force Museum, Pooler, GA......381
Mildred Lane Kemper Art Museum, Saint Louis, MO......834
Miles B. Carpenter Museum, Waverly, VA......1543
Millicent Rogers Museum of Northern New Mexico, Taos, NM......952
Milliken Gallery, Converse College, Spartanburg, SC......1341
Milton Art Museum, Canton, MA......674
Milwaukee Art Museum, Milwaukee, WI..1611

Mingei International Museum, San Diego, CA......157
Minneapolis Institute of Arts, Minneapolis, MN......782
Minnesota Landscape Arboretum, University of Minnesota, Chaska, MN....770
Minnesota Museum of American Art, Saint Paul, MN......791
Minnesota State Capitol Historic Site, Saint Paul, MN......791
Minnetrista, Muncie, IN......492
Mint Museum of Art, Charlotte, NC......1095
Mint Museum of Craft + Design, Charlotte, NC......1096
Minute Man National Historical Park, Concord, MA......676
Mission Cultural Center for Latino Arts, San Francisco, CA......166
Mission Inn Foundation/Museum, Riverside, CA......149
Mission San Carlos Borromeo Del Rio Carmelo, Carmel, CA......81
Mission San Luis Rey Museum, Oceanside, CA......135
Mission San Miguel, San Miguel, CA......175
Mission Santa Cruz, Santa Cruz, CA......182
Mississippi Museum of Art, Jackson, MS....802
Missoula Art Museum, Missoula, MT......851
Missouri Botanical Garden, Saint Louis, MO......834
The Mitchell Museum of the American Indian, Evanston, IL......435
Mizel Museum, Denver, CO......213
Mobile Museum of Art, Mobile, AL......14
Modern Art Museum of Fort Worth, Fort Worth, TX......1418
Molly Brown House Museum, Denver, CO......213
Monroe Community College, Mercer Gallery, Rochester, NY......1059
Montana Historical Society, Helena, MT.....849
Montana Museum of Art and Culture, Missoula, MT......852
Montclair Art Museum, Montclair, NJ......912
Montclair State University Art Galleries, Upper Montclair, NJ......929
Monterey History and Art Association, Monterey, CA......127
Monterey Museum of Art, Monterey, CA....128
Montgomery Museum & Lewis Miller Regional Art Center, Christiansburg, VA......1501
Montgomery Museum of Fine Arts, Montgomery, AL......16
Monticello, Home of Thomas Jefferson, Thomas Jefferson Foundation, Inc., Charlottesville, VA......1499
Montville Township Historical Museum, Montville, NJ......912
Moore County Art Association, Dumas, TX......1410
Mormon Visitors Center, Independence, MO......818
Morris Arboretum of the University of Pennsylvania, Philadelphia, PA......1283
Morris-Butler House Museum, Indianapolis, IN......485
The Morris Museum, Morristown, NJ......914
Morris Museum of Art, Augusta, GA......365
Morton House Museum, Benton Harbor, MI......728
Moses Lake Museum & Art Center, Moses Lake, WA......1559
Motts Military Museum, Groveport, OH....1167
Mount Dora Center for the Arts, Mount Dora, FL......327
Mount Holyoke College Art Museum, South Hadley, MA......709
Mount Rushmore National Memorial, Keystone, SD......1350
Mount Vernon Ladies' Association, Mount Vernon, VA......1518

The Muchnic Gallery, Atchison, KS......533
Mulvane Art Museum, Topeka, KS......559
Munson-Williams-Proctor Arts Institute Museum of Art, Utica, NY......1079
Muscarelle Museum of Art, Williamsburg, VA......1545
Muscatine Art Center, Muscatine, IA......524
Museo de Arte de Ponce (The Luis A. Ferre Foundation, Inc.), Ponce, PR......1642
Museo de las Americas, Denver, CO......213
Museo ItaloAmericano, San Francisco, CA......167
The Museum, Greenwood, SC......1334
The Museum for African Art, Long Island City, NY......1011
Museum NECCA at New England Center for Contemporary Art, Inc., Brooklyn, CT......237
The Museum of African American Art, Los Angeles, CA......119
The Museum of African Culture, Portland, ME......619
Museum of Afro-American History, Boston, MA......667
Museum of American Finance, New York, NY......1031
Museum of American Glass at Wheaton Village, Millville, NJ......911
The Museum of American Illustration at the Society of Illustrators, New York, NY......1031
Museum of American Presidents, Strasburg, VA......1539
Museum of Art and Archaeology, University of Missouri - Columbia, Columbia, MO......813
Museum of Art and History at the McPherson Center, Santa Cruz, CA......182
Museum of Art & History at Weston, Weston, CT......266
Museum of Art at Brigham Young University, Provo, UT......1469
Museum of Art/Fort Lauderdale, Fort Lauderdale, FL......307
Museum of Art of Puerto Rico, Santurce, PR......1643
Museum of Art, Rhode Island School of Design, Providence, RI......1317
Museum of Arts and Sciences, Macon, GA......378
Museum of Bad Art, Dedham, MA......679
Museum of Carousel Art & History, Sandusky, OH......1185
Museum of Church History and Art, Salt Lake City, UT......1471
Museum of Contemporary Art, Chicago, IL......424
Museum of Contemporary Art, Denver, CO......213
Museum of Contemporary Art Cleveland, Cleveland, OH......1155
The Museum of Contemporary Art, Los Angeles, Los Angeles, CA......119
Museum of Contemporary Art (MoCA), North Miami, FL......329
The Museum of Contemporary Art of Georgia (MOCA GA), Atlanta, GA......362
Museum of Contemporary Art of Puerto Rico, Santurce, PR......1644
Museum of Contemporary Art San Diego, La Jolla, CA......106
Museum of Contemporary Art San Diego - Downtown, San Diego, CA......157
Museum of Contemporary Religious Art (MOCRA)-St. Louis University, Saint Louis, MO......835
Museum of Craft and Folk Art, San Francisco, CA......167
The Museum of East Texas, Lufkin, TX....1436
Museum of Fine Arts, Boston, MA......667
Museum of Fine Arts, Santa Fe, NM......948
The Museum of Fine Arts, Houston, Houston, TX......1428

Sculpture–Continued

Museum of Fine Arts of St. Petersburg, Florida, Saint Petersburg, FL 341

Museum of Glass: International Center for Contemporary Art, Tacoma, WA 1573

Museum of Great Christian Preachers & Ministries, Orange Park, FL....................331

Museum of History & Art, Ontario, Ontario, CA 136

Museum of History, Anthropology and Art, San Juan, PR 1643

Museum of Indian Arts & Culture/Laboratory of Anthropology, Santa Fe, NM...948

Museum of Jewish Heritage-A Living Memorial to the Holocaust, New York, NY...1032

Museum of Latin American Art, Long Beach, CA 111

The Museum of Modern Art, New York, NY...1033

Museum of Nebraska Art, Kearney, NE......864

Museum of Neon Art, Los Angeles, CA 120

Museum of Northwest Art, La Conner, WA 1557

The Museum of Outdoor Arts, Englewood, CO 214

Museum of Overbeck Art Pottery, Cambridge City, IN 471

Museum of Religious Arts, Logan, IA 522

Museum of Robotics, Orinda, CA................136

The Museum of Russian Art, Minneapolis, MN...................................783

Museum of San Diego History and Research Library, San Diego, CA 158

The Museum of Southern History, Sugarland, TX..1454

Museum of Spanish Colonial Art - MoSCA, Santa Fe, NM....................949

The Museum of the Alphabet, Waxhaw, NC..1121

Museum of the American Philosophical Society, Philadelphia, PA 1283

Museum of the Big Bend, Alpine, TX 1386

Museum of the Cherokee Indian, Cherokee, NC 1096

Museum of the Mountain Man, Pinedale, WY...1637

Museum of the National Center of Afro-American Artists, Roxbury, MA 706

Museum of the Northern Great Plains, Fort Benton, MT...................................846

Museum of the Plains Indian, Browning, MT......................................843

Museum of the Southern Jewish Experience, Jackson, MS.......................803

Museum of the Southwest, Midland, TX ...1439

The Museum of Western Art, Kerrville, TX...1431

Museum of Woodcarving, Shell Lake, WI.1621

Museum of York County, Rock Hill, SC ...1340

Museums of Los Gatos, Los Gatos, CA 123

Muskegon Museum of Art, Muskegon, MI...758

Mutter Museum, College of Physicians of Philadelphia, Philadelphia, PA 1283

My Old Kentucky Home State Park, Bardstown, KY 564

Mystic Arts Center, Mystic, CT...................250

NAU Art Museum, Flagstaff, AZ 33

NCCU Art Museum, Durham, NC 1099

Naples Museum of Art and the Philharmonic Center for the Arts Galleries, Naples, FL..............................328

Napoleonic Society of America, Inc., Clearwater, FL.......................................300

Nasher Museum of Art at Duke University, Durham, NC......................1099

Nasher Sculpture Center, Dallas, TX..........1407

Nassau County Museum of Art, Roslyn Harbor, NY 1062

Nathan Manilow Sculpture Park, Governors State University, University Park, IL 461

National Academy Museum and School of Fine Arts, New York, NY..................1033

National Afro-American Museum & Cultural Center, Wilberforce, OH 1191

The National Agricultural Center & Hall of Fame, Bonner Springs, KS.................534

National Air and Space Museum, Washington, DC.....................................283

National Art Museum of Sport, Inc., Indianapolis, IN....................................485

National Arts Club, New York, NY............1034

National Automotive & Truck Museum of the United States, Inc. (NATMUS), Auburn, IN...468

National Bird Dog Museum, Grand Junction, TN 1366

The National Border Patrol Museum and Memorial Library, El Paso, TX 1412

National Buffalo Museum, Jamestown, ND...1133

National Building Museum, Washington, DC...284

National Civil Rights Museum, Memphis, TN...1375

National Cowboy & Western Heritage Museum, Oklahoma City, OK 1208

National Cowgirl Museum and Hall of Fame, Fort Worth, TX...........................1418

National Fresh Water Fishing Hall of Fame, Hayward, WI 1600

National Gallery of Art, Washington, DC 285

The National Great Blacks in Wax Museum, Inc., Baltimore, MD.................635

National Hall of Fame for Famous American Indians, Anadarko, OK..........1196

National Hispanic Cultural Center, Art Museum, Albuquerque, NM....................935

National Infantry Museum, Fort Benning, GA...372

National Liberty Museum, Philadelphia, PA...1284

National Medal of Honor Museum of Military History, Chattanooga, TN 1362

National Museum of African Art, Smithsonian Institution, Washington, DC...285

National Museum of American Illustration, Newport, RI 1314

National Museum of American Jewish Military History, Washington, DC 286

The National Museum of Catholic Art & History, New York, NY.........................1034

National Museum of Dance & Hall of Fame, Saratoga Springs, NY.................1065

National Museum of Naval Aviation, Pensacola, FL..336

National Museum of Patriotism, Atlanta, GA...362

National Museum of Polo and Hall of Fame, Inc., Lake Worth, FL...................320

National Museum of Racing and Hall of Fame, Saratoga Springs, NY.................1065

National Museum of the Morgan Horse, Shelburne, VT......................................1487

National Museum of Wildlife Art, Jackson, WY..1634

National Museum of Women in the Arts, Washington, DC.....................................287

National Museum of Woodcarving, Custer, SD...1346

National Portrait Gallery, Washington, DC...287

National Presidential Wax Museum, Keystone, SD.......................................1350

National Soaring Museum, Elmira, NY 988

National Society of the Sons of the American Revolution, Louisville, KY 578

National Steeplechase Museum, Camden, SC...1323

National Trust for Historic Preservation, Washington, DC.....................................288

National Vietnam Veterans Art Museum, Chicago, IL...425

National Wrestling Hall of Fame, Stillwater, OK.......................................1214

Native American Resource Center, Pembroke, NC......................................1114

Natural Center for the American Revolution, Wayne, PA 1306

Naugatuck Historical Society, Naugatuck, CT...251

Naumkeag, Stockbridge, MA......................712

Navajo Nation Museum, Window Rock, AZ...53

Naval War College Museum, Newport, RI...1314

Nebraska State Capitol, Lincoln, NE...........866

Negro Leagues Baseball Museum, Kansas City, MO...822

The Nelson-Atkins Museum of Art, Kansas City, MO...................................822

Nemours Mansion and Gardens, Wilmington, DE....................................274

Neuberger Museum of Art, Purchase College, State University of New York, Purchase, NY.............................1056

Nevada Museum of Art, Reno, NV 881

New Britain Museum of American Art, Inc., New Britain, CT...........................251

New Canaan Historical Society, New Canaan, CT..252

New England College Gallery, Henniker, NH...889

New Hampshire Institute of Art, Manchester, NH....................................892

New Harmony Gallery of Contemporary Art, New Harmony, IN..........................494

New Jersey Botanical Garden at Skylands (NJBG), Ringwood, NJ.........................923

New Jersey Naval Museum, Hackensack, NJ...905

New Jersey State House, Trenton, NJ 927

New Market Battlefield State Historical Park, New Market, VA............................1519

The New Museum of Contemporary Art, New York, NY......................................1035

New Orleans Museum of Art, New Orleans, LA 597

New Visions Gallery, Inc., Marshfield, WI...1608

New World Art Center/T.F. Chen Cultural Center, New York, NY.........................1035

New York City Fire Museum, New York, NY...1035

The New York Historical Society, New York, NY...1035

New York State Historical Association/Fenimore Art Museum, Cooperstown, NY.................................981

The Newark Museum, Newark, NJ 916

Newcomb Art Gallery, New Orleans, LA 598

Newport Art Museum, Newport, RI...........1314

Newport Restoration Foundation, Newport, RI..1315

Nichols House Museum, Boston, MA.........668

Nicolaysen Art Museum and Discovery Center, Casper, WY................................1629

Nita Stewart Haley Memorial Library & J. Evetts Haley History Center, Midland, TX 1439

Nora Eccles Harrison Museum of Art, Logan, UT..1466

Norfolk Botanical Garden, Norfolk, VA.....1522

Norman R. Eppink Art Gallery, Emporia State University, Emporia, KS 539

Norman Rockwell Museum, Stockbridge, MA...712

North Carolina A&T State University Galleries, Greensboro, NC 1104

North Carolina Aquarium at Fort Fisher, Kure Beach, NC.....................................1109

North Carolina Museum of Art, Raleigh,
NC 1115
North Carolina Pottery Center, Seagrove,
NC 1119
North Carolina Zoological Park,
Asheboro, NC 1088
North Country Museum of Arts, Park
Rapids, MN...786
North Dakota Museum of Art, Grand
Forks, ND...1132
The North Shore Arts Association,
Gloucester, MA......................................684
Northeast Georgia History Center at
Brenau University, Gainesville, GA 373
Northeast Louisiana Delta African
American Heritage Museum, Monroe,
LA 592
Northern Kentucky University Art
Galleries, Highland Heights, KY 571
Northwest Art Center, Minot, ND 1134
Norton Museum of Art, West Palm
Beach, FL..353
Norton Simon Museum, Pasadena, CA........140
Notah Dineh Museum, Cortez, CO..............208
The Noyes Museum of Art, Oceanville,
NJ..918

Oak Hill and The Martha Berry Museum,
Rome, GA...382
Oak Ridge Art Center, Oak Ridge, TN 1382
Oakland Museum of California, Oakland,
CA..134
Oakland Museum of California-Sculpture
Court at City Center, Oakland, CA 134
Oakland University Art Gallery,
Rochester, MI 761
Oatlands, Leesburg, VA.............................1512
Office of Cultural Affairs & Museum
Programs at Salisbury University,
Salisbury, MD..652
The Ogden Museum of Southern Art,
University of New Orleans, New
Orleans, LA 598
Ogden Union Station Museums, Ogden,
UT..1468
Oglethorpe University Museum of Art,
Atlanta, GA..362
Ogunquit Museum of American Art,
Ogunquit, ME..617
Ohr-O'Keefe Museum of Art, Biloxi, MS ...799
Ohrmann Museum and Gallery,
Drummond, MT.......................................846
Okefenokee Heritage Center, Waycross,
GA...391
Oklahoma City Museum of Art,
Oklahoma City, OK...............................1208
Oklahoma City Zoo, Oklahoma City, OK..1209
Oklahoma Firefighters Museum,
Oklahoma City, OK...............................1209
Oklahoma Forest Heritage Center,
Broken Bow, OK 1197
Oklahoma Heritage Association,
Oklahoma City, OK...............................1209
Oklahoma Visual Arts Coalition,
Oklahoma City, OK...............................1210
Old Dominion University - University
Gallery, Norfolk, VA 1523
Old Fort Harrod State Park Mansion
Museum, Harrodsburg, KY......................570
The Old Jail Art Center, Albany, TX.........1385
Old Mill Museum, Cimarron, NM...............938
Old Mission Santa Ines, Solvang, CA..........187
Old West Museum, Wimberley, TX...........1462
Old Westbury Gardens, Old Westbury,
NY..1045
Oldest House Museum Complex, Saint
Augustine, FL...339
Olympic Sculpture Park, Seattle, WA 1568
Oneida County Historical Society, Utica,
NY..1080
Oneida Nation Museum, De Pere, WI........1594
Opus 40 and the Quarryman's Museum,
Saugerties, NY......................................1066

Orange County Museum of Art, Newport
Beach, CA..130
Oregon Zoo, Portland, OR 1232
Oriental Institute Museum, University of
Chicago, Chicago, IL..............................426
Orlando Museum of Art, Orlando, FL...........332
Ormond Memorial Art Museum &
Garden, Ormond Beach, FL.....................333
Osage Nation Tribal Museum, Pawhuska,
OK...1212
Owatonna Arts Center, Owatonna, MN.......786
Owens Community College/Walter E.
Terhune Gallery, Perrysburg, OH...........1182
Owensboro Museum of Fine Art, Inc.,
Owensboro, KY......................................581

Pacem in Terris, Warwick, NY 1082
Pacific Asia Museum, Pasadena, CA............140
Pacific Grove Art Center Associates, Inc.,
Pacific Grove, CA 137
Packwood House Museum, Lewisburg,
PA..1268
Paine Art Center and Gardens, Oshkosh,
WI..1617
The Palette & Chisel, Chicago, IL 426
Palm Springs Art Museum, Palm Springs,
CA..139
Palmer Museum of Art, The Pennsylvania
State University, University Park, PA....1304
Palo Alto Art Center, Palo Alto, CA 139
Palos Verdes Art Center, Rancho Palos
Verdes, CA...145
Pamunkey Indian Museum, King
William, VA..1512
Paper Airplane Museum and the Tin Can
Man of Maui, Kahului Central Maui,
HI...399
Paris Gibson Square Museum of Art,
Great Falls, MT......................................848
Parker Tavern, Reading, MA 705
Parkersburg Art Center, Parkersburg, WV .1586
Parkland College Art Gallery,
Champaign, IL..417
Parris Island Museum, Parris Island, SC....1338
The Parrish Art Museum, Southampton,
NY..1070
Parrot Jungle Island, Miami, FL..................325
The Parthenon, Nashville, TN 1379
Passaic County Community College,
Paterson, NJ...920
The Paterson Museum, Paterson, NJ...........920
The Patricia & Phillip Frost Art Museum,
Miami, FL..325
The Patrick & Beatrice Haggerty
Museum of Art, Milwaukee, WI............1613
Patterson Homestead, Dayton, OH 1161
Paul and Lulu Hilliard University Art
Museum, University of Louisiana at
Lafayette, Lafayette, LA.........................590
Paul W. Bryant Museum, Tuscaloosa, AL......19
Pawnee Bill Ranch and Museum,
Pawnee, OK..1212
Pawnee Indian Village State Historic Site,
Republic, KS..556
The Peace Museum, Chicago, IL..................426
Pearce Collections Museum, Corsicana,
TX..1402
The Pearl S. Buck House, Perkasie, PA.....1275
The Pearson Museum, Springfield, IL..........460
Pebble Hill Plantation, Thomasville, GA 388
The Peekskill Museum, Peekskill, NY.......1051
Pen & Brush, New York, NY 1037
Pence Gallery, Davis, CA 90
Pennsylvania Academy of the Fine Arts,
Philadelphia, PA 1284
Pensacola Museum of Art, Pensacola, FL....336
The Peoria Art Guild, Peoria, IL..................451
Peoria Historical Society, Peoria, IL 451
Peter Whitmer Sr. Home and Visitors
Center, Waterloo, NY 1083
Petersburg Area Art League, Petersburg,
VA..1525

Petterson Museum of Intercultural Art,
Claremont, CA..85
The Philadelphia Art Alliance,
Philadelphia, PA 1285
Philadelphia Museum of Art,
Philadelphia, PA 1285
Philadelphia Museum of
Judaica/Congregation Rodeph Shalom,
Philadelphia, PA 1286
The Philbrook Museum of Art, Inc.,
Tulsa, OK..1215
Philip and Muriel Berman Museum of
Art at Ursinus College, Collegeville,
PA..1247
The Phillips Collection, Washington, DC....289
Phillips County Museum, Helena, AR...........59
Phippen Museum, Prescott, AZ....................42
Phoenix Art Museum, Phoenix, AZ..............41
Phoenix Museum of History, Phoenix,
AZ...41
Photographic Investments Gallery,
Atlanta, GA..363
The Picker Art Gallery, Hamilton, NY........997
The Pierpont Morgan Library, New York,
NY..1037
Pilgrim Hall Museum, Plymouth, MA 703
Pioneer Historical Museum of South
Dakota, Hot Springs, SD.......................1348
Pioneer Town, Wimberley, TX..................1462
Pioneer Woman Statue & Museum,
Ponca City, OK.....................................1212
Pioneers, Trail Drivers and Texas
Rangers Memorial Museum, San
Antonio, TX..1449
Pittock Mansion, Portland, OR 1232
Pittsburgh Center for the Arts, Pittsburgh,
PA..1293
Plains Art Museum, Fargo, ND 1130
Plattsburgh State Art Museum S.U.N.Y.,
Plattsburgh, NY 1053
Please Touch Museum, Philadelphia, PA ...1286
Plymouth Historical Museum, Plymouth,
MI...760
Polish American Museum, Port
Washington, NY 1054
Polish Heritage Center, Ashton, NE............856
Polish Museum of America, Chicago, IL.....426
Polk County Heritage Gallery, Des
Moines, IA...515
Polk Museum of Art, Lakeland, FL.............321
Ponca City Art Center, Ponca City, OK.....1212
Pony Express Museum, Saint Joseph,
MO...831
Port Angeles Fine Arts Center &
Webster's Woods Art Park, Port
Angeles, WA...1561
Portland Art Museum, Portland, OR 1232
Portland Museum of Art, Portland, ME.......619
Portland State University Galleries,
Portland, OR...1233
Portsmouth Athenaeum, Portsmouth, NH.....894
Potter's Wax Museum, Saint Augustine,
FL..339
Pratt Manhattan Gallery, New York, NY ...1037
The Preservation Society of Newport
County/The Newport Mansions,
Newport, RI..1315
The Presidential Museum and Leadership
Library, Odessa, TX 1441
Presidential Pet Museum, Lothian, MD.......649
Presidents Park Sculpture Garden, Lead,
SD..1351
Presidio La Bahia, Goliad, TX 1423
Price Tower Arts Center, Bartlesville, OK .1197
Princeton University Art Museum,
Princeton, NJ...922
Pro Rodeo Hall of Fame & Museum of
the American Cowboy, Colorado
Springs, CO...207
Project Art-University of Iowa and
Clinics, Iowa City, IA 520

Sculpture–Continued

Provincetown Art Association and Museum, Provincetown, MA 704

Pump House Regional Arts Center, La Crosse, WI.....................................1603

Purdue University Galleries, West Lafayette, IN.....................................503

Putnam County Historical Society & Foundry School Museum, Cold Spring, NY...979

Pyramid Hill Sculpture Park & Museum, Hamilton, OH 1168

QCC Art Gallery, Bayside, NY 960

Queen Mary Museum, Long Beach, CA 111

Queens Museum of Art, Queens, NY.........1056

Quietude Garden Gallery, East Brunswick, NJ....................................903

Quincy Art Center, Quincy, IL...................452

The R.W. Norton Art Gallery, Shreveport, LA..601

Racine Art Museum (RAM), Racine, WI...1619

Radford University Art Museum, Radford, VA.......................................1527

Rahr West Art Museum, Manitowoc, WI...1607

Ralph Waldo Emerson House, Concord, MA...677

Rattlesnake Museum (American International), Albuquerque, NM.............935

Rawls Museum Arts, Courtland, VA 1502

The Ray Drew Gallery-New Mexico Highlands University, Las Vegas, NM 941

The Reader's Digest Association, Inc., Pleasantville, NY....................................1053

Reading Public Museum, Reading, PA.......1296

Red Earth Museum, Oklahoma City, OK...1210

Red River Valley Museum, Vernon, TX.....1457

Red Rock Museum, Church Rock, NM 938

Redwood Library and Athenaeum, Newport, RI.......................................1315

Reese Bullen Gallery, Arcata, CA 72

The Regina A. Quick Center for the Arts, Saint Bonaventure, NY 1063

Reginald F. Lewis Museum of Maryland African American History and Culture, Baltimore, MD......................................636

Rehoboth Art League, Inc., Rehoboth Beach, DE...272

Reid Park Zoo, Tucson, AZ 50

Remington Firearms Museum and Country Store, Ilion, NY......................1002

Renee and Chaim Gross Foundation, New York, NY.....................................1037

Reynolda House Museum of American Art, Winston-Salem, NC 1126

Richard E. Peeler Art Center, Greencastle, IN.....................................479

Richard L. Nelson Gallery & The Fine Arts Collection, UC Davis, Davis, CA......90

Richmond Art Museum, Richmond, IN........497

Ripley's Believe It or Not! Museum, Orlando, FL...332

Riverside Art Museum, Riverside, CA.........149

Robbins Hunter Museum, Avery-Downer House, Granville, OH............................1167

Robert E. Wilson Gallery, Huntington, IN....481

Robert Hull Fleming Museum, Burlington, VT.....................................1478

Robert Louis Stevenson Memorial Cottage, Saranac Lake, NY...................1064

Robert Louis Stevenson Silverado Museum, Saint Helena, CA 154

Robert R. McCormick Museum at Cantigny, Wheaton, IL............................465

Robert T. Wright Community Gallery of Art, Grayslake, IL.................................439

Robert V. Fullerton Art Museum, California State University, San Bernardino, San Bernardino, CA.............155

Rockford Art Museum, Rockford, IL...........455

Rockport Art Association, Rockport, MA.....705

Rockwell Museum of Western Art, Corning, NY...982

Rocky Mount Arts Center, Rocky Mount, NC...1117

Rocky Mountain College of Art + Design Galleries, Lakewood, CO.......................225

Rodin Museum, Philadelphia, PA..............1287

Rogue Gallery & Art Center, Medford, OR...1228

Roland Gibson Gallery, Potsdam, NY....1054

Rome Art and Community Center, Rome, NY...1061

Ronald Reagan Presidential Library and Museum, Simi Valley, CA.......................187

Roosevelt Campobello International Park Commission, Lubec, ME..........................614

The Rose Art Museum, Waltham, MA.........715

Rosenbach Museum & Library, Philadelphia, PA..................................1287

Rosenberg Gallery, Goucher College, Baltimore, MD.....................................636

Rosenthal Gallery of Art, Caldwell, ID........405

Roswell Museum and Art Center, Roswell, NM.......................................946

Roswell Visual Arts Center & Gallery, Roswell, GA...382

The Rotunda, University of Virginia, Charlottesville, VA...............................1500

The Roy Rogers-Dale Evans Museum and Theater, Branson, MO.....................811

The Rubelle & Norman Schafler Gallery, Brooklyn, NY.......................................970

Rural Life Museum & Windrush Gardens, Baton Rouge, LA.....................587

Rushmore Borglum Story, Keystone, SD...1350

Russell County Historical Society/Fossil Station Museum, Russell, KS 556

The Ruth & Sherman Lee Institute for Japanese Art, Hanford, CA.....................101

Ruth Chandler Williamson Gallery, Scripps College, Claremont, CA................86

Ruthmere Museum, Elkhart, IN...................475

Sagamore Hill National Historic Site, Oyster Bay, NY...................................1049

Saginaw Art Museum, Saginaw, MI............763

Saint-Gaudens National Historic Site, Cornish, NH...885

St. George Art Museum, Saint George, UT...1470

St. Johnsbury Athenaeum, Saint Johnsbury, VT.....................................1487

Saint Joseph's University - University Gallery - Boland Hall, Philadelphia, PA...1288

St. Lawrence University - Richard F. Brush Art Gallery and Permanent Collection, Canton, NY..........................976

The Saint Louis Art Museum, Saint Louis, MO...836

St. Louis Artists' Guild, Saint Louis, MO....836

St. Louis Cardinals Hall of Fame Museum, Saint Louis, MO......................836

Salem Art Association-Bush House Museum and Bush Barn Art Center, Salem, OR...1236

Salina Art Center, Salina, KS 557

Salmagundi Museum of American Art, New York, NY.....................................1038

Salvador Dali Museum, Saint Petersburg, FL...342

Sam Bell Maxey House State Historic Site, Paris, TX.....................................1442

Sam Houston Regional Library & Research Center, Liberty, TX..................1434

Samek Art Gallery, Lewisburg, PA............1268

Samuel Cupples House of Saint Louis University, Saint Louis, MO 837

Samuel Dorsky Museum of Art, State University of New York at New Paltz, New Paltz, NY.....................................1018

Samuel P. Harn Museum of Art, Gainesville, FL....................................311

San Angelo Museum of Fine Arts, San Angelo, TX.......................................1447

San Antonio Art League Museum, San Antonio, TX.......................................1449

San Antonio de Pala Asistencia, Pala, CA...138

San Antonio Museum of Art, San Antonio, TX.......................................1450

San Buenaventura Mission Museum, Ventura, CA...195

San Diego Museum of Art, San Diego, CA...160

San Francisco Museum of Modern Art, San Francisco, CA...............................169

San Gabriel Mission Museum, San Gabriel, CA...171

San Jose Museum of Art, San Jose, CA 172

San Jose State University Art Galleries, San Jose, CA.......................................173

San Juan County Archaeological Research Center and Library at the Salmon Ruin/San Juan County Museum Association, Bloomfield, NM ...937

San Juan National Historic Site, San Juan, PR...1643

San Miguel Mission Church, Santa Fe, NM...950

The Sandor Teszler Library, Spartanburg, SC...1341

Sandwich Historical Society, Center Sandwich, NH.......................................884

Sangre de Cristo Arts Center & Buell Children's Museum, Pueblo, CO 231

Santa Barbara Botanic Garden, Santa Barbara, CA...178

The Santa Barbara Historical Museum, Santa Barbara, CA...............................179

Santa Barbara Museum of Art, Santa Barbara, CA...179

Santa Cruz Art League, Inc., Santa Cruz, CA...182

Santa Maria Museum of Flight, Inc., Santa Maria, CA...............................183

Santa Monica Museum of Art, Santa Monica, CA...183

Sapulpa Historical Museum, Sapulpa, OK.1213

Sarasota Classic Car Museum, Sarasota, FL...345

Satwiwa Native American Indian Culture Center, Thousand Oaks, CA....................191

Savannah College of Art and Design Galleries, Savannah, GA.........................386

SCAD Museum of Art, Savannah, GA 386

Scarfone/Hartley Gallery, Tampa, FL...........349

Schedel Arboretum & Gardens, Elmore, OH...1163

The Schein-Joseph International Museum of Ceramic Art, Alfred, NY....................956

The Schick Art Gallery, Skidmore College, Saratoga Springs, NY 1065

Schingoethe Center for Native American Cultures, Aurora, IL.............................412

Schmucker Art Gallery, Gettysburg, PA.....1256

Schneider Museum of Art, Ashland, OR....1217

The Schomburg Center for Research in Black Culture, New York, NY..............1038

The Schumacher Gallery, Capital University, Columbus, OH....................1159

The Schuylkill Center for Environmental Education, Philadelphia, PA...................1288

The Science Fiction Museum and Hall of Fame, Seattle, WA...............................1568

Scotchtown, Beaverdam, VA.....................1496

Scottsdale Museum of Contemporary Art, Scottsdale, AZ.......................................44

Seattle Aquarium, Seattle, WA...................1568

Seattle Art Museum, Seattle, WA...............1568

Seattle Asian Art Museum, Seattle, WA.....1569

Seminole Canyon State Park and Historic Site, Comstock, TX...............................1401

Seminole Nation Museum, Wewoka, OK...1217

Seneca County Museum, Tiffin, OH...........1186

Seneca-Iroquois National Museum, Salamanca, NY 1063
Seneca Park Zoo, Rochester, NY 1060
Sewall-Belmont House and Museum, Washington, DC............................290
Shako:wi Cultural Center, Oneida, NY 1046
The Sharon Arts Center, Inc., Sharon, NH...896
Sheehan Gallery at Whitman College, Walla Walla, WA 1577
Sheldon Memorial Art Gallery and Sculpture Garden/University of Nebraska-Lincoln, Lincoln, NE 867
Shemer Art Center & Museum, Phoenix, AZ...42
Sheppard Fine Arts Gallery, Reno, NV 881
Sherwin Miller Museum of Jewish Art, Tulsa, OK.......................................1216
Shortgrass Country Museum Society, Sayre, OK 1213
Shoshone Tribal Cultural Center, Fort Washakie, WY 1633
Sidney Mishkin Gallery of Baruch College, New York, NY 1038
Sioux City Art Center, Sioux City, IA 527
Sioux Indian Museum, Rapid City, SD 1355
Sitka National Historical Park, Sitka, AK 28
Skirball Museum Cincinnati Hebrew Union College-Jewish Institute of Religion, Cincinnati, OH.....................1151
The Slater Memorial Museum - Norwich Free Academy, Norwich, CT 258
Slidell Cultural Center, Slidell, LA 602
Slocumb Galleries, Johnson City, TN.........1368
Sloss Furnaces National Historic Landmark, Birmingham, AL 5
The Smart Museum of Art, Chicago, IL 427
Smith College Museum of Art, Northampton, MA 700
Smithsonian American Art Museum, Washington, DC............................290
Smithsonian Institution, Washington, DC.....290
The Snite Museum of Art, University of Notre Dame, Notre Dame, IN.................495
Snug Harbor Cultural Center - Visitors' Center and Newhouse Center for Contemporary Art, Staten Island, NY ...1073
The Society of the Cincinnati at Anderson House, Washington, DC 291
The Society of the Four Arts, Palm Beach, FL......................................334
Socrates Sculpture Park, Long Island City, NY......................................1012
Sod House Museum, Gothenburg, NE 862
Solomon R. Guggenheim Museum, New York, NY......................................1038
Somers Historical Society, Somers, NY 1070
Sondra & Marvin Smalley Sculpture Garden, Bel Air, CA...........................74
Sonnenberg Gardens & Mansion State Historic Park, Canandaigua, NY.............975
Sonoma County Museum, Santa Rosa, CA...185
Sordoni Art Gallery, Wilkes-Barre, PA.......1307
South Bend Regional Museum of Art, South Bend, IN.............................500
South Carolina Artisans Center, Walterboro, SC 1343
The South Carolina Botanical Garden, Clemson, SC 1328
South Carolina State Museum, Columbia, SC...1331
South Dakota Art Museum, Brookings, SD...1344
South Dakota Hall of Fame, Chamberlain, SD 1345
South Shore Arts, Munster, IN 493
Southeast Missouri Regional Museum, Cape Girardeau, MO 812
Southeastern Architectural Archive, New Orleans, LA......................................598
Southern Alleghenies Museum of Art, Loretto, PA......................................1269

Southern Alleghenies Museum of Art at Johnstown, Johnstown, PA....................1264
Southern Arts Federation, Atlanta, GA.........363
Southern Vermont Art Center, Manchester, VT 1481
Southold Historical Society and Museum, Southold, NY 1071
Spanish Governor's Palace, San Antonio, TX...1450
Spartanburg County Museum of Art, Spartanburg, SC 1341
The Speed Art Museum, Louisville, KY 579
Spelman College Museum of Fine Art, Atlanta, GA...................................363
Spencer Museum of Art, The University of Kansas, Lawrence, KS.....................548
Spertus Museum, Chicago, IL 427
Spiers Gallery, Brevard, NC 1092
The Sports Museum, Boston, MA 669
Springfield Art Association, Springfield, IL...460
Springfield Art Museum, Springfield, MO ...839
Springfield Museum of Art, Springfield, OH...1186
Springfield Museums - George Walter Vincent Smith Art Museum, Springfield, MA 710
Springfield Museums - Museum of Fine Arts, Springfield, MA 711
Springville Museum of Art, Springville, UT...1474
Spurlock Museum, University of Illinois at Urbana-Champaign, Urbana, IL...........462
Stamford Museum & Nature Center, Stamford, CT 261
Stanley Museum, Inc., Kingfield, ME.........613
Stark Museum of Art, Orange, TX 1441
State Capitol, Hartford, Conn., Hartford, CT...246
State Historical Society of Missouri, Columbia, MO...............................814
State of Illinois-Historic Preservation Agency, Historic Sites Division, Springfield, IL...............................460
Station 15, Norton, KS............................554
Stauth Memorial Museum, Montezuma, KS...553
Stedman Gallery, Camden, NJ 900
Steffen Thomas Museum and Archives, Buckhead, GA 367
Stephens African-American Museum, Shreveport, LA 602
The Stephens Museum, Fayette, MO 815
Sterling and Francine Clark Art Institute, Williamstown, MA 719
Stone House Gallery, Fredonia, KS.............540
The Stone Museum, Monroe Township, NJ...912
Stone Quarry Hill Art Park, Inc., Cazenovia, NY...............................977
Storm King Art Center, Mountainville, NY...1016
The Stowitts Museum & Library, Pacific Grove, CA......................................137
Stranahan House, Inc., Fort Lauderdale, FL...308
Strategic Air & Space Museum, Ashland, NE...856
Stuart Collection, La Jolla, CA....................107
The Studio Museum in Harlem, New York, NY......................................1040
Studio San Giuseppe Art Gallery, Cincinnati, OH..............................1151
SUArt Galleries - Syracuse University, Syracuse, NY...............................1077
Sullivan Museum and History Center, Northfield, VT 1483
Sumter Gallery of Art, Sumter, SC.............1342
Sun Gallery, Hayward, CA 102
The Supreme Court of the United States, Washington, DC............................291

Sushi Performance and Visual Art, San Diego, CA......................................161
Sutter's Fort State Historic Park, Sacramento, CA..............................153
Suzanne H. Arnold Art Gallery, Lebanon Valley College, Annville, PA 1241
Sweeney Art Gallery, University of California, Riverside, CA.......................150
Swope Art Museum, Terre Haute, IN...........501
T Rex Museum, Tucson, AZ.........................50
T.W. Wood Gallery & Arts Center, Montpelier, VT 1482
Tacoma Art Museum, Tacoma, WA.............1574
The Taft Museum of Art, Cincinnati, OH ..1151
Talkeetna Historical Society and Museum, Talkeetna, AK....................28
Tall Grass Arts Association, Park Forest, IL...449
Tampa Museum of Art, Tampa, FL.............350
Tante Blanche Museum, Madawaska, ME ...614
Taos Historic Museums, Taos, NM 953
Tarble Arts Center, Eastern Illinois University, Charleston, IL.....................417
Taube Museum of Art, Minot, ND 1135
The Tech Museum of Innovation, San Jose, CA......................................173
Ted Williams Museum and Hitters Hall of Fame, Hernando, FL....................312
The Teddy Bear Museum of Naples, Naples, FL......................................328
Telfair Museum of Art, Savannah, GA 386
The Temple Judea Museum of Reform Congregation Keneseth Israel, Elkins Park, PA......................................1251
The Temple Museum of Religious Art, Cleveland, OH 1156
Ten Broeck Mansion - Albany County Historical Association, Albany, NY.........956
Tennessee State Museum, Nashville, TN 1381
Tennessee Valley Art Center, Tuscumbia, AL...20
Terrace Gallery-City of Orlando, Orlando, FL...................................332
Terrace Hill Historic Site and Governor's Mansion, Des Moines, IA 516
Texas State Museum of Asian Cultures & Educational Center, Corpus Christi, TX...1402
Theodore Roosevelt Birthplace National Historic Site, New York, NY 1040
Thetford Historical Society Library and Museum, Thetford, VT.......................1488
This Century Art Gallery, Williamsburg, VA...1545
Thomas J. Walsh Art Gallery, Quick Center for the Arts at Fairfield University, Fairfield, CT.......................241
Thomas L. Kane Memorial Chapel, Kane, PA...1264
Thomasville Cultural Center, Inc., Thomasville, GA 388
Thorne-Sagendorph Art Gallery, Keene, NH...890
Thunderbird Foundation for the Arts, Mount Carmel, UT 1467
Timken Museum of Art, San Diego, CA 162
Tinkerton Museum, Sandia Park, NM.......947
Tinley Park Historical Society, Tinley Park, IL......................................461
The Toledo Museum of Art, Toledo, OH ..1187
Toppenish Museum, Toppenish, WA 1575
Torpedo Factory Art Center, Alexandria, VA...1494
Tougaloo College, Tougaloo, MS 808
Tower Fine Arts Gallery (SUNY Brockport), Brockport, NY 964
The Trammell & Margaret Crow Collection of Asian Art, Dallas, TX 1408
Trenton City Museum, Trenton, NJ 928
Triton Museum of Art, Santa Clara, CA 181
The Trout Gallery, Carlisle, PA 1245

Wendell Gilley Museum, Southwest Harbor, ME 623
West Bend Art Museum, West Bend, WI...1627
West Point Museum, West Point, NY 1085
West Valley Art Museum, Surprise, AZ 45
West Virginia Museum of American Glass, Weston, WV 1587
West Virginia State Museum, Charleston, WV..1581
West Virginia University-Mesaros Galleries, Morgantown, WV 1585
Western Colorado Center for the Arts, Grand Junction, CO................................221
Western Gallery, Western Washington University, Bellingham, WA 1549
Western Illinois University Art Gallery, Macomb, IL..444
Western Kentucky University Gallery, Bowling Green, KY................................566
Western Michigan University Richmond Center for Visual Arts School of Art, Kalamazoo, MI 749
Western Skisport Museum, Donner Pass, CA..91
Westmoreland Museum of American Art, Greensburg, PA..................................1257
Wexner Center for the Arts, Columbus, OH..1159
The Wharton Esherick Museum, Malvern, PA....................................1269
Whatcom Museum of History and Art, Bellingham, WA.................................1549
Wheels Through Time Museum, Inc., Maggie Valley, NC 1110
The Wheelwright Museum of the American Indian, Santa Fe, NM..............950
Whistler House Museum of Art, Lowell, MA...692
White Deer Land Museum, Pampa, TX 1442
White Hall State Historic Site, Richmond, KY.....................................583
The White House, Washington, DC............294
Whitestone Hill Battlefield State Historic Site, Kulm, ND....................................1133
Whitney Museum of American Art, New York, NY..1041
Whittier Home Association, Amesbury, MA...658
Wichita Art Museum, Wichita, KS 563
Wichita Center for the Arts, Wichita, KS.....563
Wichita Falls Museum and Art Center, Wichita Falls, TX...............................1461
Widener University Art Collection and Gallery, Chester, PA 1247
The Wiegand Gallery, Belmont, CA...............74
Wilbur D. May Museum, Reno, NV 882
Wildlife Experience Museum, Parker, CO....229
Wildling Art Museum, Los Olivos, CA 123
Wilhelm Reich Museum - Orgonon, Rangeley, ME..621
Wilkes Art Gallery, North Wilkesboro, NC..1113
Will Rogers Memorial Museum, Claremore, OK...1198
Will Rogers State Historic Park, Pacific Palisades, CA...137
William A. Farnsworth Library and Art Museum, Inc. d/b/a Farnsworth Art Museum, Rockland, ME............................621
The William Benton Museum of Art, Storrs, CT..262
William Bonifas Fine Arts Center, Escanaba, MI..741
William Cullen Bryant Homestead, Cummington, MA..678
William J. Clinton Presidential Library & Museum, Little Rock, AR 63
William S. Hart County Park & Museum, Newhall, CA..130
William Weston Clarke Emison Museum of Art, Greencastle, IN.........................479

Williams College Museum of Art, Williamstown, MA 719
Winchendon Historical Society, Inc., Winchendon, MA 720
Wing Haven Garden and Bird Sanctuary, Charlotte, NC...1096
Winston Churchill Memorial and Library, Fulton, MO.......................................816
Wiregrass Museum of Art, Dothan, AL 8
Wisconsin Fine Arts Association, Inc., Cedarburg, WI................................1594
The Wisconsin Union Galleries, University of Wisconsin-Madison, Madison, WI..1606
Wisconsin Veterans Museum-Madison, Madison, WI 1606
Wiseman & FireHouse Galleries, Rogue Community College, Grants Pass, OR ..1225
Wolf Point Area Historical Society, Inc., Wolf Point, MT 855
The Wolfsonian - Florida International University, Miami Beach, FL.................327
Woodbine International Fire Museum, Woodbine, GA...392
Wooden Sculpture Garden of Romano Gabriel, Eureka, CA................................94
Woodmere Art Museum, Philadelphia, PA.1289
Woodstock Artists Association, Woodstock, NY...................................1087
Woolaroc Museum, Bartlesville, OK 1197
Worcester Art Museum, Worcester, MA.......721
World Erotic Art Museum, Miami Beach, FL..327
World Figure Skating Museum & Hall of Fame, Colorado Springs, CO...................208
World Forestry Center, Portland, OR 1233
World Golf Hall of Fame, Saint Augustine, FL.......................................340
World O' Tools Museum, Waverly, TN......1385
World of Wings Pigeon Center, Oklahoma City, OK.............................1211
Wright Brothers National Memorial, Kill Devil Hills, NC.......................................1108
Wright Museum of Art, Beloit College, Beloit, WI..1592
Wright State University Art Galleries, Dayton, OH..1162
Wyoming Pioneer Memorial Museum, Douglas, WY...1632
Wyoming State Museum, Cheyenne, WY..1631

Xochipilli Art Gallery, Birmingham, MI......730

Yale Center for British Art, New Haven, CT..254
Yale University Art Gallery, New Haven, CT..254
Yeiser Art Center, Paducah, KY 582
Yellowstone Art Museum, Billings, MT.......842
Yeshiva University Museum at the Center for Jewish History, New York, NY........1041
Yogi Berra Museum and Learning Center, Little Falls, NJ....................................910
York W. Bailey Museum at Penn Center, Saint Helena Island, SC........................1340
Yuma Art Center Museum - Yuma Fine Arts, Yuma, AZ...54

ZAM - Zigler Art Museum, Jennings, LA ...589
Zanesville Art Center, Zanesville, OH........1194
Zenith Gallery, Washington, DC..................294
Zeum, San Francisco, CA 170
Ziibiwing Center of Anishinabe Culture & Lifeways, Mount Pleasant, MI 757

HISTORICAL COLLECTIONS

Communication Artifacts

The A.D. Buck Museum of Natural History & Science, Tonkawa, OK 1215
A.R. Mitchell Museum, Trinidad, CO..........233
A:shiwi A:wan Museum and Heritage Center, Zuni, NM 954

Abby Aldrich Rockefeller Folk Art Museum, Williamsburg, VA 1544
Ace of Clubs House, Texarkana, TX..........1455
Adair County Historical Society, Inc., Kirksville, MO...824
Adams Museum & House, Deadwood, SD...1346
Adams Old Stone Grist Mill, Bellows Falls, VT..1476
Adams State College Luther Bean Museum, Alamosa, CO 201
Admiral Nimitz National Museum of the Pacific War, Fredericksburg, TX............1419
Adventure Science Center, Nashville, TN..1377
Advertising Icon Museum, Kansas City, MO...820
African American Historical Museum & Cultural Center of Iowa, Cedar Rapids, IA...508
African American Museum, Cleveland, OH..1152
African American Museum, Dallas, TX.....1403
African-American Museum and Library at Oakland, Oakland, CA 132
The African American Museum in Philadelphia, Philadelphia, PA..............1275
African Art Museum of the S.M.A. Fathers, Tenafly, NJ 926
Afro-American Cultural Center, Charlotte, NC....................................1094
Afro-American Historical Society Museum, Jersey City, NJ 908
Agate Fossil Beds National Monument, Harrison, NE...862
Agricultural and Industrial Museum, York County Heritage Trust, York, PA...........1309
Agrirama, Georgia's Living History Museum & Village, Tifton, GA 388
Agua Mansa Pioneer Memorial Cemetery, Colton, CA..87
Ah-Tah-Thi-Ki Museum at Okalee, Hollywood, FL.....................................312
The Airborne & Special Operations Museum, Fayetteville, NC....................1100
Airline History Museum, Kansas City, MO...820
Akron Zoological Park, Akron, OH............1138
Akta Lakota Museum and Cultural Center, Chamberlain, SD.......................1345
Alabama Museum of the Health Sciences, Birmingham, AL...............................4
Alachua County Historic Trust: Matheson Museum, Inc., Gainesville, FL.............310
Alamance Battleground State Historic Site, Burlington, NC.................................1092
Alaska Indian Arts, Inc., Haines, AK 24
Albany Civil Rights Movement Museum at Old Mt. Zion Church, Albany, GA......355
Albany Institute of History & Art, Albany, NY..954
Albuquerque Museum, Albuquerque, NM....932
Alexander & Baldwin Sugar Museum, Puunene, HI...401
Alexander Brest Museum and Gallery, Jacksonville, FL..313
Alexandria Black History Resource Center, Alexandria, VA.............................1491
Alexandria Museum of Art, Alexandria, LA...584
Alice Austen House Museum, Staten Island, NY..1072
Aliceville Museum, Aliceville, AL..................3
Allaire Village Inc., Farmingdale, NJ...........903
Alling Coverlet Museum, Palmyra, NY 1050
Alutiiq Museum and Archaeological Repository, Kodiak, AK 26
Amador County Museum, Jackson, CA 105
Amana Heritage Museum, Amana, IA 504
Amelia Earhart Birthplace Museum, Atchison, KS...532
Amelia Island Museum of History, Fernandina Beach, FL 306

Communication Artifacts–Continued

America On Wheels, Inc., Allentown, PA..1239

American Airlines C.R. Smith Museum, Fort Worth, TX.....1416

American Antiquarian Society, Worcester, MA.....720

American Baptist Historical Society, Rochester, NY.....1058

American Catholic Historical Society, Philadelphia, PA.....1276

American Clock and Watch Museum, Inc., Bristol, CT.....236

American Computer Museum, Bozeman, MT.....842

American Independence Museum, Exeter, NH.....887

American Jewish Historical Society, New York, NY.....1019

American Merchant Marine Museum, Kings Point, NY.....1007

American Museum of Asmat Art, Saint Paul, MN.....789

American Museum of Nursing, Tempe, AZ.....45

American Museum of Radio and Electricity, Bellingham, WA.....1548

American Numismatic Association Money Museum, Colorado Springs, CO.....206

The American Numismatic Society, New York, NY.....1020

American Printing House for the Blind, Callahan Museum, Louisville, KY.....575

American Radio Relay League-Museum of Amateur Radio, Newington, CT.....256

American Red Cross Visitors Center and Gift Shop, Washington, DC.....275

American Royal Museum & Visitors Center, Kansas City, MO.....820

American Sign Museum, Cincinnati, OH...1148

American Swedish Historical Foundation & Museum, Philadelphia, PA.....1276

American Textile History Museum, Lowell, MA.....691

American Truck Historical Society, Kansas City, MO.....820

American Visionary Art Museum, Baltimore, MD.....629

American Water Ski Educational Foundation, Polk City, FL.....337

America's Black Holocaust Museum, Milwaukee, WI.....1610

Americas Society, New York, NY.....1020

Anacortes Museum, Anacortes, WA.....1547

Anacostia Museum and Center for African American History & Culture, Washington, DC.....275

Anadarko Heritage Museum, Anadarko, OK.....1195

Anaheim Museum, Anaheim, CA.....71

Anderson/Abruzzo Albuquerque International Balloon Museum, Albuquerque, NM.....933

Anderson County Museum, Anderson, SC.1321

Andersonville National Historic Site, Andersonville, GA.....355

Andrew J. Blackbird Museum, Harbor Springs, MI.....745

Androscoggin Historical Society, Auburn, ME.....603

Angel Mounds State Historic Site, Evansville, IN.....475

Animas Museum, Durango, CO.....214

Anna Bemis Palmer Museum, York, NE.....875

Annie Riggs Memorial Museum, Fort Stockton, TX.....1415

Anoka County Historical Society, Anoka, MN.....767

Anthropology Museum, University of San Diego, San Diego, CA.....155

The Appaloosa Museum and Heritage Center, Moscow, ID.....407

The Apple Trees Museum, Burlington, IA...506

Appomattox Court House National Historical Park, Appomattox, VA.....1495

Archives - Archdiocese of St. Paul and Minneapolis, Saint Paul, MN.....789

Archives Museum, Temple Mickve Israel, Savannah, GA.....384

Archives of J.S.G. Boggs, Brandon, FL.....298

Arden - The Helena Modjeska Historic House & Gardens, Modjeska Canyon, CA.....126

Argo Gold Mine & Mill Museum, Idaho Springs, CO.....223

Arizona Historical Society Museum, Tucson, AZ.....47

Arizona Historical Society Museum at Papago Park, Tempe, AZ.....45

Arizona Historical Society Museum - Downtown, Tucson, AZ.....47

Arizona Historical Society Pioneer Museum, Flagstaff, AZ.....32

Arizona Jewish Historical Society, Phoenix, AZ.....39

Arizona State Capitol Museum, Phoenix, AZ.....39

Arizona State Parks Board, Phoenix, AZ.....39

Arkansas Museum of Natural Resources, Smackover, AR.....68

Arlington Heights Historical Museum, Arlington Heights, IL.....411

Arlington Historical Museum, Arlington, VA.....1495

The Arlington Historical Society, Arlington, MA.....660

Armenian Library and Museum of America, Watertown, MA.....716

The Arms Family Museum of Local History, Youngstown, OH.....1193

Art Association of Randolph County, Inc., Union City, IN.....501

Art Center of Battle Creek, Battle Creek, MI.....726

The Arthur J. Moore Methodist Museum, Saint Simons Island, GA.....383

Arts Consortium of Cincinnati's African American Museum, Cincinnati, OH.....1148

Ashland Historical Society, Ashland, MA....661

Asian Art Museum of San Francisco, Chong-Moon Lee Center for Asian Art and Culture, San Francisco, CA.....163

Asian Arts & Culture Center, Towson University, Towson, MD.....655

Aspen Historical Society, Aspen, CO.....202

The Association for Gravestone Studies, Greenfield, MA.....685

Atchison County Historical Society, Atchison, KS.....533

The Athenaeum of Philadelphia, Philadelphia, PA.....1276

Atlantic City Historical Museum, Atlantic City, NJ.....897

Atwater Kent Museum of Philadelphia, Philadelphia, PA.....1276

Atwood House Museum, Home of Chatham Historical Society, Chatham, MA.....675

Au Glaize Village, Defiance, OH.....1162

Auburn Cord Duesenberg Museum, Auburn, IN.....468

Audie Murphy/American Cotton Museum, Inc, Greenville, TX.....1423

Audubon County Historical Society, Exira, IA.....517

Aurora Historical Society, Aurora, IL.....411

Aurora Historical Society, Aurora, OH.....1140

Aurora History Museum, Aurora, CO.....202

Aurora Regional Fire Museum, Aurora, IL.....411

Autry National Center of the American West, Los Angeles, CA.....112

Avery County Museum, Newland, NC.....1113

Avery Research Center for African American History & Culture, Charleston, SC.....1323

Baca House, Trinidad History Museum, Trinidad, CO.....233

The Bade Institute of Biblical Archaeology and The Howell Bible Collection, Berkeley, CA.....75

Badger Mine and Museum, Shullsburg, WI.....1622

Baldwin County Heritage Museum, Elberta, AL.....8

Baldwin-Reynolds House Museum, Meadville, PA.....1270

Baltimore & Ohio Railroad Museum, Baltimore, MD.....629

Baltimore County Historical Society, Cockeysville, MD.....640

Baltimore Museum of Industry, Baltimore, MD.....630

Bandon Historical Society Museum, Bandon, OR.....1219

Banner County Historical Society, Harrisburg, NE.....862

Bannock County Historical Museum, Pocatello, ID.....408

Barbed Wire Museum, La Crosse, KS.....547

The Bare Cove Fire Museum, Hingham, MA.....687

Barnard's Mill Art Museum, Glen Rose, TX.....1422

Barnes County Historical Museum, Valley City, ND.....1136

The Barnum Museum, Bridgeport, CT.....235

Barratt's Chapel and Museum, Frederica, DE.....270

Barron County Historical Society's Pioneer Village Museum, Cameron, WI.....1593

Bartlesville Area History Museum, Bartlesville, OK.....1196

Barton County Historical Museum & Village, Great Bend, KS.....542

Bartow History Center, Cartersville, GA.....367

Batsto Village, Hammonton, NJ.....907

The Battles Museums of Rural Life, Girard, PA.....1256

Bayou Bend Collection and Gardens, Houston, TX.....1425

The Bead Museum, Glendale, AZ.....35

Beard Gallery, Norton, MA.....700

The Beaufort Arsenal, Beaufort, SC.....1321

Beauvais Heritage Center, Clark, SD.....1345

Beaver Island Historical Society, Beaver Island, MI.....728

Beck Cultural Exchange Center, Knoxville, TN.....1369

Beckman Coulter Heritage Exhibit, Fullerton, CA.....98

Bedford City/County Museum, Bedford, VA.....1496

Beehive House, Salt Lake City, UT.....1470

Belhaven Memorial Museum, Inc., Belhaven, NC.....1092

Beltrami County History Center, Bemidji, MN.....768

Benicia Historical Museum, Benicia, CA.....74

The Benjamin & Dr. Edgar R. Cofeld Judaic Museum of Temple Beth Zion, Buffalo, NY.....971

Benjamin Harrison Presidential Site, Indianapolis, IN.....481

Benton County Historical Museum, Philomath, OR.....1230

Benzie Area Historical Museum, Benzonia, MI.....729

Berkeley County Museum & Heritage Center, Moncks Corner, SC.....1336

Bernard Judaica Museum, Congregation Emanu-El of the City of New York, New York, NY.....1021

Berrien County Historical Association, Berrien Springs, MI................729

Beth Ahabah Museum & Archives, Richmond, VA 1528

Beyer Home, Oconto County Historical Society Museum, Oconto, WI................1616

Biblical Arts Center, Dallas, TX................1404

Biblical Resource Center & Museum, Collierville, TN........................1364

Biedenharn Coca-Cola Museum, Vicksburg, MS........................809

Big Bend National Park, Big Bend, TX.....1396

Big Springs Museum, Caledonia, NY 974

Billy Graham Center Museum, Wheaton, IL........................465

Biltmore Homespun Shops - Grovewood Gallery, Asheville, NC 1089

Birmingham Civil Rights Institute, Birmingham, AL...........................4

Bisbee Mining & Historical Museum, Bisbee, AZ...........................30

Bishop Hill Heritage Museum, Bishop Hill, IL........................413

Black Hawk State Historic Site: Hauberg Indian Museum, Rock Island, IL.........453

Black Hills Mining Museum, Lead, SD.....1350

Black Kettle Museum, Cheyenne, OK 1198

Black Mountain College Museum & Arts Center, Asheville, NC..........................1089

Black River Historical Society of Lorain, Lorain, OH........................1172

Blaine County Historical Museum, Hailey, ID........................406

Bloom Mansion, Trinidad History Museum, Trinidad, CO........................233

Blue Earth County Historical Society, Mankato, MN........................780

B'nai B'rith Klutznick National Jewish Museum, Washington, DC 277

Boca Raton Historical Society, Boca Raton, FL........................296

Boca Raton Museum of Art, Boca Raton, FL........................296

Bodie Island Visitor Center, South Nags Head, NC........................1120

Bodie State Historic Park, Bridgeport, CA........................79

Boehm Gallery, San Marcos, CA 174

Bolduc House Museum, Sainte Genevieve, MO........................837

Boone County Historical Center, Boone, IA........................506

Boonsborough Museum of History, Boonsboro, MD........................637

Boonshoft Museum of Discovery, Dayton, OH........................1160

Boot Hill Museum, Inc., Dodge City, KS....536

Boothbay Railway Village, Boothbay, ME....607

Boston Childrens Museum, Boston, MA....664

Boston Public Library, Boston, MA 664

Boswell Museum of Music, Springfield Center, NY........................1071

Boulder City/Hoover Dam Museum, Boulder City, NV........................875

Bowers Museum, Santa Ana, CA 177

Bowie Heritage Children's Museum & Welcome Center, Bowie, MD 638

Bowie Railroad Station and Huntington Museum, Bowie, MD........................638

Boys Town Hall of History & Father Flanagan House, Boys Town, NE..........858

Brandywine River Museum, Chadds Ford, PA........................1246

Brec's Magnolia Mound Plantation, Baton Rouge, LA........................585

Brevard Museum of History & Science, Cocoa, FL........................300

Brick Store Museum, Kennebunk, ME 612

Bridger Valley Heritage Museum, Lyman, WY........................1636

Bridgton Historical Society, Bridgton, ME........................607

Brigham Young's Winter Home, Saint George, UT........................1470

Brimstone Museum, Sulphur, LA 602

The Bronx County Historical Society, Bronx, NY........................964

The Brooklyn Historical Society, Brooklyn, NY........................968

The Broome County Historical Society, Binghamton, NY........................962

Brunswick Railroad Museum and C&O Canal Visitors Center, Brunswick, MD ...639

Brunswick Town/Fort Anderson State Historic Site, Winnabow, NC................1124

Bucks County Civil War Library & Museum, Doylestown, PA........................1249

Buechel Memorial Lakota Museum, Saint Francis, SD........................1355

Buffalo and Erie County Historical Society, Buffalo, NY........................972

Buffalo Bill Historical Center, Cody, WY..1631

Buffalo Bill Museum & Grave, Golden, CO........................219

Buffalo Museum of Science, Buffalo, NY ...972

Bureau County Historical Society Museum, Princeton, IL........................452

Burke County Historical Powers Lake Complex, Powers Lake, ND 1136

Bushy Run Battlefield, Jeannette, PA..........1263

Butler County Historical Society, Allison, IA........................504

Butte County Pioneer Memorial Museum, Oroville, CA........................136

Byron Historical Museum, Byron, NY..........974

CDC/Global Health Odyssey, Atlanta, GA........................358

C.E. Smith Museum of Anthropology, Hayward, CA........................101

C.H. Nash Museum-Chucalissa Archaeological Museum, Memphis, TN........................1372

CU Heritage Center, Boulder, CO 203

Cabin Nature Center, Wood Dale, IL 466

Cabot Historical Society, Cabot, VT 1478

Cabrillo Marine Aquarium, San Pedro, CA........................176

California Historical Society, San Francisco, CA........................163

California Museum of Ancient Art, Beverly Hills, CA........................78

California State Capitol Museum, Sacramento, CA........................151

California State Indian Museum, Sacramento, CA........................151

Call of the Wild Museum, Gaylord, MI.......742

Calvin Coolidge Presidential Library & Museum, Northampton, MA 699

Camden County Historical Society, Camden, NJ........................899

Camp Atterbury Museum, Edinburgh, IN 474

Camp Five Museum Foundation, Inc., Laona, WI........................1604

Campbell Historical Museum & Ainsley House, Campbell, CA........................80

Campbell House Museum, Saint Louis, MO........................832

Canadian County Historical Museum, El Reno, OK........................1200

Canajoharie Library and Art Gallery, Canajoharie, NY........................974

The Cannon Village Visitor Center, Kannapolis, NC........................1107

Canton Classic Car Museum, Canton, OH.1145

Canyon County Historical Society & Museum, Nampa, ID........................408

The Cape Cod Maritime Museum, Hyannis, MA........................688

Cape Cod Museum of Natural History, Inc., Brewster, MA........................670

Cape Henry Lighthouse, Virginia Beach, VA........................1541

Cape Vincent Historical Museum, Cape Vincent, NY........................976

Capitola Historical Museum, Capitola, CA........................81

Captain Forbes House Museum, Milton, MA........................695

Carl Sandburg Home National Historic Site, Flat Rock, NC........................1101

Carlsbad Caverns National Park, Carlsbad, NM........................937

Carroll Mansion Museum Home of Leavenworth County Historical Society, Leavenworth, KS........................549

Carroll Reece Museum, Johnson City, TN.1367

Carter County Museum, Ekalaka, MT.........846

Cartoon Art Museum, San Francisco, CA....164

Caryl House and Fisher Barn, Dover, MA....680

Casa Adobe de San Rafael, Glendale, CA ...100

Casa Blanca Museum, San Juan, PR..........1642

Casa Grande Valley Historical Society & Museum, Casa Grande, AZ........................30

Cascade County Historical Society Museum, Great Falls, MT........................848

Casey Jones Home and Railroad Museum, Jackson, TN........................1367

Cass County Historical Society, Logansport, IN........................489

Cass County Historical Society Museum, Plattsmouth, NE........................872

Casteel-Linn House and Museum, Princeton, MO........................829

Castle Air Museum, Atwater, CA........................72

Castle Museum of Saginaw County History, Saginaw, MI........................762

Catalina Island Museum Society, Inc., Avalon, CA........................73

Catawba County Museum of History, Newton, NC........................1113

The Cathedral of St. John the Divine, New York, NY........................1022

Catholic Historical Society of the Roanoke Valley, Roanoke, VA................1535

Catskill Fly Fishing Center & Museum, Livingston Manor, NY........................1010

Cattaraugus Area Historical Center, Cattaraugus, NY........................976

Cayuga Museum & Case Research Lab Museum, Auburn, NY........................959

Cayuga-Owasco Lakes Historical Society, Moravia, NY........................1015

Cedar Falls Historical Society, Cedar Falls, IA........................507

Cedar Grove Historical Society, Cedar Grove, NJ........................901

Centennial Village Museum, Greeley, CO ...221

Center for American History, Austin, TX.1390

Center for American Music, Pittsburgh, PA........................1291

Center for Book Arts, New York, NY........1022

Center for History, Wheaton, IL................465

Center for Puppetry Arts, Atlanta, GA........359

Center for the Study of Political Graphics (CSPG), Los Angeles, CA........................113

Centerville - Washington Township Historical Society & Asahel Wright Community Center, Centerville, OH 1146

Central Florida Railroad Museum, Winter Garden, FL........................354

Central High School National Historic Site, Little Rock, AR........................61

Central Rappahannock Heritage Center, Fredericksburg, VA........................1505

Centre County Historical Society, State College, PA........................1301

Centre County Library and Historical Museum, Bellefonte, PA........................1241

Centre Hill Museum (The Petersburg Museums), Petersburg, VA........................1524

Chaco Culture National Historical Park, Nageezi, NM........................943

Chagrin Falls Historical Society, Chagrin Falls, OH........................1147

Chalet of the Golden Fleece, New Glarus, WI........................1614

Communication Artifacts–Continued

Champaign County Historical Museum, Champaign, IL..........416

Champaign County Historical Museum, Urbana, OH..........1188

Champion Mill State Historical Park, Champion, NE..........859

Chancellor Robert R. Livingston Masonic Library & Museum, New York, NY......1022

The Chapman Historical Museum, Glens Falls, NY..........994

Chappell Hill Historical Society Museum, Chappell Hill, TX..........1399

Charles M. Schulz Museum and Research Center, Santa Rosa, CA..........184

Charles River Museum of Industry, Waltham, MA..........715

The Charleston Museum, Charleston, SC..1324

Charlotte County Historical Center, Charlotte Harbor, FL..........299

Chattanooga African Museum/Bessie Smith Hall, Chattanooga, TN..........1360

Chattanooga Regional History Museum, Chattanooga, TN..........1361

Chemung Valley History Museum, Elmira, NY..........988

Chenango County Historical Society Museum, Norwich, NY..........1044

Cheraw Lyceum Museum, Cheraw, SC......1327

Cherokee County Historical Museum, Inc., Murphy, NC..........1112

Cherokee National Museum, Park Hill, OK..........1211

Cherokee Strip Land Rush Museum, Arkansas City, KS..........532

Cherokee Strip Museum, Alva, OK..........1195

Cherry Valley Museum, Cherry Valley, NY..........978

Chesapeake Bay Maritime Museum, Saint Michaels, MD..........652

Chesterfield County Museum, Chesterfield, VA..........1501

Cheyenne Frontier Days Old West Museum, Cheyenne, WY..........1630

The Chicago Athenaeum: Museum of Architecture and Design, Galena, IL......436

Chicago Public Library, Chicago, IL..........419

Chickamauga-Chattanooga National Military Park, Fort Oglethorpe, GA........372

Chico Museum, Chico, CA..........83

Chieftains Museum, Rome, GA..........381

Children's Discovery Museum of North San Diego, Carlsbad, CA..........81

The Children's Museum, Seattle, WA........1565

Children's Museum at La Habra, La Habra, CA..........106

Children's Museum/Detroit Public Schools, Detroit, MI..........735

Children's Museum of History, Natural History and Science at Utica, New York, Utica, NY..........1079

The Children's Museum of Indianapolis, Indianapolis, IN..........481

Children's Museum of Pittsburgh, Pittsburgh, PA..........1291

Children's Museum of the Sierra, Oakhurst, CA..........132

Chimney Point State Historic Site, Addison, VT..........1475

Chinese American Museum, Los Angeles, CA..........114

Chinese Culture Center of San Francisco, San Francisco, CA..........164

Chinqua-Penn Plantation, Reidsville, NC...1117

Chippewa County Historical Society, Montevideo, MN..........783

Chippewa Valley Museum, Inc., Eau Claire, WI..........1595

Chisholm Trail Museum, Wellington, KS....561

Chisholm Trail Museum, Kingfisher, OK...1203

Choctaw County Historical Society, Hugo, OK..........1203

Christa McAuliffe Planetarium, Concord, NH..........884

Churchill County Museum and Archives, Fallon, NV..........877

Circus World Museum, Baraboo, WI........1591

City County Pioneer Museum, Sweetwater, TX..........1454

City Island Nautical Museum, Bronx, NY...965

City of Bowie Museums, Bowie, MD..........638

City of Gilroy Museum, Gilroy, CA..........99

City of Las Vegas Museum and Rough Rider Memorial Collection, Las Vegas, NM..........941

Clallam County Historical Society, Port Angeles, WA..........1561

Clara Barton National Historic Site, Glen Echo, MD..........645

Clarion County Historical Society, Sutton-Ditz House Museum, Clarion, PA..........1247

Clark County Historical Society - Heritage Center of Clark County, Springfield, OH..........1186

Clark Hotel Museum, Van Horn, TX........1457

Clarke County Historical Association, Inc., Berryville, VA..........1496

Clarke Historical Museum, Eureka, CA........94

Clarke House Museum, Chicago, IL..........420

Clarkson Historical Museum, Clarkson, NE..........859

Clarksville-Montgomery County Museum dba Customs House Museum & Cultural Center, Clarksville, TN..........1363

Clausen Memorial Museum, Petersburg, AK..........27

Clay County Historical Museum, Liberty, MO..........826

Clay County Historical Society Museum and Archives, Moorhead, MN..........784

Clearwater Historical Museum, Orofino, ID..........408

Cleveland County Historical Museum, Shelby, NC..........1119

The Cleveland Museum of Natural History, Cleveland, OH..........1153

Cleveland State University Art Gallery, Cleveland, OH..........1153

Clifton Community Historical Society, Clifton, KS..........535

Clinton County Historical Association & Museum, Plattsburgh, NY..........1052

Clinton County Historical Society Paine-Gillam-Scott Museum, Saint Johns, MI..........763

Clinton County Museum, Frankfort, IN......478

Clymer Museum of Art, Ellensburg, WA...1553

Coe Hall, Oyster Bay, NY..........1049

The Coffey County Historical Museum, Burlington, KS..........534

Cokato Museum & Akerlund Photography Studio, Cokato, MN..........771

Colfax County Society of Art, History and Archaeology, Raton, NM..........945

Colleton Museum, Walterboro, SC..........1343

Collin County Historical Society, Inc. & History Museum, McKinney, TX..........1437

Colonial National Historical Park: Jamestown & Yorktown, Yorktown, VA..........1546

Colorado Ski Museum-Ski & Snowboard Hall of Fame, Vail, CO..........234

Colorado Springs Fine Arts Center (Taylor Museum), Colorado Springs, CO..........206

Colorado Springs Museum, Colorado Springs, CO..........206

Colton Area Museum, Colton, CA..........87

Columbia Gorge Discovery Center and Wasco County Museum, The Dalles, OR..........1237

Columbia Gorge Interpretive Center Museum, Stevenson, WA..........1572

Columbia River Maritime Museum, Astoria, OR..........1218

Command Museum, Marine Corps Recruit Depot, San Diego, San Diego, CA..........156

The Commonwealth Museum, Boston, MA..........665

Commonwealth of the Northern Mariana Islands Museum of History and Culture, Saipan, MP..........1640

Community Fine Arts Center, Rock Springs, WY..........1637

Community of Christ, Independence, MO...817

Concord Museum, Concord, MA..........676

Concordia Historical Institute, Saint Louis, MO..........832

Confederated Tribes and Bands of the Yakama Indian Nation - Cultural Heritage Center Museum, Toppenish, WA..........1575

Confederated Tribes of Grand Ronde Cultural Resources Department, Grand Ronde, OR..........1225

Conklin Reed Organ & History Museum, Hanover, MI..........745

Connecticut Historical Society, Hartford, CT..........244

Connecticut River Museum, Essex, CT........239

Cook County Historical Museum, Grand Marais, MN..........776

Cooper-Hewitt National Design Museum, Smithsonian Institution, New York, NY..........1023

Cooper Regional History Museum, Upland, CA..........193

Copia: The American Center for Wine, Food & the Arts, Napa, CA..........129

Copshaholm House Museum & Historic Oliver Gardens, South Bend, IN..........499

Cordell Hull Birthplace & Museum State Historic Park, Byrdstown, TN..........1360

Coronado State Monument, Bernalillo, NM..........937

Corry Area Historical Society, Corry, PA...1248

Cottonwood County Historical Society, Windom, MN..........796

Country Music Hall of Fame and Museum, Country Music Foundation, Nashville, TN..........1378

County of Westchester, Department of Parks, Recreation and Conservation, Mount Kisco, NY..........1016

Courthouse Square Association, Charlotte, MI..........731

Cow Neck Peninsula Historical Society Sands-Willets House, Port Washington, NY..........1053

The Cowley County Historical Society, Winfield, KS..........564

Craftsmen's Guild of Mississippi, Jackson, MS..........802

Crandall Historical Printing Museum, Provo, UT..........1469

Crane Point, Marathon, FL..........323

Crawford County Historical Museum, Pittsburg, KS..........556

Crawford W. Long Museum, Jefferson, GA..........374

Crazy Mountain Museum, Big Timber, MT..........841

Crispus Attucks Center Museum, Indianapolis, IN..........482

Croatian Heritage Museum & Library, Eastlake, OH..........1163

Crook County Museum & Art Gallery, Sundance, WY..........1638

Culbertson Museum, Culbertson, MT..........845

Culinary Archives & Museum, Johnson & Wales University, Providence, RI......1316

Cumberland Gap National Historical Park, Middlesboro, KY..........580

Custer Battlefield Museum, Garryowen, MT..........847

D.C. Booth Historic National Fish Hatchery, Spearfish, SD 1357
D.R. Barker Historical Museum, Fredonia, NY 992
Dacotah Prairie Museum, Aberdeen, SD....1344
Dakota County Historical Society, South Saint Paul, MN 793
Dakota Discovery Museum, Mitchell, SD..1352
Dal-Paso Museum, Lamesa, TX 1433
Dallam-Hartley XIT Museum, Dalhart, TX 1403
Dallas Historical Society, Dallas, TX.........1405
Dallas Holocaust Museum, Dallas, TX 1405
Dallas Museum of Art, Dallas, TX.............1405
The Dan Quayle Center & Museum, Huntington, IN 481
The Dana-Thomas House State Historic Site, Springfield, IL 458
Daniel Boone Homestead, Birdsboro, PA ..1243
Daniels County Museum and Pioneer Town, Scobey, MT 853
The Danish Immigrant Museum, Elk Horn, IA 517
Danvers Historical Society, Danvers, MA....678
Darlington Raceway Stock Car Museum, NMPA Hall of Fame, Darlington, SC....1331
Davenport House Museum, Savannah, GA 384
David Conklin Farmhouse, Huntington, NY 1000
Dawes County Historical Society Museum, Chadron, NE 859
Dawson Springs Museum and Art Center, Inc., Dawson Springs, KY 568
Dayton Historical Depot Society, Dayton, WA 1552
De Saisset Museum, Santa Clara, CA 180
Death Valley National Park Visitor Center and Museums, Death Valley, CA 91
Dedham Historical Society Museum, Dedham, MA 679
Deer Park Escondido Winery & Auto Museum, Escondido, CA 93
Degrazia Gallery In The Sun, Tucson, AZ.....48
Delaware and Hudson Canal Historical Society and Museum, High Falls, NY....998
Delta Blues Museum, Clarksdale, MS..........799
Delta County Museum, Delta, CO................209
Denali National Park and Preserve, Denali Park, AK 23
Dennys River Historical Society, Dennysville, ME 609
Denton County Historical Museum, Inc. and Texas Heritage Center, Denton, TX 1409
Denver Firefighters Museum, Denver, CO...211
Denver Museum of Miniatures, Dolls and Toys, Denver, CO 211
Denver Museum of Nature & Science, Denver, CO 211
Department of the Treasury, Washington, DC 278
Depot Museum & Fort Sedgwick Museum, Julesburg, CO 223
The Depot Museum Complex, Henderson, TX 1424
Depot Park Museum, Sonoma, CA 187
Des Moines Botanical Center, Des Moines, IA 514
Des Plaines History Center, Des Plaines, IL 430
Descanso Gardens Guild, Inc., La Canada Flintridge, CA 105
The Design Center at Philadelphia University, Philadelphia, PA.................1278
Detroit Historical Society, Detroit, MI 735
Deutschheim State Historic Site, Hermann, MO 817
DeWitt Wallace Decorative Arts Museum, Williamsburg, VA................................1545
Dexter Historical Society Campus, Dexter, ME 609

Dickinson County Heritage Center, Abilene, KS 531
The Discovery Center, Fresno, CA................96
Discovery Museum, Sacramento Museum of History, Science and Technology, Sacramento, CA 152
Disney's Animal Kingdom Theme Park, Bay Lake, FL 295
Dr. Samuel D. Harris National Museum of Dentistry, Baltimore, MD 631
Dodge County Historical Society, Mantorville, MN 780
Door County Historical Museum, Sturgeon Bay, WI 1623
Dorothy G. Page Museum, Wasilla, AK 29
Douglas County Historical Society - Carson Valley Museum & Cultural Center, Gardnerville, NV 877
Douglas County Historical Society - Genoa Courthouse Museum, Genoa, NV 877
Douglas County Museum Complex, Armour, SD 1344
Douglas County Museum of History and Natural History, Roseburg, OR 1234
Douglass Historical Museum, Douglass, KS 537
The Downers Grove Park District Museum, Downers Grove, IL 431
Downieville Museum, Downieville, CA 91
Drake Well Museum, Titusville, PA 1303
Duke Homestead State Historic Site, Durham, NC 1098
Dunbar House State Memorial, Dayton, OH 1161
Duncan Cottage Museum, Metlakatla, AK.....27
DuPage County Historical Museum, Wheaton, IL 465
Durham Center Museum/Research Library, East Durham, NY 985
Durham Historic Association Museum, Durham, NH 886
Durham Western Heritage Museum, Omaha, NE 870
Dusable Museum of African-American History, Inc., Chicago, IL........................420
Dwight D. Eisenhower Library-Museum, Abilene, KS 531
Dyer Memorial Library, Abington, MA 657

E. St. Julien Cox House, Saint Peter, MN ...792
EAA AirVenture Museum, Oshkosh, WI....1616
Eagle Historical Society & Museums, Eagle, AK..23
EarlyWorks Museums, Huntsville, AL 11
East Jordan Portside Art & Historical Museum, East Jordan, MI 739
East Texas Oil Museum at Kilgore College, Kilgore, TX 1432
Eastchester Historical Society - 1835 Marble Schoolhouse, Bronxville, NY......967
Eastern Arizona Museum and Historical Society of Graham County Inc., Pima, AZ 42
Eastern California Museum, Independence, CA 104
Eastside Heritage Center, Bellevue, WA 1548
Eckley Miners' Village, Eckley, PA............1251
Edgar Allan Poe Museum, Richmond, VA.1529
Edison & Ford Winter Estates, Fort Myers, FL 308
Edmond Historical Society Museum, Edmond, OK 1200
Edmonds South Snohomish County Historical Society, Inc., Edmonds, WA .1553
Edwards County Historical Museum, Kinsley, KS 547
Effie Yeaw Nature Center, Carmichael, CA 82
Effigy Mounds National Monument, Harpers Ferry, IA 519
Egan Maritime Foundation, Nantucket, MA 695

1859 Jail, Marshal's Home & Museum, Independence, MO....................................817
82nd Airborne Division War Memorial Museum, Fort Bragg, NC.......................1101
Eisenhower National Historic Site, Gettysburg, PA..1255
El Camino Real International Heritage Center, San Antonio, NM.........................947
El Dorado County Historical Museum, Placerville, CA 142
El Dorado Nature Center, Long Beach, CA 110
El Morro National Monument, Ramah, NM 945
El Paso Holocaust Museum & Study Center, El Paso, TX......................................1411
El Paso Museum of History, El Paso, TX...1412
El Pueblo History Museum, Pueblo, CO.....230
El Rancho de Las Golondrinas Museum, Santa Fe, NM...947
Eldridge Street Project, New York, NY 1025
Eli Whitney Museum, Inc., Hamden, CT.....244
Elkhart County Historical Museum, Bristol, IN 471
Ella Sharp Museum, Jackson, MI................748
Ellis County Historical Society, Hays, KS...543
Elmhurst Historical Museum, Elmhurst, IL 433
Elsing Museum, Tulsa, OK 1215
Enfield Historical Society Museum, Enfield Center, NH 887
Enfield Shaker Museum, Enfield, NH 887
Environmental Education Center, Somerset County Park Commission, Basking Ridge, NJ 898
Ephraim Historical Foundation, Ephraim, WI 1597
Ephrata Cloister, Ephrata, PA 1251
Erie County History Center & Cashier's House, Erie, PA 1252
Erie Maritime Museum, Homeport U.S. Brig Niagara, Erie, PA.........................1252
Ernie Pyle State Historic Site, Dana, IN 473
Essley-Noble Museum: Mercer County Historical Society, Aledo, IL....................410
Estes Park Museum, Estes Park, CO............215
Ethnic Heritage Museum, Rockford, IL 455
Eugene O'Neill National Historic Site, Danville, CA..89
Eureka School House, Springfield, VT 1487
Evansville Museum of Arts History & Science, Evansville, IN 475
Evergreen Aviation Museum, McMinnville, OR.......................................1228
Everhart Museum: Natural History, Science and Art, Scranton, PA...............1298
Experience Music Project, Seattle, WA......1565
Exploris, Raleigh, NC 1115
Explorium of Lexington, Lexington, KY 572

Fairbanks House, Dedham, MA...................679
Fairport Historical Museum, Fairport, NY...989
Fall River Historical Society Museum, Fall River, MA 682
Falls of the Ohio State Park, Clarksville, IN 472
Faninadahen Kosas Guahan-Guam Museum, Hagatna, GU.............................1640
Farmers Bank (The Petersburg Museums), Petersburg, VA.....................1525
The Fashion Institute of Design & Merchandising/FIDM Museum & Galleries, Los Angeles, CA....................114
Favell Museum Inc., Klamath Falls, OR....1227
Fayette Heritage Museum & Archives, La Grange, TX 1432
Federal Hall National Memorial, New York, NY..1025
Feet First: The Scholl Story, Rosalind Franklin University, North Chicago, IL...448
Fender Museum of Music and the Arts, Corona, CA 87

Communication Artifacts–Continued

Fick Fossil & History Museum, Oakley,
KS 554

Fillmore County Historical Center,
Fountain, MN..............776

The Finley House, Wayne, PA..............1306

Fire Museum of Maryland, Inc.,
Lutherville, MD..............649

Firehouse Art Gallery, Nassau
Community College, Garden City, NY ...992

Firelands Historical Society Museum,
Norwalk, OH..............1180

Fireman's Hall Museum, Philadelphia, PA.1279

The First Division Museum at Cantigny,
Wheaton, IL..............465

First Landing State Park, Virginia Beach,
VA 1542

Fitchburg Historical Society, Fitchburg,
MA..............683

The Five Civilized Tribes Museum,
Muskogee, OK..............1205

Florence Hawley Ellis Museum of
Anthropology and Ruth Hall Museum
of Paleontology, Abiquiu, NM..............931

Florida Holocaust Museum, Saint
Petersburg, FL..............341

Floyd County Historical Museum,
Charles City, IA..............510

The Fluvanna County Historical Society
Old Stone Jail Museum, Palmyra, VA...1524

Ford County Historical Society, Paxton,
IL..............450

Ford's Theatre National Historic Site
(Lincoln Museum), Washington, DC 279

Forest Lawn Museum, Glendale, CA 100

Fort Abraham Lincoln State Park,
Mandan, ND 1134

Fort Bliss Museum, Fort Bliss, TX 1413

Fort Bowie National Historic Site,
Bowie, AZ..............30

Fort Buford State Historic Site, Williston,
ND..............1137

Fort Caspar Museum, Casper, WY 1629

Fort Clatsop National Memorial, Astoria,
OR..............1218

Fort Davidson State Historic Site, Pilot
Knob, MO..............828

Fort de Chartres State Historic Site &
Museum, Prairie du Rocher, IL 451

Fort Dix Museum, Fort Dix, NJ 904

Fort Dodge & Frontier Village, Fort
Dodge, IA..............518

Fort Frederick State Park, Big Pool, MD.....637

Fort George G. Meade Museum, Fort
Meade, MD..............643

Fort Hays State Historic Site, Hays, KS 543

Fort Hill (The John C. Calhoun House),
Clemson, SC..............1328

Fort Kearney Museum, Kearney, NE 863

Fort Kearny State Historical Park,
Kearney, NE..............864

Fort Laramie National Historic Site, Fort
Laramie, WY 1633

Fort MacArthur Museum, San Pedro, CA....176

Fort McHenry National Monument and
Historic Shrine, Baltimore, MD..............632

Fort Morris State Historic Site, Midway,
GA..............379

Fort Payne Depot Museum, Fort Payne,
AL..............10

Fort Polk Museum Activity, Fort Polk,
LA..............588

Fort Sam Houston Museum, Fort Sam
Houston, TX..............1415

Fort Sidney Museum & Post
Commander's Home, Sidney, NE............873

Fort Smith Museum of History, Fort
Smith, AR..............58

Fort Ticonderoga, Ticonderoga, NY 1078

Fort Totten State Historic Site, Fort
Totten, ND 1131

Fort Union Trading Post National
Historic Site, Williston, ND 1138

Fort Walla Walla Museum, Walla Walla,
WA..............1576

Fort Washington Park, Fort Washington,
MD..............643

45th Infantry Division Museum,
Oklahoma City, OK..............1207

Fossil Country Museum, Kemmerer, WY..1635

Fosterfields Living Historical Farm,
Morristown, NJ..............913

Foundation For Historic Christ Church,
Inc., Irvington, VA..............1511

Four Rivers Cultural Center & Museum,
Ontario, OR..............1229

Fox Island Historical Society, Fox Island,
WA..............1554

Fox Lake Historical Museum, Inc., Fox
Lake, WI..............1598

Frank Chiarenza Museum of Glass,
Meriden, CT..............248

Frank H. Woods Telephone Museum,
Lincoln, NE..............865

Frankenmuth Historical Museum,
Frankenmuth, MI..............742

Franklin County Historical & Museum
Society & House of History, Malone,
NY..............1012

Franklin County Old Jail Museum,
Winchester, TN..............1385

The Franklin Institute, Philadelphia, PA....1280

Franklin Mineral Museum, Franklin, NJ......904

The Franklin Pierce Homestead,
Hillsborough, NH..............889

Fraternal Order of Alaska State Troopers
Museum, Anchorage, AK..............22

Frederick Douglass National Historic
Site, Washington, DC 279

Frederick Law Olmsted National Historic
Site, Brookline, MA..............671

Free Library of Philadelphia Rare Book
Department, Philadelphia, PA 1280

Freeborn County Museum and Historical
Village, Albert Lea, MN..............767

Freeport Historical Society, Freeport, ME....611

Freestone County Historical Museum,
Fairfield, TX..............1413

Fremont County Pioneer Museum,
Lander, WY..............1635

French Cable Station Museum in Orleans,
Orleans, MA..............701

The French Legation Museum, Austin,
TX..............1390

The Friends of Peace Church, Camp Hill,
PA..............1245

Frisco Historic Park & Museum, Frisco,
CO..............218

Frontier Culture Museum, Staunton, VA....1537

Frontier Museum, Williston, ND..............1138

Frontier Times Museum, Bandera, TX......1393

Frontiers of Flight Museum, Dallas, TX....1406

Fulton County Historical Museum,
Wauseon, OH..............1190

Fulton County Historical Society
Museum, Rochester, IN..............498

Fulton Mansion State Historic Site,
Rockport, TX..............1446

Furnas-Gosper Historical Society &
Museum, Arapahoe, NE..............856

Gadsden Museum of Art, Gadsden, AL 10

Gage County Historical Society and
Museum, Beatrice, NE..............857

Gaineswood, Demopolis, AL 7

Galena-Jo Daviess County Historical
Society & Museum, Galena, IL..............436

Galesburg Civic Art Center, Galesburg,
IL..............437

Galveston County Historical Museum,
Galveston, TX..............1420

Gardiner Art Gallery, Stillwater, OK..........1214

Garibaldi and Meucci Museum, Staten
Island, NY..............1072

Garrett County Historical Museum,
Oakland, MD..............649

Gatekeeper's Museum & Marion
Steinbach Indian Basket Museum,
Tahoe City, CA..............190

General Crook House Museum and
Library/Archives Center, Omaha, NE......870

General Douglas MacArthur Memorial,
Norfolk, VA 1521

General Grant National Memorial, New
York, NY..............1026

General Lew Wallace Study & Museum,
Crawfordsville, IN..............473

Geneva Historical Society &
Prouty-Chew House & Museum,
Geneva, NY..............994

Geographical Center Historical Museum,
Rugby, ND..............1136

The George Bush Presidential Library
and Museum, College Station, TX 1400

George Meany Memorial Archives, Silver
Spring, MD..............654

Georgia Museum of Art, University of
Georgia, Athens, GA..............356

Georgia Music Hall of Fame and
Museum, Macon, GA..............377

Georgia Veterans Memorial Museum,
Cordele, GA..............369

Georgia's Stone Mountain Park, Stone
Mountain, GA..............387

Gerald R. Ford Library, Ann Arbor, MI.......724

Gerald R. Ford Presidential Museum,
Grand Rapids, MI..............743

Germantown Historical Society,
Philadelphia, PA..............1280

Gettysburg National Military Park,
Gettysburg, PA..............1255

Gibbs Museum of Pioneer and Dakotah
Life, Falcon Heights, MN..............775

Gig Harbor Peninsula Historical Society,
Gig Harbor, WA..............1555

Gila County Historical Museum, Globe,
AZ..............35

The Gilbert Stuart Birthplace and
Museum, Saunderstown, RI 1319

Gilcrease Museum, Tulsa, OK 1215

Gillespie County Historical Society,
Fredericksburg, TX..............1419

Gilmore Car Museum, Hickory Corners,
MI..............746

Glacier National Park Museum, West
Glacier, MT..............854

Glencairn Museum: Academy of the New
Church, Bryn Athyn, PA..............1244

Glenn H. Curtiss Museum,
Hammondsport, NY..............997

Glenn L. Martin Maryland Aviation
Museum, Baltimore, MD..............632

Glove Museum, New York, NY..............1026

Gnadenhutten Historical Park & Museum,
Gnadenhutten, OH..............1167

Golden Gate Railroad Museum, San
Francisco, CA..............166

Gomez Foundation for Mill House,
Marlboro, NY..............1014

Goodhue County Historical Society, Red
Wing, MN..............787

Goschenhoppen Folklife Library and
Museum, Green Lane, PA..............1257

Graeme Park, Horsham, PA..............1261

Grand Canyon National Park Museum
Collection, Grand Canyon National
Park, AZ..............36

Grand Encampment Museum, Inc.,
Encampment, WY..............1632

Grand Forks County Historical Society,
Grand Forks, ND..............1132

Grand Teton National Park, Colter Bay
Indian Arts Museum, Colter Bay
Village, WY..............1631

Grand Traverse Heritage Center, Traverse
City, MI..............765

Grant County Museum, Medford, OK..........1205

Grant-Kohrs Ranch National Historic
   Site, Deer Lodge, MT 845
Granville County Historical Society
   Museum, Oxford, NC 1114
Graves Museum of Archaeology and
   Natural History, Dania Beach, FL 302
Gravette Historical Museum, Gravette,
   AR 59
Great Plains Transportation Museum,
   Wichita, KS 561
Great Smoky Mountains Heritage Center,
   Townsend, TN 1384
Greater Loveland Historical Society
   Museum, Loveland, OH 1173
Greeley History Museum, Greeley, CO 221
Greensboro Historical Museum, Inc.,
   Greensboro, NC 1103
Grout Museum District: Grout Museum
   of History and Science, Bluedorn
   Science Imaginarium, Rensselaer
   Russell House Museum, Snowden
   House, Waterloo, IA 529
Gwinnett History Museum,
   Lawrenceville, GA 376

H.G. Albee Memorial Museum,
   Estherville, IA 517
Hacienda Buena Vista, Ponce, PR 1642
Hackettstown Historical Society Museum
   & Library, Hackettstown, NJ 905
Haffenreffer Museum of Anthropology,
   Brown University, Bristol, RI 1310
The Hagley Museum and Library,
   Wilmington, DE 273
Haines Museum, Waukegan Historical
   Society, Waukegan, IL 463
The Hall of Fame for Great Americans,
   Bronx, NY 966
Hall of Flame Museum of Firefighting,
   Phoenix, AZ 40
Hammond Museum and Japanese Stroll
   Garden, North Salem, NY 1043
Hammond Museum of Bells, Eureka
   Springs, AR 57
Hampton History Museum, Hampton, VA .1509
Hampton National Historic Site, Towson,
   MD 655
Hanby House, Westerville, OH 1191
Hancock Historical Society, Hancock,
   NH 888
Hancock House, Hancock's Bridge, NJ 907
Hancock Memorial Museum, Los
   Angeles, CA 116
The Handweaving Museum & Arts
   Center, Clayton, NY 978
Hannah Lindahl Children's Museum,
   Mishawaka, IN 491
Hanover House, Clemson, SC 1328
Hans Christian Andersen Museum,
   Solvang, CA 187
Harbour House Museum, Crystal Falls,
   MI 733
Hardin County Historical Museums, Inc.,
   Kenton, OH 1170
The Harness Racing Museum and Hall of
   Fame, Goshen, NY 995
Harney County Historical Museum,
   Burns, OR 1221
Harold M. Freund American Museum of
   Baking, Manhattan, KS 550
Harper City Historical Society, Harper,
   KS 543
Harpers Ferry Center, Harpers Ferry, WV .1582
Harpers Ferry National Historical Park,
   Harpers Ferry, WV 1582
Harriet Beecher Stowe Center, Hartford,
   CT 245
Harrison County Historical Museum,
   Marshall, TX 1436
Harry Ransom Center at the University
   of Texas at Austin, Austin, TX 1390
Harry S. Truman Library-Museum,
   Independence, MO 818

Hartsville Museum, Hartsville, SC 1335
Harvard Historical Society, Still River,
   MA 711
Harvey County Historical Society,
   Newton, KS 553
Harvey Cushing/John Hay Whitney
   Medical Library, New Haven, CT 253
Hattiesburg Area Historical Society and
   HAHS Museum, Hattiesburg, MS 801
Hatton-Eielson Museum & Historical
   Association, Hatton, ND 1132
Hawaii Maritime Center, Honolulu, HI 395
Hayward Area Historical Society,
   Hayward, CA 102
Hearthstone Historic House Museum,
   Appleton, WI 1589
The Hemingway Museum and The Ernest
   Hemingway Birthplace, Oak Park, IL 448
Hennepin History Museum, Minneapolis,
   MN 782
The Henry Ford, Dearborn, MI 733
The Henry Sheldon Museum of Vermont
   History, Middlebury, VT 1481
Herbert Hoover Presidential
   Library-Museum, West Branch, IA 530
The Heritage Center, Pine Ridge, SD 1354
Heritage Center of Lancaster County,
   Inc., Lancaster, PA 1265
Heritage-Hjemkomst Interpretive Center,
   Moorhead, MN 784
Heritage House Museum of Montgomery
   County, Mount Ida, AR 64
Heritage Library Museum, Anchorage,
   AK 22
The Heritage Museum, Baltimore, MD 632
The Heritage Museum & Underhill
   Museum, Idaho Springs, CO 223
The Heritage Museum at Falfurrias, Inc.,
   Falfurrias, TX 1413
Heritage Museum of Northwest Florida,
   Valparaiso, FL 352
Heritage of the Americas Museum, El
   Cajon, CA 92
The Heritage Society, Houston, TX 1426
Heritage Square Museum, Los Angeles,
   CA 116
Heritage Station, Umatilla County
   Historical Society Museum, Pendleton,
   OR 1230
Heritage Village, Largo, FL 321
Heritage Village, Mountain Lake, MN 785
The Hermitage Foundation, Norfolk, VA ...1521
Hershey Museum, Hershey, PA 1261
The Hickories Museum of the Lorain
   County Historical Society, Elyria, OH ..1163
Hickory Grove Rural School Museum,
   Ogden, IA 525
The Higgins Museum, Okoboji, IA 525
High Cliff Historical Society & General
   Store Museum, Sherwood, WI 1622
The High Museum of Art, Atlanta, GA 360
Highland County Museum and Heritage
   Center, McDowell, VA 1517
Highland Park Historical Society,
   Highland Park, IL 439
Highlands Museum & Discovery Center,
   Ashland, KY 564
The Hill Country Museum, Kerrville, TX ..1431
Hillsboro Area Historical Society,
   Hillsboro, WI 1600
Hillsboro Museums, Hillsboro, KS 544
Hillwood Art Museum, Brookville, NY 971
Historic Bowens Mills & Pioneer Park,
   Middleville, MI 754
Historic Burlington County Prison
   Museum, Mount Holly, NJ 914
Historic Charlton Park Village and
   Museum, Hastings, MI 745
Historic Columbia Foundation, Columbia,
   SC 1329
Historic Fort Snelling, Saint Paul, MN 790

Historic General Dodge House, Council
   Bluffs, IA 512
Historic Hermann Museum, Hermann,
   MO 817
Historic Langhorne Association,
   Langhorne, PA 1267
Historic Lincoln, Lincoln, NM 941
Historic Nashville, Inc., Nashville, TN 1379
The Historic New Orleans Collection,
   New Orleans, LA 595
Historic Northampton, Northampton, MA....699
Historic Oakland Cemetery, Atlanta, GA 360
Historic Palmyra's Print Shop, Palmyra,
   NY 1050
Historic Palmyra's - Wm. Phelps General
   Store, Palmyra, NY 1050
Historic Pensacola Village, Pensacola, FL ...335
Historic Price House, Woodruff, SC 1343
Historic Richmond Town, Staten Island,
   NY 1072
Historic Schaefferstown, Inc.,
   Schaefferstown, PA 1297
Historic Warrior Run Church,
   Watsontown, PA 1306
Historical and Genealogical Society of
   Indiana County, Indiana, PA 1262
Historical Center for Southeast New
   Mexico, Roswell, NM 946
Historical Museum at Fort Missoula,
   Missoula, MT 851
Historical Museum of Bay County, Bay
   City, MI 727
Historical Museum of Southern Florida,
   Miami, FL 324
Historical Society of Brookfield,
   Brookfield Center, VT 1477
Historical Society of Cecil County,
   Elkton, MD 643
Historical Society of Cheshire County,
   Keene, NH 890
Historical Society of Delaware,
   Wilmington, DE 274
Historical Society of Fort Washington,
   Fort Washington, PA 1254
The Historical Society of Frederick
   County, Inc., Frederick, MD 644
Historical Society of Glastonbury,
   Glastonbury, CT 242
Historical Society of Millersburg &
   Upper Paxton Township Museum,
   Millersburg, PA 1272
Historical Society of Oak Park & River
   Forest, Oak Park, IL 448
Historical Society of Old Newbury,
   Cushing House Museum,
   Newburyport, MA 698
Historical Society of Palm Beach County,
   Palm Beach, FL 334
Historical Society of Pennsylvania,
   Philadelphia, PA 1281
Historical Society of Quaker Hill &
   Pawling, Pawling, NY 1051
Historical Society of Rockland County,
   New City, NY 1017
Historical Society of Saratoga Springs,
   Saratoga Springs, NY 1064
Historical Society of Talbot County,
   Easton, MD 642
Historical Society of the Cocalico Valley,
   Ephrata, PA 1252
Historical Society of the Town of
   Clarence, Clarence, NY 978
Historical Society of the Town of
   Greenwich Inc. aka Bush-Holley
   Historic Site, Cos Cob, CT 237
The History Center, Fort Wayne, IN 477
The History Center, Cedar Rapids, IA 509
The History Center in Tompkins County,
   Ithaca, NY 1003
History Museum for Springfield-Greene
   County, Springfield, MO 839
History Museum of Western Virginia,
   Roanoke, VA 1535

Communication Artifacts–Continued

History of Medicine Collections, Durham, NC.............1098

Hiwan Homestead Museum, Evergreen, CO.............215

Hoard Historical Museum and National Dairy Shrine's Visitors Center, Fort Atkinson, WI.............1598

The Holland Land Office Museum, Batavia, NY.............960

Holly History Center & Hutchinson House Museum, Waupaca, WI.............1626

Hollywood Heritage Museum, Hollywood, CA.............103

Holocaust Museum Houston, Houston, TX.............1426

Holy Trinity (Old Swedes) Church & Hendrickson House Museum, Wilmington, DE.............274

Homestead National Monument of America, Beatrice, NE.............857

Honolulu Police Department Law Enforcement Museum, Honolulu, HI.............396

Hood Museum of Art, Hanover, NH.............888

Hoover Historical Center, North Canton, OH.............1179

Hopewell Museum, Paris, KY.............582

Horatio Colony House Museum & Nature Preserve, Keene, NH.............890

Horseshoe Bend National Military Park, Daviston, AL.............7

Hot Spring County Museum - The Boyle House/1876 Log Cabin, Malvern, AR.......63

Hot Springs National Park Visitor Center, Hot Springs, AR.............60

Hotel de Paris Museum, Georgetown, CO...219

House of Broadcasting Radio & Television Museum, Scottsdale, AZ.........44

House of the Temple, Washington, DC.......280

House of Wickersham State Historical Site, Juneau, AK.............25

Howard University Museum, Moorland Spingarn Research Center, Washington, DC.............281

Hubbardton Battlefield Museum, Hubbardton, VT.............1480

Hubbell Trading Post National Historic Site, Ganado, AZ.............34

Hudson Library and Historical Society, Hudson, OH.............1168

The Hudson River Museum, Yonkers, NY.1087

Hui No'eau Visual Arts Center, Makawao, Maui, HI.............401

Hulihee Palace, Kailua-Kona, HI.............399

Hull Lifesaving Museum Inc., the Museum of Boston Harbor Heritage, Hull, MA.............687

Huntington Beach International Surfing Museum, Huntington Beach, CA.............104

Huntington County Historical Society Museum, Huntington, IN.............481

Huntington Library, Art Collections, and Botanical Gardens, San Marino, CA.......174

Huntington Sewing & Trade School, Huntington, NY.............1001

Hurst Ranch Historical Foundation, West Covina, CA.............197

Hutchinson Art Center, Hutchinson, KS.......545

The Hyde Collection, Glens Falls, NY.......994

Hyde Hall, Inc., Cooperstown, NY.............980

IMF Center, Washington, DC.............281

Idaho Military History Museum, Boise, ID.............404

Illinois and Michigan Canal Commissioners Office Museum, Lockport, IL.............443

Ilwaco Heritage Museum, Ilwaco, WA.......1556

IMA - Indianapolis Museum of Art, Indianapolis, IN.............483

The Imaginarium Science Discovery Center, Anchorage, AK.............22

Independence Historical Museum, Independence, KS.............545

Independence National Historical Park, Philadelphia, PA.............1281

Independence Seaport Museum, Philadelphia, PA.............1281

Indian City U.S.A., Anadarko, OK.............1195

Indian King Tavern Museum, Haddonfield, NJ.............906

Indian Pueblo Cultural Center, Albuquerque, NM.............933

Indiana Dunes National Lakeshore, Porter, IN.............496

Indiana Historical Society, Indianapolis, IN.............483

Indiana War Memorials, Indianapolis, IN....484

The Institute For American Indian Studies (IAIS), Washington Green, CT...263

The Interchurch Center, New York, NY.....1027

International Bluegrass Music Museum, Owensboro, KY.............581

International Bowling Museum and Hall of Fame, Saint Louis, MO.............833

International Motor Racing Research Center at Watkins Glen, Watkins Glen, NY.............1084

The International Printing Museum, Carson, CA.............82

International Spy Museum, Washington, DC.............281

International Tennis Hall of Fame & Museum, Newport, RI.............1313

Intrepid Sea-Air-Space Museum, New York, NY.............1028

Iolani Palace, Honolulu, HI.............396

Iosco County Historical Museum, East Tawas, MI.............740

Iowa Masonic Library and Museum, Cedar Rapids, IA.............509

Iraan Museum, Iraan, TX.............1430

Iredell Museum of Arts & Heritage, Statesville, NC.............1120

Irish American Heritage Museum, Albany, NY.............954

Iron County Museum, Caspian, MI.............731

Iron Mission State Park & Museum, Cedar City, UT.............1464

Ironwood Area Historical Museum, Ironwood, MI.............747

Isabel Miller Museum/Sitka Historical Society, Sitka, AK.............27

Isanti County Historical Society, Cambridge, MN.............770

Isla Center For the Arts at the University of Guam, Mangilao, GU.............1640

Island County Historical Society Museum, Coupeville, WA.............1551

Islesboro Historical Society, Islesboro, ME.............612

Islesford Historical Museum, Islesford, ME.............612

Issaquah History Museum, Issaquah, WA..1557

Italian American Museum, New York, NY.............1028

Itasca County Historical Society, Grand Rapids, MN.............777

JFK Special Warfare Museum, Fort Bragg, NC.............1101

J.J. Jackson Memorial Museum, Weaverville, CA.............197

J.W. Parmley Historical Home Society, Ipswich, SD.............1349

Jackson County Historical Museum, Lakefield, MN.............778

Jackson County Historical Museum & Research Library, Maquoketa, IA.............522

Jacob Hamblin Home, Santa Clara, UT.....1474

Jacqueline Casey Hudgens Center for the Arts, Duluth, GA.............371

Jacques Marchais Museum of Tibetan Art, Staten Island, NY.............1072

Jail Museum, Neligh, NE.............869

James K. Polk Ancestral Home, Columbia, TN.............1364

The James Madison Museum, Orange, VA.............1524

Jane L. and Robert H. Weiner Judaic Museum, Rockville, MD.............651

Jane Voorhees Zimmerli Art Museum, New Brunswick, NJ.............915

Japanese American National Museum, Los Angeles, CA.............117

Japanese Cultural Center of Hawaii, Honolulu, HI.............397

Jean Lafitte National Historical Park & Preserve, New Orleans, LA.............596

Jean P. Haydon Museum, Pago Pago, AS..1640

Jefferson Barracks Historic Site, Saint Louis, MO.............833

The Jefferson County Historical Assoc., Steubenville, OH.............1186

Jefferson County Historical Society and Farnsworth TV Pioneer Museum, Rigby, ID.............409

Jefferson National Expansion Memorial, Saint Louis, MO.............833

Jemez State Monument, Jemez Springs, NM.............940

Jersey City Museum, Jersey City, NJ.............908

The Jewish Museum, New York, NY.........1029

Jewish Museum of Florida, Miami Beach, FL.............326

Jewish Museum of Maryland, Baltimore, MD.............633

Jim Crow Museum - Ferris State University, Big Rapids, MI.............729

The Jimmy Stewart Museum, Indiana, PA.1262

John E. Conner Museum, Kingsville, TX..1432

John F. Kennedy Presidential Library & Museum, Boston, MA.............666

John G. Neihardt State Historic Site, Bancroft, NE.............856

John James Audubon Center at Mill Grove, Audubon, PA.............1241

John James Audubon Museum, Henderson, KY.............571

John Jay Homestead State Historic Site, Katonah, NY.............1006

The John Nicholas Brown Center for the Study of American Civilization, Providence, RI.............1317

John Paul Jones House Museum, Portsmouth, NH.............894

John Rivers Communications Museum, Charleston, SC.............1325

John Wornall House Museum, Kansas City, MO.............821

Johnny Appleseed Society Museum, Urbana, OH.............1189

Johnson County Historical Society, Coralville, IA.............511

Johnson County Historical Society Museum, Warrensburg, MO.............840

Johnson County Museum of History, Franklin, IN.............478

Johnson County Museums, Shawnee, KS....558

Johnson Ferry House Museum, Titusville, NJ.............926

Johnson-Humrickhouse Museum, Coshocton, OH.............1159

Johnson Victrola Museum, Dover, DE.........270

Johnstown Area Heritage Association, Johnstown, PA.............1263

Johnstown Historical Society, Johnstown, NY.............1005

Judah L. Magnes Museum, Berkeley, CA......76

Judaica Museum of Central Synagogue, New York, NY.............1029

Judy Garland Museum, Grand Rapids, MN.............777

Julia A. Purnell Museum, Snow Hill, MD...654

Julian H. Sleeper House, Saint Paul, MN 790

Juliette Gordon Low Birthplace, Savannah, GA.............385

Junction City Historical Society, Junction City, OR 1226
Juneau-Douglas City Museum, Juneau, AK 26
Juniata College Museum of Art, Huntingdon, PA 1262

Kalamazoo Valley Museum, Kalamazoo, MI 749
Kanabec History Center, Mora, MN 784
Kankakee County Museum, Kankakee, IL ... 441
Karpeles Manuscript Library Museum, Duluth, MN 773
The Kate Chopin House & Bayou Folk Museum, Cloutierville, LA 588
Kell House Museum, Wichita Falls, TX 1461
Kellogg's Cereal City USA, Battle Creek, MI 727
Kelsey Museum of Archaeology, Ann Arbor, MI 724
Kelton House Museum & Garden, Columbus, OH 1158
Kennebunkport Historical Society, Kennebunkport, ME 612
Kennedy Museum of Art, Athens, OH 1140
Kenosha County Historical Society and Museum, Inc., Kenosha, WI 1602
Kentucky Derby Museum, Louisville, KY ... 576
Kentucky Gateway Museum Center, Maysville, KY 579
Kentucky Historical Society, Frankfort, KY 569
Kentucky Military History Museum, Frankfort, KY 569
Kentucky Railway Museum, Inc., New Haven, KY 580
Ker Place, Onancock, VA 1523
Kerbyville Museum, Kerby, OR 1227
Keweenaw County Historical Society, Eagle Harbor, MI 739
Key West Museum of Art and History, Key West, FL 318
Keyport Historical Society-Steamboat Dock Museum, Keyport, NJ 909
Kidspace Children's Museum, Pasadena, CA 140
Kimball House Museum, Battle Creek, MI 727
Kirtland Temple Historic Center, Kirtland, OH 1170
Kitsap County Historical Society Museum, Bremerton, WA 1549
Klamath County Museum, Klamath Falls, OR 1227
Klickitat County Historical Society, Goldendale, WA 1555
Klondike Gold Rush National Historical Park, Skagway, AK 28
Klondike Gold Rush National Historical Park, Seattle, WA 1566
Knife River Indian Villages National Historic Site, Stanton, ND 1136
Knight Museum, Alliance, NE 855
Knights of Columbus Museum, New Haven, CT 253
Knott House Museum, Tallahassee, FL 347
Knox County Museum, Benjamin, TX 1395
Kolomoki Mounds State Park Museum, Blakely, GA 366
Koreshan State Historic Site, Estero, FL ... 306
Krannert Art Museum and Kinkead Pavilion, Champaign, IL 416

La Casa Del Libro, San Juan, PR 1642
La Raza/Galeria Posada, Sacramento, CA ... 153
Lac Qui Parle County Historical Society, Madison, MN 779
The Lace Museum, Sunnyvale, CA 190
Lacey Historical Society, Forked River, NJ 904
The Lackawanna Historical Society at the Catlin House, Scranton, PA 1298
Lafayette Miners Museum, Lafayette, CO ... 224

Lagrange County Historical Society, Inc., Lagrange, IN 488
Lake County Discovery Museum, Wauconda, IL 463
Lake County Historic Courthouse Museum, Lakeport, CA 108
Lake County Historical Society, Two Harbors, MN 794
Lake County Historical Society, Kirtland Hills, OH 1170
Lake Forest-Lake Bluff Historical Society, Lake Forest, IL 441
Lake Hopatcong Historical Museum, Landing, NJ 909
Lake Jackson Historical Museum, Lake Jackson, TX 1433
Lake Mead National Recreation Area, Boulder City, NV 875
Lake Perris Regional Indian Museum (Home of the Wind), Perris, CA 141
Lake Shore Railway Museum, North East, PA 1274
Lake Wales Depot Museum & Cultural Center, Lake Wales, FL 320
Lamar Dodd Art Center, LaGrange College, LaGrange, GA 375
Lancaster County Historical Society, Lancaster, PA 1266
Lane County Historical Society & Museum, Eugene, OR 1223
Langlade County Historical Society Museum, Antigo, WI 1589
Latvian Museum, Rockville, MD 651
Lauder Museum - Amityville Historical Society, Amityville, NY 957
Laura Ingalls Wilder Museum and Tourist Center, Walnut Grove, MN 795
Laura Ingalls Wilder-Rose Wilder Lane Historic Home & Museum, Mansfield, MO 827
The Laurel Museum, Laurel, MD 648
Laurence C. Jones Museum, Piney Woods, MS 807
Layland Museum, Cleburne, TX 1400
Le Sueur Museum, Le Sueur, MN 779
Lea County Cowboy Hall of Fame and Western Heritage Center, Hobbs, NM 940
The Lebanon County Historical Society, Lebanon, PA 1268
Lefferts Historic House, Brooklyn, NY 969
Lehigh County Historical Society, Allentown, PA 1239
Lentz Center for Asian Culture, Lincoln, NE 865
Lesbian Herstory Educational Foundation, Inc. aka Lesbian Herstory Archives, Brooklyn, NY 969
Lesueur County Historical Museum-Chapter 1, Elysian, MN 774
Levere Memorial Temple, Evanston, IL 434
Levine Museum of the New South, Charlotte, NC 1095
Lewes Historical Society, Lewes, DE 271
Liberace Museum & Foundation, Las Vegas, NV 879
Liberty Hall Historic Center, Lamoni, IA ... 522
Library of the Supreme Council, 33 Degrees, Washington, DC 282
Licking County Historical Society, Newark, OH 1178
Limberlost State Historic Site, Geneva, IN 479
Lincoln County Historical Society, North Platte, NE 869
Lincoln County Pioneer Museum, Hendricks, MN 778
The Lincoln Museum, Fort Wayne, IN 478
Lincoln Park Historical Museum, Lincoln Park, MI 751
Lincoln Tomb State Historic Site, Springfield, IL 459
Lincoln's New Salem State Historic Site, Petersburg, IL 451

The Lion and Lamb Peace Arts Center, Bluffton, OH 1143
Lisbon Historical Society, Lisbon, OH 1172
Lisle Station Museum, Lisle, IL 443
Litchfield Historical Society and Museum, Litchfield, CT 247
The Lithuanian Museum, Chicago, IL 423
Little Bighorn Battlefield National Monument, Crow Agency, MT 844
Little White House Historic Site, Warm Springs, GA 390
Little White Schoolhouse, Ripon, WI 1620
The Living Word National Bible Museum, Aledo, TX 1386
Livingston County Historical Society Museum, Geneseo, NY 993
Livingston Depot Center, Livingston, MT ... 850
Locust Lawn and Terwilliger House, Gardiner, NY 993
Log Cabin Village, Fort Worth, TX 1417
The Log House Museum of the Historical Society of Columbiana-Fairfield Township, Columbiana, OH 1157
Logan County Historical Society Museum, Bellefontaine, OH 1142
Logoly State Park, McNeil, AR 64
Lois E. Woods Museum, Norfolk, VA 1522
Lombard Historical Museum, Lombard, IL 443
Long Island Museum of American Art, History & Carriages, Stony Brook, NY 1075
Longfellow National Historic Site, Cambridge, MA 673
Longhorn Museum, Pleasanton, TX 1444
Longmont Museum, Longmont, CO 227
Longwood Gardens, Kennett Square, PA ... 1264
Longyear Museum, Chestnut Hill, MA 675
Lopez Island Historical Museum, Lopez Island, WA 1558
Los Altos History Museum aka Association of the Los Altos Historical Museum, Los Altos, CA 112
Los Angeles County Museum of Art, Los Angeles, CA 118
Los Angeles Museum of the Holocaust, Los Angeles, CA 118
Louisiana's Old State Capitol, Political History Museum, Baton Rouge, LA 587
Loveland Museum Gallery, Loveland, CO ... 227
Lovely Lane Museum, Baltimore, MD 634
Lowell Area Historical Museum, Lowell, MI 751
Lowell National Historical Park, Lowell, MA 691
Lower East Side Tenement Museum, New York, NY 1029
Lower Hudson Conference of Historical Agencies and Museums, Elmsford, NY 988
Loyola University Museum of Art, Chicago, IL 423
Lubeznik Center for the Arts, Michigan City, IN 490
Luckhard Museum - The Indian Mission, Sebewaing, MI 764
Lutz Children's Museum, Manchester, CT ... 248
Luzerne County Historical Society, Wilkes-Barre, PA 1307
The Lyceum, Alexandria's History Museum, Alexandria, VA 1493
Lyndon Baines Johnson Library and Museum, Austin, TX 1391
Lynn Museum & Historical Society, Lynn, MA 692
Lyon County Historical Society and Museum, Emporia, KS 538
Lyon County Historical Society Museum, Marshall, MN 780

Mabry-Hazen House, Knoxville, TN 1371
Macculloch Hall Historical Museum & Gardens, Morristown, NJ 913

Communication Artifacts–Continued

Mackinac State Historic Parks-Colonial Michilimackinac & Old Mackinac Point Lighthouse, Mackinaw City, MI 752

Mackinac State Historic Parks-Fort Mackinac & Mackinac Island State Park, Mackinac Island, MI......752

Madeline Island Historical Museum, La Pointe, WI......1603

Maggie L. Walker National Historic Site, Richmond, VA......1530

The Magic Lantern Castle Museum, San Antonio, TX......1448

Maine Historical Society, Portland, ME......619

Mamie Doud Eisenhower Birthplace, Boone, IA......506

Manassas Museum System, Manassas, VA......1516

Manassas National Battlefield Park, Manassas, VA......1516

Manchester Historic Association Millyard Museum, Manchester, NH......891

Manship House Museum, Jackson, MS......802

The Margaret Mitchell House & Museum, Atlanta, GA......361

Marias Museum of History and Art, Shelby, MT......853

Maridon Museum, Butler, PA......1245

Marin Museum of the American Indian, Novato, CA......131

The Mariners' Museum, Newport News, VA......1519

Marion County Historical Society, Salem, OR......1236

The Marion County Historical Society Museum, Marion, OH......1174

Marion Public Library Museum, Marion, IN......490

Mariposa Museum and History Center Inc., Mariposa, CA......124

Maritime Museum at Historic Coast Guard Station, Saint Simons Island, GA......383

Mark Twain Birthplace State Historic Site, Florida, MO......815

Marland's Grand Home, Ponca City, OK...1212

Marshall County Historical Museum, Plymouth, IN......496

Marshall County Historical Museum, Holly Springs, MS......801

Marshall County Historical Society Museum, Warren, MN......795

Marshall Gold Discovery State Historic Park, Coloma, CA......86

Martin County Historical Museum, Stanton, TX......1453

Marvin Newton House, Brookfield, VT......1477

Marvin Samson Center for History of Pharmacy/USP Museum, Philadelphia, PA......1283

The Mary Baker Eddy Library for the Betterment of Humanity, Boston, MA.....666

Mary McLeod Bethune Council House National Historic Site, Washington, DC......283

Maryland Historical Society, Baltimore, MD......634

Marywood University Art Galleries (Suraci Gallery and Mahady Gallery), Scranton, PA......1298

The Masonic Library and Museum of Pennsylvania, Philadelphia, PA......1283

Massachusetts Historical Society, Boston, MA......667

Mattapoisett Museum and Carriage House, Mattapoisett, MA......693

The Mattatuck Museum Arts and History Center, Waterbury, CT......264

Matthews Museum of Maine Heritage, Union, ME......624

Maturango Museum of the Indian Wells Valley, Ridgecrest, CA......148

Maxwell Museum of Anthropology, Albuquerque, NM......934

May Museum & Farmville Heritage Center, Farmville, NC......1100

Mayborn Museum Complex, Waco, TX......1459

Mayville Historical Society, Inc., Mayville, WI......1608

McCallum Museum, Sibley, IA......527

McConaghy House, Hayward, CA......102

McCone County Museum, Circle, MT......844

McConnell Mansion, Moscow, ID......407

McCutchen Overland Inn, McCutchenville, OH......1175

McHenry County Historical Society and Museum, Union, IL......461

McIntosh County Historical Society, Ashley, ND......1127

McLarty Treasure Museum, Vero Beach, FL......352

McLean County Historical Society Museum, Washburn, ND......1137

McLean County Museum of History, Bloomington, IL......414

McNamara House Museum, Victoria, TX..1457

McWethy Hall, Luce Gallery, Cornell College, Mount Vernon, IA......524

Meadowlands Museum, Rutherford, NJ......923

Meadows Museum, Dallas, TX......1407

Meagher County Historical Association Castle Museum, White Sulphur Springs, MT......855

Mechanicsburg Museum Association, Mechanicsburg, PA......1270

Mecosta County Historical Museum, Big Rapids, MI......729

Meeker County Historical Society Museum & G.A.R. Hall, Litchfield, MN......779

Mel Fisher Maritime Heritage Society, Key West, FL......318

The Memorial Day Museum, Waterloo, NY......1083

Mennonite Heritage Museum, Goessel, KS......542

Mennonite Library and Archives, North Newton, KS......554

Menominee County Heritage Museum, Menominee, MI......754

Merced County Courthouse Museum, Merced, CA......125

Mercer County Historical Museum, The Riley Home, Celina, OH......1146

Mercer County Historical Society, Mercer, PA......1271

Mesa Historical Museum, Mesa, AZ......37

Meux Home Museum, Fresno, CA......98

Michael C. Carlos Museum, Atlanta, GA...361

Michelson Museum of Art, Marshall, TX..1436

Michigan Maritime Museum, South Haven, MI......764

Mid-Atlantic Center for the Arts/Emlen Physick Estate/Cape May Lighthouse, Cape May, NJ......900

Mid-Continent Railway Museum, North Freedom, WI......1615

Middleborough Historical Association, Inc., Middleborough, MA......694

Middlebury Historical Society, Wyoming, NY......1087

Middlesex County Historical Society, Middletown, CT......249

Mighty Eighth Air Force Museum, Pooler, GA......381

Mildred Lane Kemper Art Museum, Saint Louis, MO......834

Military Museum of Southern New England, Danbury, CT......238

Mill Race Historical Village, Northville, MI......758

Millard Fillmore House, East Aurora, NY...985

Milton Historical Museum, Milton, VT......1482

Milton House Museum Historic Site, Milton, WI......1610

Milwaukee County Historical Society, Milwaukee, WI......1611

Milwaukee Public Museum, Milwaukee, WI......1612

Mingei International Museum, San Diego, CA......157

Minnesota Historical Society, Saint Paul, MN......791

Miracle of America Museum Inc., Polson, MT......852

Mission Mill Museum Association, Salem, OR......1236

Mission Nuestra Senora de la Soledad, Soledad, CA......187

Mission San Antonio de Padua, Jolon, CA......105

Mission San Diego de Alcala, San Diego, CA......157

Mission San Juan Capistrano Museum, San Juan Capistrano, CA......173

Mission San Luis Rey Museum, Oceanside, CA......135

Mission San Miguel, San Miguel, CA......175

Mission San Rafael Arcangel, San Rafael, CA......177

Missisquoi Valley Historical Society, North Troy, VT......1483

Mississippi Armed Forces Museum, Camp Shelby, MS......799

Mississippi Baptist Historical Commission, Clinton, MS......799

Mississippi County Historical Society, Charleston, MO......812

Mississippi River Museum at Mud Island River Park, Memphis, TN......1375

Missouri Historical Society, Saint Louis, MO......835

Missouri State Museum, Jefferson City, MO......819

The Mitchell Museum of the American Indian, Evanston, IL......435

Mizel Museum, Denver, CO......213

Mohave Museum of History and Arts, Kingman, AZ......36

Monmouth Museum & Cultural Center, Lincroft, NJ......909

Monroe County Historical Museum, Monroe, MI......756

Monroe County Local History Room & Library, Sparta, WI......1622

Montana Museum of Art and Culture, Missoula, MT......852

Montauk, Clermont, IA......511

The Montgomery County Historical Society, Dayton, OH......1161

Montville Township Historical Museum, Montville, NJ......912

Moody County Museum, Flandreau, SD....1347

Moore County Historical Museum, Dumas, TX......1410

Moravian Historical Society, Nazareth, PA......1273

Moravian Museum of Bethlehem, Inc., Bethlehem, PA......1242

Morgan Row Museum and Harrodsburg-Mercer County Research Library, Harrodsburg, KY......570

Mormon Station State Historic Park, Genoa, NV......877

Morris-Jumel Mansion, New York, NY.....1030

Morristown National Historical Park, Morristown, NJ......914

Morton Museum of Cooke County, Gainesville, TX......1420

Motorcycle Hall of Fame Museum, Pickerington, OH......1182

Motown Historical Museum, Detroit, MI....737

Mount Desert Island Historical Society, Mount Desert, ME......615

Mount Holly Community Historical Museum, Belmont, VT......1476

Mount Prospect Historical Society Museums, Mount Prospect, IL................446
Mount Vernon Hotel Museum & Garden, New York, NY.................................1031
Mount Vernon Ladies' Association, Mount Vernon, VA.................................1518
Mount Washington Museum and The Weather Discovery Center, North Conway, NH...893
Mountain Gateway Museum, Old Fort, NC...1113
The Movie Museum, Owosso, MI................759
Murfreesboro Historical Association, Murfreesboro, NC...................................1112
Muscatine History & Industry Center/Pearl Button Museum, Muscatine, IA...524
Museo de Las Americas, San Juan, PR......1642
Museum at Southwestern Michigan College, Dowagiac, MI............................738
The Museum at Warm Springs, Warm Springs, OR...1238
The Museum of African Culture, Portland, ME...619
Museum of American Finance, New York, NY...1031
The Museum of American Illustration at the Society of Illustrators, New York, NY..1031
Museum of American Political Life, West Hartford, CT......................................265
Museum of American Presidents, Strasburg, VA......................................1539
Museum of Ancient & Modern Art, Penn Valley, CA..141
Museum of Ancient Artifacts, Las Vegas, NV..879
Museum of Anthropology, Chico, CA...........83
Museum of Anthropology, University of Missouri, Columbia, MO............................813
Museum of Appalachia, Clinton, TN..........1363
Museum of Art and History at the McPherson Center, Santa Cruz, CA........182
Museum of Art/Fort Lauderdale, Fort Lauderdale, FL......................................307
Museum of Astrogeology, Meteor Crater, Winslow, AZ..53
Museum of Ceramics, East Liverpool, OH...1163
Museum of Chinese in the Americas, New York, NY...1032
Museum of Church History and Art, Salt Lake City, UT......................................1471
Museum of Connecticut History, Hartford, CT......................................245
Museum of Cultural & Natural History, Mount Pleasant, MI................................757
Museum of Design Atlanta, Atlanta, GA.....362
Museum of disAbility History, Williamsville, NY...................................1086
Museum of Discovery: Arkansas Museum of Science and History, Little Rock, AR..62
The Museum of Early Trades and Crafts, Madison, NJ...910
The Museum of Flight, Seattle, WA...........1567
Museum of Florida History, Tallahassee, FL..348
Museum of Funeral Customs, Springfield, IL...459
Museum of History & Art, Ontario, Ontario, CA..136
Museum of Indian Culture, Allentown, PA..1239
Museum of International Folk Art, Santa Fe, NM..948
Museum of Jewish Heritage-A Living Memorial to the Holocaust, New York, NY..1032
Museum of Lifestyle & Fashion History, Delray Beach, FL......................................305
The Museum of Mobile, Mobile, AL.............14
Museum of Neon Art, Los Angeles, CA......120

Museum of New Mexico, Santa Fe, NM.....949
Museum of Northern Arizona, Flagstaff, AZ..33
The Museum of Nursing History, Inc., Philadelphia, PA.....................................1283
Museum of Primitive Art and Culture, Peace Dale, RI...1316
The Museum of Printing History, Houston, TX...1428
Museum of Radio & Technology, Inc., Huntington, WV.....................................1583
Museum of Religious Arts, Logan, IA.........522
Museum of Robotics, Orinda, CA...............136
Museum of Science & History of Jacksonville, Jacksonville, FL.................315
Museum of Science and Industry, Chicago, IL...425
Museum of Seminole County History, Sanford, FL...343
The Museum of Television & Radio, Beverly Hills, CA...78
The Museum of the Alphabet, Waxhaw, NC..1121
Museum of the Cherokee Indian, Cherokee, NC.......................................1096
Museum of the Cherokee Strip, Enid, OK.1200
Museum of the City of Lake Worth, Lake Worth, FL..320
Museum of the City of New York, New York, NY...1033
The Museum of the Confederacy, Richmond, VA......................................1531
Museum of the Fur Trade, Chadron, NE......859
Museum of the Jimmy Carter Library, Atlanta, GA...362
Museum of the Llano Estacado, Plainview, TX...1443
Museum of the Mountain Man, Pinedale, WY...1637
Museum of the Moving Image, Astoria, NY...958
Museum of the National Center of Afro-American Artists, Roxbury, MA.....706
Museum of the Plains, Perryton, TX..........1443
Museum of the Puerto Rican Family of the 19th Century, San Juan, PR.............1643
Museum of the Red River, Idabel, OK......1203
Museum of the Rockies, Bozeman, MT.......842
Museum of the Southern Jewish Experience, Jackson, MS.........................803
Museum of the Western Prairie, Altus, OK..1195
Museum of Tolerance, Los Angeles, CA.....120
Museum of Transportation, Saint Louis, MO..835
Museum of Woodcarving, Shell Lake, WI.1621
Museum of Yarmouth History, Yarmouth, ME..626
Museum of York County, Rock Hill, SC...1340
Museum Village, Monroe, NY...................1015
The Music House Museum, Acme, MI........722

NASA Glenn Research Center's Visitor Center, Cleveland, OH..........................1155
Nantucket Lightship Basket Museum, Nantucket, MA.....................................696
Naper Settlement, Naperville, IL...............447
Nashville Zoo at Grassmere, Nashville, TN...1379
National Automotive & Truck Museum of the United States, Inc. (NATMUS), Auburn, IN...468
National Baseball Hall of Fame and Museum, Inc., Cooperstown, NY.............981
National Building Museum, Washington, DC..284
National Christmas Center, Paradise, PA...1275
National Civil Rights Museum, Memphis, TN...1375
National Cowgirl Museum and Hall of Fame, Fort Worth, TX............................1418
National Cryptologic Museum, Fort Meade, MD...643

National First Ladies' Library, Canton, OH...1145
National Football Museum, Inc., Canton, OH...1145
National Geographic Museum at Explorers Hall, Washington, DC...........285
National Heisey Glass Museum, Newark, OH...1178
National Heritage Museum, Lexington, MA...690
National Infantry Museum, Fort Benning, GA...372
National Mississippi River Museum & Aquarium, Dubuque, IA.........................516
National Museum of American Illustration, Newport, RI.......................1314
National Museum of American Jewish History, Philadelphia, PA......................1284
National Museum of American Jewish Military History, Washington, DC...........286
The National Museum of Catholic Art & History, New York, NY.........................1034
The National Museum of Communications, Richardson, TX.........1445
National Museum of Dance & Hall of Fame, Saratoga Springs, NY.................1065
National Museum of Health and Medicine, Washington, DC.....................286
National Museum of Roller Skating, Lincoln, NE..866
National Museum of the Morgan Horse, Shelburne, VT..1487
National New York Central Railroad Museum, Elkhart, IN.............................475
National Ornamental Metal Museum, Memphis, TN...1375
National Park Service, Washington, DC.......287
National Park Service Museum Resource Center, Landover, MD.............................648
National Plastics Center and Museum, Leominster, MA...689
National Postal Museum, Smithsonian Institution, Washington, DC...................287
National Railroad Museum, Green Bay, WI...1599
The National Science Center's Fort Discovery, Augusta, GA.........................366
National Scouting Museum, Irving, TX.....1430
National Shaving And Barbershop Museum, Meriden, CT................................249
National World War I Museum at Liberty Memorial, Kansas City, MO...................822
The National World War II Museum, New Orleans, LA......................................597
National Yiddish Book Center, Amherst, MA...659
Native American Museum, Terre Haute, IN...500
Natural Center for the American Revolution, Wayne, PA............................1306
Natural History Museum of Los Angeles County, Los Angeles, CA.......................120
Naugatuck Historical Society, Naugatuck, CT..251
Naval War College Museum, Newport, RI...1314
Nebraska Conference United Methodist Historical Center, Lincoln, NE..............866
Nebraska State Historical Society's Museum of Nebraska History, Lincoln, NE..866
Neligh Mills, Neligh, NE.............................869
The Nelson-Atkins Museum of Art, Kansas City, MO....................................822
Netherland Inn House Museum & Boatyard Complex, Kingsport, TN........1368
Nevada Historical Society, Reno, NV..........881
Nevada State Museum, Carson City, NV.....876
Nevada State Museum, Las Vegas, Las Vegas, NV...880
Neville Public Museum of Brown County, Green Bay, WI...........................1599

Communication Artifacts—Continued

New Bedford Whaling Museum, New Bedford, MA..............696

New England Fire and History Museum, Brewster, MA 670

New England Ski Museum, Franconia, NH..............888

New Hampshire Historical Society, Concord, NH..............885

The New Jersey Historical Society, Newark, NJ..............916

The New Jersey Museum of Agriculture, North Brunswick, NJ..............917

New Jersey Office of Historic Sites, Trenton, NJ..............927

New London County Historical Society, New London, CT..............255

New Orleans Pharmacy Museum, New Orleans, LA..............597

New Richmond Preservation Society, New Richmond, WI..............1615

New Windsor Cantonment State Historic Site and National Purple Heart Hall of Honor, Vails Gate, NY..............1080

New World Art Center/T.F. Chen Cultural Center, New York, NY..............1035

New York City Fire Museum, New York, NY..............1035

New York City Police Museum, New York, NY..............1035

The New York Historical Society, New York, NY..............1035

The New York Public Library for the Performing Arts, New York, NY..............1036

New York State Historical Association/Fenimore Art Museum, Cooperstown, NY..............981

Newaygo County Museum, Newaygo, MI..............758

Newseum, Washington, DC..............288

Newtown Historic Association, Newtown, PA..............1274

Nez Perce County Museum, Lewiston, ID..............407

Nez Perce National Historical Park, Spalding, ID..............409

The Niagara County Historical Center and Niagara County Genealogical Society, Lockport, NY..............1010

Ninety Six National Historic Site, Ninety Six, SC..............1338

Nishna Heritage Museum, Oakland, IA..............525

Nixon Presidential Materials Staff, College Park, MD..............641

No Man's Land Historical Society, Goodwell, OK..............1201

Noank Historical Society, Inc., Noank, CT..............256

The Noble Maritime Collection, Staten Island, NY..............1073

Nobleboro Historical Society, Nobleboro, ME..............616

Nobles County Historical Society, Worthington, MN..............797

Norfolk Historical Museum, Norfolk, CT..............257

Norman #1 Oil Well Museum, Neodesha, KS..............553

Norman Rockwell Museum, Stockbridge, MA..............712

North Andover Historical Society, North Andover, MA..............698

North Carolina Museum of History, Raleigh, NC..............1115

North Carolina Transportation Museum, Spencer, NC..............1120

North Haven Historical Society, North Haven, CT..............257

North House Museum, Lewisburg, WV..............1584

North Lee County Historic Center and Santa Fe Depot Museum Complex, Fort Madison, IA..............518

North Platte Valley Museum, Gering, NE..............861

The North Shore Arts Association, Gloucester, MA..............684

North Star Museum of Boy Scouting and Girl Scouting, North Saint Paul, MN..............785

North Tonawanda History Museum, North Tonawanda, NY..............1043

Northampton County Historical and Genealogical Society, Easton, PA..............1250

Northern Indiana Center for History, South Bend, IN..............499

Northfield Historical Society Museum, Northfield, MN..............785

Northport Historical Society Museum, Northport, NY..............1044

Northwest Museum of Arts & Culture (Eastern Washington State Historical Society), Spokane, WA..............1571

Norwood Historical Association and Museum, Norwood, NY..............1044

Novato History Museum, Novato, CA..............132

O. Henry Museum, Austin, TX..............1391

O. Winston Link Museum, Roanoke, VA..............1535

Oak Glen School House Museum, Yucaipa, CA..............200

Oak Hill and The Martha Berry Museum, Rome, GA..............382

Oakdale Museum, Oakdale, CA..............132

Oakland Museum of California, Oakland, CA..............134

Ocean City Historical Museum, Inc., Ocean City, NJ..............918

Ocean City Life-Saving Station Museum, Ocean City, MD..............650

Ocmulgee National Monument, Macon, GA..............378

The Octagon House, Hudson, WI..............1600

O'Fallon Historical Museum, Baker, MT..............840

Ohef Sholom Temple Archives, Norfolk, VA..............1523

Ohr-O'Keefe Museum of Art, Biloxi, MS..............799

Ojai Valley Historical Society and Museum, Ojai, CA..............135

Oklahoma Historical Society, Oklahoma City, OK..............1209

Oklahoma Museum of History, Oklahoma City, OK..............1210

Oklahoma Route 66 Museum, Clinton, OK..............1198

Olana State Historic Site, Hudson, NY..............1000

Old Bohemia Historical Society, Warwick, MD..............656

Old Cathedral Museum, Saint Louis, MO..............836

Old Coal Mine Museum, Madrid, NM..............943

Old Constitution House, Windsor, VT..............1490

Old Conway Homestead Complex and Museum, Camden, ME..............608

Old Courthouse Museum, Santa Ana, CA..............178

Old Cowtown Museum, Wichita, KS..............562

Old Depot Museum, Ottawa, KS..............555

Old Exchange & Provost Dungeon, Charleston, SC..............1326

Old Fort Bissell, Phillipsburg, KS..............555

Old Fort Niagara, Youngstown, NY..............1088

Old Iron County Courthouse Museum, Hurley, WI..............1601

The Old Jail Museum, Crawfordsville, IN..............473

The Old Jail Museum, Warrenton, VA..............1543

Old Jefferson Town, Oskaloosa, KS..............555

Old Lincoln County Courthouse Museum, Lincoln, NM..............942

Old Mission Santa Ines, Solvang, CA..............187

Old Sacramento State Historic Park, Old Sacramento, CA..............135

Old South Meeting House, Boston, MA..............668

Old State House Museum, Little Rock, AR..............63

Old Town Hall Museum, Fifield, WI..............1597

Old Town Museum, Old Town, ME..............617

Old Washington Historic State Park, Washington, AR..............69

Old West Movie Poster Museum, Tucson, AZ..............50

Old West Wax Museum, Thermopolis, WY..............1639

Old York Road Historical Society, Jenkintown, PA..............1263

Oldest House Museum Complex, Saint Augustine, FL..............339

Oneida Community Mansion House, Oneida, NY..............1046

Oneida County Historical Society, Utica, NY..............1080

Oneida Nation Museum, De Pere, WI..............1594

Onslow County Museum, Richlands, NC..............1117

Ontonagon County Historical Society Museum, Ontonagon, MI..............758

Orcas Island Historical Museum, Orcas Island, WA..............1560

Orchard House, Concord, MA..............677

Oregon Coast History Center, Newport, OR..............1229

Oregon Historical Society, Portland, OR..............1231

Oregon Military Museum, Clackamas, OR..............1221

Oregon Museum of Science and Industry, Portland, OR..............1231

Oregon Trail Regional Museum, Baker City, OR..............1219

Oregon Zoo, Portland, OR..............1232

Oriental Institute Museum, University of Chicago, Chicago, IL..............426

Oriskany Battlefield State Historic Site, Oriskany, NY..............1047

Oroville Chinese Temple, Oroville, CA..............136

Orpheum Children's Science Museum, Champaign, IL..............417

Osage County Historical Society Research Center, Lyndon, KS..............550

Oscar Getz Museum of Whiskey History And The Bardstown Historical Museum, Bardstown, KY..............565

Ossining Historical Society Museum, Ossining, NY..............1047

Osterville Historical Society, Inc., Osterville, MA..............701

Otero Museum Association, La Junta, CO..............224

Ottawa Scouting Museum, Ottawa, IL..............449

Otter Tail County Historical Society, Fergus Falls, MN..............775

Outagamie Museum, Appleton, WI..............1589

Overland Trail Museum, Sterling, CO..............232

Owensboro Museum of Fine Art, Inc., Owensboro, KY..............581

Owls Head Transportation Museum, Owls Head, ME..............617

Oysterponds Historical Society: The Museum of Orient and East Marion History, Orient, NY..............1047

Ozark National Scenic Riverways, Van Buren, MO..............839

The P.T. Boat Museum & Library, Germantown, TN..............1365

Pacem in Terris, Warwick, NY..............1082

Pacific County Historical Museum, South Bend, WA..............1571

Pacific Science Center, Seattle, WA..............1568

Pacific University Museum, Forest Grove, OR..............1224

Padre Island National Seashore, Corpus Christi, TX..............1402

Painted Post - Erwin Museum at the Depot, Painted Post, NY..............1050

Pajaro Valley Historical Association, Watsonville, CA..............196

Palace of the Governors/New Mexico History Museum, Santa Fe, NM..............949

The Palette & Chisel, Chicago, IL..............426

Palmer Foundation Chiropractic History, Davenport, IA..............513

Paper Airplane Museum and the Tin Can Man of Maui, Kahului Central Maui, HI..............399

Paper Discovery Center, Appleton, WI..............1590

Paris-Henry County Heritage Center,
    Paris, TN...1382
Park City Historical Society & Museum,
    Park City, UT...1468
Parson Fisher House, Blue Hill, ME...........606
Passaic County Historical Society &
    Lambert Castle Museum, Paterson, NJ...920
Patee House Museum, Saint Joseph, MO....831
The Paterson Museum, Paterson, NJ...........920
Patterson Homestead, Dayton, OH.............1161
Patterson Inn Museum/Corning - Painted
    Post Historical Society, Corning, NY......982
Paul H. Karshner Memorial Museum,
    Puyallup, WA...1564
Paul W. Bryant Museum, Tuscaloosa, AL......19
Paunsaugunt Wildlife Museum, Bryce,
    UT...1464
Pavek Museum of Broadcasting, St.
    Louis Park, MN..794
Pawnee Bill Ranch and Museum,
    Pawnee, OK...1212
Pawnee City Historical Society &
    Museum, Pawnee City, NE.......................871
Pawnee Indian Village State Historic Site,
    Republic, KS..556
Pea Ridge National Military Park,
    Garfield, AR..58
The Peace Museum, Chicago, IL.................426
Pearce Collections Museum, Corsicana,
    TX...1402
The Pearl S. Buck House, Perkasie, PA.....1275
Pearson Air Museum, Vancouver, WA.......1576
The Pearson Museum, Springfield, IL.........460
The Peary-MacMillan Arctic Museum,
    Brunswick, ME..608
The Peggy Notebaert Nature Museum,
    Chicago, IL...426
Pembina State Museum, Pembina, ND.......1135
Pennsylvania Anthracite Heritage
    Museum, Scranton, PA.............................1299
Pennyroyal Area Museum, Hopkinsville,
    KY..572
Pensacola Historical Society Museum,
    Pensacola, FL..336
Peoria Historical Society, Peoria, IL...........451
Perkins History Museum, Perkins School
    for the Blind, Watertown, MA..................716
Perry's Victory & International Peace
    Memorial, Put-in-Bay, OH......................1183
Peter Yegen Jr. Yellowstone County
    Museum, Billings, MT..............................841
Petrified Forest National Park, Petrified
    Forest National Park, AZ...........................38
Pettis County Historical Society, Sedalia,
    MO...838
Philadelphia Mummers Museum,
    Philadelphia, PA......................................1285
Philipse Manor Hall State Historic Site,
    Yonkers, NY..1087
Phoenix Museum of History, Phoenix,
    AZ...41
Piatt Castles, West Liberty, OH................1190
Piatt County Museum, Monticello, IL..........446
Piccadilly Museum of Transportation
    Memorabilia and Advertising Art,
    Butte, MT...843
The Pierpont Morgan Library, New York,
    NY...1037
Pilgrim Monument and Provincetown
    Museum, Provincetown, MA....................704
Pinal County Historical Society and
    Museum, Florence, AZ...............................34
Pine Bluff/Jefferson County Historical
    Museum, Pine Bluff, AR............................66
Pioneer Arizona Living History Village &
    Museum, Phoenix, AZ................................41
Pioneer Corner Museum, New Holstein,
    WI...1615
Pioneer Heritage Center, Cavalier, ND.......1129
Pioneer Museum and Vereins Kirche,
    Fredericksburg, TX.................................1419
Pioneer Museum of Alabama, Troy, AL.........18

Pioneer Settlement for the Creative Arts,
    Barberville, FL..295
Pioneer Village, Farmington, UT...............1465
Pipestone National Monument, Pipestone,
    MN...787
Pittsford Historical Society Museum,
    Pittsford, VT...1484
Plains Indians and Pioneers Museum,
    Woodward, OK..1217
Plantation Agriculture Museum, Scott,
    AR...67
Platen Press Printing Museum, Zion, IL......467
Plattsburgh State Art Museum S.U.N.Y.,
    Plattsburgh, NY......................................1053
Plumas County Museum, Quincy, CA.........144
Pocahontas County Iowa Historical
    Society Museum, Laurens, IA..................522
The Polk County Historical Society,
    Cedartown, GA...368
Polk County Historical Society,
    Crookston, MN...771
Polk County Memorial Museum,
    Livingston, TX..1434
Polk County Museum, Balsam Lake, WI...1590
Popular Arts Museum, San Juan, PR.........1643
Port Huron Museum, Port Huron, MI..........761
Port Orford Lifeboat Station, Port Orford,
    OR...1230
Portage County Historical Society,
    Stevens Point, WI...................................1623
Porter Thermometer Museum, Onset, MA...700
Portuguese Historical Museum, San Jose,
    CA..172
Potter County Historical Society,
    Coudersport, PA......................................1248
Powers Museum, Carthage, MO..................812
Praters Mill Foundation, Varnell, GA..........390
Pratt Building - Cohasset Historical
    Society, Cohasset, MA..............................676
Presbyterian Historical Society
    (Montreat), Montreat, NC.......................1111
Prince William Forest Park Visitor
    Center, Triangle, VA...............................1541
Pro Rodeo Hall of Fame & Museum of
    the American Cowboy, Colorado
    Springs, CO...207
Proprietary House, The Royal Governor's
    Mansion, Perth Amboy, NJ......................921
Public Museum of West Michigan, Grand
    Rapids, MI...744
Pueblo County Historical Society
    Museum and Edward H. Broadhead
    Library, Pueblo, CO..................................230
Pueblo of Pojoaque, Poeh Museum, Santa
    Fe, NM..949
Pueblo Weisbrod Aircraft Museum,
    Pueblo, CO..230
Puget Sound Coast Artillery Museum at
    Fort Worden, Port Townsend, WA.........1562
Putnam County Historical Society
    Museum, Kalida, OH...............................1169
Putnam County Museum, Greencastle, IN...479
Putney Historical Society, Putney, VT.......1485

Queen Emma Summer Palace, Honolulu,
    HI..398
Queen Mary Museum, Long Beach, CA......111
Queens Historical Society, Flushing, NY....990
Quincy Historical Society, Quincy, MA......705
Quoddy Maritime Museum, Eastport, ME...610

Racine Heritage Museum, Racine, WI.......1619
Radio & Television Museum, Bowie, MD...638
Railroad Museum of Minot, Minot, ND.....1135
Railroad Museum of Pennsylvania,
    Strasburg, PA...1302
Railroaders Memorial Museum, Altoona,
    PA...1240
Raleigh City Museum, Raleigh, NC...........1117
The Ralph Foster Museum, Point
    Lookout, MO..828
Ralston Historical Association, John
    Ralston Museum, Mendham, NJ..............911

Ramsey House Museum Plantation,
    Knoxville, TN..1371
Rancho La Patera - The Stow House
    G.V.H.S., Goleta, CA...............................100
Randall Library, Stow, MA........................713
Randolph Historical Society, Inc.,
    Randolph, VT..1485
Rankin Museum, Rankin, TX.....................1445
Rankin Museum, Inc., Ellerbe, NC............1100
Rattlesnake Museum (American
    International), Albuquerque, NM..............935
Reading Historical Society Museum,
    Reading, OH...1184
Readsboro Historical Society, Readsboro,
    VT...1486
Red Earth Museum, Oklahoma City, OK...1210
Red Mill Museum Village, Clinton, NJ........901
Red Rock Museum, Church Rock, NM.......938
Redwood County Historical Society,
    Redwood Falls, MN..................................787
Reed Gold Mine State Historic Site,
    Midland, NC..1111
Refugio County Museum, Refugio, TX......1445
Reitz Home Museum, Evansville, IN...........476
Reno County Museum, Hutchinson, KS......545
Rensselaer County Historical Society,
    Troy, NY...1079
Renville County Historical Society, Inc.,
    Mohall, ND..1135
Republic County Historical Society
    Museum, Belleville, KS............................534
Reuel B. Pritchett Museum, Bridgewater,
    VA...1497
Rhode Island Black Heritage Society,
    Providence, RI..1318
Rhode Island Historical Society,
    Providence, RI..1318
Richard Salter Storrs House,
    Longmeadow, MA.....................................691
Richardson-Bates House Museum,
    Oswego, NY..1048
Richland County Museum, Lexington,
    OH..1172
Richmond Museum of History,
    Richmond, CA..148
Riddick's Folly, Suffolk, VA.....................1539
Rifle Creek Museum, Rifle, CO..................231
Rimrocker Historical Museum of West
    Montrose County, Naturita, CO...............229
Ripley County, Indiana, Historical
    Society Museum, Versailles, IN................502
Ritz Theatre & LaVilla Museum,
    Jacksonville, FL..315
River Heritage Museum, Paducah, KY........582
Riverside Metropolitan Museum,
    Riverside, CA...150
Riverside Museum, La Crosse, WI............1603
Roane County Museum of History & Art,
    Kingston, TN..1369
Robbins Museum of Archaeology,
    Middleborough, MA..................................694
Roberson Museum and Science Center,
    Binghamton, NY......................................962
Robert C. Williams American Museum of
    Papermaking at Georgia Tech, Atlanta,
    GA...363
Robert Frost Stone House Museum,
    Shaftsbury, VT..1487
Robert Fulton Birthplace, Quarryville, PA.1295
Robert Newell House, DAR Museum,
    Saint Paul, OR..1235
Robert R. McCormick Museum at
    Cantigny, Wheaton, IL.............................465
Robert S. Kerr Museum, Poteau, OK.........1212
Robert S. Peabody Museum of
    Archaeology, Andover, MA.......................660
Robert V. Fullerton Art Museum,
    California State University, San
    Bernardino, San Bernardino, CA..............155
Robinson-Rose House, San Diego, CA........159
The Rock and Roll Hall of Fame and
    Museum, Cleveland, OH...........................1155

Communication Artifacts–Continued

Rock Springs Historical Museum, Rock Springs, WY 1638

Rockbridge Historical Society, Lexington, VA 1513

Rockingham Free Public Library and Museum, Bellows Falls, VT 1476

Rocky Ford Historical Museum, Rocky Ford, CO 231

Rocky Mountain National Park, Estes Park, CO 215

Rocky Mountain Quilt Museum, Golden, CO 220

Rocky Reach Dam, Wenatchee, WA 1577

Rodgers Tavern, Perryville, MD 650

Rogers Historical Museum, Rogers, AR 67

Rollo Jamison Museum, Platteville, WI 1617

Rome Historical Society Museum, Rome, NY 1061

Ronald Reagan Presidential Library and Museum, Simi Valley, CA............187

Roosevelt County Museum, Portales, NM ...944

Roseau County Historical Museum and Interpretive Center, Roseau, MN 788

Rosenberg Library, Galveston, TX 1422

Rosicrucian Egyptian Museum, San Jose, CA............172

The Roy Rogers-Dale Evans Museum and Theater, Branson, MO 811

Royal Gorge Regional Museum & History Center, Canon City, CO............205

Royalton Historical Society, Royalton, VT 1486

Runestone Museum, Alexandria, MN............767

Ruth and Charles Gilb Arcadia Historical Museum, Arcadia, CA............71

The Rye Historical Society and Square House Museum, Rye, NY 1062

Ryerss Museum & Library, Philadelphia, PA 1287

S.C.R.A.P. Gallery, Indio, CA............104

Saco Museum, Saco, ME............621

Sacramento Archives and Museum Collection Center, Sacramento, CA............153

Safe Haven Museum and Education Center, Oswego, NY 1048

Sag Harbor Whaling & Historical Museum, Sag Harbor, NY............1063

Sagamore Hill National Historic Site, Oyster Bay, NY 1049

Sailor's Memorial Museum, Islesboro, ME............612

St. Charles County Historical Society, Inc., Saint Charles, MO............830

St. Charles Heritage Center, Saint Charles, IL............457

St. Francis County Museum, Forrest City, AR............57

St. George's United Methodist Church, Philadelphia, PA 1287

St. John's Church and Parish Museum, Hampton, VA............1510

St. John's Episcopal Church, Richmond, VA 1531

St. John's Northwestern Military Academy Archives & Museum, Delafield, WI 1595

St. Lawrence County Historical Association - Silas Wright House, Canton, NY 975

The St. Louis County Historical Society, Duluth, MN............773

St. Marys Submarine Museum, Saint Marys, GA............382

St. Paul Museum, Randleman, NC............1117

St. Petersburg Museum of History, Saint Petersburg, FL............342

St. Photios Greek Orthodox National Shrine, Saint Augustine, FL............340

Ste. Genevieve Museum, Sainte Genevieve, MO............838

Salamanca Rail Museum, Salamanca, NY .1063

Salem Maritime National Historic Site, Salem, MA............707

The Salem Museum, Salem, VA............1536

Salisbury House Foundation, Des Moines, IA............515

Salvador Dali Museum, Saint Petersburg, FL............342

The Salvation Army Southern Historical Center & Museum, Atlanta, GA 363

Sam Brown Log House, Browns Valley, MN............770

Sam Houston Memorial Museum, Huntsville, TX............1430

Sam Houston Regional Library & Research Center, Liberty, TX............1434

Sam Noble Oklahoma Museum of Natural History, Norman, OK............1206

Sam Rayburn House Museum, Bonham, TX............1397

San Antonio de Pala Asistencia, Pala, CA ...138

San Antonio Missions National Historical Park, San Antonio, TX............1449

San Antonio Museum of Art, San Antonio, TX............1450

San Buenaventura Mission Museum, Ventura, CA............195

San Dieguito Heritage Museum, Encinitas, CA............92

San Gabriel Mission Museum, San Gabriel, CA............171

San Juan National Historic Site, San Juan, PR............1643

San Luis Obispo County Historical Museum, San Luis Obispo, CA............174

San Mateo County Historical Association and Museum, Redwood City, CA............147

Sanborn Area Historical Society, Sanborn, NY 1064

Sand Springs Cultural & Historical Museum, Sand Springs, OK............1213

Sandusky Library Follett House Museum, Sandusky, OH............1185

Sandwich Glass Museum, Sandwich, MA ...708

Sanford Museum, Sanford, FL............343

Sanilac County Historical Museum and Village, Port Sanilac, MI............761

Santa Barbara Mission Museum, Santa Barbara, CA............179

Santa Fe Trail Center, Larned, KS 547

Santa Fe Trail Museum/Trinidad History Museum, Trinidad, CO............234

Santa Monica Mountains National Recreation Area, Thousand Oaks, CA.....191

Santarella, Tyringham, MA............715

Sappington Cemetery State Historic Site, Nelson, MO............827

Sarasota Classic Car Museum, Sarasota, FL............345

Saratoga County Historical Society, Brookside Museum, Ballston Spa, NY....960

Saratoga Museum, Saratoga, WY 1638

Saratoga National Historical Park, Stillwater, NY 1075

Sarpy County Historical Museum, Bellevue, NE............857

Saunders County Historical Complex, Wahoo, NE............874

Sayville Historical Society, Sayville, NY...1066

Scantic Academy Museum, East Windsor Historical Society, Inc., East Windsor, CT............239

Scarborough Historical Museum, Scarborough, ME............621

Schenectady Museum and Suits-Bueche Planetarium, Schenectady, NY............1067

Schiele Museum of Natural History and Lynn Planetarium, Gastonia, NC............1102

Schmucker Art Gallery, Gettysburg, PA.....1256

The Schomburg Center for Research in Black Culture, New York, NY............1038

School of American Research, Indian Arts Research Center, Santa Fe, NM 950

Schoolcraft County Historical Society, Manistique, MI............753

The Schubert Club Museum of Musical Instruments, Saint Paul, MN............792

Schwartz Collection of Skiing Heritage, Tiburon, CA............192

The Science Center of Pinellas County, Saint Petersburg, FL............342

Scotland Heritage Chapel & Museum, Scotland, SD............1355

Scurry County Museum, Snyder, TX 1453

Sedgwick-Brooklin Historical Society, Sedgwick, ME............622

Seminole Canyon State Park and Historic Site, Comstock, TX............1401

Senate House State Historic Site, Kingston, NY............1008

Senator George Norris State Historic Site, McCook, NE............868

Senator John Heinz Pittsburgh Regional History Center, Pittsburgh, PA............1294

Seneca-Iroquois National Museum, Salamanca, NY............1063

Sequoia and Kings Canyon National Parks, Three Rivers, CA 191

Sequoyah Cabin, Sallisaw, OK............1213

Serra Museum/San Diego Historical Society, San Diego, CA............161

1719 Hans Herr House & Museum, Willow Street, PA............1308

The Sevier County Historical Museum, De Queen, AR............56

Seymour Community Museum, Seymour, WI............1621

Shaker Historical Society, Shaker Heights, OH............1185

Shaker Museum, New Gloucester, ME 615

The Shaker Museum and Library, Old Chatham, NY............1045

Shaker Village of Pleasant Hill, Harrodsburg, KY............571

Shako:wi Cultural Center, Oneida, NY 1046

Sharon Historical Society, Sharon, CT........260

Shawnee Town, Shawnee, KS............558

Sheboygan County Historical Museum, Sheboygan, WI............1621

Sheldon Museum and Cultural Center, Inc., Haines, AK............25

Sheldon Peck Homestead, Lombard, IL........444

Shenandoah National Park, Luray, VA........1514

Sherburne History Center, Becker, MN........768

Sherwin Miller Museum of Jewish Art, Tulsa, OK............1216

Shiloh Museum of Ozark History, Springdale, AR............68

Shippensburg Historical Society Museum, Shippensburg, PA............1300

Shore Line Trolley Museum, East Haven, CT............239

Shortgrass Country Museum Society, Sayre, OK............1213

Sibley County Historical Museum, Henderson, MN............777

Sibley House Historic Site, Mendota, MN...780

Sidney Historical Association, Sidney, NY............1069

Siege Museum (The Petersburg Museums), Petersburg, VA............1525

Siegfried H. Horn Archaeological Museum, Berrien Springs, MI............729

Sierra Mono Indian Museum, North Fork, CA............131

Silent Wings Museum, Lubbock, TX 1435

Siloam Springs Museum, Siloam Springs, AR............68

Silver City Museum, Silver City, NM........951

Sinclair Lewis House Museum & Interpretive Center/Museum, Sauk Centre, MN............793

Sindecuse Museum of Dentistry, Ann Arbor, MI............725

Sioux City Public Museum, Sioux City, IA 528
Siouxland Heritage Museums, Sioux Falls, SD 1357
Siskin Museum of Religious and Ceremonial Art, Chattanooga, TN 1362
Siskiyou County Museum, Yreka, CA 200
Sitka National Historical Park, Sitka, AK 28
The Sixth Floor Museum at Dealey Plaza, Dallas, TX...............1407
Skagit County Historical Museum, La Conner, WA 1557
Skagway Museum & Archives, Skagway, AK...............28
Skirball Cultural Center, Los Angeles, CA...............121
Skirball Museum Cincinnati Hebrew Union College-Jewish Institute of Religion, Cincinnati, OH...............1151
Skowhegan History House Inc., Skowhegan, ME...............622
Sky City Cultural Center, Pueblo of Acoma, NM...............944
The Skyscraper Museum, New York, NY ..1038
Slidell Museum, Slidell, LA 602
Sloan Museum, Flint, MI...............742
Smith Robertson Museum & Cultural Center, Jackson, MS...............804
Smith-Zimmermann Heritage Museum, Madison, SD...............1351
Smithtown Historical Society, Smithtown, NY...............1070
Snyder Museum & Creative Arts Center, Bastrop, LA...............585
Society for Contemporary Craft, Pittsburgh, PA...............1294
The Society of the Cincinnati at Anderson House, Washington, DC 291
Sonoma County Museum, Santa Rosa, CA...............185
Sonoma State Historic Park, Sonoma, CA ...188
Sony Wonder Technology Lab, New York, NY...............1039
Sophienburg Museum & Archives Inc., New Braunfels, TX...............1440
Sosa-Carrillo-Fremont House Museum, Tucson, AZ...............50
South Boston-Halifax County Museum of Fine Arts & History, South Boston, VA...............1536
South Charleston Museum, South Charleston, WV...............1586
South Coast Railroad Museum at Goleta Depot, Goleta, CA...............100
South County Historical Society, Arroyo Grande, CA...............72
South Dakota State Historical Society, Pierre, SD...............1353
South Milwaukee Historical Society Museum, South Milwaukee, WI............1622
South Park City Museum, Fairplay, CO.......215
South Pass City State Historic Site, South Pass City, WY...............1638
South Street Seaport Museum, New York, NY...............1039
South Sutton Old Store Museum, South Sutton, NH...............896
South Texas Museum, Alice, TX...............1386
South Wood County Historical Corp., Wisconsin Rapids, WI...............1628
Southeast Missouri Regional Museum, Cape Girardeau, MO...............812
Southeastern Railway Museum, Duluth, GA...............371
Southern Oregon Historical Society, Jacksonville, OR...............1226
Southern Ute Cultural Center and Museum, Ignacio, CO...............223
Southwest Florida Museum of History, Fort Myers, FL...............309
Southwest School of Art & Craft, San Antonio, TX...............1450

Southwest Virginia Museum Historical State Park, Big Stone Gap, VA...............1497
Spellman Museum of Stamps and Postal History, Weston, MA...............719
Spertus Museum, Chicago, IL...............427
Spirit of '76 Museum, Wellington, OH......1190
SPJST Library Archives & Museum, Temple, TX...............1455
Spring Grove Hospital Center, Alumni Museum, Catonsville, MD...............639
Springfield Museums - Connecticut Valley Historical Museum, Springfield, MA...............710
Spurlock Museum, University of Illinois at Urbana-Champaign, Urbana, IL...........462
Stafford County Historical Society Museum, Stafford, KS...............558
Stamford Historical Society, Inc., Stamford, CT...............260
Stan Hywet Hall and Gardens, Inc., Akron, OH...............1139
Stanley Museum, Inc., Kingfield, ME.........613
Stanly County Historic Preservation Commission and Museum, Albemarle, NC...............1088
Stanzel Model Aircraft Museum, Schulenburg, TX...............1452
Star of the Republic Museum, Washington, TX...............1460
Starhill Forest Arboretum, Petersburg, IL 451
Stars and Stripes Museum/Library, Bloomfield, MO...............811
State Agricultural Heritage Museum, Brookings, SD...............1344
State Historical Society of Iowa, Des Moines, IA...............515
State Historical Society of North Dakota, Bismarck, ND...............1128
Staten Island Institute of Arts & Sciences (SIIAS), Staten Island, NY 1074
Station 15, Norton, KS...............554
Statue of Liberty National Monument & Ellis Island Immigration Museum, New York, NY...............1039
Stauth Memorial Museum, Montezuma, KS...............553
STAX Museum of American Soul Music, Memphis, TN...............1376
Steamboat Bertrand Collection, Missouri Valley, IA...............524
Steamship Keewatin, Douglas, MI...............738
Steamship William G. Mather Museum, Cleveland, OH...............1156
Steamtown National Historic Site, Scranton, PA...............1299
Steele County Historical Society, Hope, ND...............1133
The Stephen Phillips House, Salem, MA.....707
Stephens African-American Museum, Shreveport, LA...............602
Stephens County Historical Society and Museum, Duncan, OK...............1199
Stepping Stones Museum for Children, Norwalk, CT...............257
Sterling Hill Mining Museum, Inc., Ogdensburg, NJ...............918
Sterling-Rock Falls Historical Society Museum, Sterling, IL...............461
Steuben Memorial State Historic Site, Remsen, NY...............1056
Stevens County Historical Society Museum, Morris, MN...............784
Stevens Museum, Salem, IN...............498
Stewart M. Lord Memorial Historical Society, Inc., Burlington, ME...............608
Stockbridge Library Historical Collection, Stockbridge, MA...............713
The Stone House Museum, Belchertown, MA...............662
Stonefield Historic Site, Cassville, WI 1593
Stones River National Battlefield, Murfreesboro, TN...............1377
Stonewall Jackson House, Lexington, VA ..1514

Stony Point Battlefield State Historic Site, Stony Point, NY...............1075
Storrowton Village Museum, West Springfield, MA...............718
Stoughton Historical Society, Stoughton, WI...............1623
Strong - National Museum of Play, Rochester, NY...............1060
Studebaker National Museum, Inc., South Bend, IN...............500
Stuhr Museum of the Prairie Pioneer, Grand Island, NE...............862
Suffolk County Historical Society, Riverhead, NY...............1057
Sullivan County Historical Society, Inc., Hurleyville, NY...............1001
Summit County Historical Society, Akron, OH...............1139
The Sumter County Museum, Sumter, SC .1342
Sun Prairie Historical Library & Museum, Sun Prairie, WI...............1624
The Supreme Court of the United States, Washington, DC...............291
Suquamish Museum, Poulsbo, WA...............1563
Susan B. Anthony House, Rochester, NY ..1060
Susquehanna County Historical Society & Free Library Association, Montrose, PA...............1272
Swarthout Memorial Museum, La Crosse, WI...............1603
Swedish American Museum Association of Chicago, Chicago, IL...............428
Sweet Briar Museum, Sweet Briar, VA......1540
Sweetwater County Historical Museum, Green River, WY...............1633
Swiss Historical Village, New Glarus, WI .1615
Sylvia Plotkin Judaica Museum of Congregation Beth Israel, Scottsdale, AZ...............44

Tampa Bay History Center, Inc., Tampa, FL...............350
Tannenbaum Historic Park, Greensboro, NC...............1104
Tante Blanche Museum, Madawaska, ME ...614
Taos Historic Museums, Taos, NM...............953
Telephone Museum of New Mexico, Albuquerque, NM...............935
Telephone Pioneer Museum, Phoenix, AZ 42
Telluride Historical Museum, Telluride, CO...............233
Temecula Valley Museum, Temecula, CA....191
Tempe Historical Museum, Tempe, AZ.........46
The Temple Judea Museum of Reform Congregation Keneseth Israel, Elkins Park, PA...............1251
Tennessee Central Railway Museum, Nashville, TN...............1380
Tennessee Museum of Aviation, Sevierville, TN...............1383
Terwilliger Museum, Waterloo, NY...........1083
Teutopolis Monastery Museum, Teutopolis, IL...............461
Texana Museum and Library Association, Edna, TX...............1410
Texas Baptist Historical Center Museum, Brenham, TX...............1397
Texas Forestry Museum, Lufkin, TX 1436
Texas Heritage Museum, Hillsboro, TX.....1424
Texas Maritime Museum, Rockport, TX 1446
Texas Music Museum, Austin, TX...........1392
Texas Ranger Hall of Fame and Museum, Waco, TX...............1459
Texas State Museum of Asian Cultures & Educational Center, Corpus Christi, TX...............1402
Texas Transportation Museum, San Antonio, TX...............1451
Third Cavalry Museum, Fort Carson, CO....216
Thomas E. McMillan Museum, Brewton, AL...............6
Thomas Edison House, Louisville, KY...............579

Communication Artifacts–Continued

The Thoreau Institute at Walden Woods, Lincoln, MA 691

Thornton W. Burgess Museum, Sandwich, MA 708

Three Village Historical Society, Setauket, NY.................................1069

Tinley Park Historical Society, Tinley Park, IL 461

Tioga County Historical Society Museum, Owego, NY.......................1048

Tippecanoe Battlefield, Battle Ground, IN ...468

Tippecanoe County Historical Association, Lafayette, IN.....................487

Tobacco Farm Life Museum, Inc., Kenly, NC 1107

Tolland Historical Society - Tolland County Jail and Warden's Home Museum, Tolland, CT....................262

Tom Mix Museum, Dewey, OK...........1199

Tomaquag Indian Memorial Museum, Exeter, RI...1311

Tongass Historical Museum, Ketchikan, AK...26

Torrington Historical Society, Inc., Torrington, CT....................................263

Totem Heritage Center, Ketchikan, AK.........26

Tougaloo College, Tougaloo, MS 808

Town Creek Indian Mound State Historic Site, Mount Gilead, NC...................1111

Toy & Miniature Museum of Kansas City, Kansas City, MO 823

Traill County Historical Society, Hillsboro, ND 1132

Travel Town Museum, Los Angeles, CA 121

Travellers Rest Plantation & Museum, Nashville, TN.....................................1381

Traverse County Historical Society, Wheaton, MN 796

Treasures of the Sea Exhibit, Georgetown, DE 271

Tri-County Historical Society & Museum, Inc., Herington, KS 544

Triangle Tattoo & Museum, Fort Bragg, CA 95

Trinity Museum of the Parish of Trinity Church, New York, NY.......................1040

Troutdale Historical Society, Troutdale, OR 1237

Tryon Palace Historic Sites and Gardens, New Bern, NC.....................................1112

Tsa Mo Ga Memorial Museum, Plains, TX 1443

T.T. Wentworth, Jr. Florida State Museum, Pensacola, FL.....................336

Tubac Presidio State Historic Park, Tubac, AZ..47

Tubman African-American Museum, Macon, GA..378

Tucson Museum of Art & Historic Block, Tucson, AZ...51

Tularosa Basin Historical Society Museum, Alamogordo, NM 932

Tumacacori National Historical Park, Tumacacori, AZ.......................................52

Tunica-Biloxi Native American Museum, Marksville, LA...................................591

Turquoise Museum, Albuquerque, NM 936

Tuskegee Institute National Historic Site, Tuskegee Institute, AL 21

UCLA Fowler Museum of Cultural History, Los Angeles, CA 122

UNLV Marjorie Barrick Museum, Las Vegas, NV...880

USDA Forest Service - Land Between the Lakes, Golden Pond, KY 570

U.S. Navy Museum, Washington, DC..........292

The Ukrainian Museum, New York, NY....1040

Ukrainian National Museum, Inc., Chicago, IL...428

Ulster County Historical Society, Marbletown, NY.....................................1013

Union County Historical Society, Lewisburg, PA 1268

Union Pacific Railroad Museum, Council Bluffs, IA..512

Union Station Kansas City, Inc., Kansas City, MO..823

United States Golf Association Museum & Archives, Far Hills, NJ 903

United States Holocaust Memorial Museum, Washington, DC....................293

United States Senate Commission on Art, Washington, DC....................................293

University Art Gallery, University of the South, Sewanee, TN..............................1384

University Art Museum, Binghamton, NY...963

University Galleries, Clarion, PA 1247

The University Museum, Indiana, PA 1263

University Museum, Martin, TN 1371

University Museum, New Mexico State University, Las Cruces, NM.................941

University of Alaska Museum of the North, Fairbanks, AK 24

University of Kansas Medical Center, Clendening History of Medicine Library and Museum, Kansas City, KS...546

University of Mary Washington Galleries, Fredericksburg, VA.............................1507

University of Nebraska State Museum, Lincoln, NE..867

University of Northern Iowa Museums & Collections, Cedar Falls, IA...................508

University of Pennsylvania Museum of Archaeology and Anthropology, Philadelphia, PA...............................1288

University of Richmond Museums, Richmond, VA 1532

The University of South Carolina McKissick Museum, Columbia, SC.......1331

Upham Mansion, Marshfield, WI 1608

Upper Musselshell Historical Society, Harlowton, MT......................................849

Upper Room Chapel Museum, Nashville, TN 1381

U.S. Army Chaplain Museum, Fort Jackson, SC..1332

U.S. Army Communications-Electronics Museum, Fort Monmouth, NJ.................904

U.S. Army Engineer Museum, Fort Leonard Wood, MO................................815

U.S. Army Finance Corps Museum, Fort Jackson, SC..1333

U.S. Army Medical Department Museum, Fort Sam Houston, TX........................1415

U.S. Army Women's Museum, Fort Lee, VA 1505

U.S. Capitol Historical Society, Washington, DC....................................293

U.S. Coast Guard Museum, New London, CT 255

U.S. Marconi Museum, Bedford, NH..........883

U.S. Naval Museum of Armament & Technology, China Lake, CA.....................84

U.S. Navy Seabee Museum, Port Hueneme, CA...143

USS Arizona Memorial, Honolulu, HI 398

USS Bowfin Submarine Museum & Park, Honolulu, HI 398

USS Constellation Museum, Baltimore, MD 636

USS Constitution Museum, Boston, MA 669

Utah State Historical Society, Salt Lake City, UT..1473

Ute Indian Museum/Montrose Visitor Center, Montrose, CO 228

UTSA's Institute of Texan Cultures, San Antonio, TX..1451

Vachel Lindsay Home State Historic Site, Springfield, IL......................................460

The Valdez Museum & Historical Archive Association, Inc., Valdez, AK 29

Valentine Richmond History Center, Richmond, VA 1532

Valentine-Varian House/Museum of Bronx History, Bronx, NY.....................967

Valentown Museum, Victor, NY 1081

Vallejo Naval & Historical Museum, Vallejo, CA 194

Verde Historical Society, Clemenceau Heritage Museum, Cottonwood, AZ..........32

Vermilion County Museum Society, Danville, IL..429

Vermont Ski Museum, Stowe, VT............1488

The Vestal Museum, Vestal, NY...............1081

Vesterheim Norwegian-American Museum, Decorah, IA 513

Veterans Depot Museum, West Frankfort, IL 464

Victor Heritage Museum, Victor, MT..........854

Vietnam Era Educational Center, Holmdel, NJ...908

Vigo County Historical Museum, Terre Haute, IN...501

The Vinalhaven Historical Society Museum, Vinalhaven, ME......................624

Virginia Baptist Historical Society, Richmond, VA 1532

Virginia Historical Society, Richmond, VA 1533

Virginia Holocaust Museum, Richmond, VA 1533

Virginia Military Institute Museum, Lexington, VA.....................................1514

Virginia Museum of Fine Arts, Richmond, VA 1533

Virginia War Memorial, Richmond, VA 1534

The Virginia War Museum, Newport News, VA...1520

Vista Historical Museum, Vista, CA...........196

Visual Arts Museum, New York, NY.........1040

W.C. Handy Home Museum and Library, Florence, AL...9

W.K. Gordon Center for Industrial History of Texas, Mingus, TX 1439

Wabasha County Museum, Wabasha County Historical Society at Reads Landing, Reads Landing, MN.................787

Wabaunsee County Historical Museum, Alma, KS...532

Wailoa Center for Culture and Arts, Hilo, HI 393

Wakefield House Museum, Blue Earth, MN 769

Wakefield Museum Association, Wakefield, KS....................................560

Waldensian Heritage Museum, Valdese, NC 1121

The Walker African American Museum & Research Center, Las Vegas, NV 880

Wallace District Mining Museum, Wallace, ID..410

Wallingford Historical Society, Inc., Wallingford, CT....................................263

Walnut Grove Plantation, Roebuck, SC 1340

The Waltham Museum, Waltham, MA.........716

Wapello County Historical Museum, Ottumwa, IA.......................................526

War in the Pacific National Historical Park, Piti, GU 1640

Warner House, Portsmouth, NH 895

Warren County Historical Society, Warren, PA...1304

Waseca County Historical Society, Waseca, MN 796

Washington & Jefferson College - Olin Fine Arts Center, Washington, PA 1305

Washington County Historical Association, Fort Calhoun, NE...............860

Washington County Historical Society, Washington, KS....................................560

Washington County Historical Society Inc., West Bend, WI................................1627

Washington County Historical Society
  Warden's House Museum, Stillwater,
  MN 794
Washington National Cathedral,
  Washington, DC..............................294
Washington State Historical Society,
  Tacoma, WA 1574
Waterloo Area Historical Society, Grass
  Lake, MI 744
Waterloo Center for the Arts, Waterloo,
  IA 529
Watertown Historical Society, Inc.,
  Watertown, CT...............................264
Watkins Community Museum of History,
  Lawrence, KS.................................548
Watkins Woolen Mill State Historic Site
  & Park, Lawson, MO......................825
Watson-Curtze Mansion, Erie, PA 1253
Waukesha County Museum, Waukesha,
  WI 1625
Wayne County Historical Museum,
  Richmond, IN.................................497
Wayne County Historical Society, Lyons,
  NY 1012
Weir Farm National Historic Site, Wilton,
  CT 267
Wellesley Historical Society, Inc.,
  Wellesley Hills, MA 717
Wellfleet Historical Society Museum,
  Wellfleet, MA 717
Wells County Historical Museum,
  Bluffton, IN....................................470
Wells County Museum, Fessenden, ND 1131
Wells Fargo History Museum,
  Minneapolis, MN............................783
Wendell Gilley Museum, Southwest
  Harbor, ME 623
Weslaco Museum, Weslaco, TX 1461
West Allis Historical Society Museum,
  West Allis, WI 1626
West Chicago City Museum, West
  Chicago, IL 464
West of the Pecos Museum, Pecos, TX 1443
West Pasco Historical Society Museum
  and Library, New Port Richey, FL 329
West Point Museum, West Point, NY 1085
Western Archeological & Conservation
  Center, Tucson, AZ.........................52
Western Heritage Center, Billings, MT 841
Western Historic Radio Museum, Virginia
  City, NV...882
Western Michigan University Richmond
  Center for Visual Arts School of Art,
  Kalamazoo, MI 749
Western Museum of Mining & Industry,
  Colorado Springs, CO 208
Western Reserve Historical Society,
  Cleveland, OH 1156
Westminster Historical Society,
  Westminster, VT 1490
Weston Woods Institute, Weston, CT 266
Westport Historical Society, Westport, CT ...266
The Wethersfield Historical Society,
  Wethersfield, CT.............................266
Wharton County Historical Museum,
  Wharton, TX 1461
Wheels O' Time Museum, Peoria, IL...........451
Whiskeytown Unit,
  Whiskeytown-Shasta-Trinity National
  Recreation Area, Whiskeytown, CA........198
White County Historical Society, Carmi,
  IL 415
White County Historical Society
  Museum, Monticello, IN 491
White Pine Public Museum, Ely, NV..........877
Whitehall Museum House, Middletown,
  RI 1312
Whitehead Memorial Museum, Del Rio,
  TX 1409
Whitewater Canal State Historic Site,
  Metamora, IN..................................490
Whitingham Historical Museum,
  Whitingham, VT..............................1490

Whitman Mission National Historic Site,
  Walla Walla, WA 1577
William Brewster Nickerson Memorial
  Room, Cape Cod Community College,
  West Barnstable, MA 717
William Hammond Mathers Museum,
  Bloomington, IN.............................470
William Holmes McGuffey Museum,
  Oxford, OH 1181
William Howard Taft National Historic
  Site, Cincinnati, OH 1151
William J. Clinton Presidential Library &
  Museum, Little Rock, AR................63
Williamson County Historical Society,
  Marion, IL......................................444
Wilmette Historical Museum, Wilmette,
  IL 466
Wilmington Railroad Museum,
  Wilmington, NC..............................1124
Wilson County Historical Society
  Museum, Fredonia, KS....................540
Wilson's Creek National Battlefield,
  Republic, MO 829
Wilton House Museum, Richmond, VA 1534
Winnetka Historical Society, Winnetka,
  IL 466
Winona County Historical Museum,
  Winona, MN 797
Winston Churchill Memorial and Library,
  Fulton, MO.....................................816
Wiscasset, Waterville & Farmington
  Railway Museum, Alna, ME............603
Wisconsin Automotive Museum,
  Hartford, WI 1600
Wisconsin Veterans Museum-King, King,
  WI 1602
Wisconsin Veterans Museum-Madison,
  Madison, WI 1606
Wiseman & FireHouse Galleries, Rogue
  Community College, Grants Pass, OR ..1225
Wolf Point Area Historical Society, Inc.,
  Wolf Point, MT 855
The Wolfsonian - Florida International
  University, Miami Beach, FL............327
Women's History Museum, West Liberty,
  WV 1587
The Women's Museum: An Institute for
  the Future, Dallas, TX....................1408
Wood County Historical Center and
  Museum, Bowling Green, OH 1143
Woodbine International Fire Museum,
  Woodbine, GA 392
Woodrow Wilson Presidential Library at
  His Birthplace, Staunton, VA...........1537
Woodside Store Historic Site, Woodside,
  CA 199
Woolaroc Museum, Bartlesville, OK 1197
Worcester County Horticultural
  Society/Tower Hill Botanic Garden,
  Boylston, MA 670
Worcester Historical Museum, Worcester,
  MA 721
Workman & Temple Family Homestead
  Museum, City of Industry, CA 85
The Works: Ohio Center for History, Art
  & Technology, Newark, OH..............1179
World Kite Museum & Hall of Fame,
  Long Beach, WA 1558
Wrangell Museum, Wrangell, AK...............29
Wray Museum, Wray, CO.........................235
Wren's Nest, Atlanta, GA 364
Wright County Historical Society,
  Buffalo, MN 770
Wright Museum, Wolfeboro, NH................897
Wyandotte County Museum, Bonner
  Springs, KS....................................534
Wyandotte Museum, Wyandotte, MI 766
Wyatt Earp Birthplace Home, Monmouth,
  IL 445
The Wyckoff Farmhouse Museum,
  Brooklyn, NY 970
Wyoming Pioneer Memorial Museum,
  Douglas, WY 1632

Yakima Valley Museum and Historical
  Association, Yakima, WA.................1579
Yankee Air Force, Inc. (Yankee Air
  Museum), Ypsilanti, MI 766
Yates County Genealogical and Historical
  Society and Oliver House Museum
  and L. Caroline Underwood Museum,
  Penn Yan, NY 1052
Ybor City Museum State Park, Tampa,
  FL 351
Yellowstone National Park, Gardiner, MT ...847
Yeshiva University Museum at the Center
  for Jewish History, New York, NY........1041
Yogi Berra Museum and Learning Center,
  Little Falls, NJ 910
The Yosemite Museum, National Park
  Service, Yosemite National Park, CA......199
Yucaipa Valley Historical Society
  Museum, Yucaipa, CA.....................201

Zalud House, Porterville, CA......................144
Zeum, San Francisco, CA 170
Zion Human History Museum,
  Springdale, UT................................1474
Zippo/Case Visitors Center, Bradford, PA..1244
Zoar State Memorial, Zoar, OH..................1194

Distribution and Transportation Artifacts

A.R. Bowman Memorial Museum,
  Prineville, OR.................................1234
A:shiwi A:wan Museum and Heritage
  Center, Zuni, NM 954
AT & SF Depot, Alden, KS........................532
Aberdeen Museum of History, Aberdeen,
  WA 1547
Abraham Lincoln Library & Museum,
  Lincoln Memorial University,
  Harrogate, TN.................................1366
Academy of Model Aeronautics/National
  Model Aviation Museum, Muncie, IN.....492
Adams Old Stone Grist Mill, Bellows
  Falls, VT 1476
Adan E. Treganza Anthropology
  Museum, Dept. of Anthropology, San
  Francisco State University, San
  Francisco, CA 162
Adirondack History Center,
  Elizabethtown, NY 987
The Adirondack Museum, Blue Mountain
  Lake, NY 963
Age of Steam Railroad Museum, Dallas,
  TX 1404
Agricultural and Industrial Museum, York
  County Heritage Trust, York, PA 1309
The Agricultural Memories Museum,
  Penn Yan, NY 1052
Agrirama, Georgia's Living History
  Museum & Village, Tifton, GA........388
Ah-Tah-Thi-Ki Museum at Okalee,
  Hollywood, FL................................312
Air Acres Museum, Cartersville, GA.........367
Air Classic Inc. Museum of Aviation,
  Sugar Grove, IL..............................461
Air Force Armament Museum, Eglin Air
  Force Base, FL 305
Air Force Flight Test Center Museum,
  Edwards AFB, CA...........................92
Air Mobility Command Museum, Dover
  AFB, DE...270
The Air Museum - Planes of Fame,
  Chino, CA.......................................84
Air Power Park & Museum, Hampton,
  VA 1509
Air Victory Museum, Inc., Lumberton,
  NJ 910
The Airborne & Special Operations
  Museum, Fayetteville, NC................1100
Airline History Museum, Kansas City,
  MO 820
Alabama River Museum, Finchburg, AL 9
Alamance Battleground State Historic
  Site, Burlington, NC........................1092

Distribution and Transportation Artifacts–Continued

Alamo Township Museum-John E. Gray Memorial Museum, Kalamazoo, MI........748

Alaska Aviation Heritage Museum, Anchorage, AK.........21

Alaska State Museum, Juneau, AK.........25

Albany Historical Society, Inc., Sabetha, KS.........557

Albany Institute of History & Art, Albany, NY.........954

Alexander & Baldwin Sugar Museum, Puunene, HI.........401

Alexander Ramsey House, Minnesota Historical Society, Saint Paul, MN.........789

Allegheny Portage Railroad National Historic Site and Johnstown Flood National Memorial, Gallitzin, PA.........1255

Allen County Museum, Lima, OH.........1172

Alton Museum of History and Art, Inc., Alton, IL.........410

America On Wheels, Inc., Allentown, PA..1239

American Airlines C.R. Smith Museum, Fort Worth, TX.........1416

American Airpower Heritage Museum, Inc. & Commemorative Air Force Headquarters, Midland, TX.........1438

American Helicopter Museum & Education Center, West Chester, PA.........1307

The American Heritage "Big Red" Fire Museum, Louisville, MS.........804

American Merchant Marine Museum, Kings Point, NY.........1007

American Numismatic Association Money Museum, Colorado Springs, CO.........206

American Quarter Horse Hall of Fame & Museum, Amarillo, TX.........1386

American Radio Relay League-Museum of Amateur Radio, Newington, CT.........256

American Royal Museum & Visitors Center, Kansas City, MO.........820

American Saddlebred Museum, Lexington, KY.........572

American Truck Historical Society, Kansas City, MO.........820

American West Heritage Center, Wellsville, UT.........1475

American Wings Air Museum, Blaine, MN.........769

Americana Museum, Terra Alta, WV.........1587

America's Black Holocaust Museum, Milwaukee, WI.........1610

America's Ice Cream & Dairy Museum, Medina, OH.........1175

Amherst County Museum & Historical Society, Amherst, VA.........1495

Amherst Museum, Amherst, NY.........957

Anacortes Museum, Anacortes, WA.........1547

Anadarko Heritage Museum, Anadarko, OK.........1195

Anchorage Museum at Rasmuson Center, Anchorage, AK.........22

Anderson/Abruzzo Albuquerque International Balloon Museum, Albuquerque, NM.........933

Anderson County Museum, Anderson, SC.1321

Angels Camp Museum & Carriage House, Angels Camp, CA.........71

Annie E. Woodman Institute Museum, Dover, NH.........886

Anoka County Historical Society, Anoka, MN.........767

The Antique Boat Museum, Clayton, NY....978

Antique Gas & Steam Engine Museum, Inc., Vista, CA.........196

The Appaloosa Museum and Heritage Center, Moscow, ID.........407

The Apple Trees Museum, Burlington, IA..506

Arab American National Museum, Dearborn, MI.........733

Archer County Museum, Archer City, TX.1387

Argo Gold Mine & Mill Museum, Idaho Springs, CO.........223

Arizona Historical Society Museum, Tucson, AZ.........47

Arizona Historical Society Museum at Papago Park, Tempe, AZ.........45

Arizona Historical Society Museum - Downtown, Tucson, AZ.........47

Arizona Historical Society Pioneer Museum, Flagstaff, AZ.........32

Arizona Military Museum, Phoenix, AZ.........39

Arizona Railway Museum, Chandler, AZ......31

Arizona State Parks Board, Phoenix, AZ.......39

Ark-La-Tex Antique & Classic Vehicle Museum, Shreveport, LA.........600

Arkansas Country Doctor Museum, Lincoln, AR.........61

Arkansas Museum of Natural Resources, Smackover, AR.........68

Arkansas Post National Memorial, Gillett, AR.........58

Arkansas Railroad Museum, Pine Bluff, AR.........65

Arkansas Tech University Museum of Prehistory and History, Russellville, AR.........67

Arlington Heights Historical Museum, Arlington Heights, IL.........411

Armand Bayou Nature Center, Houston, TX.........1424

The Arms Family Museum of Local History, Youngstown, OH.........1193

Ashland Historical Society Museum, Ashland, WI.........1590

Ashland Logging Museum, Inc., Ashland, ME.........603

Ashland Railroad Station Museum, Ashland, NH.........883

Ashland, The Henry Clay Estate, Lexington, KY.........572

Ashton Villa & The Heritage Visitor Center, Galveston, TX.........1420

Astronaut Memorial Planetarium and Observatory, Cocoa, FL.........300

Atchison County Historical Society, Atchison, KS.........533

The Athenaeum of Philadelphia, Philadelphia, PA.........1276

Atlanta Historical Society, Atlanta, GA.........358

Atlantic City Historical Museum, Atlantic City, NJ.........897

Atlantic 1, Swampscott, MA.........714

Atwater Kent Museum of Philadelphia, Philadelphia, PA.........1276

Au Glaize Village, Defiance, OH.........1162

Auburn Cord Duesenberg Museum, Auburn, IN.........468

Audie Murphy/American Cotton Museum, Inc, Greenville, TX.........1423

Augusta Museum of History, Augusta, GA.........364

Aurora Regional Fire Museum, Aurora, IL.........411

Automobile Driving Museum, Los Angeles, CA.........112

Automotive Hall of Fame, Inc., Dearborn, MI.........733

Autry National Center of the American West, Los Angeles, CA.........112

Aviation Hall of Fame and Museum of New Jersey, Teterboro, NJ.........926

B&O Railroad Museum: Ellicott City Station, Ellicott City, MD.........643

Baca House, Trinidad History Museum, Trinidad, CO.........233

Backing Up Classics Auto Museum, Concord, NC.........1097

Baldwin County Heritage Museum, Elberta, AL.........8

Baldwin Historical Society and Museum, Baldwin, NY.........960

Baldwin-Reynolds House Museum, Meadville, PA.........1270

Baltimore & Ohio Railroad Museum, Baltimore, MD.........629

Baltimore Civil War Museum, Baltimore, MD.........629

Baltimore Maritime Museum, Baltimore, MD.........630

Baltimore Museum of Industry, Baltimore, MD.........630

Baltimore Public Works Museum, Inc., Baltimore, MD.........630

Baltimore Streetcar Museum, Inc., Baltimore, MD.........631

Banner County Historical Society, Harrisburg, NE.........862

Banning Residence Museum, Wilmington, CA.........198

Bannock County Historical Museum, Pocatello, ID.........408

Baranov Museum, Kodiak, AK.........26

The Barbara Fritchie House, Frederick, MD.........644

Barber Vintage Motorsports Museum, Leeds, AL.........12

Barnes County Historical Museum, Valley City, ND.........1136

The Barnum Museum, Bridgeport, CT....235

Barron County Historical Society's Pioneer Village Museum, Cameron, WI.........1593

Barstow Route 66 Mother Road Museum, Barstow, CA.........74

The Bartlett Museum, Amesbury, MA.........657

Bartow History Center, Cartersville, GA.....367

Bartow-Pell Mansion Museum, Carriage House & Gardens, Bronx, NY.........964

Batsto Village, Hammonton, NJ.........907

The Battles Museums of Rural Life, Girard, PA.........1256

Battleship Texas State Historic Site, La Porte, TX.........1433

Baxter Springs Heritage Center and Museum, Baxter Springs, KS.........533

Beauvais Heritage Center, Clark, SD.........1345

Beaver Island Historical Society, Beaver Island, MI.........728

Becker County Historical Society, Detroit Lakes, MN.........772

Bedford Historical Society Museum and Library, Bedford, OH.........1142

Behringer-Crawford Museum, Covington, KY.........567

Belair Mansion, Bowie, MD.........638

Belair Stable Museum, Bowie, MD.........638

Belding Museum, Belding, MI.........728

Bell County Museum, Belton, TX.........1395

Belle Meade Plantation, Nashville, TN.........1377

Beloit Historical Society, Beloit, WI.........1592

Beltrami County History Center, Bemidji, MN.........768

Belvedere-Tiburon Landmarks Society, Tiburon, CA.........192

Benicia Fire Museum, Benicia, CA.........74

Benicia Historical Museum, Benicia, CA.....74

Benjy's Harley-Davidson, Huntington, WV.........1583

Bennington Covered Bridge Museum, Bennington, VT.........1476

Bent's Old Fort National Historic Site, La Junta, CO.........224

Berkeley County Museum & Heritage Center, Moncks Corner, SC.........1336

Berkshire County Historical Society, Inc. - Arrowhead, Pittsfield, MA.........702

Berkshire Museum, Pittsfield, MA.........702

Berkshire Scenic Railway Museum, Inc., Lenox, MA.........689

Bernard Historical Society and Museum, Delton, MI.........734

Bessemer Hall of History, Bessemer, AL.........3

Best Friend of Charleston, Charleston, SC..............................1324

Beverly Historical Society and Museum, Beverly, MA..............................662

Bexley Historical Society, Bexley, OH.......1143

Beyer Home, Oconto County Historical Society Museum, Oconto, WI..............1616

The Bicycle Museum of America, New Bremen, OH..............................1177

Big Thicket National Preserve, Kountze, TX..............................1432

Big Thunder Gold Mine, Keystone, SD.....1349

Billings Farm & Museum, Woodstock, VT..............................1490

Billy the Kid Museum, Fort Sumner, NM...939

Black Heritage Museum, Miami, FL............323

Black Hills Mining Museum, Lead, SD.....1350

Black River Historical Society of Lorain, Lorain, OH..............................1172

Blackberry Farm's Pioneer Village, Aurora, IL..............................411

Blackhawk Museum (Behring-Hofmann Educational Institute, Inc.), Danville, CA..............................89

Blaine County Historical Museum, Hailey, ID..............................406

Bluegrass Railroad Museum, Versailles, KY..............................584

Bluemont Historical Railroad Junction, Arlington, VA..............................1495

Boca Raton Historical Society, Boca Raton, FL..............................296

Bodie State Historic Park, Bridgeport, CA..............................79

Bolin Wildlife Exhibit & Antique Collection, McKinney, TX..............................1437

Bonner County Historical Museum, Sandpoint, ID..............................409

Booker T. Washington National Monument, Hardy, VA..............................1510

Boone County Historical Museum, Belvidere, IL..............................413

Boot Hill Museum, Inc., Dodge City, KS...536

Boothbay Railway Village, Boothbay, ME...607

Boothe Memorial Park and Museum, Stratford, CT..............................262

Bosque Memorial Museum, Clifton, TX....1400

Boston Fire Museum, Boston, MA..............664

Boulder City/Hoover Dam Museum, Boulder City, NV..............................875

Bowie Railroad Station and Huntington Museum, Bowie, MD..............................638

Boyertown Museum of Historic Vehicles, Boyertown, PA..............................1244

Bradford County Historical Society, Towanda, PA..............................1303

Bradford Ohio Railroad Museum, Bradford, OH..............................1143

Braintree Historical Society, Inc., Braintree, MA..............................670

Branchville Railroad Shrine and Museum, Inc., Branchville, SC..............................1322

Bridgton Historical Society, Bridgton, ME..............................607

Brigham City Museum-Gallery, Brigham City, UT..............................1463

The Bronx County Historical Society, Bronx, NY..............................964

The Broome County Historical Society, Binghamton, NY..............................962

Brownville Historical Society Museum, Brownville, NE..............................858

The Bruce Weiner Microcar Museum, Madison, GA..............................378

Brunswick Railroad Museum and C&O Canal Visitors Center, Brunswick, MD...639

Brunswick Town/Fort Anderson State Historic Site, Winnabow, NC..............................1124

Bucksport Historical Society, Inc., Bucksport, ME..............................608

Bucyrus Historical Society, Bucyrus, OH...1144

Buechel Memorial Lakota Museum, Saint Francis, SD..............................1355

Buffalo Bill Museum & Grave, Golden, CO..............................219

Buffalo Bill Museum of Le Claire, Iowa, Inc., Le Claire, IA..............................522

Buffalo County Historical Society, Kearney, NE..............................863

Buffalo Trails Museum, Epping, ND..............................1130

Bureau County Historical Society Museum, Princeton, IL..............................452

Burlington-Rock Island Railroad and Historical Museum, Teague, TX..............................1454

Burt County Museum, Tekamah, NE..............................873

Butler County History Center & Kansas Oil Museum, El Dorado, KS..............................537

C.F. Lott Historic Home, Oroville, CA........136

C. Grier Beam Truck Museum, Cherryville, NC..............................1096

C.M. Russell Museum, Great Falls, MT......848

COSI Columbus, Columbus, OH..............1157

Cabot Historical Society, Cabot, VT..............................1478

Caldwell County Railroad Museum, Princeton, KY..............................583

Calhoun County Museum, Port Lavaca, TX..............................1444

Calhoun County Museum & Cultural Center, Saint Matthews, SC..............................1341

California State Railroad Museum, Sacramento, CA..............................152

Camp Atterbury Museum, Edinburgh, IN....474

Camp Five Museum Foundation, Inc., Laona, WI..............................1604

Camp Hancock State Historic Site, Bismarck, ND..............................1127

Camp 6 Logging Museum, Tacoma, WA...1572

Campbell County Rockpile Museum, Gillette, WY..............................1633

Campbell House Museum, Saint Louis, MO..............................832

Canadian County Historical Museum, El Reno, OK..............................1200

Canal Fulton Heritage Society, Canal Fulton, OH..............................1145

Canal Society of New York State, Inc., Syracuse, NY..............................1076

Canby Historical Society, Canby, OR..............................1221

Cannon Falls Area Historical Museum, Cannon Falls, MN..............................770

Canton Classic Car Museum, Canton, OH.1145

Cape Fear Museum of History and Science, Wilmington, NC..............................1123

Cape Vincent Historical Museum, Cape Vincent, NY..............................976

Captain George Flavel House Museum, Astoria, OR..............................1218

Captain Nathaniel B. Palmer House - Home of the Discoverer of Antarctica, Stonington, CT..............................261

Carlton County Historical Society, Cloquet, MN..............................771

Carnegie Science Center, Pittsburgh, PA....1291

Carolinas Aviation Museum, Charlotte, NC..............................1094

Carriage and Western Art Museum, Santa Barbara, CA..............................178

Carriage House Museum, Colorado Springs, CO..............................206

Carroll County Historical Museum, Delphi, IN..............................474

Carson County Square House Museum, Panhandle, TX..............................1442

Carter County Museum, Ekalaka, MT..............................846

Casa Grande Valley Historical Society & Museum, Casa Grande, AZ..............................30

Cascade County Historical Society Museum, Great Falls, MT..............................848

Casey Jones Home and Railroad Museum, Jackson, TN..............................1367

Cashmere Museum & Pioneer Village, Cashmere, WA..............................1550

Cass County Historical Society at Bonanzaville, West Fargo, ND..............................1137

Cass County Museum & Pioneer School, Walker, MN..............................795

Cassia County Museum, Burley, ID..............................404

Casteel-Linn House and Museum, Princeton, MO..............................829

Castle Air Museum, Atwater, CA..............................72

Castle Clinton National Monument, New York, NY..............................1021

Castle Museum of Saginaw County History, Saginaw, MI..............................762

Castleton Historical Society, Castleton, VT..............................1478

Catalina Island Museum Society, Inc., Avalon, CA..............................73

Catawba County Museum of History, Newton, NC..............................1113

Catawissa Railroad Co., Catawissa, PA......1246

Cayuga-Owasco Lakes Historical Society, Moravia, NY..............................1015

Cedar Falls Historical Society, Cedar Falls, IA..............................507

Cedar Key Historical Society Museum, Cedar Key, FL..............................298

Cedar Key Museum State Park, Cedar Key, FL..............................299

Cedar Valley Memories, Osage, IA..............................526

Center for History, Wheaton, IL..............................465

The Center for Western Studies, Sioux Falls, SD..............................1356

Central Delta Depot Museum, Brinkley, AR..............................55

Central Florida Railroad Museum, Winter Garden, FL..............................354

Central Montana Historical Association, Inc. Museum, Lewistown, MT..............................850

The Central Museum, Central, AK..............................23

Central Nevada Museum & Historical Society, Tonopah, NV..............................882

Central Ohio Fire Museum, Columbus, OH..............................1157

Central Texas Museum of Automotive History, Rosanky, TX..............................1446

Century Village Museum, Burton, OH..............................1144

Champaign County Historical Museum, Urbana, OH..............................1188

Champion Mill State Historical Park, Champion, NE..............................859

Champoeg State Heritage Area Visitor Center, Saint Paul, OR..............................1235

Chappell Hill Historical Society Museum, Chappell Hill, TX..............................1399

Charles A. Lindbergh Historic Site, Little Falls, MN..............................779

Charles A. Weyerhaeuser Memorial Museum, Little Falls, MN..............................779

Charles H. Wright Museum of African American History, Detroit, MI..............................735

Charles River Museum of Industry, Waltham, MA..............................715

Charles Towne Landing State Historic Site, Charleston, SC..............................1324

Charlotte Museum of History and Hezekiah Alexander Homesite, Charlotte, NC..............................1094

Chateau De Mores State Historic Site, Medora, ND..............................1134

Cherokee Strip Land Rush Museum, Arkansas City, KS..............................532

Cherokee Strip Museum, Alva, OK..............................1195

Chesapeake and Ohio Canal National Historical Park, Hagerstown, MD..............................646

Chesapeake Bay Maritime Museum, Saint Michaels, MD..............................652

The Chesapeake Beach Railway Museum, Chesapeake Beach, MD..............................639

Cheyenne Frontier Days Old West Museum, Cheyenne, WY..............................1630

Chicago History Museum, Chicago, IL..............................419

Chicago Public Library, Chicago, IL..............................419

Chico Museum, Chico, CA..............................83

Distribution and Transportation Artifacts—Continued

Children's Discovery Museum of North San Diego, Carlsbad, CA 81

The Children's Museum of Indianapolis, Indianapolis, IN 481

Children's Museum of Maine, Portland, ME...618

The Children's Museum of Rose Hill Manor Park, Frederick, MD....................644

Chimney Point State Historic Site, Addison, VT..1475

Chinese House/O.R. & N. Museum & St. Peter's Catholic Church, Echo, OR 1222

Chisholm Trail Museum, Wellington, KS 561

Chisholm Trail Museum, Kingfisher, OK...1203

Christa McAuliffe Planetarium, Concord, NH...884

The Christian C. Sanderson Museum, Chadds Ford, PA...1246

Chula Vista Nature Center, Chula Vista, CA..84

Churchill County Museum and Archives, Fallon, NV..877

Cimarron Valley Railroad Museum, Cushing, OK..1199

Cincinnati Fire Museum, Cincinnati, OH...1149

City Island Nautical Museum, Bronx, NY...965

City Museum, Saint Louis, MO....................832

City of Bowie Museums, Bowie, MD.........638

City of Las Cruces Museum System, Las Cruces, NM..940

City of Las Vegas Museum and Rough Rider Memorial Collection, Las Vegas, NM 941

City of Wayne Historical Museum, Wayne, MI..766

Clallam County Historical Society, Port Angeles, WA.......................................1561

Clarion County Historical Society, Sutton-Ditz House Museum, Clarion, PA...1247

Clark County Museum, Henderson, NV 878

Classic Cars International, Salt Lake City, UT...1471

Clay County Historical Society Museum and Archives, Moorhead, MN.................784

Clear Lake Area Historical Museum, Clear Lake, WI...1594

Cleveland County Historical Museum, Shelby, NC..1119

Cleveland Police Historical Society & Museum, Cleveland, OH 1153

Clinton County Historical Association & Museum, Plattsburgh, NY.....................1052

Clinton County Historical Society, Wilmington, OH 1191

Clinton County Museum, Frankfort, IN 478

Coachella Valley Museum and Cultural Center, Indio, CA 104

Coal Miners' Museum/Van Lear Historical Society, Inc., Van Lear, KY 584

Codington County Heritage Museum, Watertown, SD..1359

The Coffey County Historical Museum, Burlington, KS...534

Cokato Museum & Akerlund Photography Studio, Cokato, MN............771

Cole Land Transportation Museum, Bangor, ME...604

College Park Aviation Museum, College Park, MD...641

Collier County Museum, Naples, FL.............328

Collin County Farm Museum, McKinney, TX..1437

Collin County Historical Society, Inc. & History Museum, McKinney, TX 1437

Collis P. Huntington Railroad Historical Society, Inc., Huntington, WV 1583

Colorado Historical Society, Denver, CO.....210

Colorado Railroad Museum, Golden, CO...220

Colton Area Museum, Colton, CA 87

Columbia Gorge Discovery Center and Wasco County Museum, The Dalles, OR..1237

Columbia Gorge Interpretive Center Museum, Stevenson, WA 1572

Columbia River Maritime Museum, Astoria, OR...1218

Combat Air Museum, Inc., Topeka, KS 559

The Commonwealth Museum, Boston, MA...665

Commonwealth of the Northern Mariana Islands Museum of History and Culture, Saipan, MP............................1640

Community Memorial Museum of Sutter County, Yuba City, CA........................200

Compass Inn Museum, Laughlintown, PA.1267

Confederate Memorial Hall-Bleak House, Knoxville, TN..1369

Conklin Reed Organ & History Museum, Hanover, MI...745

Connecticut Fire Museum, East Windsor, CT...239

Connecticut River Museum, Essex, CT........239

Connecticut Trolley Museum, East Windsor, CT...239

Constitution Convention Museum State Park, Port St. Joe, FL............................338

Conway Scenic Railroad, Inc., North Conway, NH 892

Cook County Historical Museum, Grand Marais, MN..776

Cookeville Depot Museum, Cookeville, TN..1364

Cooper-Hewitt National Design Museum, Smithsonian Institution, New York, NY..1023

Cooper Regional History Museum, Upland, CA...193

The Coopersville Area Historical Society Museum, Coopersville, MI.....................733

Coos Historical & Maritime Museum, North Bend, OR.......................................1229

Cordova Historical Museum, Cordova, AK...23

Coronado-Quivira Museum, Lyons, KS 550

Corry Area Historical Society, Corry, PA...1248

Cortland County Historical Society, Cortland, NY..982

The Country Doctor Museum, Bailey, NC.1091

The Cowley County Historical Society, Winfield, KS..564

Cowlitz County Historical Museum, Kelso, WA...1557

Cozens Ranch Museum, Fraser, CO.............218

Cracker Country, Tampa, FL.......................348

Cradle of Aviation Museum, Garden City, NY...992

Cramer-Kenyon Heritage Home, Yankton, SD...1359

Crane Point, Marathon, FL.........................323

Crawford Auto-Aviation Museum, Cleveland, OH......................................1154

Crawford County Historical Museum, Pittsburg, KS...556

Crazy Mountain Museum, Big Timber, MT...841

Creek Council House Museum, Okmulgee, OK.......................................1211

Crestline Shunk Museum, Crestline, OH ...1160

Crocker House, Mount Clemens, MI............756

Crook County Museum & Art Gallery, Sundance, WY.......................................1638

Crown Point State Historic Site, Crown Point, NY..984

Culbertson Museum, Culbertson, MT 845

Cumberland Gap National Historical Park, Middlesboro, KY.............................580

Cupertino Historical Society & Museum, Cupertino, CA..88

Curry Historical Society Museum, Gold Beach, OR...1225

Custer County 1881 Courthouse Museum, Custer, SD..1345

The Custom House Maritime Museum, Newburyport, MA.....................................697

Cuyahoga Valley National Park, Brecksville, OH.......................................1144

Cuyuna Range Historical Society & Museum, Crosby, MN 772

D.C. Booth Historic National Fish Hatchery, Spearfish, SD 1357

Dakota County Historical Society, South Saint Paul, MN.......................................793

Dakota Territory Air Museum, Minot, ND.1134

Dale & Martha Hawk Museum, Wolford, ND...1138

Dallam-Hartley XIT Museum, Dalhart, TX..1403

Dallas Firefighter's Museum, Inc., Dallas, TX..1404

Dallas Holocaust Museum, Dallas, TX 1405

The Dana-Thomas House State Historic Site, Springfield, IL.................................458

Danbury Railway Museum, Danbury, CT 238

Daniel Boone Homestead, Birdsboro, PA ..1243

Daniels County Museum and Pioneer Town, Scobey, MT.................................853

Daughters of Utah Pioneers Pioneer Memorial Museum & International Society Daughters of Utah Pioneers, Salt Lake City, UT 1471

Davidson County Historical Museum, Lexington, NC......................................1109

Dawson County Historical Museum, Lexington, NE...864

Dayton Historical Depot Society, Dayton, WA..1552

Dayton History at Carillon Park, Dayton, OH...1161

De Smet Depot Museum, De Smet, SD....1346

Dearborn Historical Museum, Dearborn, MI..733

Deer Park Escondido Winery & Auto Museum, Escondido, CA 93

Deerfield Beach Historical Society, Deerfield Beach, FL...................................304

Delaware Agricultural Museum and Village, Dover, DE.....................................269

Delaware and Hudson Canal Historical Society and Museum, High Falls, NY.....998

Delta County Historical Society Museum, Escanaba, MI..741

The Dennison Railroad Depot Museum, Dennison, OH.......................................1162

Denton County Historical Museum, Inc. and Texas Heritage Center, Denton, TX..1409

Denver Firefighters Museum, Denver, CO...211

Denver Museum of Miniatures, Dolls and Toys, Denver, CO.....................................211

The Depot Museum Complex, Henderson, TX.......................................1424

Depot Park Museum, Sonoma, CA 187

Depreciation Lands Museum, Allison Park, PA..1240

Deschutes County Historical Society, Bend, OR..1220

DeSoto County Museum, Hernando, MS.....801

Detroit Historical Society, Detroit, MI.........735

Dexter Historical Society Campus, Dexter, ME..609

Dickinson County Heritage Center, Abilene, KS...531

Discovery Museum, Sacramento Museum of History, Science and Technology, Sacramento, CA 152

Dixie Gun Works' Old Car Museum, Union City, TN.......................................1384

Dr. Daniel W. Kissam House, Huntington, NY.....................................1000

Dr. Increase Mathews House, Zanesville, OH...1194

Dr. William Robinson Plantation, Clark, NJ 901
Dog Mushing Museum, Fairbanks, AK..........24
Don F. Pratt Memorial Museum, Fort Campbell, KY.............568
Don Garlits Museum of Drag Racing Inc., Ocala, FL.............330
Door County Historical Museum, Sturgeon Bay, WI 1623
Door County Maritime Museum (at Sturgeon Bay), Sturgeon Bay, WI 1623
Dorothy G. Page Museum, Wasilla, AK 29
Douglas County Historical Society, Superior, WI.............1624
Douglas County Historical Society - Carson Valley Museum & Cultural Center, Gardnerville, NV.............877
Douglas County Historical Society - Genoa Courthouse Museum, Genoa, NV.............877
Douglas County Museum of History and Natural History, Roseburg, OR.............1234
Douglass Historical Museum, Douglass, KS.............537
The Downers Grove Park District Museum, Downers Grove, IL 431
Dows Depot Welcome Center, Dows, IA.....516
Drake Well Museum, Titusville, PA 1303
Drew County Historical Museum, Monticello, AR 64
Dublin-Laurens Museum, Dublin, GA 370
Dundy County Historical Society, Benkelman, NE.............857
Dunedin Historical Society & Museum, Dunedin, FL.............305
Dunn County Historical Society, Menomonie, WI.............1609
Durham Historic Association Museum, Durham, NH 886
Durham Western Heritage Museum, Omaha, NE 870

EAA AirVenture Museum, Oshkosh, WI....1616
Eagle Historical Society & Museums, Eagle, AK.............23
Eagle Tavern Museum, Watkinsville, GA ...391
EarlyWorks Museums, Huntsville, AL 11
East Ely Railroad Depot Museum, Ely, NV.............876
East Jordan Portside Art & Historical Museum, East Jordan, MI 739
East Texas Oil Museum at Kilgore College, Kilgore, TX.............1432
East Troy Electric Railroad Museum, East Troy, WI.............1595
Eastern Museum of Motor Racing, York Springs, PA.............1309
Eastside Heritage Center, Bellevue, WA 1548
Edmond Historical Society Museum, Edmond, OK.............1200
Edmonds South Snohomish County Historical Society, Inc., Edmonds, WA .1553
Edsel & Eleanor Ford House, Grosse Pointe Shores, MI.............745
Edwards County Historical Museum, Kinsley, KS.............547
1859 Jail, Marshal's Home & Museum, Independence, MO.............817
82nd Airborne Division War Memorial Museum, Fort Bragg, NC.............1101
El Camino Real International Heritage Center, San Antonio, NM.............947
El Dorado County Historical Museum, Placerville, CA.............142
El Paso Museum of History, El Paso, TX..1412
El Pueblo History Museum, Pueblo, CO.....230
Elgin Area Historical Society, Elgin, IL.......432
Ella Sharp Museum, Jackson, MI.............748
Ellingson Car Museum, Rogers, MN 788
Elliott Museum, Stuart, FL 346
Ellwood House Museum, DeKalb, IL.........429
Elmhurst Historical Museum, Elmhurst, IL.............433

Elwood Haynes Museum, Kokomo, IN........486
Empire Area Heritage Group, Empire, MI...740
Empire State Aerosciences Museum, Glenville, NY.............995
End-O-Line Railroad Park & Museum, Currie, MN.............772
Ephraim Historical Foundation, Ephraim, WI.............1597
Erie Canal Museum, Syracuse, NY 1076
Erie Canal Village, Rome, NY 1061
Erie Maritime Museum, Homeport U.S. Brig Niagara, Erie, PA.............1252
Ernie Pyle State Historic Site, Dana, IN.....473
Essex Shipbuilding Museum, Essex, MA 681
Essley-Noble Museum: Mercer County Historical Society, Aledo, IL.............410
Estes Park Museum, Estes Park, CO.............215
Estes-Winn Antique Automobile Museum, Asheville, NC.............1089
Eureka Pioneer Museum of McPherson County, Inc., Eureka, SD.............1346
Evansville Museum of Arts History & Science, Evansville, IN.............475
Evergreen Aviation Museum, McMinnville, OR.............1228
Exploration Station - A Children's Museum, Bourbonnais, IL.............414

Fairfax County Park Authority, Resource Management Division, Fairfax, VA.......1503
Fairfield County Museum, Winnsboro, SC.............1343
Fairport Marine Museum, Fairport Harbor, OH.............1164
Fantasy of Flight, Polk City, FL.............337
Farmers Branch Historical Park, Farmers Branch, TX.............1413
Farragut Folklife Museum, Farragut, TN ...1364
Farrar-Mansur House & Old Mill Museum, Weston, VT.............1490
FASNY Museum of Fire Fighting, Hudson, NY.............1000
Fayette County Helpers Club & Historical Society, West Union, IA.............530
Fayette Heritage Museum & Archives, La Grange, TX.............1432
Fenton History Center-Museum & Library, Jamestown, NY.............1005
Fillmore County Historical Center, Fountain, MN.............776
The Finley House, Wayne, PA.............1306
Finney County Kansas Historical Society, Inc., Garden City, KS.............541
Fire Museum of Maryland, Inc., Lutherville, MD.............649
Fire Museum of Memphis, Memphis, TN...1373
Fire Museum of Missouri, Willow Springs, MO.............840
Fire Museum of Texas, Beaumont, TX.....1394
1st Cavalry Division Museum, Fort Hood, TX.............1414
The First Division Museum at Cantigny, Wheaton, IL.............465
First Territorial Capitol of Kansas, Fort Riley, KS.............540
Fitchburg Historical Society, Fitchburg, MA.............683
Flagler Museum, Palm Beach, FL.............333
Florence Museum of Art, Science & History and the Florence Railroad Museum, Florence, SC.............1332
Florewood State Park, Greenwood, MS.......801
Florida Gulf Coast Railroad Museum, Parrish, FL.............335
Floyd County Historical Museum, Charles City, IA.............510
Folsom Museum, Inc., Folsom, NM.............939
Ford County Historical Society, Paxton, IL.............450
Forney Museum of Transportation, Denver, CO.............212
Fort Benton Museum of the Upper Missouri, Fort Benton, MT.............846

Fort Bliss Museum, Fort Bliss, TX 1413
Fort Boonesborough Museum, Richmond, KY.............583
Fort Bowie National Historic Site, Bowie, AZ.............30
Fort Buford State Historic Site, Williston, ND.............1137
Fort Caspar Museum, Casper, WY 1629
Fort Christmas Historical Park, Christmas, FL.............299
Fort Clatsop National Memorial, Astoria, OR.............1218
Fort Collins Museum, Fort Collins, CO.......217
Fort Concho National Historic Landmark, San Angelo, TX.............1447
Fort Crook Historical Museum, Fall River Mills, CA.............94
Fort Dalles Museum/Anderson Homestead, The Dalles, OR.............1237
Fort de Chartres State Historic Site & Museum, Prairie du Rocher, IL.............451
Fort Dix Museum, Fort Dix, NJ.............904
Fort Dodge & Frontier Village, Fort Dodge, IA.............518
Fort Douglas Military Museum, Fort Douglas, UT.............1465
Fort Fetterman State Historic Site, Douglas, WY.............1631
Fort Frederick State Park, Big Pool, MD.....637
Fort Garland Museum, Fort Garland, CO 217
Fort George G. Meade Museum, Fort Meade, MD.............643
Fort Hays State Historic Site, Hays, KS......543
Fort Henrietta Interpretive Park, Echo, OR.............1223
Fort Hunter Mansion & Park, Harrisburg, PA.............1258
Fort Jones Museum, Fort Jones, CA.............96
Fort Kearny State Historical Park, Kearney, NE.............864
Fort Laramie National Historic Site, Fort Laramie, WY.............1633
Fort Larned National Historic Site, Larned, KS.............547
Fort Leaton State Historical Site, Presidio, TX.............1444
Fort McKavett State Historical Site, Fort McKavett, TX.............1415
Fort Okanogan Interpretive Center, Brewster, WA.............1550
Fort Payne Depot Museum, Fort Payne, AL.............10
Fort Sidney Museum & Post Commander's Home, Sidney, NE.............873
Fort Sill National Historic Landmark, Fort Sill, OK.............1201
Fort Smith Museum of History, Fort Smith, AR.............58
Fort Smith Trolley Museum, Fort Smith, AR.............58
Fort Totten State Historic Site, Fort Totten, ND.............1131
Fort Towson Historic Site, Fort Towson, OK.............1201
Fort Union National Monument, Watrous, NM.............954
Fort Union Trading Post National Historic Site, Williston, ND.............1138
Fort Walla Walla Museum, Walla Walla, WA.............1576
Fort Washington Park, Fort Washington, MD.............643
45th Infantry Division Museum, Oklahoma City, OK.............1207
Fossil Country Museum, Kemmerer, WY..1635
Fosterfields Living Historical Farm, Morristown, NJ.............913
Fostoria Area Historical Museum, Fostoria, OH.............1164
Four Mile Historic Park, Denver, CO.........212
Four Rivers Cultural Center & Museum, Ontario, OR.............1229

Distribution and Transportation Artifacts–Continued

Four Wheel Drive Foundation, Clintonville, WI 1594

4th Infantry Division Museum, Fort Hood, TX 1415

Fox Island Historical Society, Fox Island, WA 1554

Fox Lake Historical Museum, Inc., Fox Lake, WI 1598

Fox River Trolley Museum/Fox River Trolley Association, South Elgin, IL 457

Franklin County Historical & Museum Society & House of History, Malone, NY 1012

Franklin County Historical Museum, Pasco, WA 1561

The Franklin Institute, Philadelphia, PA.....1280

The Franklin Pierce Homestead, Hillsborough, NH 889

Fraunces Tavern Museum, New York, NY 1025

Fredericksburg Area Museum & Cultural Center, Inc., Fredericksburg, VA............1506

Freeborn County Museum and Historical Village, Albert Lea, MN...........................767

Fremont County Pioneer Museum, Lander, WY 1635

The French Legation Museum, Austin, TX 1390

Fresno Metropolitan Museum, Fresno, CA 97

The Frick Art & Historical Center, Pittsburgh, PA 1292

Friends of Firemen's Museum, New Bern, NC 1112

Friendship Fire Company Museum, Woodbury, NJ 931

Friendship Firehouse, Alexandria, VA 1492

Frontier Army Museum, Fort Leavenworth, KS 539

Frontier Culture Museum, Staunton, VA 1537

Frontier Museum, Williston, ND 1138

Frontiers of Flight Museum, Dallas, TX 1406

Fulton County Historical Museum, Wauseon, OH 1190

Fulton County Historical Society Museum, Rochester, IN......................498

Gadsby's Tavern Museum, Alexandria, VA 1492

Gadsden Museum of Art, Gadsden, AL 10

Gage County Historical Society and Museum, Beatrice, NE 857

Galion Historical Museum, Galion, OH 1165

Galloway House and Village - Blakely Museum, Fond du Lac, WI....................1597

Galveston Historical Foundation, Inc., Galveston, TX.......................................1421

Galveston Railroad Museum, Galveston, TX 1421

Gardner House Museum, Albion, MI 723

Garfield Farm Museum, LaFox, IL 441

Garibaldi and Meucci Museum, Staten Island, NY 1072

Garrett Historical Museum, Garrett, IN........479

Gates Mills Historical Society, Gates Mills, OH 1166

General Patton Memorial Museum, Chiriaco Summit, CA 84

Genesee Country Village & Museum, Mumford, NY 1016

The George G. Frelinghuysen Arboretum, Morris Township, NJ..............................913

George I. Ashby Memorial Museum, Copper Center, AK 23

George Washington Carver Museum, Tuskegee Institute, AL 20

Georgia Historical Society, Savannah, GA...385

Georgia Veterans Memorial Museum, Cordele, GA 369

Georgia's Old Capital Museum, Milledgeville, GA......................................380

Georgia's Stone Mountain Park, Stone Mountain, GA 387

Gerald R. Ford Presidential Museum, Grand Rapids, MI...................................743

Gettysburg National Military Park, Gettysburg, PA 1255

Gibbs Museum of Pioneer and Dakotah Life, Falcon Heights, MN 775

Gig Harbor Peninsula Historical Society, Gig Harbor, WA.....................................1555

Gila County Historical Museum, Globe, AZ 35

Gilliam County Historical Society - Depot Museum Complex, Condon, OR.1222

Gilmore Car Museum, Hickory Corners, MI 746

Gilpin History Museum, Central City, CO...205

Glacier National Park Museum, West Glacier, MT...854

Glenn H. Curtiss Museum, Hammondsport, NY..................................997

Glenn L. Martin Maryland Aviation Museum, Baltimore, MD 632

Glensheen Historic Estate, Duluth, MN 773

Gold Coast Railroad Museum, Inc., Miami, FL 323

The Golden Age of Trucking Museum, Middlebury, CT 249

Golden Gate Railroad Museum, San Francisco, CA 166

Golden Spike National Historic Site, Brigham City, UT..................................1463

Golden State Model Railroad Museum, Point Richmond, CA 143

Golden Valley County Museum, Beach, ND 1127

Good Old Days Vintage Motorcar Museum, Inc., Hardy, AR 59

Goodyear World of Rubber Museum, Akron, OH 1139

The Grace Museum, Abilene, TX.............1385

Grand Canyon National Park Museum Collection, Grand Canyon National Park, AZ 36

Grand County Museum, Hot Sulphur Springs, CO 222

Grand Encampment Museum, Inc., Encampment, WY 1632

The Granger Homestead Society, Inc., Canandaigua, NY.................................975

Grant County Historical Society, Elbow Lake, MN..774

Grant-Kohrs Ranch National Historic Site, Deer Lodge, MT 845

Great Lakes Naval Memorial and Museum, Muskegon, MI 757

The Great Overland Station, Topeka, KS.....559

Great Plains Transportation Museum, Wichita, KS..561

Great Smoky Mountains Heritage Center, Townsend, TN......................................1384

Greater Loveland Historical Society Museum, Loveland, OH 1173

Greene County Historical Museum, Waynesburg, PA 1306

Greene County Historical Society, Xenia, OH 1193

Greybull Museum, Greybull, WY 1634

Grissom Air Museum, Peru, IN..................496

Grosse Ile Historical Society, Grosse Ile, MI 745

Groveland Yosemite Gateway Museum, Groveland, CA 101

Grumman Memorial Park, Calverton, NY ...974

Gunnison County Pioneer and Historical Society, Gunnison, CO 222

Gwinnett Historical Society, Lawrenceville, GA..................................376

Gwinnett History Museum, Lawrenceville, GA..................................376

H.G. Albee Memorial Museum, Estherville, IA...517

H.H. Franklin Foundation, Tucson, AZ..........49

Haas-Lilienthal House, San Francisco, CA 166

Hacienda Buena Vista, Ponce, PR 1642

Halifax Historical Museum, Daytona Beach, FL..303

Hall of Fame & Classic Car Museum, Weedsport, NY 1084

Hall of Flame Museum of Firefighting, Phoenix, AZ 40

Har-Ber Village, Grove, OK 1202

Hardin County Historical Museums, Inc., Kenton, OH 1170

Harney County Historical Museum, Burns, OR 1221

Harold Warp Pioneer Village Foundation, Minden, NE 868

Harpers Ferry National Historical Park, Harpers Ferry, WV 1582

Harrison County Historical Museum, Marshall, TX.......................................1436

Harry P. Leu Gardens, Orlando, FL 331

Hartsville Museum, Hartsville, SC 1335

Harvey County Historical Society, Newton, KS 553

Harvey House Museum, Florence, KS 539

Hastings Museum, Hastings, NE 863

Hattiesburg Area Historical Society and HAHS Museum, Hattiesburg, MS 801

Hatton-Eielson Museum & Historical Association, Hatton, ND 1132

Haverford Township Historical Society, Havertown, PA 1260

Hays Antique Truck Museum, Woodland, CA 199

Hayward Area Historical Society, Hayward, CA 102

Heart of Dixie Railroad Museum, Calera, AL 6

Heart of West Texas Museum, Colorado City, TX 1401

Heartland Museum of Military Vehicles, Lexington, NE 865

Hemet Museum, Hemet, CA.......................103

Henager "Memories and Nostalgia" Museum, Buckskin, IN.............................471

Hennepin History Museum, Minneapolis, MN 782

The Henry Ford, Dearborn, MI 733

Henry Ford Estate-Fair Lane, Dearborn, MI 734

Henry Guest House, New Brunswick, NJ 915

Hereford Inlet Lighthouse, North Wildwood, NJ 917

Heritage Complex Farm Equipment Museum and Learning Center, Tulare, CA 193

Heritage Farmstead Museum, Plano, TX ...1444

Heritage Hall Museum & Archives, Freeman, SD 1347

Heritage-Hjemkomst Interpretive Center, Moorhead, MN 784

The Heritage Museum, Astoria, OR 1218

Heritage Museum & Potton House, Big Spring, TX 1396

Heritage Museum of Northwest Florida, Valparaiso, FL..352

Heritage Museums & Gardens, Sandwich, MA 707

Heritage Square Museum, Los Angeles, CA 116

Heritage Village, Largo, FL 321

Heritage Village, Mountain Lake, MN 785

Hesston Steam Museum, LaPorte, IN 487

The Hickories Museum of the Lorain County Historical Society, Elyria, OH ..1163

High Desert Museum, Bend, OR...............1220

High Plains Western Heritage Center, Spearfish, SD 1357

Highland County Museum and Heritage Center, McDowell, VA 1517

Highlands Museum & Discovery Center, Ashland, KY 564

Hildene, The Lincoln Family Home, Manchester, VT 1481

Hiller Aviation Institute, San Carlos, CA 155

Hinckley Fire Museum, Hinckley, MN 778

Historic Arkansas Museum, Little Rock, AR 62

Historic Auto Attractions, Roscoe, IL 456

Historic Bethabara Park, Winston-Salem, NC 1125

Historic Charlton Park Village and Museum, Hastings, MI 745

Historic Cherry Hill, Albany, NY 954

Historic General Dodge House, Council Bluffs, IA 512

Historic Halifax State Historic Site, Halifax, NC 1105

Historic Madison, Inc., Madison, IN 489

Historic Preservation Association of Bourbon County, Inc., Fort Scott, KS 540

Historic Pullman Foundation, Chicago, IL...421

Historic Richmond Town, Staten Island, NY 1072

Historic Sauder Village, Archbold, OH 1140

Historic Walnford, Upper Freehold Twp., NJ 929

Historic Westville, Inc., Lumpkin, GA 376

Historical Museum at Fort Missoula, Missoula, MT.........851

The Historical Museum at St. Gertrude, Cottonwood, ID 405

Historical Museum of Southern Florida, Miami, FL.........324

Historical Society of Cheshire County, Keene, NH 890

Historical Society of Delaware, Wilmington, DE.........274

Historical Society of Fort Washington, Fort Washington, PA 1254

Historical Society of Greater Port Jefferson, Port Jefferson, NY 1053

Historical Society of Newburgh Bay & the Highlands - David Crawford House, Newburgh, NY 1042

Historical Society of Old Newbury, Cushing House Museum, Newburyport, MA 698

Historical Society of Santuit and Cotuit, Cotuit, MA 677

Historical Society of Stanton County Museums at Stanton and Pilger, Pilger, NE.........872

Historical Society of Talbot County, Easton, MD 642

Historical Society of the Phoenixville Area, Phoenixville, PA 1290

Historical Society of the Tonawandas, Inc., Tonawanda, NY.........1078

Historical Society of the Town of North Hempstead, Manhasset, NY 1013

The History Center in Tompkins County, Ithaca, NY.........1003

History Museum for Springfield-Greene County, Springfield, MO 839

History Museum of Western Virginia, Roanoke, VA.........1535

Holly History Center & Hutchinson House Museum, Waupaca, WI.........1626

Homestead National Monument of America, Beatrice, NE 857

Homeville Museum, Homer, NY.........999

Honolulu Police Department Law Enforcement Museum, Honolulu, HI.......396

Hood River County Historical Museum, Hood River, OR.........1226

Hopewell Furnace National Historic Site, Elverson, PA 1251

Horseless Carriage Foundation & Automotive Research Library, La Mesa, CA.........107

Hose 5 Fire Museum, Bangor, ME...............604

Hot Springs County Museum and Cultural Center, Thermopolis, WY 1639

Houghton County Historical Museum Society, Lake Linden, MI.........749

Houston Fire Museum, Houston, TX 1427

Howard County Historical Museum, Kokomo, IN.........486

Howard Steamboat Museum and Mansion, Jeffersonville, IN 486

Howard W. Cannon Aviation Museum, Henderson, NV.........878

The Hubbard Museum of the American West, Ruidoso Downs, NM.........946

Hudson River Maritime Museum, Kingston, NY.........1007

The Huguenot Historical Society, New Paltz, NY 1017

Hull Lifesaving Museum Inc., the Museum of Boston Harbor Heritage, Hull, MA.........687

Humpback Rocks Mountain Farm & Visitor Center, Waynesboro, VA 1544

The 100th Meridian Museum, Cozad, NE ...859

Hurst Ranch Historical Foundation, West Covina, CA.........197

Ice House Museum, Cedar Falls, IA 508

Idaho Military History Museum, Boise, ID.........404

Idaho Museum of Mining and Geology, Boise, ID.........404

Idaho State Historical Museum, Boise, ID...404

Illinois and Michigan Canal Commissioners Office Museum, Lockport, IL.........443

Illinois Railway Museum, Union, IL.........461

Ilwaco Heritage Museum, Ilwaco, WA.......1556

Independence Seaport Museum, Philadelphia, PA.........1281

Indian King Tavern Museum, Haddonfield, NJ.........906

Indiana Dunes National Lakeshore, Porter, IN.........496

Indiana Transportation Museum, Noblesville, IN.........495

Indianapolis Motor Speedway Hall of Fame Museum, Indianapolis, IN.........484

Inland Seas Maritime Museum, Vermilion, OH.........1189

International Motor Racing Research Center at Watkins Glen, Watkins Glen, NY.........1084

International Motorsports Hall of Fame and Museum, Lincoln, AL 13

International Museum of the Horse, Lexington, KY.........573

International Women's Air and Space Museum, Inc., Cleveland, OH.........1155

Interurban Railway Station Museum, Plano, TX.........1444

Intrepid Sea-Air-Space Museum, New York, NY.........1028

Iosco County Historical Museum, East Tawas, MI.........740

Iowa Aviation Museum, Greenfield, IA.......519

Iowa Great Lakes Maritime Museum, Arnolds Park, IA.........505

Iowa Railroad Historical Society, Boone, IA.........506

Iron & Steel Museum of Alabama, Tannehill Ironworks Historical State Park, McCalla, AL.........13

Iron Mission State Park & Museum, Cedar City, UT.........1464

Isabel Miller Museum/Sitka Historical Society, Sitka, AK.........27

Island County Historical Society Museum, Coupeville, WA.........1551

Islesboro Historical Society, Islesboro, ME.........612

Issaquah History Museum, Issaquah, WA..1557

Itasca County Historical Society, Grand Rapids, MN.........777

J.E. Reeves Home & Museum, Dover, OH.........1163

JFK Special Warfare Museum, Fort Bragg, NC.........1101

J.J. Jackson Memorial Museum, Weaverville, CA.........197

Jackson County Historical Museum & Research Library, Maquoketa, IA.........522

Jackson's Mill Historic Area, Weston, WV.........1587

Jacksonville Maritime Museum Society, Jacksonville, FL.........314

James Buchanan Foundation for the Preservation of Wheatland, Lancaster, PA.........1266

The James Madison Museum, Orange, VA.........1524

Jamestown Museum, Jamestown, RI.........1312

Jean Lafitte National Historical Park & Preserve, New Orleans, LA.........596

Jefferson Barracks Historic Site, Saint Louis, MO.........833

Jefferson County Historical Society and Farnsworth TV Pioneer Museum, Rigby, ID.........409

Jefferson County Historical Society Museum, Port Townsend, WA.........1562

Jefferson Landing State Historic Site, Jefferson City, MO.........819

Jefferson National Expansion Memorial, Saint Louis, MO.........833

Jensen Arctic Museum, Monmouth, OR....1228

Jerome County Historical Society, Inc. and Idaho Farm & Ranch Museum, Jerome, ID.........406

Jerome State Historic Park, Jerome, AZ 36

Jim Gatchell Memorial Museum, Buffalo, WY.........1629

John E. Conner Museum, Kingsville, TX ..1432

John Jay Homestead State Historic Site, Katonah, NY.........1006

John Muir National Historic Site, Martinez, CA.........124

John Stark Edwards House, Warren, OH ...1189

John Wornall House Museum, Kansas City, MO.........821

Johnson County Museum of History, Franklin, IN.........478

Johnson County Museums, Shawnee, KS 558

Johnson Hall State Historic Site, Johnstown, NY.........1005

Jonathan Hager House & Museum, Hagerstown, MD.........646

Jonesborough-Washington County History Museum, Jonesborough, TN.........1368

Julia A. Purnell Museum, Snow Hill, MD...654

Juneau-Douglas City Museum, Juneau, AK.........26

Juniata County Historical Society, Mifflintown, PA.........1271

Justice Brothers Racing Museum, Duarte, CA.........91

Kalamazoo Aviation History Museum, Kalamazoo, MI.........748

Kalkaska County Historical Museum, Kalkaska, MI.........749

Kanabec History Center, Mora, MN.........784

Kandiyohi County Historical Society, Willmar, MN.........796

Kansas Aviation Museum, Wichita, KS.......562

Kansas Cosmosphere and Space Center, Hutchinson, KS.........545

Kate Shelley Railroad Museum, Boone, IA.........506

Kaw Mission State Historic Site, Council Grove, KS.........536

Kearney County Historical Museum, Minden, NE.........868

Distribution and Transportation
Artifacts–Continued

Kelsey Museum of Archaeology, Ann Arbor, MI.......724
The Kemp-McCarthy Memorial Museum of the Rowe Historical Society, Inc., Rowe, MA.......706
Kenosha County Historical Society and Museum, Inc., Kenosha, WI.......1602
Kenosha Military Museum, Pleasant Prairie, WI.......1617
Kentucky Coal Mining Museum, Benham, KY.......565
Kentucky Derby Museum, Louisville, KY...576
Kentucky Military History Museum, Frankfort, KY.......569
Kentucky Railway Museum, Inc., New Haven, KY.......580
Keokuk River Museum, Keokuk, IA.......521
Kern County Museum, Bakersfield, CA.......73
Kewaunee County Historical Museum, Kewaunee, WI.......1602
Keyport Historical Society-Steamboat Dock Museum, Keyport, NJ.......909
Kimball House Museum, Battle Creek, MI.......727
Kimble County Historical Museum, Junction, TX.......1431
Kingman County Historical Museum, Kingman, KS.......547
Kingman Tavern Historical Museum, Cummington, MA.......678
Kinney Pioneer Museum and Historical Society of North Iowa, Clear Lake, IA...510
Kittery Historical & Naval Museum, Kittery, ME.......613
Kiwanis Van Slyke Museum Foundation Inc., Caldwell, ID.......404
Kline Creek Farm, Winfield, IL.......466
Klondike Gold Rush National Historical Park, Seattle, WA.......1566
Knight Museum, Alliance, NE.......855
Knox County Museum, Benjamin, TX.......1395
Knoxville Public Library, Knoxville, PA...1265
Kruger Street Toy & Train Museum, Wheeling, WV.......1588

LaBelle Heritage Museum, LaBelle, FL.......319
Lac Qui Parle County Historical Society, Madison, MN.......779
Lacey Historical Society, Forked River, NJ.......904
The Lackawanna Historical Society at the Catlin House, Scranton, PA.......1298
LaGrange Plantation, Cambridge, MD.......639
The Lake Champlain Maritime Museum, Vergennes, VT.......1488
Lake County Discovery Museum, Wauconda, IL.......463
Lake County Historical Museum, Tavares, FL.......351
Lake County Historical Society, Two Harbors, MN.......794
Lake Hopatcong Historical Museum, Landing, NJ.......909
Lake of the Woods County Museum, Baudette, MN.......768
Lake Pontchartrain Basin Maritime Museum, Madisonville, LA.......591
Lake Shore Railway Museum, North East, PA.......1274
Lake Superior Maritime Visitors Center, Duluth, MN.......773
Lake Superior Railroad Museum, Duluth, MN.......773
Lake Waccamaw Depot Museum, Lake Waccamaw, NC.......1109
Lake Wales Depot Museum & Cultural Center, Lake Wales, FL.......320
Lakewood's Heritage Center, Lakewood, CO.......225
Landis Valley Museum, Lancaster, PA.......1266

Landmark Park, Dothan, AL.......8
Lane County Historical Society & Museum, Eugene, OR.......1223
Langlade County Historical Society Museum, Antigo, WI.......1589
Lars Noak Blacksmith Shop, Larsson/Ostlund Log Home & One-Room Capitol School, New Sweden, ME.......616
Larz Anderson Auto Museum, Brookline, MA.......671
Laura Ingalls Wilder Museum and Tourist Center, Walnut Grove, MN.......795
Laws Railroad Museum and Historical Site, Bishop, CA.......78
Layland Museum, Cleburne, TX.......1400
Le Sault de Sainte Marie Historical Sites, Inc., Sault Ste. Marie, MI.......764
Lea County Cowboy Hall of Fame and Western Heritage Center, Hobbs, NM.......940
Leelanau Historical Museum, Leland, MI...751
Lehigh County Historical Society, Allentown, PA.......1239
Levine Museum of the New South, Charlotte, NC.......1095
Lewis County Historical Museum, Chehalis, WA.......1550
Liberty Hall Historic Site, Frankfort, KY....569
Licking County Historical Society, Newark, OH.......1178
Life on the Ohio River History Museum, Vevay, IN.......502
Limberlost State Historic Site, Geneva, IN.......479
Limon Heritage Museum, Limon, CO.......226
Lincoln County Historical Society, Lincoln, KS.......549
Lincoln County Historical Society, North Platte, NE.......869
Lincoln County Pioneer Museum, Hendricks, MN.......778
Lincoln Fire & Rescue Department Museum, Lincoln, NE.......866
Lincoln Park Historical Museum, Lincoln Park, MI.......751
The Lincoln-Tallman Restorations, Janesville, WI.......1601
Lincoln Train Museum, Gettysburg, PA.....1255
Linden Railroad Museum, Linden, IN.......488
Linn County Museum/Genealogy Library, Pleasanton, KS.......556
Lisbon Historical Society, Lisbon, OH.......1172
Lisle Station Museum, Lisle, IL.......443
Little Compton Historical Society, Little Compton, RI.......1312
Little White House Historic Site, Warm Springs, GA.......390
Livingston County Historical Society Museum, Geneseo, NY.......993
Livingston Depot Center, Livingston, MT...850
Locust Creek Covered Bridge State Historic Site, Laclede, MO.......825
Locust Lawn and Terwilliger House, Gardiner, NY.......993
Log Cabin Village, Fort Worth, TX.......1417
Logan County Historical Society Museum, Bellefontaine, OH.......1142
Lone Star Flight Museum/Texas Aviation Hall of Fame, Galveston, TX.......1421
Long Island Maritime Museum, West Sayville, NY.......1085
Long Island Museum of American Art, History & Carriages, Stony Brook, NY.......1075
Longmont Museum, Longmont, CO.......227
Longstreet Farm, Holmdel, NJ.......908
Lopez Island Historical Museum, Lopez Island, WA.......1558
Lorenzo State Historic Site, Cazenovia, NY.......976
The Los Angeles County Arboretum & Botanic Garden, Arcadia, CA.......71

Los Angeles Maritime Museum, San Pedro, CA.......176
Louis E. May Museum, Fremont, NE.......861
Louisiana Marine Fisheries Museum, Lafitte, LA.......590
Louisiana State Exhibit Museum, Shreveport, LA.......600
Louisiana State Museum, New Orleans, LA.......596
Louisville Slugger Museum & Factory, Louisville, KY.......577
Loveland Museum Gallery, Loveland, CO...227
Lowell Area Historical Museum, Lowell, MI.......751
Lowell's Boat Shop, Amesbury, MA.......658
Lucretia Vaile Museum, Palmer Lake, CO.......229
The Lyceum, Alexandria's History Museum, Alexandria, VA.......1493
Lynden Pioneer Museum, Lynden, WA.......1559
Lyndhurst, Tarrytown, NY.......1078
Lyndon B. Johnson National Historical Park, Johnson City, TX.......1431
Lynn Museum & Historical Society, Lynn, MA.......692
Lyon County Historical Society Museum, Marshall, MN.......780
The Lyons Redstone Museum, Lyons, CO...227

Mackinac State Historic Parks-Colonial Michilimackinac & Old Mackinac Point Lighthouse, Mackinaw City, MI....752
Mac's Antique Car Museum, Tulsa, OK...1215
Madison County Historical Society, Winterset, IA.......531
Mahaffie Stagecoach Stop and Farm, Olathe, KS.......554
Maine Lighthouse Museum, Rockland, ME.......621
Maine Maritime Museum, Bath, ME.......606
Maine State Museum, Augusta, ME.......604
Makoti Threshers' Museum, Makoti, ND...1133
Mamie Doud Eisenhower Birthplace, Boone, IA.......506
Mammoth Spring State Park, Depot Museum, Mammoth Spring, AR.......64
Manassas Museum System, Manassas, VA.......1516
Manassas National Battlefield Park, Manassas, VA.......1516
Maramec Museum, The James Foundation, Saint James, MO.......830
March Field Air Museum, Riverside, CA....149
Maridon Museum, Butler, PA.......1245
Marin History Museum, San Rafael, CA.....177
The Marine Museum at Fall River, Inc., Fall River, MA.......682
The Mariners' Museum, Newport News, VA.......1519
The Marion County Historical Society Museum, Marion, OH.......1174
Marion Public Library Museum, Marion, IN.......490
Maritime & Seafood Industry Museum, Biloxi, MS.......798
Maritime and Yachting Museum of the Treasure Coast, Stuart, FL.......346
Maritime Industry Museum at Fort Schuyler, Bronx, NY.......966
Maritime Museum - Cohasset Historical Society, Cohasset, MA.......676
Maritime Museum of San Diego, San Diego, CA.......157
Marquette County History Museum, Marquette, MI.......753
Marshall County Historical Society Museum, Warren, MN.......795
Marshall Gold Discovery State Historic Park, Coloma, CA.......86
Marvin Samson Center for History of Pharmacy/USP Museum, Philadelphia, PA.......1283
Maryland Science Center, Baltimore, MD...634

Mason County Historical Society/Historic White Pine Village, Ludington, MI 751
May Museum & Farmville Heritage Center, Farmville, NC 1100
Maymont, Richmond, VA 1530
Mayville Area Museum of History and Genealogy, Mayville, MI 754
Mayville Historical Society, Inc., Mayville, WI..1608
Mazomanie Historical Society, Mazomanie, WI 1608
McCallum Museum, Sibley, IA 527
McConaghy House, Hayward, CA 102
McCone County Museum, Circle, MT.........844
McHenry County Historical Society and Museum, Union, IL 461
McLarty Treasure Museum, Vero Beach, FL...352
Meade County Historical Society Museum, Meade, KS.............................552
Meagher County Historical Association Castle Museum, White Sulphur Springs, MT...855
Medina Railroad Museum, Medina, NY 1014
Mel Fisher Maritime Heritage Society, Key West, FL...318
Memoryville USA, Inc., Rolla, MO.............829
Memphis Belle B17 Flying Fortress, Memphis, TN...1374
Mendocino County Museum, Willits, CA 198
Mercer County Historical Museum, The Riley Home, Celina, OH 1146
Mercer County Historical Society, Mercer, PA..1271
Mercer Museum of the Bucks County Historical Society, Doylestown, PA.......1250
Mesa Historical Museum, Mesa, AZ..............37
Metamora Courthouse Historic Site, Metamora, IL...444
Miami County Museum, Peru, IN 496
Michigan Maritime Museum, South Haven, MI...764
Michigan Transit Museum, Inc., Mount Clemens, MI...756
Mid-America Air Museum, Liberal, KS.......549
Mid-Continent Railway Museum, North Freedom, WI...1615
Middlesex Canal Collection, Lowell, MA....691
Middlesex County Historical Society, Middletown, CT..249
Midway Village & Museum Center, Rockford, IL..455
Midwest Old Settlers & Threshers Association, Inc., Mount Pleasant, IA.....524
Mifflinburg Buggy Museum Association, Inc., Mifflinburg, PA................................1271
Mighty Eighth Air Force Museum, Pooler, GA..381
Milan Historical Museum, Inc., Milan, OH...1176
Milford Museum, Milford, DE 271
Military Aviation Museum, Virginia Beach, VA..1542
Military Museum of Southern New England, Danbury, CT...............................238
Military Veterans Museum, Inc., Oshkosh, WI...1616
Mill Race Historical Village, Northville, MI...758
The Millionaires' Cars & Disney Collection, Saint Ignace, MI...................763
Millville Army Air Field Museum, Millville, NJ..911
Milton House Museum Historic Site, Milton, WI...1610
Milwaukee County Historical Society, Milwaukee, WI......................................1611
Mingei International Museum, San Diego, CA..157
Minnesota Museum of Mining, Chisholm, MN...771

Minnesota Transportation Museum, Inc., Saint Paul, MN..792
Minnilusa Pioneer Museum, Rapid City, SD...1354
Minter Field Air Museum, Shafter, CA........186
Miracle of America Museum Inc., Polson, MT..852
Mississippi Agriculture & Forestry/National Agricultural Aviation Museum, Jackson, MS 802
Mississippi Armed Forces Museum, Camp Shelby, MS......................................799
Mississippi River Museum at Mud Island River Park, Memphis, TN......................1375
Missouri Historical Society, Saint Louis, MO..835
Missouri State Museum, Jefferson City, MO..819
Mitchell County Historical Museum, Osage, IA..526
Mitchell Gallery of Flight, Milwaukee, WI..1612
Monroe County Historical Society, Bloomington, IN.....................................469
Monroe Historical Society, Monroe, CT 250
Montana Historical Society, Helena, MT 849
Monticello Railway Museum, Monticello, IL...445
Montrose County Historical Museum, Montrose, CO...228
Moosehead Marine Museum, Greenville, ME..611
Moriarty Historical Museum, Moriarty, NM...943
Mormon Visitors Center, Independence, MO..818
Morris-Jumel Mansion, New York, NY 1030
Morton Grove Historical Museum/Haupt-Yehl House, Morton Grove, IL..446
Morton House Museum, Benton Harbor, MI..728
Morton Museum of Cooke County, Gainesville, TX..1420
Motion Unlimited Museum & Classic Car Lot, Rapid City, SD.........................1355
Motorcycle Hall of Fame Museum, Pickerington, OH.....................................1182
Mount Holly Community Historical Museum, Belmont, VT..........................1476
Mountain Gateway Museum, Old Fort, NC...1113
Mountain Heritage Center, Cullowhee, NC...1097
Mountain Life Museum, London, KY.........575
The Movie Museum, Owosso, MI...............759
Mulford Farm, East Hampton, NY..............986
Murfreesboro Historical Association, Murfreesboro, NC....................................1112
Museum and Arts Center in the Sequim Dungeness Valley, Sequim, WA.............1570
Museum at Southwestern Michigan College, Dowagiac, MI...........................738
Museum of Alaska Transportation & Industry, Inc., Wasilla, AK.......................29
Museum of Art/Fort Lauderdale, Fort Lauderdale, FL...307
Museum of Automobile Art and Design, Syracuse, NY...1076
The Museum of Automobiles, Morrilton, AR...64
The Museum of Bus Transportation, Inc., Hershey, PA...1261
The Museum of Early Trades and Crafts, Madison, NJ...910
The Museum of East Alabama, Opelika, AL...17
The Museum of Flight, Seattle, WA...........1567
Museum of Florida History, Tallahassee, FL...348
Museum of Flying, Santa Monica, CA 183
Museum of Funeral Customs, Springfield, IL...459

Museum of Great Christian Preachers & Ministries, Orange Park, FL....................331
The Museum of Man in the Sea, Inc., Panama City Beach, FL 335
Museum of Northwest Colorado, Craig, CO..208
Museum of Primitive Art and Culture, Peace Dale, RI...1316
Museum of Religious Arts, Logan, IA 522
Museum of San Diego History and Research Library, San Diego, CA 158
Museum of Science and Industry, Chicago, IL...425
Museum of Seminole County History, Sanford, FL...343
Museum of the Albemarle, Elizabeth City, NC...1099
Museum of the American Philosophical Society, Philadelphia, PA 1283
Museum of the Arkansas Grand Prairie, Stuttgart, AR..69
Museum of the Big Bend, Alpine, TX 1386
Museum of the Cape Fear Historical Complex, Fayetteville, NC....................1101
Museum of the Cherokee Indian, Cherokee, NC...1096
Museum of the Cherokee Strip, Enid, OK.1200
Museum of the City of Lake Worth, Lake Worth, FL...320
Museum of the City of New York, New York, NY...1033
Museum of the Fur Trade, Chadron, NE......859
Museum of the Great Plains, Lawton, OK.1204
Museum of the Gulf Coast, Port Arthur, TX...1444
Museum of the Llano Estacado, Plainview, TX..1443
Museum of the Middle Appalachians, Saltville, VA...1536
Museum of the Northern Great Plains, Fort Benton, MT.......................................846
Museum of Transportation, Saint Louis, MO..835
Museum of West Louisiana, Leesville, LA...591
Museum of Western Colorado, Grand Junction, CO...220
Museum of Women's History, Billings, MT..841
Museum of Yachting, Newport, RI.............1314
Museum on Main: A History Museum for West Georgia, LaGrange, GA................375
Museum Village, Monroe, NY...................1015
The Museums of Oglebay Institute - Mansion Museum & Glass Museum, Wheeling, WV.......................................1588
Muskegon County Museum, Muskegon, MI..757
Muskogee War Memorial Park & Military Museum, Muskogee, OK.........1205
NASA Glenn Research Center's Visitor Center, Cleveland, OH 1155
Nantucket Historical Association, Nantucket, MA...696
Nantucket Life-Saving Museum, Nantucket, MA...696
Narragansett Historical Society, Templeton, MA...714
NASA Kennedy Space Center, Merritt Island, FL...323
The National Agricultural Center & Hall of Fame, Bonner Springs, KS................534
National Air and Space Museum, Washington, DC......................................283
National Atomic Museum, Albuquerque, NM..934
National Automobile Museum (The Harrah Collection), Reno, NV 881
National Automotive & Truck Museum of the United States, Inc. (NATMUS), Auburn, IN..468

Distribution and Transportation Artifacts–Continued

The National Border Patrol Museum and Memorial Library, El Paso, TX 1412

National Canal Museum, Hugh Moore Historical Park and Museums, Easton, PA...1250

National Capital Trolley Museum, Silver Spring, MD 654

National Civil War Naval Museum at Port Columbus, Columbus, GA 369

National Corvette Museum, Bowling Green, KY 566

National Cowgirl Museum and Hall of Fame, Fort Worth, TX............................1418

National Frontier Trails Museum, Independence, MO..................................818

National Historic Oregon Trail Interpretive Center, Baker City, OR 1219

National Mississippi River Museum & Aquarium, Dubuque, IA.........................516

National Motorcycle Museum, Anamosa, IA 505

National Museum of American Jewish History, Philadelphia, PA 1284

National Museum of American Jewish Military History, Washington, DC 286

National Museum of Health and Medicine, Washington, DC 286

National Museum of Industrial History, Bethlehem, PA 1243

National Museum of Roller Skating, Lincoln, NE 866

National Museum of the Morgan Horse, Shelburne, VT..1487

National Museum of the United States Air Force, Wright-Patterson Air Force Base, OH...1193

National New York Central Railroad Museum, Elkhart, IN..............................475

National Ornamental Metal Museum, Memphis, TN...1375

National Packard Museum, Warren, OH 1189

National Park Service Museum Resource Center, Landover, MD.............................648

National Park Service Vicksburg National Military Park-Cairo Museum, Vicksburg, MS 809

National Postal Museum, Smithsonian Institution, Washington, DC....................287

National Railroad Museum, Green Bay, WI 1599

National Railroad Museum and Hall of Fame, Inc., Hamlet, NC 1105

National Road/Zane Grey Museum, Norwich, OH..1180

National Soaring Museum, Elmira, NY 988

National Sprint Car Hall of Fame & Museum, Knoxville, IA..........................521

National Warplane Museum, Horseheads, NY...999

Native American Exhibit, National Kateri Shrine, Fonda, NY...............................991

Natural History Museum of Los Angeles County, Los Angeles, CA.........................120

Nauticus, The National Maritime Center, Norfolk, VA 1522

Nauvoo Historical Society Museum, Nauvoo, IL..447

Navarro County Historical Society, Pioneer Village, Corsicana, TX.............1402

Nebraska Prairie Museum of the Phelps County Historical Society, Holdrege, NE 863

Neligh Mills, Neligh, NE...............................869

Nelson Pioneer Farm and Museum, Oskaloosa, IA 526

Nethercutt Collection, Sylmar, CA 190

Nevada County Historical Society, Inc., Nevada City, CA 130

Nevada Northern Railway Museum, Ely, NV..876

Nevada State Railroad Museum, Carson City, NV...876

Neversink Valley Area Museum, Cuddebackville, NY 984

New Bedford Fire Museum, New Bedford, MA..696

The New Berlin Historical Society, New Berlin, WI 1614

New Canaan Historical Society, New Canaan, CT...252

New England Air Museum of the Connecticut Aeronautical Historical Association, Inc., Windsor Locks, CT.....267

New England Fire and History Museum, Brewster, MA 670

New Hampshire Farm Museum, Inc., Milton, NH...892

New Hampshire Historical Society, Concord, NH...885

The New Hampshire Snowmobile Museum, Allenstown, NH........................883

The New Jersey Children's Museum, Paramus, NJ...919

The New Jersey Historical Society, Newark, NJ...916

The New Jersey Museum of Agriculture, North Brunswick, NJ.............................917

New Jersey Naval Museum, Hackensack, NJ...905

New Jersey State Police Museum, West Trenton, NJ...930

New London Historical Society, New London, NH...892

New Mexico Farm & Ranch Heritage Museum, Las Cruces, NM 940

New Orleans Fire Dept. Museum & Educational Center, New Orleans, LA 597

New Richmond Preservation Society, New Richmond, WI...............................1615

New York City Police Museum, New York, NY...1035

The New York Historical Society, New York, NY...1035

New York Museum of Transportation, West Henrietta, NY.............................1084

New York State Museum, Albany, NY.........955

New York Transit Museum, Brooklyn Heights, NY...970

Newark Valley Depot Museum, Newark Valley, NY...1042

Newton Fire Department, Newton, NJ.........917

Newtown Historic Association, Newtown, PA...1274

Newtown History Center, Stephens City, VA 1538

Nez Perce National Historical Park, Spalding, ID...409

The Niagara County Historical Center and Niagara County Genealogical Society, Lockport, NY.............................1010

Niles Depot Museum, Fremont, CA 96

Nishna Heritage Museum, Oakland, IA 525

No Man's Land Historical Society, Goodwell, OK...1201

The Noble Maritime Collection, Staten Island, NY...1073

Nobleboro Historical Society, Nobleboro, ME..616

North Alabama Railroad Museum, Huntsville, AL 12

North Andover Historical Society, North Andover, MA...698

North Carolina Auto Racing Hall of Fame, Mooresville, NC............................1111

North Carolina Maritime Museum, Beaufort, NC...1091

North Carolina Museum of History, Raleigh, NC...1115

North Carolina Transportation Museum, Spencer, NC...1120

North Dakota State Railroad Museum, Mandan, ND...1134

North Haven Historical Society, North Haven, CT...257

North Lee County Historic Center and Santa Fe Depot Museum Complex, Fort Madison, IA.......................................518

North Plainfield Exempt Firemen's Association, North Plainfield, NJ............917

North Platte Valley Museum, Gering, NE....861

North Tonawanda History Museum, North Tonawanda, NY 1043

Northeast Classic Car Museum, Norwich, NY...1044

Northeast Texas Rural Heritage Museum, Pittsburg, TX...1443

Northeastern Nevada Museum, Elko, NV 876

Northern Indiana Center for History, South Bend, IN.......................................499

Northern Pacific Railway Museum, Toppenish, WA 1575

Northport Historical Society Museum, Northport, NY...1044

The Northwest Carriage Museum, Raymond, WA...1564

Northwest Railway Museum, Snoqualmie, WA...1570

Novato History Museum, Novato, CA.........132

Oakland Museum of California, Oakland, CA...134

Oatlands, Leesburg, VA...............................1512

Ocean City Historical Museum, Inc., Ocean City, NJ...918

Ocean City Life-Saving Station Museum, Ocean City, MD...650

The Octagon House, Hudson, WI.............1600

Octave Chanute Aerospace Museum, Rantoul, IL...453

O'Fallon Historical Museum, Baker, MT.....840

Ohio Railway Museum, Worthington, OH .1192

Ohio River Museum, Marietta, OH 1174

Okefenokee Heritage Center, Waycross, GA...391

Oklahoma Firefighters Museum, Oklahoma City, OK...............................1209

Oklahoma Historical Society, Oklahoma City, OK...1209

Oklahoma Railway Museum, Oklahoma City, OK...1210

Oklahoma Route 66 Museum, Clinton, OK..1198

Oklahoma Territorial Museum, Guthrie, OK..1202

Old Bethpage Village Restoration, Old Bethpage, NY...1045

Old Bohemia Historical Society, Warwick, MD...656

Old Brutus Historical Society, Inc., Weedsport, NY...1084

Old Coal Mine Museum, Madrid, NM........943

Old Constitution House, Windsor, VT........1490

Old Conway Homestead Complex and Museum, Camden, ME.............................608

Old Cowtown Museum, Wichita, KS 562

Old Depot Museum, Ottawa, KS.................555

The Old Depot Railroad Museum, Dassel, MN...772

Old Dominion Railway Museum, Richmond, VA...1531

Old Firehouse Museum, Greenville, MS......800

Old Fort House Museum, Fort Edward, NY...991

Old Fort Jackson, Savannah, GA.................385

Old Fort Niagara, Youngstown, NY 1088

Old Greer County Museum & Hall of Fame, Mangum, OK.............................1204

Old Iron County Courthouse Museum, Hurley, WI...1601

Old Jefferson Town, Oskaloosa, KS 555

Old Manchester Museum, Manchester, CT...248

Old Mill Museum, Cimarron, NM................938

Old Prison Museums, Deer Lodge, MT.......845

Old Sacramento State Historic Park, Old Sacramento, CA..............135

Old Santee Canal Park, Moncks Corner, SC..............1337

Old State Capitol, Springfield, IL..............459

Old Town Hall Museum, Fifield, WI..........1597

Old Town San Diego State Historic Park, San Diego, CA..............158

Old Village Hall Museum, Lindenhurst, NY..............1009

Old World Wisconsin, Eagle, WI..............1595

The Oldest House Museum/Wrecker's Museum, Key West, FL..............318

Olympic Flight Museum, Olympia, WA....1560

Omniplex Science Museum, Oklahoma City, OK..............1210

Onondaga Historical Association Museum & Research Center, Syracuse, NY.........1077

Onslow County Museum, Richlands, NC...1117

Ontario County Historical Society, Canandaigua, NY..............975

Ontonagon County Historical Society Museum, Ontonagon, MI..............758

Orange Empire Railway Museum, Perris, CA..............141

Oregon Coast History Center, Newport, OR..............1229

Oregon Electric Railway Historical Society, Inc., Salem, OR..............1236

Oregon-Jerusalem Historical Museum, Oregon, OH..............1181

Oregon Military Museum, Clackamas, OR..............1221

Oregon Trail Regional Museum, Baker City, OR..............1219

Orpheum Children's Science Museum, Champaign, IL..............417

Otero Museum Association, La Junta, CO...224

Otter Tail County Historical Society, Fergus Falls, MN..............775

Outagamie Museum, Appleton, WI..........1589

Owls Head Transportation Museum, Owls Head, ME..............617

Ozark National Scenic Riverways, Van Buren, MO..............839

Ozaukee County Pioneer Village, Saukville, WI..............1620

P.H. Sullivan Museum and Genealogy Library, Zionsville, IN..............504

Pacific Aerospace Museum, Honolulu, HI...397

Pacific Aviation Museum - Pearl Harbor, Honolulu, HI..............397

Pacific Coast Air Museum, Santa Rosa, CA..............184

Pacific County Historical Museum, South Bend, WA..............1571

Pacific Northwest Truck Museum, Brooks, OR..............1220

Pacific Science Center, Seattle, WA..........1568

Painted Post - Erwin Museum at the Depot, Painted Post, NY..............1050

PALCO, Scotia, CA..............186

Palmer Foundation Chiropractic History, Davenport, IA..............513

Palmer House, Historical Society of Olde Northfield, Northfield, OH..............1180

Panhandle-Plains Historical Museum, Canyon, TX..............1399

Paris-Henry County Heritage Center, Paris, TN..............1382

Parishville Museum, Parishville, NY..........1050

Park City Historical Society & Museum, Park City, UT..............1468

The Park-McCullough House, North Bennington, VT..............1483

Parsons Historical Commission Museum, Parsons, KS..............555

Parsonsfield-Porter Historical Society, Porter, ME..............618

Pascack Historical Society, Park Ridge, NJ..............920

Pate Museum of Transportation, Cresson, TX..............1403

Patee House Museum, Saint Joseph, MO....831

Patriots Point Naval and Maritime Museum, Mount Pleasant, SC..............1337

Patten Lumbermen's Museum, Inc., Patten, ME..............618

Paul Bunyan Logging Camp Museum, Eau Claire, WI..............1596

Pawnee City Historical Society & Museum, Pawnee City, NE..............871

Pearson Air Museum, Vancouver, WA........1576

The Peary-MacMillan Arctic Museum, Brunswick, ME..............608

Pedaling History Bicycle Museum, Orchard Park, NY..............1047

Pembina State Museum, Pembina, ND.......1135

Pendleton District Agricultural Museum, Pendleton, SC..............1339

Pendleton Historic Foundation, Pendleton, SC..............1339

Pennsylvania Historical & Museum Commission, Harrisburg, PA..............1259

Pennsylvania Lumber Museum, Galeton, PA..............1254

Pennsylvania Military Museum and 28th Division Shrine, Boalsburg, PA..............1244

Pennsylvania Trolley Museum, Washington, PA..............1305

Pennyroyal Area Museum, Hopkinsville, KY..............572

Penobscot Marine Museum, Searsport, ME..............622

Peter Conser House, Heavener, OK..........1202

Peter Yegen Jr. Yellowstone County Museum, Billings, MT..............841

Petersen Automotive Museum, Los Angeles, CA..............121

The Petroleum Museum, Midland, TX.......1439

Phillips Historical Society, Phillips, ME......618

Phoenix Fire Museum, Mobile, AL..............15

Phoenix Museum of History, Phoenix, AZ..............41

Phoenix Police Museum, Phoenix, AZ..........41

Photomobile Model Museum, Woodstock, CT..............268

Piatt County Museum, Monticello, IL..........446

Pickens County Museum of Art & History, Pickens, SC..............1340

Pikes Peak Hill Climb Educational Museum, Colorado Springs, CO..............207

Pilgrim Monument and Provincetown Museum, Provincetown, MA..............704

Pima Air & Space Museum, Tucson, AZ.......50

Pinal County Historical Society and Museum, Florence, AZ..............34

Pine County Historical Society, Askov, MN..............768

Pink Palace Family of Museums, Memphis, TN..............1375

Pioneer Air Museum, Fairbanks, AK..............24

Pioneer Auto Museum, Murdo, SD..........1352

Pioneer Auto Trails Historical Society (PATHS), Tucson, AZ..............50

Pioneer Florida Museum Association, Inc., Dade City, FL..............302

Pioneer Museum & The Big Stampede, Fairbanks, AK..............24

Pioneer Museum and Vereins Kirche, Fredericksburg, TX..............1419

Pioneer Museum - Martin County Historical Society, Fairmont, MN..........775

Pioneer Museum of Alabama, Troy, AL........18

Pioneer Museum of Motorcycles & Conference Center, Tacoma, WA..........1574

Pioneer Settlement for the Creative Arts, Barberville, FL..............295

Pioneer Tunnel Coal Mine & Steam Train, Ashland, PA..............1241

Pioneer Village, Farmington, UT..............1465

Pioneers, Trail Drivers and Texas Rangers Memorial Museum, San Antonio, TX..............1449

Piper Aviation Museum Foundation, Lock Haven, PA..............1269

Pipestone County Historical Museum, Pipestone, MN..............786

Pithole Visitor Center, Pleasantville, PA....1295

Placer County Museums, Auburn, CA..........72

Plantation Agriculture Museum, Scott, AR..............67

Plantation Historical Museum, Plantation, FL..............337

Platt R. Spencer Memorial Archives and Special Collections Area, Geneva, OH..1166

Plymouth Historical Museum, Plymouth, MI..............760

Pocahontas County Museum, Marlinton, WV..............1584

Point Fermin Lighthouse, San Pedro, CA....176

The Polk County Historical Society, Cedartown, GA..............368

Polk County Historical Society, Crookston, MN..............771

Polk County Museum, Balsam Lake, WI...1590

Pony Express Museum, Saint Joseph, MO..............831

Port Huron Museum, Port Huron, MI..........761

Portland Harbor Museum, South Portland, ME..............623

Portola Railroad Museum, Portola, CA......144

Portsmouth Athenaeum, Portsmouth, NH....894

Powell County Museum, Deer Lodge, MT..............845

Prairie Trails Museum of Wayne County, Corydon, IA..............512

Pratt County Historical Society Museum, Pratt, KS..............556

Pro Rodeo Hall of Fame & Museum of the American Cowboy, Colorado Springs, CO..............207

Pueblo County Historical Society Museum and Edward H. Broadhead Library, Pueblo, CO..............230

Pueblo of Pojoaque, Poeh Museum, Santa Fe, NM..............949

Pueblo Weisbrod Aircraft Museum, Pueblo, CO..............230

Puget Sound Coast Artillery Museum at Fort Worden, Port Townsend, WA.........1562

Putnam County Historical Society Museum, Kalida, OH..............1169

Quincy Historical Society, Quincy, MA.......705

QV Historical Society at Carriage House Museum, Camden, NY..............974

R.E. Olds Transportation Museum, Lansing, MI..............751

RV/MH Heritage Foundation, Inc., Elkhart, IN..............475

Racine Heritage Museum, Racine, WI.......1619

Railroad and Heritage Museum Inc., Temple, TX..............1454

Railroad House Historical Association Museum, Sanford, NC..............1119

Railroad Museum of Long Island, Riverhead, NY..............1057

Railroad Museum of Minot, Minot, ND.....1135

Railroad Museum of Pennsylvania, Strasburg, PA..............1302

Railroaders Memorial Museum, Altoona, PA..............1240

Rails-to-Trails Conservancy, Washington, DC..............289

The Railway Exposition Co., Inc., Covington, KY..............567

Railway Museum of San Angelo, San Angelo, TX..............1447

Railways to Yesterday, Inc., Rockhill Furnace, PA..............1297

Raleigh City Museum, Raleigh, NC..........1117

Distribution and Transportation Artifacts–Continued

The Ralph Foster Museum, Point Lookout, MO 828

Ralston Historical Association, John Ralston Museum, Mendham, NJ 911

Randolph County Historical Museum, Winchester, IN 503

Randolph County Museum (At Beverly), Beverly, WV 1580

Randolph Historical Society, Inc., Randolph, VT 1485

Rankin Museum, Rankin, TX 1445

Raton Museum, Raton, NM 945

Raynham Hall Museum, Oyster Bay, NY .1049

Reading Railroad Heritage Museum, Reading, PA 1296

Red River Historical Museum, Sherman, TX 1452

Reedville Fishermen's Museum, Reedville, VA 1527

Reginald F. Lewis Museum of Maryland African American History and Culture, Baltimore, MD 636

Reno County Museum, Hutchinson, KS 545

Renton Historical Society and Museum, Renton, WA 1564

Renville County Historical Society, Inc., Mohall, ND 1135

Republic County Historical Society Museum, Belleville, KS 534

Rhinebeck Aerodrome Museum, Rhinebeck, NY 1056

Rhode Island Historical Society, Providence, RI 1318

Richardson-Bates House Museum, Oswego, NY 1048

Rifle Creek Museum, Rifle, CO 231

Riley County Historical Museum, Manhattan, KS 551

Rim Country Museum, Payson, AZ 38

Rio Grande Valley Museum, Harlingen, TX 1423

River Heritage Museum, Paducah, KY 582

Riverside Museum, La Crosse, WI 1603

Riverton Museum, Riverton, WY 1637

Roanoke Island Festival Park; Homeport of the "Elizabeth II", Manteo, NC 1110

Roaring Twenties Antique Car Museum, Hood, VA 1511

Robert A. Bogan Fire Museum, Baton Rouge, LA 587

Robert Fulton Birthplace, Quarryville, PA .1295

Robert S. Kerr Museum, Poteau, OK 1212

Rock Island Arsenal Museum, Rock Island, IL 454

Rock Springs Historical Museum, Rock Springs, WY 1638

Rockbridge Historical Society, Lexington, VA 1513

Rockhill Trolley Museum, Rockhill Furnace, PA 1297

Rocky Reach Dam, Wenatchee, WA 1577

Rodgers Tavern, Perryville, MD 650

Rogers Historical Museum, Rogers, AR 67

Rollo Jamison Museum, Platteville, WI 1617

Rome Historical Society Museum, Rome, NY 1061

Roosevelt County Museum, Portales, NM ...944

Roscoe Village Foundation, Coshocton, OH 1159

Rose Center Museum, Morristown, TN 1376

Rose Hill Plantation State Historic Site, Union, SC 1343

Roseau County Historical Museum and Interpretive Center, Roseau, MN 788

Rough & Tumble Engineers Historical Association, Kinzers, PA 1265

Royalton Historical Society, Royalton, VT 1486

Rural Life Museum & Windrush Gardens, Baton Rouge, LA 587

Ruth and Charles Gilb Arcadia Historical Museum, Arcadia, CA 71

Rutherford County Farm Museum, Forest City, NC 1101

S.S. Meteor Maritime Museum, Superior, WI 1624

Saginaw Valley Zoological Society, Saginaw, MI 763

Sailor's Memorial Museum, Islesboro, ME 612

St. Albans Historical Museum, Saint Albans, VT 1486

St. Charles Heritage Center, Saint Charles, IL 457

St. Joseph Museum Inc., Saint Joseph, MO 831

St. Petersburg Museum of History, Saint Petersburg, FL 342

Ste. Genevieve Museum, Sainte Genevieve, MO 838

Salamanca Rail Museum, Salamanca, NY .1063

Salem Historical Society and Museum, Salem, OH 1184

Salem Maritime National Historic Site, Salem, MA 707

Salvador Dali Museum, Saint Petersburg, FL 342

Sam Houston Memorial Museum, Huntsville, TX 1430

Sam Houston Regional Library & Research Center, Liberty, TX 1434

Sam Rayburn House Museum, Bonham, TX 1397

San Diego Air & Space Museum, San Diego, CA 159

San Diego Automotive Museum, San Diego, CA 159

San Diego Model Railroad Museum, Inc., San Diego, CA 159

San Francisco International Airport; San Francisco Airport Museums, San Francisco, CA 169

San Francisco Maritime National Historical Park, San Francisco, CA 169

San Joaquin County Historical Society & Museum, Lodi, CA 109

San Juan County Historical Society Museum, Silverton, CO 232

San Juan Historical Society, Friday Harbor, WA 1555

San Mateo County Historical Association and Museum, Redwood City, CA 147

Sanborn Area Historical Society, Sanborn, NY 1064

Sand Springs Cultural & Historical Museum, Sand Springs, OK 1213

Sandown Historical Society and Museum, Sandown, NH 896

Sandusky Library Follett House Museum, Sandusky, OH 1185

Sandy Bay Historical Society & Museums, Inc., Rockport, MA 705

Santa Fe Trail Center, Larned, KS 547

Santa Fe Trail Museum, Ingalls, KS 545

Santa Fe Trail Museum/Trinidad History Museum, Trinidad, CO 234

Santa Maria Museum of Flight, Inc., Santa Maria, CA 183

Santa Maria Valley Historical Museum, Santa Maria, CA 183

Santa Ynez Valley Historical Society, Santa Ynez, CA 185

Sapulpa Historical Museum, Sapulpa, OK .1213

Sarasota Classic Car Museum, Sarasota, FL 345

Saratoga Automobile Museum, Saratoga Springs, NY 1065

Sarpy County Historical Museum, Bellevue, NE 857

Savannah History Museum, Savannah, GA 386

Scarborough Historical Museum, Scarborough, ME 621

The Schuette Biermann Farmhouse Museum, Elk Grove Village, IL 432

Schuyler County Historical Society, Inc., Montour Falls, NY 1015

Sci-Port Discovery Center, Shreveport, LA 601

Science Museum of Virginia, Richmond, VA 1531

Scitrek, The Science and Technology Museum of Atlanta, Valdosta, GA 389

Scituate Maritime and Irish Mossing Museum, Scituate, MA 709

Scotland Heritage Chapel & Museum, Scotland, SD 1355

Scurry County Museum, Snyder, TX 1453

Seashore Trolley Museum, Kennebunkport, ME 613

Sedgwick-Brooklin Historical Society, Sedgwick, ME 622

1719 Hans Herr House & Museum, Willow Street, PA 1308

Shaker Museum, New Gloucester, ME 615

Shaker Village of Pleasant Hill, Harrodsburg, KY 571

Shakespeare Ghost Town, Lordsburg, NM ...942

Shako:wi Cultural Center, Oneida, NY 1046

Shasta College Museum & Research Center, Redding, CA 146

Shawnee Town, Shawnee, KS...................558

Sheboygan County Historical Museum, Sheboygan, WI 1621

Sheldon Jackson Museum, Sitka, AK..........27

Shiloh Museum of Ozark History, Springdale, AR 68

Shippensburg Historical Society Museum, Shippensburg, PA 1300

Ships of the Sea Maritime Museum/William Scarbrough House, Savannah, GA 386

Shirley-Eustis House, Boston, MA 669

Shore Line Trolley Museum, East Haven, CT 239

Shoreline Historical Museum, Seattle, WA 1569

Shortgrass Country Museum Society, Sayre, OK 1213

Sibley County Historical Museum, Henderson, MN 777

Sidney Historical Association, Sidney, NY 1069

Silent Wings Museum, Lubbock, TX 1435

Siloam Springs Museum, Siloam Springs, AR 68

Silt Historical Society, Silt, CO 232

Silvercreek Museum, Freeport, IL 435

Simonian Farms, Fresno, CA 98

Simsbury Historical Society, Phelps Tavern, Museum & Homestead, Simsbury, CT 260

Siouxland Heritage Museums, Sioux Falls, SD 1357

Siskiyou County Museum, Yreka, CA 200

Sisson Museum, Mount Shasta, CA 129

Skagit County Historical Museum, La Conner, WA 1557

Skagway Museum & Archives, Skagway, AK 28

Sleeping Bear Dunes National Lakeshore, Empire, MI 741

Sleepy Eye Depot Museum, Sleepy Eye, MN 793

Sloan Museum, Flint, MI 742

Sloss Furnaces National Historic Landmark, Birmingham, AL 5

Smith County Historical Society, Tyler, TX 1456

Smith Robertson Museum & Cultural Center, Jackson, MS 804

Smoky Mountain Trains, Bryson City, NC 1092
Smyth County Museum, Marion, VA 1516
The Snyder County Historical Society, Middleburg, PA................1271
The Society of California Pioneers, San Francisco, CA...............170
Sod House Museum, Aline, OK 1195
SoDus Bay Historical Society, Sodus Point, NY................1070
Somerset Historical Center, Somerset, PA .1300
Sophienburg Museum & Archives Inc., New Braunfels, TX 1440
South Boston-Halifax County Museum of Fine Arts & History, South Boston, VA................1536
South Carolina Law Enforcement Officers Hall of Fame, Columbia, SC 1330
The South Carolina Railroad Museum, Winnsboro, SC................1343
South Charleston Museum, South Charleston, WV 1586
South Coast Railroad Museum at Goleta Depot, Goleta, CA.......................100
South County Historical Society, Arroyo Grande, CA.......................72
South County Museum Inc., Narragansett, RI....................1313
South Dakota State Historical Society, Pierre, SD........................1353
South Dakota Tractor Museum, Kimball, SD.....................1350
South Florida Museum, Bishop Planetarium & Parker Manatee Aquarium, Bradenton, FL 297
South Florida Railway Museum, Deerfield Beach, FL 304
South Pass City State Historic Site, South Pass City, WY...................1638
South Street Seaport Museum, New York, NY.....................1039
South Sutton Old Store Museum, South Sutton, NH................896
South Wood County Historical Corp., Wisconsin Rapids, WI...................1628
Southampton Historical Museum, Southampton, NY................1070
Southeast Museum Association, Inc., Brewster, NY.......................964
Southeastern Railway Museum, Duluth, GA....................371
Southern California Chapter Railway & Locomotive Historical Society, Pomona, CA.................143
Southern Forest Heritage Museum, Long Leaf, LA....................591
The Southern Museum of Civil War and Locomotive History, Kennesaw, GA 375
Southern Museum of Flight, Birmingham, AL.................6
Southern Oregon Historical Society, Jacksonville, OR....................1226
Southwest Florida Museum of History, Fort Myers, FL....................309
Southwest Virginia Museum Historical State Park, Big Stone Gap, VA.............1497
Space Center Houston, Houston, TX.........1429
Space Farms Zoological Park and Museum, Sussex, NJ....................925
Spirit of '76 Museum, Wellington, OH 1190
Spiro Mounds Archaeological Center, Spiro, OK....................1214
Spring Valley Nature Center & Heritage Farm, Schaumburg, IL 457
Springfield Museums - Connecticut Valley Historical Museum, Springfield, MA....................710
Springfield Museums - Springfield Science Museum, Springfield, MA.........711
Stafford Air and Space Museum, Weatherford, OK....................1217
Stafford County Historical Society Museum, Stafford, KS....................558

Stagecoach Inn Museum Complex, Newbury Park, CA 130
Stamford Historical Society, Inc., Stamford, CT....................260
Stanley Museum, Estes Park, CO.........215
Stanley Museum, Inc., Kingfield, ME.........613
Star Cars Museum, Gatlinburg, TN............1365
State Agricultural Heritage Museum, Brookings, SD....................1344
State Historical Society of Iowa, Des Moines, IA....................515
State Historical Society of North Dakota, Bismarck, ND....................1128
State of Illinois-Historic Preservation Agency, Historic Sites Division, Springfield, IL....................460
Staten Island Institute of Arts & Sciences (SIIAS), Staten Island, NY 1074
Stauth Memorial Museum, Montezuma, KS....................553
Steam Railroading Institute, Owosso, MI 759
The Steamboat Arabia Museum, Kansas City, MO....................822
Steamboat Bertrand Collection, Missouri Valley, IA....................524
Steamship Historical Society of America, Providence, RI....................1319
Steamship Keewatin, Douglas, MI 738
Steamship William G. Mather Museum, Cleveland, OH 1156
Steamtown National Historic Site, Scranton, PA....................1299
Stearns History Museum, Saint Cloud, MN....................788
Steele County Historical Society, Hope, ND....................1133
The Stephen Phillips House, Salem, MA.....707
Stephenson County Historical Society, Freeport, IL....................436
Stephenville Museum, Stephenville, TX 1454
Stepping Stones Museum for Children, Norwalk, CT....................257
Steppingstone Museum, Havre de Grace, MD....................647
Sterling Hill Mining Museum, Inc., Ogdensburg, NJ....................918
Sterling-Rock Falls Historical Society Museum, Sterling, IL....................461
Sterne-Hoya House Museum and Library, Nacogdoches, TX....................1440
Stevens Museum, Salem, IN....................498
Stockbridge Library Historical Collection, Stockbridge, MA....................713
Stockholm Historical Society Museum, Stockholm, ME....................623
The Stone House Museum, Belchertown, MA....................662
Stonefield Historic Site, Cassville, WI 1593
Stonewall Jackson Museum at Hupp's Hill, Strasburg, VA 1539
Storrowton Village Museum, West Springfield, MA....................718
Stoughton Historical Society, Stoughton, WI....................1623
Strasburg Museum, Strasburg, VA.............1539
Strategic Air & Space Museum, Ashland, NE....................856
Stratford, Robert E. Lee Memorial Association, Inc., Stratford, VA 1539
Stuart House City Museum, Mackinac Island, MI....................752
Studebaker National Museum, Inc., South Bend, IN....................500
Suffolk County Historical Society, Riverhead, NY....................1057
Sullivan County Historical Society, Inc., Hurleyville, NY....................1001
The Sumter County Museum, Sumter, SC.1342
Sunset Crater Volcano National Monument, Flagstaff, AZ....................33
Susquehanna Museum of Havre de Grace Inc. at the Lock House, Havre de Grace, MD....................647

Swarthout Memorial Museum, La Crosse, WI....................1603
Sweetwater County Historical Museum, Green River, WY....................1633
Swisher County Archives and Museum Association, Tulia, TX....................1456
Talkeetna Historical Society and Museum, Talkeetna, AK....................28
Tallahassee Automobile Museum, Tallahassee, FL....................348
Tallahassee Museum, Tallahassee, FL 348
Tampa Bay History Center, Inc., Tampa, FL....................350
Ted Smallwood's Store, Inc., Chokoloskee, FL....................299
Temecula Valley Museum, Temecula, CA....191
Tempe Historical Museum, Tempe, AZ.........46
Temperance Tavern, Newcomerstown, OH....................1179
Tenino Depot Museum, Tenino, WA 1575
Tennessee Central Railway Museum, Nashville, TN....................1380
Tennessee Museum of Aviation, Sevierville, TN....................1383
Tennessee Valley Railroad Museum Inc., Chattanooga, TN....................1363
Territorial Capital-Lane Museum, Lecompton, KS....................549
Territorial Statehouse State Park & Museum, Fillmore, UT....................1465
Teutopolis Monastery Museum, Teutopolis, IL....................461
Tex Ark Antique Auto Museum, Texarkana, AR....................69
Texana Museum and Library Association, Edna, TX....................1410
Texarkana Museums System, Texarkana, TX....................1455
Texas Air Museum, Slaton, TX 1453
Texas City Museum, Texas City, TX..........1455
Texas Energy Museum, Beaumont, TX.......1395
Texas Forestry Museum, Lufkin, TX 1436
Texas Maritime Museum, Rockport, TX....1446
Texas Seaport Museum, Galveston, TX 1422
Texas Transportation Museum, San Antonio, TX....................1451
This Is The Place Heritage Park, Salt Lake City, UT....................1472
Thrasher Carriage Museum, Frostburg, MD....................645
Tillamook Naval Air Station Museum, Tillamook, OR....................1237
Timpanogos Cave National Monument, American Fork, UT....................1462
Tioga Point Museum, Athens, PA..............1241
Tobacco Farm Life Museum, Inc., Kenly, NC....................1107
Toledo Firefighters Museum, Toledo, OH..1187
Tomball Community Museum Center, Tomball, TX....................1455
Tombstone Courthouse State Historic Park, Tombstone, AZ....................46
Tooele County Railroad Museum, Tooele, UT....................1475
Torrington Historical Society, Inc., Torrington, CT....................263
Towe Auto Museum, Sacramento, CA 154
Town of Yorktown Museum, Yorktown Heights, NY....................1087
Toy Train Depot Museum and Train Ride, Alamogordo, NM....................932
Traill County Historical Society, Hillsboro, ND....................1132
Trails & Rails Museum, Kearney, NE..........864
Travel Town Museum, Los Angeles, CA 121
Traverse County Historical Society, Wheaton, MN....................796
Treasures of the Sea Exhibit, Georgetown, DE....................271
Trenton City Museum, Trenton, NJ.............928
Trenton Historical Museum, Trenton, MI.....765
Tri-Cities Museum, Grand Haven, MI 743

Distribution and Transportation
Artifacts—Continued

Tri-County Historical Society & Museum, Inc., Herington, KS 544
Triangle Tattoo & Museum, Fort Bragg, CA 95
Trolley Museum of New York, Kingston, NY 1008
Troutdale Historical Society, Troutdale, OR 1237
Trust for the Preservation of Maine Industrial History and Technology d/b/a Maine Narrow Gauge Railroad Co. & Museum, Portland, ME 620
T.T. Wentworth, Jr. Florida State Museum, Pensacola, FL 336
Tubac Presidio State Historic Park, Tubac, AZ 47
Tuckerton Seaport, Tuckerton, NJ 928
Tucson Rodeo Parade Museum, Tucson, AZ 52
Tulare County Museum at Mooney Grove Park, Visalia, CA 195
Tupelo Automobile Museum, Tupelo, MS ... 809
Turtle Mountain Chippewa Historical Society, Belcourt, ND 1127
Tybee Island Light Station and Tybee Museum, Tybee Island, GA 389

USDA Forest Service - Land Between the Lakes, Golden Pond, KY 570
U.S. Navy Museum, Washington, DC 292
Union County Historical Complex, Creston, IA 512
Union County Museum, Union, OR 1238
Union Pacific Historical Society (UPHS), Laramie, WY 1635
Union Pacific Railroad Museum, Council Bluffs, IA 512
United States Holocaust Memorial Museum, Washington, DC 293
The University of South Carolina McKissick Museum, Columbia, SC 1331
Upper Musselshell Historical Society, Harlowton, MT 849
U.S. Army Air Defense Artillery Museum, Fort Bliss, TX 1414
U.S. Army Aviation Museum, Fort Rucker, AL 10
U.S. Army Center of Military History, Museum Division, Fort McNair, DC 275
U.S. Army Engineer Museum, Fort Leonard Wood, MO 815
U.S. Army Medical Department Museum, Fort Sam Houston, TX 1415
U.S. Army Transportation Museum, Fort Eustis, VA 1504
U.S. Coast Guard Museum, New London, CT 255
The U.S. Space & Rocket Center, Huntsville, AL 12
USS Arizona Memorial, Honolulu, HI 398
USS Bowfin Submarine Museum & Park, Honolulu, HI 398
USS Constitution Museum, Boston, MA 669
USS Lexington Museum on the Bay, Corpus Christi, TX 1402
Utah State Historical Society, Salt Lake City, UT 1473

Vacaville Museum, Vacaville, CA 194
The Valdez Museum & Historical Archive Association, Inc., Valdez, AK 29
Valentine-Varian House/Museum of Bronx History, Bronx, NY 967
Valentown Museum, Victor, NY 1081
Valiant Air Command Warbird Air Museum, Titusville, FL 352
Vallejo Naval & Historical Museum, Vallejo, CA 194
Valley Community Historical Society, Inc., Valley, NE 874

Valley County Pioneer Museum, Glasgow, MT 847
Van Wyck Homestead Museum, Fishkill, NY 989
Ventura County Maritime Museum, Inc., Oxnard, CA 137
Ventura County Museum of History & Art, Ventura, CA 195
Vernon County Historical Museum, Viroqua, WI 1625
Victor Heritage Museum, Victor, MT 854
Vigo County Historical Museum, Terre Haute, IN 501
Vikingsholm, Tahoma, CA 191
The Vinalhaven Historical Society Museum, Vinalhaven, ME 624
Vintage Flying Museum, Fort Worth, TX .. 1419
Virginia Air & Space Center, Hampton, VA 1510
Virginia Aviation Museum, Richmond International Airport, VA 1534
Virginia Military Institute Museum, Lexington, VA 1514
Virginia Museum of Transportation, Inc., Roanoke, VA 1536
Volo Antique Auto Museum and Village, Volo, IL 463

W.H. Over Museum, Vermillion, SD 1358
The W.H. Stark House, Orange, TX 1442
W.K. Gordon Center for Industrial History of Texas, Mingus, TX 1439
Wabash Frisco and Pacific Association, Inc., Glencoe, MO 816
Wabasha County Museum, Wabasha County Historical Society at Reads Landing, Reads Landing, MN 787
Wabaunsee County Historical Museum, Alma, KS 532
Wade House Stagecoach Inn & Wesley Jung Carriage Museum State Historic Site, Greenbush, WI 1599
Wakefield House Museum, Blue Earth, MN 769
Wal-Mart Visitor's Center, Bentonville, AR 55
The Walker African American Museum & Research Center, Las Vegas, NV 880
Walkersville, Southern Railroad Museum, Walkersville, MD 656
Wallace District Mining Museum, Wallace, ID 410
Walter P. Chrysler Boyhood Home and Museum, Ellis, KS 538
Walter P. Chrysler Museum, Auburn Hills, MI 726
The Waltham Museum, Waltham, MA 716
Wantagh Historical & Preservation Society, Wantagh, NY 1081
Wapello County Historical Museum, Ottumwa, IA 526
War Eagle Air Museum, Santa Teresa, NM 951
Ward County Historical Society, Minot, ND 1135
Warhawk Air Museum, Nampa, ID 408
Warsaw Historical Museum, Warsaw, NY . 1082
Warther Museum Inc., Dover, OH 1163
Waseca County Historical Society, Waseca, MN 796
Washakie Museum, Worland, WY 1639
Washington County Historical Society and Miller House Museum, Hagerstown, MD 646
Washington County Historical Society Inc., West Bend, WI 1627
Washington County Rural Heritage Museum, Boonsboro, MD 637
Washington State Historical Society, Tacoma, WA 1574
Waterford Historical Museum and Cultural Center, Inc., Waterford, NY 1083
Waterfront Museum, Brooklyn, NY 970

Watkins Community Museum of History, Lawrence, KS 548
Watkins Woolen Mill State Historic Site & Park, Lawson, MO 825
Wayne County Historical Museum, Richmond, IN 497
Wayne County Historical Society, Lyons, NY 1012
Wayne County Historical Society, Honesdale, PA 1261
Wedell-Williams Memorial Aviation Museum, Patterson, LA 599
Wells Auto Museum, Wells, ME 625
Wells County Historical Museum, Bluffton, IN 470
Wells Fargo History Exhibit, Portland, OR 1233
Wells Fargo History Museum, Minneapolis, MN 783
Wells Fargo History Museum, Phoenix, AZ 42
Wells Fargo History Museum, Los Angeles, CA 122
Wells Fargo History Museum, Sacramento, CA 154
Wells Fargo History Museum, Sacramento, CA 154
Wells Fargo History Museum, San Diego, CA 162
Wells Fargo History Museum, San Francisco, CA 170
Wenatchee Valley Museum and Cultural Center, Wenatchee, WA 1577
Weslaco Museum, Weslaco, TX 1461
West Chicago City Museum, West Chicago, IL 464
West Florida Railroad Museum, Milton, FL 327
West of the Pecos Museum, Pecos, TX 1443
West Overton Museums, Scottdale, PA 1298
West Point Museum, West Point, NY 1085
West River Museum Society, Philip, SD 1353
West Virginia Northern Community College Alumni Association Museum, Wheeling, WV 1588
Western Aerospace Museum, Oakland, CA 134
Western Hennepin County Pioneers Association, Long Lake, MN 779
Western Mining & Railroad Museum, Helper, UT 1466
Western Museum of Flight, Hawthorne, CA 101
Western Museum of Mining & Industry, Colorado Springs, CO 208
Western North Carolina Air Museum, Hendersonville, NC 1105
The Western Railway Museum, Suisun City, CA 189
Western Reserve Historical Society, Cleveland, OH 1156
Western Springs Historical Society, Western Springs, IL 464
Westport Historical Society, Westport, CT ... 266
Westport Maritime Museum, Westport, WA 1578
The Wethersfield Historical Society, Wethersfield, CT 266
Whalers Village Museum, Lahaina, HI 401
Wheeler Historic Farm, Salt Lake City, UT 1474
Wheels O' Time Museum, Peoria, IL 451
Wheels of Yesterday, Ocean City, MD 650
Wheels Through Time Museum, Inc., Maggie Valley, NC 1110
Whippany Railway Museum, Whippany, NJ 930
Whipple House Museum, Ashland Historical Society, Ashland, NH 883
White 1 Foundation, Kissimmee, FL 319
White Pine Public Museum, Ely, NV 877

White River Valley Museum, Auburn, WA 1547
Whitehead Memorial Museum, Del Rio, TX 1409
Whitewater Canal State Historic Site, Metamora, IN 490
Whitingham Historical Museum, Whitingham, VT 1490
Whitman Mission National Historic Site, Walla Walla, WA 1577
Wilbur Wright Birthplace & Interpretive Center, Hagerstown, IN 480
Wildwood Historical Society, Inc., Wildwood, NJ 930
Wilkinson County Museum, Woodville, MS 810
William Clark Market House Museum, Paducah, KY 582
William Hammond Mathers Museum, Bloomington, IN 470
William McKinley Presidential Library & Museum, Canton, OH 1146
Willowbrook Museum Village, Newfield, ME 616
Wilmington Railroad Museum, Wilmington, NC 1124
Wilson Historical Museum, Wilson, NY 1086
Wing Luke Asian Museum, Seattle, WA 1569
Wings of History Air Museum, San Martin, CA 175
Wings Over Miami Museum, Inc., Miami, FL 326
Wings Over The Rockies Air & Space Museum, Denver, CO 213
Winnetka Historical Society, Winnetka, IL 466
Winona County Historical Museum, Winona, MN 797
Wiscasset, Waterville & Farmington Railway Museum, Alna, ME 603
Wisconsin Automotive Museum, Hartford, WI 1600
Wisconsin Maritime Museum, Manitowoc, WI 1607
Wisconsin Veterans Museum-Madison, Madison, WI 1606
The Wolfsonian - Florida International University, Miami Beach, FL 327
Woodlawn Museum/The Black House, Ellsworth, ME 610
Woodrow Wilson Presidential Library at His Birthplace, Staunton, VA 1537
Woodside Store Historic Site, Woodside, CA 199
Woodstock Museum of Shenandoah County, Inc., Woodstock, VA 1546
Worcester Historical Museum, Worcester, MA 721
Workman & Temple Family Homestead Museum, City of Industry, CA 85
The Works: Ohio Center for History, Art & Technology, Newark, OH 1179
Wrather West Kentucky Museum, Murray, KY 580
Wright Brothers National Memorial, Kill Devil Hills, NC 1108
Wright County Historical Society, Buffalo, MN 770
Wright Museum, Wolfeboro, NH 897
Wyalusing Valley Museum, Wyalusing, PA 1309
Wyandotte Museum, Wyandotte, MI 766

Yakima Valley Museum and Historical Association, Yakima, WA 1579
Yanks Air Museum, Chino, CA 84
Yates County Genealogical and Historical Society and Oliver House Museum and L. Caroline Underwood Museum, Penn Yan, NY 1052
Yellow Medicine County Historical Society and Museum, Granite Falls, MN 777

Yellowstone National Park, Gardiner, MT ...847
Yorba and Slaughter Families Adobe, Chino, CA 84
York County Heritage Trust, Fire Museum, York, PA 1309
Yorktown Historical Museum, Yorktown, TX 1462
Yucaipa Valley Historical Society Museum, Yucaipa, CA 201
Yuma Crossing State Historic Park, Yuma, AZ 54

Furnishings

A:shiwi A:wan Museum and Heritage Center, Zuni, NM 954
Abbie Gardner Cabin, Arnolds Park, IA 505
Abby Aldrich Rockefeller Folk Art Museum, Williamsburg, VA 1544
Abraham Lincoln Library & Museum, Lincoln Memorial University, Harrogate, TN 1366
Academy Hall Museum of the Rocky Hill Historical Society, Inc., Rocky Hill, CT 259
Ace of Clubs House, Texarkana, TX 1455
Adair County Historical Society, Inc., Kirksville, MO 824
Adam Thoroughgood House, Virginia Beach, VA 1541
Adams County Historical Museum, Decatur, IN 474
Adams County Historical Society, Gettysburg, PA 1255
Adams County Historical Society Museum, Lind, WA 1558
Adams County Historical Society Museum, Brighton, CO 204
Adams National Historical Park, Quincy, MA 704
Adams National Historical Park-John Adams and John Quincy Adams Birthplaces, Quincy, MA 704
Adams Old Stone Grist Mill, Bellows Falls, VT 1476
Adams State College Luther Bean Museum, Alamosa, CO 201
Adena Mansion and Gardens, Chillicothe, OH 1147
The Adirondack Museum, Blue Mountain Lake, NY 963
Adobe De Palomares, Pomona, CA 143
Adsmore Museum, Princeton, KY 583
African-American Museum and Library at Oakland, Oakland, CA 132
Afro-American Historical Society Museum, Jersey City, NJ 908
Agate Fossil Beds National Monument, Harrison, NE 862
Agecroft Hall, Richmond, VA 1527
Agricultural and Industrial Museum, York County Heritage Trust, York, PA 1309
Agrirama, Georgia's Living History Museum & Village, Tifton, GA 388
Aiken County Historical Museum, Aiken, SC 1320
Akta Lakota Museum and Cultural Center, Chamberlain, SD 1345
Al Goin Historical Museum, Portage, IN 496
Alabama Department of Archives & History, Montgomery, AL 15
Alabama Mining Museum, Dora, AL 7
Alabama Museum of the Health Sciences, Birmingham, AL 4
Alachua County Historic Trust: Matheson Museum, Inc., Gainesville, FL 310
Alamance Battleground State Historic Site, Burlington, NC 1092
Alamance County Historical Museum, Burlington, NC 1092
The Alamo, San Antonio, TX 1447
Alamo Township Museum-John E. Gray Memorial Museum, Kalamazoo, MI 748

Albany Historical Society, Inc., Sabetha, KS 557
Albany Institute of History & Art, Albany, NY 954
Albion Academy Historical Museum, Edgerton, WI 1596
Albuquerque Museum, Albuquerque, NM 932
Alden Historical Society, Inc., Alden, NY ...956
Alden House Historic Site, Duxbury, MA ...680
Alex Haley Home and Museum, Henning, TN 1367
Alexander & Baldwin Sugar Museum, Puunene, HI 401
Alexander House, Port Edwards, WI 1618
Alexander Ramsey House, Minnesota Historical Society, Saint Paul, MN 789
Alexandre Mouton House/Lafayette Museum, Lafayette, LA 589
Alexandria Museum of Art, Alexandria, LA 584
Alfred B. Maclay State Gardens, Tallahassee, FL 346
Alger County Heritage Center, Munising, MI 757
Alice Austen House Museum, Staten Island, NY 1072
Alice Moseley Folk Art and Antique Museum, Bay Saint Louis, MS 798
The Alice T. Miner Colonial Collection, Chazy, NY 977
Allaire Village Inc., Farmingdale, NJ 903
Allan Shivers Museum, Woodville, TX 1462
Allegan County Historical Society and Old Jail Museum, Allegan, MI 723
Allegany County Historical Society, Inc., Cumberland, MD 641
Allegheny Portage Railroad National Historic Site and Johnstown Flood National Memorial, Gallitzin, PA 1255
Allen County Museum, Lima, OH 1172
Alling Coverlet Museum, Palmyra, NY 1050
Allison-Antrim Museum, Inc., Greencastle, PA 1257
Almond Historical Society/Hagadorn House Museum, Almond, NY 957
Alpine County Museum, Markleeville, CA 124
Altama Museum of Art & History, Vidalia, GA 390
Alton Museum of History and Art, Inc., Alton, IL 410
Alvarado Adobe & The Blume House, San Pablo, CA 175
Amador County Museum, Jackson, CA 105
Amana Heritage Museum, Amana, IA 504
Amelia Earhart Birthplace Museum, Atchison, KS 532
Amelia Island Museum of History, Fernandina Beach, FL 306
American Catholic Historical Society, Philadelphia, PA 1276
American Clock and Watch Museum, Inc., Bristol, CT 236
American Computer Museum, Bozeman, MT 842
American Historical Society of Germans from Russia, Lincoln, NE 865
American Hungarian Foundation/Museum of the American Hungarian Foundation, New Brunswick, NJ 915
American Independence Museum, Exeter, NH 887
American Labor Museum, Botto House National Landmark, Haledon, NJ 906
American Museum of Nursing, Tempe, AZ 45
American Museum of Science & Energy, Oak Ridge, TN 1382
American Swedish Historical Foundation & Museum, Philadelphia, PA 1276
American Swedish Institute, Minneapolis, MN 781

Furnishings–Continued

American Textile History Museum, Lowell, MA 691

Americana Museum, Terra Alta, WV 1587

America's Black Holocaust Museum, Milwaukee, WI 1610

Amherst History Museum at the Strong House - Amherst Historical Society, Amherst, MA 658

Amherst Museum, Amherst, NY 957

Amity and Woodbridge Historical Society, Woodbridge, CT 268

Amos Herr House Foundation and Historic Society, Landisville, PA 1267

Anacortes Museum, Anacortes, WA 1547

Anadarko Heritage Museum, Anadarko, OK 1195

Ancient and Honorable Artillery Company, Boston, MA 663

Anderson County Historical Museum, Garnett, KS 541

Andover Historical Society, Andover, MA ...660

Andrew Johnson National Historic Site, Greeneville, TN 1366

Andrew Low House, Savannah, GA 384

Androscoggin Historical Society, Auburn, ME 603

Angels Attic Museum, Santa Monica, CA ...183

Anna Bemis Palmer Museum, York, NE.....875

Anna Miller Museum, Newcastle, WY 1637

The Anne Spencer Memorial Foundation, Inc., Lynchburg, VA 1515

Annie E. Woodman Institute Museum, Dover, NH 886

Annie Riggs Memorial Museum, Fort Stockton, TX...............1415

Anoka County Historical Society, Anoka, MN 767

Anson County Historical Society, Inc., Wadesboro, NC 1121

Antelope Valley Indian Museum, Lancaster, CA 108

The Antiquarian and Landmarks Society, Inc., Hartford, CT...............244

The Antique Boat Museum, Clayton, NY 978

Antique Gas & Steam Engine Museum, Inc., Vista, CA 196

Apostles Islands National Lakeshore, Bayfield, WI...............1591

The Apple Trees Museum, Burlington, IA...506

Appleton Museum of Art, Ocala, FL...........330

Appomattox Court House National Historical Park, Appomattox, VA 1495

Aptucxet Trading Post Museum, Bourne, MA 670

APVA Preservation Virginia, Richmond, VA 1528

APVA's John Marshall House, Richmond, VA 1528

Arab American National Museum, Dearborn, MI 733

Arbor Lodge State Historical Park, Nebraska City, NE 868

Arcadia Township Historical Commission, Arcadia, MI 726

Arches Museum of Pioneer Life, Winona, MN...............797

Archives Museum, Temple Mickve Israel, Savannah, GA...............384

Arden - The Helena Modjeska Historic House & Gardens, Modjeska Canyon, CA...............126

Ardenwood Historic Farm, Fremont, CA......96

Arizona Doll and Toy Museum, Phoenix, AZ...............39

Arizona Historical Society-Fort Lowell Museum, Tucson, AZ 47

Arizona Historical Society Museum, Tucson, AZ 47

Arizona Historical Society Museum at Papago Park, Tempe, AZ...............45

Arizona Historical Society Museum - Downtown, Tucson, AZ 47

Arizona Historical Society Pioneer Museum, Flagstaff, AZ...............32

Arizona Historical Society-Yuma: Sarguinetti House Museum and Garden, Yuma, AZ...............54

Arizona State Capitol Museum, Phoenix, AZ...............39

Arizona State Parks Board, Phoenix, AZ.......39

Ark-La-Tex Antique & Classic Vehicle Museum, Shreveport, LA...............600

Arkansas Country Doctor Museum, Lincoln, AR 61

Arkansas Museum of Natural Resources, Smackover, AR 68

Arkansas Post Museum, Gillett, AR...............58

Arkansas State University Museum, Jonesboro, AR...............60

Arkansas Tech University Museum of Prehistory and History, Russellville, AR...............67

Arlington, Birmingham, AL 4

Arlington Heights Historical Museum, Arlington Heights, IL 411

Arlington Historical Museum, Arlington, VA...............1495

The Arlington Historical Society, Arlington, MA 660

Arlington House, The Robert E. Lee Memorial, Arlington, VA...............1495

Armand Bayou Nature Center, Houston, TX...............1424

The Arms Family Museum of Local History, Youngstown, OH...............1193

Armstrong Browning Library, Waco, TX...1458

Arrow Rock State Historic Site, Arrow Rock, MO...............810

Artesia Historical Museum & Art Center, Artesia, NM 936

Arthurdale Heritage, Inc., Arthurdale, WV...............1579

Artisans Center of Virginia, Waynesboro, VA...............1543

Arvada Center for the Arts and Humanities, Arvada, CO...............201

Asa Packer Mansion, Jim Thorpe, PA........1263

Ash Lawn-Highland, Charlottesville, VA...1498

Ashland Historical Society, Ashland, MA....661

Ashland Historical Society Museum, Ashland, WI...............1590

Ashland, The Henry Clay Estate, Lexington, KY...............572

Ashtabula County Historical Society, Geneva-on-the-Lake, OH 1166

Ashtabula Historic House, Pendleton, SC..1339

Ashton Villa & The Heritage Visitor Center, Galveston, TX...............1420

Asistencia: San Gabriel Mission Outpost, Redlands, CA...............146

Aspen Historical Society, Aspen, CO...........202

Association for the Preservation of Tennessee Antiquities, Nashville, TN....1377

Astor House Museum, Golden, CO.............219

Astors' Beechwood Mansion - Living History Museum, Newport, RI...............1313

The Athenaeum of Philadelphia, Philadelphia, PA 1276

Atlanta Historical Society, Atlanta, GA.......358

Atlantic City Historical Museum, Atlantic City, NJ...............897

Atlantic Heritage Center, Somers Point, NJ...............924

Attleboro Area Industrial Museum, Inc., Attleboro, MA 661

Attmore-Oliver House, New Bern, NC.......1112

Atwood House Museum, Home of Chatham Historical Society, Chatham, MA...............675

Au Glaize Village, Defiance, OH...............1162

Auburn Cord Duesenberg Museum, Auburn, IN...............468

Audie Murphy/American Cotton Museum, Inc, Greenville, TX 1423

Audrain Historical Museum, Graceland, Mexico, MO...............827

Audubon County Historical Society, Exira, IA...............517

Audubon House & Tropical Gardens, Key West, FL...............317

Audubon State Historic Site, Saint Francisville, LA...............600

Augusta Historical Museum & Genealogy, Augusta, KS...............533

Augusta Museum of History, Augusta, GA...............364

Aurora Historical Society, Aurora, IL..........411

Aurora Historical Society, Aurora, OH.......1140

Aurora Historical Society, Inc., East Aurora, NY...............984

Aurora History Museum, Aurora, CO 202

Autry National Center of the American West, Los Angeles, CA...............112

Avery County Museum, Newland, NC.......1113

Avila Adobe, Los Angeles, CA...............113

The Avon Historical Society, Inc., Avon, CT...............235

Awbury Arboretum, Philadelphia, PA.........1277

Aztalan Museum, Jefferson, WI...............1601

Aztec Museum and Pioneer Village, Aztec, NM...............936

B&O Railroad Museum: Ellicott City Station, Ellicott City, MD 643

The Babe Ruth Museum and Sports Legends at Camden Yards, Baltimore, MD...............629

Baca House, Trinidad History Museum, Trinidad, CO...............233

Bacon's Castle, Surry County, VA...............1540

The Bade Institute of Biblical Archaeology and The Howell Bible Collection, Berkeley, CA...............75

Badger Mine and Museum, Shullsburg, WI...............1622

Bagg Bonanza Historical Farm, Mooreton, ND...............1135

Baldwin County Heritage Museum, Elberta, AL...............8

Baldwin Historical Society and Museum, Baldwin, NY...............960

Baldwin-Reynolds House Museum, Meadville, PA...............1270

Baltimore & Ohio Railroad Museum, Baltimore, MD...............629

Baltimore County Historical Society, Cockeysville, MD...............640

Bandelier National Monument, Los Alamos, NM...............942

Bandon Historical Society Museum, Bandon, OR...............1219

Bangor Museum & Center for History, Bangor, ME...............604

Banner County Historical Society, Harrisburg, NE...............862

Banning Residence Museum, Wilmington, CA...............198

Bannock County Historical Museum, Pocatello, ID...............408

Baranov Museum, Kodiak, AK...............26

The Barbara Fritchie House, Frederick, MD...............644

Barbed Wire Museum, La Crosse, KS.........547

Barker Mansion, Michigan City, IN.............490

The Barnacle Historic State Park, Coconut Grove, FL...............300

Barnard's Mill Art Museum, Glen Rose, TX...............1422

Barnes County Historical Museum, Valley City, ND...............1136

Barnes Foundation, Merion, PA...............1271

Barnes Museum, Southington, CT...............260

Barnet Historical Society, Barnet, VT...........1476

The Barnum Museum, Bridgeport, CT........235

Barnwell County Museum, Barnwell, SC..1321

Barratt's Chapel and Museum, Frederica, DE.....................................270
Barre Historical Society, Inc., Barre, MA....662
Barrett House, Forest Hall, New Ipswich, NH.....................................892
Barrington Living History Farm, Washington, TX.....................................1460
Barron County Historical Society's Pioneer Village Museum, Cameron, WI.....................................1593
Bartholomew County Historical Society, Columbus, IN.....................................472
Bartlesville Area History Museum, Bartlesville, OK.....................................1196
The Bartlett Museum, Amesbury, MA.........657
Barton County Historical Museum & Village, Great Bend, KS.....................................542
Bartow History Center, Cartersville, GA.....367
Bartow-Pell Mansion Museum, Carriage House & Gardens, Bronx, NY.................964
Bartram's Garden, Philadelphia, PA...........1277
Bassett Hall, Williamsburg, VA.....................1544
Bates-Scofield Homestead, The Darien Historical Society, Darien, CT.................238
Batsto Village, Hammonton, NJ 907
Battle of Lexington State Historic Site, Lexington, MO.....................................826
The Battles Museums of Rural Life, Girard, PA.....................................1256
Battleship New Jersey Museum & Memorial, Camden, NJ 899
Battleship North Carolina, Wilmington, NC.....................................1122
Battleship Texas State Historic Site, La Porte, TX.....................................1433
Baxter House Museum, Gorham, ME 611
Baxter Springs Heritage Center and Museum, Baxter Springs, KS.................533
Bay Area Museum, Seabrook, TX.............1452
Bay View Historical Museum, Bay View, MI.....................................728
Bayless-Selby House Museum, Denton, TX.....................................1409
Bayou Bend Collection and Gardens, Houston, TX.....................................1425
Beau Fort Plantation Home, Bermuda, LA.....................................587
Beauchamp Newman Museum, Elizabeth, WV.....................................1581
The Beaufort Arsenal, Beaufort, SC...........1321
Beaufort Historic Site, Beaufort, NC.........1091
Beauport, Sleeper-McCann House, Gloucester, MA.....................................684
Beauvais Heritage Center, Clark, SD 1345
Beauvoir, The Jefferson Davis Home and Presidential Library, Biloxi, MS.............798
Becker County Historical Society, Detroit Lakes, MN.....................................772
Bedford City/County Museum, Bedford, VA.....................................1496
Bedford Historical Society Museum and Library, Bedford, OH 1142
Bedingfield Inn Museum, Lumpkin, GA.....376
Beehive House, Salt Lake City, UT...........1470
Beith House Museum, Saint Charles, IL......456
Belair Mansion, Bowie, MD.....................638
Belair Stable Museum, Bowie, MD.............638
Belcourt Castle, Newport, RI.....................1313
Belding Museum, Belding, MI.....................728
Belhaven Memorial Museum, Inc., Belhaven, NC.....................................1092
Bell County Museum, Belton, TX.............1395
Bellamy Mansion Museum of History and Design Arts, Wilmington, NC.........1122
Belle Grove Plantation, Middletown, VA....1517
Belle Meade Plantation, Nashville, TN......1377
Bellflower Historical and Genealogical Society, Bellflower, IL.............................413
Bellingrath Gardens & Home, Theodore, AL.....................................18
Bellport-Brookhaven Historical Society and Museum, Bellport, NY.....................961

Belmont County Victorian Mansion Museum, Barnesville, OH.....................1141
Beloit Historical Society, Beloit, WI..........1592
Beltrami County History Center, Bemidji, MN.....................................768
Belvedere-Tiburon Landmarks Society, Tiburon, CA.....................................192
Bement-Billings Farmstead, Newark Valley, NY.....................................1041
Benicia Historical Museum, Benicia, CA 74
Benjamin Harrison Presidential Site, Indianapolis, IN.....................................481
Bennett Place State Historic Site, Durham, NC.....................................1098
The Bennett School, West Des Moines, IA.....................................530
Bennington Battlefield State Historic Site, Walloomsac, NY.....................................1081
The Bennington Museum, Bennington, VT.....................................1476
Benton County Historical Museum, Prosser, WA.....................................1563
Bentonville Battlefield State Historic Site, Four Oaks, NC.....................................1102
Bent's Old Fort National Historic Site, La Junta, CO.....................................224
Benzie Area Historical Museum, Benzonia, MI.....................................729
Bergen County Historical Society, River Edge, NJ.....................................923
Bergen County Zoological Park, Paramus, NJ.....................................919
Bergen Museum of Local History, Bergen, NY.....................................962
Berkeley County Museum & Heritage Center, Moncks Corner, SC.................1336
Berkeley Plantation, Charles City, VA.......1498
Berkshire County Historical Society, Inc. - Arrowhead, Pittsfield, MA.....................702
Berkshire Museum, Pittsfield, MA 702
Bernard Historical Society and Museum, Delton, MI.....................................734
Berrien County Historical Association, Berrien Springs, MI.....................................729
Bess Streeter Aldrich House & Museum, Elmwood, NE.....................................860
Bessemer Hall of History, Bessemer, AL.........3
Besser Museum for Northeast Michigan, Alpena, MI.....................................723
Bethel Historical Society Regional History Center, Bethel, ME.....................606
Betsey Williams Cottage, Providence, RI..1316
Betsy Ross House and Flag Museum, Philadelphia, PA 1277
Beverly Historical Society and Museum, Beverly, MA.....................................662
Bexley Historical Society, Bexley, OH.......1143
Beyer Home, Oconto County Historical Society Museum, Oconto, WI...............1616
The Bidwell House Museum, Monterey, MA.....................................695
Bidwell Mansion State Historic Park, Chico, CA.....................................83
Biedenharn Museum & Gardens, Monroe, LA.....................................592
Big Horn County Historical Museum, Hardin, MT.....................................849
Big Springs Museum, Caledonia, NY..........974
Big Thunder Gold Mine, Keystone, SD.....1349
Big Timbers Museum, Lamar, CO.............225
Bigelow House Museum, Olympia, WA ...1560
Bill Baggs Cape Florida State Park, Key Biscayne, FL.....................................316
Billings Farm & Museum, Woodstock, VT.....................................1490
Billy Sunday Home Museum and Visitors Center, Winona Lake, IN 504
Biltmore Estate, Asheville, NC.................1089
Biltmore Homespun Shops - Grovewood Gallery, Asheville, NC.....................................1089
Birmingham Civil Rights Institute, Birmingham, AL.....................................4

Birmingham Historical Museum & Park, Birmingham, MI.....................................730
Birthplace of John Wayne, Winterset, IA.....530
Bisbee Mining & Historical Museum, Bisbee, AZ.....................................30
Bishop Hill Heritage Museum, Bishop Hill, IL.....................................413
Bishop Hill State Historic Site, Bishop Hill, IL.....................................413
The Bishop's Palace, Galveston, TX.........1420
Black American West Museum & Heritage Center, Denver, CO.................209
Black Arts National Diaspora Museum, New Orleans, LA.....................................594
Black Heritage Museum, Miami, FL...........323
Black Mountain College Museum & Arts Center, Asheville, NC.....................................1089
Black River Historical Society of Lorain, Lorain, OH.....................................1172
Blackberry Farm's Pioneer Village, Aurora, IL.....................................411
Blackman House Museum, Snohomish, WA.....................................1570
Blaine County Historical Museum, Hailey, ID.....................................406
Blaine County Museum, Chinook, MT........844
Blaine House, Augusta, ME.....................604
Blandford Church & Reception Ctr. (The Petersburg Museums), Petersburg, VA ..1524
Blithewold Mansion, Gardens & Arboretum, Bristol, RI 1310
Block Island Historical Society, Block Island, RI.....................................1310
Bloom Mansion, Trinidad History Museum, Trinidad, CO.....................................233
Bloomfield Academy Museum, Bloomfield, NY.....................................963
Blount-Bridgers House/Hobson Pittman Memorial Gallery, Tarboro, NC...........1121
Blount County Memorial Museum, Oneonta, AL.....................................17
Blount Mansion, Knoxville, TN 1369
Blue Earth County Historical Society, Mankato, MN.....................................780
Blue Licks Battlefield Museum, Mount Olivet, KY.....................................580
Blue Ridge Institute and Museum, Ferrum, VA.....................................1504
Bluff Hall Antebellum Home and Museum, Demopolis, AL 7
Bob Jones University Museum & Gallery, Inc., Greenville, SC.....................................1333
Boca Raton Historical Society, Boca Raton, FL.....................................296
Bodie State Historic Park, Bridgeport, CA.....................................79
Bodley-Bullock House, Lexington, KY........572
Boehm Gallery, San Marcos, CA 174
Bolduc House Museum, Sainte Genevieve, MO.....................................837
Bolin Wildlife Exhibit & Antique Collection, McKinney, TX.....................1437
Bolinas Museum, Bolinas, CA.....................79
Bonnet House Museum & Gardens, Fort Lauderdale, FL.....................................306
Boonsborough Museum of History, Boonsboro, MD 637
The Boorman House - The Juneau County Historical Society, Mauston, WI.....................................1608
Boot Hill Museum, Inc., Dodge City, KS....536
Boothbay Railway Village, Boothbay, ME...607
Boothe Memorial Park and Museum, Stratford, CT.....................................262
Boscobel, Garrison, NY.....................................993
Bosque Memorial Museum, Clifton, TX....1400
Boston Center for Jewish Heritage, Boston, MA.....................................663
Boston Fire Museum, Boston, MA.............664
Boston National Historical Park, Boston, MA.....................................664

Furnishings–Continued

Boswell Museum of Music, Springfield Center, NY 1071
Botetourt County Historical Society, Fincastle, VA 1504
Bottineau County Historical Museum, Bottineau, ND 1129
Boulder City/Hoover Dam Museum, Boulder City, NV 875
Boulder History Museum, Boulder, CO 202
Boundary County Historical Society, Bonners Ferry, ID 404
Bowers Mansion, Washoe Valley, NV 882
Bowers Museum, Santa Ana, CA 177
The Bowne House Historical Society, Flushing, NY 990
Boyhood Home of President Woodrow Wilson, Augusta, GA 365
Boys Town Hall of History & Father Flanagan House, Boys Town, NE 858
Bradford Brinton Memorial & Museum, Big Horn, WY 1628
Bradford County Historical Society, Towanda, PA 1303
Bradford Historical Society Inc., Bradford, VT 1477
Bradley County Historical Museum, Warren, AR 69
Bradley House Museum, Jasper, AR 60
Bragg-Mitchell Mansion, Mobile, AL 13
Braintree Historical Society, Inc., Braintree, MA 670
Brandywine Battlefield Park, Chadds Ford, PA 1246
Brandywine River Museum, Chadds Ford, PA 1246
Branigan Cultural Center, Las Cruces, NM 940
Brazoria County Historical Museum, Angleton, TX 1387
Brec's Magnolia Mound Plantation, Baton Rouge, LA 585
Brevard Museum of History & Science, Cocoa, FL 300
Brick House, Montgomery, NY 1015
Brick Store Museum, Kennebunk, ME 612
Bridge Hampton Historical Society, Bridgehampton, NY 964
Bridger Valley Heritage Museum, Lyman, WY 1636
Bridgton Historical Society, Bridgton, ME 607
Brigham City Museum-Gallery, Brigham City, UT 1463
Brigham Young's Winter Home, Saint George, UT 1470
Brimstone Museum, Sulphur, LA 602
Bronck Museum, Coxsackie, NY 983
The Bronx County Historical Society, Bronx, NY 964
Brookings County Historical Society Museum, Volga, SD 1358
Brookline Historical Society, Brookline, MA 671
Brooklyn Historical Society, Brooklyn, OH 1144
The Broome County Historical Society, Binghamton, NY 962
Brown County Historical Society, New Ulm, MN 785
Brown County Historical Society Pioneer Museum, Nashville, IN 493
The Brown House Museum, Sandersville, GA 384
Brown Mansion, Coffeyville, KS 535
Brownella Cottage, Galion, OH 1165
Brownsville Museum of Fine Art - Brownsville Art League, Brownsville, TX 1398
Brownville Historical Society Museum, Brownville, NE 858
Brucemore, Cedar Rapids, IA 509

Brueckner Museum of Starr Commonwealth, Albion, MI 723
Brunnier Art Museum, Ames, IA 504
Brunswick Railroad Museum and C&O Canal Visitors Center, Brunswick, MD ...639
Brunswick Town/Fort Anderson State Historic Site, Winnabow, NC 1124
Brush Country Museum, Cotulla, TX 1403
Bryant Cottage, Bement, IL 413
Bryce Canyon National Park Visitor Center, Bryce, UT 1464
B's Ballpark Museum, Centennial, CO 205
Buccleuch Mansion, New Brunswick, NJ 915
Buchanan Center for the Arts, Monmouth, IL 445
Buckhorn Saloon & Museum, San Antonio, TX 1448
Bucyrus Historical Society, Bucyrus, OH ..1144
Buena Park Historical Society, Buena Park, CA 80
Buena Vista Heritage Museum, Buena Vista, CO 204
Buffalo Bill Cody Homestead, Princeton, IA 527
Buffalo Bill Historical Center, Cody, WY ..1631
Buffalo County Historical Society, Kearney, NE 863
Buffalo Gap Historic Village, Buffalo Gap, TX 1398
Buffalo Historical Museum and One-Room Schoolhouse, Buffalo, SD ...1345
Buffalo National River, Harrison, AR 59
Buffalo Trails Museum, Epping, ND 1130
Bulloch Hall, Roswell, GA 382
Bunker Hill Museum, Charlestown, MA 675
Bureau County Historical Society Museum, Princeton, IL 452
The Burgwin-Wright Museum, Wilmington, NC 1123
Burleson County Historical Museum, Caldwell, TX 1399
Burlington County Historical Society, Burlington, NJ 898
Burlington Historical Museum, Burlington, MA 672
Burlington-Rock Island Railroad and Historical Museum, Teague, TX 1454
Burnham Tavern, Machias, ME 614
Burnside Plantation, Inc., Bethlehem, PA ..1242
Burritt on the Mountain-A Living Museum, Huntsville, AL 11
Burrowes Mansion Museum, Matawan, NJ 911
Burt County Museum, Tekamah, NE 873
Bushwhacker Museum, Nevada, MO 828
Bushy Run Battlefield, Jeannette, PA 1263
Butler County History Center & Kansas Oil Museum, El Dorado, KS 537
Butler County Museum, Hamilton, OH 1168
Butte County Pioneer Memorial Museum, Oroville, CA 136
Butte-Silver Bow Arts Chateau, Butte, MT 843
Butter Pat Museum, Bigfork, MT 841
Butterfield Trail Historical Museum, Russell Springs, KS 557
Butterfly Lodge Museum, Greer, AZ 36
Byers-Evans House Museum, Denver, CO 209
Byron Historical Museum, Byron, NY 974

CDC/Global Health Odyssey, Atlanta, GA 358
C.F. Lott Historic Home, Oroville, CA 136
C. Grier Beam Truck Museum, Cherryville, NC 1096
C.H. Moore Homestead, Clinton, IL 428
CHTJ Southard House Museum, Brunswick, ME 607
C.M. Russell Museum, Great Falls, MT 848
COSI Columbus, Columbus, OH 1157
CU Heritage Center, Boulder, CO 203

Cabrillo National Monument, San Diego, CA 156
Calaveras County Museum, San Andreas, CA 155
Calhoun County Museum, Rockwell City, IA 527
Calhoun County Museum, Port Lavaca, TX 1444
Calico Ghost Town and the Lane House & Museum, Yermo, CA 199
California African-American Museum, Los Angeles, CA 113
California Heritage Museum, Santa Monica, CA 183
California State Capitol Museum, Sacramento, CA 151
Call of the Wild Museum, Gaylord, MI 742
Calvin Coolidge Historic Site, Plymouth Notch, VT 1484
Cambridge Historical Society, Cambridge, MA 672
Camden County Historical Society, Camden, NJ 899
Camp 6 Logging Museum, Tacoma, WA ...1572
Campbell County Rockpile Museum, Gillette, WY 1633
Campbell Historical Museum & Ainsley House, Campbell, CA 80
Campbell House, Grand Forks, ND 1131
Campbell House Museum, Saint Louis, MO 832
Campus Martius Museum, Marietta, OH ...1173
Canaan Historical Society, Inc., Canaan, NY 974
Canadian County Historical Museum, El Reno, OK 1200
Canal Fulton Heritage Society, Canal Fulton, OH 1145
Caney Valley Historical Society, Caney, KS 534
Cannon Falls Area Historical Museum, Cannon Falls, MN 770
The Cannon Village Visitor Center, Kannapolis, NC 1107
Canterbury Shaker Village, Inc., Canterbury, NH 883
Canton Classic Car Museum, Canton, OH.1145
Canton Historical Museum, Collinsville, CT 237
Canyon County Historical Society & Museum, Nampa, ID 408
Cape Ann Historical Museum, Gloucester, MA 684
Cape Cod National Seashore, Wellfleet, MA 717
Cape Fear Museum of History and Science, Wilmington, NC 1123
Cape May County Historical Museum and Genealogical Society, Cape May Court House, NJ 900
Cape Vincent Historical Museum, Cape Vincent, NY 976
Capitol Visitors Center, a Division of the State Preservation Board, Austin, TX....1389
Caples House Museum, Columbia City, OR 1222
Cappon & Settlers House Museums, Holland, MI 746
Captain Forbes House Museum, Milton, MA 695
Captain George Flavel House Museum, Astoria, OR 1218
Captain John Mullan Museum, Mullan, ID 407
Captain John Wilson House, Cohasset, MA 676
Captain Nathaniel B. Palmer House - Home of the Discoverer of Antarctica, Stonington, CT 261
Captain Salem Avery House Museum, Shady Side Rural Heritage Society, Inc., Shady Side, MD 653

Caramoor Center for Music & the Arts, Inc., Katonah, NY 1006
Carbon County Museum, Rawlins, WY 1637
Carl Sandburg State Historic Site, Galesburg, IL 437
Carlen House Museum, Mobile, AL 13
Carlsbad Museum & Art Center, Carlsbad, NM 938
Carlton County Historical Society, Cloquet, MN 771
Carlyle House Historic Park, Alexandria, VA 1492
Carmel Heritage Society's First Murphy House, Carmel-by-the-Sea, CA 81
Carnegie Center for Art & History, New Albany, IN 493
Carnegie Historical Museum, Fairfield, IA 517
Carnton Plantation, Franklin, TN 1365
Carolinas Aviation Museum, Charlotte, NC 1094
Carpenter Home Museum and Gallery, Cle Elum, WA 1551
Carpenter Museum, Rehoboth, MA 705
Carpinteria Valley Historical Society & Museum of History, Carpinteria, CA 82
Carroll County Farm Museum, Westminster, MD 656
Carroll Mansion Museum Home of Leavenworth County Historical Society, Leavenworth, KS 549
Carroll Reece Museum, Johnson City, TN.1367
Carry A. Nation Home Memorial, Medicine Lodge, KS 553
Carson County Square House Museum, Panhandle, TX 1442
Carter-Coile Country Doctors Museum, Winterville, GA 392
Carter County Museum, Ekalaka, MT 846
The Carter House Association, Inc., Franklin, TN 1365
Carter's Grove, Williamsburg, VA 1544
Carver County Historical Society, Waconia, MN 795
Cary Cottage, Cincinnati, OH 1148
Caryl House and Fisher Barn, Dover, MA...680
Casa Adobe de San Rafael, Glendale, CA...100
Casa Blanca Museum, San Juan, PR 1642
Casa de Rancho Cucamonga, Rancho Cucamonga, CA 144
The Casa del Herrero Foundation, Santa Barbara, CA 178
Casa Grande Valley Historical Society & Museum, Casa Grande, AZ 30
Casa Navarro State Historical Park, San Antonio, TX 1448
Cascade County Historical Society Museum, Great Falls, MT 848
Casemate Museum, Fort Monroe, VA 1505
Casey Jones Home and Railroad Museum, Jackson, TN 1367
Cashmere Museum & Pioneer Village, Cashmere, WA 1550
Cason Cottage House Museum, Delray Beach, FL 304
Cass County Historical Society, Logansport, IN 489
Cass County Historical Society at Bonanzaville, West Fargo, ND 1137
Cass County Historical Society Museum, Plattsmouth, NE 872
Cassia County Museum, Burley, ID 404
Casteel-Linn House and Museum, Princeton, MO 829
Castine Scientific Society, Castine, ME 609
The Castle, Marietta, OH 1174
Castle Air Museum, Atwater, CA 72
Castle Clinton National Monument, New York, NY 1021
Castle Museum of Saginaw County History, Saginaw, MI 762
Castle Tucker, Wiscasset, ME 625

Castleton Historical Society, Castleton, VT 1478
The Casto House and Northfield Museum, Northfield, NJ 917
Catawba County Museum of History, Newton, NC 1113
Cathedral Cultural Center, Omaha, NE 870
Catherine V. Yost Museum & Arts Center, Pontiac, IL 451
Catholic Historical Society of the Roanoke Valley, Roanoke, VA 1535
Catskill Fly Fishing Center & Museum, Livingston Manor, NY 1010
Cattaraugus Area Historical Center, Cattaraugus, NY 976
Cayuga-Owasco Lakes Historical Society, Moravia, NY 1015
Cedar Falls Historical Society, Cedar Falls, IA 507
Cedar Grove Historical Society, Cedar Grove, NJ 901
Cedar Grove Mansion Inn, Vicksburg, MS 809
Cedar Key Museum State Park, Cedar Key, FL 299
The Centennial Museum at the University of Texas at El Paso, El Paso, TX 1411
Centennial Village Museum, Greeley, CO ...221
Center for American History, Austin, TX...1390
The Center for Western Studies, Sioux Falls, SD 1356
Centerville Historical Museum, Centerville, MA 675
Centerville - Washington Township Historical Society & Asahel Wright Community Center, Centerville, OH 1146
Centerville - Washington Township Historical Society & Walton House Museum, Centerville, OH 1147
Central City Opera House Association, Central City, CO 205
Central Delta Depot Museum, Brinkley, AR 55
Central Montana Historical Association, Inc. Museum, Lewistown, MT 850
The Central Museum, Central, AK 23
Central Nevada Museum & Historical Society, Tonopah, NV 882
Centre County Historical Society, State College, PA 1301
Centre County Library and Historical Museum, Bellefonte, PA 1241
Centre Hill Museum (The Petersburg Museums), Petersburg, VA 1524
Century House Historical Society, Rosendale, NY 1061
Century Village Museum, Burton, OH 1144
Chaffee Center for the Visual Arts, Rutland, VT 1486
Chagrin Falls Historical Society, Chagrin Falls, OH 1147
Chalet of the Golden Fleece, New Glarus, WI 1614
Champaign County Historical Museum, Champaign, IL 416
Champaign County Historical Museum, Urbana, OH 1188
Champion Mill State Historical Park, Champion, NE 859
Champoeg State Heritage Area Visitor Center, Saint Paul, OR 1235
Chandler Museum, Chandler, AZ 31
The Chapman Historical Museum, Glens Falls, NY 994
Chappell Hill Historical Society Museum, Chappell Hill, TX 1399
Charles A. Grignon Mansion, Kaukauna, WI 1601
Charles A. Lindbergh Historic Site, Little Falls, MN 779
Charles A. Weyerhaeuser Memorial Museum, Little Falls, MN 779

Charles Allis Art Museum, Milwaukee, WI 1610
Charles B. Aycock Birthplace State Historic Site, Fremont, NC 1102
Charles Carroll House, Annapolis, MD 627
Charles M. Schulz Museum and Research Center, Santa Rosa, CA 184
Charles Towne Landing State Historic Site, Charleston, SC 1324
The Charleston Museum, Charleston, SC ..1324
Charlotte Museum of History and Hezekiah Alexander Homesite, Charlotte, NC 1094
Chase County Historical Society, Inc., Cottonwood Falls, KS 536
Chateau De Mores State Historic Site, Medora, ND 1134
Chatillon-DeMenil Mansion, Saint Louis, MO 832
Chattanooga African Museum/Bessie Smith Hall, Chattanooga, TN 1360
Chautauqua County Historical Society, McClurg Museum, Westfield, NY 1086
Cheboygan County Historical Museum Complex, Cheboygan, MI 732
The Chelmsford Historical Society, Inc., South Chelmsford, MA 709
Chemung Valley History Museum, Elmira, NY 988
Chenango County Historical Society Museum, Norwich, NY 1044
Cheney Homestead, Manchester, CT 248
Cherokee County Historical Museum, Inc., Murphy, NC 1112
Cherokee Courthouse Visitors Information Center & Museum, Gore, OK 1201
Cherokee National Museum, Park Hill, OK 1211
Cherokee Strip Museum, Alva, OK 1195
Cherry County Historical Society, Valentine, NE 874
Cherry Valley Museum, Cherry Valley, NY 978
Chesapeake and Ohio Canal National Historical Park, Hagerstown, MD 646
Chester County Historical Society, West Chester, PA 1307
The Chester Gould-Dick Tracy Museum, Woodstock, IL 467
Chesterwood, Stockbridge, MA 711
Chetopa Historical Museum, Chetopa, KS...535
Cheyenne County Museum, Saint Francis, KS 557
The Chicago Athenaeum: Museum of Architecture and Design, Galena, IL 436
Chicago History Museum, Chicago, IL...........419
Chickamauga-Chattanooga National Military Park, Fort Oglethorpe, GA 372
Chickasaw Council House Museum, Tishomingo, OK 1214
Chickasaw County Historical Society Bradford Pioneer Village Museum, Nashua, IA 525
Chico Museum, Chico, CA 83
The Chief John Ross House, Rossville, GA 382
Chief Plenty Coups Museum, Pryor, MT.....852
Chieftains Museum, Rome, GA 381
Children's Discovery Museum of North San Diego, Carlsbad, CA 81
Children's Hands-On Museum (CHOM), Tuscaloosa, AL 19
Children's Museum, Inc., Boca Raton, FL...296
The Children's Museum of Indianapolis, Indianapolis, IN 481
Children's Museum of Oak Ridge, Inc., Oak Ridge, TN 1382
The Children's Museum of Rose Hill Manor Park, Frederick, MD 644
Childress County Heritage Museum, Childress, TX 1400

Furnishings—Continued

Chimney Point State Historic Site, Addison, VT.............1475

Chinese American Museum, Los Angeles, CA.............114

Chinese Culture Center of San Francisco, San Francisco, CA.............164

Chinqua-Penn Plantation, Reidsville, NC...1117

Chippewa County Historical Society, Montevideo, MN.............783

Chippewa Valley Museum, Inc., Eau Claire, WI.............1595

Chiricahua National Monument, Willcox, AZ.............53

Chisholm Trail Heritage Center, Duncan, OK.............1199

Choctaw County Historical Society, Hugo, OK.............1203

Christiansted National Historic Site, Saint Croix, VI.............1644

Church Landing Farmhouse, Pennsville, NJ.............920

Church-Waddel-Brumby House Museum & Athens Welcome Center, Athens, GA.............356

Churchill County Museum and Archives, Fallon, NV.............877

Cincinnati Fire Museum, Cincinnati, OH...1149

Cincinnati Museum Center at Union Terminal, Cincinnati, OH.............1149

Circus World Museum, Baraboo, WI.........1591

City County Pioneer Museum, Sweetwater, TX.............1454

City Hall Council Chamber Gallery, Charleston, SC.............1324

City of Bowie Museums, Bowie, MD.........638

City of Burlington Historical Society, Burlington, NJ.............899

City of Gilroy Museum, Gilroy, CA.............99

City of Las Cruces Museum System, Las Cruces, NM.............940

City of Las Vegas Museum and Rough Rider Memorial Collection, Las Vegas, NM.............941

Civil War Soldiers Museum, Pensacola, FL.............335

Clallam County Historical Society, Port Angeles, WA.............1561

Clara Barton Birthplace, North Oxford, MA.............699

Clara Barton National Historic Site, Glen Echo, MD.............645

The Claremont, New Hampshire Historical Society, Inc., Claremont, NH.............884

Clarion County Historical Society, Sutton-Ditz House Museum, Clarion, PA.............1247

Clark County Historical Museum, Vancouver, WA.............1576

Clark County Historical Society - Heritage Center of Clark County, Springfield, OH.............1186

Clark County Museum, Henderson, NV.....878

Clark Hotel Museum, Van Horn, TX.........1457

Clarke Historical Museum, Eureka, CA.........94

Clarke House Museum, Chicago, IL.............420

Clarkson Historical Museum, Clarkson, NE.............859

Clarksville-Montgomery County Museum dba Customs House Museum & Cultural Center, Clarksville, TN.............1363

Clausen Memorial Museum, Petersburg, AK.............27

Clawson Historical Museum, Clawson, MI.............732

Clay County Historical Museum, Liberty, MO.............826

Clay County Historical Society Museum and Archives, Moorhead, MN.............784

Cle Elum Telephone Museum, Cle Elum, WA.............1551

Clear Creek History Park, Golden, CO.........219

Clear Lake Area Historical Museum, Clear Lake, WI.............1594

Clearwater Historical Museum, Orofino, ID.............408

Clermont State Historic Site, Clermont, NY.............979

Cleveland County Historical Museum, Shelby, NC.............1119

Cleveland Police Historical Society & Museum, Cleveland, OH.............1153

Clewiston Museum, Inc., Clewiston, FL.............300

Clifton Community Historical Society, Clifton, KS.............535

Clinton Academy, East Hampton, NY.........985

Clinton County Historical Association & Museum, Plattsburgh, NY.............1052

Clinton County Historical Society, Clinton, IA.............511

Clinton County Historical Society, Wilmington, OH.............1191

Clinton County Historical Society Paine-Gillam-Scott Museum, Saint Johns, MI.............763

Clinton County Museum, Frankfort, IN.............478

Cliveden of the National Trust, Philadelphia, PA.............1278

The Cloisters, New York, NY.............1023

Cloud County Historical Society Museum, Concordia, KS.............536

Coachella Valley Museum and Cultural Center, Indio, CA.............104

Coal Miners' Museum/Van Lear Historical Society, Inc., Van Lear, KY....584

Coarsegold Historic Museum, Coarsegold, CA.............86

Codington County Heritage Museum, Watertown, SD.............1359

Codman Estate, The Grange, Lincoln, MA.............690

Coe Hall, Oyster Bay, NY.............1049

Coeur d'Alenes Old Mission State Park, Cataldo, ID.............405

The Coffey County Historical Museum, Burlington, KS.............534

Coffin House, Newbury, MA.............697

Coggeshall Farm Museum, Bristol, RI.............1310

Cokato Museum & Akerlund Photography Studio, Cokato, MN.............771

Cole County Historical Museum, Jefferson City, MO.............819

The Coleman House Museum and Brown County Historical Society, Ainsworth, NE.............855

Colesville & Windsor Museum at St. Luke's Church, Harpursville, NY.............997

The Coley Homestead & Barn Museum, Weston, CT.............265

Colfax County Society of Art, History and Archaeology, Raton, NM.............945

Colleton Museum, Walterboro, SC.............1343

Collier County Museum, Naples, FL.............328

Collier Memorial State Park & Logging Museum, Chiloquin, OR.............1221

Collin County Farm Museum, McKinney, TX.............1437

Collin County Historical Society, Inc. & History Museum, McKinney, TX.............1437

Collingsworth County Museum, Wellington, TX.............1460

Collinsville Depot Museum, Collinsville, OK.............1198

Colonel Allensworth State Historic Park, Allensworth, CA.............70

Col. Ashley House, Ashley Falls, MA.............661

Colonel Davenport Historical Foundation, Rock Island, IL.............453

Colonel William Jones State Historic Site/Lincoln State Park & Colonel Jones Home, Lincoln City, IN.............488

Colonial Industrial Quarter, Bethlehem, PA.............1242

Colonial National Historical Park: Jamestown & Yorktown, Yorktown, VA.............1546

Colonial Pemaquid, New Harbor, ME.........615

Colonial Pennsylvania Plantation, Media, PA.............1270

The Colonial Spanish Quarter Museum, Saint Augustine, FL.............338

Colonial Williamsburg, Williamsburg, VA.1544

Colony House, Newport, RI.............1313

Colorado Historical Society, Denver, CO.....210

Colorado Ski Museum-Ski & Snowboard Hall of Fame, Vail, CO.............234

Colton Hall Museum, Monterey, CA.............127

Columbia County Historical Society, Inc., Kinderhook, NY.............1007

Columbia Gorge Interpretive Center Museum, Stevenson, WA.............1572

Columbia State Historic Park, Columbia, CA.............87

The Columbian Theatre, Museum & Art Center, Wamego, KS.............560

Columbus-Belmont Civil War Museum, Columbus, KY.............567

Columbus Chapel, Boal Mansion Museum, Boalsburg, PA.............1244

The Columbus Museum, Columbus, GA.....368

Comanche Crossing Historical Society & Museum, Strasburg, CO.............233

Communal Kitchen and Coopershop Museum, Middle Amana, IA.............523

Community Historical Museum, Maxwell, IA.............523

Community Memorial Museum of Sutter County, Yuba City, CA.............200

Compass Inn Museum, Laughlintown, PA.1267

Comstock Historic House, Moorhead, MN.............784

Concord Historical Society, Warner Museum, Springville, NY.............1071

Concord Museum, Concord, MA.............676

Concordia Historical Institute, Saint Louis, MO.............832

Confederate Memorial State Historic Site, Higginsville, MO.............817

Confederate Museum, Crawfordville, GA....369

The Conference House, Staten Island, NY.............1072

Conklin Reed Organ & History Museum, Hanover, MI.............745

Conneaut Railroad Museum, Conneaut, OH.............1159

Connecticut Historical Society, Hartford, CT.............244

Connecticut River Museum, Essex, CT.........239

Conner Prairie, Fishers, IN.............476

Conrad-Caldwell House Museum, Louisville, KY.............575

Conrad Mansion National Historic Site Museum, Kalispell, MT.............850

Conrad Weiser Homestead and Memorial Park, Womelsdorf, PA.............1308

Constitution Convention Museum State Park, Port St. Joe, FL.............338

Constitution Island Association, West Point, NY.............1085

Constitution Square State Historic Site, Danville, KY.............567

Cooper-Hewitt National Design Museum, Smithsonian Institution, New York, NY.............1023

Cooper Regional History Museum, Upland, CA.............193

Copia: The American Center for Wine, Food & the Arts, Napa, CA.............129

Copper King Mansion, Butte, MT.............843

Copper Range Historical Museum, South Range, MI.............764

Copper Village Museum & Arts Center of Deer Lodge County, Anaconda, MT.........840

Copshaholm House Museum & Historic Oliver Gardens, South Bend, IN.............499

Cordell Hull Birthplace & Museum State Historic Park, Byrdstown, TN 1360
Cordova Historical Museum, Cordova, AK..23
Cornell Museum of Art & History, Delray Beach, FL...............................304
Corry Area Historical Society, Corry, PA...1248
Cortland County Historical Society, Cortland, NY 982
Corydon Capitol Historic Site, Corydon, IN..473
Cottage Grove Museum & Annex, Cottage Grove, OR................................1222
Cottonlandia Museum, Greenwood, MS 800
Cottonwood County Historical Society, Windom, MN..796
The Country Doctor Museum, Bailey, NC.1091
Country Relics Little Village, Stanhope, IA..528
County of Westchester, Department of Parks, Recreation and Conservation, Mount Kisco, NY 1016
Courthouse Square Association, Charlotte, MI 731
Coutts Memorial Museum of Art, Inc., El Dorado, KS..537
Cow Neck Peninsula Historical Society Sands-Willets House, Port Washington, NY 1053
The Cowley County Historical Society, Winfield, KS..564
Cowlitz County Historical Museum, Kelso, WA...1557
Cozens Ranch Museum, Fraser, CO...........218
Cracker Country, Tampa, FL........................348
Craftsmen's Guild of Mississippi, Jackson, MS..802
Cragfont-Historic Cragfont, Inc., Castalian Springs, TN 1360
Cramer-Kenyon Heritage Home, Yankton, SD...1359
Cranbrook Art Museum, Bloomfield Hills, MI...730
Cranbrook House and Gardens Auxiliary, Bloomfield Hills, MI...........................730
Cranbury Historical & Preservation Society, Cranbury, NJ............................902
Cranford Historical Society, Cranford, NJ ...902
Crater Lake National Park, Crater Lake, OR...1222
Cravens House, Lookout Mountain, TN 1371
Crawford County Historical Museum, Pittsburg, KS...556
Crawford W. Long Museum, Jefferson, GA...374
Crazy Mountain Museum, Big Timber, MT..841
Creative Photographic Art Center of Maine, Lewiston, ME.............................614
Crescent Bend/The Armstrong-Lockett House and The William P. Toms Memorial Gardens, Knoxville, TN 1369
The Crescent, Valdosta Garden Center, Inc., Valdosta, GA....................................389
Crested Butte Mountain Heritage Museum, Crested Butte, CO 208
Cripple Creek District Museum, Inc., Cripple Creek, CO..................................209
Crocker House, Mount Clemens, MI............756
Crockett Tavern Museum, Morristown, TN..1376
Crosby County Pioneer Memorial Museum, Crosbyton, TX.....................1403
Crossroads Museum, Corinth, MS...............800
Crow Wing County Historical Society, Brainerd, MN..769
Crowley Museum & Nature Center, Sarasota, FL...344
Crown Gardens and Archives, Dalton, GA...370
Crown Point State Historic Site, Crown Point, NY...984

Crystal Lake Falls Historical Association, Barton, VT...1476
Crystal Rice Plantation, Crowley, LA..........588
Culbertson Mansion State Historic Site, New Albany, IN.......................................493
Culbertson Museum, Culbertson, MT.........845
Culinary Archives & Museum, Johnson & Wales University, Providence, RI......1316
Cullman County Museum, Cullman, AL..........6
Cumberland County Historical Society, Greenwich, NJ...905
Cumberland County Historical Society, The Hamilton Library and The Two Mile House, Carlisle, PA......................1245
Cumberland Island National Seashore, Saint Marys, GA...382
Cumberland Presbyterian Church Birthplace Shrine, Burns, TN................1360
Cuneo Museum & Gardens, Vernon Hills, IL..463
Cupertino Historical Society & Museum, Cupertino, CA...88
Cupola House, Egg Harbor, WI.................1596
Curry Historical Society Museum, Gold Beach, OR...1225
Curwood Castle, Owosso, MI......................759
Custer County Historical Society, Inc., Broken Bow, NE 858
Cuyuna Range Historical Society & Museum, Crosby, MN...............................772
Cyrus H. McCormick Memorial Museum, Steeles Tavern, VA 1538

DAR-Hervey Ely House, Rochester, NY ...1058
DAR John Strong Mansion Museum, Addison, VT...1475
D.C. Booth Historic National Fish Hatchery, Spearfish, SD 1357
D.R. Barker Historical Museum, Fredonia, NY...992
Dacotah Prairie Museum, Aberdeen, SD....1344
Dahlonega Gold Museum State Historic Site, Dahlonega, GA...............................369
Dakota County Historical Society, South Saint Paul, MN...793
Dakota Discovery Museum, Mitchell, SD..1352
Dakota Sunset Museum, Gettysburg, SD...1348
Dakota Territorial Museum, Yankton, SD..1359
Dakotaland Museum, Huron, SD................1348
Dal-Paso Museum, Lamesa, TX.................1433
Dallam-Hartley XIT Museum, Dalhart, TX...1403
Dallas Arboretum & Botanical Garden, Dallas, TX..1404
Dallas Heritage Village at Old City Park, Dallas, TX..1405
Dallas Historical Society, Dallas, TX.........1405
Dallas Museum of Art, Dallas, TX.............1405
Dallidet Adobe and Gardens, San Luis Obispo, CA...174
Dalton Gang Hideout, Meade, KS...............552
Dana Adobe, Nipomo, CA 130
The Dana-Thomas House State Historic Site, Springfield, IL...................................458
The Danbury Museum & Historical Society, Danbury, CT 238
Daniel Benton Homestead, Tolland, CT......262
Daniel Boone Home and Boonesfield Village, Lindenwood University, Defiance, MO...814
Daniel Boone Homestead, Birdsboro, PA ..1243
Daniels County Museum and Pioneer Town, Scobey, MT......................................853
The Danish Immigrant Museum, Elk Horn, IA..517
Danvers Historical Society, Danvers, MA....678
Danville Museum of Fine Arts & History, Danville, VA..1502
DAR Van Bunschooten Museum, Sussex, NJ..925
Darnall's Chance House Museum, M-NCPPC, Upper Marlboro, MD 655

Daughters of the American Revolution Museum, Washington, DC 277
Daughters of Utah Pioneers Pioneer Memorial Museum & International Society Daughters of Utah Pioneers, Salt Lake City, UT...............................1471
Davenport House Museum, Savannah, GA...384
David Bradford House, Washington, PA 1305
David Conklin Farmhouse, Huntington, NY...1000
David Crockett Cabin, Rutherford, TN 1383
The David Davis Mansion, Bloomington, IL..413
Dawes County Historical Society Museum, Chadron, NE............................859
Dawson County Historical Museum, Lexington, NE...864
Dayton Historical Depot Society, Dayton, WA..1552
Dayton History at Carillon Park, Dayton, OH..1161
De Graaf Nature Center, Holland, MI..........746
De Smet Depot Museum, De Smet, SD......1346
Deaf Smith County Museum, Hereford, TX...1424
Dearborn Historical Museum, Dearborn, MI...733
Death Valley National Park Visitor Center and Museums, Death Valley, CA...............91
Decatur County Last Indian Raid Museum, Oberlin, KS.................................554
Decatur House Museum, Washington, DC...277
The Decorative Arts Center of Ohio, Lancaster, OH......................................1171
Decorative Arts Collection, Inc. Museum of Decorative Painting, Wichita, KS 561
Dedham Historical Society Museum, Dedham, MA...679
Deer Isle-Stonington Historical Society, Deer Isle, ME...609
Deerfield Beach Historical Society, Deerfield Beach, FL...................................304
Degenhart Paperweight & Glass Museum, Inc., Cambridge, OH 1144
The Dekker Huis/Zeeland Historical Museum, Zeeland, MI...........................767
Del Norte County Historical Society, Crescent City, CA...87
Delaware Agricultural Museum and Village, Dover, DE.......................................269
Delaware and Hudson Canal Historical Society and Museum, High Falls, NY.....998
Delaware Division of Historical & Cultural Affairs, Dover, DE 269
Delta County Museum, Delta, CO................209
Deming Luna Mimbres Museum, Deming, NM..939
The Dennison Railroad Depot Museum, Dennison, OH......................................1162
Dennys River Historical Society, Dennysville, ME......................................609
Denver Museum of Miniatures, Dolls and Toys, Denver, CO...................................211
Department of the Treasury, Washington, DC..278
Depot Museum & Fort Sedgwick Museum, Julesburg, CO...........................223
The Depot Museum Complex, Henderson, TX...1424
Depot Park Museum, Sonoma, CA 187
Depreciation Lands Museum, Allison Park, PA...1240
Des Plaines History Center, Des Plaines, IL..430
Deschutes County Historical Society, Bend, OR..1220
Desert Caballeros Western Museum, Wickenburg, AZ...53
Desha County Museum, Dumas, AR.............56
Detroit Historical Society, Detroit, MI........735
Deutschheim State Historic Site, Hermann, MO...817

Furnishings—Continued

Dewey Hotel Museum, Dewey, OK 1199

DeWitt County Historical Museum,
Cuero, TX 1403

DeWitt Wallace Decorative Arts Museum,
Williamsburg, VA 1545

Dexter Area Historical Society &
Museum, Dexter, MI 738

Dexter Historical Society Campus,
Dexter, ME 609

Dey Mansion/Washington's Headquarters
Museum, Wayne, NJ 929

Dickinson County Heritage Center,
Abilene, KS 531

Dinsmore Homestead Foundation,
Burlington, KY 566

Diplomatic Reception Rooms,
Department of State, Washington, DC 278

The Discovery Center of the Southern
Tier, Binghamton, NY 962

Discovery Creek Children's Museum of
Washington DC, Glen Echo, MD 645

Discovery Museum, Sacramento Museum
of History, Science and Technology,
Sacramento, CA 152

Dittrick Museum of Medical History,
Cleveland, OH 1154

Doak House Museum, Greeneville, TN ..1366

Dr. Daniel W. Kissam House,
Huntington, NY 1000

Dr. Francis Medical and Apothecary
Museum, Jacksonville, AL 12

Dr. Howe-Waffle House and Medical
Museum, Santa Ana, CA 177

Dr. Increase Mathews House, Zanesville,
OH 1194

Dr. John Harris Dental Museum,
Bainbridge, OH 1141

Dr. Jose Celso Barbosa Museum &
Library, Bayamon, PR 1641

Dr. Samuel D. Harris National Museum
of Dentistry, Baltimore, MD 631

Dr. William Robinson Plantation, Clark,
NJ 901

Doctors' House Museum, Glendale, CA ...100

Dodge County Historical Society,
Mantorville, MN 780

Dodge County Historical Society
Museum, Beaver Dam, WI 1591

Don F. Pratt Memorial Museum, Fort
Campbell, KY 568

Don Garlits Museum of Drag Racing
Inc., Ocala, FL 330

Donald G. Trayser Memorial
Museum/Barnstable County Customs
House, Barnstable, MA 661

Donkey Milk House, Historic Home, Key
West, FL 317

Door County Historical Museum,
Sturgeon Bay, WI 1623

Doric House, Flemington, NJ 903

Dorothea B. Hoover Historical Museum,
Joplin, MO 819

Dorothy G. Page Museum, Wasilla, AK 29

Douglas County Historical Society,
Superior, WI 1624

Douglas County Historical Society -
Carson Valley Museum & Cultural
Center, Gardnerville, NV 877

Douglas County Historical Society -
Genoa Courthouse Museum, Genoa,
NV 877

Douglas County Museum Complex,
Armour, SD 1344

Douglass Historical Museum, Douglass,
KS 537

The Downers Grove Park District
Museum, Downers Grove, IL 431

Downieville Museum, Downieville, CA 91

Downing House Museum, Memphis, MO...827

Dragon Dreams Museum & Gift Shop,
Chattanooga, TN 1362

The Drake House Museum, Plainfield, NJ...921

Drake Well Museum, Titusville, PA 1303

Drew County Historical Museum,
Monticello, AR 64

Drum Barracks Civil War Museum,
Wilmington, CA 198

Drummond Home, Hominy, OK 1203

Drummond Island Historical Museum,
Drummond Island, MI 739

Dublin-Laurens Museum, Dublin, GA 370

Dubois Museum, Dubois, WY 1632

Duke Homestead State Historic Site,
Durham, NC 1098

Dumbarton House, Washington, DC 278

Dumbarton Oaks Research Library &
Collections, Washington, DC 278

Dunbar House State Memorial, Dayton,
OH 1161

Duncan Cottage Museum, Metlakatla, AK.....27

Dundee Township Historical Society,
Inc., Dundee, IL 431

Dundy County Historical Society,
Benkelman, NE 857

Dunedin Historical Society & Museum,
Dunedin, FL 305

Dunham Tavern Museum, Cleveland, OH..1154

Dunn County Historical Society,
Menomonie, WI 1609

Dunsmuir Historic Estate & Gardens,
Oakland, CA 133

DuPage County Historical Museum,
Wheaton, IL 465

Durant House Museum, Saint Charles, IL ...457

Durham Center Museum/Research
Library, East Durham, NY 985

Durham Historic Association Museum,
Durham, NH 886

Durham Western Heritage Museum,
Omaha, NE 870

Dutchess County Historical Society,
Poughkeepsie, NY 1054

Duxbury Rural and Historical Society,
Inc., Duxbury, MA 681

Dwight D. Eisenhower Library-Museum,
Abilene, KS 531

Dyckman Farmhouse Museum and Park,
New York, NY 1025

Dyer Memorial Library, Abington, MA 657

E. St. Julien Cox House, Saint Peter, MN ...792

Eagle Bluff Lighthouse, Fish Creek, WI....1597

Eagle Historical Society & Museums,
Eagle, AK 23

Eagle Tavern Museum, Watkinsville, GA 391

The Earle-Harrison House and Gardens
on 5th Street, Waco, TX 1458

Early American Museum, Mahomet, IL 444

EarlyWorks Museums, Huntsville, AL 11

East Brunswick Museum Corporation,
East Brunswick, NJ 902

East Hampton Historical Society, Inc.,
East Hampton, NY 985

East Hillsborough Historical Society, Inc.,
Plant City, FL 337

East Jersey Olde Towne, Piscataway, NJ 921

East Jordan Portside Art & Historical
Museum, East Jordan, MI 739

East Lyme Historical Society/Thomas
Lee House, Niantic, CT 256

East Martello Museum, Key West, FL 317

East Poultney Museum, East Poultney,
VT 1479

East Tennessee Historical Society,
Knoxville, TN 1369

East Texas Oil Museum at Kilgore
College, Kilgore, TX 1432

Eastchester Historical Society - 1835
Marble Schoolhouse, Bronxville, NY......967

Eastern Arizona Museum and Historical
Society of Graham County Inc., Pima,
AZ 42

Eastern California Museum,
Independence, CA 104

Eastern Oregon Museum on the Old
Oregon Trail, Haines, OR 1226

Eastman Lord House, Conway, NH............885

Eastside Heritage Center, Bellevue, WA 1548

The Ebenezer Maxwell Mansion, Inc.,
Philadelphia, PA 1278

The Eckhart House, Wheeling, WV 1587

Eckley Miners' Village, Eckley, PA............1251

Edgar Allan Poe Cottage, Bronx, NY 965

Edgar Allan Poe Museum, Richmond, VA.1529

Edgar County Historical Museum, Paris,
IL 449

Edison & Ford Winter Estates, Fort
Myers, FL 308

Edison National Historic Site, West
Orange, NJ 930

Edmond Historical Society Museum,
Edmond, OK 1200

Edmonds South Snohomish County
Historical Society, Inc., Edmonds, WA .1553

Edna Historical Museum, Edna, KS............537

Edsel & Eleanor Ford House, Grosse
Pointe Shores, MI 745

Edward-Dean Museum and Gardens,
Cherry Valley, CA 82

Edward Hopper Landmark Preservation
Foundation, Nyack, NY 1044

Edwards County Historical Museum,
Kinsley, KS 547

Edwin Wolters Memorial Museum,
Shiner, TX 1453

Egan Maritime Foundation, Nantucket,
MA 695

1880 Town, Murdo, SD 1352

The 1811 Old Lincoln County Jail and
Lincoln County Museum, Wiscasset,
ME 625

1859 Jail, Marshal's Home & Museum,
Independence, MO 817

The 1890 House-Museum & Center for
Arts, Cortland, NY 983

82nd Airborne Division War Memorial
Museum, Fort Bragg, NC 1101

Eisenhower Birthplace State Historical
Site, Denison, TX 1409

Eisenhower National Historic Site,
Gettysburg, PA 1255

El Dorado County Historical Museum,
Placerville, CA 142

El Monte Historical Society Museum, El
Monte, CA 92

El Paso Holocaust Museum & Study
Center, El Paso, TX 1411

El Paso Museum of History, El Paso, TX..1412

El Pueblo Historical Monument, Los
Angeles, CA 114

El Pueblo History Museum, Pueblo, CO......230

El Rancho de Las Golondrinas Museum,
Santa Fe, NM 947

Elbert Hubbard-Roycroft Museum, East
Aurora, NY 985

Eldridge Street Project, New York, NY 1025

Eleanor Roosevelt National Historic Site,
Hyde Park, NY 1002

Elfreth's Alley Association, Philadelphia,
PA 1279

Elisabet Ney Museum, Austin, TX 1390

Elizabeth Myers Mitchell Art Gallery at
St. John's College, Annapolis, MD.........627

Elkhart County Historical Museum,
Bristol, IN 471

Ella Sharp Museum, Jackson, MI 748

Elliott Museum, Stuart, FL 346

Ellis County Historical Society, Hays, KS...543

Ellis County Museum, Inc., Waxahachie,
TX 1460

Ellwood House Museum, DeKalb, IL 429

Elmhurst Historical Museum, Elmhurst,
IL 433

Elverhoj Museum of History and Art,
Solvang, CA 187

Elvis Presley Birthplace and Museum, Tupelo, MS 808

Elwood Haynes Museum, Kokomo, IN 486

Emily Dickinson Museum: The Homestead and The Evergreens, Amherst, MA 658

Emily Kimbrough House, Muncie, IN 492

Empire State Aerosciences Museum, Glenville, NY 995

End-O-Line Railroad Park & Museum, Currie, MN 772

The Endowment Fund of the Phi Kappa Psi Fraternity-Heritage Hall, Indianapolis, IN 482

Enfield Shaker Museum, Enfield, NH 887

Enoch Kelsey House, Newington, CT 256

Ephraim Historical Foundation, Ephraim, WI 1597

Ephrata Cloister, Ephrata, PA 1251

Erie Canal Village, Rome, NY 1061

Erie County History Center & Cashier's House, Erie, PA 1252

The Erlander Home Museum, Rockford, IL 454

Ernest Hemingway House Museum, Key West, FL 317

Ernie Pyle State Historic Site, Dana, IN 473

Escondido History Center, Escondido, CA 93

Essex Historical Society, Inc., Essex, CT 240

Essley-Noble Museum: Mercer County Historical Society, Aledo, IL 410

Estes Park Museum, Estes Park, CO 215

Eubie Blake National Jazz Institute and Cultural Center, Baltimore, MD 632

Eugene Field House and St. Louis Toy Museum, Saint Louis, MO 833

Eugene O'Neill National Historic Site, Danville, CA 89

Eugene V. Debs Home, Terre Haute, IN 500

Eureka Fire Museum, Milltown, NJ 911

Eureka Pioneer Museum of McPherson County, Inc., Eureka, SD 1346

Eureka School House, Springfield, VT 1487

Eustis Historical Museum & Preservation Society, Inc., Eustis, FL 306

Evanston Historical Society and Charles Gates Dawes House, Evanston, IL 434

Evansville Museum of Arts History & Science, Evansville, IN 475

Evergreen House, The Johns Hopkins University, Baltimore, MD 632

Everson Museum of Art, Syracuse, NY 1076

Excelsior House, Jefferson, TX 1431

Ezra Meeker Mansion, Puyallup, WA 1564

Fabyan Villa Museum, Geneva, IL 437

Fairbanks House, Dedham, MA 679

Fairfax County Park Authority, Resource Management Division, Fairfax, VA 1503

Fairfax Museum & Visitor Center, Fairfax, VA 1503

Fairfield County Museum, Winnsboro, SC 1343

Fairfield Historical Society, Fairfield, CT 241

Fairlawn Mansion & Museum, Superior, WI 1624

Fairport Historical Museum, Fairport, NY 989

Fairport Marine Museum, Fairport Harbor, OH 1164

Fairview Museum of History & Art, Fairview, UT 1465

Faith Trumbull Chapter, Daughters of the American Revolution, Inc., Museum and Chapter House, Norwich, CT 258

Falkirk Cultural Center, San Rafael, CA 176

Fall River County Historical Museum, Hot Springs, SD 1348

Fall River Historical Society Museum, Fall River, MA 682

Fallingwater, Mill Run, PA 1272

Falls Village-Canaan Historical Society, Falls Village, CT 241

Falmouth Historical Society, Falmouth, MA 682

Family Museum, Bettendorf, IA 505

The Farm, Sturgeon Bay, WI 1623

Farm House Museum, Ames, IA 505

Farmers Bank (The Petersburg Museums), Petersburg, VA 1525

Farmers Branch Historical Park, Farmers Branch, TX 1413

The Farmers' Museum, Inc., Cooperstown, NY 980

Farmington Historic Home, Louisville, KY 575

Farmington Museum, Farmington, NM 939

Farragut Folklife Museum, Farragut, TN 1364

Farrar-Mansur House & Old Mill Museum, Weston, VT 1490

FASNY Museum of Fire Fighting, Hudson, NY 1000

Faulkner County Museum, Conway, AR 56

Faust Park-Thornhill Historic Site & 19th Century Village, Chesterfield, MO 812

Fayette County Museum, Washington Court House, OH 1190

Fayette Heritage Museum & Archives, La Grange, TX 1432

Fayette Historic State Park, Garden, MI 742

Federal Hall National Memorial, New York, NY 1025

Felix Valle State Historic Site, Sainte Genevieve, MO 837

Fenton History Center-Museum & Library, Jamestown, NY 1005

Fern Cottage, Ferndale, CA 94

Ferndale Museum, Ferndale, CA 95

Festival-Institute, James Dick Foundation, Round Top, TX 1446

Fick Fossil & History Museum, Oakley, KS 554

Fillmore County Historical Center, Fountain, MN 776

Filoli Center, Woodside, CA 199

The Finley House, Wayne, PA 1306

Finney County Kansas Historical Society, Inc., Garden City, KS 541

Fire Island National Seashore, Patchogue, NY 1051

Firelands Historical Society Museum, Norwalk, OH 1180

Fireman's Hall Museum, Philadelphia, PA 1279

First Consolidated School in Minnesota, Saum, MN 793

The First Division Museum at Cantigny, Wheaton, IL 465

First Missouri State Capitol-State Historic Site, Saint Charles, MO 830

First Territorial Capitol of Kansas, Fort Riley, KS 540

First White House of the Confederacy, Montgomery, AL 16

Fischer-Hanlon House, Benicia, CA 75

Fisher Grove Country School/Fisher Grove State Park, Frankfort, SD 1347

Fitchburg Historical Society, Fitchburg, MA 683

The Flag House and Star-Spangled Banner Museum, Baltimore, MD 632

Flagler Museum, Palm Beach, FL 333

Fleming Historical Society, Fleming, CO 216

Flint House, Scotia, NY 1068

Florence Griswold Museum, Old Lyme, CT 258

The Florence McLeod Hazard Museum, Columbus, MS 800

Florence Museum of Art, Science & History and the Florence Railroad Museum, Florence, SC 1332

Florence Price Pioneer Museum, Florence, CO 216

Florence Ranch Homestead, Mesquite, TX 1438

Florewood State Park, Greenwood, MS 801

Florida Agricultural Museum, Palm Coast, FL 334

Florissant Valley Historical Society, Florissant, MO 815

Floyd County Historical Museum, Charles City, IA 510

The Fluvanna County Historical Society Old Stone Jail Museum, Palmyra, VA 1524

Folsom History Museum, Folsom, CA 95

The Folsom House Museum, Taylors Falls, MN 794

Folsom Museum, Inc., Folsom, NM 939

Fonthill Museum of the Bucks County Historical Society, Doylestown, PA 1249

Ford's Theatre National Historic Site (Lincoln Museum), Washington, DC 279

Forest Capital State Museum, Perry, FL 337

Forest History Center, Grand Rapids, MN 777

Forest Lawn Museum, Glendale, CA 100

Forest Park Museum and Arboretum, Perry, IA 527

Foresthill Divide Museum, Foresthill, CA 95

The Forges and Manor of Ringwood, Ringwood, NJ 923

Former Governors' Mansion State Historic Site, Bismarck, ND 1128

Fort Abercrombie State Historic Site, Abercrombie, ND 1127

Fort Abraham Lincoln State Park, Mandan, ND 1134

The Fort at No. 4 Living History Museum, Charlestown, NH 884

Fort Bedford Museum, Bedford, PA 1241

Fort Belknap Museum and Archives, Inc., Newcastle, TX 1441

Fort Bend Museum Association, Richmond, TX 1445

Fort Boonesborough Museum, Richmond, KY 583

Fort Bowie National Historic Site, Bowie, AZ 30

Fort Bridger State Museum, Fort Bridger, WY 1632

Fort Buford State Historic Site, Williston, ND 1137

Fort Christmas Historical Park, Christmas, FL 299

Fort Collins Museum, Fort Collins, CO 217

Fort Columbia House Museum, Chinook, WA 1550

Fort Columbia Interpretive Center, Chinook, WA 1551

Fort Concho National Historic Landmark, San Angelo, TX 1447

Fort Crawford Museum, Prairie du Chien, WI 1618

Fort Croghan Museum, Burnet, TX 1398

Fort Crook Historical Museum, Fall River Mills, CA 94

Fort Dalles Museum/Anderson Homestead, The Dalles, OR 1237

Fort Davis National Historic Site, Fort Davis, TX 1414

Fort de Chartres State Historic Site & Museum, Prairie du Rocher, IL 451

Fort Delaware Museum of Colonial History, Narrowsburg, NY 1017

Fort Dodge & Frontier Village, Fort Dodge, IA 518

Fort Fetterman State Historic Site, Douglas, WY 1631

Fort Frederick State Park, Big Pool, MD 637

Fort Garland Museum, Fort Garland, CO 217

Fort Harker Museum Complex, Kanopolis, KS 546

Fort Hartsuff State Historical Park, Burwell, NE 858

Fort Hays State Historic Site, Hays, KS 543

Furnishings–Continued

Fort Henrietta Interpretive Park, Echo, OR 1223

Fort Hill (The John C. Calhoun House), Clemson, SC 1328

Fort Hunter Mansion & Park, Harrisburg, PA 1258

Fort Inglish, Bonham, TX 1396

Fort Jones Museum, Fort Jones, CA 96

Fort Klock Historic Restoration, Saint Johnsville, NY 1063

Fort Laramie National Historic Site, Fort Laramie, WY 1633

Fort Larned National Historic Site, Larned, KS 547

Fort Lauderdale Historical Society, Fort Lauderdale, FL 307

Fort Leboeuf, Waterford, PA 1306

Fort Ligonier Association, Ligonier, PA 1269

Fort Macon State Park, Atlantic Beach, NC 1091

Fort McHenry National Monument and Historic Shrine, Baltimore, MD 632

Fort McKavett State Historical Site, Fort McKavett, TX 1415

Fort Nashborough, Nashville, TN 1379

Fort Necessity National Battlefield, Farmington, PA 1253

Fort Nisqually Living History Museum, Tacoma, WA 1573

Fort Ontario State Historic Site, Oswego, NY 1048

Fort Osage National Historic Landmark, Sibley, MO 838

Fort Payne Depot Museum, Fort Payne, AL 10

Fort Pitt Museum, Pittsburgh, PA 1292

Fort Plain Museum, Fort Plain, NY 991

Fort Pulaski National Monument, Savannah, GA 385

Fort St. Jean Baptiste State Historic Site, Natchitoches, LA 593

Fort St. Joseph Museum, Niles, MI 758

Fort Scott National Historic Site, Fort Scott, KS 540

Fort Sidney Museum & Post Commander's Home, Sidney, NE 873

Fort Sisseton State Historic Park, Lake City, SD 1350

Fort Smith Art Center, Fort Smith, AR 57

Fort Smith Museum of History, Fort Smith, AR 58

Fort Smith National Historic Site, Fort Smith, AR 58

Fort Sumter National Monument, Sullivan's Island, SC 1342

Fort Tejon State Historic Park, Lebec, CA 108

Fort Totten State Historic Site, Fort Totten, ND 1131

Fort Union Trading Post National Historic Site, Williston, ND 1138

Fort Vancouver National Historic Site, Vancouver, WA 1576

Fort Verde State Historic Park, Camp Verde, AZ 30

Fort Walla Walla Museum, Walla Walla, WA 1576

Fort Washington Park, Fort Washington, MD 643

Fort Washita, Durant, OK 1199

Fort Wayne Firefighters Museum, Fort Wayne, IN 477

Fort Wilkins Historic Complex, Copper Harbor, MI 733

Fort Winnebago Surgeons Quarters, Portage, WI 1618

Forts Folle Avoine Historic Park, Danbury, WI 1594

Fortuna Depot Museum, Fortuna, CA 96

45th Infantry Division Museum, Oklahoma City, OK 1207

Fossil Country Museum, Kemmerer, WY ..1635

Fossil Museum, Fossil, OR 1224

Fosterfields Living Historical Farm, Morristown, NJ 913

Fostoria Area Historical Museum, Fostoria, OH 1164

4-H Schoolhouse Museum, Clarion, IA 510

Four Mile Historic Park, Denver, CO 212

Fox Island Historical Society, Fox Island, WA 1554

Fox Lake Historical Museum, Inc., Fox Lake, WI 1598

The Foxfire Museum & Heritage Center, Mountain City, GA 380

Framingham Historical Society & Museum, Framingham, MA 683

Frances Willard House Museum, Evanston, IL 434

Francis Land House Historic Site, Virginia Beach, VA 1542

Francisco Fort Museum, La Veta, CO 224

Franconia Heritage Museum, Franconia, NH 888

Frank Chiarenza Museum of Glass, Meriden, CT 248

Frank H. McClung Museum, Knoxville, TN 1370

Frank Lloyd Wright Home and Studio, Oak Park, IL 448

Frank Lloyd Wright's Pope-Leighey House, Alexandria, VA 1492

Frank Murphy Memorial Museum, Harbor Beach, MI 745

Frank Phillips Home, Bartlesville, OK 1197

Frankenmuth Historical Museum, Frankenmuth, MI 742

Frankfort Area Historical Museum, West Frankfort, IL 464

Franklin County Historical & Museum Society & House of History, Malone, NY 1012

Franklin County Historical Museum, Mount Vernon, TX 1440

Franklin County Historical Museum, Pasco, WA 1561

Franklin County Old Jail Museum, Winchester, TN 1385

Franklin County Seminary and Museum, Brookville, IN 471

Franklin D. Roosevelt Presidential Library-Museum, Hyde Park, NY 1002

Franklin Mineral Museum, Franklin, NJ 904

The Franklin Pierce Homestead, Hillsborough, NH 889

Fraunces Tavern Museum, New York, NY 1025

Fred Harman Art Museum, Pagosa Springs, CO 229

Frederick C. Robie House, Chicago, IL 420

Frederick Douglass National Historic Site, Washington, DC 279

Frederick Law Olmsted National Historic Site, Brookline, MA 671

Fredericksburg Area Museum & Cultural Center, Inc., Fredericksburg, VA 1506

Freeborn County Museum and Historical Village, Albert Lea, MN 767

Freeport Historical Society, Freeport, ME 611

Freestone County Historical Museum, Fairfield, TX 1413

Fremont County Pioneer Museum, Lander, WY 1635

French Art Colony, Gallipolis, OH 1165

French Azilum, Inc., Towanda, PA 1303

The French Legation Museum, Austin, TX 1390

Fresno Flats Historical Park, Oakhurst, CA 132

The Frick Art & Historical Center, Pittsburgh, PA 1292

Friends of Arrow Rock, Inc., Arrow Rock, MO 811

Friends of Historic Kingston, Fred J. Johnston House Museum, Kingston, NY 1007

The Friends of Lucy Hayes Heritage Center, Chillicothe, OH 1147

The Friends of Peace Church, Camp Hill, PA 1245

The Friends of the Caleb Pusey House, Inc., Upland, PA 1304

Friendship Firehouse, Alexandria, VA 1492

Friendship Hill National Historic Site, Point Marion, PA 1295

Frisco Historic Park & Museum, Frisco, CO 218

Frontier Culture Museum, Staunton, VA 1537

Frontier Gateway Museum, Glendive, MT 847

Frontier Historical Society and Museum, Glenwood Springs, CO 219

Frontier Museum, Williston, ND 1138

Frontier Times Museum, Bandera, TX 1393

Frontiers of Flight Museum, Dallas, TX 1406

Fruitlands Museums, Harvard, MA 686

Frye's Measure Mill, Wilton, NH 897

The Fullerton Arboretum, Fullerton, CA 98

Fulton County Historical Society Museum, Rochester, IN 498

Fulton County Museum, Groversville, NY 996

Fulton Mansion State Historic Site, Rockport, TX 1446

Furnas-Gosper Historical Society & Museum, Arapahoe, NE 856

Gadsby's Tavern Museum, Alexandria, VA 1492

Gadsden Museum, Mesilla, NM 943

Gadsden Museum of Art, Gadsden, AL 10

Gage County Historical Society and Museum, Beatrice, NE 857

Gaineswood, Demopolis, AL 7

Galena-Jo Daviess County Historical Society & Museum, Galena, IL 436

Gallier House, New Orleans, LA 595

Galloping Road Compound & Poker Alley; Harbor Ranch, Dripping Springs, TX 1410

Galloway House and Village - Blakely Museum, Fond du Lac, WI 1597

Galveston County Historical Museum, Galveston, TX 1420

Galveston Historical Foundation, Inc., Galveston, TX 1421

Gamble House, Pasadena, CA 140

Garden Grove Historical Society, Garden Grove, CA 99

Gardner House Museum, Albion, MI 723

The Gardner Museum, Inc., Gardner, MA 684

Garfield Farm Museum, LaFox, IL 441

Gari Melchers Home and Studio, Fredericksburg, VA 1506

Garibaldi and Meucci Museum, Staten Island, NY 1072

Garnavillo Historical Museum, Garnavillo, IA 518

Garrett County Historical Museum, Oakland, MD 649

Gaston County Museum of Art and History, Dallas, NC 1097

Gatekeeper's Museum & Marion Steinbach Indian Basket Museum, Tahoe City, CA 190

Gates House, Machiasport Historical Society, Machiasport, ME 614

Gates Mills Historical Society, Gates Mills, OH 1166

Gateway to the Panhandle, Gate, OK 1201

Gathland State Park, Boonsboro, MD 637

Geddes Historic District Village, Geddes, SD 1347

Gem County Historical Society and Museum, Emmett, ID 405

Gene Stratton-Porter State Historic Site, Rome City, IN ... 498

General Adam Stephen House, Martinsburg, WV ... 1584

General Crook House Museum and Library/Archives Center, Omaha, NE ... 870

General Daniel Bissell House, Saint Louis, MO ... 833

General Douglas MacArthur Memorial, Norfolk, VA ... 1521

General Jacob Brown Historical Society, Brownville, NY ... 971

General John J. Pershing Boyhood Home State Historic Site, Laclede, MO ... 824

General Wait House, Waitsfield, VT ... 1489

Genesee Country Village & Museum, Mumford, NY ... 1016

Geneva Historical Society & Prouty-Chew House & Museum, Geneva, NY ... 994

Geneva Historical Society & Rose Hill Mansion, Geneva, NY ... 994

Geographical Center Historical Museum, Rugby, ND ... 1136

George Ade Memorial Association Inc., Brook, IN ... 471

The George Bush Presidential Library and Museum, College Station, TX ... 1400

George C. Marshall Museum, Lexington, VA ... 1513

George Eastman House/International Museum of Photography and Film, Rochester, NY ... 1058

George Washington Birthplace National Monument, Colonial Beach, VA ... 1502

George Washington Carver Museum, Tuskegee Institute, AL ... 20

George Washington Carver National Monument, Diamond, MO ... 814

George Washington Masonic National Memorial, Alexandria, VA ... 1493

George Washington's Fredericksburg Foundation, Historic Kenmore & Washington's Ferry Farm, Fredericksburg, VA ... 1506

George Westinghouse Museum, Wilmerding, PA ... 1308

Georgetown University Art Collection, Washington, DC ... 279

Georgia Museum of Art, University of Georgia, Athens, GA ... 356

Georgia Salzburger Society Museum, Rincon, GA ... 381

Georgia Southern University Museum, Statesboro, GA ... 387

The Georgian Museum, Lancaster, OH ... 1171

Georgia's Old Capital Museum, Milledgeville, GA ... 380

Georgia's Stone Mountain Park, Stone Mountain, GA ... 387

Germantown Historical Society, Philadelphia, PA ... 1280

Gertrude Smith House, Mount Airy, NC ... 1111

Gettysburg National Military Park, Gettysburg, PA ... 1255

Ghost Town Museum, Colorado Springs, CO ... 207

Gibbes Museum of Art, Charleston, SC ... 1325

Gibbs Museum of Pioneer and Dakotah Life, Falcon Heights, MN ... 775

The Gibson Society, Inc. dba Gibson House Museum, Boston, MA ... 665

Gig Harbor Peninsula Historical Society, Gig Harbor, WA ... 1555

Gila County Historical Museum, Globe, AZ ... 35

The Gilbert Stuart Birthplace and Museum, Saunderstown, RI ... 1319

Gillespie County Historical Society, Fredericksburg, TX ... 1419

Gillette Castle State Park, East Haddam, CT ... 239

Gilliam County Historical Society - Depot Museum Complex, Condon, OR. 1222

Gilman Garrison House, Exeter, NH ... 887

Gilman Historic Ranch and Wagon Museum, Banning, CA ... 74

Gilpin History Museum, Central City, CO ... 205

Glacier National Park Museum, West Glacier, MT ... 854

The Glebe House Museum and Gertrude Jekyll Garden, Woodbury, CT ... 268

Glencairn Museum: Academy of the New Church, Bryn Athyn, PA ... 1244

Glendower State Memorial, Lebanon, OH. 1171

Glenn H. Curtiss Museum, Hammondsport, NY ... 997

Glenn House/Historical Association of Greater Cape Girardeau, Cape Girardeau, MO ... 812

Glensheen Historic Estate, Duluth, MN ... 773

Glenview Area Historical Society, Glenview, IL ... 438

Glessner House Museum, Chicago, IL ... 421

Gloucester County Historical Society, Woodbury, NJ ... 931

Golden Ball Tavern Museum, Weston, MA ... 718

Golden Gate National Recreation Area, San Francisco, CA ... 165

Golden Pioneer Museum, Golden, CO ... 220

The Goldstein Museum of Design, Saint Paul, MN ... 789

Gomez Foundation for Mill House, Marlboro, NY ... 1014

Goochland County Museum & Historical Center, Goochland, VA ... 1508

Goodman Museum, Tyler, TX ... 1456

Goodnow Museum State Historic Site, Manhattan, KS ... 550

Goodyear World of Rubber Museum, Akron, OH ... 1139

Gore Place, Waltham, MA ... 715

Gorgas House, Tuscaloosa, AL ... 19

Goschenhoppen Folklife Library and Museum, Green Lane, PA ... 1257

Goshen Historical Society, Goshen, CT ... 242

Governor Bent Museum, Taos, NM ... 952

Governor Henry Lippitt House Museum, Providence, RI ... 1316

Governor John Langdon House, Portsmouth, NH ... 894

Governor John Sevier Memorial Association, Knoxville, TN ... 1370

Governor Printz Park, Essington, PA ... 1253

Governor Ross Plantation, Seaford, DE ... 272

Governor Seay Mansion, Kingfisher, OK ... 1204

Governor Stephen Hopkins House Museum, Providence, RI ... 1317

The Governor's Mansion, Frankfort, KY ... 569

Governor's Mansion, Columbia, SC ... 1329

Governor's Mansion State Historic Park, Sacramento, CA ... 152

Grace Armantrout Museum, George West, TX ... 1422

Grace Hudson Museum & Sun House, Ukiah, CA ... 193

The Grace Museum, Abilene, TX ... 1385

Graceland, Memphis, TN ... 1373

The Gracie Mansion Conservancy, New York, NY ... 1026

Graeme Park, Horsham, PA ... 1261

Grafton Historical Society, Grafton, VT ... 1479

Graham County Historical Society, Thatcher, AZ ... 46

Grand Army of the Republic Civil War Museum, Philadelphia, PA ... 1281

Grand County Museum, Hot Sulphur Springs, CO ... 222

Grand Forks County Historical Society, Grand Forks, ND ... 1132

Grand Gulf Military Park, Port Gibson, MS ... 807

Grand Lake Area Historical Society, Grand Lake, CO ... 221

Grand Lodge AF&AM of Virginia - Allen E. Roberts Masonic Library and Museum, Richmond, VA ... 1529

Grand Portage National Monument, Grand Marais, MN ... 776

The Grand River Historical Society & Museum, Chillicothe, MO ... 813

The Granger Homestead Society, Inc., Canandaigua, NY ... 975

Grant County Historical Museum, Canyon City, OR ... 1221

Grant County Historical Museum, Ephrata, WA ... 1553

Grant County Historical Society, Elbow Lake, MN ... 774

Grant County Museum, Carson, ND ... 1129

Grant County Museum, Medford, OK ... 1205

Grant County Museum aka Historic Adobe Museum, Ulysses, KS ... 560

Grant County Museum & Historic Society, Hyannis, NE ... 863

Grant-Humphreys Mansion, Denver, CO ... 212

Grant-Kohrs Ranch National Historic Site, Deer Lodge, MT ... 845

Granville Historical Society Museum, Granville, OH ... 1167

Granville Museum, Inc., Granville, TN ... 1366

Grass Valley Museum, Grass Valley, CA ... 100

Graue Mill and Museum, Oak Brook, IL ... 448

Gravette Historical Museum, Gravette, AR ... 59

Graycliff Conservancy, Derby, NY ... 984

Great Basin Historical Society & Museum, Delta, UT ... 1464

Great Smoky Mountains Heritage Center, Townsend, TN ... 1384

Greater Harvard Area Historical Society, Harvard, IL ... 439

Greater Hazleton Historical Society, Hazleton, PA ... 1260

Greater Loveland Historical Society Museum, Loveland, OH ... 1173

Green River Valley Museum, Big Piney, WY ... 1629

Greenbelt Museum, Greenbelt, MD ... 646

Greene County Historical Museum, Waynesburg, PA ... 1306

Greene County Historical Society, Xenia, OH ... 1193

Greenfield Historical Society, Greenfield, WI ... 1599

Greensboro Historical Museum, Inc., Greensboro, NC ... 1103

Greenwood County Historical Society, Eureka, KS ... 539

Gregg County Historical Museum, Longview, TX ... 1434

Gresham History Museum, Gresham, OR ... 1226

Grevemberg House Museum, Franklin, LA ... 588

Grier Musser Museum, Los Angeles, CA ... 115

Griggs County Historical Museum, Prairies, ND ... 1136

Grinnell Historical Museum, Grinnell, IA ... 519

Grinter Place State Historic Site, Kansas City, KS ... 546

Grissom Air Museum, Peru, IN ... 496

Gropius House, Lincoln, MA ... 690

Grosse Ile Historical Society, Grosse Ile, MI ... 745

Groton Historical Society, Groton, MA ... 685

Grout Museum District: Grout Museum of History and Science, Bluedorn Science Imaginarium, Rensselaer Russell House Museum, Snowden House, Waterloo, IA ... 529

The Grove, Glenview, IL ... 438

Groveland Yosemite Gateway Museum, Groveland, CA ... 101

Furnishings—Continued

Grover Cleveland Birthplace, Caldwell, NJ................899

Gruenewald Historic House, Anderson, IN................467

Guadalupe Mountains National Park, Salt Flat, TX................1447

Guernsey County Museum, Cambridge, OH................1144

The Guest House Museum, Fort Bragg, CA................95

Gulf Coast Exploreum Science Center, Mobile, AL................13

Gunderson House, Kenyon, MN................778

Gunn Memorial Library and Museum, Washington, CT................263

Gunnison County Pioneer and Historical Society, Gunnison, CO................222

Gunston Hall Plantation, Mason Neck, VA................1517

Guy B. Woodward Museum, Ramona, CA................144

Gwinnett Historical Society, Lawrenceville, GA................376

H.E.A.R.T.S. Veterans Museum of Texas, Huntsville, TX................1430

H.G. Albee Memorial Museum, Estherville, IA................517

Haas-Lilienthal House, San Francisco, CA................166

Hacienda Buena Vista, Ponce, PR................1642

Hackettstown Historical Society Museum & Library, Hackettstown, NJ................905

Hackley & Hume Historic Site, Muskegon, MI................757

The Haggin Museum, Stockton, CA................189

The Hagley Museum and Library, Wilmington, DE................273

Hagood-Mauldin House and Irma Morris Museum of Fine Arts, Pickens, SC................1340

Hahns Peak Area Historical Society and School House, Clark, CO................205

Haines Museum, Waukegan Historical Society, Waukegan, IL................463

Hale Farm and Village, Bath, OH................1141

Hale Pa'ahao Prison, Lahaina, HI................400

Halifax Historical Museum, Daytona Beach, FL................303

Hallockville Museum Farm, Riverhead, NY................1057

Hamden Historical Society, Inc., Hamden, CT................244

Hamilton Grange National Memorial, New York, NY................1026

Hamilton House, South Berwick, ME................622

Hamilton Township Historical Society - John Abbott II House, Hamilton, NJ................906

Hamilton Van Wagoner Museum, Clifton, NJ................901

Hamlin Garland Homestead, West Salem, WI................1627

Hammel Museum, Socorro, NM................951

Hammond Castle Museum, Gloucester, MA................684

Hammond-Harwood House Association, Annapolis, MD................628

Hampton History Museum, Hampton, VA................1509

Hampton National Historic Site, Towson, MD................655

Hampton University Museum, Hampton, VA................1509

Hanby House, Westerville, OH................1191

Hancock Historical Museum, Findlay, OH................1164

Hancock Historical Society, Hancock, NH................888

Hancock House, Hancock's Bridge, NJ................907

Hancock Memorial Museum, Los Angeles, CA................116

Hancock Shaker Village, Inc., Pittsfield, MA................703

Hanford Carnegie Museum, Hanford, CA................101

Hanford Mills Museum, East Meredith, NY................987

Hanley House, Clayton, MO................813

Hanover House, Clemson, SC................1328

Har-Ber Village, Grove, OK................1202

Harbour House Museum, Crystal Falls, MI................733

Hardin County Historical Museums, Inc., Kenton, OH................1170

Harding Home and Museum, Marion, OH................1174

Harding Museum, Franklin, OH................1164

Hardwick Historical Society, Hardwick, MA................686

Hargitt House, Norwalk, CA................131

Harlan-Lincoln House, Mount Pleasant, IA................524

Harn Homestead and 1889er Museum, Oklahoma City, OK................1207

Harold Warp Pioneer Village Foundation, Minden, NE................868

Harpers Ferry National Historical Park, Harpers Ferry, WV................1582

Harriet Beecher Stowe Center, Hartford, CT................245

The Harriet Tubman Home, Auburn, NY................959

Harrimans Falls Educational Centre and Museum, Bath, NH................883

Harrison County Historical Museum, Marshall, TX................1436

Harrison House, Branford, CT................235

Harrisonburg-Rockingham Historical Society, Dayton, VA................1503

Harry P. Leu Gardens, Orlando, FL................331

Harry Ransom Center at the University of Texas at Austin, Austin, TX................1390

Harry S Truman Birthplace State Historic Site, Lamar, MO................825

Harry S. Truman Little White House Museum, Key West, FL................317

Harry S Truman National Historic Site - Truman Farm Home, Grandview, MO................816

Harry S Truman National Historic Site - Truman Home, Independence, MO................818

Harry S. Truman Office & Courtroom, Independence, MO................818

Hartford House Museum, Manhattan, KS................551

Hartslog Heritage Museum, Alexandria, PA................1239

Hartsville Museum, Hartsville, SC................1335

Harvard Historical Society, Still River, MA................711

Harvey-Baker House, Salinas, CA................154

Harvey House Museum, Florence, KS................539

The Harwood Museum of Art of the University of New Mexico, Taos, NM................952

Haskell County Historical Society, Sublette, KS................558

Hastings Museum, Hastings, NE................863

Hathaway Ranch Museum, Santa Fe Springs, CA................182

Hattiesburg Area Historical Society and HAHS Museum, Hattiesburg, MS................801

Hatton-Eielson Museum & Historical Association, Hatton, ND................1132

Haverford Township Historical Society, Havertown, PA................1260

Haverhill Historical Society, Haverhill, MA................686

Hawaii's Plantation Village, Waipahu, HI................402

Hawkeye Log Cabin, Burlington, IA................507

Hawks Inn Historical Society, Inc., Delafield, WI................1595

Hawks Nest State Park, Ansted, WV................1579

Hay House Museum, Macon, GA................377

Hayward Area Historical Society, Hayward, CA................102

Headley-Whitney Museum, Lexington, KY................573

Headquarters House Museum, Fayetteville, AR................57

Headwaters Heritage Museum, Three Forks, MT................854

Healy House-Dexter Cabin, Leadville, CO................225

Hearst Castle, San Simeon, CA................177

Heart of West Texas Museum, Colorado City, TX................1401

Hearthstone Historic House Museum, Appleton, WI................1589

Heisey Museum, Clinton County Historical Society, Lock Haven, PA................1269

Held-Poage Memorial Home and Research Library, Ukiah, CA................193

Hellenic Museum & Cultural Center, Chicago, IL................421

Helvetia Museum, Helvetia, WV................1582

Hemet Museum, Hemet, CA................103

The Hemingway Museum and The Ernest Hemingway Birthplace, Oak Park, IL................448

Hendricks Hill Museum, Southport, ME................623

Hennepin History Museum, Minneapolis, MN................782

Henrico County Historic Preservation & Museum Services, Richmond, VA................1529

Henry B. Plant Museum, Tampa, FL................349

Henry County Historical Society, New Castle, IN................494

Henry County Museum and Cultural Arts Center, Clinton, MO................813

The Henry Ford, Dearborn, MI................733

Henry Ford Estate-Fair Lane, Dearborn, MI................734

The Henry Sheldon Museum of Vermont History, Middlebury, VT................1481

Henry Whitfield State Historical Museum, Guilford, CT................243

Herbert Hoover Presidential Library-Museum, West Branch, IA................530

Hereford Inlet Lighthouse, North Wildwood, NJ................917

The Heritage Center, Pine Ridge, SD................1354

Heritage Center Museum, Berryville, AR................55

Heritage Center of Lancaster County, Inc., Lancaster, PA................1265

Heritage Conservancy, Doylestown, PA................1249

Heritage Farm Museum & Village, Huntington, WV................1583

Heritage Farmstead Museum, Plano, TX................1444

Heritage Hall Museum & Archives, Freeman, SD................1347

Heritage Hill State Historical Park, Green Bay, WI................1599

Heritage-Hjemkomst Interpretive Center, Moorhead, MN................784

Heritage House, West Covina, CA................197

Heritage House Museum and Robert Frost Cottage, Key West, FL................318

Heritage House Museum of Montgomery County, Mount Ida, AR................64

Heritage House of Orange County Association Inc., Orange, TX................1441

The Heritage Museum, Astoria, OR................1218

Heritage Museum & Cultural Center, Baker, LA................585

Heritage Museum & Gallery, Leadville, CO................226

Heritage Museum & Potton House, Big Spring, TX................1396

The Heritage Museum & Underhill Museum, Idaho Springs, CO................223

Heritage Museum Foundation of Tate County, Inc., Senatobia, MS................808

Heritage Museum of Northwest Florida, Valparaiso, FL................352

The Heritage Society, Houston, TX................1426

Heritage Square Museum, Ontario, NY................1047

Heritage Square Museum, Los Angeles, CA................116

Heritage Station, Umatilla County Historical Society Museum, Pendleton, OR................1230

Heritage Village, Largo, FL................321

Furnishings–Continued

Historical Society of Quaker Hill & Pawling, Pawling, NY............1051

Historical Society of Quincy and Adams County, Quincy, IL..................452

Historical Society of Rockland County, New City, NY..................1017

Historical Society of St. Marys and Benzinger Township, Saint Marys, PA...1297

Historical Society of Santuit and Cotuit, Cotuit, MA..................677

Historical Society of Saratoga Springs, Saratoga Springs, NY..................1064

Historical Society of Stanton County Museums at Stanton and Pilger, Pilger, NE..................872

Historical Society of Talbot County, Easton, MD..................642

Historical Society of the Cocalico Valley, Ephrata, PA..................1252

Historical Society of the Tonawandas, Inc., Tonawanda, NY..................1078

Historical Society of the Town of Clarence, Clarence, NY..................978

Historical Society of the Town of Greenwich Inc. aka Bush-Holley Historic Site, Cos Cob, CT..................237

The Historical Society of the Town of Warwick, Warwick, NY..................1082

The Historical Society of Trappe, Collegeville, Perkiomen Valley, Inc., Trappe, PA..................1303

Historical Society of Walden & Wallkill Valley, Walden, NY..................1081

Historical Society of Wells and Ogunquit, Wells, ME..................625

Historical Society Porter County Old Jail Museum, Valparaiso, IN..................502

The Historical Society, serving Sleepy Hollow and Tarrytown, Tarrytown, NY.1078

The History Center, Cedar Rapids, IA.........509

History Museum for Springfield-Greene County, Springfield, MO..................839

The History Museum, Lake Placid-North Elba Historical Society, Lake Placid, NY..................1009

History Museum of Western Virginia, Roanoke, VA..................1535

The History Place, Morehead City, NC.....1111

History San Jose, San Jose, CA..................171

Hiwan Homestead Museum, Evergreen, CO..................215

Hixon House, La Crosse, WI..................1603

Hoard Historical Museum and National Dairy Shrine's Visitors Center, Fort Atkinson, WI..................1598

Hobart Historical Society Museum, Hobart, IN..................480

Hocking Valley Museum of Theatrical History, Inc., Nelsonville, OH..................1177

Hodgden House Museum Complex, Ellsworth, KS..................538

Hofwyl-Broadfield Plantation State Historic Site, Brunswick, GA..................366

Hoiles-Davis Museum, Greenville, IL..........439

Holiday World/Splashin' Safari, Santa Claus, IN..................498

Holland Historical Society Museum, Inc., Holland, VT..................1480

The Holland Land Office Museum, Batavia, NY..................960

The Holland Museum, Holland, MI.............746

Hollenberg Station State Historic Site, Hanover, KS..................543

Holly History Center & Hutchinson House Museum, Waupaca, WI..............1626

Hollyhock House, Los Angeles, CA............116

Hollywood Heritage Museum, Hollywood, CA..................103

Hollywood History Museum, Hollywood, CA..................103

Holmes County Historical Society, Millersburg, OH..................1176

Holyland Exhibition, Los Angeles, CA........116

Home of Franklin D. Roosevelt National Historic Site, Hyde Park, NY..............1002

Home of Stone (The Mueller-Schmidt House 1881), a Ford County Museum, curated by Ford County Historic Society, Dodge City, KS..................537

Home Sweet Home Museum, East Hampton, NY..................986

Homestead Acre and the Hill-Palmer House, Chatsworth, CA..................82

Homestead National Monument of America, Beatrice, NE..................857

Homesteader Museum, Powell, WY...........1637

Homewood House Museum, Baltimore, MD..................633

Honolulu Academy of Arts, Honolulu, HI...395

Honolulu House Museum, Marshall, MI......754

Hood River County Historical Museum, Hood River, OR..................1226

Hoover Historical Center, North Canton, OH..................1179

Hope Historical Society, Hope, NJ..............908

Hope Lodge and Mather Mill, Fort Washington, PA..................1254

Hopewell Furnace National Historic Site, Elverson, PA..................1251

Hopewell Museum, Paris, KY..................582

Hopewell Museum, Hopewell, NJ..................908

Hopsewee Plantation, Georgetown, SC......1333

Horatio Colony House Museum & Nature Preserve, Keene, NH..................890

Hornby Museum, Hornby, NY..................999

Horridge House, Vinton, IA..................529

Hot Spring County Museum - The Boyle House/1876 Log Cabin, Malvern, AR.......63

Hot Springs County Museum and Cultural Center, Thermopolis, WY........1639

Hot Springs National Park Visitor Center, Hot Springs, AR..................60

Hotel de Paris Museum, Georgetown, CO...219

Houghton County Historical Museum Society, Lake Linden, MI..................749

House in the Horseshoe State Historic Site, Sanford, NC..................1119

House of Refuge Museum, Stuart, FL..........346

The House of the Seven Gables, Salem, MA..................706

House of the Temple, Washington, DC.......280

House of Wickersham State Historical Site, Juneau, AK..................25

Houston Fire Museum, Houston, TX.........1427

Houston Museum of Decorative Arts, Chattanooga, TN..................1362

Howard County Historical Museum, Kokomo, IN..................486

Howard County Historical Society, Ellicott City, MD..................643

Howard-Dickinson House Museum, Henderson, TX..................1424

Howard Steamboat Museum and Mansion, Jeffersonville, IN..................486

Howard Weeden House Museum, Huntsville, AL..................11

Howell Historical Society & Committee Museum, Howell, NJ..................908

Howell Living History Farm, Titusville, NJ..................926

Howland House, Plymouth, MA..................703

The Hoyt Institute of Fine Arts, New Castle, PA..................1273

The Hubbard Museum of the American West, Ruidoso Downs, NM..................946

Hubbell Trading Post National Historic Site, Ganado, AZ..................34

Huddleston Farmhouse Inn Museum, Cambridge City, IN..................471

Hudson Library and Historical Society, Hudson, OH..................1168

The Hudson River Museum, Yonkers, NY.1087

Huerfano County Historical Society, including The Walsenburg Mining Museum & Ft. Francisco Museum of La Veta, Walsenburg, CO..................234

Hugh Mercer Apothecary Shop, Fredericksburg, VA..................1506

The Huguenot Historical Society, New Paltz, NY..................1017

Hulihee Palace, Kailua-Kona, HI..................399

Hull Lifesaving Museum Inc., the Museum of Boston Harbor Heritage, Hull, MA..................687

Humboldt Historical Museum, Humboldt, KS..................544

Humboldt Redwoods State Park Visitor Center, Weott, CA..................197

Humpback Rocks Mountain Farm & Visitor Center, Waynesboro, VA...........1544

Hungarian Folk-Art Museum, Port Orange, FL..................338

Hunt-Morgan House, Lexington, KY..........573

Hunter-Dawson State Historic Site, New Madrid, MO..................828

Hunter House Victorian Museum, Norfolk, VA..................1522

Huntingdon County Historical Society, Huntingdon, PA..................1262

Huntington County Historical Society Museum, Huntington, IN..................481

Huntington Museum of Art, Inc., Huntington, WV..................1583

Huron City Museums, Port Austin, MI........761

Hurst Ranch Historical Foundation, West Covina, CA..................197

The Hyde Collection, Glens Falls, NY........994

Hyde Hall, Inc., Cooperstown, NY..................980

The Hyland House, Guilford, CT..................243

Hyser Rivers Museum, Belmont, MI...........728

Idaho Museum of Mining and Geology, Boise, ID..................404

Idaho State Historical Museum, Boise, ID...404

Illinois and Michigan Canal Commissioners Office Museum, Lockport, IL..................443

Ilwaco Heritage Museum, Ilwaco, WA.......1556

IMA - Indianapolis Museum of Art, Indianapolis, IN..................483

Immaculate Conception Catholic Church, Natchitoches, LA..................593

Imperial Calcasieu Museum, Inc., Lake Charles, LA..................590

Independence Historical Museum, Independence, KS..................545

Independence National Historical Park, Philadelphia, PA..................1281

Indian City U.S.A., Anadarko, OK..................1195

Indian Hill Historical Society, Cincinnati, OH..................1150

Indian King Tavern Museum, Haddonfield, NJ..................906

Indiana Dunes National Lakeshore, Porter, IN..................496

Indiana Medical History Museum, Indianapolis, IN..................484

Indiana State Museum, Indianapolis, IN......484

The Institute For American Indian Studies (IAIS), Washington Green, CT...263

International Bluegrass Music Museum, Owensboro, KY..................581

International Institute of Metropolitan Detroit, Detroit, MI..................737

International Museum of Cultures, Dallas, TX..................1406

International Tennis Hall of Fame & Museum, Newport, RI..................1313

Iolani Palace, Honolulu, HI..................396

Iosco County Historical Museum, East Tawas, MI..................740

Iowa Department of Natural Resources, Des Moines, IA..................515

Iowa Great Lakes Maritime Museum, Arnolds Park, IA..................505

Iowa Railroad Historical Society, Boone, IA 506
Ipswich Historical Society and Museum, Ipswich, MA 688
Iraan Museum, Iraan, TX 1430
Iredell Museum of Arts & Heritage, Statesville, NC 1120
Iris & B. Gerald Cantor Center for Visual Arts at Stanford University, Stanford, CA 188
Iron & Steel Museum of Alabama, Tannehill Ironworks Historical State Park, McCalla, AL 13
Iron County Museum, Caspian, MI 731
Ironworld Discovery Center, Chisholm, MN 771
Iroquois County Historical Society, Watseka, IL 463
Isaac Farrar Mansion, Bangor, ME 604
Isaac Winslow House, Marshfield, MA 693
Isabel Miller Museum/Sitka Historical Society, Sitka, AK 27
Isabella Stewart Gardner Museum, Boston, MA 666
Isanti County Historical Society, Cambridge, MN 770
Ischua Valley Historical Society, Inc., Franklinville, NY 992
Isla Center For the Arts at the University of Guam, Mangilao, GU 1640
Island County Historical Society Museum, Coupeville, WA 1551
Isle La Motte Historical Society, Isle La Motte, VT 1480
Isle of Wight Courthouse, Smithfield, VA 1536
Isle Royale National Park, Houghton, MI 747
Islesboro Historical Society, Islesboro, ME 612
Islesford Historical Museum, Islesford, ME 612
Issaquah History Museum, Issaquah, WA 1557
Itasca County Historical Society, Grand Rapids, MN 777
Ivy Green, Birthplace of Helen Keller, Tuscumbia, AL 20

J.E. Reeves Home & Museum, Dover, OH 1163
J.W. Parmley Historical Home Society, Ipswich, SD 1349
Jack London State Historic Park, Glen Ellen, CA 99
Jackson County Historical Museum & Research Library, Maquoketa, IA 522
Jackson County Historical Society, Black River Falls, WI 1592
Jackson Hole Historical Society and Museum, Jackson, WY 1634
Jackson-Washabaugh Historical Museum, Kadoka, SD 1349
Jacksonport State Park, Jacksonport, AR 60
Jackson's Mill Historic Area, Weston, WV 1587
Jacksonville Fire Museum, Jacksonville, FL 314
Jacksonville Maritime Museum Society, Jacksonville, FL 314
Jacob Hamblin Home, Santa Clara, UT 1474
Jacob Kelley House Museum, Hartsville, SC 1335
Jacques Marchais Museum of Tibetan Art, Staten Island, NY 1072
Jail Museum, Neligh, NE 869
James A. Garfield National Historic Site, Mentor, OH 1176
James Buchanan Foundation for the Preservation of Wheatland, Lancaster, PA 1266
The James Dunklin House, Laurens, SC 1336
James J. Hill House, Saint Paul, MN 790
James K. Polk Ancestral Home, Columbia, TN 1364

The James Madison Museum, Orange, VA 1524
James Madison's Montpelier, Montpelier Station, VA 1518
James Mitchell Varnum House and Museum, East Greenwich, RI 1311
James Monroe Museum and Memorial Library, Fredericksburg, VA 1507
James S. Copley Library, La Jolla, CA 106
James W. Dillon House Museum, Dillon, SC 1331
James Whitcomb Riley Birthplace & Museum, Greenfield, IN 480
James Whitcomb Riley Museum Home, Indianapolis, IN 485
Jamestown Settlement, Yorktown Victory Center, The Jamestown-Yorktown Foundation, Williamsburg, VA 1545
Jane Addams Hull-House Museum, University of Illinois Chicago, Chicago, IL 422
Japanese Cultural Center of Hawaii, Honolulu, HI 397
Jarrell Plantation Georgia State Historic Site, Juliette, GA 374
J.C. Penney Homestead & Historical Foundation, Kemmerer, WY 1635
Jeane Dixon Museum and Library, Strasburg, VA 1538
Jeanerette Bicentennial Park and Museum, Jeanerette, LA 589
Jeff Matthews Memorial Museum, Galax, VA 1508
Jefferson Barracks Historic Site, Saint Louis, MO 833
The Jefferson County Historical Assoc., Steubenville, OH 1186
Jefferson County Historical Society, Watertown, NY 1083
Jefferson County Historical Society and Farnsworth TV Pioneer Museum, Rigby, ID 409
Jefferson County Historical Society Museum, Port Townsend, WA 1562
Jefferson County Museum, Charles Town, WV 1580
Jefferson National Expansion Memorial, Saint Louis, MO 833
Jefferson Patterson Park & Museum, Saint Leonard, MD 651
Jekyll Island Museum, Jekyll Island, GA 374
Jenkins Plantation Museum, Lesage, WV 1584
Jennings-Brown House Female Academy, Bennettsville, SC 1322
Jerome State Historic Park, Jerome, AZ 36
Jersey City Museum, Jersey City, NJ 908
Jesse James Bank Museum, Liberty, MO 826
Jesse James Farm & Museum, Kearney, MO 823
Jesse James Home Museum, Saint Joseph, MO 830
Jesse Peter Museum, Santa Rosa, CA 184
Jewell County Historical Museum, Mankato, KS 552
Jewish Museum of Florida, Miami Beach, FL 326
Jim Crow Museum - Ferris State University, Big Rapids, MI 729
Jim Gatchell Memorial Museum, Buffalo, WY 1629
Jim Thorpe Home, Yale, OK 1217
Jimmy Carter National Historic Site, Plains, GA 381
John and Mable Ringling Museum of Art, Sarasota, FL 344
John Brown Farm State Historic Site, Lake Placid, NY 1009
John Brown Museum State Historic Site, Osawatomie, KS 554
John Brown Wax Museum Inc., Harpers Ferry, WV 1582
John Burroughs Association, Inc., West Park, NY 1085

John F. Kennedy Presidential Library & Museum, Boston, MA 666
John Fitzgerald Kennedy National Historic Site, Brookline, MA 671
John G. Neihardt State Historic Site, Bancroft, NE 856
John James Audubon Center at Mill Grove, Audubon, PA 1241
John Jay French House, Beaumont Heritage Society, Beaumont, TX 1395
John Jay Homestead State Historic Site, Katonah, NY 1006
John Michael Kohler Arts Center, Sheboygan, WI 1621
John Muir National Historic Site, Martinez, CA 124
John Nance Garner Museum, Uvalde, TX 1457
The John Nicholas Brown Center for the Study of American Civilization, Providence, RI 1317
John Paul Jones House Museum, Portsmouth, NH 894
John R. Jackson House, Winlock, WA 1578
John Rains House, Rancho Cucamonga, CA 145
John S. Barry Historical Society, Constantine, MI 732
John Stark Edwards House, Warren, OH 1189
John Sydnor's 1847 Powhatan House, Galveston, TX 1421
John Waddey Carter House, Martinsville, VA 1516
John Woolman Memorial, Mount Holly, NJ 915
John Wornall House Museum, Kansas City, MO 821
Johnson County Historical Society, Coralville, IA 511
Johnson County Historical Society, Inc., Tecumseh, NE 873
Johnson County Historical Society Museum, Warrensburg, MO 840
Johnson County Museum of History, Franklin, IN 478
Johnson County Museums, Shawnee, KS 558
Johnson Ferry House Museum, Titusville, NJ 926
Johnson Hall State Historic Site, Johnstown, NY 1005
Johnstown Area Heritage Association, Johnstown, PA 1263
Johnstown Historical Society, Johnstown, NY 1005
Joliet Area Historical Museum, Joliet, IL 440
Jonathan Bailey Home, Whittier, CA 198
Jonathan Hager House & Museum, Hagerstown, MD 646
Jonesborough-Washington County History Museum, Jonesborough, TN 1368
Jonson Gallery of the University of New Mexico Art Museum, Albuquerque, NM 933
The Jordan House, West Des Moines, IA 530
Joseph Smith Historic Site, Nauvoo, IL 447
Josiah Quincy House, Quincy, MA 705
The Journey Museum, Rapid City, SD 1354
Juan Matias Sanchez Adobe, Montebello, CA 127
The Judah P. Benjamin Confederate Memorial at Gamble Plantation Historic State Park, Ellenton, FL 306
Judaica Museum of Central Synagogue, New York, NY 1029
Judith Basin County Museum, Stanford, MT 853
Judy Garland Museum, Grand Rapids, MN 777
Julian H. Sleeper House, Saint Paul, MN 790
Juliette Gordon Low Birthplace, Savannah, GA 385
Junction City Historical Society, Junction City, OR 1226

Furnishings–Continued

Juniata County Historical Society, Mifflintown, PA 1271

The Junior Museum of Bay County, Panama City, FL 334

Justin Smith Morrill Homestead, Strafford, VT 1488

Kalamazoo Nature Center, Inc., Kalamazoo, MI 748

Kaminski House Museum, Georgetown, SC 1333

Kanabec History Center, Mora, MN 784

Kandiyohi County Historical Society, Willmar, MN 796

Kankakee County Museum, Kankakee, IL...441

Kansas Museum of History, Topeka, KS 559

Karl C. Harrison Museum of George Washington, Columbiana, AL 6

The Kate Chopin House & Bayou Folk Museum, Cloutierville, LA 588

Kate Shelley Railroad Museum, Boone, IA 506

Katherine Dunham Dynamic Museum, East Saint Louis, IL...............................431

Kauffman Museum, North Newton, KS 553

Kaw Mission State Historic Site, Council Grove, KS 536

Kearney Mansion Museum, Fresno, CA 97

The Kearny Cottage, Perth Amboy, NJ 921

Keeler Tavern Museum, Ridgefield, CT......259

Kell House Museum, Wichita Falls, TX 1461

Kellogg-Eddy House and Museum, Newington, CT 256

Kellogg Historical Society, Kellogg, IA.......521

Kelly-Griggs House Museum, Red Bluff, CA 146

Kelsey Museum of Archaeology, Ann Arbor, MI 724

The Kelso House Museum, Kent, OH........1169

Kelton House Museum & Garden, Columbus, OH 1158

Kemerer Museum of Decorative Arts, Bethlehem, PA 1242

The Kemp-McCarthy Memorial Museum of the Rowe Historical Society, Inc., Rowe, MA 706

The Kenilworth Historical Society, Kenilworth, IL 441

Kennebunkport Historical Society, Kennebunkport, ME 612

Kennedy-Douglass Center for the Arts, Florence, AL 9

Kenosha County Historical Society and Museum, Inc., Kenosha, WI 1602

Kensington Mansion, Eastover, SC 1332

Kent-Delord House Museum, Plattsburgh, NY 1052

Kent Plantation House, Alexandria, LA 585

Kent State University Museum, Kent, OH.1169

Kentucky Coal Mining Museum, Benham, KY 565

Kentucky Gateway Museum Center, Maysville, KY 579

Kentucky Historical Society, Frankfort, KY 569

The Kentucky Library & Museum, Bowling Green, KY 565

Kentucky Military History Museum, Frankfort, KY 569

Kentucky State Capitol, Frankfort, KY 569

Keokuk River Museum, Keokuk, IA...........521

Ker Place, Onancock, VA 1523

Kerbyville Museum, Kerby, OR 1227

Kern County Museum, Bakersfield, CA.........73

Kershaw County Historical Society, Camden, SC 1323

Kewaunee County Historical Museum, Kewaunee, WI 1602

Keweenaw County Historical Society, Eagle Harbor, MI 739

Key West Lighthouse Museum, Key West, FL 318

Keyport Historical Society-Steamboat Dock Museum, Keyport, NJ 909

Kimball House Museum, Battle Creek, MI 727

Kimberly Crest House & Gardens, Redlands, CA 147

Kimble County Historical Museum, Junction, TX 1431

King Kamehameha V-Judiciary History Center, Honolulu, HI 397

King Manor, Jamaica, NY 1004

Kingman County Historical Museum, Kingman, KS 547

Kingman Tavern Historical Museum, Cummington, MA 678

Kings Mountain National Military Park, Blacksburg, SC 1322

Kingsley Plantation, Jacksonville, FL 315

Kingwood Center, Mansfield, OH 1173

Kinney Pioneer Museum and Historical Society of North Iowa, Clear Lake, IA ...510

Kirkland Museum of Fine & Decorative Art, Denver, CO 212

Kirtland Temple Historic Center, Kirtland, OH 1170

Kit Carson Historical Society, Kit Carson, CO 223

Kit Carson Museum, Las Animas, CO.........225

Kitsap County Historical Society Museum, Bremerton, WA 1549

Kittson County History Center Museum, Lake Bronson, MN 778

Kiwanis Van Slyke Museum Foundation Inc., Caldwell, ID 404

Klamath County Museum, Klamath Falls, OR 1227

Klein Museum, Mobridge, SD..................1352

Klickitat County Historical Society, Goldendale, WA 1555

Kline Creek Farm, Winfield, IL 466

Klyne Esopus Museum, Ulster Park, NY...1079

Knife River Indian Villages National Historic Site, Stanton, ND.....................1136

Knight Museum, Alliance, NE.....................855

Knott House Museum, Tallahassee, FL.........347

Knox County Museum, Knoxville, IL...........441

Knox Headquarters State Historic Site, Vails Gate, NY 1080

Knox House Museum, El Cajon, CA 92

Knoxville Museum of Art, Knoxville, TN.1370

Knoxville Public Library, Knoxville, PA ...1265

Knudt Salle Log Cabin, Adams, ND 1127

Koester House Museum, Marysville, KS 552

Koochiching County Historical Museum, International Falls, MN 778

Koreshan State Historic Site, Estero, FL......306

Korner's Folly, Kernersville, NC 1108

Krannert Art Museum and Kinkead Pavilion, Champaign, IL 416

Kruse House Museum, West Chicago, IL....464

Kuhlmann King Historical House and Museum, Boerne, TX 1396

Kuser Farm Mansion, Hamilton, NJ............907

L.C. Bates Museum, Hinckley, ME.............612

La Casa Primera de Rancho San Jose, Pomona, CA 143

La Porte County Historical Society Museum, La Porte, IN 487

La Puente Valley Historical Society City Hall, LaPuente, CA 107

La Purisima Mission State Historic Park, Lompoc, CA 109

LaBelle Heritage Museum, LaBelle, FL 319

Lac Qui Parle County Historical Society, Madison, MN 779

The Lace Museum, Sunnyvale, CA.............190

Lacey Historical Society, Forked River, NJ 904

The Lackawanna Historical Society at the Catlin House, Scranton, PA...................1298

Ladew Topiary Gardens, Monkton, MD.......649

Lagrange County Historical Society, Inc., Lagrange, IN..488

LaGrange Plantation, Cambridge, MD.........639

Lahaina Restoration Foundation, Lahaina, HI 400

Lake City Columbia County Historical Museum, Inc., Lake City, FL.................319

Lake County Discovery Museum, Wauconda, IL 463

Lake County Historic Courthouse Museum, Lakeport, CA 108

Lake County Historical Society, Two Harbors, MN 794

Lake County Historical Society, Kirtland Hills, OH 1170

Lake George Historical Association Museum, Lake George, NY 1008

Lake Jackson Historical Museum, Lake Jackson, TX 1433

Lake of the Red Cedars Museum, Cedar Lake, IN 472

Lake of the Woods County Museum, Baudette, MN 768

Lake Waccamaw Depot Museum, Lake Waccamaw, NC 1109

Lake Wales Depot Museum & Cultural Center, Lake Wales, FL 320

Lakewood's Heritage Center, Lakewood, CO 225

LaMoure County Museum, Grand Rapids, ND 1132

Lancaster County Historical Society, Lancaster, PA 1266

Land of the Yankee Fork Historic Association Museum, Stanley, ID............410

Landis Valley Museum, Lancaster, PA 1266

Landmark Park, Dothan, AL 8

The Landmark Society of Western New York, Rochester, NY 1058

Landmarks Foundation/Old Alabama Town, Montgomery, AL 16

Lane County Historical Museum, Dighton, KS 536

Lane County Historical Society & Museum, Eugene, OR 1223

Lane House, Roseburg, OR 1234

Lane Place, Crawfordsville, IN...................473

Lanier Mansion State Historic Site, Madison, IN 489

Lansing Manor House Museum, North Blenheim, NY 1043

Lanterman House, La Canada Flintridge, CA 105

Lapham-Patterson House, Thomasville, GA 388

The LaPointe-Krebs House & Old Spanish Fort Museum, Pascagoula, MS 807

Laramie Plains Museum, Laramie, WY 1635

Lars Noak Blacksmith Shop, Larsson/Ostlund Log Home & One-Room Capitol School, New Sweden, ME 616

LaSalle County Historical Society Museum, Utica, IL 462

Lathrop House, Redwood City, CA.............147

Lauder Museum - Amityville Historical Society, Amityville, NY 957

Laughing Brook Education Center & Wildlife Sanctuary, Hampden, MA.........686

Laura Ingalls Wilder Museum and Tourist Center, Walnut Grove, MN 795

Laura Ingalls Wilder Park & Museum, Inc., Burr Oak, IA 507

Lauren Rogers Museum of Art, Laurel, MS 804

Laurence C. Jones Museum, Piney Woods, MS 807

Lawrence County Gray House Museum, Ironton, OH 1169

Lawrence Heritage State Park, Lawrence, MA 689

Lawrence History Center: Immigrant City Archives & Museum, Lawrence, MA 689

Laws Railroad Museum and Historical Site, Bishop, CA 78

Layland Museum, Cleburne, TX 1400

Le Sault de Sainte Marie Historical Sites, Inc., Sault Ste. Marie, MI 764

Le Sueur Museum, Le Sueur, MN 779

The Lebanon County Historical Society, Lebanon, PA 1268

Lee Chapel and Museum, Lexington, VA ..1513

Lee County Historical Society, Loachapoka, AL 13

Lee-Fendall House Museum and Garden, Alexandria, VA 1493

Lee Hall Mansion, Newport News, VA 1519

Leelanau Historical Museum, Leland, MI 751

Lefferts Historic House, Brooklyn, NY 969

The Leffingwell House Museum, Norwich, CT 258

Lehigh County Historical Society, Allentown, PA 1239

The Lemee House, Natchitoches, LA 593

Lemon Hill Mansion, Philadelphia, PA 1282

Lesueur County Historical Museum-Chapter 1, Elysian, MN 774

Levere Memorial Temple, Evanston, IL 434

Leverett Historical Society, Leverett, MA 689

Levi Coffin House, Fountain City, IN 478

Levine Museum of the New South, Charlotte, NC 1095

Lewes Historical Society, Lewes, DE 271

Lewis County Historical Society Museum, Lowville, NY 1012

Lewis Ginter Botanical Garden, Richmond, VA 1530

Lexington County Museum, Lexington, SC 1336

Lexington Historical Society, Lexington, MA 689

Lexington History Museum, Lexington, KY 573

Liberace Museum & Foundation, Las Vegas, NV 879

Liberty County Museum, Chester, MT 844

Liberty Hall Historic Center, Lamoni, IA 522

Liberty Hall Historic Site, Frankfort, KY 569

Liberty Hall Museum, Union, NJ 928

Libertyville-Mundelein Historical Society, Inc., Libertyville, IL 442

Library of the Supreme Council, 33 Degrees, Washington, DC 282

Licking County Historical Society, Newark, OH 1178

Lillian Jones Museum, Jackson, OH 1169

Limberlost State Historic Site, Geneva, IN 479

Limon Heritage Museum, Limon, CO 226

Lincoln Boyhood National Memorial, Lincoln City, IN 488

Lincoln County Historical Museum, Davenport, WA 1552

Lincoln County Historical Society, North Platte, NE 869

Lincoln County Historical Society Museum of Pioneer History, Chandler, OK 1197

Lincoln County Museum, Hugo, CO 222

Lincoln County Pioneer Museum, Hendricks, MN 778

Lincoln Herdon Law Offices State Historic Site, Springfield, IL 458

Lincoln Home National Historic Site, Springfield, IL 459

Lincoln Homestead State Park, Springfield, KY 583

Lincoln Log Cabin State Historic Site, Lerna, IL 442

The Lincoln Museum, Fort Wayne, IN 478

Lincoln Parish Museum & Historical Society, Ruston, LA 600

Lincoln Park Historical Museum, Lincoln Park, MI 751

Lincoln State Monument, Lincoln, NM 941

The Lincoln-Tallman Restorations, Janesville, WI 1601

Lincoln's New Salem State Historic Site, Petersburg, IL 451

Linn County Historical Museum and Moyer House, Brownsville, OR 1220

Linn County Museum/Geneaology Library, Pleasanton, KS 556

Lisbon Historical Society, Lisbon, OH 1172

Lisle Station Museum, Lisle, IL 443

Litchfield Historical Society and Museum, Litchfield, CT 247

Little Bighorn Battlefield National Monument, Crow Agency, MT 844

The Little Brick House, Vandalia, IL 462

Little Compton Historical Society, Little Compton, RI 1312

Little Falls Historical Society Museum, Little Falls, NY 1009

Little White House Historic Site, Warm Springs, GA 390

Little White Schoolhouse, Ripon, WI 1620

Littleton Historical Museum, Littleton, CO 227

Living History Farms, Urbandale, IA 529

Livingston County Historical Society Museum, Geneseo, NY 993

Livingston Depot Center, Livingston, MT ...850

Locust Grove, Louisville, KY 577

Locust Grove, The Samuel Morse Historic Site, Poughkeepsie, NY 1055

Locust Lawn and Terwilliger House, Gardiner, NY 993

Log Cabin Village, Fort Worth, TX 1417

The Log House Museum of the Historical Society of Columbiana-Fairfield Township, Columbiana, OH 1157

Logan County Museum, Paris, AR 65

Loghurst Farm Museum, Canfield, OH 1145

Lola Montez Home, Grass Valley, CA 101

Lombard Historical Museum, Lombard, IL 443

Lompoc Valley Historical Society, Inc., Lompoc, CA 110

Long Beach Museum of Art, Long Beach, CA 111

Long Branch Historical Museum, Long Branch, NJ 910

Long Island Maritime Museum, West Sayville, NY 1085

Longfellow Evangeline State Historic Site, Saint Martinville, LA 600

Longfellow National Historic Site, Cambridge, MA 673

Longfellow's Wayside Inn, Sudbury, MA 714

Longhorn Museum, Pleasanton, TX 1444

Longmont Museum, Longmont, CO 227

Longstreet Farm, Holmdel, NJ 908

Longue Vue House & Gardens, New Orleans, LA 596

Longyear Museum, Chestnut Hill, MA 675

Lopez Adobe, San Fernando, CA 162

Lorenzo State Historic Site, Cazenovia, NY 976

Los Alamos Historical Museum, Los Alamos, NM 942

Los Altos History Museum aka Association of the Los Altos Historical Museum, Los Altos, CA 112

The Los Angeles County Arboretum & Botanic Garden, Arcadia, CA 71

Los Angeles County Museum of Art, Los Angeles, CA 118

Los Angeles Maritime Museum, San Pedro, CA 176

Los Angeles Municipal Art Gallery - Barnsdall Art Park, Los Angeles, CA 118

Los Nogales Museum, Seguin, TX 1452

Lou Holtz/Upper Ohio Valley Hall of Fame, East Liverpool, OH 1163

Loudoun Museum, Inc., Leesburg, VA 1512

Louis E. May Museum, Fremont, NE 861

Louis H. & Lena Firn Grover Museum, Shelbyville, IN 498

Louisiana State Museum, New Orleans, LA 596

Louisiana's Old State Capitol, Political History Museum, Baton Rouge, LA 587

Louisville Visual Art Association, Louisville, KY 578

Loveland Museum Gallery, Loveland, CO ...227

Lowell Area Historical Museum, Lowell, MI 751

Lowell Damon House, Wauwatosa, WI 1626

Lowell Observatory, Flagstaff, AZ 33

Lower Cape Fear Historical Society, Inc., Wilmington, NC 1123

Lower East Side Tenement Museum, New York, NY 1029

Lowndes County Historical Society and Museum, Valdosta, GA 389

Loxahatchee River Historical Society, Jupiter, FL 316

Luckhard Museum - The Indian Mission, Sebewaing, MI 764

Lucretia Vaile Museum, Palmer Lake, CO 229

Ludwig Welk Farmstead, Strasburg, ND 1136

Luis Munoz Rivera Library & Museum, Barranquitas, PR 1641

Lum & Abner Museum & Jot 'Em Down Store, Pine Ridge, AR 66

Luther Burbank Home & Gardens, Santa Rosa, CA 184

The Luther W. Brady Art Gallery, Washington, DC 282

Lutheran Heritage Center & Museum of the Perry County Lutheran Historical Society, Altenburg, MO 810

Luzerne County Historical Society, Wilkes-Barre, PA 1307

The Lyceum, Alexandria's History Museum, Alexandria, VA 1493

Lyman Allyn Art Museum, New London, CT 255

Lyman Museum, Hilo, HI 393

Lynchburg Museum System, Lynchburg, VA 1515

Lynden Pioneer Museum, Lynden, WA 1559

Lyndhurst, Tarrytown, NY 1078

Lyndon B. Johnson National Historical Park, Johnson City, TX 1431

Lyndon Baines Johnson Library and Museum, Austin, TX 1391

Lynn Museum & Historical Society, Lynn, MA 692

Lynnhaven House, Virginia Beach, VA 1542

Lyon County Historical Society and Museum, Emporia, KS 538

Lyon County Historical Society Museum, Marshall, MN 780

Mabee Farm Historic Site, Rotterdam Junction, NY 1062

Mabel Hartzell Historical Home, Alliance, OH 1139

Mabry-Hazen House, Knoxville, TN 1371

Macartney House Museum, Oakland, ME ...616

MacCallum More Museum and Gardens, Chase City, VA 1500

Macculloch Hall Historical Museum & Gardens, Morristown, NJ 913

MacGregor Ranch, Estes Park, CO 215

Mackinac Island State Park Commission-Mackinac State Historic Parks, Mackinaw City, MI 752

Mackinac State Historic Parks-Colonial Michilimackinac & Old Mackinac Point Lighthouse, Mackinaw City, MI 752

Furnishings–Continued

Mackinac State Historic Parks-Fort Mackinac & Mackinac Island State Park, Mackinac Island, MI............752

Mackinac State Historic Parks-Historic Mill Creek, Mackinaw City, MI.............753

Macktown Living History Education Center, Inc., Rockton, IL............456

Macon County Historical Society Museum Complex, Decatur, IL............430

The Madam Brett Homestead, Beacon, NY............961

Madera County Museum, Madera, CA........123

Madison County Historical Museum & Archival Library, Edwardsville, IL............432

Madison County Historical Society, Winterset, IA............531

Madison County Historical Society-Cottage Lawn, Oneida, NY......1045

Madison Historical Society, Madison, CT....247

Madison-Morgan Cultural Center, Madison, GA............378

Magevney House, Memphis, TN............1373

Maggie L. Walker National Historic Site, Richmond, VA............1530

Magnolia Grove-Historic House Museum, Greensboro, AL............10

Magnolia Manor, Cairo, IL............415

Magnolia Plantation and Gardens, Charleston, SC............1326

Magoffin Home State Historic Site, El Paso, TX............1412

Mahaffie Stagecoach Stop and Farm, Olathe, KS............554

Maine Historical Society, Portland, ME......619

Maine Lighthouse Museum, Rockland, ME............621

Maine Maritime Museum, Bath, ME............606

Maine State Museum, Augusta, ME............604

Maitland Historical Museums, Maitland, FL............322

The Major General Frederick Funston Boyhood Home and Museum, Iola, KS............546

Major John Bradford House, Kingston, MA............688

Malabar Farm State Park, Lucas, OH........1173

Malibu Lagoon Museum, Malibu, CA............123

Mallory-Neely House, Memphis, TN.........1373

Mamie Doud Eisenhower Birthplace, Boone, IA............506

Mammoth Spring State Park, Depot Museum, Mammoth Spring, AR............64

Manassas Museum System, Manassas, VA............1516

Manassas National Battlefield Park, Manassas, VA............1516

Manatee Village Historical Park, Bradenton, FL............297

Manchester Historic Association Millyard Museum, Manchester, NH............891

Manchester Historical Society, Manchester, MA............692

Manitowoc County Historical Society, Manitowoc, WI............1607

Mansfield Historical Society Museum, Storrs, CT............261

Manship House Museum, Jackson, MS........802

Maple Valley Historical Museum, Maple Valley, WA............1559

Marathon County Historical Society, Wausau, WI............1626

Marble Historical Society, Marble, CO........228

Marblehead Arts Association - King Hooper Mansion, Marblehead, MA.........693

Marblehead Museum & Historical Society, Marblehead, MA............693

Marcella Sembrich Opera Museum, Bolton Landing, NY............963

Marcellus Historical Society, Marcellus, NY............1013

Margaret Harwell Art Museum, Poplar Bluff, MO............829

The Margaret Mitchell House & Museum, Atlanta, GA............361

Maridon Museum, Butler, PA............1245

Marietta House Museum, Glenn Dale, MD............645

Marin History Museum, San Rafael, CA.....177

Marinette County Historical Museum, Marinette, WI............1607

Marion County Historical Society, Salem, OR............1236

The Marion County Historical Society Museum, Marion, OH............1174

Marion Historical Museums, Inc. - Granger House, Marion, IA............523

Marion Public Library Museum, Marion, IN............490

Mariposa Museum and History Center Inc., Mariposa, CA............124

Maritime Museum of Monterey, Monterey, CA............127

Maritime Museum of San Diego, San Diego, CA............157

Marjorie Kinnan Rawlings Historic State Park, Cross Creek, FL............301

Mark Twain Birthplace State Historic Site, Florida, MO............815

Mark Twain Home and Museum, Hannibal, MO............816

The Mark Twain House & Museum, Hartford, CT............245

Marlboro County Historical Museum, Bennettsville, SC............1322

Marlboro Historical Society, Marlboro, VT............1481

Marquette County Historical Society, Westfield, WI............1627

Marquette County History Museum, Marquette, MI............753

Marrett House, Standish, ME............623

Marshall Center School, Cedar Falls, IA.....508

Marshall County Historical Museum, Plymouth, IN............496

Marshall County Historical Museum, Holly Springs, MS............801

Marshall County Historical Society Museum, Warren, MN............795

Marshall Gold Discovery State Historic Park, Coloma, CA............86

Marshall M. Fredericks Sculpture Museum, University Center, MI............766

The Marston House/San Diego Historical Society, San Diego, CA............157

Martha A. Parsons House Museum, Enfield, CT............239

Martin County Historical Museum, Stanton, TX............1453

Martin County Museum, Shoals, IN............499

Martin Luther King, Jr. Center for Nonviolent Social Change, Inc., Atlanta, GA............361

Martin Luther King, Jr. National Historic Site and Preservation District, Atlanta, GA............361

Martin Van Buren National Historic Site, Kinderhook, NY............1007

Marvin Newton House, Brookfield, VT.....1477

Mary Aaron Memorial Museum, Marysville, CA............125

Mary Ball Washington Museum & Library, Inc., Lancaster, VA............1512

Mary McLeod Bethune Council House National Historic Site, Washington, DC............283

Mary Todd Lincoln House, Lexington, KY............574

Mary Washington House, Fredericksburg, VA............1507

Maryland Historical Society, Baltimore, MD............634

Marywood University Art Galleries (Suraci Gallery and Mahady Gallery), Scranton, PA............1298

Mason County Historical Society/Historic White Pine Village, Ludington, MI.........751

Masonic Grand Lodge Library and Museum of Texas, Waco, TX............1459

The Masonic Library and Museum of Pennsylvania, Philadelphia, PA............1283

The Massillon Museum, Massillon, OH....1175

Matchless Mine Museum (Leadville Assembly), Leadville, CO............226

Mathias Ham House Historic Site, Dubuque, IA............516

Mattapoisett Museum and Carriage House, Mattapoisett, MA............693

The Mattatuck Museum Arts and History Center, Waterbury, CT............264

Matthews Museum of Maine Heritage, Union, ME............624

May Museum & Farmville Heritage Center, Farmville, NC............1100

Mayborn Museum Complex, Waco, TX.....1459

Mayflower Society Museum, Plymouth, MA............703

Maymont, Richmond, VA............1530

Maynard Pioneer Museum & Park, Maynard, AR............64

Mayville Area Museum of History and Genealogy, Mayville, MI............754

Mayville Historical Society, Inc., Mayville, WI............1608

Mazomanie Historical Society, Mazomanie, WI............1608

Mc Cook County Historical Society and Museum, Salem, SD............1355

McAllister House Museum, Colorado Springs, CO............207

McCallum Museum, Sibley, IA............527

McConaghy House, Hayward, CA............102

McCone County Museum, Circle, MT........844

McConnell Mansion, Moscow, ID............407

McCook House, Civil War Museum, Carrollton, OH............1146

McCoy House, Lewistown, PA............1269

McCutchen Overland Inn, McCutchenville, OH............1175

McDonald's #1 Store Museum, Des Plaines, IL............431

McDowell House Museum, Danville, KY............567

McFaddin-Ward House, Beaumont, TX....1395

McFarland Historical Society, McFarland, WI............1609

McFarland State Historic Park, Florence, AZ............34

McHenry County Historical Society and Museum, Union, IL............461

McHenry Museum, Modesto, CA............126

McIntosh County Historical Society, Ashley, ND............1127

McLean-Alanreed Area Museum, McLean, TX............1438

McLean County Historical Society Museum, Washburn, ND............1137

McLean County Museum of History, Bloomington, IL............414

McMinn County Living Heritage Museum, Athens, TN............1360

McNamara House Museum, Victoria, TX..1457

McPherson County Old Mill Museum and Park, Lindsborg, KS............550

McPherson Museum & Arts Foundation, McPherson, KS............552

Meade County Historical Society Museum, Meade, KS............552

Meadow Brook Hall, Rochester, MI..........761

Meadow Garden Museum, Augusta, GA......365

Meagher County Historical Association Castle Museum, White Sulphur Springs, MT............855

Mechanicsburg Museum Association, Mechanicsburg, PA............1270

Mecosta County Historical Museum, Big Rapids, MI 729
Medina County Historical Society, The John Smart House, Medina, OH 1175
Medina Railroad Museum, Medina, NY 1014
Meeker County Historical Society Museum & G.A.R. Hall, Litchfield, MN 779
Meeker Home Museum, Greeley, CO 222
Meeteetse Museum District, Meeteetse, WY 1636
Meigs County Museum, Pomeroy, OH 1183
Mellette House, Watertown, SD 1359
Melrose Plantation Home Complex, Melrose, LA 592
Mem-Erie Historical Museum, Erie, KS 539
The Memorial Day Museum, Waterloo, NY 1083
Memorial Hall Museum, Pocumtuck Valley Memorial Assoc., Deerfield, MA 679
Memoryville USA, Inc., Rolla, MO 829
The Menczer Museum of Medicine & Dentistry, Hartford, CT 245
Mendocino Historical Research, Inc./Kelley House Museum, Mendocino, CA 125
Mennonite Heritage Center, Harleysville, PA 1258
Mennonite Heritage Museum, Goessel, KS 542
Menominee County Heritage Museum, Menominee, MI 754
Merced County Courthouse Museum, Merced, CA 125
Mercer County Genealogical and Historical Society, Princeton, MO 829
Mercer County Historical Museum, The Riley Home, Celina, OH 1146
Mercer County Historical Society, Mercer, PA 1271
Mercer Museum of the Bucks County Historical Society, Doylestown, PA 1250
Merchant's House Museum, New York, NY 1029
Meriden Historical Society, Inc., Meriden, CT 249
Meridian International Center, Washington, DC 283
Merrill Historical Museum, Merrill, WI 1609
Merwin House, Tranquility, Stockbridge, MA 712
Mesa Historical Museum, Mesa, AZ 37
Mesa Southwest Museum, Mesa, AZ 37
Mesa Verde National Park Museum, Mesa Verde National Park, CO 228
Metamora Courthouse Historic Site, Metamora, IL 444
Meux Home Museum, Fresno, CA 98
Miami County Museum, Peru, IN 496
Michel Brouillet House & Museum, Vincennes, IN 502
Michie Tavern ca. 1784, Charlottesville, VA 1499
Michigan Historical Museum, Michigan Historical Center, Lansing, MI 750
The Michigan State University Museum, East Lansing, MI 740
Michigan Transit Museum, Inc., Mount Clemens, MI 756
Mid-Atlantic Center for the Arts/Emlen Physick Estate/Cape May Lighthouse, Cape May, NJ 900
Middleborough Historical Association, Inc., Middleborough, MA 694
Middlebury Historical Society, Wyoming, NY 1087
Middlesex County Historical Society, Middletown, CT 249
Middleton Historical Society - Lura Woodside Watkins Museum, Middleton, MA 694

Middleton Place Foundation, Charleston, SC 1326
Middletown Valley Historical Society, Middletown, MD 649
Midland County Historical Society, Midland, MI 755
Midway Museum, Inc., Midway, GA 379
Midway Village & Museum Center, Rockford, IL 455
Midwest Old Settlers & Threshers Association, Inc., Mount Pleasant, IA 524
Mifflinburg Buggy Museum Association, Inc., Mifflinburg, PA 1271
Milam County Museum and Annex, Cameron, TX 1399
Milan Historical Museum, Inc., Milan, OH 1176
Miles B. Carpenter Museum, Waverly, VA 1543
Milford Historical Museum, Milford, MI 756
Milford Historical Society, Milford, CT 250
Military Veterans Museum, Inc., Oshkosh, WI 1616
Mill Race Historical Village, Northville, MI 758
Millard Fillmore House, East Aurora, NY 985
Miller-Cory House Museum, Westfield, NJ 930
Mills County Historical Society and Museum, Glenwood, IA 519
Milton Historical Museum, Milton, VT 1482
Milton House Museum Historic Site, Milton, WI 1610
Milwaukee County Historical Society, Milwaukee, WI 1611
Mineral County Museum, Hawthorne, NV 878
Minnesota Historical Society, Saint Paul, MN 791
Minnesota Pioneer Park Museum, Annandale, MN 767
Minnesota State Capitol Historic Site, Saint Paul, MN 791
Minnesota's Machinery Museum, Hanley Falls, MN 777
Minnetrista, Muncie, IN 492
Minnilusa Pioneer Museum, Rapid City, SD 1354
Minter Field Air Museum, Shafter, CA 186
Minute Man National Historical Park, Concord, MA 676
Miracle of America Museum Inc., Polson, MT 852
Miramont Castle Museum, Manitou Springs, CO 228
The Mission House, Stockbridge, MA 712
Mission Houses Museum, Honolulu, HI 397
Mission Inn Foundation/Museum, Riverside, CA 149
Mission Mill Museum Association, Salem, OR 1236
Mission San Diego de Alcala, San Diego, CA 157
Mission San Francisco de Asis (Mission Dolores), San Francisco, CA 167
Mission San Jose Chapel and Museum, Fremont, CA 96
Mission San Luis Rey Museum, Oceanside, CA 135
Missisquoi Valley Historical Society, North Troy, VT 1483
Mississippi Agriculture & Forestry/National Agricultural Aviation Museum, Jackson, MS 802
Mississippi County Historical Society, Charleston, MO 812
Mississippi Governor's Mansion, Jackson, MS 802
Mississippi River Museum at Mud Island River Park, Memphis, TN 1375
Mississippi Society Daughters of the American Revolution Rosalie House Museum, Natchez, MS 805

Missouri Historical Society, Saint Louis, MO 835
Missouri Town 1855, Lee's Summit, MO 825
Mitchell County Historical Museum, Osage, IA 526
Mobile Medical Museum, Mobile, AL 14
Moffatt-Ladd House and Garden, Portsmouth, NH 894
Mohave Museum of History and Arts, Kingman, AZ 36
Molly Brown House Museum, Denver, CO 213
Mondak Heritage Center, Sidney, MT 853
The Monhegan Museum, Monhegan, ME 615
Monocacy National Battlefield, Frederick, MD 644
Monroe County Heritage Museum, Monroeville, AL 15
Monroe County Historical Association/Stroud Mansion, Stroudsburg, PA 1302
Monroe County Historical Society, Bloomington, IN 469
Monroe Historical Society, Monroe, CT 250
Montague Museum & Historical Association, Montague, MI 756
Montalvo Arts Center, Saratoga, CA 185
Montana Historical Society, Helena, MT 849
Montauk, Clermont, IA 511
Montclair Historical Society, Montclair, NJ 912
Monterey History and Art Association, Monterey, CA 127
Monterey State Historic Park, Monterey, CA 128
The Montgomery County Historical Society, Dayton, OH 1161
The Montgomery County Historical Society, Inc., Rockville, MD 651
Montgomery Museum & Lewis Miller Regional Art Center, Christiansburg, VA 1501
Monticello, Home of Thomas Jefferson, Thomas Jefferson Foundation, Inc., Charlottesville, VA 1499
Montpelier Mansion, Laurel, MD 648
Montpelier-The General Henry Knox Museum, Thomaston, ME 624
Montville Township Historical Museum, Montville, NJ 912
Moody-Bradley House Restoration Foundation, Fairfield, TX 1413
The Moody Mansion Museum, Galveston, TX 1421
Moore County Historical Museum, Dumas, TX 1410
Moore Home, Lerna, IL 442
The Moore-Youse Home Museum, Muncie, IN 492
Moorten Botanic Garden and Cactarium, Palm Springs, CA 138
Moravian Historical Society, Nazareth, PA 1273
Moravian Museum of Bethlehem, Inc., Bethlehem, PA 1242
Mordecai Historic Park, Raleigh, NC 1115
Morgan Row Museum and Harrodsburg-Mercer County Research Library, Harrodsburg, KY 570
Moriarty Historical Museum, Moriarty, NM 943
The Morikami Museum and Japanese Gardens, Delray Beach, FL 305
Mormon Visitors Center, Independence, MO 818
Morningside Nature Center, Gainesville, FL 311
Morris-Butler House Museum, Indianapolis, IN 485
Morris County Historical Society (Acorn Hall House Museum), Morristown, NJ 914
Morris-Jumel Mansion, New York, NY 1030
The Morris Museum, Morristown, NJ 914

Furnishings—Continued

Morris Museum of Art, Augusta, GA 365

Morrison's Heritage Museum, Morrison, IL 446

Morristown National Historical Park, Morristown, NJ 914

Morton Grove Historical Museum/Haupt-Yehl House, Morton Grove, IL 446

Morton Homestead, Prospect Park, PA 1295

Morton House Museum, Benton Harbor, MI 728

Morton Museum of Cooke County, Gainesville, TX 1420

Morven Park, Leesburg, VA 1512

Moses Myers House, Norfolk, VA 1522

Moss Mansion Historic House Museum, Billings, MT 841

Mother Colony House Museum, Anaheim, CA 71

Motts Military Museum, Groveport, OH 1167

Mount Clare Museum House, Baltimore, MD 635

Mount Desert Island Historical Society, Mount Desert, ME 615

Mount Holly Community Historical Museum, Belmont, VT 1476

Mt. Horeb Area Museum, Mount Horeb, WI 1614

Mount Pleasant Historical Society, Mount Pleasant, OH 1177

Mount Prospect Historical Society Museums, Mount Prospect, IL 446

Mt. Pulaski Courthouse State Historic Site, Mount Pulaski, IL 446

Mount Vernon Hotel Museum & Garden, New York, NY 1031

Mount Vernon Ladies' Association, Mount Vernon, VA 1518

Mountain Gateway Museum, Old Fort, NC 1113

Mountain Heritage Center, Cullowhee, NC 1097

Mountain Life Museum, London, KY 575

The Movie Museum, Owosso, MI 759

The Muchnic Gallery, Atchison, KS 533

Mulford Farm, East Hampton, NY 986

Muller House Museum, San Pedro, CA 176

Murfreesboro Historical Association, Murfreesboro, NC 1112

Murphy African American Museum, Tuscaloosa, AL 19

Murray-Lindsay Mansion, Lindsay, OK 1204

Murrell Home, Park Hill, OK 1211

Muscatine Art Center, Muscatine, IA 524

Museo de las Americas, Denver, CO 213

The Museum, Greenwood, SC 1334

Museum & Archives of Georgia Education, Milledgeville, GA 380

Museum at Southwestern Michigan College, Dowagiac, MI 738

The Museum at the Fashion Institute of Technology, New York, NY 1031

Museum of Alaska Transportation & Industry, Inc., Wasilla, AK 29

Museum of American Architecture and Decorative Arts, Houston, TX 1428

Museum of American Finance, New York, NY 1031

Museum of American Glass at Wheaton Village, Millville, NJ 911

Museum of American Presidents, Strasburg, VA 1539

Museum of Ancient & Modern Art, Penn Valley, CA 141

Museum of Anthropology, Chico, CA 83

Museum of Anthropology, University of Missouri, Columbia, MO 813

Museum of Appalachia, Clinton, TN 1363

Museum of Art and History at the McPherson Center, Santa Cruz, CA 182

Museum of Art & History at Weston, Weston, CT 266

Museum of Chicot County Arkansas, Lake Village, AR 61

Museum of Chinese in the Americas, New York, NY 1032

Museum of Church History and Art, Salt Lake City, UT 1471

Museum of Cosmetology, Chicago, IL 425

Museum of Design Atlanta, Atlanta, GA 362

Museum of Early Southern Decorative Arts (MESDA), Winston-Salem, NC 1125

The Museum of Early Trades and Crafts, Madison, NJ 910

Museum of Florida History, Tallahassee, FL 348

Museum of Flying, Santa Monica, CA 183

Museum of History & Art, Ontario, Ontario, CA 136

Museum of History & Industry (MOHAI), Seattle, WA 1567

Museum of Idaho, Idaho Falls, ID 406

Museum of International Folk Art, Santa Fe, NM 948

Museum of Jewish Heritage-A Living Memorial to the Holocaust, New York, NY 1032

Museum of Migrating People, Bronx, NY 966

The Museum of Mobile, Mobile, AL 14

Museum of New Mexico, Santa Fe, NM 949

Museum of North Idaho, Coeur d'Alene, ID 405

The Museum of Nursing History, Inc., Philadelphia, PA 1283

Museum of Radio & Technology, Inc., Huntington, WV 1583

Museum of Religious Arts, Logan, IA 522

Museum of Rural Life, Denton, MD 642

Museum of San Diego History and Research Library, San Diego, CA 158

Museum of Science and Industry, Chicago, IL 425

Museum of Southern History, Jacksonville, FL 315

The Museum of Southern History, Sugarland, TX 1454

Museum of Spanish Colonial Art - MoSCA, Santa Fe, NM 949

Museum of Texas Tech University, Lubbock, TX 1435

Museum of the Albemarle, Elizabeth City, NC 1099

Museum of the American Quilter's Society (MAQS), Paducah, KY 581

Museum of the Arkansas Grand Prairie, Stuttgart, AR 69

Museum of the Bedford Historical Society, Bedford, NY 961

Museum of the Cape Fear Historical Complex, Fayetteville, NC 1101

Museum of the Cherokee Strip, Enid, OK 1200

Museum of the City of Lake Worth, Lake Worth, FL 320

Museum of the City of New York, New York, NY 1033

The Museum of the Confederacy, Richmond, VA 1531

Museum of the Great Plains, Lawton, OK 1204

Museum of the Gulf Coast, Port Arthur, TX 1444

Museum of the High Plains, McCook, NE 868

Museum of the Llano Estacado, Plainview, TX 1443

Museum of the Moving Image, Astoria, NY 958

Museum of the Northern Great Plains, Fort Benton, MT 846

Museum of the Puerto Rican Family of the 19th Century, San Juan, PR 1643

Museum of the Southern Jewish Experience, Jackson, MS 803

Museum of the Waxhaws & Andrew Jackson Memorial, Waxhaw, NC 1122

Museum of the Western Prairie, Altus, OK 1195

Museum of the Weston Historical Society, Inc., Weston, MA 718

Museum of West Louisiana, Leesville, LA 591

Museum of Wildlife, Science & Industry, Webster, SD 1359

Museum of World Cultures/University of North Carolina at Wilmington, Wilmington, NC 1123

Museum of Yachting, Newport, RI 1314

Museum of Yarmouth History, Yarmouth, ME 626

Museum on Main, Pleasanton, CA 142

Museum Village, Monroe, NY 1015

Museums of Los Gatos, Los Gatos, CA 123

The Museums of Oglebay Institute - Mansion Museum & Glass Museum, Wheeling, WV 1588

The Music House Museum, Acme, MI 722

Muskegon County Museum, Muskegon, MI 757

Musselshell Valley Historical Museum, Roundup, MT 853

My Old Kentucky Home State Park, Bardstown, KY 564

Mystic Seaport - The Museum of America and the Sea, Mystic, CT 251

NAU Art Museum, Flagstaff, AZ 33

Nantucket Historical Association, Nantucket, MA 696

Nantucket Maria Mitchell Association, Nantucket, MA 696

Naomi Wood Collection at Woodford Mansion, Philadelphia, PA 1284

Naper Settlement, Naperville, IL 447

Napoleonic Society of America, Inc., Clearwater, FL 300

Narragansett Historical Society, Templeton, MA 714

Nashville Zoo at Grassmere, Nashville, TN 1379

Nassau County, Division of Museum Services, Department of Recreation, Parks & Museums, East Meadow, NY 987

Nathan Denison Advocates, Forty Fort, PA 1254

Nathan Hale Homestead Museum, Coventry, CT 238

Nathaniel W. Faison Home and Museum, La Grange, TX 1432

National Afro-American Museum & Cultural Center, Wilberforce, OH 1191

The National Agricultural Center & Hall of Fame, Bonner Springs, KS 534

National Apple Museum, Biglerville, PA 1243

National Association of Miniature Enthusiasts, Carmel, IN 472

National Automotive & Truck Museum of the United States, Inc. (NATMUS), Auburn, IN 468

National Canal Museum, Hugh Moore Historical Park and Museums, Easton, PA 1250

National Capital Parks-East, Washington, DC 284

National Cowgirl Museum and Hall of Fame, Fort Worth, TX 1418

National Czech & Slovak Museum & Library, Cedar Rapids, IA 509

National First Ladies' Library, Canton, OH 1145

The National Great Blacks in Wax Museum, Inc., Baltimore, MD 635

National Heisey Glass Museum, Newark, OH 1178

National Heritage Museum, Lexington, MA 690

National Liberty Ship Memorial/S.S. Jeremiah O'Brien, San Francisco, CA.....168
National Mississippi River Museum & Aquarium, Dubuque, IA..........516
National Museum of American Illustration, Newport, RI......1314
National Museum of American Jewish History, Philadelphia, PA......1284
National Museum of the Morgan Horse, Shelburne, VT..........1487
National Packard Museum, Warren, OH....1189
National Park Service, Washington, DC......287
National Park Service Museum Resource Center, Landover, MD..........648
National Park Service Vicksburg National Military Park-Cairo Museum, Vicksburg, MS..........809
National Road/Zane Grey Museum, Norwich, OH..........1180
National Route 66 Museum and Old Town Complex, Elk City, OK......1200
National Shaving And Barbershop Museum, Meriden, CT......249
National Society of the Sons of the American Revolution, Louisville, KY.....578
National Temple Hill Association, Inc., New Windsor, NY..........1018
National Trust for Historic Preservation, Washington, DC..........288
Native American Exhibit, National Kateri Shrine, Fonda, NY..........991
Natural Center for the American Revolution, Wayne, PA..........1306
The Natural Science Center of Greensboro, Inc., Greensboro, NC..........1104
Naugatuck Historical Society, Naugatuck, CT..........251
Naumkeag, Stockbridge, MA..........712
Nauvoo Historical Society Museum, Nauvoo, IL..........447
Naval Undersea Museum, Keyport, WA....1557
Navarro County Historical Society, Pioneer Village, Corsicana, TX..........1402
Nebraska Conference United Methodist Historical Center, Lincoln, NE..........866
Nebraska Prairie Museum of the Phelps County Historical Society, Holdrege, NE..........863
Nebraska State Capitol, Lincoln, NE..........866
Nebraska State Historical Society's Museum of Nebraska History, Lincoln, NE..........866
Nebraska State Historical Society's Thomas P. Kennard House, Lincoln, NE..........867
Neenah Historical Society, Hiram Smith, Neenah's Heritage Park, Octagon House & Ward House, Neenah, WI.......1614
Neil Armstrong Air & Space Museum, Wapakoneta, OH..........1189
Neill-Cochran Museum House, Austin, TX..........1391
Neill Museum, Fort Davis, TX..........1414
Neligh Mills, Neligh, NE..........869
Nemours Mansion and Gardens, Wilmington, DE..........274
Nethercutt Collection, Sylmar, CA......190
Netherland Inn House Museum & Boatyard Complex, Kingsport, TN........1368
Nevada Historical Society, Reno, NV..........881
Neville Public Museum of Brown County, Green Bay, WI..........1599
New Almaden Quicksilver Mining Museum, San Jose, CA..........172
New Bedford Whaling Museum, New Bedford, MA..........696
The New Berlin Historical Society, New Berlin, WI..........1614
New Braunfels Conservation Society, New Braunfels, TX..........1440
New Britain Youth Museum, New Britain, CT..........252

New Canaan Historical Society, New Canaan, CT..........252
New Castle Historical Society, New Castle, DE..........272
New Castle Historical Society - Horace Greeley House, Chappaqua, NY..........977
New England Civil War Museum, Vernon, CT..........263
New Hampshire Farm Museum, Inc., Milton, NH..........892
New Hampshire Historical Society, Concord, NH..........885
New Harmony State Historic Site/Historic New Harmony, New Harmony, IN..........494
New Jersey Botanical Garden at Skylands (NJBG), Ringwood, NJ..........923
The New Jersey Historical Society, Newark, NJ..........916
New Jersey Office of Historic Sites, Trenton, NJ..........927
New Jersey State House, Trenton, NJ..........927
New London County Historical Society, New London, CT..........255
New London Historical Society, New London, NH..........892
New Market Battlefield State Historical Park, New Market, VA..........1519
New Mexico Farm & Ranch Heritage Museum, Las Cruces, NM..........940
The New Milford Historical Society, New Milford, CT..........256
New Orleans Fire Dept. Museum & Educational Center, New Orleans, LA....597
New Orleans Pharmacy Museum, New Orleans, LA..........597
New Richmond Preservation Society, New Richmond, WI..........1615
New Sweden Historical Society, New Sweden, ME..........616
New Windsor Cantonment State Historic Site and National Purple Heart Hall of Honor, Vails Gate, NY..........1080
New York City Police Museum, New York, NY..........1035
The New York Historical Society, New York, NY..........1035
New York State Bureau of Historic Sites, Waterford, NY..........1082
New York State Historical Association/Fenimore Art Museum, Cooperstown, NY..........981
New York State Museum, Albany, NY.........955
New York State Office of Parks, Recreation & Historic Preservation, Albany, NY..........955
Newark Valley Depot Museum, Newark Valley, NY..........1042
Newaygo County Museum, Newaygo, MI...758
Newport Historical Society & The Museum of Newport History, Newport, RI..........1315
Newport Restoration Foundation, Newport, RI..........1315
The Newsome House Museum & Cultural Center, Newport News, VA.....1520
The Newton History Museum at The Jackson Homestead, Newton, MA..........698
Newtown Historic Association, Newtown, PA..........1274
Newtown History Center, Stephens City, VA..........1538
Nez Perce County Museum, Lewiston, ID...407
Nez Perce National Historical Park, Spalding, ID..........409
The Niagara County Historical Center and Niagara County Genealogical Society, Lockport, NY..........1010
Nichols House Museum, Boston, MA..........668
Nici Self Museum, Centennial, WY..........1630
Nickels-Sortwell House, Wiscasset, ME......626
Nicollet County Historical Society, Saint Peter, MN..........793

Nishna Heritage Museum, Oakland, IA.......525
No Man's Land Historical Society, Goodwell, OK..........1201
Noah Webster House/West Hartford Historical Society, West Hartford, CT.....265
The Noble Maritime Collection, Staten Island, NY..........1073
Nobleboro Historical Society, Nobleboro, ME..........616
Nobles County Historical Society, Worthington, MN..........797
Noden-Reed Farm Museum, Windsor Locks, CT..........268
Nohwike Bagowa, The White Mountain Apache Cultural Center and Museum, Fort Apache, AZ..........34
Nordic Heritage Museum, Seattle, WA......1567
Norfolk History Museum, Norfolk, VA......1523
The Norman Cleveland County Historical Museum, Norman, OK..........1206
Norman #1 Oil Well Museum, Neodesha, KS..........553
Norman Rockwell Museum, Stockbridge, MA..........712
North Andover Historical Society, North Andover, MA..........698
North Carolina A&T State University Galleries, Greensboro, NC..........1104
North Carolina Museum of Forestry, Whiteville, NC..........1122
North Carolina Museum of History, Raleigh, NC..........1115
North Carolina Office of Archives and History, Raleigh, NC..........1116
North Castle Historical Society, Armonk, NY..........958
North House Museum, Lewisburg, WV.....1584
North Lee County Historic Center and Santa Fe Depot Museum Complex, Fort Madison, IA..........518
North Platte Valley Museum, Gering, NE....861
North Tonawanda History Museum, North Tonawanda, NY..........1043
Northampton County Historical and Genealogical Society, Easton, PA..........1250
Northborough Historical Society, Inc., Northborough, MA..........700
Northeast Louisiana Delta African American Heritage Museum, Monroe, LA..........592
Northeast Oakland Historical Museum, Oxford, MI..........759
Northern Indiana Center for History, South Bend, IN..........499
Northport Historical Society Museum, Northport, NY..........1044
The Northumberland County Historical Society, Sunbury, PA..........1302
Northwest Museum of Arts & Culture (Eastern Washington State Historical Society), Spokane, WA..........1571
Norwich Historical Society, Norwich, VT.1484
Nottawa Stone School, Centreville, MI........731
Noyes House Museum, Morrisville, VT...1483
Nutter D. Marvel Museum, Georgetown, DE..........271

O. Henry Museum, Austin, TX..........1391
O. Winston Link Museum, Roanoke, VA...1535
Oak Creek Historical Society-Pioneer Village, Oak Creek, WI..........1615
Oak Glen School House Museum, Yucaipa, CA..........200
Oak Hill and The Martha Berry Museum, Rome, GA..........382
Oakland County Pioneer and Historical Society, Pontiac, MI..........760
Oakland Museum of California, Oakland, CA..........134
Oaklands Historic House Museum, Murfreesboro, TN..........1376
Oakleigh Period House Museum, Mobile, AL..........15

Furnishings–Continued

Oakley Park, UDC Shrine, Edgefield, SC..1332
The Oaks House Museum, Jackson, MS......804
Oatland Island Education Center,
   Savannah, GA..................................385
Oatlands, Leesburg, VA.......................1512
Oberlin Heritage Center, Oberlin, OH........1180
Ocean City Historical Museum, Inc.,
   Ocean City, NJ................................918
Ocean County Historical Museum, Toms
   River, NJ......................................926
The Octagon, Washington, DC.................288
Octagon House, San Francisco, CA............168
The Octagon House, Hudson, WI..............1600
Octagon House-First Kindergarten in
   America, Watertown, WI.....................1625
O'Fallon Historical Museum, Baker, MT.....840
Ogden Historical Society, Spencerport,
   NY..1071
Ohio Historical Society, Columbus, OH.....1158
Ohio River Museum, Marietta, OH...........1174
Ohr-O'Keefe Museum of Art, Biloxi, MS...799
Okefenokee Heritage Center, Waycross,
   GA..391
Oklahoma Heritage Association,
   Oklahoma City, OK...........................1209
Oklahoma Museum of History, Oklahoma
   City, OK......................................1210
Oklahoma Territorial Museum, Guthrie,
   OK..1202
Oktibbeha County Heritage Museum,
   Starkville, MS................................808
Olana State Historic Site, Hudson, NY......1000
Old Barracks Museum, Trenton, NJ............927
Old Bethpage Village Restoration, Old
   Bethpage, NY.................................1045
Old Bohemia Historical Society,
   Warwick, MD..................................656
Old Brutus Historical Society, Inc.,
   Weedsport, NY................................1084
Old Capitol Museum, Iowa City, IA..........520
Old Cathedral Museum, Saint Louis, MO....836
The Old Church Society, Inc., Portland,
   OR..1231
Old Colony Historical Society, Taunton,
   MA..714
Old Constitution House, Windsor, VT........1490
Old Conway Homestead Complex and
   Museum, Camden, ME..........................608
Old Court House Museum-Eva Whitaker
   Davis Memorial, Vicksburg, MS............809
Old Courthouse Museum, Santa Ana, CA....178
Old Cowtown Museum, Wichita, KS........562
Old Davie School Historical Museum,
   Davie, FL.....................................302
Old Depot Museum, Ottawa, KS.............555
Old Dutch Parsonage, Somerville, NJ.........924
Old Economy Village, Ambridge, PA.........1240
Old Exchange & Provost Dungeon,
   Charleston, SC...............................1326
Old Falls Village, Menomonee Falls, WI....1609
Old Firehouse Museum, Greenville, MS......800
Old Fort Harrod State Park Mansion
   Museum, Harrodsburg, KY.....................570
Old Fort House Museum, Fort Edward,
   NY..991
Old Fort Johnson, Fort Johnson, NY............991
Old Fort Niagara, Youngstown, NY.........1088
Old Fort Western, Augusta, ME..............604
The Old Governor's Mansion, Frankfort,
   KY..570
Old Greer County Museum & Hall of
   Fame, Mangum, OK............................1204
The Old Hoxie House, Sandwich, MA........708
Old Independence Regional Museum,
   Batesville, AR.................................54
Old Iron County Courthouse Museum,
   Hurley, WI...................................1601
The Old Jail Art Center, Albany, TX.........1385
Old Jail Museum, Albion, IN..................467
The Old Jail Museum, Crawfordsville, IN...473

The Old Jail Museum, Warrenton, VA.......1543
Old Jefferson Town, Oskaloosa, KS.............555
Old Lighthouse Museum, Michigan City,
   IN..491
Old Lighthouse Museum, Stonington, CT....261
Old Lincoln County Courthouse Museum,
   Lincoln, NM..................................942
Old Log Jail and Chapel Museums,
   Greenfield, IN................................480
Old Manchester Museum, Manchester,
   CT..248
The Old Manse, Concord, MA................677
Old Market House State Historic Site,
   Galena, IL....................................436
Old Mill Museum, Cimarron, NM...........938
Old Mill Museum, El Molino Viejo - Old
   Mill Foundation, San Marino, CA..........175
Old Monterey Jail, Monterey, CA..............128
Old Ordinary House Museum, Hingham,
   MA..687
Old Prairie Town at Ward-Meade Historic
   Site, Topeka, KS..............................560
Old Sacramento Schoolhouse Museum,
   Sacramento, CA...............................153
Old Sacramento State Historic Park, Old
   Sacramento, CA...............................135
Old St. Ferdinand's Shrine, Florissant,
   MO..815
Old Salem Inc., Winston-Salem, NC.........1126
The Old Schwamb Mill, Arlington, MA.....660
Old State Capitol, Springfield, IL.................459
Old State House, Hartford, CT................245
Old State House Museum, Little Rock,
   AR...63
Old State House-The Bostonian Society,
   Boston, MA...................................668
Old Stone Fort Museum Complex,
   Schoharie, NY................................1067
The Old Stone House, Washington, DC......289
Old Stone House Museum, Windsor, NY..1086
Old Sturbridge Village, Sturbridge, MA.......713
Old Sussex County Courthouse,
   Georgetown, DE..............................271
The Old Tavern Museum, Tuscaloosa, AL.....19
Old Town Hall Museum, Fifield, WI.........1597
Old Town Museum, Old Town, ME.........617
Old Town San Diego State Historic Park,
   San Diego, CA................................158
Old Trail Museum, Choteau, MT............844
Old Village Hall Museum, Lindenhurst,
   NY..1009
Old Washington Historic State Park,
   Washington, AR...............................69
Old West Museum, Wimberley, TX..........1462
Old Westbury Gardens, Old Westbury,
   NY..1045
Old World Wisconsin, Eagle, WI............1595
Old York Historical Society, York, ME.......626
Oldest House Museum Complex, Saint
   Augustine, FL................................339
The Oldest House Museum/Wrecker's
   Museum, Key West, FL.......................318
Oldest Stone House Museum, Lakewood,
   OH..1170
The Oliver Tucker Museum, Beverly, OH.1142
Olmsted County Historical Society,
   Rochester, MN...............................788
Oneida Community Mansion House,
   Oneida, NY..................................1046
Oneida County Pioneer Museum, Malad,
   ID..407
Onondaga Historical Association Museum
   & Research Center, Syracuse, NY.........1077
Ontonagon County Historical Society
   Museum, Ontonagon, MI.....................758
Orange Beach Indian and Sea Museum,
   Orange Beach, AL............................18
Orange County Regional History Center,
   Orlando, FL..................................331
Orange Empire Railway Museum, Perris,
   CA..141

Orangetown Historical Museum and
   Archives, Pearl River, NY...................1051
Orcas Island Historical Museum, Orcas
   Island, WA...................................1560
Orchard House, Concord, MA................677
Orchard Park Historical Society, Orchard
   Park, NY.....................................1047
Orcutt Ranch, Canoga Park, CA..............81
Oregon Coast History Center, Newport,
   OR..1229
Oregon Historical Society, Portland, OR....1231
Oregon-Jerusalem Historical Museum,
   Oregon, OH..................................1181
Oregon Military Museum, Clackamas,
   OR..1221
Oregon Trail Regional Museum, Baker
   City, OR......................................1219
Oriental Institute Museum, University of
   Chicago, Chicago, IL.........................426
Orland Historical Society, Orland, ME......617
Orleans County Historical Society & The
   Old Stone House Museum,
   Brownington, VT.............................1477
Oroville Chinese Temple, Oroville, CA.......136
Osage County Historical Society
   Museum, Pawhuska, OK.....................1211
Osage County Historical Society
   Research Center, Lyndon, KS...............550
Osborn-Jackson House, East Hampton,
   NY..986
Osborne Homestead Museum, Derby, CT....238
The Oscar Anderson House Museum,
   Anchorage, AK...............................22
Oscar Getz Museum of Whiskey History
   And The Bardstown Historical
   Museum, Bardstown, KY.....................565
Oshkosh Public Museum, Oshkosh, WI.....1616
Osterville Historical Society, Inc.,
   Osterville, MA................................701
Oswego Historical Museum, Inc.,
   Oswego, KS..................................555
Otero Museum Association, La Junta, CO...224
Otoe County Museum of Memories,
   Syracuse, NE.................................873
Ottawa County Historical Museum, Port
   Clinton, OH..................................1183
Otter Tail County Historical Society,
   Fergus Falls, MN.............................775
Ouachita County Historical Society,
   Camden, AR..................................55
Our House State Memorial, Gallipolis,
   OH..1165
Outagamie Museum, Appleton, WI...........1589
Overfield Tavern Museum, Troy, OH........1188
Overholser Mansion, Oklahoma City, OK.1210
Overland Trail Museum, Sterling, CO........232
Oxford Museum, Inc., Oxford, MD..........650
Oyster Bay Historical Society, Oyster
   Bay, NY......................................1049
Oysterponds Historical Society: The
   Museum of Orient and East Marion
   History, Orient, NY..........................1047
The Ozark Folk Center, Mountain View,
   AR..65
Ozark Heritage Arts Center & Museum,
   Leslie, AR....................................61
Ozaukee County Pioneer Village,
   Saukville, WI................................1620

P.H. Sullivan Museum and Genealogy
   Library, Zionsville, IN........................504
Pacific Asia Museum, Pasadena, CA...........140
Packwood House Museum, Lewisburg,
   PA..1268
Paine Art Center and Gardens, Oshkosh,
   WI..1617
Pajaro Valley Historical Association,
   Watsonville, CA..............................196
Palace of the Governors/New Mexico
   History Museum, Santa Fe, NM............949
Palmer/Gullickson Octagon Home, West
   Salem, WI...................................1627

Palmer House, Historical Society of Olde Northfield, Northfield, OH 1180

Pamplin Historical Park and The National Museum of the Civil War Soldier, Petersburg, VA 1525

The Paperweight Museum, Santa Cruz, CA 182

The Pardee Home Museum, Oakland, CA ...134

Paris-Henry County Heritage Center, Paris, TN 1382

Park City Historical Society & Museum, Park City, UT......................................1468

The Park-McCullough House, North Bennington, VT 1483

Parker Tavern, Reading, MA 705

Parks, Recreation & Historic Sites Division, Georgia Dept. of Natural Resources, Atlanta, GA 362

The Parry Mansion Museum, New Hope, PA..1273

Parson Fisher House, Blue Hill, ME 606

Parsons Historical Commission Museum, Parsons, KS...555

Parsonsfield-Porter Historical Society, Porter, ME..618

Pasadena Museum of History, Pasadena, CA...140

Passaic County Historical Society & Lambert Castle Museum, Paterson, NJ ...920

Patee House Museum, Saint Joseph, MO 831

Patterson Homestead, Dayton, OH 1161

Patterson Inn Museum/Corning - Painted Post Historical Society, Corning, NY 982

Paul Bunyan Logging Camp Museum, Eau Claire, WI...1596

Paul Dresser Memorial Birthplace, Terre Haute, IN...500

Paul Revere House/Paul Revere Memorial Association, Boston, MA 668

Paulson House, Au Train, MI 726

Pawnee Bill Ranch and Museum, Pawnee, OK..1212

Pawnee City Historical Society & Museum, Pawnee City, NE 871

Pea Ridge National Military Park, Garfield, AR..58

Peabody Essex Museum, Salem, MA...........706

Pearl S. Buck Birthplace Foundation, Hillsboro, WV 1582

The Pearl S. Buck House, Perkasie, PA 1275

The Pearson Museum, Springfield, IL..........460

Pebble Hill Plantation, Thomasville, GA ...388

Pecos National Historical Park, Pecos, NM...944

The Peekskill Museum, Peekskill, NY 1051

Peel Mansion Museum & Historic Gardens, Bentonville, AR...........................55

Peirce Mill and Peirce Barn, Washington, DC...289

Pejepscot Historical Society, Brunswick, ME...608

Pella Historical Village, Pella, IA.................526

Pember Museum of Natural History, Granville, NY 995

Pembroke Historical Society, Inc., Pembroke, MA...701

The Pena-Peck House, Saint Augustine, FL...339

Pendarvis State Historic Site, Mineral Point, WI..1614

Pendleton District Agricultural Museum, Pendleton, SC 1339

Pendleton Historic Foundation, Pendleton, SC 1339

Pennsbury Manor, Morrisville, PA 1272

Pennsylvania German Cultural Heritage Center at Kutztown University, Kutztown, PA...1265

Pennsylvania Historical & Museum Commission, Harrisburg, PA.................1259

Pennypacker Mills, Schwenksville, PA 1297

Pennyroyal Area Museum, Hopkinsville, KY...572

Penobscot Marine Museum, Searsport, ME...622

Peralta Adobe, San Jose, CA 172

Perkins County Historical Society, Grant, NE...862

Peshtigo Fire Museum, Peshtigo, WI 1617

Peter Conser House, Heavener, OK 1202

Peter Rice Homestead, Home of Marlborough Historical Society, Inc., Marlboro, MA...693

Peter Wentz Farmstead, Worcester, PA.......1308

Peter Whitmer Sr. Home and Visitors Center, Waterloo, NY 1083

Peter Yegen Jr. Yellowstone County Museum, Billings, MT..............................841

Peterborough Historical Society, Peterborough, NH.....................................893

Petersburg National Battlefield, Petersburg, VA 1525

Petersham Historical Society, Inc., Petersham, MA...702

Petrified Forest National Park, Petrified Forest National Park, AZ.........................38

Pettaquamscutt Historical Society, Kingston, RI..1312

Pettigrew Home and Museum, Sioux Falls, SD 1356

Pewabic Pottery, Detroit, MI 737

Phelps House, Burlington, IA 507

Philadelphia Museum of Art, Philadelphia, PA.......................................1285

Philadelphia Society for the Preservation of Landmarks, Philadelphia, PA 1286

Philip and Muriel Berman Museum of Art at Ursinus College, Collegeville, PA..1247

Phillips County Museum, Helena, AR............59

Phillips County Museum, Holyoke, CO.......222

Phillips Historical Society, Phillips, ME 618

Philmont Museums, Cimarron, NM.............938

Phoenix Museum of History, Phoenix, AZ..41

Piatt Castles, West Liberty, OH 1190

Piatt County Museum, Monticello, IL..........446

Pickler Mansion, Faulkton, SD 1347

The Pierce Manse/New Hampshire Political Library, Concord, NH................885

Pierre Menard Home State Historic Site, Ellis Grove, IL...433

Pike County Historical Society, Milford, PA..1272

Pilgrim Hall Museum, Plymouth, MA 703

Pilgrim Monument and Provincetown Museum, Provincetown, MA 704

Pimeria Alta Historical Society, Nogales, AZ..37

Pinal County Historical Society and Museum, Florence, AZ...............................34

Pine Bluff/Jefferson County Historical Museum, Pine Bluff, AR............................66

Pine County Historical Society, Askov, MN...768

Pine Lodge (Ehrman Mansion), Tahoma, CA...190

Pink Palace Family of Museums, Memphis, TN...1375

Pioneer Arizona Living History Village & Museum, Phoenix, AZ................................41

Pioneer Farm Museum and Ohop Indian Village, Eatonville, WA.........................1552

Pioneer Florida Museum Association, Inc., Dade City, FL....................................302

Pioneer Heritage Center, Cavalier, ND.......1129

Pioneer Heritage Center, LSU-Shreveport, Shreveport, LA 601

Pioneer Historical Museum of South Dakota, Hot Springs, SD.......................1348

Pioneer-Krier Museum, Ashland, KS 532

Pioneer Log Cabin, Manhattan, KS..............551

The Pioneer Memorial Association of Fenton and Mundy Townships, Fenton, MI...741

Pioneer Mothers Memorial Cabin, Saint Paul, OR..1235

Pioneer Museum, Watford City, ND...........1137

Pioneer Museum, Wild Rose, WI 1628

Pioneer Museum & The Big Stampede, Fairbanks, AK..24

Pioneer Museum and Vereins Kirche, Fredericksburg, TX................................1419

Pioneer Museum - Martin County Historical Society, Fairmont, MN 775

Pioneer Museum of Alabama, Troy, AL.........18

Pioneer Settlement for the Creative Arts, Barberville, FL...295

Pioneer Town, Wimberley, TX....................1462

Pioneer Village, Farmington, UT...............1465

Pioneer Village & Virgil Grissom Memorial at Spring Mill State Park, Mitchell, IN...491

Pioneer Woman Statue & Museum, Ponca City, OK.......................................1212

Pioneers, Trail Drivers and Texas Rangers Memorial Museum, San Antonio, TX...1449

Pipestone County Historical Museum, Pipestone, MN...786

Piqua Historical Area State Memorial, Piqua, OH...1182

Pitot House Museum, New Orleans, LA......598

Pittock Mansion, Portland, OR 1232

Pittsford Historical Society Museum, Pittsford, VT..1484

Plains Conservation Center, Aurora, CO......202

Plains Indians and Pioneers Museum, Woodward, OK.......................................1217

Plainsman Museum, Aurora, NE 856

Plantation Agriculture Museum, Scott, AR..67

Plantation Historical Museum, Plantation, FL...337

Planting Fields Arboretum State Historic Park, Oyster Bay, NY..............................1049

Plimoth Plantation Inc., Plymouth, MA 703

Plum Grove Historic Home, Iowa City, IA...520

Plumas County Museum, Quincy, CA..........144

Plumas-Eureka State Park, Blairsden, CA......78

Plumb Farm Learning Center, Greeley, CO..222

Plymouth Antiquarian Society, Plymouth, MA...704

Plymouth Historical Museum, Plymouth, MI...760

Pocahontas County Iowa Historical Society Museum, Laurens, IA 522

Pocahontas County Museum, Marlinton, WV..1584

Pohick Episcopal Church, Lorton, VA 1514

Point of Honor, Lynchburg, VA 1515

Point Reyes National Seashore, Point Reyes, CA..143

Pointe Coupee Museum, New Roads, LA....599

Polish Heritage Center, Ashton, NE 856

Polish Museum of America, Chicago, IL......426

Polk County Historical Museum, Bartow, FL...295

The Polk County Historical Society, Cedartown, GA.......................................368

Polk County Historical Society, Crookston, MN......................................771

Polk County Museum, Balsam Lake, WI...1590

Polson Museum, Hoquiam, WA..................1556

Ponce DeLeon Inlet Lighthouse Preservation Association, Inc., Ponce Inlet, FL..337

Pope County Historical Society, Glenwood, MN.......................................776

Pope's Tavern Museum, Florence, AL 9

Poplar Grove Historic Plantation, Wilmington, NC.....................................1123

Furnishings–Continued

Port Gamble Historic Museum, Port
Gamble, WA 1562
Portage County Historical Society,
Ravenna, OH...1183
Portage County Historical Society,
Stevens Point, WI..................................1623
Porter-Phelps-Huntington Foundation,
Inc., Hadley, MA.......................................685
Porterville Historical Museum,
Porterville, CA..144
Portland Museum of Art, Portland, ME ....,619
Portsmouth Historical Association,
Portsmouth, VA.....................................1526
Portsmouth Historical Society,
Portsmouth, RI......................................1316
Postville Courthouse State Historic Site,
Lincoln, IL...442
Potsdam Public Museum, Potsdam, NY.....1054
Potter County Historical Society,
Coudersport, PA...................................1248
Potts Inn Museum, Pottsville, AR 66
Pottsgrove Manor, Pottstown, PA 1295
Powell County Museum, Deer Lodge,
MT..845
Powers Museum, Carthage, MO...................812
Prairie Grove Battlefield State Park,
Prairie Grove, AR.......................................66
Prairie Homestead, Philip, SD 1353
The Prairie Museum of Art & History,
Colby, KS...535
Prairie Trails Museum of Wayne County,
Corydon, IA..512
Prairie Village, Madison, SD 1351
Praters Mill Foundation, Varnell, GA...........390
Pratt Building - Cohasset Historical
Society, Cohasset, MA 676
Pratt County Historical Society Museum,
Pratt, KS..556
Pratt Museum, Homer, AK 25
The Preservation Society of Newport
County/The Newport Mansions,
Newport, RI..1315
President Andrew Johnson Museum and
Library, Greeneville, TN 1366
President James K. Polk State Historic
Site, Pineville, NC 1114
President's Cottage Museum-The
Greenbrier, White Sulphur Springs,
WV..1588
Presque Isle County Historical Museum,
Rogers City, MI..762
Prestwould Foundation, Clarksville, VA.....1501
Price Tower Arts Center, Bartlesville, OK .1197
Pricketts Fort, Fairmont, WV......................1581
Promont House Museum, Milford, OH 1176
Proprietary House, The Royal Governor's
Mansion, Perth Amboy, NJ 921
Prudence Crandall Museum, Canterbury,
CT..237
Public Museum of West Michigan, Grand
Rapids, MI..744
Pueblo County Historical Society
Museum and Edward H. Broadhead
Library, Pueblo, CO 230
Pueblo of Pojoaque, Poeh Museum, Santa
Fe, NM...949
Puget Sound Coast Artillery Museum at
Fort Worden, Port Townsend, WA.........1562
Putnam Cottage, Greenwich, CT 243
Putnam County Historical Society &
Foundry School Museum, Cold
Spring, NY..979
Putnam County Historical Society
Museum, Kalida, OH...............................1169
Putnam Museum of History & Natural
Science, Davenport, IA.............................513
Putney Historical Society, Putney, VT 1485
Pyle House Museum, Huron, SD...............1349

Queen Emma Summer Palace, Honolulu,
HI..398

Queen Mary Museum, Long Beach, CA 111
Queens County Farm Museum, Floral
Park, NY...989
Queens Historical Society, Flushing, NY.....990
Queens Museum of Art, Queens, NY.........1056
Quiet Valley Living Historical Farm,
Stroudsburg, PA.....................................1302
The Quilters Hall of Fame, Inc., Marion,
IN...490
Quincy Historical Society, Quincy, MA.......705
QV Historical Society at Carriage House
Museum, Camden, NY.............................974

R.E. Olds Transportation Museum,
Lansing, MI..751
R.P. Strathearn Historical Park and
Museum, Simi Valley, CA..........................187
Rachel Carson Homestead, Springdale,
PA...1301
Rahr West Art Museum, Manitowoc, WI...1607
Railroad and Heritage Museum Inc.,
Temple, TX...1454
Railroaders Memorial Museum, Altoona,
PA...1240
Raleigh City Museum, Raleigh, NC...........1117
Ralls Historical Museum, Ralls, TX...........1445
The Ralph Foster Museum, Point
Lookout, MO..828
Ralph Waldo Emerson House, Concord,
MA...677
Ramapogue Historical Society, West
Springfield, MA.......................................718
Ramsey House Museum Plantation,
Knoxville, TN...1371
Rancho La Patera - The Stow House
G.V.H.S., Goleta, CA...............................100
Rancho Los Alamitos, Long Beach, CA 111
Rancho Los Cerritos Historic Site, Long
Beach, CA..111
Randolph County Historical Museum,
Winchester, IN..503
Randolph County Museum (At Beverly),
Beverly, WV...1580
Randolph Historical Society, Inc.,
Randolph, VT..1485
Rankin Museum, Rankin, TX......................1445
Ransom County Historical Society, Fort
Ransom, ND...1131
Ravalli County Museum/Bitter Root
Valley Historical Society, Hamilton,
MT..848
Raynham Hall Museum, Oyster Bay, NY ..1049
Reading Historical Society, Reading, VT...1485
Reading Historical Society Museum,
Reading, OH...1184
Reading Public Museum, Reading, PA.......1296
Readsboro Historical Society, Readsboro,
VT...1486
Rebecca Nurse Homestead, Danvers, MA ...678
Rebel State Historic Site & Louisiana
Country Music Museum, Marthaville,
LA..592
Red Hill-Patrick Henry National
Memorial, Brookneal, VA 1498
Red Mill Museum Village, Clinton, NJ........901
Red River Historical Museum, Sherman,
TX...1452
Redington Museum, Waterville, ME 625
Redwood County Historical Society,
Redwood Falls, MN..................................787
Redwood Library and Athenaeum,
Newport, RI..1315
Reedville Fishermen's Museum,
Reedville, VA..1527
The Reeves Center, Washington and Lee
University, Lexington, VA........................1513
Refugio County Museum, Refugio, TX 1445
Rehoboth Art League, Inc., Rehoboth
Beach, DE..272
Reitz Home Museum, Evansville, IN...........476
Remick Country Doctor Museum and
Farm, Tamworth, NH...............................896

Renfrew Museum & Park, Waynesboro,
PA...1306
Reno County Museum, Hutchinson, KS 545
Rensselaer County Historical Society,
Troy, NY..1079
Rensselaer Russell House Museum,
Waterloo, IA..529
Renton Historical Society and Museum,
Renton, WA..1564
Renville County Historical Society, Inc.,
Mohall, ND...1135
Republic County Historical Society
Museum, Belleville, KS 534
Restoration House, Mantorville, MN...........780
Reverend Dan Foster House, Museum of
the Weathersfield Historical Society,
Weathersfield, VT..................................1489
Reynolda House Museum of American
Art, Winston-Salem, NC 1126
Reynolds Homestead, Critz, VA................1502
Rhinelander Logging Museum,
Rhinelander, WI......................................1620
Rhode Island Black Heritage Society,
Providence, RI..1318
Rhode Island Historical Preservation and
Heritage, Providence, RI.........................1318
Rhode Island Historical Society,
Providence, RI..1318
Rialto Historical Society, Rialto, CA...........148
Rice County Museum of History,
Faribault, MN..775
Richard Salter Storrs House,
Longmeadow, MA....................................691
Richards DAR House Museum, Mobile,
AL..15
Richardson-Bates House Museum,
Oswego, NY...1048
Richey Historical Society, Richey, MT 852
Richland County Historical Museum,
Wahpeton, ND..1137
Richland County Museum, Lexington,
OH..1172
Richmond Museum of History,
Richmond, CA..148
Riddick's Folly, Suffolk, VA.......................1539
Rifle Creek Museum, Rifle, CO...................231
Riley County Historical Museum,
Manhattan, KS...551
Riley House Museum of African
American History & Culture,
Tallahassee, FL..348
Rim Country Museum, Payson, AZ...............38
Rio Grande Valley Museum, Harlingen,
TX...1423
Riordan Mansion State Historic Park,
Flagstaff, AZ..33
Rip Van Winkle Gardens on Jefferson
Island, New Iberia, LA.............................593
Rising Sun Tavern, Fredericksburg, VA 1507
Ritz Theatre & LaVilla Museum,
Jacksonville, FL.......................................315
River Heritage Museum, Paducah, KY 582
River Museum, Wellsville, OH...................1190
Riversdale House Mansion, Riverdale
Park, MD..651
Riverside Heritage House, Riverside, CA 150
Riverside Metropolitan Museum,
Riverside, CA...150
Riverside, The Farnsley-Moremen
Landing, Louisville, KY.............................579
Riverton Museum, Riverton, WY...............1637
Riverview at Hobson Grove, Bowling
Green, KY..566
Roanoke Island Festival Park; Homeport
of the "Elizabeth II", Manteo, NC.........1110
Robbins Hunter Museum, Avery-Downer
House, Granville, OH.............................1167
Roberson Museum and Science Center,
Binghamton, NY.......................................962
Robert A. Bogan Fire Museum, Baton
Rouge, LA..587
Robert Frost Farm, Derry, NH.....................886

Robert Louis Stevenson House, Monterey, CA 128

Robert Louis Stevenson Silverado Museum, Saint Helena, CA 154

Robert Newell House, DAR Museum, Saint Paul, OR 1235

Robert R. McCormick Museum at Cantigny, Wheaton, IL 465

Robert S. Kerr Museum, Poteau, OK 1212

Robert Toombs House, Washington, GA 391

Roberts County Museum, Miami, TX 1438

Rochester Hills Museum at Van Hoosen Farm, Rochester Hills, MI 762

Rochester Historical Society, Rochester, NY 1059

Rochester Museum & Science Center, Rochester, NY 1059

Rock County Historical Society, Janesville, WI 1601

Rock Ford Plantation, Lancaster, PA 1267

Rock House Museum, Wytheville, VA 1546

Rock Island County Historical Society, Moline, IL 445

Rock Ledge Ranch Historic Site, Colorado Springs, CO 208

Rock Springs Historical Museum, Rock Springs, WY 1638

Rockbridge Historical Society, Lexington, VA 1513

Rockingham, Kingston, NJ 909

Rockingham Free Public Library and Museum, Bellows Falls, VT 1476

Rockwood Park, Wilmington, DE 274

Rocky Ford Historical Museum, Rocky Ford, CO 231

Rocky Mount Museum, Piney Flats, TN 1383

Rocky Mountain National Park, Estes Park, CO 215

Rodgers Tavern, Perryville, MD 650

Rogers Historical Museum, Rogers, AR 67

Rokeby (Ancestral Estate of Rowland Evans Robinson), Ferrisburgh, VT 1479

Rollo Jamison Museum, Platteville, WI 1617

Rome Area History Museum, Rome, GA 382

Rome Historical Society Museum, Rome, NY 1061

Ronald Reagan Boyhood Home, Dixon, IL 431

Ronald Reagan Presidential Library and Museum, Simi Valley, CA 187

Roosevelt Campobello International Park Commission, Lubec, ME 614

Roosevelt County Museum, Portales, NM 944

The Root House Museum, Marietta, GA 379

Rosa Ponselle Museum, Meriden, CT 249

Rosalie House, Eureka Springs, AR 57

Roscoe Village Foundation, Coshocton, OH 1159

Rose Hill Museum, Bay Village, OH 1141

Rose Hill Plantation State Historic Site, Union, SC 1343

Rose Lawn Museum, Cartersville, GA 368

Roseau County Historical Museum and Interpretive Center, Roseau, MN 788

Rosebud County Pioneer Museum, Forsyth, MT 846

Roseland Cottage, Woodstock, CT 268

Rosemont Plantation, Woodville, MS 810

Rosemount Museum, Pueblo, CO 230

Rosenbach Museum & Library, Philadelphia, PA 1287

Rosenberg Library, Galveston, TX 1422

Rosicrucian Egyptian Museum, San Jose, CA 172

Roslyn Landmark Society, Roslyn, NY 1061

Ross County Historical Society, Inc., Chillicothe, OH 1147

The Rotch-Jones-Duff House & Garden Museum, Inc., New Bedford, MA 697

Roth Living Farm Museum of Delaware Valley College, North Wales, PA 1274

Rothschild House State Park, Port Townsend, WA 1562

The Rotunda, University of Virginia, Charlottesville, VA 1500

Rowan Museum, Inc., Salisbury, NC 1118

Rowan Oak, William Faulkner's Home, Oxford, MS 806

Rowley Historical Society, Rowley, MA 706

Royal Gorge Regional Museum & History Center, Canon City, CO 205

Royall House Association, Medford, MA 694

Royalton Historical Society, Royalton, VT 1486

Ruggles House Society, Columbia Falls, ME 609

Rumford Historical Association, North Woburn, MA 699

Rundlet-May House, Portsmouth, NH 895

Runestone Museum, Alexandria, MN 767

Rural Life Museum & Windrush Gardens, Baton Rouge, LA 587

Rusk County Historical Society, Ladysmith, WI 1604

Russell County Historical Society/Fossil Station Museum, Russell, KS 556

Ruth and Charles Gilb Arcadia Historical Museum, Arcadia, CA 71

Rutherford B. Hayes Presidential Center, Fremont, OH 1165

Ruthmere Museum, Elkhart, IN 475

The Rye Historical Society and Square House Museum, Rye, NY 1062

Ryerss Museum & Library, Philadelphia, PA 1287

S.S. Meteor Maritime Museum, Superior, WI 1624

Sackets Harbor Battlefield State Historic Site, Sackets Harbor, NY 1062

Sacramento Archives and Museum Collection Center, Sacramento, CA 153

Sacramento Mountains Historical Museum, Cloudcroft, NM 938

Safety Harbor Museum of Regional History, Safety Harbor, FL 338

Safford House Historic House Museum, Tarpon Springs, FL 351

Sag Harbor Whaling & Historical Museum, Sag Harbor, NY 1063

Sagamore Hill National Historic Site, Oyster Bay, NY 1049

Saguache County Museum, Saguache, CO 231

Sahuaro Ranch Historical Area, Glendale, AZ 35

Sailor's Memorial Museum, Islesboro, ME 612

St. Albans Historical Museum, Saint Albans, VT 1486

St. Augustine Lighthouse & Museum, Inc., Saint Augustine, FL 340

St. Clair County Historical Society, Belleville, IL 412

St. Clements Island and Piney Point Museums, Colton's Point, MD 641

St. Francis County Museum, Forrest City, AR 57

Saint-Gaudens National Historic Site, Cornish, NH 885

St. George's United Methodist Church, Philadelphia, PA 1287

St. James' House, Fredericksburg, VA 1507

St. Johnsbury Athenaeum, Saint Johnsbury, VT 1487

St. Joseph Museum Inc., Saint Joseph, MO 831

St. Lawrence County Historical Association - Silas Wright House, Canton, NY 975

The St. Louis County Historical Society, Duluth, MN 773

St. Petersburg Museum of History, Saint Petersburg, FL 342

St. Simons Island Lighthouse Museum, Saint Simons Island, GA 383

Salamanca Rail Museum, Salamanca, NY 1063

Salem Art Association-Bush House Museum and Bush Barn Art Center, Salem, OR 1236

Salem County Historical Society, Salem, NJ 924

Salem Historical Society and Museum, Salem, OH 1184

Salem Maritime National Historic Site, Salem, MA 707

The Salem Museum, Salem, VA 1536

Salida Museum, Salida, CO 232

Salisbury Historical Society, Salisbury, NH 896

Salisbury House Foundation, Des Moines, IA 515

Salmon Brook Historical Society, Inc., Granby, CT 242

Saltbox Museum, New Providence, NJ 916

Salter Museum, Argonia, KS 532

Sam Bell Maxey House State Historic Site, Paris, TX 1442

Sam Brown Log House, Browns Valley, MN 770

Sam Houston Memorial Museum, Huntsville, TX 1430

Sam Rayburn House Museum, Bonham, TX 1397

The Sam Rayburn Library and Museum, a Division of the Center for American History of the University of Texas at Austin, Bonham, TX 1397

Samuel Cupples House of Saint Louis University, Saint Louis, MO 837

San Antonio Art League Museum, San Antonio, TX 1449

San Antonio Conservation Society, San Antonio, TX 1449

San Buenaventura Mission Museum, Ventura, CA 195

San Dieguito Heritage Museum, Encinitas, CA 92

San Fernando Mission, Mission Hills, CA 126

San Fernando Valley Historical Society, Inc., Mission Hills, CA 126

San Francisco Maritime National Historical Park, San Francisco, CA 169

San Gabriel Mission Museum, San Gabriel, CA 171

San Jacinto Museum, San Jacinto, CA 171

San Jacinto Museum of History Association, La Porte, TX 1433

San Juan Bautista State Historic Park, San Juan Bautista, CA 173

San Juan County Archaeological Research Center and Library at the Salmon Ruin/San Juan County Museum Association, Bloomfield, NM 937

San Juan Historical Society, Friday Harbor, WA 1555

San Luis Obispo County Historical Museum, San Luis Obispo, CA 174

San Mateo County Historical Association and Museum, Redwood City, CA 147

San Quentin Prison Museum, San Quentin, CA 176

Sanchez Adobe Historic Site, Pacifica, CA 138

Sand Springs Cultural & Historical Museum, Sand Springs, OK 1213

Sandpoint Lighthouse, Escanaba, MI 741

Sandusky Library Follett House Museum, Sandusky, OH 1185

Sandwich Glass Museum, Sandwich, MA 708

Sandwich Historical Society, Center Sandwich, NH 884

Sandy Spring Museum, Sandy Spring, MD 653

Sanford Museum, Sanford, FL 343

Sanford Museum and Planetarium, Cherokee, IA 510

Smith-McDowell House Museum, Asheville, NC 1090

Smith Robertson Museum & Cultural Center, Jackson, MS 804

Smith-Zimmermann Heritage Museum, Madison, SD 1351

Smith's Fort Plantation, Surry, VA 1540

Smithtown Historical Society, Smithtown, NY 1070

Smoki Museum - American Indian Art & Culture, Prescott, AZ 43

Smoky Hill Museum, Salina, KS 557

Smyth County Museum, Marion, VA 1516

Snake River Heritage Center, Weiser, ID.....410

The Snyder County Historical Society, Middleburg, PA 1271

Snyder Museum & Creative Arts Center, Bastrop, LA 585

Society for Contemporary Craft, Pittsburgh, PA 1294

Society for the Preservation of Long Island Antiquities, Cold Spring Harbor, NY 980

The Society of the Cincinnati at Anderson House, Washington, DC 291

Sod House Museum, Gothenburg, NE 862

Sod House Museum, Aline, OK 1195

Somers Historical Society, Somers, NY 1070

Somers Mansion, Somers Point, NJ 924

The Somerset County Historical Society, Inc., Princess Anne, MD 650

Somerset Historical Center, Somerset, PA .1300

Somerset Place State Historic Site, Creswell, NC 1097

Somervell County Historical Museum, Glen Rose, TX 1423

The Somerville Museum, Somerville, MA 709

Sonnenberg Gardens & Mansion State Historic Park, Canandaigua, NY 975

Sonoma State Historic Park, Sonoma, CA...188

Sophienburg Museum & Archives Inc., New Braunfels, TX 1440

Sosa-Carrillo-Fremont House Museum, Tucson, AZ 50

Sotterley Plantation, Hollywood, MD 647

South Bannock County Historical Center, Lava Hot Springs, ID 407

South Boston-Halifax County Museum of Fine Arts & History, South Boston, VA 1536

South Carolina Department of Parks, Recreation and Tourism, Columbia, SC 1330

South Carolina State Museum, Columbia, SC 1331

South County Historical Society, Arroyo Grande, CA 72

South County Museum Inc., Narragansett, RI 1313

South Florida Museum, Bishop Planetarium & Parker Manatee Aquarium, Bradenton, FL 297

South Hero Bicentennial Museum, South Hero, VT 1487

South Holland Historical Society, South Holland, IL 457

South Park City Museum, Fairplay, CO.......215

South Pass City State Historic Site, South Pass City, WY 1638

South Street Seaport Museum, New York, NY 1039

South Sutton Old Store Museum, South Sutton, NH 896

South Texas Museum, Alice, TX 1386

South Wood County Historical Corp., Wisconsin Rapids, WI 1628

Southampton Historical Museum, Southampton, NY 1070

Southdown Plantation House/The Terrebonne Museum, Houma, LA 589

Southeast Missouri Regional Museum, Cape Girardeau, MO 812

Southeast Museum Association, Inc., Brewster, NY 964

Southeastern Railway Museum, Duluth, GA 371

Southern California Chapter Railway & Locomotive Historical Society, Pomona, CA 143

Southern Oregon Historical Society, Jacksonville, OR 1226

Southwest Florida Museum of History, Fort Myers, FL 309

Southwest School of Art & Craft, San Antonio, TX 1450

Southwest Virginia Museum Historical State Park, Big Stone Gap, VA 1497

Space Farms Zoological Park and Museum, Sussex, NJ 925

Spartanburg County Regional Museum of History, Spartanburg, SC 1341

Spindletop/Gladys City Boomtown Museum, Beaumont, TX 1395

Spirit of '76 Museum, Wellington, OH 1190

Split Rock Lighthouse Historic Site, Two Harbors, MN 795

Spring Grove Hospital Center, Alumni Museum, Catonsville, MD 639

Spring Street Historical Museum, Shreveport, LA 602

Spring Valley Community Historical Society, Inc., Spring Valley, MN 794

Spring Valley Nature Center & Heritage Farm, Schaumburg, IL 457

Springfield Art & Historical Society - Miller Art Center, Springfield, VT.........1488

Springfield Art Association, Springfield, IL 460

Springfield Historical Society, Springfield, NJ 925

Springfield Museum, Springfield, OR 1236

Springfield Museum of Old Domestic Life, High Point, NC 1107

Springfield Museums - Connecticut Valley Historical Museum, Springfield, MA 710

Springs Museum, Springs, PA 1301

Staatsburgh State Historic Site, Staatsburg, NY 1071

Stabler-Leadbeater Apothecary Museum and Museum Shop, Alexandria, VA 1494

Stacy's Tavern Museum and Glen Ellyn Historical Society, Glen Ellyn, IL 437

Stafford County Historical Society Museum, Stafford, KS 558

Stagecoach Inn Museum Complex, Newbury Park, CA 130

Stamford Historical Society, Inc., Stamford, CT 260

Stamford Museum & Nature Center, Stamford, CT 261

Stan Hywet Hall and Gardens, Inc., Akron, OH 1139

Stanley-Whitman House, Farmington, Farmington, CT 241

Stanly County Historic Preservation Commission and Museum, Albemarle, NC 1088

Stanton House, Clinton, CT 237

Stanwood Wildlife Sanctuary, Ellsworth, ME 610

Stanzel Model Aircraft Museum, Schulenburg, TX 1452

Star of the Republic Museum, Washington, TX 1460

State Agricultural Heritage Museum, Brookings, SD 1344

State Capital Publishing Museum, Guthrie, OK 1202

State Capitol, Hartford, Conn., Hartford, CT 246

State Historical Society of North Dakota, Bismarck, ND 1128

The State House Museum, Dover, DE 270

The State Museum of Pennsylvania, Harrisburg, PA 1259

State of Illinois-Historic Preservation Agency, Historic Sites Division, Springfield, IL 460

Staten Island Historical Society, Staten Island, NY 1074

Statue of Liberty National Monument & Ellis Island Immigration Museum, New York, NY 1039

The Steamboat Arabia Museum, Kansas City, MO 822

Steamboat Bertrand Collection, Missouri Valley, IA 524

Steamship Keewatin, Douglas, MI 738

Steamship William G. Mather Museum, Cleveland, OH 1156

Stearns History Museum, Saint Cloud, MN 788

Steele County Historical Society, Hope, ND 1133

Steffen Thomas Museum and Archives, Buckhead, GA 367

Steilacoom Historical Museum Association, Steilacoom, WA 1572

Stephen Foster Folk Culture Center State Park, White Springs, FL 354

The Stephen Girard Collection, Philadelphia, PA 1288

The Stephen Phillips House, Salem, MA.....707

Stephens African-American Museum, Shreveport, LA 602

Stephens County Historical Society and Museum, Duncan, OK 1199

Stephenson County Historical Society, Freeport, IL 436

Stephenville Museum, Stephenville, TX 1454

Steppingstone Museum, Havre de Grace, MD 647

Sterling Hill Mining Museum, Inc., Ogdensburg, NJ 918

Sterling Historical Society and Little Red Schoolhouse Museum, Sterling, NY......1074

Sterling-Rock Falls Historical Society Museum, Sterling, IL 461

Sterne-Hoya House Museum and Library, Nacogdoches, TX 1440

Steuben House, River Edge, NJ 923

Steuben Memorial State Historic Site, Remsen, NY 1056

The Stevens-Coolidge Place, a property of The Trustees of Reservations, North Andover, MA 698

Stevens County Gas and Historical Museum, Hugoton, KS 544

Stevens Museum, Salem, IN 498

Steves Homestead, San Antonio, TX..........1450

Stewart M. Lord Memorial Historical Society, Inc., Burlington, ME 608

The Stickley Museum at Craftsman Farms, Parsippany, NJ 920

Still National Osteopathic Museum, Kirksville, MO 824

Stockbridge Library Historical Collection, Stockbridge, MA 713

Stockholm Historical Society Museum, Stockholm, ME 623

Stone Fort Museum, Nacogdoches, TX......1440

The Stone House Museum, Belchertown, MA 662

Stone Lagoon Red Schoolhouse Museum at Redwood Trails, Trinidad, CA 192

Stonefield Historic Site, Cassville, WI 1593

Stonewall House, Rocky Mount, NC..........1118

Stonewall Jackson House, Lexington, VA..1514

Storrowton Village Museum, West Springfield, MA 718

Stoughton Historical Society, Stoughton, MA 713

Stoughton Historical Society, Stoughton, WI 1623

Stow West School Museum, Stow, MA 713

Furnishings–Continued

Stranahan House, Inc., Fort Lauderdale, FL 308
Strasburg Museum, Strasburg, VA 1539
Strategic Air & Space Museum, Ashland, NE 856
Strater Hotel, Durango, CO 214
The Stratford Historical Society & Catherine B. Mitchell Museum, Stratford, CT 262
Stratford, Robert E. Lee Memorial Association, Inc., Stratford, VA 1539
Strawbery Banke Museum, Portsmouth, NH 895
Strong - National Museum of Play, Rochester, NY 1060
Stuart Heritage Museum, Stuart, FL 346
Stuart House City Museum, Mackinac Island, MI 752
Stuhr Museum of the Prairie Pioneer, Grand Island, NE 862
Sturdivant Hall, Selma, AL 18
Sturgis Library, Barnstable, MA 662
Stutsman County Memorial Museum, Jamestown, ND 1133
Suffolk County Historical Society, Riverhead, NY 1057
Suffolk County Vanderbilt Museum, Centerport, NY 977
Suffolk Resolves House, Milton, MA 695
Sullivan County Historical Society, Inc., Hurleyville, NY 1001
SullivanMunce Cultural Center, Zionsville, IN 504
Summit County Historical Society, Akron, OH 1139
Summit Historical Society, Breckenridge, CO 204
The Sumter County Museum, Sumter, SC .1342
Sun Inn Preservation Association Inc., Bethlehem, PA 1243
Sun Prairie Historical Library & Museum, Sun Prairie, WI 1624
Sunnyside Historical Museum, Sunnyside, WA 1572
The Supreme Court of the United States, Washington, DC 291
Surratt House Museum, Clinton, MD 640
Susan B. Anthony House, Rochester, NY ..1060
Susquehanna County Historical Society & Free Library Association, Montrose, PA 1272
Susquehanna Museum of Havre de Grace Inc. at the Lock House, Havre de Grace, MD 647
Sussex County Historical Society, Newton, NJ 917
Sutter's Fort State Historic Park, Sacramento, CA 153
Sutton County Historical Society - Miers Home Museum, Sonora, TX 1453
Swampscott Historical Society (John Humphrey House), Swampscott, MA 714
Swarthout Memorial Museum, La Crosse, WI 1603
Swedish American Museum Association of Chicago, Chicago, IL 428
Sweet Briar Museum, Sweet Briar, VA 1540
Sweetwater County Historical Museum, Green River, WY 1633
Swenson Memorial Museum of Stephens County, Breckenridge, TX 1397
Swift County Historical Society, Benson, MN 769
Swinney Homestead, Fort Wayne, IN 478
Swisher County Archives and Museum Association, Tulia, TX 1456
Swiss Historical Village, New Glarus, WI .1615
Switzerland County Historical Museum, Vevay, IN 502

T.B. Ferguson Home, Watonga, OK 1216

T.C. Steele State Historic Site, Nashville, IN 493
T.J. Elder Community Center, Sandersville, GA 384
Table Rock Historical Society and Museums, Table Rock, NE 873
Tabor Opera House Museum, Leadville, CO 226
The Taft Museum of Art, Cincinnati, OH ..1151
Tallahassee Museum, Tallahassee, FL 348
Tama County Historical Museum, Toledo, IA 528
Tannenbaum Historic Park, Greensboro, NC 1104
Tante Blanche Museum, Madawaska, ME ..614
Taoist Temple and Museum, Hanford, CA ...101
Taos Historic Museums, Taos, NM 953
Tarpon Springs Area Historical Society - Depot Museum, Tarpon Springs, FL 351
Tate House Museum, Portland, ME 620
Taylor-Grady House, Athens, GA 357
Taylor House Museum, Berlin, MD 637
Telfair Museum of Art, Savannah, GA 386
Telluride Historical Museum, Telluride, CO 233
Tempe Historical Museum, Tempe, AZ 46
Temperance Tavern, Newcomerstown, OH 1179
Ten Broeck Mansion - Albany County Historical Association, Albany, NY 956
Tenino Depot Museum, Tenino, WA 1575
Tennessee Central Railway Museum, Nashville, TN 1380
Tennessee Historical Society, Nashville, TN 1380
Tennessee State Museum, Nashville, TN ...1381
Terrace Hill Historic Site and Governor's Mansion, Des Moines, IA 516
Territorial Capital-Lane Museum, Lecompton, KS 549
Territorial Statehouse State Park & Museum, Fillmore, UT 1465
Terwilliger Museum, Waterloo, NY 1083
Teutopolis Monastery Museum, Teutopolis, IL 461
Texarkana Museums System, Texarkana, TX 1455
Texas Baptist Historical Center Museum, Brenham, TX 1397
Texas City Museum, Texas City, TX 1455
Texas Energy Museum, Beaumont, TX 1395
Texas Governor's Mansion, Austin, TX 1391
Texas Historical Commission, Austin, TX .1391
Texas Music Museum, Austin, TX 1392
Texas Parks and Wildlife Department, Austin, TX 1392
Texas Pharmacy Museum, Amarillo, TX ..1387
Texas Ranger Hall of Fame and Museum, Waco, TX 1459
Texas Transportation Museum, San Antonio, TX 1451
Theodore Roosevelt Birthplace National Historic Site, New York, NY 1040
Theodore Roosevelt Inaugural National Historic Site, Buffalo, NY 973
Theodore Roosevelt National Park-Visitor Center, Medora, ND 1134
Thetford Historical Society Library and Museum, Thetford, VT 1488
This Is The Place Heritage Park, Salt Lake City, UT 1472
Thomas Clarke House/Princeton Battlefield State Park, Princeton, NJ 922
Thomas Downs House, Charlestown, IN 472
Thomas Edison Birthplace Museum, Milan, OH 1176
Thomas Edison House, Louisville, KY 579
Thomas-Foreman Home, Muskogee, OK ...1205
The Thomas Griswold House and Museum, Guilford, CT 243
Thomas Hart Benton Home and Studio State Historic Site, Kansas City, MO 823

The Thomas J. Boyd, Wytheville, VA 1546
The Thomas T. Taber Museum of the Lycoming County Historical Society, Williamsport, PA 1308
Thomas Whaley House Museum, San Diego, CA 161
Thomas Wolfe Memorial, Asheville, NC ...1090
Thomasville Cultural Center, Inc., Thomasville, GA 388
Thousand Islands Museum, Clayton, NY 979
Thronateeska Heritage Foundation, Inc., Albany, GA 355
Thunderbird Foundation for the Arts, Mount Carmel, UT 1467
Tillamook County Pioneer Museum, Tillamook, OR 1237
Timucuan Ecological and Historic Preserve and Fort Caroline National Memorial, Jacksonville, FL 315
Tinker Swiss Cottage Museum, Rockford, IL 456
Tinley Park Historical Society, Tinley Park, IL 461
Tintic Mining Museum, Eureka, UT 1464
Tioga County Historical Society Museum, Owego, NY 1048
Tioga Point Museum, Athens, PA 1241
Tippecanoe County Historical Association, Lafayette, IN 487
Tipton-Haynes Historic Site, Johnson City, TN 1368
Tobacco Farm Life Museum, Inc., Kenly, NC 1107
Tolland Historical Society - Tolland County Jail and Warden's Home Museum, Tolland, CT 262
Tom Mix Museum, Dewey, OK 1199
Tomball Community Museum Center, Tomball, TX 1455
Tongass Historical Museum, Ketchikan, AK 26
Top of Oklahoma Historical Museum, Blackwell, OK 1197
Topsfield Historical Society, Topsfield, MA 714
Torreya State Park, Bristol, FL 298
Torrington Historical Society, Inc., Torrington, CT 263
Town of Manlius Historical Society with Museum, Manlius, NY 1013
Town of Yorktown Museum, Yorktown Heights, NY 1087
Trail End State Historic Site, Sheridan, WY 1638
Traill County Historical Society, Hillsboro, ND 1132
Trails & Rails Museum, Kearney, NE 864
Traveler's Rest State Historic Site, Toccoa, GA 389
Travellers Rest Plantation & Museum, Nashville, TN 1381
Tread of Pioneers Museum, Steamboat Springs, CO 232
Trenton City Museum, Trenton, NJ 928
Trenton Historical Museum, Trenton, MI 765
Triton Museum of Art, Santa Clara, CA 181
Troutdale Historical Society, Troutdale, OR 1237
Troy-Hayner Cultural Center, Troy, OH ...1188
Troy Museum & Historic Village, Troy, MI 765
The Trustees of Reservations, Beverly, MA 662
Tryon Palace Historic Sites and Gardens, New Bern, NC 1112
Tsa Mo Ga Memorial Museum, Plains, TX 1443
Tu-Endie-Wei State Park, Point Pleasant, WV 1586
Tubac Presidio State Historic Park, Tubac, AZ 47
Tuck Museum, Hampton, NH 888

Tucson Museum of Art & Historic Block, Tucson, AZ 51

Tucumcari Historical Research Institute, Tucumcari, NM.........................953

Tudor Place Foundation, Inc., Washington, DC.........................292

Tulare County Museum at Mooney Grove Park, Visalia, CA 195

Tularosa Basin Historical Society Museum, Alamogordo, NM 932

Turner House Museum, Hattiesburg, MS.....801

Turtle Mountain Chippewa Historical Society, Belcourt, ND.........................1127

Tuskegee Institute National Historic Site, Tuskegee Institute, AL 21

Twin Falls County Historical Museum, Filer, ID.........................405

Twin Falls State Park & Museum, Mullens, WV.........................1585

Twinsburg Historical Society, Twinsburg, OH.........................1188

Tyler Arboretum, Media, PA.........................1271

UCLA Fowler Museum of Cultural History, Los Angeles, CA 122

USDA Forest Service - Land Between the Lakes, Golden Pond, KY 570

Ulster County Historical Society, Marbletown, NY.........................1013

Ulysses S. Grant Cottage State Historic Site, Wilton, NY 1086

Umlauf Sculpture Garden & Museum, Austin, TX.........................1392

Umpqua Discovery Center, Reedsport, OR.........................1234

Uncle Remus Museum, Eatonton, GA 371

Union County Heritage Museum, New Albany, MS.........................806

The Union County Historical Society, Marysville, OH.........................1175

Union County Historical Society, Lewisburg, PA 1268

Union County Historical Society Museum, Blairsville, GA 366

Union County Museum, Union, OR...........1238

Union Mills Homestead & Grist Mill, Westminster, MD.........................656

The United States Army Quartermaster Museum, Fort Lee, VA.........................1505

United States Hockey Hall of Fame, Eveleth, MN.........................774

United States Holocaust Memorial Museum, Washington, DC 293

United States Senate Commission on Art, Washington, DC.........................293

University Art Gallery, University of the South, Sewanee, TN.........................1384

University Art Museum, Binghamton, NY...963

The University Museum, Indiana, PA 1263

University Museum & Historic Houses, The University of Mississippi, Oxford, MS.........................806

University Museum, New Mexico State University, Las Cruces, NM...................941

The University of South Carolina McKissick Museum, Columbia, SC.......1331

Upham Mansion, Marshfield, WI 1608

Upper Musselshell Historical Society, Harlowton, MT.........................849

U.S. Army Center of Military History, Museum Division, Fort McNair, DC.......275

U.S. Army Engineer Museum, Fort Leonard Wood, MO.........................815

U.S. Army Women's Museum, Fort Lee, VA.........................1505

U.S. Capitol Historical Society, Washington, DC.........................293

U.S. Cavalry Museum, Fort Riley, KS.........540

U.S. Grant's Home State Historic Site, Galena, IL.........................436

U.S. National Ski Hall of Fame & Museum, Inc., Ishpeming, MI...........747

USS Alabama Battleship Memorial Park, Mobile, AL.........................15

USS Arizona Memorial, Honolulu, HI 398

USS Constellation Museum, Baltimore, MD.........................636

Utah State Historical Society, Salt Lake City, UT.........................1473

Utica Museum, Utica, MT 854

UTSA's Institute of Texan Cultures, San Antonio, TX.........................1451

Vacaville Museum, Vacaville, CA 194

Vachel Lindsay Home State Historic Site, Springfield, IL.........................460

Vaile Mansion-Dewitt Museum, Independence, MO.........................819

The Valdez Museum & Historical Archive Association, Inc., Valdez, AK 29

Vallejo Naval & Historical Museum, Vallejo, CA 194

Valley Forge National Historical Park, King of Prussia, PA 1264

Van Buren County Historical Society, Keosauqua, IA 521

Van Cortlandt House Museum, Bronx, NY.........................967

Van Riper-Hopper House Museum, Wayne, NJ.........................929

Van Wyck Homestead Museum, Fishkill, NY.........................989

Vandalia Statehouse State Historic Site, Vandalia, IL.........................462

Vanderbilt Mansion National Historic Site, Hyde Park, NY.........................1002

Vanderbilt University Fine Arts Gallery, Nashville, TN.........................1381

Vann House, Chatsworth, GA.........................368

Varner-Hogg Plantation State Historic Site, West Columbia, TX 1461

Venango Museum of Art, Science & Industry, Oil City, PA.........................1274

Ventura County Museum of History & Art, Ventura, CA.........................195

Verde Historical Society, Clemenceau Heritage Museum, Cottonwood, AZ..........32

The Verdier House, Beaufort, SC 1321

Vermilion County Museum Society, Danville, IL.........................429

Vermont Historical Society Museum, Montpelier, VT 1482

Vermont Marble Museum, Proctor, VT......1485

Vermont Ski Museum, Stowe, VT.........................1488

Vermont Soapworks Discount Factory Outlet and Soap Museum, Middlebury, VT.........................1482

The Vermont State House, Montpelier, VT.........................1483

Vernon County Historical Museum, Viroqua, WI.........................1625

Vest-Lindsey House, Frankfort, KY 570

The Vestal Museum, Vestal, NY.................1081

Vesterheim Norwegian-American Museum, Decorah, IA 513

Victoria Mansion, Portland, ME 620

Vigo County Historical Museum, Terre Haute, IN.........................501

Vikingsholm, Tahoma, CA.........................191

Villa Louis Historic Site, Prairie du Chien, WI.........................1619

Villa Montezuma Museum/San Diego Historical Society, San Diego, CA 162

Villa Terrace Decorative Arts Museum, Milwaukee, WI.........................1613

Village Historical Society, Inc., Harrison, OH.........................1168

The Vinalhaven Historical Society Museum, Vinalhaven, ME.........................624

Vincennes State Historic Site, Indiana Territory, Vincennes, IN 503

Virginia Beach Maritime Museum, Inc./The Old Coast Guard Station, Virginia Beach, VA.........................1543

Virginia City J. Spencer Watkins Memorial Museum, Virginia City, MT....854

Virginia Holocaust Museum, Richmond, VA.........................1533

Virginia Military Institute Museum, Lexington, VA.........................1514

Virginia Museum of Fine Arts, Richmond, VA.........................1533

Virginia Robinson Gardens, Beverly Hills, CA.........................78

Virginia Sports Hall of Fame, Portsmouth, VA.........................1526

Vista Historical Museum, Vista, CA.........196

Vizcaya Museum and Gardens, Miami, FL.........................326

Volunteer Firemen's Mall and Museum of Kingston, Kingston, NY.........................1008

W.C. Handy Home Museum and Library, Florence, AL.........................9

W.H. Over Museum, Vermillion, SD.........1358

The W.H. Stark House, Orange, TX...........1442

Wade House Stagecoach Inn & Wesley Jung Carriage Museum State Historic Site, Greenbush, WI.........................1599

Wadsworth Atheneum Museum of Art, Hartford, CT.........................246

Wagner Free Institute of Science, Philadelphia, PA 1289

Wake Forest College Birthplace Society, Inc., Wake Forest, NC.........................1121

Wakefield Historical Society, Wakefield, MA.........................715

Wakefield House Museum, Blue Earth, MN.........................769

Wakefield Museum Association, Wakefield, KS.........................560

Wal-Mart Visitor's Center, Bentonville, AR.........................55

Wallace House, Somerville, NJ...................924

Wallingford Historical Society, Inc., Wallingford, CT.........................263

Walnut Grove Plantation, Roebuck, SC 1340

Walt Whitman Birthplace State Historic Site and Interpretive Center, Huntington Station, NY.........................1001

Walt Whitman House Museum and Library, Camden, NJ.........................900

Walter Reed Birthplace, Gloucester County, VA 1508

Waltham Historical Society, Waltham, MA.........................716

The Waltham Museum, Waltham, MA.........716

Wapello County Historical Museum, Ottumwa, IA.........................526

Ward County Historical Society, Minot, ND.........................1135

Ward Hall, Georgetown, KY.........................570

Ward W. O'Hara Agricultural Museum, Auburn, NY.........................959

Warner House, Portsmouth, NH.........................895

Warren County Historical Society, Warren, PA.........................1304

Warren County Historical Society Museum, Lebanon, OH.........................1171

Warren Historical Society, Warren, ME.......624

Warren ICBM & Heritage Museum, Frances E. Warren Air Force Base, WY.........................1633

Warrick County Museum, Inc., Boonville, IN.........................470

Warsaw Historical Museum, Warsaw, NY .1082

Waseca County Historical Society, Waseca, MN.........................796

Washakie Museum, Worland, WY..............1639

Washburn County Historical Society Museum, Shell Lake, WI.........................1621

Washburn Historical Museum & Cultural Center, Inc. aka Washburn Cultural Center, Washburn, WI.........................1625

Washington County Fair Farm Museum, Greenwich, NY.........................996

Winchester-Frederick County Historical Society, Inc., Winchester, VA 1546
Windham Textile and History Museum (The Mill Museum), Willimantic, CT 267
Windmill Island Municipal Park, Holland, MI 747
Winedale, Center for American History, University of Texas at Austin, Round Top, TX 1446
Wing Haven Garden and Bird Sanctuary, Charlotte, NC 1096
Winnebago Area Museum, Winnebago, MN 797
Winnetka Historical Society, Winnetka, IL 466
Winona County Historical Museum, Winona, MN 797
Winslow Crocker House, Yarmouth Port, MA 722
Winston Churchill Memorial and Library, Fulton, MO 816
Winterthur Museum & Country Estate, Winterthur, DE 274
Wisconsin Historical Museum, Madison, WI 1606
Wise County Heritage Museum, Decatur, TX 1408
Wistariahurst Museum, Holyoke, MA 687
Witte Museum, San Antonio, TX 1451
Wolcott House Museum Complex, Maumee, OH 1175
Woldumar Nature Center, Lansing, MI 751
Wolf House Museum, Manhattan, KS 552
Wolf Point Area Historical Society, Inc., Wolf Point, MT 855
Wolfeboro Historical Society, Wolfeboro, NH 897
The Wolfsonian - Florida International University, Miami Beach, FL..................327
Wood County Historical Center and Museum, Bowling Green, OH 1143
Woodburn Historic House, Pendleton, SC .1339
Woodford County Historical Society Museum, Versailles, KY 584
Woodlawn Museum/The Black House, Ellsworth, ME 610
Woodlawn Plantation Museum, Alexandria, VA 1494
Woodrow Wilson House, Washington, DC..294
Woodrow Wilson Presidential Library at His Birthplace, Staunton, VA..............1537
Woodside Store Historic Site, Woodside, CA 199
Woodson County Historical Society, Yates Center, KS..................................564
Woodstock Historical Society, Inc., Woodstock, VT 1491
Woodstock Museum of Shenandoah County, Inc., Woodstock, VA................1546
Woodville Museum, Inc., Rogue River, OR..1234
Worcester Historical Museum, Worcester, MA 721
Workman & Temple Family Homestead Museum, City of Industry, CA 85
World's First Wendy's Restaurant, Columbus, OH 1159
World's Smallest Museum, Superior, AZ.......45
Worthington Historical Society, Worthington, OH 1192
Wrather West Kentucky Museum, Murray, KY 580
Wren's Nest, Atlanta, GA 364
Wright Brothers National Memorial, Kill Devil Hills, NC 1108
Wright County Historical Society, Buffalo, MN 770
Wright Museum, Wolfeboro, NH 897
Wright's Ferry Mansion, Columbia, PA 1248
Wyandot County Historical Society, Upper Sandusky, OH 1188

Wyandotte County Museum, Bonner Springs, KS 534
Wyandotte Museum, Wyandotte, MI 766
Wyatt Earp Birthplace Home, Monmouth, IL 445
Wyck, Philadelphia, PA 1289
The Wyckoff Farmhouse Museum, Brooklyn, NY 970
Wylie House Museum, Bloomington, IN 470
The Wyman Tavern, Keene, NH....................890
Wyoming Pioneer Memorial Museum, Douglas, WY 1632
Wyoming State Museum, Cheyenne, WY ..1631
Wyoming Territorial Prison State Historic Site, Laramie, WY 1636

Yakima Valley Museum and Historical Association, Yakima, WA........................1579
Yates County Genealogical and Historical Society and Oliver House Museum and L. Caroline Underwood Museum, Penn Yan, NY..1052
Yellow Medicine County Historical Society and Museum, Granite Falls, MN 777
Yellowstone Gateway Museum of Park County, Livingston, MT 850
Yellowstone National Park, Gardiner, MT ...847
Yesteryear House-Central Mine, Clarkston, MI..732
Yesteryear Village, West Palm Beach, FL....354
Yolo County Historical Museum, Woodland, CA 199
Yorba and Slaughter Families Adobe, Chino, CA..84
Yorktown Historical Museum, Yorktown, TX 1462
Youth Museum of Southern West Virginia, Beckley, WV 1579
Ypsilanti Historical Museum, Ypsilanti, MI 767
Yucaipa Adobe, Yucaipa, CA......................200
Yucaipa Valley Historical Society Museum, Yucaipa, CA..............................201
Yuma Crossing State Historic Park, Yuma, AZ 54
Yuma Territorial Prison State Historic Park, Yuma, AZ 54

Z. Taylor Brown-Sarah Dorsey House, Midland, TX 1439
Zalud House, Porterville, CA........................144
Zebulon B. Vance Birthplace State Historic Site, Weaverville, NC................1122
Zelienople Historical Society, Zelienople, PA..1309
Zion Historical Society, Zion, IL..................467
Zippo/Case Visitors Center, Bradford, PA..1244
Zoar State Memorial, Zoar, OH..................1194

Personal Artifacts

A.C. Gilbert's Discovery Village, Salem, OR..1235
The A.D. Buck Museum of Natural History & Science, Tonkawa, OK 1215
A.R. Bowman Memorial Museum, Prineville, OR 1234
A:shiwi A:wan Museum and Heritage Center, Zuni, NM 954
Abbie Gardner Cabin, Arnolds Park, IA 505
Aberdeen Museum of History, Aberdeen, WA..1547
Abraham Lincoln Birthplace National Historic Site, Hodgenville, KY 571
Abraham Lincoln Library & Museum, Lincoln Memorial University, Harrogate, TN 1366
Abraham Lincoln Presidential Library & Museum, Springfield, IL 458
Academy Hall Museum of the Rocky Hill Historical Society, Inc., Rocky Hill, CT..259

Ace of Clubs House, Texarkana, TX..........1455
Adair County Historical Society, Inc., Kirksville, MO..824
Adam Thoroughgood House, Virginia Beach, VA 1541
Adams County Historical Society, Gettysburg, PA..1255
Adams County Historical Society Museum, Lind, WA 1558
Adams County Historical Society Museum, Brighton, CO 204
Adams Museum & House, Deadwood, SD 1346
Adams National Historical Park, Quincy, MA 704
Adams Old Stone Grist Mill, Bellows Falls, VT 1476
The Adirondack Museum, Blue Mountain Lake, NY 963
Admiral Nimitz National Museum of the Pacific War, Fredericksburg, TX...........1419
Adobe De Palomares, Pomona, CA 143
Adsmore Museum, Princeton, KY................583
African American Historical Museum & Cultural Center of Iowa, Cedar Rapids, IA 508
African American Museum, Cleveland, OH..1152
African-American Museum and Library at Oakland, Oakland, CA 132
The African American Museum in Philadelphia, Philadelphia, PA 1275
African Art Museum of the S.M.A. Fathers, Tenafly, NJ 926
Afro American Historical Association of Fauquier County, The Plains, VA 1541
Afro-American Historical Society Museum, Jersey City, NJ 908
Agate Fossil Beds National Monument, Harrison, NE..862
Agricultural and Industrial Museum, York County Heritage Trust, York, PA...........1309
Agricultural Heritage Museum, Boerne, TX 1396
Agriculture Museum, Merced, CA 125
Agrirama, Georgia's Living History Museum & Village, Tifton, GA 388
Agua Caliente Cultural Museum, Palm Springs, CA 138
Agua Mansa Pioneer Memorial Cemetery, Colton, CA..87
Ah-Tah-Thi-Ki Museum at Okalee, Hollywood, FL..312
Aiken County Historical Museum, Aiken, SC..1320
Aiken Thoroughbred Racing Hall of Fame and Museum, Aiken, SC 1320
Air Force Flight Test Center Museum, Edwards AFB, CA 92
Air Mobility Command Museum, Dover AFB, DE..270
Air Victory Museum, Inc., Lumberton, NJ..910
The Airborne & Special Operations Museum, Fayetteville, NC....................1100
Airline History Museum, Kansas City, MO..820
Airmen Memorial Museum, Suitland, MD..655
Airpower Museum Inc., Ottumwa, IA...........526
Akron Zoological Park, Akron, OH..............1138
Akta Lakota Museum and Cultural Center, Chamberlain, SD........................1345
Akwesasne Museum, Hogansburg, NY 998
Al-Goin Historical Museum, Portage, IN.....496
Alabama Center for Traditional Culture, Montgomery, AL 15
Alabama Department of Archives & History, Montgomery, AL 15
Alabama Mining Museum, Dora, AL..............7
Alabama Museum of Natural History, Tuscaloosa, AL 19

Personal Artifacts–Continued

Alabama Museum of the Health Sciences, Birmingham, AL................4

Alabama Music Hall of Fame, Tuscumbia, AL................20

Alabama Sports Hall of Fame, Birmingham, AL................4

Alabama Women's Hall of Fame, Marion, AL................13

Alachua County Historic Trust: Matheson Museum, Inc., Gainesville, FL................310

Alamance Battleground State Historic Site, Burlington, NC................1092

Alamance County Historical Museum, Burlington, NC................1092

The Alamo, San Antonio, TX................1447

Alamo Township Museum-John E. Gray Memorial Museum, Kalamazoo, MI........748

Alaska Aviation Heritage Museum, Anchorage, AK................21

Alaska Heritage Museum at Wells Fargo, Anchorage, AK................21

Alaska Museum of Natural History, Anchorage, AK................21

Alaska Native Heritage Center, Anchorage, AK................22

Alaska State Museum, Juneau, AK................25

Albany Institute of History & Art, Albany, NY................954

Albany Regional Museum, Albany, OR.....1217

Albinger Archeological Museum, Ventura, CA................194

Albuquerque Museum, Albuquerque, NM....932

Alcatraz Island, San Francisco, CA.............163

Alden Historical Society, Inc., Alden, NY....956

Alden House Historic Site, Duxbury, MA ...680

Alex Haley Home and Museum, Henning, TN................1367

Alexander & Baldwin Sugar Museum, Puunene, HI................401

Alexander Ramsey House, Minnesota Historical Society, Saint Paul, MN..........789

Alexandre Mouton House/Lafayette Museum, Lafayette, LA................589

Alexandria Black History Resource Center, Alexandria, VA................1491

Alfred B. Maclay State Gardens, Tallahassee, FL................346

Alger County Heritage Center, Munising, MI................757

Alice Austen House Museum, Staten Island, NY................1072

The Alice T. Miner Colonial Collection, Chazy, NY................977

Aliceville Museum, Aliceville, AL................3

Allaire Village Inc., Farmingdale, NJ..........903

Allan Shivers Museum, Woodville, TX......1462

Allegan County Historical Society and Old Jail Museum, Allegan, MI................723

Allegany County Historical Society, Inc., Cumberland, MD................641

Allegheny Portage Railroad National Historic Site and Johnstown Flood National Memorial, Gallitzin, PA..........1255

Allen County Historical Society, Iola, KS ...545

Allen County Museum, Lima, OH................1172

Alling Coverlet Museum, Palmyra, NY.....1050

Allison-Antrim Museum, Inc., Greencastle, PA................1257

Almond Historical Society/Hagadorn House Museum, Almond, NY................957

Alpine County Museum, Markleeville, CA................124

Alton Museum of History and Art, Inc., Alton, IL................410

Alumni Center - Husky Heritage Sports Museum, Storrs, CT................261

Alvarado Adobe & The Blume House, San Pablo, CA................175

Amador County Museum, Jackson, CA 105

Amana Heritage Museum, Amana, IA 504

Amelia Earhart Birthplace Museum, Atchison, KS................532

Amelia Island Museum of History, Fernandina Beach, FL................306

American Airlines C.R. Smith Museum, Fort Worth, TX................1416

American Airpower Heritage Museum, Inc. & Commemorative Air Force Headquarters, Midland, TX................1438

American Catholic Historical Society, Philadelphia, PA................1276

American Classical Music Hall of Fame and Museum, Cincinnati, OH................1148

American Clock and Watch Museum, Inc., Bristol, CT................236

American Computer Museum, Bozeman, MT................842

The American Film Institute, Los Angeles, CA................112

American Hungarian Foundation/Museum of the American Hungarian Foundation, New Brunswick, NJ..........915

American Independence Museum, Exeter, NH................887

American Irish Historical Society, New York, NY................1019

The American Jazz Museum, Kansas City, MO................820

American Jewish Historical Society, New York, NY................1019

American Labor Museum, Botto House National Landmark, Haledon, NJ..........906

American Maple Museum, Croghan, NY.....983

American Merchant Marine Museum, Kings Point, NY................1007

American Military Museum, Charleston, SC................1323

The American Museum of Fly Fishing, Manchester, VT................1481

American Museum of Magic & Lund Memorial Library, Inc., Marshall, MI 754

American Museum of Nursing, Tempe, AZ................45

American Museum of Science & Energy, Oak Ridge, TN................1382

The American Numismatic Society, New York, NY................1020

American Quarter Horse Hall of Fame & Museum, Amarillo, TX................1386

American Red Cross Visitors Center and Gift Shop, Washington, DC................275

American Royal Museum & Visitors Center, Kansas City, MO................820

American Swedish Institute, Minneapolis, MN................781

American Textile History Museum, Lowell, MA................691

American Truck Historical Society, Kansas City, MO................820

American Watchmakers-Clockmakers Institute, Harrison, OH................1168

American West Heritage Center, Wellsville, UT................1475

American Wings Air Museum, Blaine, MN................769

American Work Horse Museum, Lexington, VA................1513

Americana Museum, Terra Alta, WV 1587

America's Black Holocaust Museum, Milwaukee, WI................1610

Amherst County Museum & Historical Society, Amherst, VA................1495

Amherst History Museum at the Strong House - Amherst Historical Society, Amherst, MA................658

Amherst Museum, Amherst, NY................957

Amos Herr House Foundation and Historic Society, Landisville, PA..........1267

Anacortes Museum, Anacortes, WA..........1547

Anacostia Museum and Center for African American History & Culture, Washington, DC................275

Ancient and Honorable Artillery Company, Boston, MA................663

Anderson/Abruzzo Albuquerque International Balloon Museum, Albuquerque, NM................933

Anderson County Museum, Anderson, SC.1321

Andersonville National Historic Site, Andersonville, GA................355

Andover Historical Society, Andover, MA...660

Andrew County Museum & Historical Society, Savannah, MO................838

Andrew Johnson National Historic Site, Greeneville, TN................1366

Andrew Low House, Savannah, GA 384

Androscoggin Historical Society, Auburn, ME................603

Angels Attic Museum, Santa Monica, CA ...183

Angels Camp Museum & Carriage House, Angels Camp, CA................71

Animas Museum, Durango, CO................214

Anna Bemis Palmer Museum, York, NE......875

Anna Miller Museum, Newcastle, WY 1637

The Anne Spencer Memorial Foundation, Inc., Lynchburg, VA................1515

Annie Riggs Memorial Museum, Fort Stockton, TX................1415

Annmary Brown Memorial, Providence, RI................1316

Anoka County Historical Society, Anoka, MN................767

Anson County Historical Society, Inc., Wadesboro, NC................1121

Antelope Valley African American Museum, Lancaster, CA................108

Antelope Valley Indian Museum, Lancaster, CA................108

The Antiquarian and Landmarks Society, Inc., Hartford, CT................244

Antique Gas & Steam Engine Museum, Inc., Vista, CA................196

Anza-Borrego Desert State Park, Borrego Springs, CA................79

Apostles Islands National Lakeshore, Bayfield, WI................1591

The Appalachian Trail Conservancy, Harpers Ferry, WV................1581

The Appaloosa Museum and Heritage Center, Moscow, ID................407

The Apple Trees Museum, Burlington, IA...506

Appomattox Court House National Historical Park, Appomattox, VA 1495

APVA Preservation Virginia, Richmond, VA................1528

APVA's John Marshall House, Richmond, VA................1528

Arab American National Museum, Dearborn, MI................733

Arbor Lodge State Historical Park, Nebraska City, NE................868

Arcadia Township Historical Commission, Arcadia, MI................726

Arches Museum of Pioneer Life, Winona, MN................797

Archives of American Art, Smithsonian Institution, Washington, DC................276

Archives of J.S.G. Boggs, Brandon, FL.......298

Arden - The Helena Modjeska Historic House & Gardens, Modjeska Canyon, CA................126

Ardenwood Historic Farm, Fremont, CA......96

Arizona Doll and Toy Museum, Phoenix, AZ................39

Arizona Historical Society Museum, Tucson, AZ................47

Arizona Historical Society Museum - Downtown, Tucson, AZ................47

Arizona Historical Society Pioneer Museum, Flagstaff, AZ................32

Arizona Historical Society-Yuma: Sarguinetti House Museum and Garden, Yuma, AZ................54

Arizona Jewish Historical Society, Phoenix, AZ................39

Arizona Military Museum, Phoenix, AZ........39
Arizona Railway Museum, Chandler, AZ 31
Arizona State Parks Board, Phoenix, AZ 39
Ark-La-Tex Antique & Classic Vehicle
    Museum, Shreveport, LA 600
Arkansas Air Museum, Fayetteville, AR 57
Arkansas Country Doctor Museum,
    Lincoln, AR 61
Arkansas Historic Wine Museum, Paris,
    AR 65
Arkansas Museum of Natural Resources,
    Smackover, AR 68
Arkansas National Guard Museum, North
    Little Rock, AR 65
Arkansas Post Museum, Gillett, AR 58
Arkansas Post National Memorial, Gillett,
    AR 58
Arkansas Railroad Museum, Pine Bluff,
    AR 65
Arkansas State University Museum,
    Jonesboro, AR 60
Arkansas Tech University Museum of
    Prehistory and History, Russellville,
    AR 67
Arlington Heights Historical Museum,
    Arlington Heights, IL 411
Arlington Historical Museum, Arlington,
    VA 1495
The Arlington Historical Society,
    Arlington, MA 660
Arlington House, The Robert E. Lee
    Memorial, Arlington, VA........................1495
Armand Bayou Nature Center, Houston,
    TX 1424
The Arms Family Museum of Local
    History, Youngstown, OH 1193
Armstrong Browning Library, Waco, TX 1458
Arrow Rock State Historic Site, Arrow
    Rock, MO 810
Artesia Historical Museum & Art Center,
    Artesia, NM 936
Arthurdale Heritage, Inc., Arthurdale,
    WV 1579
Artillery Company of Newport Military
    Museum, Newport, RI..............................1313
Arts Consortium of Cincinnati's African
    American Museum, Cincinnati, OH 1148
Arvada Center for the Arts and
    Humanities, Arvada, CO 201
Ash Hollow State Historical Park,
    Lewellen, NE..864
Ash Lawn-Highland, Charlottesville, VA 1498
Ashland Historical Society Museum,
    Ashland, WI 1590
Ashland, The Henry Clay Estate,
    Lexington, KY 572
Ashtabula County Historical Society,
    Geneva-on-the-Lake, OH 1166
Ashton Villa & The Heritage Visitor
    Center, Galveston, TX 1420
Asian Arts & Culture Center, Towson
    University, Towson, MD 655
Asistencia: San Gabriel Mission Outpost,
    Redlands, CA...146
Aspen Historical Society, Aspen, CO 202
Association for the Preservation of
    Tennessee Antiquities, Nashville, TN 1377
Astor House Museum, Golden, CO..............219
Astronaut Ellison S. Onizuka Space
    Center, Kailua-Kona, HI 399
Astronaut Memorial Planetarium and
    Observatory, Cocoa, FL 300
Ataloa Lodge Museum, Muskogee, OK......1205
Atchison County Historical Society,
    Atchison, KS..533
The Atlanta Cyclorama, Atlanta, GA...........358
Atlanta Historical Society, Atlanta, GA......:358
Atlantic City Historical Museum, Atlantic
    City, NJ 897
Atlantic Heritage Center, Somers Point,
    NJ 924

Atlantic Wildfowl Heritage Museum,
    Virginia Beach, VA..................................1541
Atwood House Museum, Home of
    Chatham Historical Society, Chatham,
    MA 675
Au Glaize Village, Defiance, OH................1162
Auburn Cord Duesenberg Museum,
    Auburn, IN..468
Audie Murphy/American Cotton
    Museum, Inc, Greenville, TX 1423
Audrain Historical Museum, Graceland,
    Mexico, MO..827
Audubon County Historical Society,
    Exira, IA 517
Auglaize County Historical Society, Saint
    Marys, OH 1184
Augusta Museum of History, Augusta,
    GA...364
Augustana College Art Museum, Rock
    Island, IL 453
Aullwood Audubon Center and Farm,
    Dayton, OH 1160
Aurora Historical Society, Aurora, IL...........411
Aurora Historical Society, Aurora, OH.......1140
Aurora History Museum, Aurora, CO 202
Aurora Regional Fire Museum, Aurora,
    IL...411
Autry National Center of the American
    West, Los Angeles, CA..............................112
Ava Gardner Museum, Smithfield, NC.......1119
Avery County Museum, Newland, NC 1113
Avery Research Center for African
    American History & Culture,
    Charleston, SC...1323
Aviation Hall of Fame and Museum of
    New Jersey, Teterboro, NJ 926
Avila Adobe, Los Angeles, CA.....................113
The Avon Historical Society, Inc., Avon,
    CT 235
Awbury Arboretum, Philadelphia, PA.........1277
Aztalan Museum, Jefferson, WI.................1601
Aztec Museum and Pioneer Village,
    Aztec, NM 936

B&O Railroad Museum: Ellicott City
    Station, Ellicott City, MD 643
Babe Didrikson Zaharias Museum,
    Beaumont, TX 1394
The Babe Ruth Museum and Sports
    Legends at Camden Yards, Baltimore,
    MD 629
Baca House, Trinidad History Museum,
    Trinidad, CO 233
Bacon's Castle, Surry County, VA..............1540
Badger Mine and Museum, Shullsburg,
    WI 1622
Bagg Bonanza Historical Farm,
    Mooreton, ND 1135
Bailey House Museum - Maui Historical
    Society, Wailuku, HI 402
Baldwin County Heritage Museum,
    Elberta, AL 8
Baldwin Historical Society and Museum,
    Baldwin, NY..960
Baldwin-Reynolds House Museum,
    Meadville, PA 1270
Baltimore & Ohio Railroad Museum,
    Baltimore, MD..629
Baltimore Civil War Museum, Baltimore,
    MD 629
Baltimore County Historical Society,
    Cockeysville, MD......................................640
Baltimore Museum of Industry,
    Baltimore, MD...630
The Band Museum, Pine Bluff, AR...............66
Bandon Historical Society Museum,
    Bandon, OR 1219
Bangor Museum & Center for History,
    Bangor, ME...604
Banner County Historical Society,
    Harrisburg, NE..862
Banning Residence Museum,
    Wilmington, CA 198

Bannock County Historical Museum,
    Pocatello, ID 408
The Barbara Fritchie House, Frederick,
    MD 644
Barbed Wire Museum, La Crosse, KS 547
The Barker Character, Comic and
    Cartoon Museum, Cheshire, CT 237
Barker Mansion, Michigan City, IN 490
The Barnacle Historic State Park,
    Coconut Grove, FL....................................300
Barnes County Historical Museum,
    Valley City, ND 1136
Barnes Museum, Southington, CT...............260
Barnet Historical Society, Barnet, VT........1476
The Barnum Museum, Bridgeport, CT........235
Barratt's Chapel and Museum, Frederica,
    DE 270
Barre Historical Society, Inc., Barre, MA 662
Barrington Living History Farm,
    Washington, TX 1460
Barron County Historical Society's
    Pioneer Village Museum, Cameron,
    WI 1593
Barstow Route 66 Mother Road Museum,
    Barstow, CA..74
Bartholomew County Historical Society,
    Columbus, IN..472
Bartlesville Area History Museum,
    Bartlesville, OK 1196
Barton County Historical Museum &
    Village, Great Bend, KS............................542
Bartow History Center, Cartersville, GA 367
Bassett Hall, Williamsburg, VA 1544
Bates-Scofield Homestead, The Darien
    Historical Society, Darien, CT 238
Bath County Historical Society, Warm
    Springs, VA..1543
Battle of Lexington State Historic Site,
    Lexington, MO 826
Battles for Chattanooga Museum,
    Lookout Mountain, TN 1371
The Battles Museums of Rural Life,
    Girard, PA 1256
Battleship New Jersey Museum &
    Memorial, Camden, NJ 899
Battleship North Carolina, Wilmington,
    NC..1122
Battleship Texas State Historic Site, La
    Porte, TX 1433
Baxter Springs Heritage Center and
    Museum, Baxter Springs, KS....................533
Bay of Pigs Museum & Library, Miami,
    FL..323
Bay View Historical Museum, Bay View,
    MI..728
Bayless-Selby House Museum, Denton,
    TX 1409
Bayou Bend Collection and Gardens,
    Houston, TX 1425
The Bead Museum, Glendale, AZ 35
Bead Museum, Washington, DC..................276
Bear Mountain Trailside Museums and
    Zoo, Bear Mountain, NY 961
Beatty Museum and Historical Society,
    Beatty, NV...875
Beauchamp Newman Museum, Elizabeth,
    WV...1581
The Beaufort Arsenal, Beaufort, SC...........1321
Beaufort Historic Site, Beaufort, NC..........1091
Beauport, Sleeper-McCann House,
    Gloucester, MA...684
Beauvais Heritage Center, Clark, SD 1345
Beauvoir, The Jefferson Davis Home and
    Presidential Library, Biloxi, MS 798
Beaverhead County Museum, Dillon, MT ...845
Beck Cultural Exchange Center,
    Knoxville, TN 1369
Becker County Historical Society, Detroit
    Lakes, MN 772
Beckman Coulter Heritage Exhibit,
    Fullerton, CA...98

Personal Artifacts–Continued

Bedford City/County Museum, Bedford,
  VA 1496
Beehive House, Salt Lake City, UT 1470
Beith House Museum, Saint Charles, IL.....456
Belair Stable Museum, Bowie, MD.............638
Belding Museum, Belding, MI 728
Belhaven Memorial Museum, Inc.,
  Belhaven, NC..1092
Bell County Museum, Belton, TX 1395
Bellamy Mansion Museum of History
  and Design Arts, Wilmington, NC........1122
Belle Grove Plantation, Middletown, VA...1517
Belle Meade Plantation, Nashville, TN 1377
Belleville Area Museum, Belleville, MI.......728
Bellflower Historical and Genealogical
  Society, Bellflower, IL............................413
Bellingrath Gardens & Home, Theodore,
  AL 18
Bellport-Brookhaven Historical Society
  and Museum, Bellport, NY......................961
Beloit Historical Society, Beloit, WI 1592
Beltrami County History Center, Bemidji,
  MN 768
Belvedere-Tiburon Landmarks Society,
  Tiburon, CA..192
Bement-Billings Farmstead, Newark
  Valley, NY...1041
Benicia Fire Museum, Benicia, CA...............74
Benicia Historical Museum, Benicia, CA 74
The Benjamin & Dr. Edgar R. Cofeld
  Judaic Museum of Temple Beth Zion,
  Buffalo, NY...971
The Benjamin Banneker Park &
  Museum, Baltimore, MD 631
Benjamin Harrison Presidential Site,
  Indianapolis, IN.......................................481
Bennett Place State Historic Site,
  Durham, NC...1098
Bennington Battle Monument, Old
  Bennington, VT......................................1484
Bennington Center for the Natural &
  Cultural Arts, Bennington, VT...............1476
The Bennington Museum, Bennington,
  VT 1476
Benton County Historical Museum,
  Philomath, OR.......................................1230
Benton County Historical Museum,
  Prosser, WA 1563
Benzie Area Historical Museum,
  Benzonia, MI...729
Bergen County Zoological Park,
  Paramus, NJ..919
Bergen Museum of Local History,
  Bergen, NY..962
Berkeley County Museum & Heritage
  Center, Moncks Corner, SC....................1336
Berkeley Plantation, Charles City, VA 1498
Berkshire County Historical Society, Inc.
  - Arrowhead, Pittsfield, MA....................702
Berlin Area Historical Society Museum
  of Local History, Berlin, WI..................1592
Berlin Art and Historical Collections,
  Berlin, MA...662
Bernard Historical Society and Museum,
  Delton, MI...734
Berrien County Historical Association,
  Berrien Springs, MI.................................729
Besh-Ba-Gowah Archaeological Park,
  Globe, AZ...35
Bess Streeter Aldrich House & Museum,
  Elmwood, NE...860
Bessemer Hall of History, Bessemer, AL.........3
Beth Ahabah Museum & Archives,
  Richmond, VA..1528
Betsy Ross House and Flag Museum,
  Philadelphia, PA 1277
Beverly Historical Society and Museum,
  Beverly, MA...662
Bexley Historical Society, Bexley, OH.......1143

Beyer Home, Oconto County Historical
  Society Museum, Oconto, WI...............1616
BG John C.L. Scribner Texas Military
  Forces Museum, Austin, TX 1389
The Bidwell House Museum, Monterey,
  MA...695
Biedenharn Coca-Cola Museum,
  Vicksburg, MS..809
Biedenharn Museum & Gardens, Monroe,
  LA...592
Big Hole National Battlefield, Wisdom,
  MT...855
Big Horn County Historical Museum,
  Hardin, MT...849
Big Springs Museum, Caledonia, NY 974
Big Thicket National Preserve, Kountze,
  TX..1432
Big Thunder Gold Mine, Keystone, SD.....1349
Big Timbers Museum, Lamar, CO 225
Bigelow House Museum, Olympia, WA 1560
Bill Baggs Cape Florida State Park, Key
  Biscayne, FL..316
Billy Sunday Home Museum and Visitors
  Center, Winona Lake, IN 504
Billy the Kid Museum, Fort Sumner, NM ...939
Biltmore Estate, Asheville, NC.................1089
Biltmore Homespun Shops - Grovewood
  Gallery, Asheville, NC............................1089
Bily Clock Museum/Antonin Dvorak
  Exhibit, Spillville, IA 528
Birmingham Civil Rights Institute,
  Birmingham, AL...4
Birmingham Historical Museum & Park,
  Birmingham, MI.......................................730
Birthplace of John Wayne, Winterset, IA....530
Bisbee Mining & Historical Museum,
  Bisbee, AZ...30
Biscayne National Park, Homestead, FL....313
Bishop Hill Heritage Museum, Bishop
  Hill, IL...413
Bishop Hill State Historic Site, Bishop
  Hill, IL...413
Black American West Museum &
  Heritage Center, Denver, CO 209
The Black Fashion Museum, Washington,
  DC...277
Black Hawk State Historic Site: Hauberg
  Indian Museum, Rock Island, IL.............453
Black Heritage Museum, Miami, FL...........323
Black Hills Mining Museum, Lead, SD.....1350
Black History Museum and Cultural
  Center, Richmond, VA............................1528
Black Kettle Museum, Cheyenne, OK 1198
Black Mountain College Museum & Arts
  Center, Asheville, NC.............................1089
Black River Academy Museum, Ludlow,
  VT..1480
Black River Historical Society of Lorain,
  Lorain, OH...1172
Blackberry Farm's Pioneer Village,
  Aurora, IL..411
Blackman House Museum, Snohomish,
  WA...1570
Blaine County Historical Museum,
  Hailey, ID...406
Blaine County Museum, Chinook, MT 844
Blithewold Mansion, Gardens &
  Arboretum, Bristol, RI 1310
Bloom Mansion, Trinidad History
  Museum, Trinidad, CO.............................233
Bloomfield Academy Museum,
  Bloomfield, NY...963
Bloomington Historical Society,
  Minneapolis, MN......................................781
Blount-Bridgers House/Hobson Pittman
  Memorial Gallery, Tarboro, NC.............1121
Blount County Memorial Museum,
  Oneonta, AL..17
Blount Mansion, Knoxville, TN 1369
Blue and Gray Museum, Fitzgerald, GA......371
Blue Earth County Historical Society,
  Mankato, MN...780

Blue Licks Battlefield Museum, Mount
  Olivet, KY..580
Bluff Hall Antebellum Home and
  Museum, Demopolis, AL.............................7
Bob Burns Museum & River Valley
  Museum of Van Buren, Van Buren,
  AR...69
Bob Feller Museum, Van Meter, IA 529
Boca Raton Historical Society, Boca
  Raton, FL...296
Bodie State Historic Park, Bridgeport,
  CA...79
Bodley-Bullock House, Lexington, KY........572
Bolin Wildlife Exhibit & Antique
  Collection, McKinney, TX 1437
Bolinas Museum, Bolinas, CA......................79
Bolton Hall Historical Museum, Tujunga,
  CA...193
Bolton Historical Society, Inc., Bolton,
  MA...663
Bonner County Historical Museum,
  Sandpoint, ID...409
Bonnet House Museum & Gardens, Fort
  Lauderdale, FL..306
Boone County Heritage Museum,
  Harrison, AR..59
Boone County Historical Center, Boone,
  IA..506
Boonsborough Museum of History,
  Boonsboro, MD..637
The Boorman House - The Juneau
  County Historical Society, Mauston,
  WI..1608
Boot Hill Museum, Inc., Dodge City, KS....536
Booth Western Art Museum, Cartersville,
  GA...367
Boothbay Railway Village, Boothbay, ME...607
Boothe Memorial Park and Museum,
  Stratford, CT..262
Boscobel, Garrison, NY 993
Boston Childrens Museum, Boston, MA.....664
Boston National Historical Park, Boston,
  MA...664
Boswell Museum of Music, Springfield
  Center, NY...1071
Botetourt County Historical Society,
  Fincastle, VA..1504
Bottineau County Historical Museum,
  Bottineau, ND...1129
Boulder City/Hoover Dam Museum,
  Boulder City, NV......................................875
Boulder History Museum, Boulder, CO......202
Boundary County Historical Society,
  Bonners Ferry, ID....................................404
Bowers Museum, Santa Ana, CA 177
Bowie Heritage Children's Museum &
  Welcome Center, Bowie, MD..................638
The Bowne House Historical Society,
  Flushing, NY..990
Boyertown Museum of Historic Vehicles,
  Boyertown, PA..1244
Boyhood Home of President Woodrow
  Wilson, Augusta, GA...............................365
Boys Town Hall of History & Father
  Flanagan House, Boys Town, NE............858
Bradford Brinton Memorial & Museum,
  Big Horn, WY..1628
Bradford County Historical Society,
  Towanda, PA...1303
Bradley County Historical Museum,
  Warren, AR..69
Bradley House Museum, Jasper, AR 60
Bragg-Mitchell Mansion, Mobile, AL 13
Braintree Historical Society, Inc.,
  Braintree, MA...670
Branigan Cultural Center, Las Cruces,
  NM...940
Brazoria County Historical Museum,
  Angleton, TX..1387
Brazos Valley Museum of Natural
  History, Bryan, TX.................................1398
Brazosport Museum of Natural Science,
  Clute, TX..1400

Personal Artifacts–Continued

Community Memorial Museum of Sutter County, Yuba City, CA 200
Community of Christ, Independence, MO ...817
Compass Inn Museum, Laughlintown, PA .1267
Comstock Historic House, Moorhead, MN 784
Concord Historical Society, Warner Museum, Springville, NY 1071
Concord Museum, Concord, MA 676
Concordia Historical Institute, Saint Louis, MO 832
Coney Island Museum, Brooklyn, NY 969
Confederate Memorial Hall-Bleak House, Knoxville, TN 1369
Confederate Memorial Museum, Atoka, OK 1196
Confederate Memorial State Historic Site, Higginsville, MO 817
Confederate Museum, Crawfordville, GA 369
Confederate Museum, New Orleans, LA 594
Confederated Tribes of Grand Ronde Cultural Resources Department, Grand Ronde, OR 1225
Conklin Reed Organ & History Museum, Hanover, MI 745
Connecticut Historical Society, Hartford, CT 244
Connecticut River Museum, Essex, CT 239
Conner Prairie, Fishers, IN 476
Conrad-Caldwell House Museum, Louisville, KY 575
Conrad Mansion National Historic Site Museum, Kalispell, MT 850
Constitution Island Association, West Point, NY 1085
Constitution Square State Historic Site, Danville, KY 567
Conway Scenic Railroad, Inc., North Conway, NH 892
Cookeville Depot Museum, Cookeville, TN 1364
Cooper-Hewitt National Design Museum, Smithsonian Institution, New York, NY 1023
Cooper Regional History Museum, Upland, CA 193
The Coopersville Area Historical Society Museum, Coopersville, MI 733
Coos Historical & Maritime Museum, North Bend, OR 1229
Copper Range Historical Museum, South Range, MI 764
Copper Village Museum & Arts Center of Deer Lodge County, Anaconda, MT 840
Copshaholm House Museum & Historic Oliver Gardens, South Bend, IN 499
Cordell Hull Birthplace & Museum State Historic Park, Byrdstown, TN 1360
Cordova Historical Museum, Cordova, AK 23
Coronado-Quivira Museum, Lyons, KS 550
Corry Area Historical Society, Corry, PA ...1248
Cortland County Historical Society, Cortland, NY 982
Corydon Capitol Historic Site, Corydon, IN 473
Cottonlandia Museum, Greenwood, MS 800
Cottonwood County Historical Society, Windom, MN 796
The Country Doctor Museum, Bailey, NC .1091
Country Music Hall of Fame and Museum, Country Music Foundation, Nashville, TN 1378
Country Relics Little Village, Stanhope, IA 528
County of Los Angeles Fire Museum, Los Angeles, CA 114
Courthouse Square Association, Charlotte, MI 731

Cow Neck Peninsula Historical Society Sands-Willets House, Port Washington, NY 1053
The Cowley County Historical Society, Winfield, KS 564
Cowlitz County Historical Museum, Kelso, WA 1557
Cowpens National Battlefield, Chesnee, SC 1327
Cozens Ranch Museum, Fraser, CO 218
Cracker Country, Tampa, FL 348
Cradle of Aviation Museum, Garden City, NY 992
Craftsmen's Guild of Mississippi, Jackson, MS 802
Cragfont-Historic Cragfont, Inc., Castalian Springs, TN 1360
Cranbrook House and Gardens Auxiliary, Bloomfield Hills, MI 730
Cranbury Historical & Preservation Society, Cranbury, NJ 902
Cranford Historical Society, Cranford, NJ ...902
Crater Lake National Park, Crater Lake, OR 1222
Crater of Diamonds State Park Museum, Murfreesboro, AR 65
Cravens House, Lookout Mountain, TN 1371
Crawford County Historical Museum, Pittsburg, KS 556
Crawford W. Long Museum, Jefferson, GA 374
Crazy Mountain Museum, Big Timber, MT 841
Creative Photographic Art Center of Maine, Lewiston, ME 614
Crescent Bend/The Armstrong-Lockett House and The William P. Toms Memorial Gardens, Knoxville, TN 1369
The Crescent, Valdosta Garden Center, Inc., Valdosta, GA 389
Crested Butte Mountain Heritage Museum, Crested Butte, CO 208
Cripple Creek District Museum, Inc., Cripple Creek, CO 209
Crispus Attucks Center Museum, Indianapolis, IN 482
Crocker House, Mount Clemens, MI 756
Crockett County Museum, Ozona, TX 1442
Crockett Tavern Museum, Morristown, TN 1376
Crosby County Pioneer Memorial Museum, Crosbyton, TX 1403
Crossroads Museum, Corinth, MS 800
Crow Wing County Historical Society, Brainerd, MN 769
Crowley Museum & Nature Center, Sarasota, FL 344
Crown Point State Historic Site, Crown Point, NY 984
Crystal River State Archaeological Site, Crystal River, FL 302
Culbertson Mansion State Historic Site, New Albany, IN 493
Culbertson Museum, Culbertson, MT 845
Cullman County Museum, Cullman, AL 6
Cultural Rights and Protection Department/Ute Indian Tribe, Fort Duchesne, UT 1465
Cumberland County Historical Society, Greenwich, NJ 905
Cumberland County Historical Society, The Hamilton Library and The Two Mile House, Carlisle, PA 1245
Cumberland Island National Seashore, Saint Marys, GA 382
Cupertino Historical Society & Museum, Cupertino, CA 88
Cupola House, Egg Harbor, WI 1596
Curfman Gallery & Duhesa Lounge, Fort Collins, CO 216
Curry Historical Society Museum, Gold Beach, OR 1225
Curwood Castle, Owosso, MI 759

Custer Battlefield Museum, Garryowen, MT 847
Custer County 1881 Courthouse Museum, Custer, SD 1345
The Custom House Maritime Museum, Newburyport, MA 697
Cuyahoga Valley National Park, Brecksville, OH 1144
Cuyuna Range Historical Society & Museum, Crosby, MN 772
DAR-Hervey Ely House, Rochester, NY ...1058
DAR John Strong Mansion Museum, Addison, VT 1475
DAR Museum First Ladies of Texas Historic Costumes Collection, Denton, TX 1409
D.C. Booth Historic National Fish Hatchery, Spearfish, SD 1357
D.R. Barker Historical Museum, Fredonia, NY 992
Dade Battlefield Historic State Park, Bushnell, FL 298
Dahlonega Gold Museum State Historic Site, Dahlonega, GA 369
Dakota County Historical Society, South Saint Paul, MN 793
Dakota Discovery Museum, Mitchell, SD .1352
Dakota Sunset Museum, Gettysburg, SD ...1348
Dakota Territorial Museum, Yankton, SD ..1359
Dakota Territory Air Museum, Minot, ND .1134
Dakotaland Museum, Huron, SD 1348
Dal-Paso Museum, Lamesa, TX 1433
Dale & Martha Hawk Museum, Wolford, ND 1138
Dallam-Hartley XIT Museum, Dalhart, TX 1403
Dallas Firefighter's Museum, Inc., Dallas, TX 1404
Dallas Heritage Village at Old City Park, Dallas, TX 1405
Dallas Historical Society, Dallas, TX 1405
Dallas Holocaust Museum, Dallas, TX 1405
Dallidet Adobe and Gardens, San Luis Obispo, CA 174
Dalton Defenders Museum, Coffeyville, KS 535
The Dan Quayle Center & Museum, Huntington, IN 481
Dana Adobe, Nipomo, CA 130
The Dana-Thomas House State Historic Site, Springfield, IL 458
The Danbury Museum & Historical Society, Danbury, CT 238
Dancing Bear Folk Center, Thermopolis, WY 1639
Dane G. Hansen Memorial Museum, Logan, KS 550
Daniel Boone Home and Boonesfield Village, Lindenwood University, Defiance, MO 814
Daniel Boone Homestead, Birdsboro, PA ..1243
Daniels County Museum and Pioneer Town, Scobey, MT 853
The Danish Immigrant Museum, Elk Horn, IA 517
Danville Museum of Fine Arts & History, Danville, VA 1502
DAR Van Bunschooten Museum, Sussex, NJ 925
Darlington Raceway Stock Car Museum, NMPA Hall of Fame, Darlington, SC 1331
Daughters of the American Revolution Museum, Washington, DC 277
Daughters of Utah Pioneers Pioneer Memorial Museum & International Society Daughters of Utah Pioneers, Salt Lake City, UT 1471
Davenport House Museum, Savannah, GA 384
David Bradford House, Washington, PA 1305
David Conklin Farmhouse, Huntington, NY 1000

David Crockett Cabin, Rutherford, TN 1383

The David Davis Mansion, Bloomington,
IL..413

David Strawn Art Gallery, Jacksonville,
IL..440

Davidson County Historical Museum,
Lexington, NC......................................1109

The Davistown Museum, Liberty, ME.........614

The Dawes Arboretum, Newark, OH 1177

Dawes County Historical Society
Museum, Chadron, NE............................859

Dawson County Historical Museum,
Lexington, NE..864

Dawson Springs Museum and Art Center,
Inc., Dawson Springs, KY 568

De Graaf Nature Center, Holland, MI..........746

Deaf Smith County Museum, Hereford,
TX..1424

Dearborn Historical Museum, Dearborn,
MI..733

Decatur House Museum, Washington, DC...277

The Decorative Arts Center of Ohio,
Lancaster, OH.......................................1171

Dedham Historical Society Museum,
Dedham, MA..679

Deer Isle-Stonington Historical Society,
Deer Isle, ME..609

Deerfield Beach Historical Society,
Deerfield Beach, FL 304

Degenhart Paperweight & Glass Museum,
Inc., Cambridge, OH 1144

Degrazia Gallery In The Sun, Tucson, AZ.....48

DeKalb History Center Museum, Decatur,
GA..370

The Dekker Huis/Zeeland Historical
Museum, Zeeland, MI..............................767

Del Norte County Historical Society,
Crescent City, CA.....................................87

Delaware and Hudson Canal Historical
Society and Museum, High Falls, NY.....998

Delaware Archaeology Museum, Dover,
DE..269

Delaware Division of Historical &
Cultural Affairs, Dover, DE 269

Delaware Visitor's Center, Dover, DE..........270

Delta Blues Museum, Clarksdale, MS..........799

Delta County Historical Society Museum,
Escanaba, MI...741

Delta County Museum, Delta, CO................209

Delta Cultural Center, Helena, AR 59

Delta Music Museum, Ferriday, LA.............588

Denali National Park and Preserve,
Denali Park, AK..23

Dennys River Historical Society,
Dennysville, ME.......................................609

Denton County Historical Museum, Inc.
and Texas Heritage Center, Denton,
TX..1409

Denver Firefighters Museum, Denver, CO...211

Department of the Treasury, Washington,
DC..278

Depot Museum & Fort Sedgwick
Museum, Julesburg, CO...........................223

The Depot Museum Complex,
Henderson, TX.......................................1424

Depot Park Museum, Sonoma, CA 187

Depreciation Lands Museum, Allison
Park, PA...1240

Des Plaines History Center, Des Plaines,
IL..430

Deschutes County Historical Society,
Bend, OR...1220

Desert Caballeros Western Museum,
Wickenburg, AZ..53

The Design Center at Philadelphia
University, Philadelphia, PA 1278

Detroit Historical Society, Detroit, MI 735

Deutschheim State Historic Site,
Hermann, MO..817

Devils Tower Visitor Center, Devils
Tower, WY...1631

DeWitt County Historical Museum,
Cuero, TX...1403

DeWitt Wallace Decorative Arts Museum,
Williamsburg, VA 1545

Dexter Area Historical Society &
Museum, Dexter, MI................................738

Dexter Historical Society Campus,
Dexter, ME...609

Dey Mansion/Washington's Headquarters
Museum, Wayne, NJ................................929

Dickinson County Heritage Center,
Abilene, KS..531

Dinsmore Homestead Foundation,
Burlington, KY...566

DiscoverSea Shipwreck Museum,
Fenwick Island, DE.................................270

The Discovery Center of the Southern
Tier, Binghamton, NY..............................962

Discovery Museum, Sacramento Museum
of History, Science and Technology,
Sacramento, CA.......................................152

Dittrick Museum of Medical History,
Cleveland, OH.......................................1154

Dr. Daniel W. Kissam House,
Huntington, NY......................................1000

Dr. Howe-Waffle House and Medical
Museum, Santa Ana, CA..........................177

Dr. Increase Mathews House, Zanesville,
OH..1194

Dr. John Harris Dental Museum,
Bainbridge, OH......................................1141

Dr. Samuel D. Harris National Museum
of Dentistry, Baltimore, MD....................631

Dodge County Historical Society,
Mantorville, MN......................................780

Dodge County Historical Society
Museum, Beaver Dam, WI.....................1591

Dog Mushing Museum, Fairbanks, AK..........24

Don F. Pratt Memorial Museum, Fort
Campbell, KY...568

Don Garlits Museum of Drag Racing
Inc., Ocala, FL...330

Donald G. Trayser Memorial
Museum/Barnstable County Customs
House, Barnstable, MA............................661

Donkey Milk House, Historic Home, Key
West, FL...317

Donner Memorial State Park and
Emigrant Trail Museum, Truckee, CA 192

Door County Historical Museum,
Sturgeon Bay, WI..................................1623

Door County Maritime Museum (at Gills
Rock), Gills Rock, WI 1598

Door County Maritime Museum (at
Sturgeon Bay), Sturgeon Bay, WI 1623

Dorothea B. Hoover Historical Museum,
Joplin, MO...819

Dorothy G. Page Museum, Wasilla, AK 29

Douglas County Historical Society,
Superior, WI..1624

Douglas County Historical Society -
Carson Valley Museum & Cultural
Center, Gardnerville, NV 877

Douglas County Historical Society -
Genoa Courthouse Museum, Genoa,
NV..877

Douglas County Museum Complex,
Armour, SD..1344

Douglas County Museum of History and
Natural History, Roseburg, OR 1234

Douglass Historical Museum, Douglass,
KS..537

The Downers Grove Park District
Museum, Downers Grove, IL 431

Downieville Museum, Downieville, CA 91

Downing House Museum, Memphis, MO......827

Drake Well Museum, Titusville, PA...........1303

Drum Barracks Civil War Museum,
Wilmington, CA.......................................198

Drummond Home, Hominy, OK.................1203

Drummond Island Historical Museum,
Drummond Island, MI.............................739

Dublin-Laurens Museum, Dublin, GA 370

Dugger Coal Museum, Dugger, IN..............474

Duke Homestead State Historic Site,
Durham, NC...1098

Duluth Children's Museum, Duluth, MN.....772

Dunbar House State Memorial, Dayton,
OH..1161

Duncan Cottage Museum, Metlakatla, AK.....27

Dundee Township Historical Society,
Inc., Dundee, IL.......................................431

Dundy County Historical Society,
Benkelman, NE..857

Dunedin Historical Society & Museum,
Dunedin, FL...305

Dunn County Historical Society,
Menomonie, WI.....................................1609

Dunsmuir Historic Estate & Gardens,
Oakland, CA...133

DuPage County Historical Museum,
Wheaton, IL...465

Dupont Historical Society, DuPont, WA....1552

Durant House Museum, Saint Charles, IL ...457

Durham Center Museum/Research
Library, East Durham, NY.......................985

Durham Historic Association Museum,
Durham, NH...886

Durham Western Heritage Museum,
Omaha, NE..870

Dusable Museum of African-American
History, Inc., Chicago, IL........................420

Dutchess County Historical Society,
Poughkeepsie, NY..................................1054

Dwight D. Eisenhower Library-Museum,
Abilene, KS..531

Dyckman Farmhouse Museum and Park,
New York, NY..1025

E.M. Violette Museum, Kirksville, MO.......824

E. St. Julien Cox House, Saint Peter, MN ...792

EAA AirVenture Museum, Oshkosh, WI....1616

Eagle Bluff Lighthouse, Fish Creek, WI....1597

Eagle Historical Society & Museums,
Eagle, AK..23

The Earle-Harrison House and Gardens
on 5th Street, Waco, TX........................1458

Early American Museum, Mahomet, IL.......444

EarlyWorks Museums, Huntsville, AL 11

Earth & Mineral Sciences Museum and
Art Gallery, University Park, PA 1303

East Brunswick Museum Corporation,
East Brunswick, NJ 902

East Contra Costa Museum, Brentwood,
CA..79

East Hampton Historical Society, Inc.,
East Hampton, NY 985

East Hampton Town Marine Museum,
Amagansett, NY 957

East Hillsborough Historical Society, Inc.,
Plant City, FL..337

East Jersey Olde Towne, Piscataway, NJ 921

East Jordan Portside Art & Historical
Museum, East Jordan, MI........................739

East Lyme Historical Society/Thomas
Lee House, Niantic, CT 256

East Poultney Museum, East Poultney,
VT..1479

East Tennessee Historical Society,
Knoxville, TN...1369

East Texas Oil Museum at Kilgore
College, Kilgore, TX..............................1432

Eastern Arizona Museum and Historical
Society of Graham County Inc., Pima,
AZ..42

Eastern California Museum,
Independence, CA 104

Eastern Oregon Museum on the Old
Oregon Trail, Haines, OR 1226

Eastman Lord House, Conway, NH..............885

Eastside Heritage Center, Bellevue, WA 1548

The Eckhart House, Wheeling, WV.............1587

Eckley Miners' Village, Eckley, PA............1251

Edgar Allan Poe Museum, Richmond, VA.1529

Edgar County Historical Museum, Paris,
IL..449

Personal Artifacts–Continued

Edgerton-Explorit Center, Aurora, NE 856
Edison & Ford Winter Estates, Fort
    Myers, FL 308
Edisto Island Historic Preservation
    Society Museum, Edisto Island, SC 1332
Edmond Historical Society Museum,
    Edmond, OK 1200
Edmonds Art Festival Museum,
    Edmonds, WA 1553
Edmonds South Snohomish County
    Historical Society, Inc., Edmonds, WA .1553
Edna Historical Museum, Edna, KS 537
Edward H. White II Memorial Museum,
    Brooks Air Force Base, TX 1397
Edward Hopper Landmark Preservation
    Foundation, Nyack, NY 1044
Edwards County Historical Museum,
    Kinsley, KS 547
Effie Yeaw Nature Center, Carmichael,
    CA 82
1880 Town, Murdo, SD.............................1352
The 1811 Old Lincoln County Jail and
    Lincoln County Museum, Wiscasset,
    ME 625
1859 Jail, Marshal's Home & Museum,
    Independence, MO.................................817
The 1890 House-Museum & Center for
    Arts, Cortland, NY 983
82nd Airborne Division War Memorial
    Museum, Fort Bragg, NC.......................1101
Eisenhower Birthplace State Historical
    Site, Denison, TX 1409
Eisenhower National Historic Site,
    Gettysburg, PA 1255
Eiteljorg Museum of American Indians
    and Western Art, Indianapolis, IN 482
El Camino Real International Heritage
    Center, San Antonio, NM 947
El Cazador Museum, Grand Bay, AL............10
El Dorado County Historical Museum,
    Placerville, CA....................................142
El Paso Holocaust Museum & Study
    Center, El Paso, TX.............................1411
El Paso Museum of History, El Paso, TX..1412
El Pueblo History Museum, Pueblo, CO......230
El Rancho de Las Golondrinas Museum,
    Santa Fe, NM.....................................947
Elbert Hubbard-Roycroft Museum, East
    Aurora, NY 985
Eldridge Street Project, New York, NY 1025
Eleanor Roosevelt National Historic Site,
    Hyde Park, NY 1002
Elfreth's Alley Association, Philadelphia,
    PA 1279
Elgin Area Historical Society, Elgin, IL.......432
Elisabet Ney Museum, Austin, TX............1390
Eliza Cruce Hall Doll Collection,
    Ardmore, OK 1196
Elizabeth Sage Historic Costume
    Collection, Bloomington, IN 469
Elkhart County Historical Museum,
    Bristol, IN 471
Elkhorn Valley Museum & Research
    Center, Norfolk, NE 869
Ella Sharp Museum, Jackson, MI...............748
Elliott Museum, Stuart, FL......................346
Ellis County Historical Society, Hays, KS...543
Ellis County Museum, Inc., Waxahachie,
    TX 1460
Ellwood House Museum, DeKalb, IL 429
Elmhurst Historical Museum, Elmhurst,
    IL 433
Eloise Butler Wildflower Garden and
    Bird Sanctuary, Minneapolis, MN 781
Elverhoj Museum of History and Art,
    Solvang, CA.......................................187
Elwood Haynes Museum, Kokomo, IN........486
Emil A. Blackmore Museum of The
    American Legion, Indianapolis, IN 482

Emily Dickinson Museum: The
    Homestead and The Evergreens,
    Amherst, MA 658
Empire State Aerosciences Museum,
    Glenville, NY......................................995
End-O-Line Railroad Park & Museum,
    Currie, MN 772
Enfield Historical Society Museum,
    Enfield Center, NH 887
Enfield Shaker Museum, Enfield, NH 887
Enlisted Heritage Hall, Maxwell AFB -
    Gunter Annex, AL 13
Enoch Kelsey House, Newington, CT.........256
Enos Mills Cabin Museum & Gallery,
    Estes Park, CO....................................215
Ephraim Historical Foundation, Ephraim,
    WI 1597
Ephrata Cloister, Ephrata, PA 1251
Erie Canal Museum, Syracuse, NY 1076
Erie Canal Village, Rome, NY 1061
Erie Maritime Museum, Homeport U.S.
    Brig Niagara, Erie, PA 1252
The Erlander Home Museum, Rockford,
    IL 454
Ernest Hemingway House Museum, Key
    West, FL 317
Ernie Pyle State Historic Site, Dana, IN......473
Erskine Caldwell Birthplace Museum,
    Moreland, GA......................................380
Escondido History Center, Escondido,
    CA 93
Essex Shipbuilding Museum, Essex, MA 681
Essley-Noble Museum: Mercer County
    Historical Society, Aledo, IL..................410
Estes Park Museum, Estes Park, CO............215
The Esther Thomas Atkinson Museum,
    Hampden-Sydney, VA 1509
Ethan Allen Homestead Museum &
    Historic Site, Burlington, VT 1478
The Ethel Wright Mohamed Stitchery
    Museum, Belzoni, MS............................798
Ethnic Heritage Museum, Rockford, IL 455
Eubie Blake National Jazz Institute and
    Cultural Center, Baltimore, MD 632
Eugene Field House and St. Louis Toy
    Museum, Saint Louis, MO.......................833
Eugene O'Neill National Historic Site,
    Danville, CA.......................................89
Eugene V. Debs Home, Terre Haute, IN......500
Eureka Fire Museum, Milltown, NJ 911
Eureka Pioneer Museum of McPherson
    County, Inc., Eureka, SD 1346
Eureka School House, Springfield, VT 1487
Eustis Historical Museum & Preservation
    Society, Inc., Eustis, FL.......................306
Evanston Historical Society and Charles
    Gates Dawes House, Evanston, IL 434
Evansville Museum of Arts History &
    Science, Evansville, IN 475
Everglades National Park, Homestead, FL...313
Evergreen Aviation Museum,
    McMinnville, OR..................................1228
Evergreen House, The Johns Hopkins
    University, Baltimore, MD.......................632
Experience Music Project, Seattle, WA......1565
Exploris, Raleigh, NC 1115
Ezra Meeker Mansion, Puyallup, WA 1564

Fabyan Villa Museum, Geneva, IL..............437
Fairbanks House, Dedham, MA..................679
Fairfax Museum & Visitor Center,
    Fairfax, VA 1503
Fairfield County Museum, Winnsboro,
    SC 1343
Fairfield Historical Society, Fairfield, CT 241
Fairlawn Mansion & Museum, Superior,
    WI 1624
Fairmount Historical Museum & Gift
    Shop, Fairmount, IN.............................476
Fairport Historical Museum, Fairport, NY...989
Fairport Marine Museum, Fairport
    Harbor, OH 1164

Fairview Museum of History & Art,
    Fairview, UT......................................1465
Fall River County Historical Museum,
    Hot Springs, SD..................................1348
Fall River Historical Society Museum,
    Fall River, MA 682
Fallingwater, Mill Run, PA 1272
Falls Village-Canaan Historical Society,
    Falls Village, CT 241
Falmouth Historical Society, Falmouth,
    MA 682
Family Museum, Bettendorf, IA.................505
Faninadahen Kosas Guahan-Guam
    Museum, Hagatna, GU...........................1640
Fargo Air Museum, Fargo, ND 1130
The Farm, Sturgeon Bay, WI....................1623
Farm House Museum, Ames, IA.................505
Farmers Branch Historical Park, Farmers
    Branch, TX 1413
Farmington Historic Home, Louisville,
    KY 575
Farmington Museum, Farmington, NM........939
Farragut Folklife Museum, Farragut, TN ...1364
Farrar-Mansur House & Old Mill
    Museum, Weston, VT 1490
The Fashion Institute of Design &
    Merchandising/FIDM Museum &
    Galleries, Los Angeles, CA.....................114
FASNY Museum of Fire Fighting,
    Hudson, NY 1000
Faulkner County Museum, Conway, AR........56
Faust Park-Thornhill Historic Site & 19th
    Century Village, Chesterfield, MO 812
Favell Museum Inc., Klamath Falls, OR....1227
Fayette County Helpers Club &
    Historical Society, West Union, IA.........530
Fayette County Museum, Washington
    Court House, OH 1190
Fayette Heritage Museum & Archives, La
    Grange, TX 1432
Federal Bureau of Investigation,
    Washington, DC...................................278
Federal Hall National Memorial, New
    York, NY 1025
Feet First: The Scholl Story, Rosalind
    Franklin University, North Chicago, IL...448
Felix Valle State Historic Site, Sainte
    Genevieve, MO....................................837
Fenton History Center-Museum &
    Library, Jamestown, NY.........................1005
Fern Cottage, Ferndale, CA 94
Ferndale Museum, Ferndale, CA 95
Festival-Institute, James Dick Foundation,
    Round Top, TX....................................1446
Fick Fossil & History Museum, Oakley,
    KS 554
Fifth Maine Regiment Museum, Peaks
    Island, ME 618
Fillmore County Historical Center,
    Fountain, MN......................................776
Fillmore Historical Museum, Inc.,
    Fillmore, CA.......................................95
The Filson Historical Society, Inc.,
    Louisville, KY.....................................576
The Finley House, Wayne, PA..................1306
Finney County Kansas Historical Society,
    Inc., Garden City, KS............................541
Fire Museum of Maryland, Inc.,
    Lutherville, MD....................................649
Fire Museum of Memphis, Memphis, TN..1373
Fire Museum of Missouri, Willow
    Springs, MO.......................................840
The Firehouse Museum, Ellicott City,
    MD 643
Fireman's Hall Museum, Philadelphia, PA.1279
First Consolidated School in Minnesota,
    Saum, MN..793
The First Division Museum at Cantigny,
    Wheaton, IL.......................................465
First Missouri State Capitol-State Historic
    Site, Saint Charles, MO 830

The Hicksville Gregory Museum, Hicksville, NY...998

High Cliff Historical Society & General Store Museum, Sherwood, WI..............1622

High Desert Museum, Bend, OR................1220

High Plains Museum, Goodland, KS............542

High Point Museum & Historical Park, High Point, NC..................................1106

Highland County Museum and Heritage Center, McDowell, VA..........................1517

Highland House Museum, Hillsboro, OH ..1168

Highland Park Historical Society, Highland Park, IL................................439

Highlands Hammock State Park/Civilian Conservation Corps Museum, Sebring, FL...346

Hildene, The Lincoln Family Home, Manchester, VT....................................1481

The Hill Country Museum, Kerrville, TX..1431

Hiller Aviation Institute, San Carlos, CA....155

Hillforest House Museum, Aurora, IN 468

Hills and Dales Estate, LaGrange, GA.........375

Hillsboro Museums, Hillsboro, KS..............544

Hillwood Museum & Gardens, Washington, DC.......................................280

Hinckley Fire Museum, Hinckley, MN.......778

Hinsdale Historical Society, Hinsdale, IL ...440

Hiram Blauvelt Art Museum, Oradell, NJ....919

Historic Arkansas Museum, Little Rock, AR..62

Historic Auto Attractions, Roscoe, IL 456

Historic Bethany, Bethany, WV.................1580

Historic Bowens Mills & Pioneer Park, Middleville, MI......................................754

Historic Brattonsville, McConnells, SC......1336

Historic Burlington County Prison Museum, Mount Holly, NJ.....................914

Historic Carson House, Marion, NC...........1110

Historic Charleston Foundation, Charleston, SC.......................................1325

Historic Charlton Park Village and Museum, Hastings, MI............................745

Historic Cherry Hill, Albany, NY.................954

Historic Columbia Foundation, Columbia, SC...1329

Historic Columbus Foundation, Inc., Columbus, GA...369

Historic Crab Orchard Museum & Pioneer Park, Inc., Tazewell, VA............1541

Historic Deepwood Estate, Salem, OR.......1235

Historic Deerfield, Inc., Deerfield, MA........679

Historic Edenton State Historic Site, Edenton, NC..1099

Historic Fallsington, Inc., Fallsington, PA .1253

Historic Fort Snelling, Saint Paul, MN........790

Historic Fort Stockton, Fort Stockton, TX.1416

Historic General Dodge House, Council Bluffs, IA...512

Historic Georgetown Inc., Georgetown, CO...218

Historic Governors' Mansion, Cheyenne, WY...1630

Historic Halifax State Historic Site, Halifax, NC..1105

Historic Hartwood Mansion, Pittsburgh, PA...1292

Historic Hermann Museum, Hermann, MO...817

Historic Hope Foundation, Inc., Windsor, NC...1124

Historic House Trust of New York City, New York, NY.....................................1027

Historic Hudson Valley, Tarrytown, NY.....1077

Historic Jefferson College, Washington, MS...810

Historic Langhorne Association, Langhorne, PA.....................................1267

Historic Latta Plantation, Huntersville, NC...1107

Historic London Town and Gardens, Edgewater, MD......................................642

Historic Lyme Village Association, Bellevue, OH 1142

Historic Macon Foundation, Inc. - Sidney Lanier Cottage House Museum, Macon, GA 377

Historic New Harmony, New Harmony, IN..494

The Historic New Orleans Collection, New Orleans, LA....................................595

Historic Oakland Cemetery, Atlanta, GA 360

Historic Occoquan, Inc., Occoquan, VA.....1523

Historic Palmyra's - Wm. Phelps General Store, Palmyra, NY 1050

Historic Pensacola Village, Pensacola, FL ...335

Historic Pittsford, Pittsford, NY 1052

Historic Preservation Association of Bourbon County, Inc., Fort Scott, KS 540

Historic Price House, Woodruff, SC...........1343

Historic Prophetstown, Battle Ground, IN ...468

Historic Pullman Foundation, Chicago, IL...421

Historic Renville Preservation Commission, Renville, MN.....................787

Historic Richmond Town, Staten Island, NY...1072

Historic Rugby, Rugby, TN.......................1383

Historic Sauder Village, Archbold, OH 1140

Historic Schaefferstown, Inc., Schaefferstown, PA..............................1297

Historic Shepherdstown Museum, Shepherdstown, WV 1586

Historic Smithfield, Blacksburg, VA...........1497

Historic Southwest Ohio, Inc., Sharonville, OH....................................1185

Historic Spanish Point, Osprey, FL..............333

Historic Speedwell, Morristown, NJ.............913

Historic Walnford, Upper Freehold Twp., NJ...929

Historic Westville, Inc., Lumpkin, GA.........376

Historical and Genealogical Society of Indiana County, Indiana, PA 1262

Historical and Genealogical Society of Somerset County, Somerset, PA............1300

Historical and Wildlife Museum, Gridley, CA..101

Historical Center for Southeast New Mexico, Roswell, NM.............................946

Historical Museum at Fort Missoula, Missoula, MT..851

The Historical Museum at St. Gertrude, Cottonwood, ID.....................................405

Historical Museum of Bay County, Bay City, MI...727

Historical Natural History & Library Society of Natick dba Natick Historical Society, South Natick, MA 709

Historical Society of Berks County, Reading, PA...1296

Historical Society of Brookfield, Brookfield Center, VT............................1477

Historical Society of Carroll County, Westminster, MD..................................656

Historical Society of Cecil County, Elkton, MD..643

Historical Society of Cheshire County, Keene, NH...890

Historical Society of Columbia County, Saint Helens, OR...................................1234

The Historical Society of Dauphin County, Harrisburg, PA 1258

Historical Society of Delaware, Wilmington, DE.....................................274

The Historical Society of Frederick County, Inc., Frederick, MD...................644

Historical Society of Garden County, Oshkosh, NE...871

Historical Society of Glastonbury, Glastonbury, CT....................................242

Historical Society of Greater Port Jefferson, Port Jefferson, NY 1053

Historical Society of Greenfield, Greenfield, MA......................................685

Historical Society of Kent County, Inc., Chestertown, MD...................................640

Historical Society of Middletown and the Wallkill Precinct, Inc., Middletown, NY...1014

Historical Society of Millersburg & Upper Paxton Township Museum, Millersburg, PA....................................1272

Historical Society of Old Newbury, Cushing House Museum, Newburyport, MA.................................698

Historical Society of Old Randolph, Randolph, NJ..922

Historical Society of Old Yarmouth, Yarmouth Port, MA...............................722

Historical Society of Palm Beach County, Palm Beach, FL.....................................334

Historical Society of Princeton, Princeton, NJ..921

Historical Society of Quaker Hill & Pawling, Pawling, NY.........................1051

Historical Society of Quincy and Adams County, Quincy, IL.................................452

Historical Society of Santuit and Cotuit, Cotuit, MA..677

Historical Society of Saratoga Springs, Saratoga Springs, NY 1064

Historical Society of Talbot County, Easton, MD...642

Historical Society of the Cocalico Valley, Ephrata, PA...1252

Historical Society of the Phoenixville Area, Phoenixville, PA............................1290

Historical Society of the Tonawandas, Inc., Tonawanda, NY..............................1078

Historical Society of the Town of Clarence, Clarence, NY...........................978

Historical Society of the Town of Greenwich Inc. aka Bush-Holley Historic Site, Cos Cob, CT.....................237

The Historical Society of Trappe, Collegeville, Perkiomen Valley, Inc., Trappe, PA..1303

Historical Society of Wells and Ogunquit, Wells, ME..625

Historical Society Porter County Old Jail Museum, Valparaiso, IN........................502

The Historical Society, serving Sleepy Hollow and Tarrytown, Tarrytown, NY.1078

History and Traditions Museum, Lackland Air Force Base, TX................1433

The History Center, Fort Wayne, IN 477

The History Center, Cedar Rapids, IA.........509

History Museum for Springfield-Greene County, Springfield, MO 839

The History Museum, Lake Placid-North Elba Historical Society, Lake Placid, NY...1009

History Museum of Western Virginia, Roanoke, VA..1535

The History Place, Morehead City, NC 1111

History San Jose, San Jose, CA..................171

Hiwan Homestead Museum, Evergreen, CO...215

Hixon House, La Crosse, WI......................1603

Hoard Historical Museum and National Dairy Shrine's Visitors Center, Fort Atkinson, WI.......................................1598

Hobart Historical Society Museum, Hobart, IN..480

Hoboken Historical Museum, Hoboken, NJ...907

Hodgden House Museum Complex, Ellsworth, KS.......................................538

Hofwyl-Broadfield Plantation State Historic Site, Brunswick, GA 366

Hoiles-Davis Museum, Greenville, IL..........439

Holiday World/Splashin' Safari, Santa Claus, IN...498

Holland Historical Society Museum, Inc., Holland, VT..1480

The Holland Land Office Museum, Batavia, NY...960

Personal Artifacts–Continued

The Holland Museum, Holland, MI 746

Hollenberg Station State Historic Site,
Hanover, KS 543

Holly History Center & Hutchinson
House Museum, Waupaca, WI.............1626

Hollywood Heritage Museum,
Hollywood, CA...................................103

Hollywood History Museum, Hollywood,
CA...103

Holmes County Historical Society,
Millersburg, OH.............................1176

Holocaust Documentation & Education
Center, Inc., Hollywood, FL.............313

Holocaust Memorial Center, Farmington
Hills, MI..741

Holocaust Memorial Resource and
Education Center of Florida, Inc.,
Maitland, FL....................................322

Holocaust Museum Houston, Houston,
TX..1426

Holocaust Museum of Southwest Florida,
Naples, FL.......................................328

Home of Franklin D. Roosevelt National
Historic Site, Hyde Park, NY 1002

Home of Stone (The Mueller-Schmidt
House 1881), a Ford County Museum,
curated by Ford County Historic
Society, Dodge City, KS 537

Homestead National Monument of
America, Beatrice, NE.......................857

Homesteader Museum, Powell, WY...........1637

Honolulu House Museum, Marshall, MI......754

Honolulu Police Department Law
Enforcement Museum, Honolulu, HI.......396

Hood River County Historical Museum,
Hood River, OR.................................1226

Hoofprints of the Past Museum, Kaycee,
WY...1634

Hoover Historical Center, North Canton,
OH...1179

Hopewell Furnace National Historic Site,
Elverson, PA...................................1251

Hopewell Museum, Paris, KY 582

Hopewell Museum, Hopewell, NJ...............908

Hopsewee Plantation, Georgetown, SC 1333

Horatio Colony House Museum & Nature
Preserve, Keene, NH..........................890

Horridge House, Vinton, IA.......................529

Horry County Museum, Conway, SC.........1331

Horseshoe Bend National Military Park,
Daviston, AL.......................................7

Hot Spring County Museum - The Boyle
House/1876 Log Cabin, Malvern, AR.......63

Hot Springs County Museum and
Cultural Center, Thermopolis, WY........1639

Hot Springs National Park Visitor Center,
Hot Springs, AR.................................60

The Houdini Museum & Theater,
Scranton, PA..................................1298

Houghton County Historical Museum
Society, Lake Linden, MI.....................749

House of Broadcasting Radio &
Television Museum, Scottsdale, AZ 44

The House of the Seven Gables, Salem,
MA...706

House of the Temple, Washington, DC.,......280

House of Wickersham State Historical
Site, Juneau, AK.................................25

Howard County Center of African
American Culture, Columbia, MD.........641

Howard County Historical Museum,
Kokomo, IN.......................................486

Howard County Historical Society,
Ellicott City, MD...............................643

Howard Steamboat Museum and
Mansion, Jeffersonville, IN 486

Howard University Museum, Moorland
Spingarn Research Center,
Washington, DC................................281

Howard W. Cannon Aviation Museum,
Henderson, NV..................................878

Howard Weeden House Museum,
Huntsville, AL....................................11

Howell Historical Society & Committee
Museum, Howell, NJ..........................908

Howland House, Plymouth, MA.................703

The Hoyt Institute of Fine Arts, New
Castle, PA......................................1273

The Hubbard Museum of the American
West, Ruidoso Downs, NM...................946

Hubbardton Battlefield Museum,
Hubbardton, VT................................1480

Hubbell Trading Post National Historic
Site, Ganado, AZ................................34

Huddleston Farmhouse Inn Museum,
Cambridge City, IN.............................471

Hudson Library and Historical Society,
Hudson, OH....................................1168

Hudson River Maritime Museum,
Kingston, NY..................................1007

The Hudson River Museum, Yonkers, NY.1087

Hugh Mercer Apothecary Shop,
Fredericksburg, VA...........................1506

The Huguenot Historical Society, New
Paltz, NY.......................................1017

Hulihee Palace, Kailua-Kona, HI.............399

Hull Lifesaving Museum Inc., the
Museum of Boston Harbor Heritage,
Hull, MA..687

Humboldt Historical Museum, Humboldt,
KS..544

Humboldt Redwoods State Park Visitor
Center, Weott, CA..............................197

The Humphrey Forum, Minneapolis, MN....782

The 100th Meridian Museum, Cozad, NE ...859

Hungarian Folk-Art Museum, Port
Orange, FL.......................................338

Hunt-Morgan House, Lexington, KY 573

Hunter-Dawson State Historic Site, New
Madrid, MO......................................828

Huntingdon County Historical Society,
Huntingdon, PA...............................1262

Huntington Beach International Surfing
Museum, Huntington Beach, CA.............104

Huntington County Historical Society
Museum, Huntington, IN......................481

Huron City Museums, Port Austin, MI........761

Hurricane Valley Heritage Park Museum,
Hurricane, UT.................................1466

Hutchinson County Museum, Borger, TX..1397

The Hyde Collection, Glens Falls, NY 994

Hyde Hall, Inc., Cooperstown, NY 980

The Hyland House, Guilford, CT.............243

Hyrum City Museum, Hyrum, UT.............1466

The Ida Dennie Willis Museum of
Miniatures, Dolls, and Toys, Tulsa,
OK...1215

Idaho Military History Museum, Boise,
ID..404

Idaho Museum of Mining and Geology,
Boise, ID..404

Idaho State Historical Museum, Boise, ID...404

Illinois and Michigan Canal
Commissioners Office Museum,
Lockport, IL......................................443

Illinois Citizen Soldier Museum,
Galesburg, IL....................................437

Illinois Railway Museum, Union, IL............461

Ilwaco Heritage Museum, Ilwaco, WA.......1556

Immaculate Conception Catholic Church,
Natchitoches, LA...............................593

Immigration Museum of New Americans
Post WWII, San Diego, CA...................156

Immigration Station Barracks Museum,
Tiburon, CA.......................................192

Imperial Calcasieu Museum, Inc., Lake
Charles, LA.......................................590

Independence Historical Museum,
Independence, KS..............................545

Independence Seaport Museum,
Philadelphia, PA 1281

Indian Heritage Museum, Rancocas, NJ 922

Indian King Tavern Museum,
Haddonfield, NJ................................906

Indian Pueblo Cultural Center,
Albuquerque, NM..............................933

Indiana Basketball Hall of Fame, New
Castle, IN...494

Indiana Football Hall of Fame,
Richmond, IN....................................497

Indiana Historical Society, Indianapolis,
IN..483

Indiana Medical History Museum,
Indianapolis, IN................................484

Indiana State Museum, Indianapolis, IN......484

Indiana War Memorials, Indianapolis, IN 484

The Institute For American Indian
Studies (IAIS), Washington Green, CT ...263

Institute of American Indian Arts
Museum, Santa Fe, NM 947

Interlaken Historical Society, Interlaken,
NY..1002

International Bluegrass Music Museum,
Owensboro, KY.................................581

International Bowling Museum and Hall
of Fame, Saint Louis, MO....................833

The International Clown Hall of Fame &
Research Center, Inc., Milwaukee, WI..1611

International Gospel Music Hall of Fame
& Museum, Detroit, MI 737

International Institute of Metropolitan
Detroit, Detroit, MI 737

International Motor Racing Research
Center at Watkins Glen, Watkins Glen,
NY..1084

International Motorsports Hall of Fame
and Museum, Lincoln, AL 13

International Museum of Cultures, Dallas,
TX..1406

International Museum of Women, San
Francisco, CA....................................166

The International Printing Museum,
Carson, CA 82

International Spy Museum, Washington,
DC..281

International Swimming Hall of Fame,
Inc., Fort Lauderdale, FL.....................307

International Tennis Hall of Fame &
Museum, Newport, RI.......................1313

International Women's Air and Space
Museum, Inc., Cleveland, OH..............1155

Intrepid Sea-Air-Space Museum, New
York, NY..1028

Iolani Palace, Honolulu, HI 396

Iosco County Historical Museum, East
Tawas, MI.......................................740

Iowa Aviation Museum, Greenfield, IA........519

Iowa Department of Natural Resources,
Des Moines, IA..................................515

Iowa Great Lakes Maritime Museum,
Arnolds Park, IA................................505

Iowa Masonic Library and Museum,
Cedar Rapids, IA...............................509

Iowa Railroad Historical Society, Boone,
IA..506

Ipswich Historical Society and Museum,
Ipswich, MA.....................................688

Iraan Museum, Iraan, TX.......................1430

Iredell Museum of Arts & Heritage,
Statesville, NC.................................1120

Iris & B. Gerald Cantor Center for Visual
Arts at Stanford University, Stanford,
CA..188

Irish American Heritage Museum,
Albany, NY.......................................954

Iron & Steel Museum of Alabama,
Tannehill Ironworks Historical State
Park, McCalla, AL...............................13

Iron County Museum, Caspian, MI.............731

Ironwood Area Historical Museum,
Ironwood, MI....................................747

Ironworld Discovery Center, Chisholm,
MN..771

Iroquois County Historical Society,
Watseka, IL......................................463

Personal Artifacts–Continued

Lovettsville Historical Society Museum, Lovettsville, VA 1514

Lowell National Historical Park, Lowell, MA 691

Lowell Observatory, Flagstaff, AZ................33

Lower East Side Tenement Museum, New York, NY 1029

Lowndes County Historical Society and Museum, Valdosta, GA 389

Loxahatchee River Historical Society, Jupiter, FL...................................316

Luckhard Museum - The Indian Mission, Sebewaing, MI............................764

Lucretia Vaile Museum, Palmer Lake, CO..229

Lucy Craft Laney Museum of Black History and Conference Center, Augusta, GA...............................365

Ludwig Welk Farmstead, Strasburg, ND....1136

Luis Munoz Rivera Library & Museum, Barranquitas, PR.........................1641

Lum & Abner Museum & Jot 'Em Down Store, Pine Ridge, AR.....................66

Luther Burbank Home & Gardens, Santa Rosa, CA.................................184

Lutheran Heritage Center & Museum of the Perry County Lutheran Historical Society, Altenburg, MO.................810

Lutz Children's Museum, Manchester, CT...248

Luzerne County Historical Society, Wilkes-Barre, PA........................1307

The Lyceum, Alexandria's History Museum, Alexandria, VA 1493

Lynchburg Museum System, Lynchburg, VA..1515

Lynden Pioneer Museum, Lynden, WA......1559

Lyndhurst, Tarrytown, NY.....................1078

Lyndon B. Johnson National Historical Park, Johnson City, TX 1431

Lyndon Baines Johnson Library and Museum, Austin, TX 1391

Lynn Museum & Historical Society, Lynn, MA.................................692

Lyon County Historical Society and Museum, Emporia, KS 538

Lyon County Historical Society Museum, Marshall, MN..............................780

The Lyons Redstone Museum, Lyons, CO...227

MIT Museum, Cambridge, MA 674

Mabee Farm Historic Site, Rotterdam Junction, NY.............................1062

Mabel Hartzell Historical Home, Alliance, OH............................1139

Mabry-Hazen House, Knoxville, TN..........1371

MacArthur Museum of Arkansas Military History, Little Rock, AR 62

Macartney House Museum, Oakland, ME ...616

MacCallum More Museum and Gardens, Chase City, VA.........................1500

Macculloch Hall Historical Museum & Gardens, Morristown, NJ 913

Macedon Historical Society, Inc., Macedon, NY.............................1012

MacGregor Ranch, Estes Park, CO 215

Mackinac Island State Park Commission-Mackinac State Historic Parks, Mackinaw City, MI 752

Mackinac State Historic Parks-Colonial Michilimackinac & Old Mackinac Point Lighthouse, Mackinaw City, MI 752

Mackinac State Historic Parks-Fort Mackinac & Mackinac Island State Park, Mackinac Island, MI.............752

Macon County Historical Society Museum Complex, Decatur, IL...............430

Madeline Island Historical Museum, La Pointe, WI................................1603

Madera County Museum, Madera, CA 123

Madison County Historical Society, Winterset, IA.............................531

Madison County Historical Society-Cottage Lawn, Oneida, NY 1045

Magevney House, Memphis, TN 1373

Maggie L. Walker National Historic Site, Richmond, VA...........................1530

Magnolia Grove-Historic House Museum, Greensboro, AL............................10

Magnolia Manor, Cairo, IL.....................415

Magnolia Plantation and Gardens, Charleston, SC..........................1326

Magoffin Home State Historic Site, El Paso, TX................................1412

Mahaffie Stagecoach Stop and Farm, Olathe, KS...............................554

Mai Wah Society, Butte, MT...................843

Maine Historical Society, Portland, ME.......619

Maine Lighthouse Museum, Rockland, ME......................................621

Maine Maritime Museum, Bath, ME...........606

Maitland Historical Museums, Maitland, FL...322

The Major General Frederick Funston Boyhood Home and Museum, Iola, KS...546

Malabar Farm State Park, Lucas, OH.........1173

Malheur Historical Project, Stonehouse Museum, Vale, OR.......................1238

Malibu Lagoon Museum, Malibu, CA 123

Mallory-Neely House, Memphis, TN 1373

Maltz Museum of Jewish Heritage, Beachwood, OH..........................1142

Mamie Doud Eisenhower Birthplace, Boone, IA................................506

Mammoth Spring State Park, Depot Museum, Mammoth Spring, AR...............64

Manassas National Battlefield Park, Manassas, VA 1516

Manatee Village Historical Park, Bradenton, FL...........................297

Manchester Historic Association Millyard Museum, Manchester, NH...................891

Manchester Historical Society, Manchester, MA.........................692

Manitowoc County Historical Society, Manitowoc, WI..........................1607

Mann Wildlife Learning Museum, Montgomery, AL...........................16

Mansfield Historical Society Museum, Storrs, CT...............................261

Mansfield State Historic Site - Civil War Battlefield, Mansfield, LA.................591

Manship House Museum, Jackson, MS........802

Maple Valley Historical Museum, Maple Valley, WA..............................1559

Marathon County Historical Society, Wausau, WI.............................1626

Marble Historical Society, Marble, CO 228

Marblehead Arts Association - King Hooper Mansion, Marblehead, MA..........693

Marblehead Museum & Historical Society, Marblehead, MA.................693

Marcella Sembrich Opera Museum, Bolton Landing, NY......................963

Marcellus Historical Society, Marcellus, NY..1013

March Field Air Museum, Riverside, CA 149

Marfa and Presidio County Museum, Marfa, TX...............................1436

The Margaret Mitchell House & Museum, Atlanta, GA.....................361

Marianna-Lee County Museum Assoc. Inc., Marianna, AR.........................64

Marias Museum of History and Art, Shelby, MT..............................853

Maridon Museum, Butler, PA 1245

Marietta House Museum, Glenn Dale, MD..645

Marietta Museum of History, Marietta, GA..379

Marilla Historical Society Museum, Marilla, NY..............................1014

Marin History Museum, San Rafael, CA 177

Marin Museum of the American Indian, Novato, CA..............................131

The Marine Museum at Fall River, Inc., Fall River, MA...........................682

Marinette County Historical Museum, Marinette, WI...........................1607

Mario Lanza Institute/Museum, Philadelphia, PA.........................1282

Marion County Historical Society, Salem, OR..1236

The Marion County Historical Society Museum, Marion, OH 1174

Marion Heritage Center, Marion, IA 522

Marion Historical Museums, Inc. - Granger House, Marion, IA................523

Marion Public Library Museum, Marion, IN..490

Mariposa Museum and History Center Inc., Mariposa, CA.......................124

Maritime and Yachting Museum of the Treasure Coast, Stuart, FL...............346

Maritime Industry Museum at Fort Schuyler, Bronx, NY.....................966

Maritime Museum at Historic Coast Guard Station, Saint Simons Island, GA..383

Maritime Museum - Cohasset Historical Society, Cohasset, MA....................676

Maritime Museum of San Diego, San Diego, CA................................157

Marjorie Kinnan Rawlings Historic State Park, Cross Creek, FL....................301

Mark Twain Birthplace State Historic Site, Florida, MO........................815

Mark Twain Home and Museum, Hannibal, MO............................816

The Mark Twain House & Museum, Hartford, CT.............................245

Marland's Grand Home, Ponca City, OK...1212

Marlboro County Historical Museum, Bennettsville, SC.......................1322

Marlboro Historical Society, Marlboro, VT..1481

Marquette County Historical Society, Westfield, WI...........................1627

Marquette County History Museum, Marquette, MI...........................753

Marshall County Historical Museum, Plymouth, IN............................496

Marshall County Historical Museum, Holly Springs, MS.......................801

Marshall County Historical Society Museum, Warren, MN.....................795

Marshall Gold Discovery State Historic Park, Coloma, CA.........................86

Marshall Point Lighthouse Museum, Saint George, ME........................621

Martha A. Parsons House Museum, Enfield, CT..............................239

Martha's Vineyard Museum, Edgartown, MA..681

Martin and Osa Johnson Safari Museum, Inc., Chanute, KS.........................535

Martin County Historical Museum, Stanton, TX.............................1453

Martin County Museum, Shoals, IN............499

Martin Luther King, Jr. National Historic Site and Preservation District, Atlanta, GA..361

Martin Van Buren National Historic Site, Kinderhook, NY.........................1007

Martinez Museum, Martinez, CA 124

Marvin Newton House, Brookfield, VT 1477

The Mary Baker Eddy Library for the Betterment of Humanity, Boston, MA.....666

Mary Ball Washington Museum & Library, Inc., Lancaster, VA 1512

Mary McLeod Bethune Council House National Historic Site, Washington, DC..283

Mary Todd Lincoln House, Lexington, KY..574

Mary Washington House, Fredericksburg, VA.................1507

Maryhill Museum of Art, Goldendale, WA.................1556

Maryland Historical Society, Baltimore, MD.................634

Mashantucket Pequot Museum and Research Center, Mashantucket, CT........248

Mason County Historical Society/Historic White Pine Village, Ludington, MI.........751

Mason County Museum, Mason, TX.........1437

Masonic Grand Lodge Library and Museum of Texas, Waco, TX...............1459

The Masonic Library and Museum of Pennsylvania, Philadelphia, PA..............1283

Matagorda County Museum, Bay City, TX.................1393

Matchless Mine Museum (Leadville Assembly), Leadville, CO........................226

The Mattatuck Museum Arts and History Center, Waterbury, CT.................264

Matthews Museum of Maine Heritage, Union, ME.................624

Maxwell Museum of Anthropology, Albuquerque, NM.................934

May Museum & Farmville Heritage Center, Farmville, NC.................1100

May Natural History Museum and Museum of Space Exploration, Colorado Springs, CO.................207

Mayborn Museum Complex, Waco, TX.....1459

Maymont, Richmond, VA.................1530

Maynard Pioneer Museum & Park, Maynard, AR.................64

Mayville Area Museum of History and Genealogy, Mayville, MI.................754

Mayville Historical Society, Inc., Mayville, WI.................1608

Mazomanie Historical Society, Mazomanie, WI.................1608

Mc Cook County Historical Society and Museum, Salem, SD.................1355

McAllister House Museum, Colorado Springs, CO.................207

McCallum Museum, Sibley, IA.................527

McConaghy House, Hayward, CA..............102

McCone County Museum, Circle, MT........844

McConnell Mansion, Moscow, ID.................407

McCook House, Civil War Museum, Carrollton, OH.................1146

McCoy House, Lewistown, PA.................1269

McDonald's #1 Store Museum, Des Plaines, IL.................431

McDowell House Museum, Danville, KY....567

McFaddin-Ward House, Beaumont, TX....1395

McFarland Historical Society, McFarland, WI.................1609

McFarland State Historic Park, Florence, AZ.................34

McHenry County Historical Society and Museum, Union, IL.................461

McHenry Museum, Modesto, CA.................126

McIntosh County Historical Society, Ashley, ND.................1127

McKinley Birthplace Home, Niles, OH.....1179

McLarty Treasure Museum, Vero Beach, FL.................352

McLean-Alanreed Area Museum, McLean, TX.................1438

McLean County Historical Society Museum, Washburn, ND.................1137

McLean County Museum of History, Bloomington, IL.................414

McMinn County Living Heritage Museum, Athens, TN.................1360

McNamara House Museum, Victoria, TX..1457

McPherson County Old Mill Museum and Park, Lindsborg, KS.................550

McPherson Museum & Arts Foundation, McPherson, KS.................552

Meade County Historical Society Museum, Meade, KS.................552

Meadow Brook Hall, Rochester, MI.............761

Meadowlands Museum, Rutherford, NJ.......923

Meagher County Historical Association Castle Museum, White Sulphur Springs, MT.................855

Mechanicsburg Museum Association, Mechanicsburg, PA.................1270

Mecosta County Historical Museum, Big Rapids, MI.................729

Medina County Historical Society, The John Smart House, Medina, OH............1175

Meeker Home Museum, Greeley, CO.........222

Meeteetse Museum District, Meeteetse, WY.................1636

Meigs County Museum, Pomeroy, OH.......1183

Mel Fisher Maritime Heritage Society, Key West, FL.................318

Mellette House, Watertown, SD.................1359

Melrose Plantation Home Complex, Melrose, LA.................592

Melton Art Reference Library, Oklahoma City, OK.................1208

Mem-Erie Historical Museum, Erie, KS.....539

The Memorial Day Museum, Waterloo, NY.................1083

Memorial Hall Museum, Pocumtuck Valley Memorial Assoc., Deerfield, MA.................679

Memoryville USA, Inc., Rolla, MO.............829

The Menczer Museum of Medicine & Dentistry, Hartford, CT.................245

Mendocino County Museum, Willits, CA....198

Mendocino Historical Research, Inc./Kelley House Museum, Mendocino, CA.................125

Mennonite Heritage Center, Harleysville, PA.................1258

Mennonite Heritage Museum, Goessel, KS.................542

Mennonite Quilting Center, Reedley, CA.....147

Menominee County Heritage Museum, Menominee, MI.................754

Merced County Courthouse Museum, Merced, CA.................125

Mercer County Historical Museum, The Riley Home, Celina, OH.................1146

Mercer County Historical Society, Mercer, PA.................1271

Merchant's House Museum, New York, NY.................1029

Meriwether Lewis Dredge Museum, Brownville, NE.................858

Merrill Historical Museum, Merrill, WI......1609

Mesa Historical Museum, Mesa, AZ.............37

Mesa Southwest Museum, Mesa, AZ.............37

Metamora Courthouse Historic Site, Metamora, IL.................444

Meux Home Museum, Fresno, CA.................98

Mexican Fine Arts Center Museum, Chicago, IL.................424

Miami County Museum, Peru, IN...............496

Miami University Art Museum, Oxford, OH.................1181

Michael C. Carlos Museum, Atlanta, GA....361

The Michigan State University Museum, East Lansing, MI.................740

Michigan Transit Museum, Inc., Mount Clemens, MI.................756

Mid-America Air Museum, Liberal, KS.......549

Mid Atlantic Air Museum, Reading, PA....1296

Mid-Atlantic Center for the Arts/Emlen Physick Estate/Cape May Lighthouse, Cape May, NJ.................900

Mid-Continent Railway Museum, North Freedom, WI.................1615

Middleborough Historical Association, Inc., Middleborough, MA.................694

Middlebury Historical Society, Wyoming, NY.................1087

Middlesex County Historical Society, Middletown, CT.................249

Middleton Historical Society - Lura Woodside Watkins Museum, Middleton, MA.................694

Middletown Valley Historical Society, Middletown, MD.................649

Midland County Historical Museum, Midland, TX.................1438

Midland County Historical Society, Midland, MI.................755

Midland Pioneer Museum, Midland, SD....1351

Midway Village & Museum Center, Rockford, IL.................455

Midwest Old Settlers & Threshers Association, Inc., Mount Pleasant, IA.....524

Mifflinburg Buggy Museum Association, Inc., Mifflinburg, PA.................1271

Mighty Eighth Air Force Museum, Pooler, GA.................381

Milam County Museum and Annex, Cameron, TX.................1399

Milan Historical Museum, Inc., Milan, OH.................1176

Miles B. Carpenter Museum, Waverly, VA.................1543

Milford Museum, Milford, DE.................271

Military Historians, Headquarters & Museum, Westbrook, CT.................265

Military Museum of Southern New England, Danbury, CT.................238

Military Veterans Museum, Inc., Oshkosh, WI.................1616

Mill Race Historical Village, Northville, MI.................758

Millard Fillmore House, East Aurora, NY...985

Mille Lacs Indian Museum, Onamia, MN...786

Millicent Rogers Museum of Northern New Mexico, Taos, NM.................952

Mills County Historical Society and Museum, Glenwood, IA.................519

Milton Historical Museum, Milton, VT.....1482

Milton House Museum Historic Site, Milton, WI.................1610

Milwaukee County Historical Society, Milwaukee, WI.................1611

Mineral County Museum, Hawthorne, NV.................878

Mineral County Museum & Historical Society, Superior, MT.................854

Minnesota Air National Guard Historical Foundation, Inc., Saint Paul, MN...........790

Minnesota Amateur Baseball Hall of Fame, Saint Cloud, MN.................788

Minnesota Historical Society's North West Company Fur Post, Pine City, MN.................786

Minnesota Pioneer Park Museum, Annandale, MN.................767

Minnesota Transportation Museum, Inc., Saint Paul, MN.................792

Minnetrista, Muncie, IN.................492

Minnilusa Pioneer Museum, Rapid City, SD.................1354

Minter Field Air Museum, Shafter, CA....186

Minute Man National Historical Park, Concord, MA.................676

Miracle of America Museum Inc., Polson, MT.................852

Miramont Castle Museum, Manitou Springs, CO.................228

The Mission House, Stockbridge, MA.........712

Mission Houses Museum, Honolulu, HI.....397

Mission Inn Foundation/Museum, Riverside, CA.................149

Mission Mill Museum Association, Salem, OR.................1236

Mission San Luis Obispo de Tolosa, San Luis Obispo, CA.................174

Mission San Luis Rey Museum, Oceanside, CA.................135

Missisquoi Valley Historical Society, North Troy, VT.................1483

Norfolk Historical Museum, Norfolk, CT 257

Norfolk Historical Society, Norfolk, VA 1522

Norfolk History Museum, Norfolk, VA......1523

The Norman Cleveland County Historical Museum, Norman, OK............................1206

Norman #1 Oil Well Museum, Neodesha, KS...553

Norman Rockwell Museum, Stockbridge, MA...712

North Andover Historical Society, North Andover, MA..698

North Brevard Historical Museum, Titusville, FL...352

North Carolina A&T State University Galleries, Greensboro, NC 1104

North Carolina Maritime Museum, Beaufort, NC...1091

North Carolina Museum of Forestry, Whiteville, NC...1122

North Carolina Museum of History, Raleigh, NC..1115

North Carolina Transportation Museum, Spencer, NC..1120

North Dakota Fishing Hall of Fame and Museum, Garrison, ND............................1131

The North Dakota Lewis & Clark Interpretive Center, Washburn, ND........1137

North House Museum, Lewisburg, WV 1584

North Lee County Historic Center and Santa Fe Depot Museum Complex, Fort Madison, IA.......................................518

North Plainfield Exempt Firemen's Association, North Plainfield, NJ............917

North Platte Valley Museum, Gering, NE....861

North Star Museum of Boy Scouting and Girl Scouting, North Saint Paul, MN......785

North Tonawanda History Museum, North Tonawanda, NY 1043

Northborough Historical Society, Inc., Northborough, MA 700

Northeast Georgia History Center at Brenau University, Gainesville, GA 373

Northeast Oakland Historical Museum, Oxford, MI..759

Northeast Texas Rural Heritage Museum, Pittsburg, TX...1443

Northeastern Nevada Museum, Elko, NV 876

Northern Indiana Center for History, South Bend, IN.......................................499

Northern Pacific Railway Museum, Toppenish, WA..1575

Northfield Historical Society Museum, Northfield, MN 785

Northport Historical Society Museum, Northport, NY...1044

Northwest Museum of Arts & Culture (Eastern Washington State Historical Society), Spokane, WA............................1571

Northwest Railway Museum, Snoqualmie, WA......................................1570

Norwalk Museum, South Norwalk, CT........260

Norwich Historical Society, Norwich, VT .1484

Norwood Historical Association and Museum, Norwood, NY.........................1044

Novato History Museum, Novato, CA 132

Nowetah's American Indian Museum & Store, New Portland, ME...........................615

Noyes House Museum, Morrisville, VT 1483

The Noyes Museum of Art, Oceanville, NJ...918

O. Henry Museum, Austin, TX.................1391

Oak Creek Historical Society-Pioneer Village, Oak Creek, WI............................1615

Oak Hill and The Martha Berry Museum, Rome, GA.......................................382

Oakdale Cowboy Museum, Oakdale, CA ...132

Oakdale Museum, Oakdale, CA 132

Oakland County Pioneer and Historical Society, Pontiac, MI.................................760

Oaklands Historic House Museum, Murfreesboro, TN..................................1376

Oakleigh Period House Museum, Mobile, AL...15

Oakley Park, UDC Shrine, Edgefield, SC..1332

The Oaks House Museum, Jackson, MS.....804

Oatlands, Leesburg, VA..............................1512

Oberlin Heritage Center, Oberlin, OH........1180

Occoneechee State Park, Clarksville, VA...1501

Ocean City Historical Museum, Inc., Ocean City, NJ...918

Ocean City Life-Saving Station Museum, Ocean City, MD....................................650

Ocean County Historical Museum, Toms River, NJ..926

Ocmulgee National Monument, Macon, GA...378

The Octagon, Washington, DC 288

The Octagon House, Hudson, WI...............1600

Octagon House-First Kindergarten in America, Watertown, WI.........................1625

Octave Chanute Aerospace Museum, Rantoul, IL..453

O'Fallon Historical Museum, Baker, MT.....840

Ogden Historical Society, Spencerport, NY..1071

Ogden Union Station Museums, Ogden, UT..1468

Ohef Sholom Temple Archives, Norfolk, VA...1523

Ohio Historical Society, Columbus, OH.....1158

Ohio River Museum, Marietta, OH 1174

Ohr-O'Keefe Museum of Art, Biloxi, MS ...799

Okefenokee Heritage Center, Waycross, GA...391

Oklahoma City National Memorial, Oklahoma City, OK............................1209

Oklahoma Firefighters Museum, Oklahoma City, OK............................1209

Oklahoma Heritage Association, Oklahoma City, OK............................1209

Oklahoma Historical Society, Oklahoma City, OK...1209

Oklahoma Museum of History, Oklahoma City, OK..1210

Oklahoma Route 66 Museum, Clinton, OK..1198

Oklahoma Sports Museum, Guthrie, OK ...1202

Oklahoma Territorial Museum, Guthrie, OK..1202

Oktibbeha County Heritage Museum, Starkville, MS..808

Olana State Historic Site, Hudson, NY......1000

Old Brutus Historical Society, Inc., Weedsport, NY......................................1084

Old Castle Museum, Baldwin City, KS........533

Old Cathedral Museum, Saint Louis, MO....836

Old Clock Museum, Pharr, TX...................1443

Old Colony Historical Society, Taunton, MA..714

Old Constitution House, Windsor, VT........1490

Old Conway Homestead Complex and Museum, Camden, ME.........................608

Old Court House Museum-Eva Whitaker Davis Memorial, Vicksburg, MS 809

The Old Courthouse Heritage Museum, Inverness, FL..313

Old Courthouse Museum, Santa Ana, CA....178

Old Cowtown Museum, Wichita, KS 562

Old Davie School Historical Museum, Davie, FL..302

Old Depot Museum, Selma, AL 18

Old Depot Museum, Ottawa, KS.................555

The Old Depot Railroad Museum, Dassel, MN...772

Old Dominion Railway Museum, Richmond, VA..1531

Old Dorchester State Historic Site, Summerville, SC......................................1342

Old Economy Village, Ambridge, PA.........1240

Old Exchange & Provost Dungeon, Charleston, SC...1326

Old Falls Village, Menomonee Falls, WI...1609

Old Firehouse Museum, Greenville, MS.....800

Old Fort Bissell, Phillipsburg, KS 555

Old Fort House Museum, Fort Edward, NY..991

Old Fort Jackson, Savannah, GA.................385

Old Fort Johnson, Fort Johnson, NY...........991

Old Fort Meade Museum and Historic Research Association, Fort Meade, SD .1347

Old Fort Niagara, Youngstown, NY 1088

Old Greer County Museum & Hall of Fame, Mangum, OK................................1204

Old Idaho Penitentiary, Boise, ID...............404

Old Independence Regional Museum, Batesville, AR...54

Old Iron County Courthouse Museum, Hurley, WI...1601

The Old Jail Art Center, Albany, TX.........1385

Old Jail Museum, Albion, IN......................467

The Old Jail Museum, Crawfordsville, IN ...473

The Old Jail Museum, Warrenton, VA.........1543

Old Jefferson Town, Oskaloosa, KS.............555

Old Lighthouse Museum, Michigan City, IN..491

Old Lincoln County Courthouse Museum, Lincoln, NM.......................................942

Old Log Jail and Chapel Museums, Greenfield, IN...480

Old Manchester Museum, Manchester, CT..248

The Old Manse, Concord, MA 677

Old Market House State Historic Site, Galena, IL..436

Old Mill Museum, Cimarron, NM...............938

Old Monterey Jail, Monterey, CA 128

Old Ordinary House Museum, Hingham, MA..687

Old Prairie Town at Ward-Meade Historic Site, Topeka, KS..................................560

Old Sacramento Schoolhouse Museum, Sacramento, CA...153

Old Sacramento State Historic Park, Old Sacramento, CA.......................................135

Old St. Ferdinand's Shrine, Florissant, MO..815

Old Salem Inc., Winston-Salem, NC..........1126

The Old Schwamb Mill, Arlington, MA 660

Old Sod Post Office, Grassy Butte, ND 1132

Old South Meeting House, Boston, MA......668

Old State House, Hartford, CT....................245

Old State House Museum, Little Rock, AR...63

Old State House-The Bostonian Society, Boston, MA...668

Old Stone Fort Museum Complex, Schoharie, NY..1067

Old Stone House Museum, Windsor, NY ..1086

The Old Tavern Museum, Tuscaloosa, AL.....19

Old Town Hall Museum, Fifield, WI..........1597

Old Town Museum, Old Town, ME...........617

Old Town San Diego State Historic Park, San Diego, CA.....................................158

Old Trail Museum, Choteau, MT 844

Old Village Hall Museum, Lindenhurst, NY..1009

Old Washington Historic State Park, Washington, AR..69

Old West Museum, Wimberley, TX............1462

Old West Wax Museum, Thermopolis, WY..1639

Old World Wisconsin, Eagle, WI...............1595

Old York Historical Society, York, ME........626

Old York Road Historical Society, Jenkintown, PA..1263

Oldest House Museum Complex, Saint Augustine, FL..339

The Oldest House Museum/Wrecker's Museum, Key West, FL 318

Oldest Stone House Museum, Lakewood, OH..1170

Oldest Store Museum, Saint Augustine, FL...339

Oldham County History Center, La Grange, KY..572

Personal Artifacts—Continued

The Oliver Tucker Museum, Beverly, OH .1142

Olmsted County Historical Society, Rochester, MN 788

Olustee Battlefield Historic State Park, Olustee, FL 331

103rd Ohio Volunteer Infantry Civil War Museum, Sheffield Lake, OH 1185

Oneida Community Mansion House, Oneida, NY 1046

Onslow County Museum, Richlands, NC ..1117

Ontario County Historical Society, Canandaigua, NY 975

Ontonagon County Historical Society Museum, Ontonagon, MI 758

Opelousas Museum and Interpretive Center, Opelousas, LA 599

Orange County Historical Museum, Hillsborough, NC 1107

Orange County Natural History Museum, Laguna Niguel, CA 107

Orange County Regional History Center, Orlando, FL 331

Orangetown Historical Museum and Archives, Pearl River, NY 1051

Orcas Island Historical Museum, Orcas Island, WA 1560

Orchard House, Concord, MA 677

Orchard Park Historical Society, Orchard Park, NY 1047

Orcutt Ranch, Canoga Park, CA 81

Oregon Air & Space Museum, Eugene, OR 1224

Oregon Coast History Center, Newport, OR 1229

Oregon-Jerusalem Historical Museum, Oregon, OH 1181

Oregon Military Museum, Clackamas, OR 1221

Oregon Trail Regional Museum, Baker City, OR 1219

Oriental Institute Museum, University of Chicago, Chicago, IL 426

Oriskany Battlefield State Historic Site, Oriskany, NY 1047

Orland Historical Society, Orland, ME 617

Orleans County Historical Society & The Old Stone House Museum, Brownington, VT 1477

Oroville Chinese Temple, Oroville, CA 136

Osage County Historical Society Museum, Pawhuska, OK 1211

Osage County Historical Society Research Center, Lyndon, KS 550

Osborn-Jackson House, East Hampton, NY 986

Osborne Homestead Museum, Derby, CT 238

The Oscar Anderson House Museum, Anchorage, AK 22

Oscar Getz Museum of Whiskey History And The Bardstown Historical Museum, Bardstown, KY 565

Oshkosh Public Museum, Oshkosh, WI ...1616

Ossining Historical Society Museum, Ossining, NY 1047

Oswego Historical Museum, Inc., Oswego, KS 555

Otero Museum Association, La Junta, CO ...224

Otis Chidester Scout Museum of Southern Arizona, Tucson, AZ....................50

Ottawa County Historical Museum, Port Clinton, OH 1183

Ottawa Scouting Museum, Ottawa, IL 449

Otter Tail County Historical Society, Fergus Falls, MN 775

Ouachita County Historical Society, Camden, AR 55

Our House State Memorial, Gallipolis, OH 1165

Outagamie Museum, Appleton, WI 1589

Overfield Tavern Museum, Troy, OH 1188

Overholser Mansion, Oklahoma City, OK .1210

Overland Trail Museum, Sterling, CO..........232

Overstreet-Kerr Historical Farm, Keota, OK..1203

Owensboro Area Museum of Science & History, Owensboro, KY.................581

Owensboro Museum of Fine Art, Inc., Owensboro, KY............................581

Owls Head Transportation Museum, Owls Head, ME.......................................617

Owyhee County Historical Museum, Murphy, ID...407

Oxford Library Museum, Oxford, MA.........701

Oxford Museum, Inc., Oxford, MD.............650

The Oyster and Maritime Museum of Chincoteague, Chincoteague, VA...........1501

Oyster Bay Historical Society, Oyster Bay, NY..1049

Oysterponds Historical Society: The Museum of Orient and East Marion History, Orient, NY............................1047

Oz Museum, Wamego, KS.........................560

The Ozark Folk Center, Mountain View, AR...65

Ozark Heritage Arts Center & Museum, Leslie, AR..61

Ozaukee County Pioneer Village, Saukville, WI..1620

P.H. Sullivan Museum and Genealogy Library, Zionsville, IN............................504

The P.T. Boat Museum & Library, Germantown, TN...............................1365

Pablo Casals Museum, Old San Juan, PR..1641

Pacific Aviation Museum - Pearl Harbor, Honolulu, HI......................................397

Pacific Coast Air Museum, Santa Rosa, CA...184

Pacific County Historical Museum, South Bend, WA...1571

Pacific University Museum, Forest Grove, OR.......................................1224

Packwood House Museum, Lewisburg, PA...1268

Pajaro Valley Historical Association, Watsonville, CA...............................196

Palace of the Governors/New Mexico History Museum, Santa Fe, NM..............949

PALCO, Scotia, CA..................................186

Palmer Foundation Chiropractic History, Davenport, IA.....................................513

Palmer House, Historical Society of Olde Northfield, Northfield, OH 1180

Palmer Museum, Jewell, KS.....................546

Pamplin Historical Park and The National Museum of the Civil War Soldier, Petersburg, VA...................................1525

Paper Airplane Museum and the Tin Can Man of Maui, Kahului Central Maui, HI...399

The Paperweight Museum, Santa Cruz, CA...182

The Pardee Home Museum, Oakland, CA...134

Paris-Henry County Heritage Center, Paris, TN...1382

Parishville Museum, Parishville, NY..........1050

Park City Historical Society & Museum, Park City, UT....................................1468

The Park-McCullough House, North Bennington, VT................................1483

Parker-O'Malley Air Museum, Ghent, NY..994

Parks, Recreation & Historic Sites Division, Georgia Dept. of Natural Resources, Atlanta, GA........................362

Parris Island Museum, Parris Island, SC....1338

The Parry Mansion Museum, New Hope, PA...1273

Parson Fisher House, Blue Hill, ME...........606

Parsons Historical Commission Museum, Parsons, KS...555

Parsonsfield-Porter Historical Society, Porter, ME...618

Pasadena Museum of History, Pasadena, CA...140

Pascack Historical Society, Park Ridge, NJ..920

Passaic County Historical Society & Lambert Castle Museum, Paterson, NJ...920

Patee House Museum, Saint Joseph, MO 831

The Paterson Museum, Paterson, NJ...........920

Patrol Squadron Colorado, Aurora, CO........202

Patten Lumbermen's Museum, Inc., Patten, ME...618

Patterson Homestead, Dayton, OH 1161

Patterson Inn Museum/Corning - Painted Post Historical Society, Corning, NY......982

Paul Bunyan Logging Camp Museum, Eau Claire, WI..................................1596

Paul Revere House/Paul Revere Memorial Association, Boston, MA 668

Paul W. Bryant Museum, Tuscaloosa, AL......19

Pauline E. Glidden Toy Museum, Ashland, NH...883

Paulson House, Au Train, MI 726

Pawnee Bill Ranch and Museum, Pawnee, OK.......................................1212

Pawnee Indian Village State Historic Site, Republic, KS...556

Pea Ridge National Military Park, Garfield, AR...58

Peabody Essex Museum, Salem, MA...........706

The Peace Museum, Chicago, IL.................426

Pearce Collections Museum, Corsicana, TX...1402

Pearl S. Buck Birthplace Foundation, Hillsboro, WV....................................1582

The Pearl S. Buck House, Perkasie, PA.....1275

Pearson Air Museum, Vancouver, WA 1576

The Pearson Museum, Springfield, IL..........460

Pebble Hill Plantation, Thomasville, GA 388

The Peekskill Museum, Peekskill, NY.......1051

Peel Mansion Museum & Historic Gardens, Bentonville, AR........................55

The Peggy Notebaert Nature Museum, Chicago, IL...426

Pejepscot Historical Society, Brunswick, ME...608

Pembina State Museum, Pembina, ND.......1135

Pembroke Historical Society, Inc., Pembroke, MA....................................701

The Pena-Peck House, Saint Augustine, FL...339

Pendarvis State Historic Site, Mineral Point, WI...1614

Pendleton District Agricultural Museum, Pendleton, SC...................................1339

Pendleton District Historical, Recreational and Tourism Commission, Pendleton, SC...1339

Pennsbury Manor, Morrisville, PA 1272

Pennsylvania Anthracite Heritage Museum, Scranton, PA 1299

Pennsylvania German Cultural Heritage Center at Kutztown University, Kutztown, PA....................................1265

Pennsylvania Longrifle Museum, Nazareth, PA....................................1273

Pennsylvania Military Museum and 28th Division Shrine, Boalsburg, PA 1244

Pennypacker Mills, Schwenksville, PA 1297

Pennyroyal Area Museum, Hopkinsville, KY...572

Penobscot Marine Museum, Searsport, ME...622

Pensacola Historical Society Museum, Pensacola, FL.......................................336

Peoria Historical Society, Peoria, IL 451

Peralta Adobe, San Jose, CA 172

Perkins County Historical Society, Grant, NE...862

Perkins History Museum, Perkins School for the Blind, Watertown, MA.................716

Perry's Victory & International Peace Memorial, Put-in-Bay, OH 1183

Perryville Battlefield Museum, Perryville, KY 582
Peter Conser House, Heavener, OK 1202
Peter Rice Homestead, Home of Marlborough Historical Society, Inc., Marlboro, MA 693
Peter Yegen Jr. Yellowstone County Museum, Billings, MT 841
Peterborough Historical Society, Peterborough, NH 893
Petersburg National Battlefield, Petersburg, VA 1525
Petersham Historical Society, Inc., Petersham, MA 702
Peterson Air & Space Museum, Peterson Air Force Base, CO 229
Petrified Forest National Park, Petrified Forest National Park, AZ 38
Pettaquamscutt Historical Society, Kingston, RI 1312
Petterson Museum of Intercultural Art, Claremont, CA 85
Pettigrew Home and Museum, Sioux Falls, SD 1356
Pettis County Historical Society, Sedalia, MO 838
Phelps House, Burlington, IA 507
Philadelphia Society for the Preservation of Landmarks, Philadelphia, PA 1286
Philipse Manor Hall State Historic Site, Yonkers, NY 1087
Phillips County Museum, Holyoke, CO 222
Philmont Museums, Cimarron, NM 938
Phoenix Fire Museum, Mobile, AL 15
Phoenix Museum of History, Phoenix, AZ 41
Phoenix Police Museum, Phoenix, AZ 41
Piatt Castles, West Liberty, OH 1190
Piatt County Museum, Monticello, IL 446
Piccadilly Museum of Transportation Memorabilia and Advertising Art, Butte, MT 843
Pickler Mansion, Faulkton, SD 1347
The Pierce Manse/New Hampshire Political Library, Concord, NH 885
The Pierpont Morgan Library, New York, NY 1037
Pierre Menard Home State Historic Site, Ellis Grove, IL 433
Pike County Historical Society, Milford, PA 1272
Pikes Peak Hill Climb Educational Museum, Colorado Springs, CO 207
Pilgrim Hall Museum, Plymouth, MA 703
Pilgrim Monument and Provincetown Museum, Provincetown, MA 704
Pima Air & Space Museum, Tucson, AZ 50
Pimeria Alta Historical Society, Nogales, AZ 37
Pinal County Historical Society and Museum, Florence, AZ 34
Pine Bluff/Jefferson County Historical Museum, Pine Bluff, AR 66
Pine County Historical Society, Askov, MN 768
Pine Lodge (Ehrman Mansion), Tahoma, CA 190
Pioneer Air Museum, Fairbanks, AK 24
Pioneer Arizona Living History Village & Museum, Phoenix, AZ 41
Pioneer Auto Trails Historical Society (PATHS), Tucson, AZ 50
Pioneer Corner Museum, New Holstein, WI 1615
Pioneer Farm Museum and Ohop Indian Village, Eatonville, WA 1552
Pioneer Florida Museum Association, Inc., Dade City, FL 302
Pioneer Heritage Center, Cavalier, ND 1129
Pioneer Heritage Center, LSU-Shreveport, Shreveport, LA 601

Pioneer Historical Museum of South Dakota, Hot Springs, SD 1348
Pioneer-Krier Museum, Ashland, KS 532
Pioneer Mothers Memorial Cabin, Saint Paul, OR 1235
Pioneer Museum, Watford City, ND 1137
Pioneer Museum, Wild Rose, WI 1628
Pioneer Museum and Vereins Kirche, Fredericksburg, TX 1419
Pioneer Museum - Martin County Historical Society, Fairmont, MN 775
Pioneer Museum of Alabama, Troy, AL 18
Pioneer Settlement for the Creative Arts, Barberville, FL 295
Pioneer Trails Regional Museum, Bowman, ND 1129
Pioneer Village, Farmington, UT 1465
Pioneer Woman Statue & Museum, Ponca City, OK 1212
Pioneers, Trail Drivers and Texas Rangers Memorial Museum, San Antonio, TX 1449
Piper Aviation Museum Foundation, Lock Haven, PA 1269
Pipestone County Historical Museum, Pipestone, MN 786
Pipestone National Monument, Pipestone, MN 787
Piqua Historical Area State Memorial, Piqua, OH 1182
Pirate Soul Museum, Key West, FL 319
Pittock Mansion, Portland, OR 1232
Pittsford Historical Society Museum, Pittsford, VT 1484
Plains Conservation Center, Aurora, CO 202
Plains Indians and Pioneers Museum, Woodward, OK 1217
Plantation Agriculture Museum, Scott, AR 67
Plantation Historical Museum, Plantation, FL 337
Platt R. Spencer Memorial Archives and Special Collections Area, Geneva, OH ..1166
Please Touch Museum, Philadelphia, PA ...1286
Plimoth Plantation Inc., Plymouth, MA 703
Plumas County Museum, Quincy, CA 144
Plumb Farm Learning Center, Greeley, CO 222
Plymouth Antiquarian Society, Plymouth, MA 704
Plymouth Historical Museum, Plymouth, MI 760
Pocahontas County Iowa Historical Society Museum, Laurens, IA 522
Pocahontas County Museum, Marlinton, WV 1584
Point Reyes National Seashore, Point Reyes, CA 143
Pointe Coupee Museum, New Roads, LA 599
Polish Heritage Center, Ashton, NE 856
Polish Museum of America, Chicago, IL 426
Polk County Historical Museum, Bartow, FL 295
The Polk County Historical Society, Cedartown, GA 368
Polk County Historical Society, Crookston, MN 771
Polk County Memorial Museum, Livingston, TX 1434
Polk County Museum, Balsam Lake, WI ..1590
Polson Museum, Hoquiam, WA 1556
Pomeroy Living History Farm, Yacolt, WA 1578
Ponce DeLeon Inlet Lighthouse Preservation Association, Inc., Ponce Inlet, FL 337
Pony Express Museum, Saint Joseph, MO 831
Pope County Historical Society, Glenwood, MN 776
Pope John Paul II Cultural Center, Washington, DC 289

Pope's Tavern Museum, Florence, AL 9
Poplar Grove Historic Plantation, Wilmington, NC 1123
Port Gamble Historic Museum, Port Gamble, WA 1562
Portage County Historical Society, Ravenna, OH 1183
Portage County Historical Society, Stevens Point, WI 1623
Porter-Phelps-Huntington Foundation, Inc., Hadley, MA 685
Porterville Historical Museum, Porterville, CA 144
Portland Museum, Louisville, KY 578
Portsmouth Museum of Military History Inc., Portsmouth, VA 1526
Portsmouth Museums, Portsmouth, VA 1526
Portuguese Historical Museum, San Jose, CA 172
Post Rock Museum, La Crosse, KS 547
Potsdam Public Museum, Potsdam, NY 1054
Potter County Historical Society, Coudersport, PA 1248
Potts Inn Museum, Pottsville, AR 66
Pottsgrove Manor, Pottstown, PA 1295
Pound Ridge Society/Museum, Pound Ridge, NY 1055
Powell County Museum, Deer Lodge, MT 845
Powers Museum, Carthage, MO 812
Prairie Trails Museum of Wayne County, Corydon, IA 512
Prairie Village, Madison, SD 1351
Praters Mill Foundation, Varnell, GA 390
Pratt County Historical Society Museum, Pratt, KS 556
Pratt Museum, Homer, AK 25
Presbyterian Historical Society (Montreat), Montreat, NC 1111
The Preservation Society of Newport County/The Newport Mansions, Newport, RI 1315
President Andrew Johnson Museum and Library, Greeneville, TN 1366
President James K. Polk State Historic Site, Pineville, NC 1114
The Presidential Museum and Leadership Library, Odessa, TX 1441
Presidential Pet Museum, Lothian, MD 649
Presidio La Bahia, Goliad, TX 1423
Presque Isle County Historical Museum, Rogers City, MI 762
Pricketts Fort, Fairmont, WV 1581
Promont House Museum, Milford, OH 1176
Proprietary House, The Royal Governor's Mansion, Perth Amboy, NJ 921
Prudence Crandall Museum, Canterbury, CT 237
The Public Library of Nashville and Davidson County, Nashville, TN 1380
Pueblo County Historical Society Museum and Edward H. Broadhead Library, Pueblo, CO 230
Pueblo Weisbrod Aircraft Museum, Pueblo, CO 230
Puget Sound Coast Artillery Museum at Fort Worden, Port Townsend, WA 1562
Putnam County Historical Society Museum, Kalida, OH 1169
Putnam County Museum, Greencastle, IN ...479
Putney Historical Society, Putney, VT 1485
Pyle House Museum, Huron, SD 1349

Queen Emma Summer Palace, Honolulu, HI 398
Queens County Farm Museum, Floral Park, NY 989
Queens Historical Society, Flushing, NY 990
The Quilters Hall of Fame, Inc., Marion, IN 490
Quincy Historical Society, Quincy, MA 705
The Quincy Museum, Quincy, IL 452

Personal Artifacts—Continued

QV Historical Society at Carriage House Museum, Camden, NY 974

R.E. Olds Transportation Museum, Lansing, MI 751
R.P. Strathearn Historical Park and Museum, Simi Valley, CA 187
RV/MH Heritage Foundation, Inc., Elkhart, IN 475
Rachel Carson Homestead, Springdale, PA 1301
Racine Heritage Museum, Racine, WI 1619
Radford University Art Museum, Radford, VA 1527
Railroad and Heritage Museum Inc., Temple, TX 1454
Railroad Museum of Long Island, Riverhead, NY 1057
Railroad Museum of Pennsylvania, Strasburg, PA 1302
Railroaders Memorial Museum, Altoona, PA 1240
Raleigh City Museum, Raleigh, NC 1117
Ralls Historical Museum, Ralls, TX 1445
Ralph Mark Gilbert Civil Rights Museum, Savannah, GA 386
Ralston Historical Association, John Ralston Museum, Mendham, NJ 911
Ramapogue Historical Society, West Springfield, MA 718
Ramsey House Museum Plantation, Knoxville, TN 1371
Rancho La Patera - The Stow House G.V.H.S., Goleta, CA 100
Rancho Los Alamitos, Long Beach, CA 111
Rancho Los Cerritos Historic Site, Long Beach, CA 111
Randall Library, Stow, MA 713
Randolph County Historical Museum, Winchester, IN 503
Randolph County Museum (At Beverly), Beverly, WV 1580
Randolph Historical Society, Inc., Randolph, VT 1485
Randsburg Desert Museum, Randsburg, CA 146
Rangely Outdoor Museum, Rangely, CO 231
Rankin Museum, Inc., Ellerbe, NC 1100
Ransom County Historical Society, Fort Ransom, ND 1131
Raton Museum, Raton, NM 945
Rattlesnake Museum (American International), Albuquerque, NM 935
Ravalli County Museum/Bitter Root Valley Historical Society, Hamilton, MT 848
Raynham Hall Museum, Oyster Bay, NY ..1049
Reading Historical Society, Reading, VT ..1485
Reading Historical Society Museum, Reading, OH 1184
Readsboro Historical Society, Readsboro, VT 1486
Rebecca Nurse Homestead, Danvers, MA ..678
Rebel State Historic Site & Louisiana Country Music Museum, Marthaville, LA 592
Red Barn Museum, Morristown, NY 1016
Red Hill-Patrick Henry National Memorial, Brookneal, VA 1498
Red Mill Museum Village, Clinton, NJ 901
Red River Historical Museum, Sherman, TX 1452
Redington Museum, Waterville, ME 625
Redwood County Historical Society, Redwood Falls, MN 787
Redwood Library and Athenaeum, Newport, RI 1315
Redwood National and State Parks, Crescent City, CA 88
Reed Gold Mine State Historic Site, Midland, NC 1111

Refugio County Museum, Refugio, TX 1445
Reginald F. Lewis Museum of Maryland African American History and Culture, Baltimore, MD 636
Rehoboth Art League, Inc., Rehoboth Beach, DE 272
Reitz Home Museum, Evansville, IN 476
Remick Country Doctor Museum and Farm, Tamworth, NH 896
Remington Firearms Museum and Country Store, Ilion, NY 1002
Reno County Museum, Hutchinson, KS 545
Rensselaer County Historical Society, Troy, NY 1079
Renton Historical Society and Museum, Renton, WA 1564
Renville County Historical Society, Inc., Mohall, ND 1135
Republic County Historical Society Museum, Belleville, KS 534
Reston Museum, Reston, VA 1527
Retired Correctional Peace Officers Museum at Folsom Prison, Represa, CA 148
Reverend Dan Foster House, Museum of the Weathersfield Historical Society, Weathersfield, VT 1489
Rex Allen Museum, Willcox, AZ 53
Reynolda House Museum of American Art, Winston-Salem, NC 1126
Reynolds Homestead, Critz, VA 1502
Rhinebeck Aerodrome Museum, Rhinebeck, NY 1056
Rhinelander Logging Museum, Rhinelander, WI 1620
Rhode Island Black Heritage Society, Providence, RI 1318
Rhode Island State Archives, Providence, RI 1318
Rice County Museum of History, Faribault, MN 775
Richard I. Bong WWII Heritage Center, Superior, WI 1624
Richard Petty Museum, Randleman, NC 1117
Richard Salter Storrs House, Longmeadow, MA 691
Richards DAR House Museum, Mobile, AL 15
Richardson-Bates House Museum, Oswego, NY 1048
Richardson Maritime Museum, Cambridge, MD 639
Richey Historical Society, Richey, MT 852
Richland County Historical Museum, Wahpeton, ND 1137
Richland County Museum, Lexington, OH 1172
Richmond Museum of History, Richmond, CA 148
Richmond National Battlefield Park, Richmond, VA 1531
Riddick's Folly, Suffolk, VA 1539
Rifle Creek Museum, Rifle, CO 231
Riley County Historical Museum, Manhattan, KS 551
Rim Country Museum, Payson, AZ 38
Rimrocker Historical Museum of West Montrose County, Naturita, CO 229
Rio Grande Valley Museum, Harlingen, TX 1423
Rio Vista Museum, Rio Vista, CA 148
Riordan Mansion State Historic Park, Flagstaff, AZ 33
Rios-Caledonia Adobe, San Miguel, CA 175
Ripley County, Indiana, Historical Society Museum, Versailles, IN 502
Ripley's Believe it or Not!, Key West, FL 319
Ripley's Believe it or Not! Museum, Orlando, FL 332
Ripley's Believe it or Not! Museum, Atlantic City, NJ 898

Ritz Theatre & LaVilla Museum, Jacksonville, FL 315
River Heritage Museum, Paducah, KY 582
River Hills Visitor Center, Wildwood, MO 840
River Museum, Wellsville, OH 1190
Riversdale House Mansion, Riverdale Park, MD 651
Riverside Heritage House, Riverside, CA 150
Riverside Metropolitan Museum, Riverside, CA 150
Riverside Museum, La Crosse, WI 1603
Riverton Museum, Riverton, WY 1637
Riverview at Hobson Grove, Bowling Green, KY 566
Roane County Museum of History & Art, Kingston, TN 1369
Roanoke Island Festival Park; Homeport of the "Elizabeth II", Manteo, NC 1110
Roaring Twenties Antique Car Museum, Hood, VA 1511
Robbins Hunter Museum, Avery-Downer House, Granville, OH 1167
Robbins Museum of Archaeology, Middleborough, MA 694
Roberson Museum and Science Center, Binghamton, NY 962
Robert A. Bogan Fire Museum, Baton Rouge, LA 587
Robert Frost Farm, Derry, NH 886
Robert Frost Stone House Museum, Shaftsbury, VT 1487
Robert Louis Stevenson House, Monterey, CA 128
Robert Louis Stevenson Memorial Cottage, Saranac Lake, NY 1064
Robert Louis Stevenson Silverado Museum, Saint Helena, CA 154
Robert Newell House, DAR Museum, Saint Paul, OR 1235
Robert S. Kerr Museum, Poteau, OK 1212
Robert Toombs House, Washington, GA 391
Roberts County Museum, Miami, TX 1438
Robinson-Rose House, San Diego, CA 159
Rochester Hills Museum at Van Hoosen Farm, Rochester Hills, MI 762
Rochester Historical Society, Rochester, NY 1059
Rochester Museum & Science Center, Rochester, NY 1059
The Rock and Roll Hall of Fame and Museum, Cleveland, OH 1155
Rock County Historical Society, Janesville, WI 1601
Rock Ford Plantation, Lancaster, PA 1267
Rock House Museum, Wytheville, VA 1546
Rock Island Arsenal Museum, Rock Island, IL 454
Rock Island County Historical Society, Moline, IL 445
Rock Springs Historical Museum, Rock Springs, WY 1638
Rockbridge Historical Society, Lexington, VA 1513
Rockingham Free Public Library and Museum, Bellows Falls, VT 1476
Rockwell Museum of Western Art, Corning, NY 982
Rockwood Park, Wilmington, DE 274
Rocky Ford Historical Museum, Rocky Ford, CO 231
Rocky Mount Museum, Piney Flats, TN 1383
Rocky Mountain National Park, Estes Park, CO 215
Rocky Mountain Quilt Museum, Golden, CO 220
Rocky Reach Dam, Wenatchee, WA 1577
Rodgers Tavern, Perryville, MD 650
Roger Maris Museum, Fargo, ND 1131
Roger Tory Peterson Institute of Natural History, Jamestown, NY 1005

Personal Artifacts–Continued

Santa Fe Trail Museum, Ingalls, KS 545
Santa Fe Trail Museum/Trinidad History
Museum, Trinidad, CO............................234
Santa Maria Museum of Flight, Inc.,
Santa Maria, CA...183
Santa Maria Valley Historical Museum,
Santa Maria, CA...183
Santa Monica Mountains National
Recreation Area, Thousand Oaks, CA.....191
Santa Ynez Valley Historical Society,
Santa Ynez, CA...185
Santa Ysabel Asistencia, Santa Ysabel,
CA...185
Sappington House Museum, Crestwood,
MO..814
Sapulpa Historical Museum, Sapulpa, OK.1213
Sarah A. Mooney Memorial Museum,
Lemoore, CA...109
Sarah Orne Jewett House, South
Berwick, ME...622
The Sargent House Museum, Gloucester,
MA..684
Sarpy County Historical Museum,
Bellevue, NE...857
Satterlee Clark House, Horicon, WI...........1600
Sauk County Historical Museum,
Baraboo, WI..1591
Sauk Prairie Area Historical Society, Inc.,
Prairie du Sac, WI....................................1619
Saunders County Historical Complex,
Wahoo, NE..874
Saunders Memorial Museum, Berryville,
AR...55
Savannah History Museum, Savannah,
GA..386
Sawin Memorial Building, Dover, MA........680
Sawyer's Sandhills Museum, Valentine,
NE...874
Sayville Historical Society, Sayville, NY...1066
Sayward-Wheeler House, York Harbor,
ME..627
Scantic Academy Museum, East Windsor
Historical Society, Inc., East Windsor,
CT...239
Scarborough Historical Museum,
Scarborough, ME..621
The Scarsdale Historical Society,
Scarsdale, NY...1066
Schedel Arboretum & Gardens, Elmore,
OH...1163
The Schein-Joseph International Museum
of Ceramic Art, Alfred, NY.......................956
Schenectady County Historical Society,
Schenectady, NY.......................................1067
Schenectady Museum and Suits-Bueche
Planetarium, Schenectady, NY.................1067
Schmidt House Museum & Research
Library, Grants Pass, OR.........................1225
Schminck Memorial Museum, Lakeview,
OR...1227
Schofield House, Madison, IN......................489
Schoharie Colonial Heritage Association,
Schoharie, NY...1067
Scholte House Museum, Pella, IA................527
School of Nations Museum, Elsah, IL.........433
Schoolcraft County Historical Society,
Manistique, MI...753
Schoolhouse Museum of the Ridgewood
Historical Society, Inc., Ridgewood,
NJ...923
The Schuette Biermann Farmhouse
Museum, Elk Grove Village, IL.................432
Schuyler County Historical Society, Inc.,
Montour Falls, NY....................................1015
Schuyler-Hamilton House, Morristown,
NJ...914
Schuyler Mansion State Historic Site,
Albany, NY...955
Schwenkfelder Library & Heritage
Center, Pennsburg, PA.............................1275

Scituate Maritime and Irish Mossing
Museum, Scituate, MA...............................709
Scotia-Glenville Children's Museum,
Scotia, NY..1068
Scotland Heritage Chapel & Museum,
Scotland, SD...1355
Scott & Zelda Fitzgerald Museum,
Montgomery, AL...17
The Scottish Tartans Museum, Franklin,
NC..1102
Scotts Bluff National Monument, Gering,
NE...861
Scottsville Museum, Scottsville, VA..........1536
Scurry County Museum, Snyder, TX.........1453
Seacoast Science Center, Rye, NH..............896
Seagraves-Loop Museum and Art Center
Inc., Seagraves, TX.................................1452
Searchlight Historic Museum & Mining
Park, Searchlight, NV.................................882
Seaside Museum & Historical Society,
Seaside, OR..1236
The Seay House, Spartanburg, SC..............1341
Sedgwick-Brooklin Historical Society,
Sedgwick, ME...622
Senate House State Historic Site,
Kingston, NY..1008
Senator George Baldwin Hotel, Klamath
Falls, OR...1227
Senator George Norris State Historic Site,
McCook, NE..868
Senator John Heinz Pittsburgh Regional
History Center, Pittsburgh, PA.................1294
Seneca Falls Historical Society, Seneca
Falls, NY..1069
The Sequoyah Birthplace Museum,
Vonore, TN...1385
Sequoyah Cabin, Sallisaw, OK..................1213
Serra Museum/San Diego Historical
Society, San Diego, CA..............................161
1719 Hans Herr House & Museum,
Willow Street, PA.....................................1308
The 1719 William Trent House Museum,
Trenton, NJ...928
1768 Jeremiah Lee Mansion, Marblehead,
MA..693
1761 Pownalborough Courthouse,
Dresden, ME...610
The Sevier County Historical Museum,
De Queen, AR..56
Sewall-Belmont House and Museum,
Washington, DC..290
Seward House, Auburn, NY.........................959
Seward Museum, Seward, AK........................27
Seymour Community Museum, Seymour,
WI..1621
Shafer Historical Museum, Winthrop, WA.1578
Shaftsbury Historical Society, Shaftsbury,
VT...1487
Shaker Heritage Society, Albany, NY..........956
Shaker Historical Society, Shaker
Heights, OH..1185
Shaker Museum, New Gloucester, ME........615
The Shaker Museum and Library, Old
Chatham, NY..1045
Shaker Museum at South Union, South
Union, KY...583
Shaker Village of Pleasant Hill,
Harrodsburg, KY...571
Shakespeare Ghost Town, Lordsburg, NM...942
Shandy Hall, Geneva, OH..........................1166
Sharlot Hall Museum, Prescott, AZ..............43
Sharon Historical Society, Sharon, CT.......260
Sharpsteen Museum, Calistoga, CA..............80
Shasta College Museum & Research
Center, Redding, CA..................................146
Shasta State Historic Park, Shasta, CA.......186
Shawnee Town, Shawnee, KS......................558
Sheboygan County Historical Museum,
Sheboygan, WI...1621
Shelby American Collection, Boulder, CO...203
Shelby County Museum, Center, TX.........1399
Sheldon Jackson Museum, Sitka, AK............27

Sheldon Peck Homestead, Lombard, IL.......444
Shenandoal Valley Discovery Museum,
Winchester, VA...1546
Sherburne History Center, Becker, MN........768
Sherman Indian Museum, Riverside, CA.....150
Sherwin Miller Museum of Jewish Art,
Tulsa, OK...1216
Sherwood-Davidson House, Newark, OH..1178
Sherwood Forest Plantation, Charles City,
VA...1498
Shiloh Museum of Ozark History,
Springdale, AR..68
Shimmin Tveit Museum, Forbes, ND.........1131
Ship Ashore Resort Museum, Smith
River, CA...187
Shippensburg Historical Society Museum,
Shippensburg, PA.....................................1300
Ships of the Sea Maritime
Museum/William Scarbrough House,
Savannah, GA..386
Shirley-Eustis House, Boston, MA..............669
Shirley Plantation, Charles City, VA.........1498
Shoal Creek Living History Museum,
Kansas City, MO..822
Shore Line Trolley Museum, East Haven,
CT...239
Shoreline Historical Museum, Seattle,
WA...1569
Shores Memorial Museum, Lyndon
Center, VT..1481
Shorter Mansion Museum, Eufaula, AL.........8
Shortgrass Country Museum Society,
Sayre, OK...1213
Shoshone Bannock Tribal Museum, Fort
Hall, ID..406
Shoshone County Mining and Smelting
Museum d/b/a The Staff House
Museum, Kellogg, ID.................................406
Shoshone Tribal Cultural Center, Fort
Washakie, WY..1633
Sibley County Historical Museum,
Henderson, MN..777
Sibley House Historic Site, Mendota, MN...780
Siege Museum (The Petersburg
Museums), Petersburg, VA.......................1525
Siegfried H. Horn Archaeological
Museum, Berrien Springs, MI..................729
Sierra Mono Indian Museum, North Fork,
CA...131
Sierra Sacramento Valley Medical
Society Museum of Medical History,
Sacramento, CA...153
Silent Wings Museum, Lubbock, TX.........1435
Siloam Springs Museum, Siloam Springs,
AR...68
Silt Historical Society, Silt, CO.................232
Silver City Museum, Silver City, NM.........951
Silver Cliff Museum, Silver Cliff, CO.........232
Silvercreek Museum, Freeport, IL..............435
The Simon Paneak Memorial Museum,
Anaktuvuk Pass, AK....................................21
Simonian Farms, Fresno, CA........................98
Simsbury Historical Society, Phelps
Tavern, Museum & Homestead,
Simsbury, CT...260
Sinclair Lewis House Museum &
Interpretive Center/Museum, Sauk
Centre, MN...793
Siouxland Heritage Museums, Sioux
Falls, SD..1357
Siskin Museum of Religious and
Ceremonial Art, Chattanooga, TN...........1362
Siskiyou County Museum, Yreka, CA.........200
Skagit County Historical Museum, La
Conner, WA..1557
Skagway Museum & Archives, Skagway,
AK..28
Skiatook Museum, Skiatook, OK...............1214
The Skinner Museum of Mount Holyoke
College, South Hadley, MA........................709
Skowhegan History House Inc.,
Skowhegan, ME..622

Personal Artifacts–Continued

Stephenville Museum, Stephenville, TX 1454
Stepping Stones, Katonah, NY 1006
Steppingstone Museum, Havre de Grace,
  MD 647
Sterling Historical Society and Little Red
  Schoolhouse Museum, Sterling, NY......1074
Sterling-Rock Falls Historical Society
  Museum, Sterling, IL 461
Sterne-Hoya House Museum and Library,
  Nacogdoches, TX 1440
The Stevens-Coolidge Place, a property
  of The Trustees of Reservations, North
  Andover, MA 698
Stevens County Gas and Historical
  Museum, Hugoton, KS 544
Stevens County Historical Society
  Museum, Morris, MN 784
Stevens Museum, Salem, IN 498
Steves Homestead, San Antonio, TX..........1450
Stewart M. Lord Memorial Historical
  Society, Inc., Burlington, ME 608
Still National Osteopathic Museum,
  Kirksville, MO 824
Stockbridge Library Historical Collection,
  Stockbridge, MA 713
Stockholm Historical Society Museum,
  Stockholm, ME 623
Stone Fort Museum, Nacogdoches, TX....1440
The Stone House Museum, Belchertown,
  MA 662
Stonefield Historic Site, Cassville, WI 1593
Stones River National Battlefield,
  Murfreesboro, TN 1377
Stonewall House, Rocky Mount, NC..........1118
Stonewall Jackson House, Lexington, VA..1514
Stonewall Jackson Museum at Hupp's
  Hill, Strasburg, VA 1539
Storrowton Village Museum, West
  Springfield, MA 718
Stoughton Historical Society, Stoughton,
  MA 713
Stoughton Historical Society, Stoughton,
  WI 1623
Stow West School Museum, Stow, MA 713
Strasburg Museum, Strasburg, VA..............1539
Strategic Air & Space Museum, Ashland,
  NE 856
Stratford, Robert E. Lee Memorial
  Association, Inc., Stratford, VA 1539
Strawbery Banke Museum, Portsmouth,
  NH 895
Strom Thurmond Institute, Clemson, SC ...1328
Strong - National Museum of Play,
  Rochester, NY......................................1060
Stuart Heritage Museum, Stuart, FL.............346
Stuart House City Museum, Mackinac
  Island, MI 752
Stuhr Museum of the Prairie Pioneer,
  Grand Island, NE 862
Sturgis Library, Barnstable, MA..................662
Stutsman County Memorial Museum,
  Jamestown, ND 1133
Submarine Force Museum and Historic
  Ship Nautilus, Groton, CT 243
Suffolk County Historical Society,
  Riverhead, NY 1057
Suffolk Resolves House, Milton, MA 695
Sullivan County Historical Society, Inc.,
  Hurleyville, NY 1001
Sullivan Museum and History Center,
  Northfield, VT 1483
SullivanMunce Cultural Center,
  Zionsville, IN 504
Summit County Historical Society,
  Akron, OH 1139
Summit Historical Society, Breckenridge,
  CO 204
The Sumter County Museum, Sumter, SC.1342
Sumter Gallery of Art, Sumter, SC.............1342

Sun Prairie Historical Library &
  Museum, Sun Prairie, WI......................1624
Sunnyvale Historical Museum,
  Sunnyvale, CA 190
Sunset Crater Volcano National
  Monument, Flagstaff, AZ 33
SunWatch Indian Village/Archaeological
  Park, Dayton, OH 1162
Superstition Mountain Lost Dutchman
  Museum, Apache Junction, AZ.................30
The Supreme Court of the United States,
  Washington, DC 291
Suquamish Museum, Poulsbo, WA.............1563
Surratt House Museum, Clinton, MD..........640
Susan B. Anthony House, Rochester, NY ..1060
Susquehanna County Historical Society
  & Free Library Association, Montrose,
  PA 1272
Susquehanna Museum of Havre de Grace
  Inc. at the Lock House, Havre de
  Grace, MD 647
Suzanne G. Long Local History Room,
  Hammond, IN 480
Swampscott Historical Society (John
  Humphrey House), Swampscott, MA 714
Swarthout Memorial Museum, La Crosse,
  WI 1603
Swedish American Historical Society,
  Inc., Chicago, IL....................................428
Swedish American Museum Association
  of Chicago, Chicago, IL...........................428
Sweet Briar Museum, Sweet Briar, VA......1540
Sweetwater County Historical Museum,
  Green River, WY 1633
Swenson Memorial Museum of Stephens
  County, Breckenridge, TX.....................1397
Swift County Historical Society, Benson,
  MN 769
Swisher County Archives and Museum
  Association, Tulia, TX 1456
Switzerland County Historical Museum,
  Vevay, IN 502
Sylvia Plotkin Judaica Museum of
  Congregation Beth Israel, Scottsdale,
  AZ 44

T.B. Ferguson Home, Watonga, OK 1216
T.C. Steele State Historic Site, Nashville,
  IN 493
T.J. Elder Community Center,
  Sandersville, GA....................................384
T.W. Wood Gallery & Arts Center,
  Montpelier, VT 1482
Tabor Opera House Museum, Leadville,
  CO 226
Talkeetna Historical Society and
  Museum, Talkeetna, AK 28
Tallahassee Museum, Tallahassee, FL 348
Tama County Historical Museum, Toledo,
  IA 528
Tamastslikt Cultural Institute, Pendleton,
  OR 1230
Tampa Bay History Center, Inc., Tampa,
  FL...350
Tannenbaum Historic Park, Greensboro,
  NC..1104
Tante Blanche Museum, Madawaska, ME ...614
Taoist Temple and Museum, Hanford, CA...101
Taos Historic Museums, Taos, NM 953
Tate House Museum, Portland, ME 620
Taylor House Museum, Berlin, MD 637
Ted Williams Museum and Hitters Hall
  of Fame, Hernando, FL...........................312
Telluride Historical Museum, Telluride,
  CO 233
Temecula Valley Museum, Temecula, CA....191
Tempe Historical Museum, Tempe, AZ.........46
Temperance Tavern, Newcomerstown,
  OH 1179
Ten Broeck Mansion - Albany County
  Historical Association, Albany, NY 956
Ten Sleep Pioneer Museum, Ten Sleep,
  WY...1639

Tenino Depot Museum, Tenino, WA 1575
Tennessee Agricultural Museum,
  Nashville, TN...1380
Tennessee Central Railway Museum,
  Nashville, TN...1380
Tennessee Historical Society, Nashville,
  TN 1380
Tennessee Museum of Aviation,
  Sevierville, TN 1383
Tennessee State Museum, Nashville, TN ...1381
Terrace Hill Historic Site and Governor's
  Mansion, Des Moines, IA 516
Territorial Capital-Lane Museum,
  Lecompton, KS 549
Territorial Statehouse State Park &
  Museum, Fillmore, UT 1465
Teutopolis Monastery Museum,
  Teutopolis, IL 461
Texana Museum and Library Association,
  Edna, TX...1410
Texarkana Museums System, Texarkana,
  TX 1455
Texas Air Museum, Slaton, TX 1453
Texas City Museum, Texas City, TX..........1455
Texas Civil War Museum, Fort Worth,
  TX 1418
Texas Cowboy Hall of Fame, Fort Worth,
  TX 1418
Texas Heritage Museum, Hillsboro, TX.....1424
Texas Historical Commission, Austin, TX .1391
Texas Music Museum, Austin, TX 1392
Texas Parks and Wildlife Department,
  Austin, TX...1392
Texas Prison Museum, Huntsville, TX.......1430
Texas Ranger Hall of Fame and Museum,
  Waco, TX 1459
Texas Seaport Museum, Galveston, TX 1422
Texas Sports Hall of Fame, Waco, TX.......1459
Texas State Library, Austin, TX 1392
Texas Transportation Museum, San
  Antonio, TX..1451
Theodore Roosevelt Birthplace National
  Historic Site, New York, NY 1040
Theodore Roosevelt Inaugural National
  Historic Site, Buffalo, NY......................973
Theodore Roosevelt National Park-Visitor
  Center, Medora, ND 1134
Thetford Historical Society Library and
  Museum, Thetford, VT..........................1488
This Is The Place Heritage Park, Salt
  Lake City, UT 1472
Thomas E. McMillan Museum, Brewton,
  AL..6
Thomas Edison Birthplace Museum,
  Milan, OH 1176
Thomas Hart Benton Home and Studio
  State Historic Site, Kansas City, MO 823
Thomas L. Kane Memorial Chapel, Kane,
  PA 1264
The Thomas T. Taber Museum of the
  Lycoming County Historical Society,
  Williamsport, PA 1308
Thomas Warne Historical Museum &
  Library, Old Bridge, NJ 918
Thomas Whaley House Museum, San
  Diego, CA..161
Thomas Wolfe Memorial, Asheville, NC ...1090
Thomaston Historical Society,
  Thomaston, ME 624
The Thoreau Institute at Walden Woods,
  Lincoln, MA 691
Thornton W. Burgess Museum,
  Sandwich, MA 708
Thousand Islands Museum, Clayton, NY....979
Three Rivers Museum, Muskogee, OK 1205
Three Valley Museum, Durant, OK 1200
Three Village Historical Society,
  Setauket, NY 1069
Thronateeska Heritage Foundation, Inc.,
  Albany, GA..355
Thunderbird Foundation for the Arts,
  Mount Carmel, UT 1467

Tillamook County Pioneer Museum, Tillamook, OR 1237

Tillamook Naval Air Station Museum, Tillamook, OR 1237

Timucuan Ecological and Historic Preserve and Fort Caroline National Memorial, Jacksonville, FL.................315

Tinker Swiss Cottage Museum, Rockford, IL...456

Tinley Park Historical Society, Tinley Park, IL...461

Tintic Mining Museum, Eureka, UT 1464

Tioga Point Museum, Athens, PA...............1241

Tippecanoe Battlefield, Battle Ground, IN ..468

Tippecanoe County Historical Association, Lafayette, IN.....................487

Tipton County Museum, Veteran's Memorial & Nature Center, Covington, TN.......................................1364

Tobacco Farm Life Museum, Inc., Kenly, NC 1107

Toledo Firefighters Museum, Toledo, OH ..1187

Tolland Historical Society - Tolland County Jail and Warden's Home Museum, Tolland, CT.........................262

Tom Mix Museum, Dewey, OK...................1199

Tomaquag Indian Memorial Museum, Exeter, RI..1311

Tomball Community Museum Center, Tomball, TX..1455

Tombstone Courthouse State Historic Park, Tombstone, AZ................................46

Tongass Historical Museum, Ketchikan, AK 26

Top of Oklahoma Historical Museum, Blackwell, OK....................................1197

Torreya State Park, Bristol, FL.....................298

Torrington Historical Society, Inc., Torrington, CT.......................................263

Tournament House and Wrigley Gardens, Pasadena, CA...141

Towe Auto Museum, Sacramento, CA 154

Town of Manlius Historical Society with Museum, Manlius, NY..........................1013

Town of Yorktown Museum, Yorktown Heights, NY...1087

Trail End State Historic Site, Sheridan, WY 1638

Traill County Historical Society, Hillsboro, ND..1132

Trails & Rails Museum, Kearney, NE..........864

Trainland U.S.A., Colfax, IA 511

Trapper Creek Museum, Trapper Creek, AK 28

Travel Town Museum, Los Angeles, CA 121

Traveler's Rest State Historic Site, Toccoa, GA...389

Travellers Rest Plantation & Museum, Nashville, TN......................................1381

Traverse County Historical Society, Wheaton, MN..796

Tread of Pioneers Museum, Steamboat Springs, CO...232

Treasures of the Sea Exhibit, Georgetown, DE....................................271

Trenton City Museum, Trenton, NJ..............928

Tri-Cities Museum, Grand Haven, MI 743

Tri-County Historical Society & Museum, Inc., Herington, KS 544

Tri-State University, General Lewis B. Hershey Museum, Angola, IN 468

Tropic Lightning Museum, Schofield Barracks, HI...402

Troutdale Historical Society, Troutdale, OR 1237

Troy Museum & Historic Village, Troy, MI...765

Truckee-Donner Historical Society Jail Museum, Truckee, CA 193

The Trustees of Reservations, Beverly, MA..662

Tsa Mo Ga Memorial Museum, Plains, TX...1443

T.T. Wentworth, Jr. Florida State Museum, Pensacola, FL 336

Tu-Endie-Wei State Park, Point Pleasant, WV...1586

Tubac Presidio State Historic Park, Tubac, AZ...47

Tubman African-American Museum, Macon, GA..378

Tuck Museum, Hampton, NH.......................888

Tuckerton Seaport, Tuckerton, NJ................928

Tucumcari Historical Research Institute, Tucumcari, NM.....................................953

Tudor Place Foundation, Inc., Washington, DC....................................292

Tulare County Museum at Mooney Grove Park, Visalia, CA....................................195

Tularosa Basin Historical Society Museum, Alamogordo, NM 932

Tulsa Zoo & Living Museum, Tulsa, OK ..1216

Tunica-Biloxi Native American Museum, Marksville, LA.......................................591

Turquoise Museum, Albuquerque, NM 936

Turtle Bay Exploration Park, Redding, CA..146

Turtle Mountain Chippewa Historical Society, Belcourt, ND...........................1127

Tuskegee Institute National Historic Site, Tuskegee Institute, AL.............................21

Twin Falls County Historical Museum, Filer, ID...405

Twin Falls State Park & Museum, Mullens, WV.......................................1585

Twinsburg Historical Society, Twinsburg, OH 1188

Twister the Movie Museum, Wakita, OK...1216

Tybee Island Light Station and Tybee Museum, Tybee Island, GA 389

Tyler Arboretum, Media, PA......................1271

UCLA Fowler Museum of Cultural History, Los Angeles, CA 122

UNLV Marjorie Barrick Museum, Las Vegas, NV...880

U.S. Bicycling Hall of Fame, Somerville, NJ 924

USDA Forest Service - Land Between the Lakes, Golden Pond, KY.................570

U.S. Navy Museum, Washington, DC 292

USS Massachusetts Memorial Committee, Inc., Fall River, MA 682

Ukrainian-American Museum & Archives, Warren, MI...........................766

The Ukrainian Museum, New York, NY....1040

Ukrainian Museum-Archives, Inc., Cleveland, OH 1156

Ukrainian National Museum, Inc., Chicago, IL...428

Ulster County Historical Society, Marbletown, NY...................................1013

Ulysses S. Grant Cottage State Historic Site, Wilton, NY....................................1086

Umlauf Sculpture Garden & Museum, Austin, TX..1392

Umpqua Discovery Center, Reedsport, OR 1234

Uncle Remus Museum, Eatonton, GA 371

Union County Heritage Museum, New Albany, MS..806

Union County Historical Society, Lewisburg, PA.....................................1268

Union County Historical Society Museum, Blairsville, GA 366

Union County Museum, Union, OR...........1238

Union Station Kansas City, Inc., Kansas City, MO..823

Unionville Museum, Farmington, CT...........242

United States Army Heritage and Education Center - Army Heritage Museum, Carlisle, PA.............................1246

The United States Army Quartermaster Museum, Fort Lee, VA...........................1505

United States Golf Association Museum & Archives, Far Hills, NJ......................903

United States Hockey Hall of Fame, Eveleth, MN...774

United States Holocaust Memorial Museum, Washington, DC 293

United States Naval Academy Museum, Annapolis, MD.....................................628

United States Naval Shipbuilding Museum, Quincy, MA 705

University Museum, Carbondale, IL 415

The University Museum, Indiana, PA...........1263

University Museum & Historic Houses, The University of Mississippi, Oxford, MS..806

The University Museum Collections, Fayetteville, AR...57

University Museum, New Mexico State University, Las Cruces, NM....................941

University of Kentucky Basketball Museum, Lexington, KY.........................574

University of Mary Washington Galleries, Fredericksburg, VA.............................1507

University of Northern Iowa Museums & Collections, Cedar Falls, IA....................508

University of Pennsylvania Museum of Archaeology and Anthropology, Philadelphia, PA 1288

The University of South Carolina McKissick Museum, Columbia, SC.......1331

Upham Mansion, Marshfield, WI 1608

Upper Musselshell Historical Society, Harlowton, MT.......................................849

Upper Room Chapel Museum, Nashville, TN 1381

Upper Snake River Valley Historical Society, Rexburg, ID...............................409

Uppertown Firefighters Museum, Astoria, OR 1219

Upton Red Onion Museum, Upton, WY....1639

U.S. Army Air Defense Artillery Museum, Fort Bliss, TX.........................1414

U.S. Army Center of Military History, Museum Division, Fort McNair, DC.......275

U.S. Army Chaplain Museum, Fort Jackson, SC...1332

U.S. Army Finance Corps Museum, Fort Jackson, SC...1333

U.S. Army Military Police Corps Museum, Fort Leonard Wood, MO 816

U.S. Army Museum of Hawaii, Fort DeRussy, HI...392

U.S. Army Transportation Museum, Fort Eustis, VA..1504

U.S. Army Women's Museum, Fort Lee, VA 1505

U.S. Capitol Historical Society, Washington, DC....................................293

U.S. Cavalry Museum, Fort Riley, KS.........540

U.S. Coast Guard Museum, New London, CT..255

U.S. Grant's Home State Historic Site, Galena, IL...436

U.S. Marconi Museum, Bedford, NH...........883

U.S. Merchant Marine Museum, Anderson, IN...467

U.S. Navy Seabee Museum, Port Hueneme, CA..143

U.S. Navy Supply Corps Museum, Athens, GA...357

U.S. Patent and Trademark Office - Museum, Alexandria, VA.......................1494

The U.S. Space & Rocket Center, Huntsville, AL 12

USS Alabama Battleship Memorial Park, Mobile, AL...15

USS Arizona Memorial, Honolulu, HI.........398

USS Bowfin Submarine Museum & Park, Honolulu, HI...398

USS Constellation Museum, Baltimore, MD...636

USS Constitution Museum, Boston, MA 669

Personal Artifacts–Continued

USS Lexington Museum on the Bay,
Corpus Christi, TX 1402

USS Radford National Naval Museum,
Newcomerstown, OH 1179

Utah State Historical Society, Salt Lake
City, UT 1473

Utica Museum, Utica, MT 854

Vacaville Museum, Vacaville, CA 194

The Valdez Museum & Historical
Archive Association, Inc., Valdez, AK 29

Valentine Richmond History Center,
Richmond, VA 1532

Valentine-Varian House/Museum of
Bronx History, Bronx, NY 967

Valentown Museum, Victor, NY 1081

Vallejo Naval & Historical Museum,
Vallejo, CA 194

Valley Community Historical Society,
Inc., Valley, NE 874

Valley County Pioneer Museum,
Glasgow, MT 847

Van Buren County Historical Museum,
Clinton, AR 55

Van Buren County Historical Society,
Keosauqua, IA 521

Van Cortlandt House Museum, Bronx,
NY 967

Van Wyck Homestead Museum, Fishkill,
NY 989

Vanderbilt University Fine Arts Gallery,
Nashville, TN 1381

Vann House, Chatsworth, GA 368

Varnum Memorial Armory & Military
Museum, East Greenwich, RI 1311

Vashon Maury Island Heritage
Association, Vashon, WA 1576

Venango Museum of Art, Science &
Industry, Oil City, PA 1274

Vent Haven Museum, Fort Mitchell, KY 568

Ventura County Museum of History &
Art, Ventura, CA 195

Verde Historical Society, Clemenceau
Heritage Museum, Cottonwood, AZ 32

The Verdier House, Beaufort, SC 1321

Verendrye Museum, Fort Pierre, SD 1347

Vermilion County Museum Society,
Danville, IL 429

Vermont Historical Society Museum,
Montpelier, VT 1482

Vermont Ski Museum, Stowe, VT 1488

Vermont Soapworks Discount Factory
Outlet and Soap Museum, Middlebury,
VT 1482

Vernon County Historical Museum,
Viroqua, WI 1625

Vernonia Pioneer Museum, Vernonia, OR..1238

The Vestal Museum, Vestal, NY 1081

Vesterheim Norwegian-American
Museum, Decorah, IA 513

Veterans Depot Museum, West Frankfort,
IL 464

Vicksburg Battlefield Museum,
Vicksburg, MS 809

Victor Heritage Museum, Victor, MT 854

Victor Valley Museum & Art Gallery,
Apple Valley, CA 71

Victorian Dress Museum, Rugby, ND 1136

Vietnam Era Educational Center,
Holmdel, NJ 908

Vietnam War National Museum, Nelson,
NE 869

Vigo County Historical Museum, Terre
Haute, IN 501

Vikingsholm, Tahoma, CA 191

Villa Louis Historic Site, Prairie du
Chien, WI 1619

Villa Montezuma Museum/San Diego
Historical Society, San Diego, CA 162

Village Historical Society, Inc., Harrison,
OH 1168

Vincennes State Historic Site, Indiana
Territory, Vincennes, IN 503

Vintage Flying Museum, Fort Worth, TX ..1419

Virginia Air & Space Center, Hampton,
VA 1510

Virginia Baptist Historical Society,
Richmond, VA 1532

Virginia Beach Maritime Museum,
Inc./The Old Coast Guard Station,
Virginia Beach, VA 1543

Virginia City J. Spencer Watkins
Memorial Museum, Virginia City, MT....854

Virginia Historical Society, Richmond,
VA 1533

Virginia Holocaust Museum, Richmond,
VA 1533

Virginia Military Institute Museum,
Lexington, VA 1514

Virginia Museum of Transportation, Inc.,
Roanoke, VA 1536

Virginia Robinson Gardens, Beverly
Hills, CA 78

Virginia Sports Hall of Fame,
Portsmouth, VA 1526

Virginia War Memorial, Richmond, VA 1534

The Virginia War Museum, Newport
News, VA 1520

Vista Historical Museum, Vista, CA 196

Vizcaya Museum and Gardens, Miami,
FL 326

Volunteer Firemen's Mall and Museum of
Kingston, Kingston, NY 1008

W.C. Handy Home Museum and Library,
Florence, AL 9

W.H. Over Museum, Vermillion, SD 1358

The W.H. Stark House, Orange, TX 1442

W.K. Gordon Center for Industrial
History of Texas, Mingus, TX 1439

Wabasha County Museum, Wabasha
County Historical Society at Reads
Landing, Reads Landing, MN 787

Wabaunsee County Historical Museum,
Alma, KS 532

Wade House Stagecoach Inn & Wesley
Jung Carriage Museum State Historic
Site, Greenbush, WI 1599

Wagner Free Institute of Science,
Philadelphia, PA 1289

Wahkiakum County Historical Museum,
Cathlamet, WA 1550

Wailoa Center for Culture and Arts, Hilo,
HI 393

Wake Forest College Birthplace Society,
Inc., Wake Forest, NC 1121

Wakefield Historical Society, Wakefield,
MA 715

Wakefield House Museum, Blue Earth,
MN 769

Wakefield Museum Association,
Wakefield, KS 560

Wal-Mart Visitor's Center, Bentonville,
AR 55

Waldensian Heritage Museum, Valdese,
NC 1121

The Walker African American Museum &
Research Center, Las Vegas, NV 880

Wallace District Mining Museum,
Wallace, ID 410

Wallingford Historical Society, Inc.,
Wallingford, CT 263

Walnut Grove Plantation, Roebuck, SC 1340

Walt Whitman Birthplace State Historic
Site and Interpretive Center,
Huntington Station, NY 1001

Walt Whitman House Museum and
Library, Camden, NJ 900

Walter F. George Law Office Museum,
Vienna, GA 390

Walter P. Chrysler Boyhood Home and
Museum, Ellis, KS 538

Waltham Historical Society, Waltham,
MA 716

The Waltham Museum, Waltham, MA 716

Wanapum Dam Heritage Center, Beverly,
WA 1549

Wantagh Historical & Preservation
Society, Wantagh, NY 1081

Wapello County Historical Museum,
Ottumwa, IA 526

War Between the States Museum,
Florence, SC 1332

War Eagle Air Museum, Santa Teresa,
NM 951

War in the Pacific National Historical
Park, Piti, GU 1640

Ward County Historical Society, Minot,
ND 1135

Warhawk Air Museum, Nampa, ID 408

Warner House, Portsmouth, NH 895

Warren County Historical Society,
Warren, PA 1304

Warren County Historical Society
Museum, Lebanon, OH 1171

Warren Historical Society, Warren, ME 624

Warren ICBM & Heritage Museum,
Frances E. Warren Air Force Base,
WY 1633

Warren Rifles Confederate Museum,
Front Royal, VA 1508

Warrick County Museum, Inc., Boonville,
IN 470

Warsaw Historical Museum, Warsaw, NY .1082

Waseca County Historical Society,
Waseca, MN 796

Washakie Museum, Worland, WY 1639

Washburn County Historical Society
Museum, Shell Lake, WI 1621

Washburn Historical Museum & Cultural
Center, Inc. aka Washburn Cultural
Center, Washburn, WI 1625

Washington & Jefferson College - Olin
Fine Arts Center, Washington, PA 1305

Washington County Historical
Association, Fort Calhoun, NE 860

Washington County Historical Society,
Washington, KS 560

Washington County Historical Society,
Portland, OR 1233

Washington County Historical Society,
Washington, PA 1305

Washington County Historical Society
Inc., West Bend, WI 1627

Washington County Rural Heritage
Museum, Boonsboro, MD 637

Washington Historical Museum,
Washington, GA 391

Washington Museum & Tourist Center,
Washington, LA 603

Washington State Capital Museum and
Outreach Center, Olympia, WA 1560

Washington's Headquarters State Historic
Site, Newburgh, NY 1042

Washington's Lands Museum & Sayre
Log House, Ravenswood, WV 1586

Waterloo Area Historical Society, Grass
Lake, MI 744

Watermen's Museum, Yorktown, VA 1547

Watertown Historical Society, Inc.,
Watertown, CT 264

Watkins Community Museum of History,
Lawrence, KS 548

Watkins Museum, Taylorsville, MS 808

Watkins Woolen Mill State Historic Site
& Park, Lawson, MO 825

Wauconda Township Historical Society,
Wauconda, IL 463

Waukesha County Museum, Waukesha,
WI 1625

Wayland Historical Society, Wayland,
MA 716

Wayne County Historical Museum,
Richmond, IN 497

Wayne County Historical Society, Lyons,
NY 1012

Wayne County Historical Society, Wooster, OH 1192

Wayne State University Museum of Anthropology, Detroit, MI 738

Weaverville Joss House, Weaverville, CA ...197

The Webb-Deane-Stevens Museum, Wethersfield, CT............266

Webb House Museum, Newark, OH 1179

Webster County Historical Museum, Red Cloud, NE............872

Wedell-Williams Memorial Aviation Museum, Patterson, LA............599

Weems-Botts Museum, Dumfries, VA........1503

Weeping Water Valley Historical Society, Weeping Water, NE............874

Weir Farm National Historic Site, Wilton, CT............267

Wellesley Historical Society, Inc., Wellesley Hills, MA 717

Wellfleet Historical Society Museum, Wellfleet, MA 717

Wells County Historical Museum, Bluffton, IN............470

Welsh-American Heritage Museum, Oak Hill, OH............1180

Wentworth-Coolidge Mansion, Portsmouth, NH............895

Wentworth Gardner & Tobias Lear Houses Association, Portsmouth, NH......895

Weslaco Museum, Weslaco, TX............1461

West Allis Historical Society Museum, West Allis, WI............1626

West Baton Rouge Museum, Port Allen, LA............599

West Chicago City Museum, West Chicago, IL............464

West Milford Museum, West Milford, NJ....930

West of the Pecos Museum, Pecos, TX 1443

West Overton Museums, Scottdale, PA......1298

West Pasco Historical Society Museum and Library, New Port Richey, FL 329

West Point Museum, West Point, NY 1085

West River Museum Society, Philip, SD....1353

West Virginia Museum of American Glass, Weston, WV............1587

West Virginia State Farm Museum, Point Pleasant, WV 1586

West Virginia State Museum, Charleston, WV............1581

Western Aerospace Museum, Oakland, CA............134

Western Archeological & Conservation Center, Tucson, AZ............52

Western Hennepin County Pioneers Association, Long Lake, MN............779

Western Heritage Center, Billings, MT 841

Western Hotel/Museum, Lancaster, CA........108

Western Mining & Railroad Museum, Helper, UT............1466

Western Museum of Flight, Hawthorne, CA............101

Western Museum of Mining & Industry, Colorado Springs, CO............208

Western New Mexico University Museum, Silver City, NM............951

Western Reserve Historical Society, Cleveland, OH............1156

Western Rhode Island Civic Historical Society, Coventry, RI............1311

Western Skisport Museum, Donner Pass, CA............91

Western Springs Historical Society, Western Springs, IL............464

Westminster Historical Society, Westminster, VT............1490

Westport Historical Society, Westport, CT...266

Westport Maritime Museum, Westport, WA............1578

The Wethersfield Historical Society, Wethersfield, CT............266

The Whalehead Club, Corolla, NC............1097

Whalers Village Museum, Lahaina, HI 401

Wharton County Historical Museum, Wharton, TX............1461

The Wharton Esherick Museum, Malvern, PA............1269

Whatcom Museum of History and Art, Bellingham, WA 1549

Wheat Ridge Historic Park, Wheat Ridge, CO............235

Wheeler Historic Farm, Salt Lake City, UT............1474

Wheels O' Time Museum, Peoria, IL............451

Wheels Through Time Museum, Inc., Maggie Valley, NC............1110

Whipple House Museum, Ashland Historical Society, Ashland, NH............883

Whiskeytown Unit, Whiskeytown-Shasta-Trinity National Recreation Area, Whiskeytown, CA........198

White County Historical Society, Cleveland, GA............368

White County Historical Society, Carmi, IL............415

White County Historical Society Museum, Monticello, IN............491

White Deer Land Museum, Pampa, TX.....1442

White Hall State Historic Site, Richmond, KY............583

White Pine Public Museum, Ely, NV............877

The White River Museum, Meeker, CO 228

White River Valley Museum, Auburn, WA............1547

Whitehead Memorial Museum, Del Rio, TX............1409

Whitewater Canal State Historic Site, Metamora, IN............490

Whitingham Historical Museum, Whitingham, VT............1490

Whitley County Historical Museum, Columbia City, IN............472

Whitman Mission National Historic Site, Walla Walla, WA............1577

Whittier Home Association, Amesbury, MA............658

Wibaux Museum, Wibaux, MT............855

Wichita-Sedgwick County Historical Museum Association, Wichita, KS..........563

Wickersham House Museum (Tanana-Yukon Historical Society), Fairbanks, AK............24

Wilber Czech Museum, Wilber, NE............875

Wilbur D. May Museum, Reno, NV............882

Wilbur Wright Birthplace & Interpretive Center, Hagerstown, IN............480

Wilderness Road Regional Museum, Newbern, VA............1519

Wildland Firefighters Museum, Capitan, NM............937

Wildlife Prairie State Park, Hanna City, IL............439

Wildwood Center, Nebraska City, NE..........869

Wilhelm Reich Museum - Orgonon, Rangeley, ME............621

Wilkin County Historical Society, Breckenridge, MN............770

Will Rogers Memorial Museum, Claremore, OK............1198

Will Rogers State Historic Park, Pacific Palisades, CA............137

Willa Cather Pioneer Memorial and Educational Foundation, Red Cloud, NE............872

Willard House and Clock Museum, Inc., Grafton, MA............685

William A. Farnsworth Library and Art Museum, Inc. d/b/a Farnsworth Art Museum, Rockland, ME............621

The William Breman Jewish Heritage Museum, Atlanta, GA............364

William Brewster Nickerson Memorial Room, Cape Cod Community College, West Barnstable, MA 717

William Clark Market House Museum, Paducah, KY............582

William Heath Davis House Museum administered by Gaslamp Quarter Historical Foundation, San Diego, CA....162

William Henry Harrison Mansion, Grouseland, Vincennes, IN............503

William Howard Taft National Historic Site, Cincinnati, OH 1151

William J. Clinton Presidential Library & Museum, Little Rock, AR............63

William McKinley Presidential Library & Museum, Canton, OH............1146

William Otis Sawtelle Collections and Research Center, Bar Harbor, ME..........606

William Pryor Letchworth Museum, Castile, NY............976

William S. Hart County Park & Museum, Newhall, CA............130

William Whitley House State Historic Site, Stanford, KY............584

Williamson County Historical Society, Marion, IL............444

Willow Creek - China Flat Museum, Willow Creek, CA............198

Willows Museum, Willows, CA............198

Wilmette Historical Museum, Wilmette, IL............466

Wilmington Railroad Museum, Wilmington, NC............1124

Wilson County Historical Society Museum, Fredonia, KS............540

Wilson Czech Opera House Corporation, Foundation, Inc. & House of Memories Museum, Wilson, KS............564

Wilson Historical Museum, Wilson, NY....1086

Wilson's Creek National Battlefield, Republic, MO 829

Wilton House Museum, Richmond, VA 1534

Winchendon Historical Society, Inc., Winchendon, MA............720

Winchester-Frederick County Historical Society, Inc., Winchester, VA............1546

Wind Cave National Park, Hot Springs, SD............1348

Windham Textile and History Museum (The Mill Museum), Willimantic, CT 267

Windmill Island Municipal Park, Holland, MI............747

The Wine Museum of Greyton H. Taylor, Hammondsport, NY............997

Winedale, Center for American History, University of Texas at Austin, Round Top, TX............1446

Wing Haven Garden and Bird Sanctuary, Charlotte, NC............1096

Wings of History Air Museum, San Martin, CA............175

Wings Over Miami Museum, Inc., Miami, FL............326

Winnebago Area Museum, Winnebago, MN............797

Winnetka Historical Society, Winnetka, IL............466

Winona County Historical Museum, Winona, MN............797

Winston Churchill Memorial and Library, Fulton, MO............816

Winterthur Museum & Country Estate, Winterthur, DE............274

Wiscasset, Waterville & Farmington Railway Museum, Alna, ME............603

Wisconsin Automotive Museum, Hartford, WI............1600

Wisconsin Historical Museum, Madison, WI............1606

Wisconsin Maritime Museum, Manitowoc, WI............1607

Wisconsin National Guard Museum, Camp Douglas, WI............1593

Wisconsin Veterans Museum-King, King, WI............1602

Wisconsin Veterans Museum-Madison, Madison, WI............1606

Personal Artifacts–Continued

Wise County Heritage Museum, Decatur, TX 1408

Witte Museum, San Antonio, TX 1451

Wolcott House Museum Complex, Maumee, OH............1175

Woldumar Nature Center, Lansing, MI 751

Wolf Creek Indian Village and Museum, Bastian, VA 1496

Wolfeboro Historical Society, Wolfeboro, NH............897

Women's History Museum, West Liberty, WV 1587

The Women's Museum: An Institute for the Future, Dallas, TX............1408

Wonders: Memphis International Cultural Series, Memphis, TN............1376

Wood County Historical Center and Museum, Bowling Green, OH 1143

Wood Library-Museum of Anesthesiology, Park Ridge, IL 450

Woodbine International Fire Museum, Woodbine, GA............392

Woodburn Historic House, Pendleton, SC .1339

Woodford County Historical Society Museum, Versailles, KY............584

Woodlawn Museum/The Black House, Ellsworth, ME............610

Woodlawn Plantation Museum, Alexandria, VA 1494

Woodrow Wilson House, Washington, DC............294

Woodrow Wilson Presidential Library at His Birthplace, Staunton, VA............1537

Woodside Store Historic Site, Woodside, CA............199

Woodson County Historical Society, Yates Center, KS............564

Woodstock Historical Society, Bryant Pond, ME............608

Woodstock Historical Society, Inc., Woodstock, CT 268

Woodstock Historical Society, Inc., Woodstock, VT 1491

Woodstock Museum of Shenandoah County, Inc., Woodstock, VA 1546

Woodville Museum, Inc., Rogue River, OR............1234

Worcester Historical Museum, Worcester, MA............721

Working Men's Institute, New Harmony, IN............495

Workman & Temple Family Homestead Museum, City of Industry, CA 85

The Works: Ohio Center for History, Art & Technology, Newark, OH............1179

World Figure Skating Museum & Hall of Fame, Colorado Springs, CO............208

World Golf Hall of Fame, Saint Augustine, FL............340

World Methodist Museum, Lake Junaluska, NC............1109

World Museum of Mining, Butte, MT 843

World O' Tools Museum, Waverly, TN 1385

World of Scouting Museum, Valley Forge, PA............1304

World of Wings Pigeon Center, Oklahoma City, OK............1211

World's First Wendy's Restaurant, Columbus, OH............1159

World's Largest Toy Museum and Harold Bell Wright, Branson, MO............811

World's Smallest Museum, Superior, AZ.......45

Wormsloe State Historic Site, Savannah, GA............387

Worthington Historical Society, Worthington, OH............1192

Wrather West Kentucky Museum, Murray, KY............580

Wren's Nest, Atlanta, GA............364

Wright Brothers National Memorial, Kill Devil Hills, NC............1108

Wright Centennial Museum, Wright, WY..1639

Wright County Historical Society, Buffalo, MN............770

Wright Museum, Wolfeboro, NH............897

Wyandot County Historical Society, Upper Sandusky, OH............1188

Wyandotte County Museum, Bonner Springs, KS............534

Wyandotte Museum, Wyandotte, MI 766

Wyatt Earp Birthplace Home, Monmouth, IL............445

Wyck, Philadelphia, PA............1289

The Wyckoff Farmhouse Museum, Brooklyn, NY............970

Wylie House Museum, Bloomington, IN 470

The Wyman Tavern, Keene, NH............890

Wyoming Pioneer Home, Thermopolis, WY............1639

Wyoming Pioneer Memorial Museum, Douglas, WY............1632

Wyoming State Museum, Cheyenne, WY..1631

Wyoming Territorial Prison State Historic Site, Laramie, WY............1636

Yakima Valley Museum and Historical Association, Yakima, WA............1579

Yale University Collection of Musical Instruments, New Haven, CT............255

Yankee Air Force, Inc. (Yankee Air Museum), Ypsilanti, MI 766

Yanks Air Museum, Chino, CA............84

Yates County Genealogical and Historical Society and Oliver House Museum and L. Caroline Underwood Museum, Penn Yan, NY............1052

Yellow Medicine County Historical Society and Museum, Granite Falls, MN............777

Yellowstone Gateway Museum of Park County, Livingston, MT............850

Yellowstone National Park, Gardiner, MT ...847

Yeshiva University Museum at the Center for Jewish History, New York, NY............1041

Yesterday's Children Antique Doll & Toy Museum, Vicksburg, MS............809

Yesteryear House-Central Mine, Clarkston, MI............732

Yesteryear Village, West Palm Beach, FL....354

Yolo County Historical Museum, Woodland, CA............199

Yorba and Slaughter Families Adobe, Chino, CA............84

Yorktown Historical Museum, Yorktown, TX............1462

The Yosemite Museum, National Park Service, Yosemite National Park, CA......199

Ypsilanti Historical Museum, Ypsilanti, MI............767

Yucaipa Adobe, Yucaipa, CA............200

Yucaipa Valley Historical Society Museum, Yucaipa, CA............201

Yuma Crossing State Historic Park, Yuma, AZ............54

Yuma Territorial Prison State Historic Park, Yuma, AZ............54

Z. Taylor Brown-Sarah Dorsey House, Midland, TX............1439

Zalud House, Porterville, CA............144

Zane Grey Museum, Lackawaxen, PA............1265

Zebulon B. Vance Birthplace State Historic Site, Weaverville, NC............1122

Zelienople Historical Society, Zelienople, PA............1309

Ziibiwing Center of Anishinabe Culture & Lifeways, Mount Pleasant, MI............757

Zion Human History Museum, Springdale, UT............1474

Zippo/Case Visitors Center, Bradford, PA..1244

Zoar State Memorial, Zoar, OH............1194

Recreational Artifacts

A.C. Gilbert's Discovery Village, Salem, OR............1235

A.R. Bowman Memorial Museum, Prineville, OR............1234

A:shiwi A:wan Museum and Heritage Center, Zuni, NM............954

Abby Aldrich Rockefeller Folk Art Museum, Williamsburg, VA............1544

Academy of Model Aeronautics/National Model Aviation Museum, Muncie, IN.....492

Ace of Clubs House, Texarkana, TX............1455

Adair County Historical Society, Inc., Kirksville, MO............824

Adams County Historical Society, Gettysburg, PA............1255

Adams Old Stone Grist Mill, Bellows Falls, VT............1476

Adirondack History Center, Elizabethtown, NY............987

The Adirondack Museum, Blue Mountain Lake, NY............963

African-American Museum and Library at Oakland, Oakland, CA............132

The African American Museum in Philadelphia, Philadelphia, PA............1275

African Art Museum of the S.M.A. Fathers, Tenafly, NJ............926

Afro-American Historical Society Museum, Jersey City, NJ............908

Agricultural and Industrial Museum, York County Heritage Trust, York, PA............1309

Agrirama, Georgia's Living History Museum & Village, Tifton, GA............388

Ah-Tah-Thi-Ki Museum at Okalee, Hollywood, FL............312

Aiken County Historical Museum, Aiken, SC............1320

Airmen Memorial Museum, Suitland, MD............655

Akron Zoological Park, Akron, OH............1138

Akta Lakota Museum and Cultural Center, Chamberlain, SD............1345

Akwesasne Museum, Hogansburg, NY 998

Alabama Mining Museum, Dora, AL............7

Alamance Battleground State Historic Site, Burlington, NC............1092

Alden Historical Society, Inc., Alden, NY ...956

Alexander & Baldwin Sugar Museum, Puunene, HI............401

Alexander Ramsey House, Minnesota Historical Society, Saint Paul, MN............789

Alexandre Mouton House/Lafayette Museum, Lafayette, LA............589

Alger County Heritage Center, Munising, MI............757

The Alice T. Miner Colonial Collection, Chazy, NY............977

Allaire Village Inc., Farmingdale, NJ............903

Allegan County Historical Society and Old Jail Museum, Allegan, MI............723

Allegany County Historical Society, Inc., Cumberland, MD............641

Alling Coverlet Museum, Palmyra, NY 1050

Allison-Antrim Museum, Inc., Greencastle, PA............1257

Alton Museum of History and Art, Inc., Alton, IL............410

Amana Heritage Museum, Amana, IA 504

Amazement Square, The Rightmire Children's Museum, Lynchburg, VA 1514

Amelia Earhart Birthplace Museum, Atchison, KS............532

Amelia Park Children's Museum, Westfield, MA............718

The American Museum of Fly Fishing, Manchester, VT............1481

American Museum of Magic & Lund Memorial Library, Inc., Marshall, MI 754

American Museum of Nursing, Tempe, AZ............45

American Museum of Radio and Electricity, Bellingham, WA 1548

American Numismatic Association Money Museum, Colorado Springs, CO 206

The American Numismatic Society, New York, NY 1020

American Printing House for the Blind, Callahan Museum, Louisville, KY 575

American Quarter Horse Hall of Fame & Museum, Amarillo, TX 1386

American Radio Relay League-Museum of Amateur Radio, Newington, CT 256

American Royal Museum & Visitors Center, Kansas City, MO 820

American Saddlebred Museum, Lexington, KY 572

American Truck Historical Society, Kansas City, MO 820

American Visionary Art Museum, Baltimore, MD 629

American Water Ski Educational Foundation, Polk City, FL 337

Americana Museum, Terra Alta, WV 1587

America's Black Holocaust Museum, Milwaukee, WI 1610

America's Ice Cream & Dairy Museum, Medina, OH 1175

America's National Music Museum, Vermillion, SD 1358

Amherst County Museum & Historical Society, Amherst, VA 1495

Amherst History Museum at the Strong House - Amherst Historical Society, Amherst, MA 658

Anacortes Museum, Anacortes, WA 1547

Anchorage Museum at Rasmuson Center, Anchorage, AK 22

Anderson County Historical Museum, Garnett, KS 541

Anderson County Museum, Anderson, SC.1321

Andrew County Museum & Historical Society, Savannah, MO 838

Andrew J. Blackbird Museum, Harbor Springs, MI 745

Andrew Low House, Savannah, GA 384

Androscoggin Historical Society, Auburn, ME 603

Angel Mounds State Historic Site, Evansville, IN 475

Angels Attic Museum, Santa Monica, CA ...183

Animas Museum, Durango, CO 214

Annie E. Woodman Institute Museum, Dover, NH 886

Anthropology Museum, University of San Diego, San Diego, CA 155

Apostles Islands National Lakeshore, Bayfield, WI 1591

The Appaloosa Museum and Heritage Center, Moscow, ID 407

The Apple Trees Museum, Burlington, IA...506

APVA's John Marshall House, Richmond, VA 1528

Arcadia Township Historical Commission, Arcadia, MI 726

Ardenwood Historic Farm, Fremont, CA 96

Argo Gold Mine & Mill Museum, Idaho Springs, CO 223

Arizona Historical Society Museum, Tucson, AZ 47

Arizona Historical Society Museum at Papago Park, Tempe, AZ 45

Arizona Historical Society Museum - Downtown, Tucson, AZ 47

Arizona Historical Society Pioneer Museum, Flagstaff, AZ 32

Arizona Zoological Society, dba the Phoenix Zoo, Phoenix, AZ 40

Ark-La-Tex Antique & Classic Vehicle Museum, Shreveport, LA 600

Arkansas Post Museum, Gillett, AR 58

Arlington Heights Historical Museum, Arlington Heights, IL 411

Arlington Historical Museum, Arlington, VA 1495

The Arlington Historical Society, Arlington, MA 660

The Arms Family Museum of Local History, Youngstown, OH 1193

Arts Consortium of Cincinnati's African American Museum, Cincinnati, OH 1148

ArtWorks Children's Museum, Ingleside, IL 440

Ashland Historical Society Museum, Ashland, WI 1590

Ashtabula County Historical Society, Geneva-on-the-Lake, OH 1166

Ashton Villa & The Heritage Visitor Center, Galveston, TX 1420

Aspen Historical Society, Aspen, CO 202

Astor House Museum, Golden, CO 219

Ataloa Lodge Museum, Muskogee, OK 1205

The Athenaeum of Philadelphia, Philadelphia, PA 1276

The Atlanta Cyclorama, Atlanta, GA 358

Attleboro Area Industrial Museum, Inc., Attleboro, MA 661

Attmore-Oliver House, New Bern, NC 1112

Atwater Kent Museum of Philadelphia, Philadelphia, PA 1276

Atwood House Museum, Home of Chatham Historical Society, Chatham, MA 675

Au Glaize Village, Defiance, OH 1162

Audie Murphy/American Cotton Museum, Inc, Greenville, TX 1423

Audrain Historical Museum, Graceland, Mexico, MO 827

Audubon County Historical Society, Exira, IA 517

Audubon House & Tropical Gardens, Key West, FL 317

Augusta Museum of History, Augusta, GA 364

Aurora Historical Society, Aurora, IL 411

Aurora Historical Society, Aurora, OH 1140

Aurora History Museum, Aurora, CO 202

Aurora Regional Fire Museum, Aurora, IL 411

Austin Children's Museum, Austin, TX 1388

Autry National Center of the American West, Los Angeles, CA 112

B&O Railroad Museum: Ellicott City Station, Ellicott City, MD 643

BRIMS - Barren River Imaginative Museum of Science, Bowling Green, KY 565

The Babe Ruth Museum and Sports Legends at Camden Yards, Baltimore, MD 629

Baca House, Trinidad History Museum, Trinidad, CO 233

Badger Mine and Museum, Shullsburg, WI 1622

Baldwin County Heritage Museum, Elberta, AL 8

Baldwin Historical Society and Museum, Baldwin, NY 960

Baltimore County Historical Society, Cockeysville, MD 640

Bandon Historical Society Museum, Bandon, OR 1219

Banner County Historical Society, Harrisburg, NE 862

Bannock County Historical Museum, Pocatello, ID 408

Barbed Wire Museum, La Crosse, KS 547

Barnes Museum, Southington, CT 260

Barnet Historical Society, Barnet, VT 1476

Barnwell County Museum, Barnwell, SC .1321

Barre Historical Society, Inc., Barre, MA 662

Barron County Historical Society's Pioneer Village Museum, Cameron, WI 1593

Bartlesville Area History Museum, Bartlesville, OK 1196

Barton County Historical Museum & Village, Great Bend, KS 542

Bartow History Center, Cartersville, GA 367

Bayless-Selby House Museum, Denton, TX 1409

The Beaufort Arsenal, Beaufort, SC 1321

Beauvais Heritage Center, Clark, SD 1345

Beaverhead County Museum, Dillon, MT ...845

Becker County Historical Society, Detroit Lakes, MN 772

Bedingfield Inn Museum, Lumpkin, GA 376

Bell County Museum, Belton, TX 1395

Belle Meade Plantation, Nashville, TN 1377

Bellport-Brookhaven Historical Society and Museum, Bellport, NY 961

Beltrami County History Center, Bemidji, MN 768

Bement-Billings Farmstead, Newark Valley, NY 1041

Benicia Historical Museum, Benicia, CA 74

Benjamin Harrison Presidential Site, Indianapolis, IN 481

Bennington Battlefield State Historic Site, Walloomsac, NY 1081

The Bennington Museum, Bennington, VT 1476

Benton County Historical Museum, Philomath, OR 1230

Benzie Area Historical Museum, Benzonia, MI 729

Bergen Museum of Local History, Bergen, NY 962

Berkshire County Historical Society, Inc. - Arrowhead, Pittsfield, MA 702

Berkshire Museum, Pittsfield, MA 702

Bernard Historical Society and Museum, Delton, MI 734

Bess Streeter Aldrich House & Museum, Elmwood, NE 860

Bessemer Hall of History, Bessemer, AL 3

Best Friend of Charleston, Charleston, SC 1324

Betsy Ross House and Flag Museum, Philadelphia, PA 1277

Beyer Home, Oconto County Historical Society Museum, Oconto, WI 1616

The Bicycle Museum of America, New Bremen, OH 1177

Biedenharn Coca-Cola Museum, Vicksburg, MS 809

Big Springs Museum, Caledonia, NY 974

Big Thicket National Preserve, Kountze, TX 1432

Bill Baggs Cape Florida State Park, Key Biscayne, FL 316

Billings Farm & Museum, Woodstock, VT 1490

Biltmore Estate, Asheville, NC 1089

Bisbee Mining & Historical Museum, Bisbee, AZ 30

Bishop Hill Heritage Museum, Bishop Hill, IL 413

Black River Historical Society of Lorain, Lorain, OH 1172

Blackberry Farm's Pioneer Village, Aurora, IL 411

Bloom Mansion, Trinidad History Museum, Trinidad, CO 233

Blount Mansion, Knoxville, TN 1369

Blue Earth County Historical Society, Mankato, MN 780

Boone County Historical Museum, Belvidere, IL 413

Boonsborough Museum of History, Boonsboro, MD 637

Boot Hill Museum, Inc., Dodge City, KS 536

Boothbay Railway Village, Boothbay, ME...607

Bootheel Youth Museum, Malden, MO 826

Bosque Memorial Museum, Clifton, TX 1400

Boston Childrens Museum, Boston, MA 664

Recreational Artifacts–Continued

Boston Fire Museum, Boston, MA...............664

Boswell Museum of Music, Springfield
   Center, NY..1071

Bottineau County Historical Museum,
   Bottineau, ND......................................1129

Boulder City/Hoover Dam Museum,
   Boulder City, NV....................................875

Boulder History Museum, Boulder, CO.......202

Boundary County Historical Society,
   Bonners Ferry, ID..................................404

Boyertown Museum of Historic Vehicles,
   Boyertown, PA......................................1244

Bradford Brinton Memorial & Museum,
   Big Horn, WY.......................................1628

Bradford County Historical Society,
   Towanda, PA..1303

Bradford Historical Society Inc.,
   Bradford, VT...1477

Braintree Historical Society, Inc.,
   Braintree, MA...670

Branigan Cultural Center, Las Cruces,
   NM..940

Brevard Museum of History & Science,
   Cocoa, FL...300

Briar Bush Nature Center, Abington, PA...1238

Brick House, Montgomery, NY.................1015

Bridge Hampton Historical Society,
   Bridgehampton, NY................................964

Bridger Valley Heritage Museum, Lyman,
   WY...1636

The Bronx County Historical Society,
   Bronx, NY..964

Bronzeville Children's Museum,
   Evergreen Park, IL.................................435

The Brooklyn Historical Society,
   Brooklyn, NY..968

Brooklyn Historical Society, Brooklyn,
   OH...1144

Brucemore, Cedar Rapids, IA..................509

Brunswick Town/Fort Anderson State
   Historic Site, Winnabow, NC................1124

B's Ballpark Museum, Centennial, CO........205

Bucksport Historical Society, Inc.,
   Bucksport, ME..608

Bucyrus Historical Society, Bucyrus, OH..1144

Buechel Memorial Lakota Museum, Saint
   Francis, SD...1355

Buena Park Historical Society, Buena
   Park, CA..80

The Building for Kids - Fox Cities
   Children's Museum, Appleton, WI........1589

Bureau County Historical Society
   Museum, Princeton, IL...........................452

Burlingame Museum of Pez & Classic
   Toy Museum, Burlingame, CA..................80

Burlington Historical Museum,
   Burlington, MA.......................................672

Butler County History Center & Kansas
   Oil Museum, El Dorado, KS...................537

Butler County Museum, Hamilton, OH......1168

Byron Historical Museum, Byron, NY.......974

C.E. Smith Museum of Anthropology,
   Hayward, CA..101

CHTJ Southard House Museum,
   Brunswick, ME.......................................607

COSI Columbus, Columbus, OH...............1157

CU Heritage Center, Boulder, CO.............203

Cabot Historical Society, Cabot, VT..........1478

Cabrillo National Monument, San Diego,
   CA..156

California African-American Museum,
   Los Angeles, CA...................................113

California State Railroad Museum,
   Sacramento, CA....................................152

California Surf Museum, Oceanside, CA....135

Call of the Wild Museum, Gaylord, MI......742

Calvin Coolidge Historic Site, Plymouth
   Notch, VT..1484

Camden County Historical Society,
   Camden, NJ...899

Camp Atterbury Museum, Edinburgh, IN....474

Campbell County Rockpile Museum,
   Gillette, WY...1633

Campbell Historical Museum & Ainsley
   House, Campbell, CA................................80

Campbell House Museum, Saint Louis,
   MO..832

Canaan Historical Society, Inc., Canaan,
   NY..974

Cannon Falls Area Historical Museum,
   Cannon Falls, MN..................................770

Canton Classic Car Museum, Canton, OH.1145

Cape Cod Children's Museum, Mashpee,
   MA..693

Cape Fear Museum of History and
   Science, Wilmington, NC.......................1123

Cape May County Historical Museum
   and Genealogical Society, Cape May
   Court House, NJ....................................900

Capitola Historical Museum, Capitola,
   CA..81

Cappon & Settlers House Museums,
   Holland, MI..746

Captain George Flavel House Museum,
   Astoria, OR..1218

Captain John Wilson House, Cohasset,
   MA..676

Carbon County Museum, Rawlins, WY.....1637

Carlsbad Museum & Art Center,
   Carlsbad, NM...938

Carnton Plantation, Franklin, TN.............1365

Carpinteria Valley Historical Society &
   Museum of History, Carpinteria, CA.........82

Carroll Mansion Museum Home of
   Leavenworth County Historical
   Society, Leavenworth, KS.......................549

Cartoon Art Museum, San Francisco, CA....164

Carver County Historical Society,
   Waconia, MN...795

Casa Grande Valley Historical Society &
   Museum, Casa Grande, AZ........................30

Cascade County Historical Society
   Museum, Great Falls, MT.......................848

Cass County Museum & Pioneer School,
   Walker, MN...795

Casteel-Linn House and Museum,
   Princeton, MO.......................................829

Castle Air Museum, Atwater, CA................72

Castle Museum of Saginaw County
   History, Saginaw, MI.............................762

Catawba County Museum of History,
   Newton, NC..1113

Cattaraugus Area Historical Center,
   Cattaraugus, NY....................................976

Cedar Falls Historical Society, Cedar
   Falls, IA..507

Cedar Grove Historical Society, Cedar
   Grove, NJ..901

Centennial Village Museum, Greeley, CO...221

Center for American Music, Pittsburgh,
   PA...1291

Center for History, Wheaton, IL................465

Center for Puppetry Arts, Atlanta, GA.........359

Centerville Historical Museum,
   Centerville, MA.....................................675

Centerville - Washington Township
   Historical Society & Asahel Wright
   Community Center, Centerville, OH.....1146

Centerville - Washington Township
   Historical Society & Walton House
   Museum, Centerville, OH......................1147

Central Delta Depot Museum, Brinkley,
   AR..55

Central Florida Railroad Museum, Winter
   Garden, FL..354

Central Montana Historical Association,
   Inc. Museum, Lewistown, MT................850

Central Nevada Museum & Historical
   Society, Tonopah, NV.............................882

Central Ohio Fire Museum, Columbus,
   OH...1157

Central Park Conservancy, New York,
   NY...1022

Chagrin Falls Historical Society, Chagrin
   Falls, OH..1147

Chalet of the Golden Fleece, New
   Glarus, WI..1614

Challenger Learning Center of Arizona,
   Peoria, AZ...38

Champaign County Historical Museum,
   Champaign, IL..416

Champaign County Historical Museum,
   Urbana, OH..1188

Champion Mill State Historical Park,
   Champion, NE.......................................859

The Chapman Historical Museum, Glens
   Falls, NY..994

Charles A. Lindbergh Historic Site, Little
   Falls, MN..779

Charles A. Weyerhaeuser Memorial
   Museum, Little Falls, MN.......................779

Charles Pinckney National Historic Site,
   Mount Pleasant, SC..............................1337

Charles Towne Landing State Historic
   Site, Charleston, SC..............................1324

Charlotte at Play, Charlotte, NC..............1094

Charlotte County Historical Center,
   Charlotte Harbor, FL..............................299

Charlotte Museum of History and
   Hezekiah Alexander Homesite,
   Charlotte, NC..1094

Chateau De Mores State Historic Site,
   Medora, ND..1134

Chatillon-DeMenil Mansion, Saint Louis,
   MO..832

Chattanooga Regional History Museum,
   Chattanooga, TN...................................1361

Chautauqua County Historical Society,
   McClurg Museum, Westfield, NY.........1086

The Chelmsford Historical Society, Inc.,
   South Chelmsford, MA...........................709

Chenango County Historical Society
   Museum, Norwich, NY..........................1044

Cherokee County Historical Museum,
   Inc., Murphy, NC..................................1112

Cherokee Strip Museum, Alva, OK...........1195

Cherry County Historical Society,
   Valentine, NE..874

Chesapeake Bay Maritime Museum, Saint
   Michaels, MD..652

The Chesapeake Beach Railway Museum,
   Chesapeake Beach, MD...........................639

Chester County Historical Society, West
   Chester, PA..1307

Chesterfield County Museum,
   Chesterfield, VA....................................1501

The Chicago Athenaeum: Museum of
   Architecture and Design, Galena, IL.......436

Chicago Children's Museum, Chicago, IL...419

Chico Museum, Chico, CA..........................83

Children's Discovery Center, Clinton, IA....511

Children's Discovery Museum, Normal,
   IL...447

Children's Discovery Museum of North
   San Diego, Carlsbad, CA..........................81

Children's Discovery Workshop,
   Williamsport, PA..................................1308

Children's Hands-On Museum (CHOM),
   Tuscaloosa, AL.......................................19

Children's Museum, Jacksonville, OR........1226

The Children's Museum, Seattle, WA........1565

Children's Museum at Holyoke, Inc.,
   Holyoke, MA...687

The Children's Museum at Saratoga,
   Saratoga Springs, NY............................1064

Children's Museum/Detroit Public
   Schools, Detroit, MI..............................735

Children's Museum in Oak Lawn, Oak
   Lawn, IL..448

Children's Museum, Inc., Boca Raton, FL....296

The Children's Museum, Inc.,
   Bloomsburg, PA....................................1243

Children's Museum/Museo de Los Ninos,
   San Diego, CA.......................................156

Children's Museum of Acadiana,
   Lafayette, LA...589

Children's Museum of Bozeman, Bozeman, MT 842
Children's Museum of Central Nebraska, Hastings, NE 863
The Children's Museum of Cleveland, Cleveland, OH 1152
Children's Museum of Denver, Denver, CO 209
Children's Museum of Durango, Durango, CO 214
Children's Museum of Eastern Oregon, Pendleton, OR 1229
The Children's Museum of Green Bay, Green Bay, WI 1598
Children's Museum of History, Natural History and Science at Utica, New York, Utica, NY 1079
The Children's Museum of Houston, Houston, TX 1425
Children's Museum of Illinois, Decatur, IL 430
Children's Museum of Lake Charles, Inc., Lake Charles, LA 590
Children's Museum of Manhattan, New York, NY 1022
The Children's Museum of Memphis, Memphis, TN 1372
Children's Museum of Missoula, Missoula, MT 851
Children's Museum of Montana, Great Falls, MT 848
Children's Museum of Northern Nevada, Carson City, NV 875
Children's Museum of Oak Ridge, Inc., Oak Ridge, TN 1382
Children's Museum of Pittsburgh, Pittsburgh, PA 1291
The Children's Museum of Rose Hill Manor Park, Frederick, MD 644
The Children's Museum of Science and Technology, Troy, NY 1079
The Children's Museum of South Carolina, Myrtle Beach, SC 1338
Children's Museum of Stockton, Stockton, CA 189
Children's Museum of Tacoma, Tacoma, WA 1573
The Children's Museum of the Brazos Valley, Bryan, TX 1398
Children's Museum of the East End, Bridgehampton, NY 964
Children's Museum of the Highlands, Sebring, FL 345
Children's Museum of the Lowcountry, Charleston, SC 1324
Children's Museum of the Native American, New York, NY 1023
Children's Museum of the Shoals, Florence, AL 9
Children's Museum of the Three Rivers, Pasco, WA 1561
Children's Museum of the Valley, Youngstown, OH 1194
Children's Museum of Winston-Salem, Winston-Salem, NC 1125
Children's Peace Pavilion, Independence, MO 817
The Children's Playhouse, Boone, NC 1092
Children's Science Explorium at Sugar Sand Park, Boca Raton, FL 296
The Children's Toy & Doll Museum, Marietta, OH 1174
Childress County Heritage Museum, Childress, TX 1400
Chimney Point State Historic Site, Addison, VT 1475
Chinese American Museum, Los Angeles, CA 114
Chippewa County Historical Society, Montevideo, MN 783
Chippewa Nature Center, Midland, MI 755
Chippewa Valley Museum, Inc., Eau Claire, WI 1595

Chisholm Trail Historical Museum, Waurika, OK 1216
Chisholm Trail Museum, Kingfisher, OK 1203
The Christian C. Sanderson Museum, Chadds Ford, PA 1246
Churchill County Museum and Archives, Fallon, NV 877
Circus City Festival Museum, Peru, IN 495
City County Pioneer Museum, Sweetwater, TX 1454
City Island Nautical Museum, Bronx, NY 965
City Museum, Saint Louis, MO 832
City of Gilroy Museum, Gilroy, CA 99
City of Las Cruces Museum System, Las Cruces, NM 940
City of Wayne Historical Museum, Wayne, MI 766
Clallam County Historical Society, Port Angeles, WA 1561
Clark County Historical Society - Heritage Center of Clark County, Springfield, OH 1186
Clark Hotel Museum, Van Horn, TX 1457
Clarke House Museum, Chicago, IL 420
Clarkson Historical Museum, Clarkson, NE 859
Clarksville-Montgomery County Museum dba Customs House Museum & Cultural Center, Clarksville, TN 1363
Clay County Historical Society Museum and Archives, Moorhead, MN 784
Clear Creek History Park, Golden, CO 219
Clearwater Historical Museum, Orofino, ID 408
Clermont State Historic Site, Clermont, NY 979
Cleveland County Historical Museum, Shelby, NC 1119
Clewiston Museum, Inc., Clewiston, FL 300
Clinton Academy, East Hampton, NY 985
Clinton County Historical Association & Museum, Plattsburgh, NY 1052
Clinton County Historical Society, Wilmington, OH 1191
Clinton County Museum, Frankfort, IN 478
Clovis Depot Model Train Museum, Clovis, NM 939
Coal Miners' Museum/Van Lear Historical Society, Inc., Van Lear, KY 584
Codington County Heritage Museum, Watertown, SD 1359
The Coffey County Historical Museum, Burlington, KS 534
Cole County Historical Museum, Jefferson City, MO 819
Colfax County Society of Art, History and Archaeology, Raton, NM 945
College Football Hall of Fame, South Bend, IN 499
College Park Aviation Museum, College Park, MD 641
Collin County Farm Museum, McKinney, TX 1437
Collin County Historical Society, Inc. & History Museum, McKinney, TX 1437
Colorado Ski Museum-Ski & Snowboard Hall of Fame, Vail, CO 234
Columbia Gorge Discovery Center and Wasco County Museum, The Dalles, OR 1237
Columbia Gorge Interpretive Center Museum, Stevenson, WA 1572
Columbia River Maritime Museum, Astoria, OR 1218
Columbus-Belmont Civil War Museum, Columbus, KY 567
Comanche Crossing Historical Society & Museum, Strasburg, CO 233
Community Children's Museum, Dover, NJ 902
Community Memorial Museum of Sutter County, Yuba City, CA 200
Concord Museum, Concord, MA 676

Concordia Historical Institute, Saint Louis, MO 832
Coney Island Museum, Brooklyn, NY 969
Confusion Hill Gravity House, Piercy, CA 142
Conklin Reed Organ & History Museum, Hanover, MI 745
Connecticut Children's Museum, New Haven, CT 253
Connecticut Fire Museum, East Windsor, CT 239
Connecticut Historical Society, Hartford, CT 244
Conrad Mansion National Historic Site Museum, Kalispell, MT 850
Cook County Historical Museum, Grand Marais, MN 776
Cooper-Hewitt National Design Museum, Smithsonian Institution, New York, NY 1023
Cooper Regional History Museum, Upland, CA 193
Coos Historical & Maritime Museum, North Bend, OR 1229
Cortland County Historical Society, Cortland, NY 982
Cottonwood County Historical Society, Windom, MN 796
Courthouse Square Association, Charlotte, MI 731
Cow Neck Peninsula Historical Society Sands-Willets House, Port Washington, NY 1053
The Cowley County Historical Society, Winfield, KS 564
Cowlitz County Historical Museum, Kelso, WA 1557
Cradle of Aviation Museum, Garden City, NY 992
Craftsmen's Guild of Mississippi, Jackson, MS 802
Cranbury Historical & Preservation Society, Cranbury, NJ 902
Craters of the Moon National Monument, Arco, ID 403
Cravens House, Lookout Mountain, TN 1371
Crawford County Historical Museum, Pittsburg, KS 556
Creative Discovery Museum, Chattanooga, TN 1361
Crested Butte Mountain Heritage Museum, Crested Butte, CO 208
Crestline Shunk Museum, Crestline, OH 1160
Crispus Attucks Center Museum, Indianapolis, IN 482
Crossroads Museum, Corinth, MS 800
Crossroads of America, Bethlehem, NH 883
Crowley Museum & Nature Center, Sarasota, FL 344
Culbertson Mansion State Historic Site, New Albany, IN 493
Culbertson Museum, Culbertson, MT 845
Cumberland County Historical Society, Greenwich, NJ 905
Cumberland County Historical Society, The Hamilton Library and The Two Mile House, Carlisle, PA 1245
Cupertino Historical Society & Museum, Cupertino, CA 88
Custer County Historical Society, Inc., Broken Bow, NE 858
Cuyuna Range Historical Society & Museum, Crosby, MN 772

D.R. Barker Historical Museum, Fredonia, NY 992
Dacotah Prairie Museum, Aberdeen, SD 1344
Dade Battlefield Historic State Park, Bushnell, FL 298
Dakota County Historical Society, South Saint Paul, MN 793
Dakota Discovery Museum, Mitchell, SD 1352
Dakotaland Museum, Huron, SD 1348

Recreational Artifacts–Continued

Dale & Martha Hawk Museum, Wolford, ND...1138

Dallas Historical Society, Dallas, TX.........1405

The Dan Quayle Center & Museum, Huntington, IN...481

Dancing Bear Folk Center, Thermopolis, WY...1639

Daniel Boone Home and Boonesfield Village, Lindenwood University, Defiance, MO...814

Daniels County Museum and Pioneer Town, Scobey, MT...853

The Danish Immigrant Museum, Elk Horn, IA...517

Danvers Historical Society, Danvers, MA....678

Daughters of the American Revolution Museum, Washington, DC...277

Davenport House Museum, Savannah, GA...384

David Bradford House, Washington, PA....1305

De Smet Depot Museum, De Smet, SD.....1346

Deaf Smith County Museum, Hereford, TX...1424

Dearborn Historical Museum, Dearborn, MI...733

Decatur House Museum, Washington, DC....277

Decorative Arts Collection, Inc. Museum of Decorative Painting, Wichita, KS.......561

Deer Isle-Stonington Historical Society, Deer Isle, ME...609

Deer Park Escondido Winery & Auto Museum, Escondido, CA...93

Deerfield Beach Historical Society, Deerfield Beach, FL...304

Delaware and Hudson Canal Historical Society and Museum, High Falls, NY.....998

Delaware Toy and Miniature Museum, Wilmington, DE...273

Delta County Museum, Delta, CO...............209

Deming Luna Mimbres Museum, Deming, NM...939

Dennys River Historical Society, Dennysville, ME...609

Denton County Historical Museum, Inc. and Texas Heritage Center, Denton, TX...1409

Denver Museum of Miniatures, Dolls and Toys, Denver, CO...211

Depot Museum & Fort Sedgwick Museum, Julesburg, CO...223

Des Plaines History Center, Des Plaines, IL...430

Deschutes County Historical Society, Bend, OR...1220

Desert Caballeros Western Museum, Wickenburg, AZ...53

Detroit Historical Society, Detroit, MI.........735

Deutschheim State Historic Site, Hermann, MO...817

Devils Tower Visitor Center, Devils Tower, WY...1631

Dewey Hotel Museum, Dewey, OK...........1199

Dexter Area Historical Society & Museum, Dexter, MI...738

Dexter Historical Society Campus, Dexter, ME...609

Dickinson County Heritage Center, Abilene, KS...531

Discover Westfield Children's Museum, Westfield, MA...718

The Discovery Center, Fresno, CA...............96

Discovery Center at Murfree Spring, Murfreesboro, TN...1376

The Discovery Center of Idaho, Boise, ID...403

The Discovery Center of the Southern Tier, Binghamton, NY...962

Discovery Depot Children's Museum, Galesburg, IL...437

Discovery Gateway, Salt Lake City, UT....1471

The Discovery Museum, Eureka, CA.............94

Discovery Museum, Sacramento Museum of History, Science and Technology, Sacramento, CA...152

Discovery Science Place, Tyler, TX............1456

Dr. Samuel D. Harris National Museum of Dentistry, Baltimore, MD...................631

Dodge County Historical Society, Mantorville, MN...780

Dolls at Home Museum, Spearfish, SD.....1357

Don Garlits Museum of Drag Racing Inc., Ocala, FL...330

Door County Historical Museum, Sturgeon Bay, WI...1623

Dorothea B. Hoover Historical Museum, Joplin, MO...819

Dorothy G. Page Museum, Wasilla, AK.........29

Douglas County Historical Society, Superior, WI...1624

Douglas County Museum Complex, Armour, SD...1344

Douglas County Museum of History and Natural History, Roseburg, OR...........1234

Douglass Historical Museum, Douglass, KS...537

The Downers Grove Park District Museum, Downers Grove, IL...................431

Drew County Historical Museum, Monticello, AR...64

Dubois Museum, Dubois, WY...................1632

Duke Homestead State Historic Site, Durham, NC...1098

Duluth Children's Museum, Duluth, MN.....772

Duncan Cottage Museum, Metlakatla, AK.....27

Dunedin Historical Society & Museum, Dunedin, FL...305

DuPage Children's Museum, Naperville, IL...447

DuPage County Historical Museum, Wheaton, IL...465

Durham Historic Association Museum, Durham, NH...886

Durham Western Heritage Museum, Omaha, NE...870

Dwight D. Eisenhower Library-Museum, Abilene, KS...531

E. St. Julien Cox House, Saint Peter, MN ...792

Eagle Historical Society & Museums, Eagle, AK...23

EarlyWorks Museums, Huntsville, AL...........11

East Hampton Historical Society, Inc., East Hampton, NY...985

East Hampton Town Marine Museum, Amagansett, NY...957

East Jordan Portside Art & Historical Museum, East Jordan, MI...739

Eastchester Historical Society - 1835 Marble Schoolhouse, Bronxville, NY......967

Eastern Oregon Museum on the Old Oregon Trail, Haines, OR...................1226

Eastside Heritage Center, Bellevue, WA 1548

Edisto Island Historic Preservation Society Museum, Edisto Island, SC 1332

Edmond Historical Society Museum, Edmond, OK...1200

Edmonds South Snohomish County Historical Society, Inc., Edmonds, WA .1553

Edsel & Eleanor Ford House, Grosse Pointe Shores, MI...745

Edwards County Historical Museum, Kinsley, KS...547

The 1890 House-Museum & Center for Arts, Cortland, NY...983

82nd Airborne Division War Memorial Museum, Fort Bragg, NC...................1101

Eisenhower National Historic Site, Gettysburg, PA...1255

El Campo Museum of Natural History, El Campo, TX...1411

El Dorado County Historical Museum, Placerville, CA...142

El Paso Museum of History, El Paso, TX..1412

El Pueblo History Museum, Pueblo, CO......230

Elgin Area Historical Society, Elgin, IL........432

Eli Whitney Museum, Inc., Hamden, CT.....244

Elkhart County Historical Museum, Bristol, IN...471

Ella Sharp Museum, Jackson, MI.................748

Ellis County Historical Society, Hays, KS...543

Elmhurst Historical Museum, Elmhurst, IL...433

Emily Dickinson Museum: The Homestead and The Evergreens, Amherst, MA...658

The Enchanted Mansion, A Doll Museum, Baton Rouge, LA...................585

Enchanted World Doll Museum, Mitchell, SD...1352

Enfield Historical Society Museum, Enfield Center, NH...887

Ephraim Historical Foundation, Ephraim, WI...1597

Erie Canal Museum, Syracuse, NY...........1076

Erie County History Center & Cashier's House, Erie, PA...1252

Escondido Children's Museum, Escondido, CA...93

Escondido History Center, Escondido, CA...93

Essley-Noble Museum: Mercer County Historical Society, Aledo, IL...................410

Estes Park Museum, Estes Park, CO...........215

The Esther Thomas Atkinson Museum, Hampden-Sydney, VA...1509

The Ethel Wright Mohamed Stitchery Museum, Belzoni, MS...798

Eugene Field House and St. Louis Toy Museum, Saint Louis, MO...................833

Eureka School House, Springfield, VT 1487

Evanston Historical Society and Charles Gates Dawes House, Evanston, IL.........434

Evansville Museum of Arts History & Science, Evansville, IN...475

Experience Children's Museum, Erie, PA ..1253

Explora, Albuquerque, NM...933

Exploration Place, Inc., Wichita, KS...........561

Exploration Station - A Children's Museum, Bourbonnais, IL...................414

Explorations V Children's Museum, Lakeland, FL...320

Explore & More...A Children's Museum, East Aurora, NY...985

Explorium of Lexington, Lexington, KY 572

EXPO, The Children's Museum of Gainesville, Inc., Gainesville, FL............310

Fairbanks House, Dedham, MA...................679

Fairbanks Museum and Planetarium, Saint Johnsbury, VT...1486

Fairfield Historical Society, Fairfield, CT 241

Fairport Historical Museum, Fairport, NY...989

Fairview Museum of History & Art, Fairview, UT...1465

Falmouth Historical Society, Falmouth, MA...682

Farmers Branch Historical Park, Farmers Branch, TX...1413

Farragut Folklife Museum, Farragut, TN ..1364

Farrar-Mansur House & Old Mill Museum, Weston, VT...1490

Fascinate-U Children's Museum, Fayetteville, NC...1100

FASNY Museum of Fire Fighting, Hudson, NY...1000

Faust Park Foundation, Chesterfield, MO 812

Favell Museum Inc., Klamath Falls, OR....1227

Fayette County Helpers Club & Historical Society, West Union, IA.........530

Fayette Heritage Museum & Archives, La Grange, TX...1432

Fenton History Center-Museum & Library, Jamestown, NY...1005

Fillmore County Historical Center, Fountain, MN...776

Fillmore Historical Museum, Inc., Fillmore, CA...95

Fine Arts Center of Kershaw County, Inc., Camden, SC............1322
The Finley House, Wayne, PA..................1306
Fire Museum of Maryland, Inc., Lutherville, MD.........................649
Fire Museum of Texas, Beaumont, TX 1394
Firelands Historical Society Museum, Norwalk, OH...........................1180
First Territorial Capitol of Kansas, Fort Riley, KS.................................540
First White House of the Confederacy, Montgomery, AL..........................16
Fitchburg Historical Society, Fitchburg, MA...683
The Five Civilized Tribes Museum, Muskogee, OK.........................1205
Flathead Indian Museum, Saint Ignatius, MT...853
Flickertail Village and Museum, Stanley, ND..1136
Florewood State Park, Greenwood, MS.......801
Florissant Valley Historical Society, Florissant, MO...........................815
Floyd County Historical Museum, Charles City, IA.........................510
The Fluvanna County Historical Society Old Stone Jail Museum, Palmyra, VA...1524
The Folsom House Museum, Taylors Falls, MN....................................794
Fort Bowie National Historic Site, Bowie, AZ....................................30
Fort Bridger State Museum, Fort Bridger, WY..1632
Fort Buford State Historic Site, Williston, ND..1137
Fort Christmas Historical Park, Christmas, FL..............................299
Fort Collins Museum, Fort Collins, CO.......217
Fort de Chartres State Historic Site & Museum, Prairie du Rocher, IL 451
Fort Dodge & Frontier Village, Fort Dodge, IA.....................................518
Fort George G. Meade Museum, Fort Meade, MD....................................643
Fort Gibson Historic Site, Fort Gibson, OK...1200
Fort Hays State Historic Site, Hays, KS 543
Fort Hill (The John C. Calhoun House), Clemson, SC.................................1328
Fort Kearney Museum, Kearney, NE.........863
Fort Laramie National Historic Site, Fort Laramie, WY...............................1633
Fort Lauderdale Historical Society, Fort Lauderdale, FL..............................307
Fort McKavett State Historical Site, Fort McKavett, TX..............................1415
Fort Nisqually Living History Museum, Tacoma, WA..................................1573
Fort Ontario State Historic Site, Oswego, NY...1048
Fort St. Jean Baptiste State Historic Site, Natchitoches, LA.............................593
Fort Sidney Museum & Post Commander's Home, Sidney, NE.............873
Fort Smith Museum of History, Fort Smith, AR.....................................58
Fort Totten State Historic Site, Fort Totten, ND...................................1131
Fort Union Trading Post National Historic Site, Williston, ND..................1138
Fort Walla Walla Museum, Walla Walla, WA...1576
Fort Washington Park, Fort Washington, MD..643
Fort Winnebago Surgeons Quarters, Portage, WI....................................1618
Fort Worth Museum of Science and History, Fort Worth, TX 1417
Fostoria Area Historical Museum, Fostoria, OH.................................1164
Fox Island Historical Society, Fox Island, WA...1554

The Foxfire Museum & Heritage Center, Mountain City, GA........................380
Framingham Historical Society & Museum, Framingham, MA....................683
Franconia Heritage Museum, Franconia, NH..888
Frank Chiarenza Museum of Glass, Meriden, CT.................................248
Frank Phillips Home, Bartlesville, OK.......1197
Frankenmuth Historical Museum, Frankenmuth, MI.............................742
Frankfort Area Historical Museum, West Frankfort, IL..............................464
Franklin County Historical & Museum Society & House of History, Malone, NY...1012
The Franklin Pierce Homestead, Hillsborough, NH.............................889
Fraunces Tavern Museum, New York, NY...1025
Freeborn County Museum and Historical Village, Albert Lea, MN....................767
Freestone County Historical Museum, Fairfield, TX.................................1413
Fremont County Pioneer Museum, Lander, WY..................................1635
Fresno Metropolitan Museum, Fresno, CA...97
Frisco Historic Park & Museum, Frisco, CO...218
Frontier Culture Museum, Staunton, VA....1537
Frontier Historical Society and Museum, Glenwood Springs, CO 219
Frontier Museum, Williston, ND 1138
Frontiers of Flight Museum, Dallas, TX 1406
The Fullerton Arboretum, Fullerton, CA.....98
Fulton County Historical Museum, Wauseon, OH.................................1190
Fulton County Historical Society Museum, Rochester, IN.......................498
Fulton Mansion State Historic Site, Rockport, TX................................1446

Gage County Historical Society and Museum, Beatrice, NE 857
Galena-Jo Daviess County Historical Society & Museum, Galena, IL...............436
Gallier House, New Orleans, LA.................595
Galloway House and Village - Blakely Museum, Fond du Lac, WI....................1597
Galveston County Historical Museum, Galveston, TX................................1420
Galveston Historical Foundation, Inc., Galveston, TX................................1421
Galveston Railroad Museum, Galveston, TX...1421
Garden Grove Historical Society, Garden Grove, CA...99
Garden State Discovery Museum, Cherry Hill, NJ..901
Gardner House Museum, Albion, MI...........723
Garnavillo Historical Museum, Garnavillo, IA..................................518
Garrett County Historical Museum, Oakland, MD.................................649
Gaston County Museum of Art and History, Dallas, NC 1097
Gatekeeper's Museum & Marion Steinbach Indian Basket Museum, Tahoe City, CA..............................190
Gates House, Machiasport Historical Society, Machiasport, ME.....................614
General Crook House Museum and Library/Archives Center, Omaha, NE......870
General Daniel Bissell House, Saint Louis, MO.....................................833
Genesee Country Village & Museum, Mumford, NY...............................1016
Geneva Historical Society & Rose Hill Mansion, Geneva, NY.......................994
Geographical Center Historical Museum, Rugby, ND...................................1136

The George Bush Presidential Library and Museum, College Station, TX 1400
George Washington's Ferry Farm, Stafford County, VA 1537
Georgia Music Hall of Fame and Museum, Macon, GA..........................377
The Georgian Museum, Lancaster, OH 1171
Germantown Historical Society, Philadelphia, PA 1280
Ghost Town Museum, Colorado Springs, CO...207
Gibbs Museum of Pioneer and Dakotah Life, Falcon Heights, MN.....................775
Gig Harbor Peninsula Historical Society, Gig Harbor, WA..............................1555
Gila County Historical Museum, Globe, AZ..35
Gilcrease Museum, Tulsa, OK....................1215
Gillespie County Historical Society, Fredericksburg, TX.............................1419
Gilliam County Historical Society - Depot Museum Complex, Condon, OR.1222
Gilman Museum, Hellertown, PA...............1260
Gilmore Car Museum, Hickory Corners, MI...746
Gilpin History Museum, Central City, CO...205
Glendower State Memorial, Lebanon, OH.1171
Glenn H. Curtiss Museum, Hammondsport, NY.............................997
Glensheen Historic Estate, Duluth, MN.......773
Glenview Area Historical Society, Glenview, IL.....................................438
Gloucester County Historical Society, Woodbury, NJ...................................931
Gold Coast Railroad Museum, Inc., Miami, FL..323
The Golden Age of Trucking Museum, Middlebury, CT.................................249
Golden Pioneer Museum, Golden, CO.........220
Golf Museum, Newport News, VA.............1519
Goodhue County Historical Society, Red Wing, MN.....................................787
Goshen Historical Society, Goshen, CT.......242
Gouverneur Historical Association, Gouverneur, NY...............................995
Governor Ross Plantation, Seaford, DE.......272
The Grace Museum, Abilene, TX................1385
Grafton Historical Society, Grafton, VT.....1479
Graham County Historical Society, Thatcher, AZ.......................................46
Grand Encampment Museum, Inc., Encampment, WY...............................1632
Grand Forks County Historical Society, Grand Forks, ND................................1132
Grand Lake Area Historical Society, Grand Lake, CO.................................221
Grand Portage National Monument, Grand Marais, MN................................776
Grand Rapids Children's Museum, Grand Rapids, MI..743
The Grand River Historical Society & Museum, Chillicothe, MO....................813
Grand Teton National Park, Colter Bay Indian Arts Museum, Colter Bay Village, WY......................................1631
Grant County Historical Museum, Canyon City, OR.................................1221
Grant County Historical Museum, Ephrata, WA..................................1553
Grant County Museum aka Historic Adobe Museum, Ulysses, KS 560
Granville County Historical Society Museum, Oxford, NC.........................1114
Granville Historical Society Museum, Granville, OH..................................1167
Great Lakes Children's Museum, Greilickville, MI................................744
Great Smoky Mountains Heritage Center, Townsend, TN....................................1384
Greater Harvard Area Historical Society, Harvard, IL......................................439

Recreational Artifacts–Continued

Greater Hazleton Historical Society, Hazleton, PA 1260

Green Bay Packers Hall of Fame, Green Bay, WI 1598

Green Mountain Club, Inc., Waterbury Center, VT 1489

Greenbelt Museum, Greenbelt, MD 646

Greenfield Historical Society, Greenfield, WI 1599

Greensboro Children's Museum, Greensboro, NC 1103

Greensboro Historical Museum, Inc., Greensboro, NC 1103

Greenwood County Historical Society, Eureka, KS 539

Gregg County Historical Museum, Longview, TX 1434

Gresham History Museum, Gresham, OR ..1226

Greyhound Hall of Fame, Abilene, KS 531

Grinnell Historical Museum, Grinnell, IA....519

Grinter Place State Historic Site, Kansas City, KS 546

Gropius House, Lincoln, MA 690

Grosse Ile Historical Society, Grosse Ile, MI 745

Groton Historical Society, Groton, MA 685

Grout Museum District: Grout Museum of History and Science, Bluedorn Science Imaginarium, Rensselaer Russell House Museum, Snowden House, Waterloo, IA 529

Groveland Yosemite Gateway Museum, Groveland, CA 101

Guernsey County Museum, Cambridge, OH 1144

Gulf Branch Nature Center, Arlington, VA 1496

Gull Wings Children's Museum, Oxnard, CA 137

Gwinnett History Museum, Lawrenceville, GA 376

Haas-Lilienthal House, San Francisco, CA 166

Habitot Children's Museum, Berkeley, CA 75

Hackettstown Historical Society Museum & Library, Hackettstown, NJ 905

Haffenreffer Museum of Anthropology, Brown University, Bristol, RI 1310

Haines Museum, Waukegan Historical Society, Waukegan, IL 463

Halifax Historical Museum, Daytona Beach, FL 303

Hamilton House, South Berwick, ME 622

Hamilton Township Historical Society - John Abbott II House, Hamilton, NJ 906

Hammond Museum and Japanese Stroll Garden, North Salem, NY 1043

Hampton County Historical Museum, Hampton, SC 1334

Hampton History Museum, Hampton, VA .1509

Hampton National Historic Site, Towson, MD 655

Hancock Historical Museum, Findlay, OH 1164

Hancock House, Hancock's Bridge, NJ 907

Hands On Children's Museum, Olympia, WA 1560

Hands-on House, Children's Museum of Lancaster, Lancaster, PA 1265

Hannah Lindahl Children's Museum, Mishawaka, IN 491

Hanover Historical Society Museum, Hanover, VA 1510

Hanover House, Clemson, SC 1328

Happy Hollow Park & Zoo, San Jose, CA 171

Harbour House Museum, Crystal Falls, MI 733

Hardin County Historical Museums, Inc., Kenton, OH 1170

Harlan-Lincoln House, Mount Pleasant, IA 524

Harn Homestead and 1889er Museum, Oklahoma City, OK 1207

The Harness Racing Museum and Hall of Fame, Goshen, NY 995

Harney County Historical Museum, Burns, OR 1221

Harold M. Freund American Museum of Baking, Manhattan, KS 550

Harold Warp Pioneer Village Foundation, Minden, NE 868

Harpers Ferry National Historical Park, Harpers Ferry, WV 1582

Harriet Beecher Stowe Center, Hartford, CT 245

Harrison County Historical Museum, Marshall, TX 1436

Hartmann Model R.R. & Toy Museum, Intervale, NH 889

Harvard Historical Society, Still River, MA 711

Haskell County Historical Society, Sublette, KS 558

Hathaway Ranch Museum, Santa Fe Springs, CA 182

Haverford Township Historical Society, Havertown, PA 1260

Havre de Grace Decoy Museum, Havre de Grace, MD 647

Hawaii Children's Discovery Center, Honolulu, HI 395

Hawaii Loves Barbie Dolls Museum, Kailua, HI 399

Hawaii Maritime Center, Honolulu, HI 395

Hawks Inn Historical Society, Inc., Delafield, WI 1595

Hayward Area Historical Society, Hayward, CA 102

Hazel Kibler Museum, Girard, PA 1256

Health World Children's Museum, Barrington, IL 412

Healthworks! Kids' Museum, South Bend, IN 499

Healy House-Dexter Cabin, Leadville, CO 225

Hearthstone Historic House Museum, Appleton, WI 1589

Held-Poage Memorial Home and Research Library, Ukiah, CA 193

Helvetia Museum, Helvetia, WV 1582

The Hemingway Museum and The Ernest Hemingway Birthplace, Oak Park, IL 448

Hennepin History Museum, Minneapolis, MN 782

Henry County Historical Society, New Castle, IN 494

The Henry Ford, Dearborn, MI 733

Heritage Center of Lancaster County, Inc., Lancaster, PA 1265

Heritage Farmstead Museum, Plano, TX ...1444

Heritage House Museum of Montgomery County, Mount Ida, AR 64

Heritage House of Orange County Association Inc., Orange, TX 1441

The Heritage Museum of Fine Arts for Youth, Detroit, MI 736

Heritage Museum of Northwest Florida, Valparaiso, FL 352

Heritage Museums & Gardens, Sandwich, MA 707

The Heritage Society, Houston, TX 1426

Heritage Square Museum, Los Angeles, CA 116

Heritage Village, Largo, FL 321

Heritage Village, Mountain Lake, MN 785

The Hermitage, Ho-Ho-Kus, NJ 907

Herreshoff Marine Museum/America's Cup Hall of Fame, Bristol, RI 1311

Herschell Carrousel Factory Museum, North Tonawanda, NY 1043

The Hickories Museum of the Lorain County Historical Society, Elyria, OH ..1163

Hickory Grove Rural School Museum, Ogden, IA 525

Hiddenite Center, Inc., Hiddenite, NC 1106

The Higgins Museum, Okoboji, IA 525

High Point Museum & Historical Park, High Point, NC 1106

Highland County Museum and Heritage Center, McDowell, VA 1517

Highlands Hammock State Park/Civilian Conservation Corps Museum, Sebring, FL 346

Highlands Museum & Discovery Center, Ashland, KY 564

The Hill Country Museum, Kerrville, TX..1431

Hillforest House Museum, Aurora, IN 468

Hillsboro Area Historical Society, Hillsboro, WI 1600

Historic Bowens Mills & Pioneer Park, Middleville, MI 754

Historic Charlton Park Village and Museum, Hastings, MI 745

Historic Cherry Hill, Albany, NY 954

Historic Columbia Foundation, Columbia, SC 1329

Historic General Dodge House, Council Bluffs, IA 512

Historic Georgetown Inc., Georgetown, CO 218

Historic Lyme Village Association, Bellevue, OH 1142

Historic Palmyra's Print Shop, Palmyra, NY 1050

Historic Palmyra's - Wm. Phelps General Store, Palmyra, NY 1050

Historic Pensacola Village, Pensacola, FL ...335

Historic Preservation Association of Bourbon County, Inc., Fort Scott, KS 540

Historic Price House, Woodruff, SC 1343

Historic Renville Preservation Commission, Renville, MN 787

Historic Shepherdstown Museum, Shepherdstown, WV 1586

Historic Spanish Point, Osprey, FL 333

Historic Speedwell, Morristown, NJ...........913

Historical and Genealogical Society of Indiana County, Indiana, PA 1262

Historical Center for Southeast New Mexico, Roswell, NM 946

Historical Museum at Fort Missoula, Missoula, MT 851

Historical Museum of Bay County, Bay City, MI 727

Historical Museum of Southern Florida, Miami, FL 324

Historical Society of Berks County, Reading, PA 1296

Historical Society of Bloomfield New Jersey, Bloomfield, NJ 898

Historical Society of Brookfield, Brookfield Center, VT 1477

Historical Society of Carroll County, Westminster, MD 656

Historical Society of Delaware, Wilmington, DE 274

Historical Society of Fort Washington, Fort Washington, PA 1254

Historical Society of Garden County, Oshkosh, NE 871

Historical Society of Glastonbury, Glastonbury, CT 242

Historical Society of Greenfield, Greenfield, MA 685

Historical Society of Middletown and the Wallkill Precinct, Inc., Middletown, NY 1014

Historical Society of Millersburg & Upper Paxton Township Museum, Millersburg, PA 1272

Historical Society of Newburgh Bay & the Highlands - David Crawford House, Newburgh, NY 1042

Historical Society of Oak Park & River Forest, Oak Park, IL.............448
Historical Society of Old Newbury, Cushing House Museum, Newburyport, MA.............698
Historical Society of Old Randolph, Randolph, NJ.............922
Historical Society of Quaker Hill & Pawling, Pawling, NY.............1051
Historical Society of Quincy and Adams County, Quincy, IL.............452
Historical Society of Rockland County, New City, NY.............1017
Historical Society of St. Marys and Benzinger Township, Saint Marys, PA..1297
Historical Society of Stanton County Museums at Stanton and Pilger, Pilger, NE.............872
Historical Society of the Town of Clarence, Clarence, NY.............978
The History Center, Fort Wayne, IN.............477
The History Center, Cedar Rapids, IA.........509
The History Center in Tompkins County, Ithaca, NY.............1003
History Museum for Springfield-Greene County, Springfield, MO.............839
History Museum of Western Virginia, Roanoke, VA.............1535
The History Place, Morehead City, NC......1111
History San Jose, San Jose, CA.............171
Hiwan Homestead Museum, Evergreen, CO.............215
Hoard Historical Museum and National Dairy Shrine's Visitors Center, Fort Atkinson, WI.............1598
Hodgden House Museum Complex, Ellsworth, KS.............538
Hoiles-Davis Museum, Greenville, IL.........439
Holiday World/Splashin' Safari, Santa Claus, IN.............498
Holland Historical Society Museum, Inc., Holland, VT.............1480
The Holland Land Office Museum, Batavia, NY.............960
The Holland Museum, Holland, MI.............746
Holly History Center & Hutchinson House Museum, Waupaca, WI.............1626
Hollywood Guinness World of Records Museum, Hollywood, CA.............103
Hollywood Heritage Museum, Hollywood, CA.............103
Holmes County Historical Society, Millersburg, OH.............1176
Homesteader Museum, Powell, WY.........1637
Homeville Museum, Homer, NY.............999
Hood River County Historical Museum, Hood River, OR.............1226
Horatio Colony House Museum & Nature Preserve, Keene, NH.............890
Horry County Museum, Conway, SC.........1331
Hot Springs National Park Visitor Center, Hot Springs, AR.............60
Houghton County Historical Museum Society, Lake Linden, MI.............749
House of a Thousand Dolls, Loma, MT......851
Howard County Historical Society, Ellicott City, MD.............643
Howard W. Cannon Aviation Museum, Henderson, NV.............878
The Hoyt Institute of Fine Arts, New Castle, PA.............1273
The Huguenot Historical Society, New Paltz, NY.............1017
Hulihee Palace, Kailua-Kona, HI.............399
Humboldt Historical Museum, Humboldt, KS.............544
The 100th Meridian Museum, Cozad, NE...859
Hunter-Dawson State Historic Site, New Madrid, MO.............828
Huntingdon County Historical Society, Huntingdon, PA.............1262

Huntington Beach International Surfing Museum, Huntington Beach, CA.............104
Huntington County Historical Society Museum, Huntington, IN.............481
Hurst Ranch Historical Foundation, West Covina, CA.............197
Hyde Hall, Inc., Cooperstown, NY.............980
Hydroplane & Raceboat Museum, Kent, WA.............1557
The Hyland House, Guilford, CT.............243
Hyser Rivers Museum, Belmont, MI.............728
The Ida Dennie Willis Museum of Miniatures, Dolls, and Toys, Tulsa, OK.............1215
Idaho State Historical Museum, Boise, ID...404
Illinois and Michigan Canal Commissioners Office Museum, Lockport, IL.............443
The Imaginarium Science Discovery Center, Anchorage, AK.............22
Imagination Workshop - Temecula Children's Museum, Temecula, CA.........191
Imagine Children's Museum, Everett, WA.1554
Imagine It! The Children's Museum of Atlanta, Atlanta, GA.............361
Imagine Nation Museum, Bristol, CT.........236
Imagine That!, Florham Park, NJ.............904
ImagineU Children's Museum, Visalia, CA.............195
Imperial Calcasieu Museum, Inc., Lake Charles, LA.............590
Independence Historical Museum, Independence, KS.............545
Indian Pueblo Cultural Center, Albuquerque, NM.............933
Indiana Basketball Hall of Fame, New Castle, IN.............494
Indiana Historical Society, Indianapolis, IN.............483
Indiana State Museum, Indianapolis, IN......484
International Bowling Museum and Hall of Fame, Saint Louis, MO.............833
The International Clown Hall of Fame & Research Center, Inc., Milwaukee, WI..1611
International Institute of Metropolitan Detroit, Detroit, MI.............737
International Motor Racing Research Center at Watkins Glen, Watkins Glen, NY.............1084
International Museum of Carousel Art, Hood River, OR.............1226
International Museum of the Horse, Lexington, KY.............573
International Swimming Hall of Fame, Inc., Fort Lauderdale, FL.............307
International Tennis Hall of Fame & Museum, Newport, RI.............1313
Iosco County Historical Museum, East Tawas, MI.............740
The Iowa Children's Museum, Coralville, IA.............511
Iowa Great Lakes Maritime Museum, Arnolds Park, IA.............505
Ipswich Historical Society and Museum, Ipswich, MA.............688
Iredell Museum of Arts & Heritage, Statesville, NC.............1120
Irish American Heritage Museum, Albany, NY.............954
Iron & Steel Museum of Alabama, Tannehill Ironworks Historical State Park, McCalla, AL.............13
Iron Hill Museum, Newark, DE.............272
Iroquois County Historical Society, Watseka, IL.............463
Isabel Miller Museum/Sitka Historical Society, Sitka, AK.............27
Ischua Valley Historical Society, Inc., Franklinville, NY.............992
Island County Historical Society Museum, Coupeville, WA.............1551

Islesboro Historical Society, Islesboro, ME.............612
Issaquah History Museum, Issaquah, WA..1557
Itasca County Historical Society, Grand Rapids, MN.............777
J.E. Reeves Home & Museum, Dover, OH.............1163
J.J. Jackson Memorial Museum, Weaverville, CA.............197
J.W. Parmley Historical Home Society, Ipswich, SD.............1349
Jack Nicklaus Museum, Columbus, OH.....1158
Jackson County Historical Museum & Research Library, Maquoketa, IA.............522
Jackson Hole Historical Society and Museum, Jackson, WY.............1634
Jacksonport State Park, Jacksonport, AR.......60
Jail Museum, Neligh, NE.............869
The James Madison Museum, Orange, VA.............1524
James Mitchell Varnum House and Museum, East Greenwich, RI.............1311
Jamestown Settlement, Yorktown Victory Center, The Jamestown-Yorktown Foundation, Williamsburg, VA.............1545
Japanese American National Museum, Los Angeles, CA.............117
Japanese Cultural Center of Hawaii, Honolulu, HI.............397
Jarrell Plantation Georgia State Historic Site, Juliette, GA.............374
Jasmine Moran Children's Museum, Seminole, OK.............1213
Jean Lafitte National Historical Park & Preserve, New Orleans, LA.............596
Jean P. Haydon Museum, Pago Pago, AS..1640
Jeane Dixon Museum and Library, Strasburg, VA.............1538
Jeff Matthews Memorial Museum, Galax, VA.............1508
The Jefferson County Historical Assoc., Steubenville, OH.............1186
Jefferson County Historical Society and Farnsworth TV Pioneer Museum, Rigby, ID.............409
Jefferson County Historical Society Museum, Port Townsend, WA.............1562
Jefferson County Museum, Charles Town, WV.............1580
Jefferson Historical Society and Museum, Jefferson, TX.............1431
Jefferson Valley Museum, Whitehall, MT....855
Jensen Arctic Museum, Monmouth, OR....1228
Jerome County Historical Society, Inc. and Idaho Farm & Ranch Museum, Jerome, ID.............406
Jersey City Museum, Jersey City, NJ.........908
Jewell County Historical Museum, Mankato, KS.............552
Jewish Museum of Florida, Miami Beach, FL.............326
Jim Crow Museum - Ferris State University, Big Rapids, MI.............729
John D. MacArthur Beach State Park & Nature Center, North Palm Beach, FL....329
John E. Conner Museum, Kingsville, TX..1432
John F. Kennedy Presidential Library & Museum, Boston, MA.............666
John Muir National Historic Site, Martinez, CA.............124
John Wesley Powell Museum, Green River, UT.............1466
John Woolman Memorial, Mount Holly, NJ.............915
John Wornall House Museum, Kansas City, MO.............821
Johnson County Historical Society, Inc., Tecumseh, NE.............873
Johnson County Museum of History, Franklin, IN.............478
Johnson County Museums, Shawnee, KS....558

Recreational Artifacts–Continued

Johnson Ferry House Museum, Titusville, NJ......926

Johnstown Area Heritage Association, Johnstown, PA......1263

Joliet Area Historical Museum, Joliet, IL....440

Jonathan Hager House & Museum, Hagerstown, MD......646

Jonesborough-Washington County History Museum, Jonesborough, TN......1368

Josiah Quincy House, Quincy, MA......705

The Judaica Museum of the Hebrew Home at Riverdale, Riverdale, NY......1057

Judith Basin County Museum, Stanford, MT......853

Julia A. Purnell Museum, Snow Hill, MD...654

Junction City Historical Society, Junction City, OR......1226

Juneau-Douglas City Museum, Juneau, AK......26

Juniata County Historical Society, Mifflintown, PA......1271

Junior Center of Art and Science, Oakland, CA......133

Justin Smith Morrill Homestead, Strafford, VT......1488

Kalamazoo Valley Museum, Kalamazoo, MI......749

Kalkaska County Historical Museum, Kalkaska, MI......749

Kanabec History Center, Mora, MN......784

Kandiyohi County Historical Society, Willmar, MN......796

Kankakee County Museum, Kankakee, IL...441

Kansas Sports Hall of Fame, Wichita, KS...562

Kauffman Museum, North Newton, KS......553

Kearney Area Children's Museum, Kearney, NE......864

Kearney Mansion Museum, Fresno, CA......97

Kell House Museum, Wichita Falls, TX....1461

Kellogg Historical Society, Kellogg, IA......521

Kelly-Griggs House Museum, Red Bluff, CA......146

Kelton House Museum & Garden, Columbus, OH......1158

Kemerer Museum of Decorative Arts, Bethlehem, PA......1242

The Kenilworth Historical Society, Kenilworth, IL......441

Kenosha County Historical Society and Museum, Inc., Kenosha, WI......1602

Kentucky Coal Mining Museum, Benham, KY......565

Kentucky Department of Fish & Wildlife Resources-Salato Wildlife Education Center, Frankfort, KY......569

Kentucky Derby Museum, Louisville, KY...576

The Kentucky Folk Art Center, Morehead, KY......580

Kentucky Gateway Museum Center, Maysville, KY......579

The Kentucky Library & Museum, Bowling Green, KY......565

Kentucky Railway Museum, Inc., New Haven, KY......580

Key West Museum of Art and History, Key West, FL......318

Kidcity Children's Museum, Middletown, CT......249

Kids' Imagination Discovery Space, Medford, OR......1228

Kids 'N' Stuff Children's Museum, Albion, MI......723

Kidspace Children's Museum, Pasadena, CA......140

KidsQuest Children's Museum, Bellevue, WA......1548

KidZone Museum, Truckee, CA......192

The KidZone Riverside County Youth Museum, Hemet, CA......103

Kimball House Museum, Battle Creek, MI......727

Kimble County Historical Museum, Junction, TX......1431

King Manor, Jamaica, NY......1004

Kingman Tavern Historical Museum, Cummington, MA......678

Kit Carson Historical Society, Kit Carson, CO......223

Kitsap County Historical Society Museum, Bremerton, WA......1549

Klamath County Museum, Klamath Falls, OR......1227

Klickitat County Historical Society, Goldendale, WA......1555

Kline Creek Farm, Winfield, IL......466

Klyne Esopus Museum, Ulster Park, NY...1079

Knife River Indian Villages National Historic Site, Stanton, ND......1136

Knight Museum, Alliance, NE......855

Knott House Museum, Tallahassee, FL......347

Knox House Museum, El Cajon, CA......92

Knoxville Public Library, Knoxville, PA...1265

Koch Family Children's Museum of Evansville, Evansville, IN......476

Kohl Children's Museum of Greater Chicago, Glenview, IL......438

Koochiching County Historical Museum, International Falls, MN......778

Koshare Indian Museum, Inc., La Junta, CO......224

Kruger Street Toy & Train Museum, Wheeling, WV......1588

L.C. Bates Museum, Hinckley, ME......612

La Casa Del Libro, San Juan, PR......1642

La Porte County Historical Society Museum, La Porte, IN......487

La Puente Valley Historical Society City Hall, LaPuente, CA......107

LaBelle Heritage Museum, LaBelle, FL......319

Lac Qui Parle County Historical Society, Madison, MN......779

The Lace Museum, Sunnyvale, CA......190

The Lacrosse Museum & National Hall of Fame/US Lacrosse, Baltimore, MD....633

Lagrange County Historical Society, Inc., Lagrange, IN......488

LaGrange Plantation, Cambridge, MD......639

The Lake Champlain Maritime Museum, Vergennes, VT......1488

Lake County Discovery Museum, Wauconda, IL......463

Lake County Historic Courthouse Museum, Lakeport, CA......108

Lake County Historical Society, Two Harbors, MN......794

Lake of the Red Cedars Museum, Cedar Lake, IN......472

Lake Tahoe Historical Society & Museum, South Lake Tahoe, CA......188

Lakes Art Center, Okoboji, IA......525

Lancaster County Historical Society, Lancaster, PA......1266

Lane County Historical Society & Museum, Eugene, OR......1223

Lane Place, Crawfordsville, IN......473

Lanier Mansion State Historic Site, Madison, IN......489

Laramie Plains Museum, Laramie, WY......1635

Laredo Children's Museum, Laredo, TX....1434

LaSalle County Historical Society Museum, Utica, IL......462

Laura Ingalls Wilder Museum and Tourist Center, Walnut Grove, MN......795

Lawrence County Historical and Genealogical Society, Bedford, IN......469

Layland Museum, Cleburne, TX......1400

Le Sueur Museum, Le Sueur, MN......779

Leelanau Historical Museum, Leland, MI....751

Lefferts Historic House, Brooklyn, NY......969

Legends of the Game Baseball Museum and Learning Center, Arlington, TX......1388

Lehigh County Historical Society, Allentown, PA......1239

Lemon Hill Mansion, Philadelphia, PA......1282

Lesueur County Historical Museum-Chapter 1, Elysian, MN......774

Levine Museum of the New South, Charlotte, NC......1095

Lewes Historical Society, Lewes, DE......271

Lewis County Historical Museum, Chehalis, WA......1550

Lewis County Historical Society Museum, Lowville, NY......1012

Liberty Hall Historic Center, Lamoni, IA....522

Libertyville-Mundelein Historical Society, Inc., Libertyville, IL......442

Lied Discovery Children's Museum, Las Vegas, NV......879

Lightner Museum, Saint Augustine, FL......339

Limberlost State Historic Site, Geneva, IN......479

Lincoln Children's Museum, Lincoln, NE...865

Lincoln County Historical Museum, Davenport, WA......1552

Lincoln County Pioneer Museum, Hendricks, MN......778

Lincoln State Monument, Lincoln, NM......941

Linn County Historical Museum and Moyer House, Brownsville, OR......1220

Lisbon Historical Society, Lisbon, OH......1172

The Lithuanian Museum, Chicago, IL......423

The Little Brick House, Vandalia, IL......462

The Little Cowboy Bar & Museum, Fromberg, MT......847

Little White House Historic Site, Warm Springs, GA......390

Littleton Historical Museum, Littleton, CO......227

Livingston County Historical Society Museum, Geneseo, NY......993

The Log House Museum of the Historical Society of Columbiana-Fairfield Township, Columbiana, OH......1157

Logan County Museum, Paris, AR......65

Lombard Historical Museum, Lombard, IL......443

Lompoc Valley Historical Society, Inc., Lompoc, CA......110

Long Island Children's Museum, Garden City, NY......992

Long Island Maritime Museum, West Sayville, NY......1085

Lori Brock Children's Discovery Center, Bakersfield, CA......73

Los Alamos Historical Museum, Los Alamos, NM......942

Los Nogales Museum, Seguin, TX......1452

Louis E. May Museum, Fremont, NE......861

Louisiana Children's Museum, New Orleans, LA......596

Louisiana State Museum, New Orleans, LA......596

Louisiana State University Museum of Art, Baton Rouge, LA......586

Louisville Slugger Museum & Factory, Louisville, KY......577

Loveland Museum Gallery, Loveland, CO...227

Lowell Area Historical Museum, Lowell, MI......751

Lowell Damon House, Wauwatosa, WI......1626

Lower East Side Tenement Museum, New York, NY......1029

Lucretia Vaile Museum, Palmer Lake, CO......229

Lutheran Heritage Center & Museum of the Perry County Lutheran Historical Society, Altenburg, MO......810

Lutz Children's Museum, Manchester, CT...248

Lux Center for the Arts, Lincoln, NE......866

Lyman Allyn Art Museum, New London, CT......255

Lynchburg Museum System, Lynchburg, VA 1515
Lynden Pioneer Museum, Lynden, WA 1559
Lyndon B. Johnson National Historical Park, Johnson City, TX 1431
Lyndon Baines Johnson Library and Museum, Austin, TX 1391
Lynn Meadows Discovery Center, Gulfport, MS 801
Lynn Museum & Historical Society, Lynn, MA 692
Lynnhaven House, Virginia Beach, VA 1542
Lyon County Historical Society and Museum, Emporia, KS 538
Lyon County Historical Society Museum, Marshall, MN 780
The Lyons Redstone Museum, Lyons, CO 227

Mackinac State Historic Parks-Colonial Michilimackinac & Old Mackinac Point Lighthouse, Mackinaw City, MI 752
Macon County Historical Society Museum Complex, Decatur, IL 430
Madera County Museum, Madera, CA 123
Madison Children's Museum, Madison, WI 1605
Madison County Historical Society, Winterset, IA 531
Madison Historical Society, Madison, CT 247
Magnolia Manor, Cairo, IL 415
Mahaffie Stagecoach Stop and Farm, Olathe, KS 554
Maine Discovery Museum, Bangor, ME 605
Maitland Historical Museums, Maitland, FL 322
Manchester Historical Society, Manchester, MA 692
Manitowoc County Historical Society, Manitowoc, WI 1607
Mansfield Historical Society Museum, Storrs, CT 261
Manship House Museum, Jackson, MS 802
Maramec Museum, The James Foundation, Saint James, MO 830
Marathon County Historical Society, Wausau, WI 1626
Marble Historical Society, Marble, CO 228
Marblehead Museum & Historical Society, Marblehead, MA 693
Marcellus Historical Society, Marcellus, NY 1013
Marilla Historical Society Museum, Marilla, NY 1014
Marin History Museum, San Rafael, CA 177
Marin Museum of the American Indian, Novato, CA 131
Marine Science Institute, Redwood City, CA 147
The Mariners' Museum, Newport News, VA 1519
Mario Lanza Institute/Museum, Philadelphia, PA 1282
Marion County Historical Society, Salem, OR 1236
The Marion County Historical Society Museum, Marion, OH 1174
Marion Public Library Museum, Marion, IN 490
Mariposa Museum & World Culture Center, Peterborough, NH 893
Maritime & Seafood Industry Museum, Biloxi, MS 798
Maritime and Yachting Museum of the Treasure Coast, Stuart, FL 346
Maritime Museum of San Diego, San Diego, CA 157
Marlboro Historical Society, Marlboro, VT 1481
Marquette County Historical Society, Westfield, WI 1627
Marquette County History Museum, Marquette, MI 753
Marrett House, Standish, ME 623

Marshall County Historical Museum, Plymouth, IN 496
Marshall County Historical Museum, Holly Springs, MS 801
Marshall Gold Discovery State Historic Park, Coloma, CA 86
Marvin Newton House, Brookfield, VT 1477
Maryland Historical Society, Baltimore, MD 634
Mason County Historical Society/Historic White Pine Village, Ludington, MI 751
The Massillon Museum, Massillon, OH 1175
Matchbox Road Museum, Newfield, NJ 917
The Mather Homestead Museum, Library and Memorial Park, Wellsville, NY 1084
Mathias Ham House Historic Site, Dubuque, IA 516
Matthews Museum of Maine Heritage, Union, ME 624
May Museum & Farmville Heritage Center, Farmville, NC 1100
Mayville Historical Society, Inc., Mayville, WI 1608
Mazomanie Historical Society, Mazomanie, WI 1608
Mc Cook County Historical Society and Museum, Salem, SD 1355
McArthur-Burney Falls Memorial State Park, Burney, CA 80
McConaghy House, Hayward, CA 102
McCone County Museum, Circle, MT 844
McConnell Mansion, Moscow, ID 407
McHenry County Historical Society and Museum, Union, IL 461
McHenry Museum, Modesto, CA 126
McKenna Children's Museum, New Braunfels, TX 1440
McLarty Treasure Museum, Vero Beach, FL 352
McLean County Museum of History, Bloomington, IL 414
McMinn County Living Heritage Museum, Athens, TN 1360
McPherson County Old Mill Museum and Park, Lindsborg, KS 550
Meade County Historical Society Museum, Meade, KS 552
Meadowlands Museum, Rutherford, NJ 923
Meagher County Historical Association Castle Museum, White Sulphur Springs, MT 855
Mechanicsburg Museum Association, Mechanicsburg, PA 1270
Mecosta County Historical Museum, Big Rapids, MI 729
Medina Railroad Museum, Medina, NY 1014
Medora Doll House, Medora, ND 1134
Meeker County Historical Society Museum & G.A.R. Hall, Litchfield, MN 779
Meeker Home Museum, Greeley, CO 222
Meigs County Museum, Pomeroy, OH 1183
Mem-Erie Historical Museum, Erie, KS 539
Memorial Hall Museum, Pocumtuck Valley Memorial Assoc., Deerfield, MA 679
Memoryville USA, Inc., Rolla, MO 829
Mendocino County Museum, Willits, CA 198
Mennonite Heritage Museum, Goessel, KS 542
Menominee County Heritage Museum, Menominee, MI 754
Mercer County Historical Museum, The Riley Home, Celina, OH 1146
Mercer County Historical Society, Mercer, PA 1271
Meriden Historical Society, Inc., Meriden, CT 249
Merrill Historical Museum, Merrill, WI 1609
Mesa Historical Museum, Mesa, AZ 37
Meux Home Museum, Fresno, CA 98

Miami University Art Museum, Oxford, OH 1181
Michigan Maritime Museum, South Haven, MI 764
Mid Atlantic Air Museum, Reading, PA 1296
Mid-Atlantic Center for the Arts/Emlen Physick Estate/Cape May Lighthouse, Cape May, NJ 900
Mid-Hudson Children's Museum, Poughkeepsie, NY 1055
Middleborough Historical Association, Inc., Middleborough, MA 694
Middlesex County Historical Society, Middletown, CT 249
Midway Village & Museum Center, Rockford, IL 455
Milan Historical Museum, Inc., Milan, OH 1176
Military Museum of Southern New England, Danbury, CT 238
Mill Race Historical Village, Northville, MI 758
Millard Fillmore House, East Aurora, NY 985
Mills County Historical Society and Museum, Glenwood, IA 519
Milton Historical Museum, Milton, VT 1482
Milwaukee County Historical Society, Milwaukee, WI 1611
Milwaukee Public Museum, Milwaukee, WI 1612
Minnesota Amateur Baseball Hall of Fame, Saint Cloud, MN 788
Minnesota Children's Museum, Saint Paul, MN 791
Minnesota Historical Society, Saint Paul, MN 791
Minnesota Pioneer Park Museum, Annandale, MN 767
Minnetrista, Muncie, IN 492
Miracle of America Museum Inc., Polson, MT 852
Miramont Castle Museum, Manitou Springs, CO 228
Mississippi Society Daughters of the American Revolution Rosalie House Museum, Natchez, MS 805
Mississippi Sports Hall of Fame & Museum, Jackson, MS 803
Missouri State Museum, Jefferson City, MO 819
The Mitchell Museum of the American Indian, Evanston, IL 435
MOBIUS Kids, Spokane, WA 1571
Moffatt-Ladd House and Garden, Portsmouth, NH 894
Mondak Heritage Center, Sidney, MT 853
Monmouth County Historical Association, Freehold, NJ 905
Monroe County Historical Association/Stroud Mansion, Stroudsburg, PA 1302
Monroe County Historical Society, Bloomington, IN 469
Monroe County Local History Room & Library, Sparta, WI 1622
Monroe Historical Society, Monroe, CT 250
Montague Museum & Historical Association, Montague, MI 756
Montauk, Clermont, IA 511
Montclair Historical Society, Montclair, NJ 912
The Montgomery County Historical Society, Inc., Rockville, MD 651
Monticello, Home of Thomas Jefferson, Thomas Jefferson Foundation, Inc., Charlottesville, VA 1499
Montrose County Historical Museum, Montrose, CO 228
Montville Township Historical Museum, Montville, NJ 912
Moody County Museum, Flandreau, SD 1347
Moore County Historical Museum, Dumas, TX 1410

Recreational Artifacts–Continued

Moriarty Historical Museum, Moriarty, NM...............943

The Morikami Museum and Japanese Gardens, Delray Beach, FL..................305

Morris County Historical Society (Acorn Hall House Museum), Morristown, NJ ...914

The Morris Museum, Morristown, NJ.........914

Morrison's Heritage Museum, Morrison, IL................446

Morton Grove Historical Museum/Haupt-Yehl House, Morton Grove, IL................446

Morton Museum of Cooke County, Gainesville, TX................1420

Motorcycle Hall of Fame Museum, Pickerington, OH................1182

Mount Desert Island Historical Society, Mount Desert, ME................615

Mount Holly Community Historical Museum, Belmont, VT................1476

Mount Pleasant Historical Society, Mount Pleasant, OH................1177

Mount Prospect Historical Society Museums, Mount Prospect, IL................446

Mt. Rainier National Park, Ashford, WA ...1547

Mount Vernon Hotel Museum & Garden, New York, NY................1031

Mountain Gateway Museum, Old Fort, NC................1113

Mountain Heritage Center, Cullowhee, NC................1097

Mountain Skies Astronomical Society & Science Center, Lake Arrowhead, CA.....107

Mulford Farm, East Hampton, NY..............986

Muncie Children's Museum, Muncie, IN.....492

The Musee Mecanique, San Francisco, CA................167

Museo de las Americas, Denver, CO..........213

The Museum at Warm Springs, Warm Springs, OR................1238

Museum of Afro-American History, Boston, MA................667

Museum of Alaska Transportation & Industry, Inc., Wasilla, AK................29

Museum of American Architecture and Decorative Arts, Houston, TX................1428

Museum of American Finance, New York, NY................1031

Museum of American Presidents, Strasburg, VA................1539

Museum of Ancient & Modern Art, Penn Valley, CA................141

Museum of Anthropology, University of Missouri, Columbia, MO................813

Museum of Art and Archaeology, University of Missouri - Columbia, Columbia, MO................813

Museum of Art and History at the McPherson Center, Santa Cruz, CA........182

The Museum of Bus Transportation, Inc., Hershey, PA................1261

Museum of Carousel Art & History, Sandusky, OH................1185

Museum of Ceramics, East Liverpool, OH................1163

Museum of disAbility History, Williamsville, NY................1086

Museum of Discovery: Arkansas Museum of Science and History, Little Rock, AR................62

The Museum of Early Trades and Crafts, Madison, NJ................910

The Museum of East Alabama, Opelika, AL................17

Museum of Family Camping, Allenstown, NH................883

Museum of Florida History, Tallahassee, FL................348

Museum of History & Art, Ontario, Ontario, CA................136

Museum of History & Industry (MOHAI), Seattle, WA................1567

Museum of Indian Culture, Allentown, PA................1239

Museum of International Folk Art, Santa Fe, NM................948

Museum of Jewish Heritage-A Living Memorial to the Holocaust, New York, NY................1032

The Museum of Man in the Sea, Inc., Panama City Beach, FL................335

The Museum of Miniature Houses and Other Collections, Inc., Carmel, IN........471

The Museum of Mobile, Mobile, AL................14

Museum of North Idaho, Coeur d'Alene, ID................405

Museum of Radio & Technology, Inc., Huntington, WV................1583

Museum of Religious Arts, Logan, IA.......522

Museum of Robotics, Orinda, CA................136

Museum of Science & History of Jacksonville, Jacksonville, FL................315

Museum of Science and Industry, Chicago, IL................425

Museum of Seminole County History, Sanford, FL................343

Museum of Southern History, Jacksonville, FL................315

Museum of Texas Tech University, Lubbock, TX................1435

Museum of the Albemarle, Elizabeth City, NC................1099

Museum of the Bedford Historical Society, Bedford, NY................961

Museum of the Cape Fear Historical Complex, Fayetteville, NC................1101

Museum of the Cherokee Strip, Enid, OK.1200

Museum of the City of Lake Worth, Lake Worth, FL................320

The Museum of the Confederacy, Richmond, VA................1531

Museum of the Great Plains, Lawton, OK.1204

Museum of the Gulf Coast, Port Arthur, TX................1444

Museum of the Llano Estacado, Plainview, TX................1443

Museum of the Moving Image, Astoria, NY................958

Museum of the Weston Historical Society, Inc., Weston, MA................718

Museum of Vision, San Francisco, CA........167

Museum of Yachting, Newport, RI............1314

Museum of Yarmouth History, Yarmouth, ME................626

Museum Village, Monroe, NY................1015

Museums of Los Gatos, Los Gatos, CA......123

The Museums of Oglebay Institute - Mansion Museum & Glass Museum, Wheeling, WV................1588

Muskegon County Museum, Muskegon, MI................757

My Jewish Discovery Place Children's Museum, Fort Lauderdale, FL................308

MY Museum, Monterey, CA................128

Mystic Seaport - The Museum of America and the Sea, Mystic, CT................251

Naismith Memorial Basketball Hall of Fame, Springfield, MA................710

Naper Settlement, Naperville, IL................447

Narragansett Historical Society, Templeton, MA................714

Nathan Denison Advocates, Forty Fort, PA................1254

National Afro-American Museum & Cultural Center, Wilberforce, OH..........1191

The National Agricultural Center & Hall of Fame, Bonner Springs, KS................534

National Air and Space Museum, Washington, DC................283

National Archives and Records Administration, Washington, DC.............284

National Association of Miniature Enthusiasts, Carmel, IN................472

National Automotive & Truck Museum of the United States, Inc. (NATMUS), Auburn, IN................468

National Baseball Hall of Fame and Museum, Inc., Cooperstown, NY............981

The National Border Patrol Museum and Memorial Library, El Paso, TX............1412

National Capital Trolley Museum, Silver Spring, MD................654

National Children's Museum, Washington, DC................284

National Christmas Center, Paradise, PA ...1275

National Czech & Slovak Museum & Library, Cedar Rapids, IA................509

National Firearms Museum, Fairfax, VA ...1504

National Football Museum, Inc., Canton, OH................1145

National Historic Oregon Trail Interpretive Center, Baker City, OR 1219

National Italian American Sports Hall of Fame, Chicago, IL................425

National Mississippi River Museum & Aquarium, Dubuque, IA................516

National Motorcycle Museum, Anamosa, IA................505

National Museum of American Jewish History, Philadelphia, PA................1284

National Museum of Dance & Hall of Fame, Saratoga Springs, NY................1065

National Museum of Polo and Hall of Fame, Inc., Lake Worth, FL................320

National Museum of Racing and Hall of Fame, Saratoga Springs, NY................1065

National Museum of Roller Skating, Lincoln, NE................866

National New York Central Railroad Museum, Elkhart, IN................475

National Ornamental Metal Museum, Memphis, TN................1375

National Park Service Vicksburg National Military Park-Cairo Museum, Vicksburg, MS................809

National Plastics Center and Museum, Leominster, MA................689

National Postal Museum, Smithsonian Institution, Washington, DC................287

National Railroad Museum, Green Bay, WI................1599

National Railroad Museum and Hall of Fame, Inc., Hamlet, NC................1105

National Route 66 Museum and Old Town Complex, Elk City, OK................1200

National Scouting Museum, Irving, TX.....1430

National Soaring Museum, Elmira, NY.......988

The National Soccer Hall of Fame, Oneonta, NY................1046

National Sprint Car Hall of Fame & Museum, Knoxville, IA................521

The National Toy Train Museum, Strasburg, PA................1301

Nauticus, The National Maritime Center, Norfolk, VA................1522

Nauvoo Historical Society Museum, Nauvoo, IL................447

Navarro County Historical Society, Pioneer Village, Corsicana, TX............1402

Nebraska Prairie Museum of the Phelps County Historical Society, Holdrege, NE................863

Negro Leagues Baseball Museum, Kansas City, MO................822

Neligh Mills, Neligh, NE................869

Nelson Pioneer Farm and Museum, Oskaloosa, IA................526

Nemours Mansion and Gardens, Wilmington, DE................274

Nevada County Historical Society, Inc., Nevada City, CA................130

The New Berlin Historical Society, New Berlin, WI................1614

New Braunfels Conservation Society, New Braunfels, TX 1440

New Britain Youth Museum, New Britain, CT........................252

New Britain Youth Museum at Hungerford Park, Kensington, CT..........247

New Canaan Historical Society, New Canaan, CT.........................252

New Castle Historical Society, New Castle, DE.........................272

The New England Carousel Museum, Bristol, CT.........................236

New England Quilt Museum, Lowell, MA.........................692

New England Ski Museum, Franconia, NH.........................888

New England Wireless & Steam Museum Inc., East Greenwich, RI 1311

New Hampshire Farm Museum, Inc., Milton, NH.........................892

New Hampshire Historical Society, Concord, NH.........................885

The New Hampshire Snowmobile Museum, Allenstown, NH.........................883

New Haven Colony Historical Society, New Haven, CT.........................253

New Jersey Office of Historic Sites, Trenton, NJ.........................927

The New Milford Historical Society, New Milford, CT.........................256

New Orleans Fire Dept. Museum & Educational Center, New Orleans, LA 597

New Richmond Preservation Society, New Richmond, WI.........................1615

New Sweden Historical Society, New Sweden, ME.........................616

The New York Public Library for the Performing Arts, New York, NY 1036

New York State Museum, Albany, NY.........955

Newell Museum, Newell, SD 1352

Newport Historical Society & The Museum of Newport History, Newport, RI.........................1315

The Newton History Museum at The Jackson Homestead, Newton, MA...........698

Nez Perce County Museum, Lewiston, ID...407

The Niagara County Historical Center and Niagara County Genealogical Society, Lockport, NY.........................1010

Nici Self Museum, Centennial, WY 1630

Nishna Heritage Museum, Oakland, IA 525

No Man's Land Historical Society, Goodwell, OK.........................1201

Noah Webster House/West Hartford Historical Society, West Hartford, CT 265

Nobleboro Historical Society, Nobleboro, ME.........................616

Nordic Heritage Museum, Seattle, WA 1567

Norfolk Historical Museum, Norfolk, CT....257

The Norman Cleveland County Historical Museum, Norman, OK 1206

North Andover Historical Society, North Andover, MA.........................698

North Carolina A&T State University Galleries, Greensboro, NC 1104

North Carolina Auto Racing Hall of Fame, Mooresville, NC.........................1111

North Castle Historical Society, Armonk, NY.........................958

North Dakota State Railroad Museum, Mandan, ND 1134

North Haven Historical Society, North Haven, CT.........................257

North House Museum, Lewisburg, WV 1584

North Lee County Historic Center and Santa Fe Depot Museum Complex, Fort Madison, IA.........................518

North Platte Valley Museum, Gering, NE....861

North Star Museum of Boy Scouting and Girl Scouting, North Saint Paul, MN 785

North Tonawanda History Museum, North Tonawanda, NY 1043

Northborough Historical Society, Inc., Northborough, MA.........................700

Northeast Louisiana Children's Museum, Monroe, LA.........................592

Northeast Oakland Historical Museum, Oxford, MI.........................759

Northern Indiana Center for History, South Bend, IN.........................499

Northport Historical Society Museum, Northport, NY.........................1044

Northwest Museum of Arts & Culture (Eastern Washington State Historical Society), Spokane, WA.........................1571

Northwest Railway Museum, Snoqualmie, WA.........................1570

Northwoods Children's Museum, Eagle River, WI.........................1595

Norwich Historical Society, Norwich, VT .1484

Novato History Museum, Novato, CA 132

Nowetah's American Indian Museum & Store, New Portland, ME.........................615

The Noyes Museum of Art, Oceanville, NJ.........................918

O. Henry Museum, Austin, TX...................1391

Oakdale Museum, Oakdale, CA 132

Oakland County Pioneer and Historical Society, Pontiac, MI.........................760

Oatland Island Education Center, Savannah, GA.........................385

Oberlin Heritage Center, Oberlin, OH.........1180

Ocean City Historical Museum, Inc., Ocean City, NJ.........................918

Ocean City Life-Saving Station Museum, Ocean City, MD.........................650

Ocean Institute, Dana Point, CA 89

Ocmulgee National Monument, Macon, GA.........................378

The Octagon House, Hudson, WI...............1600

Odyssey Maritime Discovery Center, Seattle, WA.........................1567

The Official Marx Toy Museum, Moundsville, WV.........................1585

Ogden Historical Society, Spencerport, NY.........................1071

Ogden's George S. Eccles Dinosaur Park, Ogden, UT.........................1468

Oklahoma Museum of History, Oklahoma City, OK.........................1210

Oklahoma Route 66 Museum, Clinton, OK.........................1198

Oklahoma Sports Museum, Guthrie, OK ...1202

Old Bethpage Village Restoration, Old Bethpage, NY.........................1045

Old Colony Historical Society, Taunton, MA.........................714

Old Constitution House, Windsor, VT........1490

Old Courthouse Museum, Santa Ana, CA....178

Old Davie School Historical Museum, Davie, FL.........................302

Old Depot Museum, Ottawa, KS...................555

Old Firehouse Museum, Greenville, MS......800

Old Florida Museum, Saint Augustine, FL.........................339

Old Fort House Museum, Fort Edward, NY.........................991

Old Fort Meade Museum and Historic Research Association, Fort Meade, SD .1347

Old Greer County Museum & Hall of Fame, Mangum, OK.........................1204

Old Iron County Courthouse Museum, Hurley, WI.........................1601

Old Jail Museum, Albion, IN.........................467

The Old Jail Museum, Warrenton, VA 1543

Old Lighthouse Museum, Stonington, CT....261

Old Lincoln County Courthouse Museum, Lincoln, NM.........................942

Old Manchester Museum, Manchester, CT.........................248

Old Market House State Historic Site, Galena, IL.........................436

Old Mill Museum, Cimarron, NM...............938

Old Ordinary House Museum, Hingham, MA.........................687

Old Prairie Town at Ward-Meade Historic Site, Topeka, KS.........................560

Old Prison Museums, Deer Lodge, MT 845

Old Salem Inc., Winston-Salem, NC..........1126

Old State House Museum, Little Rock, AR.........................63

Old Sturbridge Village, Sturbridge, MA....713

Old Town Hall Museum, Fifield, WI..........1597

Old World Wisconsin, Eagle, WI...............1595

The Oldest House Museum/Wrecker's Museum, Key West, FL.........................318

Olmsted County Historical Society, Rochester, MN.........................788

Oneida County Historical Society, Utica, NY.........................1080

Oneida Nation Museum, De Pere, WI........1594

Onslow County Museum, Richlands, NC...1117

Ontario County Historical Society, Canandaigua, NY.........................975

Ontonagon County Historical Society Museum, Ontonagon, MI.........................758

Optical Science Center & Museum, Hannibal, MO.........................817

Orange County Historical Museum, Hillsborough, NC.........................1107

Orange County Regional History Center, Orlando, FL.........................331

Oregon Historical Society, Portland, OR....1231

Oregon-Jerusalem Historical Museum, Oregon, OH.........................1181

Oregon Trail Regional Museum, Baker City, OR.........................1219

Orland Historical Society, Orland, ME 617

Orleans County Historical Society & The Old Stone House Museum, Brownington, VT.........................1477

Orpheum Children's Science Museum, Champaign, IL.........................417

Osage County Historical Society Museum, Pawhuska, OK.........................1211

Osborn-Jackson House, East Hampton, NY.........................986

The Oscar Anderson House Museum, Anchorage, AK.........................22

Oscar Getz Museum of Whiskey History And The Bardstown Historical Museum, Bardstown, KY.........................565

Ossining Historical Society Museum, Ossining, NY.........................1047

Osterville Historical Society, Inc., Osterville, MA.........................701

Otero Museum Association, La Junta, CO...224

Ottawa County Historical Museum, Port Clinton, OH.........................1183

Ottawa Scouting Museum, Ottawa, IL 449

Otter Tail County Historical Society, Fergus Falls, MN.........................775

Our House State Memorial, Gallipolis, OH.........................1165

Outagamie Museum, Appleton, WI 1589

Overholser Mansion, Oklahoma City, OK .1210

Owensboro Area Museum of Science & History, Owensboro, KY.........................581

Owensboro Museum of Fine Art, Inc., Owensboro, KY.........................581

The Ozark Folk Center, Mountain View, AR.........................65

Ozark National Scenic Riverways, Van Buren, MO.........................839

The P.T. Boat Museum & Library, Germantown, TN.........................1365

Pacific Coast Air Museum, Santa Rosa, CA.........................184

Pacific County Historical Museum, South Bend, WA.........................1571

Pacific University Museum, Forest Grove, OR.........................1224

Packwood House Museum, Lewisburg, PA.........................1268

Recreational Artifacts—Continued

Pajaro Valley Historical Association, Watsonville, CA 196
PALCO, Scotia, CA 186
Palmer Foundation Chiropractic History, Davenport, IA 513
Palmer/Gullickson Octagon Home, West Salem, WI 1627
Palmer House, Historical Society of Olde Northfield, Northfield, OH 1180
Palo Alto Junior Museum and Zoo, Palo Alto, CA 139
Parishville Museum, Parishville, NY 1050
Park City Historical Society & Museum, Park City, UT 1468
Parsonsfield-Porter Historical Society, Porter, ME 618
Pasadena Museum of History, Pasadena, CA 140
Pascack Historical Society, Park Ridge, NJ 920
Passaic County Historical Society & Lambert Castle Museum, Paterson, NJ ... 920
Patee House Museum, Saint Joseph, MO 831
The Paterson Museum, Paterson, NJ 920
Patten Lumbermen's Museum, Inc., Patten, ME 618
Paul Bunyan Logging Camp Museum, Eau Claire, WI 1596
Paul W. Bryant Museum, Tuscaloosa, AL 19
Pawnee City Historical Society & Museum, Pawnee City, NE 871
Pearce Collections Museum, Corsicana, TX 1402
Pearson Air Museum, Vancouver, WA 1576
Pedaling History Bicycle Museum, Orchard Park, NY 1047
The Peekskill Museum, Peekskill, NY 1051
Peirce Mill and Peirce Barn, Washington, DC 289
Pembina State Museum, Pembina, ND 1135
Pennsylvania Anthracite Heritage Museum, Scranton, PA 1299
Pennsylvania Military Museum and 28th Division Shrine, Boalsburg, PA 1244
Pennyroyal Area Museum, Hopkinsville, KY 572
Pensacola Historical Society Museum, Pensacola, FL 336
Percussive Arts Society Museum, Lawton, OK 1204
Perkins History Museum, Perkins School for the Blind, Watertown, MA 716
Peter J. McGovern Little League Museum, South Williamsport, PA 1301
Peter Rice Homestead, Home of Marlborough Historical Society, Inc., Marlboro, MA 693
Peterborough Historical Society, Peterborough, NH 893
Pettaquamscutt Historical Society, Kingston, RI 1312
Philipse Manor Hall State Historic Site, Yonkers, NY 1087
Phoenix Museum of History, Phoenix, AZ 41
Phoenix Police Museum, Phoenix, AZ 41
Piatt County Museum, Monticello, IL 446
Pikes Peak Hill Climb Educational Museum, Colorado Springs, CO 207
Pine Bluff/Jefferson County Historical Museum, Pine Bluff, AR 66
Pink Palace Family of Museums, Memphis, TN 1375
Pioneer Arizona Living History Village & Museum, Phoenix, AZ 41
Pioneer Auto Museum, Murdo, SD 1352
Pioneer Auto Trails Historical Society (PATHS), Tucson, AZ 50
Pioneer Florida Museum Association, Inc., Dade City, FL 302
Pioneer Heritage Center, Cavalier, ND 1129

Pioneer Heritage Center, LSU-Shreveport, Shreveport, LA 601
Pioneer Museum, Wild Rose, WI 1628
Pioneer Museum and Vereins Kirche, Fredericksburg, TX 1419
Pittsford Historical Society Museum, Pittsford, VT 1484
Placer County Museums, Auburn, CA 72
Plainsman Museum, Aurora, NE 856
Playspace, Raleigh, NC 1117
Please Touch Museum, Philadelphia, PA ... 1286
Plumb Farm Learning Center, Greeley, CO 222
Plymouth Antiquarian Society, Plymouth, MA 704
Plymouth Historical Museum, Plymouth, MI 760
Pocahontas County Iowa Historical Society Museum, Laurens, IA 522
Polk County Historical Museum, Bartow, FL 295
Polk County Historical Society, Crookston, MN 771
Polk County Museum, Balsam Lake, WI ... 1590
Pope John Paul II Cultural Center, Washington, DC 289
Porter Thermometer Museum, Onset, MA ... 700
Portland Children's Museum, Portland, OR 1233
Portsmouth Historical Society, Portsmouth, RI 1316
Portsmouth Museums, Portsmouth, VA 1526
Post Rock Museum, La Crosse, KS 547
Poulsbo Marine Science Center, Poulsbo, WA 1563
Powers Museum, Carthage, MO 812
Prairie Trails Museum of Wayne County, Corydon, IA 512
Prairie Village, Madison, SD 1351
Pratt Building - Cohasset Historical Society, Cohasset, MA 676
Promont House Museum, Milford, OH 1176
Proprietary House, The Royal Governor's Mansion, Perth Amboy, NJ 921
Providence Children's Museum, Providence, RI 1317
Public Museum of West Michigan, Grand Rapids, MI 744
Pueblo County Historical Society Museum and Edward H. Broadhead Library, Pueblo, CO 230
Puget Sound Coast Artillery Museum at Fort Worden, Port Townsend, WA 1562
Putnam County Historical Society Museum, Kalida, OH 1169
Puukohola Heiau National Historic Site, Kamuela, HI 400

Queen Emma Summer Palace, Honolulu, HI 398
Queens Historical Society, Flushing, NY 990
Quincy Historical Society, Quincy, MA 705
QV Historical Society at Carriage House Museum, Camden, NY 974

Racine Heritage Museum, Racine, WI 1619
Radio & Television Museum, Bowie, MD ... 638
Railroad and Heritage Museum Inc., Temple, TX 1454
Railroad Museum of Pennsylvania, Strasburg, PA 1302
Raleigh City Museum, Raleigh, NC 1117
Ralls Historical Museum, Ralls, TX 1445
Ralph Waldo Emerson House, Concord, MA 677
Ralston Historical Association, John Ralston Museum, Mendham, NJ 911
Randolph County Historical Museum, Winchester, IN 503
Randolph Historical Society, Inc., Randolph, VT 1485
Raton Museum, Raton, NM 945
Reading Historical Society, Reading, VT ... 1485

Reading Railroad Heritage Museum, Reading, PA 1296
Readsboro Historical Society, Readsboro, VT 1486
Red Mill Museum Village, Clinton, NJ 901
Red River Valley Museum, Vernon, TX 1457
Redington Museum, Waterville, ME 625
Redwood County Historical Society, Redwood Falls, MN 787
Refugio County Museum, Refugio, TX 1445
Reno County Museum, Hutchinson, KS 545
Rensselaer County Historical Society, Troy, NY 1079
Renton Historical Society and Museum, Renton, WA 1564
Republic County Historical Society Museum, Belleville, KS 534
Reynolda House Museum of American Art, Winston-Salem, NC 1126
Rhode Island Black Heritage Society, Providence, RI 1318
Rhode Island Historical Society, Providence, RI 1318
Richard Salter Storrs House, Longmeadow, MA 691
Richardson-Bates House Museum, Oswego, NY 1048
Richland County Historical Museum, Wahpeton, ND 1137
Richland County Museum, Lexington, OH 1172
Richmond Museum of History, Richmond, CA 148
Rifle Creek Museum, Rifle, CO 231
Riley County Historical Museum, Manhattan, KS 551
Ripley's Believe It or Not!, Key West, FL 319
Riversdale House Mansion, Riverdale Park, MD 651
Riverside Museum, La Crosse, WI 1603
Riverton Museum, Riverton, WY 1637
Riverview at Hobson Grove, Bowling Green, KY 566
Roanoke Island Festival Park; Homeport of the "Elizabeth II", Manteo, NC 1110
Roaring Twenties Antique Car Museum, Hood, VA 1511
Robbins Museum of Archaeology, Middleborough, MA 694
Robert C. Williams American Museum of Papermaking at Georgia Tech, Atlanta, GA 363
Robert S. Kerr Museum, Poteau, OK 1212
Rock Ford Plantation, Lancaster, PA 1267
Rock Island County Historical Society, Moline, IL 445
Rock Springs Historical Museum, Rock Springs, WY 1638
Rockingham Free Public Library and Museum, Bellows Falls, VT 1476
Rockwell Museum of Western Art, Corning, NY 982
Rockwood Park, Wilmington, DE 274
Rocky Mount Museum, Piney Flats, TN 1383
Rocky Mountain Quilt Museum, Golden, CO 220
Roger Maris Museum, Fargo, ND 1131
Rogers Daisy Airgun Museum, Rogers, AR 67
Rogers Historical Museum, Rogers, AR 67
Rokeby (Ancestral Estate of Rowland Evans Robinson), Ferrisburgh, VT 1479
Rollo Jamison Museum, Platteville, WI 1617
Rome Historical Society Museum, Rome, NY 1061
Roosevelt County Museum, Portales, NM ... 944
Rosalie Whyel Museum of Doll Art, Bellevue, WA 1548
Rose Hill Museum, Bay Village, OH 1141
Rosenberg Library, Galveston, TX 1422

Rosicrucian Egyptian Museum, San Jose, CA 172

Ross County Historical Society, Inc., Chillicothe, OH 1147

The Rotch-Jones-Duff House & Garden Museum, Inc., New Bedford, MA 697

Rothschild House State Park, Port Townsend, WA 1562

Rowan Museum, Inc., Salisbury, NC 1118

Rowley Historical Society, Rowley, MA 706

The Roy Rogers-Dale Evans Museum and Theater, Branson, MO 811

Royalton Historical Society, Royalton, VT 1486

Ruggles House Society, Columbia Falls, ME 609

Runestone Museum, Alexandria, MN 767

Rusk County Historical Society, Ladysmith, WI 1604

Ruth and Charles Gilb Arcadia Historical Museum, Arcadia, CA 71

The Rye Historical Society and Square House Museum, Rye, NY 1062

Saco Museum, Saco, ME 621

Safety Harbor Museum of Regional History, Safety Harbor, FL 338

Sag Harbor Whaling & Historical Museum, Sag Harbor, NY 1063

Sailor's Memorial Museum, Islesboro, ME 612

St. Albans Historical Museum, Saint Albans, VT 1486

St. John Science Museum, Saint John, KS 557

St. Joseph Museum Inc., Saint Joseph, MO 831

St. Lawrence County Historical Association - Silas Wright House, Canton, NY 975

St. Louis Cardinals Hall of Fame Museum, Saint Louis, MO 836

St. Petersburg Museum of History, Saint Petersburg, FL 342

Ste. Genevieve Museum, Sainte Genevieve, MO 838

Salamanca Rail Museum, Salamanca, NY .1063

Salem County Historical Society, Salem, NJ 924

Salida Museum, Salida, CO 232

Salmon Brook Historical Society, Inc., Granby, CT 242

Sam Bell Maxey House State Historic Site, Paris, TX 1442

Sam Brown Log House, Browns Valley, MN 770

Sam Houston Memorial Museum, Huntsville, TX 1430

Sam Houston Regional Library & Research Center, Liberty, TX 1434

Sam Rayburn House Museum, Bonham, TX 1397

Samuel Cupples House of Saint Louis University, Saint Louis, MO 837

San Antonio Children's Museum, San Antonio, TX 1449

San Diego Air & Space Museum, San Diego, CA 159

San Diego Automotive Museum, San Diego, CA 159

San Diego Hall of Champions Sports Museum, San Diego, CA 159

San Diego Model Railroad Museum, Inc., San Diego, CA 159

San Dieguito Heritage Museum, Encinitas, CA 92

San Jacinto Museum of History Association, La Porte, TX 1433

San Juan Historical Society, Friday Harbor, WA 1555

San Luis Obispo County Historical Museum, San Luis Obispo, CA 174

San Mateo County Historical Association and Museum, Redwood City, CA 147

Sanborn Area Historical Society, Sanborn, NY 1064

The Sandbox, An Interactive Children's Museum, Hilton Head Island, SC 1335

Sandown Historical Society and Museum, Sandown, NH 896

Sandpoint Lighthouse, Escanaba, MI 741

Sandusky Library Follett House Museum, Sandusky, OH 1185

Sandy Bay Historical Society & Museums, Inc., Rockport, MA 705

Sandy Spring Museum, Sandy Spring, MD 653

Sanford Museum, Sanford, FL 343

Santa Fe Trail Center, Larned, KS 547

Santa Fe Trail Museum, Ingalls, KS 545

Santa Fe Trail Museum/Trinidad History Museum, Trinidad, CO 234

Santa Maria Museum of Flight, Inc., Santa Maria, CA 183

Santa Maria Valley Historical Museum, Santa Maria, CA 183

Sapulpa Historical Museum, Sapulpa, OK .1213

Sarah Orne Jewett House, South Berwick, ME 622

Sarasota Classic Car Museum, Sarasota, FL 345

Saratoga County Historical Society, Brookside Museum, Ballston Spa, NY 960

Sarpy County Historical Museum, Bellevue, NE 857

Sauk County Historical Museum, Baraboo, WI 1591

Sauk Prairie Area Historical Society, Inc., Prairie du Sac, WI 1619

Scarborough Historical Museum, Scarborough, ME 621

The Scarsdale Historical Society, Scarsdale, NY 1066

Schenectady County Historical Society, Schenectady, NY 1067

Schmidt House Museum & Research Library, Grants Pass, OR 1225

Schminck Memorial Museum, Lakeview, OR 1227

Schoolcraft County Historical Society, Manistique, MI 753

Schoolhouse Children's Museum, Boynton Beach, FL 297

Schoolhouse Museum of the Ridgewood Historical Society, Inc., Ridgewood, NJ 923

Schuyler County Historical Society, Inc., Montour Falls, NY 1015

Schwartz Collection of Skiing Heritage, Tiburon, CA 192

Sci-Quest, the North Alabama Science Center, Huntsville, AL 12

The Science Center, Carbondale, IL 415

The Science Center of Pinellas County, Saint Petersburg, FL 342

Science Central, Fort Wayne, IN 478

Scitrek, The Science and Technology Museum of Atlanta, Valdosta, GA 389

Sciworks, Winston-Salem, NC 1126

Scotia-Glenville Children's Museum, Scotia, NY 1068

Scotland Heritage Chapel & Museum, Scotland, SD 1355

Sea Cliff Village Museum, Sea Cliff, NY ..1068

SEE Science Center, Manchester, NH 892

Senate House State Historic Site, Kingston, NY 1008

Senator John Heinz Pittsburgh Regional History Center, Pittsburgh, PA 1294

Seneca Falls Historical Society, Seneca Falls, NY 1069

Sequoia and Kings Canyon National Parks, Three Rivers, CA 191

1719 Hans Herr House & Museum, Willow Street, PA 1308

The 1719 William Trent House Museum, Trenton, NJ 928

1797 Ezekiel Harris House, Augusta, GA 366

1768 Jeremiah Lee Mansion, Marblehead, MA 693

Seward County Historical Society Museum, Goehner, NE 861

Seymour Community Museum, Seymour, WI 1621

Shaker Historical Society, Shaker Heights, OH 1185

Shaker Museum, New Gloucester, ME 615

The Shaker Museum and Library, Old Chatham, NY 1045

Shalom Street, West Bloomfield, MI 766

Shawnee Town, Shawnee, KS 558

Sheboygan County Historical Museum, Sheboygan, WI 1621

Shelburne Museum, Inc., Shelburne, VT ...1487

Shenandoah National Park, Luray, VA 1514

Shenandoal Valley Discovery Museum, Winchester, VA 1546

The Sherman House, Lancaster, OH 1171

Sherwood-Davidson House, Newark, OH ..1178

Shiloh Museum of Ozark History, Springdale, AR 68

Shippensburg Historical Society Museum, Shippensburg, PA 1300

Shoal Creek Living History Museum, Kansas City, MO 822

Shoreline Historical Museum, Seattle, WA 1569

Silent Wings Museum, Lubbock, TX 1435

Siloam Springs Museum, Siloam Springs, AR 68

Silt Historical Society, Silt, CO 232

Silvercreek Museum, Freeport, IL 435

Sioux City Public Museum, Sioux City, IA 528

Siouxland Heritage Museums, Sioux Falls, SD 1357

Siskiyou County Museum, Yreka, CA 200

Skagit County Historical Museum, La Conner, WA 1557

The Skinner Museum of Mount Holyoke College, South Hadley, MA 709

Slifer House, Lewisburg, PA 1268

Smith County Historical Society, Tyler, TX 1456

Smith Robertson Museum & Cultural Center, Jackson, MS 804

Smithtown Historical Society, Smithtown, NY 1070

Smyrna Museum, Smyrna, DE 272

Snowmobile Hall of Fame and Museum, Saint Germain, WI 1620

Society for Contemporary Craft, Pittsburgh, PA 1294

Somers Mansion, Somers Point, NJ 924

The Somerset County Historical Society, Inc., Princess Anne, MD 650

Sonoma County Museum, Santa Rosa, CA 185

Sosa-Carrillo-Fremont House Museum, Tucson, AZ 50

South Bannock County Historical Center, Lava Hot Springs, ID 407

South Carolina Law Enforcement Officers Hall of Fame, Columbia, SC 1330

South Carolina State Museum, Columbia, SC 1331

South Carolina Tennis Hall of Fame, Belton, SC 1321

South County Museum Inc., Narragansett, RI 1313

South Dakota Hall of Fame, Chamberlain, SD 1345

South Dakota State Historical Society, Pierre, SD 1353

South Dakota Tractor Museum, Kimball, SD 1350

Recreational Artifacts–Continued

South Milwaukee Historical Society
Museum, South Milwaukee, WI 1622
South Park City Museum, Fairplay, CO 215
South Pass City State Historic Site, South
Pass City, WY 1638
South Street Seaport Museum, New York,
NY 1039
South Sutton Old Store Museum, South
Sutton, NH 896
South Wood County Historical Corp.,
Wisconsin Rapids, WI 1628
Southampton Historical Museum,
Southampton, NY 1070
Southeast Museum Association, Inc.,
Brewster, NY 964
Southeastern Railway Museum, Duluth,
GA 371
Southern Museum of Flight, Birmingham,
AL 6
Southern Oregon Historical Society,
Jacksonville, OR 1226
Southwest Dairy Museum, Sulphur
Springs, TX 1454
Space Farms Zoological Park and
Museum, Sussex, NJ 925
Spartanburg County Regional Museum of
History, Spartanburg, SC 1341
Spencer-Peirce-Little Farm, Newbury,
MA 697
Spirit of '76 Museum, Wellington, OH 1190
SPJST Library Archives & Museum,
Temple, TX 1455
The Sports Museum, Boston, MA 669
Spring River Park & Zoo, Roswell, NM 946
Spring Street Historical Museum,
Shreveport, LA 602
Springfield Armory National Historic
Site, Springfield, MA 710
Springfield Art & Historical Society -
Miller Art Center, Springfield, VT 1488
Springfield Art Association, Springfield,
IL 460
Springfield Museums - Connecticut
Valley Historical Museum, Springfield,
MA 710
Springs Museum, Springs, PA 1301
Stafford County Historical Society
Museum, Stafford, KS 558
Stamford Historical Society, Inc.,
Stamford, CT 260
Stan Hywet Hall and Gardens, Inc.,
Akron, OH 1139
Stanzel Model Aircraft Museum,
Schulenburg, TX 1452
State Agricultural Heritage Museum,
Brookings, SD 1344
State of Illinois-Historic Preservation
Agency, Historic Sites Division,
Springfield, IL 460
Staten Island Historical Society, Staten
Island, NY 1074
Statue of Liberty National Monument &
Ellis Island Immigration Museum,
New York, NY 1039
Steamboat Bertrand Collection, Missouri
Valley, IA 524
Stearns History Museum, Saint Cloud,
MN 788
Steilacoom Historical Museum
Association, Steilacoom, WA 1572
Stephens County Historical Society and
Museum, Duncan, OK 1199
Stephenson County Historical Society,
Freeport, IL 436
Stephenville Museum, Stephenville, TX 1454
Steppingstone Museum, Havre de Grace,
MD 647
Sterling-Rock Falls Historical Society
Museum, Sterling, IL 461
Sterne-Hoya House Museum and Library,
Nacogdoches, TX 1440

Stevens Museum, Salem, IN 498
The Stone House Museum, Belchertown,
MA 662
Stonefield Historic Site, Cassville, WI 1593
Stonewall House, Rocky Mount, NC 1118
Stonewall Jackson Museum at Hupp's
Hill, Strasburg, VA 1539
Strasburg Museum, Strasburg, VA 1539
The Stratford Historical Society &
Catherine B. Mitchell Museum,
Stratford, CT 262
Strong - National Museum of Play,
Rochester, NY 1060
Stuart Heritage Museum, Stuart, FL 346
Studebaker National Museum, Inc., South
Bend, IN 500
Stuhr Museum of the Prairie Pioneer,
Grand Island, NE 862
Stutsman County Memorial Museum,
Jamestown, ND 1133
Suffolk County Historical Society,
Riverhead, NY 1057
SullivanMunce Cultural Center,
Zionsville, IN 504
Summit County Historical Society,
Akron, OH 1139
Summit Historical Society, Breckenridge,
CO 204
The Sumter County Museum, Sumter, SC .1342
Sun Prairie Historical Library &
Museum, Sun Prairie, WI 1624
Susquehanna Museum of Havre de Grace
Inc. at the Lock House, Havre de
Grace, MD 647
Swarthout Memorial Museum, La Crosse,
WI 1603
Sweet Briar Museum, Sweet Briar, VA 1540
Sweetwater County Historical Museum,
Green River, WY 1633
Swenson Memorial Museum of Stephens
County, Breckenridge, TX 1397

T.R.E.E. House - The Rapides
Exploratory Education House,
Alexandria, LA 585
Table Rock Historical Society and
Museums, Table Rock, NE 873
Tannenbaum Historic Park, Greensboro,
NC 1104
Tante Blanche Museum, Madawaska, ME ...614
Ted Williams Museum and Hitters Hall
of Fame, Hernando, FL 312
The Teddy Bear Museum of Naples,
Naples, FL 328
Temecula Valley Museum, Temecula, CA 191
Tempe Historical Museum, Tempe, AZ 46
Tennessee Central Railway Museum,
Nashville, TN 1380
Territorial Capital-Lane Museum,
Lecompton, KS 549
Territorial Statehouse State Park &
Museum, Fillmore, UT 1465
Terwilliger Museum, Waterloo, NY 1083
Texana Museum and Library Association,
Edna, TX 1410
Texarkana Museums System, Texarkana,
TX 1455
Texas City Museum, Texas City, TX 1455
Texas Maritime Museum, Rockport, TX 1446
Texas Music Museum, Austin, TX 1392
Texas Sports Hall of Fame, Waco, TX 1459
Texas State Museum of Asian Cultures &
Educational Center, Corpus Christi,
TX 1402
Thetford Historical Society Library and
Museum, Thetford, VT 1488
This Is The Place Heritage Park, Salt
Lake City, UT 1472
The Thomas Griswold House and
Museum, Guilford, CT 243
The Thomas J. Boyd, Wytheville, VA 1546

The Thomas T. Taber Museum of the
Lycoming County Historial Society,
Williamsport, PA ....,1308
Thornton W. Burgess Museum,
Sandwich, MA 708
Three Village Historical Society,
Setauket, NY 1069
Tilden Nature Area Environmental
Education Center, Berkeley, CA 77
Tillamook County Pioneer Museum,
Tillamook, OR 1237
Tinley Park Historical Society, Tinley
Park, IL 461
Tioga County Historical Society
Museum, Owego, NY 1048
Tobacco Farm Life Museum, Inc., Kenly,
NC 1107
Tolland Historical Society - Tolland
County Jail and Warden's Home
Museum, Tolland, CT 262
Tom Mix Museum, Dewey, OK 1199
Tomball Community Museum Center,
Tomball, TX 1455
Tombstone Courthouse State Historic
Park, Tombstone, AZ 46
Tongass Historical Museum, Ketchikan,
AK 26
Torrington Historical Society, Inc.,
Torrington, CT 263
Towe Auto Museum, Sacramento, CA 154
Town of Manlius Historical Society with
Museum, Manlius, NY 1013
Town of Yorktown Museum, Yorktown
Heights, NY 1087
Toy & Miniature Museum of Kansas
City, Kansas City, MO 823
Toy Train Depot Museum and Train
Ride, Alamogordo, NM 932
Travel Town Museum, Los Angeles, CA 121
Travellers Rest Plantation & Museum,
Nashville, TN 1381
Traverse County Historical Society,
Wheaton, MN 796
Tread of Pioneers Museum, Steamboat
Springs, CO 232
Treehouse Children's Museum, Ogden,
UT 1468
Trenton Historical Museum, Trenton, MI 765
Tri-Cities Museum, Grand Haven, MI 743
Troutdale Historical Society, Troutdale,
OR 1237
Truckee-Donner Historical Society Jail
Museum, Truckee, CA 193
Tubman African-American Museum,
Macon, GA 378
Tucson Children's Museum, Tucson, AZ 51
Tudor Place Foundation, Inc.,
Washington, DC 292
Turtle Mountain Chippewa Historical
Society, Belcourt, ND 1127
Twin Falls County Historical Museum,
Filer, ID 405
Twinsburg Historical Society, Twinsburg,
OH 1188

U.S. Bicycling Hall of Fame, Somerville,
NJ 924
USDA Forest Service - Land Between
the Lakes, Golden Pond, KY 570
Ukrainian Museum-Archives, Inc.,
Cleveland, OH 1156
Ukrainian National Museum, Inc.,
Chicago, IL 428
Ulster County Historical Society,
Marbletown, NY 1013
Union County Historical Society
Museum, Blairsville, GA 366
Union County Museum, Union, OR 1238
Union Mills Homestead & Grist Mill,
Westminster, MD 656
Union Station Kansas City, Inc., Kansas
City, MO 823

United States Golf Association Museum & Archives, Far Hills, NJ 903

United States Hockey Hall of Fame, Eveleth, MN................................774

University Museum, Carbondale, IL 415

University Museum, Martin, TN 1371

University of Pennsylvania Museum of Archaeology and Anthropology, Philadelphia, PA 1288

Upham Mansion, Marshfield, WI 1608

Upper Peninsula Children's Museum, Marquette, MI.................................754

U.S. Army Air Defense Artillery Museum, Fort Bliss, TX.......................1414

U.S. Army Engineer Museum, Fort Leonard Wood, MO.............................815

U.S. Grant's Home State Historic Site, Galena, IL....................................436

U.S. National Ski Hall of Fame & Museum, Inc., Ishpeming, MI..................747

USS Constellation Museum, Baltimore, MD...636

Utah State Historical Society, Salt Lake City, UT 1473

Vacaville Museum, Vacaville, CA 194

Valentine-Varian House/Museum of Bronx History, Bronx, NY 967

Valentown Museum, Victor, NY 1081

Valley Art Center, Inc., Clarkston, WA 1551

Van Cortlandt House Museum, Bronx, NY...967

Vent Haven Museum, Fort Mitchell, KY 568

Ventura County Museum of History & Art, Ventura, CA.............................195

Verde Historical Society, Clemenceau Heritage Museum, Cottonwood, AZ..........32

Vermont Ski Museum, Stowe, VT..............1488

Vernon County Historical Museum, Viroqua, WI....................................1625

The Vestal Museum, Vestal, NY 1081

Vigo County Historical Museum, Terre Haute, IN......................................501

Villa Louis Historic Site, Prairie du Chien, WI....................................1619

Village Historical Society, Inc., Harrison, OH..1168

The Vinalhaven Historical Society Museum, Vinalhaven, ME......................624

Virginia Museum of Fine Arts, Richmond, VA 1533

Virginia Sports Hall of Fame, Portsmouth, VA................................1526

W.K. Gordon Center for Industrial History of Texas, Mingus, TX 1439

Wabaunsee County Historical Museum, Alma, KS.......................................532

Wahkiakum County Historical Museum, Cathlamet, WA................................1550

Waimea Arboretum and Botanical Garden in Waimea Valley Audubon Center, Haleiwa, HI....................................392

Wakefield House Museum, Blue Earth, MN...769

Wakefield Museum Association, Wakefield, KS..................................560

Waldensian Heritage Museum, Valdese, NC...1121

The Walker African American Museum & Research Center, Las Vegas, NV 880

Wallace District Mining Museum, Wallace, ID....................................410

Wallingford Historical Society, Inc., Wallingford, CT................................263

Walnut Grove Plantation, Roebuck, SC 1340

Waltham Historical Society, Waltham, MA...716

The Waltham Museum, Waltham, MA 716

Wantagh Historical & Preservation Society, Wantagh, NY 1081

Ward County Historical Society, Minot, ND...1135

The Ward Museum of Wildfowl Art, Salisbury University, Salisbury, MD 653

Warner House, Portsmouth, NH 895

Warrick County Museum, Inc., Boonville, IN..470

Warsaw Historical Museum, Warsaw, NY .1082

Waseca County Historical Society, Waseca, MN....................................796

Washburn Historical Museum & Cultural Center, Inc. aka Washburn Cultural Center, Washburn, WI 1625

Washington County Fair Farm Museum, Greenwich, NY..................................996

Washington County Historical Association, Fort Calhoun, NE 860

Washington County Historical Society and Miller House Museum, Hagerstown, MD 646

Washington County Historical Society Inc., West Bend, WI.........................1627

Washington County Rural Heritage Museum, Boonsboro, MD......................637

Washington Doll's House and Toy Museum, Washington, DC......................294

Washington Oaks Gardens State Park, Palm Coast, FL................................334

Washington's Lands Museum & Sayre Log House, Ravenswood, WV..............1586

Waterford Historical Museum and Cultural Center, Inc., Waterford, NY.....1083

Waterloo Area Historical Society, Grass Lake, MI......................................744

Watertown Historical Society, Inc., Watertown, CT................................264

Watkins Community Museum of History, Lawrence, KS..................................548

Watson-Curtze Mansion, Erie, PA 1253

Wauconda Township Historical Society, Wauconda, IL..................................463

Waukesha County Museum, Waukesha, WI..1625

Wayland Historical Society, Wayland, MA...716

Wayne County Historical Museum, Richmond, IN..................................497

Wayne County Historical Society, Lyons, NY...1012

Wayne County Historical Society, Honesdale, PA...............................1261

Wellesley Historical Society, Inc., Wellesley Hills, MA...........................717

Wellfleet Historical Society Museum, Wellfleet, MA..................................717

Wells County Historical Museum, Bluffton, IN...................................470

Wenatchee Valley Museum and Cultural Center, Wenatchee, WA.....................1577

Wenham Museum, Wenham, MA...............717

Weslaco Museum, Weslaco, TX 1461

West Allis Historical Society Museum, West Allis, WI.................................1626

West Bay Common School Children's Museum, League City, TX....................1434

West Chicago City Museum, West Chicago, IL....................................464

West of the Pecos Museum, Pecos, TX 1443

Western Hennepin County Pioneers Association, Long Lake, MN 779

Western Heritage Center, Billings, MT 841

Western Hotel/Museum, Lancaster, CA........108

Western Museum of Mining & Industry, Colorado Springs, CO 208

Western Reserve Historical Society, Cleveland, OH................................1156

Western Springs Historical Society, Western Springs, IL...........................464

Westminster Historical Society, Westminster, VT...............................1490

Westmoreland Museum of American Art, Greensburg, PA.................................1257

Westport Maritime Museum, Westport, WA...1578

Wexford County Historical Society & Museum, Cadillac, MI..........................731

Whatcom Museum of History and Art, Bellingham, WA...............................1549

Wheels O' Time Museum, Peoria, IL...........451

White Deer Land Museum, Pampa, TX 1442

White Pine Public Museum, Ely, NV..........877

White River Valley Museum, Auburn, WA...1547

Whitewater Canal State Historic Site, Metamora, IN....................................490

Whitingham Historical Museum, Whitingham, VT................................1490

Wichita-Sedgwick County Historical Museum Association, Wichita, KS 563

Wildcare: Terwilliger Nature Education & Wildlife, San Rafael, CA 177

Wilder Memorial Museum, Strawberry Point, IA.......................................528

Wilderness Road Regional Museum, Newbern, VA..................................1519

William A. Farnsworth Library and Art Museum, Inc. d/b/a Farnsworth Art Museum, Rockland, ME.......................621

William Clark Market House Museum, Paducah, KY....................................582

William Cullen Bryant Homestead, Cummington, MA...............................678

William Hammond Mathers Museum, Bloomington, IN...............................470

William J. Clinton Presidential Library & Museum, Little Rock, AR 63

Williamson County Historical Society, Marion, IL.......................................444

Willowbrook Museum Village, Newfield, ME...616

Wilson County Historical Society Museum, Fredonia, KS............................540

Wilton Historical Museums, Wilton, CT......267

Wilton House Museum, Richmond, VA 1534

Winchendon Historical Society, Inc., Winchendon, MA...............................720

Windham Textile and History Museum (The Mill Museum), Willimantic, CT 267

Wings Over Miami Museum, Inc., Miami, FL.......................................326

Winnetka Historical Society, Winnetka, IL...466

Winona County Historical Museum, Winona, MN....................................797

Wisconsin Historical Museum, Madison, WI..1606

Wisconsin Maritime Museum, Manitowoc, WI................................1607

Wisconsin Veterans Museum-Madison, Madison, WI....................................1606

Wise County Heritage Museum, Decatur, TX...1408

Wolcott House Museum Complex, Maumee, OH................................1175

Wolf House Museum, Manhattan, KS..........552

Wolf Point Area Historical Society, Inc., Wolf Point, MT..................................855

The Wolfsonian - Florida International University, Miami Beach, FL...................327

Wonder Works, Oak Park, IL......................449

Wonder Workshop Children's Museum, Manhattan, KS..................................552

WonderLab Museum of Science, Health and Technology, Bloomington, IN...........470

Wonderscope Children's Museum, Shawnee, KS..................................558

Woodbine International Fire Museum, Woodbine, GA..................................392

Woodlawn Museum/The Black House, Ellsworth, ME..................................610

Woodrow Wilson House, Washington, DC..294

Woodside Store Historic Site, Woodside, CA...199

Woodstock Historical Society, Inc., Woodstock, VT................................1491

Recreational Artifacts–Continued

Woodstock Museum of Shenandoah County, Inc., Woodstock, VA.....1546

Worcester Historical Museum, Worcester, MA.....721

Working Wonders Children's Museum, Bend, OR.....1220

Workman & Temple Family Homestead Museum, City of Industry, CA.....85

The Works: Ohio Center for History, Art & Technology, Newark, OH.....1179

World Awareness Children's Museum, Glen Falls, NY.....994

World Figure Skating Museum & Hall of Fame, Colorado Springs, CO.....208

World Golf Hall of Fame, Saint Augustine, FL.....340

World Kite Museum & Hall of Fame, Long Beach, WA.....1558

World Museum of Mining, Butte, MT.....843

World O' Tools Museum, Waverly, TN.....1385

World of Scouting Museum, Valley Forge, PA.....1304

World of Wings Pigeon Center, Oklahoma City, OK.....1211

World's Largest Toy Museum and Harold Bell Wright, Branson, MO.....811

Worldways Children's Museum, Ballwin, MO.....811

Worthington Historical Society, Worthington, OH.....1192

WOW! Children's Museum (World of Wonder), Lafayette, CO.....225

Wray Museum, Wray, CO.....235

Wren's Nest, Atlanta, GA.....364

Wright County Historical Society, Buffalo, MN.....770

Wright Museum, Wolfeboro, NH.....897

Wyalusing Valley Museum, Wyalusing, PA.....1309

Wyandotte County Museum, Bonner Springs, KS.....534

Wyandotte Museum, Wyandotte, MI.....766

Wyatt Earp Birthplace Home, Monmouth, IL.....445

Wyck, Philadelphia, PA.....1289

Wyoming Children's Museum & Nature Center, Laramie, WY.....1636

Yakima Valley Museum and Historical Association, Yakima, WA.....1579

Yates County Genealogical and Historical Society and Oliver House Museum and L. Caroline Underwood Museum, Penn Yan, NY.....1052

Ybor City Museum State Park, Tampa, FL.....351

Yellow Medicine County Historical Society and Museum, Granite Falls, MN.....777

Yellowstone Gateway Museum of Park County, Livingston, MT.....850

Yesterday's Children Antique Doll & Toy Museum, Vicksburg, MS.....809

Yesteryears Doll Museum, Sandwich, MA.....708

Yorktown Historical Museum, Yorktown, TX.....1462

Youth Museum of Southern West Virginia, Beckley, WV.....1579

Ypsilanti Historical Museum, Ypsilanti, MI.....767

Yucaipa Valley Historical Society Museum, Yucaipa, CA.....201

Yuma Territorial Prison State Historic Park, Yuma, AZ.....54

Zane Grey Museum, Lackawaxen, PA.....1265

Zeum, San Francisco, CA.....170

Structures

A.C. Gilbert's Discovery Village, Salem, OR.....1235

Abraham Lincoln Birthplace National Historic Site, Hodgenville, KY.....571

Abraham Lincoln Library & Museum, Lincoln Memorial University, Harrogate, TN.....1366

The Accokeek Foundation, Inc., Accokeek, MD.....627

Ace of Clubs House, Texarkana, TX.....1455

Adam Thoroughgood House, Virginia Beach, VA.....1541

Adams County Historical Society Museum, Lind, WA.....1558

Adams National Historical Park, Quincy, MA.....704

Adams Old Stone Grist Mill, Bellows Falls, VT.....1476

Adams State College Luther Bean Museum, Alamosa, CO.....201

Adena Mansion and Gardens, Chillicothe, OH.....1147

The Adirondack Museum, Blue Mountain Lake, NY.....963

Admiral Nimitz National Museum of the Pacific War, Fredericksburg, TX.....1419

Adsmore Museum, Princeton, KY.....583

Afro-American Historical Society Museum, Jersey City, NJ.....908

Age of Steam Railroad Museum, Dallas, TX.....1404

Agricultural Heritage Museum, Boerne, TX.....1396

Agrirama, Georgia's Living History Museum & Village, Tifton, GA.....388

Aiken County Historical Museum, Aiken, SC.....1320

Ak-Sar-Ben Aquarium Outdoor Education Center, Gretna, NE.....862

Akta Lakota Museum and Cultural Center, Chamberlain, SD.....1345

Alabama Agricultural Museum, Dothan, AL.....8

Alabama Mining Museum, Dora, AL.....7

Alachua County Historic Trust: Matheson Museum, Inc., Gainesville, FL.....310

Alamance Battleground State Historic Site, Burlington, NC.....1092

The Alamo, San Antonio, TX.....1447

Albany Civil Rights Movement Museum at Old Mt. Zion Church, Albany, GA.....355

Albany Historical Society, Inc., Sabetha, KS.....557

Alcatraz Island, San Francisco, CA.....163

Alden House Historic Site, Duxbury, MA.....680

Alexander Ramsey House, Minnesota Historical Society, Saint Paul, MN.....789

Alexandre Mouton House/Lafayette Museum, Lafayette, LA.....589

Alfred B. Maclay State Gardens, Tallahassee, FL.....346

Alger County Heritage Center, Munising, MI.....757

Alice Austen House Museum, Staten Island, NY.....1072

Allaire Village Inc., Farmingdale, NJ.....903

Allegan County Historical Society and Old Jail Museum, Allegan, MI.....723

Allegany County Historical Society, Inc., Cumberland, MD.....641

Allegheny Portage Railroad National Historic Site and Johnstown Flood National Memorial, Gallitzin, PA.....1255

Allen County Historical Society, Iola, KS.....545

Alley Pond Environmental Center, Inc., Douglaston, NY.....984

Almond Historical Society/Hagadorn House Museum, Almond, NY.....957

Alpine County Museum, Markleeville, CA.....124

Altama Museum of Art & History, Vidalia, GA.....390

Alton Museum of History and Art, Inc., Alton, IL.....410

Amador County Museum, Jackson, CA.....105

Amelia Earhart Birthplace Museum, Atchison, KS.....532

American Clock and Watch Museum, Inc., Bristol, CT.....236

American Independence Museum, Exeter, NH.....887

American Labor Museum, Botto House National Landmark, Haledon, NJ.....906

American Precision Museum Association, Inc., Windsor, VT.....1490

American Sign Museum, Cincinnati, OH...1148

American Swedish Historical Foundation & Museum, Philadelphia, PA.....1276

American Swedish Institute, Minneapolis, MN.....781

American Textile History Museum, Lowell, MA.....691

America's Black Holocaust Museum, Milwaukee, WI.....1610

America's Stonehenge, North Salem, NH....893

Amherst History Museum at the Strong House - Amherst Historical Society, Amherst, MA.....658

Amherst Museum, Amherst, NY.....957

Amity and Woodbridge Historical Society, Woodbridge, CT.....268

Amory Regional Museum, Amory, MS.....797

Amos Herr House Foundation and Historic Society, Landisville, PA.....1267

Anacortes Museum, Anacortes, WA.....1547

Anderson County Historical Museum, Garnett, KS.....541

Andersonville National Historic Site, Andersonville, GA.....355

Andover Historical Society, Andover, MA...660

Andrew Johnson National Historic Site, Greeneville, TN.....1366

Andrew Low House, Savannah, GA.....384

Angel Mounds State Historic Site, Evansville, IN.....475

Animas Museum, Durango, CO.....214

Anna Miller Museum, Newcastle, WY.....1637

Annie Riggs Memorial Museum, Fort Stockton, TX.....1415

Ano Nuevo State Reserve, Pescadero, CA...141

Anoka County Historical Society, Anoka, MN.....767

Anson County Historical Society, Inc., Wadesboro, NC.....1121

Antelope Valley Indian Museum, Lancaster, CA.....108

The Antiquarian and Landmarks Society, Inc., Hartford, CT.....244

The Antique Boat Museum, Clayton, NY....978

Apostles Islands National Lakeshore, Bayfield, WI.....1591

The Apple Trees Museum, Burlington, IA...506

Appomattox Court House National Historical Park, Appomattox, VA.....1495

Aptucxet Trading Post Museum, Bourne, MA.....670

APVA Preservation Virginia, Richmond, VA.....1528

APVA's John Marshall House, Richmond, VA.....1528

Arbor Lodge State Historical Park, Nebraska City, NE.....868

Arches Museum of Pioneer Life, Winona, MN.....797

Arches National Park Visitor Center, Moab, UT.....1467

Archibald Graham McIlwaine House & Visitors' Center (The Petersburg Museums), Petersburg, VA.....1524

Archives Museum, Temple Mickve Israel, Savannah, GA.....384

Arden - The Helena Modjeska Historic House & Gardens, Modjeska Canyon, CA 126

Ardenwood Historic Farm, Fremont, CA 96

Argo Gold Mine & Mill Museum, Idaho Springs, CO 223

Arizona Historical Society Pioneer Museum, Flagstaff, AZ 32

Arizona State Capitol Museum, Phoenix, AZ 39

Arizona State Parks Board, Phoenix, AZ 39

Ark-La-Tex Antique & Classic Vehicle Museum, Shreveport, LA 600

Arkansas Air Museum, Fayetteville, AR 57

Arkansas Country Doctor Museum, Lincoln, AR 61

Arkansas Post Museum, Gillett, AR..............58

Arlington Heights Historical Museum, Arlington Heights, IL 411

Arlington Historical Museum, Arlington, VA 1495

The Arlington Historical Society, Arlington, MA 660

Arlington House, The Robert E. Lee Memorial, Arlington, VA 1495

Armand Bayou Nature Center, Houston, TX 1424

The Armory Art Center, West Palm Beach, FL 353

The Arms Family Museum of Local History, Youngstown, OH 1193

Arrow Rock State Historic Site, Arrow Rock, MO 810

Artesia Historical Museum & Art Center, Artesia, NM 936

Arthurdale Heritage, Inc., Arthurdale, WV 1579

Arvada Center for the Arts and Humanities, Arvada, CO 201

Asa Packer Mansion, Jim Thorpe, PA 1263

Ash Lawn-Highland, Charlottesville, VA 1498

Ashland Historical Society, Ashland, MA 661

Ashland Railroad Station Museum, Ashland, NH 883

Ashland, The Henry Clay Estate, Lexington, KY 572

Ashtabula County Historical Society, Geneva-on-the-Lake, OH 1166

Ashton Villa & The Heritage Visitor Center, Galveston, TX 1420

Asian Art Museum of San Francisco, Chong-Moon Lee Center for Asian Art and Culture, San Francisco, CA 163

Asistencia: San Gabriel Mission Outpost, Redlands, CA 146

Aspen Historical Society, Aspen, CO..........202

Association for the Preservation of Tennessee Antiquities, Nashville, TN 1377

Astor House Museum, Golden, CO..............219

Astors' Beechwood Mansion - Living History Museum, Newport, RI..............1313

The Athenaeum of Philadelphia, Philadelphia, PA 1276

Atlanta Historical Society, Atlanta, GA.......358

Attmore-Oliver House, New Bern, NC.......1112

Atwood House Museum, Home of Chatham Historical Society, Chatham, MA 675

Au Glaize Village, Defiance, OH..............1162

Auburn Cord Duesenberg Museum, Auburn, IN 468

Audie Murphy/American Cotton Museum, Inc, Greenville, TX 1423

Audubon County Historical Society, Exira, IA 517

Audubon House & Tropical Gardens, Key West, FL..............317

Audubon State Historic Site, Saint Francisville, LA 600

Auglaize County Historical Society, Saint Marys, OH 1184

Augusta Historical Museum & Genealogy, Augusta, KS..............533

Aullwood Audubon Center and Farm, Dayton, OH..............1160

Aurora History Museum, Aurora, CO 202

Aurora Regional Fire Museum, Aurora, IL..............411

Avery County Museum, Newland, NC.......1113

The Avon Historical Society, Inc., Avon, CT..............235

Awbury Arboretum, Philadelphia, PA..........1277

Aztalan Museum, Jefferson, WI..............1601

Aztec Museum and Pioneer Village, Aztec, NM 936

B&O Railroad Museum: Ellicott City Station, Ellicott City, MD 643

Baca House, Trinidad History Museum, Trinidad, CO..............233

Bacon's Castle, Surry County, VA..............1540

Bagg Bonanza Historical Farm, Mooreton, ND..............1135

Bailey House Museum - Maui Historical Society, Wailuku, HI 402

Baldwin County Heritage Museum, Elberta, AL..............8

Baldwin-Reynolds House Museum, Meadville, PA 1270

Bale Grist Mill State Historic Park, Calistoga, CA..............80

Baltimore & Ohio Railroad Museum, Baltimore, MD..............629

Baltimore Civil War Museum, Baltimore, MD..............629

Baltimore Maritime Museum, Baltimore, MD..............630

Baltimore Museum of Industry, Baltimore, MD..............630

Baltimore Public Works Museum, Inc., Baltimore, MD..............630

Bandelier National Monument, Los Alamos, NM 942

Bandon Historical Society Museum, Bandon, OR 1219

Banner County Historical Society, Harrisburg, NE..............862

Banning Residence Museum, Wilmington, CA 198

The Barbara Fritchie House, Frederick, MD..............644

The Barnacle Historic State Park, Coconut Grove, FL..............300

Barnard's Mill Art Museum, Glen Rose, TX 1422

Barnes Foundation, Merion, PA..............1271

Barnet Historical Society, Barnet, VT.......1476

The Barnum Museum, Bridgeport, CT.........235

Barnwell County Museum, Barnwell, SC ..1321

Barratt's Chapel and Museum, Frederica, DE..............270

Barre Historical Society, Inc., Barre, MA 662

The Barrington Area Historical Society, Barrington, IL..............412

Barrington Living History Farm, Washington, TX..............1460

Barron County Historical Society's Pioneer Village Museum, Cameron, WI..............1593

The Bartlett Museum, Amesbury, MA 657

Barton County Historical Museum & Village, Great Bend, KS..............542

Bartow-Pell Mansion Museum, Carriage House & Gardens, Bronx, NY..............964

Bartram's Garden, Philadelphia, PA 1277

Bassett Hall, Williamsburg, VA..............1544

Bates-Scofield Homestead, The Darien Historical Society, Darien, CT..............238

Batsto Village, Hammonton, NJ 907

Battersea (The Petersburg Museums), Petersburg, VA..............1524

Battle of Lexington State Historic Site, Lexington, MO..............826

Battleground Historical Society, Englishtown, NJ..............903

The Battles Museums of Rural Life, Girard, PA..............1256

Battleship North Carolina, Wilmington, NC..............1122

Baxter Springs Heritage Center and Museum, Baxter Springs, KS..............533

Bay View Historical Museum, Bay View, MI..............728

Bayard Cutting Arboretum, Great River, NY..............996

Bayou Bend Collection and Gardens, Houston, TX..............1425

Bear Mountain Trailside Museums and Zoo, Bear Mountain, NY..............961

Beau Fort Plantation Home, Bermuda, LA..............587

Beauchamp Newman Museum, Elizabeth, WV..............1581

The Beaufort Arsenal, Beaufort, SC..............1321

Beaufort Historic Site, Beaufort, NC..............1091

Beauvais Heritage Center, Clark, SD 1345

Beauvoir, The Jefferson Davis Home and Presidential Library, Biloxi, MS 798

Beaver Island Historical Society, Beaver Island, MI..............728

Beaverhead County Museum, Dillon, MT ...845

Beavertail Lighthouse Museum, Jamestown, RI..............1311

Bedford City/County Museum, Bedford, VA..............1496

Bedford Historical Society Museum and Library, Bedford, OH 1142

Bedingfield Inn Museum, Lumpkin, GA......376

Belair Mansion, Bowie, MD..............638

Belair Stable Museum, Bowie, MD..............638

Belcourt Castle, Newport, RI..............1313

Belding Museum, Belding, MI 728

The Belknap Mill Society, Laconia, NH......890

Bellamy Mansion Museum of History and Design Arts, Wilmington, NC..............1122

Belle Grove Plantation, Middletown, VA ...1517

Belle Meade Plantation, Nashville, TN......1377

Bellflower Historical and Genealogical Society, Bellflower, IL..............413

Bellingrath Gardens & Home, Theodore, AL..............18

Bellport-Brookhaven Historical Society and Museum, Bellport, NY..............961

Belmont County Victorian Mansion Museum, Barnesville, OH..............1141

Beloit Historical Society, Beloit, WI..............1592

Beltrami County History Center, Bemidji, MN..............768

Belvedere-Tiburon Landmarks Society, Tiburon, CA..............192

Benicia Historical Museum, Benicia, CA 74

Benjamin Harrison Presidential Site, Indianapolis, IN..............481

Bennett Place State Historic Site, Durham, NC..............1098

Bennington Battle Monument, Old Bennington, VT..............1484

Benson Grist Mill, Stansbury Park, UT.......1475

Bentonville Battlefield State Historic Site, Four Oaks, NC..............1102

Bent's Old Fort National Historic Site, La Junta, CO..............224

Benzie Area Historical Museum, Benzonia, MI..............729

Bergen County Zoological Park, Paramus, NJ..............919

Berkshire County Historical Society, Inc. - Arrowhead, Pittsfield, MA..............702

Berkshire Museum, Pittsfield, MA..............702

Berkshire Scenic Railway Museum, Inc., Lenox, MA..............689

Berlin Art and Historical Collections, Berlin, MA..............662

Bernard Historical Society and Museum, Delton, MI 734

Structures—Continued

Berrien County Historical Association, Berrien Springs, MI...................................729

The Berry Botanic Garden, Portland, OR ..1230

Besh-Ba-Gowah Archaeological Park, Globe, AZ 35

Bess Streeter Aldrich House & Museum, Elmwood, NE 860

Bessemer Hall of History, Bessemer, AL..........3

Besser Museum for Northeast Michigan, Alpena, MI 723

Bethel Historical Society Regional History Center, Bethel, ME.....................606

Betsey Williams Cottage, Providence, RI ..1316

Betsy Ross House and Flag Museum, Philadelphia, PA 1277

Betts House Research Center, Cincinnati, OH...1148

Beverly Historical Society and Museum, Beverly, MA 662

Beyer Home, Oconto County Historical Society Museum, Oconto, WI................1616

The Bidwell House Museum, Monterey, MA 695

Biedenharn Museum & Gardens, Monroe, LA 592

Big Bend National Park, Big Bend, TX.....1396

The Big Duck, Hampton Bays, NY..............997

Big Horn County Historical Museum, Hardin, MT 849

Big Well, Greensburg, KS.........................542

Bigelow House Museum, Olympia, WA ..1560

Bill Baggs Cape Florida State Park, Key Biscayne, FL 316

Billie Creek Village, Rockville, IN 498

Billings Farm & Museum, Woodstock, VT 1490

Biltmore Estate, Asheville, NC...................1089

Biltmore Homespun Shops - Grovewood Gallery, Asheville, NC 1089

Birdsong Nature Center, Thomasville, GA 387

Birmingham Historical Museum & Park, Birmingham, MI 730

Bisbee Mining & Historical Museum, Bisbee, AZ 30

Bishop Hill State Historic Site, Bishop Hill, IL 413

The Bishop's Palace, Galveston, TX.........1420

Black American West Museum & Heritage Center, Denver, CO 209

Blackberry Farm's Pioneer Village, Aurora, IL 411

Blackman House Museum, Snohomish, WA 1570

Blaine County Historical Museum, Hailey, ID 406

Blandford Church & Reception Ctr. (The Petersburg Museums), Petersburg, VA ..1524

Blithewold Mansion, Gardens & Arboretum, Bristol, RI 1310

Block Island Historical Society, Block Island, RI 1310

Bloom Mansion, Trinidad History Museum, Trinidad, CO..........................233

Bloomfield Academy Museum, Bloomfield, NY 963

Blount-Bridgers House/Hobson Pittman Memorial Gallery, Tarboro, NC 1121

Blount County Memorial Museum, Oneonta, AL 17

Blount Mansion, Knoxville, TN 1369

Blue Earth County Historical Society, Mankato, MN...780

Blue Licks Battlefield Museum, Mount Olivet, KY 580

Blue Ridge Institute and Museum, Ferrum, VA 1504

Bluff Hall Antebellum Home and Museum, Demopolis, AL 7

Bob Burns Museum & River Valley Museum of Van Buren, Van Buren, AR 69

Boca Raton Historical Society, Boca Raton, FL 296

Bodie Island Visitor Center, South Nags Head, NC 1120

Bodie State Historic Park, Bridgeport, CA 79

Bolduc House Museum, Sainte Genevieve, MO 837

Bolinas Museum, Bolinas, CA......................79

Bollinger Mill State Historic Site, Burfordville, MO 811

Bonnet House Museum & Gardens, Fort Lauderdale, FL 306

Bonneyville Mill, Bristol, IN 471

Boot Hill Museum, Inc., Dodge City, KS 536

Boothbay Railway Village, Boothbay, ME..607

Boothe Memorial Park and Museum, Stratford, CT 262

Boscobel, Garrison, NY 993

Boston Center for Jewish Heritage, Boston, MA 663

Boston National Historical Park, Boston, MA 664

Bottineau County Historical Museum, Bottineau, ND 1129

Boulder City/Hoover Dam Museum, Boulder City, NV 875

Bowie Railroad Station and Huntington Museum, Bowie, MD 638

The Bowne House Historical Society, Flushing, NY 990

Boyhood Home of President Woodrow Wilson, Augusta, GA 365

Boys Town Hall of History & Father Flanagan Home, Boys Town, NE............858

Bradford Brinton Memorial & Museum, Big Horn, WY 1628

Bradford County Historical Society, Towanda, PA 1303

Bradford Historical Society Inc., Bradford, VT 1477

Bradford Ohio Railroad Museum, Bradford, OH 1143

Bragg-Mitchell Mansion, Mobile, AL 13

Braintree Historical Society, Inc., Braintree, MA 670

Brand Library & Art Center, Glendale, CA 100

Brandywine Battlefield Park, Chadds Ford, PA 1246

Brandywine River Museum, Chadds Ford, PA 1246

Brec's Magnolia Mound Plantation, Baton Rouge, LA..585

Brick House, Montgomery, NY 1015

Brick Store Museum, Kennebunk, ME 612

Bridge Hampton Historical Society, Bridgehampton, NY 964

Bridgton Historical Society, Bridgton, ME 607

Brigham Young's Winter Home, Saint George, UT 1470

Brimstone Museum, Sulphur, LA 602

Bronck Museum, Coxsackie, NY 983

The Bronx County Historical Society, Bronx, NY 964

Brookgreen Gardens, Murrells Inlet, SC....1337

Brooks Academy Museum, Harwich, MA ...686

The Brown House Museum, Sandersville, GA 384

Brown Mansion, Coffeyville, KS.................535

Browntown Museum, Lake City, SC..........1336

Brownville Historical Society Museum, Brownville, NE 858

Brucemore, Cedar Rapids, IA.....................509

Brueckner Museum of Starr Commonwealth, Albion, MI.....................723

Bryant Cottage, Bement, IL 413

B's Ballpark Museum, Centennial, CO 205

Buccleuch Mansion, New Brunswick, NJ 915

Buckeye Furnace State Memorial, Wellston, OH 1190

Buckhorn Saloon & Museum, San Antonio, TX 1448

Bucks County Civil War Library & Museum, Doylestown, PA.....................1249

Bucyrus Historical Society, Bucyrus, OH ..1144

Buena Park Historical Society, Buena Park, CA 80

Buffalo and Erie County Botanical Gardens, Buffalo, NY 972

Buffalo Bill Cody Homestead, Princeton, IA 527

Buffalo Bill Ranch State Historical Park, North Platte, NE 869

Buffalo County Historical Society, Kearney, NE 863

Buffalo Historical Museum and One-Room Schoolhouse, Buffalo, SD ...1345

Buffalo National River, Harrison, AR 59

Buffalo Trails Museum, Epping, ND..........1130

Buffalo Zoological Gardens, Buffalo, NY 972

Bulloch Hall, Roswell, GA 382

Bulow Plantation Ruins Historic State Park, Bunnell, FL 298

The Burgwin-Wright Museum, Wilmington, NC.......................................1123

Burke County Historical Powers Lake Complex, Powers Lake, ND 1136

Burlington County Historical Society, Burlington, NJ 898

Burlington-Rock Island Railroad and Historical Museum, Teague, TX 1454

Burnside Plantation, Inc., Bethlehem, PA ..1242

Burritt on the Mountain-A Living Museum, Huntsville, AL 11

Burrowes Mansion Museum, Matawan, NJ 911

Burt County Museum, Tekamah, NE 873

Burwell-Morgan Mill, Millwood, VA.........1518

Bushwhacker Museum, Nevada, MO 828

Butler County Historical Society, Allison, IA 504

Butler County History Center & Kansas Oil Museum, El Dorado, KS 537

Butler County Museum, Hamilton, OH....1168

Butte-Silver Bow Arts Chateau, Butte, MT 843

Byers-Evans House Museum, Denver, CO 209

C.F. Lott Historic Home, Oroville, CA 136

C.H. Nash Museum-Chucalissa Archaeological Museum, Memphis, TN 1372

CHTJ Southard House Museum, Brunswick, ME 607

C.M. Russell Museum, Great Falls, MT 848

COSI Columbus, Columbus, OH...............1157

CSS Neuse State Historic Site and Gov. Richard Caswell Memorial, Kinston, NC 1108

CU Heritage Center, Boulder, CO 203

Cabrillo National Monument, San Diego, CA 156

Cades Cove Visitor Center and Open-Air Museum, Townsend, TN 1384

Cahokia Courthouse State Historic Site, Cahokia, IL 415

Calaveras County Museum, San Andreas, CA 155

California State Railroad Museum, Sacramento, CA 152

Calusa Nature Center and Planetarium, Fort Myers, FL 308

Calvert Marine Museum, Solomons, MD 654

Calvin Coolidge Historic Site, Plymouth Notch, VT 1484

Cambridge Historical Society, Cambridge, MA 672

Camp Atterbury Museum, Edinburg, IN 474

Camp Five Museum Foundation, Inc., Laona, WI 1604
Camp Floyd/Stagecoach Inn State Park, Fairfield, UT 1465
Camp 6 Logging Museum, Tacoma, WA ...1572
Campbell Historical Museum & Ainsley House, Campbell, CA 80
Campbell House Museum, Saint Louis, MO 832
The Campus Arboretum Association Haverford College, Haverford, PA 1260
Campus Martius Museum, Marietta, OH ...1173
Canadian County Historical Museum, El Reno, OK 1200
Canal Fulton Heritage Society, Canal Fulton, OH 1145
Canby Historical Society, Canby, OR 1221
Cannon Falls Area Historical Museum, Cannon Falls, MN 770
Canterbury Shaker Village, Inc., Canterbury, NH 883
Caparra Museum and Historic Park, Guaynabo, PR 1641
Cape Ann Historical Museum, Gloucester, MA 684
Cape Cod National Seashore, Wellfleet, MA 717
Cape Henry Lighthouse, Virginia Beach, VA 1541
Capitol Visitors Center, a Division of the State Preservation Board, Austin, TX 1389
Cappon & Settlers House Museums, Holland, MI 746
Captain Forbes House Museum, Milton, MA 695
Captain George Flavel House Museum, Astoria, OR 1218
Captain Nathaniel B. Palmer House - Home of the Discoverer of Antarctica, Stonington, CT 261
Captain Salem Avery House Museum, Shady Side Rural Heritage Society, Inc., Shady Side, MD 653
Carbon County Museum, Rawlins, WY 1637
Carl Sandburg State Historic Site, Galesburg, IL 437
Carlton County Historical Society, Cloquet, MN 771
Carlyle House Historic Park, Alexandria, VA 1492
Carnegie Center for Art & History, New Albany, IN 493
Carnton Plantation, Franklin, TN 1365
Carolinas Aviation Museum, Charlotte, NC 1094
Carpenter Home Museum and Gallery, Cle Elum, WA 1551
Carroll County Farm Museum, Westminster, MD 656
Carroll Mansion Museum Home of Leavenworth County Historical Society, Leavenworth, KS 549
Carson County Square House Museum, Panhandle, TX 1442
Carter County Museum, Ekalaka, MT 846
Carter's Grove, Williamsburg, VA 1544
Cary Cottage, Cincinnati, OH 1148
Caryl House and Fisher Barn, Dover, MA ...680
Casa Adobe de San Rafael, Glendale, CA ...100
Casa Blanca Museum, San Juan, PR 1642
The Casa del Herrero Foundation, Santa Barbara, CA 178
Casa Grande Valley Historical Society & Museum, Casa Grande, AZ 30
Casa Navarro State Historical Park, San Antonio, TX 1448
Casemate Museum, Fort Monroe, VA 1505
Casey Farm, Saunderstown, RI 1319
Casey Jones Home and Railroad Museum, Jackson, TN 1367
Cashmere Museum & Pioneer Village, Cashmere, WA 1550

Cass County Historical Society, Logansport, IN 489
Cass County Historical Society at Bonanzaville, West Fargo, ND 1137
Cass County Museum & Pioneer School, Walker, MN 795
Cassia County Museum, Burley, ID 404
Castine Scientific Society, Castine, ME 609
The Castle, Marietta, OH 1174
Castle Air Museum, Atwater, CA 72
Catawba County Museum of History, Newton, NC 1113
Cathedral Cultural Center, Omaha, NE 870
The Cathedral of St. John the Divine, New York, NY 1022
Cave Creek Museum, Cave Creek, AZ 31
Cayuga Museum & Case Research Lab Museum, Auburn, NY 959
Cedar Breaks National Monument, Cedar City, UT 1464
Cedar Falls Historical Society, Cedar Falls, IA 507
Cedar Grove Historical Society, Cedar Grove, NJ 901
Cedar Key Museum State Park, Cedar Key, FL 299
Center for Wooden Boats, Seattle, WA 1565
Centerville Historical Museum, Centerville, MA 675
Centerville - Washington Township Historical Society & Asahel Wright Community Center, Centerville, OH 1146
Centerville - Washington Township Historical Society & Walton House Museum, Centerville, OH 1147
Central City Opera House Association, Central City, CO 205
Central Delta Depot Museum, Brinkley, AR 55
Central Nevada Museum & Historical Society, Tonopah, NV 882
Central Park Conservancy, New York, NY 1022
Centre County Historical Society, State College, PA 1301
Centre County Library and Historical Museum, Bellefonte, PA 1241
Centre Hill Museum (The Petersburg Museums), Petersburg, VA 1524
Century House Historical Society, Rosendale, NY 1061
Century Village Museum, Burton, OH 1144
Chalet of the Golden Fleece, New Glarus, WI 1614
Champaign County Historical Museum, Champaign, IL 416
Champion Mill State Historical Park, Champion, NE 859
Chandler Museum, Chandler, AZ 31
Chappell Hill Historical Society Museum, Chappell Hill, TX 1399
Charles A. Grignon Mansion, Kaukauna, WI 1601
Charles A. Lindbergh Historic Site, Little Falls, MN 779
Charles B. Aycock Birthplace State Historic Site, Fremont, NC 1102
Charles Pinckney National Historic Site, Mount Pleasant, SC 1337
Charles Towne Landing State Historic Site, Charleston, SC 1324
The Charleston Museum, Charleston, SC ..1324
Chateau De Mores State Historic Site, Medora, ND 1134
Chattahoochee River National Recreation Area, Atlanta, GA 359
Chautauqua County Historical Society, McClurg Museum, Westfield, NY 1086
Cheboygan County Historical Museum Complex, Cheboygan, MI 732
The Chelmsford Historical Society, Inc., South Chelmsford, MA 709
Cheney Homestead, Manchester, CT 248

Cheraw Lyceum Museum, Cheraw, SC 1327
Cherokee Courthouse Visitors Information Center & Museum, Gore, OK 1201
Cherokee National Museum, Park Hill, OK 1211
Cherokee Strip Museum, Alva, OK 1195
Cherry Valley Museum, Cherry Valley, NY 978
Chesapeake and Ohio Canal National Historical Park, Hagerstown, MD 646
Chesapeake Bay Maritime Museum, Saint Michaels, MD 652
The Chesapeake Beach Railway Museum, Chesapeake Beach, MD 639
Chesterfield County Museum, Chesterfield, VA 1501
Chesterwood, Stockbridge, MA 711
Cheyenne Depot Museum, Cheyenne, WY 1630
Chicago Architecture Foundation, Chicago, IL 418
The Chicago Athenaeum: Museum of Architecture and Design, Galena, IL 436
Chickamauga-Chattanooga National Military Park, Fort Oglethorpe, GA 372
Chickasaw Council House Museum, Tishomingo, OK 1214
Chickasaw National Recreation Area, Sulphur, OK 1214
Chieftains Museum, Rome, GA 381
Children's Hands-On Museum (CHOM), Tuscaloosa, AL 19
The Children's Museum in Easton, North Easton, MA 699
Children's Museum, Inc., Boca Raton, FL ...296
Children's Museum of Maine, Portland, ME 618
Children's Museum of Oak Ridge, Inc., Oak Ridge, TN 1382
Children's Museum of Richmond, Richmond, VA 1528
The Children's Museum of Rose Hill Manor Park, Frederick, MD 644
The Children's Museum of Science and Technology, Troy, NY 1079
Children's Museum of Southeastern Connecticut, Niantic, CT 256
Children's Museum of the Native American, New York, NY 1023
Chimney Point State Historic Site, Addison, VT 1475
Chinese Cultural Garden/Overfelt Gardens, San Jose, CA 171
Chinese House/O.R. & N. Museum & St. Peter's Catholic Church, Echo, OR 1222
Chinqua-Penn Plantation, Reidsville, NC ...1117
Chippewa County Historical Society, Montevideo, MN 783
Chiricahua National Monument, Willcox, AZ 53
Chisholm Trail Museum, Kingfisher, OK ...1203
Chittenango Landing Canal Boat Museum, Chittenango, NY 978
Choctaw County Historical Society, Hugo, OK 1203
Christiansted National Historic Site, Saint Croix, VI 1644
Cincinnati Fire Museum, Cincinnati, OH ...1149
Cincinnati Zoo & Botanical Garden, Cincinnati, OH 1149
Circus World Museum, Baraboo, WI 1591
City Museum, Saint Louis, MO 832
City of Bowie Museums, Bowie, MD 638
City of Burlington Historical Society, Burlington, NJ 899
City of Gilroy Museum, Gilroy, CA 99
Clara Barton National Historic Site, Glen Echo, MD 645
Clarion County Historical Society, Sutton-Ditz House Museum, Clarion, PA 1247

Structures—Continued

Clark County Historical Society - Heritage Center of Clark County, Springfield, OH 1186
Clark County Museum, Henderson, NV 878
Clarke House Museum, Chicago, IL 420
Clarksville-Montgomery County Museum dba Customs House Museum & Cultural Center, Clarksville, TN 1363
Clay County Historical Museum, Liberty, MO 826
Clay County Historical Society Museum and Archives, Moorhead, MN 784
Cle Elum Telephone Museum, Cle Elum, WA 1551
Clearfield County Historical Society, Clearfield, PA 1247
Clearwater County Historical Society, Shevlin, MN 793
Clermont State Historic Site, Clermont, NY 979
Cleveland County Historical Museum, Shelby, NC 1119
Clewiston Museum, Inc., Clewiston, FL 300
Cliff Dwellings Museum, Manitou Springs, CO 227
Clifton Community Historical Society, Clifton, KS 535
Clinton County Historical Association & Museum, Plattsburgh, NY 1052
Clinton County Historical Society, Wilmington, OH 1191
Clinton County Historical Society Paine-Gillam-Scott Museum, Saint Johns, MI 763
Cliveden of the National Trust, Philadelphia, PA 1278
The Cloisters, New York, NY 1023
Coachella Valley Museum and Cultural Center, Indio, CA 104
Coarsegold Historic Museum, Coarsegold, CA 86
Coastal Discovery Museum, Hilton Head Island, SC 1335
Codington County Heritage Museum, Watertown, SD 1359
Coe Hall, Oyster Bay, NY 1049
Coeur d'Alenes Old Mission State Park, Cataldo, ID 405
The Coffey County Historical Museum, Burlington, KS 534
Coffin House, Newbury, MA 697
Coggeshall Farm Museum, Bristol, RI 1310
Colesville & Windsor Museum at St. Luke's Church, Harpursville, NY 997
The Coley Homestead & Barn Museum, Weston, CT 265
College Park Aviation Museum, College Park, MD 641
Colleton Museum, Walterboro, SC 1343
Collier County Museum, Naples, FL 328
Collier Memorial State Park & Logging Museum, Chiloquin, OR 1221
Collin County Farm Museum, McKinney, TX 1437
Collin County Historical Society, Inc. & History Museum, McKinney, TX 1437
Colonel Allensworth State Historic Park, Allensworth, CA 70
Colonel Davenport Historical Foundation, Rock Island, IL 453
Colonel William Jones State Historic Site/Lincoln State Park & Colonel Jones Home, Lincoln City, IN 488
Colonial Burlington Foundation, Inc., Burlington, NJ 899
Colonial Industrial Quarter, Bethlehem, PA 1242
Colonial National Historical Park: Jamestown & Yorktown, Yorktown, VA 1546
Colonial Pemaquid, New Harbor, ME 615

Colonial Pennsylvania Plantation, Media, PA 1270
The Colonial Spanish Quarter Museum, Saint Augustine, FL 338
Colonial Williamsburg, Williamsburg, VA ..1544
Colorado Historical Society, Denver, CO 210
Colorado River Indian Tribes Museum, Parker, AZ 38
Colorado Springs Museum, Colorado Springs, CO 206
Colton Hall Museum, Monterey, CA 127
The Columbian Theatre, Museum & Art Center, Wamego, KS 560
Columbus-Belmont Civil War Museum, Columbus, KY 567
Columbus Chapel, Boal Mansion Museum, Boalsburg, PA 1244
Comanche Crossing Historical Society & Museum, Strasburg, CO 233
Combat Air Museum, Inc., Topeka, KS 559
Commonwealth of the Northern Mariana Islands Museum of History and Culture, Saipan, MP 1640
Communal Kitchen and Coopershop Museum, Middle Amana, IA 523
Compass Inn Museum, Laughlintown, PA .1267
Comstock Historic House, Moorhead, MN 784
Concord Historical Society, Warner Museum, Springville, NY 1071
Concord Museum, Concord, MA 676
Coney Island Museum, Brooklyn, NY 969
Confederate Memorial Museum, Atoka, OK 1196
Confederate Museum, Crawfordville, GA 369
The Conference House, Staten Island, NY 1072
Conklin Reed Organ & History Museum, Hanover, MI 745
Conneaut Railroad Museum, Conneaut, OH 1159
Connecticut Audubon Birdcraft Museum, Fairfield, CT 240
Connecticut River Museum, Essex, CT 239
Connecticut Trolley Museum, East Windsor, CT 239
Conner Prairie, Fishers, IN 476
Conrad Mansion National Historic Site Museum, Kalispell, MT 850
Conrad Weiser Homestead and Memorial Park, Womelsdorf, PA 1308
The Conservatory Garden, New York, NY 1023
Constitution Square State Historic Site, Danville, KY 567
Contemporary Arts Center, New Orleans, LA 594
The Contemporary Museum, Honolulu, HI 394
Cookeville Depot Museum, Cookeville, TN 1364
Cooper-Hewitt National Design Museum, Smithsonian Institution, New York, NY 1023
Copper King Mansion, Butte, MT 843
Copper Village Museum & Arts Center of Deer Lodge County, Anaconda, MT 840
Copshaholm House Museum & Historic Oliver Gardens, South Bend, IN 499
Coquille River Lighthouse/Bullards Beach State Park, Bandon, OR 1220
Cornelius Low House/Middlesex County Museum, Piscataway, NJ 921
Coronado State Monument, Bernalillo, NM 937
Corydon Capitol Historic Site, Corydon, IN 473
Cottage Grove Museum & Annex, Cottage Grove, OR 1222
The Country Doctor Museum, Bailey, NC.1091
Country Relics Little Village, Stanhope, IA 528

Courthouse Square Association, Charlotte, MI 731
Coutts Memorial Museum of Art, Inc., El Dorado, KS 537
Cow Neck Peninsula Historical Society Sands-Willets House, Port Washington, NY 1053
Cowpens National Battlefield, Chesnee, SC 1327
Cozens Ranch Museum, Fraser, CO 218
Cracker Country, Tampa, FL 348
Cragfont-Historic Cragfont, Inc., Castalian Springs, TN 1360
Crailo State Historic Site, Rensselaer, NY .1056
Cranbrook Art Museum, Bloomfield Hills, MI 730
Cranbrook House and Gardens Auxiliary, Bloomfield Hills, MI 730
Crane Point, Marathon, FL 323
Cravens House, Lookout Mountain, TN 1371
Crawford County Historical Museum, Pittsburg, KS 556
Crawford W. Long Museum, Jefferson, GA 374
Creative Photographic Art Center of Maine, Lewiston, ME 614
Creek Council House Museum, Okmulgee, OK 1211
Crescent Bend/The Armstrong-Lockett House and The William P. Toms Memorial Gardens, Knoxville, TN 1369
The Crescent, Valdosta Garden Center, Inc., Valdosta, GA 389
Cripple Creek District Museum, Inc., Cripple Creek, CO 209
Crocker House, Mount Clemens, MI 756
Crockett Tavern Museum, Morristown, TN 1376
The Crosby Arboretum, Mississippi State University, Picayune, MS 807
Crow Wing County Historical Society, Brainerd, MN 769
Crowley Museum & Nature Center, Sarasota, FL 344
Crown Point State Historic Site, Crown Point, NY 984
Crystal Lake Falls Historical Association, Barton, VT 1476
Culbertson Mansion State Historic Site, New Albany, IN 493
Cumberland County Historical Society, Greenwich, NJ 905
Cumberland Gap National Historical Park, Middlesboro, KY 580
Cumberland Island National Seashore, Saint Marys, GA 382
Cuneo Museum & Gardens, Vernon Hills, IL 463
Cupertino Historical Society & Museum, Cupertino, CA 88
Cupola House, Egg Harbor, WI 1596
Custer County 1881 Courthouse Museum, Custer, SD 1345
Cuyahoga Valley National Park, Brecksville, OH 1144
Cuyuna Range Historical Society & Museum, Crosby, MN 772
Cyrus H. McCormick Memorial Museum, Steeles Tavern, VA 1538

DAR-Hervey Ely House, Rochester, NY ...1058
DAR John Strong Mansion Museum, Addison, VT 1475
D.C. Booth Historic National Fish Hatchery, Spearfish, SD 1357
D.R. Barker Historical Museum, Fredonia, NY 992
Dahlonega Gold Museum State Historic Site, Dahlonega, GA 369
Dakota County Historical Society, South Saint Paul, MN 793
Dakota Discovery Museum, Mitchell, SD..1352
Dakota Sunset Museum, Gettysburg, SD ...1348

Dakota Territorial Museum, Yankton, SD ..1359
Dakotaland Museum, Huron, SD.............1348
Dale & Martha Hawk Museum, Wolford,
   ND...1138
Dallas Arboretum & Botanical Garden,
   Dallas, TX...1404
Dallas Heritage Village at Old City Park,
   Dallas, TX...1405
Dallas Zoo, Dallas, TX 1406
Dalton Gang Hideout, Meade, KS...........552
Dan Nagle Walnut Grove Pioneer Village,
   Long Grove, IA..522
Dana Adobe, Nipomo, CA 130
The Dana-Thomas House State Historic
   Site, Springfield, IL...............................458
The Danbury Museum & Historical
   Society, Danbury, CT..............................238
Daniel Benton Homestead, Tolland, CT.......262
Daniel Boone Home and Boonesfield
   Village, Lindenwood University,
   Defiance, MO...814
Daniel Boone Homestead, Birdsboro, PA ..1243
Daniels County Museum and Pioneer
   Town, Scobey, MT..................................853
The Danish Immigrant Museum, Elk
   Horn, IA..517
Danvers Historical Society, Danvers, MA....678
Danville Museum of Fine Arts & History,
   Danville, VA...1502
DAR Van Bunschooten Museum, Sussex,
   NJ...925
Darnall's Chance House Museum,
   M-NCPPC, Upper Marlboro, MD 655
Davenport House Museum, Savannah,
   GA..384
David Bradford House, Washington, PA 1305
David Conklin Farmhouse, Huntington,
   NY...1000
David Crockett Cabin, Rutherford, TN 1383
The David Davis Mansion, Bloomington,
   IL..413
The Dawes Arboretum, Newark, OH 1177
Dawes County Historical Society
   Museum, Chadron, NE............................859
Dawson County Historical Museum,
   Lexington, NE...864
Dayton Historical Depot Society, Dayton,
   WA..1552
Dayton History at Carillon Park, Dayton,
   OH...1161
De Graaf Nature Center, Holland, MI.........746
Deaf Smith County Museum, Hereford,
   TX..1424
Decatur County Last Indian Raid
   Museum, Oberlin, KS...............................554
Decatur House Museum, Washington, DC...277
DeKalb History Center Museum, Decatur,
   GA..370
Del Norte County Historical Society,
   Crescent City, CA.....................................87
Delano Heritage Park, Delano, CA 91
Delaware Agricultural Museum and
   Village, Dover, DE...................................269
Delaware and Hudson Canal Historical
   Society and Museum, High Falls, NY....998
The Dennison Railroad Depot Museum,
   Dennison, OH..1162
Dennys River Historical Society,
   Dennysville, ME......................................609
Denver Botanic Gardens, Inc., Denver,
   CO...210
Denver Firefighters Museum, Denver, CO...211
Denver Museum of Miniatures, Dolls and
   Toys, Denver, CO.....................................211
Department of Historic Resources,
   Richmond, VA...1529
Department of the Treasury, Washington,
   DC...278
The Depot Museum Complex,
   Henderson, TX..1424
Depreciation Lands Museum, Allison
   Park, PA...1240

Descanso Gardens Guild, Inc., La Canada
   Flintridge, CA...105
Desha County Museum, Dumas, AR...........56
DeSoto County Museum, Hernando, MS.....801
Deutschheim State Historic Site,
   Hermann, MO...817
Devils Tower Visitor Center, Devils
   Tower, WY...1631
Dewey Hotel Museum, Dewey, OK 1199
DeWitt County Historical Museum,
   Cuero, TX...1403
Dexter Historical Society Campus,
   Dexter, ME..609
Dey Mansion/Washington's Headquarters
   Museum, Wayne, NJ...............................929
Dickson Mounds Museum, Lewistown,
   IL..442
Dinsmore Homestead Foundation,
   Burlington, KY..566
Discovery Center of Springfield,
   Springfield, MO......................................839
Discovery Creek Children's Museum of
   Washington DC, Glen Echo, MD.............645
Divide County Historical Society
   Museum, Crosby, ND.............................1129
Dr. Daniel W. Kissam House,
   Huntington, NY......................................1000
Dr. Increase Mathews House, Zanesville,
   OH...1194
Dr. John Harris Dental Museum,
   Bainbridge, OH.......................................1141
Dr. William Robinson Plantation, Clark,
   NJ...901
Donald G. Trayser Memorial
   Museum/Barnstable County Customs
   House, Barnstable, MA.............................661
Donkey Milk House, Historic Home, Key
   West, FL..317
Door County Maritime Museum (at Gills
   Rock), Gills Rock, WI...........................1598
Door County Maritime Museum (at
   Sturgeon Bay), Sturgeon Bay, WI 1623
Dorothy G. Page Museum, Wasilla, AK 29
Douglas County Historical Society -
   Carson Valley Museum & Cultural
   Center, Gardnerville, NV.........................877
Douglas County Historical Society -
   Genoa Courthouse Museum, Genoa,
   NV...877
Douglas County Museum Complex,
   Armour, SD..1344
Dow Gardens, Midland, MI......................755
Downieville Museum, Downieville, CA 91
Dows Depot Welcome Center, Dows, IA.....516
Drake Well Museum, Titusville, PA 1303
Drayton Hall, Charleston, SC 1325
Drum Barracks Civil War Museum,
   Wilmington, CA......................................198
Drummond Home, Hominy, OK...............1203
Drummond Island Historical Museum,
   Drummond Island, MI.............................739
Dubois Museum, Dubois, WY..................1632
Duke Homestead State Historic Site,
   Durham, NC...1098
Dunbar House State Memorial, Dayton,
   OH...1161
Duncan Cottage Museum, Metlakatla, AK.....27
Dunedin Historical Society & Museum,
   Dunedin, FL..305
Dunham Tavern Museum, Cleveland, OH..1154
DuPage County Historical Museum,
   Wheaton, IL..465
Durham Center Museum/Research
   Library, East Durham, NY.......................985
Durham Historic Association Museum,
   Durham, NH..886
Duxbury Rural and Historical Society,
   Inc., Duxbury, MA...................................681
Dyckman Farmhouse Museum and Park,
   New York, NY..1025

E. St. Julien Cox House, Saint Peter, MN ...792
Eagle Bluff Lighthouse, Fish Creek, WI 1597

Eagle Historical Society & Museums,
   Eagle, AK..23
The Earle-Harrison House and Gardens
   on 5th Street, Waco, TX........................1458
EarlyWorks Museums, Huntsville, AL 11
East Brunswick Museum Corporation,
   East Brunswick, NJ.................................902
East Ely Railroad Depot Museum, Ely,
   NV...876
East Hampton Historical Society, Inc.,
   East Hampton, NY..................................985
East Jersey Olde Towne, Piscataway, NJ 921
East Lyme Historical Society/Thomas
   Lee House, Niantic, CT............................256
East Tennessee Historical Society,
   Knoxville, TN...1369
East Texas Oil Museum at Kilgore
   College, Kilgore, TX...............................1432
Eastern California Museum,
   Independence, CA...................................104
Eastern Shore Art Center, Fairhope, AL...........9
The Ebenezer Maxwell Mansion, Inc.,
   Philadelphia, PA.....................................1278
Eccles Community Arts Center, Ogden,
   UT..1467
Eckley Miners' Village, Eckley, PA...........1251
Edgar Allan Poe Cottage, Bronx, NY 965
Edgar Allan Poe Museum, Richmond, VA.1529
Edgar Allan Poe National Historic Site,
   Philadelphia, PA.....................................1278
Edgar County Historical Museum, Paris,
   IL..449
Edison & Ford Winter Estates, Fort
   Myers, FL..308
Edison National Historic Site, West
   Orange, NJ..930
Edsel & Eleanor Ford House, Grosse
   Pointe Shores, MI....................................745
Edward H. White II Memorial Museum,
   Brooks Air Force Base, TX....................1397
Edward Hopper Landmark Preservation
   Foundation, Nyack, NY.........................1044
Edwards County Historical Museum,
   Kinsley, KS...547
Effie Yeaw Nature Center, Carmichael,
   CA..82
Egan Maritime Foundation, Nantucket,
   MA..695
1880 Town, Murdo, SD............................1352
The 1811 Old Lincoln County Jail and
   Lincoln County Museum, Wiscasset,
   ME..625
1859 Jail, Marshal's Home & Museum,
   Independence, MO...................................817
The 1890 House-Museum & Center for
   Arts, Cortland, NY..................................983
Eisenhower Birthplace State Historical
   Site, Denison, TX..................................1409
Eisenhower National Historic Site,
   Gettysburg, PA.......................................1255
El Cazador Museum, Grand Bay, AL............10
El Pueblo Historical Monument, Los
   Angeles, CA..114
El Pueblo History Museum, Pueblo, CO......230
El Rancho de Las Golondrinas Museum,
   Santa Fe, NM..947
Elbert Hubbard-Roycroft Museum, East
   Aurora, NY...985
Eldridge Street Project, New York, NY 1025
Eleanor Roosevelt National Historic Site,
   Hyde Park, NY......................................1002
Elgin Area Historical Society, Elgin, IL......432
Elisabet Ney Museum, Austin, TX............1390
Ella Sharp Museum, Jackson, MI.............748
Ellis County Historical Society, Hays, KS...543
Ellwood House Museum, DeKalb, IL 429
Elvis Presley Birthplace and Museum,
   Tupelo, MS..808
Elwood Haynes Museum, Kokomo, IN........486
Emily Dickinson Museum: The
   Homestead and The Evergreens,
   Amherst, MA...658

Structures—Continued

End-O-Line Railroad Park & Museum, Currie, MN......772

Enfield Shaker Museum, Enfield, NH......887

Ephraim Historical Foundation, Ephraim, WI......1597

Ephrata Cloister, Ephrata, PA......1251

Erie Canal Museum, Syracuse, NY......1076

Erie Canal Village, Rome, NY......1061

Erie County History Center & Cashier's House, Erie, PA......1252

Ernest Hemingway House Museum, Key West, FL......317

Ernie Pyle State Historic Site, Dana, IN......473

Escondido History Center, Escondido, CA......93

Essex Historical Society, Inc., Essex, CT......240

Essex Shipbuilding Museum, Essex, MA......681

Estes Park Museum, Estes Park, CO......215

Ethan Allen Homestead Museum & Historic Site, Burlington, VT......1478

Eugene O'Neill National Historic Site, Danville, CA......89

Eugene V. Debs Home, Terre Haute, IN......500

Eureka Fire Museum, Milltown, NJ......911

Eureka Pioneer Museum of McPherson County, Inc., Eureka, SD......1346

Eureka School House, Springfield, VT......1487

Eustis Historical Museum & Preservation Society, Inc., Eustis, FL......306

Evanston Historical Society and Charles Gates Dawes House, Evanston, IL......434

Evergreen House, The Johns Hopkins University, Baltimore, MD......632

The Exchange Hotel Civil War Museum, Gordonsville, VA......1509

Fabyan Villa Museum, Geneva, IL......437

Fairbanks House, Dedham, MA......679

Fairbanks Museum and Planetarium, Saint Johnsbury, VT......1486

Fairfax County Park Authority, Resource Management Division, Fairfax, VA......1503

Fairfield Historical Society, Fairfield, CT......241

Fairlawn Mansion & Museum, Superior, WI......1624

Fairmont Park Horticulture Center, Philadelphia, PA......1279

Fairport Historical Museum, Fairport, NY......989

Fairport Marine Museum, Fairport Harbor, OH......1164

Fairview Museum of History & Art, Fairview, UT......1465

Faith Trumbull Chapter, Daughters of the American Revolution, Inc., Museum and Chapter House, Norwich, CT......258

Fall River County Historical Museum, Hot Springs, SD......1348

Fall River Historical Society Museum, Fall River, MA......682

Fallingwater, Mill Run, PA......1272

Falmouth Historical Society, Falmouth, MA......682

Farm House Museum, Ames, IA......505

Farmamerica, The Minnesota Agricultural Interpretive Center, Waseca, MN......796

Farmers Bank (The Petersburg Museums), Petersburg, VA......1525

Farmers Branch Historical Park, Farmers Branch, TX......1413

The Farmers' Museum, Inc., Cooperstown, NY......980

Farmington Historic Home, Louisville, KY......575

Farmington Museum, Farmington, NM......939

FASNY Museum of Fire Fighting, Hudson, NY......1000

Father Marquette National Memorial, Saint Ignace, MI......763

Faust Park-Thornhill Historic Site & 19th Century Village, Chesterfield, MO......812

Fayette Historic State Park, Garden, MI......742

Federal Hall National Memorial, New York, NY......1025

Felix Valle State Historic Site, Sainte Genevieve, MO......837

Festival-Institute, James Dick Foundation, Round Top, TX......1446

Field of Dreams Movie Site, Dyersville, IA......517

Fifth Maine Regiment Museum, Peaks Island, ME......618

Fillmore Historical Museum, Inc., Fillmore, CA......95

Filoli Center, Woodside, CA......199

Fine Arts Center of Kershaw County, Inc., Camden, SC......1322

The Finley House, Wayne, PA......1306

Fire Museum of Memphis, Memphis, TN......1373

Fire Museum of Texas, Beaumont, TX......1394

The Firehouse Museum, Ellicott City, MD......643

Firelands Historical Society Museum, Norwalk, OH......1180

Fireman's Hall Museum, Philadelphia, PA......1279

First Church of Christ Unitarian, Lancaster, MA......688

First Consolidated School in Minnesota, Saum, MN......793

First Missouri State Capitol-State Historic Site, Saint Charles, MO......830

First Territorial Capitol of Kansas, Fort Riley, KS......540

First White House of the Confederacy, Montgomery, AL......16

Fitchburg Historical Society, Fitchburg, MA......683

The Flag House and Star-Spangled Banner Museum, Baltimore, MD......632

Flagler Museum, Palm Beach, FL......333

Fleming Historical Society, Fleming, CO......216

Flickertail Village and Museum, Stanley, ND......1136

The Florence McLeod Hazard Museum, Columbus, MS......800

Florence Price Pioneer Museum, Florence, CO......216

Florewood State Park, Greenwood, MS......801

Florida Agricultural Museum, Palm Coast, FL......334

Florida Association of Museums, Tallahassee, FL......347

Florissant Fossil Beds National Monument, Florissant, CO......216

Floyd County Historical Museum, Charles City, IA......510

The Fluvanna County Historical Society Old Stone Jail Museum, Palmyra, VA......1524

The Folsom House Museum, Taylors Falls, MN......794

Folsom Museum, Inc., Folsom, NM......939

Fonthill Museum of the Bucks County Historical Society, Doylestown, PA......1249

Ford's Theatre National Historic Site (Lincoln Museum), Washington, DC......279

Forest Capital State Museum, Perry, FL......337

Forest History Center, Grand Rapids, MN......777

Forest Park Museum and Arboretum, Perry, IA......527

The Forges and Manor of Ringwood, Ringwood, NJ......923

Fort Abraham Lincoln State Park, Mandan, ND......1134

Fort Bend Museum Association, Richmond, TX......1445

Fort Benton Museum of the Upper Missouri, Fort Benton, MT......846

Fort Bowie National Historic Site, Bowie, AZ......30

Fort Bridger State Museum, Fort Bridger, WY......1632

Fort Buenaventura, Ogden, UT......1468

Fort Buford State Historic Site, Williston, ND......1137

Fort Building, Fort Bragg, CA......95

Fort Caspar Museum, Casper, WY......1629

Fort Christmas Historical Park, Christmas, FL......299

Fort Clatsop National Memorial, Astoria, OR......1218

Fort Clinch State Park, Fernandina Beach, FL......306

Fort Collins Museum, Fort Collins, CO......217

Fort Columbia Interpretive Center, Chinook, WA......1551

Fort Concho National Historic Landmark, San Angelo, TX......1447

Fort Crawford Museum, Prairie du Chien, WI......1618

Fort Croghan Museum, Burnet, TX......1398

Fort Crook Historical Museum, Fall River Mills, CA......94

Fort Dalles Museum/Anderson Homestead, The Dalles, OR......1237

Fort Davidson State Historic Site, Pilot Knob, MO......828

Fort Davis National Historic Site, Fort Davis, TX......1414

Fort Delaware Society, Delaware City, DE......268

Fort Dobbs State Historic Site, Statesville, NC......1120

Fort Dodge & Frontier Village, Fort Dodge, IA......518

Fort Douglas Military Museum, Fort Douglas, UT......1465

Fort Fetterman State Historic Site, Douglas, WY......1631

Fort Frederica National Monument, Saint Simons Island, GA......383

Fort Gibson Historic Site, Fort Gibson, OK......1200

Fort Harker Museum Complex, Kanopolis, KS......546

Fort Hartsuff State Historical Park, Burwell, NE......858

Fort Hays State Historic Site, Hays, KS......543

Fort Henrietta Interpretive Park, Echo, OR......1223

Fort Hill (The John C. Calhoun House), Clemson, SC......1328

Fort Hunter Mansion & Park, Harrisburg, PA......1258

Fort Inglish, Bonham, TX......1396

Fort King George Historic Site, Darien, GA......370

Fort Klock Historic Restoration, Saint Johnsville, NY......1063

Fort Knox State Historic Site, Prospect, ME......620

Fort Laramie National Historic Site, Fort Laramie, WY......1633

Fort Larned National Historic Site, Larned, KS......547

Fort Lauderdale Historical Society, Fort Lauderdale, FL......307

Fort Leaton State Historic Site, Presidio, TX......1444

Fort Leavenworth Historical Society, Fort Leavenworth, KS......539

Fort Lee Historic Park & Museum, Fort Lee, NJ......904

Fort Ligonier Association, Ligonier, PA......1269

Fort MacArthur Museum, San Pedro, CA......176

Fort Macon State Park, Atlantic Beach, NC......1091

Fort Massac State Park and Historic Site, Metropolis, IL......445

Fort Matanzas National Monument, Saint Augustine, FL......339

Fort McAllister, Richmond Hill, GA......381

Fort McHenry National Monument and Historic Shrine, Baltimore, MD......632

Fort McKavett State Historical Site, Fort McKavett, TX......1415

Fort Mifflin, Philadelphia, PA......1279

Fort Morgan Museum, Gulf Shores, AL 10
Fort Mountain State Park, Chatsworth, GA.........................368
Fort Necessity National Battlefield, Farmington, PA......................1253
Fort Nisqually Living History Museum, Tacoma, WA........................1573
Fort Ontario State Historic Site, Oswego, NY..................................1048
Fort Peck Interpretive Center, Fort Peck, MT.................................846
Fort Pike State Historic Site, New Orleans, LA..........................595
The Fort Pitt Block House, Pittsburgh, PA...................................1292
Fort Point and Presidio Historical Association, Presidio of San Francisco, CA...........................144
Fort Point National Historic Site, San Francisco, CA...........................165
Fort Pulaski National Monument, Savannah, GA.........................385
Fort Recovery Museum, Fort Recovery, OH..................................1164
Fort Richardson State Historical Park, Jacksboro, TX.........................1431
Fort St. Jean Baptiste State Historic Site, Natchitoches, LA.....................593
Fort Sam Houston Museum, Fort Sam Houston, TX.........................1415
Fort Scott National Historic Site, Fort Scott, KS..................................540
Fort Selden State Monument, Radium Springs, NM...........................945
Fort Sill National Historic Landmark, Fort Sill, OK.........................1201
Fort Simcoe State Park, White Swan, WA.1578
Fort Sisseton State Historic Park, Lake City, SD................................1350
Fort Smith National Historic Site, Fort Smith, AR...............................58
Fort Stanwix National Monument, Rome, NY..................................1061
Fort Sumner State Monument, Fort Sumner, NM...........................939
Fort Sumter National Monument, Sullivan's Island, SC...................1342
Fort Tejon State Historic Park, Lebec, CA...................................108
Fort Ticonderoga, Ticonderoga, NY 1078
Fort Totten State Historic Site, Fort Totten, ND..............................1131
Fort Vancouver National Historic Site, Vancouver, WA......................1576
Fort Verde State Historic Park, Camp Verde, AZ..............................30
Fort Walla Walla Museum, Walla Walla, WA...................................1576
Fort Washington Park, Fort Washington, MD...................................643
Fort Washita, Durant, OK.................1199
Fort Wayne Firefighters Museum, Fort Wayne, IN...............................477
Fort Wilkins Historic Complex, Copper Harbor, MI...........................733
Fort Winnebago Surgeons Quarters, Portage, WI...........................1618
Fort Worth Botanic Garden, Fort Worth, TX...................................1416
Fort Worth Zoological Park, Fort Worth, TX...................................1417
Fort Yargo State Park, Winder, GA 391
Fort Zachary Taylor State Historical Site, Key West, FL.........................317
Forts Folle Avoine Historic Park, Danbury, WI...........................1594
Fossil Country Museum, Kemmerer, WY ..1635
Fosterfields Living Historical Farm, Morristown, NJ......................913
Foundation For Historic Christ Church, Inc., Irvington, VA....................1511
4-H Schoolhouse Museum, Clarion, IA 510
Four Mile Historic Park, Denver, CO 212

Fox Island Historical Society, Fox Island, WA...................................1554
Fox Lake Historical Museum, Inc., Fox Lake, WI..............................1598
The Foxfire Museum & Heritage Center, Mountain City, GA...................380
Frances Willard House Museum, Evanston, IL.........................434
Francis Land House Historic Site, Virginia Beach, VA...................1542
Francisco Fort Museum, La Veta, CO.........224
Franconia Heritage Museum, Franconia, NH...................................888
Frank G. Ray House, Vinton, IA 529
Frank Lloyd Wright Home and Studio, Oak Park, IL.........................448
Frank Lloyd Wright's Pope-Leighey House, Alexandria, VA..................1492
Frank Phillips Home, Bartlesville, OK.......1197
Franklin County Historical & Museum Society & House of History, Malone, NY...................................1012
Franklin County Seminary and Museum, Brookville, IN.......................471
Franklin D. Roosevelt Presidential Library-Museum, Hyde Park, NY 1002
Franklin Mineral Museum, Franklin, NJ......904
The Franklin Pierce Homestead, Hillsborough, NH.....................889
Fraunces Tavern Museum, New York, NY...................................1025
Fred Harman Art Museum, Pagosa Springs, CO..........................229
Frederick C. Robie House, Chicago, IL.......420
Frederick Douglass National Historic Site, Washington, DC..................279
Frederick Law Olmsted National Historic Site, Brookline, MA...................671
Fredericksburg & Spotsylvania National Military Park, Fredericksburg, VA.........1506
Freeborn County Museum and Historical Village, Albert Lea, MN.................767
Freeport Historical Society, Freeport, ME....611
Freestone County Historical Museum, Fairfield, TX.......................1413
French Art Colony, Gallipolis, OH 1165
French Azilum, Inc., Towanda, PA.............1303
Fresno Flats Historical Park, Oakhurst, CA...................................132
The Frick Art & Historical Center, Pittsburgh, PA.......................1292
Friends of Arrow Rock, Inc., Arrow Rock, MO.........................811
The Friends of Lucy Hayes Heritage Center, Chillicothe, OH.................1147
The Friends of the Caleb Pusey House, Inc., Upland, PA......................1304
Friends (Quaker) Meeting House, Mount Pleasant, OH........................1177
Friendship Firehouse, Alexandria, VA........1492
Friendship Hill National Historic Site, Point Marion, PA....................1295
Frisco Historic Park & Museum, Frisco, CO...................................218
Frontier Culture Museum, Staunton, VA....1537
Frontier Gateway Museum, Glendive, MT...................................847
Frontier Museum, Williston, ND 1138
Frontiers of Flight Museum, Dallas, TX 1406
Fruitlands Museums, Harvard, MA 686
Frye's Measure Mill, Wilton, NH...............897
The Fullerton Arboretum, Fullerton, CA........98
Fulton County Historical Museum, Wauseon, OH.........................1190
Fulton County Museum, Groversville, NY...................................996
Fulton Mansion State Historic Site, Rockport, TX.......................1446
Furnace Town Living Heritage Museum, Snow Hill, MD.......................654

Gadsby's Tavern Museum, Alexandria, VA...................................1492

Gadsden Museum, Mesilla, NM 943
Gaineswood, Demopolis, AL 7
Galena-Jo Daviess County Historical Society & Museum, Galena, IL.............436
Gallier House, New Orleans, LA................595
Galloping Road Compound & Poker Alley; Harbor Ranch, Dripping Springs, TX.........................1410
Galloway House and Village - Blakely Museum, Fond du Lac, WI.............1597
Galveston Arts Center, Galveston, TX 1420
Galveston County Historical Museum, Galveston, TX.......................1420
Galveston Historical Foundation, Inc., Galveston, TX.......................1421
Garden Grove Historical Society, Garden Grove, CA.............................99
The Gardner Museum, Inc., Gardner, MA ...684
The Gardner Museum of Architecture & Design, Quincy, IL...................452
Garfield Farm Museum, LaFox, IL 441
Garfield Park Conservatory, Chicago, IL 421
Gari Melchers Home and Studio, Fredericksburg, VA.................1506
Gatekeeper's Museum & Marion Steinbach Indian Basket Museum, Tahoe City, CA........................190
Gates House, Machiasport Historical Society, Machiasport, ME..............614
Gates Mills Historical Society, Gates Mills, OH...........................1166
Gateway to the Panhandle, Gate, OK.........1201
Gathland State Park, Boonsboro, MD.........637
Geddes Historic District Village, Geddes, SD...................................1347
Gene Stratton-Porter State Historic Site, Rome City, IN.......................498
General Adam Stephen House, Martinsburg, WV...................1584
General Crook House Museum and Library/Archives Center, Omaha, NE......870
General Daniel Bissell House, Saint Louis, MO.........................833
General Grant National Memorial, New York, NY...........................1026
General John J. Pershing Boyhood Home State Historic Site, Laclede, MO............824
General Lew Wallace Study & Museum, Crawfordsville, IN.................473
Genesee Country Village & Museum, Mumford, NY.......................1016
Geneva Historical Society & Prouty-Chew House & Museum, Geneva, NY...........................994
Geneva Historical Society & Rose Hill Mansion, Geneva, NY.................994
Geographical Center Historical Museum, Rugby, ND...........................1136
The George Bush Presidential Library and Museum, College Station, TX 1400
George Eastman House/International Museum of Photography and Film, Rochester, NY.......................1058
The George G. Frelinghuysen Arboretum, Morris Township, NJ................913
George I. Ashby Memorial Museum, Copper Center, AK...................23
George Washington Carver National Monument, Diamond, MO..............814
George Washington's Ferry Farm, Stafford County, VA.................1537
George Washington's Fredericksburg Foundation, Historic Kenmore & Washington's Ferry Farm, Fredericksburg, VA.................1506
Georgia Salzburger Society Museum, Rincon, GA...........................381
Georgia State Cotton Museum, Vienna, GA...................................390
The Georgian Museum, Lancaster, OH 1171
Georgia's Old Capital Museum, Milledgeville, GA.....................380

Structures—Continued

Georgia's Stone Mountain Park, Stone Mountain, GA 387

Gertrude Herbert Institute of Art, Augusta, GA 365

Ghost Town Museum, Colorado Springs, CO 207

Gibbs Museum of Pioneer and Dakotah Life, Falcon Heights, MN 775

The Gibson Society, Inc. dba Gibson House Museum, Boston, MA 665

Gila County Historical Museum, Globe, AZ 35

The Gilbert Stuart Birthplace and Museum, Saunderstown, RI 1319

Gillespie County Historical Society, Fredericksburg, TX 1419

Gillette Castle State Park, East Haddam, CT 239

Gilliam County Historical Society - Depot Museum Complex, Condon, OR.1222

Gilman Garrison House, Exeter, NH 887

Gilman Historic Ranch and Wagon Museum, Banning, CA 74

Gilmore Car Museum, Hickory Corners, MI 746

Gingras Trading Post State Historic Site, Walhalla, ND 1137

The Glebe House Museum and Gertrude Jekyll Garden, Woodbury, CT 268

Glen Helen Ecology Institute Trailside Museum, Yellow Springs, OH 1193

Glencairn Museum: Academy of the New Church, Bryn Athyn, PA 1244

Glenn House/Historical Association of Greater Cape Girardeau, Cape Girardeau, MO 812

Glensheen Historic Estate, Duluth, MN 773

Glessner House Museum, Chicago, IL 421

Gloucester County Historical Society, Woodbury, NJ 931

Gnadenhutten Historical Park & Museum, Gnadenhutten, OH 1167

Gold Coast Railroad Museum, Inc., Miami, FL 323

Gold Nugget Museum, Paradise, CA 139

Golden Ball Tavern Museum, Weston, MA 718

Golden Gate Railroad Museum, San Francisco, CA 166

Golden Valley County Museum, Beach, ND 1127

Goliad State Park, Goliad, TX 1423

Gomez Foundation for Mill House, Marlboro, NY 1014

Goodnow Museum State Historic Site, Manhattan, KS 550

Gore Place, Waltham, MA 715

Gorgas House, Tuscaloosa, AL 19

Goschenhoppen Folklife Library and Museum, Green Lane, PA 1257

Governor John Langdon House, Portsmouth, NH 894

Governor John Sevier Memorial Association, Knoxville, TN 1370

Governor Printz Park, Essington, PA 1253

Governor Ross Plantation, Seaford, DE 272

Governor Seay Mansion, Kingfisher, OK ...1204

The Governor's Gallery, Santa Fe, NM ...947

The Governor's Mansion, Frankfort, KY 569

Graceland, Memphis, TN 1373

Graeme Park, Horsham, PA 1261

Grand Army of the Republic Civil War Museum, Philadelphia, PA 1281

Grand County Museum, Hot Sulphur Springs, CO 222

Grand Encampment Museum, Inc., Encampment, WY 1632

Grand Forks County Historical Society, Grand Forks, ND 1132

Grand Gulf Military Park, Port Gibson, MS 807

Grand Portage National Monument, Grand Marais, MN 776

Grand Traverse Heritage Center, Traverse City, MI 765

The Granger Homestead Society, Inc., Canandaigua, NY 975

Grant County Historical Museum, Canyon City, OR 1221

Grant County Historical Museum, Ephrata, WA 1553

Grant County Museum aka Historic Adobe Museum, Ulysses, KS 560

Grant-Humphreys Mansion, Denver, CO 212

Grant-Kohrs Ranch National Historic Site, Deer Lodge, MT 845

Granville Museum, Inc., Granville, TN ...1366

Gravette Historical Museum, Gravette, AR 59

Great Basin Historical Society & Museum, Delta, UT 1464

Great Smoky Mountains Heritage Center, Townsend, TN 1384

Greater Hazleton Historical Society, Hazleton, PA 1260

Greater Loveland Historical Society Museum, Loveland, OH 1173

Green Mountain Club, Inc., Waterbury Center, VT 1489

Greenbelt Museum, Greenbelt, MD 646

The Greenburgh Nature Center, Scarsdale, NY 1066

Greene County Historical Museum, Waynesburg, PA 1306

Greene County Historical Society, Xenia, OH 1193

Greenfield Historical Society, Greenfield, WI 1599

Greensboro Historical Museum, Inc., Greensboro, NC 1103

Grevemberg House Museum, Franklin, LA 588

Grinter Place State Historic Site, Kansas City, KS 546

Gropius House, Lincoln, MA 690

Grosse Ile Historical Society, Grosse Ile, MI 745

Grout Museum District: Grout Museum of History and Science, Bluedorn Science Imaginarium, Rensselaer Russell House Museum, Snowden House, Waterloo, IA 529

Guadalupe Mountains National Park, Salt Flat, TX 1447

Guernsey County Museum, Cambridge, OH 1144

Guilford Courthouse National Military Park, Greensboro, NC 1104

Gulf Islands National Seashore, Gulf Breeze, FL 312

Gunn Memorial Library and Museum, Washington, CT 263

Gunnison County Pioneer and Historical Society, Gunnison, CO 222

Gunston Hall Plantation, Mason Neck, VA 1517

Gwinnett Historical Society, Lawrenceville, GA 376

Gwinnett History Museum, Lawrenceville, GA 376

H.E.A.R.T.S. Veterans Museum of Texas, Huntsville, TX 1430

H. Earl Clack Museum, Havre, MT 849

H.G. Albee Memorial Museum, Estherville, IA 517

H.H. Franklin Foundation, Tucson, AZ 49

Haas-Lilienthal House, San Francisco, CA 166

Hacienda Buena Vista, Ponce, PR 1642

Hackley & Hume Historic Site, Muskegon, MI 757

The Hagley Museum and Library, Wilmington, DE 273

Hahns Peak Area Historical Society and School House, Clark, CO 205

Haines Museum, Waukegan Historical Society, Waukegan, IL 463

Hale Farm and Village, Bath, OH 1141

The Hall of Fame for Great Americans, Bronx, NY 966

Hallockville Museum Farm, Riverhead, NY 1057

Hamden Historical Society, Inc., Hamden, CT 244

Hammond-Harwood House Association, Annapolis, MD 628

Hampton National Historic Site, Towson, MD 655

Hampton Plantation State Historic Site, McClellanville, SC 1336

Hampton University Museum, Hampton, VA 1509

Hancock Historical Museum, Findlay, OH 1164

Hancock Historical Society, Hancock, NH 888

Hancock Shaker Village, Inc., Pittsfield, MA 703

Hanford Mills Museum, East Meredith, NY 987

Hanley House, Clayton, MO 813

Hanover House, Clemson, SC 1328

Happy Hollow Park & Zoo, San Jose, CA 171

Har-Ber Village, Grove, OK 1202

Harbor Defense Museum, Brooklyn, NY 969

Hardin County Historical Museums, Inc., Kenton, OH 1170

Harding Home and Museum, Marion, OH.1174

Harlan-Lincoln House, Mount Pleasant, IA 524

Harmonie Associates, Inc., Ambridge, PA .1240

Harn Homestead and 1889er Museum, Oklahoma City, OK 1207

Harold Warp Pioneer Village Foundation, Minden, NE 868

Harpers Ferry National Historical Park, Harpers Ferry, WV 1582

Harriet Beecher Stowe Center, Hartford, CT 245

Harrison County Historical Museum, Marshall, TX 1436

Harrison House, Branford, CT 235

Harrisonburg-Rockingham Historical Society, Dayton, VA 1503

Harry P. Leu Gardens, Orlando, FL 331

Harry S Truman Birthplace State Historic Site, Lamar, MO 825

Harry S. Truman Little White House Museum, Key West, FL 317

Harry S Truman National Historic Site - Truman Farm Home, Grandview, MO 816

Harry S Truman National Historic Site - Truman Home, Independence, MO 818

Harry S. Truman Office & Courtroom, Independence, MO 818

Hartford House Museum, Manhattan, KS 551

Hartman Reserve Nature Center, Cedar Falls, IA 507

Harvard Historical Society, Still River, MA 711

Harvey House Museum, Florence, KS 539

Hathaway Ranch Museum, Santa Fe Springs, CA 182

Hatteras Island Visitor Center, Buxton, NC 1093

Hatton-Eielson Museum & Historical Association, Hatton, ND 1132

Haverford Township Historical Society, Havertown, PA 1260

Haverhill Historical Society, Haverhill, MA 686

Havre de Grace Decoy Museum, Havre de Grace, MD 647
Hawaii's Plantation Village, Waipahu, HI 402
Hawkeye Log Cabin, Burlington, IA............507
Hawks Inn Historical Society, Inc., Delafield, WI 1595
Hawks Nest State Park, Ansted, WV 1579
Hay House Museum, Macon, GA 377
Hayward Area Historical Society, Hayward, CA..102
Headwaters Heritage Museum, Three Forks, MT..854
Heard Natural Science Museum and Wildlife Sanctuary, Inc., McKinney, TX...1437
Hearst Castle, San Simeon, CA 177
Heart of West Texas Museum, Colorado City, TX 1401
Hearthstone Historic House Museum, Appleton, WI 1589
Heathcote Botanical Gardens, Inc., Fort Pierce, FL...309
Heavener Runestone State Park, Heavener, OK 1202
Heisey Museum, Clinton County Historical Society, Lock Haven, PA 1269
Held-Poage Memorial Home and Research Library, Ukiah, CA 193
Helen Day Art Center, Stowe, VT.............1488
Helen Moe Antique Doll Museum, Paso Robles, CA..141
Helvetia Museum, Helvetia, WV 1582
The Hemingway Museum and The Ernest Hemingway Birthplace, Oak Park, IL 448
Henry B. Plant Museum, Tampa, FL...........349
Henry County Historical Society, New Castle, IN..494
Henry County Museum and Cultural Arts Center, Clinton, MO 813
The Henry Ford, Dearborn, MI 733
Henry Ford Estate-Fair Lane, Dearborn, MI...734
The Henry Sheldon Museum of Vermont History, Middlebury, VT 1481
Henry Whitfield State Historical Museum, Guilford, CT..............................243
Herbert Hoover National Historic Site, West Branch, IA 530
Hereford Inlet Lighthouse, North Wildwood, NJ 917
The Heritage Center, Pine Ridge, SD.........1354
Heritage Center of Lancaster County, Inc., Lancaster, PA..............................1265
Heritage Conservancy, Doylestown, PA 1249
Heritage Farm Museum & Village, Huntington, WV 1583
Heritage Farmstead Museum, Plano, TX 1444
Heritage Hall Museum & Archives, Freeman, SD..1347
Heritage Hill State Historical Park, Green Bay, WI 1599
Heritage House of Orange County Association Inc., Orange, TX 1441
The Heritage Museum, Astoria, OR............1218
Heritage Museum & Cultural Center, Baker, LA 585
Heritage Museum & Potton House, Big Spring, TX 1396
Heritage Museum Foundation of Tate County, Inc., Senatobia, MS 808
Heritage Museums & Gardens, Sandwich, MA...707
The Heritage Society, Houston, TX............1426
Heritage Square Museum, Ontario, NY.....1047
Heritage Square Museum, Los Angeles, CA..116
Heritage Station, Umatilla County Historical Society Museum, Pendleton, OR...1230
Heritage Village, Largo, FL........................321
Heritage Village, Mountain Lake, MN 785
Heritage Village Museum, Woodville, TX .1462

Herkimer Home State Historic Site, Little Falls, NY...1009
Hermann-Grima/Gallier Historic Houses, New Orleans, LA......................................595
The Hermitage, Ho-Ho-Kus, NJ 907
The Hermitage: Home of President Andrew Jackson, Hermitage, TN...........1367
Hernando Heritage Museum, Brooksville, FL..298
Herschell Carrousel Factory Museum, North Tonawanda, NY 1043
Hershey Gardens, Hershey, PA 1260
Hettinger County Historical Society, Regent, ND 1136
The Hickories Museum of the Lorain County Historical Society, Elyria, OH ..1163
Hickory Grove Rural School Museum, Ogden, IA 525
Hickory Hill, Thomson, GA 388
Hickory Landmarks Society-Propst House & Maple Grove, Hickory, NC.............1106
Higgins Armory Museum, Worcester, MA ..721
High Cliff Historical Society & General Store Museum, Sherwood, WI 1622
High Desert Museum, Bend, OR...............1220
High Plains Western Heritage Center, Spearfish, SD..1357
High Point Museum & Historical Park, High Point, NC 1106
Highland House Museum, Hillsboro, OH ..1168
The Highlands, Fort Washington, PA 1254
Highlands Hammock State Park/Civilian Conservation Corps Museum, Sebring, FL..346
Highlands Museum & Discovery Center, Ashland, KY...564
Hildene, The Lincoln Family Home, Manchester, VT 1481
The Hill Country Museum, Kerrville, TX..1431
Hill Cumorah Visitors Center & Historic Sites, Palmyra, NY 1050
Hill-Stead Museum, Farmington, CT 241
Hillforest House Museum, Aurora, IN 468
Hills and Dales Estate, LaGrange, GA.........375
Hillsboro Museums, Hillsboro, KS.............544
Hillwood Museum & Gardens, Washington, DC..280
Hinckley Fire Museum, Hinckley, MN 778
Hiram Blauvelt Art Museum, Oradell, NJ...919
Historic Annapolis Foundation, Annapolis, MD..628
Historic Arkansas Museum, Little Rock, AR..62
Historic Bath State Historic Site, Bath, NC..1091
Historic Bethabara Park, Winston-Salem, NC..1125
Historic Bethany, Bethany, WV 1580
Historic Bok Sanctuary, Lake Wales, FL.....320
Historic Bowens Mills & Pioneer Park, Middleville, MI..754
Historic Brattonsville, McConnells, SC......1336
Historic Burlington County Prison Museum, Mount Holly, NJ......................914
Historic Camden Revolutionary War Site, Camden, SC...1323
Historic Carson House, Marion, NC...........1110
Historic Charleston Foundation, Charleston, SC..1325
Historic Charlton Park Village and Museum, Hastings, MI...........................745
Historic Cherry Hill, Albany, NY................954
Historic Columbia Foundation, Columbia, SC..1329
Historic Columbus Foundation, Inc., Columbus, GA..369
Historic Crab Orchard Museum & Pioneer Park, Inc., Tazewell, VA...........1541
Historic Deerfield, Inc., Deerfield, MA 679
Historic Edenton State Historic Site, Edenton, NC..1099
Historic Fallsington, Inc., Fallsington, PA .1253

Historic Fort Snelling, Saint Paul, MN 790
Historic Fort Steilacoom, Lakewood, WA..1558
Historic Fort Stockton, Fort Stockton, TX.1416
Historic General Dodge House, Council Bluffs, IA 512
Historic Georgetown Inc., Georgetown, CO..218
Historic Governors' Mansion, Cheyenne, WY...1630
Historic Halifax State Historic Site, Halifax, NC...1105
Historic Homes Foundation, Inc., Louisville, KY...576
Historic Hope Foundation, Inc., Windsor, NC...1124
Historic House Trust of New York City, New York, NY 1027
Historic Hudson Valley, Tarrytown, NY.....1077
Historic Indian Agency House, Portage, WI...1618
Historic Jamestowne, Jamestown, VA 1512
Historic Jefferson College, Washington, MS..810
Historic Landmarks Foundation of Indiana, Indianapolis, IN.......................482
Historic Langhorne Association, Langhorne, PA.......................................1267
Historic Latta Plantation, Huntersville, NC...1107
Historic Lincoln, Lincoln, NM 941
Historic London Town and Gardens, Edgewater, MD......................................642
Historic Lyme Village Association, Bellevue, OH 1142
Historic Macon Foundation, Inc. - Sidney Lanier Cottage House Museum, Macon, GA...377
Historic Madison, Inc., Madison, IN...........489
Historic New England, Boston, MA............665
Historic New England/Cogswells Grant, Essex, MA...682
Historic New Harmony, New Harmony, IN...494
The Historic New Orleans Collection, New Orleans, LA......................................595
Historic Newton Home, Decatur, MI 734
Historic Northampton, Northampton, MA...699
Historic Oakland Cemetery, Atlanta, GA 360
Historic Palmyra's Print Shop, Palmyra, NY..1050
Historic Palmyra's - Wm. Phelps General Store, Palmyra, NY 1050
Historic Pensacola Village, Pensacola, FL ..335
Historic Pittsford, Pittsford, NY.................1052
Historic Preservation Association of Bourbon County, Inc., Fort Scott, KS 540
Historic Prophetstown, Battle Ground, IN ...468
Historic Pullman Foundation, Chicago, IL...421
Historic Renville Preservation Commission, Renville, MN......................787
Historic Rosedale, Charlotte, NC...............1095
Historic Rugby, Rugby, TN........................1383
Historic Sauder Village, Archbold, OH 1140
Historic Schaefferstown, Inc., Schaefferstown, PA...............................1297
Historic Smithfield, Blacksburg, VA...........1497
Historic Southwest Ohio, Inc., Sharonville, OH.......................................1185
Historic Spanish Point, Osprey, FL.............333
Historic Speedwell, Morristown, NJ............913
Historic Stagville, Durham, NC.................1098
Historic Waco Foundation, Waco, TX........1459
Historic Walnford, Upper Freehold Twp., NJ...929
Historic Warrior Run Church, Watsontown, PA.....................................1306
Historic Westville, Inc., Lumpkin, GA.........376
Historical and Genealogical Society of Somerset County, Somerset, PA 1300
Historical Center for Southeast New Mexico, Roswell, NM 946

Iowa Railroad Historical Society, Boone, IA 506
Ipswich Historical Society and Museum, Ipswich, MA 688
Iredell Museum of Arts & Heritage, Statesville, NC 1120
Iron & Steel Museum of Alabama, Tannehill Ironworks Historical State Park, McCalla, AL 13
Iron County Museum, Caspian, MI 731
Ironworld Discovery Center, Chisholm, MN 771
Isaac Farrar Mansion, Bangor, ME 604
Isaac Winslow House, Marshfield, MA 693
Isabel Anderson Comer Museum & Arts Center, Sylacauga, AL 18
Isanti County Historical Society, Cambridge, MN 770
Ischua Valley Historical Society, Inc., Franklinville, NY 992
Isle La Motte Historical Society, Isle La Motte, VT 1480
Islesboro Historical Society, Islesboro, ME 612
Issaquah History Museum, Issaquah, WA ..1557

J.E. Reeves Home & Museum, Dover, OH 1163
J.J. Jackson Memorial Museum, Weaverville, CA 197
J.W. Parmley Historical Home Society, Ipswich, SD 1349
Jacinto Foundation, Inc., Corinth, MS 800
Jackson County Historical Museum & Research Library, Maquoketa, IA 522
Jackson Hole Historical Society and Museum, Jackson, WY 1634
Jacksonport State Park, Jacksonport, AR 60
Jackson's Mill Historic Area, Weston, WV 1587
Jacksonville Fire Museum, Jacksonville, FL 314
Jacob Hamblin Home, Santa Clara, UT 1474
Jacob Kelley House Museum, Hartsville, SC 1335
James A. Garfield National Historic Site, Mentor, OH 1176
James Buchanan Foundation for the Preservation of Wheatland, Lancaster, PA 1266
The James Dunklin House, Laurens, SC 1336
James J. Hill House, Saint Paul, MN 790
James K. Polk Ancestral Home, Columbia, TN 1364
The James Madison Museum, Orange, VA 1524
James Madison's Montpelier, Montpelier Station, VA 1518
James Mitchell Varnum House and Museum, East Greenwich, RI 1311
James Whitcomb Riley Birthplace & Museum, Greenfield, IN 480
James Whitcomb Riley Museum Home, Indianapolis, IN 485
Jamestown Fire Department Memorial Museum, Jamestown, RI 1312
Jamestown Museum, Jamestown, RI 1312
Jane Addams Hull-House Museum, University of Illinois Chicago, Chicago, IL 422
Japanese American National Museum, Los Angeles, CA 117
Jarrell Plantation Georgia State Historic Site, Juliette, GA 374
Jeffers Petroglyphs Historic Site, Comfrey, MN 771
Jefferson Barracks Historic Site, Saint Louis, MO 833
Jefferson County Historical Society, Watertown, NY 1083
Jefferson Landing State Historic Site, Jefferson City, MO 819

Jefferson National Expansion Memorial, Saint Louis, MO 833
Jefferson Patterson Park & Museum, Saint Leonard, MD 651
Jekyll Island Museum, Jekyll Island, GA 374
Jemez State Monument, Jemez Springs, NM 940
Jennings-Brown House Female Academy, Bennettsville, SC 1322
Jericho Historical Society, Jericho Corners, VT 1480
Jerome County Historical Society, Inc. and Idaho Farm & Ranch Museum, Jerome, ID 406
Jerome State Historic Park, Jerome, AZ 36
Jesse James Bank Museum, Liberty, MO 826
Jesse James Farm & Museum, Kearney, MO 823
Jesse Peter Museum, Santa Rosa, CA 184
Jewish Museum of Florida, Miami Beach, FL 326
Jewish Museum of Maryland, Baltimore, MD 633
Jimmy Carter National Historic Site, Plains, GA 381
John A. Logan College Museum, Carterville, IL 416
John and Mable Ringling Museum of Art, Sarasota, FL 344
John Brown Museum State Historic Site, Osawatomie, KS 554
John Brown Wax Museum Inc., Harpers Ferry, WV 1582
John Burroughs Association, Inc., West Park, NY 1085
John Burroughs Memorial State Historic Site, Roxbury, NY 1062
John Day Fossil Beds National Monument, Kimberly, OR 1227
John Fitzgerald Kennedy National Historic Site, Brookline, MA 671
John G. Neihardt State Historic Site, Bancroft, NE 856
John G. Voigt House, Plymouth, WI 1618
John James Audubon Center at Mill Grove, Audubon, PA 1241
John Jay French House, Beaumont Heritage Society, Beaumont, TX 1395
John Jay Homestead State Historic Site, Katonah, NY 1006
John Michael Kohler Arts Center, Sheboygan, WI 1621
John Muir National Historic Site, Martinez, CA 124
John Nance Garner Museum, Uvalde, TX .1457
The John Nicholas Brown Center for the Study of American Civilization, Providence, RI 1317
John Paul Jones House Museum, Portsmouth, NH 894
John Rains House, Rancho Cucamonga, CA 145
John Stark Edwards House, Warren, OH ...1189
John Sydnor's 1847 Powhatan House, Galveston, TX 1421
John Woolman Memorial, Mount Holly, NJ 915
John Wornall House Museum, Kansas City, MO 821
Johnson County Historical Society, Inc., Tecumseh, NE 873
Johnson County Historical Society Museum, Warrensburg, MO 840
Johnson County Museums, Shawnee, KS 558
Johnson Ferry House Museum, Titusville, NJ 926
Johnson Hall State Historic Site, Johnstown, NY 1005
Johnstown Area Heritage Association, Johnstown, PA 1263
Johnstown Flood National Memorial, South Fork, PA 1300

Johnstown Historical Society, Johnstown, NY 1005
Jonathan Hager House & Museum, Hagerstown, MD 646
Jonesborough-Washington County History Museum, Jonesborough, TN 1368
Joseph Priestley House, Northumberland, PA 1274
Joseph Smith Historic Site, Nauvoo, IL 447
The Judah P. Benjamin Confederate Memorial at Gamble Plantation Historic State Park, Ellenton, FL 306
Judaica Museum of Central Synagogue, New York, NY 1029
Judge Roy Bean Visitor Center, Langtry, TX 1433
Judy Garland Museum, Grand Rapids, MN 777
Jugville Museum, Grafton, ND 1131
Juliette Gordon Low Birthplace, Savannah, GA 385
Junction City Historical Society, Junction City, OR 1226
Juneau-Douglas City Museum, Juneau, AK 26
The Junior Museum of Bay County, Panama City, FL 334
Justin Smith Morrill Homestead, Strafford, VT 1488

Kalamazoo Nature Center, Inc., Kalamazoo, MI 748
Kalaupapa National Historical Park, Kalaupapa, HI 400
Kalkaska County Historical Museum, Kalkaska, MI 749
Kaminski House Museum, Georgetown, SC 1333
Kandiyohi County Historical Society, Willmar, MN 796
Kankakee County Museum, Kankakee, IL...441
The Kate Chopin House & Bayou Folk Museum, Cloutierville, LA 588
Kate Shelley Railroad Museum, Boone, IA 506
Kauffman Museum, North Newton, KS 553
The Kearny Cottage, Perth Amboy, NJ 921
Keeler Tavern Museum, Ridgefield, CT 259
Kell House Museum, Wichita Falls, TX 1461
Kelly-Griggs House Museum, Red Bluff, CA 146
The Kelso House Museum, Kent, OH 1169
Kelton House Museum & Garden, Columbus, OH 1158
The Kemp-McCarthy Memorial Museum of the Rowe Historical Society, Inc., Rowe, MA 706
Kenilworth Aquatic Gardens, Washington, DC 281
Kennebunkport Historical Society, Kennebunkport, ME 612
Kennedy-Douglass Center for the Arts, Florence, AL 9
Kennesaw Mountain National Battlefield Park, Kennesaw, GA 374
Kenosha County Historical Society and Museum, Inc., Kenosha, WI 1602
Kensington Mansion, Eastover, SC 1332
Kent-Delord House Museum, Plattsburgh, NY 1052
The Kentucky Library & Museum, Bowling Green, KY 565
Kentucky Military History Museum, Frankfort, KY 569
Kentucky State Capitol, Frankfort, KY 569
Keokuk River Museum, Keokuk, IA 521
Ker Place, Onancock, VA 1523
Kerbyville Museum, Kerby, OR 1227
Kern County Museum, Bakersfield, CA 73
Kershaw County Historical Society, Camden, SC 1323
Kewaunee County Historical Museum, Kewaunee, WI 1602

Structures—Continued

Keweenaw County Historical Society, Eagle Harbor, MI......................739

Key West Lighthouse Museum, Key West, FL..........................318

Key West Museum of Art and History, Key West, FL..........................318

Keystone Area Historical Society, Keystone, SD..........................1350

Kid City - The Children's Museum of Tampa, Tampa, FL..........................349

Kidwell Farm at Frying Pan Park, Herndon, VA..........................1511

Kimball House Museum, Battle Creek, MI..........................727

Kimberly Crest House & Gardens, Redlands, CA..........................147

King Kamehameha V-Judiciary History Center, Honolulu, HI..........................397

King Manor, Jamaica, NY..........................1004

Kingman County Historical Museum, Kingman, KS..........................547

Kingman Tavern Historical Museum, Cummington, MA..........................678

Kings Mountain National Military Park, Blacksburg, SC..........................1322

Kingsburg Historical Park, Kingsburg, CA..........................105

Kingsley Plantation, Jacksonville, FL.......315

Kingwood Center, Mansfield, OH..............1173

Kinney Pioneer Museum and Historical Society of North Iowa, Clear Lake, IA...510

Kit Carson Historical Society, Kit Carson, CO..........................223

Kit Carson Home & Museum, Inc., Taos, NM..........................952

Kit Carson Museum, Las Animas, CO.........225

Kitsap County Historical Society Museum, Bremerton, WA..........................1549

Kittson County History Center Museum, Lake Bronson, MN..........................778

Kiwanis Van Slyke Museum Foundation Inc., Caldwell, ID..........................404

Klamath County Museum, Klamath Falls, OR..........................1227

Klein Museum, Mobridge, SD..................1352

Kline Creek Farm, Winfield, IL..................466

Klyne Esopus Museum, Ulster Park, NY...1079

Knights of Columbus Museum, New Haven, CT..........................253

Knott House Museum, Tallahassee, FL.......347

Knox County Museum, Knoxville, IL..........441

Knox Headquarters State Historic Site, Vails Gate, NY..........................1080

Kohl Children's Museum of Greater Chicago, Glenview, IL..........................438

Korean War Veterans National Museum & Library, Rantoul, IL..........................453

Koreshan State Historic Site, Estero, FL......306

Korner's Folly, Kernersville, NC..............1108

Kruse House Museum, West Chicago, IL....464

Kuhlmann King Historical House and Museum, Boerne, TX..........................1396

Kuser Farm Mansion, Hamilton, NJ.............907

L.C. Bates Museum, Hinckley, ME..............612

La Purisima Mission State Historic Park, Lompoc, CA..........................109

Lac Qui Parle County Historical Society, Madison, MN..........................779

Ladew Topiary Gardens, Monkton, MD.......649

Lafayette Miners Museum, Lafayette, CO...224

Lagrange County Historical Society, Inc., Lagrange, IN..........................488

LaGrange Plantation, Cambridge, MD.........639

Lake County Discovery Museum, Wauconda, IL..........................463

Lake County Historical Society, Two Harbors, MN..........................794

Lake Guernsey Museum-Guernsey State Park, Guernsey, WY..........................1634

Lake Jackson Mounds Archaeological State Park, Tallahassee, FL......................347

Lake Shore Railway Museum, North East, PA..........................1274

Lake Tahoe Historical Society & Museum, South Lake Tahoe, CA............188

Lake Waccamaw Depot Museum, Lake Waccamaw, NC..........................1109

Lake Wales Depot Museum & Cultural Center, Lake Wales, FL..........................320

Lakewood's Heritage Center, Lakewood, CO..........................225

Land of the Yankee Fork Historic Association Museum, Stanley, ID............410

Landis Valley Museum, Lancaster, PA.......1266

Landmark Park, Dothan, AL..........................8

The Landmark Society of Western New York, Rochester, NY..........................1058

Landmarks Foundation/Old Alabama Town, Montgomery, AL..........................16

Lane County Historical Society & Museum, Eugene, OR..........................1223

Lane House, Roseburg, OR..........................1234

Lane Place, Crawfordsville, IN......................473

Langlade County Historical Society Museum, Antigo, WI..........................1589

Lanier Mansion State Historic Site, Madison, IN..........................489

Lansing Manor House Museum, North Blenheim, NY..........................1043

Lanterman House, La Canada Flintridge, CA..........................105

Lapham-Patterson House, Thomasville, GA..........................388

Lars Noak Blacksmith Shop, Larsson/Ostlund Log Home & One-Room Capitol School, New Sweden, ME..........................616

Larz Anderson Auto Museum, Brookline, MA..........................671

Las Cabezas de San Juan Nature Reserve (El Faro), Fajardo, PR..........................1641

Lauder Museum - Amityville Historical Society, Amityville, NY..........................957

Laughing Brook Education Center & Wildlife Sanctuary, Hampden, MA..........686

Laura Ingalls Wilder Park & Museum, Inc., Burr Oak, IA..........................507

Laurence C. Jones Museum, Piney Woods, MS..........................807

Lawrence County Gray House Museum, Ironton, OH..........................1169

Lawrence Heritage State Park, Lawrence, MA..........................689

Lawrence History Center: Immigrant City Archives & Museum, Lawrence, MA.....689

Laws Railroad Museum and Historical Site, Bishop, CA..........................78

Layland Museum, Cleburne, TX...............1400

Le Sault de Sainte Marie Historical Sites, Inc., Sault Ste. Marie, MI..........................764

Lea County Museum, Lovington, NM.........943

Leander J. McCormick Observatory, Charlottesville, VA..........................1499

Lee-Fendall House Museum and Garden, Alexandria, VA..........................1493

Lefferts Historic House, Brooklyn, NY.......969

The Leffingwell House Museum, Norwich, CT..........................258

Legends of New Mexico Museum, Algodones, NM..........................936

Lehigh County Historical Society, Allentown, PA..........................1239

The Lemee House, Natchitoches, LA..........593

Lemhi County Historical Museum, Salmon, ID..........................409

Lemon Hill Mansion, Philadelphia, PA......1282

LeMoyne Art Foundation, Inc., Tallahassee, FL..........................347

Lesueur County Historical Museum-Chapter 1, Elysian, MN............774

Levere Memorial Temple, Evanston, IL......434

Levi Coffin House, Fountain City, IN.........478

Levine Museum of the New South, Charlotte, NC..........................1095

Lewis Ginter Botanical Garden, Richmond, VA..........................1530

The Lexington Cemetery, Lexington, KY....573

Lexington County Museum, Lexington, SC..........................1336

Lexington Historical Society, Lexington, MA..........................689

Lexington History Museum, Lexington, KY..........................573

Liberty Bell Memorial Museum, Melbourne, FL..........................323

Liberty County Museum, Chester, MT........844

Liberty Hall Historic Center, Lamoni, IA...522

Liberty Hall Historic Site, Frankfort, KY...569

Liberty Hall Museum, Union, NJ...............928

Liberty Jail Historic Site, Liberty, MO........826

Libertyville-Mundelein Historical Society, Inc., Libertyville, IL..........................442

Library of Congress, Washington, DC.........282

Licking County Historical Society, Newark, OH..........................1178

Lightner Museum, Saint Augustine, FL.......339

Lilacia Park-Lombard Park District, Lombard, IL..........................443

Lillian and Albert Small Jewish Museum, Washington, DC..........................282

Limberlost State Historic Site, Geneva, IN..........................479

Limon Heritage Museum, Limon, CO.........226

Lincoln Boyhood National Memorial, Lincoln City, IN..........................488

Lincoln County Historical Museum, Davenport, WA..........................1552

Lincoln County Historical Society, North Platte, NE..........................869

Lincoln County Historical Society Museum of Pioneer History, Chandler, OK..........................1197

Lincoln County Pioneer Museum, Hendricks, MN..........................778

Lincoln Herndon Law Offices State Historic Site, Springfield, IL............458

Lincoln Home National Historic Site, Springfield, IL..........................459

Lincoln Homestead State Park, Springfield, KY..........................583

Lincoln Park Conservatory, Chicago, IL.....423

Lincoln State Monument, Lincoln, NM.......941

The Lincoln-Tallman Restorations, Janesville, WI..........................1601

Lincoln Tomb State Historic Site, Springfield, IL..........................459

Lincoln's New Salem State Historic Site, Petersburg, IL..........................451

Linn County Historical Museum and Moyer House, Brownsville, OR..........1220

Lisbon Historical Society, Lisbon, OH.......1172

Lisle Station Museum, Lisle, IL..................443

Litchfield Historical Society and Museum, Litchfield, CT..........................247

Little Compton Historical Society, Little Compton, RI..........................1312

Little Falls Historical Society Museum, Little Falls, NY..........................1009

Little Norway, Inc., Blue Mounds, WI.......1593

Little White House Historic Site, Warm Springs, GA..........................390

Little White Schoolhouse, Ripon, WI.........1620

Littleton Historical Museum, Littleton, CO..........................227

Living History Farms, Urbandale, IA...........529

Livingston Depot Center, Livingston, MT...850

Locust Creek Covered Bridge State Historic Site, Laclede, MO..........................825

Locust Grove, Louisville, KY..........................577

Locust Grove, The Samuel Morse Historic Site, Poughkeepsie, NY..........1055

Locust Lawn and Terwilliger House, Gardiner, NY..........................993

Log Cabin Village, Fort Worth, TX............1417

The Log House Museum of the Historical Society of Columbiana-Fairfield Township, Columbiana, OH....................1157

Logan County Historical Society Museum, Bellefontaine, OH...................1142

Lombard Historical Museum, Lombard, IL.............443

Lompoc Valley Historical Society, Inc., Lompoc, CA.............110

Long Island Maritime Museum, West Sayville, NY.............1085

Long Island Museum of American Art, History & Carriages, Stony Brook, NY.............1075

Longfellow Evangeline State Historic Site, Saint Martinville, LA...................600

Longfellow National Historic Site, Cambridge, MA.............673

Longfellow's Wayside Inn, Sudbury, MA....714

Longmont Museum, Longmont, CO.............227

Longstreet Farm, Holmdel, NJ...................908

Longue Vue House & Gardens, New Orleans, LA.............596

Longwood Gardens, Kennett Square, PA...1264

Longyear Museum, Chestnut Hill, MA.........675

Los Alamos Historical Museum, Los Alamos, NM...................942

The Los Angeles County Arboretum & Botanic Garden, Arcadia, CA...................71

Los Angeles Municipal Art Gallery - Barnsdall Art Park, Los Angeles, CA......118

Los Nogales Museum, Seguin, TX.............1452

Loudoun Heritage Farm Museum, Sterling, VA 1538

Loudoun Museum, Inc., Leesburg, VA.......1512

Louis E. May Museum, Fremont, NE.........861

Louis H. & Lena Firn Grover Museum, Shelbyville, IN...................498

Louisiana State Oil & Gas Museum, Oil City, LA...................599

Louisville Visual Art Association, Louisville, KY...................578

Lowell Damon House, Wauwatosa, WI......1626

Lowell National Historical Park, Lowell, MA...................691

Lowell Observatory, Flagstaff, AZ...................33

Lower Cape Fear Historical Society, Inc., Wilmington, NC...................1123

Lower East Side Tenement Museum, New York, NY...................1029

Loxahatchee River Historical Society, Jupiter, FL...................316

Luckhard Museum - The Indian Mission, Sebewaing, MI...................764

Luis Munoz Rivera Library & Museum, Barranquitas, PR...................1641

Lum & Abner Museum & Jot 'Em Down Store, Pine Ridge, AR...................66

Luther Burbank Home & Gardens, Santa Rosa, CA...................184

Lutheran Heritage Center & Museum of the Perry County Lutheran Historical Society, Altenburg, MO...................810

Luzerne County Historical Society, Wilkes-Barre, PA...................1307

The Lyceum, Alexandria's History Museum, Alexandria, VA...................1493

Lyman Estate, The Vale, Waltham, MA.......715

Lyman Museum, Hilo, HI...................393

Lynchburg Museum System, Lynchburg, VA...................1515

Lyndhurst, Tarrytown, NY...................1078

Lyndon B. Johnson National Historical Park, Johnson City, TX...................1431

Lyndon House Art, Athens, GA...................356

Lynn Museum & Historical Society, Lynn, MA...................692

Lynnhaven House, Virginia Beach, VA......1542

Lyon County Historical Society and Museum, Emporia, KS...................538

Lyon County Historical Society Museum, Marshall, MN...................780

The Lyons Redstone Museum, Lyons, CO...227

MAK Center for Art and Architecture at the Schindler House, West Hollywood, CA...................197

Mabee Farm Historic Site, Rotterdam Junction, NY...................1062

Mabry-Hazen House, Knoxville, TN...................1371

MacGregor Ranch, Estes Park, CO...................215

MacKenzie Environmental Education Center, Poynette, WI...................1618

Mackinac Island State Park Commission-Mackinac State Historic Parks, Mackinaw City, MI...................752

Mackinac State Historic Parks-Colonial Michilimackinac & Old Mackinac Point Lighthouse, Mackinaw City, MI 752

Mackinac State Historic Parks-Fort Mackinac & Mackinac Island State Park, Mackinac Island, MI...................752

Mackinac State Historic Parks-Historic Mill Creek, Mackinaw City, MI...................753

Macon County Historical Society Museum Complex, Decatur, IL...................430

Madeline Island Historical Museum, La Pointe, WI...................1603

Madison County Historical Society, Winterset, IA...................531

Madison Historical Society, Madison, CT....247

Maggie L. Walker National Historic Site, Richmond, VA...................1530

The Magic House, St. Louis Children's Museum, Saint Louis, MO...................834

Magnolia Grove-Historic House Museum, Greensboro, AL...................10

Magnolia Manor, Cairo, IL...................415

Magnolia Plantation and Gardens, Charleston, SC...................1326

Magoffin Home State Historic Site, El Paso, TX...................1412

Mahaffie Stagecoach Stop and Farm, Olathe, KS...................554

Maine Maritime Museum, Bath, ME...................606

Maitland Historical Museums, Maitland, FL...................322

The Major General Frederick Funston Boyhood Home and Museum, Iola, KS...................546

Makoti Threshers' Museum, Makoti, ND...1133

Malabar Farm State Park, Lucas, OH...................1173

Malheur Historical Project, Stonehouse Museum, Vale, OR...................1238

Mallory-Neely House, Memphis, TN...................1373

Mamie Doud Eisenhower Birthplace, Boone, IA...................506

Mammoth Spring State Park, Depot Museum, Mammoth Spring, AR...................64

Manatee Village Historical Park, Bradenton, FL...................297

Manitowoc County Historical Society, Manitowoc, WI...................1607

Manship House Museum, Jackson, MS.......802

Marblehead Arts Association - King Hooper Mansion, Marblehead, MA...................693

Marblehead Museum & Historical Society, Marblehead, MA...................693

Marcella Sembrich Opera Museum, Bolton Landing, NY...................963

Marietta House Museum, Glenn Dale, MD...................645

Marietta Museum of History, Marietta, GA...................379

Marin History Museum, San Rafael, CA.....177

Mario Lanza Institute/Museum, Philadelphia, PA...................1282

The Marion County Historical Society Museum, Marion, OH...................1174

Marion Historical Museums, Inc. - Granger House, Marion, IA...................523

Mariposa Museum and History Center Inc., Mariposa, CA...................124

Maritime and Yachting Museum of the Treasure Coast, Stuart, FL...................346

Maritime Industry Museum at Fort Schuyler, Bronx, NY...................966

Maritime Museum at Historic Coast Guard Station, Saint Simons Island, GA...................383

Marjorie Kinnan Rawlings Historic State Park, Cross Creek, FL...................301

Marjorie McNeely Conservatory at Como Park, Saint Paul, MN...................790

Mark Twain Birthplace State Historic Site, Florida, MO...................815

Mark Twain Home and Museum, Hannibal, MO...................816

The Mark Twain House & Museum, Hartford, CT...................245

Marland's Grand Home, Ponca City, OK...1212

Marlboro County Historical Museum, Bennettsville, SC...................1322

Marquette County Historical Society, Westfield, WI...................1627

Marshall County Historical Museum, Plymouth, IN...................496

Marshall County Historical Museum, Holly Springs, MS...................801

Marshall County Historical Society Museum, Warren, MN...................795

Marshall Gold Discovery State Historic Park, Coloma, CA...................86

The Marston House/San Diego Historical Society, San Diego, CA...................157

Martha's Vineyard Museum, Edgartown, MA...................681

Martin County Historical Museum, Stanton, TX...................1453

Martin Luther King, Jr. National Historic Site and Preservation District, Atlanta, GA...................361

Martin Van Buren National Historic Site, Kinderhook, NY...................1007

Marvin Newton House, Brookfield, VT.....1477

The Mary Baker Eddy Library for the Betterment of Humanity, Boston, MA.....666

Mary Ball Washington Museum & Library, Inc., Lancaster, VA...................1512

Mary Todd Lincoln House, Lexington, KY...................574

Mary Washington House, Fredericksburg, VA...................1507

Maryhill Museum of Art, Goldendale, WA...................1556

Maryland Science Center, Baltimore, MD ...634

Mason County Historical Society/Historic White Pine Village, Ludington, MI...................751

Mathias Ham House Historic Site, Dubuque, IA...................516

Mattapoisett Museum and Carriage House, Mattapoisett, MA...................693

Matt's Museum, Lawtell, LA...................590

May Museum & Farmville Heritage Center, Farmville, NC...................1100

Mayborn Museum Complex, Waco, TX.....1459

Mayflower Society Museum, Plymouth, MA...................703

Maymont, Richmond, VA...................1530

Mayville Area Museum of History and Genealogy, Mayville, MI...................754

Mayville Historical Society, Inc., Mayville, WI...................1608

Mazomanie Historical Society, Mazomanie, WI...................1608

McAllister House Museum, Colorado Springs, CO...................207

McChord Air Museum, Tacoma, WA.........1573

McConaghy House, Hayward, CA...................102

McCone County Museum, Circle, MT........844

McConnell Mansion, Moscow, ID...................407

McCook House, Civil War Museum, Carrollton, OH...................1146

McDowell House Museum, Danville, KY ...567

McFaddin-Ward House, Beaumont, TX 1395

McFarland State Historic Park, Florence, AZ...................34

Motown Historical Museum, Detroit, MI.....737

Mount Clare Museum House, Baltimore, MD......635

Mount Desert Island Historical Society, Mount Desert, ME......615

Mount Holly Community Historical Museum, Belmont, VT......1476

Mt. Kearsarge Indian Museum, Warner, NH......897

Mount Pleasant Historical Society, Mount Pleasant, OH......1177

Mt. Pulaski Courthouse State Historic Site, Mount Pulaski, IL......446

Mt. Rainier National Park, Ashford, WA ...1547

Mount Rushmore National Memorial, Keystone, SD......1350

Mount Vernon Hotel Museum & Garden, New York, NY......1031

Mount Vernon Ladies' Association, Mount Vernon, VA......1518

Mountain Farm Museum-Great Smoky Mountains National Park, Cherokee, NC......1096

Mountain Life Museum, London, KY......575

The Movie Museum, Owosso, MI......759

The Municipal Art Society of New York, New York, NY......1031

Murfreesboro Historical Association, Murfreesboro, NC......1112

Murray-Lindsay Mansion, Lindsay, OK.....1204

Murrell Home, Park Hill, OK......1211

Muscatine Art Center, Muscatine, IA......524

Musee Conti Wax Museum, New Orleans, LA......597

Museo Fuerte Conde de Mirasol de Vieques, Vieques, PR......1644

Museum of Afro-American History, Boston, MA......667

Museum of Alaska Transportation & Industry, Inc., Wasilla, AK......29

Museum of American Glass at Wheaton Village, Millville, NJ......911

Museum of Appalachia, Clinton, TN......1363

The Museum of Arts and Sciences, Inc. and Center for Florida History, Daytona Beach, FL......303

Museum of Chicot County Arkansas, Lake Village, AR......61

Museum of Colorado Prisons, Canon City, CO......205

Museum of Early Southern Decorative Arts (MESDA), Winston-Salem, NC.....1125

The Museum of Early Trades and Crafts, Madison, NJ......910

Museum of Migrating People, Bronx, NY...966

The Museum of Mobile, Mobile, AL......14

Museum of New Mexico, Santa Fe, NM.....949

Museum of Northwest Colorado, Craig, CO......208

Museum of Religious Arts, Logan, IA......522

Museum of Rural Life, Denton, MD......642

Museum of Seminole County History, Sanford, FL......343

Museum of South Texas History, Edinburg, TX......1410

Museum of Surveying, Lansing, MI......750

Museum of the Arkansas Grand Prairie, Stuttgart, AR......69

Museum of the Bedford Historical Society, Bedford, NY......961

Museum of the Berkeley Springs, Berkeley Springs, WV......1580

Museum of the Cape Fear Historical Complex, Fayetteville, NC......1101

Museum of the Cherokee Strip, Enid, OK.1200

Museum of the Fur Trade, Chadron, NE......859

Museum of the Great Plains, Lawton, OK.1204

Museum of the High Plains, McCook, NE......868

Museum of the Llano Estacado, Plainview, TX......1443

Museum of the Northern Great Plains, Fort Benton, MT......846

Museum of the Plains Indian, Browning, MT......843

Museum of the Puerto Rican Family of the 19th Century, San Juan, PR......1643

Museum of the Southern Jewish Experience, Jackson, MS......803

Museum of Transportation, Saint Louis, MO......835

Museum of West Louisiana, Leesville, LA......591

Museum of Western Colorado, Grand Junction, CO......220

Museum of Wildlife, Science & Industry, Webster, SD......1359

Museum on Main: A History Museum for West Georgia, LaGrange, GA......375

Museum Village, Monroe, NY......1015

The Museums of Oglebay Institute - Mansion Museum & Glass Museum, Wheeling, WV......1588

The Music House Museum, Acme, MI......722

Muskegon County Museum, Muskegon, MI......757

Musselshell Valley Historical Museum, Roundup, MT......853

Mystic Seaport - The Museum of America and the Sea, Mystic, CT......251

Nantucket Historical Association, Nantucket, MA......696

Nantucket Maria Mitchell Association, Nantucket, MA......696

Naomi Wood Collection at Woodford Mansion, Philadelphia, PA......1284

Naper Settlement, Naperville, IL......447

NASA Kennedy Space Center, Merritt Island, FL......323

Nassau County, Division of Museum Services, Department of Recreation, Parks & Museums, East Meadow, NY....987

Nathan Denison Advocates, Forty Fort, PA......1254

Nathaniel W. Faison Home and Museum, La Grange, TX......1432

The National Agricultural Center & Hall of Fame, Bonner Springs, KS......534

National Apple Museum, Biglerville, PA..1243

National Association of Miniature Enthusiasts, Carmel, IN......472

National Automotive & Truck Museum of the United States, Inc. (NATMUS), Auburn, IN......468

National Canal Museum, Hugh Moore Historical Park and Museums, Easton, PA......1250

National Capital Parks-East, Washington, DC......284

National Cowboy & Western Heritage Museum, Oklahoma City, OK......1208

National Czech & Slovak Museum & Library, Cedar Rapids, IA......509

National First Ladies' Library, Canton, OH......1145

National Heisey Glass Museum, Newark, OH......1178

National Mississippi River Museum & Aquarium, Dubuque, IA......516

National Museum of American Illustration, Newport, RI......1314

National Museum of American Jewish History, Philadelphia, PA......1284

National Museum of Civil War Medicine, Frederick, MD......644

National Museum of Industrial History, Bethlehem, PA......1243

National New York Central Railroad Museum, Elkhart, IN......475

National Ornamental Metal Museum, Memphis, TN......1375

National Park Service-Great Falls Park, McLean, VA......1517

National Railroad Museum, Green Bay, WI......1599

National Road/Zane Grey Museum, Norwich, OH......1180

National Route 66 Museum and Old Town Complex, Elk City, OK......1200

National Temple Hill Association, Inc., New Windsor, NY......1018

National Tropical Botanical Garden, Kalaheo, HI......399

Native American Exhibit, National Kateri Shrine, Fonda, NY......991

Native American Museum, Terre Haute, IN......500

Naumkeag, Stockbridge, MA......712

Nauvoo Historical Society Museum, Nauvoo, IL......447

Naval Undersea Museum, Keyport, WA....1557

Naval War College Museum, Newport, RI......1314

Navarro County Historical Society, Pioneer Village, Corsicana, TX......1402

Nebraska State Capitol, Lincoln, NE......866

Nebraska State Historical Society's Thomas P. Kennard House, Lincoln, NE......867

Neenah Historical Society, Hiram Smith, Neenah's Heritage Park, Octagon House & Ward House, Neenah, WI......1614

Neill Museum, Fort Davis, TX......1414

Neligh Mills, Neligh, NE......869

Netherland Inn House Museum & Boatyard Complex, Kingsport, TN......1368

Nevada Northern Railway Museum, Ely, NV......876

Nevada State Railroad Museum, Carson City, NV......876

Neversink Valley Area Museum, Cuddebackville, NY......984

New Almaden Quicksilver Mining Museum, San Jose, CA......172

New Bedford Whaling Museum, New Bedford, MA......696

The New Berlin Historical Society, New Berlin, WI......1614

New Braunfels Conservation Society, New Braunfels, TX......1440

New Canaan Historical Society, New Canaan, CT......252

New Castle Historical Society, New Castle, DE......272

New Echota State Historic Site, Calhoun, GA......367

New England Civil War Museum, Vernon, CT......263

New England Fire and History Museum, Brewster, MA......670

New England Wireless & Steam Museum Inc., East Greenwich, RI......1311

New Hampshire Farm Museum, Inc., Milton, NH......892

New Harmony State Historic Site/Historic New Harmony, New Harmony, IN......494

New Jersey Association of Museums, Newark, NJ......916

New Jersey Botanical Garden at Skylands (NJBG), Ringwood, NJ......923

New Jersey Naval Museum, Hackensack, NJ......905

New Jersey Office of Historic Sites, Trenton, NJ......927

New Jersey State House, Trenton, NJ......927

New London Historical Society, New London, NH......892

New Market Battlefield State Historical Park, New Market, VA......1519

The New Milford Historical Society, New Milford, CT......256

New Orleans Fire Dept. Museum & Educational Center, New Orleans, LA....597

New Orleans Pharmacy Museum, New Orleans, LA......597

Structures—Continued

New Richmond Preservation Society, New Richmond, WI....................1615
New Sweden Historical Society, New Sweden, ME................................616
New Windsor Cantonment State Historic Site and National Purple Heart Hall of Honor, Vails Gate, NY....................1080
The New York Botanical Garden, Bronx, NY....................966
New York City Police Museum, New York, NY....................1035
New York Museum of Transportation, West Henrietta, NY....................1084
New York State Bureau of Historic Sites, Waterford, NY....................1082
New York State Council on the Arts/Museum Program, New York, NY....................1036
New York State Office of Parks, Recreation & Historic Preservation, Albany, NY....................955
Newark Valley Depot Museum, Newark Valley, NY....................1042
Newell Museum, Newell, SD....................1352
Newport Art Museum, Newport, RI....................1314
Newport Historical Society & The Museum of Newport History, Newport, RI....................1315
The Newsome House Museum & Cultural Center, Newport News, VA....................1520
The Newton History Museum at The Jackson Homestead, Newton, MA....................698
Newtown History Center, Stephens City, VA....................1538
The Niagara County Historical Center and Niagara County Genealogical Society, Lockport, NY....................1010
Nichols House Museum, Boston, MA....................668
Nici Self Museum, Centennial, WY....................1630
Noah Webster House/West Hartford Historical Society, West Hartford, CT....................265
Noank Historical Society, Inc., Noank, CT....................256
Nobleboro Historical Society, Nobleboro, ME....................616
Nobles County Historical Society, Worthington, MN....................797
Nohwike Bagowa, The White Mountain Apache Cultural Center and Museum, Fort Apache, AZ....................34
Norfolk Historical Society, Norfolk, VA....................1522
Norfolk History Museum, Norfolk, VA....................1523
The Norman Cleveland County Historical Museum, Norman, OK....................1206
Norman Rockwell Museum, Stockbridge, MA....................712
North Alabama Railroad Museum, Huntsville, AL....................12
North Andover Historical Society, North Andover, MA....................698
North Carolina Transportation Museum, Spencer, NC....................1120
The North Dakota Lewis & Clark Interpretive Center, Washburn, ND....................1137
North House Museum, Lewisburg, WV....................1584
North Lee County Historic Center and Santa Fe Depot Museum Complex, Fort Madison, IA....................518
North Platte Valley Museum, Gering, NE....................861
Northampton County Historical and Genealogical Society, Easton, PA....................1250
Northeast Texas Rural Heritage Museum, Pittsburg, TX....................1443
Northern Pacific Railway Museum, Toppenish, WA....................1575
The Northern Virginia Fine Arts Association at the Athenaeum, Alexandria, VA....................1493
Northport Historical Society Museum, Northport, NY....................1044

Northwest Railway Museum, Snoqualmie, WA....................1570
Nutter D. Marvel Museum, Georgetown, DE....................271

O. Henry Museum, Austin, TX....................1391
Oak Creek Historical Society-Pioneer Village, Oak Creek, WI....................1615
Oak Glen School House Museum, Yucaipa, CA....................200
Oak Hill and The Martha Berry Museum, Rome, GA....................382
Oakdale Museum, Oakdale, CA....................132
Oakland County Pioneer and Historical Society, Pontiac, MI....................760
Oaklands Historic House Museum, Murfreesboro, TN....................1376
Oakley Park, UDC Shrine, Edgefield, SC....................1332
The Oaks House Museum, Jackson, MS....................804
Oatland Island Education Center, Savannah, GA....................385
Oatlands, Leesburg, VA....................1512
Oberlin Heritage Center, Oberlin, OH....................1180
Ocean County Historical Museum, Toms River, NJ....................926
Oceanographic Teaching Station Inc. - Roundhouse Marine Studies Lab & Aquarium, Manhattan Beach, CA....................124
Oceanside Museum of Art, Oceanside, CA....................135
Ocmulgee National Monument, Macon, GA....................378
The Octagon, Washington, DC....................288
The Octagon House, Hudson, WI....................1600
Octagon House-First Kindergarten in America, Watertown, WI....................1625
O'Fallon Historical Museum, Baker, MT....................840
Office of Historic Alexandria, Alexandria, VA....................1494
Ogden Historical Society, Spencerport, NY....................1071
Ogden Union Station Museums, Ogden, UT....................1468
Ogden's George S. Eccles Dinosaur Park, Ogden, UT....................1468
Ohio Historical Society, Columbus, OH....................1158
Ohio River Museum, Marietta, OH....................1174
Okefenokee Heritage Center, Waycross, GA....................391
Oklahoma Firefighters Museum, Oklahoma City, OK....................1209
Oklahoma Forest Heritage Center, Broken Bow, OK....................1197
Oklahoma Heritage Association, Oklahoma City, OK....................1209
Oklahoma Historical Society, Oklahoma City, OK....................1209
Oklahoma Territorial Museum, Guthrie, OK....................1202
Olana State Historic Site, Hudson, NY....................1000
Old Barracks Museum, Trenton, NJ....................927
Old Bethpage Village Restoration, Old Bethpage, NY....................1045
Old Bohemia Historical Society, Warwick, MD....................656
Old Brutus Historical Society, Inc., Weedsport, NY....................1084
Old Castle Museum, Baldwin City, KS....................533
The Old Church Society, Inc., Portland, OR....................1231
Old Coal Mine Museum, Madrid, NM....................943
Old Constitution House, Windsor, VT....................1490
Old Courthouse Museum, Santa Ana, CA....................178
Old Cowtown Museum, Wichita, KS....................562
Old Davie School Historical Museum, Davie, FL....................302
Old Depot Museum, Ottawa, KS....................555
Old Dorchester State Historic Site, Summerville, SC....................1342
Old Economy Village, Ambridge, PA....................1240
Old Exchange & Provost Dungeon, Charleston, SC....................1326

Old Falls Village, Menomonee Falls, WI....................1609
Old Firehouse Museum, Greenville, MS....................800
Old Fort House Museum, Fort Edward, NY....................991
Old Fort Niagara, Youngstown, NY....................1088
Old Fort Western, Augusta, ME....................604
Old Greer County Museum & Hall of Fame, Mangum, OK....................1204
Old Hidalgo Pumphouse, Hidalgo, TX....................1424
Old Idaho Penitentiary, Boise, ID....................404
Old Independence Regional Museum, Batesville, AR....................54
The Old Jail Art Center, Albany, TX....................1385
Old Jail Museum, Albion, IN....................467
The Old Jail Museum, Crawfordsville, IN....................473
The Old Jail Museum, Warrenton, VA....................1543
Old Jefferson Town, Oskaloosa, KS....................555
Old Lighthouse Museum, Michigan City, IN....................491
Old Lincoln County Courthouse Museum, Lincoln, NM....................942
Old Log Jail and Chapel Museums, Greenfield, IN....................480
Old Market House State Historic Site, Galena, IL....................436
Old Mission Santa Ines, Solvang, CA....................187
Old Monterey Jail, Monterey, CA....................128
Old New-Gate Prison and Copper Mine, East Granby, CT....................238
Old Ordinary House Museum, Hingham, MA....................687
Old Prairie Town at Ward-Meade Historic Site, Topeka, KS....................560
Old Prison Museums, Deer Lodge, MT....................845
Old Sacramento State Historic Park, Old Sacramento, CA....................135
Old St. Ferdinand's Shrine, Florissant, MO....................815
Old St. Hilary's Church Museum & St. Hilary's Preserve, Tiburon, CA....................192
Old St. Paul's Cemetery, Baltimore, MD....................636
Old Salem Inc., Winston-Salem, NC....................1126
The Old Schwamb Mill, Arlington, MA....................660
Old Sod Post Office, Grassy Butte, ND....................1132
Old South Meeting House, Boston, MA....................668
Old State Capitol, Springfield, IL....................459
Old State House Museum, Little Rock, AR....................63
Old State House-The Bostonian Society, Boston, MA....................668
Old Stone Fort Museum Complex, Schoharie, NY....................1067
The Old Stone House, Washington, DC....................289
Old Stone House Museum, Windsor, NY....................1086
Old Sturbridge Village, Sturbridge, MA....................713
The Old Tavern Museum, Tuscaloosa, AL....................19
Old Town Museum, Burlington, CO....................204
Old Town San Diego State Historic Park, San Diego, CA....................158
Old Washington Historic State Park, Washington, AR....................69
Old Westbury Gardens, Old Westbury, NY....................1045
Old World Wisconsin, Eagle, WI....................1595
Old York Historical Society, York, ME....................626
Olde Colonial Courthouse, Tales of Cape Cod, Inc., Barnstable, MA....................661
Oldest House Museum Complex, Saint Augustine, FL....................339
The Oldest House Museum/Wrecker's Museum, Key West, FL....................318
Oldest Stone House Museum, Lakewood, OH....................1170
Olmsted County Historical Society, Rochester, MN....................788
103rd Ohio Volunteer Infantry Civil War Museum, Sheffield Lake, OH....................1185
Oneida Community Mansion House, Oneida, NY....................1046
The Opelousas Museum of Art, Inc., Opelousas, LA....................599

Orange County Historical Museum, Hillsborough, NC...................1107
Orange County Regional History Center, Orlando, FL...................331
Orange Empire Railway Museum, Perris, CA...................141
Orangetown Historical Museum and Archives, Pearl River, NY...................1051
Orcas Island Historical Museum, Orcas Island, WA...................1560
Orchard House, Concord, MA...................677
Orchard Park Historical Society, Orchard Park, NY...................1047
Oregon Coast History Center, Newport, OR...................1229
Oregon Military Museum, Clackamas, OR...................1221
Oregon Trail Regional Museum, Baker City, OR...................1219
Organ Pipe Cactus National Monument Museum, Ajo, AZ...................29
Oriskany Battlefield State Historic Site, Oriskany, NY...................1047
Orland E. White Arboretum, Boyce, VA....1497
Orleans County Historical Society & The Old Stone House Museum, Brownington, VT...................1477
Ormond Memorial Art Museum & Garden, Ormond Beach, FL...................333
Oroville Chinese Temple, Oroville, CA.......136
Ortega Adobe, Ventura, CA...................195
The Oscar Anderson House Museum, Anchorage, AK...................22
Osterville Historical Society, Inc., Osterville, MA...................701
Otero Museum Association, La Junta, CO...224
Otter Tail County Historical Society, Fergus Falls, MN...................775
Ouachita County Historical Society, Camden, AR...................55
Our House State Memorial, Gallipolis, OH...................1165
Outagamie Museum, Appleton, WI...........1589
Overfield Tavern Museum, Troy, OH...........1188
Overland Trail Museum, Sterling, CO..........232
Overstreet-Kerr Historical Farm, Keota, OK...................1203
Oysterponds Historical Society: The Museum of Orient and East Marion History, Orient, NY...................1047
The Ozark Folk Center, Mountain View, AR...................65
Ozark National Scenic Riverways, Van Buren, MO...................839
Ozaukee County Pioneer Village, Saukville, WI...................1620

The P.T. Boat Museum & Library, Germantown, TN...................1365
Pacem in Terris, Warwick, NY...................1082
Pacific Asia Museum, Pasadena, CA...........140
Pacific Aviation Museum - Pearl Harbor, Honolulu, HI...................397
Pacific Grove Museum of Natural History, Pacific Grove, CA...................137
Packwood House Museum, Lewisburg, PA...................1268
Paine Art Center and Gardens, Oshkosh, WI...................1617
Pajaro Valley Historical Association, Watsonville, CA...................196
Palace of the Governors/New Mexico History Museum, Santa Fe, NM.............949
PALCO, Scotia, CA...................186
Palmer/Gullickson Octagon Home, West Salem, WI...................1627
Palmer House, Historical Society of Olde Northfield, Northfield, OH...................1180
Pamplin Historical Park and The National Museum of the Civil War Soldier, Petersburg, VA...................1525
The Pardee Home Museum, Oakland, CA...134

Paris Gibson Square Museum of Art, Great Falls, MT...................848
Paris-Henry County Heritage Center, Paris, TN...................1382
Parishville Museum, Parishville, NY..........1050
The Park-McCullough House, North Bennington, VT...................1483
Parker Tavern, Reading, MA...................705
Parks, Recreation & Historic Sites Division, Georgia Dept. of Natural Resources, Atlanta, GA...................362
The Parry Mansion Museum, New Hope, PA...................1273
Parson Fisher House, Blue Hill, ME...........606
Parsonsfield-Porter Historical Society, Porter, ME...................618
The Parthenon, Nashville, TN...................1379
Pasadena Museum of History, Pasadena, CA...................140
Patee House Museum, Saint Joseph, MO....831
The Paterson Museum, Paterson, NJ...........920
Patterson Homestead, Dayton, OH...........1161
Patterson Inn Museum/Corning - Painted Post Historical Society, Corning, NY.....982
The Patuxent Rural Life Museums, Upper Marlboro, MD...................655
Paul Bunyan Logging Camp Museum, Eau Claire, WI...................1596
Paul Revere House/Paul Revere Memorial Association, Boston, MA........668
Paulson House, Au Train, MI...................726
Pawnee Bill Ranch and Museum, Pawnee, OK...................1212
Pawnee City Historical Society & Museum, Pawnee City, NE...................871
Pea Ridge National Military Park, Garfield, AR...................58
Peabody Essex Museum, Salem, MA...........706
Pearl S. Buck Birthplace Foundation, Hillsboro, WV...................1582
Pebble Hill Plantation, Thomasville, GA....388
Pecos National Historical Park, Pecos, NM...................944
Peel Mansion Museum & Historic Gardens, Bentonville, AR...................55
Pejepscot Historical Society, Brunswick, ME...................608
Pember Museum of Natural History, Granville, NY...................995
Pembroke Historical Society, Inc., Pembroke, MA...................701
The Pena-Peck House, Saint Augustine, FL...................339
Pendarvis State Historic Site, Mineral Point, WI...................1614
Pendleton Historic Foundation, Pendleton, SC...................1339
Pennsbury Manor, Morrisville, PA.............1272
Pennsylvania Historical & Museum Commission, Harrisburg, PA...................1259
Pennsylvania Trolley Museum, Washington, PA...................1305
Pennypacker Mills, Schwenksville, PA......1297
Pennyroyal Area Museum, Hopkinsville, KY...................572
Penobscot Marine Museum, Searsport, ME...................622
Peoria Historical Society, Peoria, IL...........451
Peralta Adobe, San Jose, CA...................172
Perry's Victory & International Peace Memorial, Put-in-Bay, OH...................1183
Peter Conser House, Heavener, OK...........1202
Peter J. McGovern Little League Museum, South Williamsport, PA..........1301
Peter Rice Homestead, Home of Marlborough Historical Society, Inc., Marlboro, MA...................693
Peter Wentz Farmstead, Worcester, PA.......1308
Peter Whitmer Sr. Home and Visitors Center, Waterloo, NY...................1083
Peterborough Historical Society, Peterborough, NH...................893

Petersburg National Battlefield, Petersburg, VA...................1525
Peterson Air & Space Museum, Peterson Air Force Base, CO...................229
Petrified Forest National Park, Petrified Forest National Park, AZ...................38
Pettaquamscutt Historical Society, Kingston, RI...................1312
Pewabic Pottery, Detroit, MI...................737
Phelps House, Burlington, IA...................507
The Philadelphia Art Alliance, Philadelphia, PA...................1285
Philadelphia Society for the Preservation of Landmarks, Philadelphia, PA...........1286
The Philadelphia Zoo, Philadelphia, PA.....1286
Philipse Manor Hall State Historic Site, Yonkers, NY...................1087
Philmont Museums, Cimarron, NM.............938
Phipps Conservatory and Botanical Gardens, Pittsburgh, PA...................1293
Phoenix Museum of History, Phoenix, AZ...................41
Piatt Castles, West Liberty, OH...................1190
Piccadilly Museum of Transportation Memorabilia and Advertising Art, Butte, MT...................843
The Pierce Manse/New Hampshire Political Library, Concord, NH...................885
The Pierpont Morgan Library, New York, NY...................1037
Pierre Menard Home State Historic Site, Ellis Grove, IL...................433
Pike County Historical Society, Milford, PA...................1272
Pilgrim Hall Museum, Plymouth, MA.........703
Pilgrim Monument and Provincetown Museum, Provincetown, MA...................704
Pimeria Alta Historical Society, Nogales, AZ...................37
Pine Creek Grist Mill, Muscatine, IA.........525
Pine Lodge (Ehrman Mansion), Tahoma, CA...................190
Pink Palace Family of Museums, Memphis, TN...................1375
Pioneer Air Museum, Fairbanks, AK.............24
Pioneer Arizona Living History Village & Museum, Phoenix, AZ...................41
Pioneer Auto Museum, Murdo, SD...........1352
Pioneer Farm Museum and Ohop Indian Village, Eatonville, WA...................1552
Pioneer Florida Museum Association, Inc., Dade City, FL...................302
Pioneer Heritage Center, LSU-Shreveport, Shreveport, LA...................601
Pioneer Museum, Wild Rose, WI.............1628
Pioneer Museum and Vereins Kirche, Fredericksburg, TX...................1419
Pioneer Museum of Alabama, Troy, AL.........18
Pioneer Settlement for the Creative Arts, Barberville, FL...................295
Pioneer Town, Wimberley, TX...................1462
Pioneer Village, Farmington, UT...............1465
Pioneer Village & Virgil Grissom Memorial at Spring Mill State Park, Mitchell, IN...................491
Piqua Historical Area State Memorial, Piqua, OH...................1182
Pitot House Museum, New Orleans, LA.....598
Pittock Mansion, Portland, OR...................1232
Plantation Historical Museum, Plantation, FL...................337
Planting Fields Arboretum State Historic Park, Oyster Bay, NY...................1049
Platteville Mining Museum, Platteville, WI...................1617
Plimoth Plantation Inc., Plymouth, MA.......703
Plum Grove Historic Home, Iowa City, IA...................520
Plumas County Museum, Quincy, CA..........144
Plumb Farm Learning Center, Greeley, CO...................222

Structures—Continued

Plymouth Antiquarian Society, Plymouth, MA..704
Plymouth Historical Museum, Plymouth, MI...760
Pocahontas County Iowa Historical Society Museum, Laurens, IA............522
Pocahontas County Museum, Marlinton, WV..1584
Point Arena Lighthouse and Museum, Point Arena, CA...............................142
Point Fermin Lighthouse, San Pedro, CA....176
Point of Honor, Lynchburg, VA.................1515
Point Reyes National Seashore, Point Reyes, CA..143
Pointe Coupee Museum, New Roads, LA...599
Polish Heritage Center, Ashton, NE.............856
Polk County Historical Society, Crookston, MN..771
Polk County Museum, Balsam Lake, WI...1590
Pomeroy Living History Farm, Yacolt, WA...1578
Ponce DeLeon Inlet Lighthouse Preservation Association, Inc., Ponce Inlet, FL...337
Pony Express Museum, Saint Joseph, MO...831
Pope County Historical Society, Glenwood, MN.......................................776
Pope's Tavern Museum, Florence, AL.............9
Poplar Grove Historic Plantation, Wilmington, NC....................................1123
Poricy Park Nature Center, Middletown, NJ...911
Port Discovery, The Children's Museum in Baltimore, Baltimore, MD.................636
Port Gamble Historic Museum, Port Gamble, WA..1562
Port Huron Museum, Port Huron, MI.........761
Portage County Historical Society, Ravenna, OH.......................................1183
Portage County Historical Society, Stevens Point, WI.................................1623
The Portal of the Folded Wings Shrine to Aviation and Museum, North Hollywood, CA..131
Porter-Phelps-Huntington Foundation, Inc., Hadley, MA.....................................685
Portland Museum of Art, Portland, ME.......619
Portsmouth Historical Association, Portsmouth, VA.....................................1526
Portsmouth Museums, Portsmouth, VA......1526
Postville Courthouse State Historic Site, Lincoln, IL...442
Potts Inn Museum, Pottsville, AR.................66
Pottsgrove Manor, Pottstown, PA..............1295
Prairie Grove Battlefield State Park, Prairie Grove, AR..66
Prairie Homestead, Philip, SD..................1353
Prairie Village, Madison, SD....................1351
Praters Mill Foundation, Varnell, GA...........390
Pratt County Historical Society Museum, Pratt, KS...556
Preservation Resource Center, New Orleans, LA..598
The Preservation Society of Newport County/The Newport Mansions, Newport, RI..1315
President Andrew Johnson Museum and Library, Greeneville, TN........................1366
President Chester A. Arthur Historic Site, Fairfield, VT..1479
Presidio La Bahia, Goliad, TX.................1423
Presque Isle County Historical Museum, Rogers City, MI..762
Price Tower Arts Center, Bartlesville, OK.1197
Pricketts Fort, Fairmont, WV....................1581
Prince William Forest Park Visitor Center, Triangle, VA................................1541
Promont House Museum, Milford, OH......1176

Proprietary House, The Royal Governor's Mansion, Perth Amboy, NJ.......................921
Providence Preservation Society, Providence, RI...1318
Prudence Crandall Museum, Canterbury, CT..237
Pueblo Weisbrod Aircraft Museum, Pueblo, CO..230
Pueblo Zoo, Pueblo, CO.............................230
Puget Sound Coast Artillery Museum at Fort Worden, Port Townsend, WA.........1562
Putnam Cottage, Greenwich, CT.................243
Putnam County Historical Society & Foundry School Museum, Cold Spring, NY..979
Putnam County Historical Society Museum, Kalida, OH...............................1169
Queen Mary Museum, Long Beach, CA......111
Queens County Farm Museum, Floral Park, NY...989
Queens Historical Society, Flushing, NY.....990
Queens Museum of Art, Queens, NY.........1056
The Quincy Museum, Quincy, IL.................452
Quoddy Head State Park, Lubec, ME..........614
Quoddy Maritime Museum, Eastport, ME...610
R.E. Olds Transportation Museum, Lansing, MI...751
R.P. Strathearn Historical Park and Museum, Simi Valley, CA.......................187
RV/MH Heritage Foundation, Inc., Elkhart, IN..475
Rachel Carson Homestead, Springdale, PA...1301
Rahr West Art Museum, Manitowoc, WI...1607
Railroad and Heritage Museum Inc., Temple, TX...1454
Railroad Museum of Long Island, Riverhead, NY...1057
Railroaders Memorial Museum, Altoona, PA...1240
Ralph Waldo Emerson House, Concord, MA...677
Ramapogue Historical Society, West Springfield, MA...718
Ramsay House Visitors Center, Alexandria, VA...1494
Ramsey House Museum Plantation, Knoxville, TN...1371
Rancho La Patera - The Stow House G.V.H.S., Goleta, CA..............................100
Rancho Los Alamitos, Long Beach, CA......111
Rancho Los Cerritos Historic Site, Long Beach, CA...111
Randolph County Historical Museum, Winchester, IN...503
Randolph County Museum (At Beverly), Beverly, WV...1580
Rankin House State Memorial, Ripley, OH...1184
Rankin Museum, Rankin, TX....................1445
Ransom County Historical Society, Fort Ransom, ND...1131
Raynham Hall Museum, Oyster Bay, NY..1049
Reading Railroad Heritage Museum, Reading, PA..1296
Rebecca Nurse Homestead, Danvers, MA...678
Rebel State Historic Site & Louisiana Country Music Museum, Marthaville, LA..592
Red Butte Garden & Arboretum, Salt Lake City, UT..1472
Red Hill-Patrick Henry National Memorial, Brookneal, VA......................1498
Redington Museum, Waterville, ME............625
Redwood Library and Athenaeum, Newport, RI...1315
Reed Gold Mine State Historic Site, Midland, NC...1111
Reedville Fishermen's Museum, Reedville, VA...1527
Reeves-Reed Arboretum, Summit, NJ..........925

Rehoboth Art League, Inc., Rehoboth Beach, DE..272
Reitz Home Museum, Evansville, IN..........476
Remick Country Doctor Museum and Farm, Tamworth, NH..............................896
Renfrew Museum & Park, Waynesboro, PA...1306
Rensselaer County Historical Society, Troy, NY...1079
Rensselaer Russell House Museum, Waterloo, IA..529
Renton Historical Society and Museum, Renton, WA...1564
Renville County Historical Society, Inc., Mohall, ND..1135
Republic County Historical Society Museum, Belleville, KS.............................534
Reuben H. Fleet Science Center, San Diego, CA...158
Reverend Dan Foster House, Museum of the Weathersfield Historical Society, Weathersfield, VT....................................1489
Reynolda House Museum of American Art, Winston-Salem, NC..........................1126
Reynolds Homestead, Critz, VA................1502
Rhinelander Logging Museum, Rhinelander, WI......................................1620
Rhode Island Historical Society, Providence, RI...1318
Rice County Museum of History, Faribault, MN..775
The Rice Museum, Georgetown, SC..........1333
Richard Salter Storrs House, Longmeadow, MA......................................691
Richards DAR House Museum, Mobile, AL..15
Richey Historical Society, Richey, MT........852
Richland County Historical Museum, Wahpeton, ND...1137
Richland County Museum, Lexington, OH...1172
Richmond National Battlefield Park, Richmond, VA...1531
Riddick's Folly, Suffolk, VA....................1539
The Ridges Sanctuary, Inc., Baileys Harbor, WI..1590
Riley County Historical Museum, Manhattan, KS...551
Riley House Museum of African American History & Culture, Tallahassee, FL...348
Rim Country Museum, Payson, AZ...............38
Rio Grande Valley Museum, Harlingen, TX..1423
Riordan Mansion State Historic Park, Flagstaff, AZ...33
Ripley County, Indiana, Historical Society Museum, Versailles, IN..............502
Rising Sun Tavern, Fredericksburg, VA.....1507
Rittman Historical Society, Rittman, OH...1184
Ritz Theatre & LaVilla Museum, Jacksonville, FL..315
River Museum, Wellsville, OH..................1190
Riverbanks Zoological Park & Botanical Garden, Columbia, SC.............................1329
Riverbend Environmental Education Center, Gladwyne, PA..............................1256
Riversdale House Mansion, Riverdale Park, MD...651
Riverside Metropolitan Museum, Riverside, CA..150
Riverside Museum, La Crosse, WI............1603
Riverside Nature Center, Kerrville, TX......1432
Riverside, The Farnsley-Moremen Landing, Louisville, KY..............................579
Riverview at Hobson Grove, Bowling Green, KY..566
Robbins Hunter Museum, Avery-Downer House, Granville, OH.............................1167
Robert Frost Farm, Derry, NH....................886
Robert Louis Stevenson House, Monterey, CA..128

Structures—Continued

Sautee-Nacoochee Center, Sautee, GA.........384

Sayville Historical Society, Sayville, NY....1066

Scantic Academy Museum, East Windsor Historical Society, Inc., East Windsor, CT...239

The Scarsdale Historical Society, Scarsdale, NY.....................................1066

Schenectady County Historical Society, Schenectady, NY...................................1067

Schifferstadt Architectural Museum, Frederick, MD.....................................644

Schmidt House Museum & Research Library, Grants Pass, OR......................1225

Schminck Memorial Museum, Lakeview, OR...1227

Schoenbrunn Village State Memorial, New Philadelphia, OH.........................1177

Schoharie Colonial Heritage Association, Schoharie, NY.......................................1067

Schoharie Crossing State Historic Site, Fort Hunter, NY...................................991

Scholte House Museum, Pella, IA.................527

School of American Research, Indian Arts Research Center, Santa Fe, NM......950

Schoolcraft County Historical Society, Manistique, MI.......................................753

The Schuette Biermann Farmhouse Museum, Elk Grove Village, IL..........432

Schuyler-Hamilton House, Morristown, NJ...914

Schuyler Jail Museum, Rushville, IL..........456

Schuyler Mansion State Historic Site, Albany, NY...955

Scituate Historical Society, Scituate, MA....708

Scotland Heritage Chapel & Museum, Scotland, SD..1355

Seagraves-Loop Museum and Art Center Inc., Seagraves, TX...............................1452

The Seay House, Spartanburg, SC............1341

Sedgwick-Brooklin Historical Society, Sedgwick, ME.......................................622

Seguine-Burke Plantation, Staten Island, NY...1073

Seminole Nation Museum, Wewoka, OK...1217

Senate House State Historic Site, Kingston, NY......................................1008

Senator George Baldwin Hotel, Klamath Falls, OR...1227

Seneca Falls Historical Society, Seneca Falls, NY..1069

Seneca-Iroquois National Museum, Salamanca, NY.......................................1063

Seneca Schoolhouse Museum, Poolesville, MD......................................650

Sequoyah Cabin, Sallisaw, OK...................1213

Serra Museum/San Diego Historical Society, San Diego, CA...........................161

1719 Hans Herr House & Museum, Willow Street, PA....................................1308

The 1719 William Trent House Museum, Trenton, NJ.......................................928

1797 Ezekiel Harris House, Augusta, GA....366

1768 Jeremiah Lee Mansion, Marblehead, MA...693

1761 Pownalborough Courthouse, Dresden, ME...610

The Sevier County Historical Museum, De Queen, AR...56

Sewall-Belmont House and Museum, Washington, DC.....................................290

Seward County Historical Society Museum, Goehner, NE..........................861

Seward House, Auburn, NY.........................959

Seymour Community Museum, Seymour, WI...1621

The Shadows-on-the-Teche, New Iberia, LA...593

Shafer Historical Museum, Winthrop, WA.1578

Shaftsbury Historical Society, Shaftsbury, VT...1487

Shaker Heritage Society, Albany, NY.........956

Shaker Museum, New Gloucester, ME.........615

Shaker Museum at South Union, South Union, KY..583

Shaker Village of Pleasant Hill, Harrodsburg, KY...................................571

Shakespeare Ghost Town, Lordsburg, NM...942

Shandy Hall, Geneva, OH.........................1166

Sharlot Hall Museum, Prescott, AZ..............43

Sharpsteen Museum, Calistoga, CA..............80

Shasta State Historic Park, Shasta, CA.........186

Shaw Island Library & Historical Society, Shaw Island, WA...................................1570

Shawano County Historical Society, Inc., Shawano, WI.......................................1621

Shawnee Town, Shawnee, KS......................558

Sheboygan County Historical Museum, Sheboygan, WI.......................................1621

Shelburne Museum, Inc., Shelburne, VT...1487

Shelter Island Historical Society, Shelter Island, NY..1069

Shemer Art Center & Museum, Phoenix, AZ...42

Shenandoal Valley Discovery Museum, Winchester, VA.......................................1546

Sherburne History Center, Becker, MN........768

Sherwood-Davidson House, Newark, OH..1178

Sherwood Forest Plantation, Charles City, VA...1498

Shiloh Museum of Ozark History, Springdale, AR..68

Shippensburg Historical Society Museum, Shippensburg, PA....................................1300

Ships of the Sea Maritime Museum/William Scarbrough House, Savannah, GA...386

Shirley-Eustis House, Boston, MA..............669

Shirley Plantation, Charles City, VA..........1498

Shoal Creek Living History Museum, Kansas City, MO.....................................822

Shoreline Historical Museum, Seattle, WA...1569

Shoshone Tribal Cultural Center, Fort Washakie, WY.......................................1633

Sibley County Historical Museum, Henderson, MN......................................777

Sibley House Historic Site, Mendota, MN...780

Siege Museum (The Petersburg Museums), Petersburg, VA.......................1525

Silent Wings Museum, Lubbock, TX.........1435

Silt Historical Society, Silt, CO..................232

Silver City Museum, Silver City, NM.........951

Simonian Farms, Fresno, CA........................98

Simsbury Historical Society, Phelps Tavern, Museum & Homestead, Simsbury, CT...260

Sinclair Lewis House Museum & Interpretive Center/Museum, Sauk Centre, MN...793

Siouxland Heritage Museums, Sioux Falls, SD..1357

Siskiyou County Museum, Yreka, CA.........200

Sitka National Historical Park, Sitka, AK......28

The Sixth Floor Museum at Dealey Plaza, Dallas, TX...................................1407

Skagit County Historical Museum, La Conner, WA...1557

Skagway Museum & Archives, Skagway, AK...28

Skowhegan History House Inc., Skowhegan, ME......................................622

Sky City Cultural Center, Pueblo of Acoma, NM...944

The Skyscraper Museum, New York, NY...1038

Slate Run Living Historical Farm, Metro Parks, Ashville, OH...............................1140

Slate Valley Museum, Granville, NY.........996

Slater Mill Historic Site, Pawtucket, RI....1315

Slaughter Ranch Museum, Douglas, AZ........32

Sleeping Bear Dunes National Lakeshore, Empire, MI...741

Sleepy Eye Depot Museum, Sleepy Eye, MN...793

Slidell Museum, Slidell, LA........................602

Slifer House, Lewisburg, PA......................1268

Smallwood State Park, Marbury, MD...........649

Smith County Historical Society, Tyler, TX...1456

Smith-McDowell House Museum, Asheville, NC.......................................1090

Smith Robertson Museum & Cultural Center, Jackson, MS.................................804

Smith's Fort Plantation, Surry, VA............1540

Smithtown Historical Society, Smithtown, NY...1070

Smoki Museum - American Indian Art & Culture, Prescott, AZ................................43

Snake River Heritage Center, Weiser, ID.....410

Snug Harbor Cultural Center - Visitors' Center and Newhouse Center for Contemporary Art, Staten Island, NY...1073

Society for the Preservation of Long Island Antiquities, Cold Spring Harbor, NY...980

The Society of the Cincinnati at Anderson House, Washington, DC..........291

Sod House Museum, Gothenburg, NE.........862

Sod House Museum, Aline, OK.................1195

Soldiers National Museum, Gettysburg, PA...1256

Somers Historical Society, Somers, NY.....1070

Somers Mansion, Somers Point, NJ.............924

The Somerset County Historical Society, Inc., Princess Anne, MD...........................650

Somerset Historical Center, Somerset, PA .1300

Somerset Place State Historic Site, Creswell, NC...1097

Sonnenberg Gardens & Mansion State Historic Park, Canandaigua, NY.............975

Sonoma State Historic Park, Sonoma, CA...188

Sosa-Carrillo-Fremont House Museum, Tucson, AZ...50

Sotterley Plantation, Hollywood, MD.........647

South Bannock County Historical Center, Lava Hot Springs, ID...............................407

The South Carolina Botanical Garden, Clemson, SC...1328

The South Carolina Railroad Museum, Winnsboro, SC.......................................1343

South Coast Railroad Museum at Goleta Depot, Goleta, CA...................................100

South Holland Historical Society, South Holland, IL...457

South Park City Museum, Fairplay, CO.......215

South Pass City State Historic Site, South Pass City, WY.......................................1638

South Street Seaport Museum, New York, NY...1039

South Sutton Old Store Museum, South Sutton, NH...896

South Wood County Historical Corp., Wisconsin Rapids, WI............................1628

Southdown Plantation House/The Terrebonne Museum, Houma, LA..........589

Southeastern Railway Museum, Duluth, GA...371

Southern California Chapter Railway & Locomotive Historical Society, Pomona, CA...143

Southern Forest Heritage Museum, Long Leaf, LA..591

Southern Forest World, Waycross, GA........391

The Southern Museum of Civil War and Locomotive History, Kennesaw, GA.......375

Southern Plains Indian Museum, Anadarko, OK.......................................1196

Southwest Florida Museum of History, Fort Myers, FL.......................................309

Southwest School of Art & Craft, San Antonio, TX...1450

Spirit of '76 Museum, Wellington, OH......1190

Split Rock Lighthouse Historic Site, Two Harbors, MN.......................................795

Spring Street Historical Museum, Shreveport, LA.......................................602

Structures—Continued

Tippecanoe Battlefield, Battle Ground, IN ...468

Tipton-Haynes Historic Site, Johnson City, TN 1368

Titan Missile Museum, Green Valley, AZ......36

Tobacco Farm Life Museum, Inc., Kenly, NC 1107

Tohono Chul Park Inc., Tucson, AZ...............51

The Toledo Zoo, Toledo, OH.......................1187

Tolland Historical Society - Tolland County Jail and Warden's Home Museum, Tolland, CT.............................262

Tomball Community Museum Center, Tomball, TX...1455

Tombstone Courthouse State Historic Park, Tombstone, AZ...............................46

Topsfield Historical Society, Topsfield, MA 714

Torreya State Park, Bristol, FL.....................298

Torrington Historical Society, Inc., Torrington, CT...263

Town Creek Indian Mound State Historic Site, Mount Gilead, NC........................1111

Town of Manlius Historical Society with Museum, Manlius, NY..........................1013

Traill County Historical Society, Hillsboro, ND..1132

Trails & Rails Museum, Kearney, NE...........864

Transylvania Museum, Lexington, KY..........574

Travel Town Museum, Los Angeles, CA 121

Traveler's Rest State Historic Site, Toccoa, GA..389

Travellers Rest Plantation & Museum, Nashville, TN...1381

Tread of Pioneers Museum, Steamboat Springs, CO..232

Trenton Historical Museum, Trenton, MI.....765

Troutdale Historical Society, Troutdale, OR...1237

Troy Museum & Historic Village, Troy, MI...765

Trust for the Preservation of Maine Industrial History and Technology d/b/a Maine Narrow Gauge Railroad Co. & Museum, Portland, ME.................620

The Trustees of Reservations, Beverly, MA 662

Tryon Palace Historic Sites and Gardens, New Bern, NC...1112

Tsa Mo Ga Memorial Museum, Plains, TX...1443

Tu-Endie-Wei State Park, Point Pleasant, WV...1586

Tubac Presidio State Historic Park, Tubac, AZ...47

Tuck Museum, Hampton, NH.......................888

Tucker Tower Nature Center, Ardmore, OK...1196

Tuckerton Seaport, Tuckerton, NJ 928

Tucson Museum of Art & Historic Block, Tucson, AZ...51

Tucumcari Historical Research Institute, Tucumcari, NM..953

Tudor Place Foundation, Inc., Washington, DC..292

Tulare County Museum at Mooney Grove Park, Visalia, CA......................................195

Turtle Mountain Chippewa Historical Society, Belcourt, ND............................1127

Tuskegee Institute National Historic Site, Tuskegee Institute, AL...............................21

Tuzigoot National Monument, Clarkdale, AZ...31

Tybee Island Light Station and Tybee Museum, Tybee Island, GA 389

Tyler Arboretum, Media, PA.......................1271

USDA Forest Service - Land Between the Lakes, Golden Pond, KY..................570

U.S National Arboretum, Washington, DC...292

Ulysses S. Grant Cottage State Historic Site, Wilton, NY.......................................1086

Umlauf Sculpture Garden & Museum, Austin, TX..1392

Umpqua Discovery Center, Reedsport, OR...1234

Uncle Remus Museum, Eatonton, GA 371

Union Covered Bridge State Historic Site, Paris, MO...828

Union Mills Homestead & Grist Mill, Westminster, MD......................................656

Union Pacific Historical Society (UPHS), Laramie, WY...1635

United States Botanic Garden, Washington, DC..292

United States Hockey Hall of Fame, Eveleth, MN..774

United States Naval Shipbuilding Museum, Quincy, MA...............................705

United States Senate Commission on Art, Washington, DC..293

University of Northern Iowa Museums & Collections, Cedar Falls, IA.................508

University of Washington Botanic Garden, Seattle, WA.................................1569

University of Wisconsin-Madison Arboretum, Madison, WI.......................1605

Upham Mansion, Marshfield, WI 1608

Uppertown Firefighters Museum, Astoria, OR...1219

U.S. Army Center of Military History, Museum Division, Fort McNair, DC.......275

U.S. Army Engineer Museum, Fort Leonard Wood, MO.................................815

U.S. Army Museum of Hawaii, Fort DeRussy, HI...392

U.S. Cavalry Museum, Fort Riley, KS.....540

U.S. Grant's Home State Historic Site, Galena, IL..436

USS Alabama Battleship Memorial Park, Mobile, AL...15

USS Bowfin Submarine Museum & Park, Honolulu, HI..398

USS Constellation Museum, Baltimore, MD...636

USS Lexington Museum on the Bay, Corpus Christi, TX..................................1402

UTSA's Institute of Texan Cultures, San Antonio, TX..1451

Vachel Lindsay Home State Historic Site, Springfield, IL..460

Vaile Mansion-Dewitt Museum, Independence, MO....................................819

Valentine Richmond History Center, Richmond, VA..1532

Valentine-Varian House/Museum of Bronx History, Bronx, NY......................967

Vallejo Naval & Historical Museum, Vallejo, CA..194

Valley County Pioneer Museum, Glasgow, MT..847

Valley Forge National Historical Park, King of Prussia, PA................................1264

Van Cortlandt House Museum, Bronx, NY...967

Van Meter State Park, Miami, MO..............827

Van Wyck Homestead Museum, Fishkill, NY...989

Vandalia Statehouse State Historic Site, Vandalia, IL..462

Vanderbilt Mansion National Historic Site, Hyde Park, NY....................................1002

Vann House, Chatsworth, GA......................368

Varner-Hogg Plantation State Historic Site, West Columbia, TX.....................1461

Venango Museum of Art, Science & Industry, Oil City, PA................................1274

Verde Historical Society, Clemenceau Heritage Museum, Cottonwood, AZ..........32

The Verdier House, Beaufort, SC 1321

Vermilion County Museum Society, Danville, IL...429

The Vermont State House, Montpelier, VT...1483

Vernon County Historical Museum, Viroqua, WI...1625

The Vestal Museum, Vestal, NY.................1081

Vesterheim Norwegian-American Museum, Decorah, IA..............................513

Veterans Memorial Museum, Laurel, MS 804

Victor Heritage Museum, Victor, MT...........854

Victoria Mansion, Portland, ME..................620

The Victorian Society in America, Philadelphia, PA.....................................1289

Vikingsholm, Tahoma, CA..........................191

Villa Louis Historic Site, Prairie du Chien, WI...1619

Villa Montezuma Museum/San Diego Historical Society, San Diego, CA..........162

Village Historical Society, Inc., Harrison, OH...1168

Vincennes State Historic Site, Indiana Territory, Vincennes, IN.........................503

Vincennes State Historic Site, Old State Bank, Vincennes, IN..................................503

Vintage Flying Museum, Fort Worth, TX ..1419

Virgin Islands National Park, St. John, VI.1644

Virginia Beach Maritime Museum, Inc./The Old Coast Guard Station, Virginia Beach, VA...................................1543

Virginia City J. Spencer Watkins Memorial Museum, Virginia City, MT....854

The Virginia Discovery Museum, Charlottesville, VA..................................1500

Virginia Historical Society, Richmond, VA...1533

Virginia War Memorial, Richmond, VA 1534

Visual Arts Center of Northwest Florida, Panama City, FL.......................................334

Vizcaya Museum and Gardens, Miami, FL..326

Volcano Art Center, Volcano, HI 402

Volunteer Firemen's Mall and Museum of Kingston, Kingston, NY.........................1008

W.C. Handy Home Museum and Library, Florence, AL...9

The W.H. Stark House, Orange, TX...........1442

W.W. Seymour Botanical Conservatory, Tacoma, WA...1574

Wabasha County Museum, Wabasha County Historical Society at Reads Landing, Reads Landing, MN...................787

Wade House Stagecoach Inn & Wesley Jung Carriage Museum State Historic Site, Greenbush, WI..................................1599

Wadsworth Atheneum Museum of Art, Hartford, CT..246

Wagner Free Institute of Science, Philadelphia, PA.....................................1289

Wake Forest College Birthplace Society, Inc., Wake Forest, NC............................1121

Wakefield House Museum, Blue Earth, MN...769

Walkersville, Southern Railroad Museum, Walkersville, MD......................................656

Walney Visitor Center-At Ellanor C. Lawrence Park, Chantilly, VA................1498

Walnut Grove Plantation, Roebuck, SC 1340

Walt Whitman Birthplace State Historic Site and Interpretive Center, Huntington Station, NY...........................1001

Walt Whitman House Museum and Library, Camden, NJ.................................900

Walter F. George Law Office Museum, Vienna, GA..390

Walter P. Chrysler Boyhood Home and Museum, Ellis, KS.....................................538

Wantagh Historical & Preservation Society, Wantagh, NY.............................1081

War in the Pacific National Historical Park, Piti, GU..1640

Ward County Historical Society, Minot, ND...1135

Structures—Continued

Woodside Store Historic Site, Woodside, CA 199

Woodson County Historical Society, Yates Center, KS..........................564

Woodstock Historical Society, Inc., Woodstock, VT..........................1491

Woodstock Museum of Shenandoah County, Inc., Woodstock, VA.................1546

Woodville Museum, Inc., Rogue River, OR 1234

Worcester County Horticultural Society/Tower Hill Botanic Garden, Boylston, MA 670

Worcester Historical Museum, Worcester, MA 721

Workman & Temple Family Homestead Museum, City of Industry, CA 85

World Golf Hall of Fame, Saint Augustine, FL 340

World Museum of Mining, Butte, MT 843

Wormsloe State Historic Site, Savannah, GA 387

Worthington Historical Society, Worthington, OH 1192

Wrather West Kentucky Museum, Murray, KY 580

Wren's Nest, Atlanta, GA 364

Wright County Historical Society, Buffalo, MN.................................770

Wright's Ferry Mansion, Columbia, PA 1248

Wupatki National Monument, Flagstaff, AZ 34

Wyalusing Valley Museum, Wyalusing, PA..1309

Wyandot County Historical Society, Upper Sandusky, OH 1188

Wyandotte Museum, Wyandotte, MI 766

Wyatt Earp Birthplace Home, Monmouth, IL 445

Wyck, Philadelphia, PA........................1289

The Wyckoff Farmhouse Museum, Brooklyn, NY 970

Wylie House Museum, Bloomington, IN 470

The Wyman Tavern, Keene, NH.................890

Wyoming Frontier Prison Museum, Rawlings, WY 1637

Wyoming Pioneer Memorial Museum, Douglas, WY 1632

Wyoming Territorial Prison State Historic Site, Laramie, WY.........................1636

Yakima Valley Museum and Historical Association, Yakima, WA.................1579

Yankee Air Force, Inc. (Yankee Air Museum), Ypsilanti, MI 766

Yates County Genealogical and Historical Society and Oliver House Museum and L. Caroline Underwood Museum, Penn Yan, NY 1052

Yesteryear House-Central Mine, Clarkston, MI 732

Yesteryear Village, West Palm Beach, FL....354

Yolo County Historical Museum, Woodland, CA 199

Yorba and Slaughter Families Adobe, Chino, CA 84

York County Heritage Trust, Fire Museum, York, PA 1309

Yorktown Historical Museum, Yorktown, TX 1462

Youth Museum of Southern West Virginia, Beckley, WV 1579

Yucaipa Adobe, Yucaipa, CA..................200

Yucaipa Valley Historical Society Museum, Yucaipa, CA.......................201

Yuma Crossing State Historic Park, Yuma, AZ 54

Yuma Territorial Prison State Historic Park, Yuma, AZ 54

Z. Taylor Brown-Sarah Dorsey House, Midland, TX 1439

Zalud House, Porterville, CA..................144

Zebulon B. Vance Birthplace State Historic Site, Weaverville, NC..............1122

Zelienople Historical Society, Zelienople, PA..1309

Zoar State Memorial, Zoar, OH.................1194

Zoo New England, Boston, MA 669

Tools and Equipment for Communication

A.R. Bowman Memorial Museum, Prineville, OR 1234

A.W.A. Electronic-Communication Museum, Bloomfield, NY 963

Ace of Clubs House, Texarkana, TX..........1455

Adair County Historical Society, Inc., Kirksville, MO 824

Adams County Historical Museum, Decatur, IN 474

Adams Old Stone Grist Mill, Bellows Falls, VT 1476

Adams State College Luther Bean Museum, Alamosa, CO 201

Adan E. Treganza Anthropology Museum, Dept. of Anthropology, San Francisco State University, San Francisco, CA 162

Admiral Nimitz National Museum of the Pacific War, Fredericksburg, TX............1419

Adventure Science Center, Nashville, TN..1377

African-American Museum and Library at Oakland, Oakland, CA 132

Afro-American Historical Society Museum, Jersey City, NJ 908

Agricultural and Industrial Museum, York County Heritage Trust, York, PA 1309

Agrirama, Georgia's Living History Museum & Village, Tifton, GA 388

Aiken County Historical Museum, Aiken, SC 1320

The Airborne & Special Operations Museum, Fayetteville, NC...................1100

Airline History Museum, Kansas City, MO 820

Airmen Memorial Museum, Suitland, MD 655

Airpower Museum Inc., Ottumwa, IA..........526

Alabama Museum of the Health Sciences, Birmingham, AL 4

Alamance Battleground State Historic Site, Burlington, NC..........................1092

Alaska Native Heritage Center, Anchorage, AK 22

Albany Civil Rights Movement Museum at Old Mt. Zion Church, Albany, GA......355

Albany Historical Society, Inc., Sabetha, KS 557

Albany Regional Museum, Albany, OR 1217

The Albin O. Kuhn Library & Gallery, University of Maryland-Baltimore County, Baltimore, MD 628

Albuquerque Museum, Albuquerque, NM....932

Alexander & Baldwin Sugar Museum, Puunene, HI 401

Alexandre Mouton House/Lafayette Museum, Lafayette, LA 589

Alice Austen House Museum, Staten Island, NY 1072

Aliceville Museum, Aliceville, AL....................3

Allegany County Historical Society, Inc., Cumberland, MD 641

Allegheny Portage Railroad National Historic Site and Johnstown Flood National Memorial, Gallitzin, PA 1255

Allen County Museum, Lima, OH 1172

Alling Coverlet Museum, Palmyra, NY 1050

Alton Museum of History and Art, Inc., Alton, IL 410

Amana Heritage Museum, Amana, IA 504

Amelia Island Museum of History, Fernandina Beach, FL 306

American Computer Museum, Bozeman, MT...842

The American Jazz Museum, Kansas City, MO 820

American Labor Museum, Botto House National Landmark, Haledon, NJ 906

American Merchant Marine Museum, Kings Point, NY 1007

American Museum of Asmat Art, Saint Paul, MN 789

American Museum of Radio and Electricity, Bellingham, WA 1548

American Numismatic Association Money Museum, Colorado Springs, CO 206

The American Numismatic Society, New York, NY 1020

American Precision Museum Association, Inc., Windsor, VT 1490

American Printing House for the Blind, Callahan Museum, Louisville, KY 575

American Radio Relay League-Museum of Amateur Radio, Newington, CT.........256

American Visionary Art Museum, Baltimore, MD 629

American West Heritage Center, Wellsville, UT 1475

American Wings Air Museum, Blaine, MN 769

America's Black Holocaust Museum, Milwaukee, WI 1610

America's National Music Museum, Vermillion, SD 1358

Amherst County Museum & Historical Society, Amherst, VA 1495

Amherst History Museum at the Strong House - Amherst Historical Society, Amherst, MA 658

Amherst Museum, Amherst, NY 957

Amity and Woodbridge Historical Society, Woodbridge, CT 268

Anaheim Museum, Anaheim, CA.................71

Anderson/Abruzzo Albuquerque International Balloon Museum, Albuquerque, NM.............................933

Anderson County Historical Museum, Garnett, KS 541

Anderson County Museum, Anderson, SC.1321

Andrew Low House, Savannah, GA 384

Anna Miller Museum, Newcastle, WY 1637

Annie E. Woodman Institute Museum, Dover, NH 886

Annie Riggs Memorial Museum, Fort Stockton, TX 1415

Anoka County Historical Society, Anoka, MN 767

Anthropology Museum, University of San Diego, San Diego, CA 155

The Antique Boat Museum, Clayton, NY 978

Antique Gas & Steam Engine Museum, Inc., Vista, CA 196

Apostles Islands National Lakeshore, Bayfield, WI 1591

The Appalachian Trail Conservancy, Harpers Ferry, WV 1581

The Apple Trees Museum, Burlington, IA...506

Appomattox Court House National Historical Park, Appomattox, VA 1495

APVA's John Marshall House, Richmond, VA 1528

Arbor Lodge State Historical Park, Nebraska City, NE.............................868

Arcadia Township Historical Commission, Arcadia, MI 726

Archer County Museum, Archer City, TX .1387

Ardenwood Historic Farm, Fremont, CA.......96

Argo Gold Mine & Mill Museum, Idaho Springs, CO 223

Arizona Historical Society Museum, Tucson, AZ 47

Arizona Historical Society Museum at Papago Park, Tempe, AZ.....................45
Arizona Historical Society Museum - Downtown, Tucson, AZ 47
Arizona Historical Society Pioneer Museum, Flagstaff, AZ.....................32
Arizona Military Museum, Phoenix, AZ.......39
Arkansas Air Museum, Fayetteville, AR.......57
Arkansas Post National Memorial, Gillett, AR.....................58
Arkansas Railroad Museum, Pine Bluff, AR.....................65
Arlington, Birmingham, AL.....................4
Arlington Heights Historical Museum, Arlington Heights, IL.....................411
Armenian Library and Museum of America, Watertown, MA.....................716
The Arms Family Museum of Local History, Youngstown, OH.....................1193
Artesia Historical Museum & Art Center, Artesia, NM.....................936
Ashland Historical Society Museum, Ashland, WI.....................1590
Aspen Historical Society, Aspen, CO...........202
Astor House Museum, Golden, CO..............219
Atchison County Historical Society, Atchison, KS.....................533
Attleboro Area Industrial Museum, Inc., Attleboro, MA.....................661
Atwater Kent Museum of Philadelphia, Philadelphia, PA.....................1276
Atwood House Museum, Home of Chatham Historical Society, Chatham, MA.....................675
Au Glaize Village, Defiance, OH..............1162
Auburn Cord Duesenberg Museum, Auburn, IN.....................468
Audie Murphy/American Cotton Museum, Inc, Greenville, TX.....................1423
Audrain Historical Museum, Graceland, Mexico, MO.....................827
Augusta Museum of History, Augusta, GA.....................364
Aurora Historical Society, Aurora, IL...........411
Aurora Historical Society, Aurora, OH......1140
Aurora History Museum, Aurora, CO..........202
Autry National Center of the American West, Los Angeles, CA.....................112
Aztec Museum and Pioneer Village, Aztec, NM.....................936

B&O Railroad Museum: Ellicott City Station, Ellicott City, MD.....................643
Bagpipe Music Museum, Manchester, NH...891
Baldwin County Heritage Museum, Elberta, AL.....................8
Baldwin Historical Society and Museum, Baldwin, NY.....................960
Baltimore Civil War Museum, Baltimore, MD.....................629
Baltimore County Historical Society, Cockeysville, MD.....................640
Baltimore Maritime Museum, Baltimore, MD.....................630
Baltimore Museum of Industry, Baltimore, MD.....................630
Bandon Historical Society Museum, Bandon, OR.....................1219
Banner County Historical Society, Harrisburg, NE.....................862
Banning Residence Museum, Wilmington, CA.....................198
Bannock County Historical Museum, Pocatello, ID.....................408
Barnes County Historical Museum, Valley City, ND.....................1136
Barnes Museum, Southington, CT..............260
Barratt's Chapel and Museum, Frederica, DE.....................270
Barre Historical Society, Inc., Barre, MA...662
Barrington Living History Farm, Washington, TX.....................1460

Barron County Historical Society's Pioneer Village Museum, Cameron, WI.....................1593
Bartlesville Area History Museum, Bartlesville, OK.....................1196
Barton County Historical Museum & Village, Great Bend, KS.....................542
Bartow History Center, Cartersville, GA.....367
Bartow-Pell Mansion Museum, Carriage House & Gardens, Bronx, NY.....................964
Battle of Lexington State Historic Site, Lexington, MO.....................826
The Battles Museums of Rural Life, Girard, PA.....................1256
Battleship New Jersey Museum & Memorial, Camden, NJ.....................899
Battleship North Carolina, Wilmington, NC.....................1122
Battleship Texas State Historic Site, La Porte, TX.....................1433
Bayou Bend Collection and Gardens, Houston, TX.....................1425
Beauvais Heritage Center, Clark, SD.........1345
Beaver Island Historical Society, Beaver Island, MI.....................728
Beaverhead County Museum, Dillon, MT...845
Beck Cultural Exchange Center, Knoxville, TN.....................1369
Becker County Historical Society, Detroit Lakes, MN.....................772
Bedford City/County Museum, Bedford, VA.....................1496
Bedford Historical Society Museum and Library, Bedford, OH.....................1142
Bedingfield Inn Museum, Lumpkin, GA.....376
Belhaven Memorial Museum, Inc., Belhaven, NC.....................1092
Bell County Museum, Belton, TX.....................1395
Beltrami County History Center, Bemidji, MN.....................768
Bement-Billings Farmstead, Newark Valley, NY.....................1041
Benicia Historical Museum, Benicia, CA......74
The Bennington Museum, Bennington, VT.....................1476
Benton County Historical Museum, Prosser, WA.....................1563
Bent's Old Fort National Historic Site, La Junta, CO.....................224
Benzie Area Historical Museum, Benzonia, MI.....................729
Berkeley County Museum & Heritage Center, Moncks Corner, SC.....................1336
Berkshire Museum, Pittsfield, MA.....................702
Bernard Historical Society and Museum, Delton, MI.....................734
Berrien County Historical Association, Berrien Springs, MI.....................729
Bessemer Hall of History, Bessemer, AL.........3
Bethel Historical Society Regional History Center, Bethel, ME.....................606
Beyer Home, Oconto County Historical Society Museum, Oconto, WI.....................1616
BG John C.L. Scribner Texas Military Forces Museum, Austin, TX.....................1389
Biblical Arts Center, Dallas, TX.....................1404
Big Timbers Museum, Lamar, CO.....................225
Bigelow House Museum, Olympia, WA....1560
Billy the Kid Museum, Fort Sumner, NM...939
Bily Clock Museum/Antonin Dvorak Exhibit, Spillville, IA.....................528
Birmingham Civil Rights Institute, Birmingham, AL.....................4
Bisbee Mining & Historical Museum, Bisbee, AZ.....................30
Bishop Hill Heritage Museum, Bishop Hill, IL.....................413
Black American West Museum & Heritage Center, Denver, CO.....................209
Black Arts National Diaspora Museum, New Orleans, LA.....................594
Black Hills Mining Museum, Lead, SD.....1350

Black Mountain College Museum & Arts Center, Asheville, NC.....................1089
Black River Historical Society of Lorain, Lorain, OH.....................1172
Blackberry Farm's Pioneer Village, Aurora, IL.....................411
Blackman House Museum, Snohomish, WA.....................1570
Blacksmith Shop Museum, Dover-Foxcroft, ME.....................610
Blithewold Mansion, Gardens & Arboretum, Bristol, RI.....................1310
Bloomfield Academy Museum, Bloomfield, NY.....................963
Blount Mansion, Knoxville, TN.....................1369
Bob Burns Museum & River Valley Museum of Van Buren, Van Buren, AR.....................69
Boca Raton Museum of Art, Boca Raton, FL.....................296
Bodie State Historic Park, Bridgeport, CA.....................79
Bonner County Historical Museum, Sandpoint, ID.....................409
Boone County Historical Center, Boone, IA.....................506
Boone County Historical Museum, Belvidere, IL.....................413
The Boorman House - The Juneau County Historical Society, Mauston, WI.....................1608
Boscobel, Garrison, NY.....................993
Boston Childrens Museum, Boston, MA......664
Boswell Museum of Music, Springfield Center, NY.....................1071
Bottineau County Historical Museum, Bottineau, ND.....................1129
Boulder History Museum, Boulder, CO.......202
Bowie Railroad Station and Huntington Museum, Bowie, MD.....................638
Bradbury Science Museum, Los Alamos, NM.....................942
Bradford County Historical Society, Towanda, PA.....................1303
Bradford Historical Society Inc., Bradford, VT.....................1477
Bradford Ohio Railroad Museum, Bradford, OH.....................1143
Branigan Cultural Center, Las Cruces, NM.....................940
Brazos Valley Museum of Natural History, Bryan, TX.....................1398
Brevard Museum of History & Science, Cocoa, FL.....................300
Brick Store Museum, Kennebunk, ME.........612
Bridger Valley Heritage Museum, Lyman, WY.....................1636
The Brooklyn Historical Society, Brooklyn, NY.....................968
Brooklyn Historical Society, Brooklyn, OH.....................1144
Brown County Historical Society, New Ulm, MN.....................785
Brownville Historical Society Museum, Brownville, NE.....................858
Brucemore, Cedar Rapids, IA.....................509
Brunswick Railroad Museum and C&O Canal Visitors Center, Brunswick, MD...639
Brunswick Town/Fort Anderson State Historic Site, Winnabow, NC.....................1124
Bucks County Civil War Library & Museum, Doylestown, PA.....................1249
Bucyrus Historical Society, Bucyrus, OH..1144
Buechel Memorial Lakota Museum, Saint Francis, SD.....................1355
Buffalo and Erie County Historical Society, Buffalo, NY.....................972
Buffalo Gap Historic Village, Buffalo Gap, TX.....................1398
Buffalo Trails Museum, Epping, ND..........1130
Bureau County Historical Society Museum, Princeton, IL.....................452

Tools and Equipment for
Communication–Continued

The Burgwin-Wright Museum,
  Wilmington, NC.................................1123
Burlington Historical Museum,
  Burlington, MA..................................672
Burt County Museum, Tekamah, NE 873
Butler County History Center & Kansas
  Oil Museum, El Dorado, KS 537
Butte County Pioneer Memorial Museum,
  Oroville, CA.....................................136
Butterfield Trail Historical Museum,
  Russell Springs, KS............................557
Byron Historical Museum, Byron, NY........974

CDC/Global Health Odyssey, Atlanta,
  GA...358
COSI Columbus, Columbus, OH..............1157
CTS Turner Museum, Elkhart, IN 474
Cahokia Courthouse State Historic Site,
  Cahokia, IL......................................415
Calaveras County Archives, San Andreas,
  CA...155
Calhoun County Museum, Rockwell City,
  IA..527
Calhoun County Museum, Port Lavaca,
  TX...1444
Callahan County Pioneer Museum, Baird,
  TX...1393
Calumet County Historical Society, Inc.,
  New Holstein, WI...............................1615
Calvin Coolidge Historic Site, Plymouth
  Notch, VT.......................................1484
Cambridge Museum, Cambridge, NE.........858
Camp Atterbury Museum, Edinburgh, IN ...474
Camp Five Museum Foundation, Inc.,
  Laona, WI.......................................1604
Camp 6 Logging Museum, Tacoma, WA ...1572
Campbell Historical Museum & Ainsley
  House, Campbell, CA............................80
Campbell House Museum, Saint Louis,
  MO..832
Canaan Historical Society, Inc., Canaan,
  NY...974
Canadian County Historical Museum, El
  Reno, OK..1200
Canal Fulton Heritage Society, Canal
  Fulton, OH......................................1145
Canby Historical Society, Canby, OR 1221
Canterbury Shaker Village, Inc.,
  Canterbury, NH.................................883
Canyon de Chelly National Monument,
  Chinle, AZ..31
Cape Cod National Seashore, Wellfleet,
  MA...717
Cape Fear Museum of History and
  Science, Wilmington, NC.....................1123
Cape Vincent Historical Museum, Cape
  Vincent, NY.....................................976
Captain George Flavel House Museum,
  Astoria, OR.....................................1218
Captain John Wilson House, Cohasset,
  MA...676
Caramoor Center for Music & the Arts,
  Inc., Katonah, NY.............................1006
Carlton County Historical Society,
  Cloquet, MN.....................................771
Carnton Plantation, Franklin, TN.............1365
Carpinteria Valley Historical Society &
  Museum of History, Carpinteria, CA.........82
Carroll County Farm Museum,
  Westminster, MD................................656
Cartoon Art Museum, San Francisco, CA....164
Casa Grande Valley Historical Society &
  Museum, Casa Grande, AZ.....................30
Cascade County Historical Society
  Museum, Great Falls, MT.....................848
Casey Jones Home and Railroad
  Museum, Jackson, TN.........................1367
Cashmere Museum & Pioneer Village,
  Cashmere, WA.................................1550

Cass County Historical Society at
  Bonanzaville, West Fargo, ND...............1137
Cass County Historical Society Museum,
  Plattsmouth, NE................................872
Cass County Museum & Pioneer School,
  Walker, MN......................................795
Cassia County Museum, Burley, ID 404
Casteel-Linn House and Museum,
  Princeton, MO..................................829
Castle Air Museum, Atwater, CA 72
Castle Museum of Saginaw County
  History, Saginaw, MI...........................762
Castle Tucker, Wiscasset, ME..................625
Catalina Island Museum Society, Inc.,
  Avalon, CA..73
Catawba County Museum of History,
  Newton, NC.....................................1113
Cattaraugus Area Historical Center,
  Cattaraugus, NY................................976
Cayuga Museum & Case Research Lab
  Museum, Auburn, NY..........................959
Cayuga-Owasco Lakes Historical Society,
  Moravia, NY....................................1015
Cedar Key Historical Society Museum,
  Cedar Key, FL...................................298
Cedar Key Museum State Park, Cedar
  Key, FL...299
Center for American Music, Pittsburgh,
  PA..1291
Center for Book Arts, New York, NY........1022
Center for Exploratory and Perceptual
  Art, Buffalo, NY................................973
Center for History, Wheaton, IL..............465
Centerville - Washington Township
  Historical Society & Walton House
  Museum, Centerville, OH.....................1147
Central Delta Depot Museum, Brinkley,
  AR..55
Central Florida Railroad Museum, Winter
  Garden, FL......................................354
Central High School National Historic
  Site, Little Rock, AR............................61
Central Montana Historical Association,
  Inc. Museum, Lewistown, MT...............850
Central Nevada Museum & Historical
  Society, Tonopah, NV..........................882
Centre County Historical Society, State
  College, PA.....................................1301
Centre Hill Museum (The Petersburg
  Museums), Petersburg, VA...................1524
Chalet of the Golden Fleece, New
  Glarus, WI......................................1614
Champaign County Historical Museum,
  Champaign, IL...................................416
Champion Mill State Historical Park,
  Champion, NE...................................859
Chandler Museum, Chandler, AZ 31
Channel Islands National Park, Robert J.
  Lagomarsino Visitor Center, Ventura,
  CA...194
The Chapman Historical Museum, Glens
  Falls, NY...994
Chappell Hill Historical Society Museum,
  Chappell Hill, TX..............................1399
Charles A. Grignon Mansion, Kaukauna,
  WI..1601
Charles A. Lindbergh Historic Site, Little
  Falls, MN..779
Charles A. Weyerhaeuser Memorial
  Museum, Little Falls, MN.....................779
Charles H. Wright Museum of African
  American History, Detroit, MI................735
Charles River Museum of Industry,
  Waltham, MA...................................715
Charlotte County Historical Center,
  Charlotte Harbor, FL...........................299
Charlotte Museum of History and
  Hezekiah Alexander Homesite,
  Charlotte, NC...................................1094
Chatillon-DeMenil Mansion, Saint Louis,
  MO..832
Chattanooga African Museum/Bessie
  Smith Hall, Chattanooga, TN...............1360

Chattanooga Regional History Museum,
  Chattanooga, TN...............................1361
Chemung Valley History Museum,
  Elmira, NY......................................988
Cheraw Lyceum Museum, Cheraw, SC......1327
Cherokee Strip Land Rush Museum,
  Arkansas City, KS..............................532
Cherokee Strip Museum, Alva, OK..........1195
Cherry County Historical Society,
  Valentine, NE...................................874
The Chesapeake Beach Railway Museum,
  Chesapeake Beach, MD.......................639
Chicago Public Library, Chicago, IL..........419
Chico Museum, Chico, CA......................83
Chief Plenty Coups Museum, Pryor, MT.....852
Children's Discovery Museum of North
  San Diego, Carlsbad, CA.......................81
Children's Hands-On Museum (CHOM),
  Tuscaloosa, AL...................................19
The Children's Museum, Seattle, WA 1565
Children's Museum at Holyoke, Inc.,
  Holyoke, MA....................................687
Children's Museum/Detroit Public
  Schools, Detroit, MI............................735
Children's Museum, Inc., Boca Raton, FL...296
Children's Museum of History, Natural
  History and Science at Utica, New
  York, Utica, NY................................1079
The Children's Museum of Portsmouth,
  Portsmouth, NH................................894
The Children's Museum of Rose Hill
  Manor Park, Frederick, MD...................644
Children's Museum of Southeastern
  Connecticut, Niantic, CT......................256
Children's Museum of the Sierra,
  Oakhurst, CA....................................132
Childress County Heritage Museum,
  Childress, TX...................................1400
Chimney Point State Historic Site,
  Addison, VT....................................1475
Chinese Culture Center of San Francisco,
  San Francisco, CA..............................164
Chippewa County Historical Society,
  Montevideo, MN................................783
Chisholm Trail Museum, Wellington, KS ...561
Chisholm Trail Museum, Kingfisher, OK...1203
Choctaw County Historical Society,
  Hugo, OK.......................................1203
The Christian C. Sanderson Museum,
  Chadds Ford, PA...............................1246
Churchill County Museum and Archives,
  Fallon, NV.......................................877
Cincinnati Fire Museum, Cincinnati, OH...1149
City County Pioneer Museum,
  Sweetwater, TX................................1454
City Museum, Saint Louis, MO................832
City of Burlington Historical Society,
  Burlington, NJ..................................899
City of Gilroy Museum, Gilroy, CA 99
City of Las Vegas Museum and Rough
  Rider Memorial Collection, Las Vegas,
  NM...941
City of Wayne Historical Museum,
  Wayne, MI.......................................766
Civil War and Underground Railroad
  Museum of Philadelphia, Philadelphia,
  PA..1278
Clallam County Historical Society, Port
  Angeles, WA....................................1561
Clarion County Historical Society,
  Sutton-Ditz House Museum, Clarion,
  PA..1247
Clark County Historical Museum,
  Vancouver, WA.................................1576
Clark County Historical Society -
  Heritage Center of Clark County,
  Springfield, OH.................................1186
Clark County Museum, Marshall, IL...........444
Clark Hotel Museum, Van Horn, TX 1457
Clarke Historical Museum, Eureka, CA......94
Clarkson Historical Museum, Clarkson,
  NE..859

Clarksville-Montgomery County Museum
  dba Customs House Museum &
  Cultural Center, Clarksville, TN 1363
Clausen Memorial Museum, Petersburg,
  AK...27
Clay County Historical Society Museum
  and Archives, Moorhead, MN.................784
Cle Elum Telephone Museum, Cle Elum,
  WA..1551
Clermont State Historic Site, Clermont,
  NY..979
Cleveland County Historical Museum,
  Shelby, NC...1119
Cleveland Police Historical Society &
  Museum, Cleveland, OH.......................1153
Clewiston Museum, Inc., Clewiston, FL......300
Clifton Community Historical Society,
  Clifton, KS..535
Clinton County Historical Association &
  Museum, Plattsburgh, NY.....................1052
Clinton County Historical Society
  Paine-Gillam-Scott Museum, Saint
  Johns, MI..763
Clinton County Museum, Frankfort, IN.......478
Coal Miners' Museum/Van Lear
  Historical Society, Inc., Van Lear, KY....584
Cobb County Youth Museum, Marietta,
  GA..379
Cokato Museum & Akerlund
  Photography Studio, Cokato, MN............771
The Coleman House Museum and Brown
  County Historical Society, Ainsworth,
  NE..855
The Coley Homestead & Barn Museum,
  Weston, CT..265
Colfax County Society of Art, History
  and Archaeology, Raton, NM..................945
Col. Ashley House, Ashley Falls, MA.........661
Columbia Gorge Interpretive Center
  Museum, Stevenson, WA......................1572
Comanche Crossing Historical Society &
  Museum, Strasburg, CO.........................233
Community Historical Museum,
  Maxwell, IA...523
Community Memorial Museum of Sutter
  County, Yuba City, CA...........................200
Computer History Museum, Mountain
  View, CA...129
Concord Historical Society, Warner
  Museum, Springville, NY......................1071
Confederate Museum, Crawfordville, GA....369
Conklin Reed Organ & History Museum,
  Hanover, MI...745
Conneaut Railroad Museum, Conneaut,
  OH..1159
Connecticut Fire Museum, East Windsor,
  CT..239
Connecticut Trolley Museum, East
  Windsor, CT...239
Cook County Historical Museum, Grand
  Marais, MN..776
Cookeville Depot Museum, Cookeville,
  TN..1364
Coolspring Power Museum, Coolspring,
  PA..1248
Cooper-Hewitt National Design Museum,
  Smithsonian Institution, New York,
  NY..1023
Coos Historical & Maritime Museum,
  North Bend, OR...................................1229
Copper Range Historical Museum, South
  Range, MI..764
Copper Village Museum & Arts Center of
  Deer Lodge County, Anaconda, MT........840
Cordova Historical Museum, Cordova,
  AK...23
Coronado-Quivira Museum, Lyons, KS......550
Corpus Christi Museum of Science and
  History, Corpus Christi, TX..................1401
Corry Area Historical Society, Corry, PA...1248
Cottage Grove Museum & Annex,
  Cottage Grove, OR..............................1222
Cottonlandia Museum, Greenwood, MS......800

Cottonwood County Historical Society,
  Windom, MN..796
Country Music Hall of Fame and
  Museum, Country Music Foundation,
  Nashville, TN.....................................1378
Courthouse Square Association,
  Charlotte, MI..731
Cowlitz County Historical Museum,
  Kelso, WA..1557
Cracker Country, Tampa, FL......................348
Crandall Historical Printing Museum,
  Provo, UT...1469
Crawford County Historical Museum,
  Pittsburg, KS..556
Crazy Mountain Museum, Big Timber,
  MT..841
Creative Photographic Art Center of
  Maine, Lewiston, ME.............................614
Crested Butte Mountain Heritage
  Museum, Crested Butte, CO...................208
Crestline Shunk Museum, Crestline, OH...1160
Cripple Creek District Museum, Inc.,
  Cripple Creek, CO.................................209
Croatian Heritage Museum & Library,
  Eastlake, OH.......................................1163
Crockett County Museum, Ozona, TX.......1442
Crockett Tavern Museum, Morristown,
  TN..1376
Crossroads Museum, Corinth, MS..............800
Crossroads of America, Bethlehem, NH.....883
Crow Wing County Historical Society,
  Brainerd, MN..769
Crystal Lake Falls Historical Association,
  Barton, VT...1476
Culbertson Mansion State Historic Site,
  New Albany, IN.....................................493
Culbertson Museum, Culbertson, MT.........845
Cupertino Historical Society & Museum,
  Cupertino, CA..88
The Curious Kids' Museum, Saint
  Joseph, MI...763
Curry Historical Society Museum, Gold
  Beach, OR..1225
Cuyuna Range Historical Society &
  Museum, Crosby, MN............................772

DAR John Strong Mansion Museum,
  Addison, VT.......................................1475
D.R. Barker Historical Museum,
  Fredonia, NY..992
Dakota County Historical Society, South
  Saint Paul, MN.....................................793
Dakota Discovery Museum, Mitchell, SD..1352
Dakota Sunset Museum, Gettysburg, SD...1348
Dakotaland Museum, Huron, SD...............1348
Dallam-Hartley XIT Museum, Dalhart,
  TX..1403
Dallas Firefighter's Museum, Inc., Dallas,
  TX..1404
Dallas Heritage Village at Old City Park,
  Dallas, TX..1405
Daniel Boone Home and Boonesfield
  Village, Lindenwood University,
  Defiance, MO.......................................814
Daniels County Museum and Pioneer
  Town, Scobey, MT.................................853
Danvers Historical Society, Danvers, MA....678
Daughters of the American Revolution
  Museum, Washington, DC......................277
Daughters of Utah Pioneers Pioneer
  Memorial Museum & International
  Society Daughters of Utah Pioneers,
  Salt Lake City, UT...............................1471
David Conklin Farmhouse, Huntington,
  NY..1000
Davidson County Historical Museum,
  Lexington, NC.....................................1109
Dawes County Historical Society
  Museum, Chadron, NE...........................859
Dawson County Historical Museum,
  Lexington, NE.......................................864
Dayton History at Carillon Park, Dayton,
  OH..1161

De Smet Depot Museum, De Smet, SD.....1346
Deaf Smith County Museum, Hereford,
  TX..1424
Decatur County Last Indian Raid
  Museum, Oberlin, KS.............................554
Deer Park Escondido Winery & Auto
  Museum, Escondido, CA..........................93
Degrazia Gallery In The Sun, Tucson, AZ....48
Deines Cultural Center, Russell, KS..........556
Del Norte County Historical Society,
  Crescent City, CA...................................87
Delaware and Hudson Canal Historical
  Society and Museum, High Falls, NY.....998
Delaware Division of Historical &
  Cultural Affairs, Dover, DE...................269
Delta Blues Museum, Clarksdale, MS.........799
Delta County Historical Society Museum,
  Escanaba, MI..741
Delta County Museum, Delta, CO..............209
Delta Cultural Center, Helena, AR..............59
Deming Luna Mimbres Museum,
  Deming, NM...939
Denali National Park and Preserve,
  Denali Park, AK......................................23
Denton County Historical Museum, Inc.
  and Texas Heritage Center, Denton,
  TX..1409
Denver Firefighters Museum, Denver, CO...211
Department of the Treasury, Washington,
  DC..278
Depot Museum & Fort Sedgwick
  Museum, Julesburg, CO..........................223
The Depot Museum Complex,
  Henderson, TX....................................1424
Depot Park Museum, Sonoma, CA.............187
Des Plaines History Center, Des Plaines,
  IL..430
Deschutes County Historical Society,
  Bend, OR...1220
Detroit Historical Society, Detroit, MI.......735
Deutschheim State Historic Site,
  Hermann, MO.......................................817
DeWitt County Historical Museum,
  Cuero, TX..1403
DeWitt Wallace Decorative Arts Museum,
  Williamsburg, VA................................1545
Dexter Area Historical Society &
  Museum, Dexter, MI.............................738
Dexter Historical Society Campus,
  Dexter, ME..609
Dickinson County Heritage Center,
  Abilene, KS..531
Dr. Daniel W. Kissam House,
  Huntington, NY...................................1000
Dodge County Historical Society
  Museum, Beaver Dam, WI....................1591
Dog Mushing Museum, Fairbanks, AK.........24
Don Garlits Museum of Drag Racing
  Inc., Ocala, FL......................................330
Door County Historical Museum,
  Sturgeon Bay, WI...............................1623
Door County Maritime Museum (at Gills
  Rock), Gills Rock, WI..........................1598
Dorothy G. Page Museum, Wasilla, AK.......29
Douglas County Historical Society,
  Superior, WI.......................................1624
Douglas County Historical Society -
  Carson Valley Museum & Cultural
  Center, Gardnerville, NV.......................877
Douglas County Historical Society -
  Genoa Courthouse Museum, Genoa,
  NV..877
Douglas County Museum of History and
  Natural History, Roseburg, OR.............1234
The Downers Grove Park District
  Museum, Downers Grove, IL..................431
Downieville Museum, Downieville, CA........91
Drake Well Museum, Titusville, PA..........1303
Drew County Historical Museum,
  Monticello, AR......................................64
Drummond Island Historical Museum,
  Drummond Island, MI............................739

Tools and Equipment for Communication–Continued

Duluth Children's Museum, Duluth, MN.....772
Duncan Cottage Museum, Metlakatla, AK.....27
Dunedin Historical Society & Museum, Dunedin, FL.............305
DuPage County Historical Museum, Wheaton, IL.............465
Durham Historic Association Museum, Durham, NH.............886
Dutchess County Historical Society, Poughkeepsie, NY.............1054
EAA AirVenture Museum, Oshkosh, WI....1616
Eagle Historical Society & Museums, Eagle, AK.............23
Eagle Tavern Museum, Watkinsville, GA....391
Early American Museum, Mahomet, IL.......444
EarlyWorks Museums, Huntsville, AL..........11
East Ely Railroad Depot Museum, Ely, NV.............876
East End Seaport Museum and Marine Foundation, Greenport, NY.............996
East Hillsborough Historical Society, Inc., Plant City, FL.............337
East Jordan Portside Art & Historical Museum, East Jordan, MI.............739
East Poultney Museum, East Poultney, VT.............1479
Eastern Arizona Museum and Historical Society of Graham County Inc., Pima, AZ.............42
Eastern California Museum, Independence, CA.............104
Eastern Oregon Museum on the Old Oregon Trail, Haines, OR.............1226
Eastside Heritage Center, Bellevue, WA....1548
Edgar County Historical Museum, Paris, IL.............449
Edison Museum, Beaumont, TX.............1394
Edison National Historic Site, West Orange, NJ.............930
Edisto Island Historic Preservation Society Museum, Edisto Island, SC......1332
Edmond Historical Society Museum, Edmond, OK.............1200
Edmonds South Snohomish County Historical Society, Inc., Edmonds, WA.1553
Edwards County Historical Museum, Kinsley, KS.............547
1859 Jail, Marshal's Home & Museum, Independence, MO.............817
82nd Airborne Division War Memorial Museum, Fort Bragg, NC.............1101
Eiteljorg Museum of American Indians and Western Art, Indianapolis, IN..........482
El Dorado County Historical Museum, Placerville, CA.............142
El Pueblo Historical Monument, Los Angeles, CA.............114
El Pueblo History Museum, Pueblo, CO......230
Elbert Hubbard-Roycroft Museum, East Aurora, NY.............985
Eli Whitney Museum, Inc., Hamden, CT.....244
Elkhart County Historical Museum, Bristol, IN.............471
Ella Sharp Museum, Jackson, MI.............748
Elliott Museum, Stuart, FL.............346
Ellis County Historical Society, Hays, KS..543
Ellis County Museum, Inc., Waxahachie, TX.............1460
Elmhurst Historical Museum, Elmhurst, IL.............433
Emmett Kelly Historical Museum, Sedan, KS.............558
End-O-Line Railroad Park & Museum, Currie, MN.............772
Enfield Historical Society Museum, Enfield Center, NH.............887
Englewood Textile Museum, Englewood, TN.............1364
Ephrata Cloister, Ephrata, PA.............1251

Erie Maritime Museum, Homeport U.S. Brig Niagara, Erie, PA.............1252
The Erlander Home Museum, Rockford, IL.............454
Ernie Pyle State Historic Site, Dana, IN......473
Escondido History Center, Escondido, CA.............93
Essley-Noble Museum: Mercer County Historical Society, Aledo, IL.............410
Estes Park Museum, Estes Park, CO.............215
The Esther Thomas Atkinson Museum, Hampden-Sydney, VA.............1509
Eureka Pioneer Museum of McPherson County, Inc., Eureka, SD.............1346
Eustis Historical Museum & Preservation Society, Inc., Eustis, FL.............306
Evanston Historical Society and Charles Gates Dawes House, Evanston, IL..........434
Experience Music Project, Seattle, WA......1565
Exploris, Raleigh, NC.............1115
Fairbanks House, Dedham, MA.............679
Fairbanks Museum and Planetarium, Saint Johnsbury, VT.............1486
Fairmount Historical Museum & Gift Shop, Fairmount, IN.............476
Fairport Historical Museum, Fairport, NY...989
Fairview Museum of History & Art, Fairview, UT.............1465
Fall River County Historical Museum, Hot Springs, SD.............1348
Family Museum, Bettendorf, IA.............505
Farmers Branch Historical Park, Farmers Branch, TX.............1413
Farmington Museum, Farmington, NM........939
Farragut Folklife Museum, Farragut, TN...1364
FASNY Museum of Fire Fighting, Hudson, NY.............1000
Fayette Heritage Museum & Archives, La Grange, TX.............1432
Fender Museum of Music and the Arts, Corona, CA.............87
Fenton History Center-Museum & Library, Jamestown, NY.............1005
Fillmore County Historical Center, Fountain, MN.............776
Fillmore Historical Museum, Inc., Fillmore, CA.............95
The Filson Historical Society, Inc., Louisville, KY.............576
The Finley House, Wayne, PA.............1306
Fire Museum of Maryland, Inc., Lutherville, MD.............649
Fire Museum of Memphis, Memphis, TN..1373
Fire Museum of Texas, Beaumont, TX......1394
Firelands Historical Society Museum, Norwalk, OH.............1180
Fireman's Hall Museum, Philadelphia, PA.1279
1st Cavalry Division Museum, Fort Hood, TX.............1414
First Missouri State Capitol-State Historic Site, Saint Charles, MO.............830
Fitchburg Historical Society, Fitchburg, MA.............683
Flagler Museum, Palm Beach, FL.............333
Fleming Historical Society, Fleming, CO....216
Florence Price Pioneer Museum, Florence, CO.............216
Florence Ranch Homestead, Mesquite, TX.............1438
Floyd County Historical Museum, Charles City, IA.............510
Folsom History Museum, Folsom, CA..........95
The Folsom House Museum, Taylors Falls, MN.............794
Folsom Museum, Inc., Folsom, NM.............939
Ford's Theatre National Historic Site (Lincoln Museum), Washington, DC......279
Forest History Center, Grand Rapids, MN...777
Forest Lawn Museum, Glendale, CA..........100
Fort Bedford Museum, Bedford, PA..........1241

Fort Bend Museum Association, Richmond, TX.............1445
Fort Bowie National Historic Site, Bowie, AZ.............30
Fort Bridger State Museum, Fort Bridger, WY.............1632
Fort Christmas Historical Park, Christmas, FL.............299
Fort Clatsop National Memorial, Astoria, OR.............1218
Fort Collins Museum, Fort Collins, CO.......217
Fort Concho National Historic Landmark, San Angelo, TX.............1447
Fort Croghan Museum, Burnet, TX.............1398
Fort Crook Historical Museum, Fall River Mills, CA.............94
Fort Dix Museum, Fort Dix, NJ.............904
Fort Dodge & Frontier Village, Fort Dodge, IA.............518
Fort Fetterman State Historic Site, Douglas, WY.............1631
Fort Fisher State Historic Site, Kure Beach, NC.............1108
Fort Hartsuff State Historical Park, Burwell, NE.............858
Fort Hays State Historic Site, Hays, KS......543
Fort Hill (The John C. Calhoun House), Clemson, SC.............1328
Fort Jones Museum, Fort Jones, CA.............96
Fort Kearny State Historical Park, Kearney, NE.............864
Fort Laramie National Historic Site, Fort Laramie, WY.............1633
Fort MacArthur Museum, San Pedro, CA....176
Fort McKavett State Historical Site, Fort McKavett, TX.............1415
Fort Nisqually Living History Museum, Tacoma, WA.............1573
Fort Okanogan Interpretive Center, Brewster, WA.............1550
Fort Pike State Historic Site, New Orleans, LA.............595
Fort Sidney Museum & Post Commander's Home, Sidney, NE.............873
Fort Smith Museum of History, Fort Smith, AR.............58
Fort Totten State Historic Site, Fort Totten, ND.............1131
Fort Union Trading Post National Historic Site, Williston, ND.............1138
Fort Verde State Historic Park, Camp Verde, AZ.............30
Fort Walla Walla Museum, Walla Walla, WA.............1576
Fort Ward Museum and Historic Site, Alexandria, VA.............1492
Fort Washington Park, Fort Washington, MD.............643
Forts Folle Avoine Historic Park, Danbury, WI.............1594
Fossil Country Museum, Kemmerer, WY..1635
Fostoria Area Historical Museum, Fostoria, OH.............1164
Fox Lake Historical Museum, Inc., Fox Lake, WI.............1598
The Foxfire Museum & Heritage Center, Mountain City, GA.............380
Franconia Heritage Museum, Franconia, NH.............888
Frank Phillips Home, Bartlesville, OK.......1197
Frankenmuth Historical Museum, Frankenmuth, MI.............742
Frankfort Area Historical Museum, West Frankfort, IL.............464
Franklin County Historical & Museum Society & House of History, Malone, NY.............1012
Franklin County Historical Museum, Pasco, WA.............1561
Franklin County Old Jail Museum, Winchester, TN.............1385
The Franklin Institute, Philadelphia, PA.....1280

Fraternal Order of Alaska State Troopers Museum, Anchorage, AK 22

Fred Harman Art Museum, Pagosa Springs, CO 229

Frederick Douglass National Historic Site, Washington, DC 279

Frederick Law Olmsted National Historic Site, Brookline, MA 671

Fredericksburg Area Museum & Cultural Center, Inc., Fredericksburg, VA............1506

Freeborn County Museum and Historical Village, Albert Lea, MN..............767

Freestone County Historical Museum, Fairfield, TX 1413

Fremont County Pioneer Museum, Lander, WY 1635

French Cable Station Museum in Orleans, Orleans, MA 701

Fresno Metropolitan Museum, Fresno, CA 97

The Frick Art & Historical Center, Pittsburgh, PA 1292

Friends of Arrow Rock, Inc., Arrow Rock, MO 811

Frontier Culture Museum, Staunton, VA 1537

Frontier Museum, Williston, ND 1138

Frontier Times Museum, Bandera, TX 1393

Frontiers of Flight Museum, Dallas, TX 1406

The Fullerton Arboretum, Fullerton, CA........98

Fullerton Museum Center, Fullerton, CA 98

Fulton County Historical Museum, Wauseon, OH 1190

Fulton County Historical Society Museum, Rochester, IN 498

Fulton County Museum, Groversville, NY 996

Fulton Mansion State Historic Site, Rockport, TX 1446

Furnace Town Living Heritage Museum, Snow Hill, MD 654

Furnas-Gosper Historical Society & Museum, Arapahoe, NE 856

Gage County Historical Society and Museum, Beatrice, NE 857

Gaineswood, Demopolis, AL 7

Galena-Jo Daviess County Historical Society & Museum, Galena, IL 436

Galloping Road Compound & Poker Alley; Harbor Ranch, Dripping Springs, TX..............1410

Galveston County Historical Museum, Galveston, TX..............1420

Galveston Historical Foundation, Inc., Galveston, TX..............1421

Galveston Railroad Museum, Galveston, TX 1421

Garden Grove Historical Society, Garden Grove, CA..............99

Garibaldi and Meucci Museum, Staten Island, NY..............1072

Garnavillo Historical Museum, Garnavillo, IA..............518

Gates House, Machiasport Historical Society, Machiasport, ME 614

Gates Mills Historical Society, Gates Mills, OH 1166

Gateway to the Panhandle, Gate, OK.........1201

General Lew Wallace Study & Museum, Crawfordsville, IN..............473

General Patton Memorial Museum, Chiriaco Summit, CA..............84

Genesee Country Village & Museum, Mumford, NY..............1016

Geneva Historical Society & Rose Hill Mansion, Geneva, NY..............994

Geographical Center Historical Museum, Rugby, ND..............1136

The George Bush Presidential Library and Museum, College Station, TX 1400

George Eastman House/International Museum of Photography and Film, Rochester, NY..............1058

George I. Ashby Memorial Museum, Copper Center, AK 23

George Washington Carver Museum, Tuskegee Institute, AL 20

Georgia Music Hall of Fame and Museum, Macon, GA..............377

Georgia Rural Telephone Museum, Leslie, GA..............376

Georgia State Cotton Museum, Vienna, GA..............390

Georgia Veterans Memorial Museum, Cordele, GA..............369

Georgia's Stone Mountain Park, Stone Mountain, GA..............387

Gerald R. Ford Presidential Museum, Grand Rapids, MI..............743

Gibbs Museum of Pioneer and Dakotah Life, Falcon Heights, MN..............775

The Gibson Society, Inc. dba Gibson House Museum, Boston, MA..............665

Gig Harbor Peninsula Historical Society, Gig Harbor, WA..............1555

Gila County Historical Museum, Globe, AZ..............35

Gillespie County Historical Society, Fredericksburg, TX..............1419

Gilliam County Historical Society - Depot Museum Complex, Condon, OR.1222

The Glass Museum, Dunkirk, IN..............474

Glendower State Memorial, Lebanon, OH.1171

Glenn H. Curtiss Museum, Hammondsport, NY..............997

Glenview Area Historical Society, Glenview, IL..............438

Gnadenhutten Historical Park & Museum, Gnadenhutten, OH..............1167

Golden Gate Railroad Museum, San Francisco, CA..............166

Golden Pioneer Museum, Golden, CO.........220

Golden Spike National Historic Site, Brigham City, UT..............1463

Goodhue County Historical Society, Red Wing, MN..............787

Goodman Museum, Tyler, TX..............1456

Gouverneur Historical Association, Gouverneur, NY..............995

Governor Seay Mansion, Kingfisher, OK...1204

The Grace Museum, Abilene, TX..............1385

Grafton Historical Society, Grafton, VT.....1479

Graham County Historical Society, Thatcher, AZ..............46

Grand Forks County Historical Society, Grand Forks, ND..............1132

Grand Gulf Military Park, Port Gibson, MS..............807

Grand Lodge AF&AM of Virginia - Allen E. Roberts Masonic Library and Museum, Richmond, VA..............1529

Grand Portage National Monument, Grand Marais, MN..............776

The Grand River Historical Society & Museum, Chillicothe, MO..............813

Grand Teton National Park, Colter Bay Indian Arts Museum, Colter Bay Village, WY..............1631

Grand Traverse Heritage Center, Traverse City, MI..............765

The Granger Homestead Society, Inc., Canandaigua, NY..............975

Grant County Historical Museum, Canyon City, OR..............1221

Grant County Historical Museum, Ephrata, WA..............1553

Grant County Historical Society, Elbow Lake, MN..............774

Grant County Museum, Medford, OK........1205

Grant County Museum aka Historic Adobe Museum, Ulysses, KS..............560

Granville County Historical Society Museum, Oxford, NC..............1114

Granville Historical Society Museum, Granville, OH..............1167

Gravette Historical Museum, Gravette, AR..............59

Great Basin National Park, Baker, NV.........875

Great Harbor Maritime Museum, Northeast Harbor, ME..............616

Greater Hazleton Historical Society, Hazleton, PA..............1260

Greater Loveland Historical Society Museum, Loveland, OH..............1173

Greene County Historical Museum, Waynesburg, PA..............1306

Greene County Historical Society, Xenia, OH..............1193

Greenfield Historical Society, Greenfield, WI..............1599

Greensboro Historical Museum, Inc., Greensboro, NC..............1103

Gregg County Historical Museum, Longview, TX..............1434

Gresham History Museum, Gresham, OR.1226

Greybull Museum, Greybull, WY..............1634

Grissom Air Museum, Peru, IN..............496

Grosse Ile Historical Society, Grosse Ile, MI..............745

Groveland Yosemite Gateway Museum, Groveland, CA..............101

Gunnison County Pioneer and Historical Society, Gunnison, CO..............222

Gwinnett Historical Society, Lawrenceville, GA..............376

Gwinnett History Museum, Lawrenceville, GA..............376

H.G. Albee Memorial Museum, Estherville, IA..............517

Hacienda Buena Vista, Ponce, PR..............1642

Haffenreffer Museum of Anthropology, Brown University, Bristol, RI..............1310

The Hagley Museum and Library, Wilmington, DE..............273

Haines Museum, Waukegan Historical Society, Waukegan, IL..............463

Halifax Historical Museum, Daytona Beach, FL..............303

Hall of Flame Museum of Firefighting, Phoenix, AZ..............40

Hamilton Township Historical Society - John Abbott II House, Hamilton, NJ.......906

Hamilton Wood Type Printing Museum, Two Rivers, WI..............1625

Hampton History Museum, Hampton, VA .1509

Hampton National Historic Site, Towson, MD..............655

Hanby House, Westerville, OH..............1191

Hancock Historical Museum, Findlay, OH..............1164

Hancock Historical Society, Hancock, NH..............888

Hannah Lindahl Children's Museum, Mishawaka, IN..............491

Hanover Historical Society Museum, Hanover, VA..............1510

Harbor Defense Museum, Brooklyn, NY.....969

Harlan-Lincoln House, Mount Pleasant, IA..............524

The Harness Racing Museum and Hall of Fame, Goshen, NY..............995

Harold Warp Pioneer Village Foundation, Minden, NE..............868

Harper City Historical Society, Harper, KS..............543

Harpers Ferry Center, Harpers Ferry, WV .1582

Harrison County Historical Museum, Marshall, TX..............1436

Harrisonburg-Rockingham Historical Society, Dayton, VA..............1503

Harry P. Leu Gardens, Orlando, FL 331

Harry Ransom Center at the University of Texas at Austin, Austin, TX..............1390

Harry S. Truman Library-Museum, Independence, MO..............818

Hartsville Museum, Hartsville, SC..............1335

Tools and Equipment for Communication–Continued

Harvard Historical Society, Still River, MA 711

Harvey County Historical Society, Newton, KS 553

Haskell County Historical Society, Sublette, KS 558

Hatteras Island Visitor Center, Buxton, NC 1093

Hattiesburg Area Historical Society and HAHS Museum, Hattiesburg, MS 801

Hatton-Eielson Museum & Historical Association, Hatton, ND 1132

Hawks Inn Historical Society, Inc., Delafield, WI 1595

Hayward Area Historical Society, Hayward, CA 102

Headwaters Heritage Museum, Three Forks, MT 854

Heart of West Texas Museum, Colorado City, TX 1401

Hearthstone Historic House Museum, Appleton, WI 1589

Heisey Museum, Clinton County Historical Society, Lock Haven, PA 1269

Helvetia Museum, Helvetia, WV 1582

Hemet Museum, Hemet, CA 103

Hennepin History Museum, Minneapolis, MN 782

Henrico County Historic Preservation & Museum Services, Richmond, VA 1529

Henry County Historical Society, New Castle, IN 494

Henry County Museum and Cultural Arts Center, Clinton, MO 813

The Henry Ford, Dearborn, MI 733

Henry Ford Estate-Fair Lane, Dearborn, MI 734

The Henry Sheldon Museum of Vermont History, Middlebury, VT 1481

Heritage Center Museum, Berryville, AR 55

Heritage Farm Museum & Village, Huntington, WV 1583

Heritage Farmstead Museum, Plano, TX ...1444

Heritage Hall Museum & Archives, Freeman, SD 1347

Heritage Hill State Historical Park, Green Bay, WI 1599

Heritage House Museum of Montgomery County, Mount Ida, AR 64

Heritage House of Orange County Association Inc., Orange, TX 1441

The Heritage Museum, Astoria, OR 1218

Heritage Museum & Potton House, Big Spring, TX 1396

The Heritage Museum & Underhill Museum, Idaho Springs, CO 223

The Heritage Museum at Falfurrias, Inc., Falfurrias, TX 1413

Heritage Museum Foundation of Tate County, Inc., Senatobia, MS 808

The Heritage Museum of Fine Arts for Youth, Detroit, MI 736

Heritage Museum of Northwest Florida, Valparaiso, FL 352

Heritage Square Museum, Ontario, NY 1047

Heritage Square Museum, Los Angeles, CA 116

Heritage Station, Umatilla County Historical Society Museum, Pendleton, OR 1230

Heritage Village, Largo, FL 321

Heritage Village, Mountain Lake, MN 785

Herkimer County Historical Society, Herkimer, NY 998

Hernando Heritage Museum, Brooksville, FL 298

Herschell Carrousel Factory Museum, North Tonawanda, NY 1043

Hershey Museum, Hershey, PA 1261

Hettinger County Historical Society, Regent, ND 1136

Hibbing Historical Society and Museum, Hibbing, MN 778

The Hickories Museum of the Lorain County Historical Society, Elyria, OH ..1163

Hickory Grove Rural School Museum, Ogden, IA 525

High Desert Museum, Bend, OR 1220

High Plains Museum, Goodland, KS 542

Highland County Museum and Heritage Center, McDowell, VA 1517

Highland Park Historical Society, Highland Park, IL 439

Highlands Hammock State Park/Civilian Conservation Corps Museum, Sebring, FL 346

Highlands Museum & Discovery Center, Ashland, KY 564

Hildene, The Lincoln Family Home, Manchester, VT 1481

The Hill Country Museum, Kerrville, TX..1431

Hillsboro Area Historical Society, Hillsboro, WI 1600

Hinckley Fire Museum, Hinckley, MN 778

Historic Arkansas Museum, Little Rock, AR 62

Historic Bok Sanctuary, Lake Wales, FL 320

Historic Bowens Mills & Pioneer Park, Middleville, MI 754

Historic Brattonsville, McConnells, SC......1336

Historic Carson House, Marion, NC...........1110

Historic Charlton Park Village and Museum, Hastings, MI 745

Historic Columbia Foundation, Columbia, SC 1329

Historic Edenton State Historic Site, Edenton, NC 1099

Historic Fallsington, Inc., Fallsington, PA .1253

Historic General Dodge House, Council Bluffs, IA 512

Historic Governors' Mansion, Cheyenne, WY 1630

Historic Homes Foundation, Inc., Louisville, KY 576

Historic Northampton, Northampton, MA....699

Historic Pensacola Village, Pensacola, FL ...335

Historic Preservation Association of Bourbon County, Inc., Fort Scott, KS 540

Historic Sauder Village, Archbold, OH 1140

Historic Smithfield, Blacksburg, VA...........1497

Historic Southwest Ohio, Inc., Sharonville, OH 1185

Historic Speedwell, Morristown, NJ.............913

Historic Westville, Inc., Lumpkin, GA.........376

Historical and Genealogical Society of Indiana County, Indiana, PA 1262

Historical and Genealogical Society of Somerset County, Somerset, PA 1300

Historical Center for Southeast New Mexico, Roswell, NM 946

Historical Electronics Museum, Linthicum, MD 648

Historical Museum at Fort Missoula, Missoula, MT 851

The Historical Museum at St. Gertrude, Cottonwood, ID 405

Historical Museum of Bay County, Bay City, MI 727

Historical Museum of Southern Florida, Miami, FL 324

Historical Society of Bloomfield New Jersey, Bloomfield, NJ 898

Historical Society of Cheshire County, Keene, NH 890

Historical Society of Columbia County, Saint Helens, OR 1234

The Historical Society of Dauphin County, Harrisburg, PA 1258

Historical Society of Fort Washington, Fort Washington, PA 1254

Historical Society of Garden County, Oshkosh, NE...............871

Historical Society of Greenfield, Greenfield, MA...............685

Historical Society of Middletown and the Wallkill Precinct, Inc., Middletown, NY...............1014

Historical Society of Old Newbury, Cushing House Museum, Newburyport, MA 698

Historical Society of Palm Beach County, Palm Beach, FL...............334

Historical Society of Quaker Hill & Pawling, Pawling, NY 1051

Historical Society of Rockland County, New City, NY...............1017

Historical Society of St. Marys and Benzinger Township, Saint Marys, PA..1297

Historical Society of Santuit and Cotuit, Cotuit, MA...............677

Historical Society of Stanton County Museums at Stanton and Pilger, Pilger, NE...............872

Historical Society Porter County Old Jail Museum, Valparaiso, IN...............502

The History Center, Fort Wayne, IN 477

The History Center, Cedar Rapids, IA 509

The History Center in Tompkins County, Ithaca, NY...............1003

History Museum for Springfield-Greene County, Springfield, MO...............839

History Museum of Western Virginia, Roanoke, VA...............1535

The History Place, Morehead City, NC ...1111

History San Jose, San Jose, CA...............171

Hiwan Homestead Museum, Evergreen, CO...............215

Hixon House, La Crosse, WI...............1603

Hobart Historical Society Museum, Hobart, IN...............480

Hoiles-Davis Museum, Greenville, IL...........439

Holland Historical Society Museum, Inc., Holland, VT...............1480

The Holland Land Office Museum, Batavia, NY...............960

Holly History Center & Hutchinson House Museum, Waupaca, WI...............1626

Hollywood Heritage Museum, Hollywood, CA...............103

Holmes County Historical Society, Millersburg, OH...............1176

Honolulu Police Department Law Enforcement Museum, Honolulu, HI.......396

Hood River County Historical Museum, Hood River, OR...............1226

Horry County Museum, Conway, SC.........1331

Horseshoe Bend National Military Park, Daviston, AL...............7

Houghton County Historical Museum Society, Lake Linden, MI...............749

House of the Temple, Washington, DC........280

Houston Fire Museum, Houston, TX 1427

Howard County Historical Museum, Kokomo, IN...............486

Howard County Historical Society, Ellicott City, MD...............643

Howard W. Cannon Aviation Museum, Henderson, NV...............878

Hudson River Maritime Museum, Kingston, NY...............1007

The Huguenot Historical Society, New Paltz, NY 1017

Hulihee Palace, Kailua-Kona, HI...............399

Humboldt Historical Museum, Humboldt, KS...............544

Humboldt Redwoods State Park Visitor Center, Weott, CA 197

The 100th Meridian Museum, Cozad, NE...859

Huron City Museums, Port Austin, MI 761

Hutchinson County Museum, Borger, TX..1397

Hyde Hall, Inc., Cooperstown, NY 980

Idaho State Historical Museum, Boise, ID...404

Illinois and Michigan Canal
  Commissioners Office Museum,
  Lockport, IL...................................443
Illinois Railway Museum, Union, IL............461
Imagine It! The Children's Museum of
  Atlanta, Atlanta, GA.........................361
Independence Historical Museum,
  Independence, KS.............................545
Independence National Historical Park,
  Philadelphia, PA..............................1281
Institute of American Indian Arts
  Museum, Santa Fe, NM.......................947
International Bluegrass Music Museum,
  Owensboro, KY................................581
International Museum of Cultures, Dallas,
  TX..1406
The International Printing Museum,
  Carson, CA.....................................82
International Spy Museum, Washington,
  DC...281
Intrepid Sea-Air-Space Museum, New
  York, NY.......................................1028
Iosco County Historical Museum, East
  Tawas, MI......................................740
Iowa Masonic Library and Museum,
  Cedar Rapids, IA..............................509
Iowa Railroad Historical Society, Boone,
  IA..506
Irish American Heritage Museum,
  Albany, NY....................................954
Iron & Steel Museum of Alabama,
  Tannehill Ironworks Historical State
  Park, McCalla, AL...............................13
Ironwood Area Historical Museum,
  Ironwood, MI..................................747
Ironworld Discovery Center, Chisholm,
  MN..771
Iroquois County Historical Society,
  Watseka, IL....................................463
Islesboro Historical Society, Islesboro,
  ME...612
Issaquah History Museum, Issaquah, WA..1557
Itasca County Historical Society, Grand
  Rapids, MN.....................................777

J.E. Reeves Home & Museum, Dover,
  OH..1163
JFK Special Warfare Museum, Fort
  Bragg, NC......................................1101
J.J. Jackson Memorial Museum,
  Weaverville, CA................................197
J.M. Davis Arms & Historical Museum,
  Claremore, OK.................................1198
J.W. Parmley Historical Home Society,
  Ipswich, SD....................................1349
Jackson County Historical Museum,
  Lakefield, MN..................................778
Jackson County Historical Museum &
  Research Library, Maquoketa, IA............522
Jackson County Historical Society, Black
  River Falls, WI.................................1592
Jackson Hole Historical Society and
  Museum, Jackson, WY.........................1634
Jacksonport State Park, Jacksonport, AR.......60
Jacques Marchais Museum of Tibetan
  Art, Staten Island, NY........................1072
The James Madison Museum, Orange,
  VA...1524
James Mitchell Varnum House and
  Museum, East Greenwich, RI................1311
Jamestown Settlement, Yorktown Victory
  Center, The Jamestown-Yorktown
  Foundation, Williamsburg, VA...............1545
Japanese Cultural Center of Hawaii,
  Honolulu, HI...................................397
Jean Lafitte National Historical Park &
  Preserve, New Orleans, LA...................596
Jean P. Haydon Museum, Pago Pago, AS..1640
Jeff Matthews Memorial Museum, Galax,
  VA...1508
The Jefferson County Historical Assoc.,
  Steubenville, OH..............................1186

Jefferson County Historical Society,
  Watertown, NY................................1083
Jefferson County Historical Society and
  Farnsworth TV Pioneer Museum,
  Rigby, ID.......................................409
Jefferson County Historical Society
  Museum, Port Townsend, WA...............1562
Jefferson Historical Society and Museum,
  Jefferson, TX..................................1431
Jefferson Valley Museum, Whitehall, MT....855
Jekyll Island Museum, Jekyll Island, GA....374
Jemez State Monument, Jemez Springs,
  NM..940
Jensen Arctic Museum, Monmouth, OR....1228
Jerome County Historical Society, Inc.
  and Idaho Farm & Ranch Museum,
  Jerome, ID.....................................406
Jewell County Historical Museum,
  Mankato, KS...................................552
Jim Crow Museum - Ferris State
  University, Big Rapids, MI....................729
Jim Gatchell Memorial Museum, Buffalo,
  WY..1629
Joachim Regional Museum, Dickinson,
  ND..1130
John Brown Museum State Historic Site,
  Osawatomie, KS...............................554
John Jay Homestead State Historic Site,
  Katonah, NY...................................1006
John Paul Jones House Museum,
  Portsmouth, NH...............................894
John Philip Sousa Museum, Champaign,
  IL..416
John Rivers Communications Museum,
  Charleston, SC................................1325
John Stark Edwards House, Warren, OH...1189
Johnson County Historical Society,
  Coralville, IA...................................511
Johnson County Historical Society
  Museum, Warrensburg, MO..................840
Johnson County Museum of History,
  Franklin, IN....................................478
Johnson County Museums, Shawnee, KS....558
Johnson Ferry House Museum, Titusville,
  NJ..926
Johnson Hall State Historic Site,
  Johnstown, NY................................1005
Johnson Victrola Museum, Dover, DE.........270
Joliet Area Historical Museum, Joliet, IL....440
Jonathan Hager House & Museum,
  Hagerstown, MD..............................646
Jonesborough-Washington County History
  Museum, Jonesborough, TN.................1368
Julia A. Purnell Museum, Snow Hill, MD...654
Juneau-Douglas City Museum, Juneau,
  AK...26
Juniata County Historical Society,
  Mifflintown, PA................................1271
The Junior Museum of Bay County,
  Panama City, FL...............................334
Justin Smith Morrill Homestead,
  Strafford, VT...................................1488

Kalamazoo Valley Museum, Kalamazoo,
  MI...749
Kalkaska County Historical Museum,
  Kalkaska, MI...................................749
Kanabec History Center, Mora, MN..........784
Kandiyohi County Historical Society,
  Willmar, MN...................................796
Kansas Aviation Museum, Wichita, KS........562
Kansas Cosmosphere and Space Center,
  Hutchinson, KS................................545
Kearney County Historical Museum,
  Minden, NE....................................868
The Kearny Cottage, Perth Amboy, NJ........921
Kellogg Historical Society, Kellogg, IA.......521
Kelly-Griggs House Museum, Red Bluff,
  CA...146
Kelton House Museum & Garden,
  Columbus, OH.................................1158
Kennesaw Mountain National Battlefield
  Park, Kennesaw, GA..........................374

Kenneth G. Fiske Museum of The
  Claremont Colleges, Claremont, CA.........85
Kenosha County Historical Society and
  Museum, Inc., Kenosha, WI.................1602
Kentucky Coal Mining Museum,
  Benham, KY...................................565
Kentucky Military History Museum,
  Frankfort, KY..................................569
Kentucky Railway Museum, Inc., New
  Haven, KY......................................580
Ker Place, Onancock, VA.......................1523
Kerbyville Museum, Kerby, OR...............1227
Kern County Museum, Bakersfield, CA........73
Kewaunee County Historical Museum,
  Kewaunee, WI................................1602
Key West Museum of Art and History,
  Key West, FL...................................318
Keyport Historical Society-Steamboat
  Dock Museum, Keyport, NJ..................909
Keystone Area Historical Society,
  Keystone, SD..................................1350
Kimball House Museum, Battle Creek,
  MI...727
Kimble County Historical Museum,
  Junction, TX...................................1431
Kingman County Historical Museum,
  Kingman, KS...................................547
Kingman Tavern Historical Museum,
  Cummington, MA.............................678
Kinney Pioneer Museum and Historical
  Society of North Iowa, Clear Lake, IA...510
Kit Carson Historical Society, Kit
  Carson, CO....................................223
Kitsap County Historical Society
  Museum, Bremerton, WA.....................1549
Klickitat County Historical Society,
  Goldendale, WA...............................1555
Kline Creek Farm, Winfield, IL................466
Knott House Museum, Tallahassee, FL.......347
Knox County Museum, Knoxville, IL..........441
Knox County Museum, Benjamin, TX.......1395
Knox House Museum, El Cajon, CA............92
Knoxville Public Library, Knoxville, PA...1265
Kohl Children's Museum of Greater
  Chicago, Glenview, IL........................438
Koochiching County Historical Museum,
  International Falls, MN........................778
Korean War Veterans National Museum
  & Library, Rantoul, IL........................453
Koreshan State Historic Site, Estero, FL......306
Kuhlmann King Historical House and
  Museum, Boerne, TX.........................1396

La Casa Del Libro, San Juan, PR..............1642
La Porte County Historical Society
  Museum, La Porte, IN........................487
La Puente Valley Historical Society City
  Hall, LaPuente, CA............................107
Lafayette Miners Museum, Lafayette, CO...224
Lafayette Natural History Museum and
  Planetarium, Lafayette, LA...................589
Lagrange County Historical Society, Inc.,
  Lagrange, IN...................................488
Lahaina Restoration Foundation, Lahaina,
  HI..400
Lake City Columbia County Historical
  Museum, Inc., Lake City, FL................319
Lake County Historic Courthouse
  Museum, Lakeport, CA.......................108
Lake County Historical Society, Two
  Harbors, MN...................................794
Lake Forest-Lake Bluff Historical
  Society, Lake Forest, IL......................441
Lake Meredith Aquatic and Wildlife
  Museum, Fritch, TX...........................1420
Lake of the Woods County Museum,
  Baudette, MN..................................768
Lake Shore Railway Museum, North
  East, PA..1274
Lake Tahoe Historical Society &
  Museum, South Lake Tahoe, CA.............188
Lake Waccamaw Depot Museum, Lake
  Waccamaw, NC................................1109

Tools and Equipment for Communication—Continued

Lake Wales Depot Museum & Cultural Center, Lake Wales, FL..................320
Lancaster County Historical Society, Lancaster, PA..................1266
Land of the Yankee Fork Historic Association Museum, Stanley, ID..........410
Landis Valley Museum, Lancaster, PA.......1266
Landmarks Foundation/Old Alabama Town, Montgomery, AL..................16
Lane County Historical Society & Museum, Eugene, OR..................1223
Lane Place, Crawfordsville, IN..................473
Langlade County Historical Society Museum, Antigo, WI..................1589
Lapham-Patterson House, Thomasville, GA..................388
Laramie Plains Museum, Laramie, WY.....1635
Lars Noak Blacksmith Shop, Larsson/Ostlund Log Home & One-Room Capitol School, New Sweden, ME..................616
Laura Ingalls Wilder Museum and Tourist Center, Walnut Grove, MN..................795
The Laurel Museum, Laurel, MD..................648
Lawrence County Historical and Genealogical Society, Bedford, IN..........469
Laws Railroad Museum and Historical Site, Bishop, CA..................78
Layland Museum, Cleburne, TX..................1400
Le Sueur Museum, Le Sueur, MN..................779
The Lebanon County Historical Society, Lebanon, PA..................1268
Lee County Historical Society, Loachapoka, AL..................13
Lefferts Historic House, Brooklyn, NY.......969
Legends of New Mexico Museum, Algodones, NM..................936
Legends of the Game Baseball Museum and Learning Center, Arlington, TX......1388
Lehigh County Historical Society, Allentown, PA..................1239
Lemhi County Historical Museum, Salmon, ID..................409
Lemon Hill Mansion, Philadelphia, PA......1282
Lentz Center for Asian Culture, Lincoln, NE..................865
Lesueur County Historical Museum-Chapter 1, Elysian, MN..................774
Levine Museum of the New South, Charlotte, NC..................1095
Lewes Historical Society, Lewes, DE..........271
Lewis County Historical Society Museum, Lowville, NY..................1012
Lexington History Museum, Lexington, KY..................573
Liberace Museum & Foundation, Las Vegas, NV..................879
Liberty Bell Memorial Museum, Melbourne, FL..................323
Liberty County Museum, Chester, MT..........844
Liberty Science Center, Jersey City, NJ.......909
Libertyville-Mundelein Historical Society, Inc., Libertyville, IL..................442
Licking County Historical Society, Newark, OH..................1178
Lightner Museum, Saint Augustine, FL.......339
Limberlost State Historic Site, Geneva, IN..................479
Lincoln County Historical Museum, Davenport, WA..................1552
Lincoln County Historical Society, Lincoln, KS..................549
Lincoln County Historical Society, North Platte, NE..................869
The Lincoln-Tallman Restorations, Janesville, WI..................1601
Lincoln's New Salem State Historic Site, Petersburg, IL..................451
Linden Railroad Museum, Linden, IN..........488

Lisle Station Museum, Lisle, IL..................443
The Lithuanian Museum, Chicago, IL..........423
Little Compton Historical Society, Little Compton, RI..................1312
The Little Cowboy Bar & Museum, Fromberg, MT..................847
Little White Schoolhouse, Ripon, WI........1620
Littleton Historical Museum, Littleton, CO..................227
The Living Word National Bible Museum, Aledo, TX..................1386
Livingston County Historical Society Museum, Geneseo, NY..................993
Livingston Depot Center, Livingston, MT...850
Locust Grove, The Samuel Morse Historic Site, Poughkeepsie, NY..........1055
Locust Lawn and Terwilliger House, Gardiner, NY..................993
Log Cabin Village, Fort Worth, TX..........1417
The Log House Museum of the Historical Society of Columbiana-Fairfield Township, Columbiana, OH..................1157
Logan County Museum, Paris, AR................65
Lombard Historical Museum, Lombard, IL..................443
Lompoc Valley Historical Society, Inc., Lompoc, CA..................110
Long Island Children's Museum, Garden City, NY..................992
Long Island Museum of Science and Technology, Garden City, NY..................993
Longhorn Museum, Pleasanton, TX..........1444
Longmont Museum, Longmont, CO.............227
Longwood Gardens, Kennett Square, PA...1264
Los Angeles Police Historical Society & Museum, Los Angeles, CA..................119
Louis E. May Museum, Fremont, NE..........861
Louis H. & Lena Firn Grover Museum, Shelbyville, IN..................498
Louisiana State Museum-Patterson, Patterson, LA..................599
Louisiana's Old State Capitol, Political History Museum, Baton Rouge, LA........587
Loveland Museum Gallery, Loveland, CO...227
Lowell Area Historical Museum, Lowell, MI..................751
Lucretia Vaile Museum, Palmer Lake, CO..................229
Lum & Abner Museum & Jot 'Em Down Store, Pine Ridge, AR..................66
Lutheran Heritage Center & Museum of the Perry County Lutheran Historical Society, Altenburg, MO..................810
Lutz Children's Museum, Manchester, CT...248
Lynden Pioneer Museum, Lynden, WA......1559
Lynn Museum & Historical Society, Lynn, MA..................692
Lyon County Historical Society and Museum, Emporia, KS..................538
Lyon County Historical Society Museum, Marshall, MN..................780

MIT Museum, Cambridge, MA..................674
Mabry-Hazen House, Knoxville, TN..........1371
Mackinac Island State Park Commission-Mackinac State Historic Parks, Mackinaw City, MI..................752
Madera County Museum, Madera, CA.........123
Madison County Historical Society, Winterset, IA..................531
The Magic Lantern Castle Museum, San Antonio, TX..................1448
Magnolia Manor, Cairo, IL..................415
Mahaffie Stagecoach Stop and Farm, Olathe, KS..................554
Maitland Historical Museums, Maitland, FL..................322
The Major General Frederick Funston Boyhood Home and Museum, Iola, KS..................546
Malheur Historical Project, Stonehouse Museum, Vale, OR..................1238

Mammoth Spring State Park, Depot Museum, Mammoth Spring, AR..................64
Manassas Museum System, Manassas, VA..................1516
Manassas National Battlefield Park, Manassas, VA..................1516
Manchester Historical Society, Manchester, MA..................692
Manitowoc County Historical Society, Manitowoc, WI..................1607
Manship House Museum, Jackson, MS........802
Maramec Museum, The James Foundation, Saint James, MO..................830
Marcellus Historical Society, Marcellus, NY..................1013
March Field Air Museum, Riverside, CA....149
The Margaret Mitchell House & Museum, Atlanta, GA..................361
Maridon Museum, Butler, PA..................1245
Marietta Museum of History, Marietta, GA..................379
Marin Museum of the American Indian, Novato, CA..................131
Marinette County Historical Museum, Marinette, WI..................1607
Marion County Historical Society, Salem, OR..................1236
The Marion County Historical Society Museum, Marion, OH..................1174
Marion Historical Museums, Inc. - Granger House, Marion, IA..................523
Marion Public Library Museum, Marion, IN..................490
Mariposa Museum and History Center Inc., Mariposa, CA..................124
Mark Twain Home and Museum, Hannibal, MO..................816
The Mark Twain House & Museum, Hartford, CT..................245
Marlboro County Historical Museum, Bennettsville, SC..................1322
Marquette County Historical Society, Westfield, WI..................1627
Marquette County History Museum, Marquette, MI..................753
Marshall County Historical Museum, Plymouth, IN..................496
Marshall County Historical Society Museum, Warren, MN..................795
Marshall Gold Discovery State Historic Park, Coloma, CA..................86
Martha's Vineyard Museum, Edgartown, MA..................681
Martin County Historical Museum, Stanton, TX..................1453
Martin County Museum, Shoals, IN............499
Mary McLeod Bethune Council House National Historic Site, Washington, DC..................283
Masonic Grand Lodge Library and Museum of Texas, Waco, TX..................1459
The Massillon Museum, Massillon, OH.....1175
The Mather Homestead Museum, Library and Memorial Park, Wellsville, NY......1084
Mattapoisett Museum and Carriage House, Mattapoisett, MA..................693
The Mattatuck Museum Arts and History Center, Waterbury, CT..................264
Matthews Museum of Maine Heritage, Union, ME..................624
Maturango Museum of the Indian Wells Valley, Ridgecrest, CA..................148
May Museum & Farmville Heritage Center, Farmville, NC..................1100
Mayville Historical Society, Inc., Mayville, WI..................1608
Mazomanie Historical Society, Mazomanie, WI..................1608
McConaghy House, Hayward, CA..............102
McCook House, Civil War Museum, Carrollton, OH..................1146
McCoy House, Lewistown, PA..................1269

McHenry County Historical Society and Museum, Union, IL 461
McHenry Museum, Modesto, CA 126
McIntosh County Historical Society, Ashley, ND 1127
McLean County Historical Society Museum, Washburn, ND 1137
McLean County Museum of History, Bloomington, IL 414
McMinn County Living Heritage Museum, Athens, TN 1360
McNamara House Museum, Victoria, TX ..1457
McPherson County Old Mill Museum and Park, Lindsborg, KS 550
Meade County Historical Society Museum, Meade, KS 552
Medina County Historical Society, The John Smart House, Medina, OH 1175
Medina Railroad Museum, Medina, NY 1014
Meeker County Historical Society Museum & G.A.R. Hall, Litchfield, MN 779
Meigs County Museum, Pomeroy, OH 1183
Mem-Erie Historical Museum, Erie, KS 539
Memorial Hall Museum, Pocumtuck Valley Memorial Assoc., Deerfield, MA 679
Memoryville USA, Inc., Rolla, MO 829
Mendocino County Museum, Willits, CA 198
Mennonite Heritage Museum, Goessel, KS 542
Menominee County Heritage Museum, Menominee, MI 754
Mercer County Historical Society, Mercer, PA 1271
Mercer Museum of the Bucks County Historical Society, Doylestown, PA 1250
Merrill Historical Museum, Merrill, WI 1609
Mesa Historical Museum, Mesa, AZ 37
Metamora Courthouse Historic Site, Metamora, IL 444
The Metropolitan Museum of Art, New York, NY 1030
Meux Home Museum, Fresno, CA 98
Miami County Museum, Peru, IN 496
Michael C. Carlos Museum, Atlanta, GA 361
Michelson Museum of Art, Marshall, TX ..1436
Michigan Transit Museum, Inc., Mount Clemens, MI 756
Mid-Atlantic Association of Museums, Washington, DC 283
Mid-Continent Railway Museum, North Freedom, WI 1615
Middleborough Historical Association, Inc., Middleborough, MA 694
Middlesex County Historical Society, Middletown, CT 249
Middleton Historical Society - Lura Woodside Watkins Museum, Middleton, MA 694
Midland County Historical Museum, Midland, TX 1438
Midway Village & Museum Center, Rockford, IL 455
Military Veterans Museum, Inc., Oshkosh, WI 1616
Mill Race Historical Village, Northville, MI 758
Mills County Historical Society and Museum, Glenwood, IA 519
Milton Historical Museum, Milton, VT 1482
Milton House Museum Historic Site, Milton, WI 1610
Milton J. Rubenstein Museum of Science & Technology, Syracuse, NY 1076
Milwaukee Public Museum, Milwaukee, WI 1612
Minnesota Historical Society's North West Company Fur Post, Pine City, MN 786
Minnesota Pioneer Park Museum, Annandale, MN 767

Minnesota Transportation Museum, Inc., Saint Paul, MN 792
Minnetrista, Muncie, IN 492
Minnilusa Pioneer Museum, Rapid City, SD 1354
Miracle of America Museum Inc., Polson, MT 852
Miramont Castle Museum, Manitou Springs, CO 228
Mission Houses Museum, Honolulu, HI 397
Mission San Antonio de Padua, Jolon, CA 105
Mission Santa Clara de Asis, Santa Clara, CA 181
Mississippi Agriculture & Forestry/National Agricultural Aviation Museum, Jackson, MS 802
Mississippi Armed Forces Museum, Camp Shelby, MS 799
Mississippi River Museum at Mud Island River Park, Memphis, TN 1375
Mississippi Society Daughters of the American Revolution Rosalie House Museum, Natchez, MS 805
Missouri State Museum, Jefferson City, MO 819
Mitchell County Historical Museum, Osage, IA 526
The Mitchell Museum of the American Indian, Evanston, IL 435
Mitchell Park Horticultural Conservatory, Milwaukee, WI 1612
Mobile Medical Museum, Mobile, AL 14
Modoc County Historical Museum, Alturas, CA 70
Mohave Museum of History and Arts, Kingman, AZ 36
Monroe County Historical Association/Stroud Mansion, Stroudsburg, PA 1302
Monroe County Historical Museum, Monroe, MI 756
Monroe County Historical Society, Bloomington, IN 469
Montague Museum & Historical Association, Montague, MI 756
The Montgomery County Historical Society, Dayton, OH 1161
Montgomery Museum & Lewis Miller Regional Art Center, Christiansburg, VA 1501
Monticello, Home of Thomas Jefferson, Thomas Jefferson Foundation, Inc., Charlottesville, VA 1499
Monticello Railway Museum, Monticello, IL 445
Montrose County Historical Museum, Montrose, CO 228
Montrose Historical & Telephone Pioneer Museum, Montrose, MI 756
Moody County Museum, Flandreau, SD....1347
Moore County Historical Museum, Dumas, TX 1410
Moosehead Marine Museum, Greenville, ME 611
Moravian Historical Society, Nazareth, PA 1273
Moravian Museum of Bethlehem, Inc., Bethlehem, PA 1242
Moriarty Historical Museum, Moriarty, NM 943
Mormon Station State Historic Park, Genoa, NV 877
Mormon Visitors Center, Independence, MO 818
Morris County Historical Society (Acorn Hall House Museum), Morristown, NJ ...914
The Morris Museum, Morristown, NJ 914
Morton Grove Historical Museum/Haupt-Yehl House, Morton Grove, IL 446
Morton Museum of Cooke County, Gainesville, TX 1420

Morven Park, Leesburg, VA 1512
Motown Historical Museum, Detroit, MI.....737
Motts Military Museum, Groveport, OH....1167
Mount Holly Community Historical Museum, Belmont, VT 1476
Mount Pleasant Historical Society, Mount Pleasant, OH 1177
Mount Prospect Historical Society Museums, Mount Prospect, IL 446
Mount Rushmore National Memorial, Keystone, SD 1350
Mount Washington Museum and The Weather Discovery Center, North Conway, NH 893
Mountain Heritage Center, Cullowhee, NC 1097
Mountain Life Museum, London, KY 575
The Movie Museum, Owosso, MI 759
Muscatine History & Industry Center/Pearl Button Museum, Muscatine, IA 524
The Museum, Greenwood, SC 1334
Museum at Southwestern Michigan College, Dowagiac, MI 738
The Museum of African Culture, Portland, ME 619
Museum of Afro-American History, Boston, MA 667
Museum of Alaska Transportation & Industry, Inc., Wasilla, AK 29
Museum of American Finance, New York, NY 1031
Museum of American Presidents, Strasburg, VA 1539
Museum of Ancient & Modern Art, Penn Valley, CA 141
Museum of Appalachia, Clinton, TN 1363
Museum of Art at Brigham Young University, Provo, UT 1469
Museum of Aviation at Robins Air Force Base, GA, Warner Robins, GA 390
Museum of Chicot County Arkansas, Lake Village, AR 61
Museum of Chinese in the Americas, New York, NY 1032
The Museum of Communications, Seattle, WA 1566
Museum of Cultural & Natural History, Mount Pleasant, MI 757
Museum of disAbility History, Williamsville, NY 1086
The Museum of Early Trades and Crafts, Madison, NJ 910
The Museum of East Alabama, Opelika, AL 17
The Museum of Flight, Seattle, WA 1567
Museum of Funeral Customs, Springfield, IL 459
Museum of History & Industry (MOHAI), Seattle, WA 1567
Museum of Idaho, Idaho Falls, ID 406
Museum of Independent Telephony, Abilene, KS 531
Museum of Indian Culture, Allentown, PA 1239
Museum of Jewish Heritage-A Living Memorial to the Holocaust, New York, NY 1032
Museum of Lifestyle & Fashion History, Delray Beach, FL 305
Museum of Lighthouse History, Wells, ME 625
Museum of Making Music, Carlsbad, CA 81
The Museum of Mobile, Mobile, AL 14
Museum of North Idaho, Coeur d'Alene, ID 405
Museum of Primitive Art and Culture, Peace Dale, RI 1316
The Museum of Printing History, Houston, TX 1428
Museum of Radio & Technology, Inc., Huntington, WV 1583
Museum of Robotics, Orinda, CA 136

Tools and Equipment for Communication–Continued

Museum of Science, Boston, MA................667
Museum of Science & History of Jacksonville, Jacksonville, FL................315
Museum of Science and Industry, Tampa, FL................349
Museum of Science and Industry, Chicago, IL................425
Museum of Small Town Life, Dover, DE....270
Museum of South Texas History, Edinburg, TX................1410
Museum of Southern History, Jacksonville, FL................315
The Museum of Southern History, Sugarland, TX................1454
Museum of the Albemarle, Elizabeth City, NC................1099
The Museum of the Alphabet, Waxhaw, NC................1121
Museum of the American Philosophical Society, Philadelphia, PA................1283
Museum of the Arkansas Grand Prairie, Stuttgart, AR................69
Museum of the Berkeley Springs, Berkeley Springs, WV................1580
Museum of the Cape Fear Historical Complex, Fayetteville, NC................1101
Museum of the City of Lake Worth, Lake Worth, FL................320
Museum of the Fur Trade, Chadron, NE......859
Museum of the Great Plains, Lawton, OK.1204
Museum of the High Plains, McCook, NE................868
Museum of the Hudson Highlands, Cornwall-on-Hudson, NY................982
Museum of the Llano Estacado, Plainview, TX................1443
Museum of the Moving Image, Astoria, NY................958
Museum of the Plains, Perryton, TX......1443
Museum of the Puerto Rican Family of the 19th Century, San Juan, PR............1643
Museum of the Red River, Idabel, OK......1203
Museum of the Western Prairie, Altus, OK................1195
Museum of Transportation, Saint Louis, MO................835
Museum of West Louisiana, Leesville, LA................591
Museum of Yachting, Newport, RI............1314
Museum of Yarmouth History, Yarmouth, ME................626
Museum Village, Monroe, NY................1015
The Museums of Oglebay Institute - Mansion Museum & Glass Museum, Wheeling, WV................1588
The Music House Museum, Acme, MI........722
Musical Box Society International, Houston, TX................1429
Musical Wonder House, Wiscasset, ME......626
Muskegon County Museum, Muskegon, MI................757
Muskogee War Memorial Park & Military Museum, Muskogee, OK..........1205
Mystic Seaport - The Museum of America and the Sea, Mystic, CT..........251

NASA Glenn Research Center's Visitor Center, Cleveland, OH................1155
Naper Settlement, Naperville, IL................447
The National Agricultural Center & Hall of Fame, Bonner Springs, KS................534
National Baseball Hall of Fame and Museum, Inc., Cooperstown, NY............981
The National Border Patrol Museum and Memorial Library, El Paso, TX............1412
National Building Museum, Washington, DC................284
National Civil War Naval Museum at Port Columbus, Columbus, GA............369

National Cowboy & Western Heritage Museum, Oklahoma City, OK................1208
National Cryptologic Museum, Fort Meade, MD................643
National Czech & Slovak Museum & Library, Cedar Rapids, IA................509
National Firearms Museum, Fairfax, VA...1504
National Football Museum, Inc., Canton, OH................1145
National Geographic Museum at Explorers Hall, Washington, DC................285
National Infantry Museum, Fort Benning, GA................372
National Inventors Hall of Fame, Akron, OH................1139
National Museum of American Jewish History, Philadelphia, PA................1284
National Museum of American Jewish Military History, Washington, DC..........286
National Museum of the American Indian, Smithsonian Institution, New York, NY................1034
National Museum of the United States Air Force, Wright-Patterson Air Force Base, OH................1193
National New York Central Railroad Museum, Elkhart, IN................475
National Park Service Vicksburg National Military Park-Cairo Museum, Vicksburg, MS................809
National Postal Museum, Smithsonian Institution, Washington, DC................287
National Railroad Museum, Green Bay, WI................1599
National Railroad Museum and Hall of Fame, Inc., Hamlet, NC................1105
National Route 66 Museum and Old Town Complex, Elk City, OK................1200
National Warplane Museum, Horseheads, NY................999
Native American Exhibit, National Kateri Shrine, Fonda, NY................991
Native American Museum, Terre Haute, IN................500
Naugatuck Historical Society, Naugatuck, CT................251
Nauticus, The National Maritime Center, Norfolk, VA................1522
Navajo Nation Museum, Window Rock, AZ................53
Naval Undersea Museum, Keyport, WA....1557
Navarro County Historical Society, Pioneer Village, Corsicana, TX............1402
Nebraska Prairie Museum of the Phelps County Historical Society, Holdrege, NE................863
Neil Armstrong Air & Space Museum, Wapakoneta, OH................1189
Neligh Mills, Neligh, NE................869
Nelson Pioneer Farm and Museum, Oskaloosa, IA................526
Nemours Mansion and Gardens, Wilmington, DE................274
Nethercutt Collection, Sylmar, CA................190
Netherland Inn House Museum & Boatyard Complex, Kingsport, TN........1368
Nevada County Historical Society, Inc., Nevada City, CA................130
Nevada State Museum, Carson City, NV....876
Nevada State Museum, Las Vegas, Las Vegas, NV................880
Neversink Valley Area Museum, Cuddebackville, NY................984
Neville Public Museum of Brown County, Green Bay, WI................1599
New Braunfels Conservation Society, New Braunfels, TX................1440
New Britain Youth Museum, New Britain, CT................252
New Harmony State Historic Site/Historic New Harmony, New Harmony, IN................494

New Haven Colony Historical Society, New Haven, CT................253
The New Jersey Museum of Agriculture, North Brunswick, NJ................917
New Jersey Office of Historic Sites, Trenton, NJ................927
New Jersey State Police Museum, West Trenton, NJ................930
New London Historical Society, New London, NH................892
New Mexico Museum of Space History, Alamogordo, NM................932
New Orleans Fire Dept. Museum & Educational Center, New Orleans, LA....597
New Richmond Preservation Society, New Richmond, WI................1615
New York City Police Museum, New York, NY................1035
The New York Public Library for the Performing Arts, New York, NY..........1036
Newark Valley Depot Museum, Newark Valley, NY................1042
Newaygo County Museum, Newaygo, MI...758
Newell Museum, Newell, SD................1352
Newseum, Washington, DC................288
The Newsome House Museum & Cultural Center, Newport News, VA.....1520
The Niagara County Historical Center and Niagara County Genealogical Society, Lockport, NY................1010
Nishna Heritage Museum, Oakland, IA.......525
Nobleboro Historical Society, Nobleboro, ME................616
Nobles County Historical Society, Worthington, MN................797
Norfolk Historical Museum, Norfolk, CT....257
The Norman Cleveland County Historical Museum, Norman, OK................1206
North Alabama Railroad Museum, Huntsville, AL................12
North Andover Historical Society, North Andover, MA................698
North Carolina Maritime Museum, Beaufort, NC................1091
North Carolina Transportation Museum, Spencer, NC................1120
North Haven Historical Society, North Haven, CT................257
North House Museum, Lewisburg, WV....1584
North Lee County Historic Center and Santa Fe Depot Museum Complex, Fort Madison, IA................518
North Plainfield Exempt Firemen's Association, North Plainfield, NJ............917
North Platte Valley Museum, Gering, NE....861
North Tonawanda History Museum, North Tonawanda, NY................1043
Northborough Historical Society, Inc., Northborough, MA................700
Northeast Georgia History Center at Brenau University, Gainesville, GA........373
Northeast Louisiana Delta African American Heritage Museum, Monroe, LA................592
Northeast Texas Rural Heritage Museum, Pittsburg, TX................1443
Northeastern Nevada Museum, Elko, NV....876
Northern Indiana Center for History, South Bend, IN................499
Northern Pacific Railway Museum, Toppenish, WA................1575
Northfield Historical Society Museum, Northfield, MN................785
Northport Historical Society Museum, Northport, NY................1044
Northwest Railway Museum, Snoqualmie, WA................1570
Norwood Historical Association and Museum, Norwood, NY................1044
Novato History Museum, Novato, CA........132
Nowata County Historical Society Museum, Nowata, OK................1207

Nowetah's American Indian Museum & Store, New Portland, ME..........615
The Nylander Museum of Natural History, Caribou, ME...............609

O. Henry Museum, Austin, TX..............1391
O. Winston Link Museum, Roanoke, VA...1535
Oak Hill and The Martha Berry Museum, Rome, GA.................382
Oakdale Museum, Oakdale, CA.............132
Oakfield Railroad Museum, Oakfield, ME...616
Oakland County Pioneer and Historical Society, Pontiac, MI.................760
Oaklands Historic House Museum, Murfreesboro, TN....................1376
Oberlin Heritage Center, Oberlin, OH........1180
Ocean City Historical Museum, Inc., Ocean City, NJ.................918
Ocean County Historical Museum, Toms River, NJ.................926
The Octagon House, Hudson, WI..............1600
Octagon House-First Kindergarten in America, Watertown, WI.................1625
Odyssey Maritime Discovery Center, Seattle, WA.................1567
Oklahoma Firefighters Museum, Oklahoma City, OK.................1209
Oklahoma Route 66 Museum, Clinton, OK.................1198
Old Brutus Historical Society, Inc., Weedsport, NY.................1084
Old Castle Museum, Baldwin City, KS........533
Old Coal Mine Museum, Madrid, NM.........943
Old Colony Historical Society, Taunton, MA.................714
Old Constitution House, Windsor, VT........1490
Old Conway Homestead Complex and Museum, Camden, ME.................608
Old Court House Museum-Eva Whitaker Davis Memorial, Vicksburg, MS.........809
Old Courthouse Museum, Santa Ana, CA....178
Old Cowtown Museum, Wichita, KS.........562
Old Davie School Historical Museum, Davie, FL.................302
Old Depot Museum, Ottawa, KS..............555
The Old Depot Railroad Museum, Dassel, MN.................772
Old Dominion Railway Museum, Richmond, VA.................1531
Old Dorchester State Historic Site, Summerville, SC.................1342
Old Economy Village, Ambridge, PA.........1240
Old Fort Bissell, Phillipsburg, KS.................555
Old Fort Harrod State Park Mansion Museum, Harrodsburg, KY.................570
Old Fort House Museum, Fort Edward, NY.................991
Old Fort Jackson, Savannah, GA.............385
Old Fort Meade Museum and Historic Research Association, Fort Meade, SD.1347
Old Greer County Museum & Hall of Fame, Mangum, OK.................1204
Old Iron County Courthouse Museum, Hurley, WI.................1601
The Old Jail Museum, Crawfordsville, IN...473
Old Jefferson Town, Oskaloosa, KS.............555
Old Lighthouse Museum, Stonington, CT....261
Old Mill Museum, Cimarron, NM.............938
Old Mission Santa Ines, Solvang, CA.........187
Old St. Ferdinand's Shrine, Florissant, MO.................815
Old St. Hilary's Church Museum & St. Hilary's Preserve, Tiburon, CA.................192
Old Salem Inc., Winston-Salem, NC.........1126
Old Stone Fort Museum Complex, Schoharie, NY.................1067
Old Sturbridge Village, Sturbridge, MA.......713
Old West Museum, Wimberley, TX...........1462
Old York Historical Society, York, ME.......626
The Oliver Tucker Museum, Beverly, OH.1142
Olmsted County Historical Society, Rochester, MN.................788

Oneida Nation Museum, De Pere, WI........1594
Onondaga Historical Association Museum & Research Center, Syracuse, NY.........1077
Onslow County Museum, Richlands, NC...1117
Ontario County Historical Society, Canandaigua, NY.................975
Ontonagon County Historical Society Museum, Ontonagon, MI.................758
Opelousas Museum and Interpretive Center, Opelousas, LA.................599
Orcas Island Historical Museum, Orcas Island, WA.................1560
Orchard House, Concord, MA.................677
Oregon Electric Railway Historical Society, Inc., Salem, OR.................1236
Oregon Historical Society, Portland, OR...1231
Oregon-Jerusalem Historical Museum, Oregon, OH.................1181
Oregon Military Museum, Clackamas, OR.................1221
Oregon Trail Regional Museum, Baker City, OR.................1219
Orland Historical Society, Orland, ME.......617
Orpheum Children's Science Museum, Champaign, IL.................417
Osage County Historical Society Museum, Pawhuska, OK.................1211
Osage County Historical Society Research Center, Lyndon, KS.................550
The Oscar Anderson House Museum, Anchorage, AK.................22
Oshkosh Public Museum, Oshkosh, WI.....1616
Ossining Historical Society Museum, Ossining, NY.................1047
Otero Museum Association, La Junta, CO...224
Ottawa County Historical Museum, Port Clinton, OH.................1183
Ottawa Scouting Museum, Ottawa, IL.........449
Otter Tail County Historical Society, Fergus Falls, MN.................775
Our House State Memorial, Gallipolis, OH.................1165
Outagamie Museum, Appleton, WI.................1589
Overfield Tavern Museum, Troy, OH.........1188
Overland Trail Museum, Sterling, CO.........232
Owensboro Area Museum of Science & History, Owensboro, KY.................581
Owyhee County Historical Museum, Murphy, ID.................407
Oxford Museum, Inc., Oxford, MD.............650
Ozaukee County Pioneer Village, Saukville, WI.................1620

Pablo Casals Museum, Old San Juan, PR..1641
Pacific County Historical Museum, South Bend, WA.................1571
Pacific Science Center, Seattle, WA.........1568
Painted Post - Erwin Museum at the Depot, Painted Post, NY.................1050
Pajaro Valley Historical Association, Watsonville, CA.................196
Palace of the Governors/New Mexico History Museum, Santa Fe, NM.................949
PALCO, Scotia, CA.................186
Palmer Foundation Chiropractic History, Davenport, IA.................513
Palmer House, Historical Society of Olde Northfield, Northfield, OH.................1180
Palmer Museum, Jewell, KS.................546
Park City Historical Society & Museum, Park City, UT.................1468
Parks, Recreation & Historic Sites Division, Georgia Dept. of Natural Resources, Atlanta, GA.................362
Pascack Historical Society, Park Ridge, NJ.................920
Passaic County Historical Society & Lambert Castle Museum, Paterson, NJ...920
Patee House Museum, Saint Joseph, MO....831
Patten Lumbermen's Museum, Inc., Patten, ME.................618
Patterson Inn Museum/Corning - Painted Post Historical Society, Corning, NY......982

Paul Revere House/Paul Revere Memorial Association, Boston, MA........668
Pavek Museum of Broadcasting, St. Louis Park, MN.................794
Pawnee City Historical Society & Museum, Pawnee City, NE.................871
Peabody Museum of Archaeology & Ethnology, Cambridge, MA.................674
Pearce Collections Museum, Corsicana, TX.................1402
Pearl S. Buck Birthplace Foundation, Hillsboro, WV.................1582
The Pearl S. Buck House, Perkasie, PA.....1275
The Peary-MacMillan Arctic Museum, Brunswick, ME.................608
Pejepscot Historical Society, Brunswick, ME.................608
Pembina State Museum, Pembina, ND.......1135
Pendleton District Agricultural Museum, Pendleton, SC.................1339
Pendleton District Historical, Recreational and Tourism Commission, Pendleton, SC.................1339
Pennsylvania Anthracite Heritage Museum, Scranton, PA.................1299
Pennsylvania Military Museum and 28th Division Shrine, Boalsburg, PA.................1244
Pennsylvania Trolley Museum, Washington, PA.................1305
Pennyroyal Area Museum, Hopkinsville, KY.................572
Penobscot Marine Museum, Searsport, ME.................622
Pensacola Historical Society Museum, Pensacola, FL.................336
Percussive Arts Society Museum, Lawton, OK.................1204
Perkins History Museum, Perkins School for the Blind, Watertown, MA.................716
Perry's Victory & International Peace Memorial, Put-in-Bay, OH.................1183
Petaluma Adobe State Historic Park, Petaluma, CA.................142
Pettaquamscutt Historical Society, Kingston, RI.................1312
Phillips Historical Society, Phillips, ME......618
Phoenix Museum of History, Phoenix, AZ.................41
Pickens County Museum of Art & History, Pickens, SC.................1340
Pike County Historical Society, Milford, PA.................1272
Pilgrim Monument and Provincetown Museum, Provincetown, MA.................704
Pimeria Alta Historical Society, Nogales, AZ.................37
Pinal County Historical Society and Museum, Florence, AZ.................34
Pine Bluff/Jefferson County Historical Museum, Pine Bluff, AR.................66
Pine County Historical Society, Askov, MN.................768
Pioneer Auto Museum, Murdo, SD.................1352
Pioneer Corner Museum, New Holstein, WI.................1615
Pioneer Farm Museum and Ohop Indian Village, Eatonville, WA.................1552
Pioneer Florida Museum Association, Inc., Dade City, FL.................302
Pioneer Heritage Center, Cavalier, ND.......1129
Pioneer-Krier Museum, Ashland, KS.........532
Pioneer Museum, Wild Rose, WI.................1628
Pioneer Museum & The Big Stampede, Fairbanks, AK.................24
Pioneer Museum and Vereins Kirche, Fredericksburg, TX.................1419
Pioneer Museum - Martin County Historical Society, Fairmont, MN.................775
Pioneer Settlement for the Creative Arts, Barberville, FL.................295
Pioneer Town, Wimberley, TX.................1462
Pioneer Trails Regional Museum, Bowman, ND.................1129

Tools and Equipment for Communication–Continued

Pioneers, Trail Drivers and Texas Rangers Memorial Museum, San Antonio, TX 1449

Piper Aviation Museum Foundation, Lock Haven, PA 1269

Pipestone County Historical Museum, Pipestone, MN 786

Pittsford Historical Society Museum, Pittsford, VT 1484

Placer County Museums, Auburn, CA 72

Plains Indians and Pioneers Museum, Woodward, OK 1217

Platen Press Printing Museum, Zion, IL 467

Plymouth Antiquarian Society, Plymouth, MA 704

Plymouth Historical Museum, Plymouth, MI 760

Pocahontas County Iowa Historical Society Museum, Laurens, IA 522

Pocahontas County Museum, Marlinton, WV 1584

Point Reyes National Seashore, Point Reyes, CA 143

Polish Heritage Center, Ashton, NE 856

The Polk County Historical Society, Cedartown, GA 368

Polk County Historical Society, Crookston, MN 771

Polk County Memorial Museum, Livingston, TX 1434

Polk County Museum, Balsam Lake, WI...1590

Polson Museum, Hoquiam, WA 1556

Pony Express Museum, Saint Joseph, MO 831

Pope John Paul II Cultural Center, Washington, DC 289

Portage County Historical Society, Stevens Point, WI 1623

Portsmouth Historical Society, Portsmouth, RI 1316

Post Rock Museum, La Crosse, KS 547

Potsdam Public Museum, Potsdam, NY.....1054

Potter County Historical Society, Coudersport, PA 1248

Potts Inn Museum, Pottsville, AR 66

Pound Ridge Society/Museum, Pound Ridge, NY 1055

Prairie Trails Museum of Wayne County, Corydon, IA 512

Pratt County Historical Society Museum, Pratt, KS 556

Promont House Museum, Milford, OH 1176

Public Museum of West Michigan, Grand Rapids, MI 744

Pueblo Weisbrod Aircraft Museum, Pueblo, CO 230

Puget Sound Coast Artillery Museum at Fort Worden, Port Townsend, WA 1562

Putnam County Historical Society Museum, Kalida, OH 1169

Putnam County Museum, Greencastle, IN ...479

Putnam Museum of History & Natural Science, Davenport, IA 513

Queen Emma Summer Palace, Honolulu, HI 398

Queen Mary Museum, Long Beach, CA 111

Queens Museum of Art, Queens, NY 1056

QV Historical Society at Carriage House Museum, Camden, NY 974

R.E. Olds Transportation Museum, Lansing, MI 751

Racine Heritage Museum, Racine, WI 1619

Radio & Television Museum, Bowie, MD...638

Railroad and Heritage Museum Inc., Temple, TX 1454

Railroad House Historical Association Museum, Sanford, NC 1119

Railroad Museum of Pennsylvania, Strasburg, PA 1302

Railroaders Memorial Museum, Altoona, PA 1240

Raleigh City Museum, Raleigh, NC 1117

Ralls Historical Museum, Ralls, TX...........1445

Randolph County Historical Museum, Winchester, IN 503

Randolph County Museum (At Beverly), Beverly, WV 1580

Randolph Historical Society, Inc., Randolph, VT 1485

Rankin Museum, Rankin, TX 1445

Rankin Museum, Inc., Ellerbe, NC............1100

Ransom County Historical Society, Fort Ransom, ND 1131

Raton Museum, Raton, NM 945

Reading Historical Society Museum, Reading, OH 1184

Readsboro Historical Society, Readsboro, VT 1486

Rebel State Historic Site & Louisiana Country Music Museum, Marthaville, LA 592

Red Earth Museum, Oklahoma City, OK...1210

Red Hill-Patrick Henry National Memorial, Brookneal, VA 1498

Red River Historical Museum, Sherman, TX 1452

Red River Historical Society Museum, Clay City, KY 566

Redwood County Historical Society, Redwood Falls, MN 787

Refugio County Museum, Refugio, TX 1445

Reginald F. Lewis Museum of Maryland African American History and Culture, Baltimore, MD 636

Regional Science & Discovery Center, Horseheads, NY 999

Reitz Home Museum, Evansville, IN 476

Remick Country Doctor Museum and Farm, Tamworth, NH 896

Remington Firearms Museum and Country Store, Ilion, NY 1002

Reno County Museum, Hutchinson, KS 545

Renton Historical Society and Museum, Renton, WA 1564

Renville County Historical Society, Inc., Mohall, ND 1135

Reuben H. Fleet Science Center, San Diego, CA 158

Reuel B. Pritchett Museum, Bridgewater, VA 1497

Reverend Dan Foster House, Museum of the Weathersfield Historical Society, Weathersfield, VT 1489

Rice County Museum of History, Faribault, MN 775

Richard Salter Storrs House, Longmeadow, MA 691

Richards DAR House Museum, Mobile, AL 15

Richardson-Bates House Museum, Oswego, NY 1048

Richland County Historical Museum, Wahpeton, ND 1137

Richland County Museum, Lexington, OH 1172

Richmond Museum of History, Richmond, CA 148

Rifle Creek Museum, Rifle, CO 231

Riley County Historical Museum, Manhattan, KS 551

Rim Country Museum, Payson, AZ 38

Rimrocker Historical Museum of West Montrose County, Naturita, CO 229

Riordan Mansion State Historic Park, Flagstaff, AZ 33

Ripley County, Indiana, Historical Society Museum, Versailles, IN............502

Riversdale House Mansion, Riverdale Park, MD 651

Riverton Museum, Riverton, WY 1637

Roaring Twenties Antique Car Museum, Hood, VA 1511

Robbins Hunter Museum, Avery-Downer House, Granville, OH 1167

Roberson Museum and Science Center, Binghamton, NY 962

Robert C. Williams American Museum of Papermaking at Georgia Tech, Atlanta, GA 363

Robert R. McCormick Museum at Cantigny, Wheaton, IL 465

Rochester Museum & Science Center, Rochester, NY 1059

The Rock and Roll Hall of Fame and Museum, Cleveland, OH 1155

Rock Springs Historical Museum, Rock Springs, WY 1638

Rockingham Free Public Library and Museum, Bellows Falls, VT 1476

Rocky Ford Historical Museum, Rocky Ford, CO 231

Rocky Reach Dam, Wenatchee, WA 1577

Roger Tory Peterson Institute of Natural History, Jamestown, NY 1005

Rogers Historical Museum, Rogers, AR 67

Rollo Jamison Museum, Platteville, WI.....1617

Rome Area History Museum, Rome, GA 382

Rome Historical Society Museum, Rome, NY 1061

Roosevelt County Museum, Portales, NM ...944

Rosalie House, Eureka Springs, AR 57

Rose Center Museum, Morristown, TN 1376

Roseau County Historical Museum and Interpretive Center, Roseau, MN 788

Rosenberg Library, Galveston, TX 1422

Rosicrucian Egyptian Museum, San Jose, CA 172

Ross County Historical Society, Inc., Chillicothe, OH 1147

Rothschild House State Park, Port Townsend, WA 1562

The Roy Rogers-Dale Evans Museum and Theater, Branson, MO 811

Royalton Historical Society, Royalton, VT 1486

Runestone Museum, Alexandria, MN...........767

Rural Life Museum & Windrush Gardens, Baton Rouge, LA 587

Rusk County Historical Society, Ladysmith, WI 1604

Ruth and Charles Gilb Arcadia Historical Museum, Arcadia, CA 71

Ryerss Museum & Library, Philadelphia, PA 1287

S.S. Meteor Maritime Museum, Superior, WI 1624

Sacramento Mountains Historical Museum, Cloudcroft, NM 938

Sahuaro Ranch Historical Area, Glendale, AZ 35

St. Albans Historical Museum, Saint Albans, VT 1486

St. Charles Heritage Center, Saint Charles, IL 457

St. Francis County Museum, Forrest City, AR 57

St. George's United Methodist Church, Philadelphia, PA 1287

St. John's Episcopal Church, Richmond, VA 1531

St. Louis Science Center, Saint Louis, MO 836

St. Paul Museum, Randleman, NC 1117

St. Petersburg Museum of History, Saint Petersburg, FL 342

Ste. Genevieve Museum, Sainte Genevieve, MO 838

Salamanca Rail Museum, Salamanca, NY .1063

Salem Art Association-Bush House Museum and Bush Barn Art Center, Salem, OR 1236

Salem Historical Society and Museum, Salem, OH..............1184

The Salem Museum, Salem, VA.................1536

Salisbury House Foundation, Des Moines, IA.........................515

The Salvation Army Southern Historical Center & Museum, Atlanta, GA.............363

Sam Brown Log House, Browns Valley, MN.......................770

Sam Houston Memorial Museum, Huntsville, TX.....................1430

Sam Houston Regional Library & Research Center, Liberty, TX.................1434

Sam Rayburn House Museum, Bonham, TX.................................1397

San Buenaventura Mission Museum, Ventura, CA..........................195

San Diego Air & Space Museum, San Diego, CA.............................159

San Dieguito Heritage Museum, Encinitas, CA.............................92

San Francisco Maritime National Historical Park, San Francisco, CA.........169

San Jacinto Museum of History Association, La Porte, TX.....................1433

San Joaquin County Historical Society & Museum, Lodi, CA.........................109

San Juan County Historical Society Museum, Silverton, CO.....................232

San Juan Historical Society, Friday Harbor, WA..............................1555

San Luis Obispo County Historical Museum, San Luis Obispo, CA...............174

Sanborn Area Historical Society, Sanborn, NY..............................1064

Sandown Historical Society and Museum, Sandown, NH..........................896

Sandpoint Lighthouse, Escanaba, MI..........741

Sandusky Library Follett House Museum, Sandusky, OH..........................1185

Sandwich Historical Society, Sandwich, IL..............................457

Sanford Museum, Sanford, FL..............343

Santa Fe Trail Center, Larned, KS...............547

Santa Fe Trail Museum, Ingalls, KS.............545

Santa Fe Trail Museum/Trinidad History Museum, Trinidad, CO.........................234

Santa Maria Museum of Flight, Inc., Santa Maria, CA..........................183

Santa Maria Valley Historical Museum, Santa Maria, CA..........................183

Sapulpa Historical Museum, Sapulpa, OK.1213

Sarasota Classic Car Museum, Sarasota, FL.................................345

Sarpy County Historical Museum, Bellevue, NE.............................857

Satterlee Clark House, Horicon, WI...............1600

Sauk Prairie Area Historical Society, Inc., Prairie du Sac, WI.........................1619

Sawyer's Sandhills Museum, Valentine, NE.................................874

Scarborough Historical Museum, Scarborough, ME..........................621

Schenectady County Historical Society, Schenectady, NY..........................1067

Schenectady Museum and Suits-Bueche Planetarium, Schenectady, NY.............1067

Schminck Memorial Museum, Lakeview, OR.................................1227

Scholte House Museum, Pella, IA...............527

School of Nations Museum, Elsah, IL.........433

Schoolcraft County Historical Society, Manistique, MI..........................753

The Schubert Club Museum of Musical Instruments, Saint Paul, MN..................792

Schuyler County Historical Society, Inc., Montour Falls, NY.............................1015

Schwenkfelder Library & Heritage Center, Pennsburg, PA.........................1275

Science Museum of Virginia, Richmond, VA.................................1531

Scitrek, The Science and Technology Museum of Atlanta, Valdosta, GA..........389

Scotia-Glenville Children's Museum, Scotia, NY..............................1068

Scotland Heritage Chapel & Museum, Scotland, SD.............................1355

Scurry County Museum, Snyder, TX.........1453

SEE Science Center, Manchester, NH..........892

Seminole Nation Museum, Wewoka, OK...1217

Seneca County Museum, Tiffin, OH...........1186

1797 Ezekiel Harris House, Augusta, GA....366

1768 Jeremiah Lee Mansion, Marblehead, MA..............................693

The Sevier County Historical Museum, De Queen, AR.............................56

Sewall-Belmont House and Museum, Washington, DC..........................290

Seward County Historical Society Museum, Goehner, NE..........................861

Seward Museum, Seward, AK...................27

Shaftsbury Historical Society, Shaftsbury, VT.................................1487

Shaker Heritage Society, Albany, NY..........956

Shaker Museum, New Gloucester, ME........615

The Shaker Museum and Library, Old Chatham, NY..............................1045

Shaker Village of Pleasant Hill, Harrodsburg, KY.........................571

Shandy Hall, Geneva, OH.........................1166

Sharpsteen Museum, Calistoga, CA..............80

Shasta College Museum & Research Center, Redding, CA.........................146

Shasta State Historic Park, Shasta, CA........186

Shawnee Town, Shawnee, KS....................558

Sheboygan County Historical Museum, Sheboygan, WI.............................1621

Shelburne Museum, Inc., Shelburne, VT...1487

Sheldon Museum and Cultural Center, Inc., Haines, AK.........................25

Sherwood-Davidson House, Newark, OH..1178

Shiloh Museum of Ozark History, Springdale, AR.............................68

Shippensburg Historical Society Museum, Shippensburg, PA.........................1300

Shoreline Historical Museum, Seattle, WA.................................1569

Shores Memorial Museum, Lyndon Center, VT.............................1481

Sibley County Historical Museum, Henderson, MN.............................777

Sierra Mono Indian Museum, North Fork, CA.................................131

Silent Wings Museum, Lubbock, TX.........1435

Siloam Springs Museum, Siloam Springs, AR.................................68

Silt Historical Society, Silt, CO.................232

Silver Cliff Museum, Silver Cliff, CO..........232

Silvercreek Museum, Freeport, IL.............435

Siskiyou County Museum, Yreka, CA.........200

Skagit County Historical Museum, La Conner, WA.............................1557

Skagway Museum & Archives, Skagway, AK.................................28

Slidell Museum, Slidell, LA....................602

Slifer House, Lewisburg, PA....................1268

Sloan Museum, Flint, MI.........................742

Smith County Historical Society, Tyler, TX.................................1456

Smith Robertson Museum & Cultural Center, Jackson, MS.........................804

Smith-Zimmermann Heritage Museum, Madison, SD.............................1351

Smyth County Museum, Marion, VA.........1516

Snyder Museum & Creative Arts Center, Bastrop, LA.............................585

Socrates Sculpture Park, Long Island City, NY.............................1012

Sod House Museum, Aline, OK.................1195

Somerset Historical Center, Somerset, PA.1300

Somervell County Historical Museum, Glen Rose, TX.............................1423

Sony Wonder Technology Lab, New York, NY.............................1039

Sosa-Carrillo-Fremont House Museum, Tucson, AZ.............................50

South Bannock County Historical Center, Lava Hot Springs, ID.........................407

South Boston-Halifax County Museum of Fine Arts & History, South Boston, VA.............................1536

South Carolina Law Enforcement Officers Hall of Fame, Columbia, SC.................1330

South Coast Railroad Museum at Goleta Depot, Goleta, CA.........................100

South County Historical Society, Arroyo Grande, CA.............................72

South County Museum Inc., Narragansett, RI.................................1313

South Dakota Hall of Fame, Chamberlain, SD.............................1345

South Florida Science Museum, West Palm Beach, FL.........................353

South Milwaukee Historical Society Museum, South Milwaukee, WI...........1622

South Park City Museum, Fairplay, CO.......215

South Sutton Old Store Museum, South Sutton, NH.............................896

South Texas Museum, Alice, TX.................1386

South Wood County Historical Corp., Wisconsin Rapids, WI.........................1628

Southeastern Railway Museum, Duluth, GA.................................371

Southern California Chapter Railway & Locomotive Historical Society, Pomona, CA.............................143

The Southern Museum of Civil War and Locomotive History, Kennesaw, GA.......375

Southern Museum of Flight, Birmingham, AL.................................6

Southern Oregon Historical Society, Jacksonville, OR.........................1226

Southern Plains Indian Museum, Anadarko, OK.............................1196

Southwest Florida Museum of History, Fort Myers, FL.........................309

Southwest Virginia Museum Historical State Park, Big Stone Gap, VA.............1497

Space Farms Zoological Park and Museum, Sussex, NJ.........................925

Spartanburg County Regional Museum of History, Spartanburg, SC.................1341

Spellman Museum of Stamps and Postal History, Weston, MA.........................719

Spirit of '76 Museum, Wellington, OH......1190

SPJST Library Archives & Museum, Temple, TX.............................1455

Spring Grove Hospital Center, Alumni Museum, Catonsville, MD.................639

Spring Street Historical Museum, Shreveport, LA.........................602

Springfield Museum, Springfield, OR.......1236

Springfield Museums - Connecticut Valley Historical Museum, Springfield, MA.............................710

Springfield Museums - Springfield Science Museum, Springfield, MA..........711

Springs Museum, Springs, PA...................1301

Spurlock Museum, University of Illinois at Urbana-Champaign, Urbana, IL..........462

Squished Penny Museum, Washington, DC.................................291

Stafford County Historical Society Museum, Stafford, KS.........................558

Stanley Museum, Inc., Kingfield, ME..........613

Stanly County Historic Preservation Commission and Museum, Albemarle, NC.................................1088

State Capital Publishing Museum, Guthrie, OK.............................1202

State Historical Society of Iowa, Des Moines, IA.............................515

State Historical Society of North Dakota, Bismarck, ND.............................1128

Tools and Equipment for Communication–Continued

Stauth Memorial Museum, Montezuma, KS 553

STAX Museum of American Soul Music, Memphis, TN 1376

The Steamboat Arabia Museum, Kansas City, MO 822

Steamboat Bertrand Collection, Missouri Valley, IA 524

Steamship Keewatin, Douglas, MI 738

Steamship William G. Mather Museum, Cleveland, OH 1156

Stearns Collection of Musical Instruments, Ann Arbor, MI 725

Stearns History Museum, Saint Cloud, MN 788

Steele County Historical Society, Hope, ND 1133

Steilacoom Historical Museum Association, Steilacoom, WA 1572

Stephen Foster Folk Culture Center State Park, White Springs, FL 354

Stephens County Historical Society and Museum, Duncan, OK 1199

The Stephens Museum, Fayette, MO 815

Stephenson County Historical Society, Freeport, IL 436

Stephenville Museum, Stephenville, TX ...1454

Steppingstone Museum, Havre de Grace, MD 647

Sterne-Hoya House Museum and Library, Nacogdoches, TX 1440

Stevens County Gas and Historical Museum, Hugoton, KS 544

Stevens Museum, Salem, IN 498

Stockbridge Library Historical Collection, Stockbridge, MA 713

Stockholm Historical Society Museum, Stockholm, ME 623

The Stone House Museum, Belchertown, MA 662

Stonefield Historic Site, Cassville, WI 1593

Stones River National Battlefield, Murfreesboro, TN 1377

Stonewall Jackson Museum at Hupp's Hill, Strasburg, VA 1539

Storrowton Village Museum, West Springfield, MA 718

Stoughton Historical Society, Stoughton, MA 713

Strategic Air & Space Museum, Ashland, NE 856

The Stratford Historical Society & Catherine B. Mitchell Museum, Stratford, CT 262

Strong - National Museum of Play, Rochester, NY 1060

Stuart Heritage Museum, Stuart, FL 346

Stuart House City Museum, Mackinac Island, MI 752

Stuhr Museum of the Prairie Pioneer, Grand Island, NE 862

Stutsman County Memorial Museum, Jamestown, ND 1133

Suffolk County Historical Society, Riverhead, NY 1057

Sullivan County Historical Society, Inc., Hurleyville, NY 1001

Sullivan Museum and History Center, Northfield, VT 1483

Summit County Historical Society, Akron, OH 1139

Summit Historical Society, Breckenridge, CO 204

Sun Prairie Historical Library & Museum, Sun Prairie, WI 1624

Sunset Crater Volcano National Monument, Flagstaff, AZ 33

Superstition Mountain Lost Dutchman Museum, Apache Junction, AZ 30

Susquehanna County Historical Society & Free Library Association, Montrose, PA 1272

Susquehanna Museum of Havre de Grace Inc. at the Lock House, Havre de Grace, MD 647

Swarthout Memorial Museum, La Crosse, WI 1603

Swedish American Museum Association of Chicago, Chicago, IL 428

Sweetwater County Historical Museum, Green River, WY 1633

Swenson Memorial Museum of Stephens County, Breckenridge, TX 1397

Swift County Historical Society, Benson, MN 769

Swisher County Archives and Museum Association, Tulia, TX 1456

Swiss Historical Village, New Glarus, WI .1615

T.B. Ferguson Home, Watonga, OK 1216

Talkeetna Historical Society and Museum, Talkeetna, AK 28

Tarpon Springs Cultural Center, Tarpon Springs, FL 351

The Telephone Museum, Ellsworth, ME 610

Telephone Museum of New Mexico, Albuquerque, NM 935

Telluride Historical Museum, Telluride, CO 233

Temecula Valley Museum, Temecula, CA ...191

Tempe Historical Museum, Tempe, AZ 46

Tennessee Central Railway Museum, Nashville, TN 1380

Tennessee Historical Society, Nashville, TN 1380

Tennessee Museum of Aviation, Sevierville, TN 1383

Tennessee Valley Railroad Museum Inc., Chattanooga, TN 1363

Territorial Capital-Lane Museum, Lecompton, KS 549

Territorial Statehouse State Park & Museum, Fillmore, UT 1465

Terwilliger Museum, Waterloo, NY 1083

Teutopolis Monastery Museum, Teutopolis, IL 461

Texana Museum and Library Association, Edna, TX 1410

Texas City Museum, Texas City, TX 1455

Texas Energy Museum, Beaumont, TX 1395

Texas Forestry Museum, Lufkin, TX 1436

Texas Heritage Museum, Hillsboro, TX 1424

Texas Maritime Museum, Rockport, TX ...1446

Texas Music Museum, Austin, TX 1392

Texas Ranger Hall of Fame and Museum, Waco, TX 1459

Texas Transportation Museum, San Antonio, TX 1451

This Is The Place Heritage Park, Salt Lake City, UT 1472

Thomas E. McMillan Museum, Brewton, AL 6

Thomas Edison Birthplace Museum, Milan, OH 1176

Thomas Edison House, Louisville, KY 579

Three Rivers Museum, Muskogee, OK 1205

Timpanogos Cave National Monument, American Fork, UT 1462

Tioga County Historical Society Museum, Owego, NY 1048

Tippecanoe County Historical Association, Lafayette, IN 487

Tobacco Farm Life Museum, Inc., Kenly, NC 1107

Tom Mix Museum, Dewey, OK 1199

Tombstone Courthouse State Historic Park, Tombstone, AZ 46

Top of Oklahoma Historical Museum, Blackwell, OK 1197

Torrington Historical Society, Inc., Torrington, CT 263

Totem Heritage Center, Ketchikan, AK 26

Town of Yorktown Museum, Yorktown Heights, NY 1087

Traill County Historical Society, Hillsboro, ND 1132

Traverse County Historical Society, Wheaton, MN 796

Treasures of the Sea Exhibit, Georgetown, DE 271

Trenton Historical Museum, Trenton, MI ...765

Tri-County Historical Society & Museum, Inc., Herington, KS 544

Triangle Tattoo & Museum, Fort Bragg, CA 95

Triton Museum of Art, Santa Clara, CA 181

Tryon Palace Historic Sites and Gardens, New Bern, NC 1112

Tsa Mo Ga Memorial Museum, Plains, TX 1443

T.T. Wentworth, Jr. Florida State Museum, Pensacola, FL 336

Tubac Presidio State Historic Park, Tubac, AZ 47

Tuck Museum, Hampton, NH 888

Tulare County Museum at Mooney Grove Park, Visalia, CA 195

Tularosa Basin Historical Society Museum, Alamogordo, NM 932

Turabo University, Gurabo, PR 1641

The Turner Museum, Sarasota, FL 345

Turquoise Museum, Albuquerque, NM 936

Twinsburg Historical Society, Twinsburg, OH 1188

Tyler Arboretum, Media, PA 1271

UCR/California Museum of Photography, Riverside, CA 150

USS Massachusetts Memorial Committee, Inc., Fall River, MA 682

Ukrainian-American Museum & Archives, Warren, MI 766

Ulster County Historical Society, Marbletown, NY 1013

Union County Heritage Museum, New Albany, MS 806

Union County Historical Complex, Creston, IA 512

Union County Historical Society Museum, Blairsville, GA 366

Union County Museum, Union, OR 1238

Union Mills Homestead & Grist Mill, Westminster, MD 656

Union Station Kansas City, Inc., Kansas City, MO 823

United States Senate Commission on Art, Washington, DC 293

The University Museum Collections, Fayetteville, AR 57

University of Northern Iowa Museums & Collections, Cedar Falls, IA 508

University of Pennsylvania Museum of Archaeology and Anthropology, Philadelphia, PA 1288

Upham Mansion, Marshfield, WI 1608

U.S. Army Air Defense Artillery Museum, Fort Bliss, TX 1414

U.S. Army Center of Military History, Museum Division, Fort McNair, DC 275

U.S. Army Engineer Museum, Fort Leonard Wood, MO 815

U.S. Army Finance Corps Museum, Fort Jackson, SC 1333

U.S. Army Signal Corps Museum, Fort Gordon, GA 372

U.S. Coast Guard Museum, New London, CT 255

U.S. Navy Seabee Museum, Port Hueneme, CA 143

USS Alabama Battleship Memorial Park, Mobile, AL 15

USS Constellation Museum, Baltimore, MD 636

Utah State Historical Society, Salt Lake City, UT 1473

Utica Museum, Utica, MT 854

Vacaville Museum, Vacaville, CA 194
The Valdez Museum & Historical
   Archive Association, Inc., Valdez, AK 29
Valentine Richmond History Center,
   Richmond, VA 1532
Valentown Museum, Victor, NY 1081
Vallejo Naval & Historical Museum,
   Vallejo, CA 194
Valley Community Historical Society,
   Inc., Valley, NE 874
Valley County Pioneer Museum,
   Glasgow, MT 847
Van Buren County Historical Society,
   Keosauqua, IA 521
Van Wyck Homestead Museum, Fishkill,
   NY 989
Vann House, Chatsworth, GA 368
Vashon Maury Island Heritage
   Association, Vashon, WA 1576
Vermont Marble Museum, Proctor, VT 1485
Vernon County Historical Museum,
   Viroqua, WI 1625
The Vestal Museum, Vestal, NY 1081
Victor Heritage Museum, Victor, MT...........854
Victor Valley Museum & Art Gallery,
   Apple Valley, CA..71
Vigo County Historical Museum, Terre
   Haute, IN 501
Vikingsholm, Tahoma, CA 191
Village of Elsah Museum, Elsah, IL 433
The Vinalhaven Historical Society
   Museum, Vinalhaven, ME 624
Vincennes State Historic Site, Indiana
   Territory, Vincennes, IN 503
Virginia Air & Space Center, Hampton,
   VA 1510
Virginia City J. Spencer Watkins
   Memorial Museum, Virginia City, MT....854
Virginia Museum of Transportation, Inc.,
   Roanoke, VA 1536
The Virginia War Museum, Newport
   News, VA 1520
Vista Historical Museum, Vista, CA.............196
Vizcaya Museum and Gardens, Miami,
   FL 326
Volendam Windmill Museum Inc.,
   Milford, NJ 911

W.C. Handy Home Museum and Library,
   Florence, AL 9
W.H. Over Museum, Vermillion, SD..........1358
W.K. Gordon Center for Industrial
   History of Texas, Mingus, TX 1439
Wabasha County Museum, Wabasha
   County Historical Society at Reads
   Landing, Reads Landing, MN.................787
Wabaunsee County Historical Museum,
   Alma, KS 532
Wahkiakum County Historical Museum,
   Cathlamet, WA 1550
Wakefield House Museum, Blue Earth,
   MN 769
Wakefield Museum Association,
   Wakefield, KS 560
Wallace District Mining Museum,
   Wallace, ID 410
Wantagh Historical & Preservation
   Society, Wantagh, NY 1081
Wapello County Historical Museum,
   Ottumwa, IA 526
Ward County Historical Society, Minot,
   ND 1135
Warhawk Air Museum, Nampa, ID 408
Warren County Historical Society
   Museum, Lebanon, OH 1171
Warren Historical Society, Warren, ME 624
Warrick County Museum, Inc., Boonville,
   IN 470
Warsaw Historical Museum, Warsaw, NY .1082
Waseca County Historical Society,
   Waseca, MN..796

Washakie Museum, Worland, WY 1639
Washburn County Historical Society
   Museum, Shell Lake, WI 1621
Washburn Historical Museum & Cultural
   Center, Inc. aka Washburn Cultural
   Center, Washburn, WI 1625
Washington County Historical
   Association, Fort Calhoun, NE 860
Washington County Historical Society,
   Washington, KS 560
Washington County Historical Society,
   Portland, OR 1233
Washington County Historical Society
   Inc., West Bend, WI 1627
Washington County Rural Heritage
   Museum, Boonsboro, MD 637
Washington Museum & Tourist Center,
   Washington, LA 603
Washington National Cathedral,
   Washington, DC 294
Waterloo Area Historical Society, Grass
   Lake, MI 744
Watertown Historical Society, Inc.,
   Watertown, CT 264
Watkins Community Museum of History,
   Lawrence, KS 548
Watts Towers Arts Center, Los Angeles,
   CA 122
Waukesha County Museum, Waukesha,
   WI 1625
Wayne County Historical Society,
   Honesdale, PA...1261
Wayne State University Museum of
   Anthropology, Detroit, MI 738
Webster House Museum, Elkhorn, WI 1596
Weems-Botts Museum, Dumfries, VA........1503
Wellfleet Historical Society Museum,
   Wellfleet, MA 717
Wells Auto Museum, Wells, ME 625
Wells Fargo History Museum,
   Minneapolis, MN 783
Weslaco Museum, Weslaco, TX 1461
West Allis Historical Society Museum,
   West Allis, WI 1626
West Overton Museums, Scottdale, PA 1298
West Pasco Historical Society Museum
   and Library, New Port Richey, FL 329
West Virginia State Farm Museum, Point
   Pleasant, WV 1586
West Virginia State Museum, Charleston,
   WV 1581
Western Hennepin County Pioneers
   Association, Long Lake, MN...................779
Western Historic Radio Museum, Virginia
   City, NV 882
Western Hotel/Museum, Lancaster, CA........108
Western Reserve Historical Society,
   Cleveland, OH 1156
Western Springs Historical Society,
   Western Springs, IL 464
Westminster Historical Society,
   Westminster, VT 1490
Weston Woods Institute, Weston, CT 266
Westport Maritime Museum, Westport,
   WA 1578
The Wethersfield Historical Society,
   Wethersfield, CT 266
Wexford County Historical Society &
   Museum, Cadillac, MI..............................731
Wharton County Historical Museum,
   Wharton, TX 1461
Wheels O' Time Museum, Peoria, IL...........451
Whipple House Museum, Ashland
   Historical Society, Ashland, NH 883
Whiskeytown Unit,
   Whiskeytown-Shasta-Trinity National
   Recreation Area, Whiskeytown, CA........198
White County Historical Society, Carmi,
   IL 415
White Pine Public Museum, Ely, NV...........877
Whitehead Memorial Museum, Del Rio,
   TX 1409

Whitewater Historical Museum,
   Whitewater, WI..1628
Whitley County Historical Museum,
   Columbia City, IN 472
Wilbur Wright Birthplace & Interpretive
   Center, Hagerstown, IN............................480
Wilkin County Historical Society,
   Breckenridge, MN 770
Willapa Seaport Museum, Raymond, WA..1564
William B. Ide Adobe State Historic
   Park, Red Bluff, CA 146
William Clark Market House Museum,
   Paducah, KY...582
William Hammond Mathers Museum,
   Bloomington, IN 470
William Heath Davis House Museum
   administered by Gaslamp Quarter
   Historical Foundation, San Diego, CA....162
William McKinley Presidential Library &
   Museum, Canton, OH.............................1146
Williamson County Historical Society,
   Marion, IL...444
Willowbrook Museum Village, Newfield,
   ME..616
Wilmington Railroad Museum,
   Wilmington, NC......................................1124
Wilson County Historical Society
   Museum, Fredonia, KS.............................540
Wilton House Museum, Richmond, VA 1534
Winchendon Historical Society, Inc.,
   Winchendon, MA 720
Windham Textile and History Museum
   (The Mill Museum), Willimantic, CT 267
Wing Luke Asian Museum, Seattle, WA...1569
Winnebago Area Museum, Winnebago,
   MN..797
Winnetka Historical Society, Winnetka,
   IL...466
Winona County Historical Museum,
   Winona, MN 797
Wiscasset, Waterville & Farmington
   Railway Museum, Alna, ME....................603
Wisconsin Automotive Museum,
   Hartford, WI 1600
Wisconsin Historical Museum, Madison,
   WI 1606
Wisconsin Maritime Museum,
   Manitowoc, WI.......................................1607
Wisconsin Veterans Museum-King, King,
   WI 1602
Wisconsin Veterans Museum-Madison,
   Madison, WI 1606
Wolf House Museum, Manhattan, KS..........552
Wolf Point Area Historical Society, Inc.,
   Wolf Point, MT 855
The Wolfsonian - Florida International
   University, Miami Beach, FL....................327
Wood County Historical Center and
   Museum, Bowling Green, OH 1143
Woodrow Wilson House, Washington,
   DC..294
Woodside Store Historic Site, Woodside,
   CA..199
Woodson County Historical Society,
   Yates Center, KS......................................564
Woodstock Museum of Shenandoah
   County, Inc., Woodstock, VA 1546
Worcester Historical Museum, Worcester,
   MA..721
Workman & Temple Family Homestead
   Museum, City of Industry, CA 85
The Works: Ohio Center for History, Art
   & Technology, Newark, OH...................1179
World Kite Museum & Hall of Fame,
   Long Beach, WA.....................................1558
World of Scouting Museum, Valley
   Forge, PA 1304
Wrangell Museum, Wrangell, AK..................29
Wray Museum, Wray, CO............................235
Wren's Nest, Atlanta, GA 364
Wyalusing Valley Museum, Wyalusing,
   PA...1309

Tools and Equipment for Communication–Continued

Wyandot County Historical Society, Upper Sandusky, OH...............1188
Wyandotte Museum, Wyandotte, MI...........766
Wyoming Pioneer Memorial Museum, Douglas, WY...............1632
Wyoming Territorial Prison State Historic Site, Laramie, WY...............1636

Yellowstone Gateway Museum of Park County, Livingston, MT...........850
Yucaipa Valley Historical Society Museum, Yucaipa, CA...............201
Yuma Crossing State Historic Park, Yuma, AZ...............54
Yuma Territorial Prison State Historic Park, Yuma, AZ...............54

Zeum, San Francisco, CA...............170
Zoar State Memorial, Zoar, OH...............1194

Tools and Equipment for Materials

A.R. Bowman Memorial Museum, Prineville, OR...............1234
Academy Hall Museum of the Rocky Hill Historical Society, Inc., Rocky Hill, CT...............259
The Accokeek Foundation, Inc., Accokeek, MD...............627
Adair County Historical Society, Inc., Kirksville, MO...............824
Adams County Historical Museum, Decatur, IN...............474
Adams County Historical Society, Gettysburg, PA...............1255
Adams County Historical Society Museum, Lind, WA...............1558
Adams County Historical Society Museum, Brighton, CO...............204
Adams Old Stone Grist Mill, Bellows Falls, VT...............1476
Adirondack History Center, Elizabethtown, NY...............987
The Adirondack Museum, Blue Mountain Lake, NY...............963
Adventure Science Center, Nashville, TN..1377
African American Historical Museum & Cultural Center of Iowa, Cedar Rapids, IA...............508
African-American Museum and Library at Oakland, Oakland, CA...............132
African Art Museum of the S.M.A. Fathers, Tenafly, NJ...............926
Afro-American Historical Society Museum, Jersey City, NJ...............908
Agricultural and Industrial Museum, York County Heritage Trust, York, PA...........1309
Agricultural Heritage Museum, Boerne, TX...............1396
The Agricultural Memories Museum, Penn Yan, NY...............1052
Agriculture Museum, Merced, CA...............125
Agrirama, Georgia's Living History Museum & Village, Tifton, GA...............388
Aiken County Historical Museum, Aiken, SC...............1320
Akta Lakota Museum and Cultural Center, Chamberlain, SD...............1345
Akwesasne Museum, Hogansburg, NY........998
Alabama Agricultural Museum, Dothan, AL...............8
Alabama Center for Traditional Culture, Montgomery, AL...............15
Alabama Mining Museum, Dora, AL...............7
Alabama Museum of Natural History, Tuscaloosa, AL...............19
Alachua County Historic Trust: Matheson Museum, Inc., Gainesville, FL...............310
Alamance Battleground State Historic Site, Burlington, NC...............1092

Alaska Heritage Museum at Wells Fargo, Anchorage, AK...............21
Alaska Museum of Natural History, Anchorage, AK...............21
Alaska Native Heritage Center, Anchorage, AK...............22
Alaska State Museum, Juneau, AK...............25
Albany Historical Society, Inc., Sabetha, KS...............557
Albany Regional Museum, Albany, OR.....1217
Albuquerque Museum, Albuquerque, NM....932
Alden Historical Society, Inc., Alden, NY...956
Alden House Historic Site, Duxbury, MA...680
Alexander & Baldwin Sugar Museum, Puunene, HI...............401
Alexander House, Port Edwards, WI.........1618
Alexandre Mouton House/Lafayette Museum, Lafayette, LA...............589
Alger County Heritage Center, Munising, MI...............757
Allaire Village Inc., Farmingdale, NJ...........903
Allegan County Historical Society and Old Jail Museum, Allegan, MI...............723
Allegany County Historical Society, Inc., Cumberland, MD...............641
Allegheny Portage Railroad National Historic Site and Johnstown Flood National Memorial, Gallitzin, PA...........1255
Allen County Museum, Lima, OH.............1172
Alling Coverlet Museum, Palmyra, NY.....1050
Allison-Antrim Museum, Inc., Greencastle, PA...............1257
Almond Historical Society/Hagadorn House Museum, Almond, NY...............957
Amador County Museum, Jackson, CA.......105
Amana Heritage Museum, Amana, IA.........504
Amelia Island Museum of History, Fernandina Beach, FL...............306
America On Wheels, Inc., Allentown, PA..1239
American Airlines C.R. Smith Museum, Fort Worth, TX...............1416
American Clock and Watch Museum, Inc., Bristol, CT...............236
American Craft Museum, New York, NY..1018
American Historical Society of Germans from Russia, Lincoln, NE...............865
American Labor Museum, Botto House National Landmark, Haledon, NJ.............906
American Maple Museum, Croghan, NY.....983
American Museum of Asmat Art, Saint Paul, MN...............789
The American Museum of Fly Fishing, Manchester, VT...............1481
The American Numismatic Society, New York, NY...............1020
American Precision Museum Association, Inc., Windsor, VT...............1490
American Printing House for the Blind, Callahan Museum, Louisville, KY.........575
American Quarter Horse Hall of Fame & Museum, Amarillo, TX...............1386
American Royal Museum & Visitors Center, Kansas City, MO...............820
American Textile History Museum, Lowell, MA...............691
American West Heritage Center, Wellsville, UT...............1475
American Work Horse Museum, Lexington, VA...............1513
Americana Museum, Terra Alta, WV.........1587
America's Black Holocaust Museum, Milwaukee, WI...............1610
America's Ice Cream & Dairy Museum, Medina, OH...............1175
Amherst County Museum & Historical Society, Amherst, VA...............1495
Amherst History Museum at the Strong House - Amherst Historical Society, Amherst, MA...............658
Amherst Museum, Amherst, NY...............957
Amity and Woodbridge Historical Society, Woodbridge, CT...............268

Amos Herr House Foundation and Historic Society, Landisville, PA...........1267
Anacortes Museum, Anacortes, WA...........1547
Anadarko Heritage Museum, Anadarko, OK...............1195
Anderson County Historical Museum, Garnett, KS...............541
Anderson County Museum, Anderson, SC.1321
Andover Historical Society, Andover, MA...660
Andrew County Museum & Historical Society, Savannah, MO...............838
Andrew J. Blackbird Museum, Harbor Springs, MI...............745
Androscoggin Historical Society, Auburn, ME...............603
Angel Mounds State Historic Site, Evansville, IN...............475
Angels Camp Museum & Carriage House, Angels Camp, CA...............71
Animas Museum, Durango, CO...............214
Anna B. Smith House Museum, Moundsville, WV...............1585
Anna Bemis Palmer Museum, York, NE......875
Anna Miller Museum, Newcastle, WY......1637
Ano Nuevo State Reserve, Pescadero, CA...141
Anoka County Historical Society, Anoka, MN...............767
Anson County Historical Society, Inc., Wadesboro, NC...............1121
The Antique Boat Museum, Clayton, NY....978
Antique Gas & Steam Engine Museum, Inc., Vista, CA...............196
Apostles Islands National Lakeshore, Bayfield, WI...............1591
The Apple Trees Museum, Burlington, IA...506
Arcadia Township Historical Commission, Arcadia, MI...............726
Arches Museum of Pioneer Life, Winona, MN...............797
Ardenwood Historic Farm, Fremont, CA.......96
Argo Gold Mine & Mill Museum, Idaho Springs, CO...............223
Arizona Historical Society Museum, Tucson, AZ...............47
Arizona Historical Society Museum at Papago Park, Tempe, AZ...............45
Arizona Historical Society Pioneer Museum, Flagstaff, AZ...............32
Arizona Jewish Historical Society, Phoenix, AZ...............39
Arizona State Capitol Museum, Phoenix, AZ...............39
Arkansas Historic Wine Museum, Paris, AR...............65
Arkansas Post Museum, Gillett, AR...............58
Arkansas Post National Memorial, Gillett, AR...............58
Arkansas Railroad Museum, Pine Bluff, AR...............65
Arkansas State University Museum, Jonesboro, AR...............60
Arkansas Tech University Museum of Prehistory and History, Russellville, AR...............67
Arlington Heights Historical Museum, Arlington Heights, IL...............411
Arlington Historical Museum, Arlington, VA...............1495
Armand Bayou Nature Center, Houston, TX...............1424
Armenian Library and Museum of America, Watertown, MA...............716
The Arms Family Museum of Local History, Youngstown, OH...............1193
Arrow Rock State Historic Site, Arrow Rock, MO...............810
Artesia Historical Museum & Art Center, Artesia, NM...............936
Arthurdale Heritage, Inc., Arthurdale, WV...............1579
Arvada Center for the Arts and Humanities, Arvada, CO...............201

Ashland Logging Museum, Inc., Ashland, ME 603

Ashtabula County Historical Society, Geneva-on-the-Lake, OH 1166

Asistencia: San Gabriel Mission Outpost, Redlands, CA 146

Aspen Historical Society, Aspen, CO 202

Ataloa Lodge Museum, Muskogee, OK 1205

Atchison County Historical Society, Atchison, KS 533

Atlantic Heritage Center, Somers Point, NJ 924

Atlantic Wildfowl Heritage Museum, Virginia Beach, VA 1541

Attleboro Area Industrial Museum, Inc., Attleboro, MA 661

Atwater Kent Museum of Philadelphia, Philadelphia, PA 1276

Au Glaize Village, Defiance, OH 1162

Auburn Cord Duesenberg Museum, Auburn, IN 468

Audie Murphy/American Cotton Museum, Inc, Greenville, TX 1423

Audrain Historical Museum, Graceland, Mexico, MO 827

Audubon County Historical Society, Exira, IA 517

Auglaize County Historical Society, Saint Marys, OH 1184

Augusta Historical Museum & Genealogy, Augusta, KS 533

Augusta Museum of History, Augusta, GA 364

Aullwood Audubon Center and Farm, Dayton, OH 1160

Aurora Historical Society, Aurora, OH 1140

Aurora History Museum, Aurora, CO 202

Aurora Regional Fire Museum, Aurora, IL 411

Avery County Museum, Newland, NC 1113

The Avon Historical Society, Inc., Avon, CT 235

Awbury Arboretum, Philadelphia, PA 1277

Aztalan Museum, Jefferson, WI 1601

Aztec Museum and Pioneer Village, Aztec, NM 936

B&O Railroad Museum: Ellicott City Station, Ellicott City, MD 643

The Bade Institute of Biblical Archaeology and The Howell Bible Collection, Berkeley, CA 75

Badger Mine and Museum, Shullsburg, WI 1622

Baldwin County Heritage Museum, Elberta, AL 8

Baldwin Historical Society and Museum, Baldwin, NY 960

Baldwin-Reynolds House Museum, Meadville, PA 1270

Bale Grist Mill State Historic Park, Calistoga, CA 80

Baltimore & Ohio Railroad Museum, Baltimore, MD 629

Baltimore County Historical Society, Cockeysville, MD 640

Baltimore Museum of Industry, Baltimore, MD 630

Baltimore Public Works Museum, Inc., Baltimore, MD 630

Bandon Historical Society Museum, Bandon, OR 1219

Bangor Museum & Center for History, Bangor, ME 604

Banner County Historical Society, Harrisburg, NE 862

Bannock County Historical Museum, Pocatello, ID 408

Baranov Museum, Kodiak, AK 26

Barataria Preserve, Jean Lafitte National Historical Park and Preserve, Marrero, LA 591

Barbed Wire Museum, La Crosse, KS 547

The Barnacle Historic State Park, Coconut Grove, FL 300

Barnes County Historical Museum, Valley City, ND 1136

Barnet Historical Society, Barnet, VT 1476

Barnwell County Museum, Barnwell, SC ..1321

Barre Historical Society, Inc., Barre, MA 662

The Barrington Area Historical Society, Barrington, IL 412

Barrington Living History Farm, Washington, TX 1460

Barron County Historical Society's Pioneer Village Museum, Cameron, WI 1593

Bartholomew County Historical Society, Columbus, IN 472

Bartlesville Area History Museum, Bartlesville, OK 1196

Barton County Historical Museum & Village, Great Bend, KS 542

Bartow History Center, Cartersville, GA 367

Batsto Village, Hammonton, NJ 907

Battle of Lexington State Historic Site, Lexington, MO 826

Battleship North Carolina, Wilmington, NC 1122

Battleship Texas State Historic Site, La Porte, TX 1433

Baxter Springs Heritage Center and Museum, Baxter Springs, KS 533

Bay View Historical Museum, Bay View, MI 728

The Beaufort Arsenal, Beaufort, SC 1321

Beaufort Historic Site, Beaufort, NC 1091

Beauvais Heritage Center, Clark, SD 1345

Beaver Island Historical Society, Beaver Island, MI 728

Beaverhead County Museum, Dillon, MT ...845

Becker County Historical Society, Detroit Lakes, MN 772

Bedford City/County Museum, Bedford, VA 1496

Bedford Historical Society Museum and Library, Bedford, OH 1142

Belair Stable Museum, Bowie, MD 638

Belhaven Memorial Museum, Inc., Belhaven, NC 1092

The Belknap Mill Society, Laconia, NH 890

Bell County Museum, Belton, TX 1395

Bellflower Historical and Genealogical Society, Bellflower, IL 413

Beltrami County History Center, Bemidji, MN 768

Bement-Billings Farmstead, Newark Valley, NY 1041

Benicia Historical Museum, Benicia, CA 74

The Benjamin Banneker Park & Museum, Baltimore, MD 631

Bennett Place State Historic Site, Durham, NC 1098

The Bennington Museum, Bennington, VT 1476

Benton County Historical Museum, Philomath, OR 1230

Bent's Old Fort National Historic Site, La Junta, CO 224

Benzie Area Historical Museum, Benzonia, MI 729

Bergen Museum of Local History, Bergen, NY 962

Berkeley County Museum & Heritage Center, Moncks Corner, SC 1336

Berkeley Plantation, Charles City, VA 1498

Berkshire County Historical Society, Inc. - Arrowhead, Pittsfield, MA 702

Berkshire Museum, Pittsfield, MA 702

Bernard Historical Society and Museum, Delton, MI 734

Bernhard Museum Complex, Auburn, CA 72

Berrien County Historical Association, Berrien Springs, MI 729

Bessemer Hall of History, Bessemer, AL 3

Besser Museum for Northeast Michigan, Alpena, MI 723

Bethel Historical Society Regional History Center, Bethel, ME 606

Betsy Ross House and Flag Museum, Philadelphia, PA 1277

Bexley Historical Society, Bexley, OH 1143

Beyer Home, Oconto County Historical Society Museum, Oconto, WI 1616

The Bidwell House Museum, Monterey, MA 695

Biedenharn Coca-Cola Museum, Vicksburg, MS 809

Big Bend National Park, Big Bend, TX 1396

Big Horn County Historical Museum, Hardin, MT 849

Big Springs Museum, Caledonia, NY 974

Big Thicket National Preserve, Kountze, TX 1432

Big Thunder Gold Mine, Keystone, SD 1349

Bigelow House Museum, Olympia, WA 1560

Billings Farm & Museum, Woodstock, VT 1490

Billy the Kid Museum, Fort Sumner, NM ...939

Biltmore Homespun Shops - Grovewood Gallery, Asheville, NC 1089

Bily Clock Museum/Antonin Dvorak Exhibit, Spillville, IA 528

Bisbee Mining & Historical Museum, Bisbee, AZ 30

Bishop Hill Heritage Museum, Bishop Hill, IL 413

Bishop Hill State Historic Site, Bishop Hill, IL 413

Black American West Museum & Heritage Center, Denver, CO 209

Black Hills Mining Museum, Lead, SD 1350

Black River Historical Society of Lorain, Lorain, OH 1172

Blackberry Farm's Pioneer Village, Aurora, IL 411

Blackman House Museum, Snohomish, WA 1570

Blaine County Historical Museum, Hailey, ID 406

Blaine County Museum, Chinook, MT 844

Block Island Historical Society, Block Island, RI 1310

Bloomfield Academy Museum, Bloomfield, NY 963

Blount-Bridgers House/Hobson Pittman Memorial Gallery, Tarboro, NC 1121

Blue Earth County Historical Society, Mankato, MN 780

Blue Ridge Institute and Museum, Ferrum, VA 1504

Bob Burns Museum & River Valley Museum of Van Buren, Van Buren, AR 69

Bodie Island Visitor Center, South Nags Head, NC 1120

Bodie State Historic Park, Bridgeport, CA 79

Bolin Wildlife Exhibit & Antique Collection, McKinney, TX 1437

Bolinas Museum, Bolinas, CA 79

Bolton Historical Society, Inc., Bolton, MA 663

Bonner County Historical Museum, Sandpoint, ID 409

Booker T. Washington National Monument, Hardy, VA 1510

Boone County Historical Museum, Belvidere, IL 413

Boone's Lick State Historic Site, Boonesboro, MO 811

Boonsborough Museum of History, Boonsboro, MD 637

The Boorman House - The Juneau County Historical Society, Mauston, WI 1608

Boothbay Railway Village, Boothbay, ME...607

Tools and Equipment for Materials–Continued

Boothe Memorial Park and Museum, Stratford, CT 262
Bosque Memorial Museum, Clifton, TX 1400
Boston Childrens Museum, Boston, MA 664
Boston Fire Museum, Boston, MA 664
Boston National Historical Park, Boston, MA 664
Bottineau County Historical Museum, Bottineau, ND 1129
Boulder City/Hoover Dam Museum, Boulder City, NV 875
Boulder History Museum, Boulder, CO 202
Boundary County Historical Society, Bonners Ferry, ID 404
Bowie Heritage Children's Museum & Welcome Center, Bowie, MD 638
Boyertown Museum of Historic Vehicles, Boyertown, PA 1244
Braintree Historical Society, Inc., Braintree, MA 670
Brazoria County Historical Museum, Angleton, TX 1387
Brec's Magnolia Mound Plantation, Baton Rouge, LA 585
Brick Store Museum, Kennebunk, ME 612
Bridge Hampton Historical Society, Bridgehampton, NY 964
Bridger Valley Heritage Museum, Lyman, WY 1636
Bronck Museum, Coxsackie, NY 983
The Bronx County Historical Society, Bronx, NY 964
Brookings County Historical Society Museum, Volga, SD 1358
The Brooklyn Historical Society, Brooklyn, NY 968
Brooklyn Historical Society, Brooklyn, OH 1144
Brooks Academy Museum, Harwich, MA ... 686
Brown County Historical Society, New Ulm, MN 785
Brown County Historical Society Pioneer Museum, Nashville, IN 493
Brownville Historical Society Museum, Brownville, NE 858
Brush Country Museum, Cotulla, TX 1403
Buckhorn Saloon & Museum, San Antonio, TX 1448
Bucksport Historical Society, Inc., Bucksport, ME 608
Bucyrus Historical Society, Bucyrus, OH .. 1144
Buena Park Historical Society, Buena Park, CA 80
Buffalo and Erie County Historical Society, Buffalo, NY 972
Buffalo Bill Ranch State Historical Park, North Platte, NE 869
Buffalo National River, Harrison, AR 59
Bulow Plantation Ruins Historic State Park, Bunnell, FL 298
Bunker Hill Museum, Charlestown, MA 675
Burke County Historical Powers Lake Complex, Powers Lake, ND 1136
Burlington County Historical Society, Burlington, NJ 898
Burlington Historical Museum, Burlington, MA 672
Burnside Plantation, Inc., Bethlehem, PA .. 1242
Burritt on the Mountain-A Living Museum, Huntsville, AL 11
Burt County Museum, Tekamah, NE 873
Burwell-Morgan Mill, Millwood, VA 1518
Bushwhacker Museum, Nevada, MO 828
Bushy Run Battlefield, Jeannette, PA 1263
Butler County Historical Society, Allison, IA 504
Butler County History Center & Kansas Oil Museum, El Dorado, KS 537

Butte County Pioneer Memorial Museum, Oroville, CA 136
Byron Historical Museum, Byron, NY 974

C.H. Nash Museum-Chucalissa Archaeological Museum, Memphis, TN 1372
CHTJ Southard House Museum, Brunswick, ME 607
COSI Columbus, Columbus, OH 1157
CSS Neuse State Historic Site and Gov. Richard Caswell Memorial, Kinston, NC 1108
Cabot Historical Society, Cabot, VT 1478
Calaveras County Archives, San Andreas, CA 155
Calaveras County Museum, San Andreas, CA 155
Calhoun County Museum, Rockwell City, IA 527
Calhoun County Museum, Port Lavaca, TX 1444
Calhoun County Museum & Cultural Center, Saint Matthews, SC 1341
Calico Ghost Town and the Lane House & Museum, Yermo, CA 199
California Academy of Sciences, San Francisco, CA 163
California State Capitol Museum, Sacramento, CA 151
California State Mining & Mineral Museum, Mariposa, CA 124
California State Railroad Museum, Sacramento, CA 152
California Surf Museum, Oceanside, CA 135
Calumet County Historical Society, Inc., New Holstein, WI 1615
Calvert Marine Museum, Solomons, MD 654
Calvin Coolidge Historic Site, Plymouth Notch, VT 1484
Cambridge Museum, Cambridge, NE 858
Camp Atterbury Museum, Edinburgh, IN 474
Camp Five Museum Foundation, Inc., Laona, WI 1604
Camp 6 Logging Museum, Tacoma, WA ... 1572
Campbell County Rockpile Museum, Gillette, WY 1633
Campbell Historical Museum & Ainsley House, Campbell, CA 80
Campus Martius Museum, Marietta, OH ... 1173
Canaan Historical Society, Inc., Canaan, NY 974
Canadian County Historical Museum, El Reno, OK 1200
Canby Historical Society, Canby, OR 1221
The Cannon Village Visitor Center, Kannapolis, NC 1107
Canterbury Shaker Village, Inc., Canterbury, NH 883
Canyon de Chelly National Monument, Chinle, AZ 31
Cape Ann Historical Museum, Gloucester, MA 684
Cape Cod National Seashore, Wellfleet, MA 717
Cape Fear Museum of History and Science, Wilmington, NC 1123
Cape May County Historical Museum and Genealogical Society, Cape May Court House, NJ 900
Cape Vincent Historical Museum, Cape Vincent, NY 976
Capitol Reef National Park Visitor Center, Torrey, UT 1475
Capitol Visitors Center, a Division of the State Preservation Board, Austin, TX 1389
Captain John Wilson House, Cohasset, MA 676
Captain Salem Avery House Museum, Shady Side Rural Heritage Society, Inc., Shady Side, MD 653
Carbon County Museum, Rawlins, WY 1637

Carlsbad Caverns National Park, Carlsbad, NM 937
Carlton County Historical Society, Cloquet, MN 771
Carnegie Historical Museum, Fairfield, IA 517
Carpinteria Valley Historical Society & Museum of History, Carpinteria, CA 82
Carroll County Farm Museum, Westminster, MD 656
Carroll Mansion Museum Home of Leavenworth County Historical Society, Leavenworth, KS 549
Carroll Reece Museum, Johnson City, TN.1367
Carson County Square House Museum, Panhandle, TX 1442
Carver County Historical Society, Waconia, MN 795
Caryl House and Fisher Barn, Dover, MA...680
The Casa del Herrero Foundation, Santa Barbara, CA 178
Casa Grande Valley Historical Society & Museum, Casa Grande, AZ 30
Cascade County Historical Society Museum, Great Falls, MT 848
Casemate Museum, Fort Monroe, VA 1505
Cashmere Museum & Pioneer Village, Cashmere, WA 1550
Cass County Museum & Pioneer School, Walker, MN 795
Cassia County Museum, Burley, ID 404
Castine Scientific Society, Castine, ME 609
Castle Air Museum, Atwater, CA 72
Castle Museum of Saginaw County History, Saginaw, MI 762
Castleton Historical Society, Castleton, VT 1478
Catalina Island Museum Society, Inc., Avalon, CA 73
Catawba County Museum of History, Newton, NC 1113
Catskill Fly Fishing Center & Museum, Livingston Manor, NY 1010
Cattaraugus Area Historical Center, Cattaraugus, NY 976
Cattle Raisers Museum, Fort Worth, TX.... 1416
Cave Creek Museum, Cave Creek, AZ 31
Cayuga Museum & Case Research Lab Museum, Auburn, NY 959
Cedar Falls Historical Society, Cedar Falls, IA 507
Cedar Grove Historical Society, Cedar Grove, NJ 901
Cedar Key Museum State Park, Cedar Key, FL 299
Centennial Village Museum, Greeley, CO ... 221
Center for Agricultural Science and Heritage, Indianapolis, IN 481
Center for Wooden Boats, Seattle, WA 1565
Centerville Historical Museum, Centerville, MA 675
Central Delta Depot Museum, Brinkley, AR 55
Central Nevada Museum & Historical Society, Tonopah, NV 882
Central Washington Agricultural Museum, Union Gap, WA 1575
Centre County Historical Society, State College, PA 1301
Century Village Museum, Burton, OH 1144
Chagrin Falls Historical Society, Chagrin Falls, OH 1147
Champaign County Historical Museum, Champaign, IL 416
Champaign County Historical Museum, Urbana, OH 1188
Champion Mill State Historical Park, Champion, NE 859
Champoeg State Heritage Area Visitor Center, Saint Paul, OR 1235
Chandler Museum, Chandler, AZ 31

The Chapman Historical Museum, Glens Falls, NY 994
Chappell Hill Historical Society Museum, Chappell Hill, TX 1399
Charles A. Weyerhaeuser Memorial Museum, Little Falls, MN........................779
Charles B. Aycock Birthplace State Historic Site, Fremont, NC.................1102
Charles River Museum of Industry, Waltham, MA 715
Charlotte County Historical Center, Charlotte Harbor, FL.............................299
Charlotte Museum of History and Hezekiah Alexander Homesite, Charlotte, NC...1094
Chase County Historical Society, Inc., Cottonwood Falls, KS 536
Chattahoochee River National Recreation Area, Atlanta, GA.......................359
Chattanooga Regional History Museum, Chattanooga, TN..................................1361
Chautauqua County Historical Society, McClurg Museum, Westfield, NY 1086
Cheboygan County Historical Museum Complex, Cheboygan, MI 732
The Chelmsford Historical Society, Inc., South Chelmsford, MA........................709
Chemung Valley History Museum, Elmira, NY...988
Chenango County Historical Society Museum, Norwich, NY.......................1044
Cheraw Lyceum Museum, Cheraw, SC......1327
Cherokee County Historical Museum, Inc., Murphy, NC................................1112
Cherokee Courthouse Visitors Information Center & Museum, Gore, OK...1201
Cherokee Strip Land Rush Museum, Arkansas City, KS 532
Cherokee Strip Museum, Alva, OK...........1195
Cherokee Strip Museum and Henry S. Johnston Library, Perry, OK...............1212
Cherry Valley Museum, Cherry Valley, NY...978
Chesapeake Bay Maritime Museum, Saint Michaels, MD.....................................652
Chester County Historical Society, West Chester, PA 1307
Chesterwood, Stockbridge, MA 711
Chicago History Museum, Chicago, IL........419
Chickamauga-Chattanooga National Military Park, Fort Oglethorpe, GA 372
Chickasaw National Recreation Area, Sulphur, OK..1214
Chico Museum, Chico, CA............................83
Chieftains Museum, Rome, GA.....................381
Children's Discovery Museum of North San Diego, Carlsbad, CA 81
Children's Hands-On Museum (CHOM), Tuscaloosa, AL..19
Children's Museum of History, Natural History and Science at Utica, New York, Utica, NY....................................1079
The Children's Museum of Rose Hill Manor Park, Frederick, MD...................644
Childress County Heritage Museum, Childress, TX.......................................1400
Chimney Point State Historic Site, Addison, VT...1475
Chinese American Museum, Los Angeles, CA...114
Chinese House/O.R. & N. Museum & St. Peter's Catholic Church, Echo, OR.......1222
Chippewa County Historical Society, Montevideo, MN.......................................783
Chippewa Nature Center, Midland, MI 755
Chippewa Valley Museum, Inc., Eau Claire, WI...1595
Chippokes Farm & Forestry Museum, Surry, VA 1540
Chiricahua National Monument, Willcox, AZ 53

Chisholm Trail Heritage Center, Duncan, OK..1199
Chisholm Trail Historical Museum, Waurika, OK..1216
Chisholm Trail Museum, Wellington, KS 561
Chisholm Trail Museum, Kingfisher, OK...1203
Chittenango Landing Canal Boat Museum, Chittenango, NY......................978
Churchill County Museum and Archives, Fallon, NV...877
Circus World Museum, Baraboo, WI 1591
City Island Nautical Museum, Bronx, NY...965
City Museum, Saint Louis, MO.....................832
City of Gilroy Museum, Gilroy, CA 99
City of Las Vegas Museum and Rough Rider Memorial Collection, Las Vegas, NM..941
City of Wayne Historical Museum, Wayne, MI...766
Clallam County Historical Society, Port Angeles, WA...1561
Clarion County Historical Society, Sutton-Ditz House Museum, Clarion, PA..1247
Clark County Historical Museum, Vancouver, WA..1576
Clark County Historical Society - Heritage Center of Clark County, Springfield, OH...1186
Clark County Museum, Henderson, NV 878
Clark Hotel Museum, Van Horn, TX 1457
Clarke Historical Museum, Eureka, CA........94
Clarkson Historical Museum, Clarkson, NE...859
Clarksville-Montgomery County Museum dba Customs House Museum & Cultural Center, Clarksville, TN 1363
Clausen Memorial Museum, Petersburg, AK...27
Clawson Historical Museum, Clawson, MI..732
Clay Center for Arts & Sciences West Virginia, Charleston, WV 1580
Clay County Historical Museum, Liberty, MO...826
Clear Creek History Park, Golden, CO........219
Clearwater County Historical Society, Shevlin, MN...793
Clearwater Historical Museum, Orofino, ID...408
Cleveland County Historical Museum, Shelby, NC..1119
Clewiston Museum, Inc., Clewiston, FL......300
Cliffs of the Neuse State Park, Seven Springs, NC...1119
Clinton Academy, East Hampton, NY..........985
Clinton County Historical Society, Clinton, IA...511
Clinton County Historical Society Paine-Gillam-Scott Museum, Saint Johns, MI...763
Cloud County Historical Society Museum, Concordia, KS.........................536
Coachella Valley Museum and Cultural Center, Indio, CA 104
Coal Miners' Museum/Van Lear Historical Society, Inc., Van Lear, KY 584
Coarsegold Historic Museum, Coarsegold, CA 86
Codington County Heritage Museum, Watertown, SD...1359
Coggeshall Farm Museum, Bristol, RI.......1310
Cokato Museum & Akerlund Photography Studio, Cokato, MN............771
Cold Spring Harbor Whaling Museum, Cold Spring Harbor, NY 979
Cole Land Transportation Museum, Bangor, ME...604
The Coleman House Museum and Brown County Historical Society, Ainsworth, NE...855
Colesville & Windsor Museum at St. Luke's Church, Harpursville, NY 997

The Coley Homestead & Barn Museum, Weston, CT..265
College Park Aviation Museum, College Park, MD..641
Colleton Museum, Walterboro, SC 1343
Collier County Museum, Naples, FL...........328
Collier Memorial State Park & Logging Museum, Chiloquin, OR.......................1221
Collin County Farm Museum, McKinney, TX...1437
Collinsville Depot Museum, Collinsville, OK..1198
Colonel Allensworth State Historic Park, Allensworth, CA...70
Colonial Industrial Quarter, Bethlehem, PA...1242
Colonial National Historical Park: Jamestown & Yorktown, Yorktown, VA...1546
Colonial Pemaquid, New Harbor, ME..........615
Colonial Williamsburg, Williamsburg, VA .1544
Colorado River Indian Tribes Museum, Parker, AZ..38
Colorado Ski Museum-Ski & Snowboard Hall of Fame, Vail, CO.......................234
Columbia College Chicago Center for the Book & Paper Arts, Chicago, IL 420
Columbia County Historical and Genealogical Society, Bloomsburg, PA .1243
Columbia Fire Department Museum, Columbia, SC..1328
Columbia Gorge Discovery Center and Wasco County Museum, The Dalles, OR..1237
Columbia Gorge Interpretive Center Museum, Stevenson, WA.......................1572
Columbia River Exhibition of History, Science and Technology, Richland, WA..1564
Columbia River Maritime Museum, Astoria, OR..1218
Columbia State Historic Park, Columbia, CA..87
Comanche Crossing Historical Society & Museum, Strasburg, CO.......................233
Comer Museum, Morgantown, WV 1585
Commonwealth of the Northern Mariana Islands Museum of History and Culture, Saipan, MP.......................1640
Community Historical Museum, Maxwell, IA...523
Community Memorial Museum of Sutter County, Yuba City, CA.......................200
Concord Museum, Concord, MA.................676
Confederate Museum, Crawfordville, GA....369
Connecticut Audubon Birdcraft Museum, Fairfield, CT...240
Connecticut Historical Society, Hartford, CT..244
Connecticut River Museum, Essex, CT........239
Conner Prairie, Fishers, IN 476
Constitution Convention Museum State Park, Port St. Joe, FL.........................338
Constitution Square State Historic Site, Danville, KY..567
Cook County Historical Museum, Grand Marais, MN...776
Cooper Regional History Museum, Upland, CA...193
Coos Historical & Maritime Museum, North Bend, OR..1229
Copper Range Historical Museum, South Range, MI...764
Copper Village Museum & Arts Center of Deer Lodge County, Anaconda, MT........840
Coppertown U.S.A., Calumet, MI 731
Cordova Historical Museum, Cordova, AK...23
Cornwall Iron Furnace, Cornwall, PA 1248
Coronado-Quivira Museum, Lyons, KS 550
Corpus Christi Museum of Science and History, Corpus Christi, TX 1401
Corry Area Historical Society, Corry, PA...1248

Tools and Equipment for Materials–Continued

Cortland County Historical Society, Cortland, NY 982
Cottonlandia Museum, Greenwood, MS 800
Cottonwood County Historical Society, Windom, MN 796
County of Los Angeles Fire Museum, Los Angeles, CA................114
Courthouse Square Association, Charlotte, MI 731
Cow Neck Peninsula Historical Society Sands-Willets House, Port Washington, NY................1053
Cowlitz County Historical Museum, Kelso, WA................1557
Cracker Country, Tampa, FL 348
Crafts Museum, Mequon, WI 1609
Cragfont-Historic Cragfont, Inc., Castalian Springs, TN 1360
Cranbury Historical & Preservation Society, Cranbury, NJ................902
Crane Point, Marathon, FL 323
Crater of Diamonds State Park Museum, Murfreesboro, AR................65
Crawford County Historical Museum, Pittsburg, KS................556
Crazy Mountain Museum, Big Timber, MT................841
Creede Underground Mining Museum, Creede, CO................208
Creek Council House Museum, Okmulgee, OK................1211
Crested Butte Mountain Heritage Museum, Crested Butte, CO................208
Crestline Shunk Museum, Crestline, OH ...1160
Cripple Creek District Museum, Inc., Cripple Creek, CO................209
Crocker House, Mount Clemens, MI................756
Crockett County Museum, Ozona, TX................1442
Crockett Tavern Museum, Morristown, TN................1376
Crosby County Pioneer Memorial Museum, Crosbyton, TX................1403
Crossroads Museum, Corinth, MS................800
Crow Wing County Historical Society, Brainerd, MN................769
Crowley Museum & Nature Center, Sarasota, FL................344
Crown Point State Historic Site, Crown Point, NY................984
Crystal Lake Falls Historical Association, Barton, VT................1476
Crystal Rice Plantation, Crowley, LA................588
Culbertson Mansion State Historic Site, New Albany, IN................493
Culbertson Museum, Culbertson, MT................845
Cumberland County Historical Society, Greenwich, NJ................905
Cumberland County Historical Society, The Hamilton Library and The Two Mile House, Carlisle, PA................1245
Cumberland Gap National Historical Park, Middlesboro, KY................580
Cumberland Island National Seashore, Saint Marys, GA................382
Cupertino Historical Society & Museum, Cupertino, CA................88
The Curious Kids' Museum, Saint Joseph, MI................763
Curry Historical Society Museum, Gold Beach, OR................1225
Custer Battlefield Museum, Garryowen, MT................847
Custer County 1881 Courthouse Museum, Custer, SD................1345
Custer County Historical Society, Inc., Broken Bow, NE................858
The Custom House Maritime Museum, Newburyport, MA................697

Cuyahoga Valley National Park, Brecksville, OH 1144
Cuyuna Range Historical Society & Museum, Crosby, MN 772

D.C. Booth Historic National Fish Hatchery, Spearfish, SD 1357
D.R. Barker Historical Museum, Fredonia, NY................992
Dacotah Prairie Museum, Aberdeen, SD...1344
Dahlonega Gold Museum State Historic Site, Dahlonega, GA................369
Dakota County Historical Society, South Saint Paul, MN................793
Dakota Discovery Museum, Mitchell, SD..1352
Dakota Sunset Museum, Gettysburg, SD ...1348
Dal-Paso Museum, Lamesa, TX................1433
Dale & Martha Hawk Museum, Wolford, ND................1138
Dallas Firefighter's Museum, Inc., Dallas, TX................1404
Dallas Heritage Village at Old City Park, Dallas, TX................1405
Dana Adobe, Nipomo, CA 130
The Danbury Museum & Historical Society, Danbury, CT 238
Dancing Bear Folk Center, Thermopolis, WY 1639
Daniel Boone Home and Boonesfield Village, Lindenwood University, Defiance, MO................814
Daniel Boone Homestead, Birdsboro, PA ..1243
Daniels County Museum and Pioneer Town, Scobey, MT 853
The Danish Immigrant Museum, Elk Horn, IA................517
Danvers Historical Society, Danvers, MA....678
Daughters of Utah Pioneers Pioneer Memorial Museum & International Society Daughters of Utah Pioneers, Salt Lake City, UT................1471
David Conklin Farmhouse, Huntington, NY................1000
The David Davis Mansion, Bloomington, IL................413
Davidson County Historical Museum, Lexington, NC................1109
The Davistown Museum, Liberty, ME................614
Dawson County Historical Museum, Lexington, NE................864
Dayton History at Carillon Park, Dayton, OH................1161
De Smet Depot Museum, De Smet, SD.....1346
Deaf Smith County Museum, Hereford, TX................1424
Dearborn Historical Museum, Dearborn, MI................733
Death Valley National Park Visitor Center and Museums, Death Valley, CA................91
Decatur County Last Indian Raid Museum, Oberlin, KS................554
Deer Isle-Stonington Historical Society, Deer Isle, ME................609
Deer Park Escondido Winery & Auto Museum, Escondido, CA 93
Deerfield Beach Historical Society, Deerfield Beach, FL 304
Degenhart Paperweight & Glass Museum, Inc., Cambridge, OH 1144
DeKalb History Center Museum, Decatur, GA................370
Del Norte County Historical Society, Crescent City, CA................87
Delaware Agricultural Museum and Village, Dover, DE................269
Delaware and Hudson Canal Historical Society and Museum, High Falls, NY....998
Delaware Archaeology Museum, Dover, DE................269
Delaware Division of Historical & Cultural Affairs, Dover, DE 269
Delta County Historical Society Museum, Escanaba, MI................741

Delta County Museum, Delta, CO................209
Delta Cultural Center, Helena, AR 59
Dennys River Historical Society, Dennysville, ME................609
Denton County Historical Museum, Inc. and Texas Heritage Center, Denton, TX................1409
Denver Botanic Gardens, Inc., Denver, CO................210
Depot Museum & Fort Sedgwick Museum, Julesburg, CO................223
The Depot Museum Complex, Henderson, TX................1424
Des Plaines History Center, Des Plaines, IL................430
Desert Caballeros Western Museum, Wickenburg, AZ................53
Desha County Museum, Dumas, AR................56
The Design Center at Philadelphia University, Philadelphia, PA 1278
DeSoto National Memorial, Bradenton, FL................297
Detroit Historical Society, Detroit, MI................735
Deutschheim State Historic Site, Hermann, MO................817
DeWitt County Historical Museum, Cuero, TX................1403
Dexter Area Historical Society & Museum, Dexter, MI................738
Dexter Historical Society Campus, Dexter, ME................609
Dey Mansion/Washington's Headquarters Museum, Wayne, NJ................929
Dickinson County Heritage Center, Abilene, KS................531
Dinsmore Homestead Foundation, Burlington, KY................566
DiscoverSea Shipwreck Museum, Fenwick Island, DE................270
Doak House Museum, Greeneville, TN 1366
Dr. Daniel W. Kissam House, Huntington, NY................1000
Dr. Increase Mathews House, Zanesville, OH................1194
Dr. William Robinson Plantation, Clark, NJ................901
Dodge County Historical Society, Mantorville, MN................780
Dodge County Historical Society Museum, Beaver Dam, WI................1591
Dog Mushing Museum, Fairbanks, AK................24
Don Garlits Museum of Drag Racing Inc., Ocala, FL................330
Donald G. Trayser Memorial Museum/Barnstable County Customs House, Barnstable, MA................661
Donkey Milk House, Historic Home, Key West, FL................317
Donner Memorial State Park and Emigrant Trail Museum, Truckee, CA 192
Door County Maritime Museum (at Gills Rock), Gills Rock, WI................1598
Door County Maritime Museum (at Sturgeon Bay), Sturgeon Bay, WI................1623
Dorothy G. Page Museum, Wasilla, AK................29
Douglas County Historical Society, Superior, WI................1624
Douglas County Historical Society - Carson Valley Museum & Cultural Center, Gardnerville, NV................877
Douglas County Historical Society - Genoa Courthouse Museum, Genoa, NV................877
Douglas County Museum Complex, Armour, SD................1344
Douglas County Museum of History and Natural History, Roseburg, OR................1234
Douglass Historical Museum, Douglass, KS................537
The Downers Grove Park District Museum, Downers Grove, IL................431
Downieville Museum, Downieville, CA 91
Drake Well Museum, Titusville, PA................1303

Drew County Historical Museum, Monticello, AR 64

Drummond Island Historical Museum, Drummond Island, MI....739

Dry Falls Interpretive Center, Coulee City, WA 1551

Dublin-Laurens Museum, Dublin, GA 370

Dubois Museum, Dubois, WY 1632

Dugger Coal Museum, Dugger, IN....474

Duke Homestead State Historic Site, Durham, NC....1098

Dunbar House State Memorial, Dayton, OH....1161

Dundy County Historical Society, Benkelman, NE....857

Dunham Tavern Museum, Cleveland, OH..1154

Dunn County Historical Society, Menomonie, WI....1609

DuPage County Historical Museum, Wheaton, IL....465

Dupont Historical Society, DuPont, WA 1552

Durham Center Museum/Research Library, East Durham, NY 985

Durham Historic Association Museum, Durham, NH....886

Dutchess County Historical Society, Poughkeepsie, NY 1054

EAA AirVenture Museum, Oshkosh, WI....1616

Eagle Historical Society & Museums, Eagle, AK....23

Early American Museum, Mahomet, IL....444

EarlyWorks Museums, Huntsville, AL 11

Earth & Mineral Sciences Museum and Art Gallery, University Park, PA 1303

East End Seaport Museum and Marine Foundation, Greenport, NY....996

East Hampton Historical Society, Inc., East Hampton, NY....985

East Hampton Town Marine Museum, Amagansett, NY....957

East Hillsborough Historical Society, Inc., Plant City, FL....337

East Jersey Olde Towne, Piscataway, NJ 921

East Jordan Portside Art & Historical Museum, East Jordan, MI....739

East Lyme Historical Society/Thomas Lee House, Niantic, CT....256

East Poultney Museum, East Poultney, VT....1479

East Tennessee Historical Society, Knoxville, TN....1369

East Texas Oil Museum at Kilgore College, Kilgore, TX....1432

Eastern Arizona Museum and Historical Society of Graham County Inc., Pima, AZ....42

Eastern California Museum, Independence, CA 104

Eastern Oregon Museum on the Old Oregon Trail, Haines, OR 1226

Eastside Heritage Center, Bellevue, WA 1548

Eckley Miners' Village, Eckley, PA....1251

Edgar Allan Poe Cottage, Bronx, NY 965

Edge of the Cedars State Park Museum, Blanding, UT....1463

Edison & Ford Winter Estates, Fort Myers, FL....308

Edison National Historic Site, West Orange, NJ....930

Edisto Island Historic Preservation Society Museum, Edisto Island, SC 1332

Edmond Historical Society Museum, Edmond, OK....1200

Edmonds South Snohomish County Historical Society, Inc., Edmonds, WA .1553

Edward H. White II Memorial Museum, Brooks Air Force Base, TX 1397

Edwards County Historical Museum, Kinsley, KS....547

Effie Yeaw Nature Center, Carmichael, CA....82

Ehrhart Museum, Antwerp, OH 1139

The 1811 Old Lincoln County Jail and Lincoln County Museum, Wiscasset, ME....625

1859 Jail, Marshal's Home & Museum, Independence, MO....817

The 1890 House-Museum & Center for Arts, Cortland, NY....983

82nd Airborne Division War Memorial Museum, Fort Bragg, NC....1101

Eisenhower National Historic Site, Gettysburg, PA....1255

El Camino Real International Heritage Center, San Antonio, NM....947

El Dorado County Historical Museum, Placerville, CA....142

El Paso Museum of History, El Paso, TX..1412

El Pueblo Historical Monument, Los Angeles, CA....114

El Pueblo History Museum, Pueblo, CO....230

El Rancho de Las Golondrinas Museum, Santa Fe, NM....947

Elbert Hubbard-Roycroft Museum, East Aurora, NY....985

Elberton Granite Museum & Exhibit, Elberton, GA....371

Elgin Area Historical Society, Elgin, IL....432

Eli Whitney Museum, Inc., Hamden, CT....244

Elijah Clark Memorial Museum, Lincolnton, GA....376

Elisabet Ney Museum, Austin, TX....1390

Elkhart County Historical Museum, Bristol, IN....471

Ella Sharp Museum, Jackson, MI....748

Elliott Museum, Stuart, FL 346

Ellis County Historical Society, Hays, KS...543

Ellis County Museum, Inc., Waxahachie, TX....1460

Ellwood House Museum, DeKalb, IL....429

Elmhurst Historical Museum, Elmhurst, IL....433

Elwood Haynes Museum, Kokomo, IN....486

End-O-Line Railroad Park & Museum, Currie, MN....772

Enfield Shaker Museum, Enfield, NH....887

Englewood Textile Museum, Englewood, TN....1364

Environmental Education Center, Somerset County Park Commission, Basking Ridge, NJ....898

Ephraim Historical Foundation, Ephraim, WI....1597

Erie Canal Museum, Syracuse, NY....1076

Erie Canal Village, Rome, NY....1061

Erie County History Center & Cashier's House, Erie, PA....1252

Erie Maritime Museum, Homeport U.S. Brig Niagara, Erie, PA....1252

Escondido History Center, Escondido, CA....93

Essex Shipbuilding Museum, Essex, MA 681

Essley-Noble Museum: Mercer County Historical Society, Aledo, IL....410

Eustis Historical Museum & Preservation Society, Inc., Eustis, FL 306

Evanston Historical Society and Charles Gates Dawes House, Evanston, IL 434

Everhart Museum: Natural History, Science and Art, Scranton, PA....1298

The Exhibition Alliance, Hamilton, NY....997

Explorium of Lexington, Lexington, KY 572

Fairbanks House, Dedham, MA....679

Fairfax County Park Authority, Resource Management Division, Fairfax, VA 1503

Fairfax Museum & Visitor Center, Fairfax, VA 1503

Fairfield County Museum, Winnsboro, SC....1343

Fairfield Historical Society, Fairfield, CT 241

Fairport Historical Museum, Fairport, NY...989

Fairport Marine Museum, Fairport Harbor, OH....1164

Fall River County Historical Museum, Hot Springs, SD....1348

Falmouth Historical Society, Falmouth, MA....682

Family Museum, Bettendorf, IA....505

The Farm, Sturgeon Bay, WI....1623

Farmamerica, The Minnesota Agricultural Interpretive Center, Waseca, MN....796

Farmers Branch Historical Park, Farmers Branch, TX....1413

The Farmers' Museum, Inc., Cooperstown, NY....980

Farmington Historic Home, Louisville, KY....575

Farragut Folklife Museum, Farragut, TN ...1364

Farrar-Mansur House & Old Mill Museum, Weston, VT....1490

FASNY Museum of Fire Fighting, Hudson, NY....1000

Faulkner County Museum, Conway, AR....56

Faust Park-Thornhill Historic Site & 19th Century Village, Chesterfield, MO 812

Fayette County Helpers Club & Historical Society, West Union, IA....530

Fayette Heritage Museum & Archives, La Grange, TX....1432

Fenton Glass Museum, Williamstown, WV....1589

Fenton History Center-Museum & Library, Jamestown, NY....1005

Fick Fossil & History Museum, Oakley, KS....554

Fillmore County Historical Center, Fountain, MN....776

Fillmore Historical Museum, Inc., Fillmore, CA....95

The Filson Historical Society, Inc., Louisville, KY....576

Finney County Kansas Historical Society, Inc., Garden City, KS....541

Fireman's Hall Museum, Philadelphia, PA.1279

First Landing State Park, Virginia Beach, VA....1542

First Missouri State Capitol-State Historic Site, Saint Charles, MO 830

The Fishermen's Museum, New Harbor, ME....615

Fitchburg Historical Society, Fitchburg, MA....683

The Five Civilized Tribes Museum, Muskogee, OK....1205

Fleming Historical Society, Fleming, CO 216

Flint House, Scotia, NY....1068

The Florence McLeod Hazard Museum, Columbus, MS....800

Florence Museum of Art, Science & History and the Florence Railroad Museum, Florence, SC....1332

Florence Price Pioneer Museum, Florence, CO....216

Florence Ranch Homestead, Mesquite, TX....1438

Florewood State Park, Greenwood, MS....801

Florida Agricultural Museum, Palm Coast, FL....334

Flowerdew Hundred Foundation, Hopewell, VA....1511

Floyd County Historical Museum, Charles City, IA....510

The Fluvanna County Historical Society Old Stone Jail Museum, Palmyra, VA...1524

Folsom History Museum, Folsom, CA....95

Folsom Museum, Inc., Folsom, NM....939

Ford County Historical Society, Paxton, IL....450

Forest History Center, Grand Rapids, MN...777

Forest Park Museum and Arboretum, Perry, IA....527

The Forges and Manor of Ringwood, Ringwood, NJ....923

The Fort at No. 4 Living History Museum, Charlestown, NH....884

Tools and Equipment for Materials—Continued

Fort Atkinson State Historical Park, Fort Calhoun, NE 860
Fort Bedford Museum, Bedford, PA 1241
Fort Bend Museum Association, Richmond, TX 1445
Fort Bliss Museum, Fort Bliss, TX 1413
Fort Boonesborough Museum, Richmond, KY 583
Fort Bowie National Historic Site, Bowie, AZ 30
Fort Buford State Historic Site, Williston, ND 1137
Fort Caspar Museum, Casper, WY 1629
Fort Christmas Historical Park, Christmas, FL 299
Fort Clatsop National Memorial, Astoria, OR 1218
Fort Clinch State Park, Fernandina Beach, FL 306
Fort Columbia Interpretive Center, Chinook, WA 1551
Fort Concho National Historic Landmark, San Angelo, TX 1447
Fort Crawford Museum, Prairie du Chien, WI 1618
Fort Croghan Museum, Burnet, TX 1398
Fort Crook Historical Museum, Fall River Mills, CA 94
Fort Dalles Museum/Anderson Homestead, The Dalles, OR 1237
Fort Davidson State Historic Site, Pilot Knob, MO 828
Fort Dodge & Frontier Village, Fort Dodge, IA 518
Fort Fetterman State Historic Site, Douglas, WY 1631
Fort Frederica National Monument, Saint Simons Island, GA 383
Fort Gibson Historic Site, Fort Gibson, OK 1200
Fort Hays State Historic Site, Hays, KS 543
Fort Henrietta Interpretive Park, Echo, OR 1223
Fort Hill (The John C. Calhoun House), Clemson, SC 1328
Fort Hunter Mansion & Park, Harrisburg, PA 1258
Fort Inglish, Bonham, TX 1396
Fort Jones Museum, Fort Jones, CA 96
Fort Kearny State Historical Park, Kearney, NE 864
Fort Klock Historic Restoration, Saint Johnsville, NY 1063
Fort Laramie National Historic Site, Fort Laramie, WY 1633
Fort Larned National Historic Site, Larned, KS 547
Fort Lauderdale Historical Society, Fort Lauderdale, FL 307
Fort Leaton State Historical Site, Presidio, TX 1444
Fort Lee Historic Park & Museum, Fort Lee, NJ 904
Fort Matanzas National Monument, Saint Augustine, FL 339
Fort McKavett State Historical Site, Fort McKavett, TX 1415
Fort Mifflin, Philadelphia, PA 1279
Fort Morgan Museum, Fort Morgan, CO 218
Fort Nashborough, Nashville, TN 1379
Fort Necessity National Battlefield, Farmington, PA 1253
Fort Nisqually Living History Museum, Tacoma, WA 1573
Fort Okanogan Interpretive Center, Brewster, WA 1550
Fort Ontario State Institutions Site, Oswego, NY 1048

Fort Payne Depot Museum, Fort Payne, AL 10
Fort Peck Interpretive Center, Fort Peck, MT 846
Fort Phil Kearny, Banner, WY 1628
Fort Pike State Historic Site, New Orleans, LA 595
Fort Plain Museum, Fort Plain, NY 991
Fort Recovery Museum, Fort Recovery, OH 1164
Fort St. Jean Baptiste State Historic Site, Natchitoches, LA 593
Fort St. Joseph Museum, Niles, MI 758
Fort Scott National Historic Site, Fort Scott, KS 540
Fort Sisseton State Historic Park, Lake City, SD 1350
Fort Smith Museum of History, Fort Smith, AR 58
Fort Tejon State Historic Park, Lebec, CA 108
Fort Ticonderoga, Ticonderoga, NY 1078
Fort Totten State Historic Site, Fort Totten, ND 1131
Fort Union National Monument, Watrous, NM 954
Fort Union Trading Post National Historic Site, Williston, ND 1138
Fort Vancouver National Historic Site, Vancouver, WA 1576
Fort Verde State Historic Park, Camp Verde, AZ 30
Fort Walla Walla Museum, Walla Walla, WA 1576
Fort Washington Park, Fort Washington, MD 643
Fort Washita, Durant, OK 1199
Fort Wayne Firefighters Museum, Fort Wayne, IN 477
Fort William Henry Museum, Lake George, NY 1008
Forts Folle Avoine Historic Park, Danbury, WI 1594
Fossil Country Museum, Kemmerer, WY 1635
Fossil Museum, Fossil, OR 1224
Fosterfields Living Historical Farm, Morristown, NJ 913
Fostoria Area Historical Museum, Fostoria, OH 1164
Four Mile Historic Park, Denver, CO 212
Four Rivers Cultural Center & Museum, Ontario, OR 1229
Fox Island Historical Society, Fox Island, WA 1554
Fox Lake Historical Museum, Inc., Fox Lake, WI 1598
The Foxfire Museum & Heritage Center, Mountain City, GA 380
Framingham Historical Society & Museum, Framingham, MA 683
Francis Land House Historic Site, Virginia Beach, VA 1542
Francisco Fort Museum, La Veta, CO 224
Franconia Heritage Museum, Franconia, NH 888
Frank Lloyd Wright Home and Studio, Oak Park, IL 448
Frankenmuth Historical Museum, Frankenmuth, MI 742
Frankfort Area Historical Museum, West Frankfort, IL 464
Franklin County Historical & Museum Society & House of History, Malone, NY 1012
Franklin County Historical Museum, Pasco, WA 1561
Franklin County Old Jail Museum, Winchester, TN 1385
Franklin County Seminary and Museum, Brookville, IN 471
The Franklin Institute, Philadelphia, PA 1280
The Franklin Pierce Homestead, Hillsborough, NH 889

Frederick C. Robie House, Chicago, IL 420
Fredericksburg Area Museum & Cultural Center, Inc., Fredericksburg, VA 1506
Freeborn County Museum and Historical Village, Albert Lea, MN 767
Freeport Historical Society, Freeport, ME 611
Freestone County Historical Museum, Fairfield, TX 1413
Fremont County Pioneer Museum, Lander, WY 1635
French Azilum, Inc., Towanda, PA 1303
Fresno Flats Historical Park, Oakhurst, CA 132
Friends of Arrow Rock, Inc., Arrow Rock, MO 811
Frisco Historic Park & Museum, Frisco, CO 218
Frisco Native American Museum and Natural History Center, Frisco, NC 1102
Frontier Culture Museum, Staunton, VA 1537
Frontier Gateway Museum, Glendive, MT 847
Frontier Historical Society and Museum, Glenwood Springs, CO 219
Frontier Times Museum, Bandera, TX 1393
Frontiers of Flight Museum, Dallas, TX 1406
The Fryeburg Fair Farm Museum, Fryeburg, ME 611
Fryer Memorial Museum, Munnsville, NY 1017
Frye's Measure Mill, Wilton, NH 897
Fulton County Historical Museum, Wauseon, OH 1190
Fulton County Historical Society Museum, Rochester, IN 498
Fulton County Museum, Groversville, NY 996
Furnace Town Living Heritage Museum, Snow Hill, MD 654
Furnas-Gosper Historical Society & Museum, Arapahoe, NE 856
Gage County Historical Society and Museum, Beatrice, NE 857
Galena-Jo Daviess County Historical Society & Museum, Galena, IL 436
Galena Mining & Historical Museum, Galena, KS 541
Gallier House, New Orleans, LA 595
Galloping Road Compound & Poker Alley; Harbor Ranch, Dripping Springs, TX 1410
Galloway House and Village - Blakely Museum, Fond du Lac, WI 1597
Galveston Historical Foundation, Inc., Galveston, TX 1421
Garden Grove Historical Society, Garden Grove, CA 99
Gardner House Museum, Albion, MI 723
The Gardner Museum, Inc., Gardner, MA 684
The Gardner Museum of Architecture & Design, Quincy, IL 452
Garfield Farm Museum, LaFox, IL 441
Garibaldi and Meucci Museum, Staten Island, NY 1072
Garrett County Historical Museum, Oakland, MD 649
Gates House, Machiasport Historical Society, Machiasport, ME 614
Gates Mills Historical Society, Gates Mills, OH 1166
Gateway to the Panhandle, Gate, OK 1201
Geddes Historic District Village, Geddes, SD 1347
Gemological Institute of America Museum, Carlsbad, CA 81
General Lew Wallace Study & Museum, Crawfordsville, IN 473
General Patton Memorial Museum, Chiriaco Summit, CA 84
General Wait House, Waitsfield, VT 1489
Genesee Country Village & Museum, Mumford, NY 1016

Geneva Historical Society & Prouty-Chew House & Museum, Geneva, NY....................994

Geneva Historical Society & Rose Hill Mansion, Geneva, NY....................994

Geographical Center Historical Museum, Rugby, ND....................1136

George I. Ashby Memorial Museum, Copper Center, AK....................23

George Peabody House Museum, Peabody, MA....................701

Georgia Salzburger Society Museum, Rincon, GA....................381

Georgia Southern University Museum, Statesboro, GA....................387

Georgia's Old Capital Museum, Milledgeville, GA....................380

Georgia's Stone Mountain Park, Stone Mountain, GA....................387

Germantown Historical Society, Philadelphia, PA....................1280

Geronimo Springs Museum, Truth or Consequences, NM....................953

Gibbs Museum of Pioneer and Dakotah Life, Falcon Heights, MN....................775

Gig Harbor Peninsula Historical Society, Gig Harbor, WA....................1555

Gillespie County Historical Society, Fredericksburg, TX....................1419

Gilliam County Historical Society - Depot Museum Complex, Condon, OR.1222

Gilmore Car Museum, Hickory Corners, MI....................746

Glassboro Heritage Glass Museum, Glassboro, NJ....................905

Glendower State Memorial, Lebanon, OH.1171

Glenn H. Curtiss Museum, Hammondsport, NY....................997

Glenview Area Historical Society, Glenview, IL....................438

Gloucester County Historical Society, Woodbury, NJ....................931

Glove Museum, New York, NY....................1026

Gnadenhutten Historical Park & Museum, Gnadenhutten, OH....................1167

Gold Coast Railroad Museum, Inc., Miami, FL....................323

Gold Nugget Museum, Paradise, CA....................139

Golden Ball Tavern Museum, Weston, MA....................718

Golden Gate Railroad Museum, San Francisco, CA....................166

Golden Pioneer Museum, Golden, CO....................220

Golden Spike National Historic Site, Brigham City, UT....................1463

Goliad State Park, Goliad, TX....................1423

Good Old Days Vintage Motorcar Museum, Inc., Hardy, AR....................59

Goschenhoppen Folklife Library and Museum, Green Lane, PA....................1257

Goshen Historical Society, Goshen, CT....................242

Gouverneur Historical Association, Gouverneur, NY....................995

Governor Bent Museum, Taos, NM....................952

Governor Ross Plantation, Seaford, DE....................272

Graber Olive House Museum, Ontario, CA....................135

The Grace Museum, Abilene, TX....................1385

Grafton Historical Society, Grafton, VT....................1479

Graham County Historical Society, Thatcher, AZ....................46

Grand County Museum, Hot Sulphur Springs, CO....................222

Grand Forks County Historical Society, Grand Forks, ND....................1132

Grand Gulf Military Park, Port Gibson, MS....................807

Grand Portage National Monument, Grand Marais, MN....................776

The Grand River Historical Society & Museum, Chillicothe, MO....................813

Grand Teton National Park, Colter Bay Indian Arts Museum, Colter Bay Village, WY....................1631

Grand Traverse Heritage Center, Traverse City, MI....................765

Grant County Historical Museum, Ephrata, WA....................1553

Grant County Historical Society, Elbow Lake, MN....................774

Grant County Museum, Medford, OK....................1205

Grant County Museum aka Historic Adobe Museum, Ulysses, KS....................560

Grant-Kohrs Ranch National Historic Site, Deer Lodge, MT....................845

Granville County Historical Society Museum, Oxford, NC....................1114

Granville Historical Society Museum, Granville, OH....................1167

Graves Museum of Archaeology and Natural History, Dania Beach, FL....................302

Gravette Historical Museum, Gravette, AR....................59

Great Basin Historical Society & Museum, Delta, UT....................1464

Great Harbor Maritime Museum, Northeast Harbor, ME....................616

Great Smoky Mountains Heritage Center, Townsend, TN....................1384

Greater Harvard Area Historical Society, Harvard, IL....................439

Greater Hazleton Historical Society, Hazleton, PA....................1260

Green Mountain Club, Inc., Waterbury Center, VT....................1489

Green River Valley Museum, Big Piney, WY....................1629

Greene County Historical Museum, Waynesburg, PA....................1306

Greene County Historical Society, Xenia, OH....................1193

Greenfield Historical Society, Greenfield, WI....................1599

Greentown Glass Museum, Inc., Greentown, IN....................480

Greenwood County Historical Society, Eureka, KS....................539

Gregg County Historical Museum, Longview, TX....................1434

Gresham History Museum, Gresham, OR..1226

Greybull Museum, Greybull, WY....................1634

Grinnell Historical Museum, Grinnell, IA....519

Grosse Ile Historical Society, Grosse Ile, MI....................745

Grout Museum District: Grout Museum of History and Science, Bluedorn Science Imaginarium, Rensselaer Russell House Museum, Snowden House, Waterloo, IA....................529

The Grove, Glenview, IL....................438

Guernsey County Museum, Cambridge, OH....................1144

The Guest House Museum, Fort Bragg, CA....................95

Guilford Courthouse National Military Park, Greensboro, NC....................1104

Gulf Islands National Seashore, Gulf Breeze, FL....................312

Gulf Shores Museum, Gulf Shores, AL....................11

Gunn Memorial Library and Museum, Washington, CT....................263

Gunnison County Pioneer and Historical Society, Gunnison, CO....................222

Gwinnett Historical Society, Lawrenceville, GA....................376

H. Earl Clack Museum, Havre, MT....................849

H.G. Albee Memorial Museum, Estherville, IA....................517

Hacienda Buena Vista, Ponce, PR....................1642

Haffenreffer Museum of Anthropology, Brown University, Bristol, RI....................1310

The Haggin Museum, Stockton, CA....................189

The Hagley Museum and Library, Wilmington, DE....................273

Hahns Peak Area Historical Society and School House, Clark, CO....................205

Hale Farm and Village, Bath, OH....................1141

Hallockville Museum Farm, Riverhead, NY....................1057

Hamburg State Park Museum, Mitchell, GA....................380

Hamden Historical Society, Inc., Hamden, CT....................244

Hamilton Township Historical Society - John Abbott II House, Hamilton, NJ....................906

Hamilton Van Wagoner Museum, Clifton, NJ....................901

Hampton Plantation State Historic Site, McClellanville, SC....................1336

Hampton University Museum, Hampton, VA....................1509

Hana Cultural Center, Hana, Maui, HI....................392

Hanby House, Westerville, OH....................1191

Hancock Historical Museum, Findlay, OH....................1164

Hancock Historical Society, Hancock, NH....................888

Hancock House, Hancock's Bridge, NJ....................907

Hancock Shaker Village, Inc., Pittsfield, MA....................703

The Handweaving Museum & Arts Center, Clayton, NY....................978

Hanford Mills Museum, East Meredith, NY....................987

Hanna Basin Museum, Hanna, WY....................1634

Hannah Lindahl Children's Museum, Mishawaka, IN....................491

Harbour House Museum, Crystal Falls, MI....................733

Hardin County Historical Museums, Inc., Kenton, OH....................1170

Harn Homestead and 1889er Museum, Oklahoma City, OK....................1207

Harold M. Freund American Museum of Baking, Manhattan, KS....................550

Harold Warp Pioneer Village Foundation, Minden, NE....................868

Harper City Historical Society, Harper, KS....................543

Harpers Ferry National Historical Park, Harpers Ferry, WV....................1582

Harrison House, Branford, CT....................235

Hartslog Heritage Museum, Alexandria, PA....................1239

Hartsville Museum, Hartsville, SC....................1335

Harvey House Museum, Florence, KS....................539

Haskell County Historical Society, Sublette, KS....................558

Hathaway Ranch Museum, Santa Fe Springs, CA....................182

Hatteras Island Visitor Center, Buxton, NC....................1093

Haverford Township Historical Society, Havertown, PA....................1260

Havre de Grace Decoy Museum, Havre de Grace, MD....................647

Hawaii Maritime Center, Honolulu, HI....................395

Hawaii's Plantation Village, Waipahu, HI....402

Hawkeye Log Cabin, Burlington, IA....................507

Hawks Inn Historical Society, Inc., Delafield, WI....................1595

Hawks Nest State Park, Ansted, WV....................1579

Hayward Area Historical Society, Hayward, CA....................102

Headley-Whitney Museum, Lexington, KY....................573

Headwaters Heritage Museum, Three Forks, MT....................854

Heddon Museum, Dowagiac, MI....................738

Heisey Museum, Clinton County Historical Society, Lock Haven, PA....................1269

Helvetia Museum, Helvetia, WV....................1582

Hemet Museum, Hemet, CA....................103

Tools and Equipment for
Materials—Continued

Henry County Historical Society, New
Castle, IN...494
The Henry Ford, Dearborn, MI....................733
Henry Ford Estate-Fair Lane, Dearborn,
MI...734
The Henry Sheldon Museum of Vermont
History, Middlebury, VT.......................1481
Henry Whitfield State Historical
Museum, Guilford, CT..........................243
Hereford Inlet Lighthouse, North
Wildwood, NJ......................................917
The Heritage Center and Citrus Museum,
Vero Beach, FL....................................352
Heritage Center Museum, Berryville, AR......55
Heritage Complex Farm Equipment
Museum and Learning Center, Tulare,
CA...193
Heritage Farm Museum & Village,
Huntington, WV...................................1583
Heritage Farmstead Museum, Plano, TX...1444
Heritage Hall Museum & Archives,
Freeman, SD..1347
Heritage Hill State Historical Park, Green
Bay, WI...1599
Heritage-Hjemkomst Interpretive Center,
Moorhead, MN.....................................784
Heritage House Museum of Montgomery
County, Mount Ida, AR.........................64
Heritage House of Orange County
Association Inc., Orange, TX................1441
Heritage Library Museum, Anchorage,
AK...22
The Heritage Museum, Astoria, OR..........1218
Heritage Museum & Potton House, Big
Spring, TX...1396
The Heritage Museum at Falfurrias, Inc.,
Falfurrias, TX.......................................1413
Heritage Museum Foundation of Tate
County, Inc., Senatobia, MS.................808
Heritage Museum of Northwest Florida,
Valparaiso, FL......................................352
Heritage Museums & Gardens, Sandwich,
MA..707
The Heritage Society, Houston, TX............1426
Heritage Square Museum, Ontario, NY.....1047
Heritage Square Museum, Los Angeles,
CA...116
Heritage Station, Umatilla County
Historical Society Museum, Pendleton,
OR..1230
Heritage Village, Largo, FL.......................321
Heritage Village, Mountain Lake, MN........785
The Hermitage: Home of President
Andrew Jackson, Hermitage, TN...........1367
Herreshoff Marine Museum/America's
Cup Hall of Fame, Bristol, RI...............1311
Herschell Carrousel Factory Museum,
North Tonawanda, NY...........................1043
Hershey Museum, Hershey, PA.................1261
Hibbing Historical Society and Museum,
Hibbing, MN..778
The Hickories Museum of the Lorain
County Historical Society, Elyria, OH..1163
Hickory Hill, Thomson, GA......................388
The Hicksville Gregory Museum,
Hicksville, NY......................................998
Higgins Armory Museum, Worcester, MA...721
High Cliff Historical Society & General
Store Museum, Sherwood, WI..............1622
High Plains Museum, Goodland, KS..........542
High Point Museum & Historical Park,
High Point, NC.....................................1106
Highland County Museum and Heritage
Center, McDowell, VA...........................1517
Highland House Museum, Hillsboro, OH..1168
Highland Maple Museum, Monterey, VA...1518
Highlands Hammock State Park/Civilian
Conservation Corps Museum, Sebring,
FL..346

Hillsboro Area Historical Society,
Hillsboro, WI.......................................1600
Hillsboro Museums, Hillsboro, KS.............544
Hinckley Fire Museum, Hinckley, MN........778
Historic Arkansas Museum, Little Rock,
AR...62
Historic Bethabara Park, Winston-Salem,
NC..1125
Historic Bowens Mills & Pioneer Park,
Middleville, MI.....................................754
Historic Brattonsville, McConnells, SC......1336
Historic Burlington County Prison
Museum, Mount Holly, NJ.....................914
Historic Camden Revolutionary War Site,
Camden, SC...1323
Historic Carson House, Marion, NC...........1110
Historic Charlton Park Village and
Museum, Hastings, MI..........................745
Historic Crab Orchard Museum &
Pioneer Park, Inc., Tazewell, VA..........1541
Historic Fallsington, Inc., Fallsington, PA.1253
Historic Fort Snelling, Saint Paul, MN.......790
Historic General Dodge House, Council
Bluffs, IA...512
Historic Halifax State Historic Site,
Halifax, NC..1105
Historic Homes Foundation, Inc.,
Louisville, KY......................................576
Historic Hope Foundation, Inc., Windsor,
NC..1124
Historic Indian Agency House, Portage,
WI...1618
Historic Langhorne Association,
Langhorne, PA.....................................1267
Historic Latta Plantation, Huntersville,
NC..1107
Historic Lincoln, Lincoln, NM..................941
Historic Lyme Village Association,
Bellevue, OH.......................................1142
Historic Madison, Inc., Madison, IN..........489
Historic New Harmony, New Harmony,
IN...494
Historic Occoquan, Inc., Occoquan, VA.....1523
Historic Palmyra's Print Shop, Palmyra,
NY..1050
Historic Pensacola Village, Pensacola, FL...335
Historic Preservation Association of
Bourbon County, Inc., Fort Scott, KS.....540
Historic Preservation League of Oregon,
Portland, OR..1231
Historic Price House, Woodruff, SC...........1343
Historic Prophetstown, Battle Ground, IN...468
Historic Renville Preservation
Commission, Renville, MN....................787
Historic Sauder Village, Archbold, OH......1140
Historic Schaefferstown, Inc.,
Schaefferstown, PA...............................1297
Historic Shepherdstown Museum,
Shepherdstown, WV..............................1586
Historic Smithfield, Blacksburg, VA...........1497
Historic Southwest Ohio, Inc.,
Sharonville, OH....................................1185
Historic Spanish Point, Osprey, FL............333
Historic Speedwell, Morristown, NJ...........913
Historic Walnford, Upper Freehold Twp.,
NJ..929
Historic Westville, Inc., Lumpkin, GA........376
Historical and Genealogical Society of
Indiana County, Indiana, PA.................1262
Historical Center for Southeast New
Mexico, Roswell, NM............................946
Historical Museum at Fort Missoula,
Missoula, MT.......................................851
Historical Museum of Bay County, Bay
City, MI...727
Historical Natural History & Library
Society of Natick dba Natick
Historical Society, South Natick, MA.....709
Historical Society of Bloomfield New
Jersey, Bloomfield, NJ..........................898
Historical Society of Brookfield,
Brookfield Center, VT...........................1477

Historical Society of Carroll County,
Westminster, MD..................................656
Historical Society of Cheshire County,
Keene, NH...890
Historical Society of Columbia County,
Saint Helens, OR..................................1234
Historical Society of Fort Washington,
Fort Washington, PA.............................1254
Historical Society of Garden County,
Oshkosh, NE..871
Historical Society of Greater Port
Jefferson, Port Jefferson, NY...............1053
Historical Society of Greenfield,
Greenfield, MA....................................685
Historical Society of Haddonfield,
Haddonfield, NJ...................................905
Historical Society of Middletown and the
Wallkill Precinct, Inc., Middletown,
NY..1014
Historical Society of Millersburg &
Upper Paxton Township Museum,
Millersburg, PA....................................1272
Historical Society of Newburgh Bay &
the Highlands - David Crawford
House, Newburgh, NY..........................1042
Historical Society of Old Newbury,
Cushing House Museum,
Newburyport, MA.................................698
Historical Society of Old Randolph,
Randolph, NJ.......................................922
Historical Society of Quaker Hill &
Pawling, Pawling, NY...........................1051
Historical Society of St. Marys and
Benzinger Township, Saint Marys, PA..1297
Historical Society of Santuit and Cotuit,
Cotuit, MA...677
Historical Society of Stanton County
Museums at Stanton and Pilger, Pilger,
NE..872
Historical Society of Talbot County,
Easton, MD..642
Historical Society of the Phoenixville
Area, Phoenixville, PA..........................1290
Historical Society of the Town of
Clarence, Clarence, NY........................978
Historical Society of the Town of
Greenwich Inc. aka Bush-Holley
Historic Site, Cos Cob, CT...................237
The Historical Society of the Town of
Warwick, Warwick, NY.........................1082
The Historical Society of Trappe,
Collegeville, Perkiomen Valley, Inc.,
Trappe, PA...1303
Historical Society of Walden & Wallkill
Valley, Walden, NY..............................1081
Historical Society Porter County Old Jail
Museum, Valparaiso, IN.......................502
The History Center, Fort Wayne, IN...........477
The History Center, Cedar Rapids, IA.......509
The History Center in Tompkins County,
Ithaca, NY...1003
History Museum for Springfield-Greene
County, Springfield, MO.......................839
The History Museum, Lake Placid-North
Elba Historical Society, Lake Placid,
NY..1009
History Museum of Western Virginia,
Roanoke, VA..1535
History San Jose, San Jose, CA.................171
Hoard Historical Museum and National
Dairy Shrine's Visitors Center, Fort
Atkinson, WI..1598
Hobart Historical Society Museum,
Hobart, IN...480
Hodgden House Museum Complex,
Ellsworth, KS.......................................538
Hofwyl-Broadfield Plantation State
Historic Site, Brunswick, GA................366
Holland Historical Society Museum, Inc.,
Holland, VT...1480
The Holland Land Office Museum,
Batavia, NY...960
The Holland Museum, Holland, MI............746

Holly History Center & Hutchinson House Museum, Waupaca, WI...............1626

Homestake Gold Mine Visitor Center, Lead, SD...1351

Homestead National Monument of America, Beatrice, NE 857

Homesteader Museum, Powell, WY..........1637

Homeville Antique Fire Department, Homer, NY 999

Honolulu House Museum, Marshall, MI......754

Honolulu Police Department Law Enforcement Museum, Honolulu, HI.......396

Hoo-Hoo International Forestry Museum, Gurdon, AR..59

Hood River County Historical Museum, Hood River, OR.......................................1226

Hoover Historical Center, North Canton, OH...1179

Hopewell Furnace National Historic Site, Elverson, PA 1251

Hopewell Museum, Paris, KY 582

Hornby Museum, Hornby, NY....................999

Horry County Museum, Conway, SC.........1331

Horseshoe Bend National Military Park, Daviston, AL...7

Hot Springs County Museum and Cultural Center, Thermopolis, WY.........1639

Houghton County Historical Museum Society, Lake Linden, MI..........................749

Houston Center for Contemporary Craft, Houston, TX...1426

Howard County Historical Museum, Kokomo, IN...486

Howard County Historical Society, Ellicott City, MD......................................643

Howard Steamboat Museum and Mansion, Jeffersonville, IN 486

Howell Historical Society & Committee Museum, Howell, NJ..............................908

Howell Living History Farm, Titusville, NJ..926

Howland House, Plymouth, MA..................703

The Hubbard Museum of the American West, Ruidoso Downs, NM....................946

Hubbell Trading Post National Historic Site, Ganado, AZ.......................................34

Hudson Library and Historical Society, Hudson, OH..1168

Hudson River Maritime Museum, Kingston, NY...1007

Huerfano County Historical Society, including The Walsenburg Mining Museum & Ft. Francisco Museum of La Veta, Walsenburg, CO.......................234

The Huguenot Historical Society, New Paltz, NY 1017

Hull Lifesaving Museum Inc., the Museum of Boston Harbor Heritage, Hull, MA...687

Humboldt Historical Museum, Humboldt, KS...544

Humboldt Redwoods State Park Visitor Center, Weott, CA 197

Humpback Rocks Mountain Farm & Visitor Center, Waynesboro, VA 1544

The 100th Meridian Museum, Cozad, NE ...859

Huntington Beach International Surfing Museum, Huntington Beach, CA.............104

Huntington County Historical Society Museum, Huntington, IN 481

Huron City Museums, Port Austin, MI........761

Hurricane Valley Heritage Park Museum, Hurricane, UT.......................................1466

Hurst Ranch Historical Foundation, West Covina, CA 197

Hutchinson County Museum, Borger, TX..1397

Hyde Hall, Inc., Cooperstown, NY 980

Ice House Museum, Cedar Falls, IA 508

Idaho State Historical Museum, Boise, ID...404

Illinois and Michigan Canal Commissioners Office Museum, Lockport, IL..443

Illinois Railway Museum, Union, IL.............461

Ilwaco Heritage Museum, Ilwaco, WA.......1556

Imagine It! The Children's Museum of Atlanta, Atlanta, GA................................361

Independence Historical Museum, Independence, KS....................................545

Independence Seaport Museum, Philadelphia, PA....................................1281

Indian City U.S.A., Anadarko, OK 1195

Indian King Tavern Museum, Haddonfield, NJ.......................................906

Indiana Dunes National Lakeshore, Porter, IN...496

Indiana State Museum, Indianapolis, IN 484

Indiana War Memorials, Indianapolis, IN 484

The Institute For American Indian Studies (IAIS), Washington Green, CT...263

Interlaken Historical Society, Interlaken, NY...1002

International Bluegrass Music Museum, Owensboro, KY...581

International Institute of Metropolitan Detroit, Detroit, MI................................737

International Museum of the Horse, Lexington, KY..573

The International Printing Museum, Carson, CA...82

Intrepid Sea-Air-Space Museum, New York, NY...1028

Iolani Palace, Honolulu, HI 396

Iosco County Historical Museum, East Tawas, MI...740

Iowa Department of Natural Resources, Des Moines, IA 515

Iowa Railroad Historical Society, Boone, IA..506

Irish American Heritage Museum, Albany, NY...954

Iron & Steel Museum of Alabama, Tannehill Ironworks Historical State Park, McCalla, AL.....................................13

Iron Mission State Park & Museum, Cedar City, UT....................................1464

Iron Mountain Iron Mine, Vulcan, MI 766

Ironworld Discovery Center, Chisholm, MN...771

Isabel Anderson Comer Museum & Arts Center, Sylacauga, AL 18

Isabel Miller Museum/Sitka Historical Society, Sitka, AK 27

Isanti County Historical Society, Cambridge, MN.......................................770

Ischua Valley Historical Society, Inc., Franklinville, NY.......................................992

Island County Historical Society Museum, Coupeville, WA 1551

Isle La Motte Historical Society, Isle La Motte, VT...1480

Isle Royale National Park, Houghton, MI....747

Islesboro Historical Society, Islesboro, ME...612

Islesford Historical Museum, Islesford, ME...612

Issaquah History Museum, Issaquah, WA ..1557

Itasca County Historical Society, Grand Rapids, MN...777

J.E. Reeves Home & Museum, Dover, OH...1163

JFK Special Warfare Museum, Fort Bragg, NC...1101

J.J. Jackson Memorial Museum, Weaverville, CA 197

J.W. Parmley Historical Home Society, Ipswich, SD...1349

Jackson County Historical Museum & Research Library, Maquoketa, IA............522

Jackson County Historical Society, Black River Falls, WI.......................................1592

Jackson-Washabaugh Historical Museum, Kadoka, SD...1349

Jacksonport State Park, Jacksonport, AR 60

Jackson's Mill Historic Area, Weston, WV..1587

Jacob Kelley House Museum, Hartsville, SC...1335

Jail Museum, Neligh, NE............................869

The James Madison Museum, Orange, VA...1524

James Whitcomb Riley Birthplace & Museum, Greenfield, IN........................480

Jamestown Settlement, Yorktown Victory Center, The Jamestown-Yorktown Foundation, Williamsburg, VA...............1545

Japanese Cultural Center of Hawaii, Honolulu, HI..397

Jarrell Plantation Georgia State Historic Site, Juliette, GA......................................374

Jean Lafitte National Historical Park & Preserve, New Orleans, LA.....................596

Jean P. Haydon Museum, Pago Pago, AS ..1640

Jeff Matthews Memorial Museum, Galax, VA...1508

Jefferson Barracks Historic Site, Saint Louis, MO...833

Jefferson County Historical Society, Watertown, NY..1083

Jefferson County Historical Society and Farnsworth TV Pioneer Museum, Rigby, ID..409

Jefferson County Historical Society Museum, Port Townsend, WA 1562

Jefferson Historical Society and Museum, Jefferson, TX..1431

Jefferson National Expansion Memorial, Saint Louis, MO.......................................833

Jefferson Patterson Park & Museum, Saint Leonard, MD.................................651

Jefferson Valley Museum, Whitehall, MT....855

Jensen Arctic Museum, Monmouth, OR 1228

Jerome County Historical Society, Inc. and Idaho Farm & Ranch Museum, Jerome, ID...406

Jewell County Historical Museum, Mankato, KS..552

Jim Gatchell Memorial Museum, Buffalo, WY..1629

John Day Fossil Beds National Monument, Kimberly, OR.....................1227

John E. Conner Museum, Kingsville, TX ..1432

John Jay Homestead State Historic Site, Katonah, NY...1006

John Rains House, Rancho Cucamonga, CA...145

John Stark Edwards House, Warren, OH ...1189

John Wesley Powell Memorial Museum, Page, AZ..37

Johnson County Historical Society, Coralville, IA...511

Johnson County Historical Society, Inc., Tecumseh, NE...873

Johnson County Historical Society Museum, Warrensburg, MO...................840

Johnson County Museum of History, Franklin, IN..478

Johnson County Museums, Shawnee, KS ...558

Johnson Ferry House Museum, Titusville, NJ...926

Johnson-Humrickhouse Museum, Coshocton, OH 1159

Johnstown Area Heritage Association, Johnstown, PA......................................1263

Johnstown Flood National Memorial, South Fork, PA......................................1300

Joliet Area Historical Museum, Joliet, IL 440

Jonathan Bailey Home, Whittier, CA 198

Jonathan Hager House & Museum, Hagerstown, MD.....................................646

Jonesborough-Washington County History Museum, Jonesborough, TN 1368

The Journey Museum, Rapid City, SD.......1354

The Judah P. Benjamin Confederate Memorial at Gamble Plantation Historic State Park, Ellenton, FL............306

Tools and Equipment for Materials—Continued

Judith Basin County Museum, Stanford, MT.................853
Jugville Museum, Grafton, ND.................1131
Julia A. Purnell Museum, Snow Hill, MD...654
Junction City Historical Society, Junction City, OR.................1226
Juneau-Douglas City Museum, Juneau, AK.................26
The Junior Museum of Bay County, Panama City, FL.................334

Kalamazoo Nature Center, Inc., Kalamazoo, MI.................748
Kalaupapa National Historical Park, Kalaupapa, HI.................400
Kalkaska County Historical Museum, Kalkaska, MI.................749
Kanabec History Center, Mora, MN.................784
Kandiyohi County Historical Society, Willmar, MN.................796
Kankakee County Museum, Kankakee, IL...441
Kansas Aviation Museum, Wichita, KS.................562
Kauai Museum, Lihue, HI.................401
Kauffman Museum, North Newton, KS.................553
Kaw Mission State Historic Site, Council Grove, KS.................536
Kearney County Historical Museum, Minden, NE.................868
Keeler Tavern Museum, Ridgefield, CT.................259
Kellogg Historical Society, Kellogg, IA.................521
The Kelso House Museum, Kent, OH.................1169
Kennebunkport Historical Society, Kennebunkport, ME.................612
Kenosha County Historical Society and Museum, Inc., Kenosha, WI.................1602
Kensington Mansion, Eastover, SC.................1332
Kentucky Coal Mining Museum, Benham, KY.................565
Kentucky Department of Fish & Wildlife Resources-Salato Wildlife Education Center, Frankfort, KY.................569
Kentucky Gateway Museum Center, Maysville, KY.................579
Kentucky Historical Society, Frankfort, KY.................569
Kentucky Military History Museum, Frankfort, KY.................569
Kentucky Railway Museum, Inc., New Haven, KY.................580
Ker Place, Onancock, VA.................1523
Kerbyville Museum, Kerby, OR.................1227
Kern County Museum, Bakersfield, CA.................73
Kewaunee County Historical Museum, Kewaunee, WI.................1602
Keweenaw County Historical Society, Eagle Harbor, MI.................739
Keyport Historical Society-Steamboat Dock Museum, Keyport, NJ.................909
Keystone Area Historical Society, Keystone, SD.................1350
Kidwell Farm at Frying Pan Park, Herndon, VA.................1511
Kimball House Museum, Battle Creek, MI.................727
Kimble County Historical Museum, Junction, TX.................1431
King Saddlery Museum, Sheridan, WY.................1638
Kingman County Historical Museum, Kingman, KS.................547
Kingman Tavern Historical Museum, Cummington, MA.................678
Kings Mountain National Military Park, Blacksburg, SC.................1322
Kingsley Plantation, Jacksonville, FL.................315
Kinney Pioneer Museum and Historical Society of North Iowa, Clear Lake, IA...510
Kit Carson Historical Society, Kit Carson, CO.................223

Kitsap County Historical Society Museum, Bremerton, WA.................1549
Kittery Historical & Naval Museum, Kittery, ME.................613
Kiwanis Van Slyke Museum Foundation Inc., Caldwell, ID.................404
Klamath County Museum, Klamath Falls, OR.................1227
Klickitat County Historical Society, Goldendale, WA.................1555
Kline Creek Farm, Winfield, IL.................466
Klondike Gold Rush National Historical Park, Seattle, WA.................1566
Klyne Esopus Museum, Ulster Park, NY...1079
Knife River Indian Villages National Historic Site, Stanton, ND.................1136
Knight Museum, Alliance, NE.................855
Knox County Museum, Knoxville, IL.................441
Knox County Museum, Benjamin, TX.................1395
Knoxville Public Library, Knoxville, PA...1265
Koochiching County Historical Museum, International Falls, MN.................778
Koreshan State Historic Site, Estero, FL.................306
Koshare Indian Museum, Inc., La Junta, CO.................224

L.C. Bates Museum, Hinckley, ME.................612
La Puente Valley Historical Society City Hall, LaPuente, CA.................107
La Purisima Mission State Historic Park, Lompoc, CA.................109
LaBelle Heritage Museum, LaBelle, FL.................319
Lac Qui Parle County Historical Society, Madison, MN.................779
The Lackawanna Historical Society at the Catlin House, Scranton, PA.................1298
Lafayette Miners Museum, Lafayette, CO...224
Lafayette Natural History Museum and Planetarium, Lafayette, LA.................589
Lagrange County Historical Society, Inc., Lagrange, IN.................488
LaGrange Plantation, Cambridge, MD.................639
The Lake Champlain Maritime Museum, Vergennes, VT.................1488
Lake County Discovery Museum, Wauconda, IL.................463
Lake County Historical Museum, Tavares, FL.................351
Lake County Historical Society, Two Harbors, MN.................794
Lake County Historical Society, Kirtland Hills, OH.................1170
Lake George Historical Association Museum, Lake George, NY.................1008
Lake of the Red Cedars Museum, Cedar Lake, IN.................472
Lake of the Woods County Museum, Baudette, MN.................768
Lake Superior Maritime Visitors Center, Duluth, MN.................773
Lake Tahoe Historical Society & Museum, South Lake Tahoe, CA.................188
Lake Waccamaw Depot Museum, Lake Waccamaw, NC.................1109
Lake Wales Depot Museum & Cultural Center, Lake Wales, FL.................320
Lakewood's Heritage Center, Lakewood, CO.................225
Land of the Yankee Fork Historic Association Museum, Stanley, ID.................410
Landis Valley Museum, Lancaster, PA.................1266
Landmark Park, Dothan, AL.................8
Landmarks Foundation/Old Alabama Town, Montgomery, AL.................16
Lane County Historical Museum, Dighton, KS.................536
Lane County Historical Society & Museum, Eugene, OR.................1223
Langlade County Historical Society Museum, Antigo, WI.................1589

Lars Noak Blacksmith Shop, Larsson/Ostlund Log Home & One-Room Capitol School, New Sweden, ME.................616
Larz Anderson Auto Museum, Brookline, MA.................671
Las Cabezas de San Juan Nature Reserve (El Faro), Fajardo, PR.................1641
LaSalle County Historical Society Museum, Utica, IL.................462
Latvian Museum, Rockville, MD.................651
Lauder Museum - Amityville Historical Society, Amityville, NY.................957
Laura Ingalls Wilder Park & Museum, Inc., Burr Oak, IA.................507
Laurence C. Jones Museum, Piney Woods, MS.................807
Lawrence County Gray House Museum, Ironton, OH.................1169
Lawrence County Historical and Genealogical Society, Bedford, IN.................469
Lawrence Heritage State Park, Lawrence, MA.................689
Lawrence History Center: Immigrant City Archives & Museum, Lawrence, MA.................689
Layland Museum, Cleburne, TX.................1400
Le Sueur Museum, Le Sueur, MN.................779
Lea County Cowboy Hall of Fame and Western Heritage Center, Hobbs, NM.................940
Leadville National Mining Hall of Fame & Museum, Leadville, CO.................226
Lee County Historical Society, Loachapoka, AL.................13
Leelanau Historical Museum, Leland, MI...751
The Leffingwell House Museum, Norwich, CT.................258
Legends of the Game Baseball Museum and Learning Center, Arlington, TX.................1388
Lehigh County Historical Society, Allentown, PA.................1239
Leverett Historical Society, Leverett, MA...689
Levi Coffin House, Fountain City, IN.................478
Levine Museum of the New South, Charlotte, NC.................1095
Lewis County Historical Museum, Chehalis, WA.................1550
Lewis County Historical Society Museum, Lowville, NY.................1012
Lexington County Museum, Lexington, SC.................1336
Liberty County Museum, Chester, MT.................844
Liberty Hall Historic Site, Frankfort, KY.................569
Liberty Hall Museum, Union, NJ.................928
Life on the Ohio River History Museum, Vevay, IN.................502
Lightner Museum, Saint Augustine, FL.................339
Limberlost State Historic Site, Geneva, IN.................479
Limon Heritage Museum, Limon, CO.................226
Lincoln Boyhood National Memorial, Lincoln City, IN.................488
Lincoln County Historical Museum, Davenport, WA.................1552
Lincoln County Historical Society, Lincoln, KS.................549
Lincoln County Historical Society, North Platte, NE.................869
Lincoln County Pioneer Museum, Hendricks, MN.................778
Lincoln Homestead State Park, Springfield, KY.................583
Lincoln Log Cabin State Historic Site, Lerna, IL.................442
Lincoln Parish Museum & Historical Society, Ruston, LA.................600
Lincoln Park Historical Museum, Lincoln Park, MI.................751
Lincoln's New Salem State Historic Site, Petersburg, IL.................451
Linn County Historical Museum and Moyer House, Brownsville, OR.................1220
Linn County Museum/Genealogy Library, Pleasanton, KS.................556

Lisbon Historical Society, Lisbon, OH.......1172
Lisle Station Museum, Lisle, IL...................443
Litchfield Historical Society and
    Museum, Litchfield, CT.........................247
Little Compton Historical Society, Little
    Compton, RI.......................................1312
The Little Cowboy Bar & Museum,
    Fromberg, MT......................................847
Littleton Historical Museum, Littleton,
    CO...227
Living Bible Museum, Mansfield, OH.......1173
Living History Farms, Urbandale, IA.........529
Livingston County Historical Society
    Museum, Geneseo, NY...........................993
Lock Museum of America, Inc.,
    Terryville, CT.......................................262
Locust Grove, Louisville, KY....................577
Locust Grove, The Samuel Morse
    Historic Site, Poughkeepsie, NY...........1055
Log Cabin Village, Fort Worth, TX..........1417
The Log House Museum of the Historical
    Society of Columbiana-Fairfield
    Township, Columbiana, OH...................1157
Logan County Historical Society
    Museum, Bellefontaine, OH...................1142
Logan County Museum, Paris, AR................65
Lombard Historical Museum, Lombard,
    IL...443
Lompoc Valley Historical Society, Inc.,
    Lompoc, CA...110
Long Island Culture History Lab &
    Museum, Commack, NY..........................980
Long Island Maritime Museum, West
    Sayville, NY.......................................1085
Long Island Museum of American Art,
    History & Carriages, Stony Brook,
    NY..1075
Longfellow Evangeline State Historic
    Site, Saint Martinville, LA......................600
Longfellow's Wayside Inn, Sudbury, MA....714
Longhorn Museum, Pleasanton, TX...........1444
Longmont Museum, Longmont, CO,...........227
Longstreet Farm, Holmdel, NJ...................908
Lopez Island Historical Museum, Lopez
    Island, WA..1558
Loriks Peterson Heritage House, Oldham,
    SD..1352
Los Altos History Museum aka
    Association of the Los Altos Historical
    Museum, Los Altos, CA..........................112
Los Angeles Maritime Museum, San
    Pedro, CA..176
Los Nogales Museum, Seguin, TX............1452
Lost City Museum, Overton, NV................880
Loudoun Heritage Farm Museum,
    Sterling, VA.......................................1538
Louis E. May Museum, Fremont, NE.........861
The Louisiana Cotton Museum, Lake
    Providence, LA.....................................590
Louisville Science Center, Louisville, KY...577
Louisville Slugger Museum & Factory,
    Louisville, KY......................................577
Loveland Museum Gallery, Loveland, CO...227
Lovettsville Historical Society Museum,
    Lovettsville, VA..................................1514
Lowell Area Historical Museum, Lowell,
    MI...751
Lowell National Historical Park, Lowell,
    MA..691
Lowell's Boat Shop, Amesbury, MA...........658
Lower East Side Tenement Museum,
    New York, NY....................................1029
Lower White River Museum, Des Arc,
    AR..56
Lowndes County Historical Society and
    Museum, Valdosta, GA...........................389
Luckhard Museum - The Indian Mission,
    Sebewaing, MI.....................................764
Lucretia Vaile Museum, Palmer Lake,
    CO...229
Luther Burbank Home & Gardens, Santa
    Rosa, CA...184

Lutz Children's Museum, Manchester, CT...248
Luzerne County Historical Society,
    Wilkes-Barre, PA................................1307
The Lyceum, Alexandria's History
    Museum, Alexandria, VA.......................1493
Lynchburg Museum System, Lynchburg,
    VA..1515
Lynden Pioneer Museum, Lynden, WA......1559
Lynn Museum & Historical Society,
    Lynn, MA..692
Lyon County Historical Society Museum,
    Marshall, MN.......................................780
The Lyons Redstone Museum, Lyons, CO...227

Mabee Farm Historic Site, Rotterdam
    Junction, NY......................................1062
MacGregor Ranch, Estes Park, CO.............215
MacKenzie Environmental Education
    Center, Poynette, WI...........................1618
Mackinac Island State Park
    Commission-Mackinac State Historic
    Parks, Mackinaw City, MI.......................752
Mackinac State Historic Parks-Colonial
    Michilimackinac & Old Mackinac
    Point Lighthouse, Mackinaw City, MI....752
Mackinac State Historic Parks-Fort
    Mackinac & Mackinac Island State
    Park, Mackinac Island, MI......................752
Mackinac State Historic Parks-Historic
    Mill Creek, Mackinaw City, MI..............753
Macon County Historical Society
    Museum Complex, Decatur, IL................430
The Madam Brett Homestead, Beacon,
    NY..961
Madeline Island Historical Museum, La
    Pointe, WI...1603
Madera County Museum, Madera, CA........123
Madison County Historical Society,
    Winterset, IA.......................................531
Madison Historical Society, Madison, CT....247
Magnolia Plantation and Gardens,
    Charleston, SC...................................1326
Mahaffie Stagecoach Stop and Farm,
    Olathe, KS...554
Maine Maritime Museum, Bath, ME...........606
Maine State Museum, Augusta, ME............604
Maitland Historical Museums, Maitland,
    FL..322
The Major General Frederick Funston
    Boyhood Home and Museum, Iola,
    KS...546
Makoti Threshers' Museum, Makoti, ND...1133
Malabar Farm State Park, Lucas, OH.........1173
Malheur Historical Project, Stonehouse
    Museum, Vale, OR..............................1238
Mammoth Spring State Park, Depot
    Museum, Mammoth Spring, AR...............64
Manassas Museum System, Manassas,
    VA..1516
Manassas National Battlefield Park,
    Manassas, VA.....................................1516
Manatee Village Historical Park,
    Bradenton, FL......................................297
Manitowoc County Historical Society,
    Manitowoc, WI...................................1607
Mann Wildlife Learning Museum,
    Montgomery, AL.....................................16
Mansfield Historical Society Museum,
    Storrs, CT..261
Manship House Museum, Jackson, MS........802
Maple Valley Historical Museum, Maple
    Valley, WA...1559
Marathon County Historical Society,
    Wausau, WI.......................................1626
Marble Historical Society, Marble, CO........228
Marblehead Museum & Historical
    Society, Marblehead, MA.......................693
Marcellus Historical Society, Marcellus,
    NY...1013
Marias Museum of History and Art,
    Shelby, MT..853
Marietta Museum of History, Marietta,
    GA...379

Marilla Historical Society Museum,
    Marilla, NY..1014
Marin Museum of the American Indian,
    Novato, CA..131
The Mariners' Museum, Newport News,
    VA..1519
Marinette County Historical Museum,
    Marinette, WI.....................................1607
Marion County Historical Society, Salem,
    OR...1236
The Marion County Historical Society
    Museum, Marion, OH...........................1174
Marion Historical Museums, Inc. -
    Granger House, Marion, IA.....................523
Mariposa Museum and History Center
    Inc., Mariposa, CA...............................124
Mariposa Museum & World Culture
    Center, Peterborough, NH......................893
Maritime & Seafood Industry Museum,
    Biloxi, MS...798
The Maritime Aquarium, Norwalk, CT........257
Maritime Museum - Cohasset Historical
    Society, Cohasset, MA...........................676
Maritime Museum of Monterey,
    Monterey, CA.......................................127
Maritime Museum of San Diego, San
    Diego, CA..157
Marjorie Kinnan Rawlings Historic State
    Park, Cross Creek, FL............................301
Marlboro County Historical Museum,
    Bennettsville, SC................................1322
Marlboro Historical Society, Marlboro,
    VT..1481
Marquette County Historical Society,
    Westfield, WI.....................................1627
Marquette County History Museum,
    Marquette, MI......................................753
Marshall County Historical Museum,
    Plymouth, IN..496
Marshall County Historical Museum,
    Holly Springs, MS................................801
Marshall County Historical Society
    Museum, Warren, MN............................795
Marshall Gold Discovery State Historic
    Park, Coloma, CA...................................86
Marshall M. Fredericks Sculpture
    Museum, University Center, MI..............766
Marshall Point Lighthouse Museum,
    Saint George, ME..................................621
Martha's Vineyard Museum, Edgartown,
    MA..681
Martin County Historical Museum,
    Stanton, TX..1453
Martinez Museum, Martinez, CA...............124
Marvin Newton House, Brookfield, VT.....1477
Mason County Historical Society/Historic
    White Pine Village, Ludington, MI..........751
Mason County Museum, Mason, TX.........1437
Mattapoisett Museum and Carriage
    House, Mattapoisett, MA........................693
The Mattatuck Museum Arts and History
    Center, Waterbury, CT...........................264
Matthew Edel Blacksmith Shop,
    Haverhill, IA..519
Matthews Museum of Maine Heritage,
    Union, ME..624
Maui Ocean Center, Maalaea, HI...............401
May Natural History Museum and
    Museum of Space Exploration,
    Colorado Springs, CO............................207
Mayborn Museum Complex, Waco, TX.....1459
Mayville Area Museum of History and
    Genealogy, Mayville, MI........................754
Mayville Historical Society, Inc.,
    Mayville, WI......................................1608
Mazomanie Historical Society,
    Mazomanie, WI..................................1608
Mc Cook County Historical Society and
    Museum, Salem, SD.............................1355
McCallum Museum, Sibley, IA..................527
McConaghy House, Hayward, CA...............102
McCone County Museum, Circle, MT.........844
McConnell Mansion, Moscow, ID...............407

Tools and Equipment for Materials—Continued

McCoy House, Lewistown, PA..................1269

McFarland Historical Society, McFarland, WI..............................1609

McHenry County Historical Society and Museum, Union, IL..........................461

McHenry Museum, Modesto, CA................126

McLean-Alanreed Area Museum, McLean, TX......................................1438

McLean County Museum of History, Bloomington, IL............................414

McMinn County Living Heritage Museum, Athens, TN.........................1360

McPherson County Old Mill Museum and Park, Lindsborg, KS...................550

McPherson Museum & Arts Foundation, McPherson, KS..............................552

Meade County Historical Society Museum, Meade, KS..........................552

Mecosta County Historical Museum, Big Rapids, MI..................................729

Medicine Bow Museum, Medicine Bow, WY..1636

Medina County Historical Society, The John Smart House, Medina, OH......1175

Medina Railroad Museum, Medina, NY....1014

Meeteetse Museum District, Meeteetse, WY..1636

Mel Fisher Maritime Heritage Society, Key West, FL...............................318

Melrose Plantation Home Complex, Melrose, LA................................592

Mem-Erie Historical Museum, Erie, KS......539

Memorial Hall Museum, Pocumtuck Valley Memorial Assoc., Deerfield, MA..679

Memoryville USA, Inc., Rolla, MO............829

Mendocino Historical Research, Inc./Kelley House Museum, Mendocino, CA.............................125

Mennonite Heritage Center, Harleysville, PA..1258

Mennonite Heritage Museum, Goessel, KS..542

Menominee County Heritage Museum, Menominee, MI..............................754

Merced County Courthouse Museum, Merced, CA....................................125

Mercer County Historical Museum, The Riley Home, Celina, OH....................1146

Mercer County Historical Society, Mercer, PA....................................1271

Mercer Museum of the Bucks County Historical Society, Doylestown, PA.......1250

Meriwether Lewis Dredge Museum, Brownville, NE..............................858

Merrill Historical Museum, Merrill, WI....1609

Mesa Historical Museum, Mesa, AZ..............37

Metamora Courthouse Historic Site, Metamora, IL................................444

Miami County Museum, Peru, IN................496

Michael C. Carlos Museum, Atlanta, GA....361

Michie Tavern ca. 1784, Charlottesville, VA..1499

Michigan Maritime Museum, South Haven, MI....................................764

Mid Atlantic Air Museum, Reading, PA....1296

Mid-Atlantic Center for the Arts/Emlen Physick Estate/Cape May Lighthouse, Cape May, NJ................................900

Middleborough Historical Association, Inc., Middleborough, MA....................694

Middlebury Historical Society, Wyoming, NY..1087

Middlesex Canal Collection, Lowell, MA....691

Middlesex County Historical Society, Middletown, CT............................249

Middleton Historical Society - Lura Woodside Watkins Museum, Middleton, MA..............................694

Middleton Place Foundation, Charleston, SC..1326

Midway Village & Museum Center, Rockford, IL................................455

Midwest Old Settlers & Threshers Association, Inc., Mount Pleasant, IA.....524

Mifflinburg Buggy Museum Association, Inc., Mifflinburg, PA....................1271

Milam County Museum and Annex, Cameron, TX................................1399

Milan Historical Museum, Inc., Milan, OH..1176

Miles B. Carpenter Museum, Waverly, VA..1543

Milford Historical Society, Milford, CT.......250

Milford Museum, Milford, DE...................271

Military Veterans Museum, Inc., Oshkosh, WI..................................1616

Mill Race Historical Village, Northville, MI..758

Millard Fillmore House, East Aurora, NY...985

Miller-Cory House Museum, Westfield, NJ..930

Mills County Historical Society and Museum, Glenwood, IA...................519

Milton Historical Museum, Milton, VT.....1482

Milton House Museum Historic Site, Milton, WI..................................1610

Milwaukee County Historical Society, Milwaukee, WI..............................1611

Minnesota Air National Guard Historical Foundation, Inc., Saint Paul, MN............790

Minnesota Museum of Mining, Chisholm, MN..771

Minnesota Pioneer Park Museum, Annandale, MN..............................767

Minnesota Transportation Museum, Inc., Saint Paul, MN..............................792

Minnesota's Machinery Museum, Hanley Falls, MN....................................777

Minnetrista, Muncie, IN........................492

Minnilusa Pioneer Museum, Rapid City, SD..1354

Miracle of America Museum Inc., Polson, MT..852

Miramont Castle Museum, Manitou Springs, CO..................................228

Mission Mill Museum Association, Salem, OR..................................1236

Mission San Antonio de Padua, Jolon, CA..105

Mission San Diego de Alcala, San Diego, CA..157

Mississippi Agriculture & Forestry/National Agricultural Aviation Museum, Jackson, MS.....................802

Mississippi County Historical Society, Charleston, MO..............................812

Missouri Town 1855, Lee's Summit, MO....825

Mitchell County Historical Museum, Osage, IA....................................526

The Mitchell Museum of the American Indian, Evanston, IL........................435

Mobile Medical Museum, Mobile, AL...........14

Moccasin Lake Nature Park, An Environmental & Energy Education Center, Clearwater, FL....................299

Modoc County Historical Museum, Alturas, CA....................................70

Mohave Museum of History and Arts, Kingman, AZ..................................36

Mondak Heritage Center, Sidney, MT.........853

The Monhegan Museum, Monhegan, ME....615

Monmouth County Historical Association, Freehold, NJ..................................905

Monroe County Historical Association/Stroud Mansion, Stroudsburg, PA............................1302

Monroe County Historical Museum, Monroe, MI....................................756

Monroe County Historical Society, Bloomington, IN............................469

Monroe County Local History Room & Library, Sparta, WI........................1622

Montague Museum & Historical Association, Montague, MI...................756

Montauk, Clermont, IA..........................511

Montclair Historical Society, Montclair, NJ..912

Monterey Bay Aquarium, Monterey, CA.....127

The Montgomery County Historical Society, Dayton, OH........................1161

Montrose County Historical Museum, Montrose, CO..................................228

Montville Township Historical Museum, Montville, NJ..................................912

Moody County Museum, Flandreau, SD....1347

Moore County Historical Museum, Dumas, TX..................................1410

Moores Creek National Battlefield, Currie, NC..................................1097

Moorten Botanic Garden and Cactarium, Palm Springs, CA..............................138

Morgan Row Museum and Harrodsburg-Mercer County Research Library, Harrodsburg, KY...................570

Moriarty Historical Museum, Moriarty, NM..943

Mormon Station State Historic Park, Genoa, NV..................................877

Morristown National Historical Park, Morristown, NJ..............................914

Morton Grove Historical Museum/Haupt-Yehl House, Morton Grove, IL....................................446

Morton Museum of Cooke County, Gainesville, TX..............................1420

Morven Park, Leesburg, VA...................1512

Mount Desert Island Historical Society, Mount Desert, ME..........................615

Mount Desert Oceanarium, Southwest Harbor, ME..................................623

Mount Holly Community Historical Museum, Belmont, VT....................1476

Mount Pleasant Historical Society, Mount Pleasant, OH................................1177

Mount Prospect Historical Society Museums, Mount Prospect, IL..............446

Mt. Rainier National Park, Ashford, WA...1547

Mount Rushmore National Memorial, Keystone, SD................................1350

Mountain Gateway Museum, Old Fort, NC..1113

Mountain Heritage Center, Cullowhee, NC..1097

Mountain Life Museum, London, KY.........575

Mulford Farm, East Hampton, NY.............986

Murfreesboro Historical Association, Murfreesboro, NC............................1112

Murray-Lindsay Mansion, Lindsay, OK.....1204

Muscatine History & Industry Center/Pearl Button Museum, Muscatine, IA..............................524

Museo Fuerte Conde de Mirasol de Vieques, Vieques, PR........................1644

Museum and Arts Center in the Sequim Dungeness Valley, Sequim, WA............1570

Museum at Southwestern Michigan College, Dowagiac, MI....................738

The Museum at Warm Springs, Warm Springs, OR................................1238

Museum of Alaska Transportation & Industry, Inc., Wasilla, AK.................29

Museum of American Cut and Engraved Glass, Highlands, NC........................1107

Museum of American Glass at Wheaton Village, Millville, NJ........................911

Museum of Anthracite Mining, Weatherly, PA................................1307

Museum of Anthropology, University of Missouri, Columbia, MO...................813

Museum of Appalachia, Clinton, TN.........1363

Museum of Carousel Art & History, Sandusky, OH................................1185

Museum of Ceramics, East Liverpool, OH.......1163
Museum of Church History and Art, Salt Lake City, UT.......1471
Museum of Connecticut History, Hartford, CT.......245
Museum of Cosmetology, Chicago, IL.......425
Museum of Cultural & Natural History, Mount Pleasant, MI.......757
Museum of disAbility History, Williamsville, NY.......1086
Museum of Discovery: Arkansas Museum of Science and History, Little Rock, AR.......62
The Museum of Early Trades and Crafts, Madison, NJ.......910
The Museum of East Alabama, Opelika, AL.......17
Museum of Flying, Santa Monica, CA.......183
Museum of History & Art, Ontario, Ontario, CA.......136
Museum of History & Industry (MOHAI), Seattle, WA.......1567
Museum of Idaho, Idaho Falls, ID.......406
Museum of Indian Culture, Allentown, PA.......1239
Museum of International Folk Art, Santa Fe, NM.......948
Museum of Jewish Heritage-A Living Memorial to the Holocaust, New York, NY.......1032
The Museum of Man in the Sea, Inc., Panama City Beach, FL.......335
Museum of North Idaho, Coeur d'Alene, ID.......405
Museum of Northwest Colorado, Craig, CO.......208
Museum of Primitive Art and Culture, Peace Dale, RI.......1316
Museum of Rural Life, Denton, MD.......642
Museum of Science, Boston, MA.......667
Museum of Science & History of Jacksonville, Jacksonville, FL.......315
Museum of Science and Industry, Chicago, IL.......425
Museum of Seminole County History, Sanford, FL.......343
Museum of Small Town Life, Dover, DE.......270
Museum of South Texas History, Edinburg, TX.......1410
The Museum of Southern History, Sugarland, TX.......1454
Museum of Spanish Colonial Art - MoSCA, Santa Fe, NM.......949
Museum of Surveying, Lansing, MI.......750
Museum of the Albemarle, Elizabeth City, NC.......1099
Museum of the Aleutians, Unalaska, AK.......28
Museum of the Arkansas Grand Prairie, Stuttgart, AR.......69
Museum of the Bedford Historical Society, Bedford, NY.......961
Museum of the Big Bend, Alpine, TX.......1386
Museum of the Cape Fear Historical Complex, Fayetteville, NC.......1101
Museum of the Cherokee Strip, Enid, OK.......1200
Museum of the City of Lake Worth, Lake Worth, FL.......320
Museum of the Great Plains, Lawton, OK.......1204
Museum of the Hudson Highlands, Cornwall-on-Hudson, NY.......982
Museum of the Llano Estacado, Plainview, TX.......1443
Museum of the Mountain Man, Pinedale, WY.......1637
Museum of the Northern Great Plains, Fort Benton, MT.......846
Museum of the Plains, Perryton, TX.......1443
Museum of the Red River, Idabel, OK.......1203
Museum of the Western Prairie, Altus, OK.......1195

Museum of the Weston Historical Society, Inc., Weston, MA.......718
Museum of West Louisiana, Leesville, LA.......591
Museum of Woodcarving, Shell Lake, WI.......1621
Museum Village, Monroe, NY.......1015
Museums of Los Gatos, Los Gatos, CA.......123
The Museums of Oglebay Institute - Mansion Museum & Glass Museum, Wheeling, WV.......1588
Muskegon County Museum, Muskegon, MI.......757
Musselshell Valley Historical Museum, Roundup, MT.......853
Mystic Seaport - The Museum of America and the Sea, Mystic, CT.......251
NASA Glenn Research Center's Visitor Center, Cleveland, OH.......1155
Nantucket Historical Association, Nantucket, MA.......696
Napa Valley Museum, Yountville, CA.......200
Naper Settlement, Naperville, IL.......447
Narragansett Historical Society, Templeton, MA.......714
Nathan Denison Advocates, Forty Fort, PA.......1254
The National Agricultural Center & Hall of Fame, Bonner Springs, KS.......534
National Apple Museum, Biglerville, PA.......1243
National Canal Museum, Hugh Moore Historical Park and Museums, Easton, PA.......1250
National Cowboy & Western Heritage Museum, Oklahoma City, OK.......1208
National Fresh Water Fishing Hall of Fame, Hayward, WI.......1600
National Frontier Trails Museum, Independence, MO.......818
National Heisey Glass Museum, Newark, OH.......1178
National Heritage Museum, Lexington, MA.......690
National Historic Oregon Trail Interpretive Center, Baker City, OR.......1219
National Inventors Hall of Fame, Akron, OH.......1139
National Knife Museum, Inc., Chattanooga, TN.......1362
National Medal of Honor Museum of Military History, Chattanooga, TN.......1362
National Mississippi River Museum & Aquarium, Dubuque, IA.......516
National Museum of American Jewish History, Philadelphia, PA.......1284
National Museum of Industrial History, Bethlehem, PA.......1243
National Museum of the Morgan Horse, Shelburne, VT.......1487
National Museum of Woodcarving, Custer, SD.......1346
National New York Central Railroad Museum, Elkhart, IN.......475
National Ornamental Metal Museum, Memphis, TN.......1375
National Park Service, Washington, DC.......287
National Park Service Vicksburg National Military Park-Cairo Museum, Vicksburg, MS.......809
National Plastics Center and Museum, Leominster, MA.......689
National Railroad Museum, Green Bay, WI.......1599
National Railroad Museum and Hall of Fame, Inc., Hamlet, NC.......1105
National Soaring Museum, Elmira, NY.......988
National Temple Hill Association, Inc., New Windsor, NY.......1018
National Tropical Botanical Garden, Kalaheo, HI.......399
National Warplane Museum, Horseheads, NY.......999

Native American Exhibit, National Kateri Shrine, Fonda, NY.......991
Native American Museum, Terre Haute, IN.......500
Naugatuck Historical Society, Naugatuck, CT.......251
Nauvoo Historical Society Museum, Nauvoo, IL.......447
Naval Undersea Museum, Keyport, WA.......1557
Navarro County Historical Society, Pioneer Village, Corsicana, TX.......1402
Nebraska Prairie Museum of the Phelps County Historical Society, Holdrege, NE.......863
Nebraska State Historical Society's Museum of Nebraska History, Lincoln, NE.......866
Neeses Farm Museum, Neeses, SC.......1338
Neligh Mills, Neligh, NE.......869
Nelson Pioneer Farm and Museum, Oskaloosa, IA.......526
Nemours Mansion and Gardens, Wilmington, DE.......274
Netherland Inn House Museum & Boatyard Complex, Kingsport, TN.......1368
Nevada State Railroad Museum, Carson City, NV.......876
Neversink Valley Area Museum, Cuddebackville, NY.......984
Neville Public Museum of Brown County, Green Bay, WI.......1599
New Bedford Whaling Museum, New Bedford, MA.......696
New Braunfels Conservation Society, New Braunfels, TX.......1440
New Britain Industrial Museum, New Britain, CT.......251
New Britain Youth Museum, New Britain, CT.......252
New Britain Youth Museum at Hungerford Park, Kensington, CT.......247
New Canaan Historical Society, New Canaan, CT.......252
New Castle Historical Society, New Castle, DE.......272
New Castle Historical Society - Horace Greeley House, Chappaqua, NY.......977
New England Fire and History Museum, Brewster, MA.......670
New England Maple Museum, Pittsford, VT.......1484
New Hampshire Antiquarian Society, Hopkinton, NH.......889
New Hampshire Farm Museum, Inc., Milton, NH.......892
The New Jersey Center for Life Science, Trenton, NJ.......927
The New Jersey Historical Society, Newark, NJ.......916
The New Jersey Museum of Agriculture, North Brunswick, NJ.......917
New Jersey Office of Historic Sites, Trenton, NJ.......927
New London County Historical Society, New London, CT.......255
New London Historical Society, New London, NH.......892
New Mexico Bureau of Geology Mineral Museum, Socorro, NM.......951
New Mexico Farm & Ranch Heritage Museum, Las Cruces, NM.......940
New Mexico Museum of Space History, Alamogordo, NM.......932
New Orleans Fire Dept. Museum & Educational Center, New Orleans, LA.......597
New Richmond Preservation Society, New Richmond, WI.......1615
New Sweden Farmstead Museum, Inc., Bridgeton, NJ.......898
New Sweden Historical Society, New Sweden, ME.......616

Tools and Equipment for Materials—Continued

New Windsor Cantonment State Historic Site and National Purple Heart Hall of Honor, Vails Gate, NY 1080
Newark Valley Depot Museum, Newark Valley, NY 1042
Newaygo County Museum, Newaygo, MI...758
Newell Museum, Newell, SD 1352
Newport Restoration Foundation, Newport, RI 1315
The Newton History Museum at The Jackson Homestead, Newton, MA..........698
Newtown Historic Association, Newtown, PA..........1274
Newtown History Center, Stephens City, VA 1538
Nez Perce County Museum, Lewiston, ID...407
Nez Perce National Historical Park, Spalding, ID..........409
Nicollet County Historical Society, Saint Peter, MN..........793
Ninety Six National Historic Site, Ninety Six, SC 1338
Nishna Heritage Museum, Oakland, IA 525
No Man's Land Historical Society, Goodwell, OK..........1201
Noank Historical Society, Inc., Noank, CT 256
Noden-Reed Farm Museum, Windsor Locks, CT 268
Nohwike Bagowa, The White Mountain Apache Cultural Center and Museum, Fort Apache, AZ..........34
Nordic Heritage Museum, Seattle, WA 1567
Norfolk Historical Museum, Norfolk, CT....257
Norfolk Historical Society, Norfolk, VA 1522
The Norman Cleveland County Historical Museum, Norman, OK 1206
Norman #1 Oil Well Museum, Neodesha, KS 553
North Andover Historical Society, North Andover, MA 698
North Carolina Maritime Museum, Beaufort, NC 1091
North Carolina Museum of Forestry, Whiteville, NC 1122
North Carolina Museum of History, Raleigh, NC 1115
North Carolina Transportation Museum, Spencer, NC 1120
North Cascades National Park Service Complex, Marblemount, WA 1559
North Castle Historical Society, Armonk, NY..........958
North Haven Historical Society, North Haven, CT..........257
North Lee County Historic Center and Santa Fe Depot Museum Complex, Fort Madison, IA 518
North Platte Valley Museum, Gering, NE....861
Northborough Historical Society, Inc., Northborough, MA 700
Northeast Georgia History Center at Brenau University, Gainesville, GA 373
Northeast Louisiana Delta African American Heritage Museum, Monroe, LA 592
Northeast Oakland Historical Museum, Oxford, MI..........759
Northeastern Montana Threshers and Antique Association, Culbertson, MT 845
Northern Indiana Center for History, South Bend, IN..........499
Northern New York Agricultural Historical Society, Agricultural Museum at Stone Mills, LaFargeville, NY..........1008
Northfield Historical Society Museum, Northfield, MN 785
Northport Historical Society Museum, Northport, NY..........1044

Northwest Railway Museum, Snoqualmie, WA..........1570
Norwich Historical Society, Norwich, VT .1484
Notah Dineh Museum, Cortez, CO 208
Novato History Museum, Novato, CA 132
Nowata County Historical Society Museum, Nowata, OK..........1207
Nowetah's American Indian Museum & Store, New Portland, ME..........615
Oak Creek Historical Society-Pioneer Village, Oak Creek, WI..........1615
Oakland County Pioneer and Historical Society, Pontiac, MI 760
Oaklands Historic House Museum, Murfreesboro, TN..........1376
Oatland Island Education Center, Savannah, GA..........385
Ocean City Life-Saving Station Museum, Ocean City, MD..........650
Ocean County Historical Museum, Toms River, NJ..........926
Ocmulgee National Monument, Macon, GA..........378
Ocracoke Island Visitor Center, Ocracoke, NC..........1113
The Octagon House, Hudson, WI..........1600
Odyssey Maritime Discovery Center, Seattle, WA..........1567
O'Fallon Historical Museum, Baker, MT....840
Ogden Historical Society, Spencerport, NY..........1071
Ohio Historical Society, Columbus, OH.....1158
Ohio River Museum, Marietta, OH 1174
Ojai Valley Historical Society and Museum, Ojai, CA 135
Okefenokee Heritage Center, Waycross, GA..........391
Oklahoma Firefighters Museum, Oklahoma City, OK..........1209
Oklahoma Forest Heritage Center, Broken Bow, OK..........1197
Oklahoma Historical Society, Oklahoma City, OK..........1209
Oklahoma Museum of History, Oklahoma City, OK..........1210
Oklahoma Route 66 Museum, Clinton, OK..........1198
Oklahoma Territorial Museum, Guthrie, OK..........1202
Oktibbeha County Heritage Museum, Starkville, MS..........808
Old Bethpage Village Restoration, Old Bethpage, NY..........1045
Old Bohemia Historical Society, Warwick, MD 656
Old Brutus Historical Society, Inc., Weedsport, NY..........1084
Old Castle Museum, Baldwin City, KS........533
Old Colony Historical Society, Taunton, MA..........714
Old Constitution House, Windsor, VT........1490
Old Conway Homestead Complex and Museum, Camden, ME..........608
Old Court House Museum-Eva Whitaker Davis Memorial, Vicksburg, MS 809
The Old Courthouse Heritage Museum, Inverness, FL..........313
Old Cowtown Museum, Wichita, KS 562
Old Davie School Historical Museum, Davie, FL..........302
Old Depot Museum, Ottawa, KS..........555
The Old Depot Railroad Museum, Dassel, MN..........772
Old Dorchester State Historic Site, Summerville, SC..........1342
Old Economy Village, Ambridge, PA.........1240
Old Exchange & Provost Dungeon, Charleston, SC..........1326
Old Falls Village, Menomonee Falls, WI...1609
Old Fort Bissell, Phillipsburg, KS..........555
Old Fort Harrod State Park Mansion Museum, Harrodsburg, KY..........570

Old Fort Jackson, Savannah, GA..........385
Old Fort Niagara, Youngstown, NY..........1088
Old Greer County Museum & Hall of Fame, Mangum, OK..........1204
Old Hidalgo Pumphouse, Hidalgo, TX 1424
Old Iron County Courthouse Museum, Hurley, WI..........1601
Old Jail Museum, Albion, IN..........467
Old Jefferson Town, Oskaloosa, KS 555
Old Lighthouse Museum, Stonington, CT....261
Old Lincoln County Courthouse Museum, Lincoln, NM..........942
Old Log Jail and Chapel Museums, Greenfield, IN..........480
Old Manchester Museum, Manchester, CT..........248
Old Market House State Historic Site, Galena, IL..........436
Old Ordinary House Museum, Hingham, MA..........687
Old Prairie Town at Ward-Meade Historic Site, Topeka, KS..........560
The Old Schwamb Mill, Arlington, MA 660
Old Stone Fort Museum Complex, Schoharie, NY..........1067
The Old Stone House, Washington, DC.......289
Old Sturbridge Village, Sturbridge, MA.....713
Old Town Hall Museum, Fifield, WI.........1597
Old Town Museum, Old Town, ME..........617
Old Town Museum, Burlington, CO 204
Old Town San Diego State Historic Park, San Diego, CA..........158
Old Washington Historic State Park, Washington, AR..........69
Old West Wax Museum, Thermopolis, WY..........1639
Old World Wisconsin, Eagle, WI..........1595
Oldham County History Center, La Grange, KY..........572
Oliver Kelley Farm, Elk River, MN..........774
The Oliver Tucker Museum, Beverly, OH .1142
Olmsted County Historical Society, Rochester, MN..........788
Olympic National Park Visitor Center, Port Angeles, WA..........1561
Oneida County Historical Society, Utica, NY..........1080
Oneida Nation Museum, De Pere, WI........1594
Onslow County Museum, Richlands, NC...1117
Ontario County Historical Society, Canandaigua, NY..........975
Ontonagon County Historical Society Museum, Ontonagon, MI..........758
Opus 40 and the Quarryman's Museum, Saugerties, NY..........1066
Orange County Regional History Center, Orlando, FL..........331
Orange Empire Railway Museum, Perris, CA..........141
Orangetown Historical Museum and Archives, Pearl River, NY 1051
Orcas Island Historical Museum, Orcas Island, WA..........1560
Orchard Park Historical Society, Orchard Park, NY..........1047
Oregon Electric Railway Historical Society, Inc., Salem, OR..........1236
Oregon Historical Society, Portland, OR....1231
Oregon-Jerusalem Historical Museum, Oregon, OH..........1181
Oregon Military Museum, Clackamas, OR..........1221
Oregon Museum of Science and Industry, Portland, OR..........1231
Oregon Trail Regional Museum, Baker City, OR..........1219
Oriental Institute Museum, University of Chicago, Chicago, IL 426
Orland Historical Society, Orland, ME 617
Orleans County Historical Society & The Old Stone House Museum, Brownington, VT..........1477

Osage County Historical Society Research Center, Lyndon, KS 550
Osborn-Jackson House, East Hampton, NY 986
Oshkosh Public Museum, Oshkosh, WI 1616
Ossining Historical Society Museum, Ossining, NY 1047
Osterville Historical Society, Inc., Osterville, MA 701
Otero Museum Association, La Junta, CO ...224
Ottawa County Historical Museum, Port Clinton, OH 1183
Otter Tail County Historical Society, Fergus Falls, MN 775
Outagamie Museum, Appleton, WI 1589
Overfield Tavern Museum, Troy, OH 1188
Overland Trail Museum, Sterling, CO 232
Overstreet-Kerr Historical Farm, Keota, OK 1203
Owensboro Area Museum of Science & History, Owensboro, KY 581
Oxford Museum, Inc., Oxford, MD 650
The Oyster and Maritime Museum of Chincoteague, Chincoteague, VA 1501
Oyster Bay Historical Society, Oyster Bay, NY 1049
Oysterponds Historical Society: The Museum of Orient and East Marion History, Orient, NY 1047
Ozark National Scenic Riverways, Van Buren, MO 839
Ozaukee County Pioneer Village, Saukville, WI 1620

P.H. Sullivan Museum and Genealogy Library, Zionsville, IN 504
Pacific County Historical Museum, South Bend, WA 1571
Pacific Science Center, Seattle, WA 1568
Palace of the Governors/New Mexico History Museum, Santa Fe, NM 949
PALCO, Scotia, CA 186
Palm Beach Zoo at Dreher Park, West Palm Beach, FL 353
Palmer House, Historical Society of Olde Northfield, Northfield, OH 1180
Pamplin Historical Park and The National Museum of the Civil War Soldier, Petersburg, VA 1525
Panhandle-Plains Historical Museum, Canyon, TX 1399
Parishville Museum, Parishville, NY 1050
Park City Historical Society & Museum, Park City, UT 1468
Parks, Recreation & Historic Sites Division, Georgia Dept. of Natural Resources, Atlanta, GA 362
The Parry Mansion Museum, New Hope, PA 1273
Parson Fisher House, Blue Hill, ME 606
Pascack Historical Society, Park Ridge, NJ 920
Patee House Museum, Saint Joseph, MO 831
Patten Lumbermen's Museum, Inc., Patten, ME 618
Patterson Inn Museum/Corning - Painted Post Historical Society, Corning, NY 982
The Patuxent Rural Life Museums, Upper Marlboro, MD 655
Paul Bunyan Logging Camp Museum, Eau Claire, WI 1596
Paul Revere House/Paul Revere Memorial Association, Boston, MA 668
Paunsaugunt Wildlife Museum, Bryce, UT 1464
Pawnee Bill Ranch and Museum, Pawnee, OK 1212
Pawnee City Historical Society & Museum, Pawnee City, NE 871
Paynes Creek Historic State Park, Bowling Green, FL 297
Peabody Museum of Archaeology & Ethnology, Cambridge, MA 674

Pearl S. Buck Birthplace Foundation, Hillsboro, WV 1582
Pearson Air Museum, Vancouver, WA 1576
Pejepscot Historical Society, Brunswick, ME 608
Pembina State Museum, Pembina, ND 1135
Pembroke Historical Society, Inc., Pembroke, MA 701
Pendarvis State Historic Site, Mineral Point, WI 1614
Pendleton District Agricultural Museum, Pendleton, SC 1339
Pendleton District Historical, Recreational and Tourism Commission, Pendleton, SC 1339
Pennsbury Manor, Morrisville, PA 1272
Pennsylvania Anthracite Heritage Museum, Scranton, PA 1299
Pennsylvania German Cultural Heritage Center at Kutztown University, Kutztown, PA 1265
Pennsylvania Historical & Museum Commission, Harrisburg, PA 1259
Pennsylvania Military Museum and 28th Division Shrine, Boalsburg, PA 1244
Pennsylvania Trolley Museum, Washington, PA 1305
Pennyroyal Area Museum, Hopkinsville, KY 572
Penobscot Marine Museum, Searsport, ME 622
Peoria Historical Society, Peoria, IL 451
Perkins County Historical Society, Grant, NE 862
Petaluma Adobe State Historic Park, Petaluma, CA 142
Peter Conser House, Heavener, OK 1202
Peter Rice Homestead, Home of Marlborough Historical Society, Inc., Marlboro, MA 693
Peter Wentz Farmstead, Worcester, PA.......1308
Peterborough Historical Society, Peterborough, NH 893
Petersburg Area Art League, Petersburg, VA 1525
Petersen Automotive Museum, Los Angeles, CA 121
Petersham Historical Society, Inc., Petersham, MA 702
The Petroleum Museum, Midland, TX.......1439
Pettaquamscutt Historical Society, Kingston, RI 1312
Philadelphia Society for the Preservation of Landmarks, Philadelphia, PA 1286
Philip and Muriel Berman Museum of Art at Ursinus College, Collegeville, PA 1247
Philipse Manor Hall State Historic Site, Yonkers, NY 1087
Phillips County Museum, Holyoke, CO.......222
Phillips Historical Society, Phillips, ME 618
Phoenix Museum of History, Phoenix, AZ 41
Piatt Castles, West Liberty, OH 1190
Piatt County Museum, Monticello, IL..........446
Pilgrim Hall Museum, Plymouth, MA 703
Pinal County Historical Society and Museum, Florence, AZ 34
Pine Bluff/Jefferson County Historical Museum, Pine Bluff, AR 66
Pine County Historical Society, Askov, MN 768
Pine Creek Grist Mill, Muscatine, IA 525
Pink Palace Family of Museums, Memphis, TN 1375
Pioneer Auto Museum, Murdo, SD 1352
Pioneer Corner Museum, New Holstein, WI 1615
Pioneer Farm Museum and Ohop Indian Village, Eatonville, WA 1552
Pioneer Florida Museum Association, Inc., Dade City, FL 302

Pioneer Heritage Center, Cavalier, ND.......1129
Pioneer Heritage Center, LSU-Shreveport, Shreveport, LA 601
Pioneer-Krier Museum, Ashland, KS 532
Pioneer Log Cabin, Manhattan, KS.............551
Pioneer Museum, Wild Rose, WI 1628
Pioneer Museum and Vereins Kirche, Fredericksburg, TX 1419
Pioneer Museum - Martin County Historical Society, Fairmont, MN 775
Pioneer Settlement for the Creative Arts, Barberville, FL 295
Pioneer Town, Wimberley, TX...................1462
Pioneers, Trail Drivers and Texas Rangers Memorial Museum, San Antonio, TX 1449
Piper Aviation Museum Foundation, Lock Haven, PA 1269
Pipestone County Historical Museum, Pipestone, MN 786
Piqua Historical Area State Memorial, Piqua, OH 1182
Pithole Visitor Center, Pleasantville, PA 1295
Pittsford Historical Society Museum, Pittsford, VT 1484
Plains Conservation Center, Aurora, CO......202
Plains Indians and Pioneers Museum, Woodward, OK 1217
Plantation Agriculture Museum, Scott, AR 67
Plantation Historical Museum, Plantation, FL 337
Platteville Mining Museum, Platteville, WI 1617
Plimoth Plantation Inc., Plymouth, MA 703
Plumb Farm Learning Center, Greeley, CO 222
Plymouth Historical Museum, Plymouth, MI 760
Pocahontas County Museum, Marlinton, WV 1584
Polk County Historical Museum, Bartow, FL 295
The Polk County Historical Society, Cedartown, GA 368
Polk County Memorial Museum, Livingston, TX 1434
Polk County Museum, Balsam Lake, WI...1590
Polson Museum, Hoquiam, WA 1556
Pomeroy Living History Farm, Yacolt, WA 1578
Pony Express Museum, Saint Joseph, MO 831
Poplar Grove Historic Plantation, Wilmington, NC 1123
Port Gamble Historic Museum, Port Gamble, WA 1562
Port Huron Museum, Port Huron, MI 761
Portage County Historical Society, Ravenna, OH 1183
Portage County Historical Society, Stevens Point, WI 1623
Porterville Historical Museum, Porterville, CA 144
Portland Harbor Museum, South Portland, ME 623
Portola Railroad Museum, Portola, CA........144
Potsdam Public Museum, Potsdam, NY 1054
Potter County Historical Society, Coudersport, PA 1248
Pound Ridge Society/Museum, Pound Ridge, NY 1055
Powell County Museum, Deer Lodge, MT 845
Prairie Homestead, Philip, SD 1353
Prairie Trails Museum of Wayne County, Corydon, IA 512
Prairie Village, Madison, SD 1351
Praters Mill Foundation, Varnell, GA..........390
Pratt Building - Cohasset Historical Society, Cohasset, MA 676

Tools and Equipment for Materials—Continued

Pratt County Historical Society Museum, Pratt, KS.....556

Pratt Museum, Homer, AK 25

President James K. Polk State Historic Site, Pineville, NC 1114

Presidio La Bahia, Goliad, TX 1423

Pricketts Fort, Fairmont, WV.....1581

Public Museum of West Michigan, Grand Rapids, MI.....744

Putnam County Historical Society & Foundry School Museum, Cold Spring, NY.....979

Putnam County Historical Society Museum, Kalida, OH.....1169

Putnam County Museum, Greencastle, IN.....479

Quasdorf Blacksmith and Wagon Museum, Dows, IA 516

Queens County Farm Museum, Floral Park, NY.....989

Quiet Valley Living Historical Farm, Stroudsburg, PA.....1302

Quincy Historical Society, Quincy, MA.....705

QV Historical Society at Carriage House Museum, Camden, NY.....974

R.E. Olds Transportation Museum, Lansing, MI.....751

R.P. Strathearn Historical Park and Museum, Simi Valley, CA.....187

Racine Heritage Museum, Racine, WI.....1619

Railroad and Heritage Museum Inc., Temple, TX.....1454

Railroad House Historical Association Museum, Sanford, NC.....1119

Railroad Museum of Pennsylvania, Strasburg, PA.....1302

Railroaders Memorial Museum, Altoona, PA.....1240

Raleigh City Museum, Raleigh, NC.....1117

Ralls Historical Museum, Ralls, TX.....1445

The Ralph Foster Museum, Point Lookout, MO.....828

Ralston Historical Association, John Ralston Museum, Mendham, NJ.....911

Ramapogue Historical Society, West Springfield, MA.....718

Ramsey House Museum Plantation, Knoxville, TN.....1371

Rancho La Patera - The Stow House G.V.H.S., Goleta, CA.....100

Rancho Los Alamitos, Long Beach, CA.....111

Rancho Los Cerritos Historic Site, Long Beach, CA.....111

Randolph County Museum (At Beverly), Beverly, WV.....1580

Randolph Historical Society, Inc., Randolph, VT.....1485

Rankin Museum, Inc., Ellerbe, NC.....1100

Ransom County Historical Society, Fort Ransom, ND.....1131

Reading Historical Society, Reading, VT.....1485

Readsboro Historical Society, Readsboro, VT.....1486

Rebecca Nurse Homestead, Danvers, MA.....678

Rebel State Historic Site & Louisiana Country Music Museum, Marthaville, LA.....592

Red Mill Museum Village, Clinton, NJ.....901

Red River Historical Society Museum, Clay City, KY.....566

Redwood County Historical Society, Redwood Falls, MN.....787

Redwood National and State Parks, Crescent City, CA.....88

Reed Gold Mine State Historic Site, Midland, NC.....1111

Reedville Fishermen's Museum, Reedville, VA.....1527

Refugio County Museum, Refugio, TX.....1445

Reginald F. Lewis Museum of Maryland African American History and Culture, Baltimore, MD.....636

Remick Country Doctor Museum and Farm, Tamworth, NH.....896

Remington Firearms Museum and Country Store, Ilion, NY.....1002

Reno County Museum, Hutchinson, KS.....545

Rensselaer County Historical Society, Troy, NY.....1079

Renton Historical Society and Museum, Renton, WA.....1564

Renville County Historical Society, Inc., Mohall, ND.....1135

Republic County Historical Society Museum, Belleville, KS.....534

Retired Correctional Peace Officers Museum at Folsom Prison, Represa, CA.....148

Reuel B. Pritchett Museum, Bridgewater, VA.....1497

Reverend Dan Foster House, Museum of the Weathersfield Historical Society, Weathersfield, VT.....1489

Rhinebeck Aerodrome Museum, Rhinebeck, NY.....1056

Rhinelander Logging Museum, Rhinelander, WI.....1620

Rice County Museum of History, Faribault, MN.....775

Richard Salter Storrs House, Longmeadow, MA.....691

Richardson-Bates House Museum, Oswego, NY.....1048

Richardson Maritime Museum, Cambridge, MD.....639

Richey Historical Society, Richey, MT.....852

Richmond Museum of History, Richmond, CA.....148

Rifle Creek Museum, Rifle, CO.....231

Rikard's Mill Historical Park, Beatrice, AL.....3

Riley County Historical Museum, Manhattan, KS.....551

Rim Country Museum, Payson, AZ.....38

Rimrocker Historical Museum of West Montrose County, Naturita, CO.....229

Rio Vista Museum, Rio Vista, CA.....148

Ripley County, Indiana, Historical Society Museum, Versailles, IN.....502

River Heritage Museum, Paducah, KY.....582

Riverside Museum, La Crosse, WI.....1603

Riverside, The Farnsley-Moremen Landing, Louisville, KY.....579

Riverton Museum, Riverton, WY.....1637

Roanoke Island Festival Park; Homeport of the "Elizabeth II", Manteo, NC.....1110

Roaring Twenties Antique Car Museum, Hood, VA.....1511

Robbins Museum of Archaeology, Middleborough, MA.....694

Robert A. Bogan Fire Museum, Baton Rouge, LA.....587

Robert C. Williams American Museum of Papermaking at Georgia Tech, Atlanta, GA.....363

Robert Fulton Birthplace, Quarryville, PA.1295

Rochester Hills Museum at Van Hoosen Farm, Rochester Hills, MI.....762

Rock County Historical Society, Janesville, WI.....1601

Rock Island Arsenal Museum, Rock Island, IL.....454

Rock Island County Historical Society, Moline, IL.....445

Rock Ledge Ranch Historic Site, Colorado Springs, CO.....208

Rock Springs Historical Museum, Rock Springs, WY.....1638

Rockingham Free Public Library and Museum, Bellows Falls, VT.....1476

Rocky Ford Historical Museum, Rocky Ford, CO.....231

Rocky Mount Museum, Piney Flats, TN.....1383

Rocky Reach Dam, Wenatchee, WA.....1577

Rogers Historical Museum, Rogers, AR.....67

Rokeby (Ancestral Estate of Rowland Evans Robinson), Ferrisburgh, VT.....1479

Rollo Jamison Museum, Platteville, WI.....1617

Rome Historical Society Museum, Rome, NY.....1061

Roosevelt County Museum, Portales, NM.....944

Roscoe Village Foundation, Coshocton, OH.....1159

Rose Center Museum, Morristown, TN.....1376

Rose Hill Museum, Bay Village, OH.....1141

Roseau County Historical Museum and Interpretive Center, Roseau, MN.....788

Rosebud County Pioneer Museum, Forsyth, MT.....846

Rosemont Plantation, Woodville, MS.....810

Rosicrucian Egyptian Museum, San Jose, CA.....172

Roslyn Landmark Society, Roslyn, NY.....1061

Roswell Museum and Art Center, Roswell, NM.....946

Roth Living Farm Museum of Delaware Valley College, North Wales, PA.....1274

Rowley Historical Society, Rowley, MA.....706

The Roy Rogers-Dale Evans Museum and Theater, Branson, MO.....811

Royalton Historical Society, Royalton, VT.....1486

Runestone Museum, Alexandria, MN.....767

Rusk County Historical Society, Ladysmith, WI.....1604

Russell Cave National Monument, Bridgeport, AL.....6

Rutherford County Farm Museum, Forest City, NC.....1101

The Rye Historical Society and Square House Museum, Rye, NY.....1062

S.C. Tobacco Museum, Mullins, SC.....1337

Saco Museum, Saco, ME.....621

Sacramento Archives and Museum Collection Center, Sacramento, CA.....153

Safety Harbor Museum of Regional History, Safety Harbor, FL.....338

Sag Harbor Whaling & Historical Museum, Sag Harbor, NY.....1063

Saginaw Valley Zoological Society, Saginaw, MI.....763

Saguache County Museum, Saguache, CO.....231

Sahuaro Ranch Historical Area, Glendale, AZ.....35

Sailor's Memorial Museum, Islesboro, ME.....612

St. Augustine Lighthouse & Museum, Inc., Saint Augustine, FL.....340

St. Francis County Museum, Forrest City, AR.....57

St. Lawrence County Historical Association - Silas Wright House, Canton, NY.....975

St. Petersburg Museum of History, Saint Petersburg, FL.....342

St. Photios Greek Orthodox National Shrine, Saint Augustine, FL.....340

Salamanca Rail Museum, Salamanca, NY.1063

Salem County Historical Society, Salem, NJ.....924

Salem Historical Society and Museum, Salem, OH.....1184

Salmon Brook Historical Society, Inc., Granby, CT.....242

Salt Museum, Liverpool, NY.....1010

Sam Brown Log House, Browns Valley, MN.....770

Sam Houston Memorial Museum, Huntsville, TX.....1430

Sam Noble Oklahoma Museum of Natural History, Norman, OK.....1206

Samoa Cookhouse & Logging Museum, Samoa, CA.....155

San Antonio Missions National Historical Park, San Antonio, TX 1449
San Dieguito Heritage Museum, Encinitas, CA 92
San Francisco Maritime National Historical Park, San Francisco, CA 169
San Gabriel Mission Museum, San Gabriel, CA 171
San Jacinto Museum, San Jacinto, CA 171
San Jacinto Museum of History Association, La Porte, TX 1433
San Joaquin County Historical Society & Museum, Lodi, CA 109
San Juan Bautista State Historic Park, San Juan Bautista, CA 173
San Juan County Archaeological Research Center and Library at the Salmon Ruin/San Juan County Museum Association, Bloomfield, NM ...937
San Juan Historical Society, Friday Harbor, WA 1555
San Juan Island National Historical Park, Friday Harbor, WA 1555
San Juan National Historic Site, San Juan, PR 1643
San Luis Obispo County Historical Museum, San Luis Obispo, CA 174
San Mateo County Historical Association and Museum, Redwood City, CA 147
Sanborn Area Historical Society, Sanborn, NY 1064
Sanchez Adobe Historic Site, Pacifica, CA 138
Sandown Historical Society and Museum, Sandown, NH 896
Sandusky Library Follett House Museum, Sandusky, OH 1185
Sandwich Historical Society, Sandwich, IL 457
Sandy Bay Historical Society & Museums, Inc., Rockport, MA 705
Sandy Spring Museum, Sandy Spring, MD 653
Sanford Museum, Sanford, FL.....................343
Santa Barbara Maritime Museum, Santa Barbara, CA 179
Santa Cruz Museum of Natural History, Santa Cruz, CA 182
Santa Fe Trail Center, Larned, KS 547
Santa Fe Trail Museum, Ingalls, KS 545
Santa Fe Trail Museum/Trinidad History Museum, Trinidad, CO 234
Santa Maria Valley Historical Museum, Santa Maria, CA 183
Santa Ynez Valley Historical Society, Santa Ynez, CA 185
Saratoga County Historical Society, Brookside Museum, Ballston Spa, NY....960
Saratoga National Historical Park, Stillwater, NY 1075
Sarpy County Historical Museum, Bellevue, NE..857
Satterlee Clark House, Horicon, WI..........1600
Saugus Iron Works National Historic Site, Saugus, MA..708
Sauk Prairie Area Historical Society, Inc., Prairie du Sac, WI 1619
Saunders County Historical Complex, Wahoo, NE..874
Sawin Memorial Building, Dover, MA 680
Sawyer's Sandhills Museum, Valentine, NE..874
Scantic Academy Museum, East Windsor Historical Society, Inc., East Windsor, CT..239
Scarborough Historical Museum, Scarborough, ME 621
Schenectady County Historical Society, Schenectady, NY 1067
Schiele Museum of Natural History and Lynn Planetarium, Gastonia, NC 1102
Schifferstadt Architectural Museum, Frederick, MD 644

Schoenbrunn Village State Memorial, New Philadelphia, OH.............................1177
Schoharie Colonial Heritage Association, Schoharie, NY 1067
School of Nations Museum, Elsah, IL 433
Schoolcraft County Historical Society, Manistique, MI 753
Schoolhouse Museum of the Ridgewood Historical Society, Inc., Ridgewood, NJ 923
The Schuette Biermann Farmhouse Museum, Elk Grove Village, IL 432
Schuyler County Historical Society, Inc., Montour Falls, NY 1015
Schwenkfelder Library & Heritage Center, Pennsburg, PA 1275
Sci-Port Discovery Center, Shreveport, LA 601
Science Museum of Long Island, Manhasset, NY 1013
Scitrek, The Science and Technology Museum of Atlanta, Valdosta, GA...........389
Scituate Historical Society, Scituate, MA 708
Scituate Maritime and Irish Mossing Museum, Scituate, MA.........................709
Scotchtown, Beaverdam, VA 1496
Scotia-Glenville Children's Museum, Scotia, NY 1068
Scotland Heritage Chapel & Museum, Scotland, SD 1355
Scotts Bluff National Monument, Gering, NE 861
Scurry County Museum, Snyder, TX 1453
Sea Cliff Village Museum, Sea Cliff, NY ...1068
Seacoast Science Center, Rye, NH 896
Seagraves-Loop Museum and Art Center Inc., Seagraves, TX 1452
Sedgwick-Brooklin Historical Society, Sedgwick, ME 622
Seneca Falls Historical Society, Seneca Falls, NY 1069
Seneca-Iroquois National Museum, Salamanca, NY 1063
Serra Museum/San Diego Historical Society, San Diego, CA 161
1719 Hans Herr House & Museum, Willow Street, PA 1308
1768 Jeremiah Lee Mansion, Marblehead, MA 693
1761 Pownalborough Courthouse, Dresden, ME 610
Seward County Historical Society Museum, Goehner, NE 861
Seward Museum, Seward, AK 27
Seymour Community Museum, Seymour, WI 1621
Shaftsbury Historical Society, Shaftsbury, VT 1487
Shaker Heritage Society, Albany, NY 956
Shaker Historical Society, Shaker Heights, OH 1185
Shaker Museum, New Gloucester, ME 615
The Shaker Museum and Library, Old Chatham, NY 1045
Shaker Museum at South Union, South Union, KY 583
Shaker Village of Pleasant Hill, Harrodsburg, KY 571
Shakespeare Ghost Town, Lordsburg, NM...942
Shandy Hall, Geneva, OH 1166
Sharlot Hall Museum, Prescott, AZ................43
Shasta College Museum & Research Center, Redding, CA 146
Shawano County Historical Society, Inc., Shawano, WI 1621
Shawnee Town, Shawnee, KS 558
Sheboygan County Historical Museum, Sheboygan, WI 1621
Shelburne Museum, Inc., Shelburne, VT ...1487
Sheldon Jackson Museum, Sitka, AK.............27
Sheldon Museum and Cultural Center, Inc., Haines, AK 25

Shelter House Society, Emmaus, PA 1251
Shelter Island Historical Society, Shelter Island, NY 1069
Shenandoal Valley Discovery Museum, Winchester, VA 1546
Sherburne History Center, Becker, MN........768
Sherwood Forest Plantation, Charles City, VA 1498
Shiloh Museum of Ozark History, Springdale, AR..68
Shippensburg Historical Society Museum, Shippensburg, PA 1300
Shirley Plantation, Charles City, VA 1498
Shoal Creek Living History Museum, Kansas City, MO 822
Shore Line Trolley Museum, East Haven, CT 239
Shoreline Historical Museum, Seattle, WA 1569
Shoshone County Mining and Smelting Museum d/b/a The Staff House Museum, Kellogg, ID 406
Shoshone Tribal Cultural Center, Fort Washakie, WY 1633
Sibley County Historical Museum, Henderson, MN 777
Sibley House Historic Site, Mendota, MN...780
Siegfried H. Horn Archaeological Museum, Berrien Springs, MI 729
Sierra Mono Indian Museum, North Fork, CA 131
Siloam Springs Museum, Siloam Springs, AR 68
Silt Historical Society, Silt, CO 232
Silver Cliff Museum, Silver Cliff, CO.........232
Silvercreek Museum, Freeport, IL 435
The Simon Paneak Memorial Museum, Anaktuvuk Pass, AK 21
Simsbury Historical Society, Phelps Tavern, Museum & Homestead, Simsbury, CT 260
Skagit County Historical Museum, La Conner, WA 1557
Skagway Museum & Archives, Skagway, AK 28
The Skinner Museum of Mount Holyoke College, South Hadley, MA 709
The Skyscraper Museum, New York, NY ..1038
Slate Run Living Historical Farm, Metro Parks, Ashville, OH 1140
Slate Valley Museum, Granville, NY 996
Slater Mill Historic Site, Pawtucket, RI.....1315
Sleeping Bear Dunes National Lakeshore, Empire, MI 741
Slidell Museum, Slidell, LA 602
Slifer House, Lewisburg, PA 1268
Sloan Museum, Flint, MI 742
Sloane-Stanley Museum and Kent Furnace, Kent, CT 247
Sloss Furnaces National Historic Landmark, Birmingham, AL 5
Smith County Historical Society, Tyler, TX 1456
Smith-McDowell House Museum, Asheville, NC 1090
Smith Robertson Museum & Cultural Center, Jackson, MS 804
Smith-Zimmermann Heritage Museum, Madison, SD 1351
Smithtown Historical Society, Smithtown, NY 1070
Smoki Museum - American Indian Art & Culture, Prescott, AZ................................43
Smoky Hill Museum, Salina, KS 557
Snake River Heritage Center, Weiser, ID.....410
Snoqualmie Valley Historical Museum, North Bend, WA 1559
The Snyder County Historical Society, Middleburg, PA..1271
Society for the Preservation of Long Island Antiquities, Cold Spring Harbor, NY 980

Tools and Equipment for Materials—Continued

Sod House Museum, Gothenburg, NE 862
Sod House Museum, Aline, OK 1195
SoDus Bay Historical Society, Sodus Point, NY 1070
Somers Historical Society, Somers, NY 1070
Somers Mansion, Somers Point, NJ 924
The Somerset County Historical Society, Inc., Princess Anne, MD 650
Somerset Historical Center, Somerset, PA .1300
Somervell County Historical Museum, Glen Rose, TX 1423
Sonoma County Museum, Santa Rosa, CA 185
Sophienburg Museum & Archives Inc., New Braunfels, TX 1440
Sosa-Carrillo-Fremont House Museum, Tucson, AZ 50
Sotterley Plantation, Hollywood, MD 647
South Carolina Cotton Museum, Bishopville, SC 1322
South County Historical Society, Arroyo Grande, CA 72
South County Museum Inc., Narragansett, RI 1313
South Dakota State Historical Society, Pierre, SD..1353
South Dakota Tractor Museum, Kimball, SD 1350
South Florida Museum, Bishop Planetarium & Parker Manatee Aquarium, Bradenton, FL 297
South Hero Bicentennial Museum, South Hero, VT 1487
South Holland Historical Society, South Holland, IL 457
South Park City Museum, Fairplay, CO.......215
South Pass City State Historic Site, South Pass City, WY 1638
South Street Seaport Museum, New York, NY 1039
South Texas Museum, Alice, TX.................1386
South Wood County Historical Corp., Wisconsin Rapids, WI 1628
Southampton Historical Museum, Southampton, NY 1070
Southdown Plantation House/The Terrebonne Museum, Houma, LA 589
Southeast Museum Association, Inc., Brewster, NY 964
Southeastern Railway Museum, Duluth, GA 371
Southern Forest Heritage Museum, Long Leaf, LA 591
Southern Forest World, Waycross, GA.........391
Southern Highland Craft Guild at the Folk Art Center, Asheville, NC.............1090
The Southern Museum of Civil War and Locomotive History, Kennesaw, GA 375
Southern Oregon Historical Society, Jacksonville, OR 1226
Southern Plains Indian Museum, Anadarko, OK...1196
Southern Ute Cultural Center and Museum, Ignacio, CO 223
Southwest Dairy Museum, Sulphur Springs, TX......................................1454
Southwest Florida Museum of History, Fort Myers, FL 309
Southwest Virginia Museum Historical State Park, Big Stone Gap, VA...............1497
Space Farms Zoological Park and Museum, Sussex, NJ 925
The SPAM Museum, Austin, MN................768
Spindletop/Gladys City Boomtown Museum, Beaumont, TX.........................1395
Spirit of '76 Museum, Wellington, OH 1190
Spiro Mounds Archaeological Center, Spiro, OK.......................................1214

Spokane House Interpretive Center, Nine Mile Falls, WA 1559
Spring Grove Hospital Center, Alumni Museum, Catonsville, MD 639
Spring Valley Community Historical Society, Inc., Spring Valley, MN 794
Spring Valley Nature Center & Heritage Farm, Schaumburg, IL 457
Springfield Armory National Historic Site, Springfield, MA 710
Springfield Historical Society, Springfield, NJ 925
Springfield Museum, Springfield, OR 1236
Springfield Museum of Old Domestic Life, High Point, NC 1107
Springfield Museums - Connecticut Valley Historical Museum, Springfield, MA 710
Springfield Museums - Springfield Science Museum, Springfield, MA 711
Springs Museum, Springs, PA 1301
Spurlock Museum, University of Illinois at Urbana-Champaign, Urbana, IL..........462
Stafford County Historical Society Museum, Stafford, KS 558
Stagecoach Inn Museum Complex, Newbury Park, CA 130
Stamford Historical Society, Inc., Stamford, CT 260
Stamford Museum & Nature Center, Stamford, CT 261
Stanley-Whitman House, Farmington, Farmington, CT 241
Stanly County Historic Preservation Commission and Museum, Albemarle, NC 1088
Star of the Republic Museum, Washington, TX 1460
State Agricultural Heritage Museum, Brookings, SD 1344
State Historical Society of Iowa, Des Moines, IA 515
State Historical Society of North Dakota, Bismarck, ND 1128
The State Museum of Pennsylvania, Harrisburg, PA 1259
Steam Railroading Institute, Owosso, MI ...759
The Steamboat Arabia Museum, Kansas City, MO.......................................822
Steamboat Bertrand Collection, Missouri Valley, IA 524
Steamship Keewatin, Douglas, MI 738
Steamship William G. Mather Museum, Cleveland, OH 1156
Stearns History Museum, Saint Cloud, MN 788
Steele County Historical Society, Hope, ND 1133
Steilacoom Historical Museum Association, Steilacoom, WA 1572
Stephen C. Foster State Park, Fargo, GA.....371
Stephenson County Historical Society, Freeport, IL 436
Stephenville Museum, Stephenville, TX 1454
Steppingstone Museum, Havre de Grace, MD 647
Sterling Historical Society and Little Red Schoolhouse Museum, Sterling, NY......1074
Sterling-Rock Falls Historical Society Museum, Sterling, IL 461
Sterne-Hoya House Museum and Library, Nacogdoches, TX 1440
Stevens County Historical Society Museum, Morris, MN 784
Stevens Museum, Salem, IN 498
Stewart M. Lord Memorial Historical Society, Inc., Burlington, ME 608
Stockbridge Library Historical Collection, Stockbridge, MA 713
Stockholm Historical Society Museum, Stockholm, ME 623
Stone Fort Museum, Nacogdoches, TX......1440

The Stone House Museum, Belchertown, MA 662
Stonefield Historic Site, Cassville, WI.......1593
Stonewall House, Rocky Mount, NC..........1118
Stonewall Jackson Museum at Hupp's Hill, Strasburg, VA 1539
Storrowton Village Museum, West Springfield, MA 718
Stoughton Historical Society, Stoughton, WI 1623
Strasburg Museum, Strasburg, VA..............1539
Strategic Air & Space Museum, Ashland, NE 856
The Stratford Historical Society & Catherine B. Mitchell Museum, Stratford, CT 262
Strawbery Banke Museum, Portsmouth, NH...895
Stuart Heritage Museum, Stuart, FL...........346
Stuart House City Museum, Mackinac Island, MI 752
Studebaker National Museum, Inc., South Bend, IN 500
Stutsman County Memorial Museum, Jamestown, ND..1133
Sullivan County Historical Society, Inc., Hurleyville, NY 1001
Summit County Historical Society, Akron, OH...1139
The Sumter County Museum, Sumter, SC.1342
Sun Prairie Historical Library & Museum, Sun Prairie, WI.............................1624
Sunnyside Historical Museum, Sunnyside, WA 1572
Sunnyvale Historical Museum, Sunnyvale, CA 190
SunWatch Indian Village/Archaeological Park, Dayton, OH 1162
Susquehanna County Historical Society & Free Library Association, Montrose, PA 1272
Swampscott Historical Society (John Humphrey House), Swampscott, MA......714
Swarthout Memorial Museum, La Crosse, WI 1603
Swedish American Museum Association of Chicago, Chicago, IL..........................428
Sweet Briar Museum, Sweet Briar, VA.......1540
Sweetwater County Historical Museum, Green River, WY 1633
Swenson Memorial Museum of Stephens County, Breckenridge, TX.....................1397
Swift County Historical Society, Benson, MN 769
Swisher County Archives and Museum Association, Tulia, TX 1456
Swiss Historical Village, New Glarus, WI.1615
Switzerland County Historical Museum, Vevay, IN 502

T.B. Ferguson Home, Watonga, OK 1216
Talkeetna Historical Society and Museum, Talkeetna, AK 28
Tallahassee Museum, Tallahassee, FL 348
Tama County Historical Museum, Toledo, IA 528
Tamastslikt Cultural Institute, Pendleton, OR 1230
Tampa Bay History Center, Inc., Tampa, FL...350
Tarpon Springs Area Historical Society - Depot Museum, Tarpon Springs, FL 351
Temecula Valley Museum, Temecula, CA...191
Tempe Historical Museum, Tempe, AZ........46
Ten Broeck Mansion - Albany County Historical Association, Albany, NY 956
Ten Sleep Pioneer Museum, Ten Sleep, WY 1639
Tenino Depot Museum, Tenino, WA 1575
Tennessee Agricultural Museum, Nashville, TN.......................................1380
Tennessee Central Railway Museum, Nashville, TN.......................................1380

Territorial Statehouse State Park &
    Museum, Fillmore, UT............1465
Terwilliger Museum, Waterloo, NY...........1083
Teutopolis Monastery Museum,
    Teutopolis, IL............461
Texana Museum and Library Association,
    Edna, TX............1410
Texas Baptist Historical Center Museum,
    Brenham, TX............1397
Texas City Museum, Texas City, TX............1455
Texas Energy Museum, Beaumont, TX......1395
Texas Forestry Museum, Lufkin, TX............1436
Texas Maritime Museum, Rockport, TX....1446
Texas Ranger Hall of Fame and Museum,
    Waco, TX............1459
Texas Seaport Museum, Galveston, TX....1422
Texas Transportation Museum, San
    Antonio, TX............1451
Thetford Historical Society Library and
    Museum, Thetford, VT............1488
This Is The Place Heritage Park, Salt
    Lake City, UT............1472
Thomas E. McMillan Museum, Brewton,
    AL............6
The Thomas Griswold House and
    Museum, Guilford, CT............243
The Thomas J. Boyd, Wytheville, VA........1546
Thomas Jefferson's Poplar Forest, Forest,
    VA............1504
The Thomas T. Taber Museum of the
    Lycoming County Historical Society,
    Williamsport, PA............1308
Thomas Warne Historical Museum &
    Library, Old Bridge, NJ............918
Thomaston Historical Society,
    Thomaston, ME............624
Thousand Islands Museum, Clayton, NY.....979
Three Rivers Museum, Muskogee, OK......1205
Thronateeska Heritage Foundation, Inc.,
    Albany, GA............355
Tillamook County Pioneer Museum,
    Tillamook, OR............1237
Timpanogos Cave National Monument,
    American Fork, UT............1462
Tinkertown Museum, Sandia Park, NM......947
Tioga County Historical Society
    Museum, Owego, NY............1048
Tioga Point Museum, Athens, PA............1241
Tipton-Haynes Historic Site, Johnson
    City, TN............1368
Tobacco Farm Life Museum, Inc., Kenly,
    NC............1107
Tolland Historical Society - Tolland
    County Jail and Warden's Home
    Museum, Tolland, CT............262
Tombstone Courthouse State Historic
    Park, Tombstone, AZ............46
Tongass Historical Museum, Ketchikan,
    AK............26
Tooele County Railroad Museum, Tooele,
    UT............1475
Top of Oklahoma Historical Museum,
    Blackwell, OK............1197
Torrington Historical Society, Inc.,
    Torrington, CT............263
Towe Auto Museum, Sacramento, CA.........154
Town of Manlius Historical Society with
    Museum, Manlius, NY............1013
Town of Yorktown Museum, Yorktown
    Heights, NY............1087
Traverse County Historical Society,
    Wheaton, MN............796
Tread of Pioneers Museum, Steamboat
    Springs, CO............232
Treasures of the Sea Exhibit,
    Georgetown, DE............271
Trenton City Museum, Trenton, NJ............928
Trenton Historical Museum, Trenton, MI.....765
Tri-Cities Museum, Grand Haven, MI.........743
Tri-County Historical Society &
    Museum, Inc., Herington, KS............544

Tri-State Mineral Museum, Joplin, MO.......820
Tropic Lightning Museum, Schofield
    Barracks, HI............402
Troutdale Historical Society, Troutdale,
    OR............1237
Troy Museum & Historic Village, Troy,
    MI............765
Tsa Mo Ga Memorial Museum, Plains,
    TX............1443
T.T. Wentworth, Jr. Florida State
    Museum, Pensacola, FL............336
Tuck Museum, Hampton, NH............888
Tucker Tower Nature Center, Ardmore,
    OK............1196
Tuckerton Seaport, Tuckerton, NJ............928
Tucson Rodeo Parade Museum, Tucson,
    AZ............52
Tulare County Museum at Mooney Grove
    Park, Visalia, CA............195
Tularosa Basin Historical Society
    Museum, Alamogordo, NM............932
Turquoise Museum, Albuquerque, NM........936
Turtle Bay Exploration Park, Redding,
    CA............146
Twin Falls County Historical Museum,
    Filer, ID............405
Twin Falls State Park & Museum,
    Mullens, WV............1585
Twinsburg Historical Society, Twinsburg,
    OH............1188
Tybee Island Light Station and Tybee
    Museum, Tybee Island, GA............389

USS Massachusetts Memorial Committee,
    Inc., Fall River, MA............682
Umlauf Sculpture Garden & Museum,
    Austin, TX............1392
Umpqua Discovery Center, Reedsport,
    OR............1234
Uncle Remus Museum, Eatonton, GA.........371
Union County Historical Complex,
    Creston, IA............512
Union County Historical Society,
    Lewisburg, PA............1268
Union County Historical Society
    Museum, Blairsville, GA............366
Union County Museum, Union, OR............1238
Union Mills Homestead & Grist Mill,
    Westminster, MD............656
Union Station Kansas City, Inc., Kansas
    City, MO............823
Unionville Museum, Farmington, CT...........242
University Museum, Carbondale, IL............415
The University Museum Collections,
    Fayetteville, AR............57
University of Nebraska State Museum,
    Lincoln, NE............867
University of Pennsylvania Museum of
    Archaeology and Anthropology,
    Philadelphia, PA............1288
Upper Musselshell Historical Society,
    Harlowton, MT............849
Upper Snake River Valley Historical
    Society, Rexburg, ID............409
U.S. Army Engineer Museum, Fort
    Leonard Wood, MO............815
U.S. Army Transportation Museum, Fort
    Eustis, VA............1504
U.S. Grant's Home State Historic Site,
    Galena, IL............436
U.S. Mint-Philadelphia, Philadelphia, PA...1289
U.S. Navy Seabee Museum, Port
    Hueneme, CA............143
USS Alabama Battleship Memorial Park,
    Mobile, AL............15
USS Constellation Museum, Baltimore,
    MD............636
USS Constitution Museum, Boston, MA.....669
USS Lexington Museum on the Bay,
    Corpus Christi, TX............1402
Utah State Historical Society, Salt Lake
    City, UT............1473
Utica Museum, Utica, MT............854

Vacaville Museum, Vacaville, CA...............194
The Valdez Museum & Historical
    Archive Association, Inc., Valdez, AK......29
Valentine-Varian House/Museum of
    Bronx History, Bronx, NY............967
Valentown Museum, Victor, NY............1081
Vallejo Naval & Historical Museum,
    Vallejo, CA............194
Valley County Pioneer Museum,
    Glasgow, MT............847
Van Buren County Historical Society,
    Keosauqua, IA............521
Van Riper-Hopper House Museum,
    Wayne, NJ............929
Van Wyck Homestead Museum, Fishkill,
    NY............989
Vanderbilt University Fine Arts Gallery,
    Nashville, TN............1381
Vashon Maury Island Heritage
    Association, Vashon, WA............1576
Venango Museum of Art, Science &
    Industry, Oil City, PA............1274
Ventura County Maritime Museum, Inc.,
    Oxnard, CA............137
Ventura County Museum of History &
    Art, Ventura, CA............195
Verde Historical Society, Clemenceau
    Heritage Museum, Cottonwood, AZ..........32
Vermont Historical Society Museum,
    Montpelier, VT............1482
Vermont Marble Museum, Proctor, VT......1485
Vermont Ski Museum, Stowe, VT............1488
Vernon County Historical Museum,
    Viroqua, WI............1625
Vernon Historians, Inc., Vernon, VT............1489
Vernonia Pioneer Museum, Vernonia, OR..1238
The Vestal Museum, Vestal, NY............1081
Vesterheim Norwegian-American
    Museum, Decorah, IA............513
Victor Heritage Museum, Victor, MT..........854
Victor Valley Museum & Art Gallery,
    Apple Valley, CA............71
Village of Elsah Museum, Elsah, IL............433
The Vinalhaven Historical Society
    Museum, Vinalhaven, ME............624
Vintage Flying Museum, Fort Worth, TX..1419
Virginia Museum of Transportation, Inc.,
    Roanoke, VA............1536
Vista Historical Museum, Vista, CA............196

W.H. Over Museum, Vermillion, SD..........1358
Wabasha County Museum, Wabasha
    County Historical Society at Reads
    Landing, Reads Landing, MN............787
Wabaunsee County Historical Museum,
    Alma, KS............532
Wade House Stagecoach Inn & Wesley
    Jung Carriage Museum State Historic
    Site, Greenbush, WI............1599
Wahkiakum County Historical Museum,
    Cathlamet, WA............1550
Waimea Arboretum and Botanical Garden
    in Waimea Valley Audubon Center,
    Haleiwa, HI............392
Wakefield Historical Society, Wakefield,
    MA............715
Wakefield House Museum, Blue Earth,
    MN............769
Wakefield Museum Association,
    Wakefield, KS............560
Waldensian Heritage Museum, Valdese,
    NC............1121
Wallace District Mining Museum,
    Wallace, ID............410
Wallingford Historical Society, Inc.,
    Wallingford, CT............263
Walney Visitor Center-At Ellanor C.
    Lawrence Park, Chantilly, VA............1498
Walnut Grove Plantation, Roebuck, SC......1340
The Waltham Museum, Waltham, MA.........716
Wapello County Historical Museum,
    Ottumwa, IA............526

Tools and Equipment for Materials—Continued

Ward County Historical Society, Minot, ND 1135

The Ward Museum of Wildfowl Art, Salisbury University, Salisbury, MD 653

Ward W. O'Hara Agricultural Museum, Auburn, NY 959

Warren County Historical Society Museum, Lebanon, OH 1171

Warren Historical Society, Warren, ME 624

Warrick County Museum, Inc., Boonville, IN 470

Warsaw Historical Museum, Warsaw, NY .1082

Warther Museum Inc., Dover, OH 1163

Washburn County Historical Society Museum, Shell Lake, WI 1621

Washburn Historical Museum & Cultural Center, Inc. aka Washburn Cultural Center, Washburn, WI 1625

Washington County Fair Farm Museum, Greenwich, NY 996

Washington County Historical Association, Fort Calhoun, NE 860

Washington County Historical Society, Washington, KS 560

Washington County Historical Society, Portland, OR 1233

Washington County Historical Society Inc., West Bend, WI 1627

Washington County Rural Heritage Museum, Boonsboro, MD 637

Washington Crossing Historic Park, Washington Crossing, PA 1305

Washington Museum & Tourist Center, Washington, LA 603

Washington's Lands Museum & Sayre Log House, Ravenswood, WV 1586

Water Mill Museum, Water Mill, NY 1082

Waterfront Museum, Brooklyn, NY 970

Waterloo Area Historical Society, Grass Lake, MI 744

Watermen's Museum, Yorktown, VA 1547

Watertown Historical Society, Inc., Watertown, CT 264

Watervliet Arsenal's Museum of the Big Guns, Watervliet, NY 1084

Watkins Community Museum of History, Lawrence, KS 548

Watkins Woolen Mill State Historic Site & Park, Lawson, MO 825

Watters Smith Memorial State Park, Lost Creek, WV 1584

Wauconda Township Historical Society, Wauconda, IL 463

Waukesha County Museum, Waukesha, WI 1625

Wayland Historical Society, Wayland, MA 716

Wayne County Historical Society, Lyons, NY 1012

Wayne County Historical Society, Honesdale, PA 1261

Webster House Museum, Elkhorn, WI 1596

Weir Farm National Historic Site, Wilton, CT 267

Wellfleet Historical Society Museum, Wellfleet, MA 717

Wells Auto Museum, Wells, ME 625

Wells County Historical Museum, Bluffton, IN 470

Wells County Museum, Fessenden, ND 1131

Wenatchee Valley Museum and Cultural Center, Wenatchee, WA 1577

Wendell Gilley Museum, Southwest Harbor, ME 623

Wenham Museum, Wenham, MA 717

Weslaco Museum, Weslaco, TX 1461

West Allis Historical Society Museum, West Allis, WI 1626

West Baton Rouge Museum, Port Allen, LA 599

West Chicago City Museum, West Chicago, IL 464

West Milford Museum, West Milford, NJ ...930

West of the Pecos Museum, Pecos, TX 1443

West Pasco Historical Society Museum and Library, New Port Richey, FL 329

West Point Museum, West Point, NY 1085

West Virginia Museum of American Glass, Weston, WV 1587

West Virginia State Farm Museum, Point Pleasant, WV 1586

West Virginia State Museum, Charleston, WV 1581

Western Hennepin County Pioneers Association, Long Lake, MN 779

Western Heritage Center, Billings, MT 841

Western Mining & Railroad Museum, Helper, UT 1466

Western New Mexico University Museum, Silver City, NM 951

The Western Railway Museum, Suisun City, CA 189

Western Rhode Island Civic Historical Society, Coventry, RI 1311

Western Springs Historical Society, Western Springs, IL 464

Westminster Historical Society, Westminster, VT 1490

Westmoreland Sanctuary, Inc., Bedford Corners, NY 961

Westport Historical Society, Westport, CT ...266

Westport Maritime Museum, Westport, WA 1578

The Wethersfield Historical Society, Wethersfield, CT 266

Wexford County Historical Society & Museum, Cadillac, MI 731

The Whale Museum, Friday Harbor, WA ...1555

Wharton County Historical Museum, Wharton, TX 1461

Wheat Ridge Historic Park, Wheat Ridge, CO 235

Wheeler Historic Farm, Salt Lake City, UT 1474

Wheels O' Time Museum, Peoria, IL 451

Whipple House Museum, Ashland Historical Society, Ashland, NH 883

White County Historical Society Museum, Monticello, IN 491

White Deer Land Museum, Pampa, TX 1442

White Hall State Historic Site, Richmond, KY 583

White Pine Public Museum, Ely, NV 877

White River Valley Museum, Auburn, WA 1547

Whitehead Memorial Museum, Del Rio, TX 1409

Whitewater Canal State Historic Site, Metamora, IN 490

Whitewater Historical Museum, Whitewater, WI 1628

Whitingham Historical Museum, Whitingham, VT 1490

Whitley County Historical Museum, Columbia City, IN 472

Whitman Mission National Historic Site, Walla Walla, WA 1577

Wild Turkey Center and Winchester Museum, Edgefield, SC 1332

Wilder Memorial Museum, Strawberry Point, IA 528

Wilderness Road Regional Museum, Newbern, VA 1519

Wilkin County Historical Society, Breckenridge, MN 770

Willard House and Clock Museum, Inc., Grafton, MA 685

William B. Ide Adobe State Historic Park, Red Bluff, CA 146

William Clark Market House Museum, Paducah, KY 582

William Cullen Bryant Homestead, Cummington, MA 678

William Otis Sawtelle Collections and Research Center, Bar Harbor, ME 606

Williamson County Historical Society, Marion, IL 444

Willowbrook Museum Village, Newfield, ME 616

Wilmette Historical Museum, Wilmette, IL 466

Wilmington Railroad Museum, Wilmington, NC 1124

Wilson County Historical Society Museum, Fredonia, KS 540

Wilson Czech Opera House Corporation, Foundation, Inc. & House of Memories Museum, Wilson, KS 564

Wilson Historical Museum, Wilson, NY 1086

Wilton Historical Museums, Wilton, CT 267

Winchester-Frederick County Historical Society, Inc., Winchester, VA 1546

Windham Textile and History Museum (The Mill Museum), Willimantic, CT ...267

Wing Luke Asian Museum, Seattle, WA 1569

Winnebago Area Museum, Winnebago, MN 797

Winnetka Historical Society, Winnetka, IL 466

Winona County Historical Museum, Winona, MN 797

Winterthur Museum & Country Estate, Winterthur, DE..274

Wiscasset, Waterville & Farmington Railway Museum, Alna, ME 603

Wisconsin Automotive Museum, Hartford, WI 1600

Wisconsin Historical Museum, Madison, WI 1606

Wisconsin Maritime Museum, Manitowoc, WI 1607

Wolcott House Museum Complex, Maumee, OH 1175

Woldumar Nature Center, Lansing, MI 751

Wolf Point Area Historical Society, Inc., Wolf Point, MT 855

Wolfeboro Historical Society, Wolfeboro, NH 897

Wood County Historical Center and Museum, Bowling Green, OH 1143

Woodbine International Fire Museum, Woodbine, GA 392

Woodburn Historic House, Pendleton, SC .1339

Wooden Nickel Historical Museum, San Antonio, TX 1452

Woodruff Museum of Indian Artifacts, Bridgeton, NJ 898

Woodside Store Historic Site, Woodside, CA 199

Woodson County Historical Society, Yates Center, KS 564

Woodstock Historical Society, Bryant Pond, ME 608

Woodstock Historical Society, Inc., Woodstock, VT 1491

Worcester Historical Museum, Worcester, MA 721

Workman & Temple Family Homestead Museum, City of Industry, CA 85

The Works: Ohio Center for History, Art & Technology, Newark, OH 1179

World Kite Museum & Hall of Fame, Long Beach, WA 1558

World O' Tools Museum, Waverly, TN 1385

Wormsloe State Historic Site, Savannah, GA 387

Worthington Historical Society, Worthington, OH 1192

Wrangell Museum, Wrangell, AK 29

Wrather West Kentucky Museum, Murray, KY 580

Wray Museum, Wray, CO 235

Wright Brothers National Memorial, Kill Devil Hills, NC 1108

Wright Centennial Museum, Wright, WY ..1639
Wyalusing Valley Museum, Wyalusing, PA 1309
Wyandot County Historical Society, Upper Sandusky, OH 1188
Wyandotte County Museum, Bonner Springs, KS 534
Wyandotte Museum, Wyandotte, MI 766
The Wyckoff Farmhouse Museum, Brooklyn, NY 970
Wyoming Territorial Prison State Historic Site, Laramie, WY 1636

Yakima Valley Museum and Historical Association, Yakima, WA 1579
Yates County Genealogical and Historical Society and Oliver House Museum and L. Caroline Underwood Museum, Penn Yan, NY 1052
Ybor City Museum State Park, Tampa, FL 351
Yellow Medicine County Historical Society and Museum, Granite Falls, MN 777
Yellowstone Gateway Museum of Park County, Livingston, MT 850
Yorba and Slaughter Families Adobe, Chino, CA 84
Youth Museum of Southern West Virginia, Beckley, WV 1579
Youth Science Institute, San Jose, CA 173
Yucaipa Adobe, Yucaipa, CA 200
Yucaipa Valley Historical Society Museum, Yucaipa, CA 201
Yuma Crossing State Historic Park, Yuma, AZ 54
Yuma Territorial Prison State Historic Park, Yuma, AZ 54

Zane Grey Museum, Lackawaxen, PA 1265
Zebulon B. Vance Birthplace State Historic Site, Weaverville, NC 1122
Zelienople Historical Society, Zelienople, PA 1309
Zion Human History Museum, Springdale, UT 1474
Zippo/Case Visitors Center, Bradford, PA ..1244
Zoar State Memorial, Zoar, OH 1194

Tools and Equipment for Science and Technology

A.C. Gilbert's Discovery Village, Salem, OR 1235
A.R. Bowman Memorial Museum, Prineville, OR 1234
Abraham Lincoln Library & Museum, Lincoln Memorial University, Harrogate, TN 1366
Academy of Model Aeronautics/National Model Aviation Museum, Muncie, IN 492
The Academy of Natural Sciences of Philadelphia, Philadelphia, PA 1275
Adams County Historical Museum, Decatur, IN 474
Adler Planetarium & Astronomy Museum, Chicago, IL 417
Admiral Nimitz National Museum of the Pacific War, Fredericksburg, TX 1419
Adventure Science Center, Nashville, TN..1377
Afro-American Historical Society Museum, Jersey City, NJ 908
Agate Fossil Beds National Monument, Harrison, NE 862
Agriculture Museum, Merced, CA 125
Agrirama, Georgia's Living History Museum & Village, Tifton, GA 388
Aiken County Historical Museum, Aiken, SC 1320
Air Force Flight Test Center Museum, Edwards AFB, CA 92
Air Mobility Command Museum, Dover AFB, DE 270

Air Victory Museum, Inc., Lumberton, NJ 910
The Airborne & Special Operations Museum, Fayetteville, NC 1100
Airline History Museum, Kansas City, MO 820
Airmen Memorial Museum, Suitland, MD 655
Airpower Museum Inc., Ottumwa, IA 526
Alabama Mining Museum, Dora, AL 7
Alabama Museum of the Health Sciences, Birmingham, AL 4
Alamance Battleground State Historic Site, Burlington, NC 1092
Alamance County Historical Museum, Burlington, NC 1092
Alaska Heritage Museum at Wells Fargo, Anchorage, AK 21
Alaska State Museum, Juneau, AK 25
Albany Historical Society, Inc., Sabetha, KS 557
Albuquerque Museum, Albuquerque, NM...932
Aliceville Museum, Aliceville, AL 3
Allegany County Historical Society, Inc., Cumberland, MD 641
Allen County Historical Society, Iola, KS ...545
Allen County Museum, Lima, OH 1172
Alling Coverlet Museum, Palmyra, NY 1050
Allison-Antrim Museum, Inc., Greencastle, PA 1257
Almond Historical Society/Hagadorn House Museum, Almond, NY 957
Amador County Museum, Jackson, CA 105
American Airpower Heritage Museum, Inc. & Commemorative Air Force Headquarters, Midland, TX 1438
American Clock and Watch Museum, Inc., Bristol, CT 236
American Heart Association - Halle Heart Center, Tempe, AZ 45
American Merchant Marine Museum, Kings Point, NY 1007
American Museum of Nursing, Tempe, AZ 45
American Museum of Radio and Electricity, Bellingham, WA 1548
American Museum of Science & Energy, Oak Ridge, TN 1382
American Precision Museum Association, Inc., Windsor, VT 1490
American Printing House for the Blind, Callahan Museum, Louisville, KY 575
American Textile History Museum, Lowell, MA 691
American Watchmakers-Clockmakers Institute, Harrison, OH 1168
Americana Museum, Terra Alta, WV 1587
America's Black Holocaust Museum, Milwaukee, WI 1610
America's Stonehenge, North Salem, NH ...893
Amherst County Museum & Historical Society, Amherst, VA 1495
Anacortes Museum, Anacortes, WA 1547
Anacostia Museum and Center for African American History & Culture, Washington, DC 275
Anadarko Heritage Museum, Anadarko, OK 1195
Ancient and Honorable Artillery Company, Boston, MA 663
Anderson/Abruzzo Albuquerque International Balloon Museum, Albuquerque, NM 933
Anderson County Historical Museum, Garnett, KS 541
Anderson County Museum, Anderson, SC.1321
Andersonville National Historic Site, Andersonville, GA 355
Androscoggin Historical Society, Auburn, ME 603
The Anne Spencer Memorial Foundation, Inc., Lynchburg, VA 1515

Anoka County Historical Society, Anoka, MN 767
Anson County Historical Society, Inc., Wadesboro, NC 1121
The Antique Boat Museum, Clayton, NY 978
Apostles Islands National Lakeshore, Bayfield, WI 1591
Apple Farm Mill House, San Luis Obispo, CA 174
The Apple Trees Museum, Burlington, IA ...506
Arab American National Museum, Dearborn, MI 733
Archer County Museum, Archer City, TX .1387
Archives of J.S.G. Boggs, Brandon, FL 298
Argo Gold Mine & Mill Museum, Idaho Springs, CO 223
Arizona Historical Society Museum, Tucson, AZ 47
Arizona Historical Society Museum at Papago Park, Tempe, AZ 45
Arizona Historical Society Museum - Downtown, Tucson, AZ 47
Arizona Historical Society Pioneer Museum, Flagstaff, AZ 32
Arizona Military Museum, Phoenix, AZ 39
Arizona State Capitol Museum, Phoenix, AZ 39
Arizona State Museum, Tucson, AZ 48
Arkansas Country Doctor Museum, Lincoln, AR 61
Arkansas Museum of Natural Resources, Smackover, AR 68
Arkansas Post Museum, Gillett, AR 58
Armand Bayou Nature Center, Houston, TX 1424
The Arms Family Museum of Local History, Youngstown, OH 1193
Arrow Rock State Historic Site, Arrow Rock, MO 810
Artesia Historical Museum & Art Center, Artesia, NM 936
The Arthur & Kriebel Herbaria, Purdue University, West Lafayette, IN 503
Artillery Company of Newport Military Museum, Newport, RI 1313
Ashland Historical Society, Ashland, MA 661
Ashland Historical Society Museum, Ashland, WI 1590
Astronaut Memorial Planetarium and Observatory, Cocoa, FL 300
Ataloa Lodge Museum, Muskogee, OK 1205
Atchison County Historical Society, Atchison, KS 533
Atlanta Historical Society, Atlanta, GA 358
Atlantic Heritage Center, Somers Point, NJ 924
The Atomic Testing Museum, Las Vegas, NV 878
Au Glaize Village, Defiance, OH 1162
Audie Murphy/American Cotton Museum, Inc, Greenville, TX 1423
Auglaize County Historical Society, Saint Marys, OH 1184
Augusta Museum of History, Augusta, GA 364
Aullwood Audubon Center and Farm, Dayton, OH 1160
Aurora History Museum, Aurora, CO 202
Aurora Regional Fire Museum, Aurora, IL 411
Avery County Museum, Newland, NC 1113
Aviation Cadet Museum, Eureka Springs, AR 57
Aviation Museum of Kentucky Inc., Lexington, KY 572

BRIMS - Barren River Imaginative Museum of Science, Bowling Green, KY 565
Badger Mine and Museum, Shullsburg, WI 1622
Baker-Cederberg Museum & Archives, Rochester, NY 1058

Tools and Equipment for Science and Technology—Continued

The Bakken Library and Museum, Minneapolis, MN......................781

Baldwin County Heritage Museum, Elberta, AL..............................8

Baldwin Historical Society and Museum, Baldwin, NY.................960

Baldwin-Reynolds House Museum, Meadville, PA............................1270

Baltimore Civil War Museum, Baltimore, MD....................................629

Baltimore Maritime Museum, Baltimore, MD....................................630

Baltimore Museum of Industry, Baltimore, MD................................630

Banner County Historical Society, Harrisburg, NE...........................862

Bannock County Historical Museum, Pocatello, ID............................408

The Bare Cove Fire Museum, Hingham, MA.....................................687

The Barnacle Historic State Park, Coconut Grove, FL........................300

Barnes County Historical Museum, Valley City, ND..........................1136

Barnet Historical Society, Barnet, VT........1476

Barratt's Chapel and Museum, Frederica, DE......................................270

Barre Historical Society, Inc., Barre, MA....662

Barrington Living History Farm, Washington, TX.............................1460

Barron County Historical Society's Pioneer Village Museum, Cameron, WI..1593

Bartlesville Area History Museum, Bartlesville, OK............................1196

Bartow History Center, Cartersville, GA.....367

Battle of Lexington State Historic Site, Lexington, MO..............................826

Battleship North Carolina, Wilmington, NC..1122

Battleship Texas State Historic Site, La Porte, TX..1433

Beauvais Heritage Center, Clark, SD.........1345

Beckman Coulter Heritage Exhibit, Fullerton, CA.................................98

Bedford City/County Museum, Bedford, VA..1496

Belhaven Memorial Museum, Inc., Belhaven, NC.................................1092

Bell County Museum, Belton, TX..............1395

Belle Isle Nature Zoo, Detroit, MI..............735

Bellflower Historical and Genealogical Society, Bellflower, IL.......................413

Bellport-Brookhaven Historical Society and Museum, Bellport, NY.................961

Beltrami County History Center, Bemidji, MN..768

Benicia Historical Museum, Benicia, CA......74

The Benjamin Banneker Park & Museum, Baltimore, MD.................631

Bennington Battle Monument, Old Bennington, VT..............................1484

Benton County Historical Museum, Philomath, OR...............................1230

Benton County Historical Museum, Prosser, WA.................................1563

Bentonville Battlefield State Historic Site, Four Oaks, NC.........................1102

Benzie Area Historical Museum, Benzonia, MI..................................729

Berkeley County Museum & Heritage Center, Moncks Corner, SC.........1336

Bernard Historical Society and Museum, Delton, MI.....................................734

Berrien County Historical Association, Berrien Springs, MI.......................729

Bessemer Hall of History, Bessemer, AL.........3

Besser Museum for Northeast Michigan, Alpena, MI..723

Beyer Home, Oconto County Historical Society Museum, Oconto, WI..............1616

BG John C.L. Scribner Texas Military Forces Museum, Austin, TX..................1389

Big Bear Solar Observatory, Big Bear City, CA..78

Birch Aquarium at Scripps, Scripps Institution of Oceanography, University of California, San Diego, La Jolla, CA..106

Bisbee Mining & Historical Museum, Bisbee, AZ..30

Bishop Hill Heritage Museum, Bishop Hill, IL..413

Black American West Museum & Heritage Center, Denver, CO..................209

Black Hills Mining Museum, Lead, SD.....1350

Black Kettle Museum, Cheyenne, OK........1198

Black River Historical Society of Lorain, Lorain, OH.......................................1172

Blackberry Farm's Pioneer Village, Aurora, IL..411

Blaine County Historical Museum, Hailey, ID...406

Blaine County Museum, Chinook, MT........844

Bluegrass Railroad Museum, Versailles, KY...584

Bob Campbell Geology Museum, Clemson, SC...1328

Bodie State Historic Park, Bridgeport, CA..79

Bonner County Historical Museum, Sandpoint, ID...409

Boone County Heritage Museum, Harrison, AR...59

Boone County Historical Center, Boone, IA..506

Boonsborough Museum of History, Boonsboro, MD.......................................637

The Boorman House - The Juneau County Historical Society, Mauston, WI...1608

Boscobel, Garrison, NY..............................993

Bosque Memorial Museum, Clifton, TX....1400

Boston Childrens Museum, Boston, MA......664

Bottineau County Historical Museum, Bottineau, ND......................................1129

Boulder City/Hoover Dam Museum, Boulder City, NV.......................................875

Boulder History Museum, Boulder, CO........202

Bradbury Science Museum, Los Alamos, NM...942

Braintree Historical Society, Inc., Braintree, MA...670

Brandywine Battlefield Park, Chadds Ford, PA...1246

Brazos Valley Museum of Natural History, Bryan, TX.................................1398

Bremerton Naval Museum, Bremerton, WA..1549

Bridger Valley Heritage Museum, Lyman, WY.....................................1636

Brockton Fire Museum, Brockton, MA........671

The Bronx County Historical Society, Bronx, NY...964

Brookhaven National Laboratory-Science Museum, Upton, NY.........................1079

Brookings County Historical Society Museum, Volga, SD.........................1358

The Brooklyn Historical Society, Brooklyn, NY...968

Brooklyn Historical Society, Brooklyn, OH..1144

Bucyrus Historical Society, Bucyrus, OH..1144

Buehler Challenger & Science Center, Paramus, NJ...919

Buena Vista Museum of Natural History, Bakersfield, CA.....................................73

Buffalo and Erie County Historical Society, Buffalo, NY.................................972

Buffalo and Erie County Naval & Military Park, Buffalo, NY.................972

Burritt on the Mountain-A Living Museum, Huntsville, AL.......................11

Burt County Museum, Tekamah, NE.........873

Bushwhacker Museum, Nevada, MO.........828

Butler County History Center & Kansas Oil Museum, El Dorado, KS.................537

Butte County Pioneer Memorial Museum, Oroville, CA.......................................136

CDC/Global Health Odyssey, Atlanta, GA..358

COSI Columbus, Columbus, OH..............1157

CTS Turner Museum, Elkhart, IN.............474

CU Heritage Center, Boulder, CO.............203

Cabrillo Marine Aquarium, San Pedro, CA..176

Cabrillo National Monument, San Diego, CA..156

Caldwell County Railroad Museum, Princeton, KY.......................................583

Calhoun County Museum, Rockwell City, IA..527

Calhoun County Museum & Cultural Center, Saint Matthews, SC.................1341

California Academy of Sciences, San Francisco, CA.......................................163

California Oil Museum, Santa Paula, CA....183

California State Railroad Museum, Sacramento, CA.......................................152

Calusa Nature Center and Planetarium, Fort Myers, FL.......................................308

Calvin Coolidge Historic Site, Plymouth Notch, VT...1484

Cambridge Museum, Cambridge, NE.........858

Camp 6 Logging Museum, Tacoma, WA....1572

Campbell Historical Museum & Ainsley House, Campbell, CA.............................80

Canterbury Shaker Village, Inc., Canterbury, NH.......................................883

Canton Classic Car Museum, Canton, OH.1145

Canyon de Chelly National Monument, Chinle, AZ..31

Cape May County Historical Museum and Genealogical Society, Cape May Court House, NJ.......................................900

Capitola Historical Museum, Capitola, CA..81

Captain Forbes House Museum, Milton, MA..695

Carbon County Museum, Rawlins, WY.....1637

Carlsbad Caverns National Park, Carlsbad, NM.......................................937

Carnegie Science Center, Pittsburgh, PA....1291

Carroll Mansion Museum Home of Leavenworth County Historical Society, Leavenworth, KS.......................549

Carroll Reece Museum, Johnson City, TN.1367

Cashmere Museum & Pioneer Village, Cashmere, WA.......................................1550

Cass County Museum & Pioneer School, Walker, MN.......................................795

Castle Air Museum, Atwater, CA................72

Castle Museum of Saginaw County History, Saginaw, MI.............................762

Catawba County Museum of History, Newton, NC.......................................1113

Catawba Science Center, Hickory, NC.......1106

Cattaraugus Area Historical Center, Cattaraugus, NY.......................................976

Cayuga Museum & Case Research Lab Museum, Auburn, NY.............................959

Cedar Key Historical Society Museum, Cedar Key, FL.......................................298

Cedar Key Museum State Park, Cedar Key, FL..299

Centennial Village Museum, Greeley, CO...221

Center for Agricultural Science and Heritage, Indianapolis, IN.................481

Centerville Historical Museum, Centerville, MA.......................................675

Central Delta Depot Museum, Brinkley, AR..55

Central Nevada Museum & Historical Society, Tonopah, NV 882
Chabot Space & Science Center, Oakland, CA 133
Challenger Learning Center of Arizona, Peoria, AZ 38
Champaign County Historical Museum, Champaign, IL 416
Champaign County Historical Museum, Urbana, OH 1188
Champion Mill State Historical Park, Champion, NE 859
Charles A. Weyerhaeuser Memorial Museum, Little Falls, MN 779
Charles River Museum of Industry, Waltham, MA 715
Charlotte Museum of History and Hezekiah Alexander Homesite, Charlotte, NC 1094
Chattanooga African Museum/Bessie Smith Hall, Chattanooga, TN 1360
Chenango County Historical Society Museum, Norwich, NY 1044
Cherokee National Museum, Park Hill, OK 1211
Cherokee Strip Land Rush Museum, Arkansas City, KS 532
Cherokee Strip Museum, Alva, OK 1195
Cherokee Strip Museum and Henry S. Johnston Library, Perry, OK 1212
Cherry Valley Museum, Cherry Valley, NY 978
Chester County Historical Society, West Chester, PA 1307
Chester County Historical Society Museum, Chester, SC 1327
The Chicago Athenaeum: Museum of Architecture and Design, Galena, IL 436
Chicago History Museum, Chicago, IL 419
Children's Discovery Museum of North San Diego, Carlsbad, CA 81
Children's Hands-On Museum (CHOM), Tuscaloosa, AL 19
Children's Health Museum, Charlottesville, VA 1499
Children's Museum at Holyoke, Inc., Holyoke, MA 687
The Children's Museum of Science and Technology, Troy, NY 1079
Childress County Heritage Museum, Childress, TX 1400
Chippewa County Historical Society, Montevideo, MN 783
Chisholm Trail Museum, Kingfisher, OK 1203
Christa McAuliffe Planetarium, Concord, NH 884
Christiansted National Historic Site, Saint Croix, VI 1644
Chula Vista Nature Center, Chula Vista, CA 84
Cincinnati Fire Museum, Cincinnati, OH 1149
The Citadel Archives & Museum, Charleston, SC 1324
City County Pioneer Museum, Sweetwater, TX 1454
City of Gilroy Museum, Gilroy, CA 99
City of Wayne Historical Museum, Wayne, MI 766
Civil War and Underground Railroad Museum of Philadelphia, Philadelphia, PA 1278
Civil War Life - The Soldier's Museum, Fredericksburg, VA 1505
Civil War Museum of Lonejack, Jackson County, Lone Jack, MO 826
Civil War Soldiers Museum, Pensacola, FL 335
Clark County Historical Museum, Vancouver, WA 1576
Clark County Historical Society - Heritage Center of Clark County, Springfield, OH 1186

Clarksville-Montgomery County Museum dba Customs House Museum & Cultural Center, Clarksville, TN 1363
Clay County Historical Museum, Liberty, MO 826
Cleveland County Historical Museum, Shelby, NC 1119
Cleveland Police Historical Society & Museum, Cleveland, OH 1153
Clinton County Historical Association & Museum, Plattsburgh, NY 1052
Cloud County Historical Society Museum, Concordia, KS 536
Clovis Big Dry Creek Historical Museum, Clovis, CA 86
Coastal Discovery Museum, Hilton Head Island, SC 1335
Coastal Science Center at Hutchinson Island, Stuart, FL 346
Coca-Cola Space Science Center, Columbus, GA 368
Cokato Museum & Akerlund Photography Studio, Cokato, MN 771
The Coleman House Museum and Brown County Historical Society, Ainsworth, NE 855
Collin County Historical Society, Inc. & History Museum, McKinney, TX 1437
Colonial National Historical Park: Jamestown & Yorktown, Yorktown, VA 1546
Colonial Williamsburg, Williamsburg, VA 1544
Colorado School of Mines Geology Museum, Golden, CO 220
Colton Area Museum, Colton, CA 87
Columbia Fire Department Museum, Columbia, SC 1328
Columbia Gorge Interpretive Center Museum, Stevenson, WA 1572
Columbia River Exhibition of History, Science and Technology, Richland, WA 1564
Columbus-Belmont Civil War Museum, Columbus, KY 567
Columbus Chapel, Boal Mansion Museum, Boalsburg, PA 1244
Combat Air Museum, Inc., Topeka, KS 559
The Commonwealth Museum, Boston, MA 665
Commonwealth of the Northern Mariana Islands Museum of History and Culture, Saipan, MP 1640
Communal Agriculture Museum, South Amana, IA 528
Computer History Museum, Mountain View, CA 129
Concord Historical Society, Warner Museum, Springville, NY 1071
Confederate Memorial Museum, Atoka, OK 1196
Confederate Museum, Crawfordville, GA 369
Congaree National Park, Hopkins, SC 1336
Connecticut River Museum, Essex, CT 239
Conner Prairie, Fishers, IN 476
Coolspring Power Museum, Coolspring, PA 1248
Cooper-Hewitt National Design Museum, Smithsonian Institution, New York, NY 1023
Copper Village Museum & Arts Center of Deer Lodge County, Anaconda, MT 840
Coppertown U.S.A., Calumet, MI 731
Coronado National Memorial, Hereford, AZ 36
Corpus Christi Museum of Science and History, Corpus Christi, TX 1401
Cottage Grove Museum & Annex, Cottage Grove, OR 1222
The Country Doctor Museum, Bailey, NC 1091
Courthouse Square Association, Charlotte, MI 731
Cradle of Aviation Museum, Garden City, NY 992

Crawford County Historical Museum, Pittsburg, KS 556
Crawford W. Long Museum, Jefferson, GA 374
Crazy Mountain Museum, Big Timber, MT 841
Crockett Tavern Museum, Morristown, TN 1376
Crossroads Museum, Corinth, MS 800
Crown Point State Historic Site, Crown Point, NY 984
Culinary Archives & Museum, Johnson & Wales University, Providence, RI 1316
The Curious Kids' Museum, Saint Joseph, MI 763
Curry Historical Society Museum, Gold Beach, OR 1225
Custer Battlefield Museum, Garryowen, MT 847
Custer County Historical Society, Inc., Broken Bow, NE 858
Cuyuna Range Historical Society & Museum, Crosby, MN 772

D.C. Booth Historic National Fish Hatchery, Spearfish, SD 1357
D.R. Barker Historical Museum, Fredonia, NY 992
Dade Battlefield Historic State Park, Bushnell, FL 298
Dakota County Historical Society, South Saint Paul, MN 793
Dakota Territorial Museum, Yankton, SD 1359
Dakotaland Museum, Huron, SD 1348
Dale & Martha Hawk Museum, Wolford, ND 1138
Dallam-Hartley XIT Museum, Dalhart, TX 1403
Dallas Heritage Village at Old City Park, Dallas, TX 1405
Daniels County Museum and Pioneer Town, Scobey, MT 853
Darlington Raceway Stock Car Museum, NMPA Hall of Fame, Darlington, SC 1331
Daughters of the American Revolution Museum, Washington, DC 277
Davidson County Historical Museum, Lexington, NC 1109
Dayton History at Carillon Park, Dayton, OH 1161
De Anza Planetarium, Cupertino, CA 88
Death Valley National Park Visitor Center and Museums, Death Valley, CA 91
Delaware Division of Historical & Cultural Affairs, Dover, DE 269
Delaware Nature Society, Hockessin, DE 271
Delta County Museum, Delta, CO 209
Deming Luna Mimbres Museum, Deming, NM 939
Denton County Historical Museum, Inc. and Texas Heritage Center, Denton, TX 1409
Denver Museum of Nature & Science, Denver, CO 211
Depot Museum & Fort Sedgwick Museum, Julesburg, CO 223
The Depot Museum Complex, Henderson, TX 1424
Des Plaines History Center, Des Plaines, IL 430
Deschutes County Historical Society, Bend, OR 1220
DeSoto National Memorial, Bradenton, FL 297
Detroit Historical Society, Detroit, MI 735
Detroit Science Center, Detroit, MI 736
DeWitt Stetten, Jr., Museum of Medical Research, Bethesda, MD 637
DeWitt Wallace Decorative Arts Museum, Williamsburg, VA 1545
Dexter Historical Society Campus, Dexter, ME 609
Dia Center for the Arts, Quemado, NM 945

Tools and Equipment for Science and Technology–Continued

Dickinson County Heritage Center, Abilene, KS 531

Dinosaur Depot Museum, Canon City, CO............204

The Discovery Center, Fresno, CA............96

Discovery Center (East Tennessee Discovery Center), Knoxville, TN............1369

Discovery Park, Safford, AZ............43

Discovery World - The James Lovell Museum of Science, Economics and Technology, Milwaukee, WI 1610

Dittrick Museum of Medical History, Cleveland, OH 1154

Dixie Gun Works' Old Car Museum, Union City, TN............1384

Dr. Howe-Waffle House and Medical Museum, Santa Ana, CA............177

Dr. John Harris Dental Museum, Bainbridge, OH............1141

Dr. Samuel D. Harris National Museum of Dentistry, Baltimore, MD 631

Dr. William Robinson Plantation, Clark, NJ............901

Doctors' House Museum, Glendale, CA 100

Dodge County Historical Society Museum, Beaver Dam, WI 1591

Don F. Pratt Memorial Museum, Fort Campbell, KY............568

Door County Historical Museum, Sturgeon Bay, WI............1623

Dorothy G. Page Museum, Wasilla, AK 29

Douglas County Historical Society, Superior, WI............1624

Douglas County Museum Complex, Armour, SD............1344

Douglas County Museum of History and Natural History, Roseburg, OR............1234

Douglass Historical Museum, Douglass, KS............537

Downing Planetarium, Fresno, CA............96

Drum Barracks Civil War Museum, Wilmington, CA............198

Drummond Island Historical Museum, Drummond Island, MI............739

Dubois Museum, Dubois, WY............1632

Duncan Cottage Museum, Metlakatla, AK......27

Dunn County Historical Society, Menomonie, WI............1609

DuPage County Historical Museum, Wheaton, IL............465

Durham Historic Association Museum, Durham, NH 886

EAA AirVenture Museum, Oshkosh, WI....1616

Earth & Mineral Sciences Museum and Art Gallery, University Park, PA 1303

East Hampton Town Marine Museum, Amagansett, NY............957

East Hillsborough Historical Society, Inc., Plant City, FL............337

East Jordan Portside Art & Historical Museum, East Jordan, MI............739

East Tennessee Historical Society, Knoxville, TN............1369

Eastern Arizona Museum and Historical Society of Graham County Inc., Pima, AZ............42

Eastern California Museum, Independence, CA............104

Edgar County Historical Museum, Paris, IL............449

Edison & Ford Winter Estates, Fort Myers, FL............308

Edison Museum, Beaumont, TX............1394

Edison National Historic Site, West Orange, NJ............930

Edmonds South Snohomish County Historical Society, Inc., Edmonds, WA .1553

Edward H. White II Memorial Museum, Brooks Air Force Base, TX 1397

1859 Jail, Marshal's Home & Museum, Independence, MO............817

82nd Airborne Division War Memorial Museum, Fort Bragg, NC............1101

El Dorado County Historical Museum, Placerville, CA............142

El Pueblo History Museum, Pueblo, CO......230

Eli Whitney Museum, Inc., Hamden, CT......244

Elkhart County Historical Museum, Bristol, IN............471

Elkhorn Slough National Estuarine Research, Wastsonville, CA............196

Ella Sharp Museum, Jackson, MI............748

Ellis County Historical Society, Hays, KS...543

Ellis County Museum, Inc., Waxahachie, TX............1460

Elmhurst Historical Museum, Elmhurst, IL............433

Empire State Aerosciences Museum, Glenville, NY............995

Epcot at Walt Disney World Resort, Lake Buena Vista, FL............319

Erie Maritime Museum, Homeport U.S. Brig Niagara, Erie, PA 1252

Erie Planetarium, Erie, PA............1253

Essley-Noble Museum: Mercer County Historical Society, Aledo, IL............410

The Esther Thomas Atkinson Museum, Hampden-Sydney, VA............1509

Eustis Historical Museum & Preservation Society, Inc., Eustis, FL 306

Everglades National Park, Homestead, FL...313

Evergreen Aviation Museum, McMinnville, OR............1228

The Exchange Hotel Civil War Museum, Gordonsville, VA............1509

Explorit Science Center, Davis, CA 89

Explorium of Lexington, Lexington, KY 572

FPL Energy Encounter, Jensen Beach, FL...316

Fabyan Villa Museum, Geneva, IL............437

Fairbanks House, Dedham, MA............679

Fairbanks Museum and Planetarium, Saint Johnsbury, VT 1486

Fairport Historical Museum, Fairport, NY...989

Falmouth Historical Society, Falmouth, MA............682

Family Museum, Bettendorf, IA............505

Farm and Ranch Museum, Gering, NE........861

The Farmers' Museum, Inc., Cooperstown, NY............980

FASNY Museum of Fire Fighting, Hudson, NY............1000

Faulkner County Museum, Conway, AR........56

Fayette County Helpers Club & Historical Society, West Union, IA............530

Feet First: The Scholl Story, Rosalind Franklin University, North Chicago, IL...448

The Finley House, Wayne, PA............1306

Finney County Kansas Historical Society, Inc., Garden City, KS............541

Fire Museum of Memphis, Memphis, TN..1373

Fire Museum of Texas, Beaumont, TX 1394

The Firehouse Museum, Ellicott City, MD............643

Firehouse Museum, San Diego, CA 156

Fireman's Hall Museum, Philadelphia, PA.1279

1st Cavalry Division Museum, Fort Hood, TX............1414

First Missouri State Capitol-State Historic Site, Saint Charles, MO 830

Fitchburg Historical Society, Fitchburg, MA............683

Flandrau Science Center and Planetarium, Tucson, AZ............49

Florence Price Pioneer Museum, Florence, CO............216

Florida Agricultural Museum, Palm Coast, FL............334

Florida Air Museum At Sun'n Fun, Lakeland, FL............321

Floyd County Historical Museum, Charles City, IA............510

Flying Heritage Collection, Arlington, WA............1547

Folsom History Museum, Folsom, CA............95

Ford County Historical Society, Paxton, IL............450

Forest History Center, Grand Rapids, MN...777

Forest Park Museum and Arboretum, Perry, IA............527

Fort Abercrombie State Historic Site, Abercrombie, ND 1127

Fort Bend Museum Association, Richmond, TX............1445

Fort Benton Museum of the Upper Missouri, Fort Benton, MT............846

Fort Bliss Museum, Fort Bliss, TX 1413

Fort Boonesborough Museum, Richmond, KY............583

Fort Bowie National Historic Site, Bowie, AZ............30

Fort Bridger State Museum, Fort Bridger, WY............1632

Fort Clatsop National Memorial, Astoria, OR............1218

Fort Collins Museum, Fort Collins, CO.......217

Fort Columbia Interpretive Center, Chinook, WA............1551

Fort Concho National Historic Landmark, San Angelo, TX............1447

Fort Crawford Museum, Prairie du Chien, WI............1618

Fort Croghan Museum, Burnet, TX............1398

Fort Davidson State Historic Site, Pilot Knob, MO............828

Fort Delaware Society, Delaware City, DE............268

Fort Dix Museum, Fort Dix, NJ............904

Fort Dodge & Frontier Village, Fort Dodge, IA............518

Fort Douglas Military Museum, Fort Douglas, UT............1465

Fort Fetterman State Historic Site, Douglas, WY............1631

Fort Fisher State Historic Site, Kure Beach, NC............1108

Fort Frederick State Park, Big Pool, MD...637

Fort Gibson Historic Site, Fort Gibson, OK............1200

Fort Harker Museum Complex, Kanopolis, KS............546

Fort Hartsuff State Historical Park, Burwell, NE............858

Fort Hays State Historic Site, Hays, KS 543

Fort Hill (The John C. Calhoun House), Clemson, SC............1328

Fort Jones Museum, Fort Jones, CA 96

Fort Kearney Museum, Kearney, NE............863

Fort Knox State Historic Site, Prospect, ME............620

Fort Laramie National Historic Site, Fort Laramie, WY............1633

Fort Larned National Historic Site, Larned, KS............547

Fort Laurens State Memorial, Bolivar, OH............1143

Fort Ligonier Association, Ligonier, PA.....1269

Fort MacArthur Museum, San Pedro, CA....176

Fort Macon State Park, Atlantic Beach, NC............1091

Fort Matanzas National Monument, Saint Augustine, FL............339

Fort McHenry National Monument and Historic Shrine, Baltimore, MD.............632

Fort McKavett State Historical Site, Fort McKavett, TX............1415

Fort Mifflin, Philadelphia, PA............1279

Fort Morgan Museum, Gulf Shores, AL 10

Fort Nisqually Living History Museum, Tacoma, WA............1573

Fort Ontario State Historic Site, Oswego, NY............1048

Fort Phil Kearny, Banner, WY 1628

Fort Pike State Historic Site, New
   Orleans, LA 595

Fort Point National Historic Site, San
   Francisco, CA 165

Fort Polk Museum Activity, Fort Polk,
   LA 588

Fort Pulaski National Monument,
   Savannah, GA 385

Fort Raleigh National Historic Site,
   Manteo, NC 1110

Fort Recovery Museum, Fort Recovery,
   OH 1164

Fort Sam Houston Museum, Fort Sam
   Houston, TX 1415

Fort Sill National Historic Landmark,
   Fort Sill, OK 1201

Fort Sisseton State Historic Park, Lake
   City, SD 1350

Fort Smith Museum of History, Fort
   Smith, AR 58

Fort Stanwix National Monument, Rome,
   NY 1061

Fort Sumter National Monument,
   Sullivan's Island, SC 1342

Fort Tejon State Historic Park, Lebec,
   CA 108

Fort Ticonderoga, Ticonderoga, NY 1078

Fort Union National Monument, Watrous,
   NM 954

Fort Union Trading Post National
   Historic Site, Williston, ND 1138

Fort Walla Walla Museum, Walla Walla,
   WA 1576

Fort Ward Museum and Historic Site,
   Alexandria, VA 1492

Fort Washington Park, Fort Washington,
   MD 643

Fort Winnebago Surgeons Quarters,
   Portage, WI 1618

Fort Worth Museum of Science and
   History, Fort Worth, TX 1417

Fossil Country Museum, Kemmerer, WY .. 1635

4th Infantry Division Museum, Fort
   Hood, TX 1415

Fox Island Historical Society, Fox Island,
   WA 1554

Frank H. Woods Telephone Museum,
   Lincoln, NE 865

Frankfort Area Historical Museum, West
   Frankfort, IL 464

Franklin County Historical & Museum
   Society & House of History, Malone,
   NY 1012

Franklin County Historical Museum,
   Pasco, WA 1561

The Franklin Institute, Philadelphia, PA 1280

Franklin Mineral Museum, Franklin, NJ 904

Fraternal Order of Alaska State Troopers
   Museum, Anchorage, AK 22

The Frazier International History
   Museum, Louisville, KY 576

Freeborn County Museum and Historical
   Village, Albert Lea, MN 767

Freestone County Historical Museum,
   Fairfield, TX 1413

Fremont County Pioneer Museum,
   Lander, WY 1635

Fresno Metropolitan Museum, Fresno,
   CA 97

Friends of Firemen's Museum, New
   Bern, NC 1112

Friendship Firehouse, Alexandria, VA 1492

Frontier Army Museum, Fort
   Leavenworth, KS 539

Frontier Culture Museum, Staunton, VA ... 1537

Frontier Gateway Museum, Glendive,
   MT 847

Frontier Historical Society and Museum,
   Glenwood Springs, CO 219

Frontier Museum, Williston, ND 1138

Frontiers of Flight Museum, Dallas, TX 1406

The Fullerton Arboretum, Fullerton, CA 98

Furnas-Gosper Historical Society &
   Museum, Arapahoe, NE 856

Gadsden Museum, Mesilla, NM 943

Gadsden Museum of Art, Gadsden, AL 10

Gage County Historical Society and
   Museum, Beatrice, NE 857

Galena-Jo Daviess County Historical
   Society & Museum, Galena, IL 436

Garden Grove Historical Society, Garden
   Grove, CA 99

Gardner House Museum, Albion, MI 723

Garibaldi and Meucci Museum, Staten
   Island, NY 1072

Garrett County Historical Museum,
   Oakland, MD 649

Gaston County Museum of Art and
   History, Dallas, NC 1097

Gateway to Science, Bismarck, ND 1128

General Adam Stephen House,
   Martinsburg, WV 1584

General Douglas MacArthur Memorial,
   Norfolk, VA 1521

General Lew Wallace Study & Museum,
   Crawfordsville, IN 473

General Patton Memorial Museum,
   Chiriaco Summit, CA 84

Geographical Center Historical Museum,
   Rugby, ND 1136

George Key Ranch, Placentia, CA 142

Georgetown Energy Museum,
   Georgetown, CO 218

Georgia Southern University Museum,
   Statesboro, GA 387

Georgia Veterans Memorial Museum,
   Cordele, GA 369

Gerald E. Eddy Discovery Center,
   Chelsea, MI 732

Gettysburg National Military Park,
   Gettysburg, PA 1255

Gibbs Museum of Pioneer and Dakotah
   Life, Falcon Heights, MN 775

Gig Harbor Peninsula Historical Society,
   Gig Harbor, WA 1555

Gila County Historical Museum, Globe,
   AZ 35

Gilcrease Museum, Tulsa, OK 1215

Gillespie County Historical Society,
   Fredericksburg, TX 1419

Gilman Museum, Hellertown, PA 1260

Gilpin History Museum, Central City, CO ... 205

Glendower State Memorial, Lebanon, OH . 1171

Glenn H. Curtiss Museum,
   Hammondsport, NY 997

Glenn L. Martin Maryland Aviation
   Museum, Baltimore, MD 632

Golden Gate National Recreation Area,
   San Francisco, CA 165

Golden Gate Railroad Museum, San
   Francisco, CA 166

Golden Valley County Museum, Beach,
   ND 1127

Goldendale Observatory, Goldendale, WA . 1555

Goodhue County Historical Society, Red
   Wing, MN 787

Goodyear World of Rubber Museum,
   Akron, OH 1139

Gorgas House, Tuscaloosa, AL 19

Gouverneur Historical Association,
   Gouverneur, NY 995

The Grand River Historical Society &
   Museum, Chillicothe, MO 813

Grand Teton National Park, Colter Bay
   Indian Arts Museum, Colter Bay
   Village, WY 1631

Grant County Historical Society, Elbow
   Lake, MN 774

Grant County Museum, Medford, OK 1205

Grant County Museum & Historic
   Society, Hyannis, NE 863

Granville County Historical Society
   Museum, Oxford, NC 1114

Gravette Historical Museum, Gravette,
   AR 59

Great Basin Historical Society &
   Museum, Delta, UT 1464

Great Lakes Museum of Military History,
   Michigan City, IN 490

Great Lakes Science Center, Cleveland,
   OH 1154

Great Lakes Shipwreck Museum,
   Paradise, MI 760

Great Plains Transportation Museum,
   Wichita, KS 561

Greater Hazleton Historical Society,
   Hazleton, PA 1260

Greater Loveland Historical Society
   Museum, Loveland, OH 1173

Greene County Historical Museum,
   Waynesburg, PA 1306

Greensboro Historical Museum, Inc.,
   Greensboro, NC 1103

Gregg County Historical Museum,
   Longview, TX 1434

Greybull Museum, Greybull, WY 1634

Grissom Air Museum, Peru, IN 496

Grout Museum District: Grout Museum
   of History and Science, Bluedorn
   Science Imaginarium, Rensselaer
   Russell House Museum, Snowden
   House, Waterloo, IA 529

Guadalupe Mountains National Park, Salt
   Flat, TX 1447

Guernsey County Museum, Cambridge,
   OH 1144

Guilford Courthouse National Military
   Park, Greensboro, NC 1104

Gulf Coast Exploreum Science Center,
   Mobile, AL 13

Gulf Islands National Seashore, Gulf
   Breeze, FL 312

Gulfcoast Wonder and Imagination Zone,
   dba G.WIZ, Sarasota, FL 344

Gwinnett Historical Society,
   Lawrenceville, GA 376

Gwinnett History Museum,
   Lawrenceville, GA 376

H.G. Albee Memorial Museum,
   Estherville, IA 517

Hadley Farm Museum, Hadley, MA 685

The Haggin Museum, Stockton, CA 189

Halifax Historical Museum, Daytona
   Beach, FL 303

Hall of Flame Museum of Firefighting,
   Phoenix, AZ 40

Hall of Health, Berkeley, CA 75

Hamilton Township Historical Society -
   John Abbott II House, Hamilton, NJ 906

Hammel Museum, Socorro, NM 951

Hammond Museum of Bells, Eureka
   Springs, AR 57

Hampton County Historical Museum,
   Hampton, SC 1334

Hancock Historical Society, Hancock,
   NH 888

Harbor Defense Museum, Brooklyn, NY 969

Hardin County Historical Museums, Inc.,
   Kenton, OH 1170

Harney County Historical Museum,
   Burns, OR 1221

Harper City Historical Society, Harper,
   KS 543

Harpers Ferry Center, Harpers Ferry, WV . 1582

Harrison County Historical Museum,
   Marshall, TX 1436

Harvey Cushing/John Hay Whitney
   Medical Library, New Haven, CT 253

Haskell County Historical Society,
   Sublette, KS 558

Hastings Museum, Hastings, NE 863

Hatfield Marine Science Center, Oregon
   State University, Newport, OR 1228

Hatton-Eielson Museum & Historical
   Association, Hatton, ND 1132

Tools and Equipment for Science and Technology–Continued

Haverford Township Historical Society, Havertown, PA............................1260
Hawaii's Plantation Village, Waipahu, HI....402
Hayward Area Historical Society, Hayward, CA 102
Headwaters Heritage Museum, Three Forks, MT 854
Heard Natural Science Museum and Wildlife Sanctuary, Inc., McKinney, TX 1437
Heart of West Texas Museum, Colorado City, TX 1401
Hearthstone Historic House Museum, Appleton, WI 1589
Heisey Museum, Clinton County Historical Society, Lock Haven, PA 1269
Helvetia Museum, Helvetia, WV................1582
Henager "Memories and Nostalgia" Museum, Buckskin, IN 471
The Henry Ford, Dearborn, MI 733
Henry Ford Estate-Fair Lane, Dearborn, MI 734
Heritage Center Museum, Berryville, AR 55
Heritage Complex Farm Equipment Museum and Learning Center, Tulare, CA 193
Heritage House Museum of Montgomery County, Mount Ida, AR 64
Heritage House of Orange County Association Inc., Orange, TX 1441
The Heritage Museum at Falfurrias, Inc., Falfurrias, TX 1413
Heritage Museum Foundation of Tate County, Inc., Senatobia, MS 808
Heritage Museums & Gardens, Sandwich, MA 707
Heritage Square Museum, Ontario, NY 1047
Heritage Village, Largo, FL 321
Heritage Village, Mountain Lake, MN.........785
Herreshoff Marine Museum/America's Cup Hall of Fame, Bristol, RI 1311
Hesston Steam Museum, LaPorte, IN 487
Higgins Armory Museum, Worcester, MA...721
High Desert Museum, Bend, OR................1220
High Plains Museum, Goodland, KS............542
Highland Park Historical Society, Highland Park, IL...............................439
Highlands Museum & Discovery Center, Ashland, KY 564
Hildene, The Lincoln Family Home, Manchester, VT 1481
Hill Aerospace Museum, Hill Air Force Base, UT 1466
Hiller Aviation Institute, San Carlos, CA 155
Historic Arkansas Museum, Little Rock, AR 62
Historic Bethabara Park, Winston-Salem, NC 1125
Historic Bowens Mills & Pioneer Park, Middleville, MI 754
Historic Charlton Park Village and Museum, Hastings, MI 745
Historic Crab Orchard Museum & Pioneer Park, Inc., Tazewell, VA 1541
Historic Fort Snelling, Saint Paul, MN 790
Historic General Dodge House, Council Bluffs, IA 512
Historic Lincoln, Lincoln, NM 941
Historic New Harmony, New Harmony, IN 494
The Historic New Orleans Collection, New Orleans, LA 595
Historic Pensacola Village, Pensacola, FL ...335
Historic Preservation Association of Bourbon County, Inc., Fort Scott, KS 540
Historic Renville Preservation Commission, Renville, MN 787
Historic Shepherdstown Museum, Shepherdstown, WV 1586

Historic Speedwell, Morristown, NJ.............913
Historical and Genealogical Society of Indiana County, Indiana, PA 1262
Historical Center for Southeast New Mexico, Roswell, NM 946
Historical Electronics Museum, Linthicum, MD 648
Historical Museum at Fort Missoula, Missoula, MT 851
Historical Museum of Bay County, Bay City, MI 727
Historical Society of Berks County, Reading, PA 1296
Historical Society of Carroll County, Westminster, MD 656
Historical Society of Cheshire County, Keene, NH 890
Historical Society of Columbia County, Saint Helens, OR 1234
Historical Society of Greenfield, Greenfield, MA 685
Historical Society of Middletown and the Wallkill Precinct, Inc., Middletown, NY 1014
Historical Society of Millersburg & Upper Paxton Township Museum, Millersburg, PA 1272
Historical Society of Oak Park & River Forest, Oak Park, IL 448
Historical Society of Old Newbury, Cushing House Museum, Newburyport, MA 698
Historical Society of Quaker Hill & Pawling, Pawling, NY 1051
Historical Society of Santuit and Cotuit, Cotuit, MA 677
Historical Society of the Phoenixville Area, Phoenixville, PA 1290
Historical Society of the Town of Clarence, Clarence, NY 978
Historical Society Porter County Old Jail Museum, Valparaiso, IN 502
The History Center, Cedar Rapids, IA 509
History Museum of Western Virginia, Roanoke, VA 1535
History of Medicine Collections, Durham, NC 1098
History of Pharmacy Museum, Tucson, AZ 49
The History Place, Morehead City, NC 1111
History San Jose, San Jose, CA 171
Hixon House, La Crosse, WI......................1603
Homeopathy Works, Berkeley Springs, WV 1580
Honolulu Police Department Law Enforcement Museum, Honolulu, HI.......396
Hoo-Hoo International Forestry Museum, Gurdon, AR..59
Horseshoe Bend National Military Park, Daviston, AL 7
Hot Springs County Museum and Cultural Center, Thermopolis, WY 1639
Hot Springs National Park Visitor Center, Hot Springs, AR 60
Houghton County Historical Museum Society, Lake Linden, MI....................749
Houston Fire Museum, Houston, TX 1427
Houston Museum of Natural Science, Houston, TX 1427
Howard County Historical Society, Ellicott City, MD 643
Howard Steamboat Museum and Mansion, Jeffersonville, IN 486
Howard W. Cannon Aviation Museum, Henderson, NV 878
Hugh Mercer Apothecary Shop, Fredericksburg, VA 1506
Hui No'eau Visual Arts Center, Makawao, Maui, HI 401
Hull Lifesaving Museum Inc., the Museum of Boston Harbor Heritage, Hull, MA 687
Hunt-Morgan House, Lexington, KY 573

Hurricane Valley Heritage Park Museum, Hurricane, UT...1466
Hurst Ranch Historical Foundation, West Covina, CA 197
ICR Museum of Creation & Earth History, Santee, CA 185
Idaho Museum of Mining and Geology, Boise, ID 404
Idaho State Historical Museum, Boise, ID...404
The Imaginarium Science Discovery Center, Anchorage, AK 22
Imagine It! The Children's Museum of Atlanta, Atlanta, GA 361
Impression 5 Science Center, Lansing, MI...750
Independence Historical Museum, Independence, KS 545
Independence Seaport Museum, Philadelphia, PA 1281
Indiana Medical History Museum, Indianapolis, IN 484
Indiana War Memorials, Indianapolis, IN 484
Insights-El Paso Science Center, Inc., El Paso, TX 1412
Intel Museum, Santa Clara, CA....................181
Interlaken Historical Society, Interlaken, NY 1002
International Museum of Surgical Science, Chicago, IL 422
The International Printing Museum, Carson, CA 82
Intrepid Sea-Air-Space Museum, New York, NY 1028
Iolani Palace, Honolulu, HI 396
Iosco County Historical Museum, East Tawas, MI 740
Iron & Steel Museum of Alabama, Tannehill Ironworks Historical State Park, McCalla, AL 13
Islesboro Historical Society, Islesboro, ME 612
Issaquah History Museum, Issaquah, WA ..1557
Itasca County Historical Society, Grand Rapids, MN 777

J.E. Reeves Home & Museum, Dover, OH 1163
JFK Special Warfare Museum, Fort Bragg, NC 1101
J.I. Holcomb Observatory and Planetarium, Indianapolis, IN 485
J.J. Jackson Memorial Museum, Weaverville, CA 197
J.M. Davis Arms & Historical Museum, Claremore, OK 1198
Jackson County Historical Museum, Lakefield, MN 778
Jacksonville Fire Museum, Jacksonville, FL 314
Jail Museum, Neligh, NE 869
Jamestown Settlement, Yorktown Victory Center, The Jamestown-Yorktown Foundation, Williamsburg, VA 1545
Jean P. Haydon Museum, Pago Pago, AS ..1640
Jefferson Barracks Historic Site, Saint Louis, MO 833
The Jefferson County Historical Assoc., Steubenville, OH 1186
Jefferson County Historical Society and Farnsworth TV Pioneer Museum, Rigby, ID 409
Jefferson County Historical Society Museum, Port Townsend, WA 1562
Jefferson Planetarium, Richmond, VA 1530
Jefferson Telephone Museum, Jefferson, IA 521
Jerome State Historic Park, Jerome, AZ 36
Jewell County Historical Museum, Mankato, KS 552
Jim Gatchell Memorial Museum, Buffalo, WY 1629

Joachim Regional Museum, Dickinson, ND 1130
John E. Conner Museum, Kingsville, TX ..1432
John Gorrie Museum State Park, Apalachicola, FL 295
John P. McGovern Museum of Health & Medical Science, Houston, TX 1427
John Paul Jones House Museum, Portsmouth, NH 894
The John Q. Adams Center for the History of Otolaryngology - Head and Neck Surgery, Alexandria, VA 1493
Johnson County Museums, Shawnee, KS ..558
Jonesborough-Washington County History Museum, Jonesborough, TN 1368
Joseph A. Tallman Museum, Cherokee, IA 510
Joseph Priestley House, Northumberland, PA 1274
Julia A. Purnell Museum, Snow Hill, MD ...654
Junction City Historical Society, Junction City, OR 1226
Juneau-Douglas City Museum, Juneau, AK 26
Juniata County Historical Society, Mifflintown, PA 1271
The Junior Museum of Bay County, Panama City, FL 334
Justin Smith Morrill Homestead, Strafford, VT 1488

Kalamazoo Aviation History Museum, Kalamazoo, MI 748
Kalkaska County Historical Museum, Kalkaska, MI 749
Kanabec History Center, Mora, MN 784
Kandiyohi County Historical Society, Willmar, MN 796
Kansas Aviation Museum, Wichita, KS 562
Kansas Cosmosphere and Space Center, Hutchinson, KS 545
Kate Shelley Railroad Museum, Boone, IA 506
The Kearny Cottage, Perth Amboy, NJ 921
Kellogg's Cereal City USA, Battle Creek, MI 727
Kennesaw Mountain National Battlefield Park, Kennesaw, GA 374
Kenosha County Historical Society and Museum, Inc., Kenosha, WI 1602
Kenosha Military Museum, Pleasant Prairie, WI 1617
Kentucky Coal Mining Museum, Benham, KY 565
Kentucky Historical Society, Frankfort, KY 569
Kentucky Military History Museum, Frankfort, KY 569
Kentucky Railway Museum, Inc., New Haven, KY 580
Kerbyville Museum, Kerby, OR 1227
Kern County Museum, Bakersfield, CA 73
Kewaunee County Historical Museum, Kewaunee, WI 1602
Key West Lighthouse Museum, Key West, FL 318
Kimball House Museum, Battle Creek, MI 727
Kimble County Historical Museum, Junction, TX 1431
King Saddlery Museum, Sheridan, WY 1638
Kingman Tavern Historical Museum, Cummington, MA 678
Kings Mountain National Military Park, Blacksburg, SC 1322
Kinney Pioneer Museum and Historical Society of North Iowa, Clear Lake, IA ...510
Kitsap County Historical Society Museum, Bremerton, WA 1549
Kitt Peak National Observatory, Tucson, AZ 49
Kittery Historical & Naval Museum, Kittery, ME 613

Kiwanis Van Slyke Museum Foundation Inc., Caldwell, ID 404
Klamath County Museum, Klamath Falls, OR 1227
Kline Creek Farm, Winfield, IL 466
Klyne Esopus Museum, Ulster Park, NY ...1079
Knight Museum, Alliance, NE 855
Knox County Museum, Knoxville, IL 441
Kodiak Military History Museum, Kodiak, AK 27
Kohl Children's Museum of Greater Chicago, Glenview, IL 438
Koreshan State Historic Site, Estero, FL 306
Lafayette Natural History Museum and Planetarium, Lafayette, LA 589
Lagrange County Historical Society, Inc., Lagrange, IN 488
LaGrange Plantation, Cambridge, MD 639
The Lake Champlain Maritime Museum, Vergennes, VT 1488
Lake County Discovery Museum, Wauconda, IL 463
Lake County Historical Society, Two Harbors, MN 794
Lake of the Woods County Museum, Baudette, MN 768
Lake Shore Railway Museum, North East, PA 1274
Lake Superior Maritime Visitors Center, Duluth, MN 773
Lancaster County Historical Society, Lancaster, PA 1266
Lane County Historical Society & Museum, Eugene, OR 1223
Lane Place, Crawfordsville, IN 473
Langlade County Historical Society Museum, Antigo, WI 1589
Lanterman House, La Canada Flintridge, CA 105
Las Cabezas de San Juan Nature Reserve (El Faro), Fajardo, PR 1641
The Laurel Museum, Laurel, MD 648
Laurence C. Jones Museum, Piney Woods, MS 807
Lawrence History Center: Immigrant City Archives & Museum, Lawrence, MA 689
Layton P. Ott Planetarium, Ogden, UT 1468
Le Sault de Sainte Marie Historical Sites, Inc., Sault Ste. Marie, MI 764
Leander J. McCormick Observatory, Charlottesville, VA 1499
Lehigh County Historical Society, Allentown, PA 1239
Lesueur County Historical Museum-Chapter 1, Elysian, MN 774
Levine Museum of the New South, Charlotte, NC 1095
Lewes Historical Society, Lewes, DE 271
Lewis & Clark Boat House and Nature Center, Saint Charles, MO 830
Lewis and Clark Visitor Center, Yankton, SD 1360
Lewis County Historical Museum, Chehalis, WA 1550
Lexington History Museum, Lexington, KY 573
Liberty County Museum, Chester, MT 844
Liberty Science Center, Jersey City, NJ 909
Licking County Historical Society, Newark, OH 1178
Life on the Ohio River History Museum, Vevay, IN 502
Lightner Museum, Saint Augustine, FL 339
Limberlost State Historic Site, Geneva, IN 479
Lincoln County Historical Museum, Davenport, WA 1552
Lincoln County Historical Society, Lincoln, KS 549
Lincoln County Historical Society, North Platte, NE 869
Lincoln Memorial Shrine, Redlands, CA 147

The Lincoln Museum, Fort Wayne, IN 478
Lincoln Park Historical Museum, Lincoln Park, MI 751
Lincoln's New Salem State Historic Site, Petersburg, IL 451
Linn County Historical Museum and Moyer House, Brownsville, OR 1220
Lisbon Historical Society, Lisbon, OH 1172
The Lithuanian Museum, Chicago, IL 423
Livingston County Historical Society Museum, Geneseo, NY 993
The Log House Museum of the Historical Society of Columbiana-Fairfield Township, Columbiana, OH 1157
Logan County Historical Society Museum, Bellefontaine, OH 1142
Logan County Museum, Paris, AR 65
Lompoc Valley Historical Society, Inc., Lompoc, CA 110
Lone Star Flight Museum/Texas Aviation Hall of Fame, Galveston, TX 1421
Long Beach Fire Museum, Long Beach, CA 111
Long Island Museum of Science and Technology, Garden City, NY 993
Longhorn Museum, Pleasanton, TX 1444
Longmont Museum, Longmont, CO 227
Lorenzo State Historic Site, Cazenovia, NY 976
Los Alamos Historical Museum, Los Alamos, NM 942
Los Nogales Museum, Seguin, TX 1452
Louisiana Art & Science Museum - Irene W. Pennington Planetarium, Baton Rouge, LA 586
Louisiana State Exhibit Museum, Shreveport, LA 600
Louisiana State Oil & Gas Museum, Oil City, LA 599
Louisiana Tech Museum, Ruston, LA 600
Louisiana's Old State Capitol, Political History Museum, Baton Rouge, LA 587
Louisville Science Center, Louisville, KY ...577
Lowell Area Historical Museum, Lowell, MI 751
Lowell Observatory, Flagstaff, AZ 33
Lowndes County Historical Society and Museum, Valdosta, GA 389
Lucretia Vaile Museum, Palmer Lake, CO 229
Lynden Pioneer Museum, Lynden, WA 1559
Lynn Museum & Historical Society, Lynn, MA 692
Lyon County Historical Society and Museum, Emporia, KS 538
Lyon County Historical Society Museum, Marshall, MN 780

MIT Museum, Cambridge, MA 674
Mabee Farm Historic Site, Rotterdam Junction, NY 1062
Macaulay Museum of Dental History, Charleston, SC 1326
Mackinac Island State Park Commission-Mackinac State Historic Parks, Mackinaw City, MI 752
Madera County Museum, Madera, CA 123
Madison County Historical Society, Winterset, IA 531
Madison Historical Society, Madison, CT ...247
The Magic Lantern Castle Museum, San Antonio, TX 1448
Mahaffie Stagecoach Stop and Farm, Olathe, KS 554
Maine Historical Society, Portland, ME 619
Maine Maritime Museum, Bath, ME 606
Maine State Museum, Augusta, ME 604
Maitland Historical Museums, Maitland, FL 322
Manassas National Battlefield Park, Manassas, VA 1516
Manchester Historic Association Millyard Museum, Manchester, NH 891

Tools and Equipment for Science and Technology–Continued

Manitowoc County Historical Society, Manitowoc, WI...........1607

Mansfield State Historic Site - Civil War Battlefield, Mansfield, LA...........591

Marathon County Historical Society, Wausau, WI...........1626

Marblehead Museum & Historical Society, Marblehead, MA...........693

Marcellus Historical Society, Marcellus, NY...........1013

March Field Air Museum, Riverside, CA....149

Marian Koshland Science Museum, Washington, DC...........283

Marias Museum of History and Art, Shelby, MT...........853

Marietta Museum of History, Marietta, GA...........379

Marin Museum of the American Indian, Novato, CA...........131

Marine Science Institute, Redwood City, CA...........147

The Mariners' Museum, Newport News, VA...........1519

Marinette County Historical Museum, Marinette, WI...........1607

Marion County Historical Society, Salem, OR...........1236

Marion Public Library Museum, Marion, IN...........490

Maritime & Seafood Industry Museum, Biloxi, MS...........798

Maritime and Yachting Museum of the Treasure Coast, Stuart, FL...........346

The Maritime Aquarium, Norwalk, CT........257

Maritime Museum of Monterey, Monterey, CA...........127

Maritime Museum of San Diego, San Diego, CA...........157

Marquette County History Museum, Marquette, MI...........753

Marshall Gold Discovery State Historic Park, Coloma, CA...........86

Marvin Samson Center for History of Pharmacy/USP Museum, Philadelphia, PA...........1283

Mary McLeod Bethune Council House National Historic Site, Washington, DC...........283

Mary Vagle Museum & Nature Center, Fontana, CA...........95

Maryland Science Center, Baltimore, MD...634

Mazomanie Historical Society, Mazomanie, WI...........1608

McCallum Museum, Sibley, IA...........527

McConaghy House, Hayward, CA...........102

McCone County Museum, Circle, MT........844

McConnell Mansion, Moscow, ID...........407

McDowell House Museum, Danville, KY...567

McFarland Historical Society, McFarland, WI...........1609

McFarland State Historic Park, Florence, AZ...........34

McLarty Treasure Museum, Vero Beach, FL...........352

Meade County Historical Society Museum, Meade, KS...........552

Medina County Historical Society, The John Smart House, Medina, OH...........1175

Meeker County Historical Society Museum & G.A.R. Hall, Litchfield, MN...........779

Mem-Erie Historical Museum, Erie, KS......539

The Memorial Day Museum, Waterloo, NY...........1083

The Menczer Museum of Medicine & Dentistry, Hartford, CT...........245

Mennonite Heritage Museum, Goessel, KS...........542

Merced County Courthouse Museum, Merced, CA...........125

Mercer County Historical Society, Mercer, PA...........1271

Merrill Historical Museum, Merrill, WI.....1609

Merrillville Community Planetarium, Merrillville, IN...........490

Mesa Historical Museum, Mesa, AZ...........37

The Metropolitan Museum of Art, New York, NY...........1030

Meux Home Museum, Fresno, CA...........98

Miami Museum of Science & Planetarium, Miami, FL...........325

Michigan Historical Museum, Michigan Historical Center, Lansing, MI...........750

Mid-America Air Museum, Liberal, KS.......549

Mid-America Science Museum, Hot Springs, AR...........60

Mid-America Windmill Museum, Kendallville, IN...........486

Mid Atlantic Air Museum, Reading, PA...1296

Mid-Hudson Children's Museum, Poughkeepsie, NY...........1055

Middlesex County Historical Society, Middletown, CT...........249

Midway Village & Museum Center, Rockford, IL...........455

Mighty Eighth Air Force Museum, Pooler, GA...........381

Milan Historical Museum, Inc., Milan, OH...........1176

Milford Museum, Milford, DE...........271

Military Museum of Southern New England, Danbury, CT...........238

Military Veterans Museum, Inc., Oshkosh, WI...........1616

Mill Race Historical Village, Northville, MI...........758

Milton Historical Museum, Milton, VT.....1482

Milton House Museum Historic Site, Milton, WI...........1610

Milton J. Rubenstein Museum of Science & Technology, Syracuse, NY...........1076

Milwaukee County Historical Society, Milwaukee, WI...........1611

Milwaukee Public Museum, Milwaukee, WI...........1612

Minnesota Air National Guard Historical Foundation, Inc., Saint Paul, MN...........790

Minnesota Pioneer Park Museum, Annandale, MN...........767

Minnesota Veterinary Historical Museum, Saint Paul, MN...........792

Minnilusa Pioneer Museum, Rapid City, SD...........1354

Minter Field Air Museum, Shafter, CA........186

Miracle of America Museum Inc., Polson, MT...........852

Mississippi Armed Forces Museum, Camp Shelby, MS...........799

Mitchell County Historical Museum, Osage, IA...........526

Mitchell Gallery of Flight, Milwaukee, WI...........1612

Mobile Medical Museum, Mobile, AL...........14

Moccasin Lake Nature Park, An Environmental & Energy Education Center, Clearwater, FL...........299

Monroe County Historical Association/Stroud Mansion, Stroudsburg, PA...........1302

Monroe County Historical Museum, Monroe, MI...........756

Monroe County Historical Society, Bloomington, IN...........469

Montana Historical Society, Helena, MT.....849

Montclair Historical Society, Montclair, NJ...........912

The Montgomery County Historical Society, Dayton, OH...........1161

The Montgomery County Historical Society, Inc., Rockville, MD...........651

Montrose County Historical Museum, Montrose, CO...........228

Montshire Museum of Science, Inc., Norwich, VT...........1483

Moody County Museum, Flandreau, SD....1347

Moores Creek National Battlefield, Currie, NC...........1097

Moravian Museum of Bethlehem, Inc., Bethlehem, PA...........1242

Morehead Planetarium and Science Center, Chapel Hill, NC...........1093

Morton Grove Historical Museum/Haupt-Yehl House, Morton Grove, IL...........446

Morton Museum of Cooke County, Gainesville, TX...........1420

Moses Lake Museum & Art Center, Moses Lake, WA...........1559

Mount Rushmore National Memorial, Keystone, SD...........1350

Mount Washington Museum and The Weather Discovery Center, North Conway, NH...........893

Mount Wilson Observatory & Museum, Atlanta, GA...........362

Mountain Gateway Museum, Old Fort, NC...........1113

Mountain Skies Astronomical Society & Science Center, Lake Arrowhead, CA.....107

Museum at Mountain Home - East Tennessee State University, Johnson City, TN...........1368

Museum of Alaska Transportation & Industry, Inc., Wasilla, AK...........29

Museum of American Glass at Wheaton Village, Millville, NJ...........911

Museum of Anthropology, University of Missouri, Columbia, MO...........813

Museum of Appalachia, Clinton, TN...........1363

Museum of Archaeology & Material Culture, Cedar Crest, NM...........938

Museum of Astrogeology, Meteor Crater, Winslow, AZ...........53

Museum of Aviation at Robins Air Force Base, GA, Warner Robins, GA...........390

Museum of Chicot County Arkansas, Lake Village, AR...........61

Museum of Church History and Art, Salt Lake City, UT...........1471

Museum of Connecticut History, Hartford, CT...........245

Museum of disAbility History, Williamsville, NY...........1086

Museum of Discovery: Arkansas Museum of Science and History, Little Rock, AR...........62

The Museum of Early Trades and Crafts, Madison, NJ...........910

The Museum of Flight, Seattle, WA...........1567

Museum of Funeral Customs, Springfield, IL...........459

Museum of History & Industry (MOHAI), Seattle, WA...........1567

Museum of Indian Culture, Allentown, PA...........1239

The Museum of Man in the Sea, Inc., Panama City Beach, FL...........335

Museum of Natural Science, Ogden, UT...1468

The Museum of Northwest Colorado, Craig, CO...........208

The Museum of Nursing History, Inc., Philadelphia, PA...........1283

Museum of Photographic Arts, San Diego, CA...........158

Museum of Robotics, Orinda, CA...........136

Museum of Science, Boston, MA...........667

Museum of Science and Industry, Tampa, FL...........349

Museum of Science and Industry, Chicago, IL...........425

Museum of Small Town Life, Dover, DE....270

Museum of South Texas History, Edinburg, TX...........1410

Museum of Southern History, Jacksonville, FL............315
Museum of Surveying, Lansing, MI............750
Museum of Texas Tech University, Lubbock, TX............1435
Museum of the American Philosophical Society, Philadelphia, PA............1283
Museum of the Big Bend, Alpine, TX.......1386
Museum of the Cape Fear Historical Complex, Fayetteville, NC............1101
Museum of the City of Lake Worth, Lake Worth, FL............320
The Museum of the Confederacy, Richmond, VA............1531
Museum of the Fur Trade, Chadron, NE......859
Museum of the High Plains, McCook, NE............868
Museum of the Llano Estacado, Plainview, TX............1443
Museum of the Soldier, Portland, IN 496
Museum of the Western Prairie, Altus, OK............1195
Museum of Vision, San Francisco, CA........167
Museum of Weapons and Early American History, Saint Augustine, FL............339
Museum of Wildlife, Science & Industry, Webster, SD............1359
Museum on Main: A History Museum for West Georgia, LaGrange, GA............375
Museum Village, Monroe, NY............1015
The Museums of Oglebay Institute - Mansion Museum & Glass Museum, Wheeling, WV............1588
Muskegon County Museum, Muskegon, MI............757
Mutter Museum, College of Physicians of Philadelphia, Philadelphia, PA 1283
Mystic Aquarium & Institute for Exploration, Mystic, CT............250

NASA Glenn Research Center's Visitor Center, Cleveland, OH 1155
Nantucket Historical Association, Nantucket, MA............696
Napoleonic Society of America, Inc., Clearwater, FL............300
NASA Kennedy Space Center, Merritt Island, FL............323
National Air and Space Museum, Washington, DC............283
National Atomic Museum, Albuquerque, NM............934
National Building Museum, Washington, DC............284
The National Civil War Museum, Harrisburg, PA............1258
National Civil War Naval Museum at Port Columbus, Columbus, GA............369
National Cowboy & Western Heritage Museum, Oklahoma City, OK............1208
National Cryptologic Museum, Fort Meade, MD............643
National Farm Toy Museum, Dyersville, IA............517
National Firearms Museum, Fairfax, VA...1504
The National Great Blacks in Wax Museum, Inc., Baltimore, MD............635
National Great Rivers Museum, East Alton, IL............431
National Inventors Hall of Fame, Akron, OH............1139
National Liberty Ship Memorial/S.S. Jeremiah O'Brien, San Francisco, CA.....168
National Museum of American Jewish History, Philadelphia, PA............1284
National Museum of American Jewish Military History, Washington, DC............286
National Museum of Civil War Medicine, Frederick, MD............644
National Museum of Health and Medicine, Washington, DC............286
National Museum of Industrial History, Bethlehem, PA............1243

National Museum of Roller Skating, Lincoln, NE............866
National Museum of the United States Air Force, Wright-Patterson Air Force Base, OH............1193
National New York Central Railroad Museum, Elkhart, IN............475
National Ornamental Metal Museum, Memphis, TN............1375
National Packard Museum, Warren, OH....1189
National Park Service Vicksburg National Military Park-Cairo Museum, Vicksburg, MS............809
National Plastics Center and Museum, Leominster, MA............689
National Route 66 Museum and Old Town Complex, Elk City, OK 1200
The National Science Center's Fort Discovery, Augusta, GA............366
National Soaring Museum, Elmira, NY.......988
National Warplane Museum, Horseheads, NY............999
The National Watch & Clock Museum, Columbia, PA............1247
National Wildlife Visitor Center, Patuxent Research Refuge, Laurel, MD 648
National World War I Museum at Liberty Memorial, Kansas City, MO............822
The National World War II Museum, New Orleans, LA............597
Native American Exhibit, National Kateri Shrine, Fonda, NY............991
Native American Museum, Terre Haute, IN............500
The Natural Science Center of Greensboro, Inc., Greensboro, NC........1104
Nauticus, The National Maritime Center, Norfolk, VA............1522
Naval Undersea Museum, Keyport, WA....1557
Naval War College Museum, Newport, RI............1314
Navarro County Historical Society, Pioneer Village, Corsicana, TX............1402
Navy UDT-SEAL Museum, Fort Pierce, FL............309
Nebraska Prairie Museum of the Phelps County Historical Society, Holdrege, NE............863
Nebraska State Historical Society's Museum of Nebraska History, Lincoln, NE............866
Neil Armstrong Air & Space Museum, Wapakoneta, OH............1189
Neligh Mills, Neligh, NE............869
Nevada State Fire Museum & Comstock Firemen's Museum, Virginia City, NV....882
New Almaden Quicksilver Mining Museum, San Jose, CA............172
New Britain Industrial Museum, New Britain, CT............251
New England Air Museum of the Connecticut Aeronautical Historical Association, Inc., Windsor Locks, CT.....267
New England Civil War Museum, Vernon, CT............263
New England Wireless & Steam Museum Inc., East Greenwich, RI............1311
The New Jersey Center for Life Science, Trenton, NJ............927
The New Jersey Museum of Agriculture, North Brunswick, NJ............917
New Jersey Naval Museum, Hackensack, NJ............905
New Jersey State Police Museum, West Trenton, NJ............930
New Mexico Museum of Space History, Alamogordo, NM............932
New Orleans Fire Dept. Museum & Educational Center, New Orleans, LA....597
New Orleans Pharmacy Museum, New Orleans, LA............597

New Windsor Cantonment State Historic Site and National Purple Heart Hall of Honor, Vails Gate, NY............1080
New York City Fire Museum, New York, NY............1035
New York City Police Museum, New York, NY............1035
New York Hall of Science, Flushing Meadows, NY............990
New York Power Authority-Niagara Power Project Visitors' Center, Lewiston, NY............1009
New York State Military Museum and Veterans Research Center, Saratoga Springs, NY............1065
Newark Valley Depot Museum, Newark Valley, NY............1042
Newaygo County Museum, Newaygo, MI....758
Nez Perce County Museum, Lewiston, ID....407
Nicollet County Historical Society, Saint Peter, MN............793
Nobleboro Historical Society, Nobleboro, ME............616
Norfolk Historical Museum, Norfolk, CT....257
Norman #1 Oil Well Museum, Neodesha, KS............553
North Andover Historical Society, North Andover, MA............698
North Anna Nuclear Information Center, Mineral, VA............1518
North Carolina Maritime Museum, Beaufort, NC............1091
North Carolina Museum of History, Raleigh, NC............1115
North Carolina Transportation Museum, Spencer, NC............1120
North Lee County Historic Center and Santa Fe Depot Museum Complex, Fort Madison, IA............518
North Platte Valley Museum, Gering, NE....861
Northborough Historical Society, Inc., Northborough, MA............700
Northern New York Agricultural Historical Society, Agricultural Museum at Stone Mills, LaFargeville, NY............1008
Northwest Railway Museum, Snoqualmie, WA............1570
Northwestern Oklahoma State University Museum, Alva, OK............1195

Oakfield Railroad Museum, Oakfield, ME...616
Oakland County Pioneer and Historical Society, Pontiac, MI............760
Oaklands Historic House Museum, Murfreesboro, TN............1376
Oatland Island Education Center, Savannah, GA............385
Ocean Star Offshore Drilling Rig & Museum, Galveston, TX............1421
Oceanographic Teaching Station Inc. - Roundhouse Marine Studies Lab & Aquarium, Manhattan Beach, CA............124
Ocmulgee National Monument, Macon, GA............378
Ocracoke Island Visitor Center, Ocracoke, NC............1113
The Octagon House, Hudson, WI............1600
Octave Chanute Aerospace Museum, Rantoul, IL............453
Odyssey Maritime Discovery Center, Seattle, WA 1567
O'Fallon Historical Museum, Baker, MT.....840
Ohio Historical Society, Columbus, OH.....1158
Okefenokee Heritage Center, Waycross, GA............391
Oklahoma Museums Association, Oklahoma City, OK............1210
Oktibbeha County Heritage Museum, Starkville, MS............808
Old Barracks Museum, Trenton, NJ............927
Old Colony Historical Society, Taunton, MA............714

Tools and Equipment for Science and Technology–Continued

Old Constitution House, Windsor, VT........1490
Old Cowtown Museum, Wichita, KS...........562
Old Depot Museum, Ottawa, KS.................555
Old Dominion Railway Museum,
Richmond, VA..1531
Old Fort Bissell, Phillipsburg, KS.............555
Old Fort House Museum, Fort Edward,
NY..991
Old Fort Jackson, Savannah, GA.................385
Old Fort Niagara, Youngstown, NY..........1088
Old Fort Western, Augusta, ME.................604
Old Greer County Museum & Hall of
Fame, Mangum, OK...............................1204
The Old Guard Museum, Fort Myer, VA..1505
Old Iron County Courthouse Museum,
Hurley, WI...1601
Old Jail Museum, Albion, IN.....................467
The Old Jail Museum, Warrenton, VA.......1543
Old Jefferson Town, Oskaloosa, KS...........555
Old Lighthouse Museum, Michigan City,
IN..491
Old Lighthouse Museum, Stonington, CT....261
Old Lincoln County Courthouse Museum,
Lincoln, NM...942
Old Ordinary House Museum, Hingham,
MA...687
Old Salem Inc., Winston-Salem, NC..........1126
The Old Schwamb Mill, Arlington, MA......660
Old Stone Fort Museum Complex,
Schoharie, NY.......................................1067
Old Stone House Museum, Windsor, NY...1086
The Oliver Tucker Museum, Beverly, OH.1142
Olmstead Funeral & Historical Museum,
Heber Springs, AR...................................59
Olmstead Place State Park, Ellensburg,
WA..1553
Omaha Children's Museum, Omaha, NE.....871
Omniplex Science Museum, Oklahoma
City, OK...1210
103rd Ohio Volunteer Infantry Civil War
Museum, Sheffield Lake, OH.................1185
Oneida County Historical Society, Utica,
NY..1080
Onondaga Historical Association Museum
& Research Center, Syracuse, NY.........1077
Onslow County Museum, Richlands, NC...1117
Ontario County Historical Society,
Canandaigua, NY...................................975
Opelousas Museum and Interpretive
Center, Opelousas, LA............................599
Oregon Air & Space Museum, Eugene,
OR..1224
Oregon Military Museum, Clackamas,
OR..1221
Oregon Museum of Science and Industry,
Portland, OR..1231
Orpheum Children's Science Museum,
Champaign, IL...417
Osage County Historical Society
Museum, Pawhuska, OK.........................1211
Otero Museum Association, La Junta, CO...224
Ottawa County Historical Museum, Port
Clinton, OH...1183
Otter Tail County Historical Society,
Fergus Falls, MN.....................................775
Outagamie Museum, Appleton, WI............1589
Owensboro Area Museum of Science &
History, Owensboro, KY.........................581
Owls Head Transportation Museum, Owls
Head, ME...617
Owyhee County Historical Museum,
Murphy, ID..407
Oxford Museum, Inc., Oxford, MD............650

The P.T. Boat Museum & Library,
Germantown, TN...................................1365
Pacific Aerospace Museum, Honolulu, HI...397
Pacific Aviation Museum - Pearl Harbor,
Honolulu, HI...397

Pacific Coast Air Museum, Santa Rosa,
CA..184
Pacific County Historical Museum, South
Bend, WA...1571
Pacific Northwest Truck Museum,
Brooks, OR...1220
Pacific University Museum, Forest
Grove, OR..1224
Packwood House Museum, Lewisburg,
PA..1268
Page Museum at the La Brea Tar Pits,
Los Angeles, CA.....................................121
Painted Post - Erwin Museum at the
Depot, Painted Post, NY.......................1050
Paleontological Research Institution,
Ithaca, NY...1004
Palmer Foundation Chiropractic History,
Davenport, IA..513
Palmer House, Historical Society of Olde
Northfield, Northfield, OH...................1180
Palomar Observatory, Palomar Mountain,
CA..139
Pamplin Historical Park and The National
Museum of the Civil War Soldier,
Petersburg, VA......................................1525
Panhandle-Plains Historical Museum,
Canyon, TX..1399
Paper Discovery Center, Appleton, WI......1590
Parker-O'Malley Air Museum, Ghent,
NY..994
Parks, Recreation & Historic Sites
Division, Georgia Dept. of Natural
Resources, Atlanta, GA...........................362
Parris Island Museum, Parris Island, SC....1338
Parson Fisher House, Blue Hill, ME...........606
Parsonsfield-Porter Historical Society,
Porter, ME...618
Patriots Point Naval and Maritime
Museum, Mount Pleasant, SC...............1337
Patten Lumbermen's Museum, Inc.,
Patten, ME...618
The Patuxent Rural Life Museums, Upper
Marlboro, MD..655
Paunsaugunt Wildlife Museum, Bryce,
UT..1464
Pavek Museum of Broadcasting, St.
Louis Park, MN..794
Pawnee City Historical Society &
Museum, Pawnee City, NE......................871
Pawnee Indian Village State Historic Site,
Republic, KS...556
Pea Ridge National Military Park,
Garfield, AR..58
Peabody Museum of Natural History,
New Haven, CT..253
Pearson Air Museum, Vancouver, WA.......1576
The Pearson Museum, Springfield, IL..........460
Pejepscot Historical Society, Brunswick,
ME...608
Pendleton District Historical, Recreational
and Tourism Commission, Pendleton,
SC..1339
Pennsylvania Anthracite Heritage
Museum, Scranton, PA...........................1299
Pennsylvania Longrifle Museum,
Nazareth, PA...1273
Pensacola Historical Society Museum,
Pensacola, FL...336
Perkins County Historical Society, Grant,
NE..862
Perry's Victory & International Peace
Memorial, Put-in-Bay, OH....................1183
Perryville Battlefield Museum, Perryville,
KY..582
Petersen Automotive Museum, Los
Angeles, CA...121
Peterson Air & Space Museum, Peterson
Air Force Base, CO.................................229
The Petroleum Museum, Midland, TX......1439
Pettaquamscutt Historical Society,
Kingston, RI...1312
Pettis County Historical Society, Sedalia,
MO...838

Phelps House, Burlington, IA.....................507
Philadelphia Society for the Preservation
of Landmarks, Philadelphia, PA...........1286
Phoenix Fire Museum, Mobile, AL...............15
Piatt County Museum, Monticello, IL..........446
Pickens County Museum of Art &
History, Pickens, SC.............................1340
Piedmont Environmental Center, High
Point, NC...1107
Pikes Peak Hill Climb Educational
Museum, Colorado Springs, CO.............207
Pima Air & Space Museum, Tucson, AZ......50
Pinal County Historical Society and
Museum, Florence, AZ..............................34
Pink Palace Family of Museums,
Memphis, TN...1375
Pioneer Arizona Living History Village &
Museum, Phoenix, AZ...............................41
Pioneer Florida Museum Association,
Inc., Dade City, FL.................................302
Pioneer Heritage Center, LSU-Shreveport,
Shreveport, LA.......................................601
Pioneer-Krier Museum, Ashland, KS..........532
Pioneer Museum & The Big Stampede,
Fairbanks, AK..24
Pioneer Museum - Martin County
Historical Society, Fairmont, MN...........775
Pioneer Village & Virgil Grissom
Memorial at Spring Mill State Park,
Mitchell, IN..491
Pioneers, Trail Drivers and Texas
Rangers Memorial Museum, San
Antonio, TX...1449
Pipestone County Historical Museum,
Pipestone, MN...786
Plainsman Museum, Aurora, NE.................856
Please Touch Museum, Philadelphia, PA...1286
Pocahontas County Museum, Marlinton,
WV..1584
Polk County Historical Museum, Bartow,
FL..295
Polk County Memorial Museum,
Livingston, TX.......................................1434
Polk County Museum, Balsam Lake, WI...1590
Portage County Historical Society,
Stevens Point, WI..................................1623
Porter Thermometer Museum, Onset, MA...700
Portland Harbor Museum, South
Portland, ME...623
Portsmouth Museums, Portsmouth, VA....1526
Post Rock Museum, La Crosse, KS.............547
Potts Inn Museum, Pottsville, AR................66
Poulsbo Marine Science Center, Poulsbo,
WA..1563
Powers Museum, Carthage, MO.................812
Prairie Trails Museum of Wayne County,
Corydon, IA...512
Pratt County Historical Society Museum,
Pratt, KS...556
Pretlow Planetarium, Norfolk, VA............1523
Public Museum of West Michigan, Grand
Rapids, MI...744
Pueblo Weisbrod Aircraft Museum,
Pueblo, CO..230
Putnam County Historical Society
Museum, Kalida, OH.............................1169

Queen Mary Museum, Long Beach, CA......111
The Quincy Museum, Quincy, IL................452

Racine Heritage Museum, Racine, WI.......1619
Railroad Museum of Pennsylvania,
Strasburg, PA...1302
Railroaders Memorial Museum, Altoona,
PA..1240
Raleigh City Museum, Raleigh, NC..........1117
The Ralph Foster Museum, Point
Lookout, MO..828
Randolph County Museum (At Beverly),
Beverly, WV...1580
Rangely Outdoor Museum, Rangely, CO.....231
Rankin Museum, Rankin, TX....................1445

Ransom County Historical Society, Fort Ransom, ND 1131

Ravalli County Museum/Bitter Root Valley Historical Society, Hamilton, MT..848

Red Mill Museum Village, Clinton, NJ.......901

Red River Historical Society Museum, Clay City, KY................................566

Redington Museum, Waterville, ME 625

Redwood County Historical Society, Redwood Falls, MN............................787

Reed Gold Mine State Historic Site, Midland, NC..................................1111

Regional Science & Discovery Center, Horseheads, NY..............................999

Remick Country Doctor Museum and Farm, Tamworth, NH 896

Remington Firearms Museum and Country Store, Ilion, NY....................1002

Renton Historical Society and Museum, Renton, WA 1564

Renville County Historical Society, Inc., Mohall, ND..................................1135

Reuben H. Fleet Science Center, San Diego, CA..................................158

Reuel B. Pritchett Museum, Bridgewater, VA..1497

Rhinebeck Aerodrome Museum, Rhinebeck, NY...............................1056

Rhode Island Black Heritage Society, Providence, RI...............................1318

Richard I. Bong WWII Heritage Center, Superior, WI................................1624

Richard Salter Storrs House, Longmeadow, MA............................691

Richardson-Bates House Museum, Oswego, NY.................................1048

Richland County Historical Museum, Wahpeton, ND...............................1137

Richmond Museum of History, Richmond, CA................................148

Richmond National Battlefield Park, Richmond, VA...............................1531

Rifle Creek Museum, Rifle, CO...................231

Riley County Historical Museum, Manhattan, KS...............................551

Riley House Museum of African American History & Culture, Tallahassee, FL..............................348

Rim Country Museum, Payson, AZ................38

Rio Grande Valley Museum, Harlingen, TX..1423

Ripley County, Indiana, Historical Society Museum, Versailles, IN...............502

Riverside Museum, La Crosse, WI.............1603

Riverton Museum, Riverton, WY 1637

Roanoke Island Festival Park; Homeport of the "Elizabeth II", Manteo, NC.........1110

Robert R. Meyer Planetarium, Birmingham, AL..................................5

Robeson Planetarium and Science Center, Lumberton, NC..............................1110

Rock Island Arsenal Museum, Rock Island, IL..................................454

Rock Springs Historical Museum, Rock Springs, WY.................................1638

Rockingham Free Public Library and Museum, Bellows Falls, VT 1476

Rocky Ford Historical Museum, Rocky Ford, CO..................................231

Rocky Mount Children's Museum and Science Center, Inc., Rocky Mount, NC..1118

Rogers Historical Museum, Rogers, AR 67

Rollo Jamison Museum, Platteville, WI.....1617

Roosevelt County Museum, Portales, NM ..944

Roper Mountain Science Center, Greenville, SC...............................1334

Roseau County Historical Museum and Interpretive Center, Roseau, MN..........788

Rosicrucian Egyptian Museum, San Jose, CA..172

Royal Gorge Regional Museum & History Center, Canon City, CO..............205

Royalton Historical Society, Royalton, VT..1486

Runestone Museum, Alexandria, MN..........767

Rusk County Historical Society, Ladysmith, WI...............................1604

Russell C. Davis Planetarium, Jackson, MS..804

Sacramento Archives and Museum Collection Center, Sacramento, CA.........153

Sacramento Mountains Historical Museum, Cloudcroft, NM.....................938

Sag Harbor Whaling & Historical Museum, Sag Harbor, NY.....................1063

Sailor's Memorial Museum, Islesboro, ME..612

St. Albans Historical Museum, Saint Albans, VT...............................1486

St. John Science Museum, Saint John, KS..557

St. Joseph Museum Inc., Saint Joseph, MO..831

St. Louis Science Center, Saint Louis, MO..836

St. Marys Submarine Museum, Saint Marys, GA.................................382

Salem Maritime National Historic Site, Salem, MA.................................707

The Salem Museum, Salem, VA.................1536

Salt Museum, Liverpool, NY.....................1010

Sam Houston Memorial Museum, Huntsville, TX..............................1430

Sam Houston Regional Library & Research Center, Liberty, TX...............1434

San Diego Air & Space Museum, San Diego, CA..................................159

San Diego Automotive Museum, San Diego, CA..................................159

San Francisco Bay Model Visitor Center, Sausalito, CA..............................186

San Joaquin County Historical Society & Museum, Lodi, CA.......................109

San Juan County Historical Society Museum, Silverton, CO.....................232

San Juan Historical Society, Friday Harbor, WA...............................1555

San Juan National Historic Site, San Juan, PR.................................1643

San Mateo County Historical Association and Museum, Redwood City, CA............147

Sandwich Glass Museum, Sandwich, MA ...708

Sandwich Historical Society, Center Sandwich, NH...............................884

Santa Barbara Botanic Garden, Santa Barbara, CA..................................178

Santa Barbara Maritime Museum, Santa Barbara, CA..................................179

Santa Maria Museum of Flight, Inc., Santa Maria, CA............................183

Santa Maria Valley Historical Museum, Santa Maria, CA............................183

Saratoga Museum, Saratoga, WY..............1638

Saratoga National Historical Park, Stillwater, NY...............................1075

Sarpy County Historical Museum, Bellevue, NE.................................857

Saunders Memorial Museum, Berryville, AR..55

Scantic Academy Museum, East Windsor Historical Society, Inc., East Windsor, CT..239

Schenectady Museum and Suits-Bueche Planetarium, Schenectady, NY..............1067

Schuyler County Historical Society, Inc., Montour Falls, NY............................1015

Schwenkfelder Library & Heritage Center, Pennsburg, PA.......................1275

Sci-Port Discovery Center, Shreveport, LA..601

Science Center of Connecticut, West Hartford, CT................................265

Science Center of Iowa, Des Moines, IA.....515

The Science Center of Pinellas County, Saint Petersburg, FL..........................342

The Science Center of West Virginia, Bluefield, WV...............................1580

Science Discovery Center of Oneonta, Oneonta, NY.................................1046

The Science Fiction Museum and Hall of Fame, Seattle, WA.............................1568

Science Museum of Long Island, Manhasset, NY...............................1013

Science Spectrum, Lubbock, TX 1435

Science Station-IMAX Dome Theatre, Cedar Rapids, IA............................510

Sciencenter, Ithaca, NY...........................1004

ScienceWorks Hands-On Museum, Ashland, OR.................................1218

SciTech, Aurora, IL..................................412

Scitrek, The Science and Technology Museum of Atlanta, Valdosta, GA...........389

Sciworks, Winston-Salem, NC..................1126

Scotland Heritage Chapel & Museum, Scotland, SD.................................1355

Scurry County Museum, Snyder, TX 1453

Sea Cliff Village Museum, Sea Cliff, NY ..1068

Seacoast Science Center, Rye, NH...............896

SEE Science Center, Manchester, NH.........892

Senator George Baldwin Hotel, Klamath Falls, OR..................................1227

Serra Museum/San Diego Historical Society, San Diego, CA 161

Shaftsbury Historical Society, Shaftsbury, VT..1487

The Shaker Museum and Library, Old Chatham, NY...............................1045

Shaker Village of Pleasant Hill, Harrodsburg, KY............................571

Shasta College Museum & Research Center, Redding, CA............................146

Shasta State Historic Park, Shasta, CA........186

Shawnee Town, Shawnee, KS.....................558

Shenandoal Valley Discovery Museum, Winchester, VA...............................1546

Sherwood-Davidson House, Newark, OH ..1178

Shiloh National Military Park & Cemetery, Shiloh, TN.........................1384

Shippensburg Historical Society Museum, Shippensburg, PA............................1300

Ships of the Sea Maritime Museum/William Scarbrough House, Savannah, GA.................................386

Shoal Creek Living History Museum, Kansas City, MO............................822

Shoreline Historical Museum, Seattle, WA..1569

Shoshone County Mining and Smelting Museum d/b/a The Staff House Museum, Kellogg, ID.........................406

Siege Museum (The Petersburg Museums), Petersburg, VA.....................1525

Sierra Sacramento Valley Medical Society Museum of Medical History, Sacramento, CA...............................153

Silent Wings Museum, Lubbock, TX 1435

Siloam Springs Museum, Siloam Springs, AR..68

Sindecuse Museum of Dentistry, Ann Arbor, MI..................................725

Sioux City Public Museum, Sioux City, IA..528

Sioux Empire Medical Museum, Sioux Falls, SD..................................1356

Siouxland Heritage Museums, Sioux Falls, SD..................................1357

Siskiyou County Museum, Yreka, CA 200

Skagit County Historical Museum, La Conner, WA................................1557

Slate Valley Museum, Granville, NY 996

Sloan Museum, Flint, MI..........................742

Smith County Historical Society, Tyler, TX..1456

Tools and Equipment for Science and Technology–Continued

Smith Robertson Museum & Cultural Center, Jackson, MS......804
Smithsonian Institution, Washington, DC.....290
Snyder Museum & Creative Arts Center, Bastrop, LA......585
The Society of the Cincinnati at Anderson House, Washington, DC......291
Sony Wonder Technology Lab, New York, NY......1039
Sophienburg Museum & Archives Inc., New Braunfels, TX......1440
South Boston-Halifax County Museum of Fine Arts & History, South Boston, VA......1536
South Carolina Law Enforcement Officers Hall of Fame, Columbia, SC......1330
South Carolina State Museum, Columbia, SC......1331
South Charleston Museum, South Charleston, WV......1586
South Coast Railroad Museum at Goleta Depot, Goleta, CA......100
South County Historical Society, Arroyo Grande, CA......72
South County Museum Inc., Narragansett, RI......1313
South Florida Museum, Bishop Planetarium & Parker Manatee Aquarium, Bradenton, FL......297
South Holland Historical Society, South Holland, IL......457
South Park City Museum, Fairplay, CO......215
South Street Seaport Museum, New York, NY......1039
South Sutton Old Store Museum, South Sutton, NH......896
South Texas Museum, Alice, TX......1386
South Wood County Historical Corp., Wisconsin Rapids, WI......1628
Southeast Missouri Regional Museum, Cape Girardeau, MO......812
Southeast Museum Association, Inc., Brewster, NY......964
Southern Forest Heritage Museum, Long Leaf, LA......591
The Southern Museum of Civil War and Locomotive History, Kennesaw, GA......375
Southwest Museum of Engineering, Communications and Computation, Glendale, AZ......35
Southwest Museum of Science and Technology, The Science Place & TI Founders IMAX Theater, Dallas, TX......1407
Southwest Virginia Museum Historical State Park, Big Stone Gap, VA......1497
Spartanburg County Regional Museum of History, Spartanburg, SC......1341
Spirit of '76 Museum, Wellington, OH......1190
SPJST Library Archives & Museum, Temple, TX......1455
Split Rock Lighthouse Historic Site, Two Harbors, MN......795
Spring Grove Hospital Center, Alumni Museum, Catonsville, MD......639
Spring Street Historical Museum, Shreveport, LA......602
Springfield Armory National Historic Site, Springfield, MA......710
Springfield Museums - Springfield Science Museum, Springfield, MA......711
Springs Museum, Springs, PA......1301
Spurlock Museum, University of Illinois at Urbana-Champaign, Urbana, IL......462
Stabler-Leadbeater Apothecary Museum and Museum Shop, Alexandria, VA......1494
Stafford Air and Space Museum, Weatherford, OK......1217
Stafford County Historical Society Museum, Stafford, KS......558
Stanley Museum, Inc., Kingfield, ME......613

Stanly County Historic Preservation Commission and Museum, Albemarle, NC......1088
State Historical Society of Iowa, Des Moines, IA......515
The State Museum of Pennsylvania, Harrisburg, PA......1259
The Steamboat Arabia Museum, Kansas City, MO......822
Steamboat Bertrand Collection, Missouri Valley, IA......524
Steamship William G. Mather Museum, Cleveland, OH......1156
Steamtown National Historic Site, Scranton, PA......1299
Stearns History Museum, Saint Cloud, MN......788
Steele County Historical Society, Hope, ND......1133
Stephens County Historical Society and Museum, Duncan, OK......1199
Stepping Stones Museum for Children, Norwalk, CT......257
Steppingstone Museum, Havre de Grace, MD......647
Sterling Hill Mining Museum, Inc., Ogdensburg, NJ......918
Sterling-Rock Falls Historical Society Museum, Sterling, IL......461
Sterne-Hoya House Museum and Library, Nacogdoches, TX......1440
Stevens Museum, Salem, IN......498
Still National Osteopathic Museum, Kirksville, MO......824
Stone Fort Museum, Nacogdoches, TX......1440
The Stone House Museum, Belchertown, MA......662
Stonefield Historic Site, Cassville, WI......1593
Stones River National Battlefield, Murfreesboro, TN......1377
Stonewall Jackson House, Lexington, VA......1514
Stonewall Jackson Museum at Hupp's Hill, Strasburg, VA......1539
Storrowton Village Museum, West Springfield, MA......718
Stuart House City Museum, Mackinac Island, MI......752
Stutsman County Memorial Museum, Jamestown, ND......1133
Submarine Force Museum and Historic Ship Nautilus, Groton, CT......243
Suffolk County Historical Society, Riverhead, NY......1057
Sullivan Museum and History Center, Northfield, VT......1483
Summit County Historical Society, Akron, OH......1139
Sunset Crater Volcano National Monument, Flagstaff, AZ......33
Superstition Mountain Lost Dutchman Museum, Apache Junction, AZ......30
Susquehanna County Historical Society & Free Library Association, Montrose, PA......1272
Susquehanna Museum of Havre de Grace Inc. at the Lock House, Havre de Grace, MD......647
Swampscott Historical Society (John Humphrey House), Swampscott, MA......714
Swarthout Memorial Museum, La Crosse, WI......1603
Sweetwater County Historical Museum, Green River, WY......1633
Swenson Memorial Museum of Stephens County, Breckenridge, TX......1397
Tampa Bay History Center, Inc., Tampa, FL......350
The Tech Museum of Innovation, San Jose, CA......173
Telephone Museum of New Mexico, Albuquerque, NM......935

Telluride Historical Museum, Telluride, CO......233
Tempe Historical Museum, Tempe, AZ......46
Tennessee Central Railway Museum, Nashville, TN......1380
Tennessee Museum of Aviation, Sevierville, TN......1383
Tennessee Valley Railroad Museum Inc., Chattanooga, TN......1363
Territorial Statehouse State Park & Museum, Fillmore, UT......1465
Terwilliger Museum, Waterloo, NY......1083
Texana Museum and Library Association, Edna, TX......1410
Texas Air Museum, Slaton, TX......1453
Texas City Museum, Texas City, TX......1455
Texas Civil War Museum, Fort Worth, TX......1418
Texas Energy Museum, Beaumont, TX......1395
Texas Forestry Museum, Lufkin, TX......1436
Texas Heritage Museum, Hillsboro, TX......1424
Texas Maritime Museum, Rockport, TX......1446
Texas Parks and Wildlife Department, Austin, TX......1392
Texas Pharmacy Museum, Amarillo, TX......1387
Texas Ranger Hall of Fame and Museum, Waco, TX......1459
Texas Transportation Museum, San Antonio, TX......1451
Third Cavalry Museum, Fort Carson, CO......216
Thomas E. McMillan Museum, Brewton, AL......6
Thomas Edison House, Louisville, KY......579
The Thomas J. Boyd, Wytheville, VA......1546
Three Rivers Museum, Muskogee, OK......1205
Thronateeska Heritage Foundation, Inc., Albany, GA......355
Tillamook County Pioneer Museum, Tillamook, OR......1237
Tillamook Naval Air Station Museum, Tillamook, OR......1237
Timexpo Museum, Waterbury, CT......264
Timpanogos Cave National Monument, American Fork, UT......1462
Timucuan Ecological and Historic Preserve and Fort Caroline National Memorial, Jacksonville, FL......315
Tioga County Historical Society Museum, Owego, NY......1048
Titan Missile Museum, Green Valley, AZ......36
Tobacco Farm Life Museum, Inc., Kenly, NC......1107
Toledo Firefighters Museum, Toledo, OH......1187
Tombstone Courthouse State Historic Park, Tombstone, AZ......46
Top of Oklahoma Historical Museum, Blackwell, OK......1197
Torrington Historical Society, Inc., Torrington, CT......263
Town of Manlius Historical Society with Museum, Manlius, NY......1013
Transylvania Museum, Lexington, KY......574
Traverse County Historical Society, Wheaton, MN......796
Treasures of the Sea Exhibit, Georgetown, DE......271
Tri-Cities Museum, Grand Haven, MI......743
Tri-County Historical Society & Museum, Inc., Herington, KS......544
T.T. Wentworth, Jr. Florida State Museum, Pensacola, FL......336
Tubac Presidio State Historic Park, Tubac, AZ......47
Tularosa Basin Historical Society Museum, Alamogordo, NM......932
Tuskegee Institute National Historic Site, Tuskegee Institute, AL......21
Twinsburg Historical Society, Twinsburg, OH......1188
Tyler Arboretum, Media, PA......1271
U.S. Navy Museum, Washington, DC......292

USS Massachusetts Memorial Committee, Inc., Fall River, MA 682
Umpqua Discovery Center, Reedsport, OR 1234
Union County Historical Complex, Creston, IA 512
Union County Museum, Union, OR 1238
Union Pacific Railroad Museum, Council Bluffs, IA 512
Union Station Kansas City, Inc., Kansas City, MO 823
United States Department of the Interior Museum, Washington, DC 293
United States Naval Academy Museum, Annapolis, MD 628
University Museum, Carbondale, IL 415
University Museum & Historic Houses, The University of Mississippi, Oxford, MS 806
University Museum, New Mexico State University, Las Cruces, NM 941
University of Iowa Hospitals & Clinics Medical Museum, Iowa City, IA 520
University of Kansas Medical Center, Clendening History of Medicine Library and Museum, Kansas City, KS ...546
The University of South Carolina McKissick Museum, Columbia, SC 1331
University of Wisconsin Zoological Museum, Madison, WI 1606
Upham Mansion, Marshfield, WI 1608
Uppertown Firefighters Museum, Astoria, OR 1219
U.S. Army Air Defense Artillery Museum, Fort Bliss, TX 1414
U.S. Army Center of Military History, Museum Division, Fort McNair, DC 275
U.S. Army Engineer Museum, Fort Leonard Wood, MO 815
U.S. Army Medical Department Museum, Fort Sam Houston, TX 1415
U.S. Army Museum of Hawaii, Fort DeRussy, HI 392
U.S. Army Ordnance Museum, Aberdeen Proving Ground, MD 627
U.S. Army Transportation Museum, Fort Eustis, VA 1504
U.S. Coast Guard Museum, New London, CT 255
U.S. Marconi Museum, Bedford, NH 883
U.S. Merchant Marine Museum, Anderson, IN 467
U.S. Naval Museum of Armament & Technology, China Lake, CA 84
U.S. Navy Seabee Museum, Port Hueneme, CA 143
U.S. Navy Supply Corps Museum, Athens, GA 357
U.S. Patent and Trademark Office - Museum, Alexandria, VA 1494
The U.S. Space & Rocket Center, Huntsville, AL 12
USS Alabama Battleship Memorial Park, Mobile, AL 15
USS Bowfin Submarine Museum & Park, Honolulu, HI 398
USS Constellation Museum, Baltimore, MD 636
USS Constitution Museum, Boston, MA 669
USS Radford National Naval Museum, Newcomerstown, OH 1179
Utah State Historical Society, Salt Lake City, UT 1473

Vachel Lindsay Home State Historic Site, Springfield, IL 460
The Valdez Museum & Historical Archive Association, Inc., Valdez, AK 29
Valentine Richmond History Center, Richmond, VA 1532
Valentown Museum, Victor, NY 1081
Valiant Air Command Warbird Air Museum, Titusville, FL 352

Vallejo Naval & Historical Museum, Vallejo, CA 194
Valley Art Center, Inc., Clarkston, WA 1551
Van Buren County Historical Museum, Clinton, AR 55
Van Buren County Historical Society, Keosauqua, IA 521
Venango Museum of Art, Science & Industry, Oil City, PA 1274
Ventura County Maritime Museum, Inc., Oxnard, CA 137
Ventura County Museum of History & Art, Ventura, CA 195
Vermont Historical Society Museum, Montpelier, VT 1482
Village Historical Society, Inc., Harrison, OH 1168
Vincennes State Historic Site, Indiana Territory, Vincennes, IN 503
Virginia Air & Space Center, Hampton, VA 1510
Virginia Aquarium & Marine Science Center, Virginia Beach, VA 1542
Virginia Holocaust Museum, Richmond, VA 1533
Virginia Military Institute Museum, Lexington, VA 1514
Virginia War Memorial, Richmond, VA 1534
The Virginia War Museum, Newport News, VA 1520

W.H. Over Museum, Vermillion, SD 1358
W.K. Gordon Center for Industrial History of Texas, Mingus, TX 1439
Wabaunsee County Historical Museum, Alma, KS 532
Wagner Free Institute of Science, Philadelphia, PA 1289
Wake Forest College Birthplace Society, Inc., Wake Forest, NC 1121
Wakefield House Museum, Blue Earth, MN 769
Wallingford Historical Society, Inc., Wallingford, CT 263
Wapello County Historical Museum, Ottumwa, IA 526
War in the Pacific National Historical Park, Piti, GU 1640
Ward County Historical Society, Minot, ND 1135
Warhawk Air Museum, Nampa, ID 408
Waring Historical Library, Charleston, SC .1327
Warren County Historical Society, Warren, PA 1304
Warren Historical Society, Warren, ME 624
Warrick County Museum, Inc., Boonville, IN 470
Warsaw Historical Museum, Warsaw, NY .1082
Waseca County Historical Society, Waseca, MN 796
Washburn Historical Museum & Cultural Center, Inc. aka Washburn Cultural Center, Washburn, WI 1625
Washington County Historical Association, Fort Calhoun, NE 860
Washington County Historical Society, Portland, OR 1233
Washington County Historical Society, Washington, PA 1305
Washington County Rural Heritage Museum, Boonsboro, MD 637
Washington Irving Trail Museum, Ripley, OK 1213
Washington Museum & Tourist Center, Washington, LA 603
Waterford Historical Museum and Cultural Center, Inc., Waterford, NY 1083
Watervliet Arsenal's Museum of the Big Guns, Watervliet, NY 1084
Watkins Community Museum of History, Lawrence, KS 548
Waukesha County Museum, Waukesha, WI 1625

Weinman Mineral Museum, White, GA 391
Wellfleet Historical Society Museum, Wellfleet, MA 717
West Allis Historical Society Museum, West Allis, WI 1626
West Pasco Historical Society Museum and Library, New Port Richey, FL 329
West Virginia State Farm Museum, Point Pleasant, WV 1586
Western Aerospace Museum, Oakland, CA 134
Western Heritage Center, Billings, MT 841
Western Museum of Flight, Hawthorne, CA 101
Western Museum of Mining & Industry, Colorado Springs, CO 208
Western Rhode Island Civic Historical Society, Coventry, RI 1311
Western Springs Historical Society, Western Springs, IL 464
Westminster Historical Society, Westminster, VT 1490
Wexford County Historical Society & Museum, Cadillac, MI 731
The Whale Museum, Friday Harbor, WA ...1555
Whalers Village Museum, Lahaina, HI 401
Wharton County Historical Museum, Wharton, TX 1461
Wheels O' Time Museum, Peoria, IL 451
Whipple House Museum, Ashland Historical Society, Ashland, NH 883
Whiskeytown Unit, Whiskeytown-Shasta-Trinity National Recreation Area, Whiskeytown, CA 198
Whitaker Center for Science and the Arts, Harrisburg, PA 1259
White County Historical Society, Carmi, IL 415
White County Historical Society Museum, Monticello, IN 491
White 1 Foundation, Kissimmee, FL............319
White Pine Public Museum, Ely, NV 877
Whitewater Canal State Historic Site, Metamora, IN 490
Whitingham Historical Museum, Whitingham, VT 1490
Whitman Mission National Historic Site, Walla Walla, WA 1577
Wilbur Wright Birthplace & Interpretive Center, Hagerstown, IN 480
Wilhelm Reich Museum - Orgonon, Rangeley, ME 621
Willapa Seaport Museum, Raymond, WA ..1564
Willard House and Clock Museum, Inc., Grafton, MA 685
William Clark Market House Museum, Paducah, KY 582
William Heath Davis House Museum administered by Gaslamp Quarter Historical Foundation, San Diego, CA 162
William McKinley Presidential Library & Museum, Canton, OH 1146
Williamson County Historical Society, Marion, IL 444
Willowbrook Museum Village, Newfield, ME 616
Wilson County Historical Society Museum, Fredonia, KS 540
Wilson Czech Opera House Corporation, Foundation, Inc. & House of Memories Museum, Wilson, KS 564
Wilson's Creek National Battlefield, Republic, MO 829
Windham Textile and History Museum (The Mill Museum), Willimantic, CT 267
The Wine Museum of Greyton H. Taylor, Hammondsport, NY 997
Wings Over Miami Museum, Inc., Miami, FL 326
Winnebago Area Museum, Winnebago, MN 797
Wisconsin National Guard Museum, Camp Douglas, WI 1593

Tools and Equipment for Science and Technology–Continued

Wisconsin Veterans Museum-King, King, WI 1602

Wisconsin Veterans Museum-Madison, Madison, WI 1606

Wise County Heritage Museum, Decatur, TX 1408

Wolf Point Area Historical Society, Inc., Wolf Point, MT 855

Wood Library-Museum of Anesthesiology, Park Ridge, IL 450

Woodburn Historic House, Pendleton, SC .1339

Woods Hole Oceanographic Institution Exhibit Center, Woods Hole, MA............720

Woods Hole Science Aquarium, Woods Hole, MA 720

Woodside Store Historic Site, Woodside, CA 199

Woodson County Historical Society, Yates Center, KS 564

Woodstock Museum of Shenandoah County, Inc., Woodstock, VA 1546

Woolaroc Museum, Bartlesville, OK 1197

Worcester Historical Museum, Worcester, MA 721

Workman & Temple Family Homestead Museum, City of Industry, CA 85

The Works: Ohio Center for History, Art & Technology, Newark, OH...................1179

World Kite Museum & Hall of Fame, Long Beach, WA 1558

The World of Energy, Seneca, SC 1341

Wrangell Museum, Wrangell, AK.................29

Wray Museum, Wray, CO 235

Wright Brothers National Memorial, Kill Devil Hills, NC 1108

Wright Museum, Wolfeboro, NH 897

Wyck, Philadelphia, PA 1289

The Wyman Tavern, Keene, NH.................890

Wyoming State Museum, Cheyenne, WY ..1631

Yanks Air Museum, Chino, CA 84

Yellow Medicine County Historical Society and Museum, Granite Falls, MN 777

Youth Science Center, Hacienda Heights, CA 101

Yucaipa Valley Historical Society Museum, Yucaipa, CA..........................201

Zane Grey Museum, Lackawaxen, PA 1265

Zeum, San Francisco, CA 170

NATURAL COLLECTIONS

Botanical (Living)

A.L. Fetterman Educational Museum, Fort Valley, GA.....................................372

ASRI Environmental Education Center, Bristol, RI 1310

Abilene Zoological Gardens, Abilene, TX .1385

The Accokeek Foundation, Inc., Accokeek, MD.......................................627

Adena Mansion and Gardens, Chillicothe, OH 1147

Adventure Aquarium, Camden, NJ.............899

Adventure Science Center, Nashville, TN..1377

Agate Fossil Beds National Monument, Harrison, NE 862

Ah-Tah-Thi-Ki Museum, Big Cypress Seminole Indian Reservation, FL 295

Ak-Sar-Ben Aquarium Outdoor Education Center, Gretna, NE 862

Akron Zoological Park, Akron, OH............1138

Alameda Park Zoo, Alamogordo, NM.........931

The Alamo, San Antonio, TX 1447

Alaska SeaLife Center, Seward, AK.............27

Alaska Zoo, Anchorage, AK 22

Albuquerque Biological Park, Albuquerque, NM..................................932

Alfred B. Maclay State Gardens, Tallahassee, FL 346

Allegany County Museum, Belmont, NY 961

Amy B.H. Greenwell Ethnobotanical Garden, Captain Cook, HI 392

Anna Scripps Whitcomb Conservatory, Detroit, MI 734

The Anne Spencer Memorial Foundation, Inc., Lynchburg, VA 1515

Anniston Museum of Natural History, Anniston, AL 3

Antelope Valley California Poppy Reserve, Lancaster, CA 108

The Antiquarian and Landmarks Society, Inc., Hartford, CT 244

Anza-Borrego Desert State Park, Borrego Springs, CA 79

Apple Farm Mill House, San Luis Obispo, CA 174

Applegate Park Zoo, Merced, CA 125

Aptucxet Trading Post Museum, Bourne, MA 670

The Arboretum at Flagstaff, Flagstaff, AZ 32

Arboretum at UC Santa Cruz, Santa Cruz, CA 181

Arden - The Helena Modjeska Historic House & Gardens, Modjeska Canyon, CA 126

Ardenwood Historic Farm, Fremont, CA........96

Arizona-Sonora Desert Museum, Tucson, AZ 48

Arizona Zoological Society, dba the Phoenix Zoo, Phoenix, AZ......................40

Arkansas Country Doctor Museum, Lincoln, AR 61

Armand Bayou Nature Center, Houston, TX 1424

Arnold Arboretum of Harvard University, Jamaica Plain, MA 688

Ash Lawn-Highland, Charlottesville, VA ...1498

Ashland, The Henry Clay Estate, Lexington, KY 572

Astors' Beechwood Mansion - Living History Museum, Newport, RI...............1313

Atlanta Botanical Garden, Atlanta, GA 357

Atlanta Historical Society, Atlanta, GA........358

Audubon Greenwich, Greenwich, CT 242

Audubon House & Tropical Gardens, Key West, FL...317

Audubon Louisiana Nature Center, New Orleans, LA 594

Audubon Naturalist Society, Chevy Chase, MD...640

Audubon Society of New Hampshire, Concord, NH 884

Audubon Society of Rhode Island, Smithfield, RI..1319

Audubon Zoo, New Orleans, LA..................594

Aullwood Audubon Center and Farm, Dayton, OH...1160

Austin Nature & Science Center, Austin, TX 1389

Awbury Arboretum, Philadelphia, PA.........1277

Baca House, Trinidad History Museum, Trinidad, CO 233

The Bakken Library and Museum, Minneapolis, MN.....................................781

Baldwin County Heritage Museum, Elberta, AL...8

Barnes Foundation, Merion, PA................1271

Barrington Living History Farm, Washington, TX 1460

Bartlett Arboretum & Gardens, Stamford, CT 260

Bartow-Pell Mansion Museum, Carriage House & Gardens, Bronx, NY...............964

Bartram's Garden, Philadelphia, PA 1277

Baton Rouge Zoo, Baton Rouge, LA 585

Batsto Village, Hammonton, NJ 907

Bayard Cutting Arboretum, Great River, NY 996

Bayou Bend Collection and Gardens, Houston, TX 1425

Beaumont Botanical Gardens, Beaumont, TX 1394

Belle Grove Plantation, Middletown, VA ..1517

Belle Isle Nature Zoo, Detroit, MI..............735

Bellingrath Gardens & Home, Theodore, AL 18

Belvedere-Tiburon Landmarks Society, Tiburon, CA...192

Bement-Billings Farmstead, Newark Valley, NY 1041

The Benjamin Banneker Park & Museum, Baltimore, MD 631

Bennington Battlefield State Historic Site, Walloomsac, NY 1081

Bergen County Zoological Park, Paramus, NJ 919

Berkeley Plantation, Charles City, VA 1498

Berkeley Rose Garden, Berkeley, CA 75

Berkshire Botanical Garden, Stockbridge, MA 711

Bernhard Museum Complex, Auburn, CA 72

Bernheim Arboretum and Research Forest, Clermont, KY 567

The Berry Botanic Garden, Portland, OR ..1230

Bickelhaupt Arboretum, Clinton, IA 511

Biedenharn Museum & Gardens, Monroe, LA 592

Big Thunder Gold Mine, Keystone, SD.....1349

Bigelow House Museum, Olympia, WA 1560

Binder Park Zoo, Battle Creek, MI 727

Birch Aquarium at Scripps, Scripps Institution of Oceanography, University of California, San Diego, La Jolla, CA...106

Birdsong Nature Center, Thomasville, GA...387

Birmingham Botanical Gardens, Birmingham, AL..4

Birmingham Zoo, Birmingham, AL................5

Biscayne National Park, Homestead, FL......313

Black Hawk State Historic Site: Hauberg Indian Museum, Rock Island, IL............453

Black Hills Reptile Gardens, Inc., Rapid City, SD 1354

Blithewold Mansion, Gardens & Arboretum, Bristol, RI 1310

Blue Hills Trailside Museum, Milton, MA 695

Bodie Island Visitor Center, South Nags Head, NC 1120

Boerner Botanical Gardens, Hales Corners, WI 1600

Bolsa Chica Conservancy, Huntington Beach, CA...104

Bonnet House Museum & Gardens, Fort Lauderdale, FL.......................................306

Boonshoft Museum of Discovery, Dayton, OH...1160

Boscobel, Garrison, NY 993

The Botanic Garden of Smith College, Northampton, MA 699

Botanica, The Wichita Gardens, Wichita, KS 561

Botanical Gardens at Asheville, Asheville, NC......................................1089

Bowman's Hill Wildflower Preserve, New Hope, PA 1273

Boyce Thompson Arboretum, Superior, AZ 44

Boyhood Home of President Woodrow Wilson, Augusta, GA................................365

Bramble Park Zoo, Watertown, SD 1359

Briar Bush Nature Center, Abington, PA 1238

Brookgreen Gardens, Murrells Inlet, SC 1337

Brooklyn Botanic Garden, Brooklyn, NY 967

Brooklyn Historical Society, Brooklyn, OH 1144

Brookside Gardens, Wheaton, MD..............657

Brucemore, Cedar Rapids, IA.....................509

Buffalo and Erie County Botanical Gardens, Buffalo, NY 972
Buffalo Zoological Gardens, Buffalo, NY 972
The Burgwin-Wright Museum, Wilmington, NC 1123
Burke County Historical Powers Lake Complex, Powers Lake, ND 1136
COSI Columbus, Columbus, OH 1157
Cabin Nature Center, Wood Dale, IL 466
Cable Natural History Museum, Cable, WI 1593
Cabrillo Marine Aquarium, San Pedro, CA 176
Cal State Northridge Botanic Garden, Northridge, CA 131
Caldwell Zoo, Tyler, TX 1456
Calkins Nature Area/Field Museum, Iowa Falls, IA 521
Calusa Nature Center and Planetarium, Fort Myers, FL 308
Cameron Park Zoo, Waco, TX 1458
The Campus Arboretum Association Haverford College, Haverford, PA 1260
Cape Cod Museum of Natural History, Inc., Brewster, MA 670
Cape May County Park and Zoo, Cape May Court House, NJ 901
Carl G. Fenner Nature Center, Lansing, MI 749
Carl S. English Botanical Gardens, Seattle, WA 1565
Carleen Bright Arboretum, Woodway, TX .1462
The Casa del Herrero Foundation, Santa Barbara, CA 178
The Cathedral of St. John the Divine, New York, NY 1022
Catherine Montgomery Interpretive Center, Greenwater, WA 1556
Catoctin Wildlife Preserve & Zoo, Thurmont, MD 655
Cedar Key Museum State Park, Cedar Key, FL 299
The Centennial Museum at the University of Texas at El Paso, El Paso, TX 1411
Center for Agricultural Science and Heritage, Indianapolis, IN 481
Central Florida Zoo, Sanford, FL 342
Central Park Conservancy, New York, NY 1022
Channel Islands National Park, Robert J. Lagomarsino Visitor Center, Ventura, CA 194
Charles Paddock Zoo, Atascadero, CA 72
Charles Towne Landing State Historic Site, Charleston, SC 1324
The Charleston Museum, Charleston, SC ..1324
Charlotte Nature Museum, Charlotte, NC..1094
The Chattanooga Nature Center, Chattanooga, TN 1361
Cheekwood-Tennessee Botanical Garden & Museum of Art, Nashville, TN 1378
The Chelmsford Historical Society, Inc., South Chelmsford, MA 709
Chesapeake and Ohio Canal National Historical Park, Hagerstown, MD 646
Chesterwood, Stockbridge, MA 711
Cheyenne Botanic Gardens, Cheyenne, WY 1630
Cheyenne Mountain Zoological Park, Colorado Springs, CO 206
Chicago Botanic Garden, Glencoe, IL..........438
Chicago Zoological Park (Brookfield Zoo), Brookfield, IL 414
Chico Creek Nature Center, Chico, CA 83
Chihuahuan Desert Research Institute, Fort Davis, TX 1414
Children's Discovery Museum of San Jose, San Jose, CA 171
The Children's Metamorphosis, Children's Museum, Derry, NH 886
Children's Museum, Inc., Boca Raton, FL...296

The Children's Museum, Inc., Bloomsburg, PA 1243
Chinese Cultural Garden/Overfelt Gardens, San Jose, CA 171
Chinqua-Penn Plantation, Reidsville, NC...1117
Chippewa Nature Center, Midland, MI..........755
Chula Vista Nature Center, Chula Vista, CA 84
Cincinnati Zoo & Botanical Garden, Cincinnati, OH 1149
Civic Garden Center of Greater Cincinnati, Cincinnati, OH 1149
Clark Botanic Garden, Albertson, NY 956
Clark County Museum, Henderson, NV 878
Clearwater Marine Aquarium, Clearwater, FL 299
Cleveland Botanical Garden, Cleveland, OH 1152
Cleveland Metroparks Outdoor Education Division, Garfield Heights, OH 1165
Cleveland Metroparks Zoo, Cleveland, OH 1152
The Cleveland Museum of Natural History, Cleveland, OH 1153
The Cloisters, New York, NY 1023
Coastal Discovery Museum, Hilton Head Island, SC 1335
Coe Hall, Oyster Bay, NY 1049
Coker Arboretum of the North Carolina Botanical Garden, Chapel Hill, NC 1093
The Coley Homestead & Barn Museum, Weston, CT 265
Collier County Museum, Naples, FL 328
The Colonial Spanish Quarter Museum, Saint Augustine, FL 338
Colorado Plateau Biodiversity Center, Flagstaff, AZ 32
Columbus Zoo and Aquarium, Powell, OH 1183
Congaree National Park, Hopkins, SC 1336
Connecticut Audubon Birdcraft Museum, Fairfield, CT 240
Connecticut Audubon Center at Fairfield, Fairfield, CT 240
Connecticut College Arboretum, New London, CT 255
Connecticut State Museum of Natural History and Connecticut Archaeology Center, Storrs, CT 261
Connecticut's Beardsley Zoo, Bridgeport, CT 236
Conservancy Nature Center, Naples, FL 328
The Conservatory Garden, New York, NY 1023
Constitution Square State Historic Site, Danville, KY 567
The Contemporary Museum, Honolulu, HI 394
Core Arboretum, Morgantown, WV 1585
The Cornell Plantations, Ithaca, NY 1003
The Country Doctor Museum, Bailey, NC.1091
County of Westchester, Department of Parks, Recreation and Conservation, Mount Kisco, NY 1016
Cox Arboretum & Gardens MetroPark, Dayton, OH 1160
Coyote Point Museum for Environmental Education, San Mateo, CA 175
Cragfont-Historic Cragfont, Inc., Castalian Springs, TN 1360
Cranbrook House and Gardens Auxiliary, Bloomfield Hills, MI 730
Crane Point, Marathon, FL 323
Craters of the Moon National Monument, Arco, ID 403
The Crosby Arboretum, Mississippi State University, Picayune, MS 807
Cuneo Museum & Gardens, Vernon Hills, IL 463
Curry Historical Society Museum, Gold Beach, OR 1225
Custer State Park, Custer, SD 1346

Cutler Botanic Garden, Binghamton, NY 962
Cylburn Arboretum, Baltimore, MD 631
DAR John Strong Mansion Museum, Addison, VT 1475
Dakota Zoo, Bismarck, ND 1128
Dallas Arboretum & Botanical Garden, Dallas, TX 1404
The Dallas World Aquarium, Dallas, TX ...1406
Dallas Zoo, Dallas, TX 1406
Daniel Stowe Botanical Garden, Belmont, NC 1092
Danvers Historical Society, Danvers, MA....678
David Bradford House, Washington, PA ..1305
David Trayol Zoo of Emporia, Emporia, KS 538
The Dawes Arboretum, Newark, OH 1177
De Graaf Nature Center, Holland, MI..........746
Deer Isle-Stonington Historical Society, Deer Isle, ME 609
Deer Park Escondido Winery & Auto Museum, Escondido, CA 93
Degrazia Gallery In The Sun, Tucson, AZ.....48
Delaware Nature Society, Hockessin, DE 271
Delta Cultural Center, Helena, AR 59
Denison Pequotsepos Nature Center, Mystic, CT 250
Denver Botanic Gardens, Inc., Denver, CO 210
Des Moines Botanical Center, Des Moines, IA 514
Descanso Gardens Guild, Inc., La Canada Flintridge, CA 105
Desert Botanical Garden, Phoenix, AZ 40
Detroit Zoo, Royal Oak, MI 762
DeWitt County Historical Museum, Cuero, TX 1403
Dinosaur State Park, Rocky Hill, CT 259
The Discovery Center, Fresno, CA 96
Discovery Creek Children's Museum of Washington DC, Glen Echo, MD 645
Discovery Museum, Sacramento Museum of History, Science and Technology, Sacramento, CA 152
Discovery Science and Outdoor Center, Ocala, FL 330
Discovery Seashell Museum, Ocean City, NJ 918
Disney's Animal Kingdom Theme Park, Bay Lake, FL 295
Dr. William Robinson Plantation, Clark, NJ 901
Dodge Nature Center, West Saint Paul, MN 796
Dothan Area Botanical Gardens, Dothan, AL 8
Douglas County Museum of History and Natural History, Roseburg, OR 1234
Dow Gardens, Midland, MI 755
Drayton Hall, Charleston, SC 1325
Drumlin Farm Education Center, Lincoln, MA 690
Dubuque Arboretum & Botanical Gardens, Dubuque, IA 516
Duke Homestead State Historic Site, Durham, NC 1098
Dumbarton Oaks Research Library & Collections, Washington, DC 278
Dungeness River Audubon Center, Sequim, WA 1570
Dunham Tavern Museum, Cleveland, OH..1154
E. St. Julien Cox House, Saint Peter, MN ...792
Earl Burns Miller Japanese Garden, Long Beach, CA 110
The Earle-Harrison House and Gardens on 5th Street, Waco, TX 1458
Earthplace - The Nature Discovery Center, Westport, CT 266
ECHO at the Leahy Center for Lake Champlain, Burlington, VT 1478
EcoTarium, Worcester, MA 720

Botanical (Living)–Continued

Edison & Ford Winter Estates, Fort Myers, FL................................308

Edsel & Eleanor Ford House, Grosse Pointe Shores, MI........................745

Effie Yeaw Nature Center, Carmichael, CA..82

El Dorado Nature Center, Long Beach, CA..110

El Morro National Monument, Ramah, NM..945

El Paso Museum of Archaeology, El Paso, TX......................................1411

El Paso Zoo, El Paso, TX.......................1412

El Rancho de Las Golondrinas Museum, Santa Fe, NM....................947

Elachee Nature Science Center, Gainesville, GA................................373

Elkhorn Slough National Estuarine Research, Wastsonville, CA.........196

Ellen Trout Zoo, Lufkin, TX...............1435

Eloise Butler Wildflower Garden and Bird Sanctuary, Minneapolis, MN..........781

Enfield Shaker Museum, Enfield, NH.........887

Epcot at Walt Disney World Resort, Lake Buena Vista, FL......................319

Erie Zoological Park & Botanical Gardens of Northwestern Pennsylvania, Erie, PA.................1253

Ernest Hemingway House Museum, Key West, FL............................317

Essex County's Turtle Back Zoo, West Orange, NJ.............................930

Evanston Environmental Association/Evanston Ecology Center, Evanston, IL........................434

Explorium of Lexington, Lexington, KY.....572

Fabyan Villa Museum, Geneva, IL...............437

Fairchild Tropical Botanic Garden, Coral Gables, FL.........................301

Fairfax County Park Authority, Resource Management Division, Fairfax, VA........1503

Fairmont Park Horticulture Center, Philadelphia, PA.........................1279

The Farm, Sturgeon Bay, WI..................1623

The Farmers' Museum, Inc., Cooperstown, NY...........................980

Farmington Museum, Farmington, NM........939

Faust Park-Thornhill Historic Site & 19th Century Village, Chesterfield, MO.........812

The Fay Hyland Botanical Plantation, Orono, ME............................617

Fernbank Museum of Natural History, Atlanta, GA..............................359

Fernbank Science Center, Atlanta, GA.........360

Ferndell Nature Museum, Los Angeles, CA....................................115

Fernwood Botanical Garden & Nature Preserve, Niles, MI.....................758

Filoli Center, Woodside, CA.....................199

Finnup Park and Lee Richardson Zoo, Garden City, KS.........................541

First Landing State Park, Virginia Beach, VA....................................1542

Fisher Museum of Forestry, Petersham, MA....................................702

Flint River Quarium, Albany, GA...........355

Florida Institute of Technology Botanical Gardens, Melbourne, FL..............323

Flowerdew Hundred Foundation, Hopewell, VA.........................1511

Foellinger-Freimann Botanical Conservatory, Fort Wayne, IN.............477

Fontenelle Nature Association, Bellevue, NE....................................857

Forest Park Museum and Arboretum, Perry, IA................................527

Forestiere Underground Gardens, Fresno, CA.....................................97

Fort Ancient Museum, Oregonia, OH.........1181

Fort Boonesborough Museum, Richmond, KY....................................583

Fort Kearny State Historical Park, Kearney, NE.........................864

Fort Leaton State Historical Site, Presidio, TX..........................1444

Fort Matanzas National Monument, Saint Augustine, FL......................339

Fort Mifflin, Philadelphia, PA............1279

Fort Raleigh National Historic Site, Manteo, NC............................1110

Fort Ticonderoga, Ticonderoga, NY...........1078

Fort Wayne Children's Zoo, Fort Wayne, IN....................................477

Fort Worth Botanic Garden, Fort Worth, TX....................................1416

Fort Worth Zoological Park, Fort Worth, TX....................................1417

Fossil Rim Wildlife Center, Glen Rose, TX....................................1422

Foster Botanical Garden, Honolulu, HI........395

Fosterfields Living Historical Farm, Morristown, NJ.........................913

Four Mile Historic Park, Denver, CO..........212

Four Rivers Cultural Center & Museum, Ontario, OR.........................1229

Frank Lloyd Wright's Pope-Leighey House, Alexandria, VA.................1492

Franklin Park Conservatory, Columbus, OH....................................1158

Fresno Chaffee Zoo, Fresno, CA................97

The Friends of Lucy Hayes Heritage Center, Chillicothe, OH..............1147

The Friends of Peace Church, Camp Hill, PA....................................1245

Fruitlands Museums, Harvard, MA............686

Fuller Gardens, North Hampton, NH...........893

The Fullerton Arboretum, Fullerton, CA........98

Garden in the Woods of the New England Wild Flower Society, Framingham, MA.........................683

Gardens at Callaway, Pine Mountain, GA...380

Gardenview Horticultural Park, Strongsville, OH..........................1186

Garfield Farm Museum, LaFox, IL............441

Garfield Park Conservatory, Chicago, IL.....421

Gene Stratton-Porter State Historic Site, Rome City, IN.........................498

General Crook House Museum and Library/Archives Center, Omaha, NE......870

George Eastman House/International Museum of Photography and Film, Rochester, NY.........................1058

The George G. Frelinghuysen Arboretum, Morris Township, NJ...................913

George L. Luthy Memorial Botanical Garden, Peoria, IL....................450

George Landis Arboretum, Esperance, NY....................................989

George Washington Birthplace National Monument, Colonial Beach, VA.........1502

George Washington Carver National Monument, Diamond, MO...............814

Georgia State Cotton Museum, Vienna, GA....................................390

George B. Dorr Museum of Natural History, Bar Harbor, ME...............605

Gladys Porter Zoo, Brownsville, TX.........1398

The Glebe House Museum and Gertrude Jekyll Garden, Woodbury, CT..........268

Glen Oak Zoo, Peoria, IL.....................450

Gold Coast Railroad Museum, Inc., Miami, FL.............................323

Good Zoo, Wheeling, WV.....................1587

Gore Place, Waltham, MA.....................715

Governor John Sevier Memorial Association, Knoxville, TN.............1370

Graber Olive House Museum, Ontario, CA....................................135

Graves Museum of Archaeology and Natural History, Dania Beach, FL.........302

Great Valley Museum of Natural History, Modesto, CA...........................126

Greater Loveland Historical Society Museum, Loveland, OH...............1173

Green Bay Botanical Garden, Green Bay, WI....................................1598

The Greenburgh Nature Center, Scarsdale, NY.........................1066

Gropius House, Lincoln, MA.................690

The Grove, Glenview, IL.....................438

Gruenewald Historic House, Anderson, IN....................................467

Gulf Branch Nature Center, Arlington, VA....................................1496

Gulfcoast Wonder and Imagination Zone, dba G.WIZ, Sarasota, FL.............344

Hakone Gardens, Saratoga, CA...............185

Hammond Museum and Japanese Stroll Garden, North Salem, NY.............1043

Hana Cultural Center, Hana, Maui, HI........392

Hancock Shaker Village, Inc., Pittsfield, MA....................................703

Happy Hollow Park & Zoo, San Jose, CA....................................171

Harding Home and Museum, Marion, OH.1174

Harkness Memorial State Park, Waterford, CT.........................264

Harold L. Lyon Arboretum, Honolulu, HI...395

Harriet Alexander Nature Center, Roseville, MN.........................788

Harry P. Leu Gardens, Orlando, FL.............331

Harry S. Truman Little White House Museum, Key West, FL...............317

Hartman Reserve Nature Center, Cedar Falls, IA................................507

Hathaway Ranch Museum, Santa Fe Springs, CA...........................182

Hawaii Tropical Botanical Garden, Papaikou, HI.........................401

Hawk Mountain Sanctuary, Kempton, PA.1264

Hayes Regional Arboretum, Richmond, IN....................................497

Heard Natural Science Museum and Wildlife Sanctuary, Inc., McKinney, TX....................................1437

Hearst Castle, San Simeon, CA...............177

Heathcote Botanical Gardens, Inc., Fort Pierce, FL.............................309

Henry Doorly Zoo, Omaha, NE.................871

Henry Foundation for Botanical Research, Gladwyne, PA...............1256

Henry Vilas Park Zoo, Madison, WI.........1605

The Herbarium of the University of the Pacific, Stockton, CA.............189

Hereford Inlet Lighthouse, North Wildwood, NJ.........................917

The Heritage Museum, Baltimore, MD........632

Heritage Museums & Gardens, Sandwich, MA....................................707

Heritage of the Americas Museum, El Cajon, CA................................92

The Hermitage Foundation, Norfolk, VA...1521

Hershey Gardens, Hershey, PA...............1260

Hickory Hill, Thomson, GA...................388

Hidden Lake Gardens, Tipton, MI.............765

High Desert Museum, Bend, OR...............1220

Highland Botanical Park, Rochester, NY...1058

Highland Community College Arboretum, Freeport, IL.........................435

The Highlands, Fort Washington, PA.........1254

Highlands Center for Natural History, Prescott, AZ...........................42

Hildene, The Lincoln Family Home, Manchester, VT.........................1481

Hill-Stead Museum, Farmington, CT..........241

Hills and Dales Estate, LaGrange, GA........375

Hillsboro Museums, Hillsboro, KS.............544

Hilltop Garden and Nature Center, Bloomington, IN......................469

Hillwood Museum & Gardens, Washington, DC.........................280

Historic Annapolis Foundation, Annapolis, MD 628
Historic Bethabara Park, Winston-Salem, NC 1125
Historic Bok Sanctuary, Lake Wales, FL 320
Historic Hudson Valley, Tarrytown, NY...1077
Historic Jefferson College, Washington, MS 810
Historic London Town and Gardens, Edgewater, MD 642
Historic Oakland Cemetery, Atlanta, GA 360
Historic Price House, Woodruff, SC 1343
Historic Rosedale, Charlotte, NC...............1095
Historic Sauder Village, Archbold, OH 1140
Historic Smithfield, Blacksburg, VA...........1497
Historic Spanish Point, Osprey, FL 333
Historic Walnford, Upper Freehold Twp., NJ 929
Historic Westville, Inc., Lumpkin, GA........376
Historical Shrine Foundation of San Diego County, San Diego, CA................156
Historical Society of Old Yarmouth, Yarmouth Port, MA 722
History of Medicine Collections, Durham, NC 1098
The Holden Arboretum, Kirtland, OH 1170
Home of Stone (The Mueller-Schmidt House 1881), a Ford County Museum, curated by Ford County Historic Society, Dodge City, KS 537
Homeopathy Works, Berkeley Springs, WV 1580
Homestead Acre and the Hill-Palmer House, Chatsworth, CA............82
Honolulu Botanical Gardens, Honolulu, HI 396
Honolulu Zoo, Honolulu, HI 396
Hoover Historical Center, North Canton, OH 1179
Houston Museum of Natural Science, Houston, TX 1427
Houston Zoo, Inc., Houston, TX 1427
Hoyt Arboretum, Portland, OR 1231
Hugh Mercer Apothecary Shop, Fredericksburg, VA 1506
Hui No'eau Visual Arts Center, Makawao, Maui, HI 401
Humboldt Redwoods State Park Visitor Center, Weott, CA 197
Humboldt State University Natural History Museum, Arcata, CA............72
Huntington Library, Art Collections, and Botanical Gardens, San Marino, CA 174
Huntington Museum of Art, Inc., Huntington, WV 1583
Huntsville/Madison County Botanical Garden, Huntsville, AL 11
Hurst Ranch Historical Foundation, West Covina, CA 197
The Hyland House, Guilford, CT 243

Idaho Botanical Garden, Boise, ID..............403
Illinois and Michigan Canal Commissioners Office Museum, Lockport, IL............443
Imaginarium Hands-On Museum, Fort Myers, FL 309
The Imaginarium Science Discovery Center, Anchorage, AK 22
Indianapolis Zoo, Indianapolis, IN 485
Institute of Ecosystem Studies, Millbrook, NY 1014
International Crane Foundation, Baraboo, WI 1591
Isabella Stewart Gardner Museum, Boston, MA 666

J.L. Scott Marine Education Center and Aquarium, Gulf Coast Research Laboratory College of Marine Sciences, The U. of Southern Mississippi, Biloxi, MS 798

Jacksonville Zoo and Gardens, Jacksonville, FL............315
James A. Garfield National Historic Site, Mentor, OH 1176
James A. McFaul Environmental Center of Bergen County, Wyckoff, NJ............931
James & Meryl Hearst Center for the Arts and Sculpture Garden, Cedar Falls, IA............508
James Madison's Montpelier, Montpelier Station, VA............1518
Japanese Friendship Garden, San Diego, CA............156
The Japanese Garden, Van Nuys, CA...........194
JC Raulston Arboretum at NC State University, Raleigh, NC............1115
Jenkins Arboretum, Devon, PA 1249
Jerome Ford Nature Center, Alexandria, VA 1493
Jesse Hepler Lilac Arboretum, University of New Hampshire, Durham, NH............886
Jimmie Rodgers Museum, Meridian, MS....805
John A. Finch Arboretum, Spokane, WA.....1571
John and Mable Ringling Museum of Art, Sarasota, FL............344
John Burroughs Association, Inc., West Park, NY 1085
John G. Neihardt State Historic Site, Bancroft, NE............856
John G. Shedd Aquarium, Chicago, IL 422
John James Audubon Center at Mill Grove, Audubon, PA 1241
John Sydnor's 1847 Powhatan House, Galveston, TX............1421
John Wornall House Museum, Kansas City, MO 821
Johnson Ferry House Museum, Titusville, NJ 926
Joshua Tree National Park, Oasis Visitor Center, Twentynine Palms, CA 193
The Journey Museum, Rapid City, SD.......1354
The Junior Museum of Bay County, Panama City, FL............334
Jurupa Mountains Cultural Center, Riverside, CA 149

Kalamazoo Nature Center, Inc., Kalamazoo, MI............748
Kalaupapa National Historical Park, Kalaupapa, HI............400
Kanapaha Botanical Gardens, Gainesville, FL............311
Kansas City Zoo, Kansas City, MO 821
Kauffman Museum, North Newton, KS....553
Keeler Tavern Museum, Ridgefield, CT.......259
Kenilworth Aquatic Gardens, Washington, DC............281
Kensington Metropark Nature Center, Milford, MI............755
Kentucky Department of Fish & Wildlife Resources-Salato Wildlife Education Center, Frankfort, KY 569
Ker Place, Onancock, VA............1523
Key West Tropical Forest & Botanical Garden, Key West, FL............318
Kid City - The Children's Museum of Tampa, Tampa, FL............349
Kidspace Children's Museum, Pasadena, CA............140
Kimberly Crest House & Gardens, Redlands, CA............147
Kingwood Center, Mansfield, OH 1173
Klehm Arboretum & Botanical Garden, Rockford, IL............455
Knott House Museum, Tallahassee, FL.......347
Knox Headquarters State Historic Site, Vails Gate, NY............1080
Knoxville Zoological Gardens, Knoxville, TN............1370
Kohl Children's Museum of Greater Chicago, Glenview, IL 438
Koreshan State Historic Site, Estero, FL......306
Krohn Conservatory, Cincinnati, OH.........1150

Kruse House Museum, West Chicago, IL....464
La Purisima Mission State Historic Park, Lompoc, CA 109
Ladew Topiary Gardens, Monkton, MD.......649
Lady Bird Johnson Wildflower Center, Austin, TX 1390
Lake Erie Nature & Science Center, Bay Village, OH 1141
Lake Mead National Recreation Area, Boulder City, NV 875
Lake View Nature Center, Oakbrook Terrace, IL 449
Landis Valley Museum, Lancaster, PA 1266
Landmark Park, Dothan, AL............8
Lanterman House, La Canada Flintridge, CA 105
LaSalle County Historical Society Museum, Utica, IL 462
Laughing Brook Education Center & Wildlife Sanctuary, Hampden, MA........686
Laurens Henry Cohn, Sr. Memorial Plant Arboretum, Baton Rouge, LA................586
Lawrence County Gray House Museum, Ironton, OH 1169
Lewis Ginter Botanical Garden, Richmond, VA 1530
Liberty Science Center, Jersey City, NJ 909
Lichterman Nature Center, Memphis, TN..1373
Lilacia Park-Lombard Park District, Lombard, IL............443
Lincoln Children's Zoo, Lincoln, NE...........866
Lincoln Memorial Garden and Nature Center, Springfield, IL 459
Lincoln Park Conservatory, Chicago, IL......423
Lindsay Wildlife Museum, Walnut Creek, CA............196
The Living Arts and Science Center, Inc., Lexington, KY 573
The Living Desert, Palm Desert, CA 138
Living Desert Zoo and Gardens State Park, Carlsbad, NM 938
Living History Farms, Urbandale, IA...........529
Log Cabin Village, Fort Worth, TX...........1417
Long Branch Nature Center, Arlington, VA............1496
Longue Vue House & Gardens, New Orleans, LA............596
Longwood Gardens, Kennett Square, PA ...1264
The Los Angeles County Arboretum & Botanic Garden, Arcadia, CA 71
The Los Angeles Zoo and Botanical Gardens, Los Angeles, CA 119
Louisiana Arboretum, State Preservation Area, Ville Platte, LA............603
Louisville Science Center, Louisville, KY ...577
Louisville Zoological Garden, Louisville, KY............578
Lower Rio Grande Valley Nature Center, Weslaco, TX 1460
Lummis Home: El Alisal, Los Angeles, CA............119
Luther Burbank Home & Gardens, Santa Rosa, CA............184
Lyman Estate, The Vale, Waltham, MA 715
Lyndhurst, Tarrytown, NY............1078
Lynnhaven House, Virginia Beach, VA 1542

MacCallum More Museum and Gardens, Chase City, VA............1500
MacKenzie Environmental Education Center, Poynette, WI 1618
Mackinac Island State Park Commission-Mackinac State Historic Parks, Mackinaw City, MI 752
Mackinac State Historic Parks-Fort Mackinac & Mackinac Island State Park, Mackinac Island, MI............752
Mackinac State Historic Parks-Historic Mill Creek, Mackinaw City, MI 753
Madison Museum of Fine Art, Madison, GA............378

Botanical (Living)–Continued

Magnolia Plantation and Gardens, Charleston, SC 1326
Malabar Farm State Park, Lucas, OH ... 1173
Malheur Historical Project, Stonehouse Museum, Vale, OR 1238
Maramec Museum, The James Foundation, Saint James, MO 830
The Marie Selby Botanical Gardens, Inc., Sarasota, FL 344
Marjorie Kinnan Rawlings Historic State Park, Cross Creek, FL 301
Marjorie McNeely Conservatory at Como Park, Saint Paul, MN 790
Maryhill Museum of Art, Goldendale, WA 1556
The Maryland Zoo in Baltimore, Baltimore, MD 635
Massachusetts Audubon at Connecticut River Valley Sanctuaries, Easthampton, MA 681
Massee Lane Gardens, Home of American Camellia Society, Fort Valley, GA 373
Matagorda County Museum, Bay City, TX 1393
Matthaei Botanical Gardens and Nichols Arboretum, Ann Arbor, MI 725
Maymont, Richmond, VA 1530
McCrory Gardens at South Dakota State University, Brookings, SD 1344
McDowell House Museum, Danville, KY ... 567
McKee Botanical Garden, Vero Beach, FL 352
McWane Science Center, Birmingham, AL 5
Melrose Plantation Home Complex, Melrose, LA 592
Memphis Botanic Garden, Goldsmith Civic Garden Center, Memphis, TN 1374
Mendocino Coast Botanic Garden, Fort Bragg, CA 95
Mesker Park Zoo & Botanic Garden, Evansville, IN 476
Middleton Place Foundation, Charleston, SC 1326
Mildred E. Mathias Botanical Garden, Los Angeles, CA 119
Milwaukee County Zoological Gardens, Milwaukee, WI 1612
The Minna Anthony Common Nature Center at Wellesley State Park, Fineview, NY 989
Minnesota Landscape Arboretum, University of Minnesota, Chaska, MN 770
Minnesota Zoo, Apple Valley, MN 768
Minnetrista, Muncie, IN 492
The Mission House, Stockbridge, MA 712
Mission San Antonio de Padua, Jolon, CA 105
Mission San Juan Capistrano Museum, San Juan Capistrano, CA 173
Mission San Miguel, San Miguel, CA 175
Mississippi Agriculture & Forestry/National Agricultural Aviation Museum, Jackson, MS 802
Mississippi Museum of Natural Science, Jackson, MS 803
Mississippi Petrified Forest, Flora, MS 800
Mississippi Society Daughters of the American Revolution Rosalie House Museum, Natchez, MS 805
Missouri Botanical Garden, Saint Louis, MO 834
Mitchell Park Horticultural Conservatory, Milwaukee, WI 1612
Moanalua Gardens Foundation, Honolulu, HI 397
Mobile Botanical Gardens, Mobile, AL 14
Moccasin Lake Nature Park, An Environmental & Energy Education Center, Clearwater, FL 299

Moffatt-Ladd House and Garden, Portsmouth, NH 894
Mohonk Preserve, Inc., Gardiner, NY 993
Montalvo Arts Center, Saratoga, CA 185
Montclair Historical Society, Montclair, NJ 912
Monterey Bay Aquarium, Monterey, CA 127
Montgomery Zoo, Montgomery, AL 17
Montpelier Mansion, Laurel, MD 648
Moorten Botanic Garden and Cactarium, Palm Springs, CA 138
The Morikami Museum and Japanese Gardens, Delray Beach, FL 305
Mormon Station State Historic Park, Genoa, NV 877
Morningside Nature Center, Gainesville, FL 311
Morris Arboretum of the University of Pennsylvania, Philadelphia, PA 1283
Morris-Jumel Mansion, New York, NY 1030
Morrow Mountain State Park, Albemarle, NC 1088
The Morton Arboretum, Lisle, IL 443
Morven Park, Leesburg, VA 1512
Mount Airy Arboretum, Cincinnati, OH ... 1150
Mt. Kearsarge Indian Museum, Warner, NH 897
Mount Pisgah Arboretum, Eugene, OR 1224
Mount Vernon Hotel Museum & Garden, New York, NY 1031
Mountain Skies Astronomical Society & Science Center, Lake Arrowhead, CA 107
Mounts Botanical Garden, West Palm Beach, FL 353
Muir Woods National Monument, Mill Valley, CA 125
Mulford Farm, East Hampton, NY 986
Museum of Ancient Artifacts, Las Vegas, NV 879
The Museum of Arts and Sciences, Inc. and Center for Florida History, Daytona Beach, FL 303
Museum of Discovery and Science, Fort Lauderdale, FL 307
Museum of Indian Culture, Allentown, PA 1239
Museum of Life and Science, Durham, NC 1098
Museum of Science and Industry, Tampa, FL 349
Museum of Seminole County History, Sanford, FL 343
Museum of South Texas History, Edinburg, TX 1410
Museum of Spanish Colonial Art - MoSCA, Santa Fe, NM 949
Museum of the Hudson Highlands, Cornwall-on-Hudson, NY 982
Myriad Botanical Gardens, Oklahoma City, OK 1208
Mystic Aquarium & Institute for Exploration, Mystic, CT 250

Nani Mau Gardens, Hilo, HI 393
Nantucket Lightship Basket Museum, Nantucket, MA 696
Nantucket Maria Mitchell Association, Nantucket, MA 696
Nashville Zoo at Grassmere, Nashville, TN 1379
The National Aquarium, Washington, DC 284
National Aquarium in Baltimore, Baltimore, MD 635
National Aviary in Pittsburgh, Inc., Pittsburgh, PA 1293
National Capital Parks-East, Washington, DC 284
National Museum of Natural History, Washington, DC 286
National Museum of the American Indian, Washington, DC 286
National Tropical Botanical Garden, Kalaheo, HI 399

National Wildlife Visitor Center, Patuxent Research Refuge, Laurel, MD 648
Native American Heritage Museum at Highland Mission State Historic Site, Highland, KS 544
Native American Museum, Terre Haute, IN 500
The Natural Science Center of Greensboro, Inc., Greensboro, NC 1104
The Nature Center at Shaker Lakes, Cleveland, OH 1155
Naumkeag, Stockbridge, MA 712
Nebraska State Capitol, Lincoln, NE 866
New Canaan Nature Center, New Canaan, CT 252
New Jersey Botanical Garden at Skylands (NJBG), Ringwood, NJ 923
New Jersey Meadowlands Environment Center, Lyndhurst, NJ 910
New Mexico Farm & Ranch Heritage Museum, Las Cruces, NM 940
New Orleans Pharmacy Museum, New Orleans, LA 597
New Richmond Preservation Society, New Richmond, WI 1615
The New York Botanical Garden, Bronx, NY 966
New York State Bureau of Historic Sites, Waterford, NY 1082
New York State Office of Parks, Recreation & Historic Preservation, Albany, NY 955
Newport State Park, Ellison Bay, WI 1597
Nicollet County Historical Society, Saint Peter, MN 793
Norfolk Botanical Garden, Norfolk, VA 1522
North Carolina Aquarium at Fort Fisher, Kure Beach, NC 1109
North Carolina Aquarium at Pine Knoll Shores, Pine Knoll Shores, NC 1114
North Carolina Aquarium on Roanoke Island, Manteo, NC 1110
North Carolina Botanical Garden, Chapel Hill, NC 1093
North Carolina Museum of Natural Sciences, Raleigh, NC 1116
North Carolina Zoological Park, Asheboro, NC 1088
North Central Oklahoma Cactus Botanical Garden, Covington, OK 1198
Northland Arboretum, Brainerd, MN 769
Northwest Trek Wildlife Park, Eatonville, WA 1552
The Nylander Museum of Natural History, Caribou, ME 609

The Oak Park Conservatory, Oak Park, IL 449
Oakwoods Metropark Nature Center, Belleville, MI 728
Oatland Island Education Center, Savannah, GA 385
Ojai Valley Historical Society and Museum, Ojai, CA 135
Oklahoma City Zoo, Oklahoma City, OK .. 1209
Oklahoma State University Botanical Garden, Stillwater, OK 1214
Olbrich Botanical Gardens, Madison, WI .. 1605
Old Bethpage Village Restoration, Old Bethpage, NY 1045
Old Cowtown Museum, Wichita, KS 562
The Old Manse, Concord, MA 677
Old Prairie Town at Ward-Meade Historic Site, Topeka, KS 560
Old Santee Canal Park, Moncks Corner, SC 1337
The Old Stone House, Washington, DC 289
Old Sturbridge Village, Sturbridge, MA 713
Old Trail Museum, Choteau, MT 844
Old Westbury Gardens, Old Westbury, NY 1045
Old World Wisconsin, Eagle, WI 1595
Oliver Kelley Farm, Elk River, MN 774

Olympic Sculpture Park, Seattle, WA 1568
Omniplex Science Museum, Oklahoma
    City, OK...1210
Orcutt Ranch, Canoga Park, CA....................81
Oregon Coast Aquarium, Newport, OR......1229
Oregon Trail Arboretum, Echo, OR............1223
Oregon Zoo, Portland, OR..........................1232
Orland E. White Arboretum, Boyce, VA....1497
Ormond Memorial Art Museum &
    Garden, Ormond Beach, FL....................333
Oroville Chinese Temple, Oroville, CA.......136
Orpheum Children's Science Museum,
    Champaign, IL...417
Overstreet-Kerr Historical Farm, Keota,
    OK..1203

Pacem in Terris, Warwick, NY 1082
Pacific Grove Museum of Natural
    History, Pacific Grove, CA......................137
Pacific Rim Bonsai Collection, Federal
    Way, WA...1554
Pacific Science Center, Seattle, WA 1568
Packwood House Museum, Lewisburg,
    PA...1268
Paine Art Center and Gardens, Oshkosh,
    WI...1617
Palm Beach Zoo at Dreher Park, West
    Palm Beach, FL.......................................353
Panola Mountain State Conservation
    Park, Stockbridge, GA.............................387
The Park-McCullough House, North
    Bennington, VT......................................1483
Parrot Jungle Island, Miami, FL...................325
Patterson Homestead, Dayton, OH 1161
Peel Mansion Museum & Historic
    Gardens, Bentonville, AR..........................55
Pember Museum of Natural History,
    Granville, NY...995
Pendarvis State Historic Site, Mineral
    Point, WI...1614
Peninsula State Park, Fish Creek, WI 1597
Pennsbury Manor, Morrisville, PA 1272
Pennsylvania German Cultural Heritage
    Center at Kutztown University,
    Kutztown, PA...1265
Pennsylvania Historical & Museum
    Commission, Harrisburg, PA..................1259
Pennypacker Mills, Schwenksville, PA 1297
Perryville Battlefield Museum, Perryville,
    KY..582
Petrified Creatures Museum of Natural
    History, Richfield Springs, NY 1057
Petrified Forest Museum, Calistoga, CA........80
Petrified Sea Gardens, Saratoga Springs,
    NY..1065
Philadelphia Society for the Preservation
    of Landmarks, Philadelphia, PA 1286
The Philadelphia Zoo, Philadelphia, PA.....1286
Phipps Conservatory and Botanical
    Gardens, Pittsburgh, PA 1293
Pickens County Museum of Art &
    History, Pickens, SC.............................1340
Pioneer Heritage Center, LSU-Shreveport,
    Shreveport, LA..601
Pioneer Museum and Vereins Kirche,
    Fredericksburg, TX...............................1419
Pioneers Park Nature Center, Lincoln, NE...867
Piqua Historical Area State Memorial,
    Piqua, OH...1182
Pitot House Museum, New Orleans, LA......598
Pittock Mansion, Portland, OR 1232
Pittsburgh Zoo and Aquarium, Pittsburgh,
    PA...1293
Plains Conservation Center, Aurora, CO......202
Planting Fields Arboretum State Historic
    Park, Oyster Bay, NY............................1049
Pointe Coupee Museum, New Roads, LA...599
Postville Courthouse State Historic Site,
    Lincoln, IL..442
Potawatomi State Park, Sturgeon Bay, WI.1624
Potawatomi Zoo, South Bend, IN................499
Pratt Museum, Homer, AK............................25

The Presby Memorial Iris Gardens,
    Upper Montclair, NJ................................929
The Preservation Society of Newport
    County/The Newport Mansions,
    Newport, RI...1315
Providence Canyon State Park, Lumpkin,
    GA..377
Providence Children's Museum,
    Providence, RI.......................................1317
Pueblo of Pojoaque, Poeh Museum, Santa
    Fe, NM...949
Pueblo Zoo, Pueblo, CO..............................230
Pyramid Hill Sculpture Park & Museum,
    Hamilton, OH..1168

Quail Botanical Gardens, Encinitas, CA 92
Quail Ridge Wilderness Conservancy,
    Davis, CA...90
Queen Emma Summer Palace, Honolulu,
    HI...398
Queens Botanical Garden, Flushing, NY 990
Queens County Farm Museum, Floral
    Park, NY...989
Quoddy Head State Park, Lubec, ME..........614

R.S. Barnwell Memorial Garden and Art
    Center, Shreveport, LA............................601
Rachel Carson Homestead, Springdale,
    PA...1301
Racine Zoological Gardens, Racine, WI 1619
Rancho La Patera - The Stow House
    G.V.H.S., Goleta, CA..............................100
Rancho Los Alamitos, Long Beach, CA 111
Rancho Los Cerritos Historic Site, Long
    Beach, CA...111
Rancho Santa Ana Botanic Garden at
    Claremont, Claremont, CA........................85
Randall Museum, San Francisco, CA...........168
Ravine Gardens State Park, Palatka, FL 333
Red Butte Garden & Arboretum, Salt
    Lake City, UT..1472
Red Rock Museum, Church Rock, NM 938
Reeves-Reed Arboretum, Summit, NJ..........925
Reid Park Zoo, Tucson, AZ...........................50
Reynolda Gardens of Wake Forest
    University, Winston-Salem, NC 1126
Rhododendron Species Botanical Garden,
    Federal Way, WA...................................1554
The Ridges Sanctuary, Inc., Baileys
    Harbor, WI..1590
Riley House Museum of African
    American History & Culture,
    Tallahassee, FL..348
Rio Grande Nature Center State Park,
    Albuquerque, NM...................................935
Riverbanks Zoological Park & Botanical
    Garden, Columbia, SC...........................1329
Riverbend Environmental Education
    Center, Gladwyne, PA............................1256
Riverside Nature Center, Kerrville, TX......1432
Riverside Zoo, Scottsbluff, NE....................872
Riverview at Hobson Grove, Bowling
    Green, KY...566
Robert A. Vines Environmental Science
    Center, Houston, TX..............................1429
Robert Bebb Herbarium, Norman, OK.......1206
Robert Fulton Birthplace, Quarryville, PA.1295
Robert Louis Stevenson House,
    Monterey, CA..128
Rock Creek Nature Center, Washington,
    DC..290
Rockingham, Kingston, NJ...........................909
Rockwood Park, Wilmington, DE................274
Rockwoods Reservation, Wildwood, MO 840
Rocky Mount Children's Museum and
    Science Center, Inc., Rocky Mount,
    NC..1118
Rocky Mount Museum, Piney Flats, TN....1383
Rodef Shalom Biblical Botanical Garden,
    Pittsburgh, PA.......................................1294
Roger Williams Park Zoo, Providence, RI.1318
The Root House Museum, Marietta, GA 379

Rose Hill Plantation State Historic Site,
    Union, SC..1343
Roseland Cottage, Woodstock, CT..............268
Rotary Nature Center, Oakland, CA............134
The Rotch-Jones-Duff House & Garden
    Museum, Inc., New Bedford, MA...........697
Rusch Botanical Garden, Citrus Heights,
    CA..84
The Rutgers Gardens, New Brunswick,
    NJ...916
Ruthmere Museum, Elkhart, IN...................475

Sacramento Zoo, Sacramento, CA...............153
Saginaw Valley Zoological Society,
    Saginaw, MI..763
St. Augustine Alligator Farm, Saint
    Augustine, FL..340
Saint-Gaudens National Historic Site,
    Cornish, NH..885
San Antonio Botanical Garden, San
    Antonio, TX..1449
San Antonio Zoological Society, San
    Antonio, TX..1450
San Bernardino County Museum,
    Redlands, CA...147
San Diego Wild Animal Park, Escondido,
    CA..93
San Diego Zoo, San Diego, CA 161
San Francisco Botanical Garden at
    Strybing Arboretum, San Francisco,
    CA..168
San Francisco Zoological Gardens, San
    Francisco, CA..170
San Gabriel Mission Museum, San
    Gabriel, CA...171
San Joaquin County Historical Society &
    Museum, Lodi, CA..................................109
San Mateo Arboretum Society, Inc., San
    Mateo, CA..175
Sanibel-Captiva Conservation Foundation,
    Inc., Sanibel, FL......................................343
Sanilac County Historical Museum and
    Village, Port Sanilac, MI.........................761
Santa Barbara Botanic Garden, Santa
    Barbara, CA...178
Santa Barbara Orchid Estate, Santa
    Barbara, CA...180
Santa Barbara Zoological Gardens, Santa
    Barbara, CA...180
Santa Fe Children's Museum, Santa Fe,
    NM..950
Santarella, Tyringham, MA 715
Saratoga Museum, Saratoga, WY..............1638
Sarett Nature Center, Benton Harbor, MI....729
Schedel Arboretum & Gardens, Elmore,
    OH..1163
Schiele Museum of Natural History and
    Lynn Planetarium, Gastonia, NC...........1102
Schifferstadt Architectural Museum,
    Frederick, MD...644
Schuyler-Hamilton House, Morristown,
    NJ...914
The Schuylkill Center for Environmental
    Education, Philadelphia, PA...................1288
Sci-Port Discovery Center, Shreveport,
    LA...601
Science Museum of Long Island,
    Manhasset, NY......................................1013
Sciworks, Winston-Salem, NC....................1126
Scott Arboretum of Swarthmore College,
    Swarthmore, PA.....................................1302
Seacoast Science Center, Rye, NH..............896
Seattle Aquarium, Seattle, WA..................1568
Sedgwick County Zoo, Wichita, KS............562
Senator Fong's Plantation & Gardens,
    Kaneohe, HI..400
Seneca Park Zoo, Rochester, NY 1060
Seney National Wildlife Refuge Visitor
    Center, Seney, MI...................................764
Shaker Historical Society, Shaker
    Heights, OH...1185
Sharon Audubon Center, Sharon, CT..........259

Botanical (Living)–Continued

Shenandoal Valley Discovery Museum, Winchester, VA ...1546
Sherman Gardens, Corona del Mar, CA ...87
Sherwood Forest Plantation, Charles City, VA ...1498
Ships of the Sea Maritime Museum/William Scarbrough House, Savannah, GA ...386
Sieur de Monts Springs Nature Center, Bar Harbor, ME ...605
Six Flags Marine World, Vallejo, CA ...194
Slate Run Living Historical Farm, Metro Parks, Ashville, OH ...1140
Smithsonian Institution, Washington, DC ...290
Snug Harbor Cultural Center - Visitors' Center and Newhouse Center for Contemporary Art, Staten Island, NY ...1073
Socrates Sculpture Park, Long Island City, NY ...1012
Sonnenberg Gardens & Mansion State Historic Park, Canandaigua, NY ...975
South Carolina Aquarium, Charleston, SC ...1326
The South Carolina Botanical Garden, Clemson, SC ...1328
South Dakota Discovery Center and Aquarium, Pierre, SD ...1353
South Shore Natural Science Center, Inc., Norwell, MA ...700
Southern Forest Heritage Museum, Long Leaf, LA ...591
Southern Forest World, Waycross, GA ...391
Spiro Mounds Archaeological Center, Spiro, OK ...1214
Spring Valley Nature Center & Heritage Farm, Schaumburg, IL ...457
Springbrook Nature Center, Fridley, MN ...776
Squam Lakes Natural Science Center, Holderness, NH ...889
Stagecoach Inn Museum Complex, Newbury Park, CA ...130
Stan Hywet Hall and Gardens, Inc., Akron, OH ...1139
Starhill Forest Arboretum, Petersburg, IL ...451
The State Botanical Garden of Georgia, Athens, GA ...357
Staten Island Botanical Garden, Staten Island, NY ...1073
Stephenson County Historical Society, Freeport, IL ...436
The Stevens-Coolidge Place, a property of The Trustees of Reservations, North Andover, MA ...698
Still National Osteopathic Museum, Kirksville, MO ...824
Stone Quarry Hill Art Park, Inc., Cazenovia, NY ...977
Storrowton Village Museum, West Springfield, MA ...718
Stranahan House, Inc., Fort Lauderdale, FL ...308
Stuhr Museum of the Prairie Pioneer, Grand Island, NE ...862
Sturdivant Hall, Selma, AL ...18
Sulphur Creek Nature Center, Hayward, CA ...102
Susan B. Anthony House, Rochester, NY ...1060
Sylvia Plotkin Judaica Museum of Congregation Beth Israel, Scottsdale, AZ ...44

Tallahassee Museum, Tallahassee, FL ...348
Tampa's Lowry Park Zoo, Tampa, FL ...350
Tanglewood Nature Center and Museum, Elmira, NY ...988
Telluride Historical Museum, Telluride, CO ...233
Texas Discovery Gardens, Dallas, TX ...1408
The Texas Zoo, Victoria, TX ...1457
Thomas-Foreman Home, Muskogee, OK ...1205
Thornton W. Burgess Museum, Sandwich, MA ...708

Tinker Swiss Cottage Museum, Rockford, IL ...456
Tohono Chul Park Inc., Tucson, AZ ...51
Toledo Botanical Garden, Toledo, OH ...1187
The Toledo Zoo, Toledo, OH ...1187
Topeka Zoological Park, Topeka, KS ...560
Trailside Nature and Science Center, Mountainside, NJ ...915
The Trustees of Reservations, Beverly, MA ...662
Tryon Palace Historic Sites and Gardens, New Bern, NC ...1112
Tu-Endie-Wei State Park, Point Pleasant, WV ...1586
Tucker Tower Nature Center, Ardmore, OK ...1196
Tucson Botanical Gardens, Tucson, AZ ...51
Tudor Place Foundation, Inc., Washington, DC ...292
Tulsa Zoo & Living Museum, Tulsa, OK ...1216
Turabo University, Gurabo, PR ...1641
Turtle Bay Exploration Park, Redding, CA ...146
Tyler Arboretum, Media, PA ...1271
Tyler Rose Museum, Tyler, TX ...1457

USDA Forest Service - Land Between the Lakes, Golden Pond, KY ...570
U.S National Arboretum, Washington, DC ...292
UC Davis Arboretum, Davis, CA ...90
Umpqua Discovery Center, Reedsport, OR ...1234
Union County Heritage Museum, New Albany, MS ...806
United States Botanic Garden, Washington, DC ...292
University of Alabama Arboretum, Tuscaloosa, AL ...20
University of California Botanical Garden, Berkeley, CA ...77
University of California Irvine Arboretum, Irvine, CA ...105
University of Oregon Museum of Natural and Cultural History, Eugene, OR ...1224
University of Puerto Rico Department of Marine Sciences Museum, Mayaguez, PR ...1641
University of South Florida Botanical Garden, Tampa, FL ...350
University of Tennessee Arboretum, Oak Ridge, TN ...1382
University of Washington Botanic Garden, Seattle, WA ...1569
University of Wisconsin-Madison Arboretum, Madison, WI ...1605
Upham Mansion, Marshfield, WI ...1608
Utah's Hogle Zoo, Salt Lake City, UT ...1473
Ute Indian Museum/Montrose Visitor Center, Montrose, CO ...228
Utica Zoo, Utica, NY ...1080

Varner-Hogg Plantation State Historic Site, West Columbia, TX ...1461
Victor Valley Museum & Art Gallery, Apple Valley, CA ...71
Virginia Aquarium & Marine Science Center, Virginia Beach, VA ...1542
Virginia Living Museum, Newport News, VA ...1520
Virginia Robinson Gardens, Beverly Hills, CA ...78
Virginia Zoological Park, Norfolk, VA ...1523
The Voas Nature Area/Voas Museum, Minburn, IA ...523

W.J. Beal Botanical Garden, East Lansing, MI ...740
W.K. Kellogg Bird Sanctuary of Michigan State University, Augusta, MI ...726
W.W. Seymour Botanical Conservatory, Tacoma, WA ...1574

Wahkeena Nature Preserve, Sugar Grove, OH ...1186
Waikiki Aquarium, Honolulu, HI ...399
Waimea Arboretum and Botanical Garden in Waimea Valley Audubon Center, Haleiwa, HI ...392
The Walker Art Collection of the Garnett Public Library, Garnett, KS ...541
Walter B. Jacobs Memorial Nature Park, Shreveport, LA ...602
Walter E. Heller Nature Center, Highland Park, IL ...439
Washington County Historical Society, Washington, PA ...1305
Washington National Cathedral, Washington, DC ...294
Washington Oaks Gardens State Park, Palm Coast, FL ...334
Washington Park Botanical Garden, Springfield, IL ...460
Washington Park Zoological Gardens, Michigan City, IN ...491
Washington State Capital Museum and Outreach Center, Olympia, WA ...1560
Wave Hill, Bronx, NY ...967
Wentworth-Coolidge Mansion, Portsmouth, NH ...895
West Rock Nature Center, New Haven, CT ...254
Westerly Public Library, Westerly, RI ...1320
Western North Carolina Nature Center, Asheville, NC ...1090
The Wetlands Institute, Stone Harbor, NJ ...925
Whitefish Dunes State Park, Sturgeon Bay, WI ...1624
Whitehouse Nature Center, Albion, MI ...723
Wilbur D. May Museum, Reno, NV ...882
Wilbur Wright Birthplace & Interpretive Center, Hagerstown, IN ...480
The Wilderness Center Inc., Wilmot, OH ...1192
Wildlife Museum at Petaluma High School, Petaluma, CA ...142
Wildlife Prairie State Park, Hanna City, IL ...439
Wildlife World Zoo, Litchfield Park, AZ ...37
Wing Haven Garden and Bird Sanctuary, Charlotte, NC ...1096
Winterthur Museum & Country Estate, Winterthur, DE ...274
Woldumar Nature Center, Lansing, MI ...751
Woodland Park Zoo, Seattle, WA ...1570
Woodlawn Plantation Museum, Alexandria, VA ...1494
Woodrow Wilson Presidential Library at His Birthplace, Staunton, VA ...1537
Worcester County Horticultural Society/Tower Hill Botanic Garden, Boylston, MA ...670
World Forestry Center, Portland, OR ...1233
Wupatki National Monument, Flagstaff, AZ ...34
Wylie House Museum, Bloomington, IN ...470

Yakima Area Arboretum & Botanical Garden, Yakima, WA ...1579
Ybor City Museum State Park, Tampa, FL ...351
Youth Science Institute, San Jose, CA ...173
Youth Science Institute at Vasona Park, Los Gatos, CA ...123

Zalud House, Porterville, CA ...144
The Zoo, Gulf Breeze, FL ...312
Zoo Atlanta, Atlanta, GA ...364
Zoo Montana, Billings, MT ...842
Zoo New England, Boston, MA ...669
Zooamerica North America Wildlife Park, Hershey, PA ...1261

Botanical (Nonliving)

ASRI Environmental Education Center, Bristol, RI ...1310

The Academy of Natural Sciences of Philadelphia, Philadelphia, PA 1275

The Accokeek Foundation, Inc., Accokeek, MD..............................627

Adventure Science Center, Nashville, TN..1377

Alabama Museum of Natural History, Tuscaloosa, AL 19

Alaska Museum of Natural History, Anchorage, AK...............................21

Alaska State Museum, Juneau, AK 25

Allegany County Museum, Belmont, NY 961

Alutiiq Museum and Archaeological Repository, Kodiak, AK........................26

Anniston Museum of Natural History, Anniston, AL 3

Antelope Valley California Poppy Reserve, Lancaster, CA........................108

Anza-Borrego Desert State Park, Borrego Springs, CA.......................................79

Apostles Islands National Lakeshore, Bayfield, WI...................................1591

Applegate Park Zoo, Merced, CA 125

The Arboretum at Flagstaff, Flagstaff, AZ 32

Arches National Park Visitor Center, Moab, UT......................................1467

Arizona Zoological Society, dba the Phoenix Zoo, Phoenix, AZ..................40

Arkansas Post National Memorial, Gillett, AR...58

Armand Bayou Nature Center, Houston, TX..1424

Arnold Arboretum of Harvard University, Jamaica Plain, MA............................688

The Arthur & Kriebel Herbaria, Purdue University, West Lafayette, IN............503

Atlanta Botanical Garden, Atlanta, GA........357

Audubon Greenwich, Greenwich, CT 242

Audubon House & Tropical Gardens, Key West, FL..................................317

Audubon Louisiana Nature Center, New Orleans, LA.....................................594

Aullwood Audubon Center and Farm, Dayton, OH..................................1160

Aztec Museum and Pioneer Village, Aztec, NM....................................936

Barnes Foundation, Merion, PA.................1271

Bear Mountain Trailside Museums and Zoo, Bear Mountain, NY..................961

Belvedere Castle-Henry Luce Nature Observatory, New York, NY.................1021

Belvedere-Tiburon Landmarks Society, Tiburon, CA....................................192

Benson Memorial Museum, Malheur National Wildlife Refuge, Princeton, OR..1233

Bent's Old Fort National Historic Site, La Junta, CO..224

Berea College Burroughs Geological Museum, Berea, KY..........................565

Bernheim Arboretum and Research Forest, Clermont, KY.......................567

The Berry Botanic Garden, Portland, OR ..1230

Big Bend National Park, Big Bend, TX.....1396

Big Cypress National Preserve, Ochopee, FL...330

Big Thicket National Preserve, Kountze, TX..1432

Big Thunder Gold Mine, Keystone, SD.....1349

Billings Farm & Museum, Woodstock, VT..1490

Biltmore Estate, Asheville, NC.................1089

Birmingham Botanical Gardens, Birmingham, AL....................................4

Bishop Museum, Honolulu, HI..................394

Black Hills Reptile Gardens, Inc., Rapid City, SD..1354

Boerner Botanical Gardens, Hales Corners, WI..................................1600

Bonner County Historical Museum, Sandpoint, ID...................................409

Boonshoft Museum of Discovery, Dayton, OH..................................1160

The Botanic Garden of Smith College, Northampton, MA............................699

Botanical Museum of Harvard University, Cambridge, MA..............................672

Bowers Science Museum, Cortland, NY......982

Bowman's Hill Wildflower Preserve, New Hope, PA......................................1273

Boyce Thompson Arboretum, Superior, AZ...44

Brazosport Museum of Natural Science, Clute, TX.......................................1400

Brevard Museum of History & Science, Cocoa, FL......................................300

Brooklyn Botanic Garden, Brooklyn, NY 967

Brookside Gardens, Wheaton, MD..............657

Bryce Canyon National Park Visitor Center, Bryce, UT.............................1464

Buffalo Museum of Science, Buffalo, NY ..972

Buffalo National River, Harrison, AR 59

Buffalo Zoological Gardens, Buffalo, NY....972

Burke Museum of Natural History and Culture, Seattle, WA........................1565

Burpee Museum of Natural History, Rockford, IL....................................454

Cabin Nature Center, Wood Dale, IL..........466

Cable Natural History Museum, Cable, WI..1593

Cabrillo Marine Aquarium, San Pedro, CA...176

California Academy of Sciences, San Francisco, CA...................................163

Calkins Nature Area/Field Museum, Iowa Falls, IA..521

Call of the Wild Museum, Gaylord, MI.......742

Calusa Nature Center and Planetarium, Fort Myers, FL..................................308

Cape Cod Museum of Natural History, Inc., Brewster, MA...........................670

Capitol Reef National Park Visitor Center, Torrey, UT............................1475

Capitola Historical Museum, Capitola, CA..81

Capulin Volcano National Monument, Capulin, NM..................................937

Carlsbad Caverns National Park, Carlsbad, NM..................................937

Carnegie Museum of Natural History, Pittsburgh, PA................................1291

Cashmere Museum & Pioneer Village, Cashmere, WA...............................1550

Catherine Montgomery Interpretive Center, Greenwater, WA....................1556

Cedar Breaks National Monument, Cedar City, UT..1464

The Centennial Museum at the University of Texas at El Paso, El Paso, TX..........1411

The Central Museum, Central, AK................23

Cheyenne Mountain Zoological Park, Colorado Springs, CO.......................206

Chicago Botanic Garden, Glencoe, IL..........438

Chicago Zoological Park (Brookfield Zoo), Brookfield, IL...........................414

Chickasaw National Recreation Area, Sulphur, OK...................................1214

Chico Creek Nature Center, Chico, CA 83

Children's Museum/Detroit Public Schools, Detroit, MI..........................735

The Children's Museum of Science and Technology, Troy, NY.......................1079

Children's Museum of Southeastern Connecticut, Niantic, CT....................256

Chippewa Nature Center, Midland, MI........755

Chiricahua National Monument, Willcox, AZ..53

Chula Vista Nature Center, Chula Vista, CA..84

Cincinnati Museum Center at Union Terminal, Cincinnati, OH....................1149

Clark County Historical Society - Heritage Center of Clark County, Springfield, OH................................1186

Cleveland Botanical Garden, Cleveland, OH..1152

The Cleveland Museum of Natural History, Cleveland, OH........................1153

Cliffs of the Neuse State Park, Seven Springs, NC....................................1119

Clyde E. Buckley Wildlife Sanctuary, Frankfort, KY..................................568

Coe Hall, Oyster Bay, NY 1049

Colleton Museum, Walterboro, SC.............1343

Colorado National Monument, Fruita, CO...218

Colorado Plateau Biodiversity Center, Flagstaff, AZ......................................32

Congaree National Park, Hopkins, SC 1336

Connecticut Audubon Birdcraft Museum, Fairfield, CT....................................240

Connecticut Audubon Center at Fairfield, Fairfield, CT....................................240

Connecticut College Arboretum, New London, CT......................................255

Connecticut State Museum of Natural History and Connecticut Archaeology Center, Storrs, CT................................261

Corpus Christi Museum of Science and History, Corpus Christi, TX................1401

County of Westchester, Department of Parks, Recreation and Conservation, Mount Kisco, NY.............................1016

Coyote Point Museum for Environmental Education, San Mateo, CA.................175

Cranbrook Institute of Science, Bloomfield Hills, MI..........................730

Crane Point, Marathon, FL 323

Crater Lake National Park, Crater Lake, OR...1222

The Crosby Arboretum, Mississippi State University, Picayune, MS......................807

Crowley Museum & Nature Center, Sarasota, FL....................................344

Cumberland Island National Seashore, Saint Marys, GA................................382

Curry Historical Society Museum, Gold Beach, OR.....................................1225

Cuyahoga Valley National Park, Brecksville, OH..............................1144

Cylburn Arboretum, Baltimore, MD............631

D. Ralph Hostetter Museum of Natural History, Harrisonburg, VA..................1510

Dakota Zoo, Bismarck, ND.......................1128

The Dawes Arboretum, Newark, OH.........1177

De Graaf Nature Center, Holland, MI..........746

Death Valley National Park Visitor Center and Museums, Death Valley, CA...............91

Delaware Archaeology Museum, Dover, DE..269

Delaware Nature Society, Hockessin, DE 271

Denali National Park and Preserve, Denali Park, AK..................................23

Denver Botanic Gardens, Inc., Denver, CO..210

Des Moines Botanical Center, Des Moines, IA......................................514

Desert Botanical Garden, Phoenix, AZ 40

Devils Tower Visitor Center, Devils Tower, WY....................................1631

Dickson Mounds Museum, Lewistown, IL..442

Dinosaur State Park, Rocky Hill, CT..........259

The Discovery Center, Fresno, CA................96

Discovery Museum, Sacramento Museum of History, Science and Technology, Sacramento, CA................................152

Dodge Nature Center, West Saint Paul, MN...796

Earthplace - The Nature Discovery Center, Westport, CT..........................266

Effie Yeaw Nature Center, Carmichael, CA..82

Effigy Mounds National Monument, Harpers Ferry, IA.............................519

Botanical (Nonliving)–Continued

El Dorado Nature Center, Long Beach, CA 110

Eloise Butler Wildflower Garden and Bird Sanctuary, Minneapolis, MN 781

Environmental Education Center, Somerset County Park Commission, Basking Ridge, NJ 898

Everglades National Park, Homestead, FL ...313

Everhart Museum: Natural History, Science and Art, Scranton, PA 1298

Fairbanks Museum and Planetarium, Saint Johnsbury, VT 1486

Fairchild Tropical Botanic Garden, Coral Gables, FL 301

Family Museum, Bettendorf, IA 505

Fernbank Museum of Natural History, Atlanta, GA 359

Filoli Center, Woodside, CA 199

Florida Museum of Natural History, Gainesville, FL 310

Florissant Fossil Beds National Monument, Florissant, CO 216

Flowerdew Hundred Foundation, Hopewell, VA 1511

Fontenelle Nature Association, Bellevue, NE 857

Fort Clatsop National Memorial, Astoria, OR 1218

Fort Wayne Children's Zoo, Fort Wayne, IN 477

Fort Worth Museum of Science and History, Fort Worth, TX 1417

Fountain County War Museum, Inc., Veedersburg, IN 502

Frank H. McClung Museum, Knoxville, TN 1370

Garden in the Woods of the New England Wild Flower Society, Framingham, MA 683

Geology Museum, Huntington, WV 1583

George Landis Arboretum, Esperance, NY 989

Georgia Museum of Natural History, Athens, GA 356

Gerald E. Eddy Discovery Center, Chelsea, MI 732

George B. Dorr Museum of Natural History, Bar Harbor, ME 605

Gilman Museum, Hellertown, PA 1260

Glacier National Park Museum, West Glacier, MT 854

Golden Gate National Recreation Area, San Francisco, CA 165

Goodnow Museum State Historic Site, Manhattan, KS 550

Governor's Mansion State Historic Park, Sacramento, CA 152

Grand Canyon National Park Museum Collection, Grand Canyon National Park, AZ 36

Graves Museum of Archaeology and Natural History, Dania Beach, FL .....:..302

Great Basin National Park, Baker, NV 875

Great Sand Dunes National Monument and Preserve, Mosca, CO 229

Great Valley Museum of Natural History, Modesto, CA 126

Greene-Nieuwland Herbarium, Notre Dame, IN 495

Groveland Yosemite Gateway Museum, Groveland, CA 101

Guadalupe Mountains National Park, Salt Flat, TX 1447

Gulf Islands National Seashore, Gulf Breeze, FL 312

Gunnison Museum of Natural History, Pawling, NY 1051

Gwinnett County Parks & Recreation Outdoor Interpretive Section, Lawrenceville, GA 375

Hampton County Historical Museum, Hampton, SC 1334

Harold L. Lyon Arboretum, Honolulu, HI ...395

Hartman Reserve Nature Center, Cedar Falls, IA 507

Harvard Museum of Natural History, Cambridge, MA 672

The Harvard University Herbaria, Cambridge, MA 673

Henry Foundation for Botanical Research, Gladwyne, PA 1256

Henry Vilas Park Zoo, Madison, WI 1605

Herbarium of the University of Michigan, Ann Arbor, MI 724

The Herbarium of the University of the Pacific, Stockton, CA 189

Heritage of the Americas Museum, El Cajon, CA 92

Hi-Desert Nature Museum, Yucca Valley, CA 201

Highlands Center for Natural History, Prescott, AZ 42

Historic New Harmony, New Harmony, IN 494

Historical Society of Brookfield, Brookfield Center, VT 1477

The Holden Arboretum, Kirtland, OH 1170

Honolulu Botanical Gardens, Honolulu, HI 396

Hopewell Culture National Historical Park, Chillicothe, OH 1147

Hopewell Furnace National Historic Site, Elverson, PA 1251

Hot Springs National Park Visitor Center, Hot Springs, AR 60

Hubbell Trading Post National Historic Site, Ganado, AZ 34

Hugh Mercer Apothecary Shop, Fredericksburg, VA 1506

Idaho Museum of Natural History, Pocatello, ID 408

Illinois State Museum, Springfield, IL 458

Indiana Dunes National Lakeshore, Porter, IN 496

The Institute For American Indian Studies (IAIS), Washington Green, CT ...263

Intermountain Herbarium, Utah State University, Logan, UT 1466

International Crane Foundation, Baraboo, WI 1591

Isle Royale National Park, Houghton, MI 747

James Ford Bell Museum of Natural History, Minneapolis, MN 782

James R. Slater Museum of Natural History, Tacoma, WA 1573

Jean Lafitte National Historical Park & Preserve, New Orleans, LA 596

Jean P. Haydon Museum, Pago Pago, AS ..1640

Jimmie Rodgers Museum, Meridian, MS.....805

John G. Shedd Aquarium, Chicago, IL 422

John Muir National Historic Site, Martinez, CA 124

Joshua Tree National Park, Oasis Visitor Center, Twentynine Palms, CA 193

KU Natural History Museum and Biodiversity Research Center, Lawrence, KS 548

Kalamazoo Nature Center, Inc., Kalamazoo, MI 748

Kansas State University Herbarium, Manhattan, KS 551

Kauai Museum, Lihue, HI 401

Kensington Metropark Nature Center, Milford, MI 755

Kentucky Department of Fish & Wildlife Resources-Salato Wildlife Education Center, Frankfort, KY 569

Kidspace Children's Museum, Pasadena, CA 140

Kingman Museum, Battle Creek, MI 727

Kings Mountain National Military Park, Blacksburg, SC 1322

Kittson County History Center Museum, Lake Bronson, MN 778

Klondike Gold Rush National Historical Park, Skagway, AK 28

Knife River Indian Villages National Historic Site, Stanton, ND 1136

Koke'e Natural History Museum, Kauai, HI 400

L.H. Bailey Hortorium, Ithaca, NY 1003

Lady Bird Johnson Wildflower Center, Austin, TX 1390

Las Cabezas de San Juan Nature Reserve (El Faro), Fajardo, PR 1641

Las Vegas Natural History Museum, Las Vegas, NV 879

Lava Beds National Monument, Tulelake, CA 193

Lewis & Clark Boat House and Nature Center, Saint Charles, MO 830

Lewis Ginter Botanical Garden, Richmond, VA 1530

Lichterman Nature Center, Memphis, TN ..1373

Lightner Museum, Saint Augustine, FL 339

Lilacia Park-Lombard Park District, Lombard, IL 443

Lincoln Boyhood National Memorial, Lincoln City, IN 488

Lindsay Wildlife Museum, Walnut Creek, CA 196

Little Bighorn Battlefield National Monument, Crow Agency, MT 844

Longfellow Evangeline State Historic Site, Saint Martinville, LA 600

Longwood Gardens, Kennett Square, PA ...1264

The Los Angeles County Arboretum & Botanic Garden, Arcadia, CA 71

Louisiana Arboretum, State Preservation Area, Ville Platte, LA 603

Louisiana State University Herbarium, Baton Rouge, LA 586

Louisville Science Center, Louisville, KY ...577

Lower Rio Grande Valley Nature Center, Weslaco, TX 1460

Lyndon B. Johnson National Historical Park, Johnson City, TX 1431

Madison County Historical Society-Cottage Lawn, Oneida, NY 1045

Maidu Interpretive Center, Roseville, CA 151

Maine State Museum, Augusta, ME 604

Maramec Museum, The James Foundation, Saint James, MO 830

The Marie Selby Botanical Gardens, Inc., Sarasota, FL 344

Martha's Vineyard Museum, Edgartown, MA 681

Matagorda County Museum, Bay City, TX 1393

Matthaei Botanical Gardens and Nichols Arboretum, Ann Arbor, MI 725

Maturango Museum of the Indian Wells Valley, Ridgecrest, CA 148

May Natural History Museum and Museum of Space Exploration, Colorado Springs, CO 207

Meeteetse Museum District, Meeteetse, WY 1636

Memphis Botanic Garden, Goldsmith Civic Garden Center, Memphis, TN 1374

Mesa Verde National Park Museum, Mesa Verde National Park, CO 228

Michigan State University Herbarium, East Lansing, MI 740

Mildred E. Mathias Botanical Garden, Los Angeles, CA 119

Milwaukee County Zoological Gardens, Milwaukee, WI 1612

Milwaukee Public Museum, Milwaukee, WI 1612

Minnesota Landscape Arboretum, University of Minnesota, Chaska, MN 770

Mission San Miguel, San Miguel, CA 175

Mississippi Museum of Natural Science, Jackson, MS................803

Mississippi Petrified Forest, Flora, MS 800

Missouri Botanical Garden, Saint Louis, MO................834

Mobile Medical Museum, Mobile, AL...........14

Moccasin Lake Nature Park, An Environmental & Energy Education Center, Clearwater, FL................299

Mohonk Preserve, Inc., Gardiner, NY 993

The Monhegan Museum, Monhegan, ME....615

Monte L. Bean Life Science Museum, Provo, UT................1469

Montgomery Zoo, Montgomery, AL 17

Moorten Botanic Garden and Cactarium, Palm Springs, CA................138

Mormon Station State Historic Park, Genoa, NV................877

Morningside Nature Center, Gainesville, FL................311

Morris Arboretum of the University of Pennsylvania, Philadelphia, PA....1283

Morro Bay State Park Museum of Natural History, Morro Bay, CA 129

The Morton Arboretum, Lisle, IL................443

Mount Pisgah Arboretum, Eugene, OR......1224

Mount Washington Museum and The Weather Discovery Center, North Conway, NH................893

Muir Woods National Monument, Mill Valley, CA................125

The Murie Museum, Kelly, WY 1634

The Museum at Warm Springs, Warm Springs, OR................1238

Museum of Discovery and Science, Fort Lauderdale, FL................307

Museum of Long Island Natural Sciences, Stony Brook, NY 1075

Museum of Natural History, Marshall, MN................780

Museum of Natural History and Planetarium, Providence, RI...................1317

Museum of Northern Arizona, Flagstaff, AZ................33

Museum of Paleontology, Berkeley, CA 76

Museum of Southwestern Biology, Albuquerque, NM................934

Museum of Western Colorado, Grand Junction, CO................220

Museum of Woodcarving, Shell Lake, WI.1621

Museum of York County, Rock Hill, SC ...1340

Myrtle Beach State Park Nature Center, Myrtle Beach, SC................1338

Nantucket Maria Mitchell Association, Nantucket, MA 696

The National Aquarium, Washington, DC....284

National Capital Parks-East, Washington, DC................284

National Museum of Natural History, Washington, DC................286

National Park Service, Washington, DC.......287

National Park Service-Great Falls Park, McLean, VA................1517

National Park Service Museum Resource Center, Landover, MD................648

National Park Service Vicksburg National Military Park-Cairo Museum, Vicksburg, MS................809

National Tropical Botanical Garden, Kalaheo, HI................399

National Wildlife Visitor Center, Patuxent Research Refuge, Laurel, MD 648

Natural History Museum, Portales, NM.......944

Natural History Museum of Los Angeles County, Los Angeles, CA................120

The Natural Science Center of Greensboro, Inc., Greensboro, NC.........1104

The Nature Center at Shaker Lakes, Cleveland, OH 1155

Nature Interpretive Center, Lebanon, MO....825

The Nature Museum at Grafton, Grafton, VT................1479

Nevada State Museum, Carson City, NV 876

New Britain Youth Museum, New Britain, CT................252

New Canaan Nature Center, New Canaan, CT................252

New Jersey State Museum, Trenton, NJ 927

New Mexico Museum of Natural History & Science, Albuquerque, NM................935

New Orleans Pharmacy Museum, New Orleans, LA................597

The New York Botanical Garden, Bronx, NY................966

New York State Museum, Albany, NY.........955

The Newark Museum, Newark, NJ................916

Newport State Park, Ellison Bay, WI.........1597

North Carolina Aquarium at Pine Knoll Shores, Pine Knoll Shores, NC................1114

North Carolina Botanical Garden, Chapel Hill, NC................1093

North Carolina Maritime Museum, Beaufort, NC................1091

North Carolina Museum of Forestry, Whiteville, NC................1122

North Cascades National Park Service Complex, Marblemount, WA 1559

The North Museum of Natural History & Science, Lancaster, PA................1266

The Northern Maine Museum of Science, University of Maine, Presque Isle, ME...620

Northwest Trek Wildlife Park, Eatonville, WA................1552

Nowetah's American Indian Museum & Store, New Portland, ME................615

Oak Glen School House Museum, Yucaipa, CA................200

Oakland Museum of California, Oakland, CA................134

Oakley Park, UDC Shrine, Edgefield, SC..1332

Oatland Island Education Center, Savannah, GA................385

Ohio Historical Society, Columbus, OH.....1158

Ojai Valley Historical Society and Museum, Ojai, CA 135

Old Santee Canal Park, Moncks Corner, SC................1337

Old State House, Hartford, CT................245

Old Trail Museum, Choteau, MT 844

Olympic National Park Visitor Center, Port Angeles, WA 1561

Oregon Museum of Science and Industry, Portland, OR................1231

Organ Pipe Cactus National Monument Museum, Ajo, AZ................29

Orland E. White Arboretum, Boyce, VA....1497

Orlando Science Center, Inc., Orlando, FL................332

Orma J. Smith Museum of Natural History, Caldwell, ID 405

Ormond Memorial Art Museum & Garden, Ormond Beach, FL................333

Ottawa Scouting Museum, Ottawa, IL 449

Ozark National Scenic Riverways, Van Buren, MO................839

Pacific Grove Museum of Natural History, Pacific Grove, CA 137

Padre Island National Seashore, Corpus Christi, TX................1402

Paleontological Research Institution, Ithaca, NY................1004

Panola Mountain State Conservation Park, Stockbridge, GA................387

Patten Lumbermen's Museum, Inc., Patten, ME................618

Paul Bunyan Logging Camp Museum, Eau Claire, WI................1596

Paul H. Karshner Memorial Museum, Puyallup, WA................1564

Peabody Museum of Natural History, New Haven, CT................253

The Pearson Museum, Springfield, IL..........460

Pecos National Historical Park, Pecos, NM................944

The Peggy Notebaert Nature Museum, Chicago, IL................426

Pember Museum of Natural History, Granville, NY................995

Petrified Creatures Museum of Natural History, Richfield Springs, NY.........1057

Petrified Forest Museum, Calistoga, CA........80

Philip L. Wright Zoological Museum and University of Montana Herbarium, Missoula, MT................852

Piedmont Environmental Center, High Point, NC................1107

Pink Palace Family of Museums, Memphis, TN................1375

Pinnacles National Monument, Paicines, CA................138

Pioneers Park Nature Center, Lincoln, NE...867

Pipestone National Monument, Pipestone, MN................787

Pitot House Museum, New Orleans, LA......598

Pittsburgh Zoo and Aquarium, Pittsburgh, PA................1293

Planting Fields Arboretum State Historic Park, Oyster Bay, NY................1049

Point Reyes National Seashore, Point Reyes, CA................143

Pratt Museum, Homer, AK................25

Presque Isle County Historical Museum, Rogers City, MI................762

Prince William Forest Park Visitor Center, Triangle, VA................1541

Providence Canyon State Park, Lumpkin, GA................377

Putnam Museum of History & Natural Science, Davenport, IA 513

Puukohola Heiau National Historic Site, Kamuela, HI................400

Quail Botanical Gardens, Encinitas, CA 92

Rancho Santa Ana Botanic Garden at Claremont, Claremont, CA................85

Randall Museum, San Francisco, CA..........168

Rangeley Lakes Region Logging Museum, Rangeley, ME................620

Redwood National and State Parks, Crescent City, CA................88

Riley House Museum of African American History & Culture, Tallahassee, FL................348

Rio Grande Nature Center State Park, Albuquerque, NM................935

River Hills Visitor Center, Wildwood, MO................840

River Legacy Living Science Center, Arlington, TX................1388

Riverbend Environmental Education Center, Gladwyne, PA................1256

Riverside Metropolitan Museum, Riverside, CA................150

Riverside Nature Center, Kerrville, TX......1432

Robert A. Vines Environmental Science Center, Houston, TX................1429

Robert Bebb Herbarium, Norman, OK......1206

Rock Creek Nature Center, Washington, DC................290

Rocky Mount Children's Museum and Science Center, Inc., Rocky Mount, NC................1118

Rocky Mountain Herbarium, Laramie, WY................1635

Rocky Mountain National Park, Estes Park, CO................215

Rotary Nature Center, Oakland, CA.............134

The Rutgers Gardens, New Brunswick, NJ................916

Botanical (Nonliving)–Continued

St. Croix National Scenic Riverway, Saint Croix Falls, WI 1620

St. Joseph Museum Inc., Saint Joseph, MO 831

Salida Museum, Salida, CO 232

Salinas Pueblo Missions National Monument, Mountainair, NM 943

Sam Noble Oklahoma Museum of Natural History, Norman, OK 1206

San Bernardino County Museum, Redlands, CA...147

San Diego Natural History Museum, San Diego, CA 160

San Francisco Bay Model Visitor Center, Sausalito, CA 186

San Francisco Botanical Garden at Strybing Arboretum, San Francisco, CA...168

Sanibel-Captiva Conservation Foundation, Inc., Sanibel, FL 343

Santa Barbara Botanic Garden, Santa Barbara, CA 178

Santa Monica Mountains National Recreation Area, Thousand Oaks, CA.....191

Sarett Nature Center, Benton Harbor, MI.....729

Schiele Museum of Natural History and Lynn Planetarium, Gastonia, NC 1102

The Schuylkill Center for Environmental Education, Philadelphia, PA 1288

Schwenkfelder Library & Heritage Center, Pennsburg, PA 1275

Sci-Port Discovery Center, Shreveport, LA...601

Sci-Tech Center of Northern New York, Watertown, NY.......................................1084

Science Museum of Long Island, Manhasset, NY 1013

The Science Museum of Minnesota, Saint Paul, MN 792

Seacoast Science Center, Rye, NH 896

Seneca County Museum, Tiffin, OH 1186

Seney National Wildlife Refuge Visitor Center, Seney, MI 764

Sequoia and Kings Canyon National Parks, Three Rivers, CA 191

Sierra Sacramento Valley Medical Society Museum of Medical History, Sacramento, CA 153

Sieur de Monts Springs Nature Center, Bar Harbor, ME 605

Silver River Museum & Environmental Education Center, Ocala, FL..................330

Sleeping Bear Dunes National Lakeshore, Empire, MI...741

South Carolina Department of Parks, Recreation and Tourism, Columbia, SC...1330

South Shore Natural Science Center, Inc., Norwell, MA...700

Southern Vermont Natural History Museum, West Marlboro, VT 1489

Spartanburg Science Center, Spartanburg, SC...1342

Springbrook Nature Center, Fridley, MN 776

Springfield Museums - Springfield Science Museum, Springfield, MA 711

Stabler-Leadbeater Apothecary Museum and Museum Shop, Alexandria, VA 1494

Star Eco Station, Culver City, CA..................88

The State Botanical Garden of Georgia, Athens, GA 357

The State Museum of Pennsylvania, Harrisburg, PA 1259

Staten Island Institute of Arts & Sciences (SIIAS), Staten Island, NY 1074

Stephen C. Foster State Park, Fargo, GA.....371

The Stephens Museum, Fayette, MO 815

Stepping Stones Museum for Children, Norwalk, CT 257

Sternberg Museum of Natural History, Hays, KS 543

The Stone Museum, Monroe Township, NJ 912

Stones River National Battlefield, Murfreesboro, TN 1377

Suffolk County Vanderbilt Museum, Centerport, NY 977

Sugarlands Visitor Center, Gatlinburg, TN.1365

Sulphur Creek Nature Center, Hayward, CA...102

Summit Historical Society, Breckenridge, CO...204

Sunset Crater Volcano National Monument, Flagstaff, AZ 33

Tanglewood Nature Center and Museum, Elmira, NY 988

Texas Forestry Museum, Lufkin, TX 1436

The Texas Zoo, Victoria, TX 1457

Theodore Roosevelt National Park-Visitor Center, Medora, ND 1134

Thornton W. Burgess Museum, Sandwich, MA... 708

Timpanogos Cave National Monument, American Fork, UT 1462

Tipton County Museum, Veteran's Memorial & Nature Center, Covington, TN.......................................1364

Tobacco Farm Life Museum, Inc., Kenly, NC 1107

Tonto National Monument, Roosevelt, AZ...43

Trailside Nature and Science Center, Mountainside, NJ 915

Trailside Nature Museum, Cross River, NY 983

Transylvania Museum, Lexington, KY.........574

Tucker Tower Nature Center, Ardmore, OK 1196

Tucson Botanical Gardens, Tucson, AZ 51

Tucumcari Historical Research Institute, Tucumcari, NM......................................953

Tyler Arboretum, Media, PA 1271

U.S National Arboretum, Washington, DC...292

United States Botanic Garden, Washington, DC 292

University Herbarium & Jepson Herbarium, Berkeley, CA..........................77

University of Alaska Museum of the North, Fairbanks, AK 24

University of Colorado Museum, Boulder, CO..203

University of Iowa Hospitals & Clinics Medical Museum, Iowa City, IA 520

University of Iowa Museum of Natural History, Iowa City, IA 520

The University of Michigan Exhibit Museum of Natural History, Ann Arbor, MI 725

University of Michigan Museum of Anthropology, Ann Arbor, MI.................725

The University of Montana-Western Art Gallery & Museum, Dillon, MT.............846

University of Nebraska State Museum, Lincoln, NE 867

University of Northern Iowa Museums & Collections, Cedar Falls, IA...................508

University of Richmond Museums, Richmond, VA 1532

University of Washington Botanic Garden, Seattle, WA 1569

Utah Field House of Natural History State Park, Vernal, UT 1475

Utah Museum of Natural History, Salt Lake City, UT 1473

Virgin Islands National Park, St. John, VI.1644

Virginia Aquarium & Marine Science Center, Virginia Beach, VA...................1542

Virginia Living Museum, Newport News, VA.. 1520

Virginia Museum of Natural History, Martinsville, VA 1516

W.K. Kellogg Bird Sanctuary of Michigan State University, Augusta, MI..726

Wagner Free Institute of Science, Philadelphia, PA 1289

Waimea Arboretum and Botanical Garden in Waimea Valley Audubon Center, Haleiwa, HI 392

Walnut Canyon National Monument, Flagstaff, AZ 34

Walter B. Jacobs Memorial Nature Park, Shreveport, LA 602

The Wayne State University Museum of Natural History, Detroit, MI....................738

Weir Farm National Historic Site, Wilton, CT...267

Welder Wildlife Foundation & Refuge, Sinton, TX 1453

Western Archeological & Conservation Center, Tucson, AZ....................................52

Western North Carolina Nature Center, Asheville, NC 1090

Weymouth Woods-Sandhills Nature Preserve Museum, Southern Pines, NC.1120

Whiskeytown Unit, Whiskeytown-Shasta-Trinity National Recreation Area, Whiskeytown, CA........198

White Sands National Monument, Alamogordo, NM....................................932

Whitehouse Nature Center, Albion, MI.......723

Wildlife Museum at Petaluma High School, Petaluma, CA 142

William Cullen Bryant Homestead, Cummington, MA...................................678

William M. Colmer Visitor Center, Ocean Springs, MS...806

William Pryor Letchworth Museum, Castile, NY 976

Winedale, Center for American History, University of Texas at Austin, Round Top, TX 1446

World Forestry Center, Portland, OR 1233

Wupatki National Monument, Flagstaff, AZ...34

Yellowstone National Park, Gardiner, MT ...847

The Yosemite Museum, National Park Service, Yosemite National Park, CA......199

Youth Science Institute, San Jose, CA 173

Zion Human History Museum, Springdale, UT..1474

Zooamerica North America Wildlife Park, Hershey, PA..1261

Geological

The A.D. Buck Museum of Natural History & Science, Tonkawa, OK 1215

A. E. Seaman Mineral Museum, Houghton, MI 747

ASRI Environmental Education Center, Bristol, RI 1310

Abrams Planetarium, Michigan State University, East Lansing, MI 739

The Academy of Natural Sciences of Philadelphia, Philadelphia, PA 1275

Adair County Historical Society, Inc., Kirksville, MO..824

Adams County Historical Society Museum, Brighton, CO 204

Adams Museum & House, Deadwood, SD...1346

Adirondack Park Visitor Interpretive Center, Paul Smiths, NY 1051

Adler Planetarium & Astronomy Museum, Chicago, IL................................417

Alabama Museum of Natural History, Tuscaloosa, AL 19

Alaska Museum of Natural History, Anchorage, AK 21

Alden Historical Society, Inc., Alden, NY ...956
Alexander F. Morrison Planetarium, San Francisco, CA ...163
Allegany County Museum, Belmont, NY ...961
Alpine County Museum, Markleeville, CA ...124
Alutiiq Museum and Archaeological Repository, Kodiak, AK ...26
American Bald Eagle Foundation, Haines, AK ...25
American Museum of Natural History, New York, NY ...1019
Anderson County Historical Museum, Garnett, KS ...541
Andrew County Museum & Historical Society, Savannah, MO ...838
Anna Bemis Palmer Museum, York, NE ...875
Anna Miller Museum, Newcastle, WY ...1637
Annie E. Woodman Institute Museum, Dover, NH ...886
Annie Riggs Memorial Museum, Fort Stockton, TX ...1415
Anniston Museum of Natural History, Anniston, AL ...3
Ano Nuevo State Reserve, Pescadero, CA ...141
Anthropology Teaching Museum, California State University, Fullerton, Fullerton, CA ...98
Anza-Borrego Desert State Park, Borrego Springs, CA ...79
Archer County Museum, Archer City, TX .1387
Arches National Park Visitor Center, Moab, UT ...1467
Argus Planetarium, Ann Arbor, MI ...724
Arizona Mining and Mineral Museum, Phoenix, AZ ...39
Arizona Science Center, Phoenix, AZ ...39
Arizona-Sonora Desert Museum, Tucson, AZ ...48
Arkansas Museum of Natural Resources, Smackover, AR ...68
Arkansas State University Museum, Jonesboro, AR ...60
Arkansas Tech University Museum of Prehistory and History, Russellville, AR ...67
Artesia Historical Museum & Art Center, Artesia, NM ...936
Ash Hollow State Historical Park, Lewellen, NE ...864
Aspen Historical Society, Aspen, CO ...202
Astronaut Ellison S. Onizuka Space Center, Kailua-Kona, HI ...399
Ataloa Lodge Museum, Muskogee, OK ...1205
Au Glaize Village, Defiance, OH ...1162
Audubon Greenwich, Greenwich, CT ...242
Audubon Louisiana Nature Center, New Orleans, LA ...594
Audubon Society of Rhode Island, Smithfield, RI ...1319
Augusta Museum of History, Augusta, GA ...364
Aullwood Audubon Center and Farm, Dayton, OH ...1160
Aurora Fossil Museum, Aurora, NC ...1091
Austin Nature & Science Center, Austin, TX ...1389
Autry National Center of the American West, Los Angeles, CA ...112
Avery County Museum, Newland, NC ...1113
Awbury Arboretum, Philadelphia, PA ...1277

Badlands National Park, Interior, SD ...1349
Badlands Petrified Gardens, Kadoka, SD ...1349
Barataria Preserve, Jean Lafitte National Historical Park and Preserve, Marrero, LA ...591
The Bartlett Museum, Amesbury, MA ...657
Battle Hill Museum of Natural History, Battle Creek, IA ...505
Baxter Springs Heritage Center and Museum, Baxter Springs, KS ...533
Bay Area Museum, Seabrook, TX ...1452

The Bead Museum, Glendale, AZ ...35
Bear Brook Nature Center, Suncook, NH ...896
Bear Butte State Park Visitors Center, Sturgis, SD ...1358
Belle Isle Nature Zoo, Detroit, MI ...735
Berea College Burroughs Geological Museum, Berea, KY ...565
Berea College Weatherford Planetarium, Berea, KY ...565
Bergen Museum of Art & Science, Paramus, NJ ...919
Berkshire Museum, Pittsfield, MA ...702
Bernard Historical Society and Museum, Delton, MI ...734
Bernheim Arboretum and Research Forest, Clermont, KY ...567
Besh-Ba-Gowah Archaeological Park, Globe, AZ ...35
Big Bear Solar Observatory, Big Bear City, CA ...78
Big Bend National Park, Big Bend, TX ...1396
Big Bone Lick State Park Museum, Union, KY ...584
Big Thicket National Preserve, Kountze, TX ...1432
Big Thunder Gold Mine, Keystone, SD ...1349
Big Timbers Museum, Lamar, CO ...225
Big Well, Greensburg, KS ...542
Birmingham Botanical Gardens, Birmingham, AL ...4
Black Hawk State Historic Site: Hauberg Indian Museum, Rock Island, IL ...453
Black Hills Museum of Natural History, Hill City, SD ...1348
Black Hills Reptile Gardens, Inc., Rapid City, SD ...1354
Black Kettle Museum, Cheyenne, OK ...1198
Blackwater Draw Museum, Portales, NM ...944
Blue Hills Trailside Museum, Milton, MA ...695
Bob Campbell Geology Museum, Clemson, SC ...1328
Boone County Historical Center, Boone, IA ...506
Boonshoft Museum of Discovery, Dayton, OH ...1160
Boothe Memorial Park and Museum, Stratford, CT ...262
Bosque Memorial Museum, Clifton, TX ...1400
Bowers Science Museum, Cortland, NY ...982
Boyce Thompson Arboretum, Superior, AZ ...44
Brasstown Bald Visitor Center, Hiawassee, GA ...374
Brazos Valley Museum of Natural History, Bryan, TX ...1398
Brazosport Museum of Natural Science, Clute, TX ...1400
Brevard Museum of History & Science, Cocoa, FL ...300
Briar Bush Nature Center, Abington, PA ...1238
Bridger Valley Heritage Museum, Lyman, WY ...1636
Brigham Young University Earth Science Museum, Provo, UT ...1469
Brooklyn Children's Museum, Brooklyn, NY ...968
Bruce Museum, Greenwich, CT ...243
Bryce Canyon National Park Visitor Center, Bryce, UT ...1464
Buena Vista Heritage Museum, Buena Vista, CO ...204
Buena Vista Museum of Natural History, Bakersfield, CA ...73
Buffalo Museum of Science, Buffalo, NY ...972
Buffalo National River, Harrison, AR ...59
Buffalo Trails Museum, Epping, ND ...1130
Burke Museum of Natural History and Culture, Seattle, WA ...1565
Burpee Museum of Natural History, Rockford, IL ...454

Burritt on the Mountain-A Living Museum, Huntsville, AL ...11
Bushwhacker Museum, Nevada, MO ...828
Butte County Pioneer Memorial Museum, Oroville, CA ...136

C.H. Nash Museum-Chucalissa Archaeological Museum, Memphis, TN ...1372
Cabin Nature Center, Wood Dale, IL ...466
Cable Natural History Museum, Cable, WI ...1593
Cabrillo National Monument, San Diego, CA ...156
Calhoun County Museum, Rockwell City, IA ...527
Calhoun County Museum, Port Lavaca, TX ...1444
Calico Ghost Town and the Lane House & Museum, Yermo, CA ...199
California Academy of Sciences, San Francisco, CA ...163
California Science Center, Los Angeles, CA ...113
California State Mining & Mineral Museum, Mariposa, CA ...124
Calkins Nature Area/Field Museum, Iowa Falls, IA ...521
Calusa Nature Center and Planetarium, Fort Myers, FL ...308
Cambridge Museum, Cambridge, NE ...858
Camp Five Museum Foundation, Inc., Laona, WI ...1604
Cape Cod Museum of Natural History, Inc., Brewster, MA ...670
Capitol Reef National Park Visitor Center, Torrey, UT ...1475
Capulin Volcano National Monument, Capulin, NM ...937
Carbon County Museum, Rawlins, WY ...1637
Carlsbad Caverns National Park, Carlsbad, NM ...937
Carnegie Museum of Natural History, Pittsburgh, PA ...1291
Carrie Weedon Natural Science Museum, Galesville, MD ...645
Carter County Museum, Ekalaka, MT ...846
Cashmere Museum & Pioneer Village, Cashmere, WA ...1550
Cass County Historical Society, Logansport, IN ...489
Cass County Museum & Pioneer School, Walker, MN ...795
Castine Scientific Society, Castine, ME ...609
Catalina Island Museum Society, Inc., Avalon, CA ...73
Catherine Montgomery Interpretive Center, Greenwater, WA ...1556
Cedar Breaks National Monument, Cedar City, UT ...1464
The Centennial Museum at the University of Texas at El Paso, El Paso, TX ...1411
Center for Agricultural Science and Heritage, Indianapolis, IN ...481
Center for Meteorite Studies, Tempe, AZ ...46
Central Montana Historical Association, Inc. Museum, Lewistown, MT ...850
The Central Museum, Central, AK ...23
Central Park Conservancy, New York, NY ...1022
Century House Historical Society, Rosendale, NY ...1061
Chabot Space & Science Center, Oakland, CA ...133
Chapman's Gem and Mineral Museum, Fortuna, CA ...96
Charlotte County Historical Center, Charlotte Harbor, FL ...299
Charlotte Nature Museum, Charlotte, NC ...1094
The Chattanooga Nature Center, Chattanooga, TN ...1361
Cherokee County Historical Museum, Inc., Murphy, NC ...1112

Geological–Continued

Chesapeake and Ohio Canal National Historical Park, Hagerstown, MD............646
Chesapeake Planetarium, Chesapeake, VA.1501
Chesterfield County Museum, Chesterfield, VA.........................1501
Chickasaw National Recreation Area, Sulphur, OK.........................1214
Chico Creek Nature Center, Chico, CA 83
Chihuahuan Desert Research Institute, Fort Davis, TX........................1414
Children's Museum at La Habra, La Habra, CA.........................106
Children's Museum of History, Natural History and Science at Utica, New York, Utica, NY.........................1079
Children's Museum of Oak Ridge, Inc., Oak Ridge, TN.........................1382
The Children's Museum of Science and Technology, Troy, NY.........................1079
Children's Museum of Southeastern Connecticut, Niantic, CT.........................256
Children's Museum of the Sierra, Oakhurst, CA.........................132
Chippewa Nature Center, Midland, MI.....755
Chiricahua National Monument, Willcox, AZ.........................53
Christa McAuliffe Planetarium, Concord, NH.........................884
Cincinnati Museum Center at Union Terminal, Cincinnati, OH.........................1149
City County Pioneer Museum, Sweetwater, TX.........................1454
City of Las Cruces Museum System, Las Cruces, NM.........................940
City of Las Vegas Museum and Rough Rider Memorial Collection, Las Vegas, NM.........................941
The Claremont, New Hampshire Historical Society, Inc., Claremont, NH.........................884
Clark Hotel Museum, Van Horn, TX 1457
Clark Planetarium, Salt Lake City, UT 1470
Clausen Memorial Museum, Petersburg, AK.........................27
Clearwater Historical Museum, Orofino, ID.........................408
The Cleveland Museum of Natural History, Cleveland, OH.........................1153
Cliffs of the Neuse State Park, Seven Springs, NC.........................1119
Clifton Community Historical Society, Clifton, KS.........................535
Clinton County Historical Society Paine-Gillam-Scott Museum, Saint Johns, MI.........................763
Cloud County Historical Society Museum, Concordia, KS.........................536
Clyde E. Buckley Wildlife Sanctuary, Frankfort, KY.........................568
Colburn Earth Science Museum, Asheville, NC.........................1089
College of Eastern Utah Prehistoric Museum, Price, UT.........................1469
Colorado National Monument, Fruita, CO...218
Colorado School of Mines Geology Museum, Golden, CO.........................220
Columbia River Exhibition of History, Science and Technology, Richland, WA.........................1564
Comanche Crossing Historical Society & Museum, Strasburg, CO.........................233
Comer Museum, Morgantown, WV 1585
Community Historical Museum, Maxwell, IA.........................523
Connecticut State Museum of Natural History and Connecticut Archaeology Center, Storrs, CT.........................261
Cook's Natural Science Museum, Decatur, AL.........................7
Copper Village Museum & Arts Center of Deer Lodge County, Anaconda, MT........840

Core Arboretum, Morgantown, WV 1585
The Cornell Plantations, Ithaca, NY...........1003
Cornwall Iron Furnace, Cornwall, PA 1248
Corpus Christi Museum of Science and History, Corpus Christi, TX...................1401
Cottage Grove Museum & Annex, Cottage Grove, OR.........................1222
Cottonlandia Museum, Greenwood, MS 800
Cranbrook House and Gardens Auxiliary, Bloomfield Hills, MI.........................730
Cranbrook Institute of Science, Bloomfield Hills, MI.........................730
Crater Lake National Park, Crater Lake, OR.........................1222
Crater of Diamonds State Park Museum, Murfreesboro, AR.........................65
Craters of the Moon National Monument, Arco, ID.........................403
Creation Evidence Museum, Glen Rose, TX.........................1422
Creation Museum, Petersburg, KY.............583
Crockett County Museum, Ozona, TX.......1442
The Crosby Arboretum, Mississippi State University, Picayune, MS.........................807
Crossroads Museum, Corinth, MS.............800
Crown Point State Historic Site, Crown Point, NY.........................984
Crystal Caverns at Hupp's Hill, Strasburg, VA.........................1538
Curry Historical Society Museum, Gold Beach, OR.........................1225
Custer County 1881 Courthouse Museum, Custer, SD.........................1345
Custer State Park, Custer, SD.........................1346
Cuyuna Range Historical Society & Museum, Crosby, MN.........................772
Cylburn Arboretum, Baltimore, MD............631

D. Ralph Hostetter Museum of Natural History, Harrisonburg, VA.........................1510
Dahlonega Gold Museum State Historic Site, Dahlonega, GA.........................369
Dakota Dinosaur Museum, Dickinson, ND.........................1129
Dakota Sunset Museum, Gettysburg, SD...1348
Dallas Museum of Natural History, Dallas, TX.........................1406
Dan O'Laurie Museum of Moab, Moab, UT.........................1467
Dana Adobe, Nipomo, CA.........................130
Danville Science Center, Danville, VA.......1502
Dawson County Historical Museum, Lexington, NE.........................864
De Graaf Nature Center, Holland, MI.........746
Dead Horse Point State Park, Moab, UT...1467
Death Valley National Park Visitor Center and Museums, Death Valley, CA..............91
Delaware County Institute of Science, Media, PA.........................1270
Delaware Nature Society, Hockessin, DE 271
Delta County Museum, Delta, CO.................209
Deming Luna Mimbres Museum, Deming, NM.........................939
Denali National Park and Preserve, Denali Park, AK.........................23
Denison Pequotsepos Nature Center, Mystic, CT.........................250
Denver Museum of Nature & Science, Denver, CO.........................211
Detroit Science Center, Detroit, MI.........736
Devils Postpile National Monument, Mammoth Lakes, CA.........................124
Dinosaur Depot Museum, Canon City, CO.........................204
Dinosaur Discovery Museum, Kenosha, WI.........................1602
Dinosaur Journey, Fruita, CO.........................218
Dinosaur State Park, Rocky Hill, CT...........259
The Discovery Center, Fresno, CA.................96
Discovery Center (East Tennessee Discovery Center), Knoxville, TN.........1369
Discovery Center Museum, Rockford, IL 454

The Discovery Center of the Southern Tier, Binghamton, NY.........................962
Discovery Creek Children's Museum of Washington DC, Glen Echo, MD............645
Discovery Museum, Sacramento Museum of History, Science and Technology, Sacramento, CA.........................152
The Discovery Museums, Acton, MA.........657
Discovery Place, Inc., Charlotte, NC.........1094
Discovery Seashell Museum, Ocean City, NJ.........................918
Don Harrington Discovery Center, Amarillo, TX.........................1387
Door County Historical Museum, Sturgeon Bay, WI.........................1623
Douglass Historical Museum, Douglass, KS.........................537
Downieville Museum, Downieville, CA 91
Drumlin Farm Education Center, Lincoln, MA.........................690
Dry Falls Interpretive Center, Coulee City, WA.........................1551
Dublin-Laurens Museum, Dublin, GA 370
Dubois Museum, Dubois, WY.........................1632
Dungeness River Audubon Center, Sequim, WA.........................1570
Dunn-Seiler Museum, Mississippi State University, MS.........................805
Durham Center Museum/Research Library, East Durham, NY.........................985

Earth & Mineral Sciences Museum and Art Gallery, University Park, PA...........1303
Earthplace - The Nature Discovery Center, Westport, CT.........................266
East Kentucky Center for Science, Mathematics, and Technology, Prestonsburg, KY.........................583
Eastern California Museum, Independence, CA.........................104
ECHO at the Leahy Center for Lake Champlain, Burlington, VT.........................1478
EcoTarium, Worcester, MA.........................720
Ed Clark Museum of Missouri Geology, Rolla, MO.........................829
Edisto Island Historic Preservation Society Museum, Edisto Island, SC 1332
Effigy Mounds National Monument, Harpers Ferry, IA.........................519
Ehrhart Museum, Antwerp, OH.........................1139
El Campo Museum of Natural History, El Campo, TX.........................1411
El Dorado County Historical Museum, Placerville, CA.........................142
Elberton Granite Museum & Exhibit, Elberton, GA.........................371
Eleanor Barbour Cook Museum of Geology, Chadron, NE.........................859
Elgin Public Museum, Elgin, IL.........................432
Elkhorn Slough National Estuarine Research, Wastsonville, CA.........................196
Elsing Museum, Tulsa, OK.........................1215
Emporia State University Johnston Geology Museum, Emporia, KS.............538
Environmental Education Center, Somerset County Park Commission, Basking Ridge, NJ.........................898
Erie Planetarium, Erie, PA.........................1253
Eugene Historical Society, Eugene, OR 1223
Eureka Pioneer Museum of McPherson County, Inc., Eureka, SD.........................1346
Exploration Station - A Children's Museum, Bourbonnais, IL.........................414
Explorit Science Center, Davis, CA 89
Explorium of Lexington, Lexington, KY 572

Fairbanks Museum and Planetarium, Saint Johnsbury, VT.........................1486
Falls of the Ohio State Park, Clarksville, IN.........................472
Family Museum, Bettendorf, IA...................505
Faninadahen Kosas Guahan-Guam Museum, Hagatna, GU.........................1640

The Farm, Sturgeon Bay, WI......................1623
Favell Museum Inc., Klamath Falls, OR....1227
Fernbank Museum of Natural History,
    Atlanta, GA...359
Fernbank Science Center, Atlanta, GA.........360
Festival-Institute, James Dick Foundation,
    Round Top, TX..1446
Fick Fossil & History Museum, Oakley,
    KS..554
Fiedler Memorial Museum, Seguin, TX.....1452
Field Museum of Natural History,
    Chicago, IL..420
Fillmore Historical Museum, Inc.,
    Fillmore, CA..95
Fisher Museum of Forestry, Petersham,
    MA..702
Flandrau Science Center and Planetarium,
    Tucson, AZ..49
Fleischmann Planetarium, Reno, NV............880
Flint Ridge State Memorial Museum,
    Glenford, OH..1166
Florence Hawley Ellis Museum of
    Anthropology and Ruth Hall Museum
    of Paleontology, Abiquiu, NM.................931
Florence Price Pioneer Museum,
    Florence, CO...216
Florida Museum of Natural History,
    Gainesville, FL..310
Florissant Fossil Beds National
    Monument, Florissant, CO.......................216
The Fluvanna County Historical Society
    Old Stone Jail Museum, Palmyra, VA....1524
Folsom Museum, Inc., Folsom, NM............939
Fontenelle Nature Association, Bellevue,
    NE..857
Forestiere Underground Gardens, Fresno,
    CA..97
Fort Buford State Historic Site, Williston,
    ND..1137
Fort Casey Interpretive Center,
    Coupeville, WA.......................................1551
Fort Davidson State Historic Site, Pilot
    Knob, MO..828
Fort Wayne Children's Zoo, Fort Wayne,
    IN..477
Fort Worth Museum of Science and
    History, Fort Worth, TX.........................1417
Fossil Museum, Fossil, OR........................1224
Fossil Rim Wildlife Center, Glen Rose,
    TX...1422
Fostoria Area Historical Museum,
    Fostoria, OH...1164
Fountain Rock Nature Center,
    Walkersville, MD......................................656
Francisco Fort Museum, La Veta, CO.........224
Frankfort Area Historical Museum, West
    Frankfort, IL...464
Franklin Mineral Museum, Franklin, NJ.....904
Frontera Audubon Society, Weslaco, TX....1460
Frontier Historical Society and Museum,
    Glenwood Springs, CO............................219
Fryxell Geology Museum, Rock Island,
    IL..454

Galena Mining & Historical Museum,
    Galena, KS..541
Garrett County Historical Museum,
    Oakland, MD...649
Gateway to the Panhandle, Gate, OK.........1201
Gemological Institute of America
    Museum, Carlsbad, CA...............................81
General Patton Memorial Museum,
    Chiriaco Summit, CA..................................84
General Sterling Price Museum,
    Keytesville, MO...824
Genesee Country Village & Museum,
    Mumford, NY..1016
The Geological Museum, The University
    of Wyoming, Laramie, WY.....................1635
Geology Museum, Huntington, WV...........1583
George Washington Carver National
    Monument, Diamond, MO........................814
Georgia Capitol Museum, Atlanta, GA........360

Georgia Museum of Natural History,
    Athens, GA..356
Georgia Southern University Museum,
    Statesboro, GA..387
Gerald E. Eddy Discovery Center,
    Chelsea, MI...732
Geronimo Springs Museum, Truth or
    Consequences, NM....................................953
Gheens Science Hall and Rauch
    Planetarium, Louisville, KY.....................576
The Gillespie Museum - Stetson
    University, De Land, FL............................304
Gilman Museum, Hellertown, PA..............1260
Gilpin History Museum, Central City, CO...205
Ginkgo Petrified Forest State Park,
    Vantage, WA..1576
Glacier National Park Museum, West
    Glacier, MT...854
Gonzales Memorial Museum, Gonzales,
    TX...1423
Goodhue County Historical Society, Red
    Wing, MN..787
Goodnow Museum State Historic Site,
    Manhattan, KS...550
Gouverneur Historical Association,
    Gouverneur, NY..995
Grand Canyon National Park Museum
    Collection, Grand Canyon National
    Park, AZ..36
Grand Gulf Military Park, Port Gibson,
    MS..807
Grand Traverse Heritage Center, Traverse
    City, MI..765
Grant County Historical Museum,
    Canyon City, OR......................................1221
Grant County Museum, Medford, OK........1205
Granville Historical Society Museum,
    Granville, OH..1167
Graves Museum of Archaeology and
    Natural History, Dania Beach, FL...........302
Gravette Historical Museum, Gravette,
    AR..59
Great Basin Historical Society &
    Museum, Delta, UT.................................1464
Great Basin National Park, Baker, NV........875
Great Valley Museum of Natural History,
    Modesto, CA..126
The Greenburgh Nature Center,
    Scarsdale, NY..1066
Greene Memorial Museum, University of
    Wisconsin-Milwaukee, Milwaukee, WI.1611
Greenwood County Historical Society,
    Eureka, KS..539
Greybull Museum, Greybull, WY.............1634
Griffith Observatory, Los Angeles, CA......115
Grosse Ile Historical Society, Grosse Ile,
    MI..745
Grout Museum District: Grout Museum
    of History and Science, Bluedorn
    Science Imaginarium, Rensselaer
    Russell House Museum, Snowden
    House, Waterloo, IA.................................529
Groveland Yosemite Gateway Museum,
    Groveland, CA...101
Gunnison County Pioneer and Historical
    Society, Gunnison, CO.............................222
Gunnison Museum of Natural History,
    Pawling, NY..1051
Gwinnett County Parks & Recreation
    Outdoor Interpretive Section,
    Lawrenceville, GA....................................375

H. Earl Clack Museum, Havre, MT............849
Hampton County Historical Museum,
    Hampton, SC...1334
Hannah Lindahl Children's Museum,
    Mishawaka, IN..491
Harney County Historical Museum,
    Burns, OR..1221
Harvard Museum of Natural History,
    Cambridge, MA...672
Haskell County Historical Society,
    Sublette, KS...558

Hatfield Marine Science Center, Oregon
    State University, Newport, OR 1228
Hattiesburg Area Historical Society and
    HAHS Museum, Hattiesburg, MS...........801
Hawk Mountain Sanctuary, Kempton, PA..1264
Headwaters Heritage Museum, Three
    Forks, MT..854
Heard Natural Science Museum and
    Wildlife Sanctuary, Inc., McKinney,
    TX...1437
Henry S. Reuss Ice Age Visitor Center,
    Campbellsport, WI...................................1593
Heritage Center Museum, Berryville, AR 55
Heritage House Museum of Montgomery
    County, Mount Ida, AR.............................64
The Heritage Museum, Astoria, OR..........1218
The Heritage Museum & Underhill
    Museum, Idaho Springs, CO....................223
The Heritage Museum at Falfurrias, Inc.,
    Falfurrias, TX..1413
Herrett Center for Arts & Science,
    Faulkner Planetarium and Centennial
    Observatory, Twin Falls, ID....................410
Hi-Desert Nature Museum, Yucca Valley,
    CA..201
Hibbing Historical Society and Museum,
    Hibbing, MN...778
The Hicksville Gregory Museum,
    Hicksville, NY...998
Hiddenite Center, Inc., Hiddenite, NC....1106
High Cliff Historical Society & General
    Store Museum, Sherwood, WI................1622
Highlands Center for Natural History,
    Prescott, AZ..42
Historic Crab Orchard Museum &
    Pioneer Park, Inc., Tazewell, VA............1541
Historic New Harmony, New Harmony,
    IN..494
The Historical Museum at St. Gertrude,
    Cottonwood, ID..405
Historical Natural History & Library
    Society of Natick dba Natick
    Historical Society, South Natick, MA.....709
Historical Society of Columbia County,
    Saint Helens, OR.....................................1234
Historical Society of Quaker Hill &
    Pawling, Pawling, NY.............................1051
Historical Society of the Town of North
    Hempstead, Manhasset, NY...................1013
The Historical Society of the Town of
    Warwick, Warwick, NY...........................1082
Hollywood Guinness World of Records
    Museum, Hollywood, CA.........................103
Homesteader Museum, Powell, WY...........1637
Hopewell Culture National Historical
    Park, Chillicothe, OH.............................1147
Hot Spring County Museum - The Boyle
    House/1876 Log Cabin, Malvern, AR.......63
Hot Springs County Museum and
    Cultural Center, Thermopolis, WY........1639
Hot Springs National Park Visitor Center,
    Hot Springs, AR...60
Houston Museum of Natural Science,
    Houston, TX..1427
Howard B. Owens Science Center and
    Challenger Learning Center,
    Lanham-Seabrook, MD.............................648
Huerfano County Historical Society,
    including The Walsenburg Mining
    Museum & Ft. Francisco Museum of
    La Veta, Walsenburg, CO..........................234
Humboldt State University Natural
    History Museum, Arcata, CA......................72
Huntington County Historical Society
    Museum, Huntington, IN..........................481
Hyrum City Museum, Hyrum, UT.............1466

ICR Museum of Creation & Earth
    History, Santee, CA..................................185
Idaho Museum of Mining and Geology,
    Boise, ID...404
Idaho Museum of Natural History,
    Pocatello, ID...408

Geological–Continued

Illinois State Museum, Springfield, IL 458
Illinois State Museum, Chicago Gallery,
   Chicago, IL 422
The Imaginarium Science Discovery
   Center, Anchorage, AK 22
Independence Historical Museum,
   Independence, KS 545
Insights-El Paso Science Center, Inc., El
   Paso, TX 1412
Institute of Meteoritics Meteorite
   Museum, Albuquerque, NM 933
International Museum of Art and Science,
   McAllen, TX 1437
Iraan Museum, Iraan, TX 1430
Iron Mountain Iron Mine, Vulcan, MI 766
Ironworld Discovery Center, Chisholm,
   MN 771
Isabel Anderson Comer Museum & Arts
   Center, Sylacauga, AL 18

Jackson County Historical Museum,
   Lakefield, MN 778
James A. McFaul Environmental Center
   of Bergen County, Wyckoff, NJ 931
Jean P. Haydon Museum, Pago Pago, AS ..1640
Jeffers Petroglyphs Historic Site,
   Comfrey, MN 771
Robert H. Johnson Planetarium,
   Lakewood, CO 225
Jerome Ford Nature Center, Alexandria,
   VA 1493
Jerome State Historic Park, Jerome, AZ 36
Jim Gatchell Memorial Museum, Buffalo,
   WY 1629
Jimmie Rodgers Museum, Meridian, MS.....805
John C. Wells Planetarium, Harrisonburg,
   VA 1511
John Day Fossil Beds National
   Monument, Kimberly, OR 1227
John Deere Planetarium, Rock Island, IL 454
John Hutchings Museum of Natural
   History, Lehi, UT 1466
John Wesley Powell Memorial Museum,
   Page, AZ 37
Joshua Tree National Park, Oasis Visitor
   Center, Twentynine Palms, CA 193
The Journey Museum, Rapid City, SD.......1354
The Junior Museum of Bay County,
   Panama City, FL 334
Jurica Nature Museum, Lisle, IL 442
Jurupa Mountains Cultural Center,
   Riverside, CA 149

KU Natural History Museum and
   Biodiversity Research Center,
   Lawrence, KS 548
Kalamazoo Nature Center, Inc.,
   Kalamazoo, MI 748
Kateri Galleries, The National Shrine of
   the North American Martyrs,
   Auriesville, NY 959
Kauai Children's Discovery Museum,
   Kapaa, HI 400
Kauai Museum, Lihue, HI 401
Kenosha Public Museum, Kenosha, WI.....1602
Kensington Metropark Nature Center,
   Milford, MI 755
Kentucky Coal Mining Museum,
   Benham, KY 565
Kentucky Historical Society, Frankfort,
   KY 569
Kerbyville Museum, Kerby, OR 1227
Keweenaw County Historical Society,
   Eagle Harbor, MI 739
Keystone Area Historical Society,
   Keystone, SD 1350
Kidspace Children's Museum, Pasadena,
   CA 140
Kingman Museum, Battle Creek, MI 727
Kirby Science Discovery Center at the
   Washington Pavilion, Sioux Falls, SD...1356

Kittson County History Center Museum,
   Lake Bronson, MN 778
Knight Museum, Alliance, NE......................855
Koke'e Natural History Museum, Kauai,
   HI 400

L.C. Bates Museum, Hinckley, ME.............612
La Porte County Historical Society
   Museum, La Porte, IN 487
Lafayette Miners Museum, Lafayette, CO ...224
Lafayette Natural History Museum and
   Planetarium, Lafayette, LA 589
Lake Afton Public Observatory, Goddard,
   KS 541
Lake Mead National Recreation Area,
   Boulder City, NV 875
Lake of the Woods County Museum,
   Baudette, MN 768
Lake Perris Regional Indian Museum
   (Home of the Wind), Perris, CA 141
Lake View Nature Center, Oakbrook
   Terrace, IL 449
Lake Waccamaw Depot Museum, Lake
   Waccamaw, NC 1109
Lakeview Museum of Arts and Sciences,
   Peoria, IL 450
Land of the Yankee Fork Historic
   Association Museum, Stanley, ID...........410
Las Vegas Natural History Museum, Las
   Vegas, NV 879
Laughing Brook Education Center &
   Wildlife Sanctuary, Hampden, MA..........686
Lava Beds National Monument, Tulelake,
   CA 193
Lawrence County Historical and
   Genealogical Society, Bedford, IN 469
Lawrence Hall of Science, Berkeley, CA.......76
Lewis & Clark Boat House and Nature
   Center, Saint Charles, MO 830
Lewis County Historical Society
   Museum, Lowville, NY 1012
Libby Museum, Wolfeboro, NH 897
Liberty County Museum, Chester, MT.......844
Liberty Science Center, Jersey City, NJ.......909
Lincoln County Historical Society,
   Lincoln, KS 549
Lindsay Wildlife Museum, Walnut Creek,
   CA 196
The Little Cowboy Bar & Museum,
   Fromberg, MT 847
Little White House Historic Site, Warm
   Springs, GA 390
The Living Desert, Palm Desert, CA 138
Living Desert Zoo and Gardens State
   Park, Carlsbad, NM 938
Lizzadro Museum of Lapidary Art,
   Elmhurst, IL 433
Lompoc Valley Historical Society, Inc.,
   Lompoc, CA 110
Lorenzo State Historic Site, Cazenovia,
   NY 976
Lost City Museum, Overton, NV 880
Louden-Henritze Archaeology Museum,
   Trinidad, CO 234
Louisiana State Exhibit Museum,
   Shreveport, LA 600
Louisiana State Oil & Gas Museum, Oil
   City, LA 599
Louisiana Tech Museum, Ruston, LA 600
Louisville Science Center, Louisville, KY ...577
Lowell Observatory, Flagstaff, AZ................33
Lyman Museum, Hilo, HI 393
Lyon County Historical Society Museum,
   Marshall, MN 780

Mackinac State Historic Parks-Fort
   Mackinac & Mackinac Island State
   Park, Mackinac Island, MI........................752
Madison County Historical Society,
   Winterset, IA 531
Madison Museum of Fine Art, Madison,
   GA 378
Maine State Museum, Augusta, ME.............604

Mammoth Site of Hot Springs, Inc., Hot
   Springs, SD...1348
Maramec Museum, The James
   Foundation, Saint James, MO.................830
Marengo Cave, Marengo, IN 489
Marias Museum of History and Art,
   Shelby, MT 853
Maritime Museum at Historic Coast
   Guard Station, Saint Simons Island,
   GA 383
Marlboro County Historical Museum,
   Bennettsville, SC 1322
Martin County Museum, Shoals, IN............499
Mary Vagle Museum & Nature Center,
   Fontana, CA...95
Mason County Museum, Mason, TX 1437
Massachusetts Audubon at Connecticut
   River Valley Sanctuaries,
   Easthampton, MA 681
Matagorda County Museum, Bay City,
   TX 1393
Matchless Mine Museum (Leadville
   Assembly), Leadville, CO 226
Maturango Museum of the Indian Wells
   Valley, Ridgecrest, CA 148
May Natural History Museum and
   Museum of Space Exploration,
   Colorado Springs, CO 207
Mayborn Museum Complex, Waco, TX.....1459
McIntosh County Historical Society,
   Ashley, ND 1127
McLean County Historical Society
   Museum, Washburn, ND 1137
McPherson Museum & Arts Foundation,
   McPherson, KS 552
McWane Science Center, Birmingham,
   AL 5
Meadowlands Museum, Rutherford, NJ.......923
Meagher County Historical Association
   Castle Museum, White Sulphur
   Springs, MT 855
Mercer County Genealogical and
   Historical Society, Princeton, MO 829
The Merrick Art Gallery, New Brighton,
   PA 1273
Mesa Southwest Museum, Mesa, AZ 37
Mesa Verde National Park Museum,
   Mesa Verde National Park, CO................228
Mesalands Community College's
   Dinosaur Museum, Tucumcari, NM 953
Mesker Park Zoo & Botanic Garden,
   Evansville, IN 476
Middlebury Historical Society, Wyoming,
   NY 1087
Midland County Historical Museum,
   Midland, TX 1438
Miles Mineral Museum, Portales, NM 944
Millerton Courthouse, Friant, CA................98
Mineral and Lapidary Museum of
   Henderson County Inc.,
   Hendersonville, NC 1105
Mineral County Museum, Hawthorne,
   NV 878
Mineral County Museum & Historical
   Society, Superior, MT 854
Mineral Museum, Butte, MT 843
The Minna Anthony Common Nature
   Center at Wellesley State Park,
   Fineview, NY...989
Minnesota Planetarium & Space
   Discovery Center, Minneapolis, MN 783
Mississippi Museum of Natural Science,
   Jackson, MS 803
Mississippi Petrified Forest, Flora, MS 800
Moccasin Lake Nature Park, An
   Environmental & Energy Education
   Center, Clearwater, FL 299
Mohonk Preserve, Inc., Gardiner, NY.........993
Mondak Heritage Center, Sidney, MT.........853
Montrose County Historical Museum,
   Montrose, CO 228
Moorten Botanic Garden and Cactarium,
   Palm Springs, CA 138

Morgan Row Museum and Harrodsburg-Mercer County Research Library, Harrodsburg, KY 570
Morningside Nature Center, Gainesville, FL 311
Morro Bay State Park Museum of Natural History, Morro Bay, CA 129
Morrow Mountain State Park, Albemarle, NC 1088
Moses Lake Museum & Art Center, Moses Lake, WA 1559
Mote Marine Laboratory/Aquarium, Sarasota, FL 345
Mt. Rainier National Park, Ashford, WA ...1547
Mount Washington Museum and The Weather Discovery Center, North Conway, NH 893
Mountain Skies Astronomical Society & Science Center, Lake Arrowhead, CA 107
The Museum, Greenwood, SC 1334
Museum of Ancient & Modern Art, Penn Valley, CA 141
Museum of Ancient Artifacts, Las Vegas, NV 879
Museum of Anthracite Mining, Weatherly, PA 1307
Museum of Archaeology & Material Culture, Cedar Crest, NM 938
Museum of Arts and Sciences, Macon, GA 378
Museum of Astrogeology, Meteor Crater, Winslow, AZ 53
Museum of Chicot County Arkansas, Lake Village, AR 61
Museum of Discovery and Science, Fort Lauderdale, FL 307
Museum of Earth and Life History, Lynchburg, VA 1515
Museum of Geology and Paleontology, South Dakota School of Mines and Technology, Rapid City, SD 1355
Museum of Jurassic Technology, Culver City, CA 88
Museum of Life and Science, Durham, NC 1098
Museum of Long Island Natural Sciences, Stony Brook, NY 1075
Museum of Natural History and Planetarium, Providence, RI..................1317
Museum of Natural Science, Ogden, UT ...1468
Museum of North Carolina Minerals, Spruce Pine, NC 1120
Museum of Northern Arizona, Flagstaff, AZ 33
Museum of Paleontology, Berkeley, CA 76
Museum of Rim Country Archaeology, Payson, AZ 38
Museum of Science, Boston, MA.................667
Museum of Science and Industry, Tampa, FL 349
Museum of the Berkeley Springs, Berkeley Springs, WV.........................1580
Museum of the Big Bend, Alpine, TX 1386
Museum of the Geosciences, Blacksburg, VA 1497
Museum of the Hudson Highlands, Cornwall-on-Hudson, NY 982
Museum of the Middle Appalachians, Saltville, VA 1536
Museum of the Rockies, Bozeman, MT.......842
Museum of the Southwest, Midland, TX ...1439
Museum of Western Colorado, Grand Junction, CO 220
Museum of World Treasures, Wichita, KS...562
Museum of Yarmouth History, Yarmouth, ME 626
Museum of York County, Rock Hill, SC ...1340
Museums of Los Gatos, Los Gatos, CA 123
Musselshell Valley Historical Museum, Roundup, MT 853

Napa Valley Museum, Yountville, CA ...200

NASA Kennedy Space Center, Merritt Island, FL...323
Natchez Trace Parkway, Tupelo, MS...........808
National Capital Parks-East, Washington, DC 284
National Museum of Natural History, Washington, DC.......................................286
National Park Service-Great Falls Park, McLean, VA...1517
The Natural History Museum, Santa Maria, CA..182
Natural History Museum of Los Angeles County, Los Angeles, CA.....................120
The Natural Science Center of Greensboro, Inc., Greensboro, NC.........1104
The Nature Center at Shaker Lakes, Cleveland, OH..1155
The Nature Museum at Grafton, Grafton, VT 1479
Nauvoo Historical Society Museum, Nauvoo, IL..447
Navajo Nation Museum, Window Rock, AZ 53
Nevada State Museum, Carson City, NV 876
New Almaden Quicksilver Mining Museum, San Jose, CA 172
New Britain Youth Museum, New Britain, CT..252
New Britain Youth Museum at Hungerford Park, Kensington, CT...........247
New Canaan Nature Center, New Canaan, CT..252
New Jersey State Museum, Trenton, NJ 927
New London Public Museum, New London, WI..1615
New Mexico Bureau of Geology Mineral Museum, Socorro, NM...........................951
New Mexico Museum of Natural History & Science, Albuquerque, NM..................935
New York State Museum, Albany, NY.........955
The Newark Museum, Newark, NJ 916
Newell Museum, Newell, SD 1352
Newport State Park, Ellison Bay, WI.........1597
Niagara Gorge Discovery Center, Niagara Falls, NY..1042
Nishna Heritage Museum, Oakland, IA 525
No Man's Land Historical Society, Goodwell, OK..1201
Norman #1 Oil Well Museum, Neodesha, KS 553
North Carolina Maritime Museum, Beaufort, NC..1091
North Carolina Museum of Natural Sciences, Raleigh, NC 1116
North Cascades National Park Service Complex, Marblemount, WA 1559
The North Museum of Natural History & Science, Lancaster, PA 1266
The Northern Maine Museum of Science, University of Maine, Presque Isle, ME...620
Northwestern Oklahoma State University Museum, Alva, OK..................................1195
The Nylander Museum of Natural History, Caribou, ME 609

Oakes Museum Messiah College, Grantham, PA 1257
Ogden Union Station Museums, Ogden, UT 1468
Ojai Valley Historical Society and Museum, Ojai, CA 135
The Old Courthouse Heritage Museum, Inverness, FL..313
The Old Jail Museum, Crawfordsville, IN...473
Old New-Gate Prison and Copper Mine, East Granby, CT..238
Old State House, Hartford, CT 245
Old Stone Fort Museum Complex, Schoharie, NY..1067
Old Trail Museum, Choteau, MT 844
Oregon Museum of Science and Industry, Portland, OR..1231
Oregon Trail Museum, Gering, NE 861

Oregon Trail Regional Museum, Baker City, OR..1219
Organ Pipe Cactus National Monument Museum, Ajo, AZ...29
Orlando Science Center, Inc., Orlando, FL 332
Orma J. Smith Museum of Natural History, Caldwell, ID 405
Ormond Memorial Art Museum & Garden, Ormond Beach, FL.....................333
Orpheum Children's Science Museum, Champaign, IL..417
Orton Geological Museum, Ohio State University, Columbus, OH...................1158
Oscar Getz Museum of Whiskey History And The Bardstown Historical Museum, Bardstown, KY.....................565
Ottawa County Historical Museum, Port Clinton, OH..1183
Owensboro Area Museum of Science & History, Owensboro, KY.......................581
Owyhee County Historical Museum, Murphy, ID..407
The Oyster and Maritime Museum of Chincoteague, Chincoteague, VA...........1501

Pacific County Historical Museum, South Bend, WA..1571
Pacific Grove Museum of Natural History, Pacific Grove, CA............................137
Pacific Science Center, Seattle, WA 1568
Pacific University Museum, Forest Grove, OR..1224
Painted Post - Erwin Museum at the Depot, Painted Post, NY 1050
Paleontological Research Institution, Ithaca, NY..1004
Palo Alto Junior Museum and Zoo, Palo Alto, CA..139
Panhandle-Plains Historical Museum, Canyon, TX..1399
Panola Mountain State Conservation Park, Stockbridge, GA............................387
The Pardee Home Museum, Oakland, CA...134
Park City Historical Society & Museum, Park City, UT..1468
The Park-McCullough House, North Bennington, VT..1483
Parsonsfield-Porter Historical Society, Porter, ME..618
Peabody Museum of Natural History, New Haven, CT..253
Pecos National Historical Park, Pecos, NM 944
The Peggy Notebaert Nature Museum, Chicago, IL..426
Pember Museum of Natural History, Granville, NY..995
Pembina State Museum, Pembina, ND.......1135
Peninsula State Park, Fish Creek, WI 1597
Pennsylvania Historical & Museum Commission, Harrisburg, PA..................1259
Peoria Historical Society, Peoria, IL 451
Petrified Creatures Museum of Natural History, Richfield Springs, NY 1057
Petrified Forest Museum, Calistoga, CA........80
Petrified Forest National Park, Petrified Forest National Park, AZ 38
Petrified Forest of the Black Hills, Piedmont, SD..1353
Petrified Sea Gardens, Saratoga Springs, NY 1065
The Petroleum Museum, Midland, TX.......1439
Philmont Museums, Cimarron, NM.............938
Pickens County Museum of Art & History, Pickens, SC............................1340
Piedmont Environmental Center, High Point, NC..1107
Pinnacle Mountain State Park, Little Rock, AR..63
Pinnacles National Monument, Paicines, CA 138
Pioneer Auto Museum, Murdo, SD 1352

Geological–Continued

Pioneer Corner Museum, New Holstein,
WI 1615
Pioneer-Krier Museum, Ashland, KS 532
Pioneer Tunnel Coal Mine & Steam
Train, Ashland, PA 1241
Pioneers Park Nature Center, Lincoln, NE...867
Pipestone National Monument, Pipestone,
MN 787
Piqua Historical Area State Memorial,
Piqua, OH 1182
Placer County Museums, Auburn, CA 72
Plains Conservation Center, Aurora, CO.....202
Platteville Mining Museum, Platteville,
WI 1617
Plumas County Museum, Quincy, CA.........144
Plymouth Historical Society, Inc.,
Plymouth, PA 1295
Pocahontas County Museum, Marlinton,
WV 1584
Point Reyes National Seashore, Point
Reyes, CA 143
Polk County Historical Society,
Crookston, MN 771
Portland Planetarium, Portland, ME 620
Potter County Historical Society,
Coudersport, PA 1248
Pound Ridge Society/Museum, Pound
Ridge, NY 1055
Pratt County Historical Society Museum,
Pratt, KS 556
The Pratt Museum of Natural History,
Amherst, MA 659
The Prehistoric Life Museum, Evanston,
IL 435
Presque Isle County Historical Museum,
Rogers City, MI 762
Prince William Forest Park Visitor
Center, Triangle, VA 1541
Princeton University Museum of Natural
History, Princeton, NJ 922
Providence Canyon State Park, Lumpkin,
GA 377
Pueblo County Historical Society
Museum and Edward H. Broadhead
Library, Pueblo, CO 230
Putnam Museum of History & Natural
Science, Davenport, IA 513

The Quincy Museum, Quincy, IL 452
Quoddy Head State Park, Lubec, ME 614

Railroad House Historical Association
Museum, Sanford, NC 1119
Randall Museum, San Francisco, CA..........168
Randsburg Desert Museum, Randsburg,
CA 146
The Raymond M. Alf Museum of
Paleontology, Claremont, CA......................86
Reading Public Museum, Reading, PA.......1296
Red River Valley Museum, Vernon, TX.....1457
Redwood National and State Parks,
Crescent City, CA 88
Reed Gold Mine State Historic Site,
Midland, NC 1111
Rimrocker Historical Museum of West
Montrose County, Naturita, CO 229
Rio Grande Valley Museum, Harlingen,
TX 1423
Ripley County, Indiana, Historical
Society Museum, Versailles, IN 502
River Legacy Living Science Center,
Arlington, TX 1388
Riverbend Environmental Education
Center, Gladwyne, PA 1256
Riverside Metropolitan Museum,
Riverside, CA 150
Riverside Nature Center, Kerrville, TX......1432
Robert A. Vines Environmental Science
Center, Houston, TX..............................1429
Robert T. Longway Planetarium, Flint,
MI 742

Robeson Planetarium and Science Center,
Lumberton, NC 1110
Rochester Museum & Science Center,
Rochester, NY 1059
Rock Creek Nature Center, Washington,
DC 290
Rockwoods Reservation, Wildwood, MO 840
Rocky Ford Historical Museum, Rocky
Ford, CO 231
Rocky Mount Children's Museum and
Science Center, Inc., Rocky Mount,
NC 1118
Rocky Mountain National Park, Estes
Park, CO 215
Rocky Reach Dam, Wenatchee, WA 1577
Roper Mountain Science Center,
Greenville, SC 1334
Rotary Nature Center, Oakland, CA.............134
Royal Gorge Regional Museum &
History Center, Canon City, CO 205
Rural Farming & Agriculture Museum,
Warner, OK 1216
Rusk County Historical Society,
Ladysmith, WI 1604
Ruth and Charles Gilb Arcadia Historical
Museum, Arcadia, CA 71

Safety Harbor Museum of Regional
History, Safety Harbor, FL.......................338
Saguache County Museum, Saguache,
CO 231
St. Francis County Museum, Forrest City,
AR 57
St. Joseph Museum Inc., Saint Joseph,
MO 831
St. Louis Science Center, Saint Louis,
MO 836
Sam Noble Oklahoma Museum of
Natural History, Norman, OK 1206
San Bernardino County Museum,
Redlands, CA 147
San Diego Natural History Museum, San
Diego, CA 160
San Juan County Historical Society
Museum, Silverton, CO...........................232
Sandy Bay Historical Society &
Museums, Inc., Rockport, MA..................705
Sanford Museum and Planetarium,
Cherokee, IA 510
Sanilac County Historical Museum and
Village, Port Sanilac, MI.........................761
Santa Barbara Museum of Natural
History, Santa Barbara, CA......................179
Santa Cruz Museum of Natural History,
Santa Cruz, CA 182
Santa Monica Mountains National
Recreation Area, Thousand Oaks, CA.....191
Saratoga Museum, Saratoga, WY 1638
Sarett Nature Center, Benton Harbor, MI.....729
Sauk County Historical Museum,
Baraboo, WI 1591
Schiele Museum of Natural History and
Lynn Planetarium, Gastonia, NC 1102
The Schuylkill Center for Environmental
Education, Philadelphia, PA....................1288
Sci-Port Discovery Center, Shreveport,
LA 601
Sci-Tech Center of Northern New York,
Watertown, NY 1084
The Science Center of Pinellas County,
Saint Petersburg, FL 342
Science Factory Children's Museum &
Planetarium, Eugene, OR.......................1224
Science Museum of Long Island,
Manhasset, NY 1013
The Science Museum of Minnesota, Saint
Paul, MN 792
Science Museum of Western Virginia,
Roanoke, VA 1535
Sciworks, Winston-Salem, NC 1126
Scotia-Glenville Children's Museum,
Scotia, NY 1068
Seacoast Science Center, Rye, NH 896

Searchlight Historic Museum & Mining
Park, Searchlight, NV.............................882
Seminole Nation Museum, Wewoka, OK...1217
Shenandoah National Park, Luray, VA 1514
Shenandoal Valley Discovery Museum,
Winchester, VA 1546
Ship Ashore Resort Museum, Smith
River, CA 187
Shoshone County Mining and Smelting
Museum d/b/a The Staff House
Museum, Kellogg, ID.............................406
Sidney Historical Association, Sidney,
NY 1069
Silver River Museum & Environmental
Education Center, Ocala, FL.....................330
Sioux City Public Museum, Sioux City,
IA 528
Sisson Museum, Mount Shasta, CA 129
The Skinner Museum of Mount Holyoke
College, South Hadley, MA......................709
Slate Valley Museum, Granville, NY 996
Sleeping Bear Dunes National Lakeshore,
Empire, MI 741
Smithsonian Institution, Washington, DC.....290
Smyth County Museum, Marion, VA 1516
Somervell County Historical Museum,
Glen Rose, TX 1423
South Bannock County Historical Center,
Lava Hot Springs, ID.............................407
South Boston-Halifax County Museum of
Fine Arts & History, South Boston,
VA 1536
The South Carolina Botanical Garden,
Clemson, SC 1328
South Carolina State Museum, Columbia,
SC 1331
South Florida Museum, Bishop
Planetarium & Parker Manatee
Aquarium, Bradenton, FL 297
South Florida Science Museum, West
Palm Beach, FL 353
South Milwaukee Historical Society
Museum, South Milwaukee, WI...........1622
South Shore Natural Science Center, Inc.,
Norwell, MA 700
Southeast Museum Association, Inc.,
Brewster, NY 964
Southern Vermont Natural History
Museum, West Marlboro, VT 1489
Space Farms Zoological Park and
Museum, Sussex, NJ 925
Spartanburg Science Center, Spartanburg,
SC 1342
Springfield Museums - Springfield
Science Museum, Springfield, MA 711
Stamford Museum & Nature Center,
Stamford, CT 261
Starved Rock State Park, Utica, IL 462
The State Museum of Pennsylvania,
Harrisburg, PA 1259
Staten Island Institute of Arts & Sciences
(SIIAS), Staten Island, NY 1074
Stephens County Historical Society and
Museum, Duncan, OK 1199
The Stephens Museum, Fayette, MO 815
Sterling Hill Mining Museum, Inc.,
Ogdensburg, NJ 918
Sterling-Rock Falls Historical Society
Museum, Sterling, IL 461
Sternberg Museum of Natural History,
Hays, KS 543
The Stone Museum, Monroe Township,
NJ 912
Stoughton Historical Society, Stoughton,
WI 1623
Strasenburgh Planetarium/Rochester
Museum & Science Center, Rochester,
NY 1060
Summit Historical Society, Breckenridge,
CO 204
Sunset Crater Volcano National
Monument, Flagstaff, AZ.........................33

Superstition Mountain Lost Dutchman Museum, Apache Junction, AZ..................30

Tate Geological Museum, Casper, WY 1629

Telluride Historical Museum, Telluride, CO..233

Tenino Depot Museum, Tenino, WA 1575

Texas Energy Museum, Beaumont, TX......1395

Texas Natural Science Center, Austin, TX.1392

The Texas Zoo, Victoria, TX 1457

Theodore Roosevelt National Park-Visitor Center, Medora, ND 1134

Thomas E. McMillan Museum, Brewton, AL..6

Thronateeska Heritage Foundation, Inc., Albany, GA...355

Tillamook County Pioneer Museum, Tillamook, OR...................................1237

Timberlake Rose Rock Museum, Noble, OK...1206

Timpanogos Cave National Monument, American Fork, UT.................................1462

Tintic Mining Museum, Eureka, UT 1464

Tipton County Museum, Veteran's Memorial & Nature Center, Covington, TN......................................1364

Tipton-Haynes Historic Site, Johnson City, TN..1368

Tohono Chul Park Inc., Tucson, AZ..............51

The Toledo Zoo, Toledo, OH......................1187

Tombstone Courthouse State Historic Park, Tombstone, AZ...............................46

Tonto National Monument, Roosevelt, AZ...43

Toppenish Museum, Toppenish, WA 1575

Trailside Nature and Science Center, Mountainside, NJ..915

Trailside Nature Center, Cincinnati, OH ...1151

Trailside Nature Museum, Cross River, NY..983

Transylvania Museum, Lexington, KY.........574

Treasures of the Sea Exhibit, Georgetown, DE..271

Tri-State Mineral Museum, Joplin, MO 820

The Trustees of Reservations, Beverly, MA...662

Tu-Endie-Wei State Park, Point Pleasant, WV..1586

Tucker Tower Nature Center, Ardmore, OK..1196

Tucker Wildlife Sanctuary, Silverado, CA ...186

Tucumcari Historical Research Institute, Tucumcari, NM.......................................953

Tulsa Zoo & Living Museum, Tulsa, OK ..1216

Turquoise Museum, Albuquerque, NM 936

Underground Gold Miners Museum, Alleghany, CA...70

United States Department of the Interior Museum, Washington, DC 293

The University Museum Collections, Fayetteville, AR..57

University of Alaska Museum of the North, Fairbanks, AK..................................24

University of Arizona Mineral Museum, Tucson, AZ...52

University of Iowa Museum of Natural History, Iowa City, IA................................520

The University of Michigan Exhibit Museum of Natural History, Ann Arbor, MI..725

University of Missouri-Rolla Minerals Museum, Rolla, MO................................829

University of Nebraska State Museum, Lincoln, NE..867

University of Northern Iowa Museums & Collections, Cedar Falls, IA...................508

University of Oregon Museum of Natural and Cultural History, Eugene, OR 1224

University of Richmond Museums, Richmond, VA.......................................1532

The University of South Carolina McKissick Museum, Columbia, SC.......1331

Upper Musselshell Historical Society, Harlowton, MT.......................................849

Utah Field House of Natural History State Park, Vernal, UT 1475

Utah Museum of Natural History, Salt Lake City, UT...1473

Van Buren County Historical Museum, Clinton, AR...55

Vermont Marble Museum, Proctor, VT......1485

The Vermont State House, Montpelier, VT..1483

Victor Valley Museum & Art Gallery, Apple Valley, CA...71

Village of Elsah Museum, Elsah, IL 433

Virgin Islands National Park, St. John, VI.1644

Virginia Aquarium & Marine Science Center, Virginia Beach, VA....................1542

Virginia Department of Conservation and Recreation, Richmond, VA.....................1533

Virginia Living Museum, Newport News, VA..1520

Virginia Museum of Natural History, Martinsville, VA 1516

Vista Historical Museum, Vista, CA.............196

The Voas Nature Area/Voas Museum, Minburn, IA..523

W.A. Gayle Planetarium, Montgomery, AL..17

W.H. Over Museum, Vermillion, SD..........1358

W.M. Keck Museum, Reno, NV..................881

Wagner Free Institute of Science, Philadelphia, PA....................................1289

Walney Visitor Center-At Ellanor C. Lawrence Park, Chantilly, VA...............1498

Walter B. Jacobs Memorial Nature Park, Shreveport, LA...602

Walter E. Heller Nature Center, Highland Park, IL..439

Warrick County Museum, Inc., Boonville, IN..470

Washakie Museum, Worland, WY 1639

Washburn Historical Museum & Cultural Center, Inc. aka Washburn Cultural Center, Washburn, WI 1625

Washington County Historical Association, Fort Calhoun, NE.....................860

Watermen's Museum, Yorktown, VA..........1547

Wayne County Historical Society, Wooster, OH...1192

Weinberg Nature Center, Scarsdale, NY 1066

Weinman Mineral Museum, White, GA.......391

Weitkamp Observatory and Planetarium, Westerville, OH......................................1191

Weslaco Museum, Weslaco, TX 1461

West of the Pecos Museum, Pecos, TX......1443

West Rock Nature Center, New Haven, CT..254

West Virginia State Museum, Charleston, WV..1581

Western Museum of Mining & Industry, Colorado Springs, CO 208

Western New Mexico University Museum, Silver City, NM......................951

Western North Carolina Nature Center, Asheville, NC..1090

Westport Maritime Museum, Westport, WA..1578

White Sands National Monument, Alamogordo, NM....................................932

Whitley County Historical Museum, Columbia City, IN....................................472

Wilder Memorial Museum, Strawberry Point, IA...528

The Wilderness Center Inc., Wilmot, OH ..1192

Wildlife Museum at Petaluma High School, Petaluma, CA 142

William M. Colmer Visitor Center, Ocean Springs, MS...806

William McKinley Presidential Library & Museum, Canton, OH.............................1146

William Otis Sawtelle Collections and Research Center, Bar Harbor, ME...........606

William Pryor Letchworth Museum, Castile, NY...976

Wilson County Historical Society Museum, Fredonia, KS............................540

Witte Museum, San Antonio, TX 1451

Working Men's Institute, New Harmony, IN..495

World Forestry Center, Portland, OR 1233

World Museum of Mining, Butte, MT 843

World Museum of Natural History, Riverside, CA...150

Wrangell Museum, Wrangell, AK..................29

Wupatki National Monument, Flagstaff, AZ...34

Yakima Valley Museum and Historical Association, Yakima, WA......................1579

Yellowstone Gateway Museum of Park County, Livingston, MT..........................850

Yellowstone National Park, Gardiner, MT ...847

Yorktown Historical Museum, Yorktown, TX..1462

The Yosemite Museum, National Park Service, Yosemite National Park, CA.......199

Youth Science Center, Hacienda Heights, CA..101

Youth Science Institute, San Jose, CA 173

Youth Science Institute, Sanborn Nature Center, Saratoga, CA.................................185

Zion Human History Museum, Springdale, UT..1474

Paleontological

The Academy of Natural Sciences of Philadelphia, Philadelphia, PA 1275

Adams County Historical Society Museum, Brighton, CO..........................204

Adams Museum & House, Deadwood, SD 1346

Agate Fossil Beds National Monument, Harrison, NE..862

Alabama Museum of Natural History, Tuscaloosa, AL..19

Alaska Museum of Natural History, Anchorage, AK...21

Allegany County Museum, Belmont, NY 961

American Museum of Natural History, New York, NY...1019

Anna Miller Museum, Newcastle, WY 1637

Anniston Museum of Natural History, Anniston, AL..3

Anza-Borrego Desert State Park, Borrego Springs, CA...79

Archer County Museum, Archer City, TX .1387

Arizona Mining and Mineral Museum, Phoenix, AZ..39

Arizona-Sonora Desert Museum, Tucson, AZ...48

Arkansas State University Museum, Jonesboro, AR..60

Ash Hollow State Historical Park, Lewellen, NE..864

Audubon Louisiana Nature Center, New Orleans, LA...594

Aurora Fossil Museum, Aurora, NC..........1091

Badlands National Park, Interior, SD 1349

Badlands Petrified Gardens, Kadoka, SD...1349

The Bailey-Matthews Shell Museum, Sanibel, FL..343

Battle Hill Museum of Natural History, Battle Creek, IA.......................................505

Behringer-Crawford Museum, Covington, KY..567

Belle Isle Nature Zoo, Detroit, MI 735

Belvedere Castle-Henry Luce Nature Observatory, New York, NY.................1021

Bent's Old Fort National Historic Site, La Junta, CO..224

Paleontological—Continued

Berea College Burroughs Geological Museum, Berea, KY 565

Bergen Museum of Art & Science, Paramus, NJ 919

Big Bend National Park, Big Bend, TX 1396

Big Bone Lick State Park Museum, Union, KY 584

Big Timbers Museum, Lamar, CO 225

Black Hills Museum of Natural History, Hill City, SD 1348

Black Hills Reptile Gardens, Inc., Rapid City, SD 1354

Blackwater Draw Museum, Portales, NM 944

Blaine County Museum, Chinook, MT 844

Blue Licks Battlefield Museum, Mount Olivet, KY 580

Bob Campbell Geology Museum, Clemson, SC 1328

Boone County Historical Center, Boone, IA 506

Boonshoft Museum of Discovery, Dayton, OH 1160

Bosque Memorial Museum, Clifton, TX 1400

Bowers Science Museum, Cortland, NY 982

Brazos Valley Museum of Natural History, Bryan, TX 1398

Brazosport Museum of Natural Science, Clute, TX 1400

Brevard Museum of History & Science, Cocoa, FL 300

Briar Bush Nature Center, Abington, PA ...1238

Bridger Valley Heritage Museum, Lyman, WY 1636

Brigham Young University Earth Science Museum, Provo, UT 1469

Brooklyn Children's Museum, Brooklyn, NY 968

Bruce Museum, Greenwich, CT 243

Buena Vista Museum of Natural History, Bakersfield, CA 73

Buffalo Museum of Science, Buffalo, NY ..972

Buffalo Trails Museum, Epping, ND 1130

Burke Museum of Natural History and Culture, Seattle, WA 1565

Burpee Museum of Natural History, Rockford, IL 454

Bushwhacker Museum, Nevada, MO 828

Cabrillo Marine Aquarium, San Pedro, CA 176

Calhoun County Museum, Port Lavaca, TX 1444

California Academy of Sciences, San Francisco, CA 163

Calkins Nature Area/Field Museum, Iowa Falls, IA 521

Calusa Nature Center and Planetarium, Fort Myers, FL 308

Calvert Marine Museum, Solomons, MD 654

Capitol Reef National Park Visitor Center, Torrey, UT 1475

Carlsbad Caverns National Park, Carlsbad, NM 937

Carnegie Museum of Natural History, Pittsburgh, PA 1291

Carrie Weedon Natural Science Museum, Galesville, MD 645

Carter County Museum, Ekalaka, MT 846

Cassia County Museum, Burley, ID 404

Castine Scientific Society, Castine, ME 609

Cedar Breaks National Monument, Cedar City, UT 1464

The Centennial Museum at the University of Texas at El Paso, El Paso, TX 1411

Channel Islands National Park, Robert J. Lagomarsino Visitor Center, Ventura, CA 194

Chapman's Gem and Mineral Museum, Fortuna, CA 96

The Charleston Museum, Charleston, SC ...1324

Charlotte County Historical Center, Charlotte Harbor, FL 299

Chickasaw National Recreation Area, Sulphur, OK 1214

Children's Museum at La Habra, La Habra, CA 106

The Children's Museum of Kansas City, Kansas City, KS 546

The Children's Museum of Portsmouth, Portsmouth, NH 894

Children's Museum of Southeastern Connecticut, Niantic, CT 256

Children's Museum of the Sierra, Oakhurst, CA 132

Childress County Heritage Museum, Childress, TX 1400

Chula Vista Nature Center, Chula Vista, CA 84

City County Pioneer Museum, Sweetwater, TX 1454

City of Las Cruces Museum System, Las Cruces, NM 940

Clark Hotel Museum, Van Horn, TX 1457

Clarke County Historical Association, Inc., Berryville, VA 1496

The Cleveland Museum of Natural History, Cleveland, OH 1153

Colburn Earth Science Museum, Asheville, NC 1089

College of Eastern Utah Prehistoric Museum, Price, UT 1469

Colorado National Monument, Fruita, CO ...218

Colorado Plateau Biodiversity Center, Flagstaff, AZ 32

Colorado School of Mines Geology Museum, Golden, CO 220

Community Historical Museum, Maxwell, IA 523

Cottonlandia Museum, Greenwood, MS 800

Coyote Point Museum for Environmental Education, San Mateo, CA 175

Cranbrook Institute of Science, Bloomfield Hills, MI 730

Creation Evidence Museum, Glen Rose, TX 1422

Creative Photographic Art Center of Maine, Lewiston, ME 614

Crowley Museum & Nature Center, Sarasota, FL 344

Crystal River State Archaeological Site, Crystal River, FL 302

The Curious Kids' Museum, Saint Joseph, MI 763

Custer County 1881 Courthouse Museum, Custer, SD 1345

Cylburn Arboretum, Baltimore, MD 631

D. Ralph Hostetter Museum of Natural History, Harrisonburg, VA 1510

Dakota Dinosaur Museum, Dickinson, ND 1129

Dallas Museum of Natural History, Dallas, TX 1406

Dana Adobe, Nipomo, CA 130

Dawson County Historical Museum, Lexington, NE 864

Death Valley National Park Visitor Center and Museums, Death Valley, CA 91

Delaware Division of Historical & Cultural Affairs, Dover, DE 269

Denver Museum of Nature & Science, Denver, CO 211

Des Moines Botanical Center, Des Moines, IA 514

Dinosaur Depot Museum, Canon City, CO 204

Dinosaur Discovery Museum, Kenosha, WI 1602

Dinosaur Gardens, LLC, Ossineke, MI 759

Dinosaur Journey, Fruita, CO 218

The Dinosaur Museum, Blanding, UT 1463

Dinosaur State Park, Rocky Hill, CT 259

Dinosaur Valley State Park, Glen Rose, TX 1422

Dinosaur Walk Museum, Pigeon Forge, TN 1383

The Discovery Center, Fresno, CA 96

Discovery Center (East Tennessee Discovery Center), Knoxville, TN 1369

The Discovery Center of the Southern Tier, Binghamton, NY 962

Discovery Creek Children's Museum of Washington DC, Glen Echo, MD 645

Disney's Animal Kingdom Theme Park, Bay Lake, FL 295

Dorothy G. Page Museum, Wasilla, AK 29

Drummond Island Historical Museum, Drummond Island, MI 739

Dry Falls Interpretive Center, Coulee City, WA 1551

Dunn-Seiler Museum, Mississippi State University, MS 805

Durham Center Museum/Research Library, East Durham, NY 985

Earth & Mineral Sciences Museum and Art Gallery, University Park, PA 1303

Eastern Arizona Museum and Historical Society of Graham County Inc., Pima, AZ 42

ECHO at the Leahy Center for Lake Champlain, Burlington, VT 1478

Ed Clark Museum of Missouri Geology, Rolla, MO 829

Effigy Mounds National Monument, Harpers Ferry, IA 519

Eleanor Barbour Cook Museum of Geology, Chadron, NE 859

Elgin Public Museum, Elgin, IL 432

Emporia State University Johnston Geology Museum, Emporia, KS 538

Erie Planetarium, Erie, PA 1253

Everhart Museum: Natural History, Science and Art, Scranton, PA 1298

Exploration Station - A Children's Museum, Bourbonnais, IL 414

Explorium of Lexington, Lexington, KY 572

Fairbanks Museum and Planetarium, Saint Johnsbury, VT 1486

Fairview Museum of History & Art, Fairview, UT 1465

Falls of the Ohio State Park, Clarksville, IN 472

Fernbank Museum of Natural History, Atlanta, GA 359

Fick Fossil & History Museum, Oakley, KS 554

Fiedler Memorial Museum, Seguin, TX 1452

First Landing State Park, Virginia Beach, VA 1542

Flint Ridge State Memorial Museum, Glenford, OH 1166

Florence Hawley Ellis Museum of Anthropology and Ruth Hall Museum of Paleontology, Abiquiu, NM 931

Florida Museum of Natural History, Gainesville, FL 310

Florissant Fossil Beds National Monument, Florissant, CO 216

Ford County Historical Society, Paxton, IL 450

Fort Kearney Museum, Kearney, NE 863

Fort Peck Interpretive Center, Fort Peck, MT 846

Fort Recovery Museum, Fort Recovery, OH 1164

Fort Wayne Children's Zoo, Fort Wayne, IN 477

Fort Worth Museum of Science and History, Fort Worth, TX 1417

Francisco Fort Museum, La Veta, CO 224

Frank H. McClung Museum, Knoxville, TN 1370

Franklin Mineral Museum, Franklin, NJ 904

Frontier Gateway Museum, Glendive, MT...........847
Frontier Historical Society and Museum, Glenwood Springs, CO 219
Fryxell Geology Museum, Rock Island, IL...........454

Galion Historical Museum, Galion, OH.....1165
The Geological Museum, The University of Wyoming, Laramie, WY...........1635
Geology Museum, Huntington, WV...........1583
Georgia Museum of Natural History, Athens, GA...........356
Georgia Southern University Museum, Statesboro, GA...........387
The Gillespie Museum - Stetson University, De Land, FL...........304
Gilman Museum, Hellertown, PA...........1260
Glenrock Paleontological Museum, Glenrock, WY...........1633
Gonzales Memorial Museum, Gonzales, TX...........1423
Goodhue County Historical Society, Red Wing, MN...........787
Grand Canyon National Park Museum Collection, Grand Canyon National Park, AZ...........36
Grand Gulf Military Park, Port Gibson, MS...........807
Grand River Museum, Lemmon, SD...........1351
Grant County Historical Museum, Canyon City, OR...........1221
Grant County Historical Society, Elbow Lake, MN...........774
Grave Creek Mound Archaeology Complex, Moundsville, WV...........1585
Graves Museum of Archaeology and Natural History, Dania Beach, FL...........302
Greater Hazleton Historical Society, Hazleton, PA...........1260
Greene Memorial Museum, University of Wisconsin-Milwaukee, Milwaukee, WI.1611
Greybull Museum, Greybull, WY...........1634
Grout Museum District: Grout Museum of History and Science, Bluedorn Science Imaginarium, Rensselaer Russell House Museum, Snowden House, Waterloo, IA...........529
Gwinnett County Parks & Recreation Outdoor Interpretive Section, Lawrenceville, GA...........375

H. Earl Clack Museum, Havre, MT...........849
Harvard Museum of Natural History, Cambridge, MA...........672
Hastings Museum, Hastings, NE...........863
Heard Natural Science Museum and Wildlife Sanctuary, Inc., McKinney, TX...........1437
Heart of West Texas Museum, Colorado City, TX...........1401
Hefner Zoology Museum, Oxford, OH...........1181
Hemet Museum, Hemet, CA...........103
Heritage of the Americas Museum, El Cajon, CA...........92
The Hicksville Gregory Museum, Hicksville, NY...........998
Historic St. Mary's City, Saint Mary's City, MD...........652
The Historical Museum at St. Gertrude, Cottonwood, ID...........405
Historical Society of Greenfield, Greenfield, MA...........685
Houston Museum of Natural Science, Houston, TX...........1427
Humboldt State University Natural History Museum, Arcata, CA...........72
Hyrum City Museum, Hyrum, UT...........1466

Idaho Museum of Mining and Geology, Boise, ID...........404
Idaho Museum of Natural History, Pocatello, ID...........408

Illinois State Museum, Springfield, IL...........458
Illinois State Museum, Chicago Gallery, Chicago, IL...........422
The Imaginarium Science Discovery Center, Anchorage, AK...........22
Insights-El Paso Science Center, Inc., El Paso, TX...........1412
International Museum of Art and Science, McAllen, TX...........1437
International Wildlife Museum, Tucson, AZ...........49
Iraan Museum, Iraan, TX...........1430
Iron Hill Museum, Newark, DE...........272

Jackson County Historical Museum & Research Library, Maquoketa, IA...........522
James A. McFaul Environmental Center of Bergen County, Wyckoff, NJ...........931
Jefferson Patterson Park & Museum, Saint Leonard, MD...........651
Jensen Arctic Museum, Monmouth, OR...........1228
Jimmie Rodgers Museum, Meridian, MS...........805
John Burroughs Association, Inc., West Park, NY...........1085
John Day Fossil Beds National Monument, Kimberly, OR...........1227
John Hutchings Museum of Natural History, Lehi, UT...........1466
John Wesley Powell Memorial Museum, Page, AZ...........37
Joseph Moore Museum, Richmond, IN...........497
The Journey Museum, Rapid City, SD...........1354
The Junior Museum of Bay County, Panama City, FL...........334
Jurica Nature Museum, Lisle, IN...........442
Jurupa Mountains Cultural Center, Riverside, CA...........149

KU Natural History Museum and Biodiversity Research Center, Lawrence, KS...........548
Kenosha Public Museum, Kenosha, WI...........1602
Kensington Metropark Nature Center, Milford, MI...........755
Kidspace Children's Museum, Pasadena, CA...........140
Kingman Museum, Battle Creek, MI...........727
Kirby Science Discovery Center at the Washington Pavilion, Sioux Falls, SD...1356
Kittson County History Center Museum, Lake Bronson, MN...........778
Klamath County Museum, Klamath Falls, OR...........1227
Klyne Esopus Museum, Ulster Park, NY...1079

LaBelle Heritage Museum, LaBelle, FL...........319
Lake County Historical Museum, Tavares, FL...........351
Lake Mead National Recreation Area, Boulder City, NV...........875
Lake Meredith Aquatic and Wildlife Museum, Fritch, TX...........1420
Lake Perris Regional Indian Museum (Home of the Wind), Perris, CA...........141
Lakeview Museum of Arts and Sciences, Peoria, IL...........450
Las Vegas Natural History Museum, Las Vegas, NV...........879
Lincoln Park Zoo, Manitowoc, WI...........1607
Lizzadro Museum of Lapidary Art, Elmhurst, IL...........433
Lorenzo State Historic Site, Cazenovia, NY...........976
Lost City Museum, Overton, NV...........880
Louden-Henritze Archaeology Museum, Trinidad, CO...........234
Louisa County Historical Society, Louisa, VA...........1514
Louisiana Tech Museum, Ruston, LA...........600
Louisville Science Center, Louisville, KY...577
Loxahatchee River Historical Society, Jupiter, FL...........316

MacCallum More Museum and Gardens, Chase City, VA...........1500
Madison County Historical Society-Cottage Lawn, Oneida, NY...........1045
Makoshika Dinosaur Museum, Glendive, MT...........848
Mammoth Cave National Park, Mammoth Cave, KY...........579
Mammoth Site of Hot Springs, Inc., Hot Springs, SD...........1348
Marias Museum of History and Art, Shelby, MT...........853
Marin Museum of the American Indian, Novato, CA...........131
Maritime Museum at Historic Coast Guard Station, Saint Simons Island, GA...........383
Maryland Science Center, Baltimore, MD...634
Matagorda County Museum, Bay City, TX...........1393
Maturango Museum of the Indian Wells Valley, Ridgecrest, CA...........148
Mayborn Museum Complex, Waco, TX...........1459
McPherson Museum & Arts Foundation, McPherson, KS...........552
McWane Science Center, Birmingham, AL...........5
Mesa Southwest Museum, Mesa, AZ...........37
Mesa Verde National Park Museum, Mesa Verde National Park, CO...........228
Mesalands Community College's Dinosaur Museum, Tucumcari, NM...........953
Miami Museum of Science & Planetarium, Miami, FL...........325
The Michigan State University Museum, East Lansing, MI...........740
Milam County Museum and Annex, Cameron, TX...........1399
Miles Mineral Museum, Portales, NM...........944
Milwaukee Public Museum, Milwaukee, WI...........1612
Mineral and Lapidary Museum of Henderson County Inc., Hendersonville, NC...........1105
Mineral Museum, Butte, MT...........843
The Minna Anthony Common Nature Center at Wellesley State Park, Fineview, NY...........989
Mississippi Museum of Natural Science, Jackson, MS...........803
Mississippi Petrified Forest, Flora, MS...........800
Mohonk Preserve, Inc., Gardiner, NY...........993
Moorten Botanic Garden and Cactarium, Palm Springs, CA...........138
Morningside Nature Center, Gainesville, FL...........311
Moses Lake Museum & Art Center, Moses Lake, WA...........1559
Mote Marine Laboratory/Aquarium, Sarasota, FL...........345
Mulberry Phospate Museum, Mulberry, FL...........327
Museum and Arts Center in the Sequim Dungeness Valley, Sequim, WA...........1570
Museum of Ancient & Modern Art, Penn Valley, CA...........141
Museum of Arts and Sciences, Macon, GA...........378
The Museum of Arts and Sciences, Inc. and Center for Florida History, Daytona Beach, FL...........303
Museum of Comparative Zoology, Cambridge, MA...........674
Museum of Cultural & Natural History, Mount Pleasant, MI...........757
Museum of Discovery and Science, Fort Lauderdale, FL...........307
Museum of Earth and Life History, Lynchburg, VA...........1515
Museum of Geology and Paleontology, South Dakota School of Mines and Technology, Rapid City, SD...........1355

Paleontological–Continued

Museum of Long Island Natural
  Sciences, Stony Brook, NY 1075
Museum of Natural History and
  Planetarium, Providence, RI...................1317
Museum of Natural Science, Baton
  Rouge, LA 587
Museum of Northern Arizona, Flagstaff,
  AZ 33
Museum of Rim Country Archaeology,
  Payson, AZ 38
Museum of Science, Boston, MA...............667
Museum of Science and Industry, Tampa,
  FL..349
Museum of South Texas History,
  Edinburg, TX 1410
Museum of Texas Tech University,
  Lubbock, TX 1435
Museum of the Big Bend, Alpine, TX 1386
Museum of the Geosciences, Blacksburg,
  VA 1497
Museum of the High Plains, McCook,
  NE 868
Museum of the Middle Appalachians,
  Saltville, VA 1536
Museum of the Red River, Idabel, OK 1203
Museum of the Rockies, Bozeman, MT.......842
Museum of West Louisiana, Leesville,
  LA 591
Museum of Western Colorado, Grand
  Junction, CO 220
Museum of World Treasures, Wichita, KS...562
Museum on Main: A History Museum for
  West Georgia, LaGrange, GA 375

Napa Valley Museum, Yountville, CA 200
Nassau County, Division of Museum
  Services, Department of Recreation,
  Parks & Museums, East Meadow, NY 987
National Geographic Museum at
  Explorers Hall, Washington, DC..............285
National Park Service, Washington, DC.......287
The Natural History Museum, Santa
  Maria, CA 182
Natural History Museum of Los Angeles
  County, Los Angeles, CA.........................120
The Natural Science Center of
  Greensboro, Inc., Greensboro, NC.........1104
The Nature Center at Shaker Lakes,
  Cleveland, OH 1155
The Nature Museum at Grafton, Grafton,
  VT 1479
Nevada State Museum, Las Vegas, Las
  Vegas, NV 880
New Canaan Nature Center, New
  Canaan, CT 252
New Jersey State Museum, Trenton, NJ 927
New London Public Museum, New
  London, WI...1615
New Mexico Bureau of Geology Mineral
  Museum, Socorro, NM 951
New Mexico Museum of Natural History
  & Science, Albuquerque, NM..................935
New York State Museum, Albany, NY.........955
Niagara Gorge Discovery Center, Niagara
  Falls, NY 1042
No Man's Land Historical Society,
  Goodwell, OK 1201
North Carolina Museum of Forestry,
  Whiteville, NC 1122
North Carolina Museum of Natural
  Sciences, Raleigh, NC 1116
The North Museum of Natural History &
  Science, Lancaster, PA 1266
The Northern Maine Museum of Science,
  University of Maine, Presque Isle, ME...620
Northwestern Oklahoma State University
  Museum, Alva, OK 1195
The Nylander Museum of Natural
  History, Caribou, ME 609

Oakley Park, UDC Shrine, Edgefield, SC..1332

O'Fallon Historical Museum, Baker, MT.....840
Ogden's George S. Eccles Dinosaur Park,
  Ogden, UT 1468
Old Courthouse Museum, Santa Ana, CA....178
Old Trail Museum, Choteau, MT................844
Oregon Museum of Science and Industry,
  Portland, OR 1231
Oregon Zoo, Portland, OR 1232
Orlando Science Center, Inc., Orlando,
  FL..332
Orma J. Smith Museum of Natural
  History, Caldwell, ID 405
Orpheum Children's Science Museum,
  Champaign, IL 417
Orton Geological Museum, Ohio State
  University, Columbus, OH 1158
Ottawa County Historical Museum, Port
  Clinton, OH 1183
Owensboro Area Museum of Science &
  History, Owensboro, KY 581

Pacific County Historical Museum, South
  Bend, WA..1571
Pacific Grove Museum of Natural
  History, Pacific Grove, CA 137
Page Museum at the La Brea Tar Pits,
  Los Angeles, CA 121
Paleontological Research Institution,
  Ithaca, NY 1004
Palo Alto Junior Museum and Zoo, Palo
  Alto, CA 139
Panhandle-Plains Historical Museum,
  Canyon, TX 1399
Peabody Museum of Natural History,
  New Haven, CT 253
The Peggy Notebaert Nature Museum,
  Chicago, IL 426
Pember Museum of Natural History,
  Granville, NY 995
Pembina State Museum, Pembina, ND.......1135
Pennsylvania Historical & Museum
  Commission, Harrisburg, PA..................1259
Petrified Creatures Museum of Natural
  History, Richfield Springs, NY 1057
Petrified Forest National Park, Petrified
  Forest National Park, AZ..........................38
Petrified Forest of the Black Hills,
  Piedmont, SD 1353
Petrified Sea Gardens, Saratoga Springs,
  NY 1065
The Petroleum Museum, Midland, TX.......1439
Pink Palace Family of Museums,
  Memphis, TN 1375
Pioneer-Krier Museum, Ashland, KS 532
Pioneer Trails Regional Museum,
  Bowman, ND 1129
Piqua Historical Area State Memorial,
  Piqua, OH 1182
Plains Conservation Center, Aurora, CO......202
Pocahontas County Museum, Marlinton,
  WV 1584
Polk County Historical Museum, Bartow,
  FL..295
Poricy Park Nature Center, Middletown,
  NJ 911
Port Townsend Marine Science Center,
  Port Townsend, WA 1562
Potawatomi Zoo, South Bend, IN...............499
Pound Ridge Society/Museum, Pound
  Ridge, NY 1055
The Pratt Museum of Natural History,
  Amherst, MA 659
The Prehistoric Life Museum, Evanston,
  IL 435
Princeton University Museum of Natural
  History, Princeton, NJ 922
Providence Canyon State Park, Lumpkin,
  GA 377
Putnam Museum of History & Natural
  Science, Davenport, IA 513

Railroad House Historical Association
  Museum, Sanford, NC 1119

Randall Museum, San Francisco, CA...........168
Rankin Museum, Inc., Ellerbe, NC.............1100
The Raymond M. Alf Museum of
  Paleontology, Claremont, CA....................86
Red Mill Museum Village, Clinton, NJ........901
Red River Valley Museum, Vernon, TX.....1457
Reuel B. Pritchett Museum, Bridgewater,
  VA 1497
Richland County Historical Museum,
  Wahpeton, ND 1137
Rimrocker Historical Museum of West
  Montrose County, Naturita, CO 229
River Legacy Living Science Center,
  Arlington, TX 1388
Riverside Metropolitan Museum,
  Riverside, CA 150
Roberts County Museum, Miami, TX........1438
Rochester Museum & Science Center,
  Rochester, NY.......................................1059
Rocky Ford Historical Museum, Rocky
  Ford, CO 231
Rocky Mount Children's Museum and
  Science Center, Inc., Rocky Mount,
  NC 1118
Rocky Mountain Dinosaur Resource
  Center, Woodland Park, CO 235
Ross County Historical Society, Inc.,
  Chillicothe, OH 1147

Sag Harbor Whaling & Historical
  Museum, Sag Harbor, NY 1063
St. Francis County Museum, Forrest City,
  AR 57
St. Louis Science Center, Saint Louis,
  MO 836
St. Simons Island Lighthouse Museum,
  Saint Simons Island, GA 383
Salinas Pueblo Missions National
  Monument, Mountainair, NM 943
Sam Noble Oklahoma Museum of
  Natural History, Norman, OK 1206
San Bernardino County Museum,
  Redlands, CA 147
San Diego Natural History Museum, San
  Diego, CA 160
San Jacinto Museum, San Jacinto, CA.........171
Sanford Museum and Planetarium,
  Cherokee, IA 510
Santa Barbara Museum of Natural
  History, Santa Barbara, CA 179
Santa Cruz Museum of Natural History,
  Santa Cruz, CA 182
Santa Monica Mountains National
  Recreation Area, Thousand Oaks, CA....191
Sarett Nature Center, Benton Harbor, MI....729
Sci-Port Discovery Center, Shreveport,
  LA 601
Sci-Tech Center of Northern New York,
  Watertown, NY 1084
Science Museum of Long Island,
  Manhasset, NY 1013
The Science Museum of Minnesota, Saint
  Paul, MN 792
Science Museum of Western Virginia,
  Roanoke, VA 1535
Sciworks, Winston-Salem, NC 1126
Scotts Bluff National Monument, Gering,
  NE 861
Shenandoal Valley Discovery Museum,
  Winchester, VA 1546
Silver River Museum & Environmental
  Education Center, Ocala, FL 330
Sioux City Public Museum, Sioux City,
  IA 528
Smithsonian Institution, Washington, DC.....290
Somervell County Historical Museum,
  Glen Rose, TX 1423
South Carolina State Museum, Columbia,
  SC 1331
South Florida Museum, Bishop
  Planetarium & Parker Manatee
  Aquarium, Bradenton, FL 297

South Florida Science Museum, West Palm Beach, FL............353
Southern Vermont Natural History Museum, West Marlboro, VT............1489
Spartanburg Science Center, Spartanburg, SC............1342
Springfield Museums - Springfield Science Museum, Springfield, MA............711
State Historical Society of Iowa, Des Moines, IA............515
The State Museum of Pennsylvania, Harrisburg, PA............1259
Sternberg Museum of Natural History, Hays, KS............543
The Stone Museum, Monroe Township, NJ............912

T Rex Museum, Tucson, AZ............50
Tate Geological Museum, Casper, WY............1629
Texas Energy Museum, Beaumont, TX............1395
Texas Natural Science Center, Austin, TX............1392
Texas Parks and Wildlife Department, Austin, TX............1392
The Texas Zoo, Victoria, TX............1457
Timpanogos Cave National Monument, American Fork, UT............1462
Tipton-Haynes Historic Site, Johnson City, TN............1368
Trailside Nature and Science Center, Mountainside, NJ............915
Trailside Nature Center, Cincinnati, OH............1151
Tucker Tower Nature Center, Ardmore, OK............1196
Tucumcari Historical Research Institute, Tucumcari, NM............953
Tularosa Basin Historical Society Museum, Alamogordo, NM............932
Tulsa Zoo & Living Museum, Tulsa, OK............1216
Tuzigoot National Monument, Clarkdale, AZ............31
Two Medicine Dinosaur Center, Bynum, MO............812

Union County Heritage Museum, New Albany, MS............806
University Museum, Carbondale, IL............415
The University Museum, Edwardsville, IL............432
The University Museum Collections, Fayetteville, AR............57
University of Alaska Museum of the North, Fairbanks, AK............24
University of Colorado Museum, Boulder, CO............203
University of Iowa Museum of Natural History, Iowa City, IA............520
The University of Michigan Exhibit Museum of Natural History, Ann Arbor, MI............725
University of Missouri-Rolla Minerals Museum, Rolla, MO............829
University of Nebraska State Museum, Lincoln, NE............867
University of Northern Iowa Museums & Collections, Cedar Falls, IA............508
University of Oregon Museum of Natural and Cultural History, Eugene, OR............1224
University of Richmond Museums, Richmond, VA............1532
University of Wisconsin Zoological Museum, Madison, WI............1606
Upper Musselshell Historical Society, Harlowton, MT............849
Utah Field House of Natural History State Park, Vernal, UT............1475
Utah Museum of Natural History, Salt Lake City, UT............1473

Valley Community Historical Society, Inc., Valley, NE............874
Van Meter State Park, Miami, MO............827
Virginia Living Museum, Newport News, VA............1520

Virginia Museum of Natural History, Martinsville, VA............1516
The Voas Nature Area/Voas Museum, Minburn, IA............523

Wagner Free Institute of Science, Philadelphia, PA............1289
Walter B. Jacobs Memorial Nature Park, Shreveport, LA............602
Wapello County Historical Museum, Ottumwa, IA............526
Warren County Historical Society Museum, Lebanon, OH............1171
Washakie Museum, Worland, WY............1639
Wayne County Historical Society, Wooster, OH............1192
Weinman Mineral Museum, White, GA............391
Wenatchee Valley Museum and Cultural Center, Wenatchee, WA............1577
Western New Mexico University Museum, Silver City, NM............951
The Whale Museum, Friday Harbor, WA............1555
White County Historical Society, Carmi, IL............415
Wildlife Museum at Petaluma High School, Petaluma, CA............142
William Pryor Letchworth Museum, Castile, NY............976
William S. Webb Museum of Anthropology, Lexington, KY............575
Wilson County Historical Society Museum, Fredonia, KS............540
Winona County Historical Museum, Winona, MN............797
Wise County Heritage Museum, Decatur, TX............1408
World Museum of Natural History, Riverside, CA............150
Wray Museum, Wray, CO............235
The Wyoming Dinosaur Center, Thermopolis, WY............1639

Yakima Valley Museum and Historical Association, Yakima, WA............1579
Youth Science Center, Hacienda Heights, CA............101
Youth Science Institute, San Jose, CA............173

Zion Human History Museum, Springdale, UT............1474

Zoological (Living)

A.K.C. Museum of The Dog, Saint Louis, MO............831
ASRI Environmental Education Center, Bristol, RI............1310
Abilene Zoological Gardens, Abilene, TX............1385
The Academy of Natural Sciences of Philadelphia, Philadelphia, PA............1275
Action Wildlife Foundation, Goshen, CT............242
Adventure Aquarium, Camden, NJ............899
Adventure Science Center, Nashville, TN............1377
Ak-Sar-Ben Aquarium Outdoor Education Center, Gretna, NE............862
Akron Zoological Park, Akron, OH............1138
Alameda Park Zoo, Alamogordo, NM............931
Alaska Zoo, Anchorage, AK............22
Albuquerque Biological Park, Albuquerque, NM............932
Allegany County Museum, Belmont, NY............961
Alley Pond Environmental Center, Inc., Douglaston, NY............984
American Bald Eagle Foundation, Haines, AK............25
Anniston Museum of Natural History, Anniston, AL............3
Ano Nuevo State Reserve, Pescadero, CA............141
Applegate Park Zoo, Merced, CA............125
Aquarium of Niagara, Niagara Falls, NY............1042
Aquarium of the Pacific, Long Beach, CA............110
Arizona-Sonora Desert Museum, Tucson, AZ............48

Arizona Zoological Society, dba the Phoenix Zoo, Phoenix, AZ............40
Armand Bayou Nature Center, Houston, TX............1424
Arthur D. Feiro Marine Life Center c/o Peninsula College, Port Angeles, WA............1561
Ash Lawn-Highland, Charlottesville, VA............1498
Atlanta Botanical Garden, Atlanta, GA............357
Audubon Aquarium of the Americas, New Orleans, LA............593
Audubon Greenwich, Greenwich, CT............242
Audubon Louisiana Nature Center, New Orleans, LA............594
Audubon Naturalist Society, Chevy Chase, MD............640
Audubon Society of New Hampshire, Concord, NH............884
Audubon Zoo, New Orleans, LA............594
Aullwood Audubon Center and Farm, Dayton, OH............1160
Austin Nature & Science Center, Austin, TX............1389
Awbury Arboretum, Philadelphia, PA............1277

Barrington Living History Farm, Washington, TX............1460
Baton Rouge Zoo, Baton Rouge, LA............585
Batsto Village, Hammonton, NJ............907
Battle Hill Museum of Natural History, Battle Creek, IA............505
Bear Country U.S.A., Rapid City, SD............1354
Bear Mountain Trailside Museums and Zoo, Bear Mountain, NY............961
Belle Isle Aquarium, Detroit, MI............734
Belle Isle Nature Zoo, Detroit, MI............735
Bent's Old Fort National Historic Site, La Junta, CO............224
Bergen County Zoological Park, Paramus, NJ............919
Berkshire Museum, Pittsfield, MA............702
Bernheim Arboretum and Research Forest, Clermont, KY............567
Big Thunder Gold Mine, Keystone, SD............1349
Binder Park Zoo, Battle Creek, MI............727
Binghamton Zoo at Ross Park, Binghamton, NY............962
Birch Aquarium at Scripps, Scripps Institution of Oceanography, University of California, San Diego, La Jolla, CA............106
Birdsong Nature Center, Thomasville, GA............387
Birmingham Zoo, Birmingham, AL............5
Biscayne National Park, Homestead, FL............313
Black Hills Reptile Gardens, Inc., Rapid City, SD............1354
Blank Park Zoo, Des Moines, IA............514
Blue Hills Trailside Museum, Milton, MA............695
Bonnet House Museum & Gardens, Fort Lauderdale, FL............306
Boone's Lick State Historic Site, Boonesboro, MO............811
Boonshoft Museum of Discovery, Dayton, OH............1160
Boyce Thompson Arboretum, Superior, AZ............44
Bramble Park Zoo, Watertown, SD............1359
Brandywine Zoo, Wilmington, DE............272
Brazos Valley Museum of Natural History, Bryan, TX............1398
Briar Bush Nature Center, Abington, PA............1238
Bronx Zoo, Bronx, NY............965
Brookgreen Gardens, Murrells Inlet, SC............1337
Buffalo Zoological Gardens, Buffalo, NY............972
Burpee Museum of Natural History, Rockford, IL............454

Cabin Nature Center, Wood Dale, IL............466
Cabrillo Marine Aquarium, San Pedro, CA............176
Caldwell Zoo, Tyler, TX............1456

Zoological (Living)—Continued

California Academy of Sciences, San Francisco, CA 163
Calkins Nature Area/Field Museum, Iowa Falls, IA 521
Calusa Nature Center and Planetarium, Fort Myers, FL 308
Calvert Marine Museum, Solomons, MD 654
Cameron Park Zoo, Waco, TX 1458
The Campus Arboretum Association Haverford College, Haverford, PA 1260
Cape Cod Museum of Natural History, Inc., Brewster, MA 670
Cape May County Park and Zoo, Cape May Court House, NJ 901
Capron Park Zoo, Attleboro, MA 661
Carl G. Fenner Nature Center, Lansing, MI 749
Carlsbad Caverns National Park, Carlsbad, NM 937
Cass County Historical Society, Logansport, IN 489
The Cathedral of St. John the Divine, New York, NY 1022
Catoctin Wildlife Preserve & Zoo, Thurmont, MD 655
Cedar Bog Nature Preserve, Urbana, OH ..1188
Central Florida Zoo, Sanford, FL 342
Central Park Conservancy, New York, NY 1022
Channel Islands National Park, Robert J. Lagomarsino Visitor Center, Ventura, CA 194
Charles Paddock Zoo, Atascadero, CA 72
Charles Towne Landing State Historic Site, Charleston, SC 1324
The Chattanooga Nature Center, Chattanooga, TN 1361
Chattanooga Zoo at Warner Park, Chattanooga, TN 1361
The Chesapeake Children's Museum, Annapolis, MD 627
Cheyenne Mountain Zoological Park, Colorado Springs, CO 206
Chicago Zoological Park (Brookfield Zoo), Brookfield, IL 414
Chickasaw National Recreation Area, Sulphur, OK 1214
Chico Creek Nature Center, Chico, CA 83
Children's Hands-On Museum (CHOM), Tuscaloosa, AL 19
Children's Museum at La Habra, La Habra, CA 106
Children's Museum of History, Natural History and Science at Utica, New York, Utica, NY 1079
The Children's Museum of Science and Technology, Troy, NY 1079
Chippewa Nature Center, Midland, MI 755
Chula Vista Nature Center, Chula Vista, CA 84
Cincinnati Zoo & Botanical Garden, Cincinnati, OH 1149
City of Las Cruces Museum System, Las Cruces, NM 940
Clearwater Marine Aquarium, Clearwater, FL 299
Cleveland Metroparks Outdoor Education Division, Garfield Heights, OH 1165
Cleveland Metroparks Zoo, Cleveland, OH 1152
The Cleveland Museum of Natural History, Cleveland, OH 1153
Clyde E. Buckley Wildlife Sanctuary, Frankfort, KY 568
Clyde Peeling's Reptiland, Allenwood, PA 1240
Coastal Science Center at Hutchinson Island, Stuart, FL 346
Coggeshall Farm Museum, Bristol, RI 1310
Columbian Park Zoo, Lafayette, IN 487

Columbus Zoo and Aquarium, Powell, OH 1183
Como Park Zoo and Conservatory, Saint Paul, MN 789
Congaree National Park, Hopkins, SC 1336
Connecticut Audubon Center at Fairfield, Fairfield, CT 240
Connecticut's Beardsley Zoo, Bridgeport, CT 236
Conservancy Nature Center, Naples, FL 328
Cora Hartshorn Arboretum and Bird Sanctuary, Short Hills, NJ 924
Core Arboretum, Morgantown, WV 1585
County of Westchester, Department of Parks, Recreation and Conservation, Mount Kisco, NY 1016
Cox Arboretum & Gardens MetroPark, Dayton, OH 1160
Coyote Point Museum for Environmental Education, San Mateo, CA 175
Crane Point, Marathon, FL 323
Craters of the Moon National Monument, Arco, ID 403
Creation Museum, Petersburg, KY 583
Creepy Hollow Living Museum, Oklahoma City, OK 1207
The Crosby Arboretum, Mississippi State University, Picayune, MS 807
Cuneo Museum & Gardens, Vernon Hills, IL 463
Custer State Park, Custer, SD 1346
The Custom House Maritime Museum, Newburyport, MA 697
Cylburn Arboretum, Baltimore, MD 631

D.C. Booth Historic National Fish Hatchery, Spearfish, SD 1357
Dakota Zoo, Bismarck, ND 1128
The Dallas Aquarium at Fair Park, Dallas, TX 1404
The Dallas World Aquarium, Dallas, TX ..1406
Dallas Zoo, Dallas, TX 1406
Dan Nicholas Park Nature Center, Salisbury, NC 1118
Danville Science Center, Danville, VA 1502
David Trayol Zoo of Emporia, Emporia, KS 538
The Dawes Arboretum, Newark, OH 1177
De Graaf Nature Center, Holland, MI 746
Dead Horse Point State Park, Moab, UT 1467
Delaware Nature Society, Hockessin, DE 271
Denison Pequotsepos Nature Center, Mystic, CT 250
Denver Zoological Gardens, Denver, CO.....211
Des Moines Botanical Center, Des Moines, IA 514
Descanso Gardens Guild, Inc., La Canada Flintridge, CA 105
Detroit Zoo, Royal Oak, MI 762
Dickerson Park Zoo, Springfield, MO 838
Dinosaur State Park, Rocky Hill, CT 259
The Discovery Center, Fresno, CA 96
Discovery Center (East Tennessee Discovery Center), Knoxville, TN 1369
Discovery Creek Children's Museum of Washington DC, Glen Echo, MD 645
Discovery Museum, Sacramento Museum of History, Science and Technology, Sacramento, CA 152
Discovery Place, Inc., Charlotte, NC 1094
Disney's Animal Kingdom Theme Park, Bay Lake, FL 295
Douglas County Museum of History and Natural History, Roseburg, OR 1234
Drayton Hall, Charleston, SC 1325
Drumlin Farm Education Center, Lincoln, MA 690
Dry Tortugas National Park, Key West, FL 317

Earthplace - The Nature Discovery Center, Westport, CT 266

ECHO at the Leahy Center for Lake Champlain, Burlington, VT 1478
EcoTarium, Worcester, MA 720
Effie Yeaw Nature Center, Carmichael, CA 82
El Dorado Nature Center, Long Beach, CA 110
El Paso Zoo, El Paso, TX 1412
El Rancho de Las Golondrinas Museum, Santa Fe, NM 947
Elachee Nature Science Center, Gainesville, GA 373
Elgin Public Museum, Elgin, IL 432
Ellen Trout Zoo, Lufkin, TX 1435
Environmental Education Center, Somerset County Park Commission, Basking Ridge, NJ 898
Epcot at Walt Disney World Resort, Lake Buena Vista, FL 319
Erie Zoological Park & Botanical Gardens of Northwestern Pennsylvania, Erie, PA 1253
Ernest Hemingway House Museum, Key West, FL 317
Essex County's Turtle Back Zoo, West Orange, NJ 930
Exploration Station - A Children's Museum, Bourbonnais, IL 414

Fairfax County Park Authority, Resource Management Division, Fairfax, VA 1503
Falls of the Ohio State Park, Clarksville, IN 472
The Farm, Sturgeon Bay, WI 1623
The Farmers' Museum, Inc., Cooperstown, NY 980
Fejervary Zoo, Davenport, IA 512
Finnup Park and Lee Richardson Zoo, Garden City, KS 541
Flandrau Science Center and Planetarium, Tucson, AZ 49
Flint River Quarium, Albany, GA 355
Florida Agricultural Museum, Palm Coast, FL 334
Florida Aquarium, Tampa, FL 349
Fontenelle Nature Association, Bellevue, NE 857
Ford Nature Education Center, Youngstown, OH 1194
Forest Park Museum and Arboretum, Perry, IA 527
Fort Leaton State Historical Site, Presidio, TX 1444
Fort Matanzas National Monument, Saint Augustine, FL 339
Fort Niobrara National Wildlife Refuge, Valentine, NE 874
Fort Wayne Children's Zoo, Fort Wayne, IN 477
Fort Worth Museum of Science and History, Fort Worth, TX 1417
Fort Worth Zoological Park, Fort Worth, TX 1417
Fossil Rim Wildlife Center, Glen Rose, TX 1422
Fosterfields Living Historical Farm, Morristown, NJ 913
Fountain Rock Nature Center, Walkersville, MD 656
Four Mile Historic Park, Denver, CO 212
Fresno Chaffee Zoo, Fresno, CA 97
The Frost Entomological Museum, Dept. of Entomology, The Pennsylvania State University, University Park, PA....1304

Gardens at Callaway, Pine Mountain, GA ...380
Garfield Farm Museum, LaFox, IL 441
Gavins Point National Fish Hatchery and Aquarium, Yankton, SD 1359
Georgia Aquarium, Atlanta, GA 360
George B. Dorr Museum of Natural History, Bar Harbor, ME 605
Gilman Museum, Hellertown, PA 1260

Gladys Porter Zoo, Brownsville, TX..........1398
Glen Oak Zoo, Peoria, IL 450
Gloucester County Historical Society,
    Woodbury, NJ.......................................931
Good Zoo, Wheeling, WV 1587
Gore Place, Waltham, MA...........................715
Great Explorations, The Childrens
    Museum, Saint Petersburg, FL................341
Great Plains Zoo & Delbridge Museum,
    Sioux Falls, SD....................................1356
Great Valley Museum of Natural History,
    Modesto, CA..126
The Greenburgh Nature Center,
    Scarsdale, NY......................................1066
Greenville Zoo, Greenville, SC 1334
Grizzly & Wolf Discovery Center, West
    Yellowstone, MT 854
The Grove, Glenview, IL 438
Gulf Branch Nature Center, Arlington,
    VA...1496
Gulfcoast Wonder and Imagination Zone,
    dba G.WIZ, Sarasota, FL 344
Gull Wings Children's Museum, Oxnard,
    CA..137
Gwinnett County Parks & Recreation
    Outdoor Interpretive Section,
    Lawrenceville, GA..................................375

Hands On! Regional Museum, Johnson
    City, TN..1367
Happy Hollow Park & Zoo, San Jose,
    CA..171
Harriet Alexander Nature Center,
    Roseville, MN...788
Hartman Reserve Nature Center, Cedar
    Falls, IA..507
Hatfield Marine Science Center, Oregon
    State University, Newport, OR 1228
Hawk Mountain Sanctuary, Kempton, PA..1264
Heard Natural Science Museum and
    Wildlife Sanctuary, Inc., McKinney,
    TX...1437
Henry Doorly Zoo, Omaha, NE..................871
Henry Vilas Park Zoo, Madison, WI..........1605
Henson Robinson Zoo, Springfield, IL.........458
Herrett Center for Arts & Science,
    Faulkner Planetarium and Centennial
    Observatory, Twin Falls, ID....................410
Hi-Desert Nature Museum, Yucca Valley,
    CA..201
Hickory Hill, Thomson, GA.........................388
High Desert Museum, Bend, OR................1220
Hilltop Garden and Nature Center,
    Bloomington, IN.....................................469
Historic Bethabara Park, Winston-Salem,
    NC..1125
Historic Jefferson College, Washington,
    MS..810
Historic Sauder Village, Archbold, OH 1140
Honolulu Zoo, Honolulu, HI.......................396
Houston Museum of Natural Science,
    Houston, TX..1427
Houston Zoo, Inc., Houston, TX 1427
Hugh Mercer Apothecary Shop,
    Fredericksburg, VA...............................1506
Humboldt State University Natural
    History Museum, Arcata, CA....................72

ICR Museum of Creation & Earth
    History, Santee, CA...............................185
Imaginarium Hands-On Museum, Fort
    Myers, FL..309
The Imaginarium Science Discovery
    Center, Anchorage, AK 22
Imagination Station Science Museum,
    Wilson, NC..1124
Indianapolis Zoo, Indianapolis, IN..............485
International Crane Foundation, Baraboo,
    WI...1591
International Museum of the Horse,
    Lexington, KY..573
International Peace Garden, Dunseith,
    ND..1130

International Wildlife Museum, Tucson,
    AZ...49
Ipswich River Wildlife Sanctuary
    (Massachusetts Audubon Society),
    Topsfield, MA..714

J.L. Scott Marine Education Center and
    Aquarium, Gulf Coast Research
    Laboratory College of Marine
    Sciences, The U. of Southern
    Mississippi, Biloxi, MS 798
Jackson Zoological Park, Inc., Jackson,
    MS..802
Jacksonville Zoo and Gardens,
    Jacksonville, FL......................................315
James A. McFaul Environmental Center
    of Bergen County, Wyckoff, NJ..............931
Jerome Ford Nature Center, Alexandria,
    VA...1493
Jimmie Rodgers Museum, Meridian, MS.....805
John Ball Zoological Garden, Grand
    Rapids, MI...744
John Burroughs Association, Inc., West
    Park, NY..1085
John D. MacArthur Beach State Park &
    Nature Center, North Palm Beach, FL 329
John G. Shedd Aquarium, Chicago, IL 422
John James Audubon Center at Mill
    Grove, Audubon, PA 1241
John James Audubon Museum,
    Henderson, KY.......................................571
The Junior Museum of Bay County,
    Panama City, FL.....................................334

Kalamazoo Nature Center, Inc.,
    Kalamazoo, MI.......................................748
Kalaupapa National Historical Park,
    Kalaupapa, HI..400
Kansas City Zoo, Kansas City, MO 821
Kansas Department of Wildlife & Parks,
    Pratt, KS...556
Kenilworth Aquatic Gardens, Washington,
    DC..281
Kensington Metropark Nature Center,
    Milford, MI..755
Kentucky Department of Fish & Wildlife
    Resources-Salato Wildlife Education
    Center, Frankfort, KY 569
Kidspace Children's Museum, Pasadena,
    CA..140
Knoxville Zoological Gardens, Knoxville,
    TN..1370

Lake Erie Nature & Science Center, Bay
    Village, OH..1141
Lake Mead National Recreation Area,
    Boulder City, NV....................................875
Lake Meredith Aquatic and Wildlife
    Museum, Fritch, TX..............................1420
Lake Superior Zoological Gardens,
    Duluth, MN..773
Lake View Nature Center, Oakbrook
    Terrace, IL...449
Landis Valley Museum, Lancaster, PA.......1266
Landmark Park, Dothan, AL............................8
Las Vegas Natural History Museum, Las
    Vegas, NV...879
Lawrence Hall of Science, Berkeley, CA.......76
Leaming's Run Garden & Colonial Farm,
    Swainton, NJ...926
Liberty Science Center, Jersey City, NJ.......909
Lichterman Nature Center, Memphis, TN..1373
Lincoln Children's Zoo, Lincoln, NE...........866
Lincoln Memorial Garden and Nature
    Center, Springfield, IL............................459
Lincoln Park Zoo, Manitowoc, WI............1607
Lincoln Park Zoological Gardens,
    Chicago, IL..423
Lindsay Wildlife Museum, Walnut Creek,
    CA..196
Little River Zoo, Norman, OK..................1206
Little Rock Zoological Gardens, Little
    Rock, AR..62

The Living Desert, Palm Desert, CA 138
Living Desert Zoo and Gardens State
    Park, Carlsbad, NM................................938
Living History Farms, Urbandale, IA...........529
Loggerhead Marinelife Center, Juno
    Beach, FL..316
Logoly State Park, McNeil, AR.....................64
Long Branch Nature Center, Arlington,
    VA...1496
The Los Angeles Zoo and Botanical
    Gardens, Los Angeles, CA......................119
Loudoun Heritage Farm Museum,
    Sterling, VA...1538
Louisiana Arboretum, State Preservation
    Area, Ville Platte, LA..............................603
Louisville Zoological Garden, Louisville,
    KY..578
Lower Rio Grande Valley Nature Center,
    Weslaco, TX...1460
Lutz Children's Museum, Manchester, CT...248

MacKenzie Environmental Education
    Center, Poynette, WI.............................1618
Madison County Historical Society,
    Winterset, IA...531
Magnolia Plantation and Gardens,
    Charleston, SC......................................1326
Malabar Farm State Park, Lucas, OH.........1173
Mammoth Cave Wildlife Museum, Cave
    City, KY..566
Manchester Zoo, Manchester, CT..............248
The Maritime Aquarium, Norwalk, CT........257
The Maryland Zoo in Baltimore,
    Baltimore, MD..635
Matagorda County Museum, Bay City,
    TX...1393
Maui Ocean Center, Maalaea, HI 401
May Natural History Museum and
    Museum of Space Exploration,
    Colorado Springs, CO.............................207
Maymont, Richmond, VA 1530
McWane Science Center, Birmingham,
    AL..5
Memphis Botanic Garden, Goldsmith
    Civic Garden Center, Memphis, TN 1374
Memphis Zoo, Memphis, TN.....................1374
Mendocino Coast Botanic Garden, Fort
    Bragg, CA..95
ME's Zoo, Parker City, IN..........................495
Mesker Park Zoo & Botanic Garden,
    Evansville, IN...476
Miami Metrozoo, Miami, FL.......................324
Miami Museum of Science &
    Planetarium, Miami, FL...........................325
Miami Seaquarium, Miami, FL 325
Micke Grove Zoo, Lodi, CA........................109
Mill Mountain Zoo, Roanoke, VA.............1535
Millbrook School, Trevor Zoo, Millbrook,
    NY...1014
Miller Park Zoo, Bloomington, IL................414
Milwaukee County Zoological Gardens,
    Milwaukee, WI.....................................1612
The Minna Anthony Common Nature
    Center at Wellesley State Park,
    Fineview, NY..989
Minnesota Zoo, Apple Valley, MN..............768
Mississippi Museum of Natural Science,
    Jackson, MS...803
Missouri Botanical Garden, Saint Louis,
    MO..834
Mitchell Park Horticultural Conservatory,
    Milwaukee, WI.....................................1612
MOBIUS Kids, Spokane, WA 1571
Moccasin Lake Nature Park, An
    Environmental & Energy Education
    Center, Clearwater, FL...........................299
Mohonk Preserve, Inc., Gardiner, NY..........993
Monterey Bay Aquarium, Monterey, CA 127
Montgomery Zoo, Montgomery, AL 17
Morningside Nature Center, Gainesville,
    FL..311
Morro Bay Aquarium, Morro Bay, CA 129

Zoological (Living)–Continued

Mote Marine Laboratory/Aquarium, Sarasota, FL 345
Mount Desert Oceanarium, Southwest Harbor, ME 623
Mount Pisgah Arboretum, Eugene, OR 1224
Museum of Ancient & Modern Art, Penn Valley, CA 141
Museum of Arts and Sciences, Macon, GA 378
Museum of Discovery and Science, Fort Lauderdale, FL 307
Museum of Discovery: Arkansas Museum of Science and History, Little Rock, AR 62
Museum of Life and Science, Durham, NC 1098
Museum of Paleontology, Berkeley, CA 76
Museum of Science, Boston, MA 667
Museum of Science & History of Jacksonville, Jacksonville, FL 315
Museum of Science and Industry, Tampa, FL 349
Museum of the Hudson Highlands, Cornwall-on-Hudson, NY 982
Museum of the Northern Great Plains, Fort Benton, MT 846
Museum of Zoology, Amherst, MA 659
Myrtle Beach State Park Nature Center, Myrtle Beach, SC 1338
Mystic Aquarium & Institute for Exploration, Mystic, CT 250

Nantucket Maria Mitchell Association, Nantucket, MA 696
Nashville Zoo at Grassmere, Nashville, TN 1379
Natchitoches National Fish Hatchery, Natchitoches, LA 593
The National Aquarium, Washington, DC 284
National Aquarium in Baltimore, Baltimore, MD 635
National Audubon Society, New York, NY 1034
National Aviary in Pittsburgh, Inc., Pittsburgh, PA 1293
National Bird Dog Museum, Grand Junction, TN 1366
National Buffalo Museum, Jamestown, ND 1133
National Wildlife Visitor Center, Patuxent Research Refuge, Laurel, MD 648
National Zoological Park, Smithsonian Institution, Washington, DC 288
Natural Bridge Zoological Park, Natural Bridge, VA 1519
Natural History Museum, Portales, NM 944
The Natural Science Center of Greensboro, Inc., Greensboro, NC 1104
The Nature Center at Shaker Lakes, Cleveland, OH 1155
The Nature Conservancy, Arlington, VA 1496
Nauticus, The National Maritime Center, Norfolk, VA 1522
New Britain Youth Museum, New Britain, CT 252
New Britain Youth Museum at Hungerford Park, Kensington, CT 247
New Canaan Nature Center, New Canaan, CT 252
New England Aquarium Corporation, Boston, MA 668
New Jersey Meadowlands Environment Center, Lyndhurst, NJ 910
New Mexico Farm & Ranch Heritage Museum, Las Cruces, NM 940
New York Aquarium, Brooklyn, NY 969
The Newark Museum, Newark, NJ 916
Niabi Zoo, Coal Valley, IL 428
No Man's Land Historical Society, Goodwell, OK 1201

North Carolina Aquarium at Fort Fisher, Kure Beach, NC 1109
North Carolina Aquarium at Pine Knoll Shores, Pine Knoll Shores, NC 1114
North Carolina Aquarium on Roanoke Island, Manteo, NC 1110
North Carolina Museum of Natural Sciences, Raleigh, NC 1116
North Carolina Zoological Park, Asheboro, NC 1088
The North Museum of Natural History & Science, Lancaster, PA 1266
Northwest Trek Wildlife Park, Eatonville, WA 1552

The Oak Park Conservatory, Oak Park, IL 449
Oakland Zoo, Oakland, CA 134
Oakwoods Metropark Nature Center, Belleville, MI 728
Oatland Island Education Center, Savannah, GA 385
Ocean City Life-Saving Station Museum, Ocean City, MD 650
Oceanographic Teaching Station Inc. - Roundhouse Marine Studies Lab & Aquarium, Manhattan Beach, CA 124
Oklahoma City Zoo, Oklahoma City, OK ..1209
Old Bethpage Village Restoration, Old Bethpage, NY 1045
Old Cowtown Museum, Wichita, KS 562
Old Santee Canal Park, Moncks Corner, SC 1337
Old World Wisconsin, Eagle, WI 1595
Oregon Coast Aquarium, Newport, OR 1229
Oregon Zoo, Portland, OR 1232
Orlando Science Center, Inc., Orlando, FL 332
Ormond Memorial Art Museum & Garden, Ormond Beach, FL 333
Orpheum Children's Science Museum, Champaign, IL 417
Overstreet-Kerr Historical Farm, Keota, OK 1203
Oxon Cove Park, Oxon Hill, MD 650
The Oyster and Maritime Museum of Chincoteague, Chincoteague, VA 1501

Pacific Science Center, Seattle, WA 1568
Paducah Aquarium, Paducah, KY 582
Palm Beach Zoo at Dreher Park, West Palm Beach, FL 353
Palo Alto Junior Museum and Zoo, Palo Alto, CA 139
Panaewa Rainforest Zoo, Hilo, HI 393
Panola Mountain State Conservation Park, Stockbridge, GA 387
Paradise Point Nature Center, East Hebron, NH 887
Parrot Jungle Island, Miami, FL 325
Pawnee Bill Ranch and Museum, Pawnee, OK 1212
Pember Museum of Natural History, Granville, NY 995
Pennsbury Manor, Morrisville, PA 1272
The Philadelphia Zoo, Philadelphia, PA 1286
The Pier Aquarium, Saint Petersburg, FL ...341
Pioneers Park Nature Center, Lincoln, NE ...867
Piqua Historical Area State Memorial, Piqua, OH 1182
Pittsburgh Zoo and Aquarium, Pittsburgh, PA 1293
Plains Conservation Center, Aurora, CO 202
Pocatello Zoo, Pocatello, ID 409
Point Defiance Zoo & Aquarium, Tacoma, WA 1574
Port Townsend Marine Science Center, Port Townsend, WA 1562
Potawatomi Zoo, South Bend, IN 499
Potter Park Zoo, Lansing, MI 750
Pratt Museum, Homer, AK 25
The Pratt Museum of Natural History, Amherst, MA 659

Prospect Park Zoo, Brooklyn, NY 970
Providence Canyon State Park, Lumpkin, GA 377
Pueblo Zoo, Pueblo, CO 230

Quail Ridge Wilderness Conservancy, Davis, CA 90
Queens County Farm Museum, Floral Park, NY 989

Rachel Carson Homestead, Springdale, PA 1301
Racine Zoological Gardens, Racine, WI 1619
Randall Museum, San Francisco, CA 168
Rattlesnake Museum (American International), Albuquerque, NM 935
Reid Park Zoo, Tucson, AZ 50
The Ridges Sanctuary, Inc., Baileys Harbor, WI 1590
Riley House Museum of African American History & Culture, Tallahassee, FL 348
Rio Grande Nature Center State Park, Albuquerque, NM 935
River Hills Visitor Center, Wildwood, MO 840
River Legacy Living Science Center, Arlington, TX 1388
Riverbanks Zoological Park & Botanical Garden, Columbia, SC 1329
Riverbend Environmental Education Center, Gladwyne, PA 1256
Riverside Zoo, Scottsbluff, NE 872
Robert A. Vines Environmental Science Center, Houston, TX 1429
Rock Creek Nature Center, Washington, DC 290
Rockwoods Reservation, Wildwood, MO 840
Rocky Mount Children's Museum and Science Center, Inc., Rocky Mount, NC 1118
Rocky Mount Museum, Piney Flats, TN 1383
Roger Williams Park Zoo, Providence, RI.1318
Roosevelt Park Zoo, Minot, ND 1135
Roper Mountain Science Center, Greenville, SC 1334
Rosamond Gifford Zoo at Burnet Park, Syracuse, NY 1077
Rotary Nature Center, Oakland, CA 134
Roth Living Farm Museum of Delaware Valley College, North Wales, PA 1274
The Rutgers Gardens, New Brunswick, NJ 916

Sacramento Zoo, Sacramento, CA 153
Saginaw Valley Zoological Society, Saginaw, MI 763
St. Augustine Alligator Farm, Saint Augustine, FL 340
St. Catherine's Wildlife Survival Center, Midway, GA 380
Saint Louis Zoo, Saint Louis, MO 837
The Salisbury Zoological Park, Salisbury, MD 652
San Antonio Zoological Society, San Antonio, TX 1450
San Diego Wild Animal Park, Escondido, CA 93
San Diego Zoo, San Diego, CA 161
San Francisco Bay Bird Observatory, Alviso, CA 70
San Francisco Zoological Gardens, San Francisco, CA 170
Sanibel-Captiva Conservation Foundation, Inc., Sanibel, FL 343
Santa Ana Zoo, Santa Ana, CA 178
Santa Barbara Zoological Gardens, Santa Barbara, CA 180
Santa Cruz Museum of Natural History, Santa Cruz, CA 182
Santa Fe Children's Museum, Santa Fe, NM 950

Santa Fe Community College Teaching Zoo, Gainesville, FL....................................311
Schiele Museum of Natural History and Lynn Planetarium, Gastonia, NC 1102
The Schuylkill Center for Environmental Education, Philadelphia, PA....................1288
Sci-Port Discovery Center, Shreveport, LA..601
Sci-Tech Center of Northern New York, Watertown, NY..1084
Science Center of Connecticut, West Hartford, CT 265
Science Center of Iowa, Des Moines, IA.....515
The Science Center of Pinellas County, Saint Petersburg, FL.................................342
Science Museum of Long Island, Manhasset, NY..1013
Science Museum of Western Virginia, Roanoke, VA...1535
Science Spectrum, Lubbock, TX 1435
Sciworks, Winston-Salem, NC..................1126
Scovill Children's Zoo, Decatur, IL 430
Seacoast Science Center, Rye, NH 896
Seattle Aquarium, Seattle, WA..................1568
SeaWorld San Diego, San Diego, CA...........161
Sedgwick County Zoo, Wichita, KS.............562
Seneca Park Zoo, Rochester, NY 1060
Seney National Wildlife Refuge Visitor Center, Seney, MI.................................764
Sharon Audubon Center, Sharon, CT 259
Shenandoal Valley Discovery Museum, Winchester, VA.................................1546
Sierra Safari Zoo, Reno, NV.......................881
Six Flags Marine World, Vallejo, CA..........194
Slate Run Living Historical Farm, Metro Parks, Ashville, OH 1140
Smithsonian Institution, Washington, DC.....290
South Carolina Aquarium, Charleston, SC.1326
South County Museum Inc., Narragansett, RI...1313
South Florida Museum, Bishop Planetarium & Parker Manatee Aquarium, Bradenton, FL.......................297
South Shore Natural Science Center, Inc., Norwell, MA..700
Southern Vermont Natural History Museum, West Marlboro, VT 1489
Space Farms Zoological Park and Museum, Sussex, NJ 925
Spartanburg Science Center, Spartanburg, SC...1342
Spiro Mounds Archaeological Center, Spiro, OK...1214
Spring River Park & Zoo, Roswell, NM......946
Spring Valley Nature Center & Heritage Farm, Schaumburg, IL 457
Springbrook Nature Center, Fridley, MN.....776
Springfield Museums - Springfield Science Museum, Springfield, MA..........711
Squam Lakes Natural Science Center, Holderness, NH.....................................889
Stanwood Wildlife Sanctuary, Ellsworth, ME...610
Star Eco Station, Culver City, CA................88
Staten Island Children's Museum, Staten Island, NY...1073
Staten Island Zoo, Staten Island, NY 1074
Stephen C. Foster State Park, Fargo, GA.....371
Strong - National Museum of Play, Rochester, NY..................................1060
Sulphur Creek Nature Center, Hayward, CA...102
Sunset Zoological Park, Manhattan, KS.......552

T Rex Museum, Tucson, AZ.........................50
Tallahassee Museum, Tallahassee, FL 348
Tampa's Lowry Park Zoo, Tampa, FL 350
Tanglewood Nature Center and Museum, Elmira, NY...988
Tautphaus Park Zoo, Idaho Falls, ID...........406
Tennessee Aquarium, Chattanooga, TN......1362

Tewaukon National Wildlife Refuge, Cayuga, ND...1129
Texarkana Museums System, Texarkana, TX...1455
Texas Discovery Gardens, Dallas, TX........1408
Texas Energy Museum, Beaumont, TX.......1395
The Texas Zoo, Victoria, TX 1457
Tilden Nature Area Environmental Education Center, Berkeley, CA 77
Tohono Chul Park Inc., Tucson, AZ...............51
The Toledo Zoo, Toledo, OH....................1187
Topeka Zoological Park, Topeka, KS 560
Tracy Aviary, Salt Lake City, UT 1472
Trailside Nature and Science Center, Mountainside, NJ...................................915
Trailside Nature Center, Cincinnati, OH 1151
The Trustees of Reservations, Beverly, MA...662
Tucker Tower Nature Center, Ardmore, OK..1196
Tulsa Zoo & Living Museum, Tulsa, OK..1216
Turtle Bay Exploration Park, Redding, CA...146

UNLV Marjorie Barrick Museum, Las Vegas, NV..880
USDA Forest Service - Land Between the Lakes, Golden Pond, KY 570
University of Michigan, Museum of Zoology, Ann Arbor, MI 726
University of North Dakota Zoology Museum, Grand Forks, ND....................1132
University of Puerto Rico Department of Marine Sciences Museum, Mayaguez, PR..1641
Upper Souris National Wildlife Refuge, Berthhold, ND.......................................1127
Utah's Hogle Zoo, Salt Lake City, UT.......1473
Utica Zoo, Utica, NY 1080

Vermont Institute of Natural Science, Quechee, VT.......................................1485
Virginia Aquarium & Marine Science Center, Virginia Beach, VA...................1542
Virginia Living Museum, Newport News, VA...1520
Virginia Museum of Natural History, Martinsville, VA 1516
Virginia Zoological Park, Norfolk, VA.......1523

W.K. Kellogg Bird Sanctuary of Michigan State University, Augusta, MI...726
Wabasha County Museum, Wabasha County Historical Society at Reads Landing, Reads Landing, MN..................787
Wahkeena Nature Preserve, Sugar Grove, OH...1186
Waikiki Aquarium, Honolulu, HI.................399
Waimea Arboretum and Botanical Garden in Waimea Valley Audubon Center, Haleiwa, HI..392
Walney Visitor Center-At Ellanor C. Lawrence Park, Chantilly, VA..............1498
Walter B. Jacobs Memorial Nature Park, Shreveport, LA.....................................602
Walter E. Heller Nature Center, Highland Park, IL...439
Washington Park Zoological Gardens, Michigan City, IN..................................491
Welder Wildlife Foundation & Refuge, Sinton, TX..1453
West Rock Nature Center, New Haven, CT..254
West Virginia State Wildlife Center, French Creek, WV.................................1581
Western North Carolina Nature Center, Asheville, NC......................................1090
Westmoreland Sanctuary, Inc., Bedford Corners, NY..961
The Wetlands Institute, Stone Harbor, NJ 925
White Memorial Conservation Center, Inc., Litchfield, CT.................................247

Whitehouse Nature Center, Albion, MI........723
The Wilderness Center Inc., Wilmot, OH ..1192
Wildlife Conservation Society, Queens Zoo, Flushing, NY..................................990
Wildlife Museum at Petaluma High School, Petaluma, CA.............................142
Wildlife Prairie State Park, Hanna City, IL...439
Wildlife World Zoo, Litchfield Park, AZ 37
Willow Park Zoo, Logan, UT....................1467
Woldumar Nature Center, Lansing, MI 751
Woodland Park Zoo, Seattle, WA 1570
Woods Hole Science Aquarium, Woods Hole, MA..720

Youth Science Center, Hacienda Heights, CA...101
Youth Science Institute, San Jose, CA 173
Youth Science Institute at Vasona Park, Los Gatos, CA..123
Youth Science Institute, Sanborn Nature Center, Saratoga, CA...............................185

The Zoo, Gulf Breeze, FL 312
Zoo Atlanta, Atlanta, GA 364
Zoo Boise, Boise, ID..................................404
Zoo Montana, Billings, MT 842
Zoo New England, Boston, MA 669
Zooamerica North America Wildlife Park, Hershey, PA...1261

Zoological (Nonliving)

The A.D. Buck Museum of Natural History & Science, Tonkawa, OK 1215
A.K.C. Museum of The Dog, Saint Louis, MO...831
ASRI Environmental Education Center, Bristol, RI..1310
Abilene Zoological Gardens, Abilene, TX .1385
The Academy of Natural Sciences of Philadelphia, Philadelphia, PA 1275
Action Wildlife Foundation, Goshen, CT.....242
Adams Museum & House, Deadwood, SD...1346
Adventure Science Center, Nashville, TN..1377
Aiken County Historical Museum, Aiken, SC...1320
Ak-Sar-Ben Aquarium Outdoor Education Center, Gretna, NE..................................862
Akron Zoological Park, Akron, OH...........1138
Alabama Museum of Natural History, Tuscaloosa, AL 19
Alaska Museum of Natural History, Anchorage, AK.......................................21
Alfred B. Maclay State Gardens, Tallahassee, FL......................................346
Allan Shivers Museum, Woodville, TX.......1462
Allegany County Museum, Belmont, NY 961
Alley Pond Environmental Center, Inc., Douglaston, NY......................................984
American Bald Eagle Foundation, Haines, AK..25
American Museum of Natural History, New York, NY.....................................1019
American Saddlebred Museum, Lexington, KY......................................572
Androscoggin Historical Society, Auburn, ME...603
Angel Mounds State Historic Site, Evansville, IN....................................475
Anniston Museum of Natural History, Anniston, AL...3
Ano Nuevo State Reserve, Pescadero, CA...141
Antelope Valley California Poppy Reserve, Lancaster, CA........................108
Anthropology Teaching Museum, California State University, Fullerton, Fullerton, CA...98
Anza-Borrego Desert State Park, Borrego Springs, CA..79
Applegate Park Zoo, Merced, CA 125
Aquarium of Niagara, Niagara Falls, NY ..1042

Zoological (Nonliving)—Continued

Arizona Zoological Society, dba the
  Phoenix Zoo, Phoenix, AZ..........................40
Arkansas Game and Fish Commission,
  Little Rock, AR 61
Arkansas Post National Memorial, Gillett,
  AR 58
Arkansas State University Museum,
  Jonesboro, AR...60
Armand Bayou Nature Center, Houston,
  TX 1424
Arthur D. Feiro Marine Life Center c/o
  Peninsula College, Port Angeles, WA ...1561
Audubon Greenwich, Greenwich, CT 242
Audubon Louisiana Nature Center, New
  Orleans, LA 594
Audubon Society of New Hampshire,
  Concord, NH 884
Audubon Society of Rhode Island,
  Smithfield, RI...1319
Aullwood Audubon Center and Farm,
  Dayton, OH...1160

The Bailey-Matthews Shell Museum,
  Sanibel, FL...343
Baranov Museum, Kodiak, AK.......................26
The Bartlett Museum, Amesbury, MA 657
Baton Rouge Zoo, Baton Rouge, LA 585
Battle Hill Museum of Natural History,
  Battle Creek, IA...505
Bayard Cutting Arboretum, Great River,
  NY..996
Bear Mountain Trailside Museums and
  Zoo, Bear Mountain, NY 961
Belding Museum, Belding, MI 728
Belle Isle Nature Zoo, Detroit, MI 735
Belvedere Castle-Henry Luce Nature
  Observatory, New York, NY....................1021
Benson Memorial Museum, Malheur
  National Wildlife Refuge, Princeton,
  OR...1233
Benton County Historical Museum,
  Prosser, WA..1563
Bent's Old Fort National Historic Site, La
  Junta, CO...224
Berea College Burroughs Geological
  Museum, Berea, KY...................................565
Bergen County Zoological Park,
  Paramus, NJ...919
Bergen Museum of Art & Science,
  Paramus, NJ...919
Berkshire Museum, Pittsfield, MA 702
Bernard Historical Society and Museum,
  Delton, MI...734
Bernheim Arboretum and Research
  Forest, Clermont, KY.................................567
Besser Museum for Northeast Michigan,
  Alpena, MI...723
Bickelhaupt Arboretum, Clinton, IA............511
Big Basin Redwoods State Park, Boulder
  Creek, CA..79
Big Bend National Park, Big Bend, TX.....1396
Big Cypress National Preserve, Ochopee,
  FL...330
Big Thicket National Preserve, Kountze,
  TX 1432
Big Thunder Gold Mine, Keystone, SD 1349
Birch Aquarium at Scripps, Scripps
  Institution of Oceanography,
  University of California, San Diego,
  La Jolla, CA...106
Bishop Museum, Honolulu, HI.....................394
Black Hills Reptile Gardens, Inc., Rapid
  City, SD..1354
Black Kettle Museum, Cheyenne, OK 1198
Blue Hills Trailside Museum, Milton,
  MA...695
Bolin Wildlife Exhibit & Antique
  Collection, McKinney, TX 1437
Booker T. Washington National
  Monument, Hardy, VA 1510

Boone County Historical Center, Boone,
  IA...506
Boonshoft Museum of Discovery,
  Dayton, OH...1160
Boston Childrens Museum, Boston, MA......664
Bowers Science Museum, Cortland, NY......982
Bowman's Hill Wildflower Preserve, New
  Hope, PA..1273
Boyce Thompson Arboretum, Superior,
  AZ..44
Bramble Park Zoo, Watertown, SD 1359
Brazos Valley Museum of Natural
  History, Bryan, TX...................................1398
Brazosport Museum of Natural Science,
  Clute, TX..1400
Brevard Museum of History & Science,
  Cocoa, FL...300
Briar Bush Nature Center, Abington, PA ...1238
Bruce Museum, Greenwich, CT...................243
Buckhorn Saloon & Museum, San
  Antonio, TX...1448
Buffalo Museum of Science, Buffalo, NY ...972
Buffalo National River, Harrison, AR 59
Burke Museum of Natural History and
  Culture, Seattle, WA................................1565
Burpee Museum of Natural History,
  Rockford, IL...454
Byron Historical Museum, Byron, NY........974

Cabin Nature Center, Wood Dale, IL 466
Cable Natural History Museum, Cable,
  WI..1593
Cabrillo Marine Aquarium, San Pedro,
  CA..176
Calhoun County Museum, Rockwell City,
  IA...527
California Academy of Sciences, San
  Francisco, CA...163
Calkins Nature Area/Field Museum, Iowa
  Falls, IA...521
Call of the Wild Museum, Gaylord, MI.......742
Calusa Nature Center and Planetarium,
  Fort Myers, FL...308
Calvin Coolidge Historic Site, Plymouth
  Notch, VT...1484
Cambridge Museum, Cambridge, NE...........858
Cape Cod Museum of Natural History,
  Inc., Brewster, MA....................................670
Capitol Reef National Park Visitor
  Center, Torrey, UT...................................1475
Capitola Historical Museum, Capitola,
  CA..81
Capulin Volcano National Monument,
  Capulin, NM..937
Carbon County Museum, Rawlins, WY 1637
Carnegie Museum of Natural History,
  Pittsburgh, PA..1291
Carrie Weedon Natural Science Museum,
  Galesville, MD...645
Carson County Square House Museum,
  Panhandle, TX..1442
Carter County Museum, Ekalaka, MT..........846
Cashmere Museum & Pioneer Village,
  Cashmere, WA..1550
The Cathedral of St. John the Divine,
  New York, NY..1022
Cattle Raisers Museum, Fort Worth, TX....1416
Cedar Breaks National Monument, Cedar
  City, UT...1464
The Centennial Museum at the University
  of Texas at El Paso, El Paso, TX 1411
Central Florida Zoo, Sanford, FL 342
Central Missouri State University
  Archives and Museum, Warrensburg,
  MO...839
Channel Islands National Park, Robert J.
  Lagomarsino Visitor Center, Ventura,
  CA..194
Charles R. Conner Museum, Pullman,
  WA...1563
The Charleston Museum, Charleston, SC ..1324
Charlotte Nature Museum, Charlotte, NC..1094

Chester County Historical Society
  Museum, Chester, SC...............................1327
Cheyenne Mountain Zoological Park,
  Colorado Springs, CO 206
Chicago Zoological Park (Brookfield
  Zoo), Brookfield, IL..................................414
Chickasaw National Recreation Area,
  Sulphur, OK...1214
Chico Creek Nature Center, Chico, CA 83
Children's Hands-On Museum (CHOM),
  Tuscaloosa, AL..19
Children's Museum at La Habra, La
  Habra, CA..106
The Children's Museum at Yunker Farm,
  Fargo, ND...1130
Children's Museum/Detroit Public
  Schools, Detroit, MI..................................735
The Children's Museum, Inc.,
  Bloomsburg, PA..1243
Children's Museum of History, Natural
  History and Science at Utica, New
  York, Utica, NY.......................................1079
The Children's Museum of Science and
  Technology, Troy, NY..............................1079
Children's Museum of Southeastern
  Connecticut, Niantic, CT...........................256
Children's Museum of the Sierra,
  Oakhurst, CA...132
Chippewa Nature Center, Midland, MI........755
Chiricahua National Monument, Willcox,
  AZ..53
Chula Vista Nature Center, Chula Vista,
  CA..84
Cincinnati Museum Center at Union
  Terminal, Cincinnati, OH........................1149
The Claremont, New Hampshire
  Historical Society, Inc., Claremont,
  NH...884
Clearwater Marine Aquarium, Clearwater,
  FL...299
Cleveland Metroparks Outdoor Education
  Division, Garfield Heights, OH...............1165
The Cleveland Museum of Natural
  History, Cleveland, OH............................1153
Cliffs of the Neuse State Park, Seven
  Springs, NC..1119
Clinton County Museum, Frankfort, IN......478
Clyde E. Buckley Wildlife Sanctuary,
  Frankfort, KY..568
Coastal Discovery Museum, Hilton Head
  Island, SC...1335
Coastal Science Center at Hutchinson
  Island, Stuart, FL......................................346
Cold Spring Harbor Whaling Museum,
  Cold Spring Harbor, NY............................979
Colleton Museum, Walterboro, SC.............1343
Collier County Museum, Naples, FL............328
Colorado National Monument, Fruita, CO...218
Colorado Plateau Biodiversity Center,
  Flagstaff, AZ..32
Columbia River Exhibition of History,
  Science and Technology, Richland,
  WA...1564
Columbus Zoo and Aquarium, Powell,
  OH..1183
Congaree National Park, Hopkins, SC 1336
Connecticut Audubon Birdcraft Museum,
  Fairfield, CT..240
Connecticut Audubon Center at Fairfield,
  Fairfield, CT..240
Connecticut Audubon Society, Fairfield,
  CT..240
Connecticut State Museum of Natural
  History and Connecticut Archaeology
  Center, Storrs, CT.....................................261
Cook's Natural Science Museum,
  Decatur, AL...7
Coronado National Memorial, Hereford,
  AZ..36
Corpus Christi Museum of Science and
  History, Corpus Christi, TX.....................1401
Cottonwood County Historical Society,
  Windom, MN...796

County of Westchester, Department of Parks, Recreation and Conservation, Mount Kisco, NY 1016
Coyote Point Museum for Environmental Education, San Mateo, CA.......................175
Cranbrook Institute of Science, Bloomfield Hills, MI 730
Crane Point, Marathon, FL 323
Crater Lake National Park, Crater Lake, OR.......................1222
Crowley Museum & Nature Center, Sarasota, FL 344
Curry Historical Society Museum, Gold Beach, OR.......................1225
Custer County 1881 Courthouse Museum, Custer, SD.......................1345
Cylburn Arboretum, Baltimore, MD...........631

D. Ralph Hostetter Museum of Natural History, Harrisonburg, VA.......................1510
Dacotah Prairie Museum, Aberdeen, SD....1344
Dakota Sunset Museum, Gettysburg, SD ...1348
Dakota Zoo, Bismarck, ND.......................1128
Dallas Museum of Natural History, Dallas, TX.......................1406
The Dawes Arboretum, Newark, OH 1177
De Graaf Nature Center, Holland, MI...........746
De Smet Depot Museum, De Smet, SD.....1346
Delaware Archaeology Museum, Dover, DE.......................269
Delaware County Institute of Science, Media, PA.......................1270
Delaware Museum of Natural History, Wilmington, DE.......................273
Delaware Nature Society, Hockessin, DE 271
Denali National Park and Preserve, Denali Park, AK 23
Denison Pequotsepos Nature Center, Mystic, CT.......................250
Denver Museum of Nature & Science, Denver, CO.......................211
Devils Tower Visitor Center, Devils Tower, WY.......................1631
Dickson Mounds Museum, Lewistown, IL.......................442
Dinosaur Discovery Museum, Kenosha, WI.......................1602
The Discovery Center, Fresno, CA.................96
Discovery Center (East Tennessee Discovery Center), Knoxville, TN.........1369
Discovery Creek Children's Museum of Washington DC, Glen Echo, MD...........645
Discovery Museum, Sacramento Museum of History, Science and Technology, Sacramento, CA.......................152
Discovery Place, Inc., Charlotte, NC...........1094
Disney's Animal Kingdom Theme Park, Bay Lake, FL.......................295

Earthplace - The Nature Discovery Center, Westport, CT.......................266
ECHO at the Leahy Center for Lake Champlain, Burlington, VT.......................1478
EcoTarium, Worcester, MA.......................720
Edisto Island Historic Preservation Society Museum, Edisto Island, SC 1332
Effie Yeaw Nature Center, Carmichael, CA.......................82
Effigy Mounds National Monument, Harpers Ferry, IA.......................519
Ehrhart Museum, Antwerp, OH 1139
El Campo Museum of Natural History, El Campo, TX.......................1411
El Dorado Nature Center, Long Beach, CA.......................110
El Paso Zoo, El Paso, TX 1412
Entomology Research Museum, Riverside, CA.......................149
Environmental Education Center, Somerset County Park Commission, Basking Ridge, NJ.......................898
Essig Museum of Entomology, University of California, Berkeley, Berkeley, CA.......75

Estelle H. Womack Museum of Natural History, Danville, VA.......................1503
Everglades National Park, Homestead, FL...313
Everhart Museum: Natural History, Science and Art, Scranton, PA.......................1298
Exploration Station - A Children's Museum, Bourbonnais, IL.......................414
Explorit Science Center, Davis, CA.................89

Fabyan Villa Museum, Geneva, IL.......................437
Fairbanks Museum and Planetarium, Saint Johnsbury, VT.......................1486
Fairfax County Park Authority, Resource Management Division, Fairfax, VA.......1503
Falls of the Ohio State Park, Clarksville, IN.......................472
Family Museum, Bettendorf, IA.......................505
Faninadahen Kosas Guahan-Guam Museum, Hagatna, GU.......................1640
Fernbank Museum of Natural History, Atlanta, GA.......................359
Fernbank Science Center, Atlanta, GA.........360
Fernwood Botanical Garden & Nature Preserve, Niles, MI.......................758
Finnup Park and Lee Richardson Zoo, Garden City, KS.......................541
First Landing State Park, Virginia Beach, VA.......................1542
Florida Museum of Natural History, Gainesville, FL.......................310
Fontenelle Nature Association, Bellevue, NE.......................857
Ford Nature Education Center, Youngstown, OH.......................1194
Forest Park Museum and Arboretum, Perry, IA.......................527
Fort Kearney Museum, Kearney, NE 863
Fort Matanzas National Monument, Saint Augustine, FL.......................339
Fort Okanogan Interpretive Center, Brewster, WA.......................1550
Fort Peck Interpretive Center, Fort Peck, MT.......................846
Fort Wayne Children's Zoo, Fort Wayne, IN.......................477
Fort Worth Museum of Science and History, Fort Worth, TX.......................1417
Fort Worth Zoological Park, Fort Worth, TX.......................1417
Fossil Rim Wildlife Center, Glen Rose, TX.......................1422
Fountain Rock Nature Center, Walkersville, MD.......................656
Francisco Fort Museum, La Veta, CO.........224
Frank H. McClung Museum, Knoxville, TN.......................1370
Fred Dana Marsh Museum, Ormond Beach, FL.......................333
Freeborn County Museum and Historical Village, Albert Lea, MN.......................767
Fresno Chaffee Zoo, Fresno, CA.......................97
The Frost Entomological Museum, Dept. of Entomology, The Pennsylvania State University, University Park, PA....1304

Gardens at Callaway, Pine Mountain, GA ...380
Gavins Point National Fish Hatchery and Aquarium, Yankton, SD 1359
Georgia Museum of Natural History, Athens, GA.......................356
Georgia Southern University Museum, Statesboro, GA.......................387
Gerald E. Eddy Discovery Center, Chelsea, MI.......................732
George B. Dorr Museum of Natural History, Bar Harbor, ME.......................605
Gilman Museum, Hellertown, PA.......................1260
Gladys Porter Zoo, Brownsville, TX.......................1398
Golden Gate National Recreation Area, San Francisco, CA.......................165
Goodnow Museum State Historic Site, Manhattan, KS.......................550

Grand Canyon National Park Museum Collection, Grand Canyon National Park, AZ.......................36
Great Basin National Park, Baker, NV.......875
Great Plains Zoo & Delbridge Museum, Sioux Falls, SD.......................1356
Great Sand Dunes National Monument and Preserve, Mosca, CO.......................229
Great Valley Museum of Natural History, Modesto, CA.......................126
Greater Hazleton Historical Society, Hazleton, PA.......................1260
Grizzly & Wolf Discovery Center, West Yellowstone, MT.......................854
The Grove, Glenview, IL 438
Gunnison Museum of Natural History, Pawling, NY.......................1051
Gwinnett County Parks & Recreation Outdoor Interpretive Section, Lawrenceville, GA.......................375

Hampton County Historical Museum, Hampton, SC 1334
Hands On! Regional Museum, Johnson City, TN.......................1367
Happy Hollow Park & Zoo, San Jose, CA.......................171
Hartman Reserve Nature Center, Cedar Falls, IA.......................507
Harvard Museum of Natural History, Cambridge, MA.......................672
Hastings Museum, Hastings, NE.......................863
Hatteras Island Visitor Center, Buxton, NC.......................1093
Havre de Grace Decoy Museum, Havre de Grace, MD.......................647
Hefner Zoology Museum, Oxford, OH 1181
Henry County Historical Society, New Castle, IN.......................494
Henry Vilas Park Zoo, Madison, WI.........1605
Heritage Hall Museum & Archives, Freeman, SD.......................1347
Heritage of the Americas Museum, El Cajon, CA.......................92
Hi-Desert Nature Museum, Yucca Valley, CA.......................201
The Hicksville Gregory Museum, Hicksville, NY.......................998
Hilltop Garden and Nature Center, Bloomington, IN.......................469
Historic Auto Attractions, Roscoe, IL 456
Historic Renville Preservation Commission, Renville, MN.......................787
The Historical Museum at St. Gertrude, Cottonwood, ID.......................405
Historical Natural History & Library Society of Natick dba Natick Historical Society, South Natick, MA 709
Historical Society Porter County Old Jail Museum, Valparaiso, IN.......................502
Hoard Historical Museum and National Dairy Shrine's Visitors Center, Fort Atkinson, WI.......................1598
Horry County Museum, Conway, SC.........1331
Hot Springs National Park Visitor Center, Hot Springs, AR.......................60
Houston Museum of Natural Science, Houston, TX.......................1427
Humboldt State University Natural History Museum, Arcata, CA.......................72
Huron City Museums, Port Austin, MI 761

ICR Museum of Creation & Earth History, Santee, CA.......................185
Idaho Museum of Natural History, Pocatello, ID.......................408
Illinois State Museum, Springfield, IL 458
The Imaginarium Science Discovery Center, Anchorage, AK.......................22
Indiana Dunes National Lakeshore, Porter, IN.......................496
International Crane Foundation, Baraboo, WI.......................1591

Zoological (Nonliving)–Continued

International Museum of Art and Science, McAllen, TX 1437

International Peace Garden, Dunseith, ND 1130

International Wildlife Museum, Tucson, AZ 49

Isle Royale National Park, Houghton, MI 747

J.L. Scott Marine Education Center and Aquarium, Gulf Coast Research Laboratory College of Marine Sciences, The U. of Southern Mississippi, Biloxi, MS 798

Jacksonville Zoo and Gardens, Jacksonville, FL 315

James A. McFaul Environmental Center of Bergen County, Wyckoff, NJ 931

James Ford Bell Museum of Natural History, Minneapolis, MN 782

James R. Slater Museum of Natural History, Tacoma, WA 1573

Jean Lafitte National Historical Park & Preserve, New Orleans, LA 596

Jeff Matthews Memorial Museum, Galax, VA 1508

Jensen Arctic Museum, Monmouth, OR 1228

Jerome Ford Nature Center, Alexandria, VA 1493

Jersey City Museum, Jersey City, NJ 908

Jimmie Rodgers Museum, Meridian, MS.....805

John E. Conner Museum, Kingsville, TX ..1432

John James Audubon Center at Mill Grove, Audubon, PA 1241

Joseph Moore Museum, Richmond, IN........497

Joshua Tree National Park, Oasis Visitor Center, Twentynine Palms, CA 193

The Junior Museum of Bay County, Panama City, FL 334

Jurica Nature Museum, Lisle, IL 442

KU Natural History Museum and Biodiversity Research Center, Lawrence, KS 548

Kalamazoo Nature Center, Inc., Kalamazoo, MI 748

Kansas City Zoo, Kansas City, MO 821

Kansas Department of Wildlife & Parks, Pratt, KS 556

Kauffman Museum, North Newton, KS 553

Kenosha Public Museum, Kenosha, WI.....1602

Kensington Metropark Nature Center, Milford, MI 755

Kentucky Department of Fish & Wildlife Resources-Salato Wildlife Education Center, Frankfort, KY 569

Kidspace Children's Museum, Pasadena, CA 140

Kingman Museum, Battle Creek, MI 727

Kings Mountain National Military Park, Blacksburg, SC 1322

Kittson County History Center Museum, Lake Bronson, MN 778

Klamath County Museum, Klamath Falls, OR 1227

Klondike Gold Rush National Historical Park, Skagway, AK 28

Knife River Indian Villages National Historic Site, Stanton, ND............................1136

Koke'e Natural History Museum, Kauai, HI 400

L.C. Bates Museum, Hinckley, ME.............612

La Porte County Historical Society Museum, La Porte, IN............................487

Lac Qui Parle County Historical Society, Madison, MN 779

Lake Erie Nature & Science Center, Bay Village, OH 1141

Lake Meredith Aquatic and Wildlife Museum, Fritch, TX 1420

Lake Perris Regional Indian Museum (Home of the Wind), Perris, CA..............141

Lake View Nature Center, Oakbrook Terrace, IL 449

Lake Waccamaw Depot Museum, Lake Waccamaw, NC............................1109

Lakeview Museum of Arts and Sciences, Peoria, IL 450

Las Cabezas de San Juan Nature Reserve (El Faro), Fajardo, PR 1641

Las Vegas Natural History Museum, Las Vegas, NV 879

Lawrence County Historical and Genealogical Society, Bedford, IN 469

The Lebanon County Historical Society, Lebanon, PA 1268

Lewis & Clark Boat House and Nature Center, Saint Charles, MO............................830

Lewis and Clark Visitor Center, Yankton, SD 1360

Libby Museum, Wolfeboro, NH 897

Lichterman Nature Center, Memphis, TN ..1373

Lincoln Memorial Garden and Nature Center, Springfield, IL............................459

Lindsay Wildlife Museum, Walnut Creek, CA 196

Little Rock Zoological Gardens, Little Rock, AR 62

Loggerhead Marinelife Center, Juno Beach, FL 316

Logoly State Park, McNeil, AR 64

Lopez Island Historical Museum, Lopez Island, WA 1558

Lorenzo State Historic Site, Cazenovia, NY 976

Louisville Science Center, Louisville, KY ...577

Louisville Zoological Garden, Louisville, KY 578

Lower Rio Grande Valley Nature Center, Weslaco, TX 1460

Loxahatchee River Historical Society, Jupiter, FL............................316

Lutz Children's Museum, Manchester, CT...248

Lyman Museum, Hilo, HI 393

M.T. Brackbill Planetarium, Harrisonburg, VA............................1511

MacKenzie Environmental Education Center, Poynette, WI 1618

Madison County Historical Society-Cottage Lawn, Oneida, NY 1045

Maidu Interpretive Center, Roseville, CA....151

Mammoth Cave National Park, Mammoth Cave, KY 579

Mann Wildlife Learning Museum, Montgomery, AL 16

Martha's Vineyard Museum, Edgartown, MA 681

Martin and Osa Johnson Safari Museum, Inc., Chanute, KS 535

The Maryland Zoo in Baltimore, Baltimore, MD............................635

Massachusetts Audubon at Connecticut River Valley Sanctuaries, Easthampton, MA 681

Matagorda County Museum, Bay City, TX 1393

Maturango Museum of the Indian Wells Valley, Ridgecrest, CA 148

May Natural History Museum and Museum of Space Exploration, Colorado Springs, CO 207

Mayborn Museum Complex, Waco, TX.....1459

McCone County Museum, Circle, MT........844

McLean County Historical Society Museum, Washburn, ND 1137

McPherson County Old Mill Museum and Park, Lindsborg, KS 550

Meeteetse Museum District, Meeteetse, WY 1636

The Merrick Art Gallery, New Brighton, PA 1273

Mesa Verde National Park Museum, Mesa Verde National Park, CO................228

Mesker Park Zoo & Botanic Garden, Evansville, IN 476

Miami Museum of Science & Planetarium, Miami, FL 325

The Michigan State University Museum, East Lansing, MI............................740

Millerton Courthouse, Friant, CA.................98

Milwaukee County Zoological Gardens, Milwaukee, WI 1612

Milwaukee Public Museum, Milwaukee, WI 1612

The Minna Anthony Common Nature Center at Wellesley State Park, Fineview, NY 989

Minnesota Zoo, Apple Valley, MN 768

Mississippi Entomological Museum, Mississippi State University, MS............805

Mississippi Museum of Natural Science, Jackson, MS............................803

Moccasin Lake Nature Park, An Environmental & Energy Education Center, Clearwater, FL 299

Mohonk Preserve, Inc., Gardiner, NY 993

The Monhegan Museum, Monhegan, ME....615

Montague Museum & Historical Association, Montague, MI............................756

Monte L. Bean Life Science Museum, Provo, UT 1469

Monterey Bay Aquarium, Monterey, CA 127

Montgomery Zoo, Montgomery, AL 17

Moore County Historical Museum, Dumas, TX............................1410

Mormon Station State Historic Park, Genoa, NV 877

Morningside Nature Center, Gainesville, FL............................311

Morro Bay State Park Museum of Natural History, Morro Bay, CA 129

Mote Marine Laboratory/Aquarium, Sarasota, FL............................345

Mount Desert Oceanarium, Southwest Harbor, ME 623

Mount Pisgah Arboretum, Eugene, OR.......1224

Mt. Rainier National Park, Ashford, WA ..1547

Muir Woods National Monument, Mill Valley, CA............................125

The Murie Museum, Kelly, WY 1634

The Museum, Greenwood, SC 1334

Museum and Arts Center in the Sequim Dungeness Valley, Sequim, WA.............1570

Museum of Ancient & Modern Art, Penn Valley, CA............................141

Museum of Arts and Sciences, Macon, GA............................378

Museum of Comparative Zoology, Cambridge, MA............................674

Museum of Cultural & Natural History, Mount Pleasant, MI............................757

Museum of Discovery and Science, Fort Lauderdale, FL............................307

Museum of Discovery: Arkansas Museum of Science and History, Little Rock, AR............................62

Museum of Geology and Paleontology, South Dakota School of Mines and Technology, Rapid City, SD................1355

Museum of Natural History, Marshall, MN............................780

Museum of Natural History and Planetarium, Providence, RI................1317

Museum of Natural Science, Baton Rouge, LA............................587

Museum of Northern Arizona, Flagstaff, AZ............................33

Museum of Paleontology, Berkeley, CA 76

Museum of Primitive Art and Culture, Peace Dale, RI............................1316

Museum of San Rafael, Castle Dale, UT...1464

Museum of Science, Boston, MA................667

Museum of Science & History of Jacksonville, Jacksonville, FL................315

Museum of Southwestern Biology, Albuquerque, NM.............934
Museum of Texas Tech University, Lubbock, TX.............1435
Museum of the Fur Trade, Chadron, NE......859
Museum of the Hudson Highlands, Cornwall-on-Hudson, NY.............982
Museum of Vertebrate Zoology, Berkeley, CA.............76
Museum of Western Colorado, Grand Junction, CO.............220
Museum of Woodcarving, Shell Lake, WI.1621
Museum of World Treasures, Wichita, KS...562
Museum of York County, Rock Hill, SC ...1340
Museum of Zoology, Amherst, MA.............659
Museum Village, Monroe, NY.............1015
Museums of Los Gatos, Los Gatos, CA 123
Mutter Museum, College of Physicians of Philadelphia, Philadelphia, PA.............1283
Myrtle Beach State Park Nature Center, Myrtle Beach, SC.............1338
Mystic Aquarium & Institute for Exploration, Mystic, CT.............250

Nantucket Maria Mitchell Association, Nantucket, MA.............696
National Aquarium in Baltimore, Baltimore, MD.............635
National Aviary in Pittsburgh, Inc., Pittsburgh, PA.............1293
National Bighorn Sheep Interpretive Center, Dubois, WY.............1632
National Bird Dog Museum, Grand Junction, TN.............1366
National Great Rivers Museum, East Alton, IL.............431
National Museum of Health and Medicine, Washington, DC.............286
National Museum of Natural History, Washington, DC.............286
National Museum of Racing and Hall of Fame, Saratoga Springs, NY.............1065
National Wildlife Visitor Center, Patuxent Research Refuge, Laurel, MD.............648
Natural History Museum, Portales, NM.......944
The Natural History Museum, Santa Maria, CA.............182
Natural History Museum of Los Angeles County, Los Angeles, CA.............120
The Natural Science Center of Greensboro, Inc., Greensboro, NC.........1104
Nature Interpretive Center, Lebanon, MO....825
The Nature Museum at Grafton, Grafton, VT.............1479
Nauticus, The National Maritime Center, Norfolk, VA.............1522
Nevada State Museum, Carson City, NV.....876
Nevada State Museum, Las Vegas, Las Vegas, NV.............880
New Canaan Nature Center, New Canaan, CT.............252
New England Aquarium Corporation, Boston, MA.............668
New Jersey Meadowlands Environment Center, Lyndhurst, NJ.............910
New Jersey State Museum, Trenton, NJ 927
New London Public Museum, New London, WI.............1615
New Mexico Museum of Natural History & Science, Albuquerque, NM.............935
New York State Museum, Albany, NY........955
The Newark Museum, Newark, NJ.............916
Newell Museum, Newell, SD.............1352
Newport State Park, Ellison Bay, WI.........1597
Nici Self Museum, Centennial, WY.........1630
North Carolina Aquarium at Fort Fisher, Kure Beach, NC.............1109
North Carolina Aquarium at Pine Knoll Shores, Pine Knoll Shores, NC.............1114
North Carolina Museum of Forestry, Whiteville, NC.............1122
North Carolina Museum of Natural Sciences, Raleigh, NC.............1116

North Cascades National Park Service Complex, Marblemount, WA.............1559
The North Museum of Natural History & Science, Lancaster, PA.............1266
Northeastern Nevada Museum, Elko, NV....876
The Northern Maine Museum of Science, University of Maine, Presque Isle, ME...620
Northwest Trek Wildlife Park, Eatonville, WA.............1552
Northwestern Oklahoma State University Museum, Alva, OK.............1195
Nowetah's American Indian Museum & Store, New Portland, ME.............615
The Nylander Museum of Natural History, Caribou, ME.............609

Oakes Museum Messiah College, Grantham, PA.............1257
Oakland Museum of California, Oakland, CA.............134
Oakley Park, UDC Shrine, Edgefield, SC..1332
Oatland Island Education Center, Savannah, GA.............385
Oceanographic Teaching Station Inc. - Roundhouse Marine Studies Lab & Aquarium, Manhattan Beach, CA.............124
Oklahoma City Zoo, Oklahoma City, OK...1209
Old Santee Canal Park, Moncks Corner, SC.............1337
Old State House, Hartford, CT.............245
Old West Museum, Wimberley, TX............1462
Olympic National Park Visitor Center, Port Angeles, WA.............1561
Ontonagon County Historical Society Museum, Ontonagon, MI.............758
Oregon Museum of Science and Industry, Portland, OR.............1231
Oregon Zoo, Portland, OR.............1232
Organ Pipe Cactus National Monument Museum, Ajo, AZ.............29
Orlando Science Center, Inc., Orlando, FL.............332
Orma J. Smith Museum of Natural History, Caldwell, ID.............405
Ormond Memorial Art Museum & Garden, Ormond Beach, FL.............333
Ottawa Scouting Museum, Ottawa, IL.........449
Owensboro Area Museum of Science & History, Owensboro, KY.............581
The Oyster and Maritime Museum of Chincoteague, Chincoteague, VA...........1501
Ozark National Scenic Riverways, Van Buren, MO.............839

Pacific Grove Museum of Natural History, Pacific Grove, CA.............137
Padre Island National Seashore, Corpus Christi, TX.............1402
Page Museum at the La Brea Tar Pits, Los Angeles, CA.............121
Paleontological Research Institution, Ithaca, NY.............1004
Palm Beach Zoo at Dreher Park, West Palm Beach, FL.............353
Palo Alto Junior Museum and Zoo, Palo Alto, CA.............139
Panola Mountain State Conservation Park, Stockbridge, GA.............387
The Paterson Museum, Paterson, NJ............920
Paul H. Karshner Memorial Museum, Puyallup, WA.............1564
Paunsaugunt Wildlife Museum, Bryce, UT.............1464
Peabody Essex Museum, Salem, MA...........706
Peabody Museum of Natural History, New Haven, CT.............253
The Peary-MacMillan Arctic Museum, Brunswick, ME.............608
Pecos National Historical Park, Pecos, NM.............944
The Peggy Notebaert Nature Museum, Chicago, IL.............426

Pember Museum of Natural History, Granville, NY.............995
Petrified Creatures Museum of Natural History, Richfield Springs, NY.............1057
Philip L. Wright Zoological Museum and University of Montana Herbarium, Missoula, MT.............852
Piedmont Environmental Center, High Point, NC.............1107
Pilgrim Monument and Provincetown Museum, Provincetown, MA.............704
Pine Lodge (Ehrman Mansion), Tahoma, CA.............190
Pink Palace Family of Museums, Memphis, TN.............1375
Pinnacles National Monument, Paicines, CA.............138
Pioneers Park Nature Center, Lincoln, NE...867
Pittsburgh Zoo and Aquarium, Pittsburgh, PA.............1293
Plains Conservation Center, Aurora, CO......202
Plantation Historical Museum, Plantation, FL.............337
Plumas County Museum, Quincy, CA.........144
Point Reyes National Seashore, Point Reyes, CA.............143
Poricy Park Nature Center, Middletown, NJ.............911
Port Townsend Marine Science Center, Port Townsend, WA.............1562
Portland Children's Museum, Portland, OR.............1233
Prairie Trails Museum of Wayne County, Corydon, IA.............512
Pratt Museum, Homer, AK.............25
The Pratt Museum of Natural History, Amherst, MA.............659
Presque Isle County Historical Museum, Rogers City, MI.............762
Prince William Forest Park Visitor Center, Triangle, VA.............1541
Princeton University Museum of Natural History, Princeton, NJ.............922
Providence Canyon State Park, Lumpkin, GA.............377
Public Museum of West Michigan, Grand Rapids, MI.............744
Pueblo Zoo, Pueblo, CO.............230
Putnam Museum of History & Natural Science, Davenport, IA.............513

The Quincy Museum, Quincy, IL.............452

R.M. Bohart Museum of Entomology, Davis, CA.............90
Racine Zoological Gardens, Racine, WI....1619
Randall Museum, San Francisco, CA...........168
Rankin Museum, Inc., Ellerbe, NC.............1100
Rattlesnake Museum (American International), Albuquerque, NM.............935
Reading Public Museum, Reading, PA.......1296
Red River Valley Museum, Vernon, TX.....1457
Redwood County Historical Society, Redwood Falls, MN.............787
Redwood National and State Parks, Crescent City, CA.............88
Richard H. Schmidt Museum of Natural History, Emporia, KS.............539
Riley House Museum of African American History & Culture, Tallahassee, FL.............348
Rio Grande Nature Center State Park, Albuquerque, NM.............935
Rio Grande Valley Museum, Harlingen, TX.............1423
River Legacy Living Science Center, Arlington, TX.............1388
Riverbanks Zoological Park & Botanical Garden, Columbia, SC.............1329
Riverbend Environmental Education Center, Gladwyne, PA.............1256
Riverside Metropolitan Museum, Riverside, CA.............150

Zoological (Nonliving)–Continued

Riverside Nature Center, Kerrville, TX......1432
Robert A. Vines Environmental Science Center, Houston, TX..............................1429
Rochester Museum & Science Center, Rochester, NY..................................1059
Rock Creek Nature Center, Washington, DC..290
Rockwoods Reservation, Wildwood, MO....840
Rocky Mount Children's Museum and Science Center, Inc., Rocky Mount, NC...1118
Rocky Mountain National Park, Estes Park, CO...215
Roger Tory Peterson Institute of Natural History, Jamestown, NY........................1005
Roger Williams Park Zoo, Providence, RI.1318
Rosenbruch Wildlife Museum, St. George, UT...1474
Rotary Nature Center, Oakland, CA.............134
The Rotch-Jones-Duff House & Garden Museum, Inc., New Bedford, MA...........697
Royal Gorge Regional Museum & History Center, Canon City, CO..............205
Runestone Museum, Alexandria, MN..........767
Rural Life Museum & Windrush Gardens, Baton Rouge, LA.....................587
Ryerss Museum & Library, Philadelphia, PA...1287

Sacramento Zoo, Sacramento, CA................153
St. Augustine Alligator Farm, Saint Augustine, FL......................................340
St. Croix National Scenic Riverway, Saint Croix Falls, WI.............................1620
St. Louis Science Center, Saint Louis, MO..836
Saint Louis Zoo, Saint Louis, MO..............837
Salida Museum, Salida, CO........................232
Sam Noble Oklahoma Museum of Natural History, Norman, OK.................1206
San Bernardino County Museum, Redlands, CA.......................................147
San Diego Natural History Museum, San Diego, CA...160
Sanford Museum and Planetarium, Cherokee, IA.......................................510
Sanibel-Captiva Conservation Foundation, Inc., Sanibel, FL......................................343
Sanilac County Historical Museum and Village, Port Sanilac, MI........................761
Santa Barbara Museum of Natural History, Santa Barbara, CA...................179
Santa Cruz Museum of Natural History, Santa Cruz, CA......................................182
Santa Monica Mountains National Recreation Area, Thousand Oaks, CA.....191
Saratoga Museum, Saratoga, WY...............1638
Schiele Museum of Natural History and Lynn Planetarium, Gastonia, NC...........1102
The Schuylkill Center for Environmental Education, Philadelphia, PA....................1288
Sci-Port Discovery Center, Shreveport, LA...601
The Science Center of Pinellas County, Saint Petersburg, FL.............................342
Science Museum of Long Island, Manhasset, NY......................................1013
The Science Museum of Minnesota, Saint Paul, MN..792
Science Museum of Western Virginia, Roanoke, VA.......................................1535
Sciworks, Winston-Salem, NC....................1126
Scotia-Glenville Children's Museum, Scotia, NY...1068
Seacoast Science Center, Rye, NH..............896
Seneca Park Zoo, Rochester, NY 1060
Seney National Wildlife Refuge Visitor Center, Seney, MI..................................764
Sequoia and Kings Canyon National Parks, Three Rivers, CA.......................191
Sharon Audubon Center, Sharon, CT...........259

Sierra Mono Indian Museum, North Fork, CA...131
Sierra Sacramento Valley Medical Society Museum of Medical History, Sacramento, CA.....................................153
Sieur de Monts Springs Nature Center, Bar Harbor, ME......................................605
Silver River Museum & Environmental Education Center, Ocala, FL.................330
The Skinner Museum of Mount Holyoke College, South Hadley, MA....................709
South Florida Science Museum, West Palm Beach, FL......................................353
South Park City Museum, Fairplay, CO......215
South Shore Natural Science Center, Inc., Norwell, MA...700
Southern Forest World, Waycross, GA.........391
Southern Oregon University Museum of Vertebrate Natural History, Ashland, OR...1218
Southern Vermont Natural History Museum, West Marlboro, VT 1489
Space Farms Zoological Park and Museum, Sussex, NJ..................................925
Spartanburg Science Center, Spartanburg, SC..1342
Spiro Mounds Archaeological Center, Spiro, OK...1214
Spring Valley Nature Center & Heritage Farm, Schaumburg, IL...........................457
Springbrook Nature Center, Fridley, MN.....776
Springfield Museums - Springfield Science Museum, Springfield, MA..........711
Squam Lakes Natural Science Center, Holderness, NH......................................889
Stamford Museum & Nature Center, Stamford, CT..261
Stanwood Wildlife Sanctuary, Ellsworth, ME...610
State Historical Society of Iowa, Des Moines, IA..515
The State Museum of Pennsylvania, Harrisburg, PA....................................1259
Staten Island Children's Museum, Staten Island, NY...1073
Staten Island Institute of Arts & Sciences (SIIAS), Staten Island, NY 1074
Stauth Memorial Museum, Montezuma, KS...553
Stephen C. Foster State Park, Fargo, GA.....371
Stepping Stones Museum for Children, Norwalk, CT..257
Sternberg Museum of Natural History, Hays, KS...543
Still National Osteopathic Museum, Kirksville, MO.......................................824
Suffolk County Vanderbilt Museum, Centerport, NY......................................977
Sugarlands Visitor Center, Gatlinburg, TN.1365
Sulphur Creek Nature Center, Hayward, CA...102
Summit Historical Society, Breckenridge, CO...204
Sunset Zoological Park, Manhattan, KS.......552

T Rex Museum, Tucson, AZ...........................50
Tanglewood Nature Center and Museum, Elmira, NY...988
Texas Discovery Gardens, Dallas, TX........1408
Texas Maritime Museum, Rockport, TX.....1446
Texas Natural Science Center, Austin, TX.1392
The Texas Zoo, Victoria, TX......................1457
Theodore Roosevelt National Park-Visitor Center, Medora, ND...............................1134
Thronateeska Heritage Foundation, Inc., Albany, GA...355
Tillamook County Pioneer Museum, Tillamook, OR.......................................1237
Timpanogos Cave National Monument, American Fork, UT.................................1462
Tipton County Museum, Veteran's Memorial & Nature Center, Covington, TN.......................................1364

The Toledo Zoo, Toledo, OH.....................1187
Tonto National Monument, Roosevelt, AZ..43
Topeka Zoological Park, Topeka, KS...........560
Trailside Nature and Science Center, Mountainside, NJ......................................915
Trailside Nature Center, Cincinnati, OH 1151
Trailside Nature Museum, Cross River, NY...983
Transylvania Museum, Lexington, KY.........574
Tucker Tower Nature Center, Ardmore, OK...1196
Tucumcari Historical Research Institute, Tucumcari, NM.......................................953
Tulsa Zoo & Living Museum, Tulsa, OK..1216

UNLV Marjorie Barrick Museum, Las Vegas, NV...880
USDA Forest Service - Land Between the Lakes, Golden Pond, KY.................570
The University Museum Collections, Fayetteville, AR.......................................57
University of Alaska Museum of the North, Fairbanks, AK................................24
University of Colorado Museum, Boulder, CO...203
University of Iowa Hospitals & Clinics Medical Museum, Iowa City, IA.............520
University of Iowa Museum of Natural History, Iowa City, IA................................520
The University of Michigan Exhibit Museum of Natural History, Ann Arbor, MI..725
University of Michigan Museum of Anthropology, Ann Arbor, MI..................725
University of Michigan, Museum of Zoology, Ann Arbor, MI 726
The University of Montana-Western Art Gallery & Museum, Dillon, MT............846
University of Nebraska State Museum, Lincoln, NE...867
University of Northern Iowa Museums & Collections, Cedar Falls, IA....................508
University of Oregon Museum of Natural and Cultural History, Eugene, OR 1224
University of Wisconsin Zoological Museum, Madison, WI............................1606
University of Wyoming Anthropology Museum, Laramie, WY............................1636
Utah Field House of Natural History State Park, Vernal, UT 1475
Utah Museum of Natural History, Salt Lake City, UT...1473
Utica Museum, Utica, MT.........................854
Utica Zoo, Utica, NY...............................1080

Valley County Pioneer Museum, Glasgow, MT..847
Victor Valley Museum & Art Gallery, Apple Valley, CA......................................71
Virgin Islands National Park, St. John, VI.1644
Virginia Aquarium & Marine Science Center, Virginia Beach, VA...................1542
Virginia City J. Spencer Watkins Memorial Museum, Virginia City, MT....854
Virginia Institute of Marine Science, Gloucester Point, VA............................1508
Virginia Living Museum, Newport News, VA...1520
Virginia Museum of Natural History, Martinsville, VA 1516
Virginia Zoological Park, Norfolk, VA.......1523

W.K. Kellogg Bird Sanctuary of Michigan State University, Augusta, MI...726
Wagner Free Institute of Science, Philadelphia, PA 1289
Waikiki Aquarium, Honolulu, HI...............399
Walney Visitor Center-At Ellanor C. Lawrence Park, Chantilly, VA...............1498
Walnut Canyon National Monument, Flagstaff, AZ..34

Walter B. Jacobs Memorial Nature Park, Shreveport, LA 602
War in the Pacific National Historical Park, Piti, GU 1640
Warrick County Museum, Inc., Boonville, IN 470
Watermen's Museum, Yorktown, VA 1547
Wayne County Historical Society, Wooster, OH 1192
The Wayne State University Museum of Natural History, Detroit, MI.....................738
Webster House Museum, Elkhorn, WI.......1596
Welder Wildlife Foundation & Refuge, Sinton, TX 1453
Wellesley Historical Society, Inc., Wellesley Hills, MA 717
Wenatchee Valley Museum and Cultural Center, Wenatchee, WA 1577
Wendell Gilley Museum, Southwest Harbor, ME 623
Werner Wildlife Museum, Casper, WY 1630
West Virginia State Wildlife Center, French Creek, WV....................................1581
Western Archeological & Conservation Center, Tucson, AZ......................................52
Western North Carolina Nature Center, Asheville, NC 1090

Westmoreland Sanctuary, Inc., Bedford Corners, NY..961
Westport Maritime Museum, Westport, WA 1578
The Wetlands Institute, Stone Harbor, NJ....925
Weymouth Woods-Sandhills Nature Preserve Museum, Southern Pines, NC.1120
The Whale Museum, Friday Harbor, WA...1555
Whatcom Museum of History and Art, Bellingham, WA 1549
White Sands National Monument, Alamogordo, NM.................................932
Whitehouse Nature Center, Albion, MI........723
Wild Turkey Center and Winchester Museum, Edgefield, SC.........................1332
Wildcare: Terwilliger Nature Education & Wildlife, San Rafael, CA 177
Wildlife Museum at Petaluma High School, Petaluma, CA 142
Wildlife Prairie State Park, Hanna City, IL...439
William S. Webb Museum of Anthropology, Lexington, KY 575
Woldumar Nature Center, Lansing, MI 751
Woods Hole Science Aquarium, Woods Hole, MA...720

Working Men's Institute, New Harmony, IN 495
World Forestry Center, Portland, OR 1233
World Museum of Natural History, Riverside, CA 150
Wrangell Museum, Wrangell, AK..................29
Wray Museum, Wray, CO..............................235
Wupatki National Monument, Flagstaff, AZ 34

Yellowstone National Park, Gardiner, MT ...847
The Yosemite Museum, National Park Service, Yosemite National Park, CA......199
Youth Science Center, Hacienda Heights, CA 101
Youth Science Institute, San Jose, CA 173
Youth Science Institute at Vasona Park, Los Gatos, CA 123
Youth Science Institute, Sanborn Nature Center, Saratoga, CA................................185

Zion Human History Museum, Springdale, UT......................................1474
The Zoo, Gulf Breeze, FL 312
Zoo Atlanta, Atlanta, GA 364
Zooamerica North America Wildlife Park, Hershey, PA 1261